# *Textbook of* GENETICS

AF659396

Dr. Ajoy Paul

CELEBRATING 55 YEARS 1960-2015

Since 1960

*[For Undergraduate & Postgraduate students of Genetics, Zoology, Botany, Microbiology, Physiology, Biochemistry, Biophysics, Biotechnology, and other Bio-Science courses. Also useful for NET, SET, GATE, JAM, JEST, and other competitive examinations.]*

# Textbook of GENETICS


**Dr. Ajoy Paul**, M.Sc., Ph.D., FICCE, FISBT, FZSEI

*Formerly Professor-in-Charge, Chakdaha College, Chakdaha, Nadia, West Bengal, Affiliated to University of Kalyani, Kalyani, Nadia, W.B., India, Formerly Associate Professor and Head of the Department of Zoology, Chakdaha College, Chakdaha, Nadia, West Bengal, Fellow, International Congress of Chemistry and Environment, Fellow, International Society of Biotechnology, Fellow, Zoological Society of Eastern India.*



**BOOKS AND ALLIED (P) Ltd.**

No. 1-E(1) "Shubham Plaza" (1st Floor)
83/1, Beliaghata Main Road, Kolkata 700010 (India)

*Tel* : 8961053844 • 8274085530

*e-mail* : booksandallied1960@gmail.com • booksmktng@gmail.com

# *Textbook of* GENETICS

First Published : September, 2011
**Second Edition** (thoroughly revised & updated) **: 2018**



***Publisher*** : Arunabha Sen
BOOKS & ALLIED (P) LTD.
8/1 Chintamoni Das Lane, Kolkata 700009

***Typesetter*** : BOOKS & ALLIED (P) LTD.
8/1 Chintamoni Das Lane, Kolkata 700009

***Printer*** : CALCUTTA ART STUDIO (P) LTD.
185/1, B. B. Ganguly Street, Kolkata 700012

***Project Supervisor*** : Sudhangsu De

**ISBN** 978-93-84294-11-3

**Price :** **₹ 1,250.00**

*I dedicate this book to my*

***father** and **mother***

*who are my god and goddess.*

---

*Thanks to my family members,*

*especially **wife**, **daughter** and **son**,*

*for their love and support,*

*without which this book*

*would not have been completed.*

# About the Author

**AJOY PAUL** is retired Professor-in-Charge of Chakdaha College, affiliated to University of Kalyani, West Bengal, India, and taught there as Associate Professor and Head of the Department of Zoology since 1981. After obtaining his M.Sc. degree in Zoology in the year 1976, he started his research work in Immunology and earned his Ph.D. in Cytogenetics at Department of Zoology from University of Kalyani, India in 1994. Dr. Paul always had a keen interest in teaching, research, research paper publication and writing text books in the field of different subjects of Biological Sciences. Over the years, he has taught courses in general Zoology, Immunology, Molecular Biology, Biotechnology, Genetics and Microbiology. He has published a number of research papers in many journals and delivered lectures in the seminars. He has been elected to Fellowships in the International Congress of Chemistry and Environment, International Society of Biotechnology and also Zoological Society of Eastern India. Besides this book, he is also the author of *"Textbook of Cell and Molecular Biology"*, and *"Textbook of Immunology (including Immuno-technology & Immunotherapy)"* and also five other textbooks on *Environmental Studies* for undergraduate courses of Indian Universities. Besides reading and writing, he enjoys flower gardening, travelling and spending time with his family members. His email address is *ajoypaul.genetics@gmail.com*

# Preface to the Second Edition

My humble endeavour **Textbook of Genetics** was first published in the year 2011. Now it is my great pleasure to bring out the second edition of this book within only seven years.

My sincere thanks to the readers, both students and teachers, as well as lovers of genetics for their overwhelming response and their kind acceptance of the book.

The printing mistakes which were obviously present in the first edition have been corrected as far possible. If any mistake still remains and is kindly brought to my notice, it will definitely be rectified in the next reprint.

The first edition of *Textbook of Genetics* was a voluminous one. After revision, updation and addition of new chapters and further elaboration of subject topics, the book became more voluminous. To overcome this situation, the book has been divided into two separate volumes. The first volume comprises of six parts, viz., *Basic Mechanisms of Inheritance; Microbial Genetics; Molecular Genetics; Human Genetics; Quantitative & Behavioural Genetics* and *Evolutionary Genetics*. The remaining portion of the previous edition will be segregated and published under the title *"Genetic Engineering including Tools & Techniques in Genetics"*.

The current edition of the book is presented with more multi-coloured figures and illustrations, which would certainly help the readers to grasp the subject-matter easily and more precisely.

I owe a deep debt of gratitude to my parents; their blessings have made me achieve peace and prosperity in my life.

I also express my gratitude to Mr. Arunabha Sen, Director, Books & Allied (P) Ltd., Kolkata, for his whole-hearted cooperation in bringing out this book to my satisfaction. My sincere thanks to all the staffs of Books & Allied (P) Ltd., particularly to Sudhangsu De for composing, drawing and supervising the book.

Last but not the least, I thank to my wife, daughter, son and son-in-law for their constant cooperation, support and encouragement.

"Bhuban Smriti"
Plot No. A-10/17
Kalyani, Nadia,
West Bengal, India
Pin - 741235

**Dr. Ajoy Paul**
*e-mail* : ajoypaul.genetics@gmail.com

# Preface to the First Edition

Charles Darwin, in 1868, wrote *"The whole subject of inheritance is wonderful"*. Biology of his days provided no solution for what continued for many years to be called the *"riddle of heredity"*. Yet at the time of Darwin made his remark, the great biologist, Gregor Mendel took the essential steps which led to the solution of the *riddle*. He published his work in 1866 in a scientific journal in his native Austria, but remained unknown and the scientific world failed to recognize or to appreciate the work until 1900, because, he was not primarily a biologist but a monk in the Augustinian monastery at Brunn (now Brno, Czechoslovakia), Austria.

Before Mendel's time, heredity was supposed to be transmitted as though it were a misceble fluid, like blood in animals and human. The "bloods" of the parents were assumed to mix or fuse in the offspring. Mendel provided the first proof for the theory that explained heredity by the transmission of units in the reproductive cells and thus put an end to vague notions such as those concerning *"blood"*. According to this theory, genotypes of all organisms consist of genes. Because of the universal applicablility of this theory throughout the range of life from virus to human, the *"gene"* may be regarded as the fundamental unit of life. After the rediscovery of Mendel's work by DeVries in Holland, Correns in Germany and Tschermak in Austria, the Mendel's theory of inheritance *"law of segregation"* was reestablished and was extended by experiments carried on in various parts of the world on many kinds of animals and plants.

After rediscovery of Mendel's law of inheritance, a number of great biologists did several experiments on the inheritance of characters from *E.coli* to yeast to insects to mammals including humans and they confirmed the existence of genes, which are transmitted from generation to generation and express their phenotypes.

The epoch-making discovery of the three dimensional structure of DNA (gene) by Watson, Crick and Wilkins in 1955 was possibly the best of all the achievements in the scientific world of research during the last century. It outlines the possibilities for an understanding in the finest details of the molecular configuration of genes which dictate the general as well as individual characteristics of living organisms.

Discovery of *"Central dogma"*, *i.e.* flow of information from gene to mRNA by transcription and then to protein by translation presented us how the genes work in our body to express phenotypes. The mechanism of gene expression, replication, mutation, repair and recombination, all were disclosed in details at the molecular level and the science *"Molecular biology"* took birth at the last decade of last century, which gave detailed mechanism of inheritance of genes.

Each and every organism possesses its own genes and thus each of them has a separate phenotype. Thus the term *"genome"* has come to us which can give detailed description of the entire genetic complement of a living organism. The *genomics* deals with the study of the total genetic material of a living organism which dictates the shaping of body function. Modern molecular biology describes the detailed mapping of genome in the chromosomes of the organisms, analysis of genomes, sequencing of genomes, comparative studies of genomes at interspecific as well as intraspecific levels, origin and evolution of genome, manipulation of genome and how genome functions in the living body. *Proteomics* deals with the proper shaping of the organism. Thus, genomics and proteomics are the two branches of the molecular biology.

Genetic manipulation of individual species by breeding experiments became very popular among geneticists which improves its quality. By the discovery of Genetic Engineering, genetic manipulation of an individual became easier and more distinct to produce genetically modified organisms as well as genetically modified food. This field of research in genetics might provide us tremendous impacts and importance in agriculture, medicine and commerce. Discovery of SNP gave birth to a new field of research for pharmacogenomics which has a target to produce personalized medicine, *i.e. "right drug to right patient"*. Eugenics and euphenics and euphenics are now become the two branches of Human genetics for the benefit of human being. The latest epoch-making event, which has occurred on 3rd Sept, 2007 by Dr. Craig Venter when entire human genome was unvailed.

The first edition of this book is being published at the time when the revolution in molecular biology with gene cloning is at its heart, had progressed to encompass a variety of other techniques and advances, especially genome sequencing, the polymerase chain reaction and microarray technologies. The main title of the book *"The Textbook of Genetics"* with subtitle *"From Genes to Genomes"* is supposed to be appropriate as the book deals with the Mendelian classical genetics and hereditary principles as well as new large-scale techniques, bioinformatic analyses of complete genome sequence, isolation and identification of genome, genome manipulation and also the whole new range of technologies (post-genomics) that are designed for genome-wide analysis of gene structure and expression. This book has also covered the field of immunogenetics, developmental genetics, molecular phenetics and molecular evolution. The book is written in a lucid style with theoritical discussions and coloured illustrations as far as possible; the tables for easy understanding and explained the subject matter in a simple precise language and also sequence the points and with solved answers to the problems on genetics.

I have tried my level best to make it free from errors and printing mistakes by correcting the galley proof several times. Notwithstanding, some unwanted mistakes may crop up. Mistakes noticed by readers and suggestion for improvement if any may kindly be brought to the notice of the auther at the email address so that the next edition may be useful to those for whom the book has been written.

I owe a deep sense of gratitude to my parents because their blessings are my assets. My family members are my inspiration; without their tolerance and interaction, writing of this book would never be possible. I also express my cordial gratefulness to Prof. A.K. Saha my teacher, Zoology department, Kalyani University, WB, India, and also to Prof. A.R. Khudabakash and Prof. P.D. Ghosh of Kalyani University; Dr. Subrata De, Director, School of Biotechnology and Biological Sciences, West Bengal University of Technology, Saltlake, Kolkata, Dr. Anil Ghosh; Dy. Director, Indian institute of Chemical Biology Kolkata, those who inspired me continuously all through the writing of this book.

Nothing is sufficient to express my gratitude to Mr. Arunabha Sen, Director, Books & Allied (P) Ltd., Kolkata for readily concenting to my request of publishing the book. My special thanks to Sri Sudhangsu De for page makeup computer graphic work of this book and also to other members of the Books & Allied (P) Ltd.

Lastly, but not the least in importance, I dedicate this book to the readers who are lovers of genetics.

"Bhuban Smriti"
Plot No. A-10/17
Kalyani, Nadia,
West Bengal, India
Pincode No. 741235

**Dr. Ajoy Paul**

*e-mail* : ajoypaul.genetics@gmail.com

# Brief Contents

# Detailed Contents

# 1

# Basis of Heredity and Mendelism

**CHAPTER AGENDA**

## 1.1 CONCEPT

The term "Genetics" was used for the first time by W. Bateson (1905). The branch of science, which embodies studies of biological make up, environment and also the analysis of the laws and principles that govern transmission of characters is called *Genetics.*

**Heredity** is the term where the traits or characteristics are transmitted from generation to generation.

**Variations** are the differences in characters or traits, which are observed during transmission from generation to generation.

**Genetics** is described as a science, which deals with heredity and variation.

Genetics is barely one hundred years old. The first marked pioneer and experimental work in this field was started by **Gregor Johan Mendel** (1822-84). Therefore, the name **"Father of modern genetics"** was given to him.

## 1.2 PRE-MENDELIAN WORK

The breeding experiments for the improvement of races of domesticated plants and animals were conducted by Babylonians and Assyrians, thousands of years before the Christian Era. Genetics was not known exactly and how is passed on from parent to offspring to make them similar or different.

1. **Vapour and Fluid Theory** : Early Greek philosopher Pythagoras (500 BC) proposed that some moist vapour is given out from brain, nerves and other parts of the body of male during coitus that makes the offspring resemble male parent.

2. **Semen Theory** : It was suggested by Empedocies that both parents produce semen that arise from their various body parts. The semen from both parents mixes to produce the new individual.

3. **Particulate Theory** : French biologist Mauperitus (1689-1795) proposed that the body of each parent gives rise to minute particles. In sexual reproduction, these particles from the both parents blend together to form the daughter individual.

4. **Pangenesis Theory** : Charles Darwin proposed that every cell, tissue and organ of animal body produce many minute particles known as *gemmules* or *pangenes*. These are discharged in the blood stream and are deposited in the reproductive organs. The reproductive cells contain these pangenes and an offspring develops as a result of blending of pangenes from two parents.

5. **Pre-formation Theory** : J. Swammerdam (1679) advanced the idea that one of the sex cells or gametes either sperm or egg contains inside the miniature of the adult in perfect form. This preformed individual was called *homunculus.*

## 1.3 BLENDING AND PARTICULATE THEORY OF INHERITANCE

The scientists of pre-Mendelian era believed in blending inheritance that the qualities of two parents get blended or mixed up in the offspring, which exhibit some intermediate results. However, this concept is not acceptable now.

According to the particulate theory given by Mauperitus, the parental characters do not blend in the offspring. These remain discrete and may reappear after several generations. German botanist Kolreuter, presented experimental evidence to show that characters remain discrete. Although his observations were similar to Mendel. He could not interpret them.

Fig.1.1 : *Gregor Johan Mendel, the father of genetics.*

**Exceptions to blending inheritance :**

1. Character of sex does not blend because offsprings are either male or female.
2. John Gross crossed yellow and green seed pea plants. The $F_1$ hybrids had yellow seeds. The hybrids were not intermediate. It means, there is no blending of characters.
3. **Atavism** or **reversion** is the appearance of a character present in distant ancestor and not shown by parents or grand parents, e.g., appearance of rudimentary tail in a human child. The character remains unexpected for several generations and suddenly reappears. Thus atavism is just opposite to blending inheritance.

## 1.4 MENDEL'S PRINCIPLE

The modern science of heredity starts with the experiments which the Austrian monk, Gregor Johan Mendel, made on pea plants (Fig. 1.1). Mendel published his results in 1866 in the journal *The Annual Proceedings of the Natural History* Society of Brunn, in the paper entitled "Experiments in Plant Hybridization". but he received very little attention and his work was overlooked for a number of years. In 1900, the principles of heredity, which Mendel had discovered were independently, rediscovered by three biologists, **Hugo de Vries** in Holland, **Carl Correns** in Germany and **Eric von Tschermark** in Austria. From this time on the science of heredity has made rapid progress.

Before Mendel's time, heredity was supposed to be transmitted as though it were a miscible fluid, like blood in animal and man. The *bloods* of parents were assumed to mix or fuse in the offspring. Mendel provided the first proof for a theory that explained heredity by the transmission of units in the reproductive cells and thus put an end to vague notions such as those concerning "**bloods**".

### 1.4.1 Mendel's Experimental Material

In his garden, Mendel carried on a series of experiments with the common garden pea (*Pisum sativum*) and established some definite principles. These principles have since been tested and found correct in numerous cases and have thus become established as Laws of Mendel.

He took the garden peas for his experiments because:

1. The pea flowers are regularly self-pollinated.
2. The plants exhibited constant and clear distinguishing features.
3. The hybrids were usually perfectly fertile.
4. Life cycle is short.
5. It can be maintained properly even in the laboratory.
6. Large number of offsprings are produced that help in deducing the correct conclusions.

Mendel mainly considered seven pairs of contrasting characters (Fig. 1.2) :

(i) Smooth and wrinkled seed.

(ii) Yellow and green seed coat.

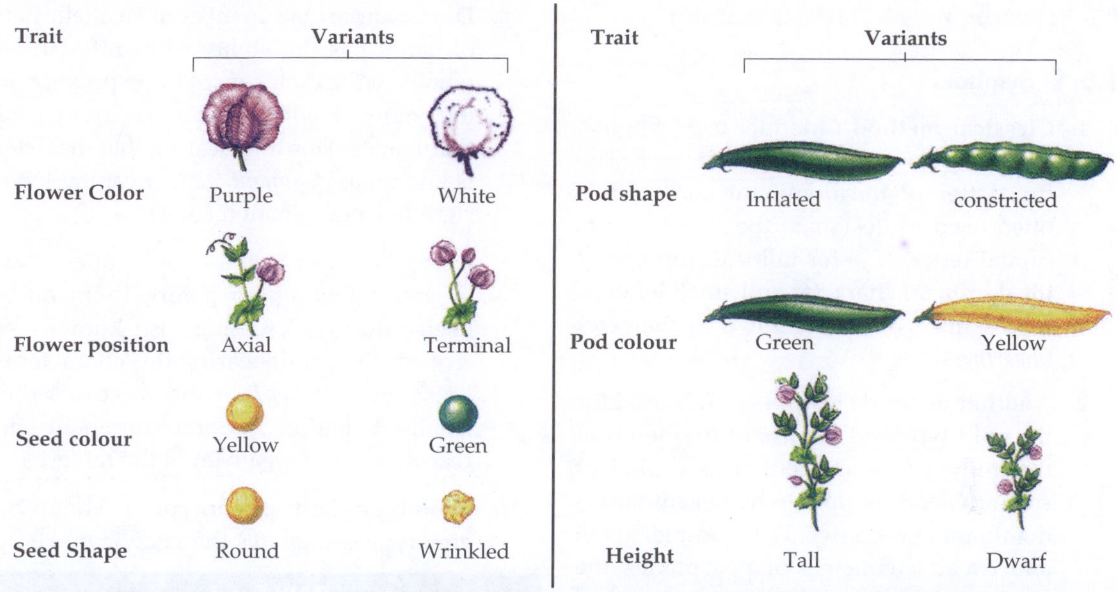


**Fig.1.2 :** *An illustration of the seven traits that Mendel studied.*

(iii) Tall and dwarf plants.

(iv) Colored and white flowers.

(v) Axial and terminal flowers.

(vi) Inflated and constricted pods.

(vii) Green and yellow pods.

Mendel's success was mainly due to the facts that:

(i) He always worked with pure homogeneous materials.

(ii) He considered with character independently.

(iii) The records of the offspring of each individual were kept separately.

(iv) The records were kept up to at least the third filial generations.

### 1.4.2 Crossing techniques:

Since garden pea is self-pollinating, a great care was taken during the experiments.

1. To prevent the possibility of self-fertilization, the anthers were removed from the plants taken as seed parents, even before the stigma was fully mature.
2. The pollens from the parent plant were transferred at the dehiscence stage and were dusted on the feathery stigma of those flowers from which anthers were removed.
3. These cross-pollinated flowers were enclosed in separate bags to avoid further deposition of pollens from some other sources.
4. Seeds were collected separately in marked bottles. In case of seed characters, seeds were studied immediately but for other plant characters, seeds were sown to raise the plants for the pod characters, flower characters and stem characters.

The plants used as parents are said to represent *parental generation*, designated by $P_1$. The progeny obtained as a result of crossing between parents is called *first filial generation*, represented by $F_1$ (*the word filial means offspring*). The progeny obtained as a result of self-fertilization among $F_1$ plants represents *second filial generation* ($F_2$-*generation*).

## 1.5 SYMBOLS AND TERMINOLOGIES

### 1.5.1 Symbols

1. **Classical method :** Mendel used English alphabets to represent the factors. The first letter of the dominant character is often used to designate the character. Its capital letter, '*T*'—for tallness, represents the dominant character and small letter '*t*' represents its recessive character (*dwarfness*).
2. **Another method :** Here '+' sign is used for the wild type and the use of first letter of the mutant character either as capital or small depending upon whether mutant is dominant or recessive. For example, in tall and dwarf characters of pea plants, the wild or tall character is represented as +/+ and dwarf as *d/d*. The genotype of $F_1$ hybrids will be represented by +/*d*.

### 1.5.2 Terminologies

1. **Factors :** Mendel presumed that a character is determined by a pair of factors or determiners (*hereditary units*) present in each cells of the individual. These are known as genes in modern genetics.
2. **Alleles or allelomorphs :** *Allele* is a Greek word which means "belonging to one another". It is used to refer to one member of a gene pair. According to Mendel, two genes representing two alternatives of a character are present on two separate homologous chromosomes but at the corresponding loci. For example, in a gene pair *Tt*, *T* is present on one chromosome and *t* on the other homologous chromosome but at the same locus. Each of them is *called an allele* to the other, i.e., *T* is an allele to *t* and vice versa.
3. **Locus :** The physical location of a particular gene on a chromosome is known as locus.
4. **Dominance :** One member of an allelic pair of genes has the ability to manifest itself wholly at the exclusion of the expression of the other member. This is known as dominance. This trait bearing this character is known as *dominant trait.* A capital letter signified a dominant (*D* or *T*).
5. **Recessive :** One member of an allelic pair of genes having no ability to manifest itself during crossing is known as *recessive*. The trait bearing this character is known as *recessive trait* and is expressed in small letter (*d* or *t*). Some dominant and recessive traits are given in the table 1.1.
6. **Genotype and phenotype :** The term genotype designates the genetic make up

**TABLE 1.1**
**Some Dominant and Recessive Traits**

| | *Dominant* | *Recessive* |
|---|---|---|
| ***Pea Plant*** | Tall | Dwarf |
| | Red flower | White flower |
| | Greeen pod | Yellow pod |
| | Round seed | Wrinkled seed |
| | Yellow Cotyledon | White cotyledon |
| ***Drosophila*** | Red eye | White eye |
| | Flat & Yellow wing | Curled and white wing |
| | Grey body colour | Black body colour |
| ***Human*** | Curly, dark hair | Straight light hair |
| | Skin with melanin | Albinism |
| | Brown irish | Blue irish |
| | Webbed finger | Normal finger |
| | Extra finger | Normal 5 fingers |
| | Normal hearing | Deaf mutism |
| | Glaucoma | Normal |
| | Opaque lens | Normal |
| | Teeth absent | Present |
| | Ability to roll the tongue | Inability to roll |
| | Taste bitter to PTC | Tasteless to PTC |
| | Free ear lobe | Attached ear lobe |
| | Long eye lashes | Short eye lashes |
| | Large ear | Smaller ear |

of an organism, whereas, phenotype is used to indicate the external appearance of an individual. For example, a pure tall phenotype has a genotype (*TT*), hybrid tall phenotype has a genotype (*Tt*), and dwarf phenotype of the pea plant has a genotype (**tt**). **Johanssen** used these terms in 1911.

7. **Homozygous and heterozygous :** If in an organism, the two genes for a particular character are identical, it is said to be pure or homozygous. For example, tall plants with *TT* or dwarf plants with *tt* are homozygous.

   If in an organism, the two contrasting genes of a pair are present it is said to be impure or hybrid or heterozygous. For example, the tall plant but with *Tt* genotype would be heterozygous.

## 1.6 MONOHYBRID CROSS (CROSS INVOLVING SINGLE PAIR OF CONTRASTING CHARACTERS)

### 1.6.1 Mendel's experiments with Garden peas for single pair of contrasting characters

Mendel's first experiments were done by crossing a tall variety of pea plant with one of a dwarf variety. He artificially pollinated the stigma of the flowers of the dwarf plants with pollen from those of the tall plants and vice versa. He kept a very careful record of the result of these crossings. Mendel found that irrespective of the heights of the plants and in whichever way crosses were made (reciprocal cross), the progenies of the $F_1$ generation were all tall plants.

Next, the flowers of this $F_1$ generation were allowed to self-pollinate. On germination of seeds obtained as a result of this selfing in the $F_1$ generation, the $F_2$ generation was obtained, about one-fourth of whose progeny was all dwarf and rest three-fourth all tall showing varying degrees of tallness, *i.e.*, the ratio of tall individuals and dwarf individuals was 3 : 1. Mendel actually obtained 787 tall and 277 dwarf plants.

When these dwarf plants were self pollinated, in $F_3$ all the offsprings were dwarf. Of all tall plants of $F_2$ only one-third were found to breed true for tallness. The rest two-third produced tall and dwarf in the ratio of 3 : 1 in $F_3$ generation. It means that $F_2$ generation consisted of three types of plants instead of apparent two types (Fig. 1.3).

Tall homozygous (*Pure*) = 25%.

Tall heterozygous = 50%.

Dwarf homozygous = 25%.

#### Mendel's Explanation and Interpretation

When Mendel began his studies of inheritance, there was no knowledge of chromosomes and the role and mechanism of meiosis. He concluded that inheritance of characters is controlled by particles called *hereditary units* or *factors*.

Mendel explained above results by presuming that:

(a) Tallness and dwarfness are determined by a pair of contrasting factors or determiners (*now these are called genes*). A plant is tall because it possesses determiners for tallness (*represented by **T***) and a plant is dwarf because it has determiners for dwarfness (*represented by **t***).

(b) These determiners occur in pairs. Each parent contributes to one member of this pair.

(c) When two factors for alternative expression of a trait are brought together by fertilization, only one (*the dominant trait—tallness*) expresses itself masking the expression of the other (*the recessive trait dwarfness*).

   On the basis of this behaviour the tallness is described as dominant character and dwarfness as recessive.

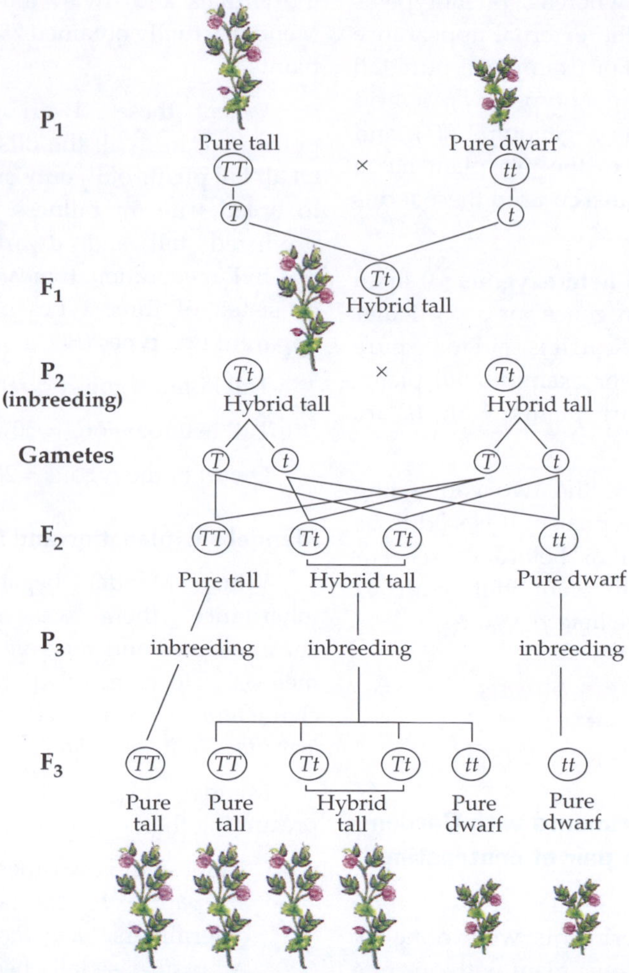


**Fig.1.3 :** *Mendel's experiment on garden peas for single pair of contrasting characters, tall and dwarf variety.*

From the above experiment Mendel proposed the **Law of dominance and recessiveness.**

*"When two homozygous individuals with one or more sets of contrasting characters are crossed, the characters that appear in the $F_1$ hybrid are dominant and those which do not appear in $F_1$ are recessive characters."*

(d) The determiners are never contaminated but when gametes are formed those unit factors segregate so that each gamete gets only one of the two alternative factors. It means factors for tallness (*T*) and dwarfness (*t*) are separate entities and in a gamete either *T* or *t* is present. When $F_1$ hybrids (*Tt*) are self-pollinated the two entities separate out and unites independently producing tall and dwarf plants. From this observation, Mendel proposed "**Law of Segregation**" (Fig. 1.3).

The law of segregation states that, *"When a pair of contrasting factors or genes or allelomorphs are brought together in a*

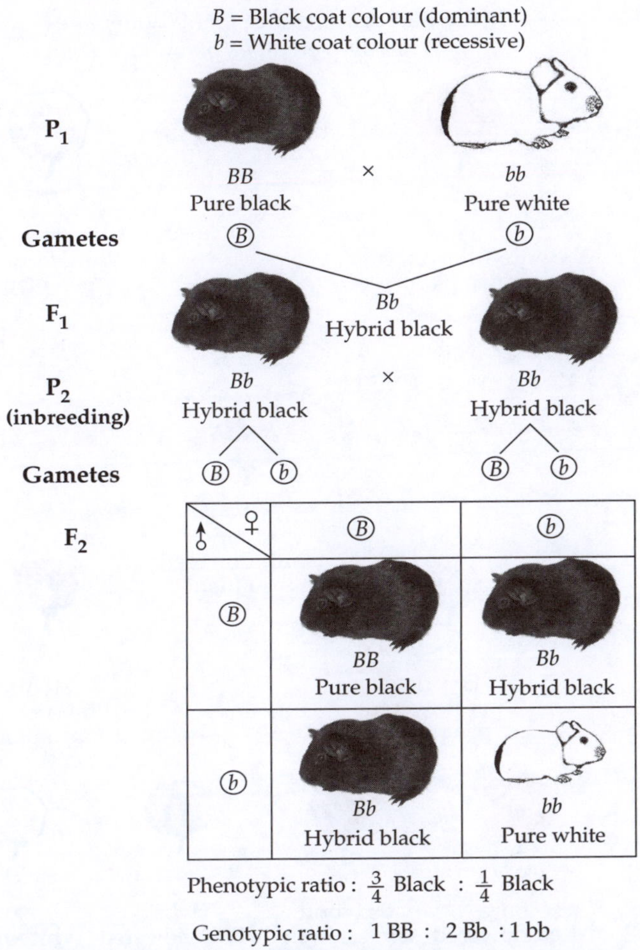


**Fig.1.4 :** *Monohybrid cross taking coat color in Guineapig.*

*heterozygote, the two members of the allelic pair remain together without being contaminated and when gametes are formed from the hybrid, the two separate out from each other and only one enters each gamete".*

### 1.6.2 Monohybrid cross taking coat color in Guinea Pig

When a homozygous black-coated guinea pig is mated to a homozygous white one, the offspring in the $F_1$ progeny are all with black-coat colour. If two of them are inbred, out of the total population produced in the $F_2$ generation, 25% will be homozygous black. 50% will be heterozygous black and 25% will be homozygous white.

The phenotypic ratio in $F_2$ is 3 (*black*) : 1 (*white*) and genotypic ratio is 1 (*pure dominant*) : 2 (hybrid) : 1 (*pure recessive*) (Fig. 1.4).

### 1.6.3 Incomplete Dominance

The law of dominance does not occur universally. In some plants, *e.g.*, red and white flowered pea plant, snapdragon and also in some animals such as Andalusian fowl with black and white feathers and also the red and white coat colour of cattle, such **incomplete dominance,** also called semidominance is found.

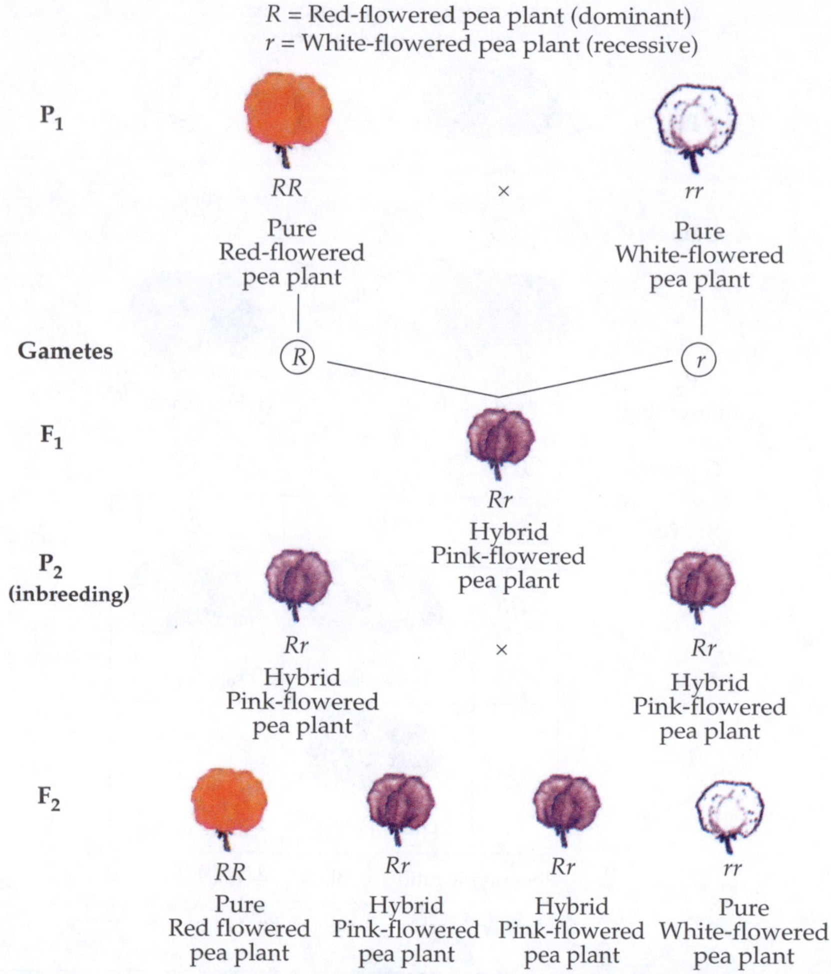


**Fig.1.5 :** *Incomplete dominance in red-white flowered pea plants.*

**Red-White flowered pea plant**

When a red flowered pea plant (*RR*) is crossed with white flowered pea plant (*rr*) the $F_1$ hybrid pea plants are found to have pink flowers. It shows that gene for red colour could not dominate the gene for white colour as shown in the **figure 1.5**. The appearance of this intermediate character in $F_1$ generation is known as *incomplete dominance*. Again, when these $F_1$ hybrids are inbred, the red, pink and white coloured flower plants are produced in 1 : 2 : 1 ratio.

### 1.6.4 Black and White Feathered Andalusian Fowl

When a homozygous Andalusian fowl with black feathers crossed with a homozygous fowl with splashed white feathers, the $F_1$-hybrids are found to contain blue feathers. When these hybrids are inbred, again black, blue and white feathered birds are produced in 1 : 2 : 1 ratio (Fig. 1.6).

Thus non-mixing of alleles, i.e., the *law of segregation* could be firmly proved.

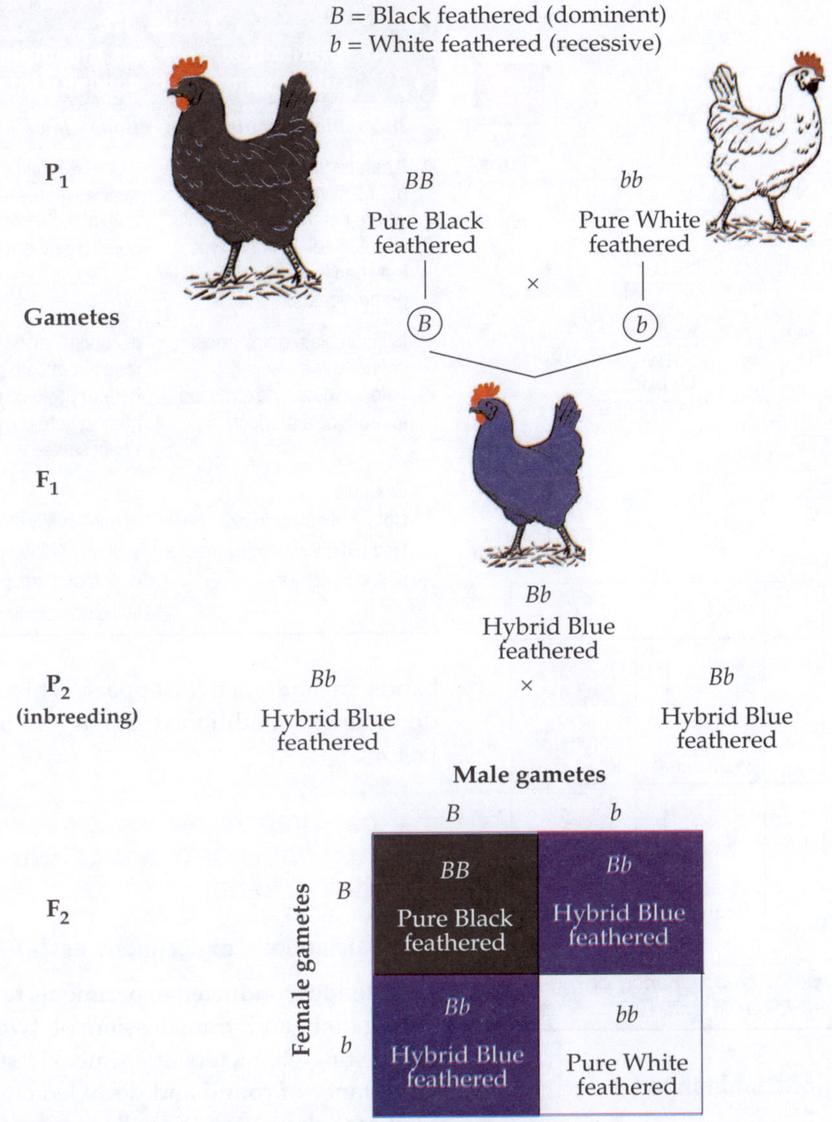


**Fig.1.6 :** *Inheritance of incomplete dominance in black and white feathered Andalusian fowl.*

### 1.6.5 Co-dominance

In co-dominance both the dominant and recessive characters occur side by side in $F_1$ hybrids to give a mixed colour. Best example of co-dominance has been observed in cattle, when a cattle of red coat is crossed with the cattle of white coat, the $F_1$-heterozygote or hybrid is found to posses roan coat. In roan coat the red and white (Fig. 1.7) hairs occur in definite patches but no hair has intermediate colour of red and white (Table 1.2).

### 1.6.6 Delayed Dominance

A character, which is truly dominant but becomes expressive late. Dark haired individuals do not acquire their definitive hair colour until adulthood.

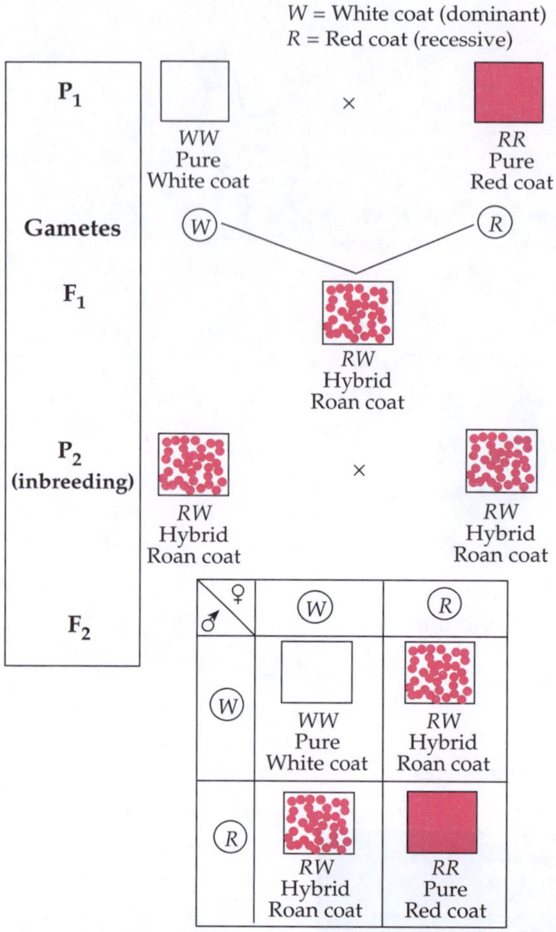


**Fig.1.7** : *Inheritance of co-dominance of red-white coat colour in cattle.*

### 1.6.7 Reversal of Dominance

A recessive character may become dominant. In snail (*Helix*) the colour of red shell is dominant over the colour of yellow shell. Sometimes, an exception occurs and during crosses snails with yellow shells dominate over red shells.

### 1.6.8 Conditioned Dominance

Morgan described a case in *Drosophila* where an abnormality, the banded abdomen becomes expressive only when they are provided with fresh food and moisture. When food becomes dry and there is less moisture, the bands in abdomen disappear. This a type of dominance conditioned upon environmental factors.

**TABLE 1.2**
**Distinction between Incomplete dominance and codominance**

| *Incomplete dominance* | *Codominancl* |
|---|---|
| 1. It can be found more as a quantitative phenomenon where heterozygote exhibits an intemediate phenotype between the limits set by the homozygotes. | It can be found more as a qualitative manner where both of the alleles in the homozygate are expressed. |
| 2. In incomplete dominance, only one allele in a heterozygote in expressed to produce a product. | In codominance, products result from both alleles in a heterozygote so that both homozygote phenotypes are observed . |
| Example : Colour of flower in pea plaints Red (RR) × white (rr) results pink (Rr) colour. | In human MN blood group system M blood group (MM) × N blood group (NN) result MN blood group person. |

## 1.7 DIHYBRID CROSS (CROSS INVOLVING TWO PAIRS OF CONTRASTING CHARACTERS)

### 1.7.1 Mendel's experiment with Pea Seeds

Mendel conducted experiments to study the segregation and transmission of two pairs of contrasting characters at a time. He studied the inheritance of round and wrinkled characters of seed coat along with the yellow or green color of seeds. He found that, a cross between round-yellow and wrinkled-green seeds ($P_1$) produced only round-yellow seeds in $F_1$ generation. But when these $F_1$ plants are inbred, in $F_2$ four types of combinations were observed, two of these combinations were similar to parental combinations while the other two were new combinations (Fig. 1.8).

**Results:**

Yellow-round – 9 (Parental combination).

Green-round – 3 (New combination)

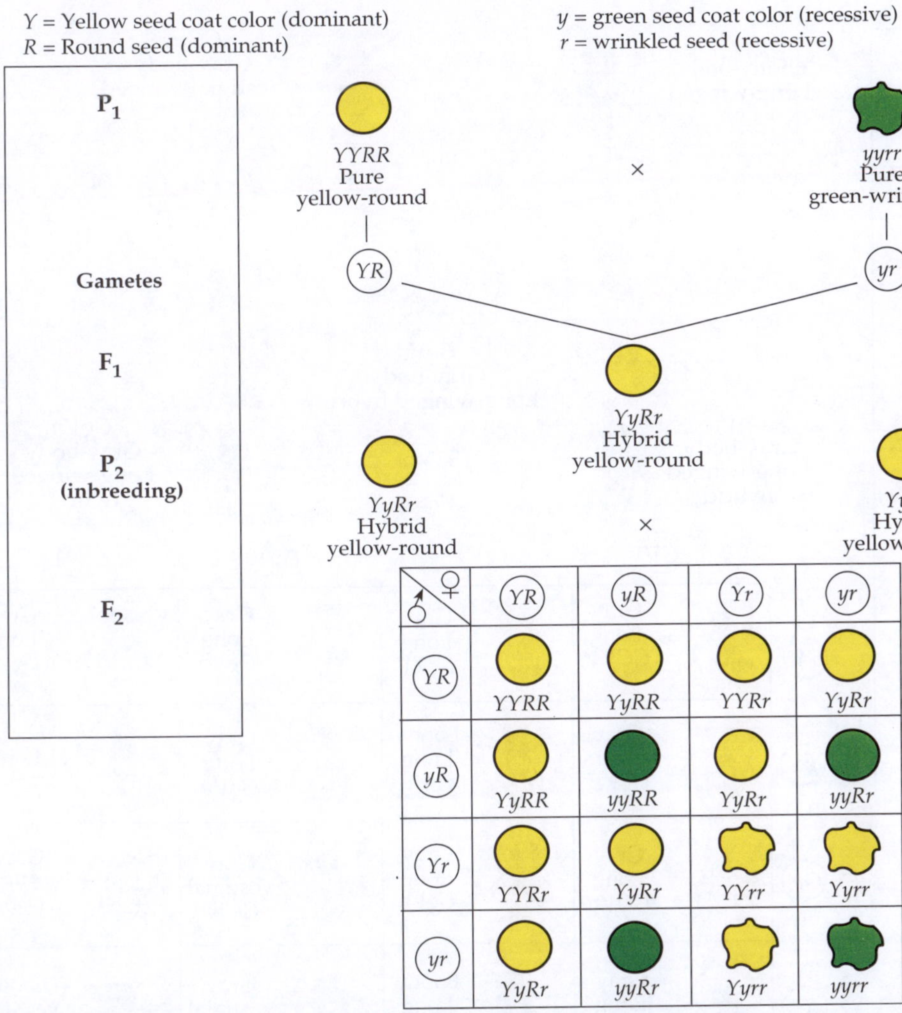


**Fig.1.8 :** *Cross involving two pairs of contrasting characters of seed coat colour and shape in pea plants.*

Yellow-wrinkled – 3 (New combination).

Green-wrinkled – 1(Parental combination).

Thus the offsprings of $F_2$ generation were produced in the ratio of 9:3:3:1. This ratio is called *dihybrid cross ratio.*

**Explanation :** Mendel explained the results by assuming that the round and yellow characters are dominant over wrinkled and green respectively so that all the $F_1$ offsprings are yellow-round. In $F_2$ generation, since all the characters assorted out independent of the others, he said that a pair of alternate or contrasting characters behave independently of the other pair, *i.e.,* seed colour is independent of seed coat. Therefore, at the time of gamete formation genes for round or wrinkled character of seed coat is assorted out independently of the yellow or green colour of the seed. As a result, four types of gametes with two old and two new combinations, *i.e., RY, ry, Ry, rY* are formed from $F_1$ hybrid. These four types of gametes on random mating produced four types of offspring in the ratio of 9:3:3:1 in $F_2$ generation. From this result Mendel proposed his *"Law of Independent Assortment"*.

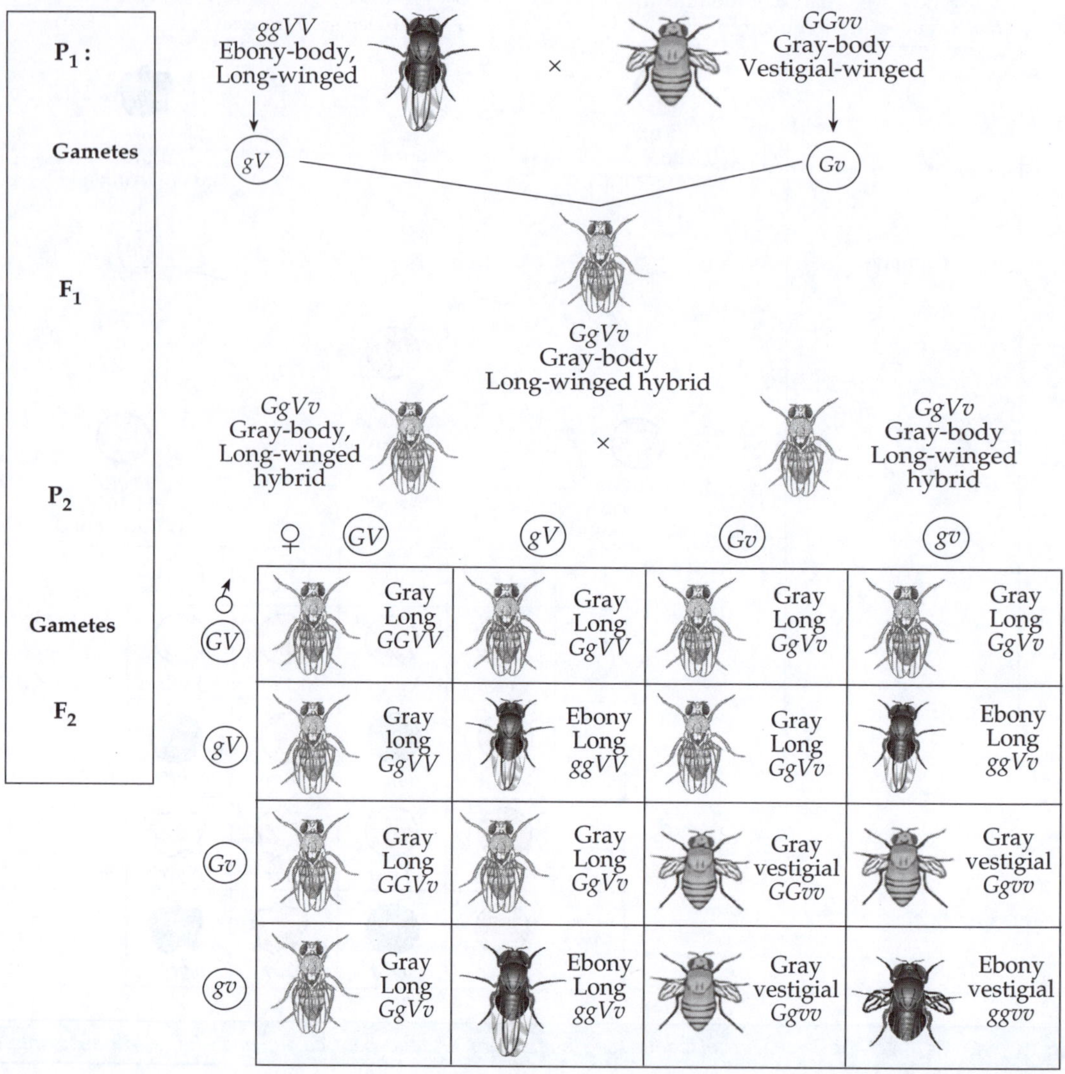


**Fig.1.9 :** *Dihybrid cross in Drosophila.*

*"If the inheritance of more than one pair of characters (two pairs or more) is studied simultaneously, the factors or genes for each pair of characters assort out independently of the other pairs".*

### 1.7.2 Dihybrid cross in *Drosophila*

In a dihybrid cross homozygous long winged and ebony-bodied *Drosophila* fly is crossed with a vestigial winged, gray-bodied fly; they produced in $F_1$ long-winged gray-bodied *Drosophila*. The hybrids of $F_1$ generation after mating with each other produced $F_2$ generation 9 long-winged gray- bodied, 3 long-winged ebony-bodied, 3-vestigial-winged gray-bodied and 1 vestigial winged ebony bodied *Drosophila*. Out of total 16, therefore, the $F_2$ have the ratio 9 : 3 : 3 : 1 (Fig. 1.9) .

*G* = Gray-bodied individual (*dominant*).

*g* = Ebony-bodied individual (*recessive*).

*V* = Long-winged individual (*dominant*).

*v* = Vestigial-winged individual (*recessive*).

## 1.8 TRIHYBRID CROSS

Cross involving three pairs of contrasting characters is called trihybrid cross.

Mendel conducted experiments to study on inheritance of three pairs of characters and observed independent assortment of characters in pea. The three pairs of contrasting characters are :

*T* = Tall stem (*dominant*).

*t* = short stem (*recessive*).

*Y* = yellow seed coat (*dominant*).

*y* = green seed coat (*recessive*).

*R* = round seed (*dominant*).

*r* = wrinkled seed (*recessive*).

Mendel crossed homozygous tall, round and yellow (*TTRRYY*) with dwarf, wrinkled green (*ttrryy*) plants. All the $F_1$ offspring were tall, round and yellow (*TtRrYy*). These are called *trihybrids*.

On selfing, they produced:

27 tall, round-yellow.

9 tall, round-green.

9 tall, wrinkled-yellow.

9 dwarf, round-yellow.

3 tall, wrinkled-green.

3 dwarf, round-green.

3 dwarf, wrinkled-yellow.

1 dwarf, wrinkled-green.

Thus the trihybrid phenotypic ratio is 27:9:9:9:3:3:3:1.

## 1.9 BACK CROSS AND TEST CROSS

When $F_1$ individuals are crossed with one of the two parents from which they were derived, then such a cross is called *back cross*. Therefore, in the back, cross both the parents either homozygous dominant or homozygous recessive can take part in the cross with the $F_1$ hybrid.

When $F_1$ individuals are crossed only with the homozygous recessive parent, it is called *test cross*.

Therefore, test cross is also a back cross but one of the back crosses where $F_1$ hybrid is crossed with only the pure recessive parent; it would be a **test cross**.

### 1.9.1 Monohybrid test cross ratio (Fig. 1.10)

*T* = tall pea plant (*dominant*).

*t* = dwarf pea plant (*recessive*).

Phenotypic and genotypic ratio both are 1:1.

### 1.9.2 Dihybrid test cross ratio (Fig. 1.11)

*Y* = Yellow seed of pea (*dominant*).

*y* = Green seed of pea (*recessive*).

*R* = Round seed of pea (*dominant*).

*r* = Wrinkled seed of pea (*recessive*).

Genotypic and phenotypic ratio both are 1 : 1 : 1 : 1.

## 1.10 APPLICATION OF MENDEL'S PRINCIPLES

When genetic basis of a trait is known, Mendel's principles can be used to predict the outcome of cross. There are three general procedures, two are based on the systematic enumeration of all the zygotic genotypes and phenotypes and one is based on mathematical insight.

### 1.10.1 The Punnett Square Method

To predict the outcome of simple genetic crosses Punnett square method is used, which was proposed by Reginald Punnett. For situations involving one or two genes, it is

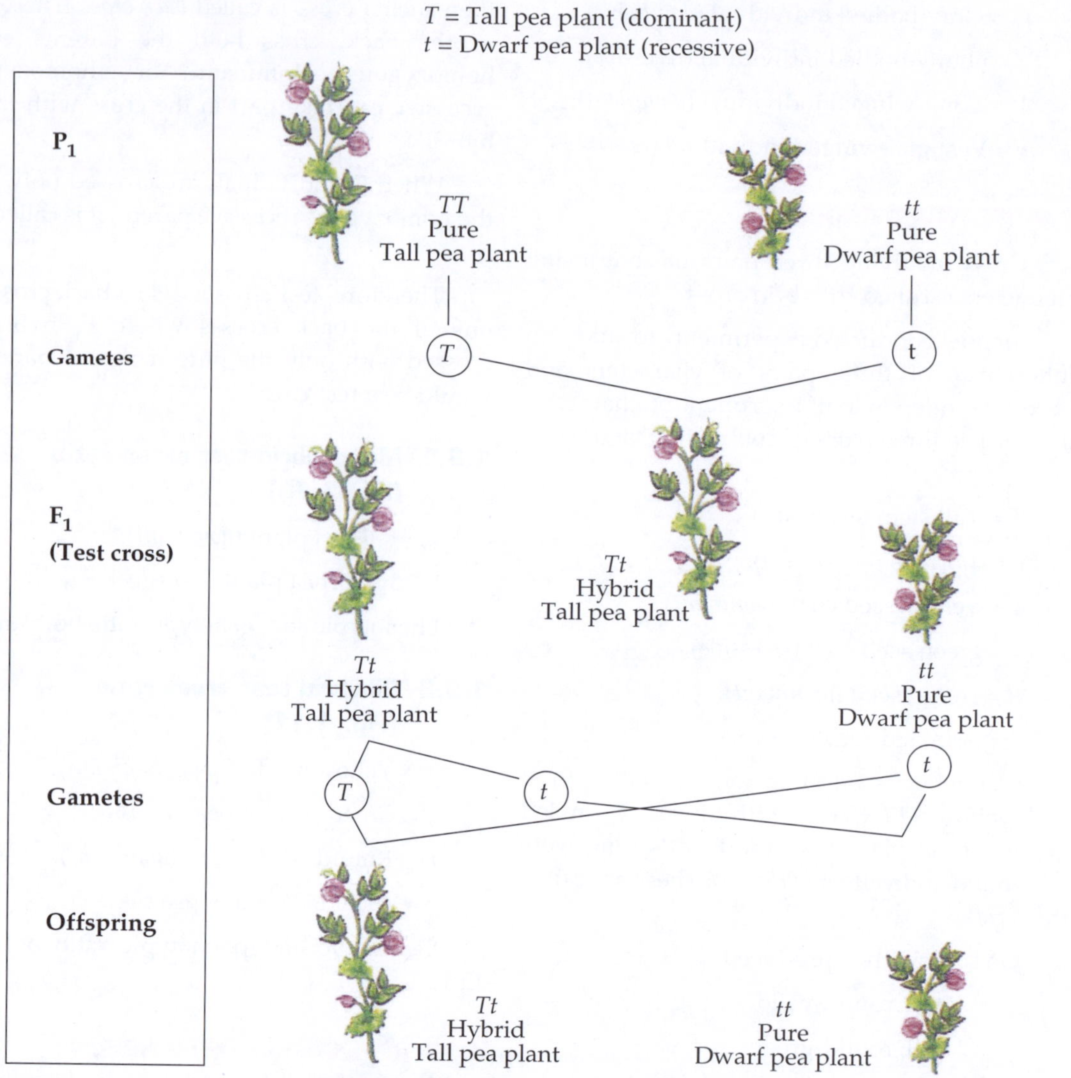


**Fig.1.10 :** *Monohybrid test cross involving tall and dwarf traits in pea plants.*

possible to write down all the gametes and combine them systematically to generate the array of zygotic genotypes. Then the principles of dominance can be used to determine the associated phenotypes. With this information, the Punnett square enables us to predict the types of offspring the parent will produce and in what proportions. However, in more complicated situations, like those involving more than two genes, the Punnett square method is unwieldy.

For the construction of Punnett square several steps are used.

Step 1 : To write down the genotypes of both parents.

Step 2 : To write down the possible gametes that each parent can produce.

*Y* = Yellow seed coat (dominant)

*y* = Green seed coat (recessive)

*R* = Round seed coat (dominant)

*r* = Wrinkled seed coat (recessive)

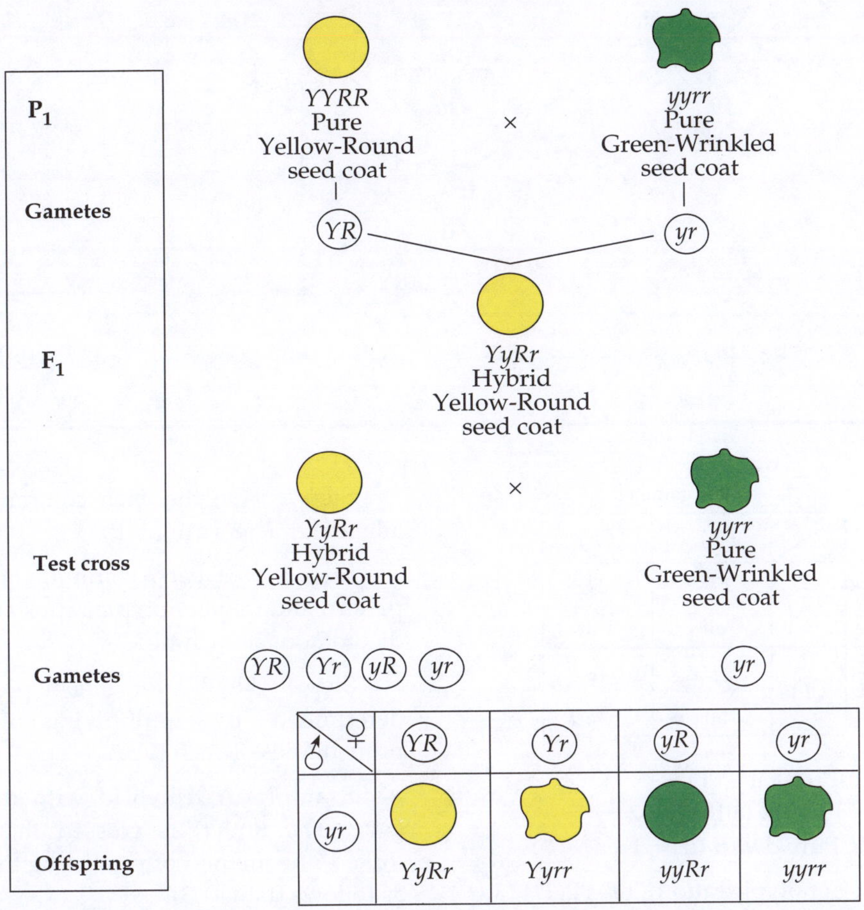


**Fig.1.11 :** *Dihybrid test cross involving two pairs of contrasting characters in the seed of pea plant.*

Step 3 : To create an empty Punnett square

Step 4 : To fill in the possible genotypes of the offspring by combining the alleles of the gametes in the empty boxes.

Step 5 : To determine the relative proportions of genotypes and phenotypes of the offspring.

Step 6 : To calculate the genotypic and phenotypic ratios of the offspring produced in the squares.

**For example :** A cross occurs between two heterozygous tall pea plants.

Step 1 : Male parent *Tt*
Female parent *Tt*

Step 2 : Male gametes *T* and *t*
Female gametes *T* and *t*

Step 3 : Empty Punnett square

Step 4 : Filling in the squares

**TABLE 1.3**
**Fork-lined method in trihybrid cross**

| *Yellow/green* | *Round/Wrinkled* | *Tall/dwarf* | *Observed product* | *Phenotype* |
|---|---|---|---|---|
| $\frac{3}{4}$ Yellow | $\frac{3}{4}$ Round | $\frac{3}{4}$ tall | $\frac{3}{4} \times \frac{3}{4} \times \frac{3}{4} = \frac{27}{64}$ | Yellow round tall |
| | | $\frac{1}{4}$ dwarf | $\frac{3}{4} \times \frac{3}{4} \times \frac{1}{4} = \frac{9}{64}$ | Yellow round dwarf |
| | $\frac{1}{4}$ Wrinkled | $\frac{3}{4}$ tall | $\frac{3}{4} \times \frac{1}{4} \times \frac{3}{4} = \frac{9}{64}$ | Yellow wrinkled tall |
| | | $\frac{1}{4}$ dwarf | $\frac{3}{4} \times \frac{1}{4} \times \frac{1}{4} = \frac{3}{64}$ | Yellow wrinkled dwarf |
| $\frac{1}{4}$ Green | $\frac{3}{4}$ Round | $\frac{3}{4}$ tall | $\frac{1}{4} \times \frac{3}{4} \times \frac{3}{4} = \frac{9}{64}$ | Green round tall |
| | | $\frac{1}{4}$ dwarf | $\frac{1}{4} \times \frac{3}{4} \times \frac{1}{4} = \frac{3}{64}$ | Green round dwarf |
| | $\frac{1}{4}$ Wrinkled | $\frac{3}{4}$ tall | $\frac{1}{4} \times \frac{1}{4} \times \frac{3}{4} = \frac{3}{64}$ | Green wrinkled tall |
| | | $\frac{1}{4}$ dwarf | $\frac{1}{4} \times \frac{1}{4} \times \frac{1}{4} = \frac{1}{64}$ | Green wrinkled dwarf |

Male gametes

| Female gametes: ♀ \ ♂ | (*T*) | (*t*) |
|---|---|---|
| (*T*) | *TT* Tall | *Tt* Tall |
| (*t*) | *Tt* Tall | *tt* dwarf |

Step 5 : Pure tall (*TT*) = 1
Hybrid tall (*Tt*) = 2
Pure dwarf (*tt*) = 1

Step 6 : Genotypic ratio 1 (*TT*) : 2(*Tt*) : 1 (*tt*)
Phenotypic ratio 3 (tall) : 1 (dwarf)

## 1.10.2 The Forked - line method

Another procedure for predicting the outcome of a cross involving two or more genes is the forked-line method where by combining the gametes systematically, branching lines of a diagram is constructed.

For this purpose, few steps are taken into account.

Step 1 : The table consists of seveal columns, therefore for the inheritance of three genes, first three columns are made.

Step 2 : On the each column, the pair of allelic characters are written.

Step 3 : At each column, the inheritance pattern and its phenotypic ratios are written by dicotomous branching.

Step 4 : Finally, the genetic proportions are determined by multiplying together the probabilities of each type.

Example. A trihybrid with three pairs of genes (*Yy Rr Tt*) is crossed themselves, the forked-line method of predicting the outcome is as follows (table 1.3).

## 1.10.3 Probability and Statistics

A powerful application of Mendel's work is that the laws of inheritance can be used to predict the outcome of genetic crosses. Before going to its application we have to know few definitions of statistical terms.

The word **probability** literally means the "chance". The theory of probability deals with laws governing the chances of occurrence of phenomena which are unpredictable in nature.

The "**experiment**" is used to describe an act which can be repeated under some given conditions.

**Random experiments** are those experiments whose results depend upon the chance. Eg, tossing of coins or throwing of a die.

The result of the random experiment is called **outcome.** Eg. a coin is tossed several times, there are two outcomes "head" or "tail".

**Event** is any phenomenon which occurs in a random experiment. For instance, one or more outcomes are said to constitute an "event". Events may be elimentary or composites. If it cannot be decomposed into simpler events, it is called *elementary event* and aggregate of several elementary events is called **composite event**.

Events are said to be **mutually exclusive**, when two or more of them can not occur simultaneously. Therefore, mutually exclusive events can always be connected by a word "either .............. or". Eg. when a coin tossed, either head or tail would be resulted.

Several events are said to form "**exhaustive set**", if at least one of them must necessarily occur. Eg, if a coin is tossed, the two events "head" and "tail" form an exhaustive set, because one of these two must necessarily occur.

Any particular performance of the random experiment is called **trial.**

The outcomes of a random experiment are said to be "**equally likely**" if after taking into consideration all relevent evidence, none of them can be expected in preference to another.

Among all the possible outcomes of a random experiment those cases which entail occurrence of an event "A" are called "**Cases of favourable to A**". For example, when a die is thrown, the odd number of points are 1, 3 and 5. Thus, these three cases are favourable to event "**odd number points**".

- **Classical definition of probability**

If a random experiment has "n" possible outcomes, which are mutually exclusive, exhaustive and equally likely and "m" of these are favourable to an event "A", then the probability of the event is the ratio $\frac{m}{n}$.

$$\text{So, } P(A) = \frac{m}{n}$$

$$= \frac{\text{Number of outcomes favourable to the event}}{\text{Total number of mutually exclusive exhaustive and equally likely outcomes of the random experiment.}}$$

For example, in a tossing of an unbiased coin, the probability of head is $\frac{1}{2}$, In a die, the probability of point 1 (one) is $\frac{1}{6}$.

In the genetic problem, when two heterozygous tall pea plants (Tt) are crossed themselves, the phenotypic ratio of the offspring is 3 tall : 1 dwarf. This information can be used to calculate the probability for tall and dwarf offspring.

Here, the probability

$$= \frac{\text{Number of individuals with a given phenotype}}{\text{Total number of individuals}}$$

$$P(\text{tall}) = \frac{3}{3+1} = \frac{3}{4} = 0.75 = 75\%$$

$$P(\text{dwarf}) = \frac{1}{3+1} = \frac{1}{4} = 0.25 = 25\%$$

The probability ranges from 0 and 1 *i.e.* $0 \leqslant P \leqslant 1$.

When P = 0, there is no chance of its occurrence.

When P=1, the chances of an event happening are 100%.

**Theorem of total probability or the addition rule or sum rule :**

*If two events are mutually exclussive, then the probability of happening of any one of them is equal to the sum of the probabilities of the happening of the separate events.*

If two events "A" and "B" are mutually exclusive, then the probability of occurrence of either "A" or "B" is given by the sum of their probabilities. i.e.,

Probability of (A or B) = Probability of A+ Probability of B.

or P(A + B) = P(A) + P(B)

Similarly, for three mutually exclussive events A, B and C

P(A+B+C) = P(A) + P(B) + P(C).

If we consider a cross between two pea plants heterozygous for genes affecting the seed colour and flower colour. Yellow seed colour (Y) is dominant over recessive green seed colour(y). Similarly, red flower (R) is dominant over the recessive white flower colour (r). If a cross is made between them, normal dihybrid ratio is observed as 9 yellow seed red flower : 3 yellow seed white flower : 3 green seed -red flower : 1 green seed -white flower. These four phenotypes yellow seed - red flower cannot have green seed white flower.

The question in such dihybrid cross (*YyRr* × *YyRr*), what is the probability that an offspring will have yellow seed-red flower or have green seed white flower phenotype?

To solve the problem following steps are to be followed.

**Step 1 :** First to calculate the individual probabilities of each phenotype. This can be accomplished by using Punnet square.

The probability of yellow seed - red flower is $\frac{9}{9+3+3+1} = \frac{9}{16}$

The probability of green seed – white flower is $\frac{1}{9+3+3+1} = \frac{1}{16}$

**Step 2 :** The individual probilities are to be added together $\frac{9}{16} + \frac{1}{16} = \frac{10}{16}$

This means that $\frac{10}{16}$ is the probability that an offspring will have either yellow seed red flower or green seed-white flower. We can convert $\frac{10}{16}$ = 0.625, which means that 62.5% of offspring are predicted to have yellow seed red flower or green seed white flower.

**Compound probability**

• *Compound event* : When two or more than two simple events occur in connection with each other, then their simultaneous occurrence is called **compound event.**

• *Conditional event* : The probability of happening of an event A, when it is known that B has already happened, is called **conditional probability** of A which is denoted by P(A/B).

*i.e.,* P(A/B) = Conditional probability of A given that B has already happened.

P(B/A) = Conditional probability of B given that A has already happened.

• *Independent event or unconditional event* : An event is said to be *independent* of the event B, if P(A/B) = P(A), *i.e.,* the probabilility of the happening of B.

For example, if two dice are tossed, the events (A), "six" on Die-I and B "six" on Die-II are independent, because, the probability of obtaining a six, suppose on die-II which is $\frac{1}{6}$ does not change if it be known that die-I has resulted in a six or not *i.e.,* unconditional.

**• Theorems of compound Probability**

The probability of occurrence of the event A as well as B is given by the product of (unconditional) probability of A and conditional probability of B, assuming that A has actually occurred, *i.e.* probability of A and B = Probability of A × Conditional probability of B assuming A.

So, P(AB) = P(A) × P(B/A)

*Example* : If a bag contains 6 white and 3 black balls, two balls are drawn at random one after the other without replacement.

For example, Suppose,

"A" denotes the event "first drawing gives 3 black balls" *i.e.* P(A)

"B" denotes the second attempt P(B/A)

Probability of dwawing a black ball in the first attempt

$$P(A) = \frac{\text{Favourable event}}{\text{Total exhaustive event}}$$

$$= \frac{m}{n} = \frac{3}{6+3} = \frac{1}{3}$$

Probability of drawing the second ball given the first ball drawn is black

$$P(\tfrac{B}{A}) = \frac{\text{Favourable event}}{\text{Total exhaustive event}}$$

$$= \frac{m}{n} = \frac{2}{6+2} = \frac{1}{4}$$

Then, Probability that both the balls drawn are black

$$\text{i.e. } P(AB) = P(A) \times P(\tfrac{B}{A})$$

$$= \frac{1}{3} \times \frac{1}{4} = \frac{1}{12}$$

Similarly, for any three events A, B and C

$$P(ABC) = P(A) \times P(\tfrac{B}{A}) \times P(\tfrac{C}{AB})$$

- **The multiplication rule or Product rule**

If the events A and B are independent, the probability that they occur together, denoted P(A and B) is P(A) × P(B).

For example, if a card drawn from a deck turns out to be an ace, we have no clue about the curds' suit. Thus drawing the ace of spade represents the joint occurrence of two independent events — the card is an ace(A) and it is a spade (S). According to the multiplicative rule. P(A and S) = P(A) × P(S) and because P(A) $= \frac{4}{52}$ and P(S) $= \frac{1}{4}$, then P(A and S) $= \frac{4}{52} \times \frac{1}{4} = \frac{1}{52}$

- **Binomial expansion and prediction of probability**

Binomial distribution is a discrete probability distribution and is defined by the probability mass function (p.m.f).

$$f(x) = {}^nC_x p^x q^{n-x}$$

Where, x = 0, 1, 2 ..............n

p and q are positive functions

and p+q = 1

In general, the occurrence of the event is called "success" and its non-occurrence is known as "failure".

In a series of n independent trials, if the probability of success in each trial is a constant p and the probability of failure is q, then the binomial distribution would be as follows.

| (x) | 0 | 1 | 2 | 3 | .......n |
|---|---|---|---|---|---|
| f(x) | $q^n$, | ${}^nC_1pq^{n-1}$, | ${}^nC_2p^2q^{n-2}$, | ${}^nC_3p^3q^{n-3}$, | .......$p^n$ |

The distribution is known as "binomial" because, the probabilities are given by the binomial series :

$$(q+p)^n = q^n + {}^nC_1pq^{n-1} + {}^nC_2p^2q^{n-2} \text{ ...... } + p^n$$

The constants n and p appearing in the expression for f(x) are known as parameters of the binomial distribution.

The important properties of such distribution is that the mean of the distribution = np, variance = npq and standard deviation is $\sqrt{npq}$ .

## 1.11 FORMULATING AND TESTING GENETIC HYPOTHESIS

### 1.11.1 Concept

Any statement or assertion about a statistical population or the values of its parameters is called **statistical hypothesis.**

The validity of hypothesis will be tested by analyzing the sample. The procedure which enables us to decide whether a certain hypothesis is true or not is called **test of significance** or **test of hypothesis**.

**Null hypothesis :** A statistical hypothesis which is set up and whose validity is tested for possible rejection on the basis of sample observation is called *Null hypothesis*.

Tests of hypothesis deals with rejection or acceptance of Null hypothesis only. This is denoted by the symbol $H_0$. For example, the Null hypothesis may be that the population mean is 40, we write $H_0$ ($\mu = 40$).

Any hypothesis which differs from the Null hypothesis is called Alternative hypothesis and is denoted by the symbol $H_A$.

Null hypothesis is tested against an alternative hypothesis which in the above case, may be either that the population mean is not 40 or that it is greater than 40 or that it is less than 40, *ie* any case of

$$H_A\ (\mu \neq 40)$$
$$H_A\ (\mu > 40)$$
$$H_A\ (\mu < 40)$$

The alternative hypothesis is not tested but its acceptance/rejection depends upon the rejection/acceptance of the Null hypothesis, the choice of an appropriate critical region depends upon the type of alternative hypothesis whether, both-sided or one-sided.

**Test of significance :** The sample analyzed to decide whether to reject or not to reject the Null hypothesis $H_0$ is based on the probability consideration.

We first choose a *"test statistic"* assuming that $H_0$ is really true.

If the difference between observed value and the expected value is large, then the Null hypothesis is rejected and we doubt the validity of our assumption. If the difference is not large, $H_0$ is not rejected and the difference may be considered to have arisen solely due to the fluctuation during sampling.

If the observed difference is larger than the set value at certain probability (say 5%) of cases, the Null hypothesis is rejected. If it is less, there is no reason to reject the Null hypothesis.

Then it is necessary to decide how much of difference is tolerable before we are able to conclude that Null hypothesis is acceptable.

The set values of the test statistic which led to rejection of Null hypothesis is called **critical region** or **rejection region** of the test. The probability with which a true Null hypothesis is rejected by the test is referred to as **size of the critical region.** On the other hand, the values that led to the acceptance of the hypothesis is said to be acceptance region. The boundary of the region of acceptance and rejection is called **critical value.**

The maximum probability with which a true Null hypothesis is rejected is known as **level of significance.**

If the probability of the test statistic lies in the critical region then the Null hypothesis is rejected only be significant at this level of probability. Then we may say that the observed difference is significant (means significantly different) say 5% and hence, Null hypothesis is rejected at 5% level of significance.

So, size of critical region $\leqslant$ level of significance

**Steps in Test of Significance :**

1. Set up the Null hypothesis *ie,* $H_0$ ($\theta = \theta_0$) and the alternative hypothesis *ie* $H_A$ ($\theta \neq \theta_0$), whether to use a two-tailed or one tailed test (right or left)
2. Set an appropriate "test statistic" and also its sample distribution.
3. Select level of significance of the test. Usually 5% or 1% level is used. If nothing is mentioned, 5% level is used.
4. Find the critical region of the test at the chosen level of significance.
5. Compute the value of test statistic on the basis of data and the Null hypothesis.
6. If the computed value of the test statistic lies in the critical region then $H_0$ is rejected, otherwise donot reject $H_0$.
7. If $H_0$ is rejected, the interpretation is that the data are not consistent with the assumption that Null hypothesis is true and hence $H_0$ is not tenable.

If $H_0$ is not rejected the data cannot provide any evidence against the Null hypothesis and hence $H_0$ may be accepted to be true.

### 1.11.2 Test for goodness of fit (Pearsonian chi-square test)

This test is used to decide whether the observations are in good aggrement with a hypothetical distribution; *i.e.,* whether the sample may be supposed to have arisen from a specified population.

The observed frequency ($f_0$) of different classes are compared with the expected frequency ($f_e$) by the test statistic

$$\chi^2 = \sum \frac{(f_0 - f_e)^2}{f_e}$$

This is goodness of fit chisquare or Pearson's chi-square.

When Null hypothesis $H_0$ (data are in aggrement with hypothetical population) is true, the statistic approximately follows $\chi^2$ distribution between (K-1) degree of freedom, where K is the number of classes.

If the observed value of the statistic exceeds the tabulated value of $\chi^2$ at a given level, the Null hypothesis is rejected.

## 1.12 SOLVED PROBLEMS

### 1.12.1 Solved problems on Probability

**Problem 1**

If a cross between plants heterozygous for four different genes, each assorting independently. What fraction of the progeny will be homozygous for all four recessive alleles?

**Solution :**

For one gene, the fraction of offspring that will be recessive homozygous is $\frac{1}{4}$, as it will be for the second, third and fourth genes.

Therefore, the principle of Independent assortment, the fraction of offspring that will be quadruple recessive homozygotes is $\frac{1}{4} \times \frac{1}{4} \times \frac{1}{4} \times \frac{1}{4} = \frac{1}{256}$.

**Problem 2**

What fraction of the offspring will be homozygous for all four genes?

**Solution :**

For each gene there are two types of homozygotes, the dominant and the recessive, and together they constitute half of the progeny.

The fraction of progeney that will be homozygous for all four genes will therefore be $\frac{1}{2} \times \frac{1}{2} \times \frac{1}{2} \times \frac{1}{2} = \frac{1}{16}$.

**Problem 3**

A cross between *AaBb* and *AaBb*, what fraction of the progeny will show recessive phenotype for at least one gene?

**Solution :**

Three kinds of genotypes would satisfy this condition.

1. *AAbb* or *Aabb*
2. *aaBB* or *aaBb*

and 3. *aabb*

The answer to the question must therefore be the sum of the probabilities corresponding to each of these genotypes.

The probability for AAbb or Aabb is $\frac{3}{4} \times \frac{1}{4} = \frac{3}{16}$.

The probability for aaBB or aaBb is $\frac{1}{4} \times \frac{3}{4} = \frac{3}{16}$.

The probability for aabb is $\frac{1}{4} \times \frac{1}{4} = \frac{1}{16}$.

Adding these together we find that the answer is $\frac{3}{16} + \frac{3}{16} + \frac{1}{16} = \frac{7}{16}$.

**Problem 4**

P is normal and p is the recessive congenital disease alleles (a) what is the probability that the couple's first three offspring will have congenital disease if both of the parents are carrier (Pp)? (b) What is the probability that the first offspring will be normal second offspring will have the congenital disease and the third will be normal again?

**Solution :**

(a) If the parents both are carrier then their genotype for the both is Pp.

The probability of an affected offspring is $\frac{1}{4}$.

In this case we are asking about the first three offspring, and so we multiply $\frac{1}{4}$ three times.

$$\frac{1}{4} \times \frac{1}{4} \times \frac{1}{4} = \frac{1}{64} = 0.016$$

Thus the probability that the first three offspring will have this trait it 0.016 or 16%.

(b) In the monohybrid cross, the normal is $\frac{3}{4}$, congenital diseased = $\frac{1}{4}$.

The probability that these three phenotypes will occur in the specified order is

$$\frac{3}{4} \times \frac{1}{4} \times \frac{3}{4} = \frac{9}{64} = 0.14$$

Therefore, this sequence of events is expected to occur only 14% of cases.

**Problem 5**

Suppose, an individual with the genotype *AaBbCC* was crossed to an individual with the genotype *AabbCc*. What is the probability that an offspring will have the genotype AAbbCc? If the three genes are independely assorted.

**Solution :**

The cross is *AaBbCC* × *AabbCc*.

Probability that an offspring will *AA* = $\frac{1}{4}$

Probability that an offspring will be *bb* = $\frac{1}{2}$

Probability that an offspring will *Cc* = $\frac{1}{2}$

We can use the product rule to determine the probabilty that an offspring will be *AAbbCc*.

$$P = \frac{1}{4} \times \frac{1}{2} \times \frac{1}{2} = \frac{1}{16} = 0.0625 = 6.25\%$$

### 1.12.2 Solved Problems on Binomial Expansion

**Problem 1**

Three coins are tossed at a time. Find the probabilities of

(i) Zero head
(ii) One head
(iii) Two heads
(iv) Three heads
(v) More than one head
(vi) At least one head

**Solution :**

Here, p= probability of success (head) in a single trial = $\frac{1}{2}$

So, $q = 1 - p = 1 - \frac{1}{2} = \frac{1}{2}$

Number of independent trials = 3

The variable (x) follows binomial distribution with parameters

Therefore, probability of x success is

$$f(x) = {}^nC_x\, p^x\, q^{n-x}$$

$$= {}^3C_x \left(\frac{1}{2}\right)^3$$

$$= \frac{1}{8}\, {}^3C_x$$

Putting the values of x = 0, 1, 2, 3

(i) f(0) = Probability of 0 success (head) = $\frac{1}{8}\,{}^{3}C_{0} = \frac{1}{8}$

(ii) f(1) = Probability of 1 success (head) = $\frac{1}{8}\,{}^{3}C_{1} = \frac{3}{8}$

(iii) f(2) = Probability of 2 success (head) = $\frac{1}{8}\,{}^{3}C_{2} = \frac{3}{8}$

(iv) f(3) = Probability of 3 success (head) = $\frac{1}{8}\,{}^{3}C_{3} = \frac{1}{8}$

(v) Probability more than one success (head) $= f(2) + f(3) = \frac{3}{8} + \frac{1}{8} = \frac{1}{2}$

(vi) Probability at least one success (head) $= 1 - f(0) = 1 - \frac{1}{8} = \frac{7}{8}$

### Problem 2

Five coins are tossed 3200 times. Find the expected frequencies of the distribution of head and tail and tabulate the result. Calculate the mean number of heads and standard deviation.

**Solution :**

Here, the probability of head = $\frac{1}{2}$

and tail = $\frac{1}{2}$

Then, the expansion of the binomial structure

$$\left(\frac{1}{2} \times \frac{1}{2}\right)^5 = \left(\frac{1}{2}\right)^5 + {}^5C_1\left(\frac{1}{2}\right)\left(\frac{1}{2}\right)^{5-1} + {}^5C_2\left(\frac{1}{2}\right)^2\left(\frac{1}{2}\right)^{5-2} + {}^5C_3\left(\frac{1}{2}\right)^3\left(\frac{1}{2}\right)^{5-3} + {}^5C_4\left(\frac{1}{2}\right)^4\left(\frac{1}{2}\right)^{5-4} + \left(\frac{1}{2}\right)^5$$

$$= \frac{1}{32} + \frac{5}{32} + \frac{10}{32} + \frac{10}{32} + \frac{5}{32} + \frac{1}{32}$$

In a single toss of 5 coins, the probabilities of the different numbers of head and tails and their expected frequencies in 3200 tosses are shown as follows :

| *Number of head* | *Number of tail* | *Probability* | *Expected frequency 3200 × Probability* |
|---|---|---|---|
| 0 | 5 | $\frac{1}{32}$ | 100 |
| 1 | 4 | $\frac{5}{32}$ | 500 |
| 2 | 3 | $\frac{10}{32}$ | 1000 |
| 3 | 2 | $\frac{10}{32}$ | 1000 |
| 4 | 1 | $\frac{5}{32}$ | 500 |
| 5 | 0 | $\frac{1}{32}$ | 100 |

Mean $\bar{x} = n.p = 5 \times \frac{1}{2} = 2.5$

Standard deviation $= \sqrt{npq}$

$$= \sqrt{5 \times \frac{1}{2} \times \frac{1}{2}} = \frac{\sqrt{5}}{2} = 1.118$$

### Problem 3

In a cross *Bb* × *Bb*, what is the probability that two out of five offspring will have blue eyes?

**Solution :**

The individual probability of the blue eye and brown eye phenotypes are to be obtained from Punnet square method. The probability of blue eye (p) = $\frac{1}{4}$ and the probability of brown eye (q) = $\frac{3}{4}$.

In this question total number n = 5

number of success x = 2

Therefore, the probability of two blue eyes out of 5 offspring putting the values in the equation

$$f(x) = {}^nC_x\, p^x q^{n-x}$$

$$= {}^5C_2\left(\frac{1}{4}\right)^2\left(\frac{3}{4}\right)^{5-2}$$

$$= \frac{\underline{|5}}{\underline{|2}\,\underline{|3}} \times \frac{1}{16} \times \frac{27}{64} = 0.263 = 26.3\%$$

**Problem 4**

Albino-carrying heterozygous parents have five children, what is the probability that we will have two normal sons, two normal daughters and one albino son?

**Solution :**

According to product rule :

Probability of a normal son $= \frac{3}{4} \times \frac{1}{2} = \frac{3}{8}$

Probability of a normal daughter

$$= \frac{3}{4} \times \frac{1}{2} = \frac{3}{8}$$

Probability of a albino son $= \frac{1}{4} \times \frac{1}{2} = \frac{1}{8}$

Probability of a albino daughter

$$= \frac{1}{4} \times \frac{1}{2} = \frac{1}{8}$$

Thus :

$$P = \frac{5!}{2!\,2!\,1!\,0!} \times \left(\frac{3}{8}\right)^2 \times \left(\frac{3}{8}\right)^2 \times \left(\frac{1}{8}\right)^1 \times \left(\frac{1}{8}\right)^0$$

$$= 0.074$$

Note : If there are more than two outcomes, the general form of multinominal expansion is $(p + q + r + \ldots\ldots\ldots\ldots)^n$ and the general formula for the probability is

$$P = \frac{n!}{s!\,t!\,u!} \times p^S\, q^t\, r^u$$

where $s + t + u + \ldots\ldots\ldots\ldots = n$

and $p + q + r + \ldots\ldots\ldots\ldots = 1$

## 1.12.3 Solved Problems on Goodness of fit

**Problem 1**

Crossing a grey-bodied scarlet-eyed *Drosophila* with a black-bodied red-eyed one, produced all grey bodied and red eyed flies in $F_1$ generation. On crossing $F_1$ flies, $F_2$ generation gave following phenotypes :

1. Grey-bodied red-eyed = 362
2. Black-bodied red-eyed = 128
3. Gray-bodied scarlet-eyed = 122
4. Black body scarlet eyed = 44

Do the data have a goodness of fit with the Mendelian cross phenotypic ratio

[ given $\chi^2_{0.05(3)} = 7.82$ ]

**Solution :**

The phenotypic ratio of Mendelian dihybrid cross is 9 : 3 : 3 : 1

The Null hypothesis is that the observed ratio follows the Mendelian dihybrid cross ratio.

Here degree of freedom = k–1 = 4 – 1 = 3

Total observation n = 362 + 128 + 122 + 44 = 656

$\chi^2$ - **Table :**

| *Phenotype* | $f_0$ | $f_e$ | $(f_0-f_e)$ | $(f_0-f_e)^2$ | $\frac{(f_0-f_e)^2}{f_e}$ |
|---|---|---|---|---|---|
| Grey body red eye | 362 | 369 | –7 | 49 | 0.132 |
| Black body red eye | 128 | 123 | 5 | 25 | 0.203 |
| Grey body scarlet eye | 122 | 123 | –1 | 1 | 0.008 |
| Black body scarlet eye | 44 | 41 | 3 | 9 | 0.219 |
| | | | | | $\sum\frac{(f_0-f_e)^2}{f_e} = 0.562$ |

The tabulated value of $\chi^2_{0.05(3)} = 7.81$. But the calculated value of $\chi^2 = 0.562$, which is less than the tabulated value. Therefore, Null hypothesis is accepted.

The conclusion is that the observed ratio has goodness of fit with the Mendelian dihybrid cross ratio.

**Problem 2**

Heterozygote snapdragon plants having the pink flower is self crossed, which give three phenotypes with Red 62, pink 131 and white 57 plants. This is to be noted that. Red and white colour flower traits show incomplete dominance. Carefully deduce the data and conclude about its goodness of fit. [given $\chi^2_{0.05(2)} = 5.991$ ]

**Solution :**

Here the Mendelian inheritance is a monohybrid cross and the dominant is incomplete. Hence the expected ratio of the offspring is 1 red : 2 pink : 1 white.

The degree of freedom = 3 – 1 = 2

**$\chi^2$ - Table :**

| *Phenotype* | $f_0$ | $f_e$ | $(f_0 - f_e)$ | $(f_0 - f_e)^2$ | $\frac{(f_0 - f_e)^2}{f_e}$ |
|---|---|---|---|---|---|
| Red | 62 | 62.5 | –0.5 | 0.25 | 0.004 |
| Pink | 131 | 125 | 6 | 36 | 0.228 |
| White | 57 | 62.5 | 5.5 | 30.25 | 0.484 |
| Total | 250 | | | | $\sum\frac{(f_0 - f_e)^2}{f_e} = 0.776$ |

The tabulated value of $\chi^2_{0.05(2)}$ = 5.991, But the calculated value from the observed data $\chi^2$ = 0.776 which is lesser than the tabulated value. Therefore, Null hypothesis is accepted. The conclusion is that the hypothesis is an adequate explanation for the data.

### Problem 3

In an experiment of test cross was preformed between yellow round seed coat heterozygous pea plant with a double recessive green-wrinkled variety. The reasult is as follows.

| | |
|---|---|
| Yellow-round | 165 |
| Yellow-wrinkled | 140 |
| Green-round | 175 |
| Green-wrinkled | 170 |

Comment on the goodness of fit for this result with Mendelian dihybrid test cross ratio.

[given $\chi^2_{0.05(3)} = 7.82$]

**Solution :**

The phenotypic ratio of Mendelian test cross ratio is 1:1:1:1

The Null hypothesis is that the observed test cross ratio follows the Mendelian test cross ratio.

**$\chi^2$ - Table :**

| *Phenotype* | $f_0$ | $f_e$ | $(f_0 - f_e)$ | $(f_0 - f_e)^2$ | $\frac{(f_0 - f_e)^2}{f_e}$ |
|---|---|---|---|---|---|
| Yellow-round | 165 | 162.5 | 2.5 | 6.25 | 0.0384 |
| Yellow-wrinkled | 140 | 162.5 | –22.5 | 506.25 | 3.1153 |
| Green-round | 175 | 162.5 | 12.5 | 156.25 | 0.9615 |
| Green-wrinkled | 170 | 162.5 | 7.5 | 56.25 | 0.3461 |
| Total | 650 | | | | $\sum\frac{(f_0 - f_e)^2}{f_e} = 4.461$ |

Degree of freedom = 4–1 = 3

The tabulated value of $\chi^2_{0.05(3)}$ = 7.82. But the calculated value of $\chi^2$ = 4.461 which is less than the tabulated value. Thus Null hypothesis is accepted. It is concluded that the observed data have goodness of fit with the Mendelian test cross ratio.

### Problem 4

A cross between black and white coat coloured mice, the $F_2$ individuals are segregated into 787 black and 277 white coat colour. If you have to test that this result agrees with the expected monohybrid cross ratio. [given $\chi^2_{0.05(1)} = 3.84$]

**Solution :**

The Mendelian monohybrid cross ratio is 3 : 1. The Null hypothesis is that the observed frequency followed the Mendelian test cross frequency.

$\chi^2$ - **Table :**

| *Phenotype* | $f_0$ | $f_e$ | $(f_0-f_e)$ | $(f_0-f_e)^2$ | $\frac{(f_0-f_e)^2}{f_e}$ |
|---|---|---|---|---|---|
| Black | 787 | 798 | –11 | 121 | 0.1516 |
| White | 277 | 266 | +11 | 121 | 0.4548 |
| Total | 1064 | | | | $\sum\frac{(f_0-f_e)^2}{f_e} = 0.606$ |

The tabulated value of $\chi^2_{0.05(1)} = 3.84$. But the calculated value is 0.606, which is less than the tabulated value. Thus Null hypothesis is accepted. It is concluded that the observed value has goodness of fit with the Mendelian monohybrid cross ratio.

## Chapter Glossary/Key Terms

**Alleles :** A pair of genes showing Mendelian segregation in a 3:1 ratio after crossing.

**Atavism :** Appearance of a character present in distant ancestor and not shown by parents or grand parents.

**Backcross :** The cross of an individual with one of its parents or with an organism with the same genotype of the parent.

*Contd.*

**Codominance :** The relationship of alleles in a heterozygote that shows the individuals expression of each allele in the phenotype.

**Conditioned dominance :** The dominant trait would be expressed only in presence of certain environmental conditions.

**Critical region:** The set values of a test statistic which led to rejection of Null hypothesis.

**Dominant gene :** When a gene responsible for a certain character, becomes expressive in $F_1$.

**Exhaustive set :** At least one of the events must necessarily occur.

**Factor :** See "gene".

**Gametes :** A mature germ cell.

**Gemmule :** Tissues, cells and organs of the animal body are discharged in the blood stream and are deposited as gemmules in the reproductive organs.

**Gene :** The hypothetical "factor" of Mendel.

**Genetics :** The branch of science which embodies studies of biological makeup, environement and also the analysis of the laws and principles that govern transmission of character.

**Genotype :** The genetical constitution of an indivudual.

**Heredity :** Inheritance of characters from parent to their offspring

**Heterozygous :** An individual containing a pair of unlike genes, a dominant and its recessive alleles.

**Homozygous :** An individual containing a pair of identical alleles, either two dominants or two recessives.

**Incomplete dominance :** The situation in which both alleles of the heterozygote influence the phenotype whch is usually intermediate between the two homozygous forms.

**Level of significance :** The maximum probability with which a true Null hypothesis is rejected.

**locus :** The physical location of a particular gene on a chromosome.

**Mutually exclusive :** Two or more of the events can not occur simultaneously.

**Null hypothesis :** The statistical hypothesis that there are no differences between observed data and those data expected based on the assumption of no experimental effect.

**Outcome :** Result of the random experiment.

**Phenotype :** The external appearance of an individual.

**Probability :** The expression of the occurrence of a particular event.

**Probability theory :** The coceptual framework concerned with qualification of probabities.

**Recessive gene :** A gene responsible for a certain character but remains hidden in $F_1$.

**Testcross :** The cross of an organism with a homozygous recessive.

**Trait :** Any characteristics that an organism displays.

**Trial :** Any particular performance of the random experiment.

**Variation:** Members of a species which shows differences amongst themselves.

**Zygote :** Union of two gametes that form the cell.

# Exercise

## A. Long answer type questions :

1. What is blending theory of inheritance. What are the exceptions of blending inheritance?
2. Why Mendel preferred to take garden peas for genetic experiments and what are the causes of the success?
3. What contrasting pairs of characters of garden pea did Mendel considered?
4. What is dihybrid cross? Give an example and find out the genotypic and phenotypic ratios in $F_2$. From this cross what did Mendel come to his conclusion?
5. What is incomplete dominance? Give an example? From this cross what did Mendel come to his conclusion?
6. What are the Mendel principles of inheritance?
7. What is codominance? Give an example with suitable cross.
8. What is trihybrid cross? Give the example. Find out their phenotypic ratios in $F_2$.
9. Define and distinguish back-cross and test-cross. Find out monohybrid and dihybrid test-cross ratios?
10. How outcome of genetic crosses can be predicted by Punnet square method and the forked line method?
11. What is statistical probability? What is the classical definition of probability? What are limitations? Deduce sum-rules, product-rule of probability.
12. How prediction of probability is done by binomial expansion.
13. What is statistical hypothesis? What is meant by a test of null hypothesis?
14. Explain the term : Tests of signifinance, Null hypothesis, Critical region, level of significance, region of acceptance.
15. A particular variety of corn has a gene for kernel colour and a gene for height with the following phenotypes.

    CC, Cc : purple kernel

    cc : White kernel

    TT : tall stem

    Tt : Medium height of stem

    tt : dwarf stem

    Give the proportions of genotypes and phenotypes if a dihybrid plant is selfed.
15. A brown-eyed, long-winged fly is mated with a red-eyed, long-winged fly. The progeny are

    51 long, red

    53 long, brown

    18 Short, red

    16 Short, brown

    What are the genotypes of the parent?
16. In *Drosophila*, two red-eyed flies mate and yield 110 red eyed and 35 brown-eyed offsprings. Diagram the cross and determine which allele is dominant?
17. A purple-flowered pea plant is crossed with a white-flowered pea plant. All the $F_1$ plants produce purple flowers. When the $F_1$ plants are allowed to self-pollinate, 401 of the $F_2$ s have purple and 131 have white flowers. What are the genotypes of the parental and $F_1$ generation plants?
18. Grey seed colour (*G*) in garden peas is dominant to white seed color (*g*). In the following crosses, the indicated parents with known phenotypes, but unknown genotypes, produced the progeny listed :

| Parent | Progeny | | Female parent genotype |
|---|---|---|---|
| Female × Male | Grey | white | |
| Grey × White | 81 | 82 | ? |
| Grey × Grey | 118 | 39 | ? |
| Grey × White | 74 | 0 | ? |
| Grey × Grey | 90 | 0 | ? |

On the basis of the segregation data, give the possible genotypes of each female parent.

19. In Jimsonweed, purple flower (*P*) is dominant to white (*p*) and spiny pods (*S*) are dominant to smooth (*s*). A true-breeding plant with white flowers and spiny pods is crossed to a true breeding plant with purple flowers and smooth pods. Determine the phenotype of

    (a) the $F_1$ generation

    (b) the $F_2$ generation

    (c) the progeny of a cross of the $F_1$ s back to the white spiny parent.

    (d) the progeny of a cross of the $F_1$ back to the purple smooth parent.

20. Phenylthiocarbamide (PTC) tasting is dominant (T) to nontasting (*t*). If a taster woman (with a nontaster father) produces children with a taster man and the man previously had a nontaster daughter, what would be the probability that

    (a) their first child would be a nontaster?

    (b) their first child would be a nontaster girl?

    (c) if they had six children, they would have two nontaster sons, two nontaster daughters and two taster sons?

    (d) their fourth child would be a taster daughter?

21. What chance do a man and a woman have of producing one son and one daughter?

22. If a heterozygous taster mates with a nontaster, what is the probability that of their five children, only one will be a taster?

23. Mendel self-fertilized pea plants with round and yellow peas. In the next generation he recovered the following numbers of peas

    round and yellow : 315

    round and green : 108

    wrinkled and yellow : 101

    wrinkled and green : 32

    What is yours hypothesis about the genetic control of the phenotype? Do the data support this hypothesis?

24. A violet-flowered, long stemmed plant was crossed with a white-flowered, short stemmed plant producing the following offspring.

    47 violet, long stemmed

    40 White, long stemmed

    38 violet, short-stemmed

    41 white, short-stemmed plants.

    Suggest a hypothesis with different levels of significance.

25. Two agouti mice are crossed and over a period of a year 48 offspring are produced with the following phenotypes :

    28 agauti, 7 black and 13 albino.

    What is your hypothesis about the genetic control of coat colour in these mice? Do the data support that hypothesis?

26. What offspring will a blue Andulasian fowl have if bred to birds of the following plumage colour : (a) black, (b) blue, (c) white?

27. Destinguish between incomplete dominance and codominance.

## B. Short answer type questions.

1. Who first used the term "Genetics"?
2. Define genetics?
3. What are heredity and variation?
4. Who is known as the "Father of modern genetics"?
5. Define blending and particulate theories?
6. What are the exceptions of blending inheritance?
7. Who rediscovered the Mendel's work?
8. Why Mendel preferred garden peas in his experiments?
9. What are the seven pairs of contrasting characters of peas that Mendel considered?
10. How Mendel performed his experiments?
11. What are meant by parental generation, first filial generations and second filial generations?
12. Define factors, alleles locus, dominance recessive, genotype, phenotype, homozygote, heterozygote.
13. What is monohybrid cross? What are its genetypic and phenotypic ratios?
14. What is the law of dominance and recessiveness?

15. Define Mendel's law of segregation.
16. Define Mendel's law of independent assortment.
17. What is incomplete dominance? Give example
18. What is codominance? Give example.
19. What is delayed dominance? Give example.
20. What is reversal of dominance? Give example.
21. What is conditioned dominance? Give example.
22. What is meant by dihybrid cross? Give example. What is its phenotypic ratio in $F_2$?
23. What is meant by trihybrid cross? Give an example.
24. Define back-cross and test-cross.
25. "All test-crosses are backcrosses but all back crosses are not test crosses" — explain.
26. Give monohybrid and dihybrid test cross ratios?
27. Define probability, experiments, random experiments, outcome, events, mutually exclusive event, exhaustive set, trial, equally likely etc.
28. What is classical definition of probability?
29. What is addition rule of probability?
30. What is compound probability?
31. What are conditional probability.
32. What are independent and unconditional events?
33. Define the theorems of compound probability.
34. What is product rule?
35. What is success and failure?
36. What is statistical hypothesis?
37. What is meant by test of hypothesis?
38. What are null and alternative hypotheses?
39. What is rejection region?
40. What are critical value and size of the critical region?
41. What is meant by level of significance?
42. Define Pearson's chi-square.

# 2

# Model Genetic Organisms

**CHAPTER AGENDA**

## 2.1 CONCEPT

Genetic studies are conducted on thousands of different species, including almost all major groups of bacteria, fungi, protists, plants and animals. These organisms are used widely in genetic studies, because they have the characteristics, such as short generation time and large number of progeny and adaptibility to a laboratory environment that make them well suited to genetic analysis. Six model organisms are taken into account for many genetic researches and their genomes were sequenced as a part of the Human Genome Project. These six organisms are

1. *Escherichia coli*, a bacterium
2. *Saccharomyces cerevisiae*, the baker's yeast
3. *Caenorhabditis elegans*, a nematode
4. *Mus musculus*, the house rat,
5. *Drosophila melanogaster*, the fruit fly and
6. *Arabidopsis thaliana*, the mustard plant.

Other species that are frequently the subject of genetic research include

1. *Neurospora crassa*, the bread mold.
2. *Zea mays*, the corn
3. *Danio rerio*, the zebrafish.
4. *Xenopus laevis*, the clawed frog, and
5. grasshoppers.

## 2.2 *ESCHERICHIA COLI*

This is one of the best prokaryotic organisms studied for genetic experiments and analysis. These are naturally occuring bacteria in the intestinal tract of human and other warm-blooded animals. Some strains are disease causing organisms [Fig. 2.1(a)].

### 2.2.1 Life Cycle

1. It can grow in the minimal medium that contains only glucose and some inorganic salts.
2. It undergoes division once an hour. But in richer medium with sufficient glucose and amino acids, it can divide every 20 minutes.
3. It reproduces normally by simple binary fission where chromosomes divide first and followed by division of the cell.
4. Sexual reproduction occurs through conjugation, which is controlled by fertility genes located on its F-plasmids. This occurs by transfer and recombination.
5. Genetic recombination may occur by transformation and transduction processes.

### 2.2.2 Genomics

1. Its chromosome is single circular highly coiled
2. Total 4638858 base pairs in the chromosome.
3. Total number of gene is approximately 4289.
4. Only 8% of the genes are common with humans.
5. Average gene size is 1000 base pairs.
6. Half of the genes are more than one copy called *orphane genes* which may play an important role in adapting to unusual environment, coordinating metabolic pathways and communicating with other bacterial cells.
7. G+C content is 51%.

### 2.2.3 Advantages

1. The cell is very small with rapid reproduction.
2. Under optimal condition, it can divide every 20 minutes, Thus within a day, more than few million descendents can be obtained.

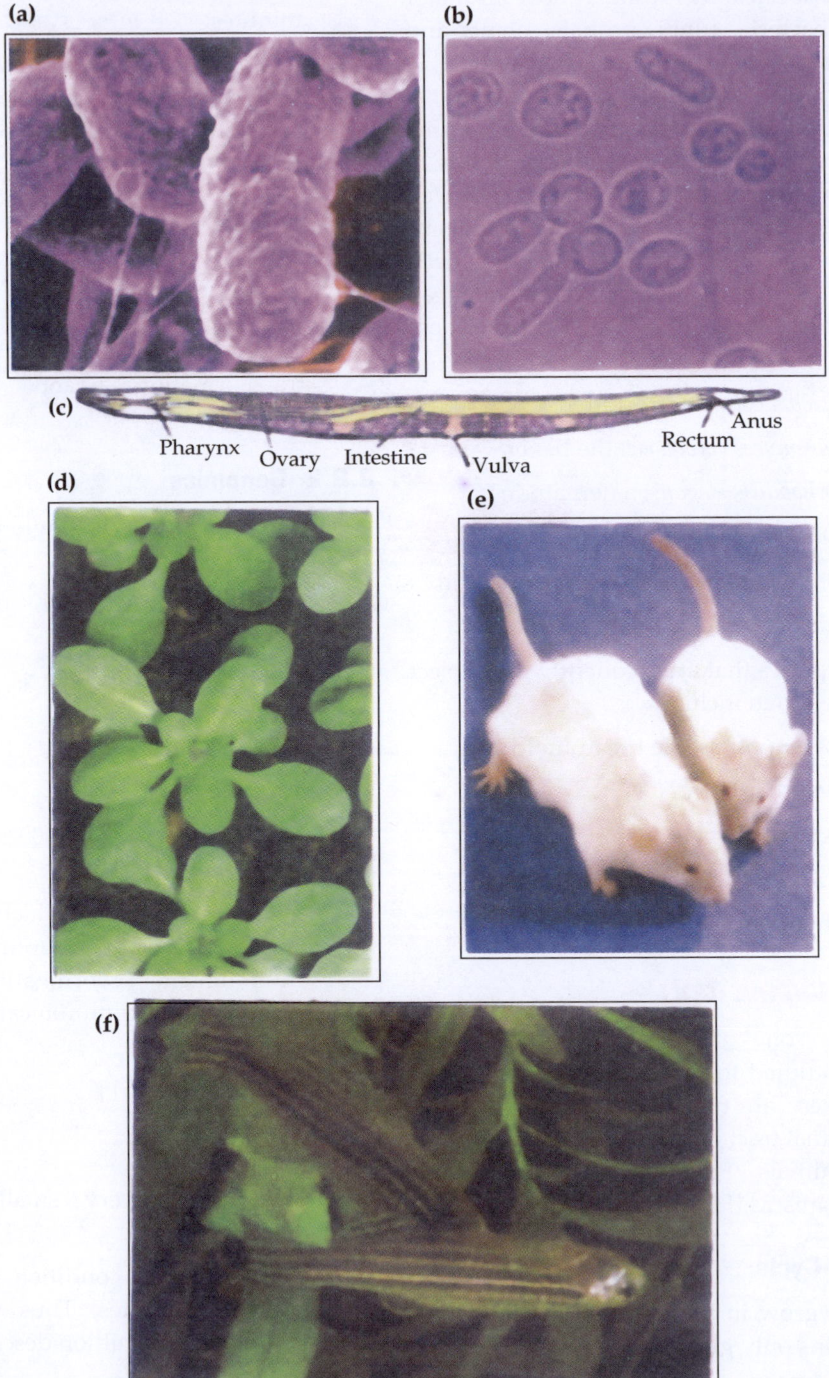


**Fig. 2.1 :** *Some Model genetic organisms*
*(a) E. coli ; (b) S. cerevisiae; (c) C. elegans; (d) Arabidopsis thaliana; (e) Mus musculus; (f) Danio rerio*

3. Easy to culture in liquid or solid medium in the laboratory.
4. It forms colony on the petridish and therefore this is very easy to isolate.
5. Genome is very small.
6. They undergo mutations with distinct phenotypes.
7. Various methods are available for genetic engineering.

### 2.2.4 Contribution to Genetics

1. For isolation of restriction enzymes
2. For isolation of plasmids
3. For the production of recombinant DNA and cloning of genes.
4. Gene regulation and expression studies
5. To study genetic processes such as resplication, transcription, translation and recombination etc.
6. Gene fine structure
7. To study on gene mutaions
8. *E. coli* gives the basic knowledge about the genetic processes and discoveries in molecular genetics.

## 2.3 *SACCHAROMYCES CEREVISIAE*

*S. cerevisiae* is known as common baker's yeast, an eukaryotic organism provides a powerful model for the study in classical as well as molecular biology and reseach [(Fig. 2.1(b)].

### 2.3.1 Life Cycle

1. Life cycle exists in two forms, haploid and diploid.
2. When the organism is starved for nutrition, it exists in haploid form. Then it reproduces mitotically by producing haploid daughter cells through budding.
3. In optimum nutrient condition, they undergo sexual reproduction. There are two mating types " α" and 'a'. Haploid cells of two different mating types fuse to form a diploid cell. These cells reproduce mitotically through budding process.
4. Starvation induces these diploid cells to undergo meiosis to form haploid spores.
5. Four spores form a tetrad and enclosed in a common structure called ascus.
6. Spores germinate into yeast cells.

### 2.3.2 Genomics

1. In haploid cells chromosome number is 16. Thus in diploid cells 16 paires of chromosomes.
2. The size of the organism is about 2μ diameter.
3. Single-celled eukaryotic organism.
4. The amount of DNA is 12.1 million base pairs.
5. Total number of genes 6144 of which 5900 encode proteins.
6. Average gene size is 1500 base pairs
7. 25% of their genes are common to humans.
8. G + C content is 38%.
9. Number of estimated protein domains encoded by some eukaryotic genomes is 581.
10. *S. pombe* has introns and fewer transposable elements. It has only 4900 genes.

### 2.3.3. Advantages

1. Most simple eukaryotic unicellular organism with molecular and genetic systems similar to those of higher organisms including human beings.
2. It can be grown easily in the laboratory with a very short life cycle of only 90 minutes.
3. Exists in both haploid and diploid forms. So when in haploid forms, single allele at each locus will be expressed as it's phenotype. On the contrary when in

diploid forms some recessive alleles are masked by dominant alleles. Thus the recessive and dominant alleles can be easily identified and the interactions between them can also be analysed.

4. All the products of meiosis are present in a single struture called ascus. These four cells from a single zygote are called *tetrads*. From tetrad analysis, it is possible to identify all the products from the single meiosis, which is called *tetrad analysis*.
5. In spite of unicellular structure, yeast cells possess many genes which are found in humans and other eukaryotic organisms which have several contributions to Human Genome Project.

### 2.3.4 Contribution to Genetics

1. The rate of recombination is high and therefore a relatively long genetic map compared with other organisms.
2. It's mitochondrial genome is studied extensively.
3. It's plasmid is 2μ with 6300 bp. long, and is transmitted to daughter cells in both mitosis and meiosis. This plasmid has been engineered to provide an efficient vector for gene transfer into yeast. Shuttle vectors are produced which are propagated in both yeasts and bacteria are used for genetic manipulation.
4. Yeast Artificial Chromosome has been developed for the purpose of cloning of large DNA fragments.

## 2.4 *CAENORHABDITIS ELEGANS*

*C. elegans,* a soil-living nematode, first introduced to the study of genetics by Sydney Brenner in 1962 for genetic dissection of behaviour. The species has made important contribution to the study of development, cell death, aging and behaviour (Fig. 2.3c).

### 2.4.1 Life Cycle

1. *C. elegans* is 1mm is length, unsegmented elongated body, lives and reproduces in the soil.
2. The mature forms are either males but maximum are hermaphrodites. Hermaphrodites are with XX genetic constitutions produce both eggs and sperms. They may self fertilize to produce only females but sometimes may produce males due to non-disjunction of X-chromosomes. The males are with XO genetic constitution produce two kinds of gametes. When hermaphrodites mate with males, half of the progeny are XX hermaphrodites and other half are XO males.
3. Fertilization is internal. Eggs are laid in the soil and the development is completed externally. After 14 hours of fertilization, a larva is hatched out called $L_1$. After 10 hrs, 11 hrs, 13 hrs, three successive larval stages $L_2$, $L_3$ and $L_4$ are produced. The $L_4$ larva undergoes final molt and after 26 hours, an adult worm is produced.
4. In normal laboratory condition, it survives only 2-3 weeks.

### 2.4.2 Genomics

1. It contains 5 pairs of autosomes plus two X-chromosomes in females (hermaphrodites) but one-X-chromosome in males.
2. Number of predicted protein domains 1014
3. Percentage of genome consisting of interspersed repeats derived from transposable element is 6.5%.
4. Amout of DNA is 103 million base pairs
5. Number of genes 20598 of which 20000 are protein encoding genes.
6. 25% of its gene is common with humans.
7. Average gene size is 5000 base pairs.
8. G+C content is 49%.

### 2.4.3 Advantages

1. The worm is small, non-parasitic and so it is easy to culture in the laboratory.
2. It produces large numbers of eggs (200–1000) and offspring.
3. Generation time is 3 days only at room tempeature.
4. It may be cultured on agar-filled petridishes and covered with bacteria for their food.
5. The body is transparent and so the cells of their developmental stages can be observed easily.
6. Body is simple with invariable number 959 cells in a mature hermaphrodite organism and 1031 cells in a mature female.
7. Self-fertilization and cross-fertilization both are taking place.

### 2.4.4 Contribution to Genetics

1. This is the smallest multicellular animal and having 25% common genetic homology with human, thus it becomes an important model organism in Human Genome Project.
2. During its development, all the cells and their lineages are traced back to the original zygote stage. The programmed cell death of each cell is known in advance and thus the mechanism of apoptosis and tumor suppression, gene regulations during cell division cycle, the role of genes in cancer are often clearly traced out.
3. Chemical mutagens are routinely used to generate mutation in *C.elegans* which are easy to identify and isolate.
4. The interferance RNA technology is widely used on these worms to investigate gene silencing studies.
5. Transgenic worms can be produced by injecting DNA directly into ovary to observe expression of different genes.

## 2.5 *MUS MUSCULUS*

After the rediscovery of Mendel's principles of heredity, geneticists began to use mice to their inheritance of traits. The Jackson Laboratory, Maine, in Bar Harbor first recognized inbreed strain of mice in 1929 then it became the centre for mouse genetics (Fig. 2.1c).

### 2.5.1 Life Cycle

Mice are rodent mammals, weighing about 20 gms and size is about 2–3 inches in length. They inhabit in fields, houses and other places surrounding us.

Secondary oocytes are ovulated from the ovaries and enter into oviduct.

Following fertilization, the diploid embryo implants into the uterus. Gestation period is 21 days.

The mice reach puberty in about 5–6 weeks. Life span is 2 years. Generation time is about 8 weeks.

### 2.5.2 Genomics

1. Chromosome number is 2n=40, of which 19 pairs of autosomes and one pair of sex chromosome. Males have one X and One Y, while females have two Xs.
2. Total amount of DNA is 2.6 billion base pairs
3. Total number of genes 26762
4. Average gene size 40000 base pairs
5. 99% genes are common to human beings
6. In the year 2002 all the genes have been sequenced.
7. G+C content is 42%
8. There are large segments of chromosomes in which gene content and even gene order are the same with human beings. 2300 genes of mouse are very similar with human beings.

### 2.5.3 Advantages

1. The foremost among many advantages that mouse has its close relationship to human. About 99% homology in genes makes it an alternative experimental mammal in place of human beings because human being are not used for experimental purpose.
2. The oestrus cycle is only 4 days, easy to breed and culture in the laboratory and tremendous geneation with only 21 days gestation period and 8–10 pups per litter make it's use in genetic studies.
3. Sex determining mechanism, chromosome karyotype etc. are very similar to human beings.

### 2.5.4 Contribution to Genetics

1. Due to vast similarities between human and mouse genomes, it becomes an important tool for determining the function of unknown genes in humans.
2. The linkage relations of many genes are similar to those of humans. Thus the linkage relation of genes in mice may provide many informations about these related genes in humans.
3. Production of transgenic mice by simple injection of DNA into the mouse embryo and gene knockout studies are made possible to study mutational and functional studies of many genes.
4. A number of human diseases have been created to mice by manipulating their genes, which make possible to know the cause and mechanism of origin as well as the remedies of these diseases.

## 2.6 *DROSOPHILA MELANOGASTER*

*Drosophila* is commonly known as fruit fly which was among the first organisms used for genetic studies and analysis even today. The genus has more than 1000 species, of which *D. melanogaster* is widely used but the studies have also been extended to many other species of the genus. Thomas Hunt Morgan began using fruit flies in the experimental studies of heredity at Columbia University in the year 1900. In the year 2000 all the genes were sequenced (Fig. 2.2).

### 2.6.1 Life Cycle

1. The insect is 2–3 mm in length, three body segments and one pair of wings. It feeds on fruit.
2. The mode of development is holometabolous type, *ie* complete metamerphosis where eggs through a series of stages larva and pupa, it transforms into adult. The time of development from egg to adult depends upon the temperature of the environment. Usually it requires 10 days at 25°C. At higher temperature, the generation time is faster *i.e.* 12–13 days at 21–22°C , on the other hand below 18°C the generation time is slower, about 19 days.
3. **Eggs** : Fertilized females lay eggs upto 100/day. Virgin females lay unfertilized eggs but these are sterile.

   Eggs are 0.5 mm in length, undergo rapid cleavage. Within one day at optimum temperature *i.e.* at 25°C, a protruding structure is found which is to be used for the coming out larva stage. The larva is clearly visible in the growing medium if the medium is white for the black head of the larva.
4. Larvae are motile. They feed and grow very rapidly. During each instar, larval growth occurs and between the instars they discard their own cuticle and skin, which is called molting and a new skin and cuticle are formed. At late stages of larva, they grow to a larger size and attain maximum size on 6th day of fertilization after third and final instar.

   (a) The eggs are first fertilized (day-0)

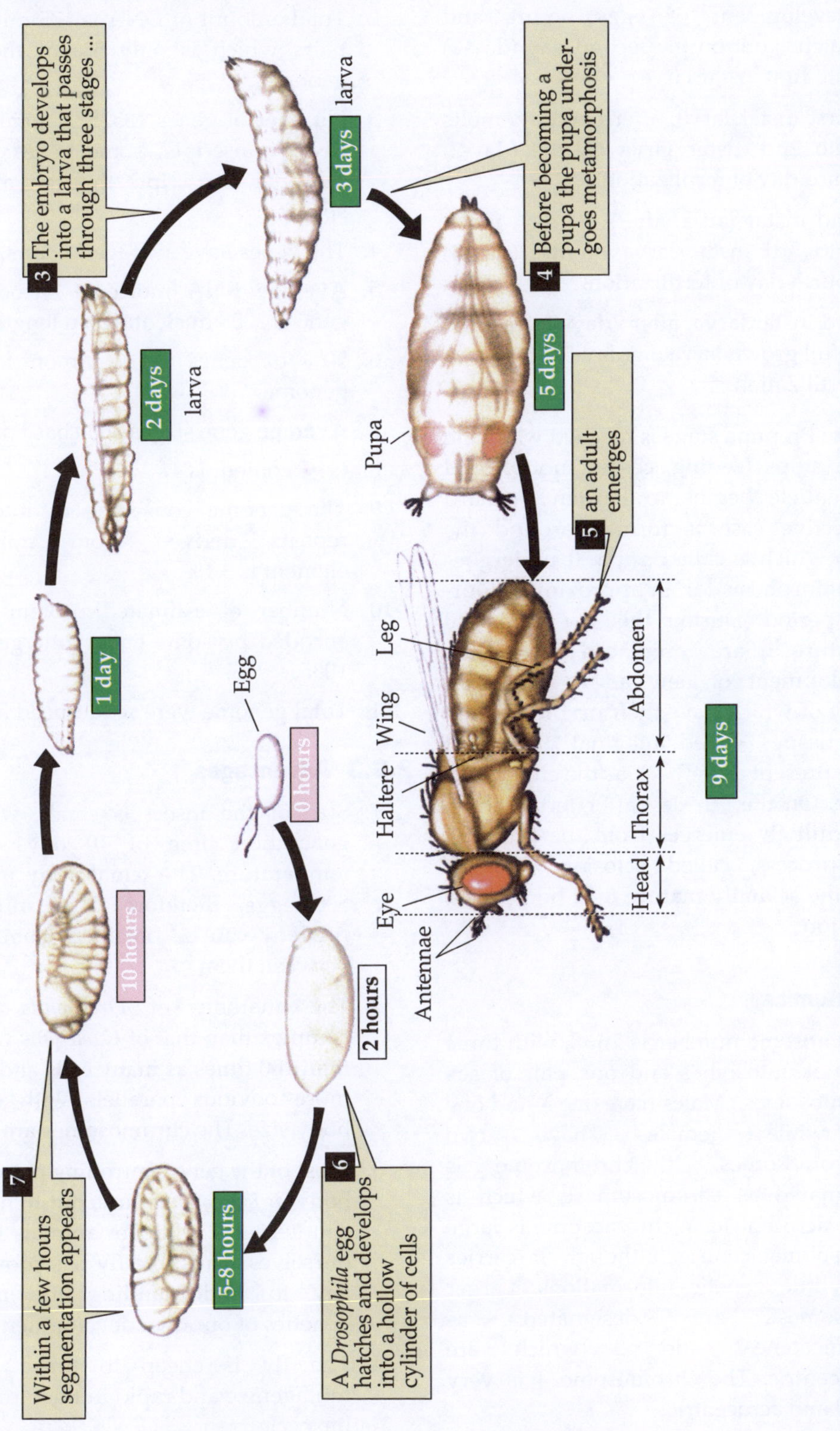


**Fig. 2.2 :** *Life cycle of Drosophila melanogaster.*

(b) Development of eggs occurs and hatches out on the second day (day-1) into first instar larva.

(c) First instar larva, after one day, molts into 2nd instar larva on the (day-2) third day of fertilization.

(d) 2nd instar larva, after one day, molts into 3rd instar larva on the (day-3) fourth day of fertilization.

(e) 3rd instar larva, after 2days forms into a full grown larva on (day-5) 6th day of fertilization.

5. **Pupa :** Prepupa stage is reached when the larva stops feeding, ceases motion and the cuticle begins to harden. A hard protective case is formed around the larva which is called pupa. It undergoes metamorphosis for an approximate four-day period. During this period, larval structures are replaced by the development of new adult structures, many of which have their origin in small disc tissues, called imaginal discs, that were present as far back as the embryonic stage. On the 9th day after fertilization, an adult fly emerges from the pupa by the process, called eclosion. Females become sexually mature 8-10 hours after eclosion.

### 2.6.2 Genomics

1. Chromosome number is 2n=8, with three pairs of autosomes and one pair of sex chromosomes. Males have one X and one Y while females have two X-chromosomes. X chromosome is designated as chromosome-1, which is large acrocentric. Y chromosome is large but submetacentric, although it carries very little genetic informations. Larger autosomes are designated as chromosome-2 and 3 which are metacentric. The chromosome 4 is very small and acrocentric.
2. Total amount of DNA is 175 million base pairs which is only 5% of the human genome.
3. Number of genes 13525, A total of 14113 RNA transcripts, some genes encoding multiple transcripts through alternative splicing.
4. The genes have average 4 exons/gene.
5. Average RNA molecule encoded by a gene is 3058 nucleotides in length.
6. 50% of genes are common to human genome.
7. Average gene size is 3000 base pairs.
8. G+C content is 41%.
9. The genome consisting of interspersed repeats derived from transposable element is 3.1%.
10. Number of estimated protein domains encoded by some eukaryotic genomes is 1035.
11. Total genome were sequesnced in 2000.

### 2.6.3 Advantages

1. Size of the insect is small, with short generation time of 10 days at room temperature. The females lay more than 500 eggs, therefore, large number of progeny can be obtained from crossing between them.
2. The anatomy of *Drosophila* is more complex than that of *C. elegans* with more than 100 times as many cells and it shows more obvious parallels with our own body size. The chromosomes are large.
3. Most of the gene controlling pattern of the body in *Drosophila* turns out to have close counterparts in higher animals including ourselves. Thus, the fly has provided the key to understanding the molecular genetics of our own development.
4. The fly is cheap to breed, easy to mutagenize and rapid in the reproductive life cycle.

5. In *Drosophila*, only one copy of gene of one specific character and therefore, for the mutation study, the phenotype of a single mutation in the fly often directly uncovers the function of the mutant genes. Besides, the wild and mutant characters are very prominent to distinguish between them.

### 2.6.4 Contribution to genetics

1. It plays an important role in studies of linkage, epistasis, chromosome genetics, development, behaviour and evolution.
2. By understanding the processes of replication and transcription in fruit fly helps us to understand the same processes in humans and other eukaryotes.
3. Salivary gland chromosome of *Drosophila* larva is an important tool for cytogenetic mapping of genes and the location of genes.
4. This is a tool for the study of induced mutations and chromosome aberrations.
5. Genetic control of pattern formation during development is a classical study which can be done with *Drosophila*.
6. There are several species of *Drosophila*, their chromosome numbers are different. By their chromosome study, the role of centric fusion of chromosomes in evolution can be traced out.

## 2.7 *ARABIDOPSIS THALIANA*

The molecular biology of plants has lagged behind the other groups of organisms. Though, much of the early works in genetics were carried out on plants, including Mendel's discoveries on pea plants and other important aspects of heredity.

*Arabidopsis thaliana,* a mustard plant commonly known as mouse-ear cress has become the model for the molecular genetics of higher plants (Fig. 2.1d).

### 2.7.1 Life Cycle

1. *A. thaliana* is a flowering plant, with roots, one primary shoot, simple leaves and flowers. Height of the plant is 10–20 cm. They live on medows as weeds. Excepts for genetic studies, these plants have no economic importance.
2. Alternation of generation occurs through diploid vegetative plant and haploid gametes produced in the pollen and ovaries.
3. Polination causes to fall the pollen grains on the stigma of flower. Pollen tube migrates through the pistil upto the ovary and fertiliation occurs there. The zygotes develop within the seeds which are produced in a long pod.
4. At appropriate conditions, the embryo germinates and grows into a plant.

### 2.7.2 Genomics

1. It consists of 5 pairs of linear chromosomes.
2. Genome size is about 125 million base pairs.
3. Total number of gene is 25706 average with 4 introns. Although, it has many proteins in common with yeast, *C. elegans*, *Drosophila* and also humans.
4. It has roughly 150 protein families which are not seen in other eukaryotes including structural proteins, transcription factors, enzymes and proteins of unknown function.
5. About 18% of the genes have been found to be common with humans.
6. Average gene size is 2000 b.p.
7. Genome of *Arabidopsis* consisting of interspersed repeats derived from transposable elements of about 10.5%, which is much less than human beings (44%). Most of the transposable elements

are not transcribed and many of them are concentrated near the centromere.

8. 60% of the genome consisting of duplicated segments. 17% in tandem arrays which are multiple copies of same gene. This may be due to unequal crossing over. Large extent of such genes suggests that species has tetraploid ancertors.
9. Number of estimated protein domains encoded by some eukaryotic genes is 1012.
10. G+C content is 47%

### 2.7.3 Advantages

1. The chief advantages are its small size and (maximum height of 10–20 cm), prolific reproduction.
2. Life cycle, from seed germination to seed production requires only 6 weeks and producing 10000 to 40000 seeds per plant. This large numbers of progeny help to study genetic crosses more correctly.
3. Its genome is small in comparison to maize genome (2-5 billion). Therefore its genome has been sequenced in the year 2000 providing detailed informations about the structure and organization of the species.
4. It can be grown in the laboratory under low illumination conditions.
5. Many variants are available.
6. Self-fertilization or out-crosses can be done in the laboratory.

### 2.7.4 Contribution to Genetics

1. Self-fertilization occurs in *A. thaliana*, thus any recessive mutation may appear in the immediate progeny. Cross-fertilization is also possible by removing anther and dusting pollen into the stigma of other plants.
2. New mutations can be produced by exposing to mutagens, radiation and inserting the transposable elements.
3. By using Ti plasmid, transgenic *A. thaliana* can be produced where genes can be transferred from other organisms.
4. Today, *Arabidopsis* figures prominently in the study of plant genome structure, gene regulation, genetics of plant development, genetics of flowering and evolution.

## 2.8 AN OUTLINE OF HUMAN GENOMICS

1. Human being consists of 2n=46 chromosomes with 22 pairs of autosomes and two sex chromosomes. Females have two Xs while the males have one X and one Y.
2. Human genome is 3.2 billion base pairs in length, only 25% of the DNA is transcribed into RNA and less than 2% encode proteins.
3. Active genes are separated by vast non-coding DNA, much of which consists of repeated sequences derived from transposable elements. About 44.4% of such repeats are found which are derived from transposable elements.
4. Total number of gene is 32000.
5. The average gene in the human genome is approximately 27000 bp average in length which contains about 9 exons, the exceptional gene has 234 exons. Size of internal exon is about 145 bp in average.
6. The introns are much longer than other genomes which may be 3365 b.p. (average).
7. The number of estimated protein domains encoded by some eukaryotic genomes is 1262. The domains are combined relatively diverse proteomes.
8. A single gene may encode multiple proteins through alternative splicing. Each gene encodes on the average, 2-3 different mRNA molecules. Thus human genome with 32000 genes might encode as many as 96000 proteins.

9. G + C content is 41%.
10. Maximum gene density is observed in chromosome 17, 19 and 22, whereas, in chromosome 4, 13, 18, X and Y have least gene density.
11. X chromosome constitutes about 89% of DNA which is made up of transposable elements.
12. Human genome contains various types of transposable elements including LINEs, SINEs, retrotransposons and DNA transposons. Most of them are evolutionary defective.
13. Some proteins are exclusively encoded by human genome which include those affecting immune functions; neural development, structure and function; intercellular and intracellular signaling pathways in development; hemostasis; and apoptosis. Summary of human genome is described in the table 2.1.

## 2.9 ZEBRAFISH *(DANIO RERIO)*

*Danio rerio* was previously known as *Brachydanio rerio*. In the late 1960s and early 1970s George Streisinger, a bacteriophage geneticist turned his attention on the genetic analysis of this species. He believed that this species may be used as a model organism for the study of vertebrate physiology and development (Fig. 2.1f).

### 2.9.1 Life Cycle

1. Zebrafish is native to the slow freshwater streams and rice paddies of East India and Myanmar including Ganges river.
2. They are small hardy fishes about an inch long that have been bred for many years and may survive for about five years. The "wild type" is clear-coloured with black stripes that run lengthwise down its body.
3. The eggs are laid in cluthes of about 200. They are clear and develop outside the mother's body.

**Table 2.1**
**Summary of human genome**

| *Characteristics* | *Quantity* |
|---|---|
| 1. Chromosome number | 2n=46,<br>Males 44 autosomes + X, Y<br>Females 44 autosomes + XX |
| 2. Total genome | 3.2 billion b.p. |
| 3. DNA transcribed into RNA | 25% of the genome |
| 4. Encoded proteins | < 2% |
| 5. Repeated sequence derived from transposable element | 44.4% |
| 6. Total number of genes | 32000 |
| 7. G + C content | 41% |
| 8. Number estimated protein domains encoded by some eukaryotic genomes | 1264 |
| 9. Number of produced proteins by the genome | 96000 (approximately) |
| 10. Transposable elements in X chromosomes | 89% |
| 11. Number of exons | 8.8 (average) |
| 12. Size of internal exon | 145 bp (average) |
| 13. Size of intron | 3365 bp (average) |
| 14. Size of 5′ untranslated region | 770 bp (average) |
| 15. Size of coding region | 1340 bp (average) |

4. Development from egg to adult takes about three months.

### 2.9.2 Genomics

1. They have about 1700 Mb of DNA on 25 chromosomes, about the half size of human genome.
2. Shows 75% homology with human genome.
3. The genome contains 22000 genes.
4. It's haploid eggs can be induced to begin development by exposure to sperm rendered biologically inactive by UV radiation.

### 2.9.3 Advantages

1. The eggs are clear and develop outside the body of mother's body, so it is possible to watch a zebrafish egg grow into a newly formed fish under the light microscope.
2. Gene-tagging is relatively easy and microinjecting the egg with DNA is straightforward.
3. Within just a few years, thousands of mutant strains have been collected.

### 2.9.4 Contribution to genetics

1. In 2003, zebrafish became the first commercially available genetically engineered pet. Fluorescent red zebrafish is marketed in the USA by Yorktown Technologies as **GolFish$^{TM}$**. They fluoresce red white light or better black light due to presence of a gene for a fluorescent protein taken from the sea coral.
2. Another interest is their use as a biomonitoring organism for surveillance of environmental pollutants such as heavy meals. A second generation of more specialized red fluorescent zebrafish will fluoresce in response to environmental toxins or pollutants.
3. Zebrafish geneticists have developed procedures to mimic the effects of mutations in specific genes. This procedure does not induce mutations that is, they do not change the DNA itself. Indeed they block or attenuate the expression of the information encoded in the DNA. this is achieved by injecting a synthetic molecule to specific mRNA and prevent its translation. This injected material is a stable DNA analogue that is designed to base pair specifically to the 5′untranslated region and start codon of mRNA. The sugar phosphate backbone of the DNA analog is built from **morpholine** moieties. The injected molecule is **morpholino**. Only 10 nanograms of morpholino injected into the yolk of a fertilized zebrafish egg or early embryo are effective in disrupting gene expression for a considerable period of time. These are also known as **phenocopies** of the mutant phenotype.

## Chapter Glossary/Key Terms

**Genome :** The entire genetic complement of a living organism.

**Larva :** An immature, free living stage in the life cycle of various animals, which reach the adult form by undergoing metamorphosis.

**Orphan gene family :** A group of homologous genes whose functions are unknown.

**Pupa :** Developmental stage in the complete metamorphosis of an insect.

**Sex chromosome :** A chromosome that is involved in sex determination.

## Exercise

### A. Long answer type questions :

1. What is the criteria of the model organism in genetics? Give the names of such organism.
2. Briefly diescribe the life cycle, genomics, advantage and contribution to genetics of *E. coli*.
3. What is baker's yeast? What is its important characteristics of life cycle? Briefly describe the genomics, advantage and it's contribution to genetics.
4. What is *C. elegans?* Describe its life cycle, genomics, advantage and its contribution to genetics.
5. Why mice is regarded as the best model organism in the experimental molecular biology and human genetics?
6. Why *Drosophila* became the most important model organisms in the mutation study?
7. What is the contribution of *Arabidopsis* in plant molecular biology and genetics?
8. Briefly describe the human genomics.
9. What is the advantages of zebrafish as the model organism? What is its contribution to molecular biology.

### B. Short answer type questions.

1. What do you mean by model organisms? What are their characteristics?
2. What model organisms are used in genetic experiments?
3. What are orphan genes?
4. What are the characteristics of *E. coli* genome?
5. Why *E. coli* is considered as model organism in genetics.
6. What is the contribution of *E. coli* to genetics?
7. What is common baker's yeast?
8. What is the peculiarities in the life cyte of *S. cerevisiae*.
9. What are the genomic constitutions of *S. cerevisiae*?
10. How the recessive and dominant alleles can be analyzed by the *S. cerevisiae* genomics?
11. What is *C. elegans?*
12. What is the chromosome constituents in different sexes of *C. elegans*.
13. What are the successive larval stages and how do they produce during the development of *C. elegans?*

14. What are the genetic composition of *C. elegans*?
15. Why *C. elegans* is considered to be a model organism in genetics?
16. Why *C. elegans* becomes an important model organisms in HGP?
17. What is the genetic composition of mice genome?
18. Why mice is considered as the most important model organism?
19. What is the importance of mice genomics in the experimental genetics?
20. What is the genetic composition of *Drosophila* genome.
21. Why *Drosophila* is very useful in the mutation study?
22. What is mouse-ear cress?
23. Write a note on genomics of *A. thaliana.*
24. What is the advantage of *A. thaliania* in molecular genetics studies?
25. What is the genetic constitution of human genome?
26. What is about zebrafish life cycle?
27. What is the genetic constituent of zebrafish?
28. Why zebrafish is considered as a model organism is molecular genetic studies?
29. What is GlowFish™?
30. What is morpholine?
31. What is the effect of morpholine if this is injected into zebrafish egg?

3

# Interaction and Expression of Genes

**CHAPTER AGENDA**

**3.1** Concept; **3.2** Dominant Epistasis; **3.3** Recessive Epistasis; **3.4** Duplicate Genes with cumulative effect; **3.5** Duplicate Dominant genes; **3.6** Duplicate Recessive genes; **3.7** Dominant and Recessive Interactions; **3.8** Non-epistatic Inter-allelic Genetic Interactions; **3.9** Interaction of Genes for coat colour in mice; **3.10** Modifier genes; **3.11** Problems on Gene interaction; Chapter Glossary/Key Terms; Exercise

## 3.1 CONCEPT

For the determination of a single gene, interacted in various ways, such as, out of two allelomorphs of a single gene, one allelomorph might show simple dominance (*complete*) over the action of other which was recessive, or both allelomorphs might have partial or incomplete dominance relationship or both allelomorphs might have equal expression or co-dominance relationship. These kinds of genic interactions occur in between the two allelomorphs of a single type of gene and are usually referred to as **Intra-Allelic** or **Allelic-Genetic interactions**. These kinds of genetic interactions give the classical ratio of 3:1 (monohybrid cross) or 9:3:3:1(dihybrid cross).

In **Interallelic genic interaction or non-Allelic Interactions,** (non homologous) genes located on the same or on different chromosomes interact with one another for the expression of single phenotypic trait of an organism.

A gene or locus, which suppressed or masked the action of a gene at another locus, is termed as EPISTATIC GENE. The gene locus, which is suppressed by an epistatic gene, is called HYPOSTATIC GENE.

When, in dihybrid crosses, the epistatic interactions occur between two genes, less than 4 phenotypes appear in $F_2$. Such bigenic epistatic interactions may be of 6 types:

## 3.2 DOMINANT EPISTASIS (12 : 3 : 1)

When out of two genes, the dominant allele (e.g., *A*) of one gene masked the activity of another gene (e.g., *B*) and is expressed itself phenotypically, the "*A*" gene-locus is said to be epistatic to *B* gene locus. Because the dominant allele "*A*" can express itself only in the presence of either *B* or *b* allele, therefore such type of epistasis is termed as dominant epistasis. The alleles of hypostatic locus or gene *B* will be able to express themselves phenotypically only when gene locus "*A*" can have only two recessive alleles (*aa*). Thus genotype *AABB* or *AaBb*, *Aabb* or *AAbb* would produce same genotypes.

### Example

Among dogs, the colour of coat depends upon the action of two genes.

One gene locus has a dominant epistatic inhibitor allele (*I*) of coat colour pigment. The allele prevents the expression of colour allele at another independently assorting, hypostatic gene locus *B* or *b* and produce white coat colour. The alleles of hypostatic gene locus *BB*, *Bb*, *bb* express only when two recessive alleles (ii) occur on the epistatic locus, i.e., *iiBB* or *iiBb* produces black and *iibb* produces brown individuals.

When two white coat colour dogs are crossed in $F_1$, the white, black and brown coat colours will appears in 12 : 3 : 1 ratio (Fig. 3.1).

## 3.3 RECESSIVE EPISTASIS (9 : 3 : 4)

Sometimes, the recessive alleles of one gene locus at homozygous condition *aa* masked the action (phenotypic expression) of alleles of another locus. This type of epistasis is called recessive epistasis.

### Example 1

In common house mice, a number of coat colours *i.e.*, agouti, black and albino are present. The agouti colour is commonly occurred and is wild type, characterized by colour banded hairs in which the part near the skin is gray, then a yellow band and finally black or brown. The albino mouse lacks totally in pigments and with white hair and pink eyes.

When homozygous agouti (*BBAA*) is crossed with a homozygous albino (*bbaa*), in $F_1$ all the offspring will appear agouti. When $F_1$-agouti is crossed among themselves in $F_2$ agouti, black and albino will appear in 9 : 3 : 4 ratio (Fig. 3.2).

$B$ = Black coat colour (dominant)
$b$ = brown coat colour (recessive)
$I$ = Inhibitor of the colour gene (dominant)
$i$ = Non inhibitor of the coat colour (recessive)

| | | | |
|---|---|---|---|
| $P_1$ | *IIBB* White coat colour | × | *iibb* Brown coat colour |
| $F_1$ | | *IiBb* White coat colour Hybrid | |
| $P_2$ inbreeding | *IiBb* White coat colour Hybrid | × | *IiBb* White coat colour Hybrid |
| $F_2$ | | | |

Male gametes

| ♀ (female gametes) \ ♂ | *IB* | *Ib* | *iB* | *ib* |
|---|---|---|---|---|
| *IB* | *IIBB* white | *IIBb* white | *IiBB* white | *IiBb* white |
| *Ib* | *IIBb* white | *IIbb* white | *IiBb* white | *Iibb* white |
| *iB* | *IiBB* white | *IiBb* white | *iiBB* black | *iiBb* black |
| *ib* | *IiBb* white | *Iibb* white | *iiBb* black | *iibb* brown |

Phenotypic ratio : $\frac{12}{16}$ white : $\frac{3}{16}$ Black : $\frac{1}{16}$ Brown

**Fig. 3.1 :** *Dominant epistasis in coat color of dogs.*

$B$ = Agauti gene (dominant hypostatic)
$b$ = Black gene (recessive)
$A$ = Colour producing gene (dominant)
$a$ = Non colour gene (recessive)

| | | | |
|---|---|---|---|
| $P_1$ | *BBAA* Agauti | × | *bbaa* Albino |
| $F_1$ | | *BbAa* Hybrid Agauti | |
| $P_2$ inbreeding | *BbAa* Agauti Hybrid | × | *BbAa* Hybrid Agauti |
| $F_2$ | | | |

Male gametes

| ♀ (female gametes) \ ♂ | *BA* | *Ba* | *bA* | *ba* |
|---|---|---|---|---|
| *BA* | *BBAA* Agouti | *BBAa* Agouti | *BbAA* Agouti | *BbAa* Agouti |
| *Ba* | *BBAa* Agouti | *BBaa* Albino | *BbAa* Agouti | *Bbaa* Albino |
| *bA* | *BbAA* Agouti | *BbAa* Agouti | *bbAA* Black | *bbAa* Black |
| *ba* | *BbAa* Agouti | *Bbaa* Albino | *bbAa* Black | *bbaa* Albino |

Phenotypic ratio : $\frac{9}{16}$ Agauti : $\frac{3}{16}$ Black : $\frac{4}{16}$ Albino

**Fig. 3.2 :** *Recessive epistasis in coat colour of house mouse.*

$r$ = red flower (recessive)
+ = purple flower (dominant)
$a$ = Non-color gene (recessive)
+ = Colour gene (dominant)

**P₁**: $\frac{a}{a}\frac{+}{+}$ white flower × $\frac{+}{+}\frac{r}{r}$ red flower

**F₁**: $\frac{a}{+}\frac{+}{r}$ purple flower Hybrid

**P₂ inbreeding**: $\frac{a}{+}\frac{+}{r}$ purple flower × $\frac{a}{+}\frac{+}{r}$ purple flower

**F₂**

Male gametes

| female gametes ♀ \ ♂ | $a$ + | $a$ $r$ | + + | + $r$ |
|---|---|---|---|---|
| $a$ + | $\frac{a}{a}\frac{+}{+}$ white | $\frac{a}{a}\frac{r}{+}$ white | $\frac{+}{a}\frac{+}{+}$ purple | $\frac{+}{a}\frac{r}{+}$ purple |
| $a$ $r$ | $\frac{a}{a}\frac{+}{r}$ white | $\frac{a}{a}\frac{r}{r}$ white | $\frac{+}{a}\frac{+}{r}$ purple | $\frac{+}{a}\frac{r}{r}$ red |
| + + | $\frac{a}{+}\frac{+}{+}$ purple | $\frac{a}{+}\frac{r}{+}$ purple | $\frac{+}{+}\frac{+}{+}$ purple | $\frac{+}{+}\frac{r}{+}$ purple |
| + $r$ | $\frac{a}{+}\frac{+}{r}$ purple | $\frac{a}{+}\frac{r}{r}$ red | $\frac{+}{+}\frac{+}{r}$ purple | $\frac{+}{+}\frac{r}{r}$ red |

Phenotypic ratio : $\frac{9}{16}$ purple : $\frac{3}{16}$ red : $\frac{4}{16}$ white

**Fig.3.3** : *Recessive epistasis in flower colour of sweet pea*

**Example 2**

Considering a cross with sweet peas.

Red ($r$) flower due to recessive mutation of normal purple (+) gene. Two white mutations '$a$' and '$r$'.

We might now cross one of the white races '$a$' to the red. The genotype of the parent $\frac{a}{a}\frac{+}{+}$ white and $\frac{+}{+}\frac{r}{r}$ red. Then $F_1$ would be $\frac{a}{+}\frac{+}{r}$ purple (Fig. 3.3).

## 3.4 DUPLICATE GENES WITH CUMULATIVE EFFECT (9 : 6 : 1)

Certain phenotypic traits (e.g. coat colouration) depend upon the dominant alleles of two gene loci. When the dominant condition (homo or heterozygous) at either locus (but not both) produces the same phenotype, the $F_2$ ratio would be 9 : 6 : 1.

**Example**

In the Duroc-Jersey breed of pigs, coat colour is influenced by two pairs of genes that interact in a particular manner.

Sandy coat colour results from a dominant 'S' gene and its recessive 's' is white. Sandy coat colour may also result from a non-allelic dominant R-gene, its recessive 'r' is also white.

When a Sandy pig (*SSrr*) is crossed with a second Sandy pig (*ssRR*), the $F_1$ offspring would be red coloured coat. Such interactions are said to be the result of **mutually supplementary genes**. When $F_1$ red coated pigs crossbreed among themselves, they produce red; sandy and white in 9 : 6 : 1 ratio (Fig. 3.4).

## 3.5 DUPLICATE DOMINANT GENES (15 : 1) (G. H. SHULL)

In the wild plant known as Shepherd's purse, the seed case or capsule is normally triangular. But there is also a race of round capsules produced by the combinations of two mutations in a different chromosome and each is recessive to its normal allele.

We designate the mutated genes by *a* and *b* and their normal alleles by + signs.

Neither mutation by itself has any influence on the shape of the capsule even the plant is pure for it.

A cross of the two races $\left(\frac{+}{+}\frac{+}{+}\right)\times\left(\frac{a}{a}\frac{b}{b}\right)$ gives $F_1$ of $\left(\frac{a}{+}\frac{b}{+}\right)$ genotype with normal triangular capsule. When they inbreed give the ratio 15 : 1 in $F_2$ (Fig. 3.5).

## 3.6 DUPLICATE RECESSIVE GENES (9 : 7) OR COMPLEMENTARY GENES

In sweet peas (*Lathyrus odoratus*) the flowers are normally purple, but there are two white flowered varieties, which we can refer to as *white race-a* and *white race-b*. Each white race is due to a recessive mutation and in two separate chromosomes (Fig. 3.6).

We can designate the mutant genes by *a* and *b* and their normal alleles by + sign. *The two (+) normal alleles are both necessary for purple flowers and therefore they are referred to as complementary genes.*

A cross of two white races $\left(\frac{a}{a}\frac{+}{+}\right)\times\left(\frac{+}{+}\frac{b}{b}\right)$ produces $F_1$ of genotype $\left(\frac{a}{+}\frac{+}{b}\right)$ is purple, because the (+,+) alleles are dominant. When $F_1$ is inbred the result would be like as follows (Fig. 3.7).

## 3.7 DOMINANT AND RECESSIVE INTERACTIONS (BATESON AND PUNNET)

The white plumage of White Leghorn fowl is almost completely dominant over the coloured plumage. White plumage of White Plymouth Rock has often found to be recessive to coloured plumage and to be due to a gene distinct from that which produces the White Leghorn. Experiments showed that *White Leghorn contains a colour gene and with it a gene that inhibits its expression.* They are genetically coloured birds that are unable to develop their colours (Fig. 3.8).

Denoting such an inhibitor by 'I' and a colour gene by 'C'. Thus the White Leghorn is *IICC* and White Plymouth Rock is iicc.

By crossing these two varieties, the $F_1$ genotype is *IiCc*, is white phenotype. When these two $F_1$ phenotypes were crossed in $F_2$ $\frac{13}{16}$ white fowls and 3/16 coloured fowls are observed. Here the colour genes are hypostatic to the white of Leghorn, which is thus epistatic to the variety of gene determining colours and patterns. Only *iiCC* and *iiCc* genotype would be coloured.

## 3.8 NON EPISTATIC INTERALLELIC GENETIC INTERACTIONS

In certain cases, two pairs of genes determine the same phenotype but are assorted independently, produce new phenotypes by mutual non-epistatic interactions and the $F_2$ phenotypic ratio 9 : 3 : 3 : 1 remains unaltered. Two pairs of genes, which interact to affect comb size and shape but are independently transmitted.

$S$ = Sandy coat color (dominant)
$s$ = White coat color (recessive)
$R$ = Sandy coat color (dominant)
$r$ = White coat color (recessive)

| | | | |
|---|---|---|---|
| **P₁** | *SSrr* Sandy Pig | × | *ssRR* Sandy Pig |
| **F₁** | | *SsRr* Red coat color Hybrid | |
| **P₂ inbreeding** | *SsRr* Red coat color Hybrid | × | *SsRr* Red coat color Hybrid |
| **F₂** | | | |

Male gametes (columns) / Female gametes (rows)

| ♀ \ ♂ | *SR* | *Sr* | *sR* | *sr* |
|---|---|---|---|---|
| *SR* | *SSRR* Red | *SSRr* Red | *SsRR* Red | *SsRr* Red |
| *Sr* | *SSRr* Red | *SSrr* Sandy | *SsRr* Red | *Ssrr* Sandy |
| *sR* | *SsRR* Red | *SsRr* Red | *ssRR* Sandy | *ssRr* Sandy |
| *sr* | *SsRr* Red | *Ssrr* Sandy | *ssRr* Sandy | *ssrr* White |

Phenotypic ratio : $\frac{9}{16}$ Red : $\frac{6}{16}$ Sandy : $\frac{1}{16}$ White

**Fig.3.4 :** *Duplicate genes with cumulative effect in coat colour of Pig.*

| | | | |
|---|---|---|---|
| **P₁** | $\frac{+}{+}\frac{+}{+}$ Triangular | × | $\frac{a}{a}\frac{b}{b}$ Round |
| **F₁** | | $\frac{+}{a}\frac{+}{b}$ Triangular | |
| **P₂** | $\frac{+}{a}\frac{+}{b}$ Triangular | × | $\frac{+}{a}\frac{+}{b}$ Triangular |
| **F₂** | | | |

Male gametes (columns) / female gametes (rows)

| ♀ \ ♂ | $\overline{+}\ \overline{+}$ | $\overline{a}\ \overline{+}$ | $\overline{+}\ \overline{b}$ | $\overline{a}\ \overline{b}$ |
|---|---|---|---|---|
| $\overline{+}\ \overline{+}$ | $\frac{+}{+}\frac{+}{+}$ Triangular | $\frac{a}{+}\frac{+}{+}$ Triangular | $\frac{+}{+}\frac{b}{+}$ Triangular | $\frac{a}{+}\frac{b}{+}$ Triangular |
| $\overline{a}\ \overline{+}$ | $\frac{+}{a}\frac{+}{+}$ Triangular | $\frac{a}{a}\frac{+}{+}$ Triangular | $\frac{+}{a}\frac{b}{+}$ Triangular | $\frac{a}{a}\frac{b}{+}$ Triangular |
| $\overline{+}\ \overline{b}$ | $\frac{+}{+}\frac{+}{b}$ Triangular | $\frac{a}{+}\frac{+}{b}$ Triangular | $\frac{+}{+}\frac{b}{b}$ Triangular | $\frac{a}{+}\frac{b}{b}$ Triangular |
| $\overline{a}\ \overline{b}$ | $\frac{+}{a}\frac{+}{b}$ Triangular | $\frac{a}{a}\frac{+}{b}$ Triangular | $\frac{+}{a}\frac{b}{b}$ Triangular | $\frac{a}{a}\frac{b}{b}$ Round |

Phenotypic ratio : $\frac{15}{16}$ Triangular : $\frac{1}{16}$ Round

**Fig.3.5 :** *Duplicate dominant genes in Shepherd's purse.*

**Fig.3.6 :** *Purple and white flowered variety in sweet pea.*

| | | | |
|---|---|---|---|
| $P_1$ | $\frac{a}{a}\ \frac{+}{+}$ White | × | $\frac{+}{+}\ \frac{b}{b}$ White |
| $F_1$ | | $\frac{a}{+}\ \frac{+}{b}$ Purple | |
| $P_2$ | $\frac{a}{+}\ \frac{+}{b}$ Purple | × | $\frac{a}{+}\ \frac{+}{b}$ Purple |
| $F_2$ | | | |

**Male gametes**

**Female gametes** (rows)

| ♀ \ ♂ | + + | a + | + b | a b |
|---|---|---|---|---|
| + + | $\frac{+}{+}\ \frac{+}{+}$ **Purple** | $\frac{a}{+}\ \frac{+}{+}$ **Purple** | $\frac{+}{+}\ \frac{b}{+}$ **Purple** | $\frac{a}{+}\ \frac{b}{+}$ **Purple** |
| a + | $\frac{+}{a}\ \frac{+}{+}$ **Purple** | $\frac{a}{a}\ \frac{+}{+}$ **White** | $\frac{+}{a}\ \frac{b}{+}$ **Purple** | $\frac{a}{a}\ \frac{b}{+}$ **White** |
| + b | $\frac{+}{+}\ \frac{+}{b}$ **Purple** | $\frac{a}{+}\ \frac{+}{b}$ **Purple** | $\frac{+}{+}\ \frac{b}{b}$ **White** | $\frac{a}{+}\ \frac{b}{b}$ **White** |
| a b | $\frac{+}{a}\ \frac{+}{b}$ **Purple** | $\frac{a}{a}\ \frac{+}{b}$ **White** | $\frac{+}{a}\ \frac{b}{b}$ **White** | $\frac{a}{a}\ \frac{b}{b}$ **White** |

Phenotypic ratio : $\frac{9}{16}$ Purple : $\frac{7}{16}$ White

**Fig.3.7 :** *Complementary genes in sweet pea.*

$I$ = Inhibitor of colour gene (dominant)
$i$ = Non inhibitor of color gene (recessive)
$C$ = Color producing gene (dominant)
$c$ = White gene (recessive)

$P_1$ — *II CC* White Leghorn × *ii cc* White Plymouth Rock

$F_1$ — *Ii Cc* Hybrid White

$P_2$ — *Ii Cc* Hybrid White × *Ii Cc* Hybrid White

$F_2$

Male gametes

| ♀ \ ♂ (Female gametes) | *IC* | *Ic* | *iC* | *ic* |
|---|---|---|---|---|
| *IC* | *II CC* white | *II Cc* white | *Ii CC* white | *Ii Cc* white |
| *Ic* | *II Cc* white | *II cc* white | *Ii Cc* white | *Ii cc* white |
| *iC* | *Ii CC* white | *Ii Cc* white | *ii CC* Colored | *ii Cc* Colored |
| *ic* | *Ii Cc* white | *Ii cc* white | *ii Cc* Colored | *ii cc* White |

Phenotypic ratio : $\frac{13}{16}$ white : $\frac{3}{16}$ Coloured

**Fig.3.8 :** *Dominant - recessive interaction in the plumage colour of fowl.*

The classical case of genetic interaction of two genes is discovered by Bateson and Punnet (1905-08) in fowls. There are many different breeds of domestic chicken. Each breed possesses a characteristic type of comb. The Wyandotte breed has a comb called ROSE, the Brahmas breed has a comb called PEA, and the Leghorn has a comb called SINGLE. Each of these types can breed true (Fig. 3.9).

A cross of chicken with a 'rose' comb with a "single" comb, produces ¾ rose and ¼ single showing dominance of rose over single.

Another cross between "pea" combed chicken and single combed chicken produces ¾ pea and ¼ single, showing dominance of pea over single.

But when a "rose" combed chicken is crossed with that of "pea" combed, the $F_1$ progeny was found with a different type of comb known as WALNUT. When $F_1$–walnut combed fowls were breed together, in $F_2$ all four types of comb appeared.

Bateson and Punnet interpreted these peculiar results as follows:

The "rose" comb is caused by the combinations of homozygous recessive genes (*pp*) and a homozygous or heterozygous dominant genes *RR* and *Rr*. The "pea" comb is supposed to be produced by combination of a homozygous recessive condition (*rr*) and homozygous or heterozygous dominant condition (*PP* or *Pp*), while; the "single" type comb is produce by the double recessive (*rrpp*) genes. Thus *R* gene determines the shape of "rose" comb and *P* gene determines the shape of "pea" comb, but when both genes happen to come together in single individual due to cross between "rose" and "pea" combed chicken they interact to produce a 'walnut' comb in $F_1$.

In the cases of two walnut chickens, two genes interact variously and produce 4 types of offspring in $F_2$.

In the inheritance of comb in fowls, the genes themselves do not determine the development of a character (presence or absence of comb) and simply modify a character determined by a basic gene and therefore known as **Supplementary or Modifying genes** (Fig. 3.10).

**Fig.3.9 :** *Comb shapes in chickens of different breeds (a) Rose of Wyandottes ; (b) Pea of Brahmas ; (c) Walnut hybrid from cross between rose and pea comb chicken ; (d) Single of Leghorn.*

$P_1$ — *RR pp* Rose comb × *rr PP* Pea comb

$F_1$ — *Rr Pp* Walnut comb

$P_2$ — *Rr Pp* Walnut comb × *Rr Pp* Walnut comb

$F_2$ —

Male gametes

| Female gametes ♀ \ ♂ | (*RP*) | (*Rp*) | (*rP*) | (*rp*) |
|---|---|---|---|---|
| (*RP*) | *RR PP* Walnut | *RR Pp* Walnut | *Rr PP* Walnut | *Rr Pp* Walnut |
| (*Rp*) | *RR Pp* Walnut | *RR pp* Rose | *Rr Pp* Walnut | *Rr pp* Rose |
| (*rP*) | *Rr PP* Walnut | *Rr Pp* Walnut | *rr PP* Pea | *rr Pp* Pea |
| (*rp*) | *Rr Pp* Walnut | *Rr pp* Rose | *rr Pp* Pea | *rr pp* Single |

Phenotypic ratio : $\frac{9}{16}$ Walnut : $\frac{3}{16}$ Rose : $\frac{3}{16}$ Pea : $\frac{1}{16}$ Single

**Fig.3.10 :** *Nonepistatic interallelic genetic interaction in the comb pattern of fowl.*

## 3.9 INTERACTION OF GENES FOR COAT COLOUR IN MICE

In house mouse, *C* is the fundamental colour gene, necessary for the production of any pigment in the coat. Another gene *"A"* determines the development of the **agouti** pattern. It's recessive allele *"a"* is present in the non- agouti mice such as brown.

Another gene *"B"* governs the development of **black** pigment and is dominant over its allelic conditions of **brown or chocolate** *'b'*.

Many varieties are spotted with white in a **blotched** or **piebald** pattern, and such mice contain a gene *"s"* which is recessive to **solid colour** *'S'*.

Another gene *'d'* brings about **clumping of the black and brown pigment** granules in the hair and makes these colours appear **faded** or **dilute**, as opposed to the normal fully pigmented form *'D'*.

Another gene reduces the amount of black and brown pigment in the fur, giving it a **pale**, washed out appearance, and also reduces the pigment in the iris making the eyes appear reddish or pink like the eyes of albinos. This gene, which is called pink eye (*p*) from its most noticeable effect is recessive to the normal intense dark colour condition (*P*). [*for* Table 2.1 see next page]

These genes all segregate and may occur in any combination. There must be present at least 6 genes and each of which has a definite effect on coat colours. If a single gene is changed the coat pattern is also changed.

All these recessive genes have been arisen from its normal allele by mutation and they show complete dominance. The wild colour is due to interaction of all the 6 dominant genes either in homozygous or in heterozygous condition, partly or fully. Therefore *AABBCCDDPPSS* and *AaBbCcDdPpSs* both will show agouti in appearance.

## 3.10 MODIFIER GENES

Modifier genes are such that they change the phenotypic effects of other gene in a quantitative fashion. For example, the coat color in mammals are modified through dilution or enhancement of the effect of color genes. Similarly, the inhibitor genes that prevent the appearance of feather colour in chickens, which is the modifier gene of normal fowl colour gene.

Both the modifiers and complementary genes as well as the epistatic genes modify or affect the nature of gene expression of normal genes, but the difference is that, the action of complementary gene is due to the additive or the mixing effect of the both dominant and recessive gene products. *The action of epistatic gene is the musking or hiding the effect of the gene by increasing or decreasing enzyme activity or, changes in the acidity of the cellular environment that affect the appearance of the color.* But the modifier genes change the phenotypic effect of the other genes in quantitative fashion.

Modifiers always do not act upon normal genes. They may also act upon mutant gene and in some cases they completely reduce the phenotypic expression of the mutant gene. These are called *suppressor* genes. Example, In *Drosophila, su-Hw* gene suppresses the expression of hairy wing phenotype caused by a mutant gene. This *su-Hw* also reduces the mutant phenotype caused by genes for forked bristles, interrupted wing veins etc.

Modifier genes may be dominant or recessive. For example, white spotting in mice is due to the homozygous recessive gene *"s"* but may be greatly enhanced by many genetic factors, so an almost completely white animal is produced.

Ford in his experiment on *Abraxas grossulariata,* the current moth, illustrated the influence of modifier genes on the dominant or recessive effects of a gene. The *lutea* gene produces yellow colour in homozygous

**Table 3.1**
**Interaction of genes for coat color in mice**

| Genes | | | | | | Zygotic formula | Phenotype |
|---|---|---|---|---|---|---|---|
| C | A | B | D | P | S | CABDPS | Wild agouti |
| | | | | | s | CABDPS | Spolled agouti |
| | | | | p | S | CABDps | Pink-eyed aqouti |
| | | | | | s | CABDps | Pink-eyed spotted agouti |
| | | | d | P | S | CABdPS | Dilute agouti |
| | | | | | s | CABdPs | Spotted dilute agouti |
| | | | | p | S | CABdpS | pink-eyed dilute agouti |
| | | | | | s | CABdps | pinkeyed spotted dilute agouts |
| | | b | D | P | S | CAbDPS | Cinnamos |
| | | | | | s | CAbDPS | Spotted Cinnamon |
| | | | | p | S | CabDPS | Pink eyed Cinnamon |
| | | | | | s | CAbDps | Pinkeyed spotted Cinnamon |
| | | | d | P | S | CAbdPS | Dilute Cinnamon |
| | | | | | s | CAbdPs | Spotted dilute Cinnamon |
| | | | | p | S | CAbdpS | Pink eyed dilute Cinnamons |
| | | | | | s | Cabdps | Pink eyed spotted dilute Cinnamons |
| | a | B | D | P | S | CaBDPS | Black |
| | | | | | s | CaBDPs | Spotted black |
| | | | | p | S | CaBDpS | Pink eyed black |
| | | | | | s | CaBDps | Pink eyed spotted black |
| | | | d | P | S | CaBdPS | dilute Black |
| | | | | | s | CaBdPs | Spotted dilute black |
| | | | | p | S | CaBdpS | Pink eyed dilute black |
| | | | | | s | CaBdps | Pink eyed spotted dilute black |
| | | b | D | P | S | CabDPS | Brown |
| | | | | | s | CabDPs | Spotted brown |
| | | | | p | S | CabDPs | Pink eyed brown |
| | | | | | s | CabDPs | Pink eyed spotted brown |
| | | | d | p | S | CabdPS | Dilute brown |
| | | | | | s | CabdpS | Spotted dilute brown |
| | | | | p | S | CabdPs | Pink eyed dilute brown |
| | | | | | s | Cabdps | Pink eyed spotted brown |
| c with any other genes .............Albino may be of 32 genotypes | | | | | | | |

condition instead of normal white colour. Heterozygous has an intermediate effect. After four generations of selecting moths for greater and lesser expression of lutea-phenotype in the heterozygote. He was able to show two distinct strains, in one case *lutea* acted almost as a complete dominant and in the other case almost as a complete rcessive. In each strain special modifiers had been chosen, some enhancing and some detracting from the dominance of this particular gene.

## 3.11 PROBLEMS ON GENE INTERACTION

### Problem 1

Given peas of the genotypes designated below, derive the phenotypic ratios in which the offspring are produced.

(a) $\frac{d}{T}\frac{w}{R} \times \frac{d}{d}\frac{w}{w}$ (b) $\frac{d}{T}\frac{w}{R} \times \frac{d}{T}\frac{w}{w}$ (c) $\frac{d}{d}\frac{w}{R} \times \frac{d}{d}\frac{w}{w}$ (d) $\frac{d}{T}\frac{R}{R} \times \frac{T}{T}\frac{w}{w}$

**Solution :**

(a) $P_1$ : $\frac{d}{T}\frac{w}{R}$ × $\frac{d}{d}\frac{w}{w}$

Tall round dwarf wrinkled

$F_2$ :

| $\underline{d}\ \underline{w}$ | $\underline{T}\ \underline{R}$ | $\underline{T}\ \underline{w}$ | $\underline{d}\ \underline{R}$ | ♀ / ♂ |
|---|---|---|---|---|
| $\frac{d}{d}\frac{w}{w}$ Dwarf wrinkled | $\frac{T}{d}\frac{R}{w}$ Tall round | $\frac{T}{d}\frac{w}{w}$ Tall wrinkled | $\frac{d}{d}\frac{R}{w}$ Dwarf round | $\underline{d}\ \underline{w}$ |

Genotypic ratio : 1 : 1 : 1 : 1; Phenotypic ratio : 1 : 1 : 1 : 1

### Problem 2

A cross of a tall round pea to a dwarf white, produces the following count of offspring 58 tall round and 49 dwarf round. Give the genotype of the parent.

**Solution :**

Genotype of Tall round would be $\frac{T}{T}\frac{R}{R}$, $\frac{T}{d}\frac{R}{w}$, $\frac{T}{T}\frac{R}{w}$ or $\frac{T}{d}\frac{R}{R}$

Genotype of dwarf wrinkled $\frac{d}{d}\frac{w}{w}$.

Genotype of the parent would be : $\frac{T}{d}\frac{R}{R}$ × $\frac{d}{d}\frac{w}{w}$

Gametes : $\underline{T}\ \underline{R}$ $\underline{d}\ \underline{R}$ $\underline{d}\ \underline{w}$

Offspring : $\frac{T}{d}\frac{R}{w}$ and $\frac{d}{d}\frac{R}{w}$

Tall round dwarf round

Ratio : 1 : 1

### Problem 3

A tall round × a dwarf round produces a dwarf wrinkled offspring. Give the genotypes of the parent.

**Solution :**

Genotypes of tall round $\frac{T}{T}\frac{R}{R}, \frac{T}{d}\frac{R}{w}, \frac{T}{T}\frac{R}{w}, \frac{T}{d}\frac{R}{R}$   Dwarf round $\frac{d}{d}\frac{R}{R}, \frac{d}{d}\frac{R}{w}$

The offspring is dwarf wrinkled is $\frac{d}{d}\frac{w}{w}$;   So, the parent's genotypes are $\frac{T}{d}\frac{R}{w}$ and $\frac{d}{w}\frac{w}{w}$

$P_1$ : $\frac{T}{d}\frac{R}{w}$ × $\frac{d}{d}\frac{w}{w}$

Gametes : (dR) (Tw) (TR) (dw)   (dw)

Offspring : $\frac{d}{d}\frac{w}{w}$ (dwarf wrinkled)

### Problem 4

In man, brown eyes (*B*) are dominated to blue(*b*) and dark hair (*D*) to red *(r)*. A man has brown eyes and red hair. He marries a woman with blue eyes and dark hair. They have a child with brown eyes and red hair and one with blue eyes and dark hair. Give the genotypic ratio of the parent and children.

**Solution :**

Genotypes of the parents would be :

Brown eyes, red hair $\frac{B}{b}\frac{r}{r}$ or $\frac{B}{B}\frac{r}{r}$;   Blue eyes , dark hair $\frac{b}{b}\frac{D}{r}$ or $\frac{b}{b}\frac{D}{D}$

The genotypes of the children would be :

Brown eyes, red hair $\frac{B}{b}\frac{r}{r}$ or $\frac{B}{B}\frac{r}{r}$;   Blue eyes, Dark hair $\frac{b}{b}\frac{D}{r}$ or $\frac{b}{b}\frac{D}{D}$

Here the genotypes of the parent would be :

$\frac{B}{b}\frac{r}{r}$ × $\frac{b}{b}\frac{D}{r}$

Gametes : (Br) (br) (br) (bD)

Offspring : $\frac{B}{b}\frac{r}{r}$ and $\frac{b}{b}\frac{r}{D}$

(Brown eyes, red hair)   (Blue eyes, Dark hair)

### Problem 5

In horses, Black ($B$) is dominant to Chestnut ($c$) and Trotting ($T$) a gait in which the legs move in pair diagonally but not quite simultaneously, is dominant to Pacing ($p$), in which legs move in lateral pairs. A Black Pacer is breed to a Chestnut Trotter and resulting colt is a Chestnut Pacer. Give the genotypes of parent and offspring.

**Solution :**

Genotypes of parents would be :

1. Black Pacer $\frac{B}{B}\,\frac{p}{p}$ or $\frac{B}{c}\,\frac{p}{p}$ 2. Chestnut Trotter $\frac{c}{c}\,\frac{T}{T}$ or $\frac{c}{c}\,\frac{T}{p}$

Offspring : Chestnut Trotter $\frac{C}{C}\,\frac{P}{P}$

The genotypes of the parents would be :

$$\frac{B}{B}\,\frac{p}{p} \times \frac{c}{c}\,\frac{T}{p}$$

Gametes : ($\underline{B}\ \underline{p}$) ($\underline{c}\ \underline{p}$) ($\underline{c}\ \underline{T}$) ($\underline{c}\ \underline{p}$)

Offspring : $\frac{c}{c}\,\frac{p}{p}$

Chestnut Pacer

### Problem 6

In snapdragon, tall ($T$) is dominant to dwarf ($d$) and red flowers ($R$) are incompletely dominant to white ($w$), the hybrid being pink. A pure tall white crossed with pure dwarf red and the $F_1$ are self-fertilized, give the $F_2$ ratio.

**Solution :**

Parental phenotypes and genotypes are :

Pure tall white $\frac{T}{T}\,\frac{w}{w}$; Pure dwarf red $\frac{d}{d}\,\frac{R}{R}$

So, The $F_1$ would be $\frac{T}{d}\,\frac{w}{R}$ (hybrid tall pink)

When these $F_1$ are self fertilized the result would be : $\frac{T}{d}\,\frac{w}{R} \times \frac{T}{d}\,\frac{w}{R}$

Offsprings :

| (Tw) | (dR) | (dw) | (TR) | ♀ / ♂ |
|---|---|---|---|---|
| *TTww* Tall white | *TdRw* Tall pink | *Tdww* Tall white | *TTRw* Tall pink | (Tw) |
| *TdRw* Tall Pink | *ddRR* dwarf red | *ddRw* dwarf pink | *TdRR* Tall red | (dR) |
| *Tdww* Tall White | *ddRw* dwarf pink | *ddww* dwarf White | *TdRw* Tall pink | (dw) |
| *TTRw* Tall Pink | *TdRR* Tall red | *TdRw* Tall pink | *TTRR* Tall red | (TR) |

Ratio : 3 tall red : 1 dwarf red : 3 tall white : 1 dwarf white : 6 tall pink : 2 dwarf pink

### Problem 7

In snapdragon, broad leaves (*B*) are incompletely dominant to narrow (*n*), the hybrid leaves being of intermediate width. A broad red plant is crossed to a narrow white. Give the genotype and phenotype of $F_1$ and the $F_2$ phenotypic ratio when $F_1$ is self fertilized.

**Solution :**

Phenotype and genotype of parents.

Pure Broad red $\frac{B}{B}\frac{R}{R}$; Narrow white $\frac{n}{n}\frac{w}{w}$

$F_1$ hybrid would be $\frac{B}{n}\frac{R}{w}$ (intermediate with of leave and pink).

$P_1$: $F_1 \times F_1$ *i.e.* $\frac{B}{n}\frac{R}{w} \times \frac{B}{n}\frac{R}{w}$

$F_2$ :

| *BR* | *nR* | *Bw* | *nw* | ♀ / ♂ |
|---|---|---|---|---|
| *BBRR* Broad-red | *BnRR* Int.-red | *BBRw* Broad-Pink | *BnRw* Int.-Pink | *BR* |
| *BnRR* Int.-red | *nnRR* Narrow-red | *BnRw* Int.-pink | *nnRw* narrow-Pink | *nR* |
| *BBRw* Broad-pink | *BnRw* Int.-pink | *BBww* Broad-white | *Bnww* Int.-white | *Bw* |
| *BnRw* Int.-pink | *nnRw* Narrow-pink | *Bnww* Int.-white | *nnww* narrow-white | *nw* |

Phenotypic ratio :

Narrow-white = 1 Broad-red = 1 Intermediate-red = 2 Broad-pink = 2

Intermedite-pink = 4 Narrow-red = 1 Narrow-pink = 2 Broad-white = 1

Intermediate-white = 2

### Problem 8

The *Drosophila* has gray body red eyes and straight wings. Black body (*b*) pink eyes (*p*) and bent wing (*bt*) are the three recessive mutants, each on a separate chromosome. The normal allele of each being designated by (+).

A pure gray red fly is crossed to a black pink bent and the F1 is inbred. Give the $P_1$ phenotype and genotype, the $P_1$ gametes, the $F_1$ genotype and phenotype. Derive the $F_1$ classes of gametes by the branching method and below each abbreviated genotype put its phenotype.

**Solution :**

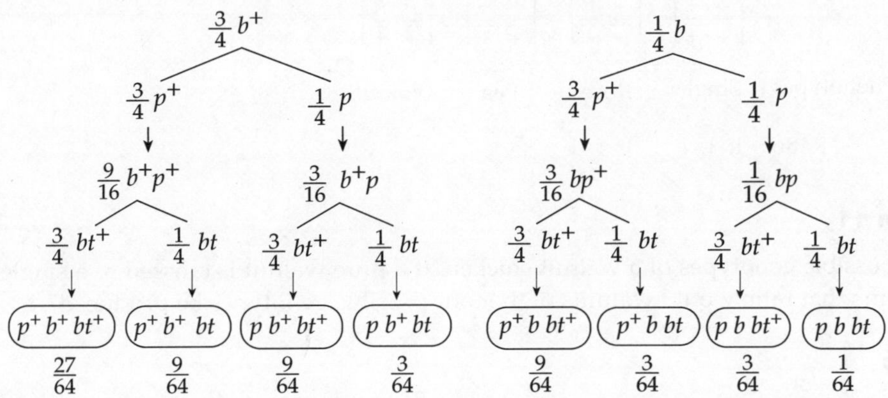


**Problem 9**

In the cross of a pure gray red straight fly by a black pink bent. What fraction of the $F_2$ are gray pink straight. What fraction of the $F_2$ are gray pink straight of genotype $\frac{b}{+}\ \frac{p}{p}\ \frac{bt}{+}$?

**Solution :**

The genotypes of gray pink straight are $\frac{b}{+}\ \frac{p}{p}\ \frac{bt}{+}$, $\frac{b}{+}\ \frac{p}{p}\ \frac{+}{bt}$.

Which are formed by the union of ($b\ \ p\ \ bt$) and ($+\ \ p\ \ +$) these two types of gametes from both parents.

Thus, there are 4 such offspring among 64 zygotes.

Out of them 2 would be of genotype containing $\left(\frac{b}{+}\ \frac{p}{p}\ \frac{bt}{+}\right)$.

**Problem 10**

A chicken pure for pea comb is crossed to a pure rose, each being pure normal at the other locus and the $F_1$ is crossed to a single. Give the phenotypes and genotypes of the $P_1$, the genotypic and phenotypic ratios in $F_2$.

**Solution :**

Pure rose $\frac{+}{+}\ \frac{R}{R}$, Pure Pea $\frac{P}{P}\ \frac{+}{+}$, Single $\frac{+}{+}\ \frac{+}{+}$, Walnut $\frac{P}{P}\ \frac{R}{R}$.

$$P_1 : \frac{+}{+}\ \frac{R}{R} \times \frac{P}{P}\ \frac{+}{+}$$

(Rose) ↓ (Pea)

$$F_1 : \boxed{\frac{+}{P}\ \frac{R}{+}}$$ (Walnut)

$P_1$ : $F_1$ is crossed to single $\frac{+}{P}\frac{R}{+} \times \frac{+}{+}\frac{+}{+}$

gametes : (++) (+R) (P+) (PR) (++)

$\left[\frac{+}{+}\frac{+}{+}\right]$ $\left[\frac{+}{+}\frac{R}{+}\right]$ $\left[\frac{P}{+}\frac{+}{+}\right]$ $\left[\frac{P}{+}\frac{R}{+}\right]$

Phenotypes : Single Rose Pea Walnut

Ratio : 1 : 1 : 1 : 1

### ➧ Problem 11

Give possible genotypes of a walnut chicken. If a pure walnut is crossed to a single and the $F_1$ interbred, in what ratio would walnuts of the four possible genotypes be produced?

**Solution :**

The possible genotypes of walnut are $\frac{+}{P}\frac{+}{R}$ , $\frac{P}{P}\frac{+}{R}$ , $\frac{P}{+}\frac{R}{R}$ , $\frac{P}{P}\frac{R}{R}$

$P_1$ : Pure walnut is crossed with single $\frac{P}{P}\frac{R}{R} \times \frac{+}{+}\frac{+}{+}$

$F_1$ : $\frac{P}{+}\frac{R}{+}$ (walnut)

$P_2$ : $\frac{P}{+}\frac{R}{+} \times \frac{P}{+}\frac{R}{+}$

$F_2$ :

| (++) | (P+) | (+R) | (PR) | ♀ / ♂ |
|---|---|---|---|---|
| $\frac{+}{+}\frac{+}{+}$ Single | $\frac{P}{+}\frac{+}{+}$ Pea | $\frac{+}{+}\frac{R}{+}$ rose | $\frac{P}{+}\frac{R}{+}$ Walnut | (++) |
| $\frac{+}{P}\frac{+}{+}$ Pea | $\frac{P}{P}\frac{+}{+}$ Pea | $\frac{+}{P}\frac{R}{+}$ Walnut | $\frac{P}{P}\frac{R}{+}$ Walnut | (P+) |
| $\frac{+}{+}\frac{+}{R}$ Rose | $\frac{P}{+}\frac{+}{R}$ Walnut | $\frac{+}{+}\frac{R}{R}$ Rose | $\frac{P}{+}\frac{R}{R}$ Walnut | (+R) |
| $\frac{+}{P}\frac{+}{R}$ Walnut | $\frac{P}{P}\frac{+}{R}$ Walnut | $\frac{+}{P}\frac{R}{R}$ Walnut | $\frac{P}{P}\frac{R}{R}$ Walnut | (PR) |

Genotypic ratio of 4 walnuts : $1\frac{P}{P}\frac{R}{R} : 4\frac{+}{P}\frac{+}{R} : 2\frac{P}{+}\frac{R}{R} : 2\frac{P}{P}\frac{R}{+}$

### Problem 12

Suppose we were given one of the $F_2$ walnuts from a cross of the pure walnut by single and asked to determine its genotype. How might we do this?

**Solution :**

The possible walnut genotypes in $F_2$ would be $\frac{P}{P}\frac{R}{R}$, $\frac{P}{P}\frac{R}{+}$, $\frac{P}{+}\frac{R}{R}$, $\frac{P}{+}\frac{R}{+}$

We have to cross this $F_2$ walnut with a single-combed hen.

1. If all are walnut, then the genotype of walnut is $\frac{P}{P}\frac{R}{R}$
2. If the ratio is 1 walnut : 1 Pea, then the genotype is $\frac{P}{P}\frac{R}{+}$
3. If the ratio is 1 walnut : 1 rose, then the genotype is $\frac{P}{+}\frac{R}{R}$
4. If the ratio is 1 walnut : 1 single, then genotype is $\frac{P}{+}\frac{R}{+}$

### Problem 13

In corn the seeds are normally purple, due to pigment in the "aleurone" layer of the seed. Two recessive mutations in separate chromosomes changed purple aleurone to white. In the nomenclature of "the presence or absence" theory, two normal alleles of the mutant genes are designated as *C, R*, meaning the gene for colour red and two white genes are designated as c and r meaning the absence of *C* or *R*. Instead, let us designate the white genes as $w_1$ and $w_2$ and normal alleles of each as (+).

Two plants, each of which grows from a seed (on their cobs) all with purple aleurone. Give the phenotypes and genotypes of the $P_1$, the gametes of $P_1$, the genotype and phenotype of $F_1$ and the gametes of $F_1$. Give the abbreviated genotypic ratio in the $F_2$ and below each abbreviated genotype put its phenotype.

**Solution :**

One white race = $w_1$, the normal is (+); Other white race = $w_2$, the normal is (+)

So, the genotype of pure purple is $\frac{+}{+}\frac{+}{+}$; genotype of pure white is $\frac{w_1}{w_1}\frac{w_2}{w_2}$

When they are crossed

$$P_1: \quad \frac{+}{+}\frac{+}{+} \quad \times \quad \frac{w_1}{w_1}\frac{w_2}{w_2}$$

$$\text{Gemetes}: \quad (\underline{+}\,\underline{+}) \qquad (\underline{w_1}\,\underline{w_2})$$

$$F_1: \quad \frac{+}{w_1}\frac{+}{w_2} \quad \text{Purple phenotype}$$

$P_2$ : When $F_1$ is crossed themselves

$$\frac{+}{w_1}\frac{+}{w_2} \times \frac{+}{w_1}\frac{+}{w_2}$$

Gemetes : (+ +) (+ $w_2$) ($w_1$ +) ($w_1$ $w_2$) (+ +) (+ $w_2$) ($w_1$ +) ($w_1$ $w_2$)

$F_2$ :

| (+ +) | (+ $w_2$) | ($w_1$ +) | ($w_1$ $w_2$) | ♀ / ♂ |
|---|---|---|---|---|
| $\frac{+}{+}\frac{+}{+}$ Purple | $\frac{+}{+}\frac{+}{w_2}$ Purple | $\frac{+}{w_1}\frac{+}{+}$ Purple | $\frac{+}{w_1}\frac{+}{w_2}$ Purple | (+ +) |
| $\frac{+}{+}\frac{+}{w_2}$ Purple | $\frac{+}{+}\frac{w_2}{w_2}$ White | $\frac{w_1}{+}\frac{+}{w_2}$ Purple | $\frac{w_1}{+}\frac{w_2}{w_2}$ White | (+ $w_2$) |
| $\frac{+}{w_1}\frac{+}{+}$ Purple | $\frac{+}{w_1}\frac{w_2}{+}$ Purple | $\frac{w_1}{w_1}\frac{+}{+}$ White | $\frac{w_1}{w_1}\frac{w_2}{+}$ White | ($w_1$ +) |
| $\frac{+}{w_1}\frac{+}{w_2}$ Purple | $\frac{+}{w_1}\frac{w_2}{w_2}$ White | $\frac{w_1}{w_1}\frac{+}{w_2}$ White | $\frac{w_1}{w_1}\frac{w_2}{w_2}$ White | ($w_1$ $w_2$) |

The phenotypic ratio : 9 Purple : 7 White

### ➧ Problem 14

Give the phenotypic ratio in which the offspring are produced if a purple aleurone of the genotype $\left(\frac{+}{w_1}\frac{+}{w_2}\right)$ is crossed to a plant of genotype

(a) $\frac{w_1}{w_1}\frac{w_2}{w_2}$ ; (b) $\frac{w_1}{w_1}\frac{+}{+}$ ; (c) $\frac{+}{+}\frac{w_2}{w_2}$

**Solution :**

(a) $\frac{+}{w_1}\frac{+}{w_2} \times \frac{w_1}{w_1}\frac{w_2}{w_2}$

Gemetes : (++) (+$w_2$) ($w_1$+) ($w_1w_2$) ($w_1w_2$)

Offspring :

| $\frac{+}{w_1}\frac{+}{w_2}$ | $\frac{+}{w_1}\frac{w_2}{w_2}$ | $\frac{w_1}{w_1}\frac{+}{w_2}$ | $\frac{w_1}{w_1}\frac{w_2}{w_2}$ |
|---|---|---|---|
| Purple | White | White | White |

Ratio : 1 Purple : 3 White

(b) $\frac{+}{w_1}\frac{+}{w_2} \times \frac{w_1}{w_1}\frac{+}{+}$

Gemetes : (++) (+$w_2$) ($w_1$+) ($w_1w_2$) ($w_1$+)

Offspring :

| $\frac{+}{w_1}\frac{+}{+}$ | $\frac{+}{w_1}\frac{w_2}{+}$ | $\frac{w_1}{w_1}\frac{+}{+}$ | $\frac{w_1}{w_1}\frac{w_2}{+}$ |
|---|---|---|---|
| Purple | Purple | White | White |

Ratio : 1 Purple : 1 White

(c) $$\frac{+}{w_1}\frac{+}{w_2} \times \frac{+}{+}\frac{w_1}{w_1}$$

Gemetes : $(++)$ $(+w_2)$ $(w_1+)$ $(w_1w_2)$ $(+w_2)$

Offspring :

| $\frac{+}{+}\frac{+}{w_1}$ | $\frac{+}{+}\frac{w_2}{w_2}$ | $\frac{w_1}{+}\frac{+}{w_2}$ | $\frac{w_1}{+}\frac{w_2}{w_2}$ |
|---|---|---|---|
| Purple | White | Purple | White |

Ratio : 1 Purple : 1 White

### ➧ Problem 15

Two corn plants are crossed. One grew from a seed with purple aleurone. The other from a seed with white aleurone. The offspring seeds from the cross are produced in the ratio of 1 purple : 3 white, give the genotype.

**Solution :**

Genotypes of white phenotype are $\frac{w_1}{w_1}\frac{w_2}{w_2}$, $\frac{w_1}{w_1}\frac{+}{w_2}$, $\frac{+}{w_1}\frac{w_2}{w_2}$, $\frac{w_1}{w_1}\frac{+}{+}$ and $\frac{+}{+}\frac{w_2}{w_2}$

Genotypes of purple phenotype are $\frac{+}{+}\frac{+}{+}$, $\frac{+}{+}\frac{+}{w_2}$, $\frac{+}{w_1}\frac{+}{+}$, $\frac{+}{w_1}\frac{+}{w_2}$

Next see the cross of Problem No. 14a.

### ➧ Problem 16

In corn, a recessive mutation changed purple aleurone to red. Designate the mutant gene as $r$ (red) and its normal allele as (+). A pure purple seed contains the normal alleles of $w_1$, $w_2$ and $r$ and therefore is $\frac{+}{+}\frac{+}{+}\frac{+}{+}$ a pure red contains normal alleles of $w_1$ and $w_2$ is $\frac{+}{+}\frac{+}{+}\frac{r}{r}$. Both r and its normal alleles are without effect in a seed pure for either $w_1$ or $w_2$ or for both $w_1$ or $w_2$. Thus for example $\frac{w_1}{w_1}\frac{+}{+}\frac{+}{+}$ is white $\frac{+}{+}\frac{w_2}{w_2}\frac{r}{r}$ is white.

A plant of genotype $\frac{+}{+}\frac{+}{+}\frac{r}{r}$(red) is crossed to one of genotype $\frac{w_1}{w_1}\frac{w_2}{w_2}\frac{+}{+}$(white). Give the genotype and phenotype of $F_1$.

**Solution :**

$$P_1 : \frac{+}{+}\frac{+}{+}\frac{r}{r} \quad \times \quad \frac{w_1}{w_1}\frac{w_2}{w_2}\frac{+}{+}$$

Gametes : $(++r)$ $\qquad$ $(w_1 w_2 +)$

$$P_1 : \frac{+}{w_1}\frac{+}{w_2}\frac{r}{+} \text{ (White)}$$

$F_1$ :

$\frac{3}{4}+$ → $\frac{3}{4}+$ → $\frac{9}{16}(++)$ → $\frac{3}{4}+$ → $\frac{27}{64}(+++)$ Purple; $\frac{1}{4}r$ → $\frac{9}{64}(++r)$ Red

$\frac{3}{4}+$ → $\frac{1}{4}w_2$ → $\frac{3}{16}(+w_2)$ → $\frac{3}{4}+$ → $\frac{9}{64}(+w_2+)$ White; $\frac{1}{4}r$ → $\frac{3}{64}(+w_2r)$ White

$\frac{1}{4}w_1$ → $\frac{3}{4}+$ → $\frac{3}{16}(w_1+)$ → $\frac{3}{4}+$ → $\frac{9}{64}(w_1++)$ White; $\frac{1}{4}r$ → $\frac{3}{64}(w_1+r)$ White

$\frac{1}{4}w_1$ → $\frac{1}{4}w_2$ → $\frac{1}{16}(w_1w_2)$ → $\frac{3}{4}+$ → $\frac{3}{64}(w_1w_2+)$ White; $\frac{1}{4}r$ → $\frac{1}{64}(w_1w_2r)$ White

So, the phenotypic ratio is 27 Purple : 9 red : 28 white

## Problem 17

In poultry, the genes for rose comb (*R*) and pea comb (*P*) if present together produce walnut comb. The recessive allele of both of which present together produce single comb.

What will be the comb character of the offspring of the following crosses in which genotypes of parent are given :

*RrPp* × *RrPp*

*RRPp* × *rrPp*

*RrPP* × *RrPp*

*RrPp* × *Rrpp*

*Rrpp* × *Rrpp*

**Hints :** Here the crosses are to be made and the genotypes with.

*RP* would be walnut comb

*Rp* be rose comb.

*rP* be pea comb.

*rp* be single comb.

**Problem 18**

In the following questions all of which concerned comb form in poultry, determine the genotype of the parent.

**(a)** A rose combed hen is crossed with a walnut comb, produces offspring three-eighths of which are walnut, three-eighths rose, one-eighths pea and one eighth single.

**Solution :**

Genotypes of Walnut comb are $\frac{+}{+}\frac{+}{+}$, $\frac{+}{+}\frac{+}{p}$, $\frac{+}{r}\frac{+}{+}$, $\frac{+}{r}\frac{+}{p}$

Genotypes of rose comb are $\frac{+}{+}\frac{r}{r}$, $\frac{p}{+}\frac{r}{r}$

$P_1$ : $\frac{p}{+}\frac{r}{r}$ × $\frac{+}{p}\frac{+}{r}$

Gametes : (+r) (pr) (+r) (p+) (++) (pr)

Offspring :

| ♀ \ ♂ | (++) | (p+) | (+r) | (pr) |
|---|---|---|---|---|
| (+r) | $\frac{+}{+}\frac{+}{r}$ walnut | $\frac{p}{+}\frac{+}{r}$ walnut | $\frac{+}{+}\frac{r}{r}$ rose | $\frac{p}{+}\frac{r}{r}$ rose |
| (pr) | $\frac{+}{p}\frac{+}{r}$ walnut | $\frac{p}{p}\frac{+}{r}$ pea | $\frac{+}{p}\frac{r}{r}$ rose | $\frac{p}{p}\frac{r}{r}$ single |

Ratio : 3 walnut : 3 rose : 1 pea : 1 single

**(b)** A walnut crossed with a single, produces in $F_1$ ¼ walnut, ¼ pea, ¼ rose and ¼ single.

**Solution :**

Genotypes of walnut comb : $\frac{+}{p}\frac{+}{r}$, $\frac{+}{+}\frac{r}{+}$, $\frac{p}{+}\frac{+}{+}$, $\frac{+}{+}\frac{+}{+}$ ; Genotype of single : $\frac{p}{p}\frac{r}{r}$

Here the genotypes of the parent would be $\frac{+}{p}\frac{+}{r}$ and $\frac{p}{p}\frac{r}{r}$

Parent : $\frac{+}{p}\frac{+}{r}$ × $\frac{p}{p}\frac{r}{r}$

Gametes : (++) (+r) (p+) (pr) (pr)

Offspring :

| (++) | (+r) | (p+) | (pr) | ♀ / ♂ |
|---|---|---|---|---|
| $\frac{+}{p}\frac{+}{r}$ walnut | $\frac{+}{p}\frac{r}{r}$ rose | $\frac{p}{p}\frac{+}{r}$ pea | $\frac{p}{p}\frac{r}{r}$ single | (pr) |

**(c)** A rose is crossed with a pea, produces 6 walnut and 5 rose offspring.

**Solution :**

Genotypes of rose comb are : $\frac{+}{+}\frac{r}{r}$ , $\frac{+}{p}\frac{r}{r}$ Genotypes of pea comb are : $\frac{p}{p}\frac{+}{+}$ , $\frac{p}{p}\frac{+}{r}$

Here the ratio is 1 : 1 (approx)

Therefore, genotypes of the parent would be

Parent : $\frac{+}{+}\frac{r}{r} \times \frac{p}{p}\frac{+}{r}$

Gametes : (+r) (pr) (p+)

Offspring : $\left(\frac{+}{p}\frac{r}{r}\right)$ and $\left(\frac{+}{p}\frac{r}{+}\right)$

rose walnut

**(d)** A walnut crossed with a single produces one single comb offspring.

**Solution :**

One of the offspring is single, whose genotype would be $\frac{p}{p}\frac{r}{r}$.

Therefore the genotypes of the walnut might be $\frac{+}{p}\frac{+}{r}$.

Parent : $\frac{+}{p}\frac{+}{r} \times \frac{p}{p}\frac{r}{r}$

Gametes : (++) (+r) (p+) (pr) (pr)

Offspring : $\frac{p}{p}\frac{r}{r}$ Single comb

**Problem 19**

In poultry, feathered shanks (*F*) are dominant over clean shank (*f*) and the white plumage of Leghorn (*I*) is dominant over black (*i*).

What will be the appearance of the offspring of the following crosses, in which the genotypes of the parents are given?

(a) $\frac{f}{f}\frac{R}{r}\frac{P}{p} \times \frac{F}{f}\frac{R}{r}\frac{p}{p}$

Clean shank walnut comb × Shanks feathered rose comb

(b) *Ff ii Rrpp* × *ff II RrPp*

Shank black rose comb × Clean white walnut comb

**Solution :**

(a) $P_1$ : *ff Rr Pp* Clean-walnut × *Ff Rr pp* Shank-rose

Gametes : (fRP) (frp) (fRp) (frP) (FRp) (frp) (Frp) (fRp)

$F_1$ :

| fRP | frp | fRp | frP | ♀ / ♂ |
|---|---|---|---|---|
| *Ff RR Pp* Shank walnut | *Ff Rr pp* Shank rose | *Ff RR pp* Shank rose | *FfRrPp* Shank walnut | FRp |
| *ff Rr Pp* Clean walnut | *ff rr pp* clean single | *ff Rr pp* Clean rose | *ffrrPp* Clean Pea | frp |
| *Ff Rr Pp* Shank walnut | *Ff rr pp* Shank single | *Ff Rr pp* Shank rose | *FfrrPp* Shank pea | Frp |
| *ff RR Pp* Clean walnut | *ff Rr pp* Clean rose | *ff RR pp* Clean rose | *ffRrPp* Clean walnut | fRp |

Shank walnut = 3, Shank rose = 3, Shank pea = 1, Shank single = 1,

Clean walnut = 3, Clean rose = 3, Clean pea = 1, Clean single = 1

(b) $P_1$ : *ii Ff Rr pp* Shank black rose × *II ff Rr Pp* Clean white walnut

Gametes : (iFRp) (ifrp) (iFrp) (ifRp) (IfRP) (Ifrp) (IfRp) (IfrP)

$F_1$ :

| iFRp | ifrp | iFrp | ifRp | ♀ / ♂ |
|---|---|---|---|---|
| *Ii Ff RR Pp* Shank -black walnut | *Ii ff Rr Pp* Clean -black walnut | *Ii Ff Rr Pp* Shank -black walnut | *Ii ff RR Pp* Clean -black walnut | IfRP |
| *Ii Ff Rr pp* Shank -black rose | *Ii ff rr pp* Clean -black single | *Ii Ff rr pp* Shank -black single | *Ii ff Rr pp* Clean -black rose | Ifrp |
| *Ii Ff RR pp* Shank -black rose | *Ii ff Rr pp* Clean -black rose | *Ii Ff Rr pp* Shank -black rose | *Ii ff RR pp* Clean -black rose | IfRp |
| *Ii Ff Rr Pp* Shank -black walnut | *Ii ff rr Pp* Clean -black pea | *Ii Ff rr Pp* Shank -black pea | *Ii ff Rr Pp* Clean -black walnut | IfrP |

**Result :**

Shank-black walnut = 3

Shank black pea = 1

Clean black walnut = 3

Clean black pea = 1

Shank black rose = 3

Shank black single = 1

Clean black rose = 3

Clean black single = 1

### Problem 20

A feathered-shanked, rose comb bird, crossed with a clean-shanked pea comb one produces 25 feathered-pea, 24 feathered walnut, 26-feathered rose and 22 feathered single. What are the genotypes of parents?

**Solution :**

Genotypes of the parent may be

Feathered shanked rose comb bird : *FF RR pp, Ff RR pp, Ff Rr pp, FF Rr pp*

Clean shanked pea combed bird : *ff rr PP, ff rr Pp*

Here the ratio is 1 : 1 : 1 : 1

Therefore, the genotypes of the parent would be *FF Rr pp* and *ff rr Pp*

P : *FF Rr pp* × *ff rr Pp*

Offspring :

| (FRp) | (Frp) | ♀ / ♂ |
|---|---|---|
| *Ff Rr Pp* feathered walnut | *Ff rr Pp* feathered Pea | (frP) |
| *Ff Rr pp* Feathered rose | *ff rr pp* Feathered single | (frp) |

### ➧ Problem 21

A breeder has a homozygous race of feathered shank–black-rose combed bird and another clean shank-white pea combed ones. He wants a race of black birds with clean shank-walnut combs. What proportion of the $F_2$ raised from a cross between these two races will be what he desires in appearance? What proportion of these birds will be homologous for desired characters?

**Solution :**

Genotype of homozygous feathered-shank-black rose combed bird *FF ii RR pp*

Genotype of homozygous clean-shank-white pea combed bird *ff II rr PP*

Genotype of $F_1$ hybrid is *Ff Ii Rr Pp*

Phenotype is Feathered shank-black-walnut

$F_2$ : Cross between $F_1$ and $F_1$

*Ff Ii Rr Pp* × *Ff Ii Rr Pp*

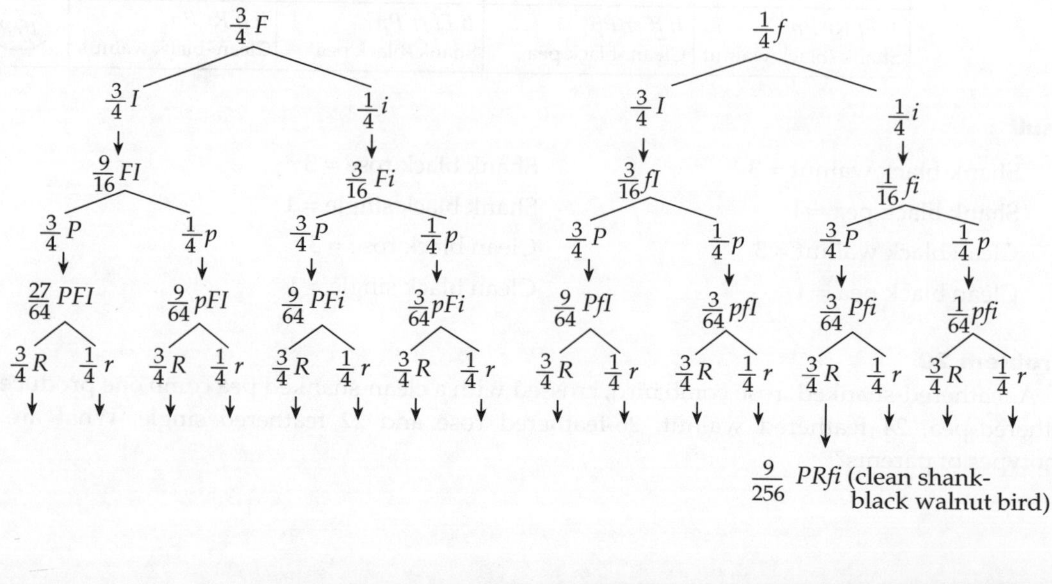

He will get a fraction $\left[\frac{9}{256}\right]$ of $F_2$ progenies.

**Problem 22**

In sweet peas *C* or *P* alone produces white flower, the purple colour being due to the presence of both these factors.

What will be the flower colour of the offspring of the following crosses in which the genotypes of the parent are given.

(a) *CcPp* × *ccPp*

(b) *ccPp* × *CCpp*

(c) *CcPp* × *CcPP*

(d) *Ccpp* × *ccPp*

**Solution :**

(a) Parent : *Cc Pp* × *cc Pp*

Gametes : (*CP*) (*Cp*) (*cP*) (*cp*)   (*cP*) (*cp*)

Offspring :

| (*CP*) | (*Cp*) | (*cP*) | (*cp*) | ♀ / ♂ |
|---|---|---|---|---|
| *Cc PP* Purple | *Cc Pp* Purple | *cc PP* White | *cc Pp* White | (*cP*) |
| *Cc Pp* Purple | *Cc pp* White | *cc Pp* White | *cc pp* White | (*cp*) |

Ratio : 3 Purple : 5 White

**Problem 23**

In the following three crosses of sweet peas, what are the genotypes of the parent?

**(a)** A white-flowered plant crossed with a purple produces offspring of which $\frac{3}{8}$ are purple and $\frac{5}{8}$ are white?

**Solution :**

Genotypes of white flower are *cc Pp, Cc pp, CCpp, cc Pp*

Genotypes of purple flower are *CCPp, CcPP, CCPp* and *CcPp*

Here the genotypes of the parent would be *cc Pp* × *Cc Pp*

or, *Cc pp* × *Cc Pp*

**(b)** A purple flowered plant crossed with a white one produces offspring of which one half are purple and one half white.

**Solution :**

Here the genotypes of the parent would be

| | CC Pp | × | cc pp |
|---|---|---|---|
| | (Purple) | | (White) |
| Gametes : | (CP) (Cp) | | (cp) |
| Offspring : | Cc Pp | × | Cc pp |
| | (Purple) | | (White) |

**(c)** A white flowered plant crossed with another white produces offspring of which $\frac{3}{4}$ are white and $\frac{1}{4}$ purple.

**Solution :**

Genotype of white plants are *cc PP, cc Pp, Cc pp, CC pp*

Here the genotype of the parent would be : *cc Pp* and *Cc pp*

Parent : *cc Pp* × *Cc pp*

Offspring :

| ♂ \ ♀ | (Cp) | (cp) |
|---|---|---|
| (cP) | Cc Pp Purple | cc Pp White |
| (cp) | Cc pp White | cc pp White |

Ratio : $\frac{3}{4}$ White : $\frac{1}{4}$ Purple

**Problem 24**

In maize plant-A when crossed with B, produces 255 green, 89 white and when selfed produce 153 green and 118 white offspring. What are the genotypes of the two plants? What should plant-B produce when selfed?

**Solution :**

When A × B, then green : white = 255 : 89 = 3 : 1

Again, when A × A, then green : white= 153 : 118 = 9 : 7

In corn many genes affecting the development of green chlorophyll pigment are known. The normal green colour of maize results from the combined action of the normal allele of these genes.

If one of these genes mutates to a recessive allele, the seedlings are albinoic i.e. white. If the mutants are $w_1$ and $w_2$ and their normal genes are +'s.

Then their genotypes and phenotypes would be

$$\frac{+}{w_1}\,\frac{w_2}{w_2}\text{ (white)},\quad \frac{w_1}{w_1}\,\frac{w_2}{w_2}\text{ (white)},\quad \frac{w_1}{w_1}\,\frac{+}{w_2}\text{ (white)}$$

$$\frac{+}{w_1}\,\frac{+}{w_2}\text{ (green)},\quad \frac{+}{+}\,\frac{+}{w_2}\text{ (green)},\quad \frac{+}{w_1}\,\frac{+}{+}\text{ (green)}$$

When, $\frac{+}{w_1}\frac{+}{w_2}$ × $\frac{w_1}{w_1}\frac{w_2}{w_2}$, the result is 3 white : 1 green

When, $\frac{+}{w_1}\frac{+}{w_2}$ × $\frac{+}{w_1}\frac{+}{w_2}$, the result is 9 : 7

When, $\frac{+}{+}\frac{+}{w_2}$ × $\frac{+}{w_1}\frac{+}{w_2}$, the result is 3 : 1

Therefore, the genotype of A is $\frac{+}{w_1}\frac{+}{w_2}$ and genotype of B is $\frac{+}{+}\frac{+}{w_2}$

Parent : $\frac{+}{+}\frac{+}{w_2}$ × $\frac{+}{+}\frac{+}{w_2}$

Gemetes : (+ +) (+$w_2$) (+ +) (+$w_2$)

$F_2$ :

| ♀ \ ♂ | (++) | (+$w_2$) |
|---|---|---|
| (++) | $\frac{+}{+}\frac{+}{+}$ green | $\frac{+}{+}\frac{+}{w_2}$ green |
| (+$w_2$) | $\frac{+}{+}\frac{+}{w_2}$ green | $\frac{+}{+}\frac{w_2}{w_2}$ white |

The ratio is 3 green : 1 white

**Problem 25**

A green maize plant when selfed, produces about $\frac{15}{16}$ green and $\frac{1}{16}$ white (lethal) seedlings. What would be the genotype?

**Solution :**

The genotypes of green maize may be $\frac{+}{+}\frac{+}{+}\frac{+}{+}$, $\frac{+}{w_1}\frac{+}{w_2}\frac{+}{+}$, $\frac{+}{w_1}\frac{+}{+}\frac{+}{+}$, $\frac{+}{+}\frac{+}{w_2}\frac{+}{+}$

when $\frac{+}{w_1}\frac{+}{w_2}\frac{+}{+}$ is selfed $\left(i.e,\ \frac{+}{w_1}\frac{+}{w_2}\frac{+}{+} \times \frac{+}{w_1}\frac{+}{w_2}\frac{+}{+}\right)$, the result is as follows.

| ♂ \ ♀ | (+++) | (+$w_2$+) | ($w_1$++) | ($w_1w_2$+) |
|---|---|---|---|---|
| (+++) | $\frac{+}{+}\frac{+}{+}\frac{+}{+}$ green | $\frac{+}{+}\frac{w_2}{+}\frac{+}{+}$ green | $\frac{w_1}{+}\frac{+}{+}\frac{+}{+}$ green | $\frac{w_1}{+}\frac{w_2}{+}\frac{+}{+}$ green |
| (+$w_2$+) | $\frac{+}{+}\frac{+}{w_2}\frac{+}{+}$ green | $\frac{+}{+}\frac{w_2}{w_2}\frac{+}{+}$ green | $\frac{w_1}{+}\frac{+}{w_2}\frac{+}{+}$ green | $\frac{w_1}{+}\frac{w_2}{w_2}\frac{+}{+}$ green |
| ($w_1$++) | $\frac{+}{w_1}\frac{+}{+}\frac{+}{+}$ green | $\frac{+}{w_1}\frac{w_2}{+}\frac{+}{+}$ green | $\frac{w_1}{w_1}\frac{+}{+}\frac{+}{+}$ green | $\frac{w_1}{w_1}\frac{w_2}{+}\frac{+}{+}$ green |
| ($w_1w_2$+) | $\frac{+}{w_1}\frac{+}{w_2}\frac{+}{+}$ green | $\frac{+}{w_1}\frac{w_2}{w_2}\frac{+}{+}$ green | $\frac{w_1}{w_1}\frac{+}{w_2}\frac{+}{+}$ green | $\frac{w_1}{w_1}\frac{w_2}{w_2}\frac{+}{+}$ white |

**Problem 26**

In maize, *C* and *R* are both necessary for the production of red aleurone colour, the absence of either resulting in white aleurone. If *P* is present in addition to *C* and *R*, then the aleurone is purple but *P* has no effect in the absence of either *C* or *R* or both.

What would be aleurone colour of the offspring of the following crosses, the genotypes of the parent are being given.

(a) *Cc Rr pp* × *cc Rr Pp*

(b) *CC rr Pp* × *Cc Rr pp*

(c) *Cc Rr Pp* × *Cc Rr pp*

(d) *cc RR Pp* × *Cc Rr pp*

**Solution :**

(a) *Cc Rr pp* (Red) × *cc Rr Pp* (purple)

Gametes : *Crp* *CRp* *crp* *cRp*    *crp* *cRP* *cRp* *crP*

Offsprings :

| ♀ \ ♂ | *Crp* | *CRp* | *crp* | *cRp* |
|---|---|---|---|---|
| *crp* | *Cc rr pp* white | *Cc Rr pp* red | *cc rr pp* white | *cc Rr pp* white |
| *cRP* | *Cc Rr Pp* purple | *Cc RR Pp* purple | *cc Rr Pp* purple | *cc RR Pp* Purple |
| *cRp* | *Cc Rr pp* red | *Cc RR pp* red | *cc Rr pp* white | *cc RR pp* white |
| *crP* | *Cc rr Pp* purple | *Cc Rr Pp* purple | *cc rr Pp* white | *cc Rr Pp* purple |

Ratio : 7 purple : 6 white : 3 red

(d) *cc RR Pp* (purple) × *Cc Rr pp* (red)

Offsprings :

| ♀ \ ♂ | *CRp* | *crp* | *Crp* | *cRp* |
|---|---|---|---|---|
| *cRp* | *Cc RR pp* red | *cc Rr pp* white | *Cc Rr pp* red | *cc RR pp* white |
| *cRP* | *Cc RR Pp* purple | *cc Rr Pp* purple | *Cc Rr Pp* purple | *cc RR Pp* purple |

Ratio : 4 purple : 2 red : 2 white

(c) *Cc Rr Pp* (purple) × *Cc Rr Pp* (purple)

$\frac{3}{4}C$

- $\frac{3}{4}R$ → $\frac{9}{16}CR$
  - $\frac{3}{4}P$ → $\frac{27}{64}CRP$
  - $\frac{1}{4}p$ → $\frac{9}{64}CRp$
- $\frac{1}{4}r$ → $\frac{3}{16}Cr$
  - $\frac{3}{4}P$ → $\frac{9}{64}CrP$
  - $\frac{1}{4}p$ → $\frac{3}{64}Crp$

$\frac{1}{4}c$

- $\frac{3}{4}R$ → $\frac{3}{16}cR$
  - $\frac{3}{4}P$ → $\frac{9}{64}cRP$
  - $\frac{1}{4}p$ → $\frac{3}{64}cRp$
- $\frac{1}{4}r$ → $\frac{1}{16}cr$
  - $\frac{3}{4}P$ → $\frac{3}{64}crP$
  - $\frac{1}{4}p$ → $\frac{1}{64}crp$

| | $\frac{27}{64}CRP$ | $\frac{9}{64}CRp$ | $\frac{9}{64}CrP$ | $\frac{3}{64}Crp$ | $\frac{9}{64}cRP$ | $\frac{3}{64}cRp$ | $\frac{3}{64}crP$ | $\frac{1}{64}crp$ |
|---|---|---|---|---|---|---|---|---|
| Phenotype : | purple | red | purple | white | purple | white | purple | white |

Ratio : 48 purple : 9 red : 7 white

(d) *cc RR Pp* (purple) × *Cc Rr pp* (red)

Offsprings :

| ♂ \ ♀ | *CRp* | *crp* | *Crp* | *cRp* |
|---|---|---|---|---|
| *cRp* | *Cc RR pp* red | *cc Rr pp* white | *Cc Rr pp* red | *cc RR pp* white |
| *cRP* | *Cc RR Pp* purple | *cc Rr Pp* purple | *Cc Rr Pp* purple | *cc RR Pp* purple |

Ratio : 4 purple : 2 red : 2 white

## Chapter Glossary/Key Terms

**Complementary gene :** The duplicate recessive gene in the separate chromosomes, which interact to produce a different phenotype when Come to the same genotype.

**Duplicate gene :** The alleles of two gene loci either dominant or recessive, combinely produces a trait.

**Epistasis :** The masking of the action of alleles of one gene by allelic combinations of another gene.

*Contd.*

**Hypostatic gene:** A gene whose expression is masked by an epistatic gene.

**Interallelic interaction :** The genes located on the same or different chromosomes that interact with one another for the expression of phenotype.

**Intra-allelic interaction :** The kind of genic interaction occurs in between the two allelomorphs of a single type of gene.

**Modifier gene :** The gene that changes the phenotypic effects of the other gene in a quantitative fashion.

**Modifying gene :** The genes whose phenotypic expression is modified by the presence of modifier gene.

**Mutually supplementary gene:** The dominant duplicate genes interact to produce a different phenotype when come to the same genotype.

# EXERCISE

**A. Long answer type questions :**

1. What is meant by epistasis? Define dominant epistasis. Give an example with $F_1$ and $F_2$ phenotypes, genotypes and ratio.
2. Define recessive epistasis. Give an example with $F_1$ and $F_2$ genetypes and phenotypes and also phenotypic ratio.
3. What is duplicate gene with cumulative effect? Give an example. Make a cross with $F_1$ and $F_2$ genotypes and phenotypes. What is the $F_2$ phenotypic ratio?
4. What is meant by duplicate dominant gene? Give an example. Make a cross with $F_1$ and $F_2$ genotypes and phenotypes and also $F_2$ phenotypic ratio.
5. What is meatn by duplicate recessive gene. Why it is called complement gene? Give an example. Make a cross with $F_1$ and $F_2$ geneotypes and phenotypes and also $F_2$ phenotypic ratio.
6. Give an example of dominant and recessive interaction. Make a cross with $F_1$ and $F_2$ phenotypes and genotypes and also $F_2$ phenotypic ratio.
7. What is meant by non-epistatic interallelic interaction? Give an example.
8. What is meant by modifier gene? Give suitable example.
9. What are the differences among dominance, epistasis and pleiotropy? How can you determine that pleiotropic effect, such as those seen in sickle-cell anemia are due to different genes?
10. In a variety of onions, three bulbs colours segragate : red, yellow and white. A plant with a red bulb is crossed to a plant with a white bulb, and all the offspring have red bulbs. When these are selfed, the following plants are obtained :

| | |
|---|---|
| Red-bulbed | 119 |
| Yellow-bulbed | 32 |
| White-bulbed | 9 |

What is the mode of inheritance of bulb color and how do you account for the ratio?

11. How you can determine the nature of the genetic control of comb type in the rooster . How would you proceed if both your rooster and hen had rose combs?

**B. Short answer type questions.**

1. What is intra-allelic interaction?
2. What is inter-allelic interaction?
3. What are epistatic and hypotatic genes?
4. What are epistatic and hypostatic interactions?
5. What is bigenic epistatic interaction?
6. What do you mean by dominant epistasis? What is its $F_2$ phenotypic ratio?
7. What do you mean by recessive epistasis? What is its $F_2$ phenotypic ratio?
8. Distinguish dominant epistasis and recessive epistasis.
9. What is cumulative effect of duplicate gene? What is its $F_2$ phenotypic ratio?
10. Why duplicate genes with cumulative effect is known as mutually supplementry genes?
11. What is duplicate dominant gene? What is its $F_2$ phenotypic ratio?
12. What is duplicate recessive gene? What is its $F_2$ phenotypic ratio? Why duplicate recessive genes are called complementary gene?
13. Distinguish duplicate dominant and duplicate recessive gene interactions.
14. What do you mean by dominant-recessive interaction? Give an example.
15. What is non epistatic interaction?
16. How comb pattern of hen is inherited?
17. What is modifier genes?
18. What is suppressor genes?

# 4

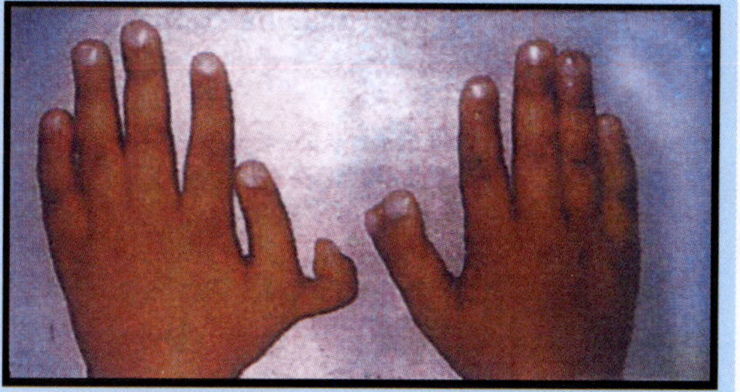

# Lethality : Expressivities and Penetrance

**CHAPTER AGENDA**

## 4.1 CONCEPT

According to the phenotypic manifestation of genes, it can be grouped into lethal, semi lethal and non-lethals.

Certain genes, which can cause death from zygote upto sexually mature adult stage, are called **lethal genes**. It can be sex-linked or autosomal.

When the genes cause death of some individuals but the individuals could survive and get maturity and reproduce, are known as **semi lethals or sub vitals**. It can also be sex-linked or autosomal.

The distinction between these categories is not sharp, especially some genes that are lethal under some conditions may permit survival under special medical treatment.

Conventionally, genes that kill fewer than 100% but more than 50% of their victims are called semi lethals, whereas, those that cause less than 50% mortality are known as sub vital genes.

## 4.2 INHERITANCE OF AUTOSOMAL LETHAL GENES (RECESSIVE) IN MICE

$A^Y$ = dominant gene for yellow fur

a = recessive allele for non yellow

It has been found that when yellow furred male mice are mated with yellow furred females, some of the yellow furred embryos die in the uterus in an early stage. It has also been noticed that the progenies of such cross showed 2 yellow : one non yellow phenotypes (Fig. 4.1).

It has been concluded from the result that:

(i) Homozygous $A^YA^Y$ dies before birth.

(ii) The **lethality of** $A^Y$ **gene is recessive**; therefore when it is heterozygous, this lethal gene cannot be expressed due to the presence of normal gene on one of its chromosome.

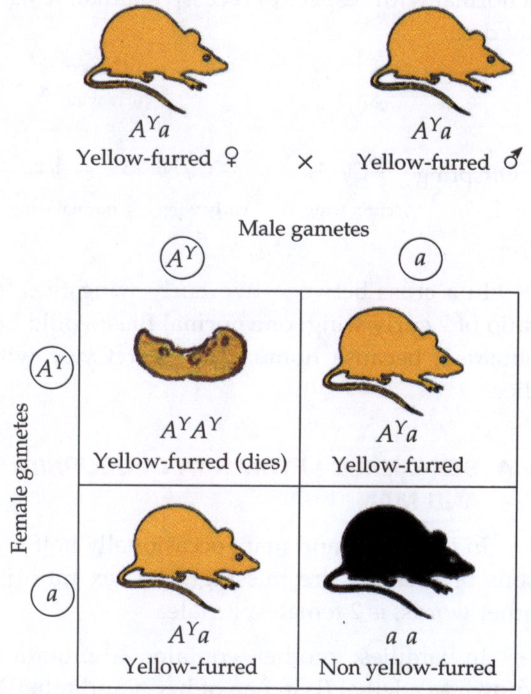


**Fig.4.1 :** *inheritance of a lethal gene in mice.*

(iii) When it is heterozygous, the dominant colour gene is expressed to give yellow fur to the mice.

## 4.3 AUTOSOMAL LETHAL GENES IN *DROSOPHILA*

Cy = curly wings (dominant gene)

cy = normal wings (recessive gene).

Curly wings in *Drosophila* is dominant over its normal recessive wing, but **curly wing gene is recessive** to its lethality therefore when it is homozygous for curly wing genes (*CyCy*), the fly will die because of the presence of recessive lethal genes in their two chromosomes. The heterozygous *Drosophila* (*Cycy*) will be curly wing in it's phenotype because of the presence of dominant wing character but one of its gene is normal with respect to recessive lethal. It will not die.

Parent : *Cy cy* (curly wing ♀) × *Cy cy* (curly wing ♂)

Offspring : $\frac{1}{4}$ *Cy Cy* (curly wing dies) : $\frac{2}{4}$ *Cy cy* (curly wing) : $\frac{1}{4}$ *cy cy* (normal wing)

In a cross between two curly wing flies, a ratio of 2 curly wing: one normal flies would be obtained, because homozygous for CyCy will die.

## 4.4 SEX-LINKED LETHALS IN *DROSOPHILA* AND MAN

In *Drosophila* and man, occasionally half the sons of a family are missing. The sex ratio in other words, is 2 females: 1 male.

In families, mother contains a mutation known as a lethal (l) in one of her X and other X chromosome has its normal allele (+). The hybrid mother survives because she contains the dominant normal allele in one of her X-chromosome and this prevents the lethal from expressing itself. But half of her sons receive her lethal containing X and die. The remaining offspring receives at least one normal X and survives. Hence a sex ratio of 2 females: 1 male results.

Parent : $X^+X^l$ (♀) × $X^+Y$ (♂)

Offspring : $X^+X^+$ ♀ normal; $X^+X^l$ ♀ carrier; $X^+Y$ ♂ normal; $X^lY$ ♂ lethal (dies)

## 4.5 LETHAL HEREDITARY DISEASES IN MAN

**Juvenile amaurotic idiocy** is a lethal hereditary disease. Infants homozygous for this gene appear to be normal at birth; their eyesight begins to fail between the age of 4 to 7 years resulting in blindness, physical and mental retardation and die before attaining adolescence. It is a **lethal recessive gene.**

**Tay-sachs disease** or **infantile amaurotic idiocy** is also another such recessive lethal genetic disease, causing early death at homozygous condition.

**Phenyl-ketonuric imbecility** is a lethal hereditary disease, caused by recessive lethal gene, in homozygous condition. It is characterized by the presence of phenyl pyruvic acid in the urine, mental retardation, defects in muscular reflex, dilution of hair and skin pigments. Characteristic posture and have reduced life expectancy and seldom have children.

Sickle cell anemia, thalassemia are the examples of such recessive lethal genes.

It is probable that many prenatal deaths such as stillbirths and abortions in man are due to lethal genes.

## 4.6 SEMI-LETHAL AND SUB-VITAL GENES IN MAN

A dominant semi lethal gene in man causes a disease called **epiloia**. The heterozygous carriers of this gene have symptoms of mental deficiency, abnormal growths on the skin and tumors in internal organs and may die when the disease is caused in childhood. But some of them manage to survive and become adult, marry and then half of their heterozygote offspring develop the disease epiloia.

The gene epiloia has been appeared due to dominant mutation of the normal gene. The rate of mutation is so rare (only ten per million) that union between two such carriers are rare and thus the dominant heterozygotes of such gene have not been observed.

The disease **retinoblastoma** is caused by another dominant mutant gene in man. The symptoms are the malignant tumors in the eyes and caused death in their childhood in heterozygous as well as homozygous conditions. This is due to mutation of normal gene and shows complete lethal. Sometimes the child may grow to an adult.

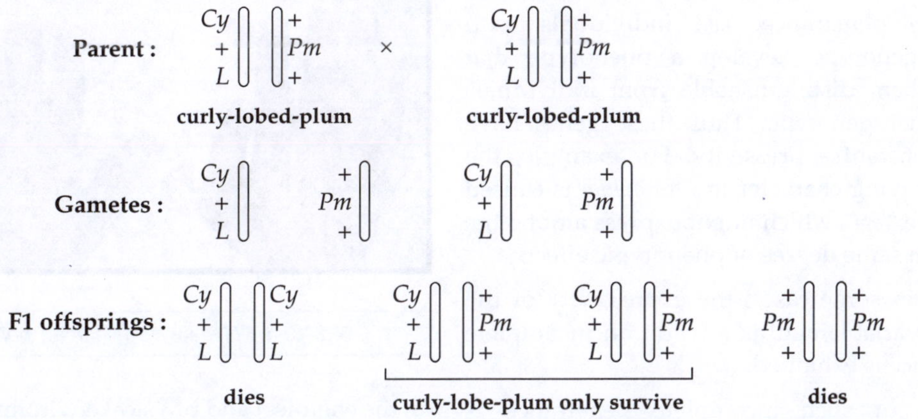


**Fig.4.2 :** *Inheritance of balanced lethal genes.*

**Sickle cell anaemia**, **thalassemia** and **haemophilia** (sex-linked gene) genes have been classified as semi lethal rather than complete lethal, because by modern treatment and medicine these patients can survive long upto adult and produce their offsprings.

## 4.7 SEMI LETHAL AND SUB-VITAL GENES IN *DROSOPHILA*

*Drosophila* shows some conspicuous external appearance, which is caused due to expression of sub vital or semi lethal genes.

One of such semi-lethal gene is that causes vestigial wing where the wing is less sturdy than the normal winged flies. This gene is recessive to normal wings. When a normal dominant (homozygous) fly is crossed with a vestigial winged homozygous recessive one, $F_1$ progenies would have all normal winged hybrid. In $F_2$, one-fourth of the progenies would have a double recessive vestigial winged flies. These flies after hatching out from the eggs can not fly in the nature, as a result they will die on the spot and thus the gene would become complete lethal. But in culture medium, with proper care and food these flies can survive and reach to adult and successfully may produce their progenies. Thus it becomes semi lethal.

## 4.8 BALANCED LETHAL GENE

Balanced lethal stock is one which carries mutant lethal alleles (markers) on specific homologous chromosomes, their normal allele being present on its homologue, consequently homozygous individuals (both for normal and mutants) will not survive.

In *Drosophila*, a stock carried the dominant genes *Cy* (curly wing) and *L* (lobed eye) on one chromosome and *Pm* (plum eye i.e., brown eye) on the other homologue, so that the organism can be designated as *Cy* + *L*/ + *Pm* + (Fig. 4.2).

Phenotype of the stock, which is heterozygous for *Cy*, *L* and *Pm* is curly-lobe-plum. If such individuals are crossed among themselves, progeny is always heterozygous because, each of the two homologous chromosomes carried lethal mutant genes. Through the presence of inversion, crossing over was also suppressed, so that *Cy* and/or *L* may not be transferred to the chromosome carrying *Pm* and vice versa.

## 4.9 PENETRANCE AND EXPRESSIVITY OF LETHAL AND NONLETHAL GENES

It is difficult to draw a line between categories of lethals. The genes causing lethality may differ in their penetrance and expressivity.

Some lethal genes are said to have a complete penetrance, *i.e.*, individuals with proper genotype develop a phenotype that makes them distinguishable from individuals with other genotype. Thus these genes have fairly constant expressivity. For example, the vestigial wing character in *Drosophila* is caused by a gene "*vg*", which might express among the flies with same degree of phenotypic effect.

But in some cases, the expressivity of the gene is variable and as a result an incomplete penetrance is exhibited.

One of such incomplete penetrance is observed in man through a dominant gene causes a disease, **Huntington's chorea**. The symptoms of this disease start with involuntary twitching of the head, limbs and body and degenerative changes in nervous system, loss of mental and physical power and death. The onset of the disease may be noticed at any stage as early as the first year of birth up to an age of 70. Thus the gene is said to have incomplete penetrance and the expressivity is also variable. As the person carrying this gene may attain their reproductive stage, it is to be regarded as semi lethal gene.

Another gene of incomplete penetrance and variable expressivities is observed among human beings that cause the ability and inability of bitter taste of phenyl-thio-carbamide (PTC). The tasters bear a dominant gene (*T*) in homozygous or heterozygous conditions and non-tasters would have homozygous recessive gene(t). It has been found that some tasters taste an intensely bitter, while the other requires a more concentration of PTC to be a taster.

Possibly this sensitivity is due to the presence of two *T* genes one *T* and one t gene. However, the existence of a minority of persons who are found to be intermediate in sensitivity i.e., the expressivity of the alleles *T* and *t* is variable. This gene also shows Mendelian inheritance, for example, two heterozygous tasters may have a non-taster child.

Actually the expression of a gene depends not only upon their genetic constitution but also on the chemical and physical environment of the cell. Thus various environmental conditions may interfere with the various biochemical paths that are required for the development of the body and mind of the organism. The expressivity and penetrance of the gene may certainly be due to interaction between genetic constitution of the organism and the environmental factors.

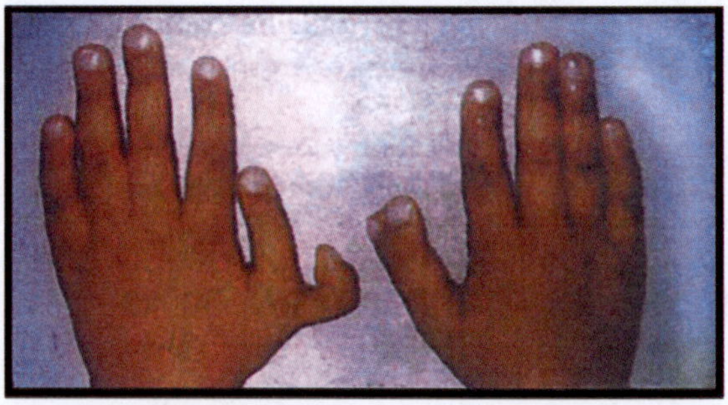

**Fig.4.3 :** *Polydactyly in human beings.*

Other genetic factors, modifiers, etc may also cause variations in penetrance and expressivity of the gene.

For some characters, the genotype does not always produce the expected phenotype, a phenomenon termed *incomplete penetrance.*

Incomplete penetrance is seen in **human polydactyly**, the condition of having extra finger and toes (Fig. 4.3). There are several different forms of human polydactyly, but the trait is usually caused by a dominant allele. Occasionally, people possess the allele for polydactyly, but nevertheless, have a normal number of fingers and toes. In these cases, the gene for polydactyly is not fully penetrant.

**Penetrance** is defined as the percentage of individuals having a particular genotype that expresses the expected phenotype. For example, if we examine 100 people having an allele for polydactyly and found that only 90 of them were polydactylous, the penetrance would be 90% (= 0.90).

**Expressivity** is the degree to which a character is expressed. Polydactyly also exhibits variable expressivity. Some polydactylous persons possess extra fingers and toes that are fully functional, whereas, others possess only a small tag of extra skin.

The incomplete penetrance and variable expressivity are due to the effects of other genes and also due to environmental factors that partially or completely suppress the effect of the said gene.

## 4.10 CONDITIONAL ALLELES

When the absence of a specific protein results in a lethal phenotype, then it is considered that these genes encode essential proteins for the survival of the organisms. These are called *essential gene.*

The allele that has the potential to cause the death of the organism is called *lethal gene.* There are many genes which are not absolutely required for the survival although they are likely to be beneficial to the organism. These are called **nonessential genes.** Loss of function mutations do not cause death. Sometimes, its mutation or overproduction may cause death and leads to a lethal phenotype.

Lethal phenotypes may express at the early age of the individual or may exert effects later in life. Then lethality is appeared in the individual. For example, **Huntington disease,** the symptoms appear usually between the age of 30 and 50. In some cases lethality may be expressed only at a cerain environmental condition. These are called **conditional lethal alleles.** For example, in *Drosophila,* such lethality occurs and kills the organism only at a particular temperature sensitive (*ts*) lethal. This allele can kill the developing larva at a high temperature (30°C) but it will survive if grown at a lower temperature (22°C). The mutation of the normal allele alters the structure of the encoded protein so that it can not function properly at the nonpermissive temperature. The proteins would then be unfolded or degraded.

Conditional alleles can be identified by exposing the individuals at that particular nonpermissive environment. For example, the people with a defect in the gene for the enzyme glucose -6-phosphate dehydrogenase, have a negative reaction when ingested with fava beans, which can lead to **hemolytic syndrome** and death.

## 4.11 PROBLEMS ON LETHAL GENE

### Problem 1

In *Drosophila,* a dominant gene *D* for a phenotype "dichoete" is homozygous lethal. Summarise the result.

(a) Two dichaete heterozygous flies *Dd* are crossed.

(b) Cross between dichaete and wildtype.

**Solution :**

*D* is dichaete gene, lethal dominant
*d* is normal gene, wild recessive

(a)

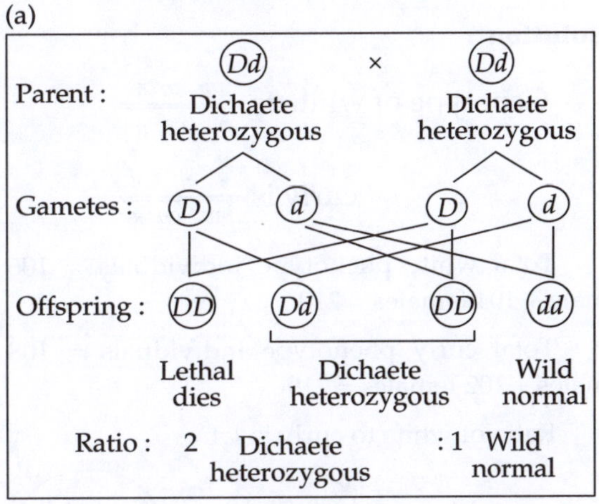


(b)

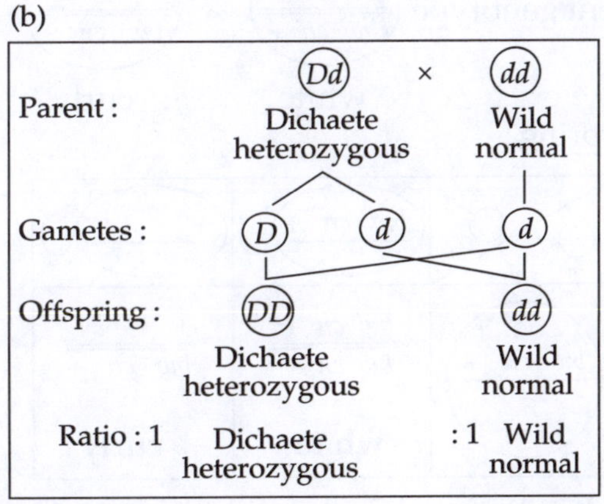

### Problem 2

In *Drosophila*, two mutants, brown eye (*bw*) and Cinnabar (*cn*) are recessive to their respective normal wild alleles (+). If both mutants present in homozygous condition, eye becomes white. Curly wind (*Cy*) is dominant over wild normal wing (+), when homozygous for two dominant alleles becomes lethal.

**Question (a)**

A cross between curly-white flies, the following progenies are obtained

Curly male - 108

Curly female - 102

White male - 106

White female - 104

Determine the genotype and phenotype of the parent and offspring and also design the cross.

**Solution :**

Genotype of white is $\dfrac{bw\ cn\ +}{bw\ cn\ +}$

curly is $\dfrac{+\ +\ Cy}{bw\ cn\ +}$

Total white phenotype individuals = 106 male + 104 females = 210

Total curly phenotype individuals = 108 males + 102 females = 210

Ratio of white to curly is 1:1

Parent genotype $\dfrac{bw\ cn\ +}{bw\ cn\ +}$ × $\dfrac{+\ +\ Cy}{bw\ cn\ +}$

white curly

Offspring

| ♀ \ ♂ | $bw\ cn\ +$ | $+\ +\ Cy$ |
|---|---|---|
| $bw\ cn\ +$ | $\dfrac{bw\ cn\ +}{bw\ cn\ +}$ white | $\dfrac{+\ +\ Cy}{bw\ cn\ +}$ curly |

Result : Ratio : Curly : white = 1 : 1

**Question (b)**

A Cross between curly and curly files, the following progenies are recovered

Curly male 214

Curly female 216

White male 110

White female 105

Determine genotype of parent and offspring. Also design the cross.

**Solution :**

Total number of curly males and females = 214 + 216 = 430

Total number of white males and females = 110 + 105 = 215

Parent genotype $\dfrac{+\ +\ Cy}{bw\ cn\ +}$ × $\dfrac{bw\ cn\ +}{bw\ cn\ Cy}$

Curly Curly

Offspring

| ♀ \ ♂ | $bw\ cn\ +$ | $+\ +\ Cy$ |
|---|---|---|
| $bw\ cn\ +$ | $\dfrac{bw\ cn\ +}{bw\ cn\ +}$ White | $\dfrac{+\ +\ Cy}{bw\ cn\ +}$ Curly |
| $bw\ cn\ Cy$ | $\dfrac{bw\ cn\ +}{bw\ cn\ Cy}$ Curly | $\dfrac{+\ +\ Cy}{bw\ cn\ Cy}$ Dies |

Result : Ratio : Curly : white = 2 : 1

### Problem 3

Two fruit files of wild phenotype of X-linked genes were crossed and in the progeny, there were (a) 202 females and 98 males in a cross and (b) 208 females and 206 males all are wild in another cross. Discuss the results.

**Solution :**

Let, the recessive gene is "c"
and its normal alele is "+"

| *Genotype* | *Phenotype* |
|---|---|
| c c | Female homozygous, mutant phenotype (dies) |
| + + | Female homozygous, wild phenotype |
| c + | Female heterozygous, wild phenotype |
| + | Male, wild phenotype |
| c | Male, mutant phenotype (dies) |

**Question (a)**

Sex ratio Male : Female = 1:2

Parent :

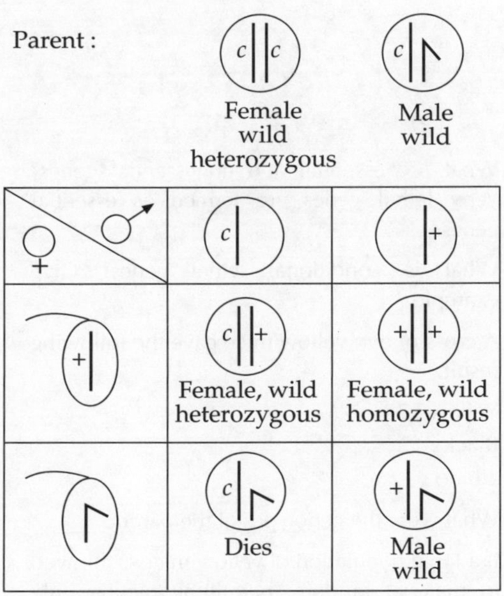


Result : All wild, Sex ratio Male : Female = 1:2

**Question (b)**

Sex ratio Male : Female = 1:1 All wild

Parent :

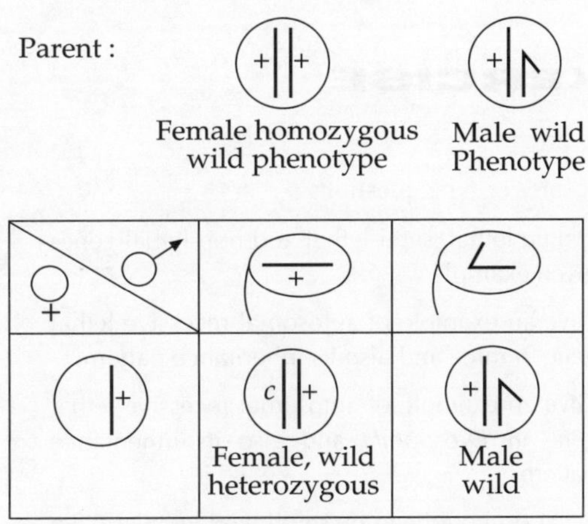


Result : All wild, Sex ratio Male : Female = 1:1

## Chapter Glossary/Key Terms

**Balanced lethal stock :** The stock carries mutant lethal alleles, the homozygous for lethal genes or homozygous for normal genes will not survive.

**Conditional-lethal mutant :** A mutant that is lethal under one condition but not lethal under another.

**Expressivity :** The degree of expression of a genetically controlled trait.

**Lethal genes :** The genes which can cause death from zygote upto sexually mature adult stage.

**Non-essential genes :** The genes which are not absolutely required for the survival, although they are likely to be beneficial to the organism.

**Penetrance :** The normal appearance of genetically controlled traits in the phenotype.

**Retinoblastoma :** A malignant disease of retina which is caused by a dominant mutant gene.

**Semilethal genes :** The genes that can cause death of some individuals but the individuals could survive and get maturity and reproduce.

## Exercise

### A. Long answer type questions :

1. Define lethal, semi-lethal and non-lethal genes given example.
2. Give an example of autosomal recessive lethal gene in mice and also its inheritance pattern.
3. Give an example of autosomal recessive lethal gene in *Drosophila* and also its inhentance pattern.
4. What do you mean by sex-linked lethals? Give examples for man and *Drosophila* and also its pattern of inheritance.
5. Distinguish semilethal and subvital genes.
6. What do you mean by balanced lethal genes? illustrate its pattern of inheritance.
7. What is penetrance and expressivity of lethal and non lethal genes. Give an example of incomplete penetrance.
8. What are essential and nonessential genes? Why lethal genes are termed as essential genes?
9. What is conditional lethal genes? Give example.
10. A cross of two yellow mice gave the following result.

    Yellow : 24

    Black : 12

    albino : 12

    What were the genotypes of the parent.
11. If a large population of yellow mice is allowed to mate at random, permitting mating only among members of the same generation, what would be the expected frequency of yellows and nonyellows in the $F_1$–$F_5$ generation? Plot graphically the changes in the frequency of the gene $A^Y$ during this period. Assume that yellow and nonyellow have equal fecundity.

12. In cattle, short-legged animals of the Dexter-Kerry breed occasionally produce abnormal calves dead at birth or dying shortly thereafter. Outline an experimental test of the hypothesis that such deaths are due to hyomozygosis of lethal gene.
13. The allele *(l)* in *Drosophila* is recessive, sex-linked and lethal when homozygous or hemizygons (the condition in the males). If a female of genotype *L/l* is crossed with a normal male, what is the probability that the first two surviving progeny will be males?
14. In *Drosophila,* crosses of Dichaete-winged flies X Dichaete always give two-thirds Dichaete to one-third normal-winged offspring. Dichaete X normal gives one-half Dichaete and one-half normal. How would you explain these results?

**B. Short answer type questions.**

1. Define lethal, semilethal and nonlethals.
2. What are essential and nonessential genes?
3. Why lethal genes are called invisible genes?
4. Give example of autosomal recessive genes in mice. What is its $F_1$ ratio?
5. Give the example of autosomal lethal genes in *Drosophila*.
6. Give the example of sex-linked lethal in man.
7. Distinguish semi-lethal and subvital genes. Give examples.
8. What do you mean by balanced lethal?
9. Define penetrance and expressivity of genes, give example.
10. What is incomplete penetrance?
11. Why polydactyly shows variable expressivity?
12. What is conditional gene? Give example.
13. What do you mean by 0.8 penetrance?

5

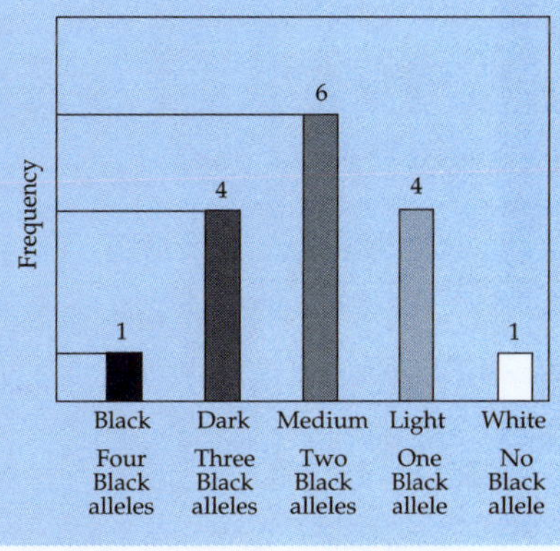


# Multiple – Factor Inheritance

**CHAPTER AGENDA**

**5.1** Concept ; **5.2** Skin colour in Human being; **5.3** Kernel colour in wheat; **5.4** Ear size in Maize; **5.5** White-spotting in mice; **5.6** Problems on Multiple factors; Chapter Glossary/Key Terms; Exercise

## 5.1 CONCEPT

The Mendelian inheritance is not acceptable in certain cases. There are no definite or distinct traits on the otherhand there is a gradual or continuous trait. This may be found in the case of certain economic fruits or meat, egg, milk, body colour and also intelligence. There is not a sharp demarkation between them.

The general gradations are usually between large and small, heavy and light etc. There is no dominance of genes and each gene has some almost of determining character. The phenotype of the zygote would be determined by the additive values of the TOTAL GENE composition of the individual.

East (1910,16) and Nilson-Ehle (1908) termed this type of inheritance as **blending** or **mixing type of inheritance** due to the additive effect of multiple alleles or simply it is termed as **multiple factors of inheritance**. Mather called it as **polygenic inheritance**.

## 5.2. SKIN COLOUR IN HUMAN BEING

C. B. Davenport (1913) described the polygenic inheritance in man about the skin colour of Black-man (formerly called as Negro) and White.

According to him, Negros have two pairs of skin colour-producing genes $P_1P_1P_2P_2$ and White races have no-colour producing genes, $p_1p_1p_2p_2$.

When a Black man crossed with a White, the resulting hybrids would be intermediate between the two parents. It would be neither black as Black man nor be white as one of the parent. This is termed as MULATTO. Again if such two Mulattos are crossed, the result would be like as follows (Fig. 5.1):

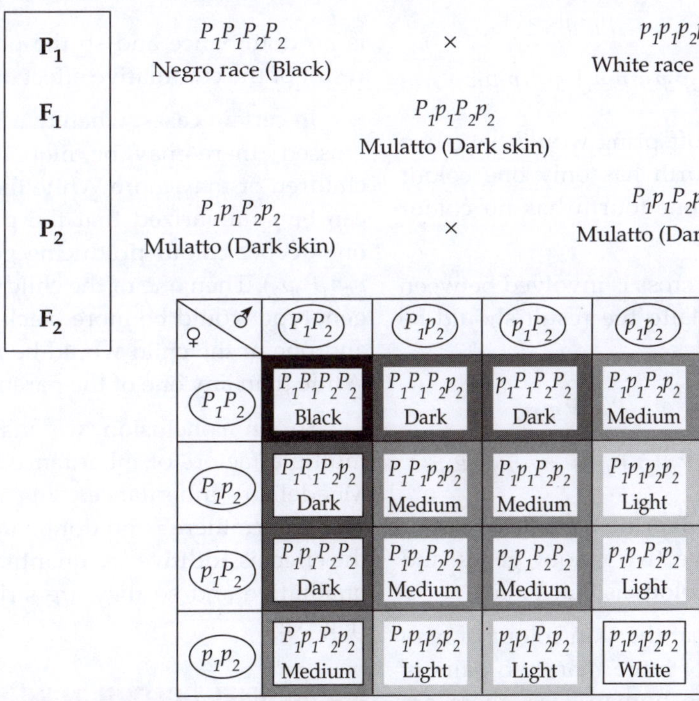


**Fig.5.1 :** *Inheritance of skin colour in human beings*

**Results :**

(i) One out of 16 has four colour-genes and becomes black skin as Black man.

(ii) Four out of 16 have three colour genes and resembled to the intermediate between Black men and Mulattos.

(iii) Six out of 16 have two colour genes, which would be intermediate skin colour between Balck man and White, called Mulatto.

(iv) Four out of 16 have only one colour gene, which would be intermediate between Mulattos and White.

(v) One out of 16 has no colour genes and would be as like as White.

**Back cross :**

When back cross is involved between Mulatto and White. The result would be like this

$P_1$ : $P_1p_1P_2p_2$ × $p_1p_1p_2p_2$

$F_1$ : $P_1P_1p_2p_2$, $P_1p_1p_2p_2$, $p_1p_1P_2p_2$, $p_1p_1p_2p_2$

Here, half of the offspring would have two colour genes, one fourth has only one colour gene and remaining one-fourth has no colour genes.

Again when back cross is involved between a Black man and Mulatto the result should be like this.

$P_1$ : $P_1P_1P_2P_2$ × $P_1p_1P_2p_2$

$F_1$ : $P_1P_1P_2P_2$, $P_1p_1P_2P_2$, $P_1P_1P_2p_2$, $P_1p_1P_2p_2$

Here, half of the offspring have three colour genes, one-fourth have two colour genes and one fourth have four colour as Black man.

Davenport said that the skin colour of man is due to interaction of more than two pairs of genes, because, in the human race, there are varieties of skin colour genes. Each gene has definite amount of colour producing property.

Davenport also said that the skin colour of man is example of **polygenic inheritance**. There is no dominance and so the phenotype is as a result of the cumulative effect of these genes.

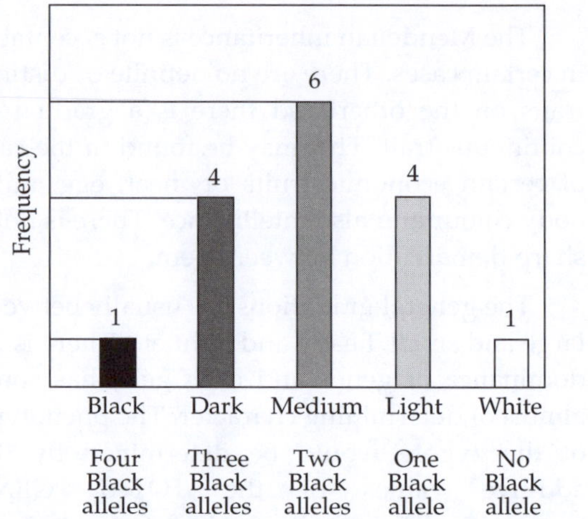


**Fig.5.2 :** *Number of black alleles and body-color of human beings where two independently assorted genes, each having two alleles. The frequency of offsping where cross involved between two Mulattos.*

In certain cases, when two White (semi) are crossed, there may be more Black (Mulatto) children or may more White than the parent. It can be summarized that the parent have only one deeper colour producing genes ($P_1p_1P_2p_2$ × $p_1p_1P_2p_2$). Then one of the children has $P_1p_1P_2p_2$ genotype would be more black than the parent and one of the child would be $p_1p_1p_2p_2$ is more White than any one of the parent.

So, in conclusion we may say that the multiple factors of inheritance are not same as Mendelian inheritance. In multiple factor inheritance there is no dominance of genes and the effect is additive *i.e.*, quantitative rather than qualitative and so they are strikingly different (Fig. 5.2).

## 5.3. KERNEL COLOUR IN WHEAT

Nilsson-Ehal crossed several varieties of wheat. Red kernel is incompletely dominant over white and thus a series of shades of red colour has been found of their $F_2$ generation. It

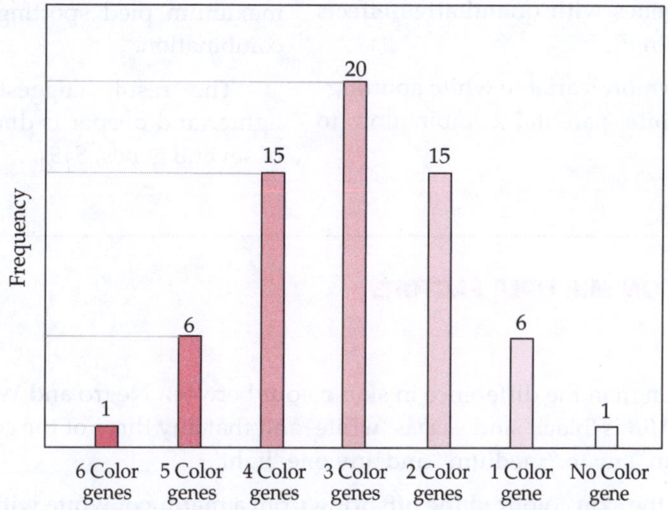


**Fig.5.3 :** *Number of colour genes in a wheet, where three independently assorting genes, each has two alleles. The frequency of offspring where cross involving between two heterozygotes.*

is known that there are three genes involved in kernel colour of wheat. The red allele is designated as *R* and white allele as *r*. If the red parent is represented by $R_1R_1R_2R_2R_3R_3$ and white by $r_1r_1r_2r_2r_3r_3$, $F_1$ generation would have three colour genes and the genotype would be $R_1r_1R_2r_2R_3r_3$. The genotypes that appear in the $F_2$ generation can easily be predicted by constructing a checker board with 64 cells.

About

1 in 64 will be red, having 6 colour genes.

6 in 64 will have five colour genes.

15 in 64 will have four colour genes.

20 in 64 will have three colour genes.

15 in 64 will have two colour genes.

6 in 64 will have one colour gene.

1 in 64 will have no colour gene.

In this experiment they reached to the conclusion that the effect of each dominant allele was cumulative and thus they put forwarded the multiple factor hypothesis (Fig. 5.3).

## 5.4. EAR SIZE IN MAIZE

East worked with two varieties of maize, long-eared black Mexican sweet corn and short eared Tom Thumb popcorn. In $F_1$, one plant is 9cm long, 12 were 10cm long. In $F_2$ there is a greater range, from plants with ears as short as the shorter-eared grandparent and as long as the longer grand-parent. There are relatively few of these extreme types and relatively large numbers of those have intermediate like that of the $F_1$. Thus it can be concluded that the ear size of the maize is inherited by the multiple factors of inheritance.

## 5.5. WHITE – SPOTTING IN MICE

In mice, *ss* zygote is represented for **pied spotting**, animals occur ranging from those with only a small white spot on the belly to those with an entirely white coat.

When these two strains were crossed in $F_1$, a series of intermediates are obtained. In a back cross of $F_1$ with animals of the nearly all white stock, the parental type was recovered with about the frequency that would be expected as if three or four genes with quantitative effects were segregating in $F_1$.

The $F_2$ shows more variable white spottings ranging from white parental combination to maximum pied spotting of the other parental combination.

The result suggested that the spotting lighter and deeper is due to the additive effects of several genes, $S_1S_2, .... S_n$.

## 5.6. PROBLEMS ON MULTIPLE FACTORS

### Problem 1

Assume that in man the difference in skin colour between Negro and White is due to two pairs of factors, that *AABB* is 'black' and *aabb* is 'white' and that any three of the colour producing factors produce 'dark skin' any to "medium" and any one 'light'.

What will be the skin colour of the offspring from a mating of white with black? From a mating of two individuals genotypically like these $F_1$ offspring.

**Solution :**

$P_1$ : *AA BB* (Black) × *aa bb* (White)

$F_1$ : *Aa Bb* (Medium coloured skin)

$P_2$ : *Aa Bb* × *Aa Bb*

$F_2$ :

| (AB) | (Ab) | (aB) | (ab) | ♀ / ♂ |
|---|---|---|---|---|
| *AA BB* black | *AA Bb* dark | *Aa BB* dark | *Aa Bb* medium | (AB) |
| *AA Bb* dark | *AA bb* medium | *Aa Bb* medium | *Aa bb* light | (Ab) |
| *Aa BB* dark | *Aa Bb* medium | *aa BB* medium | *aa Bb* light | (aB) |
| *Aa Bb* medium | *Aa bb* light | *aa Bb* light | *aa bb* white | (ab) |

Phenotypic ratio : 1 black : 5 dark : 6 medium : 5 light : 1 white

### Problem 2

What are the genotypes of the parents in the two following mating of Negros?

(a) Medium × light giving $\frac{1}{8}$ dark, $\frac{3}{8}$ medium, $\frac{3}{8}$ light, $\frac{1}{8}$ white

(b) Medium × light giving one half medium and one half light

**Solution :**

(a)

| Genotypes of medium | their gametes |
|---|---|
| *Aa Bb* | (AB) (ab) (aB) (Ab) |
| *AA bb* | (Ab) |
| *aa BB* | (aB) |

| Genotypes of light | their gametes |
|---|---|
| *Aa bb* | (Ab) (ab) |
| *aa Bb* | (aB) (ab) |

So, the cross between

*Aa Bb* × *Aa bb*
medium white

Offspring :

| (AB) | (aB) | (Ab) | (ab) | ♀ / ♂ |
|---|---|---|---|---|
| *Ab Bb* medium | *aa Bb* light | *Aa bb* light | *ab ab* white | (ab) |
| *AA Bb* dark | *Aa Bb* medium | *AA bb* medium | *Aa bb* light | (Ab) |

The ratio $\frac{1}{8}$ dark : $\frac{3}{8}$ medium : $\frac{3}{8}$ light : $\frac{1}{8}$ white

(b)

medium × light
*AA bb* *Aa bb*

Gametes : (Ab) (Ab) (ab)

Offspring : *AA bb* medium *Aa bb* light

The result is that 50% is medium and 50% light.

### ➧ Problem 3

Assume that the red kernel colour of a certain race of wheat is due to the presence of three independent genes $R_1$, $R_2$, $R_3$.

Any one of the genes singly will cause the red colour, white is $r_1r_1r_2r_2r_3r_3$. What are the genotypes of parent in each of the following crosses?

(a) Red × Red gives 3 red : 1 white

(b) Red × Red gives 15 red : 1 white

(c) Red × Red gives 63 red : 1 white

(d) Red × Red gives 7 red : 1 white

(e) Red × white gives 1 red : 1 white

(f) Red × white gives 3 red : 1 white

(g) Red × white gives 7 red : 1 white

(h) Red × white gives all red

**Solution :**

**(a)**

Red × Red

$P_1$ : $R_1r_1r_2r_2r_3r_3$ $R_1r_1r_2r_2r_3r_3$

Gametes : $R_1r_2r_3$ $r_1r_2r_3$ $R_1r_2r_3$ $r_1r_2r_3$

$P_1$ : $R_1R_1r_2r_2r_3r_3$ (red) $R_1r_1r_2r_2r_3r_3$ (red) $R_1r_1r_2r_2r_3r_3$ (red) $r_1r_1r_2r_2r_3r_3$ (white)

The ratio : 3 red : 1 white

**(b)**

Red × Red

$P_1$ : $R_1r_1R_2r_2r_3r_3$ $R_1r_1R_2r_2r_3r_3$

$F_1$ :

| $R_1R_2r_3$ | $r_1r_2r_3$ | $R_1r_2r_3$ | $r_1R_2r_3$ | ♀ / ♂ |
|---|---|---|---|---|
| $R_1R_1R_2R_2r_3r_3$ red | $R_1r_1R_2r_2r_3r_3$ red | $R_1R_1R_2r_2r_3r_3$ red | $R_1r_1R_2R_2r_3r_3$ red | $R_1R_2r_3$ |
| $R_1r_1R_2r_2r_3r_3$ red | $r_1r_1r_2r_2r_3r_3$ white | $R_1r_1r_2r_2r_3r_3$ red | $r_1r_1R_2r_2r_3r_3$ red | $r_1r_2r_3$ |
| $R_1R_1R_2r_2r_3r_3$ red | $R_1r_1r_2r_2r_3r_3$ red | $R_1R_1r_2r_2r_3r_3$ red | $R_1r_1R_2r_2r_3r_3$ red | $R_1r_2r_3$ |
| $R_1r_1R_2R_2r_3r_3$ red | $r_1r_1R_2r_2r_3r_3$ red | $R_1r_1R_2r_2r_3r_3$ red | $r_1r_1R_2R_2r_3r_3$ red | $r_1R_2r_3$ |

The ratio is 15 red : 1 white

**(c)**

Red × Red

$R_1r_1R_2r_2R_3r_3$ $R_1r_1R_2r_2R_3r_3$

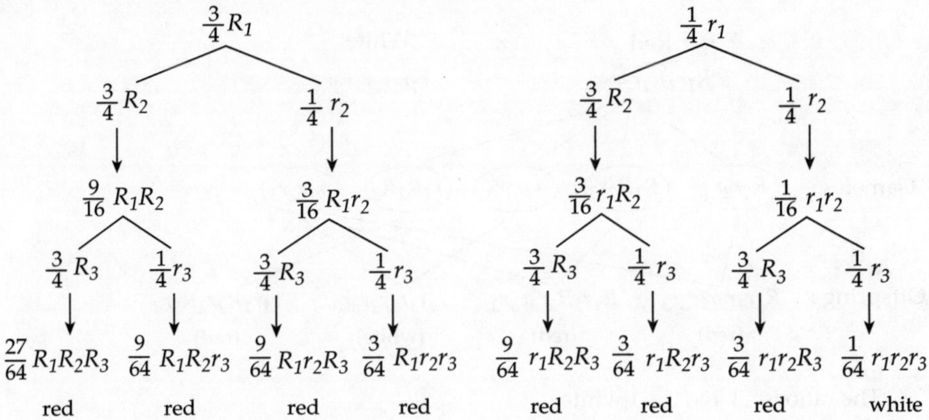


The ratio is $\frac{63}{64}$ red : $\frac{1}{64}$ white

**(d)**

Red × Red

$R_1r_1R_2r_2r_3r_3$ $R_1r_1r_2r_2r_3r_3$

Offspring :

| $R_1R_2r_3$ | $r_1r_2r_3$ | $R_1r_2r_3$ | $r_1R_2r_3$ | ♀ / ♂ |
|---|---|---|---|---|
| $R_1R_1R_2r_2r_3r_3$ red | $R_1r_1r_2r_2r_3r_3$ red | $R_1R_1r_2r_2r_3r_3$ red | $R_1r_1R_2r_2r_3r_3$ red | $R_1r_2r_3$ |
| $R_1r_1R_2r_2r_3r_3$ red | $r_1r_1r_2r_2r_3r_3$ white | $R_1r_1r_2r_2r_3r_3$ red | $r_1r_1R_2r_2r_3r_3$ red | $r_1r_2r_3$ |

The phenotypic ratio is 7 red : 1 white

**(e)**

Red × White

$R_1r_1r_2r_2r_3r_3$ $r_1r_1r_2r_2r_3r_3$

Gametes : $R_1r_2r_3$ $r_1r_2r_3$ $r_1r_2r_3$

$R_1r_1r_2r_2r_3r_3$ (red) $r_1r_1r_2r_2r_3r_3$ (white)

The ratio : 1 red : 1 white

**(f)**

Red × White

$R_1r_1R_2r_2r_3r_3$ $r_1r_1r_2r_2r_3r_3$

Gametes : $(R_1r_2r_3)$ $(R_1R_2r_3)$ $(r_1r_2r_3)$ $(r_1R_2R_3)$ $(r_1r_2r_3)$

Offspring : $R_1r_1r_2r_2r_3r_3$ (red) $R_1r_1R_2r_2r_3r_3$ (red) $r_1r_1r_2r_2r_3r_3$ (white) $r_1r_1R_2r_2R_3r_3$ (red)

The ratio is 3 red : 1 white

**(g)**

red × white

$R_1r_1\ R_2r_2\ R_3r_3$ $r_1r_1\ r_2r_2\ r_3r_3$

Gametes :

| $R_1R_2r_3$ | $r_1r_2r_3$ | $R_1r_2r_3$ | $r_1R_2R_3$ | $r_1r_2R_3$ | $R_1R_2r_3$ | $R_1r_2R_3$ | $r_1R_2r_3$ | ♀ / ♂ |
|---|---|---|---|---|---|---|---|---|
| red | white | red | red | red | red | red | red | $r_1r_2r_3$ |

Ratio is 8 red : 1 white

**(h)**

red × white

$R_1R_1\ r_2r_2\ R_3r_3$ $r_1r_1\ r_2r_2\ r_3r_3$

$R_1R_1\ R_2r_2\ R_3r_3$

$R_1R_1\ R_2R_2\ r_3r_3$

$R_1R_1\ R_2R_2\ R_3r_3$

$R_1R_1\ R_2R_2\ R_3R_3$

(At least one homozygous red factor
must present in the red zygote then all the
offspring would have any one R gene which will represent red phenotype).

## Problem 4

Assume that the difference between a race of oats yielding about 4gms per plant and one yielding 10 gms is due to three equal and cumulative multiple factor pairs *AABBCC*. Cross one with the other. What will be phenotype in $F_1$ and $F_2$?

**Solution :**

Factors containing *AA BB CC* will yield 10 gms/plant

*aa bb cc* will yield 4 gms/plant

So, the unit value of $A$, $B$ or $C = \frac{10}{6} = 1\frac{2}{3}$ gm,

$$a, b \text{ or } c = \frac{4}{6} = \frac{2}{3} \text{ gm}$$

$P_1$ : *AA BB CC* × *aa bb cc*

$F_1$ : *Aa Bb Cc* would yield $3 \times \frac{10}{6} + 3 \times \frac{4}{6} = 7$ gm

$F_2$ :

| Gametes : (quantitative value) | *ABC* ⑤ | *ABc* ④ | *abC* ③ | *AbC* ④ | *aBc* ③ | *aBC* ④ | *Abc* ③ | *abc* ② | ♀ / ♂ |
|---|---|---|---|---|---|---|---|---|---|
| | 10 | 9 | 8 | 9 | 8 | 9 | 8 | 7 | *ABC* ⑤ |
| | 9 | 8 | 7 | 8 | 7 | 8 | 7 | 6 | *ABc* ④ |
| | 8 | 7 | 6 | 7 | 6 | 7 | 6 | 5 | *abC* ③ |
| | 9 | 8 | 7 | 8 | 7 | 8 | 7 | 6 | *AbC* ④ |
| | 8 | 7 | 6 | 7 | 6 | 7 | 6 | 5 | *aBc* ③ |
| | 9 | 8 | 7 | 8 | 7 | 8 | 7 | 6 | *aBC* ④ |
| | 8 | 7 | 6 | 7 | 6 | 7 | 6 | 5 | *Abc* ③ |
| | 7 | 6 | 5 | 6 | 5 | 6 | 5 | 4 | *abc* ($1\frac{1}{2}$) |

(Right-hand column: Gametes (quantitative value))

In the checker board showing only their quantitative values.

The result is that :

| Frequency of | | | | |
|---|---|---|---|---|
| | 10 | gms plants | = | 1 |
| | 9 | " | = | 6 |
| | 8 | " | = | 15 |
| | 7 | " | = | 20 |
| | 6 | " | = | 15 |
| | 5 | " | = | 6 |
| | 4 | " | = | 1 |

### ➧ Problem 5

Assume that in squashes the difference in fruit weight between 3 pound type and a 6 pound type is due to 3 factor pairs *AA, BB, CC* each for containing one pound weight and *aa bb cc* each for containing ½ pound weight.

Cross a 3-pound (*aabbcc*) with a 6-pound (*AABBCC*), what would be the phenotype?

**Solution :**

$P_1$ : *AA BB CC* × *aa bb cc*

$F_1$ : *Aa Bb Cc* The phenotype is $4\frac{1}{2}$ pound

$F_2$ :

| Gametes (quantitative value) | *ABC* (3) | ABc ($2\frac{1}{2}$) | *abC* (2) | *AbC* ($2\frac{1}{2}$) | *aBc* (2) | *Abc* (2) | *aBC* ($2\frac{1}{2}$) | *abc* ($1\frac{1}{2}$) | ♀ / ♂ |
|---|---|---|---|---|---|---|---|---|---|
| | 6 | $5\frac{1}{2}$ | 5 | $5\frac{1}{2}$ | 5 | 5 | $5\frac{1}{2}$ | $4\frac{1}{2}$ | *ABC* (3) |
| | $5\frac{1}{2}$ | 5 | $4\frac{1}{2}$ | 5 | $4\frac{1}{2}$ | $4\frac{1}{2}$ | 5 | 4 | *ABc* ($2\frac{1}{2}$) |
| | 5 | $4\frac{1}{2}$ | 4 | $4\frac{1}{2}$ | 4 | 4 | $4\frac{1}{2}$ | $3\frac{1}{2}$ | *abC* (2) |
| | $5\frac{1}{2}$ | 5 | $4\frac{1}{2}$ | 5 | $4\frac{1}{2}$ | $4\frac{1}{2}$ | 5 | 4 | *AbC* ($2\frac{1}{2}$) |
| | 5 | $4\frac{1}{2}$ | 4 | $4\frac{1}{2}$ | 4 | 4 | $4\frac{1}{2}$ | $3\frac{1}{2}$ | *aBc* (2) |
| | 5 | $4\frac{1}{2}$ | 4 | $4\frac{1}{2}$ | 4 | 4 | $4\frac{1}{2}$ | $3\frac{1}{2}$ | *Abc* (2) |
| | $5\frac{1}{2}$ | 5 | $4\frac{1}{2}$ | 5 | $4\frac{1}{2}$ | $4\frac{1}{2}$ | 5 | 4 | *aBC* ($2\frac{1}{2}$) |
| | $4\frac{1}{2}$ | 4 | $3\frac{1}{2}$ | 4 | $3\frac{1}{2}$ | $3\frac{1}{2}$ | 4 | 3 | *abc* ($1\frac{1}{2}$) |

The result is that

| The Frequency of | | | |
|---|---|---|---|
| 6 pound | | = | 1 |
| $5\frac{1}{2}$ | " | = | 6 |
| 5 | " | = | 15 |
| $4\frac{1}{2}$ | " | = | 20 |
| 4 | " | = | 15 |
| $3\frac{1}{2}$ | " | = | 6 |
| 3 | " | = | 1 |

**Problem 6**

Assume in the following three problems that difference between a corn plant 10 decimeters high and 26 decimeters high is due (in so far as it is caused by inheritance) to four pairs of equal and cumulative multiple factors, the 26 dm plant being *AABBCCDD* and 10 dm one *aabbccdd* that will be the size and genotype of an $F_1$ from a cross between these two pure types? Give the limits of variation in height which the offspring of the following crosses will show:-

*Aa BBcc dd* × *Aa bb Ccdd*

*aa BBcc dd* × *Aa Bb Ccdd*

*AA BBCc dd* × *aa BBcc Dd*

**Solution :**

Unit value of *A* or *B* or *C* or *D* = $\frac{26}{8} = 3\frac{1}{4}$ dm

*a* or *b* or *c* or *d* = $\frac{10}{8} = 1\frac{1}{4}$ dm

When Two pure types were crosseed.

$P_1$ : *AABBCC* × *aabbcc*

$F_1$ : *Aa Bb Cc Dd* (18 dm)

$P_2$ : *Aa BBcc dd* × *Aa bbCc dd*

$F_2$ : Offspring :

| ♀ \ ♂ | *AbCd* (9 dm) | *abCd* (7 dm) | *Abcd* (7 dm) | *abcd* (5 dm) |
|---|---|---|---|---|
| *ABcd* (9 dm) | 18 dm | 16 dm | 16 dm | 14 dm |
| *aBcd* (7 dm) | 16 dm | 14 dm | 14 dm | 12 dm |

So, there would be one offspring of 18 dm, three offspring of 16 dm and three Offspring of 14 dm and one offspring of 12 dm

$P_1$ : *aa BBcc dd* *Aa BbCc dd*

Offspring :

| ♀ \ ♂ | *ABCd* (11) | *abcd* (5) | *ABcd* (9) | *abCd* (7) | *AbCd* (9) | *aBcd* (7) | *aBCd* (9) | *Abcd* (7) |
|---|---|---|---|---|---|---|---|---|
| *aBcd* (7 dm) | 18 | 12 | 16 | 14 | 16 | 14 | 16 | 14 |

Result is that one offspring of 18 dm, 3 offspring 16 dm, 3 offspring 14 dm and one offspring 12 dm.

*AABBCcdd* × *aaBBccDd*

Offspring :

| ♂ \ ♀ | *aBcD* (9 dm) | *aBcd* (7 dm) |
|---|---|---|
| *ABCd* (11 dm) | 20 dm | 18 dm |
| *ABcd* (9 dm) | 18 dm | 16 dm |

Result would be one 20 dm height, two 18 dm and another one 16 dm.

## Chapter Glossary/Key Terms

**Blending theory of inheritance :** The seeds that dictate hereditary traits are able to blend together from generation to generation. The blended traits would then be passed to the next generation.

**Mulatto :** The person originated from a cross between Black-man and a White. The body colour is intermediate.

**Multiple factor inheritance :** The phenotype of the zygote would be determined by the additive values of total gene composition of the individual. There is no dominance of genes.

**Pied spotting :** Mice occur ranging those with only a small white spot on the belly to those with an entirely white coat.

**Polygenic inheritance :** Refers to the transmission of traits that are governed by two or more different genes.

# EXERCISE

**A. Long answer type questions :**

1. What is multiple factors of inheritance? Why this is called polygenic inherilance?
2. How does the skin color of human beings is inherited? Explain the mode of inheritance.
3. How does the kernal colour of wheat is inherited? Explain the mode of inheritance.
4. Describe the mode of inheritance of ear size in maize and white spotting in mice.
5. The $F_1$ generation from pure parent types differing in a size character is usually no more variable than the parents. Explain.
6. If two pure types, differing in size character are crossed, is it possible for individual in the $F_2$ to be, more exptreme than either grand-parent? explain.
7. If frequency happens that one character of a plant, such as number of seeds, is much more variable than another character, such as weight of seeds. What explanations for this difference can you suggest.
8. Assume that height in people depends on four pairs of alleles. How can two persons of moderate height produce children who are much taller than they are? Assume that the environment is exerting a negligible effect.

**B. Short answer type questions.**

1. What is multiple factor of inheritance?
2. What is polygenic inheritance?
3. Why Negro and White cross produces different phenotype.
4. Can two mulattoes have white-skined offspring? Can two white-skined people have dark-skined offspring? Explain.
5. How do polygenes differ from traditional Mendelian genes?
6. What is the characteristics of polygenic

6

# Multiple Alleles

**CHAPTER AGENDA**

## 6.1 CONCEPT

*When any of the three or more allelic forms of a gene occupy the same locus in a given pair of homologous chromosomes, they are said to constitute a series of multiple alleles.*

Characteristics of multiple alleles :

1. Multiple alleles of a series always occupy the same locus in the chromosome.
2. All the alleles of multiple series occupy the same locus in chromosome, therefore, no crossing over occurs within the alleles of a same multiple allele series.
3. Multiple alleles always influence the same trait.
4. The wild type allele is nearly always docoument, while the other mutant alleles in the series may show dominance or there may be an intermediate phenotypic effect.
5. When any two of the mutant multiple alleles are crossed, the phenotype is mutant type and not the wild type.

## 6.2 COAT COLOUR IN RABBITS:

Coat colour in rabbit may have following different colours (Fig. 6.1).

1. **Full colour :** The ordinary wild type rabbits are referred to as agouti or full colour in which, individuals have banded hairs, the portion nearest to the skin being gray, succeeded by a yellow band and finally a black or brown tip. "C" may represent the gene for full colour.

**Fig.6.1 :** *Coat colour in rabbits.*
*(a) Full coat colour; (b) Chinchilla coat colour; (c) Himalayan coat colour; (d) Albino coat colour.*

2. **Chinchilla :** In some individuals, the coat lacking the yellow pigment and due to the optical effect of black and gray hairs, have the appearance of silvery gray. The gene for chinchilla as represented "$C^{ch}$".
3. **Himalayan :** The Himalayan type coat is white except for black extremities (nose, ear, feet and tail). The eyes are pigmented. "$C^h$" represents the gene for Himalayan coat.
4. **Albino :** The albino coat totally lacks in pigmentation and the eyes of an albino also remain pink due to lack of pigment in iris of eye. "$C^a$" represents the gene for albino.

When crosses are made between rabbits with different coat colours, it is revealed that full colour "C" is dominant to $C^{Ch}$, $C^h$, and $C^a$. The $C^{Ch}$ is found recessive to C but dominant over gene $C^h$ and $C^a$. Likewise, the allele for Himalayan $C^h$ is found to be recessive to C and $C^{Ch}$ but dominant to allele '$C^a$'. The allele '$C^a$' albino is found to be recessive to all alleles of the multiple allelic series. Thus, hierarchy of dominance may be expressed as follows.

$$C > C^{Ch} > C^h > C^a$$

The genotypes and phenotypes of these members of the albino series of coat colours in rabbits may therefore be written as follows:

| Genotype | Phenotype |
|---|---|
| $CC, CC^{Ch}, CC^h, CC^a$ | Wild |
| $C^{Ch}C^{Ch}$ | Chinchilla |
| $C^{Ch}C^h, C^{Ch}C^a$ | Light gray |
| $C^hC^h, C^hC^a$ | Himalayan |
| $C^aC^a$ | Albino |

The number of genes in a series of multiple alleles increases the variety of genotypes when alleles in series are 'n' the total possible genotypes would be $\frac{n(n-1)}{2}$.

## 6.3 WING-SIZE IN *DROSOPHILA*

*Drosophila* comprises three alleles of genes for wing size.

(i) $L^+$ for normal wild type wing size.

(ii) $L^{vg}$ for vestigial wing.

(iii) $L^a$ antlered wing.

The wild type ($L^+$) gene is dominant over vestigial ($L^{vg}$ and antlered ($L^a$) wings.

The $L^{vg}$ and $L^a$ has an incomplete dominance relationship. Therefore when the zygote having a hybrid genotype ($L^{vg}$ $L^a$), then an intermediate wing size is developed, again when these are inbred, vestigial and antlered wings are obtained.

$P_1$: $L^{vg}L^{vg}$ (Vestigial wing) × $L^aL^a$ (antlered wing)

↓

$F_1$: $L^{vg}L^a$ (Intermediate wing)

$P_2$: $L^{vg}L^a$ × $L^{vg}L^a$ (inbreeding)

↓

$F_2$: $L^{vg}L^{vg}$ (Vestigial) $L^{vg}L^a$ (Intermediate) $L^aL^a$ (antlered)

Thus, in *L* gene locus of *Drosophila* three allelic forms are possible and their hierarchy of dominance is as follows :

$$L^+ > L^{vg} > L^a$$

## 6.4 ABO - BLOOD GROUPS (MULTIPLE ALLELES)

### 6.4.1 Concept

Karl Landsteiner in 1900 observed that red cells of one person are agglutinated in the serum of other person. In 1901, he suggested that these results could be explained by the existence of three phenotypes A, B and O. In 1902, he added a fourth phenotype AB. The ABO system of blood grouping is still today the most important, although more than 19 other blood group systems have been documented till now.

It is found that there can be two antigens A and B and result four blood groups.

Blood groups are genetically controlled and they are determined by the presence of specific surface antigens on the erythrocytes and of specific antibodies in the plasma. In ABO system two types of surface antigens, designated A and B are recognized and in plasma two types of naturally occurring antibodies have been found against antigen-A is Anti-A and antibody against antigen-B is Anti-B.

The phenotypes of different ABO blood groups are dependent upon the presence or absence of antigen-A and antigen-B on the surface of their RBC.

| *Blood group* | *Antigen on RBC* | *Antibody in plasma* |
|---|---|---|
| A | A | anti-b |
| B | B | anti-a |
| AB | A and B | None |
| O | None | anti-a and anti-b |

The transfusion of blood from one person to another person depends upon the presence of types of antigen in donor's blood (RBC) and the types of antibody in recipients' serum. If they are of same types the transfused blood may get agglutinated.

Therefore, A-group blood could not be transfused to B-group containing persons.

In AB-group, RBC possesses both antigens and no antibody in plasma and therefore if could not be given to other groups except its own, but could receive blood from all other groups. Therefore, it is **universal receipient**.

In O-group, RBC does not have the antigen A and B, but serum has both antibodies and therefore, it could be given to all other groups and can not receive blood except its own. So, it is **universal donor**.

### 6.4.2 Genetic constitution of ABO blood group

Both group O and A are fairly numerous and either might be considered the normal. ABO locus is present in chromosome-9 in band $q_{34}$. For convenience, Group-O is regarded as the normal and group A and B arose from group-O as a result of two dominant mutations. The mutant genes can be given the symbols A and B respectively. Both of these arose in the same locus from one of the normal genes in group-O.

The symbol which is commonly used where

$I^A$ is for antigen – A

$I^B$ for antigen – B

$i$ for their normal recessive allele

Thus, the genotypes of different blood groups can also be symbolized as

| *Group* | *Genotypes* |
|---|---|
| A | $I^A I^A$ and $I^A i$ |
| B | $I^B I^B$ and $I^B i$ |
| AB | $I^A I^B$ |
| O | ii |

The inheritance of ABO-blood group system in human is described in the Table 6.1.

**TABLE 5.1**
**The inheritance of ABO system is as follows**

| *Parental Groups* | *Parental genotypes* | *Offsprings genotype* | *Offsprings phenotype (groups)* |
|---|---|---|---|
| A × A | $I^A I^A \times I^A I^A$ | $I^A I^A$ | A |
| | $I^A I^A \times I^A i$ | $I^A I^A$, $I^A i$ | A |
| | $I^A i \times I^A i$ | $I^A I^A$, $I^A i$ | A |
| | | $ii$ | O |
| B × B | $I^B I^B \times I^B I^B$ | $I^B I^B$ | B |
| | $I^B I^B \times I^B i$ | $I^B I^B$, $I^B i$ | B |
| | $I^B i \times I^B i$ | $I^B I^B$, $I^B i$ | B |
| | | $ii$ | O |
| A × B | $I^A I^A \times I^B I^B$ | $I^A I^B$ | AB |
| | $I^A I^A \times I^B i$ | $I^A I^B$ | AB |
| | | $I^A i$ | A |
| | $I^A i \times I^B I^B$ | $I^A I^B$ | AB |
| | | $I^B i$ | B |
| | $I^A i \times I^B i$ | $I^A I^B$ | AB |
| | | $I^A i$ | A |
| | | $I^B i$ | B |
| | | $ii$ | O |
| AB × A | $I^A I^B \times I^A I^A$ | $I^A I^A$ | A |
| | | $I^B I^A$ | AB |
| | $I^A I^B \times I^A i$ | $I^A I^A$, $I^A i$ | A |
| | | $I^B i$ | B |
| | | $I^A I^B$ | AB |
| AB × B | $I^A I^B \times I^B I^B$ | $I^A I^B$ | AB |
| | | $I^B I^B$ | B |
| | $I^A I^B \times I^B i$ | $I^A I^B$ | AB |
| | | $I^A i$ | A |
| | | $I^B I^B$, $I^B i$ | B |
| AB × AB | $I^A I^B \times I^A I^B$ | $I^A I^A$ | A |
| | | $I^A I^B$ | AB |
| | | $I^B I^B$ | B |
| O × O | $ii \times ii$ | $ii$ | O |
| A × O | $I^A I^A \times ii$ | $I^A i$ | A |
| | $I^A i \times ii$ | $A^A i$ | A |
| | | $ii$ | O |
| B × O | $I^B I^B \times ii$ | $I^B i$ | B |
| | $I^B i \times ii$ | $I^B i$ | B |
| | | $ii$ | O |
| AB × O | $I^A I^B \times ii$ | $I^A i$ | A |
| | | $I^B i$ | B |

### 6.4.3 Chemistry of antigen-A and antigen-B

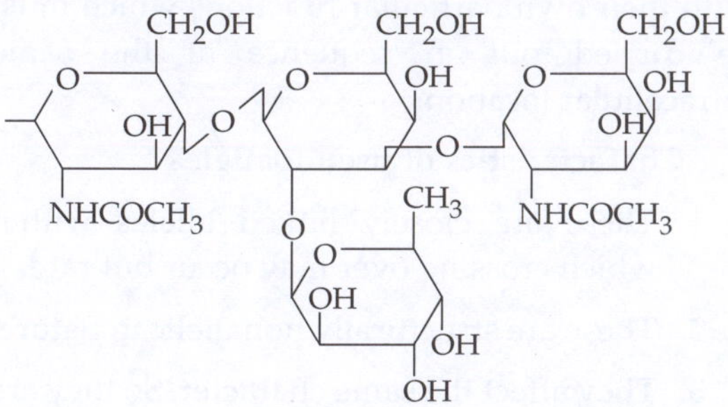

A-substance

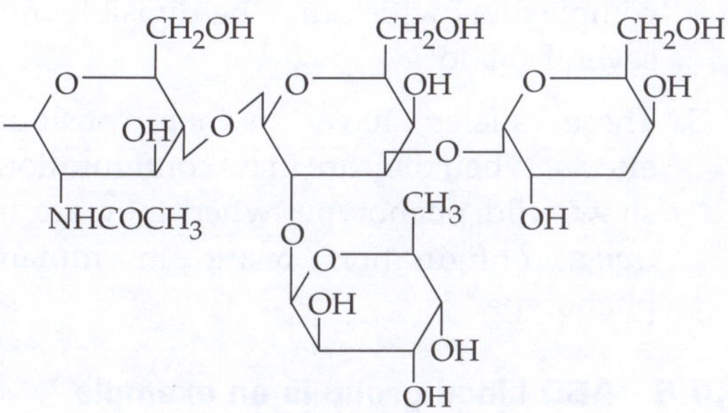

B-substance

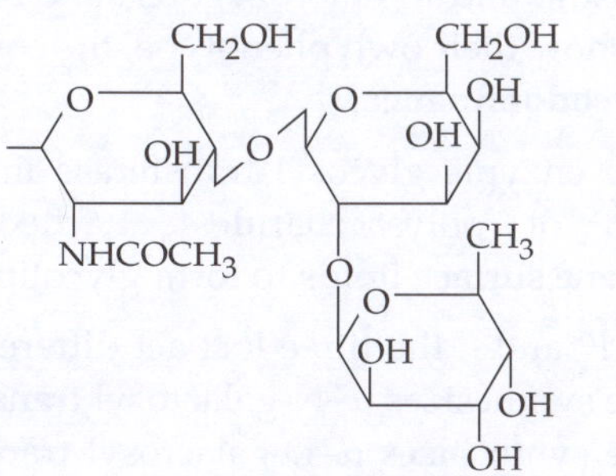

O-substance

According to Kabat, Watkins and others, the A-substance bears an N-acetyl group at number 2 position of the terminal galactose sugar. The B-substance carries a hydroxyl group at this position and the O-substance lacks the terminal galactose sugar entirely.

The A and B substances are produced from the precursors by the action of A and B alleles; each allele produces a transferase enzyme but one as N-acetyl galactosaminyl transferase (*A*) and other as a galactosyl transferase (*B*). In case of 'O' allele no **terminal transferase enzyme** appears to be produced and it can therefore be called a '**null**' allele. This helps to explain a number of findings that *A* and *B* both are codominant and 'O'-substance is not antigenically detectable by antibodies that act on the terminal galactose sugar and 'O' allele acts as a recessive.

### 6.4.4 Secretion of blood group substances

The "A" and "B" are not only found on RBC but often in the body fluid and saliva. The person who possess such antigens are called "secretors" and can be shown to be either homozygous(*SeSe*) or heterozygous (*Se se*) for the dominant secretor allele (controlled by a different gene pair than the ABO blood group genes). These antigens are present as protein-sugar compounds on RBC and fat -sugar compound in secretors.

### 6.4.5 Close-linkage versus Allelism in explanation of the ABO-blood groups

It is theoretically possible that the ABO blood groups are determined by genes at two adjacent loci, *a* and *b*.

| *Blood group* | *Haploid element* |
|---|---|
| O | a b |
| AB | A B |
| B | a B |

The haploid element of gene A will be *Ab* and gene *B* will be *aB*. If there were never any crossing over between loci *a* and *b*, then in each instance, the two linked genes would act as a single unit of heredity. Hence, *Ab* and *aB* would behave as though they were alleles of one another. The hybrid *Ab/aB* would represent the AB blood group and this hybrid would form only two classes of gametes *Aa* and *aB*.

There is no simple way of knowing whether the ABO blood groups are determined by alleles or by linked genes between which there is no crossing over, since, in either event, the hybrid *A/B* would form only two classes of gametes. However, it is customary to consider the haploid elements involved in determining the ABO blood group as alleles rather than closely linked genes, possibly because the alleles theory is somewhat simpler than the "close linkage theory". In any event, the ABO blood groups are determined either by alleles or by allele like elements (in close linkage).

### 6.4.6 Subdivisions of A-blood group

It we would add an excess of A-corpuscles to the B-serum; we would then expect to remove all anti A from the serum. We would then expect that this absorbed B serum would no longer agglutinate any fresh A-corpuscles that were added to it, since the B-serum would expectically no longer contain any anti-A. But the corpuscles of some people belonging to group-A do not remove all the anti-A. It can still agglutinate additional corpuscles of a particular person. Thus, the corpuscles of these exceptional group-A people must be different from those of most other group-A people. Additional multiple alleles at the ABO locus have recently been found ($A_1$, $A_2$, $A_3$, $A_4$) which probably differ in even more minor respects.

Since, $A_1$ is not rare, people homozygous for $A_1$ ($A_1/A_1$) would not be unusual, but people homozygous for $A_2$, $A_3$ and $A_4$ would be very unusual, since these alleles are rare. The rare alleles would usually occur in combination with $A_1$ ($A_1/A_2$, $A_1/A_3$, $A_1/A_4$).

In a person of group AB, A-might be $A_1$, $A_2$, $A_3$ or $A_4$, hence group AB is subdivided into $A_1B$, $A_2B$, $A_3B$, $A_4B$. There is some evidences, not yet conclusive that the B group is also subdivided into subgroups.

### 6.4.7 Pseudoalleles

Such genes which have two separate gene loci, but often inherit together due to close linkage and have a very rare chance of crossing over area called Pseudoalleles.

According to Lewis (1955) and Green the pseudoalleles may be regarded as distinct genes with their own particular functions which must be carried out in sequence at the same intracellular location.

**Characteristics of pseudoalleles**

1. These are closely linked alleles within which crossing over may occur but rare.
2. These are structurally nonallelic in nature.
3. They affect the same character. So they are allelic in function.
4. These are arranged in linear order within complex loci which may be divisible into several sub loci.
5. These alleles have *cis-trans* position effects. When they are in *cis* configuration, show wild phenotype, when they are in *trans* configuration result in mutant phenotype.

### 6.4.8 ABO blood group is an example of Codominance

If the alleles lack dominant-recessive relationship and in heterozygous state both the alleles show their own phenotype, the condition is alled **codominance**.

The enzyme glycosyl transferase mediates reaction of polysaccharides attached with membrane surface lipids to form glycolipids.

$I^A$, $I^B$ and *i*, the three loci act differentially. $I^A$ allele synthesizes α–N-galactosyl transferase, $I^B$ allele synthesizes α–D-galactosyl transferase and *i* lacks the enzyme.

The homozygote $I^AI^A$ synthesizes only α-N-galactosyl transferase.

The homozygate $I^BI^B$ synthesizes only α-D-galactosyl transferase.

While the heterozygote $I^AI^B$ *ie* AB blood group synthesizes both α-N and α–D galactosyl transferase enzymes. Thus $I^A$ and $I^B$ both alleles are condominants.

### 6.4.9 Isoalleles

The alleles which express the same phenotypic range, are called *isoalleles.*

1. **Mutant isoalleles** *i.e.* the alleles within the phenotypic range of abnormal characters.
2. **Normal isoalleles** *i.e.* the alleles within the phenotypic range of wild type.

Example : *Drasophila,* many alleles of white eye colour have been found to occur which have a quantitative effect between white and wild type (red). This can be distinguished by the relative amounts of pigments.

| *Genotype* | *Colour of eye* | *Relative amount of Pigment* |
|---|---|---|
| *ww* | White | 0.0044 |
| $w^a w^a$ | Apricot | 0.0197 |
| $w^e w^e$ | Eosin | 0.0324 |

## 6.5 RHESUS ALLELES : (PSEUDOALLELISM)

### 6.5.1 Concept

An important agglutinogen has been demonstrated (1940) in human corpuscles also by Landsteiner and Wiener. It is agglutingen of Rhesus monkey (*Macaca mulatta*) and is present in about 85% of the white people. Among Indians and Ceylonese the percentage is high above 95%. *There are no naturally occurring antibodies in the human plasma.*

When the serum of rabbits, immunized by the blood of rhesus monkey, is agglutinated by RBC of a person is called **Rhesus positive**.

When a woman has an erythroblastotic child, by selective absorption, two kinds of antibodies may be separated from such a serum, one known as **anti-D** which agglutinates only Rhesus Positive cells, the other is known as **anti-C** which agglutinates cells of a particular rare type of Rhesus negative. The later type has therefore be a specific antigen 'C' but no D-antigen and is designated as Cd. The Rhesus positives that do not agglutinate with anti C is designated as cD. Another antibody known as **anti-c**, agglutinates all cells that lack C-antigen.

No antiserum has been available for detecting 'd' (the alternate of D). D-positive person may be homozygous (*DD*) or heterozygous (*Dd*) because some D positive person may have D negative child.

But *C* and *c*, each allele produces it's own antigen in the *Cc* heterozygous condition. Therefore, there is obviously no dominance.

Two other specific antibodies; **anti E** and **anti-e** have been found, these detect the antigens E and e determined by a pair of alleles *E* and *e.*

Therefore, there are three pairs of Rh agglutinogens, C, c, D, E and e. *C, D* and *E* are Mendelian dominants and *c, d* and *e* are recessives. These three pairs of alleles in fixed combinations that are always inherited together as alleles of a single gene. **Therefore Rh genes are regarded as the pseudoalleles.**

### 6.5.2 Genetic Control

Two major hypotheses have been advanced to explain the genetic mechanism that controls the Rh antigens.

Wiener proposed a series of alleles at a single locus and a pair of chromosomes different from those carrying any other genes for blood grouping antigens, i.e., one gene determining three specificities (antigen).

Fisher and Race postulate that three pairs of closely linked alleles at three separate loci, *i.e.,* three genes each determining single specificities (antigen). They are so closely linked that really no cross-overs occur.

Wiener's concept postulates a basic series of 8 allelic genes, any two of which can occur in single heterozygous individuals. Each of these genes determines an antigen able to induce and combine with one to three kinds of antibodies. The symbol $Rh_o$ is capitalized and represents the Rh antigen. rh' and rh'' stands for another additional antigens. hr' occurs on all cells

**TABLE 6.2**
**Genetic composition of Rh blood group**

| | Wiener's view | Antigenic specificity | | Antiserum (Wiener's/Fisher's symbol) | | | | |
|---|---|---|---|---|---|---|---|---|
| | | Wiener's view | Fisher's view | Anti-$Rh_0$ | Anti-rh′ | Anti-rh″ | Anti-hr′ | Anti-hr″ |
| | Gene | | | Anti-D | Anti-C | Anti-E | Anti-c | anti-e |
| Rh +ve | $R^1$ | $Rh_0$, rh′, hr″ | CDe | ⊕ | ⊕ | | | ⊕ |
| | $R^2$ | $Rh_0$, rh″, hr′ | cDE | ⊕ | | ⊕ | ⊕ | |
| | $R^0$ | $Rh_0$, hr′, hr″ | cDe | ⊕ | | | ⊕ | ⊕ |
| | $R^z$ | $Rh_0$, rh′, rh″ | CDE | ⊕ | ⊕ | ⊕ | | |
| Rh –ve | r′ | rh′, hr″ | Cde | | ⊕ | | | ⊕ |
| | r″ | rh″, hr′ | cdE | | | ⊕ | ⊕ | |
| | r | hr′, hr″ | cde | | | | ⊕ | ⊕ |
| | $r^y$ | rh′, rh″ | CdE | | ⊕ | ⊕ | | |

lacking rh′ and hr″ occurs on all cells lacking the rh″ specificity. Antigenic counterpart of $Rh_o$ antigen is $Hr_o$ has yet to be identified.

R. A. Fisher and Race proposed that three pairs of closely linked alleles *C-c, D-d* and *E-e* produce a distinct antigen by each gene showing co-dominance. These three pairs of alleles in fixed combinations are always inherited together (Table 6.2).

The existence of such a series of eight different alternative arrangements of three kinds of antigens has of course led to the suspicion that these are not alletic states of the same gene but rather than the Rh locus consists of a cluster of three closely associated genes *C-c, D-d* and *E-e*. The inheritance of these properties in families can be explained by assuming that they are multiple alleles.

Rh null individuals have no Rh antigen. They are comparable to the Bombay phenotype of ABO blood group system. They do not have a precursor, which is needed as a substance for the formation of the antigens of the Rh system. They are homozygous for a rare gene $X^0r$, whose allele $X^lr$ is responsible for the synthesis of a precursor of both Rh and LW antigens (Rh null people also lack LW). The Rh null phenotype is very rare and was first found in an Australian aborigine. There is a rare Rh blood group, where the *C* and *E* series of antigens are missing and only *D* is present called *D/D* genotype . This was attributed to a deletion of the part of chromosome that carries the *C* and *E* loci (It should be noted that the order of the genes on the chromosome is now believed to be *DCE* and not *CDE*). However, the genotype is more likely to be due to a separate suppressor gene such as $X^0r$.

### 6.5.3 Clinical Importance of Rh factor

1. At the time of transfusion of blood into a patient, along with the ABO system compatibility, presence or absence of Rh factor in the donor and recipient blood is necessary to know. If Rh +ve blood is transfused to a Rh –ve blood, within 12 days Anti-Rh factor will develop in their serum. If a second transfusion is made by Rh +ve blood after this period, haemo-agglutination of donor's corpuscles will take place.

2. When the father is Rh +ve and the mother is Rh –ve, she might have a Rh+ve baby in her uterus. Due to the influence of Rh+ve antigen of the fetus, mother develops sufficient anti-Rh antibody in her serum. During his second pregnancy, if her child is Rh+ve, the antibody then attacks the RBC of the fetus, causing destruction of RBC of her unborn baby provokes hemolysis and anaemia. This may be serious enough to cause death of the newborn infant or abortion of the fetus. This disease is known as **erythroblastosis fetalis.** If Rh-ve mother receives Rh+ blood previously through transfusion then the first child might have such anaemia.

## 6.6 SELF STERILITY ALLELES: (MULTIPLE ALLELES)

Self sterility means that the pollen from a plant will not be able to bring about fertilization in the ovules of the same plant.

A series of multiple alleles for self sterility in tobacco (*Nicotiana*) was reported by E.M. East. The alleles in such a series of 15 can be designated as $S_1, S_2, S_3 .........S_{15}$. Pollen grains containing $S_1$ fail to grow properly on the style of the plant that carries the same allele. Thus, the plant never be homozygous.

If $S_1S_2$ is pollinated by the pollen by another $S_1S_2$ plant, no pollen grains will reach the ovule after fertilization. Again when $S_1S_2$ is crossed with $S_1S_3$ only $S_1S_3$ and $S_2S_3$ will be produced. It means that if one allele of the mother is same with the allele of the pollen, the mothers' tissue prevents growth of that pollen grains and prevents fertilization and growth of the embryo. This hypothesis is illustrated in the following crosses where three genotypic classes involved.

In *Oenothera organensis*, Sterling Emersion observed 37 such different compatibility alleles.

The self-sleterity effect is exerted by the slowing of pollen tube growth rate. It is too slow that when the tube reaches the ovule, the flower already becomes withered. It is probably due to the gene controlled reaction between haploid pollen and diploid tissue of the female plant. Therefore such alleles are called **oppositional alleles.**

**Parents :**

| ♀ \ ♂ | $S_1S_2$ | $S_1S_3$ | $S_2S_3$ |
|---|---|---|---|
| $S_1S_2$ | No Offspring | $S_1S_3$, $S_2S_3$ | $S_1S_3$, $S_2S_3$ |
| $S_1S_3$ | $S_1S_2$, $S_2S_3$ | No Offspring | $S_1S_2$, $S_2S_3$ |
| $S_2S_3$ | $S_1S_2$, $S_1S_3$ | $S_1S_2$, $S_1S_3$ | No Offspring |

The mechanism of S-allele has been worked out by Nasralla *et al.* (1985) at the molecular level. They proposed after cloning DNA from $S_6$ gene of *Brassica oleracea*, that the gene synthesizes a glycoprotein and they also have shown that different *S*-alleles have different DNA sequences.

## 6.7 MN-BLOOD GROUPS (CO-DOMINANCE)

Another blood group system which is called the **MN system**; having no relation with ABO blood groups, though it has no importance in the blood transfusion. It was discovered by Landsteiner and Levine and considered three general types called M, N and MN. The M type elicited antibodies (anti-M serum) specific for M which could not agglutinate N, while the N red cells caused the production of antibodies specific for N (anti-N serum). Both types of antibodies could agglutinate MN red cells.

It is found that the genes for M and N appeared to be alleles for each other.

In the honour of Landsteiner, this gene was named L and the allele for M and N were named as $L^M$ and $L^N$ respectively. Therefore, M-blood group person comprises homozygous $L^ML^M$ alleles; N-blood group person comprises homozygous $L^NL^N$ alleles, whereas MN blood group person comprises $L^ML^N$ alleles. Thus, *M* and *N* genes show co-dominance. The inheritance is as follows in Table 6.3.

**TABLE 6.3**
**Inheritance of MN blood group**

| *Blood group of the parent* | *Geneotypes of the parent* | *genotypes of offspring* | *Blood groups of the offspring* |
|---|---|---|---|
| M × M | $L^ML^M \times L^ML^M$ | $L^ML^M$ | M |
| N × N | $L^NL^N \times L^NL^N$ | $L^NL^N$ | N |
| MN × MN | $L^ML^N \times L^ML^N$ | $L^ML^M, L^ML^N, L^NL^N$ | M, MN, N |
| MN × N | $L^ML^N \times L^NL^N$ | $L^ML^M, L^NL^N$ | MN, N |
| MN × M | $L^ML^N \times L^NL^M$ | $L^ML^N, L^ML^M$ | MN, M |
| M × N | $L^ML^M \times L^NL^N$ | $L^ML^N$ | MN |

In 1947 Walsh and Montgomery observed that a certain human population of human blood serum could be used to distinguish new varieties of MN blood groups. Another blood type which is called **Ss**, closely tied to the inheritance of *MN* gene. Thus, four co-dominant genes have been found to be inherited to give nine four different phenotypic combinations. The multiple allelic nature of **MNSs system** can be deduced by the following possible combinations (Table 6.4).

## 6.8 SPECIAL GENETIC CASES OF ABO BLOOD GROUP

Another antigen known as 'H'-antigen also identified on the RBC of man, which can be demonstrated by agglutinations by anti-H serum. This antigen is believed to be an intermediate between antigen A and B. The dominant gene-*H* is responsible for the production of H-antigen and the genotypes are as follows (Table 6.5)

**TABLE 6.4**
**Composition of MN blood group**

| *Genotypes* | *Phenotypes* | *Reaction with antigens* | | | |
|---|---|---|---|---|---|
| | | *anti-M* | *anti-N* | *anti-S* | *anti-s* |
| $L^{MS}L^{MS}$ | MS | + | | + | |
| $L^{MS}L^{Ms}$ | MSs | + | | + | + |
| $L^{Ms}L^{Ms}$ | Ms | + | | | + |
| $L^{MS}L^{NS}$ | MNS | + | + | + | |
| $L^{MS}L^{Ns}$ | MNSs | + | + | + | + |
| $L^{Ms}L^{NS}$ | MNSs | + | + | + | + |
| $L^{NS}L^{NS}$ | NS | | + | + | |
| $L^{Ns}L^{Ns}$ | Ns | | + | | + |
| $L^{NS}L^{Ns}$ | NSs | | + | + | + |
| $L^{Ms}L^{Ns}$ | MNs | + | + | | + |

**TABLE 6.5**
**Relation of H gene with ABO blood group**

| *Genotype* | *Phenotype* |
|---|---|
| *HH* | H-antigen |
| *Hh* | H-antigen |
| *hh* | no H-antigen |
| A group + *HH* or *Hh* | A + H-antigen |
| B group + *HH* or *Hh* | B + H-antigen |
| O group + *HH* or *Hh* | none + H - antigen |
| AB group + *HH* or *Hh* | A + B + H-antigen |
| O group + *h/h* | none (Bombay Phenotype) |

The chemical structure of H-substance is

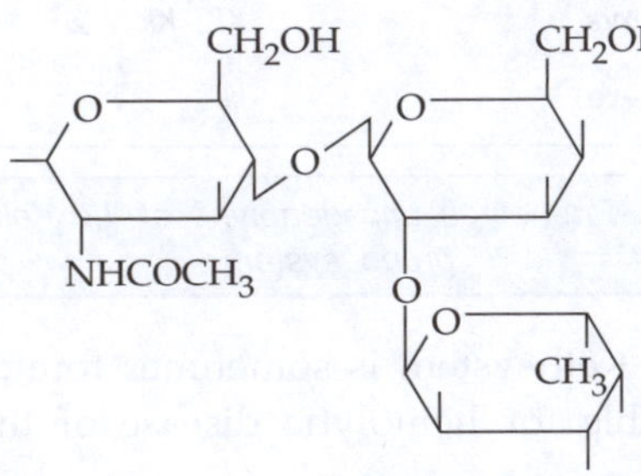


In the construction of RBC surface molecules that determine blood type, type-A individuals make an enzyme that adds polysaccharide -A onto a base consisting of a sugar polymer, known as **substance-H**; type -B similarly adds polysaccharide B; but type-O individuals make neither A-adding nor B-adding enzymes. Thus substance-H is exposed on the RBC surface. All people of A, B or O phenotype at least have dominant wild-type H-allele for the second gene and this produce some substance-H.

It is interesting to note that the individuals whose blood gives no reaction with Anti-A or Anti-B or Anti-H belong to very rare group and are known as "**Bombay Phenotype**", because it was first described in a very small group of people in the Bombay city. It resembles type-O, having homozygous mutant alleles (*hh*) of a second gene that masks the effects of any ABO alleles that might be present. The anti-H antibody is found naturally in the serum of subjects of Bombay Phenotype who have genotype *bb*. Because of the anti-H antibody, individuals with Bombay phenotype cannot form A or B antigens even if they carry genotype $I^AI^A$, $I^Ai$, $I^BI^B$ or $I^Bi$. The RBCs of such individuals in spite of genotypically having the *A* or *B* gene, cannot be agglutinated by Anti-A, Anti-B or anti -H as their sera contain all three antibodies. This leads to misadjusting of blood groups in individuals having the Bombay Phenotype (Table 6.5).

## 6.9 HISTOCOMPATIBILITY GENES IN MICE AND MAN.

The genes involved in the production of cell surface antigens that are recognized by the rejection or tolerance of tissue transplants are collectively called **histocompatibility genes**. The action of alleles that produce antigens seems to be co-dominant. The rejection of donor tissues occurs where the host does not carry the alleles of the donor. For example, if we confine ourselves to only three pairs of genes *A*, *B* and *C*, an inbred strain of mice may bear the histocompatibility genotype $A^1A^1B^1B^1C^2C^2$. Such mice can tolerate the tissue transplants from the mice of the same genotype but will reject transplants from the inbred mice of genotype $A^2A^2B^2B^2C^1C^1$. When these two such strains are crossed the resultant ($F_1$) hybrid is $A^1A^2B^1B^2C^1C^2$ will accept transplants from either parental strain but it's tissue will be rejected by either parental strain.

If $F_1XF_1$ mating is made, $F_2$ will show a wide varieties of possible genotypic combinations. Some of $F_2$ offspring lacking one or more alleles present in $F_1$ genotype, such $F_2$ individuals will reject the $F_1$ donor tissue, while tissues of $F_2$ individuals will not be rejected by $F_1$ hosts.

In mice more than 50 genes are known to be involved in histocompatibility genes and some maintaining multiple alleles.

Four separate genes linked together on the same chromosome (chromosome no-6) have been proposed for the HLA system, each gene possessing from 8 to 40 multiple alleles, each allele specifying a particular antigen. HLA-A gene has 20 possible alleles HLA-B gene has 40 alleles. In chromosome No.6, one from each gene has possible combinations of 75000 types. Each particular combination is called haplotype. An individual might have two such haplotypes obtained one from each parent. Thus, such enormous populational variability helps to explain the difficulties in successful tissue transplantation. Therefore, unrelated person will differ markedly in their HLA genotype; the differences can even be expected among close relatives.

## 6.10 OTHER BLOOD GROUP SYSTEMS

**1. P Blood group system** (Landsteiner and Levine 1927) : This type of blood group is characterised by the dominant gene $p_1$ and its multiple allele series $p^1$, $p^2$ and p and there are four recognisable phenotypes, viz $p_1$, $p_2$, $p$ and $pk$. The group $pk$ lacking an independent dominant gene as in the Bombay phenotype.

| *Phenotype Group* | *Genotype* |
|---|---|
| **P1** | $p^1p^1$, $p^1p^2$, $p^1p$ |
| **P2** | $p^2p^2$, $p^2p$ |
| **P** | p p |
| **$P^k$** | $p_1p^2$ |

**Fig.6.2 :** *Phenotype and genotype of the P blood group system*

**2. Lutheran Blood group system** (Callender *et al*, 1946) : This system of blood group was the first example studied of autosomal linkage and autosomal crossing over in man — the Lutheran secretor linkage. The locus for myotonic disrophy is also linked to the Lutheran and secretor loci. Two genes are responsible for such phenotype $Lu^a$ and $Lu^b$ and presence of *Lu* suppressor gene affecting the expression of all $Lu^a$ and $Lu^b$ genes at the *Lu* locus.

| *Phenotype Group* | *Genotype* |
|---|---|
| **Lu** ($a^+$ $b^-$) | $Lu^a$ $Lu^a$ |
| **Lu** ($a^+$ $b^+$) | $Lu^a$ $Lu^b$ |
| **Lu** ($a^-$ $b^+$) | $Lu^b$ $Lu^b$ |
| **Lu** ($a^-$ $b^-$) | *Lu silent* |

**Fig.6.3 :** *Phenotype and genotype of the Lutheran blood group system.*

**3. Kell Blood group system** (Coombs *et al* 1946) : The Kell blood group system was described as having two alternative phenotypes : Kell positive (K+) and Kell negative (K–) determined by a pair of alleles *K* and *k*.

| *Phenotype* | *Genotype* |
|---|---|
| **K +ve** | *KK, Kk* |
| **K –ve** | *kk* |

**Fig.6.4 :** *Phenotype and genotype of the Kell blood group system.*

The Kell system is sometimes found to be responsible for hemolytic disease of the new born.

**4. Lewis Blood group system (Mourant, 1946) :** The Lewis blood group system interacts with ABO and secretor system. Lewis substances are not primarily red cell antigens but antigens of body fluids such as plasma and saliva. The antigens get absorbed into RBCs from the plasma

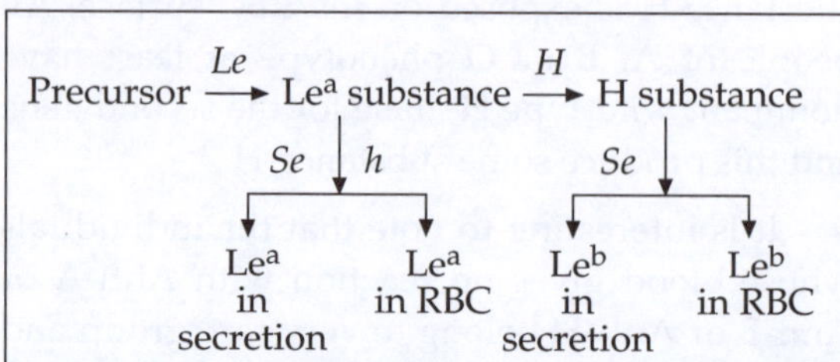


**Fig.6.5 :** *Steps involved in the synthesis of Le blood group antigens and its relationship to ABO system and secretor system.*

The $Le^a$ and $Le^b$ antigens in the serum and saliva are determined by a pair of alleles *Le* and *le.*

The phenotype and genotype of the lewis system is as follows

| *Phenotype* | *Genotype* | *Comment* |
|---|---|---|
| **Le** ($a^+$ $b^-$) | $Le^a$ $Le^a$ | RBC does not secrete ABH substance |
| **Le** ($a^+$ $b^+$) | $Le^a$ $Le^b$ | RBC secretes ABH substance |
| **Le** ($a^-$ $b^+$) | $Le^b$ $Le^b$ | Not observed in adult |
| **Le** ($a^-$ $b^-$) | *Le silent* | *Rare* |

**Fig.6.6 :** *Phenotype and genotype of the Lewis blood group system.*

5. **Duffy Blood group system** (Cutbush *et al* 1950) : This gene is located on the chromosome-1. There are three allelic genes in this Duffy locus $Fy^a$, $Fy^b$ *and* $Fy^c$.

6. **Kidd Blood group system** (Allen *et al* 1951) : There are three allelic genes at the Kidd locus $Jk^a$, $Jk^b$ and *Jk*. The anti $Jk^a$ is responsible for hemolytic disease of newborn and also for some transfusion reactions.

7. **Diego Blood group system** (Layrisse *et al* 1955) : $Di^a$ antigen is the specific marker for such blood group and found in Mongolians. The two alleles responsible for such phenotype are $Di^a$ and *Di*.

The phenetype and genotypes are as follows :

| *Phenotype* | *Genotype* |
|---|---|
| **Di** ($a^+$) | $Di^a$ $Di^a$, $Di^a$ *Di* |
| **Di** ($a^-$) | *Di Di* |

**Fig.6.7 :** *Phenotype and genotype of the Diego blood group system.*

8. **I-Blood group system** (Wiener *et al* 1956) : I-antigen is known as **public antigens,** which is present almost all members of human species. The I-negative adults are very rare.

I-antigen is adult antigen and its counterpart i-antigen is fetal antigen. At birth i-antigen is strong and thereafter it decreases. On the other hand I-antigen is poorly developed at birth and gradually increases as i-antigen decreases.

In many disorders in adults such as thalassaemia major, the RBCs are agglutinated by both anti-I and anti-i.

9. $\mathbf{Y_T}$ **(Cartwright) Blood group system** (Eaton *et al 1956)* : About 98% of the populations are Yt(a+) . This type fo blood group is determined by $Yl^a$ and $Y1^b$. The genotype and phenotype are as follows :

| *Phenotype* | *Genotype* |
|---|---|
| **Yt** ($a^+$ $b^-$) | $Y1^a$ $Y1^a$ |
| **Yt** ($a^+$ $b^+$) | $Y1^a$ $Y1^a$ |
| **Yt** ($a^-$ $b^+$) | $Y1^b$ $Y1^b$ |

**Fig.6.8 :** *Phenotype and genotype of the $Y_T$ Cartwright blood group system.*

10. $\mathbf{X_G}$ **Blood group system** (Mann *et al* 1962) : Xg locus is present on the X-chromosome and appears not to participate in X-inactivation like other X-linked loci. This locus contains two alleles $Xg^a$ and *Xg*. The phenotype and genotype of this system is as follows :

| *Sex* | *Phenotype* | *Genotype* |
|---|---|---|
| Male | **Xg** ($a^+$) | $Xg^a$/Y |
| | **Xg** ($a^-$) | Xg /Y |
| Female | **Xg** ($a^+$) | $Xg^a$/$Xg^a$ |
| | **Xg**($a^-$) | Xg/Xg |

**Fig.6.9 :** *Phenotype and genotype of the $X_G$ blood group system.*

11. **Dombrock blood group system** (Swanson *et al* 1965) : About 64% of northern Europeans are Do (a+) phenotype. Two allelic genes determine this blood group systems : $Do^a$ and $Do^b$. The phenotype and genotype are as follows :

| *Phenotype* | *Genotype* |
|---|---|
| **Di** ($a^+$ $b^-$) | *$Do^a$ $Do^a$* |
| **Di** ($a^-$ $b^+$) | *$Do^b$ $Do^b$* |

**Fig.6.10 :** *Phenotype and genotype and Dombrock blood group system.*

## 6.11 BLOOD GROUP CHIMERAS

A person with blood cells of two different genotypes derived from two differnt zygotes is said to have a blood group chimera.

In blood group chimeras, **the excahnge of hemopoietic cells** takes place in fetal life, prior to the development of **immune Competence.**

These antibodies persist in the host's bone marrow and remain throughout life and so foreign cells do not stimulate the host to form antibodies agaisnt them.

If the hemopoietic cells are exchanged, the host will transmit only his on her own blood group to his or her daughter.

The possible mode of origin of chimeric blood group is the sharing of circulation in prenatal life by dizygotic twin . The dispermic chimera is also formed by the fusion of dizygotic twin zygotes or very early embryos. This is rare event, so incidence of chimeric blood group is very low.

## 6.12 COMPLEX "R" LOCI IN MAIZE (MOSAIC DOMINANCE)

Sometimes members of a series of multiple alleles may affect different combinations of traits. For example, a series of genes-R in maize which determine the purple coloration of different parts of the plant due to production of anthocyanin. Four of these alleles have the following effects:

$R^r$ - coloured seed (aleurone), coloured plant.

$R^g$ - coloured seed (aleurone), colourless plant.

$r^r$ - colourless seed (aleurone), coloured plant.

$r^g$ - colourless seed (aleurone), colourless plant.

The coloured genes are dominant over colourless because of the ability to produce the anthocyanin in their respective body parts. Therefore $R^g r^r$ plants have coloured aleurone as well as coloured leaves and stem. The gene behaves as though it consists of at least two parts or components. One of which determines aleurone colour and the plant colour.

## 6.13 EYE COLOR IN *DROSOPHILA*

Normal eye color in *Drosophila* is red. Several mutations have been found to occur in this red eye color gene locus. The first mutation is white, which shows simple dominant-recessive relationship. Normal red eye colour is also found to be dominant over all other mutants. In homozygous condition, these recessive mutant genes show a series of eye colour shades. But if any two different recessive alleles come together in heterozygous condition, an intermediate type of eye colour is obtained. These are actually not allelic but pseudoallelic in nature. (Table 6.6)

**TABLE 6.6**
**Multiple alleles for eye colour in *Drosophila***

| *Allele* | *Phenotype in homozygous condition* | *Genotype and phenotype in heterozygous condition* |
|---|---|---|
| + | red | |
| $w$ | white | $+/w$ (red) |
| $w^{ch}$ | Cherry | $+/w^{ch}$ (red) |
| $w^b$ | blood | $+/w^b$ (red) |
| $w^e$ | eosin | $+/w^e$ (red) |
| $w^{apr}$ | apricot | $+/w^{apr}$ (red) |
| $w^{iv}$ | ivory | $+/w^{iv}$ (red) |
| $w^{cr}$ | Cream | $+/w^{cr}$ (red) |
| | | other heterozygotes (intermediate) |

## 6.14 PLEIOTROPISM

The term pleiotropy is derived from the Greek work *pleio* = many and *tropic* - affecting. So, genes that affect multiple apparently unrelated phenotypes and thus called **pleiotropic genes**.

**Pleiotropism** is defined as when one gene influences multiple unrelated phenotypic traits in the same organism.

**Pleiotropy** describes the genetic effects of a single gene on multiple phenotypic traits.

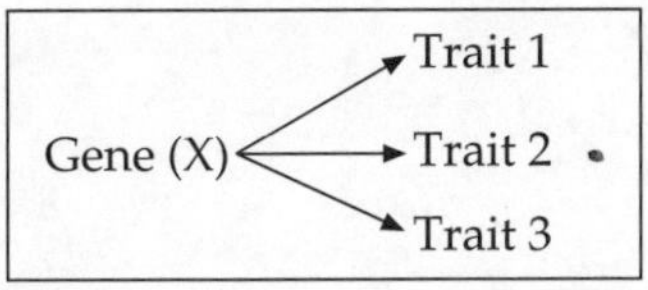


*Examples*

1. Marfan syndrome is a disorder in humans in which one gene is responsible for a constellation of symptoms including thinnes, joint hypermobility, limb elongation, lens dislocation and increased susceptibility to heart disease.
2. Phenylketoneuria (PKU), a disorder in humans which is a caused by deficiency of the enzyme *phenylalanine hydroxylase*, which is necessary to convert the essential amino acid phenylalanine to tyrosine. A defect in the single gene that codes for this enzyme may result in multiple phenotypes associated PKU including mental retardation, eczema, and pigment defects that make affected individuals lighter skinned.
3. Sickle cell anaemia is caused by homozygosity abnormal β-hemoglobuin gene leading to formation of crescent shaped RBC and impairs $O_2$ carrying capacity. This often led to renal failure, cardiac failure and thrombosis. Thus a single gene mutation causes multiple effects on different sites and tissues.

*Significance of Pleiotropism :*

1. Single genes may impose in multiple systems, often give us insight into biological function of specific genes.
2. This gene can provide us valuable information regarding the evolution of different genes and gene families which are coopted for new purposes beyond its original functions.
3. It reflects that most proteins have multiple roles in distinct cell types and wide range effects in a variety of tissues.

*Examples :*

1. Mendel noticed that pea plants with coloured seed coats always had coloured flowers and coloured leaf axils and also observed that colorless seed coats always had white flowers and no pigmentation on their axils. The seed coat color gene is not only responsible for seed coat colour, but also for flower and axil pigmentation.
2. Vestigial gene of *Drosophila,* is recessive, in homozygous condition they develop short wings and unable to fly. This *vg* gene is pleotropic , indirectly this gene changes that number of egg strings in the ovary of fly, alter the position of bristles on the scutellum of fly and decreases the length of a fly's life.
3. Dominant *frizzle* gene of chicken produces feathers that curled outward rather than lying flat against their bodies. This gene is pleiotropic, also produces defective feathers, abnormal body temperature higher metabolic and blood flow rates, greater digestive capacity etc.
4. *p53* gene of human directs damaged cells to stop reproducing, thereby esulting in cell death. This gene helps avert cancer by preventing cells with DNA damage from dividing. But it also suppresses the division of stem cell which allows the body to renew and replace deteriorating tissues during aging. Therefore this is an examples of *antagonistic pleiotropy*, in which the expression of a single gene causes completing effects, some of which are beneficial and some of which are detrimental to the fitness of an organism. This idea is called antagonistic pleiotropy. This gene is not eliminated through natural selection.

## 6.15 PROBLEMS ON ALLELISM

### Problem 1

In rabbits full colour (C), himalayan ($C^h$) and albinism ($C^a$) for a series of multiple alleles with dominance in the order given. What will be the appearance of the offspring of the following crosses?

(a) Coloured × Himalayan (both homozygous) (b) $F_2$ from the above cross.

(c) Himalayan × Albino (both homozygous) (d) $F_2$ from above.

(e) $F_1$ from (a) × $F_1$ from (c)

**Solution :**

**(a)**

Coloured × Hymalyan (both homozygous)

$P_1$ : $CC$ $C^h C^h$

$F_1$ : $CC^h$
(Coloured phenotype heterozygote)

**(b)**

$P_2$ : $CC^h$ × $CC^h$

Gametes : (C) ($C^h$) (C) ($C^h$)

$F_2$ : $CC$ $CC^h$ $CC^h$ $C^hC^h$

Coloured Himalayan

The phenotypic ratio 3 coloured : 1 Himalayan

**(c)**

Himalayan × Albino (both homozygous)

$P_1$ : $C^hC^h$ $C^aC^a$

$F_1$ : $C^hC^a$
(himalayan heterozygote)

**(d)**

$P_2$ : $C^hC^a$ × $C^hC^a$

Gametes : ($C^h$) ($C^a$) ($C^h$) ($C^a$)

$F_2$ : ($C^hC^h$) ($C^hC^a$) ($C^hC^a$) ($C^aC^a$)

Himalayan Albino

The phenotypic ratio 3 Himalayan : 1 Albino

**(e)** Crosses between two $F_1$ heterozygotes.

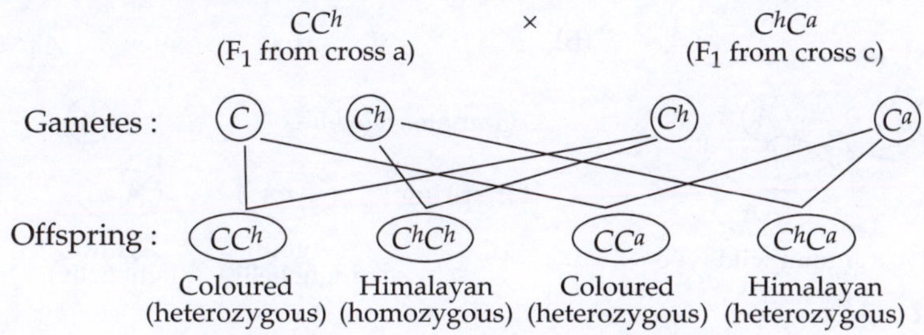


Phenotypic ratio 2 coloured : 2 Himalayan

### Problem 2

What are the genotypes of the parents in the following crosses in rabbits?

(a) Wild type × Wild type giving ¾ Wild, ¼ Himalayan.

**[Ans :** $CC^h \times CC^h$]

(b) Wild type × Wild type giving ¾ Wild, ¼ Gray.

**[Ans :** $CC^{ch} \times CC^a$ or $CC^{ch} \times CC^h$]

(c) Wild type × Himalayan giving ½ Wild,¼ Himalayan, ¼ Albino.

**[Ans :** $CC^a \times C^hC^a$]

### Problem 3

What will be the appearance of the offspring from the following crosses in rabbits.

(a) $CC^h \times CC^a$

**[Ans :** ¾ wild and ¼ gray]

(b) $C^{ch}C^h \times C^hC^h$

**[Ans :** 1:1 light gray and himalayan]

(c) $C^hC^a \times C^{ch}C^{ch}$

**[Ans :** All light gray]

(d) $CC^h \times C^{ch}C^h$

**[Ans :** 2 coloured : 1 light gray : 1 himalayan]

### Problem 4

In mice, the following genes affecting coat color form a series of multiple alleles $A^Y$ = yellow, $A^L$ = agouti (light belly), $A$ = agouti (light belly wild type), $a^t$ = black and tan (black back light belly), a = black (non agouti), $Aa^t$ = agouti with light belly.

What will be the appearance of the offspring of the following crosses?

(a) $A^LA \times AA$

(b) $A^LA^L \times Aa$

(c) $Aa^t \times Aa$

(d) $A^LA \times a^ta$

(e) $A^Ya \times aA^L$

(f) $A^Ya \times Aa^t$

(g) $A^Ya^t \times Aa^t$

**Solution :**

**(a)** $A^LA \times AA$

Gametes : $(A^L)$ $(A)$ $(A)$

Offspring : $A^LA$ — Agouti light belly; $AA$ — Agouti wild type

**(b)** $A^LA^L \times Aa$

Gametes : $(A^L)$ $(A)$ $(a)$

Offspring : $A^LA$ — Agouti (light belly); $A^La$ — Agouti (light belly)

**(c)** $Aa^t \times Aa$

Gametes : $(A)$ $(a^t)$ $(A)$ $(a)$

Offspring : $AA$ — Agouti (wild); $Aa^t$ — Agouti (wild); $Aa$ — Agouti (wild); $a^ta$ — black & tan

**(d)** $A^LA \times a^ta$

Gametes : $(A^L)$ $(A)$ $(a^t)$ $(a)$

Offspring : $A^La^t$ — Agouti light belly; $Aa^t$ — Agouti wild; $A^La$ — Agouti light belly; $Aa$ — Agouti wild

**(e)** $A^YA \times aA^L$

Gametes : $(A^Y)$ $(A)$ $(A^L)$ $(a)$

Offspring : $A^Ya$ — yellow; $A^YA^L$ — yellow; $Aa$ — Agouti wild; $AA^L$ — Agouti light belly

**(f)** $A^Ya \times Aa^t$

Gametes : $(A^Y)$ $(a)$ $(A)$ $(a^t)$

Offspring : $A^YA$ — yellow; $A^Ya^t$ — yellow; $Aa$ — wild agouti; $a^ta$ — black-tan

**(g)** $A^Ya^t \times Aa^t$

Gametes : $(A^Y)$ $(a^t)$ $(A)$ $(a^t)$

Offspring : $A^YA$ — yellow; $A^Ya^t$ — yellow; $Aa^t$ — Agouti light belly; $a^ta$ — tan-black

### ➧ Problem 5

What are the genotypes of the parents in the following crosses?

(a) Agouti light belly × Agouti light belly giving ¼ agouti, ½ agouti light belly and ¼ black tan.

(b) Agouti light belly × Agouti giving ½ agouti light belly, ¼ agouti and ¼ black.

(c) Albino × Agouti giving all agouti light belly in $F_1$. Also find $F_2$ phenotypes, where "C" is color gene and "c" is its recessive non-color gene.

**Solution :**

**(a)** $Aa^t \times Aa^t$

Gametes : (A) ($a^t$) (A) ($a^t$)

Offspring : $AA$ — Wild; $Aa^t$, $Aa^t$ — Agouti light belly; $a^ta^t$ — tan-black

**(b)** $A^La \times Aa$

Gametes : ($A^L$) (a) (A) (a)

Offspring : $A^LA$, $A^La$ — Agouti light belly; $Aa$ — Agouti; $aa$ — black

**(c)** $cc\,a^t a^t$ (albino) × $CC\,AA$ (agouti)

$F_1$ : $Cc\,Aa^t$

All agouti light belly

$P_2$ : $Cc\,Aa^t \times Cc\,Aa^t$

Offspring :

| ♀ \ ♂ | (CA) | (cA) | ($Ca^t$) | ($ca^t$) |
|---|---|---|---|---|
| (CA) | $CC\,AA$ agouti | $Cc\,AA$ agouti | $CC\,Aa^t$ light agouti | $Cc\,Aa^t$ light agouti |
| (cA) | $Cc\,AA$ agouti | $cc\,AA$ albino | $Cc\,Aa^t$ light agouti | $cc\,Aa^t$ albino |
| ($Ca^t$) | $CC\,Aa^t$ agouti | $Cc\,Aa^t$ light agouts | $CC\,a^t a^t$ tan black | $Cc\,a^ta^t$ tan black |
| ($ca^t$) | $Cc\,Aa^t$ light agouti | $cc\,Aa^t$ albino | $Cc\,a^t a^t$ tan black | $cc\,a^ta^t$ albino |

Phenotypic ratio : Wild agouti $= \frac{3}{16}$

Light belly agouti $= \frac{6}{16}$

Colored tan black $= \frac{3}{16}$

Albino $= \frac{4}{16}$

**Problem 6**

In maize, there are several factors that affect plant colour. Three of these are sun red, weak sun red and dilute sun red with decreasing intensities in order named. Following are the results of crosses between three types.

(a) Sun red × Dilute sun red = all sun red in $F_1$ and 998 sun red : 314 dilute sun red in $F_2$, *i.e.*, 3:1.

(b) Weak Sun red × Dilute sun red gave all weak sun red in $F_1$ and 1300 weak sun red : 420 dilute sun red in $F_2$, *i.e.*, 3:1.

(c) Sun red × Weak sun red gave all sun red in $F_1$ and 71 sun red and 16 weak sun red in $F_2$, *i.e.*, 3:1.

Explain three results stating the relationship among three plant colours.

**Solution :**

Suppose Sun red = $S$

weak sun red = $S^w$

dilute sun red = $S^d$

**(a)** $SS$ (Sun red) × $S^d S^d$ (dilute sun red)

in $F_1$ all are $SS^d$ or sun red

When in $F_1 \times F_2$ crossed

$SS^d \times SS^d$

Offspring : $SS$ $SS^d$ $SS^d$ — 3 weak sun red; $S^dS^d$ — 1 dilute sun red

**(b)** $S^wS^w$ (weak sun red) × $S^d S^d$ (dilute sun red)

in $F_1$ all are $S^wS^d$ *i.e.* weak sun red

When in $F_1 \times F_1$ is crossed

$S^wS^d \times S^wS^d$

Offspring : $S^wS^w$ $S^wS^d$ $S^wS^d$ — 3 weak sun red; $S^dS^d$ — 1 dilute sun red

**(c)** $SS$ (sun red) × $S^wS^w$ (weak sun red)

in $F_1$ all are $SS^w$ or sun red

When, $F_1 \times F_1$ is crossed

$SS^w \times SS^w$

Offspring : $SS$ $SS^w$ $SS^w$ — 3 sun red; $S^wS^w$ — 1 weak sun red

### ➧ Problem 7

What will be the phenotype, as to blood groups of offspring of parents of the following genotypes for blood group?

$I^Ai \times I^Bi$ $\quad$ $I^AI^B \times I^Bi$ $\quad$ $I^Bi \times I^Bi$

**Solution :**

$I^Ai \times I^Bi$

| $I^A$ | $i$ | ♀ / ♂ |
|---|---|---|
| $I^AI^B$ AB-group | $I^Bi$ B-group | $I^B$ |
| $I^Ai$ A-group | $ii$ O-group | $i$ |

$I^AI^B \times I^Bi$

| $I^A$ | $I^B$ | ♀ / ♂ |
|---|---|---|
| $I^AI^B$ AB-group | $I^BI^B$ B-group | $I^B$ |
| $I^Ai$ A-group | $I^Bi$ B-group | $i$ |

$I^Bi \times I^Bi$

| $I^B$ | $i$ | ♀ / ♂ |
|---|---|---|
| $I^BI^B$ B-group | $I^Bi$ B-group | $I^B$ |
| $I^Bi$ B-group | $ii$ O-group | $i$ |

### ➧ Problem 8

If a person of blood group B marries one belonging to group-O. What will be the blood group of their children?

**Solution :**

Person belonging to B-blood group would have the genotype $I^BI^B$ or $I^Bi$ and the person belonging to O-blood group would have the genotype –ii.

When $I^BI^B \times ii$

$F_1$ $\quad$ $I^Bi$

All would be of B blood group

When the cross is $I^Bi \times ii$

$F_1 = I^Bi$ and $ii$

½ of the children would be B-blood group

Other ½ of the children would be O-blood group.

### Problem 8

In the three following problems on blood groups, determine genotypes of the parent.

(a) One parent is group A and the other group B but all four groups are represented among the children.

(b) Both parents are group-A but three-fourth of the children belong to group-A and one fourth to group-O

(c) One parent is AB and the other is B but of the children, one fourth are A, one fourth AB and one half B.

**Solution :**

**(a)**

$I^Ai \times I^Bi$

| | | | | |
|---|---|---|---|---|
| Children | $I^AI^B$ | $I^Ai$ | $I^Bi$ | $ii$ |
| Blood group | AB | A | B | O |

**(b)**

$I^Ai \times I^Ai$

| | | | | |
|---|---|---|---|---|
| Children | $I^AI^A$ | $I^Ai$ | $I^Ai$ | $ii$ |
| Blood group | A | A | A | O |

¾ group-A ¼ group-O

**(c)**

$I^AI^B \times I^Bi$

| | | | | |
|---|---|---|---|---|
| Children | $I^AI^B$ | $I^BI^B$ | $I^Bi$ | $I^Ai$ |
| Blood group | AB | B | B | A |

¼ group-AB ½ group-B ¼ group-A

### Problem 10

In the two following cases of disputed paternity, determine the probable father of the child.

(a) The mother belongs to group-B, the child to O, one possible father to A and the other to AB.

(b) The mother belonging to group B, the child is AB. Who is possible father A or B?

**Solution :**

(a) The mother belonging to group B

So, the genotype is $I^BI^B$ or $I^Bi$

Child is group-O.

So, the genotype of the child is *ii*. If the father is AB, his genotype would be $I^AI^B$, if his mother is B, his child would be either A, AB or B but not O because he has no genes for i to produce homozygosity ii to his child. Therefore AB group person would not be father of that child.

If the father is blood group-A his genotype would be $I^AI^A$ or $I^Ai$.

The genotype $I^Ai$ can produce a homozygous *ii* child if the mother is $I^Bi$.

Therefore, the person belonging to Blood group A ($I^Ai$) would be actual father of the child.

(b) Mother is belonging to blood group B, her genotype would be $I^BI^B$ or $I^Bi$.

The child is belonging to AB blood group the genotype would be $I^AI^B$.

If the father is A, his genotype is $I^AI^A$ or $I^Ai$ and if the father is B his genotype is $I^BI^B$ or $I^Bi$

When Father and mother both B group

$$B \times B$$

$$I^BI^B \text{ or } I^Bi \times I^BI^B \text{ or } I^Bi$$

They would have the children with genotype $I^BI^B$ or $I^Bi$, *i.e.*, group B and also in some cases *ii*, *ie* group-O.

But the child is group AB. Therefore father would not be B-blood group.

$$A \text{ (father)} \times B \text{ (mother)}$$

$$I^AI^A \text{ or } I^Ai \times I^BI^B \text{ or } I^Bi$$

The genotype of their children would be $I^AI^B$, $I^Ai$, $I^Bi$, *ii*, i.e., AB, A, B or O group.

Therefore, the person belonging to group A is the actual father here.

### Problem 11

In the choice of donors for blood transfusion, a patient's brother or sister is often selected. Would these be more likely to be successful donors if both parents' belong to group AB or if both belonged to group-O? Explain.

**Solution :**

When parents are both AB then their genotype would be $I^AI^B$.

$$I^AI^B \times I^AI^B$$

| | | | | |
|---|---|---|---|---|
| Children genotypes | $I^AI^A$ | $I^AI^B$ | $I^AI^B$ | $I^BI^B$ |
| Blood group | A | AB | AB | B |

Brothers and sisters would be A, AB or B. So, when they are selected they likely to be successful but not for every case.

But when both parents are O-group then their genotype would be ii.

Their all children would be *ii, i.e.*, O-group then, the brother and sister is successful to donate blood at every case.

## Chapter Glossary/Key Terms

**Codominance :** A pattern of inheritance in which two alleles are both expressed in the heterozygous condition.

**Histocompatibility antigens :** Family of proteins that determine the ability of one individual accepts tissue or cell grafts from another.

**Histocompatibility genes :** The genes involved in the production of histocompatibility antigens.

**Masaic dominance :** The genes behave as though they consist of at least two components and two different phenotypes of two different traits.

**Multiple allele :** When the same gene exists in two or more alleles within a population.

**Pheotropy :** The phenomenon whereby a single mutant affects several apparently unrelated aspects of the phenotype.

**Pseudoallele :** Genes that are not functionally but structurally allelic. Within gene families, pseudoalleles are alleles that are not expressed.

**Secretors :** These are antigens present in the saliva and body fluid.

**Universal donor :** Human O-group blood can be given to any other groups but cannot receive blood except its own.

**Universal recipient :** Human AB-group blood can not be given to other group except its own but can receive blood from other groups.

## Exercise

**A. Long answer type questions :**

1. Define multiple allele. What are the characteristics of multiple alleles?
2. "Coat colours of rabbit exhibit multiple allele series" - explain
3. How the blood groups of human beings are genotypically and phenotypically controlled? Describle the patterns of inheritance of blood groups in humans.
4. What are secretor alleles? How these alleles are inherited? What is the difference in antigenic constituents of secretors and ABO antigens.
5. Describe the chemistry of antigin – A, B and O. How do these antigens are derived from the precursor H substance?
6. Explain whether ABO locus is explained as closely linked alleles or a multiple allele series.
7. What do you mean by subtypes in A blood group? How does the AB group divided into subgroups?
8. What do you mean by Rh+ve person? What is pseudoallele? Why Rh genes are regarded as pseudoalleles?
9. What antigenes and antibodies are required to designated Rhessus blood group in human?
10. Describe defferent genetic conpositions and their antigenic constituents used in both Wiener's and Fisher's views.
11. Describe the clinical importance of Rh factor.

12. Describe the self sterility multiple allelic series in tobacco, also describe its inheritance.
13. Describe the genetic regulation of MN blood group in human beings.
14. How do *Hh* allele regulates the ABO blood group system?
15. What is HLA? What is its importance .
16. What is mosaic dominance? Describe the inheritance of complex "R" - locus in maize.
17. Described the multiple allelic series of eye colour in *Drosophila*.
18. What is pleotropism? Give an example and cite the pleiotropic effects.
19. In about 85% of Europeans knowns as *secretors,* antigen-A or B found in saliva and other body fluids if it occurs in blood, whereas 15% do not have an antigen in saliva and are known as *nonsecretors.* If *S* (secretor) is dominant to *s* (nonsecretor) and *S* and *s* are inherited independently of the classical blood-group alleles, calculate the proportion of offspring from the following matings which would be expected to give A or B reactions in salwa.

    (i) AB secretor (*Ss*) × O (Ss)

    (ii) O (*ss*) × AB secretor (Ss)
20. A sibship of seven children gave the following reactions to Rh-testing sera.

| | Anti-C | Anti-c | Anti-D | Anti-E | Anti-e |
|---|---|---|---|---|---|
| Child 1 | – | + | – | – | + |
| 2 | + | + | + | + | + |
| 3 | – | + | – | – | + |
| 4 | – | + | + | + | + |
| 5 | + | + | + | – | + |
| 6 | + | + | + | + | + |
| 7 | – | + | + | + | + |

Give the probable genotypes of the children and the two parents and predict the reactions of parent-1 and parent-2 to the testing sera.

21. Which of the following matings would run the risk of having a baby with erythroblastosis fetalis?

| | ♀ | ♂ |
|---|---|---|
| A | $\frac{CDe}{cde}$ | $\frac{cde}{cde}$ |
| B | $\frac{cde}{cde}$ | $\frac{cDe}{cde}$ |
| C | $\frac{Cde}{cde}$ | $\frac{CDe}{cDE}$ |
| D | $\frac{cDe}{CDe}$ | $\frac{Cde}{cde}$ |

In which mating would the risk be greatest?

22. A man belongs to AB blood group while his wife is B blood group. Predict the probable genotypes and phenotypes of their offspring.

### B. Short answer type questions.

1. Define multiple allele?
2. How you can determine the coat colours in rabbit *viz* agouti, chichilla, Himalayan and albino are in multiple allelic series?
3. Give the phenotypes and different genotypes of multiple allelic series of coat color in rabbit.
4. If the number of genes in a multiple allelic series is "n" what would be the total possible its genotypes?
5. What are the multiple allelic series of L-gene locus in wing character of *Drosophila?* Give its inheritance pattern.
6. What antigens are responsible for ABO blood group and how these antigens determine the ABO blood group system?
7. What are the criteria for the transfusion of blood?
8. Why A-group of blood can not be given to B group?
9. Why AB group is universal recepient and O-group is universal donor?
10. A woman of blood group-AB marries a man of blood group-A whose father was of group-O. What is the probability that

    (a) their two children will both be a group-A?

    (b) one children will be of group-B, the other of group -O

    (c) the first child will be a son of group AB and the second child a son of group B.

11. If a mother and her child belong to blood group-O, what blood group could the father not belong to?
12. A man of what blood group could not be the father of a child of blood type-AB?
13. Under what circumstances can be phenotypes of the ABO system be used to refute paternity.
14. What are secretor and non secretor alleles? How do they inherited? What is the difference between secretor antigen and ABO blood group antigens?
15. What is null gene?
16. What is the precursor molecule of ABO blood group antigens? What are the differences from the precursor?
17. Distinguish A, B, O and H-subtances in blood group system.
18. How could you distinguish different A-group antigens? What are the AB subgroups?
19. What is pseudoallele?
20. What is rhesus antigen?
21. What do you mean by Rh+ve and R–ve?
22. What antigens and antibodies are found in Rh system? Which of the antibody of the Rh-antigen is not found in Rh system of blood grouping?
23. Which alleles are responsible for determining Rh blood group system? Of there which gene is essential for Rh+ve blood gmpt?
24. Why Rh genes are regarded as pseudoalleles?
25. What is erythroblastosis fetatis? What are the causes of this disease?
26. What do you meant by self sterility allele? Give example.
27. Why self sterility allele is called oppositional allele?
28. Waht is MN blood group systems? What allleles control this blood groups system?
29. How do S-s alleles give different conbinations of MN systems?
30. What is H-antigen? How do the *H-h* alleles are related to ABO blood group systems?
31. What is Bombay phenotype? What is its genetic and antigenic constitutions?
32. What enzymes are responsible for the determination of blood antigen A and antigen B?
33. What histocompatibility genes! What is histocompatibility haplotype?
34. Why $F_2$ individuals usually reject the $F_1$ graft tissue but tissues of $F_2$ individuals usually not be rejected by $F_1$ hosts?
35. What do you meant by mosaic dominance? Give example.
36. Why the eye colors in *Drosophila* show pseudodominance?
37. What do you mean by pleotropism and pleiotropic effect? Give an example.

**Write Short notes :**

1. Multiple allele, ABO-antigens, H-substance, Secretor alleles, Pseudoallele, Erythroblastosis fetalis, Sterility alleles, oppositional alleles, *H-h*-alleles, Mosaic dominance, Pleiotropic affect.

# 7

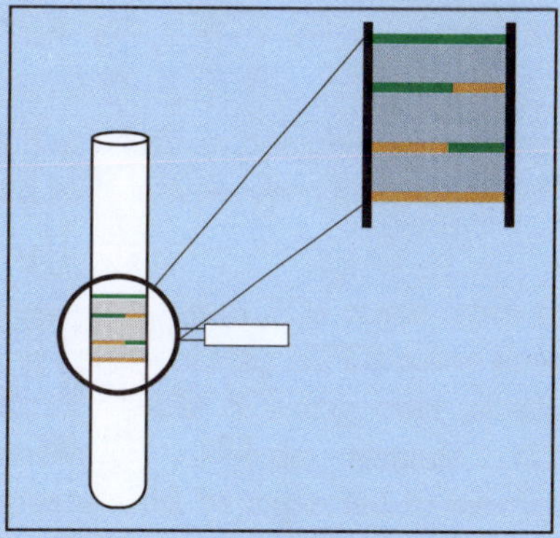

# Linkage and Crossing – over

**CHAPTER AGENDA**

## 7.1 CONCEPT

Certain genes, located on the same chromosome tend to remain linked together while passing from one generation to another. This tendency of certain genes to stick together in the way in which they entered the cross has been termed as **linkage** and such genes are called **linked genes**.

## 7.2 COMPLETE LINKAGE IN *DROSOPHILA*

In *Drosophila*, ordinary normal fly has gray body and long wing. But a stock can be got having the recessive mutations black and vestigial; both in the same chromosome.

$B$ = gray body (dominant)

$b$ = black body (recessive)

$V$ = long wing (dominant)

$v$ = vestigial wing (recessive)

When a pure gray-long $\left(\frac{B\,V}{B\,V}\right)$ is crossed with a black vestigial $\left(\frac{b\,v}{b\,v}\right)$, the gametes of the two parents combine, giving offspring of genotype $\frac{B\,V}{b\,v}$.

Now if we take a hybrid male having a genotype $\frac{B\,V}{b\,v}$ and a test cross is performed with a female having genotype $\frac{b\,v}{b\,v}$, the result would be as follows :

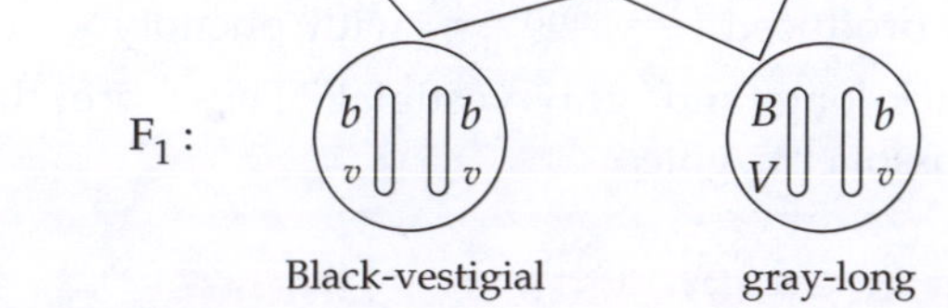


In *Drosophila*, crossing over is rarely or never taken place in the males. Therefore, male hybrid would produce only two kinds of gametes and only two kinds of offspring would be produced like the two parental combinations in 1:1 ratio. This shows that gray body and long wings entering the dihybrid cross, the two genes are linked together and do not abide by the Mendel's principles of Independent Assortment.

Cytological study of spermatogenesis in male *Drosophila* made by Darlington and others disclosed that the homologous chromosomes undergo as usual pairing in the spermatocytes, no chiasma are established. 4 chromatids lying parallel to one another and at anaphase-I, it goes to each pole.

## 7.3 INCOMPLETE LINKAGE IN *DROSOPHILA* (OR CROSSING-OVER)

Morgan (1919) in his experiment when a female hybrid gray-long fly is crossed with a black-vestigial pure recessive male. The following results were obtained.

Gray-long – 41.5%

Black-vestigial – 41.5%

Gray-vestigial - 8.5%

Black-long – 8.5%

The result does not show the dihybrid test cross ratio (1:1:1:1). Therefore, the independent assortment is not sufficient to describe it.

Again if the genes were linked i.e., having on the same chromosome then all the offspring should be with parental combinations i.e., gray-long and black-vestigial in 1:1 ratio.

But in the result, the parental combinations gray-long and black-vestigial flies are more frequent, about 83% of the offspring. The association of the characters has been changed. This result could be explained as follows in Fig 7.1.

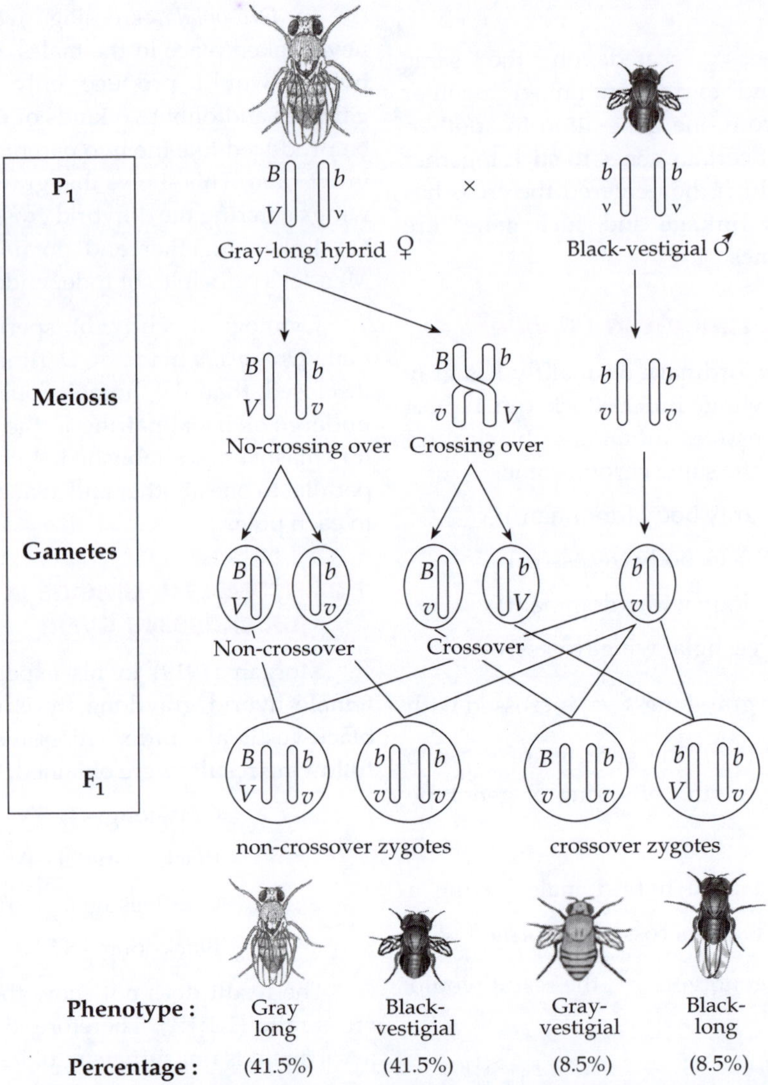


**Fig.7.1 :** *Incomplete linkage in Drosophila*

It is obvious that the two pairs of genes *B-b* and *V-v* have not assorted independently. The parental combinations are greatly exceeded the expected 50%, they remain combined or linked in 83% and the other 17% of the offspring were produced with association of changed characters are due to crossing over between these two genes during first meiotic division of spermatocytes.

Due to crossing over between the two genes, two types of cross over gametes could be produced ($\underline{b\ V}$) and ($\underline{B\ v}$) and after fertilization with ($\underline{b\ v}$) sperms, two types of zygotes could be produced $\left(\frac{b\ V}{b\ v} \text{ and } \frac{B\ v}{b\ v}\right)$ with phenotypes of black-long and gray-vestigial. These are the crossover zygotes.

## 7.4. CHARACTERISTICS OF LINKAGE

1. Linkage is an exception to Mendel's principle of independent assortment.

2. Linked genes are located in the same pair of chromosomes.
3. Lesser the distance between the linked genes, stronger is the linkage bond. Genes lying farther apart show less linkage.
4. Linked genes tend to be transmitted together from one generation to the other.
5. Separation of linked genes occurs very seldom.

## 7.5. LINKAGE GROUPS

If a certain gene '*X*' is linked to two other genes *Y* and *Z*, then it is true that *Y* and *Z* are linked. In plants or animals where several genes exist, crosses are rearranged to assertain the existence of linkage of pairs or of groups of several pairs of genes. The genes known to exist in a species and are thus divided into linkage groups. The haploid number of autosomes plus sex chromosome is the measure of linkage group.

In *Drosophila melanogaster*, 4 pairs of chromosomes, has (3 autosomes+X+Y) five linkage groups. *Pisum sativum* (2n = 14) has 7 linkage groups. Man has (2n = 46) 24 linkage groups. In mouse (2n = 40) has 21 linkage groups. In tomato (2n = 24) has 13 linkage groups.

## 7.6. RELATION BETWEEN LINKAGE AND CROSSING-OVER

1. Linkage is an exception to Mendel's principles of independent assortment, the crossing over is also the exceptions of independent assortment.
2. Linkage and crossing over are inversely related. The more distance between two genes on a chromosome, decreases the linkage but increases the crossing over between these genes.
3. Crossing over occurs between two non-sister chomatids of the homologous chromosomes and exchange of chromatin segment is involved. But in linkage, it is not involved.
4. New combinations of genes are involved in crossover gametes but in linkage the genes remain in their original combinations.

## 7.7. COUPLING AND REPULSION

Due to linkage, there is a tendency of dominant or recessive alleles to remain together and the result after performing test cross is different from the test cross of Mendelian independent assortment. This is called *genetic coupling*. W. Bateson (1905) explained the law of independent assortment in the experiment when *BbLl* hybrid is crossed with *bbll*, the ratio was not 1 : 1 : 1 : 1, it is 7 : 1; 1 : 7. [*B* = blue colour of sweet pea flower, *b* = red (recessive) *L* = round pollen, dominant over *l* = long pollen]. Here two dominant or recessive alleles came from same parents.

When two dominant alleles or recessive alleles came from different parents, they tend to remain separate, which is called **gametic repulsion** :- when *BBll* is crossed with *bbLL*, $F_1$ is *BblL* when it is crossed with *bbll* then the result is 1 : 7 : 7 : 1 ratio instead of expected dihybrid test-ratio 1 : 1 : 1 : 1.

Thus, coupling and repulsion appear to be the two aspects of the same phenomenon called linkage (Fig. 7.2).

## 7.8. CYTOLOGICAL DEMONSTRATION OF CROSSING OVER

### 7.8.1 Stern's experiment on *Drosophila*

Stern had a stain of *Drosophila* in which a portion of a Y-chromosome had through translocation become attached to the end of one of the X-chromosome forming an L-shaped body, can easily be distinguishable from normal rod like X-chromosome.

In another strain, one of the X-chromosome had broken into two approximately equal parts. The terminal portion containing the centromere remained in its normal position.

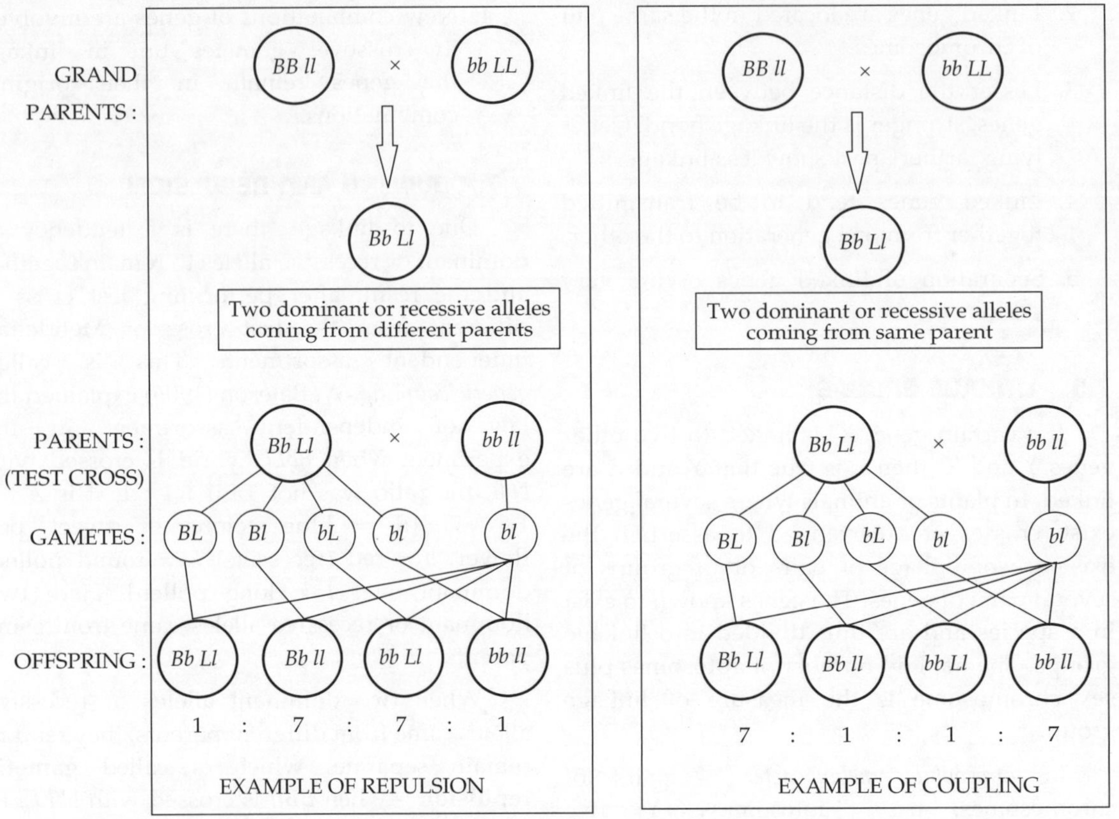


**Fig.7.2** : *Genetic coupling and Repulsion*

The other portion was translocated to one of the small fourth chromosome. The strain was viable, since the entire material of the X-chromosomes was present although in two separate pieces.

By crossing these strains, females were produced in which one X-chromosome showed one of these translocations and other X-chromosome from the other. It was thus possible to distinguish both the X-chromosomes in the same individual from each other and also from autosomes.

Stern made such female heterozygous taking two sex-linked mutations located in the X-chromosome.

*Car* – Carnation or dark red eye colour (recessive)

*Car*$^+$ – Red eye colour (Dominant)

*Bar* – Rod shaped eye (dominant)

*Bar*$^+$ – Rounded eye (recessive)

In Stern's experiment the modified females have such *Car* and *Bar* genes in the broken X-chromosome and their two normal alleles *Car*$^+$ and *Bar*$^+$ genes are remained in the X-chromosome bearing the translocated Y-segment.

Such females were breed to a male having both recessive genes (*Car* and *Bar*$^+$).

Only the female offspring were studied. There would be 4 types of gametes. Two non crossover gametes ($\frac{Car\ \ Bar}{}$ and $\frac{+\ \ +}{}$) and another two types of crossover gametes ($\frac{Car\ \ +}{}$ and $\frac{+\ \ Bar}{}$), if crossing over occurs in between *Car* and *Bar* genes (Fig. 7.3).

When the chromosomes of these offspring are examined under the microscope

1. The class of offspring which appear Carnation-Bar eye is found to have the broken X without the fragment of Y.
2. In the second class red-round eyed females are found to have the unbroken X-with the attached Y-fragment.
3. The third, Carnation-round eyed females have the unbroken X without an attached Y-chromosome.
4. In fourth class red-bar females have the broken X with an attached Y-fragment.

So, there was a complete correspondence between the genetic and cytological facts. In other words, genetic recombination was proved to be accompanied by cytological crossing over and actual exchange of chromatin material between homologous chromosomes.

### 7.8.2 Creighton and Mc. Clintock's experiment on Corn

H. S. Creighton and Barbara Mc.Clintock (1931) have obtained a plant, which has a knob on the 9$^{th}$ chromosome. This 9$^{th}$ chromosome was also involved in a reciprocal translocation with 8$^{th}$ chromosome.

*C* = coloured seed (dominant)

*c* = colourless seed (recessive)

*Wx* = Non-waxy endosperm (dominant)

*wx* = Waxy endosperm (recessive)

The plant is heterozygous for coloured aleurone and waxy endosperm character $\frac{C\ \ wx}{c\ \ Wx}$. The $\frac{C\ \ wx}{}$ chromosome carries a knob, while $\frac{c\ \ Wx}{}$ is knobless chromosome.

Such a plant was test crossed with plants homozygous recessive for both characters. From the hybrid two types of non-crossover gametes and six types of crossover gametes would be produced and 8 types of offspring can be observed (Fig. 7.4).

### 7.8.3 Meselson and Weigle's experiment using lambda phage

In their experiment they (1961) used two strains of lambda phage, one strain has the genetic markers *'c'* and *mi* at one of the chromosome and this chromosome was heavy because the phage strain was produced in *E.coli* containing $C^{13}$ and $C^{15}$ (heavy isotopes). Another strain was (+ +) for the markers and had light DNA (Fig. 7.5).

After double infection of these two strains, *E. coli* cells were grown in $C^{12}$ and $C^{14}$ contained medium. After lysis of the phage, particles are analyzed by CsCl density gradient centrifugation.

A wide band was observed, which indicated that the phage DNA ranged in density from heavy parental value to light parental value.

Recombinant phages (*c* +) and (+ *mi*) have been recovered which had the density close to heavy and light parental values respectively.

These experiments suggested the physical breakage and reunion of DNA during recombination.

## 7.9. FACTORS AFFECTING THE STRENGTH OF LINKAGE

The frequency of crossing over between genes *ie.,* the frequency of chiasma formation between their loci in the chromosome may be influenced by a number of physiological and environmental factors.

1. **Effect of Sex :** The frequency of crossing over depends upon the sex, e.g., in male *Drosophila,* does not get any crossing over according to Whitting Hill (1937-47).

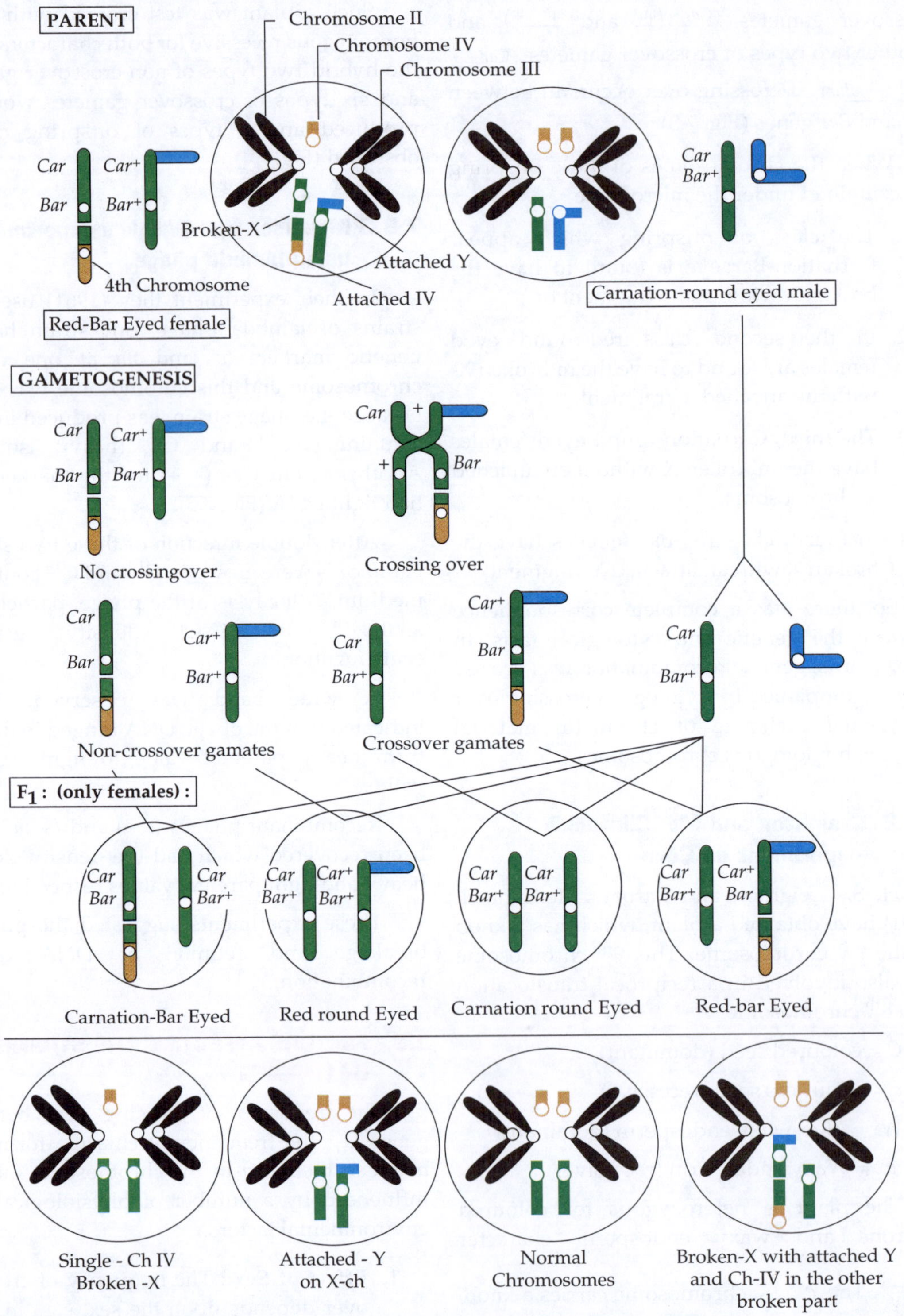


**Fig.7.3 :** *Cytological demostration of crossing over in Drosophila.*

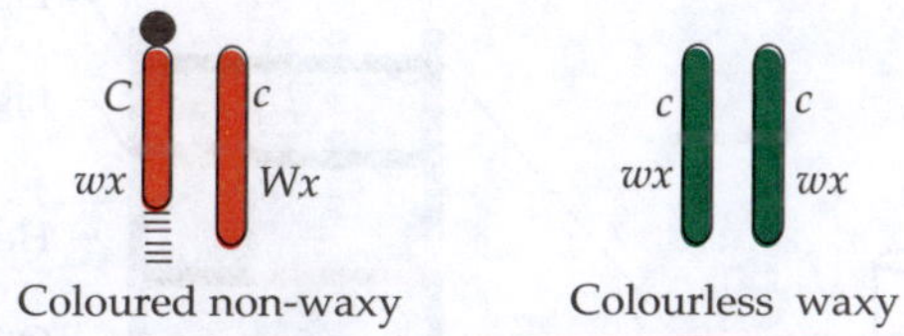


| | Gamates | Zygote | Phenotypes | Comments |
|---|---|---|---|---|
| C wx / c Wx<br>Non-crossover | C wx | c wx / C wx | Coloured waxy<br>Class I | No Crossing over |
| | c Wx | c wx / c Wx | Colourless non-waxy<br>Class II | No Crossing over |
| C wx / c Wx<br>Single crossover between knob & C | c Wx | c wx / c Wx | Colourless non-waxy<br>Class III | Knob was present in C (coloured) gene containing chromosome. But cytologically at metaphase I, the knob is observed and quadrivalent ring |
| | C wx | c wx / C wx | Coloured waxy<br>Like Class IV | At metaphase-I, presence of a ring of four chromosomes without a knob was associated, with 9th chromosome carrying translocation. |
| C wx / c Wx<br>Single crossover between C & *Wx* | C Wx | c wx / C Wx | Coloured non-waxy<br>Like Class V | Like Class-III |
| | c wx | c wx / c wx | Colourless waxy<br>Like Class VI | Like Class-IV |
| C wx / c Wx<br>Double crossover between knob & C and C & *Wx* | c wx | c wx / c wx | Colourless waxy<br>Like Class VII | Knob is also transferred to colourless gene which can be seen cytologically |
| | C Wx | c wx / C Wx | Coloured non-waxy<br>Like Class VIII | Absence of knob at the end even the gene C (coloured) is present |

**Fig.7.4 :** *Creighton and McClintock's experiment on corn for cytological demonstration of crossing-over.*

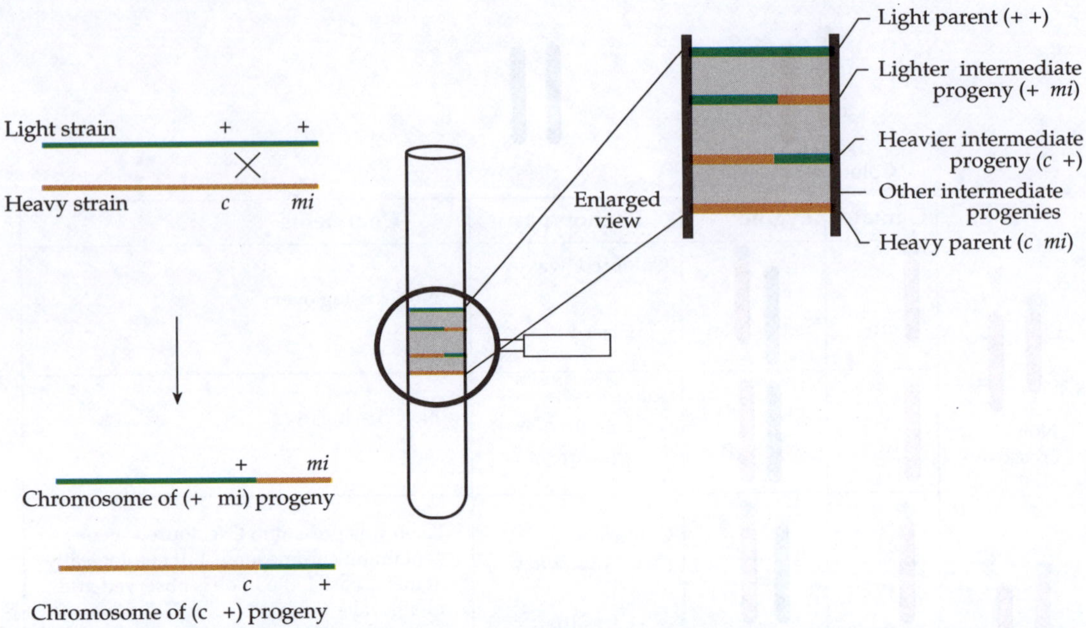


**Fig.7.5 :** *Meselson and Weigle's experiment using λ-phage for the demonstration of crossing-over.*

In silk worm, no crossing over occurs in female.

In some organisms, both sexes have crossing over. The presence of crossing over between any two genes may be identical in two sexes, in case of garden pea in equal percentage.

Percentage of CO is higher in females and lower in males as in case of mouse (Dunn 1920, Castle 1925).

The percentage of crossing over is higher in males and less in females in pigeon (Holloender 1938).

It has been pointed out by Hollander (1922) that, where linkage differences exist between two sexes, it is heterogametic sex.

2. **Effect of Age :** The potency of crossing over also varies with the age. Bridges (1915) showed the crossing over of *Drosophila,* which is markedly vary with age.

Collection of eggs over three periods *ie* 30 days intervals of 10 days and the region tested in second chromosome is in between black-purple, crossing over is 6%. The crossing over data of first 10 days is 5.9%, which is dropped in next 10 days results 1.8% during second 10 days and then 3.8% during third 10 days period. So, initial higher rate is followed by a mark of 1.8% after which again rises.

3. **Effect of temperature :** Plough (1917-21) and Stern (1926) had shown that temperature greatly affects on percentage of crossing over. Three genes in second chromosome *b*, *pr* and *c* (c = curled wing, *pr* = purple eye and *b* = black body) have been taken and crossing over picture is as follows:

At 9°C between *b* and *pr* = 13.6%,
*pr* and *c* = 25.5%.

At 20°C between *b* and *pr* = 6%,
*pr* and *c* = 19.6%

At 32°C between *b* and *pr* = 15.5%,

*pr* and *c* = 25.5%

4. **Effect of centromere :** Centromeres have some sorts of influence on crossing over. For example, if the centromere was at the left end of the chromosome, the chiasma would form near the left end of the chromosome toward the right end and first chiasma would form nearest to the centromere.

   If the centromere is centrally located the crossing over starts on either side of it and proceeds toward the end of the chromosome. Effect of centromere is indicated in *Drosophila* by the experiment of Beadle (1932) and Graubard (1932).

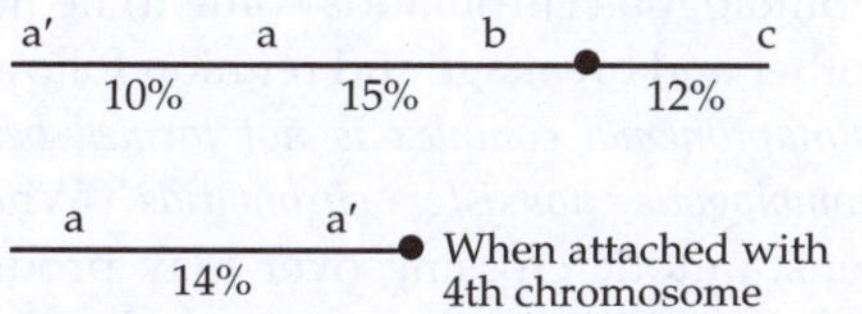


5. **Effect of Heterochromatin :** Heterochromatin is situated near about the centromere. The experiment was carried out on an X-chromosome in which a piece of heterochromatin was inserted in a median portion. The data obtained indicated that heterochromatin is mostly unsuitable than euchromatin in its response to environmental variability. So, the heterochromatin in an inert region and crossing over does not take place in this region. But when a piece of heterochromatin is translocated to the median portion, the crossing over percentage drops from 10% to 5%.

6. **Inter-chromosomal effect :** Sturtevant (1919) pointed out that decrease in percentage of crossing over between a pair of homologues increase the percentage of crossing over of unrelated homologues pair of chromosomes.

   Due to phenomenon of inversion the homozygote or heterozygote increases the percentage of crossing over in non-homologues chromosomes. It is seemed that a certain amount of potential energy is available for crossing over in a particular cell in each meiotic cell. But if one pair of homologous chromosomes did not utilize the amount of energy, other pair of chromosomes would utilize to increase the crossing over.

7. **Effect of chromosomal aberration or intra-chromosomal effect :** The internal rearrangement exists in heterozygous condition would be expected not only to the linear order of chromosomes but also to change the percentage of crossing over between it and its normal homologue. Frequently references were made on *Drosophila* that presence of suppressor reduces or eliminates the crossover type of offspring. They are shown to be inversion for the most part.

   Muller said that the crossover suppression has been known to be inversion heterozygote.

## 7.10 SINGLE AND DOUBLE CROSSING-OVER BETWEEN TWO GENE LOCI

Crossing-over involved between two linked genes at two points is called *two point crossing over*.

Single crossing-over occurs between two loci in every event. In reality, that will not happen, since crossing overs are random events such that no crossing over will occur in same events, double crossing over will occur in others and so on. But assume that it does happen. Crossing over occurs after chromosome duplication when each homologous chromosome is represented by two chromatids.

Single crossing over occurs between two loci among two non-sisters of the four chromatids. As a result, four classes of products would be obtained after meiosis. Half of them

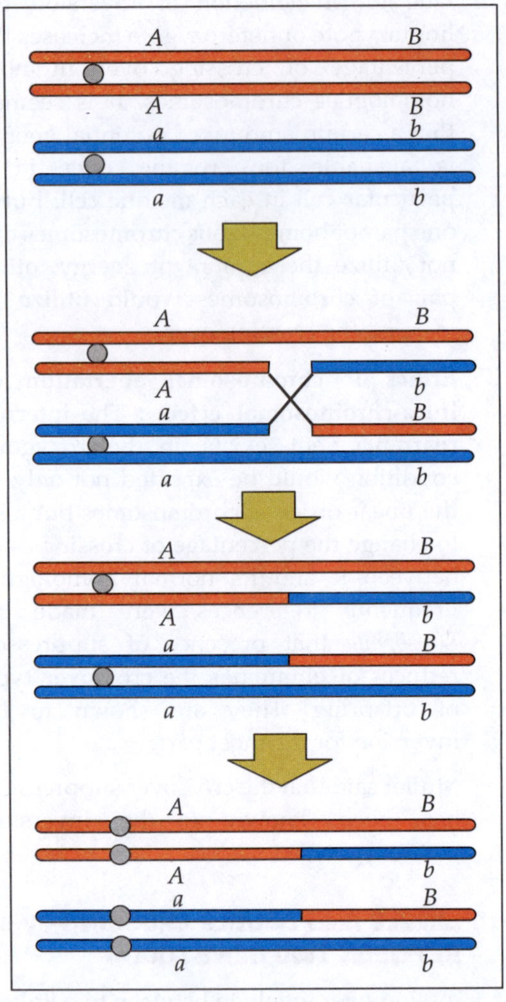


**Fig.7.6 :** *Single crossing-over between two genes.*

are parental combinations and half of them are recombinants (Fig. 7.6).

Double crossing over may occur in three different ways between two gene loci.

1. *Two-strand double crossing over* which occur when both cross-over involve the same two non-sister chromatids.
2. *Three-strand double crossing over*, in which the second cross-over involves one of the same two chromatids as the first cross-over plus one different chromatid.
3. *Four-strand double crossing over*, which occurs when the second cross-over involves the two chromatids not in the first crossover.

If the second cross-over in a letrad involves two chromatids at random irrespective of which chromatids were involved in the first crossing over, then the ratio of two-strand to three-strand to four-strand crossing over will be 1:2:1 (Fig. 7.7).

## 7.11 MITOTIC CROSSING OVER

Recombination, *i.e.*, the exchange of chromatin is a rare event in mitotic division. In fungus, *Aspergillus nidulans*, mitotic crossing over occurs about once in every one hundred cell divisions. During mitotic recombination, two homologous chromatids come to lie next to each other and breakage and reunion follow, but *here synaptonemal complex is not formed between the homologous nonsister chromatids*. When it happens, mitotic crossing over may produce a pair of recombinant chromosomes that have a new combination of alleles. If it occurs during an early stage of embryonic development, the daughter cells containing the recombinant chromosomes continue to divide many times to produce a patch of tissue in the adult. This may result in a portion of tissue with characteristics different from those of the rest of the organism.

Mitotic recombination was discovered by Curt Stern (1936), who noticed the occurrence of **twin spots** on the bodies of certain *Drosophila* strains. These strains carrying alleles for body colour and bristle morphology (Fig. 7.8).

$y$ = Yellow body colour (recessive)

$y^+$ = Grey body colour (dominant)

$sn$ = Singed morphology confers shorter body bristle (recessive)

$sn^+$ = Normal bristle (dominant)

A dihybrid with a genotype $\frac{y^+ \; sn}{y \; sn^+}$ is allowed to develop, it will have normal bristles and grey body colour. If a mitotic crossing over

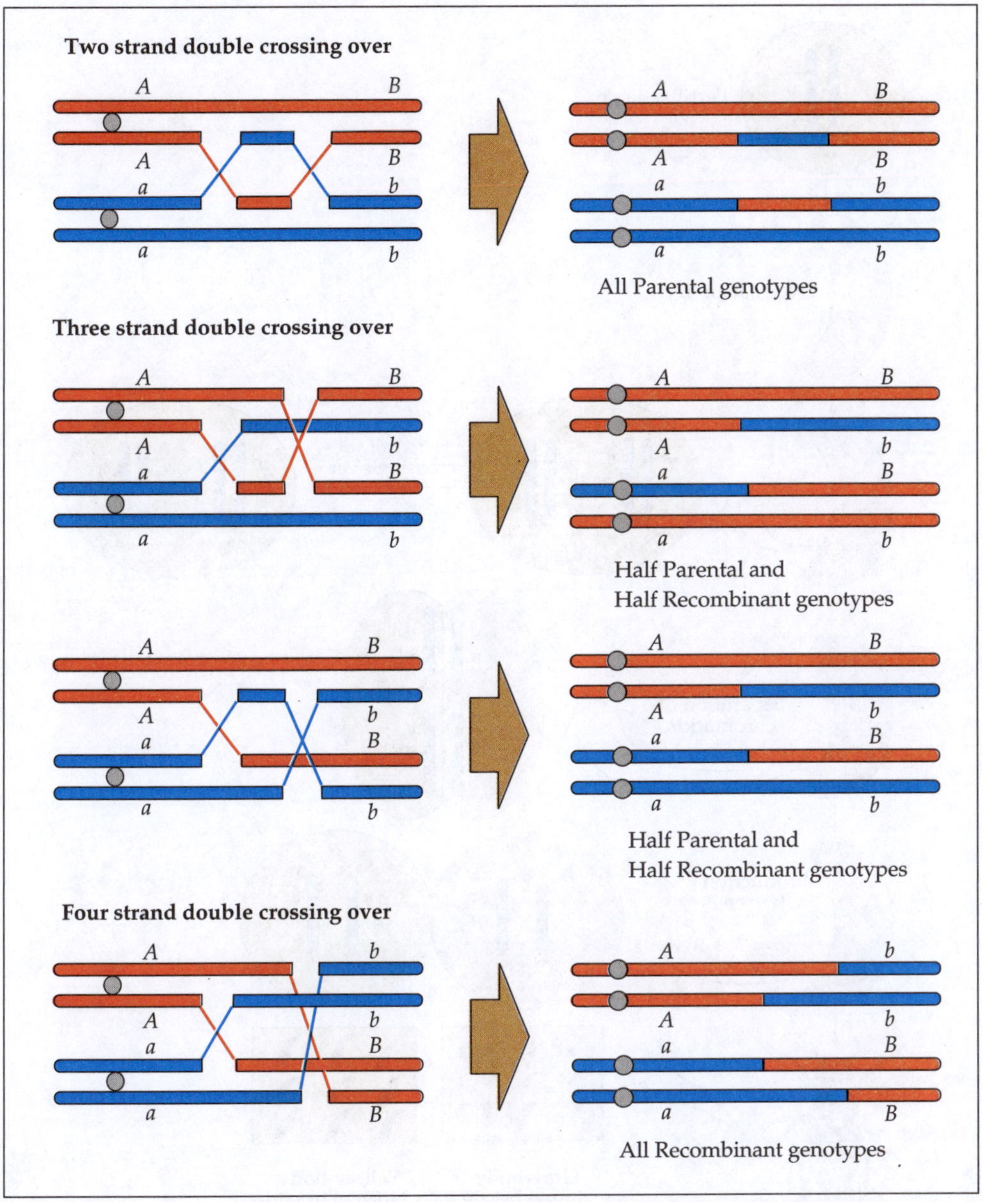


**Fig.7.7 :** *Double crossing over between two genes.*

occurs in a cell, then two cell lines would be resulted. One cell line would have a genotype $\frac{y^+ \ sn}{y^+ \ sn}$ and the other cell line would have the genotype $\frac{y \ sn^+}{y \ sn^+}$.

The former cell line gives rise to a group of cells with a phenotype grey body and singed bristles while the other would have a phenotype yellow body and normal bristles. These two groups of cells will produce twin spots side by side on the body of the fly.

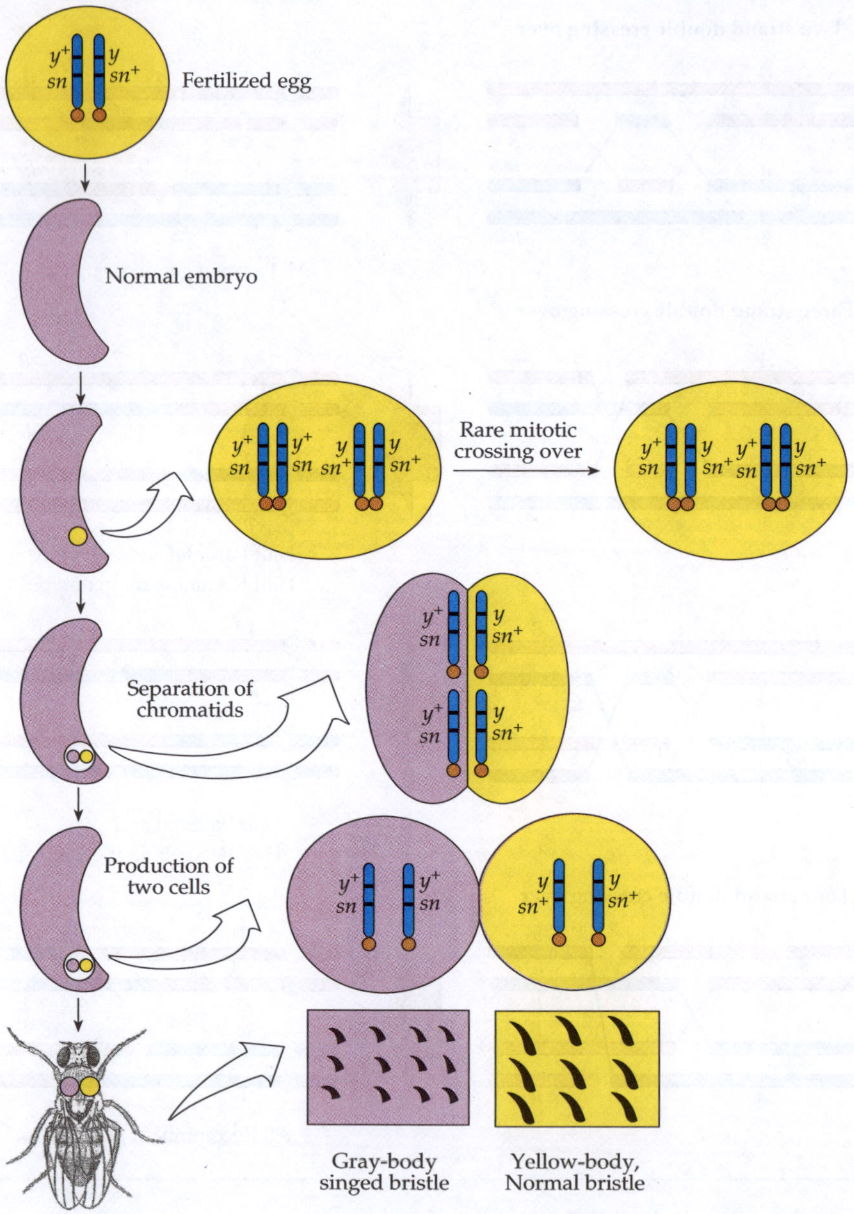


**Fig.7.8 :** *Mitotic crossing-over in Drosophila produces twin spotting.*

Mitotic crossing over has been used in fungal genetics supplemental or even a primary method for determining linkage relations.

## 7.12. SOLVED PROBLEMS ON LINKAGE AND CROSSING OVER

### Problem 1

Assume that genes $a$ and $b$ are linked and show 40% of recombination. If an $\frac{+\;\;+}{+\;\;+}$ individual is crossed with one that is $\frac{a\;\;b}{a\;\;b}$, what will be genotype of $F_1$? What gametes will the $F_1$ produce and in what proportion? If the $F_1$ is crossed with a double recessive, what will be the appearance and genotypes of the offspring?

**Solution :**

Linkage = 60%, Recombination = 40%

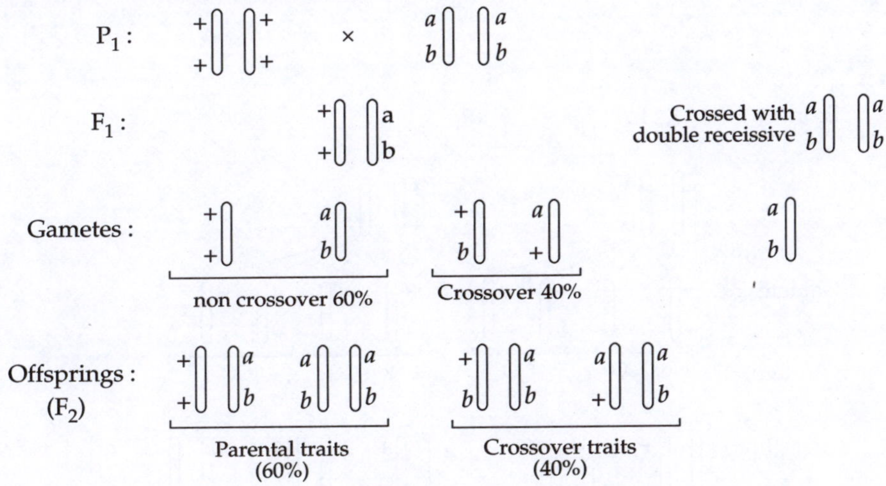


### Problem 2

If the original cross is $\frac{+\;b}{+\;b} \times \frac{a\;+}{a\;+}$, what will be the genotype of $F_1$? What gametes will it produce? If $F_1$ is crossed back with double recessive, what will be the appearance of the offspring?

**Solution :**

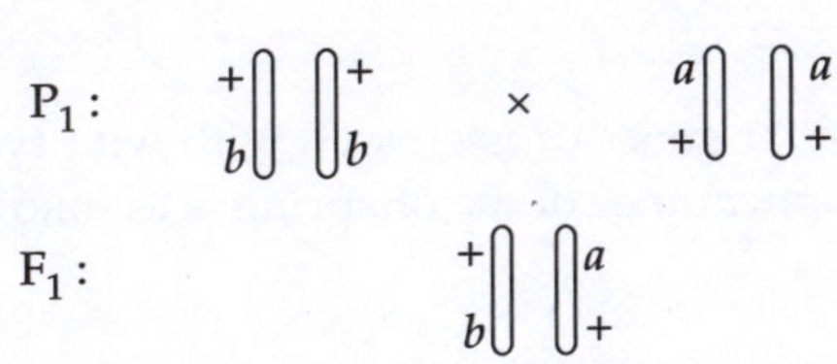


back cross with double recessive :

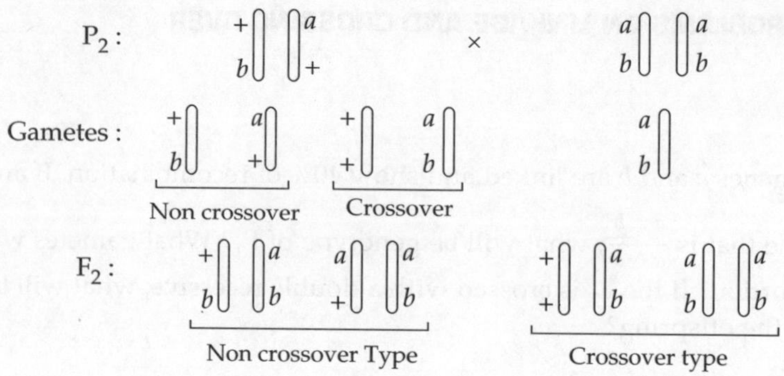


## ➧ Problem 3

What will be the appearance of the $F_2$ ($F_1 \times F_1$) of the crosses described in two preceding questions?

**Solution :**

From Q-1 $F_1$ × $F_1$

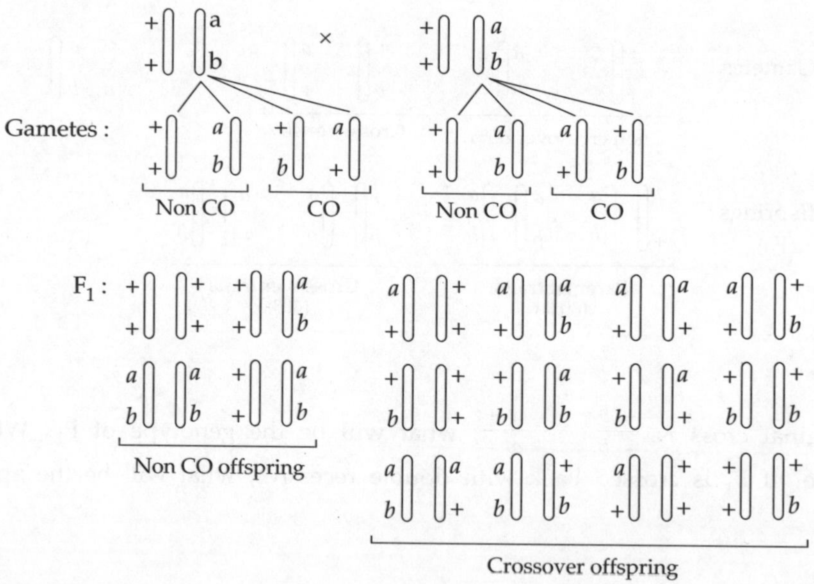


## ➧ Problem 4

An individual homozygous for genes *cd* is crossed with wild type and the F1 is crossed back with the double recessive. The appearance of the offspring is as follows.

| | |
|---|---|
| + + | 903 |
| *c d* | 897 |
| + *d* | 98 |
| *c* + | 102 |

Explain this result giving the strength of linkage between *c* and *d*. If assortment between c and d were independent, what would the result of this cross?

**Solution :**

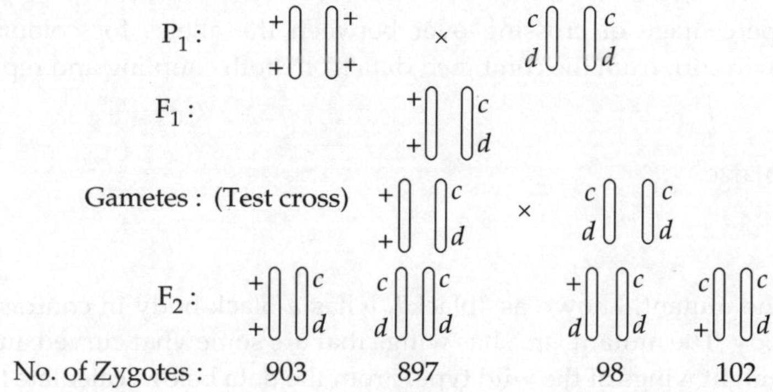


$$\therefore \text{Linkage} = \frac{1800}{1800 + 200} = 0.9 = 90\%$$

$$\text{Crossover value} = \frac{200}{2000} = 0.1 = 10\%$$

If assortment between *c* and *d* occurs, 4 kind of gametes will be produced in equal proportion and then the result would be as follows.

$$++ = \frac{2000}{4} = 500$$

$$cd = 500$$

$$c+ = 500$$

$$+d = 500$$

**➧ Problem 5**

If the cross in the preceeding question had been between a homologous *+d* individuals and a homologous *c+* one, what would be the result of the cross of F1 with a double recessive?

**Solution :**

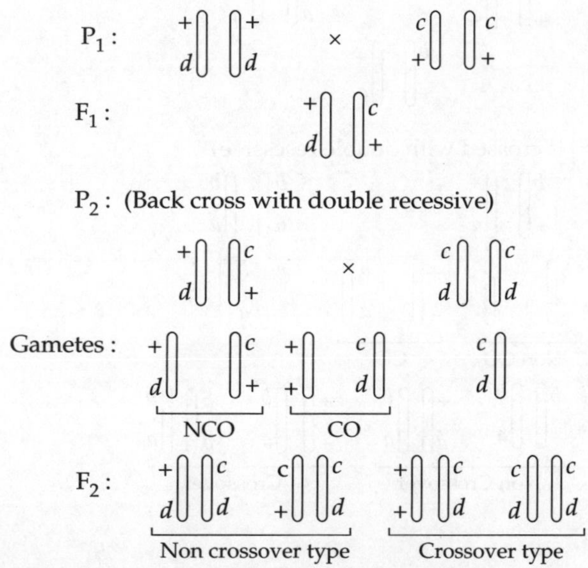

### Problem 6

Calculate the percentage of crossing over between the alleles for colourless aleurone and shunken endosperm in corn from the combined data from both coupling and repulsion experiment.

**Solution :**

See linkage in maize.

### Problem 7

In *Drosophila*, the mutant, known as "black", *b* has a black body in contrast to the wild type, which has a gray body. The mutant *'arc'*, has wings that are somewhat curved and bent downward, in contrast to the straight wings of the wild type. From the data below, calculate the crossover value between black and arc.

(a) Black straight (♀) × Gray arc (♂) then

Gray straight = 281 (++)

Gray arc = 335 (+*a*)

Black straight = 335 (*b*+)

Black arc = 239 (*ba*)

(b) Black arc × wild type then

$F_1$ (♀) × black arc (♂) gives

Gray straight = 1641 (++)

Gray arc = 1251 (+*a*)

Black straight = 1180 (*b*+)

Black arc = 1532 (*ba*)

**Solution :**

(a)

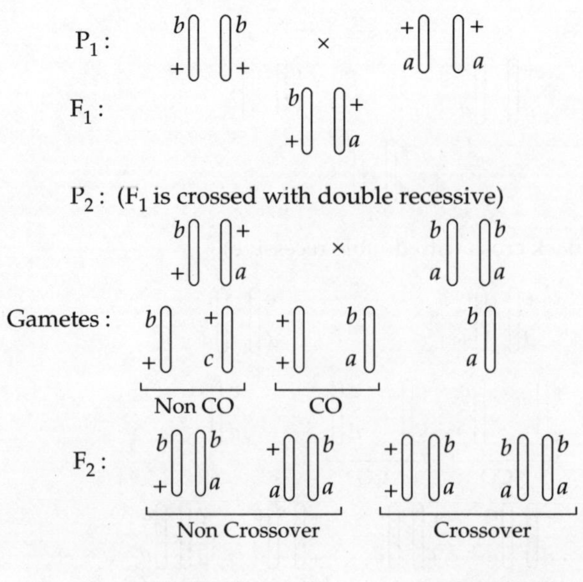

Here; Non-crossover type = 335 + 335 = 670

Non-crossover type = 281 + 239 = 520

Total = 1190

$$\text{Non crossover value} = \frac{670}{1190} = 0.571$$

Non crossover percentage = 57.1%

Linkage = 57.1%

Crossover value between black and arc genes = 100 – 57.1 = 42.9%

(b)

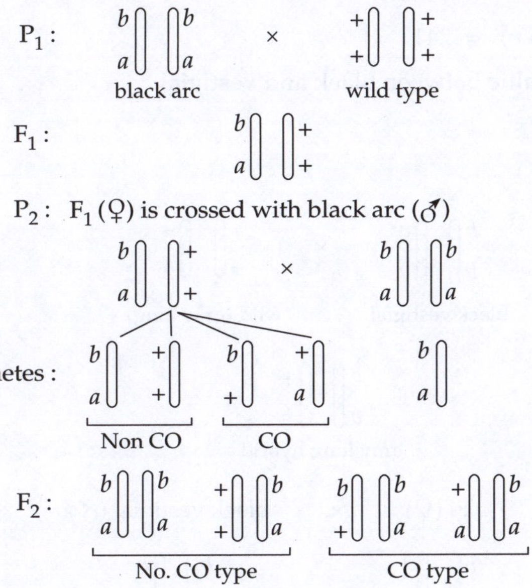


Here; Crossover type = 1180 + 1251 = 2431

Non-crossover type = 1641 + 1532 = 3173

Total = 2431 + 3173 = 5604

$$\text{Crossover value} = \frac{2431}{5604} \times 100\% = 43.4\%$$

Linkage value = 100 – 43.4 = 56.6%

### Problem 8

In the two following crosses, the parents are given, as in the previous question, together with the count of offspring of $F_1$(♀) × black vestigial (♂).

(a) Black vestigeal × wild type,

then $F_1$(♀) × black vestigial (♂)

Gray long 822 (++)

Gray vestigial 130 (+*v*)

Black log 161 (*b*+)

Black vestigial 652 (*bv*)

find the crossover value between black and vestigial.

(b) Black long × gray vestigeal

then $F_1$(♀) × black vestigial (♂)

Result : Gray long (+ +) = 283

Gray vestigial (+ *v*) = 1294

Black log (b +) = 1418

Black vestigial (b *v*) = 241

Calculate the crossover value between black and vestigial.

**Solution :**

**(a)**

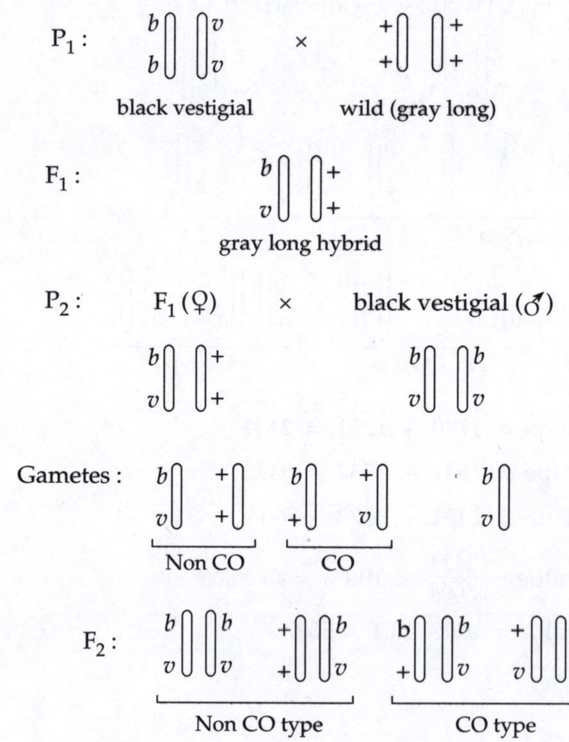


Here; parental (non-CO) types = 822 + 652 = 1474

Crossover types = 130 + 161 = 291

Total = 1474 + 291 = 1765

$$\text{Crossover value} = \frac{291}{1765} \times 100\% = 16.5\%$$

**(b)**

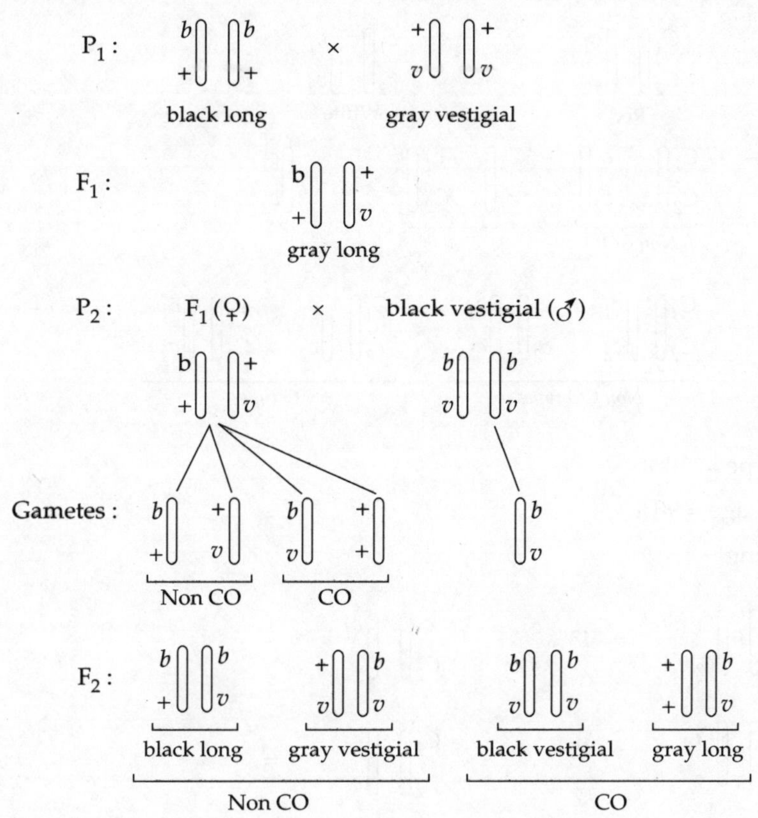


Here; Total number of crossover types = 283 + 241 = 525

Non crossover types = 1294 + 1418 = 2712

Total = 525 + 2712 = 3237

$$\text{Crossover value} = \frac{525}{3237} \times 100\% = 16.2\%$$

**➧ Problem 9**

What would be the $F_2$ ratio of red and white grains from a cross red with white if two duplicate factors for red were linked with a crossover value of 10% (Assume the red parent to be homozygous for both genes)?

**Solution :**

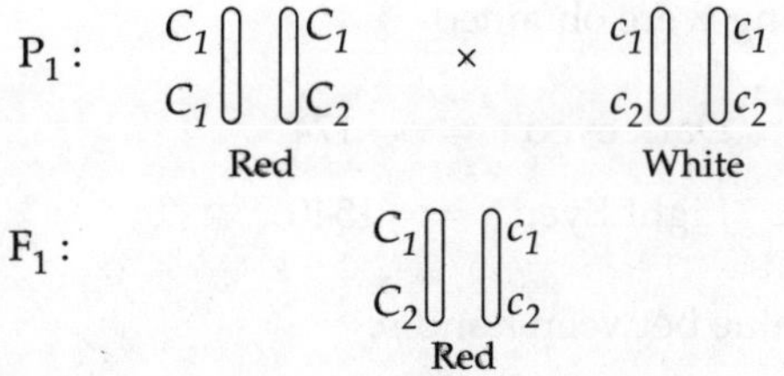

*$P_2$ : $F_1$ with double recessive back cross*

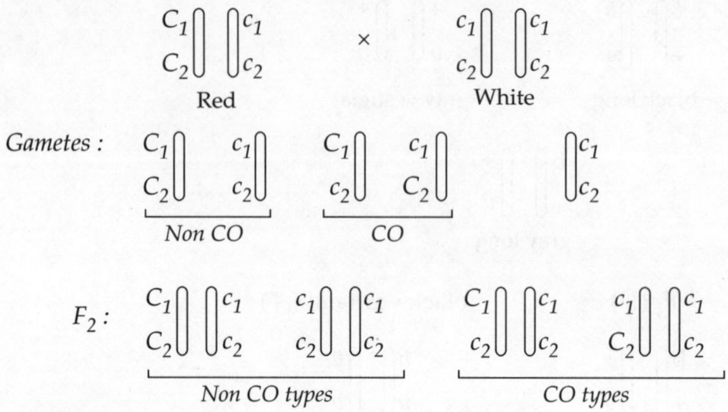


Here the Crossover type = 10%

Linkage = 90%

The ratio of the offspring

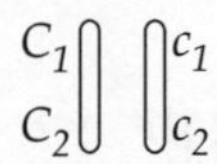 = 45% 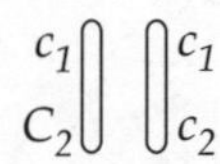 = 5%

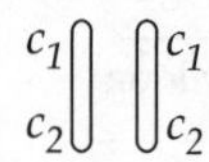 = 45% 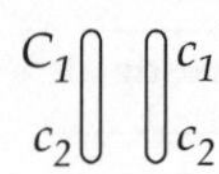 = 5%

*i.e.* 9 : 9 : 1 : 1

**Problem 10**

In rats, dark eyes are due to the interaction of two genes *R* and *P*. The recessive allele of either producing light colour eyes. These genes are on the same chromosome.

When homologous dark eyed rats $\frac{+\ +}{+\ +}$ were crossed back with double recessive $\frac{r\ p}{r\ p}$ and the $F_1$ is crossed black with the double recessive the following offsprings were obtained

Dark eyed = 1255 (+ +)

Light eyed = 1777 (*r p*)

When $\frac{+\ p}{+\ p}$ animals were crossed with $\frac{r\ +}{r\ +}$ ones and the $F_1$ is crossed back with the double recessive the following offspring were obtained

Dark eyed = 174

Light Eyed = 1540

Calculate the crossover value between *r* and *p*.

**Solution :**

In the first cross

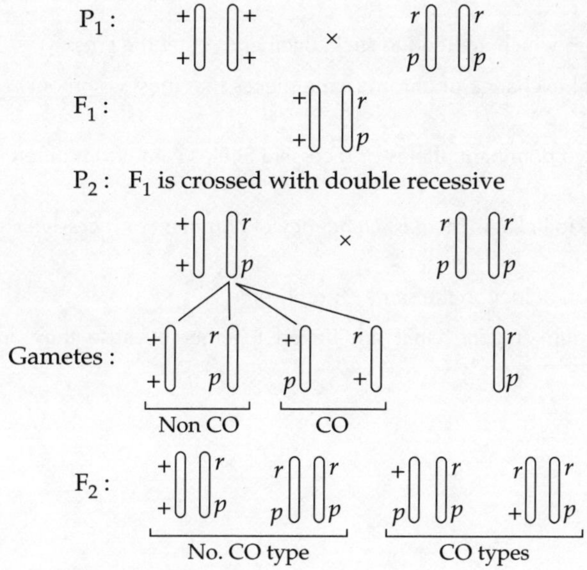


Here non CO = 1255 + 1777 = 3032

Again when :

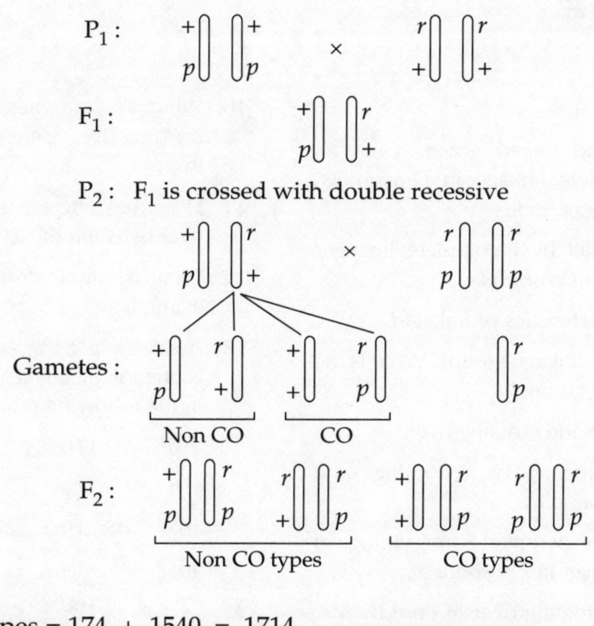


Here, Crossover types = 174 + 1540 = 1714

Total offspring = 3032 + 1714 = 4746

$$\text{Crossover value} = \frac{1714}{4746} \times 100\% = 36.1\%$$

## Chapter Glossary/Key Terms

**Linked genes :** The genes which are tend to stick together to enter the cross.

**Crossing over :** Physical exchange of chromosome pieces that most commonly occurs during prophase of meiosis-I.

**Gametic repulsion :** Two dominant alleles or recessive alleles came from different parents, they tend to remain separate.

**Genetic coupling :** Due to linkage, there is a tendency of dominant or recessive alleles to remain together in the cross.

**Linkage :** The association of loci on the same chromosome.

**Linkage group :** A group of genes that are linked together because they are found on the same chromosome.

## Exercise

### A. Long answer type questions :

1. Define linkage and linked genes. Give an example of complete linkage in *Drosophila*. Why such experiment is closen?
2. What do you meant by incomplete linkage? Give an example in *Drosophila*.
3. What are the characteristics of linkage?
4. What do you mean linkage groups. What is the measure of linkage groups?
5. Distinguish linkage and crossing over.
6. What do you meant by coupling and repulsion? Give examples.
7. Describe Stern's experiment on cytological proof of crossing-over in *Drosophila* .
8. Demonstrate the crossing over in corn by Mc. Clintock's experiment and in Lambda phage by Meselson and Weigle's experiment.
9. What are the factors affecting the strength of crossing over.
10. What do you mean by single and double crossing-over between two loci? Illustrate this.
11. Describe different types of double crossing over between the two loci.
12. What is mitotic crossing over? Illustrate with example.
13. A cross $a^+a^+b^+b^+ \times aabb$ produces an $F_1$ that is phenotypically $a^+b^+$. Its phenotypes appear in the following numbers :

| | |
|---|---|
| $a^+b^+$ | 110 |
| $a^+b$ | 16 |
| $ab^+$ | 19 |
| $ab$ | 15 |
| | 160 |

What $F_2$ numbers would be expected if the *a* and *b* loci assort independently? Use a chi-sequare test to evaluate whether the two loci are linked or assort independently

14. In corn, a dihybrid for the recessives *a* and *b* is test crossed. The distribution of the phenotypes is as follows

| | |
|---|---|
| *AB* | 112 |
| *Ab* | 118 |
| *aB* | 81 |
| ab | *79* |

Test the hypothesis that these genes are assorting independently using a chi-sequare test. Explain tentatively any deviation from expected values, and tell how you would test your explanation.

15. The $F_1$ from a cross of *AB/AB* ×*ab/ab* is test crossed, resulting in the following phenotypic ratios :

| | |
|---|---|
| *AB* | 308 |
| *Ab* | 190 |
| *ab* | 292 |
| *aB* | 210 |

What is the frequency of recombination between genes *a* and *b*

16. Genes *a* and *b* are linked with 10% recombination. What would be the phenotypes and the probability of each, among progeny of the following cross?

$$\frac{a\,b^+}{a^+\,b} \times \frac{ab}{ab}$$

17. Genes *a* and *b* are sex-linked and are located 7 mu apart on the X-chromosome of *Drosophila*. A female of genotype $a^+b/ab^+$ is mated with a wild type male $a^+b^+/Y$

(a) What is the probability that one of her sons will be either $a^+b^+$ or $ab^+$ in phenotype?

(b) What is the probability that one of her daughters will be $a^+b^+$ in phenotype?

**B. Short answer type questions.**

1. What is linkage?
2. What is linked genes?
3. What do you meant by complete linkage?
4. What is incomplete linkage?
5. What is linkage group?
6. How do linkage groups are measured?
7. What are the linkage groups of *Drosophila* grasshopper, Woman and Man?
8. What the relation between linkage and crossing-over?
9. Define repulsion and coupling.
10. How does sex of the animal affect strength of crosing over.
11. How does temperature affect strength of crossing over in *Drosophila*.
12. How does heterochromatin affect strength of crossing over.
13. What do you mean by intrachromosomal and interchromosomal effects on the strength of crossing over.
14. What do you mean by single and double crossing over between two loci?
15. What are two-strand, three-strand, four strand double crossing over?
16. What is mitotic crossing over?
17. What is twin spot in *Drosophila*.

**Short Notes on :**

Linkage, Complete linkage, Incomplete linkage, Linkage groups, Coupling and repulsion, Stern's experiment on cytological demonstration of crossing-over, Mitotic crossing over, Twin spot in *Drosophila*.

# 8

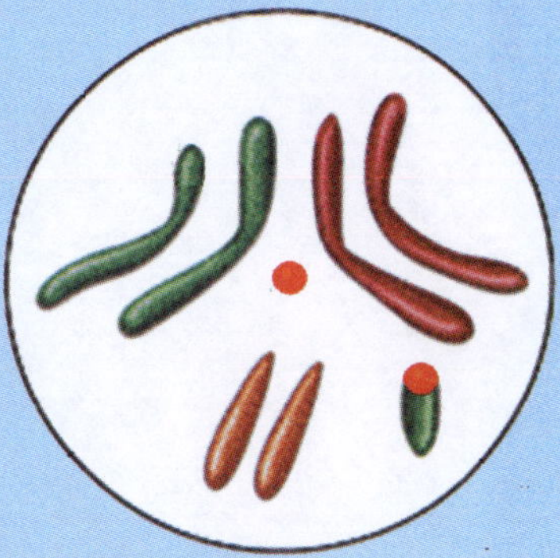

# Genetic and Cytogenetic maps of Chromosomes

**CHAPTER AGENDA**

**8.1**Concept; **8.2** Two-point test cross; **8.3** Three point test cross; **8.4** Accounting unseen multiple crossing over; **8.5** Coefficient of Coincidence; **8.6** Tetrad analysis or Haploid mapping; **8.7** Genetic mapping by human pedigree analysis; **8.8** Lod score; **8.9** Cytogenetic map; **8.10** Construction of Cytogenetic map; **8.11** Solved problems on Genetic maps; Chapter Glossary/Key Terms; Exercise

## 8.1. CONCEPT

T. H. Morgan put forward the hypothesis (1911) that the strength of linkage of a pair of genes *i.e.*, the amount of crossing over or recombination observed is a function of the distance in the chromosome between the genes. It has also been assumed that crossing over occurs between the genes which are present as linear arrays on the chromosomes.

The recombination frequencies are directly proportional to the distance between genes on the chromosome and these values can be used for the preparation of **linkage maps** or **genetic maps**.

Physical location of a gene in a chromosome is accomplished by identifying a gene locus with relation to some visible landmarks viz chromosome cross bands, is termed as physical map or cytological map of chromosomes.

*Distinguish between linkage map and physical map*

1. Frequency of crossing over usually varies in different segments of chromosome, but it is highly predictable event between two gene loci, whereas, actual physical distances between linked genes bear no direct relationship to the linkage map distances.
2. In both cases the genes are arranged in the chromosoems in a linear order.

## 8.2. TWO-POINT TEST CROSS

The percentage of crossing over between two linked genes is calculated by test crosses in which a $F_1$ dihybrid is crossed with a double recessive parent. Such crosses, because involved crossing over at two points, it is called two point tests cross.

Let us, there are two genes *A* and *C* which are dominant over *a* and *c* respectively. The dihybrid of these two genes *AC/ac* is test crossed with double recessive (*ac/ac*). A hypothetical result may be obtained from the following cross.

Parents : *AC/ac* × *ac/ac*

Gametes : (*AC*) (*ac*) [non crossover] (*Ac*) (*aC*) [crossover] (*ac*)

Offsprings : *Aa Cc* *aa cc* [non crossover zygotes] *Aa cc* *aa Cc* [Crossover zygotes]

Suppose the phenotype of the offspring with parental combinations is 40% each i.e., 80% in total and frequency of the crossing over zygotes with non-parental phenotype is 10% each *i.e.*, 20% in total, then the distance between the loci *A* and *C* is estimated to be 20 centi Morgans.

Two-point test cross would only give the knowledge of distance between the two gene loci. But their position whether to the left or to the right is not to be understood.

**Recomination fraction** is the index of the distance between two loci. eg. At the end of first meiosis, each daughter cell will have a 50% chance of receiving each locus. This recombination fraction is 0.5.

## 8.3. THREE-POINT TEST CROSS AND LINKAGE MAP

A three-point test cross or trihybrid test cross, involving three genes gives us information regarding relative distance between these genes. It also shows us the linear arrays of genes whether on the left or on the right side of their sequence on the chromosome. For this purpose along with two marker genes another third marker gene is used (eg. *A, B* and *C*), which are located in fairly, close proximity in the same linkage group. All the three markers may be used together conducting the analysis of the map distance and relative position of the three points.

There are three possible arrangements of these three marker genes, these are *A-B-C*, *A-C-B* or *B-A-C*. Three point tests cross is used to find out which one (gene) is at the middle. For this purpose a trihybrid *ABC/abc* is test crossed with a double recessive *abc/abc*.

| | *Genotype* | *Phenotype* | *Supposed frequency* |
|---|---|---|---|
| 1. Non crossover | *ABC/abc* | ABC | a |
| | *abc/abc* | abc | b |
| 2. Crossing over between (A – B) | *Abc/abc* | Abc | c |
| | *aBC/abc* | aBC | d |
| 3. Crossing over between (B–C) | *ABc/abc* | ABc | e |
| | *abC/abc* | abC | f |
| 4. Double crossing over between A–B and B–C | *AbC/abc* | AbC | g |
| | *aBc/abc* | aBc | h |
| | | | Total = T |

A hypothetical frequency of 8 classes of progenies is as follows.

If crossing over value between A and B is 'X', between B and C is Y and between A and C is Z.

Then,

1. Crossing over between A and B (where A and B or *a* and *b* are separated)

$$X = \frac{c+d+g+h}{T} \times 100\%$$

2. Crossing over between B and C (where B and C or b and c are separated)

$$Y = \frac{e+f+g+h}{T} \times 100\%$$

3. Crossing over between A and C (where A and C or a and c are separated)

$$Z = \frac{c+d+e+f}{T} \times 100\%$$

From the above values of X, Y and Z, order of genes can be worked out and a linkage map can be prepared using the following criteria.

If X+Y=Z, then the order of gene is A–B–C

X–Y=Z, then the order of gene is A–C–B

And Y–X=Z, then the order of gene is B–A–C

| *Phenotype* | *Genotype* | *frequencies* | | |
|---|---|---|---|---|
| Echinus | *+ ec +/sc ec cv* | 810 | 1638 | 1980 |
| Scute-cross veinless | *sc + cv/sc ec cv* | 828 | | |
| Scute echinus | *sc ec +/sc ec cv* | 62 | 150 | |
| Crossveinless | *+ + cv/sc ec cv* | 88 | | |
| Scute | *sc + +/sc ec cv* | 89 | 192 | |
| Echinus-cross veinless | *+ ec cv/sc ec cv* | 103 | | |
| Wild type | *+ + +/sc ec cv* | 0 | 0 | |
| Scute-echinus-cross veinless | *sc ec cv/sc ec cv* | 0 | | |

- **An example of genetic map**

Bridges and Olbryct crossed *Drosophila melangaster* flies with rough eyes due to gene, *echinus (ec)*, certain bristles missing, *scute (sc)* and absence of the cross veins in the wings, *cross veinless (cv)*.

These three genes are recessive to the corresponding normal condition and are sex-linked, the hybrid females are normal or wild type in phenotype, *i.e.*, they had non-rough eyes, presence of all bristles and presence of cross-veins.

The hybrid females had one X-chromosome, carrying the gene *ec* and normal alleles of scute *sc* and *cv*. Another X-chromosome with a normal allele of echinus and mutant alleles *sc* and *cv*. The normal alleles in wild flies are denoted by + sings. So the genotype of the hybrid is (*+ ec +/ sc + cv*).

1. Parental combinations are more frequent. So, the genotypes of the parent are $\frac{+\ ec\ +}{sc\ +\ cv}$(♀) and $\frac{sc\ \ ec\ \ cv}{}$(♂).

2. Crossing over between *sc* and *ec*, where *ec* and *sc* or their normal genes (+ and +) come together.

The recombination frequency between *sc* and *ec* is $\frac{62 + 88}{1980} \times 100\% = 7.6\%$.

3. Crossing over between *ec* and *cv*, where *ec* and *cv* or their normal genes (+ and +) come together.

   The recombination frequency between *ec* ad *cv* is $\frac{89 + 103}{1980} \times 100\% = 9.7\%$.

4. Crossing over between *sc* and *cv*, where *sc* and *cv* or their normal genes are separated.

   The recombination frequency between *sc* and *cv* is $\frac{62 + 88 + 89 + 103}{1980} \times 100\% = 17.3\%$.

So, the recombination frequencies between

*sc* and *ec* = 7.6%

*ec* and *cv* = 9.7%

*sc* and *cv* = 17.3%

According to Morgan's hypothesis, the frequency of crossing over giving rise to recombination of linked genes is a function of the distance between these genes in the chromosome.

Hence, distance between (*sc* – *cv*) = distance between (*sc* – *ec*) + (*ec* – *cv*).

According to geometrical rule, if *sc*, *ec* and *cv* lie on a straight line we can draw a genetic map of the part of the chromosome in which these genes are located in the following order.

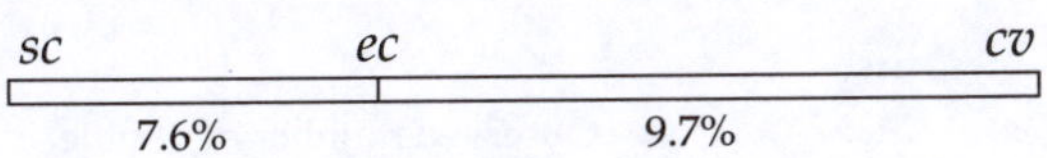


After knowing total number of genes in each linkage group of a species, the relative distance between each linked gene have to be determined. The distance between two given genes is calculated according to the percentage of crossing over, because crossing over frequency is directly proportional to the distance between the genes and if the percentage of crossing over between two linked genes is 1% it means that the distance between two linked genes is one unit of the map distance which is known as **map unit** or **centi-Morgan** (cM) in honour of Thomas Hunt Morgan.

## 8.4 ACCOUNTING UNSEEN MULTIPLE CROSSING OVER

In general, as the average number of physical crossover events increases and the map distance gets longer; the observed number of recombinants will also increase but will still never exceed 50% and recombination frequency will remain smaller than the actual map distance, because more than one crossover event between them takes place.

Multiple crossover events between two loci may be quite difficult to detect. For example, if the crossover is restricted between two loci of nonsister chromatids and is double or even-numbered then the crossover events cannot produce recombinants. On the otherhand, if the crossover event is odd numbered multiple, then the products would be recombinants.

Thus the presence of multiple crossovers makes it difficult to estimate map distances accurately, whereas small map distance with fewer multiple crossovers are estimated more reliably (Fig. 8.1).

## 8.5 COEFFICIENT OF COINCIDENCE

If the frequency of single crossing over is 10% between *A* and *B* genes and 8% between *B* and *C* genes and the occurrence of crossing over in one part of a chromosome is independent of its occurrence in other parts of the same chromosome, then we can predict the frequency of simultaneous occurrence of crossing over between *A* and *B* and between *B* and *C*. On the assumption of independence, the frequency of such double crossing over should be 10% of 8% i.e. 0.8%.

Actually, the observed frequency of double crossing over would not be so *i.e* less then 0.8% or zero (no double crossing over occurs). It seems

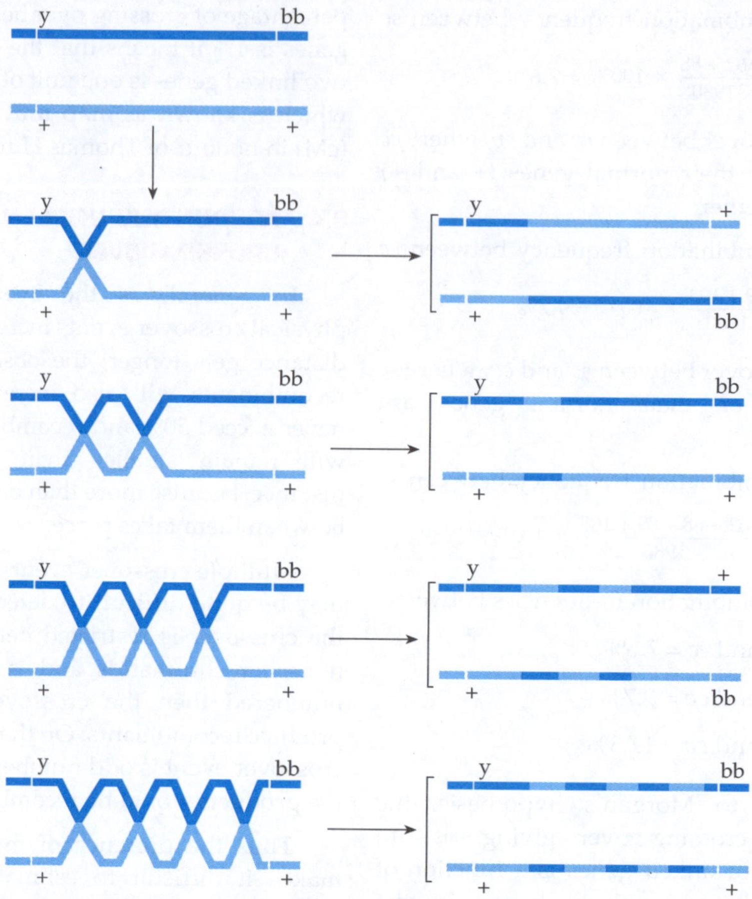


Fig.8.1 : *Unseen multiple crossing-over.*

that, the occurrence of crossing over at one point in the chromosome decreases the probability of its occurrence elsewhere in the same chromosome. This phenomenon is called *interference*.

If the observed frequency of double crossing over is lower than the expected number, this implies a *positive interference*. Therefore, we can say the occurrence of the first crossing over reduces the chance of the second. Its value lies between 0 to 1.

On the contrary, if the observed frequency of double crossing over is more than the expected number, this is *negative interference*. Its value is below Zero.

An inverse measure of interference is called **coincidence**. The *coefficient of coincidence* is defined as the ratio between the observed number of double crossing over to the expected number of such doubles.

Thus,

$$\text{Coefficient of coincidence} = \frac{\text{Observed number of double crossing over}}{\text{Expected number of double crossing over}}$$

The reduced quantity of double crossing overs is expressed as the *degree of interference*.

Thus, Degree of interference

= 1 – Coefficient of coincidence.

For example,

If crossing over percentage between $A$ and $B$ is 10 and between $B$ and $C$ is 8. Then the expected number of double crossing over is 0.8%. Again, if, the observed double crossing over is 0.2%, then coefficient of coincedence is $\frac{0.2}{0.8} = 0.25$ and the degree of interference is 1–0.25 = 0.75.

## 8.6 TETRAD ANALYSIS OR HAPLOID MAPPING

Ascomycetes group of fungi retain the four haploid products of meiosis as ascospores in a sac, called *ascus*. It provides an unique opportunity to look at the total products of meiosis in a tetrad. The two such fungi, the common baker's yeast *Saccharomyces cerevisiae* and the pink bread mold, *Neurospora crassa*, both of them retain their products of meiosis as ascospores in ascus (Fig. 8.2).

### 8.6.1 Tetrad analysis of Yeast

The budding yeast, *Saccharomyces cerevisiae* exists in both haploid and diploid forms. The haploid form is usually formed under nutritional stress (starvation) But in optimum condition, these haploid cells of the two sexes, called *"a" and "α" mating types* fuse to form the diploid. Again after starvation condition, haploid form is established by meiosis. The important feature of such meiosis is that all the products of meiosis are contained in the ascus.

**Mapping procedure** : Let, we like to map genes at the two loci *"a"* and *"b"*.

When an *ab* spore fuses with $a^+b^+$ spore (or gamete), then the diploid zygote undergoes meiosis. The haploid spores can be isolated and grown as haploid colonies. We may then get three types of asci.

Class I has two types of spores, which are identical to the parental haploid spores. Such ascus type is called as *Parental ditype* (PD)[$ab$, $ab$, $a^+b^+$ and $a^+b^+$].

Class II has only two types of spores, but these are recombinants. The ascus type is called as *Nonparental ditype* (NPD) [$ab^+$, $ab^+$, $a^+b$ and $a^+b$].

Class III has all four possible spore types and is referred to as a *tetratype (TT)* [$ab$, $ab^+$, $a^+b$ and $a^+b^+$].

If the genes are linked, PDs come from the lack of crossing over whereas NPDs come about from four-strand double crossing over (double crossovers between all four strands). The parental ditypes would be expected to be more than nonparental ditypes for such linked loci.

If the loci are not linked, both parential and nonparental ditypes come out through independent assortment and so they would occur in equal frequencies.

Now we can thus determine whether the two loci are linked or not linked *i.e.*, on the same chromosome or on the separate chromosomes.

Thus in a NPD, all four chromatids are recombinants, whereas in tetratype only half of the chromatids are recombinants. The maps unit can be determined by the following formula.

$$\text{Map units} = \frac{\frac{1}{2} \times \text{the number of TT loci} + \text{the number of NPD asci}}{\text{Total number of asci}} \times 100$$

If total number asci counted as 100 and the total number of TT asci is 30 and the number of NPD asci is 5. Then the value of map unit would be

$$\frac{\frac{1}{2} \times 30 + 5}{100} \times 100 = 20$$

### 8.6.2 Tetrad analysis in *Neurospora*

*Neurospora*, the pink bread mold has three phenotypic categories : Colony morphology, drug resistance and nutritional requirements.

Wild type *Neurospora* generally grows in a filamentous form. Their mutant growth forms are fluffy (*fl*), tuft (*tu*), durty (*dir*) and colonial (*col4*).

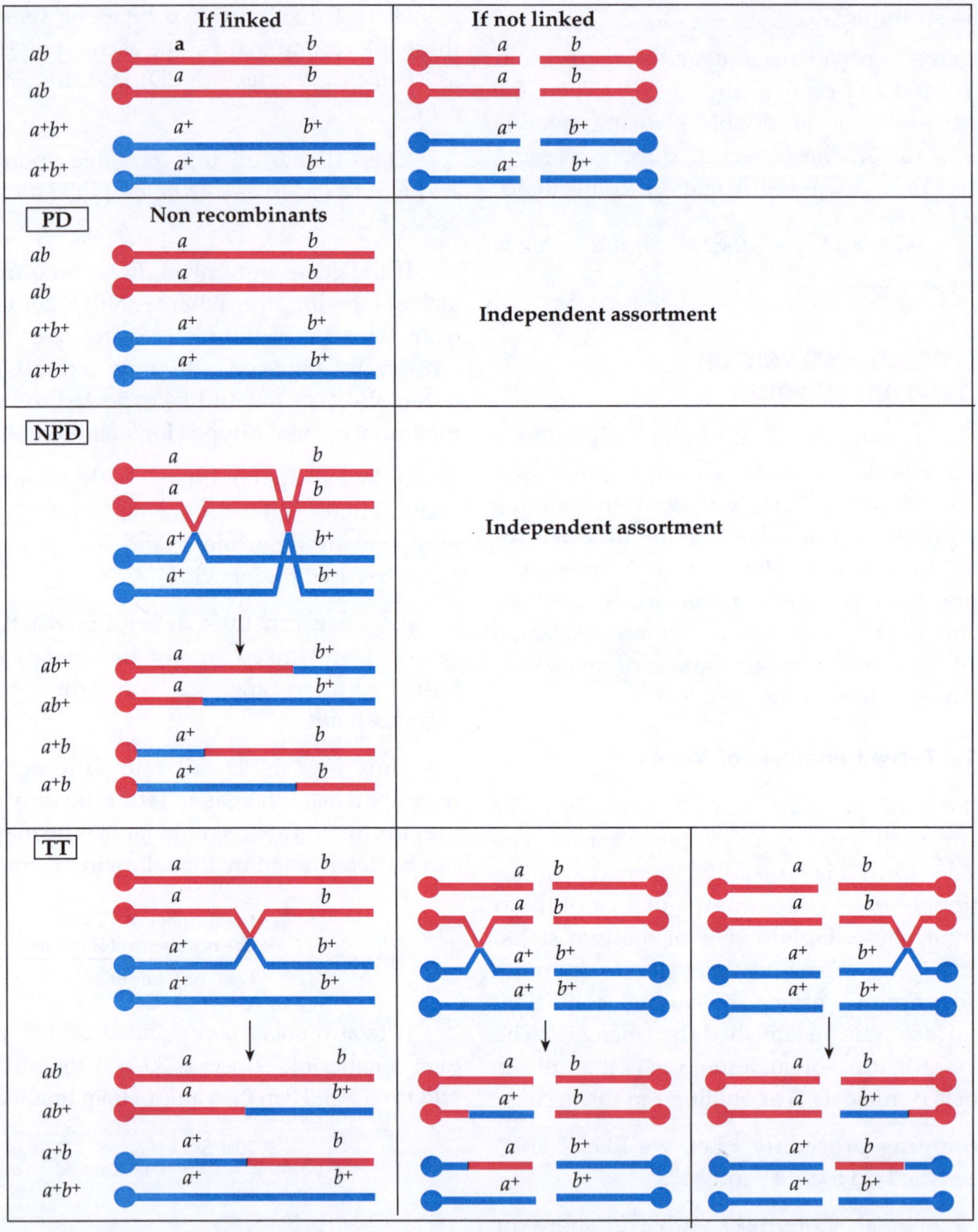


**Fig.8.2 :** *Tetrad analysis in S. cerevisiae*

Wild-type *Neurospora* is sensitive to sulfa drug sulfonamide, whereas one of its mutant (*Sfo*) requires sulfonamide in order to grow and survive.

Wild-type *Neurospora* can grow on a medium containing only sugar, a nitrogen source, some organic acids and salts and the vitamin biotin which is called minimal medium. Several different mutants cannot grow on this minimal media, but require some essential nutrients.

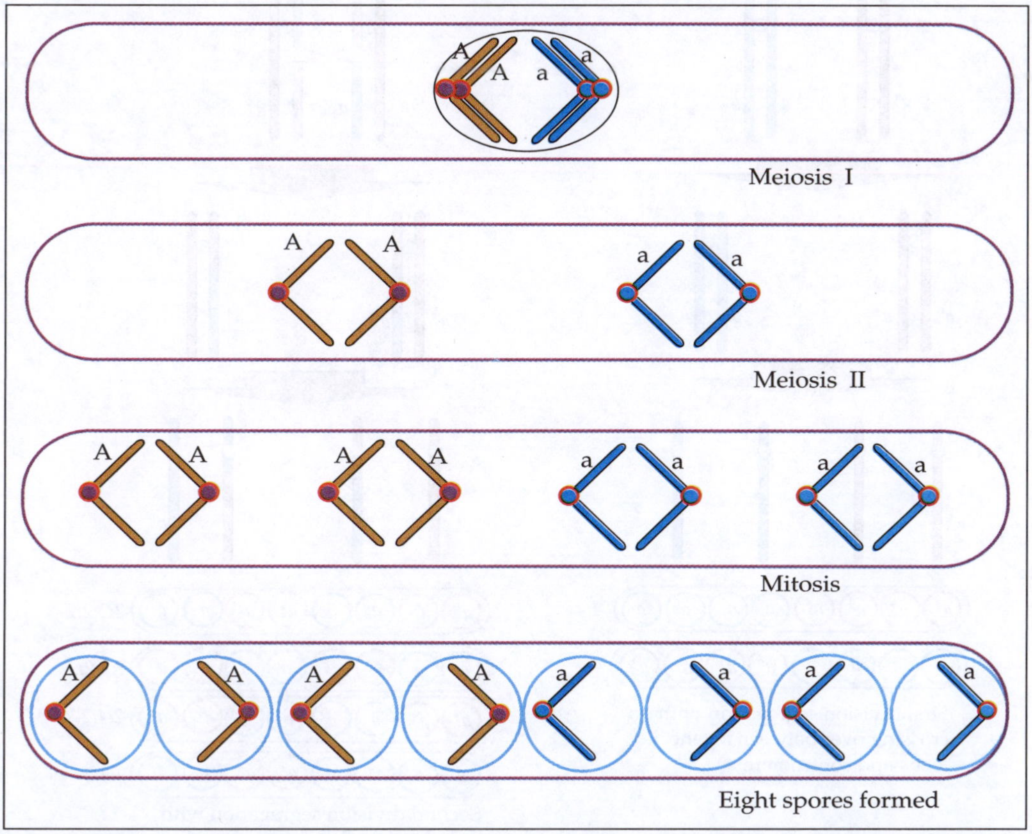


**Fig.8.3 :** *Meiosis in Neurospora and formation of spores.*

*Neurospora* vegetative hyphae (n) are developed from haploid ascospores. Fertilization takes place within an immature fruiting body after a spore or filament of one mating type contacts with a special filament extending from the fruiting body of the opposite mating type. Zygote undergoes meiosis. The meiotic spindle forced to lie along the cell's long axis of the ascus. As a result, four spores are formed and ordered according to their centromeres. Before the ascospores mature, a mitosis takes place in each nucleus so that four pairs of spores are formed which are arranged in a ordered series in the ascus (Fig. 8.3).

**Mapping Procedure :**

Two kinds of patterns appear among the loci on their chromosomes.

If there is *no crossover between the locus (a) and its centromere*, the allelic pattern is same as the centromerie pattern. This is referred to as **first division segregation** (FDS) because the alleles separate from each other at meiosis. The pattern is 4:4 (Fig. 8.4).

But if there is *a crossover between the locus and centromere*, the pattern would be 2:4:2 or 2:2:2:2, each of which is referred to as **second division segregation** (SDS)

Every SDS configuration has four recombinant and four nonrecombinant chromatids (spores) *i.e.* half of the spores are recombinant. The map unit is defined as the 1% recombinant chromatids

Therefore

$$\text{Map distance} = \frac{\frac{1}{2} \times \text{the number of SDS asci}}{\text{Total number of asci}} \times 100$$

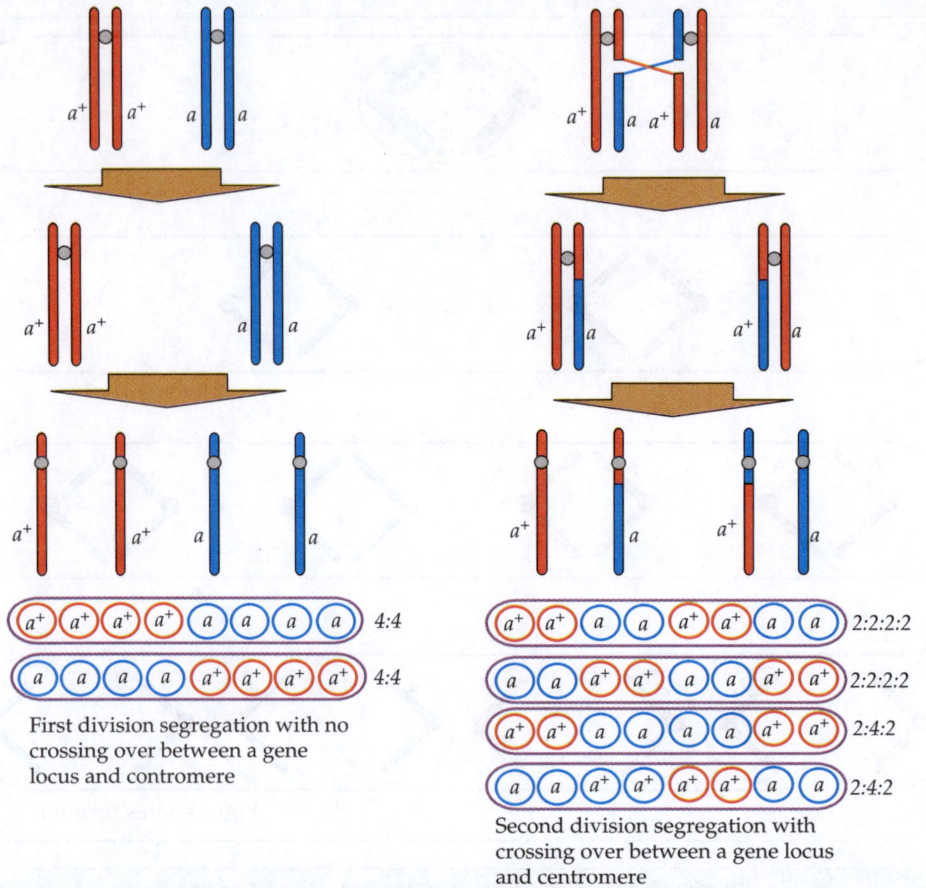


**Fig.8.4 :** *Six possible Neurospora ascospore patterns in respect to one locus.*

The calculation of map distance of a locus from the centromere can be calculated from the following data (Fig. 8.5).

In *Neurospora,* three-point cross can be studied to map two gene loci and the centromere.

The fertilization between fused mycelia with genotypes *ab* and $a^+b^+$ results in a zygote, whose asci can be analysed. Since each locus can show 6 different patterns, two loci may show 36 possible spore arrangements.

The tetrad in meiosis is a three dimensional entity and therefore, at meiotic division, either centromere can go to the left or to the right. When the centromere splits at the second meiotic division the segregation of the chromosome would be at random and therefore eight different patterns of spores can be produced with different gene compositions. All eight arrangements are equally likely. Then the 36 possible patterns can be grouped into 7 unique patterns. These patterns may be parental ditypes, nonparental ditypes and tetratypes (Fig. 8.7 & 8.8).

**Determination of gene order :**

In the above table, class-I is PD and class-II is NPD. If class-I represents maximum (here it is $x_1$) and class-II represents very few (here it is $x_2$), then can say that these two genes *a* and *b* are linked. If these two categories are more or less equally present, then it may be said that these two genes are not linked.

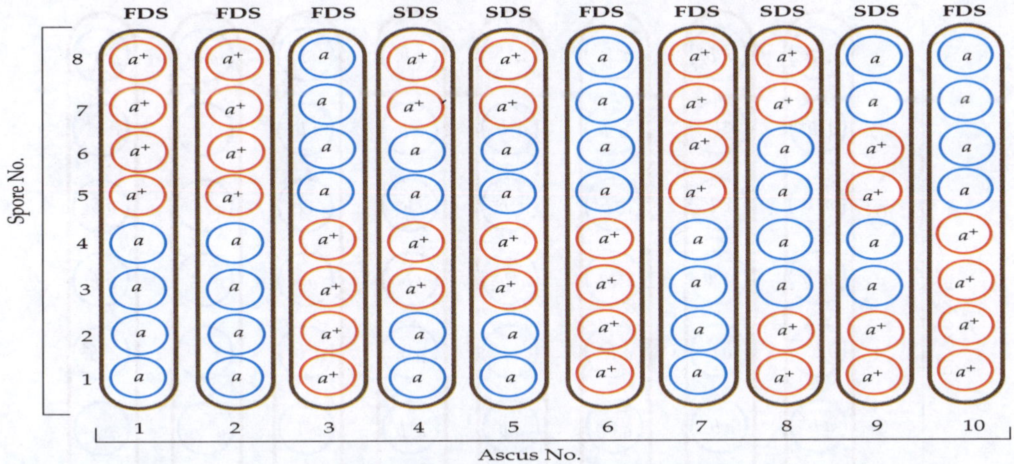


**Fig.8.5 :** *Genetic patterns following meiosis in an a+a heterozygous Neurospora (10 loci examined)*

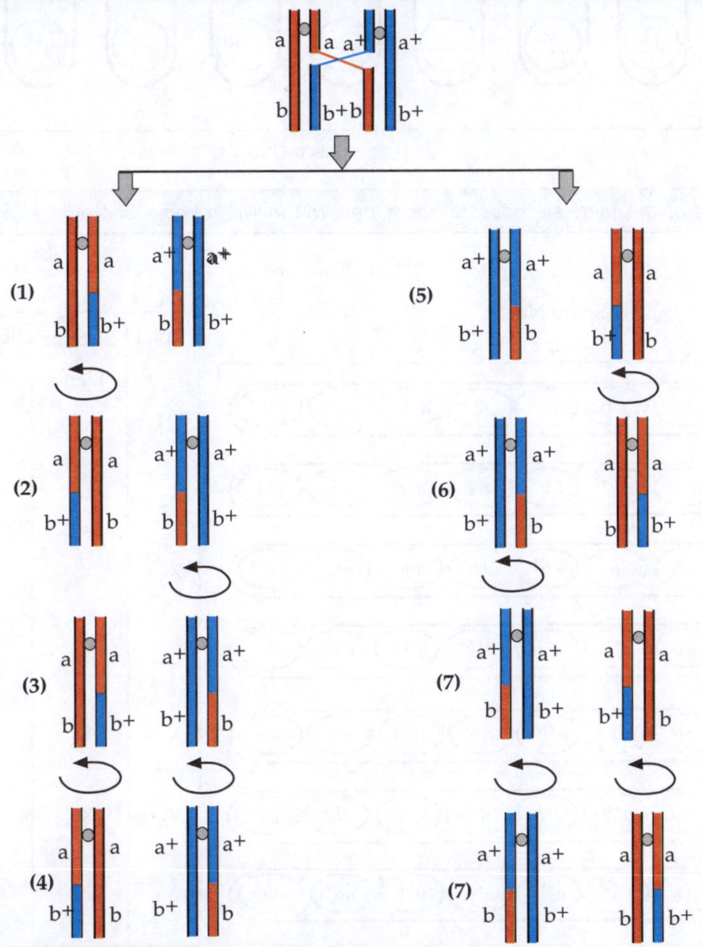


**Fig.8.6 :** *The eight Random arrangements possible when a single crossover occurs between a and b loci in Neurospora.*

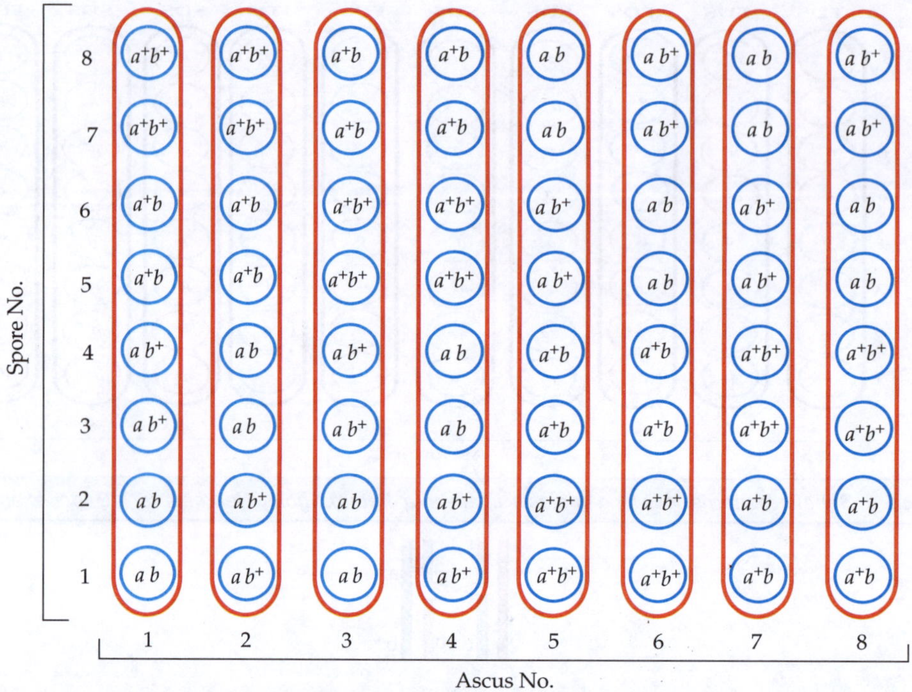


**Fig.8.7 :** *Eight of the thirty-six possble spore patterns in Neurospora scored for two loci a and b.*

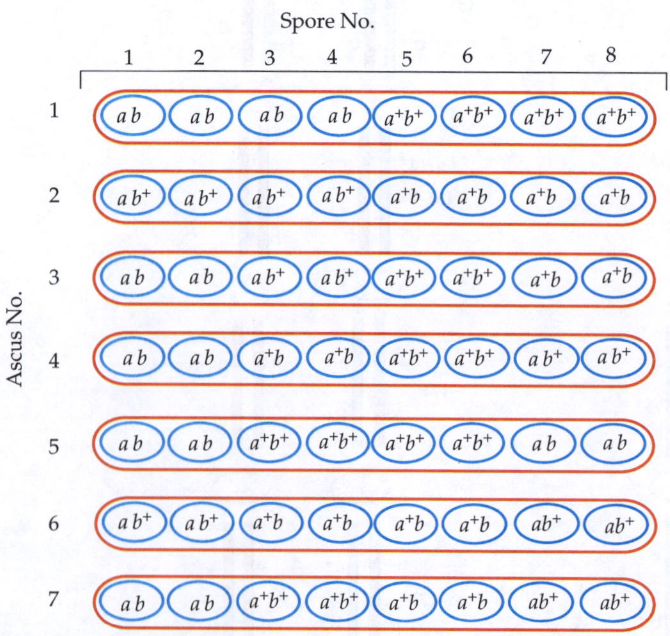


| Total | SDS for "a" locus | SDS for "b" locus | Unordered |
|---|---|---|---|
| $X_1$ | | | PD |
| $X_2$ | | | NPD |
| $X_3$ | | $X_3$ | TT |
| $X_4$ | $X_4$ | $X_4$ | TT |
| $X_5$ | $X_5$ | $X_5$ | PD |
| $X_6$ | $X_6$ | $X_6$ | NPD |
| $X_7$ = N | $X_7$ | $X_7$ | TT |

**Fig.8.8 :** *Seven unique classes of asci resulting from meiosis in a dihybrid cross $ab/a^+b^+$*

The distance of each gene from the centromere is to be measured

Distance of any locus from the centromere

$$= \frac{\frac{1}{2} \times \text{SDS of that locus}}{\text{Total number of asci}} \times 100$$

Thus the distance of locus *a* from the centromere

$$= \frac{\frac{1}{2} \times (x_4 + x_5 + x_6 + x_7)}{N} \times 100$$

= "A" map unit (centimorgans)

Distance of locus *b* from the centromere

$$= \frac{\frac{1}{2} \times \text{SDS of locus } b}{N} \times 100$$

= "B" map units (centimorgans)

The distance between locus-*a* and locus-*b* can be determined by the formula.

$$\frac{\frac{1}{2} \times \text{the number of TT asci} + \text{the number of NPD asci}}{\text{Total number of SC}} \times 100$$

$$= \frac{\frac{1}{2} \times (x_3 + x_4 + x_7) + (x_2 + x_6)}{N} \times 100$$

= "C" map units (centimorgans)

These two genes may be on the two opposite sides of the centromere.

If the distance (C) between locus *a* and locus *b* is equal to (A + B), then these two loci lie on the two opposite sides of the centromere. On the otherhand if the distance (C) between them is (A~B) then, centromere and these two loci are at the one side of the chromosome.

If the value of A>B then the gene order is "*Centromere—b—a*". But if the value of A<B then the order is "*Centromere—a—b*".

## 8.7 GENETIC MAPPING BY HUMAN PEDIGREE ANALYSIS

Convensional linkage mapping is impossible for the human beings, because

1. It is impossible to preselect the genotypes of parents and set up croses designed for mapping purpose.
2. If the generations are taken into account, data for the calculation of recombination frequencies becomes insufficient, as the number of offspring p is very few even may be only one.
3. Human marriage rarely results in a convenaint test cross.
4. Genotypes of one or more family members are unobtainable because those individuals are dead (the actual cause is not known) or unwilling to cooperate.

For genetic mapping in humans, pedigree analysis is used where genetic diseases are frequently used as a *gene marker.* To establish a recombination frequency between the disease gene and microsatellite-M (which is present on the same chromosome) we have to know how many of the children are recombinants (Fig. 8.9a).

If we consider the pedigree of a family, where Mother is diseased but not the father. Six children, four of them are diseased. The disease allele is dominant over the healthy allele. $M_1$, $M_2$, $M_3$, $M_4$ are four alleles for microsatellites. The objective is to determine the degree of linkage between the disease gene and the microsatellite (Fig. 8.9b)

Here the genotype of mother is $M_1M_2$ where disease dominant gene is located near $M_1$ (*disease—$M_1$*) while the healthy recessive gene is located near $M_2$ (*healthy—$M_2$*).

1. Among children, No.-1, 3, 4 are with parental genotypes as they have disease allele and $M_1$ microsatellite.
2. No.-2 and 5 also have parental genotype because of the presence of healthy allele and $M_2$.
3. No. -6 is the only recombinant, because the child is diseased but with $M_2$ microsatellite.

From of above analysis we can say that the disease gene and the microsatellite are linked and crossover occurs between them infrequently (only $\frac{1}{6}$ = 16.66%).

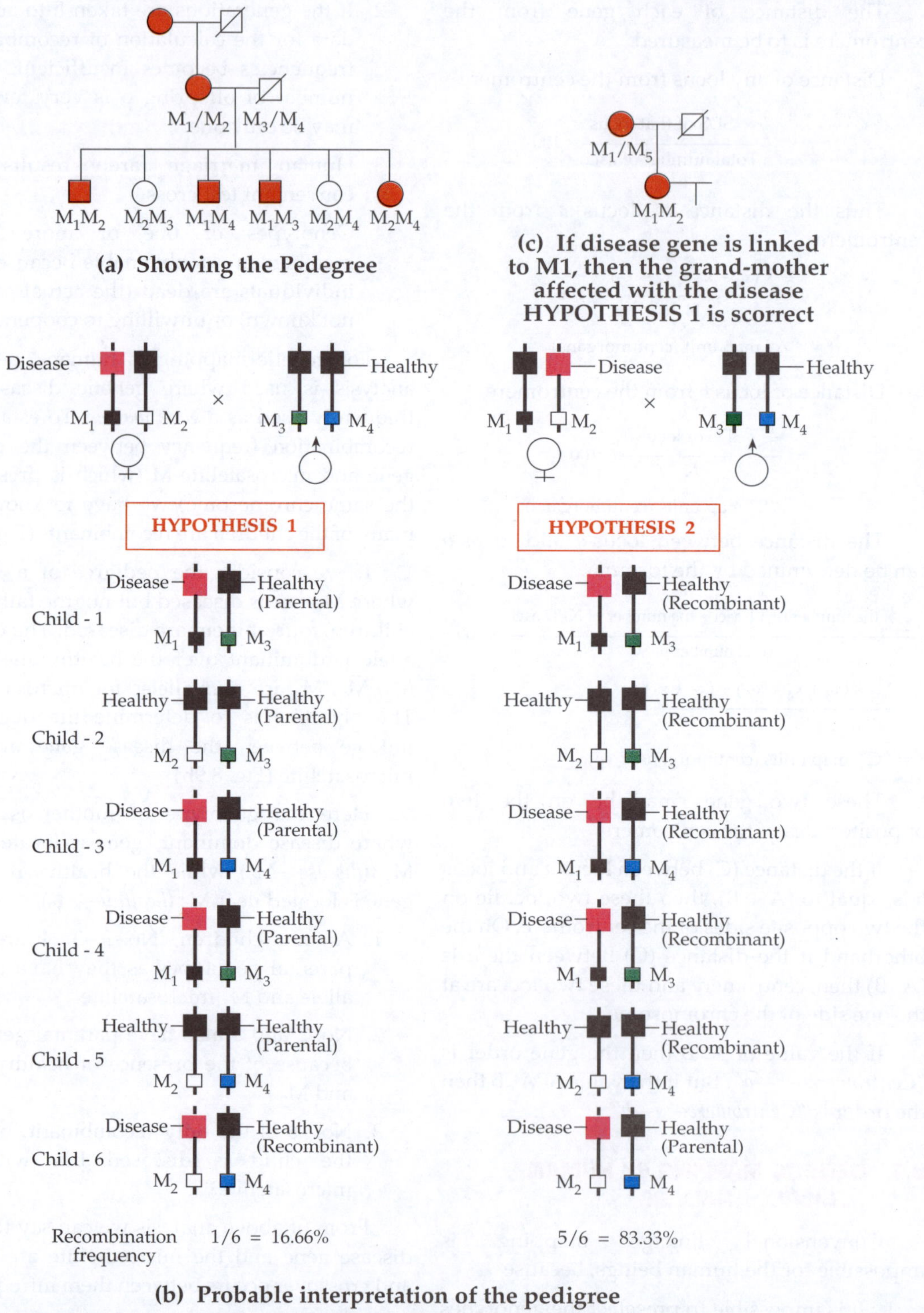


**Fig.8.9 :** *An example of human pedigree analysis*

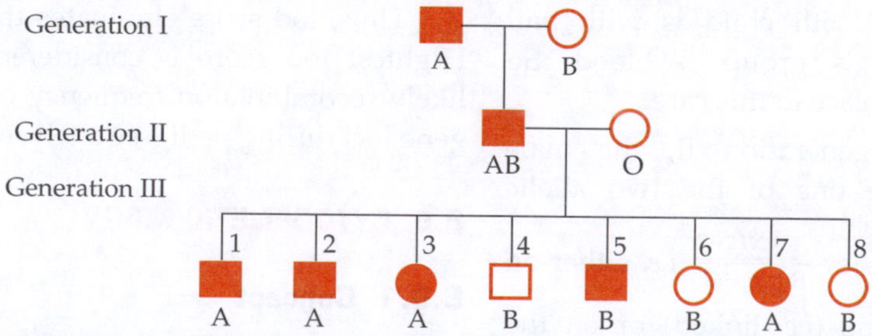


**Fig.8.10 :** *An example of Pedigree analysis showing three generations where the two genes nail-patella syndrome and ABO blood group.*

This can be analysed by other way where disease gene is linked to $M_2$ and healthy gene is with $M_1$. Then we may say that No. 1, 2, 3, 4 and 5 children are recombinants and No. 6 child is nonrecombinant which shows a recombination frequency of $\frac{5}{6}$ = 83.33%.

We cannot easily determine which of the above hypothesis is correct. This is only possible if the genotype of grandmother is known by any means such as her reappearance (who was not actually dead) or by obtaining her DNA from her pathology specimen. If she is diseased and the disease gene is with $M_1$ then the first hypothesis is correct and the genotype may be ($M_1M_2$). If she is not diseased then the disease gene is with $M_2$ and her genotype is $M_2M_5$ and the second hypothesis is correct (Fig. 8.9c).

Imperfect pedigree can be analyzed statistically using a measure called the *lod score.*

## 8.8 LOD SCORE

Imperfect pedigrees are analyzed statistically, using a measure called **lod score**. This stands for logarithm of the odds that the genes are linked, and is used primarily to determine if the two markers being studied lie on the same chromosome. If the lod analysis establishes linkage then it can also provide measure of the most likely recombination frequency.

1. The available data will be derived from more than one pedigree which will increase the confidence of the result.
2. The analysis would be less ambiguous if the families with large number of children.
3. At least three generations are to be taken

These are the three criteria regarding the analysis of lod score.

This probability technique was developed by Newton Morton. The measure is based on the ratio of the probability of genotypes in a family given a certain crossover frequency compared with the probability of those genotypes if, the loci are unlinked (*ie.* the probaility assuming independent assortment). Logarithm is used for the ratio to calculate a parameter called lod score (sigmbolired by Z)

$$\text{So, } Z = \frac{\text{Probability of a particular pedigree assuming a particular recombination frequency}}{\text{Probability assuming independent assortment}}$$

The highest lod score is to be considered and from this the most likely recombination frequency is to be judged and accepted (Fig. 8.10)

The above pedigree analsysis shows three generations where the two genes. **Nail-patella syndrome** (abnormal nail growth coupled with the absence or underdevelopment of kneecap); a dominant trait (*NPS-1*) which has a recessive normal trait (*nps-1*) and ABO blood group is tested in the lod score analysis *NPS-1* gene is linked with blood group 'A' gene.

In generation II, male individual is AB and nail patella disease is linked to *A* gene with no recombination.

In generation III, 5th child is with nail patella disease but is group B blood. So recombination takes place in this care.

**Analysis :** In generation II, the male individual can have one of the two allelic arrangements $\frac{A-NPS}{B-nps}$ or $\frac{A}{B}\ \frac{NPS\text{-}1}{nps\text{-}1}$ *i.e.* either on the same chromosome (*i.e.* linked) or on the separate chromosomes.

The recombination estimate from the pedigree analysis is $\frac{1}{8} \times 100 = 12.5$ map units *ie* the probability is 0.125.

The probability of child-1 of genration III is 0.4375. The child would be non-recombinant.

So, his probability of having the nail-patella syndrome and type A blood is half the probability of no crossover during meiosis *ie* $\frac{1-0.125}{2} = 0.4375$. The same probability is fact for all the children except the 5th one, which is recombinant. It's probability is $\frac{0.125}{2} = 0.0625$.

[We divide by two, because there are two non recombinant types]

The numerator, *ie* the probabily, assuming 12.5 map units would be $(0.4375)^7(0.0625)$.

If the two loci are not linked, then probability of any genotype is $\frac{1}{4} = 0.25$.

The denominator, *ie* the probability of the children assuming the independent assortment of the gene is $(0.25)^8$.

$$\text{The lod score } z = \log \frac{(0.4375)^7(0.0625)^1}{(0.25)^8}$$

$$= \log (12.566) = 1.099$$

The lod score would always be greater than zero if linkage takes place. On the contrary if the lod score is less than zero then recombination frequency has been underestimated. If lod score is 4, then the recombination frequency would be $10^4 = 10{,}000$ times more likely than independent assortment. This considered a strong likelyhood of linkage.

Thus, lod score eliminates the odd results. Hightest lod score is considered as the most likely recombination frequency of the said two gene loci during pedigree analysis.

## 8.9. CYTOGENETIC MAP

### 8.9.1 Concept

It has been found that linkage map distances between genes are not necessarily proportional to physical linear measurements. Special cytological techniques have been used to determine the physical locations of a gene in a chromosome. Localization has been accomplished by identifying a gene locus with relation to some visible landmark such as a chromomere or cross band. This process of chromosome mapping is called **cytological mapping of chromosomes**.

T.H.Pointer was the first geneticist who used polytene chromosomes of *Drosophila* in the cytological verification of genetic data, and hence it is also called **cytogenetic mapping** of chromosomes.

In this process, it is possible to determine the actual locations of the genes. This might be done first by removing a small segment of chromosome by means of X-rays or other means. Then we determine which gene had been removed by means of genetic tests, that can be observed under the microscope which part has been removed. Thus the actual location of genes can be determined.

Bridges made extensive detailed investigation on the salivary gland chromosomes and in course of his investigations, develop a tool of practical usefulness in reading genes of chromosomes. Applying this method on *Drosophila melanogaster*, he prepared a series of cytological or chromosome maps to correspond with the linkage maps already available.

The cytogenetic mapping of chromosomes is based on the study of chromosome aberration in salivary gland chromosomes of *Drosophila*; such as deficiency, duplication, translocation and inversions of chromosome segments.

### 8.9.2 Deficiency

A mutant called "NOTCH" produces a notched margin in wings, it is sex-linked dominant in females but lethal in males. So, male zygote carrying "notch" gene will die.

When 'notch' female with red eyes were crossed to white eyes with normal wings males.

In $F_1$ females, with notch wing had also white eyes, as though the gene white eye was dominant in presence of notch.

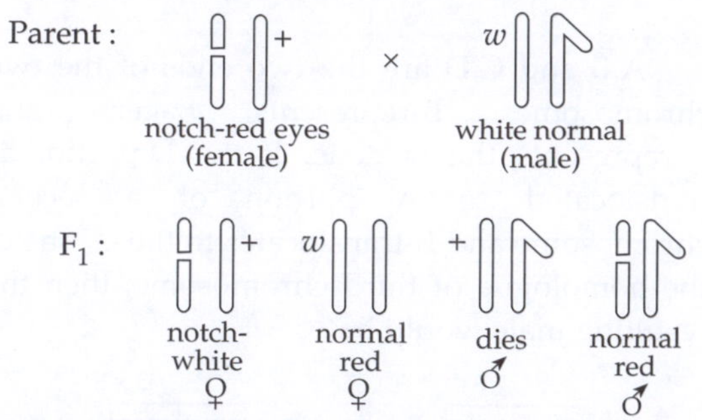


A hypothesis was formulated according to which notch arose as a result of the loss of a piece of chromosome containing the genes that show **pseudodominance**. But he was unable to confirm his hypothesis cytologically because the section of chromosome deficiency in notch is too small to produce appreciable shortening of the X-chromosome. It was confirmed by studying salivary gland chromosome in course of time.

It is found that one of the paired homologues is shorter than the other and since pairing occurs only between homologous discs. The section of the normal chromosome, which contains discs, the missing in the other chromosome forms a buckle.

The genes, which on the basis of the genetic tests, are known to be missing in the deficiency, must be located in the part of the chromosome that forms the buckle in the deficiency heterozygote. Thus the certain positions of the genes can be determined. From this, it is found in salivary gland chromosome the genes are located as a single or a group of discs. The deficient heterozygotes are not usually lethal so they are viable (Fig. 8.11)

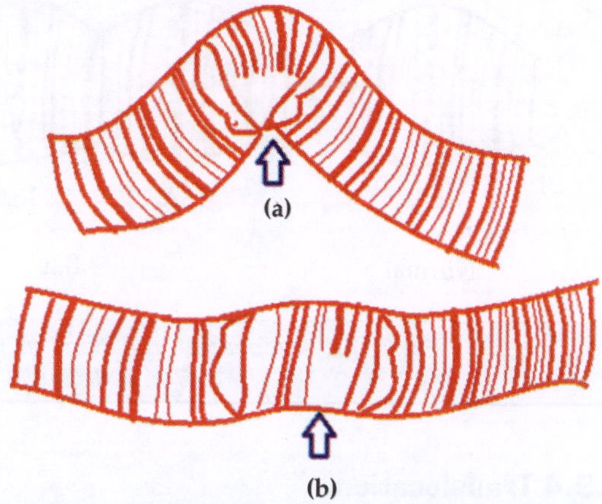


**Fig.8.11 :** *Portion of salivary gland chromosome of Drosophila showing a deficiency of 8 bands (a) and 3 bands (b)*

### 8.9.3 Duplication

Bridges (1919) observed that, in *Drosophila melanogaster*, has homozygous for certain recessive genes failed to manifest the effects in the phenotype.

An analysis showed that dominant alleles of the genes in question were present in addition to the recessive one. The flies evidently contain an extra piece of chromosome in addition to a complete duplex chromosome. One dominant allele of a gene is sufficient to suppress the effects of the recessives. The exceptional individuals with extra piece of chromosome showed the effect of a dominant allele in the phenotype. Cytologically duplication may produce the same kind of configuration in the chromosome as a deficiency does, one is larger than the other and forms a buckle in pairing.

In *Drosophila*, the mutant *bar* (narrow eye) is due to a small repeat of 16A segment. Still in another case two repeats of 16A segments resulting **double bar**.

The duplicated individuals are viable and show various abnormal bodily characters, which can be identified cytologically (Fig. 8.12).

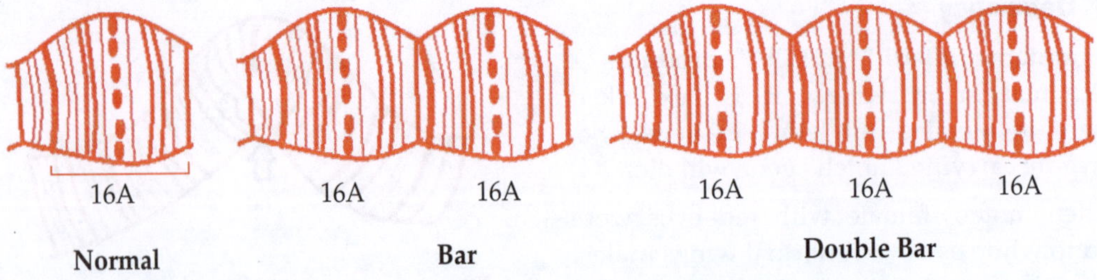


**Fig.8.12 :** *A repeat of 16A band in the salivary gland chromosome in a normal, Bar and double Bar eye in Drosophila.*

### 8.9.4 Translocation

Translocation means the exchange of parts with the other chromosome.

**Genetic detection of translocations :** Second chromosome of *Drosophila* contains the recessive mutant gene, *vestigial wing (vg)* and third chromosome contains the recessive mutant *spineless (ss)*.

When *vestigial spineless* fly is crossed with pure (normal) fly, the $F_1$ would have $\frac{vg}{+}\ \frac{ss}{+}$ genotype.

When this $F_1$ hybrid is crossed with double recessive, 4 types of combinations would get. These are $\left(\frac{vg}{vg}\ \frac{ss}{ss}\right), \left(\frac{+}{vg}\ \frac{+}{ss}\right), \left(\frac{vg}{vg}\ \frac{+}{ss}\right)$ and $\left(\frac{+}{vg}\ \frac{ss}{ss}\right)$ and the ratio is 1:1:1:1.

But in certain test crosses only wild and double recessive is obtained as though they are linked and located on the same chromosome.

This can be produced as follows :

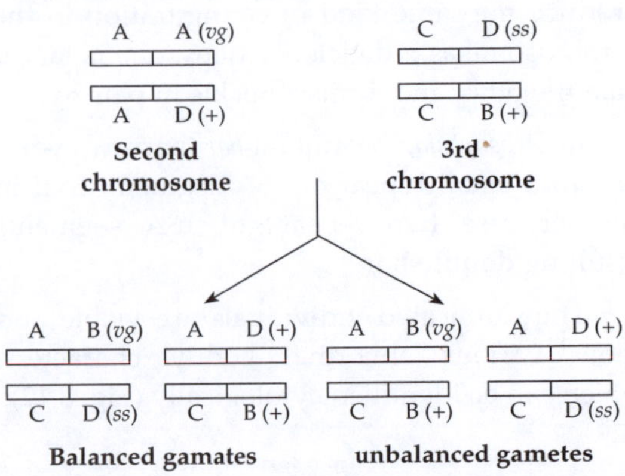


A.B and C.D are the two ends of the two chromosomes. B-represents *vg*-gene and D-represents the *ss* gene. If the D-portion is translocated to A portion of a second chromosome and B-translocates to the C, one of the homologue of third chromosome, then the resulting male would be

They would produce 4 kinds of gametes and when this is crossed with vestigial-spineless female, only two kinds of offspring would be produced. Other two classes will die. So the vg and ss seem to be linked and located on the same chromosome.

**Locating the breaking points in translocation :** The translocation of vg and ss segment could be easily understood. The individual of translocation heterozygote is easily seen in the meiotic prophase or in the salivary gland chromosome.

The translocation heterozygote may be expected to produce a cross-shaped pairing configuration and during metaphase a ring or circle or twisted structure is observed under the microscope, or if chiasma is failed to form, an open chain of four chromosomes are observed.

In salivary gland chromosome, a four-armed structure is appeared. Each arm of a figure appears to be a single chromosome, but actually it is made up of a pair homologous

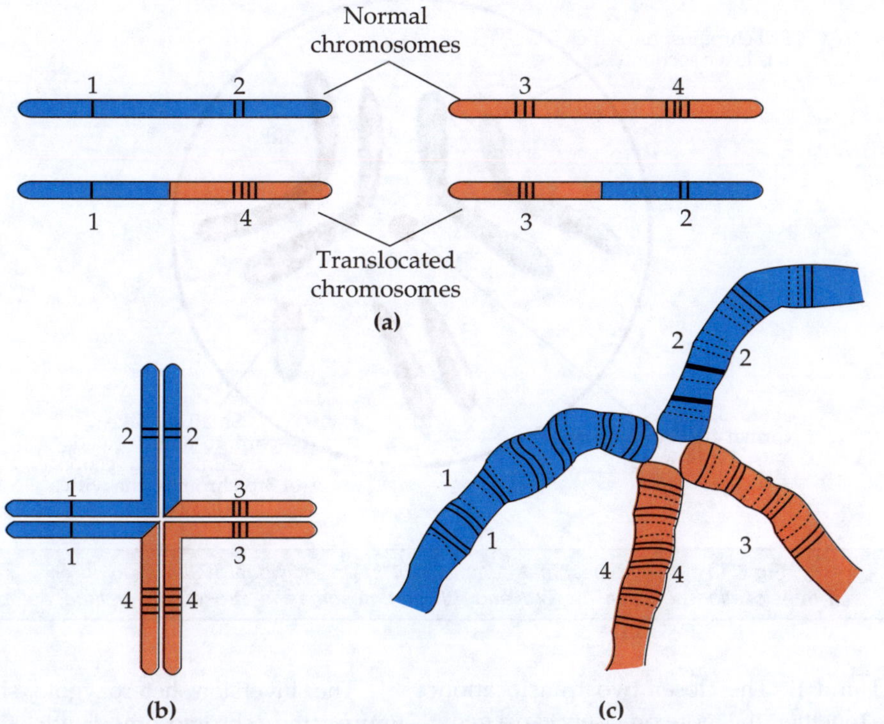


**Fig.8.13 :** *Salivary gland chromosomes of a translocation heterozygote, (a) and (b) are diagramatic; (c) is actual specimen under microscope.*

segments which can be seen at the base of the arm where the two segments are pulled singly apart.

Here we can understand at what point (or between bands) the breakage occurred with normal arrangement of the bands (Fig. 8.13).

In *Drosophila*, a small 4th chromosome might be involved in a translocation with one of the large one. A study of recombination disclosed that the third chromosome has been broken between loci of the gene *pink* and *curled*. The chromosome of female heterozygote for this, translocation may appear as the fig. 8.13. One of the large V-shaped chromosome, one of its limbs becomes much shortened. There is only one free dot like 4th chromosome which is not present in the normal chromosome component (Fig. 8.14). The interpretation is that :

The shortened V-shaped chromosome is the third chromosome, which has lost in the section corresponding to the *cu* and *Mg* interval of the linkage map. This section is attached to a part of the $4^{th}$ chromosome giving rise to a new rod like chromosome. The analysis shows that this is due to translocation.

### Locating genes by means of translocation

When a break occurs between two genes in the map of chromosome, it is possible to locate the break in the map by means of linkage tests. In this way we can determine which genes in the map are to the left of the break and which to the right. Suppose, two translocations and that each involved a break in a given kind of chromosome as indicated by broken lines I and II (Fig. 8.15).

Further linkage test would told us that a certain gene *p* was to the right to break-I and left to the break-II and therefore *p* is located between I and II and that is must, therefore, be represented by one or more of the bands included

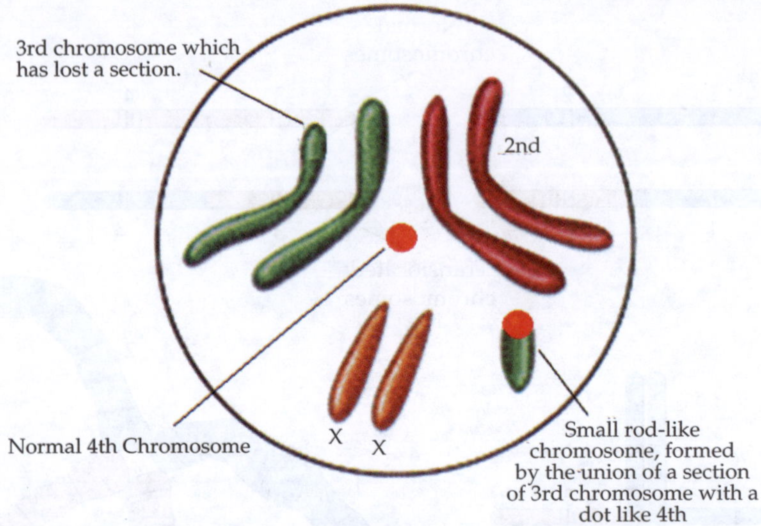


**Fig.8.14 :** *A chromosomal complement in an individual heterozygous for a translocation between the 3rd and 4th chromosomes in Drosophila melanogaster.*

between I and II. The closer two translocation breaks are together, the more precisely can a gene be located by means of them.

### 8.9.5 Inversion

The part of the chromosome rotates 180$^{o}$ without loss of genes are known as inversions.

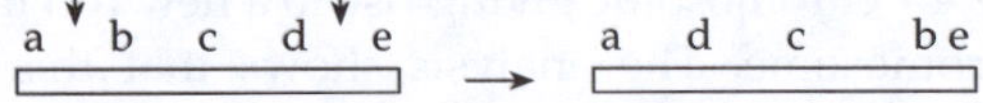


It is found that the inverted heterozygotes form a loop in meiosis and at anaphase there would produce some normal as well as abnormal gametes (Fig. 8.16).

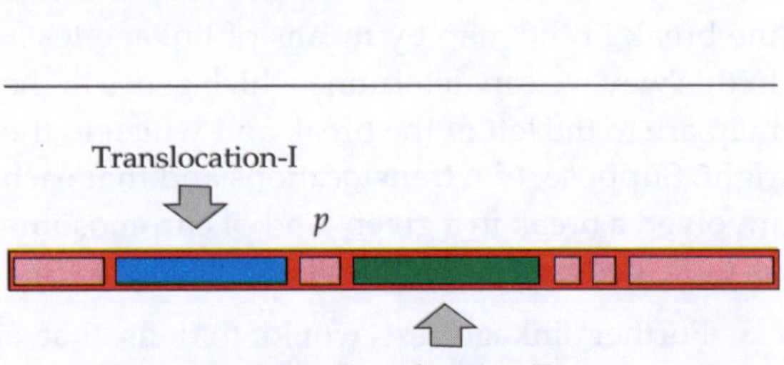


**Fig.8.15 :** *Locating a gene in a salivary gland chromosome by means of translocation.*

The inversion heterozygote shown in the figure, the chromosome with the inversion contains one break within segment 45 and other within segment 53. If we examine segments 44 and 45, it will be noted that the sequence of the bands in the inversion chromosome corresponds with that in the normal down to the line which separates segments 45 from 53 in the inversion chromosome, but here the band sequence in two chromosomes no longer corresponds. In the second figure shown in which the band sequence can be seen to correspond down to the segment marked 'X'. Now in normal chromosome (left), this band is followed by a thin continuous, dark band in the inversion (right) by a thin broken band. We know therefore that with reference to the normal chromosome (or the normal band sequence) the left inversion break (one in segment 45) occurred between the light band marked 'X' and the dark band that immediately follows it. The right inversion break (the one in segment 53) could be very precisely located in a similar manner.

### Locating genes by means of inversion

Soon after the discovery of linkage and recombination in *Drosophila melanogaster*, it was

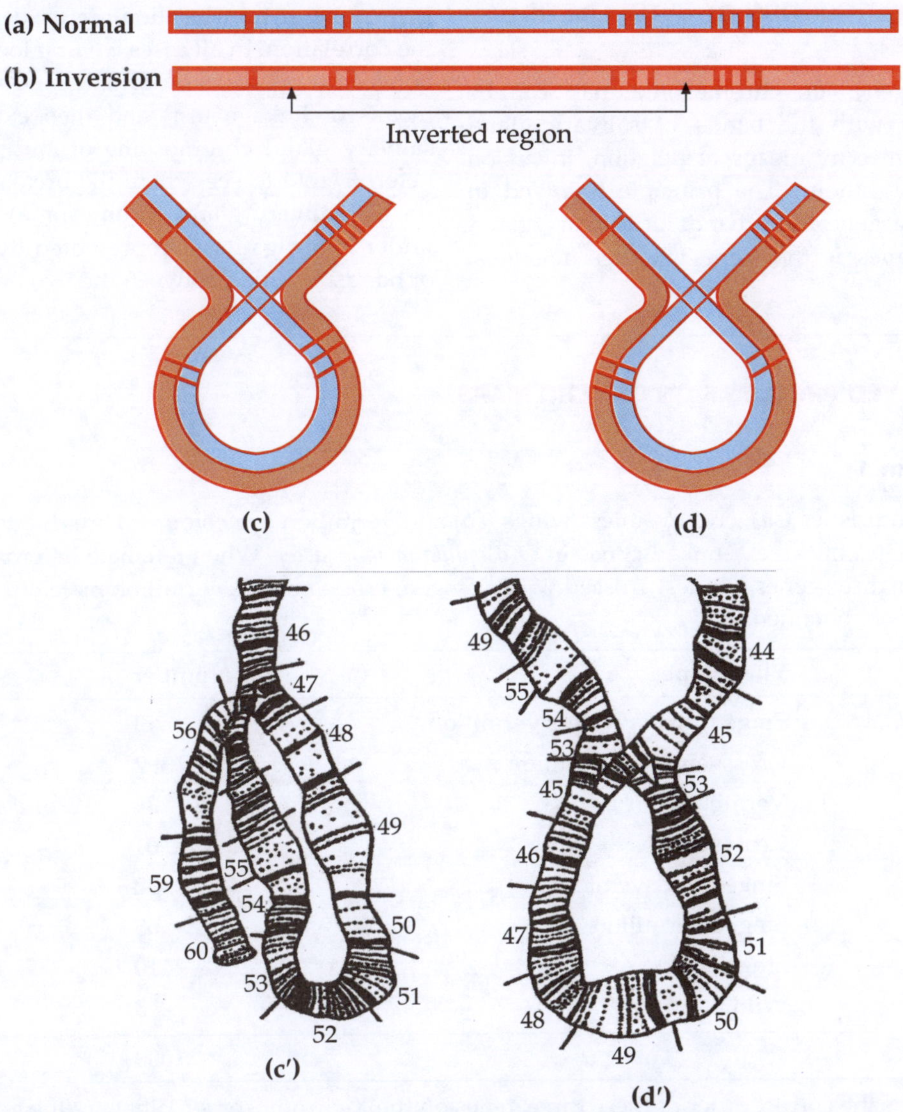


**Fig.8.16 :** *The salivary gland chromosome of an inversion heterozygote in c and c′, the normal chromosome is on the outside of the loop; in d and d′ on the inside.*

noticed that some strains of the fly contain *c-factor*, which reduces or suppresses the cross over or recombination in certain chromosome or part of a chromosome in female heterozygotes.

Sturtivant (1926) found that c-factor is nothing but the **position effect** of chromosome or inversion of chromosome.

So, in an inversion heterozygote, the cross over within the inversion is suppressed but not outside. Hence, linkage test would tell us whether a given gene was inside or outside the limits of an inversion. In case, the genes were outside, the linkage test will tell us whether the gene was to the left or to the right of the inversion.

## 8.10. CONSTRUCTION OF CYTOGENETIC MAP

The genes on chromosome map can be correlated with the bands of salivary gland chromosomes by means of deletion, inversion and translocations. The principle involved in correlating genes with bands of salivary gland chromosomes is the same whether deletions, inversions or translocation are used in making the correlation. In all cases we first locate a gene between two breaks by genetic method (i.e., by means of linkage test) and then examine the salivary gland chromosome of an appropriate heterozygote to see where the breaks occurred (in the salivary gland chromosome). The gene under investigation is represented by the band or bands included between the two breaks.

## 8.11 SOLVED PROBLEMS ON GENETIC MAPS

### Problem 1

Singed bristles (*sn*), cross-veinless wings (*cv*) and vermilion eye colour (*v*) are due to recessive mutant alleles of three X-linked genes in *Drosophila melanogaster*. When a female heterozygous for each of the three genes was test crossed with a singed, crossveinless, vermilion male, the following progeny were obtained.

| Phenotype | Number |
|---|---|
| Singed, crossveinless vermilion | 3 |
| Crossveinless, vermilion | 392 |
| Vermilion | 34 |
| Crossveinless | 61 |
| Singed crossveinless | 32 |
| Singed vermilion | 65 |
| Singed | 410 |
| Wild type | 3 |
| **Total** | **1000** |

What is the correct order of these three genes on the X-chromosome? What are the genetic map distances between *sn* and *cv*, *sn* and *v* and *cv* and *v* ? What is the coefficient of coincidence?

**Solution :**

Here the two classes of offspring, the crossveinless, vermilion and the singed are more numerous and so the genotype of heterozygous female is $\frac{cv \; + \; v}{+ \; sn \; +}$ . *i.e. cv* and *v* are on the same chromosome while *sn* is on the other.

1. The noncrossover zygotes where either *cv* and *v* or their normal genes are remained together are 392 + 410 = 802.
2. Crossing over between *cv* and *sn* genes where either *cv* and *sn* or their normal genes come together are 34 + 32 + 3 + 3 = 72. Frequency of crossing over between cv and sn = $\frac{72}{1000} \times 100 = 7.2\%$ .

3. Crossing over between $v$ and $sn$ where either $v$ and $sn$ or their normal genes come tegether is $61 + 65 + 3 + 3 = 132$. Frequency of crossing over between $v$ and $sn = \frac{132}{1000} \times 100 = 13.2\%$.

4. Crossing over between $cv$ and $v$ where either $cv$ and $v$ or their normal alleles are separated $34 + 61 + 32 + 65 = 192$. The frequency of crossing over between $cv$ and $v = \frac{192}{1000} \times 100 = 19.2\%$.

According to Morgan's hypothesis :

distance between $cv$ and $sn$ = 7.2 cM

distance between $sn$ and $v$ = 13.2 cM

distance between $cv$ and $v$ = 19.2 cM

Thus we can conclude that these three genes are arranged in the other of $cv - sn - v$

Observed frequency of double crossing over = $\frac{3+3}{1000} = 0.006$

Expected frequency of double crossing over is $0.072 \times 0.132 = 0.0095$

$$\text{Coefficient of coincedence} = \frac{\text{observed frequency of double crossing over}}{\text{Expected frequency of double crossing over}} = \frac{0.006}{0.0095} = 0.63$$

This indicates only moderate interferance.

### Problem 2

A geneticist crossed *Drosophila* females homozygous for three X-linked mutations yellow body ($y$), bar eyes ($B$) and vermilion eye color ($v$) to a wild type males. $F_1$ females, which had gray bodied bar eyes with dark red pigment were then crossed to $yB^+v$ males yielding the following results :

| Phenotype | Number |
|---|---|
| Yellow, bar, vermilion<br>Wild type | 546 |
| Yellow<br>Bar, Vermilion | 244 |
| Yellow, Vermilion<br>Bar | 160 |
| Yellow, bar<br>Vermilion | 50 |

Determine the order these loci on the X-chromosome and estimate the distances between them.

**Solution :**

According to the genotype of the homozygous female is $\frac{y\ B\ v}{y\ B\ v}$, which is then crossed with wild type of male where on the X-chromosome three normal genes are present, so its genotype would be $\underline{\underline{y^+\ B^+\ v^+}}$.

The genotype of female $F_1$ offspring would be $\frac{y\ B\ v}{y^+\ B^+\ v^+}$. It's phenotype is gray body, bar eyes and dark red pigment.

If this $F_1$ female is test crossed with $\underline{y\ B^+\ v}$, the results we get as follows.

1. Crossing over between *y* and *B* where either *y* and *B* or their normal genes are separated, which results $yB^+v/yB^+v$ (i.e. yellow, vermilion) and $yBv/yB^+v$ (bar eye) the recombintion frequency between *y* and *B* is $\frac{244 + 160}{1000} \times 100 = 40.4\%$.

2. Crossing over between *B* and *v* where *B* and *v* or their normal genes are separated.

   The recombination frequency between B and v is $\frac{160 + 50}{1000} \times 100 = 21\%$.

3. Crossing over between *y* and *v* where either *y* and *v* or their normal alleles are separated.

   The recombination frequency between *y* and *v* $= \frac{244 + 50}{1000} \times 100 = 29.4\%$

According to Morgan's hypothesis the distance between

*y* and *B* is 40.4 cM

*B* and *v* is 21 cM

*y* and *v* is 29.4 cM

Thus, the distance between *B* and *v* plus *y* and *v* is approximately equal to distance between *y* and *B*.

Therefore, *v* gene is located between *y* and *B*. The sequence of the genetic maps is

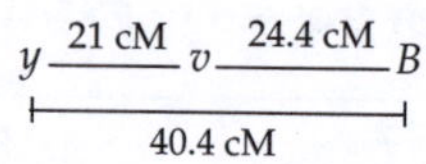


### ➧ Problem 3

Assume that in *Drosophila* there are three genes *x*, *y* and *z* with each mutant allele recessive to the wild type allele. A cross between female heterozygous for these three loci and wild type males yielded the following progeny

| | | |
|---|---|---|
| Females : | +++ | 1010 |
| Males : | +++ | 39 |
| | ++*z* | 430 |
| | +*yz* | 32 |
| | *x*++ | 27 |
| | *xy*+ | 441 |
| | *xyz* | 31 |
| | **Total** | **2010** |

Using the data, construct a linkage map of the three genes and calculate the coefficient of coincidence

**Solution :**

The parental combinations would be nummerous. Here frequencies of ++z and *xy*+ are numerous, therefore the genotype of female heterozygous is $\frac{xy+}{++z}$. This is then crossed with wild type $\frac{+++}{\longrightarrow}$ males.

Only male offspring are to be considered.

1. When crossing over has taken place between *x* and *y* then *x* and *y* or their normal alleles are separated. The recombination frequency is $\frac{39+32}{1000} = 0.71$ *i.e.* 7.1%.

2. When crossing over has taken place between *y* and *z* then both *y* and *z* or their normal alleles come together.

   The recombination frequency is $\frac{39+32+27+31}{1000} = 0.129$ *i.e.* 12.9%.

3. When crossing over has taken place between x and z, then x an z or their normal alleles come together.

   The recombination frequency = $\frac{27+31}{1000} = 0.58$ *i.e* 5.8%.

   According to Morgan's hypothesis distance between *x* and *y* = 7.1 cM

   *y* and *z* = 12.9 cM

   *x* and *z* = 5.8 cM

   Here, the distance between x and y plus between *x* and *z* is equal to *y* and *z*

   Therefore *x* gene lies between *y* and *z*.

   The sequence of there genes in the genetic map is y —7.1 cM— x —5.8 cM— z (12.9 cM)

The genotype of $F_1$ female is $\frac{y\ x\ +}{+\ +\ z}$.

Due to double crossing over the offspring would be $\underline{y\ +\ +}$ and $\underline{+\ x\ z}$. Their frequencies are zero.

Therefore the coefficient of coincidence is zero.

### Problem 4

Female *Drosophila* heterozygous for three recessive mutations ebony body (*e*) scarlet eyes (*st*) and spineless bristles (*ss*) were test crossed, and the following results were obtained.

| Phenotype | Number | Phenotype | Number |
|---|---|---|---|
| Wild type | 67 | ebony | 8 |
| ebony, scarlet | 68 | ebony, spineless | 347 |
| ebony, scarlet, spineless | 78 | scarlet | 368 |
| scarlet, spineless | 10 | spineless | 54 |

(a) What indicates that the genes are linked?

(b) What was the genotype of the original heterozygous females?

(c) What is the order of the genes?

(d) What is the map distance between *e* and *st* and between *st*, *e* and *ss*?

(e) What is the coefficient of coincidence?

(f) Diagram of crosses of the experiment.

**Solution :**

Here, the frequency of ebony, opineless is 347 and scarlet is 368, which are numerous. Hence female heterozygote possesses *e* and *ss* genes on one cromosome and *st* on the other chromosome. Thus its genotype would be $\frac{e\ ss\ +}{+\ +\ st}$.

1. When crossing over occurs between *e* and *ss*, these genes or their normal genes are separated. The recombination frequency between *e* and *ss* is $\frac{8+68+10+54}{1000} = 0.140 = 14\%$.
2. When crossing over occurs between *ss* and *st*, these genes or their normal genes come together. The recombintion frquency between *ss* and *st* is $\frac{10+8+78+67}{1000} = 0.163 = 16.3\%$.
3. When crossing over occurs between *e* and *st*, these genes or their normal genes come together. The recombination frequency is $\frac{67+68+78+54}{1000} = 0.267 = 26.7\%$

According to Morgan's hypothesis distance between *e* and *ss* is 14 cM

*ss* and *st* is 16.3 cM

*e* and *st* is 26.7 cM

Therefore, distance between *e* and *ss* plus between *ss* and *st* is approximately equal to distance between *e* and *st* The sequence fo genes is as follows $\overset{e \xrightarrow{14\text{ cM}} ss \xrightarrow{16.3\text{ cM}} st}{\underset{26.7\text{ cM}}{\longmapsto}}$.

Therefore, the genotype of $F_1$ female is $\frac{e\ ss\ +}{+\ +\ st}$.

Due to double crossing over the gametes would be $\underline{e\ +\ +}$ and $\underline{+\ ss\ st}$. The zygotes would be $\frac{e\ +\ +}{e\ ss\ st}$ and $\frac{+\ ss\ st}{e\ ss\ st}$ Their frequencies are 8 + 10.

The recombintion frequency of double crossing over is $\frac{8+10}{1000} = 0.018$.

The expected double crossing over frequency is $0.14 \times 0.163 = 0.02282$.

The coefficient of coincidence = $\frac{0.018}{0.02282} = 0.7887$.

The diagram of the cross is as follows :

Genotype of female heterozygote $\frac{e\ ss\ +}{+\ +\ st}$

Genotype of male $\frac{e\ ss\ st}{\ }$. Then see the table

| Crossing over between | ♀ gametes | ♂ gametes | ♀ Zygotes | ♂ Zygotes | Phenotype |
|---|---|---|---|---|---|
| No crossing over | *e*<br>*ss*<br>+ | *e*<br>*ss*<br>*st* | *e* ‖ *e*<br>*ss* ‖ *ss*<br>+ ‖ *st* | *e*<br>*ss*<br>+ | ebony, spineles |
| | +<br>+<br>*st* | | + ‖ *e*<br>+ ‖ *ss*<br>*st* ‖ *st* | +<br>+<br>*st* | scarlet |
| e and ss | *e*<br>+<br>*st* | *e*<br>*ss*<br>*st* | *e* ‖ *e*<br>+ ‖ *ss*<br>*st* ‖ *st* | *e*<br>+<br>*st* | ebony, scarlet |
| | +<br>*ss*<br>+ | | + ‖ *e*<br>*ss* ‖ *ss*<br>+ ‖ *st* | +<br>*ss*<br>+ | spineless |
| ss and st | *e*<br>*ss*<br>*st* | *e*<br>*ss*<br>*st* | *e* ‖ *e*<br>*ss* ‖ *ss*<br>*st* ‖ *st* | *e*<br>*ss*<br>*st* | ebony, spineless, scarlet |
| | +<br>+<br>+ | | + ‖ *e*<br>+ ‖ *ss*<br>+ ‖ *st* | +<br>+<br>+ | wild-type |
| e and ss, ss and st double crossing over | *e*<br>+<br>+ | *e*<br>*ss*<br>*st* | *e* ‖ *e*<br>+ ‖ *ss*<br>+ ‖ *st* | *e*<br>+<br>+ | ebony |
| | +<br>*ss*<br>*st* | | + ‖ *e*<br>*ss* ‖ *ss*<br>*st* ‖ *st* | +<br>*ss*<br>*st* | Spneless, scarlet |

### Problem 5

The following three recessive genes are found in corn : *bt* (brittle endosperm), *gl* (glossy leaf) *rgdl* (ragged seedling). A trihybrid of unknown origin is test crossed, producing the following offspring.

| Phenotype | Number |
|---|---|
| brittle, glossy, ragged | 236 |
| brittle glossy | 241 |
| ragged | 219 |
| glossy | 23 |
| wild-type | 224 |
| brittle ragged | 17 |
| glossy ragged | 21 |
| brittle | 19 |
| **Title** | **1000** |

(a) If the genes are linked, determine the relative order and map distances.

(b) Reconstruct the chromosomes of the trihybrid.

(c) If there any cross over interferance? If yes, how much?

**Solution :**

Here the parental gentoype may be $\frac{bt\ \ gl\ \ rgdl}{+\ \ +\ \ +}$ or $\frac{bt\ \ gl\ \ +}{+\ \ +\ \ rgdl}$ because the number of offspring brittle, glossy ragged plus wild type is 460 which is also equals with the brittle glossy plus ragged phenotypes.

We may consider the first one as the trihybrid. If this is crossed with tripple recessive the following results we get

1. Crossing over between *bt* and *gl* causes separation of these genes or their normal genes.

   The recombintion frequency between *bt* and *gl* is $\frac{21+19}{1000} = 0.04 = 4\%$.

2. Crossing over between *gl* and *rdgl* causes the separation of *gl* and *rdgl* and their normal genes.

   The recombination frequency = $\frac{241+219+17+23}{1000} = 0.500 = 50\%$.

3. Crossing over between *bt* and *rgdl* causes the separation of these genes or their normal genes.

   The recombination frequency between *bt* and *rgdl* is $\frac{241+219+21+19}{1000} = 0.500 = 50\%$.

   Here the distance between *bt* and *rgdl* is (= 50 cM) equals with the distance between *bt* and *rdgl* ( = 50 cM). The distance between *bt* and *gl* is 4 cM.

   This indicates that *bt* and *gl* genes are located very close together either on the left or right sides of each other. The arrangement of these genes would be as follows

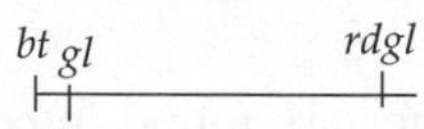


*or*

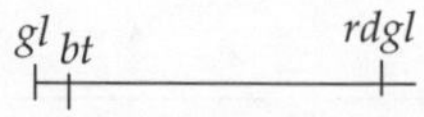


The observed double crossing over is $\frac{17+23}{1000} = 0.04$ when *bt, gl* and *rdgl* is the sequence and $\frac{21+19}{1000} = 0.04$ when *gl, bt rdgl* is the sequence. In both cases expected double crossing over is = 0.04 × 0.50.

The coefficient of coincidence = $\frac{0.04}{0.04 \times 0.5} = 2$.

The crossover interference = 1 – 2 = –1 = –100%

The crossover interference is negative which means that more double crossing overs than the expected. In this situation, the occurrence of one crossover seems to enhance the probability, that crossovers will occur in adjacent regions.

## Chapter Glossary/Key Terms

**Ascus :** The sac in Ascomycete fungi that holds the ascospores.

**Centi-Morgan (cM) :** Same as mapunit.

**Coefficient of coincidence :** The number of observed double crossover, divided by the number expected based on the independent occurrence of crossovers.

**Degree of interference :** Reduced quantity of double crossing over.

**First division segregation :** The allelic arrangement of ordered spores that indicate the lack of recombination between a locus and its centromere.

**Genetic mapping :** Any method used to determine the linear order of genes as they are linked to each other along the same chromosome.

**Interference :** The occurrence of crossing over at one point affects the probability of its occurrence elsewhere in th same chromosome.

**Linkage mapping :** The mapping of genes of other genetic sequences along a chromosome by analyzing the outcome of crosses.

**Lod score method :** The technique logarithmic odds for determining the most likely recombination frequency between two loci from pedigree data.

**Map distance :** The relative distance between sites along a single chromosome.

**Map unit :** A unit of map distance obtained from genetic cross, which is equivalent to 1% recombinant offspring in a test cross.

**Mating type :** In some microorganisms, mating can take place only between dividuals of opposite mating types due to the interaction of cell surface components.

**Negative interference :** The phenomenon whereby a crossover in a particular region facilitates the occurrence of other apparent corssover in the same region of the cromosome.

**Nonparental ditype :** A spore arrangement in ascomycete fungi that contains only the two recombinant type ascospores.

**Parental ditype :** A spore arrangement in ascomycete fungi that contains only the two nonrecombinant type ascospores.

**Positive interference :** When the occurrence of one crossover reduces the probability that a second will occur in the same region.

**Pseudodominance :** A pattern of inheritance that occurs when a single copy of a recessive allele is phenotypically expressed because the second copy of the gene has been deleted from the homologous chromosome.

**Second division segregation :** The allelic arrangement in the spores of Ascomycete fungi with ordered spores that indicates a crossover between a locus and its centromere.

**Tetratype :** A spore arrangement in Ascomycete fungi that consists of the two parental and two recombinant spores.

**Three-point cross :** A cross involving three loci.

**Two-point cross :** A cross involving two loci.

# EXERCISE

## A. Long answer type questions :

1. Define linkage map.
2. What is two-point test cross? Describe it with example.
3. Define three-point test cross. Describe the method of linkage mapping of genes by three-point test cross.
4. What is coincidence and coefficient of coincedence?
5. What is degree of interference? How do the degree of interference is measured?
6. Why multiple crossing over causing difficulties to map genes?
7. Describe tetrad analysis of yeast.
8. Describe the tetrad analysis of *Neurospora* and determining the gene order.
9. What are the drawbacks of genetic mapping in human by pedigree analysis?
10. Describe the mechanism of gene mapping in human beings by pedigree analysis.
11. What is lod score? How the lod score is calculated? Give an example to use lod score in the human pedigree analysis.
12. Distinguish genetic map and cytogenetic map. How the cytogenetic mapping is done in *Drosophila*.
13. In the house mouse, the autosomal alleles, *"trembling"* and *"rex"* (short hair) are dominant to not trembling (normal) and long hair respectively. Heterozygous trembling, rex females were crossed with normal, long-haired males and yielded the following offspring :

| | |
|---|---|
| Trembling, Rex | 42 |
| Trembling, long-haired | 105 |
| Normal, Rex | 109 |
| Normal, long haired | 44 |

(a) Are the two genes linked? How do you know?

(b) In the heterozygous females, were *trembling*, and *rex* in *cis* or *trans* positions? Explain.

(c) Calculate the percent recombination between the two genes.

14. In *Drosophila*, a cross of

$$\frac{a^+b^+c\ d\ e}{a b c^+d^+e^+} \times \frac{a\ b\ c\ d\ e}{a\ b\ c\ d\ e}$$

gave 1000 progeny of the following phenotypes.

| | Genotype | Phenotype |
|---|---|---|
| 01. | $a^+\ b^+\ c\ d\ e$ | 220 |
| 02. | $a^+\ b^+ c\ d\ e^+$ | 230 |
| 03. | $a\ b\ c^+\ d^+\ e$ | 210 |
| 04. | $a\ b\ c^+\ d^+\ e^+$ | 215 |
| 05. | $a\ b^+ c^+\ d^+\ e$ | 12 |
| 06. | $a\ b^+\ c^+\ d^+\ e^+$ | 13 |
| 07. | $a^+\ b\ c\ d\ e^+$ | 16 |
| 08. | $a^+\ b\ c\ d\ e$ | 14 |
| 09. | $a\ b^+\ c^+\ d\ e^+$ | 14 |
| 10. | $a\ b^+ c^+\ d\ e$ | 13 |
| 11. | $a^+\ b\ c\ d^+\ e^+$ | 8 |
| 12. | $a^+\ b\ c\ d^+\ e$ | 8 |
| 13. | $a^+\ b^+\ c^+\ d\ e^+$ | 7 |
| 14. | $a^+\ b^+\ c^+\ d\ e$ | 7 |
| 15. | $a\ b\ c\ d^+\ e^+$ | 6 |
| 16. | $a\ b\ c\ d^+\ e$ | 7 |

(a) Draw a genetic map of the chromosome indicating the linkage of the five genes and the number of map units separating each.

(b) From the single-crossover frequencies, what would be the expected frequency of $a^+b^+c^+d^+e^+$ flies.

[ **Hints :** At first to be considered two genes at a time suppose a and b gene pair. Calculate parental type progeny and the recombinant type progeny. Then calculate recom-bination frequency by the formula

$$\left[\frac{\text{recombinant type progeny}}{\text{parental type progeny}}\right]$$

If this is 50% then this pair is not linked.

Develop map starting with the smallest distances, as they are the most accurate.]

16. In the tomato three mutant genes on the same chromosome are oblate (flattened fluit) gne-*o*, peach (hairy fruit) gene *p* and compound inflorescence gene-*s*.

When $F_1$ heterozygate was test crossed following results obtained

| Phenotype | Frequency |
|---|---|
| + + + | 73 |
| + + s | 348 |
| + p + | 2 |
| + p s | 96 |
| o + + | 110 |
| o + s | 2 |
| o p + | 306 |
| o p s | 63 |
| Total | 1000 |

(a) Determine the genotype of F1 hybrid

(b) Determine the sequence of these three genes

(c) Draw a linkage map

(d) Calculate the coefficient of coincidence

17. Two normal *Drosophhila* are crossed and yield following phenotypes among the progeny. Give the parental genotypes, gene arrangement in the female parent, map distances the coefficient of coincidence and cross-over interferance.

| | *Phenotype* | *Frequency* |
|---|---|---|
| Females : | + + + | 2000 |
| Males : | + + + | 3 |
| | a b c | 1 |
| | + b c | 840 |
| | a + + | 85 |
| | a b + | 825 |
| | + + c | 100 |
| | a + c | 72 |
| | + b + | 74 |
| | Total | 4000 |

**B. Short answer type questions.**

1. What is genetic map? Why this is also called linkage map?
2. What is two-point test cross?
3. What is the principle of gene mapping by using two-point test cross?
4. What is the drawbacks of two-point test related gene mapping?
5. What is three-point test cross? Why third marker is used? What is the advantage of three-point test-cross?
6. What is centiMorgan unit in linkage mapping?
7. What are the difficulties in linkage mapping when multiple crossing over takes place?
8. What is interference in crossing over?
9. Define positive and negative interference.
10. What is coefficient of coincidence? How it can be measured?
11. How the degree of interference can be measured?
12. What is haploid mapping?
13. Define parental ditype, nonparental ditype and tetratype with examples.
14. How the map unit is determined in tetrad analysis?
15. Define first division segregation and second division segregation?
16. How the map distance is measured in tetrad analysis?
17. How the gene order and its centromere position can be determined in tetrad analysis.
18. Why linkage mapping is virtually impossible in human beings?
19. For gene mapping in human by pedigree analysis, what kind of gene marker is used?
20. What is lod score?
21. What are the criteria for lod score measure?
22. What is the parameter of the lod scrore?
23. What kind of lod score can be considered and accepted?
24. What is cytological mapping of chromosome?

25. What is cytogenetic mapping of chromosome?
26. How the cytogenetic map is done?
27. What are the basis of cytogenetic mapping?
28. How deletion can be the basis of cytogenetic mapping? Give example.
29. How duplication can be the basis of cytogenetic mapping? Give example.
30. How translocation can be used for genetic detection, locating breakpoints and locating the genes?
31. What is the advantage of using Neurospora in tetrad analysis than yeast?

**Write short notes on :**

Two-point and three-point test cross

Coefficient of coincidence

Interference on crossing over

Unseen multiple crossing over.

Tetrad analysis in Yeast and its map distance.

Tetrad analysis in *Neurospora* and its map distance.

Lod score.

Cytogenetic map.

# 9

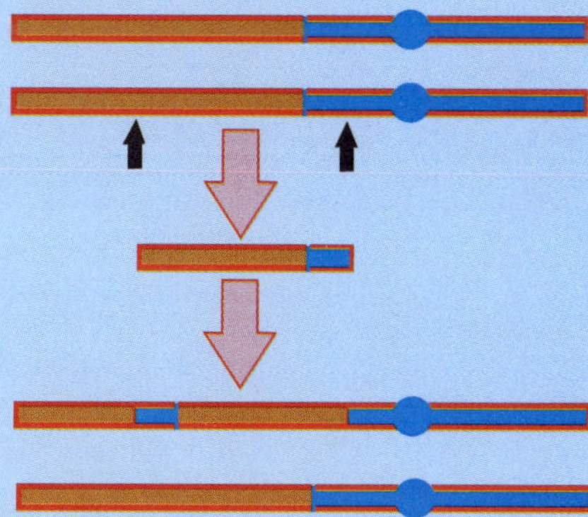

# Sex-linked inheritance

**CHAPTER AGENDA**

**9.1** Concept; **9.2** Sex-linkage in *Drosophila*; **9.3** Sex-linked inheritance in man; **9.4** Sex-linked lethals in man; **9.5** Sex-linked genes in Poultry and in Moths; **9.6** Sex-influenced gene; **9.7** Sex-limited gene; **9.8** Solved Problems on Sex-linked inheritance; Chapter Glossary/Key Terms; Exercise

## 9.1 CONCEPT

Sex-linked inheritance is a type of inheritance in which characters other than sex are inherited alongwith X and Y chromosomes, because the genes for these characters are located on the sex chromosomes. Therefore, inheritance of sex-linked characters is related to sex determination.

Sex-linked genes could be grouped into lethal, semi-lethal and non-lethals.

Certain sex-linked genes can cause death from zygote upto sexually mature adult stage is called lethals. When the sex linked genes can cause death of some individuals but the individual could survive and get maturity and reproduce are known as semi-lethal or sub-vitals.

The distinction between these categories is not sharp, especially, since genes that are lethal under some conditions may permit survival under special medical treatment.

Conventionally, genes that kill fewer that 100% but more than 50% of their victims are called semi-lethals, whereas, those that cause less than 50% mortality are known as sub-vital genes.

Sex-linked genes could be classified into three types:

(a) **X-linked :** The genes are localized in the homologous sections of X-chromosomes and that have no corresponding alleles in Y-chromosome. The X-linked genes are commonly known as sex-linked genes.

(b) **Y-linked :** The Y-linked type sex-linked inheritance is performed by those genes which are localized in the section of Y-chromosome. The Y-linked genes are commonly known as **holandric genes.**

(c) **X-Y-linked :** The X-Y linked type sex-linked inheritance is performed by those genes which are localized in homologous sections of X and Y chromosomes.

## 9.2 SEX-LINKAGE IN *DROSOPHILA*

### 9.2.1 Inheritance of X-linked gene for eye-colour in *Drosophila* (Non lethal).

In *Drosophila*, the gene for white eye colour is X-linked and recessive to another X-linked dominant gene for red eye colour. It is discovered by Morgan (1910) and showed characteristics of **criss-cross** inheritance.

$w$ = white eye colour (recessive)

$W$= Red eye colour (dominant)

(a) **Red eyed female X white eyed male :**

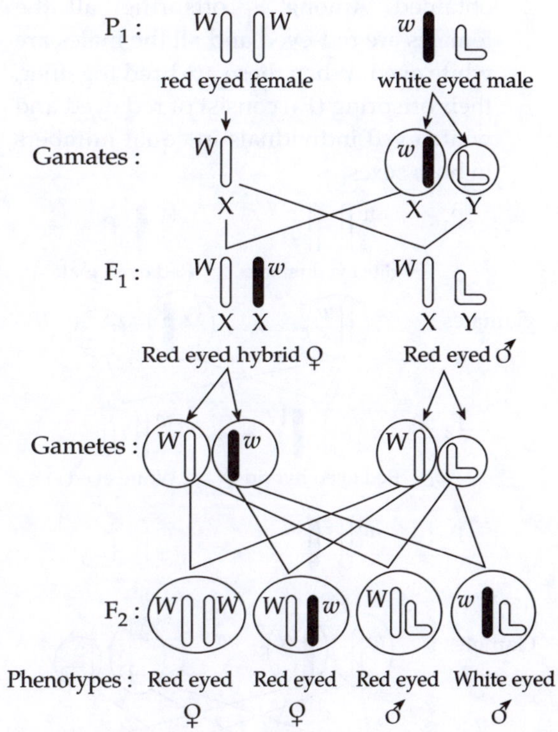


From the cross, the first generation flies are red-eyed in both sexes. When these bred together, white reappears in a quarter of the $F_2$ offspring indicating that red and white eye colours are due to an allelic pair of genes of which red acts as the dominant. However, of the $F_2$ offspring all the females are red, whereas, half the males are red and half are white. The females are of two kinds genotypically. Half of them give nothing but the red offspring, half must carry the recessive white, for in their offspring half the males are white eyed.

So, in *Drosophila*, sex-linked traits such as white eye color follow a criss-cross inheritance. **The male (grand-father) transmits his sex-linked recessive traits to his grand-sons through his daughters, never to or through his sons.**

(b) **Red eyed male X white eyed female :** When a red eyed male is bred to a white eyed female, quite different result is obtained. Among $F_1$ offspring, all the females are red-eyed and all the males are white eyed. When these are bred together, their offspring ($F_2$) consist of red eyed and white eyed individuals in equal numbers in both sexes.

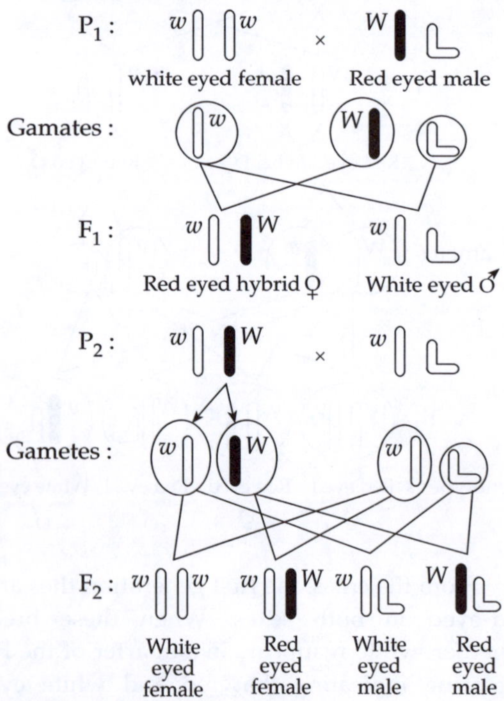


## 9.2.2 X-Y linked inheritance

The sex-linked genes contained in the X-chromosome of *Drosophila* have no alleles in the Y-chromosome. This is the reason why a male that carries a single dose of a recessive sex-linked gene shows its effects in the phenotype. The Y-chromosome is therefore genetically "empty" or "inert" at least compared with X-chromosome. One gene **bobbed**, however, has alleles both in the X and in the Y-chromosomes. The recessive mutant allele of bobbed, when present in both X-chromosomes of a female, causes bristles on the body of the fly to be shorter and slender than the normal. A male carrying bobbed in the X-chromosome but normal allele of the gene in the Y-has normal bristles. If such a male is crossed with bobbed females all the sons have normal bristles and all the daughters are bobbed. The normal bristles are transmitted from father to sons.

*b* = Bobbed bristles (Recessive)

\+ = Normal bristles (Dominant)

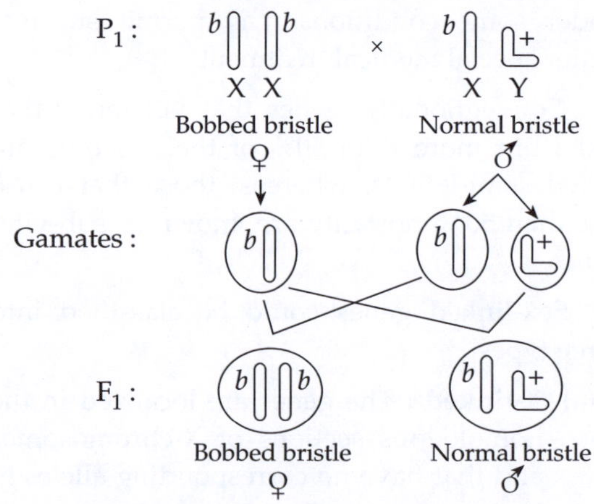


## 9.2.3 Sex-linked Lethals in *Drosophila*

In *Drosophila*, occasionally half the sons in a family are missing. The sex ratio is 2 females : 1 male.

In families, mother contains a mutation known as a lethal *(l)* in one of her X-chromosome and other X-chromosome has its normal allele (+). The hybrid mother survives because she contains the dominant normal allele in one of her X-chromosomes and this prevents the lethal from expressing itself. But half of her sons receive her lethal containing-X-chromosome and die. The remaining offspring receive at least one normal X-chromosome and survive. Hence a sex ratio of 2 females : 1 male results.

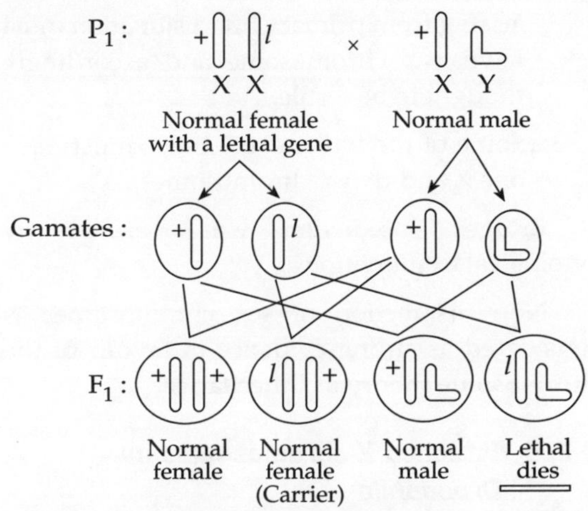


### 9.2.4 Primary Nondisjunction of X-chromosome in *Drosophila*

Normally, when white-eyed *Drosophila* females crossed with red-eyed males produce red eyed daughters and white eyed sons in the $F_1$ generation.

However, there are some exceptions of this rule. About one fly in 2000 $F_1$ offspring has the unexpected eye colour, red in males and white in females. This appearance contradicts the Morgan's assumption. Bridges solved the problem. His reasoning was as follows.

The white eyed exceptional females must carry two X-chromosomes, since their sex is female and they must have inherited both their X-chromosomes from their mothers, since the colour of their eyes is white. Similarly, the red eyed exceptional males must have one X-chromosome which must have come from their father since their eyes are red.

$w$ = white eye (recessive)

$W$ = red eye (dominant)

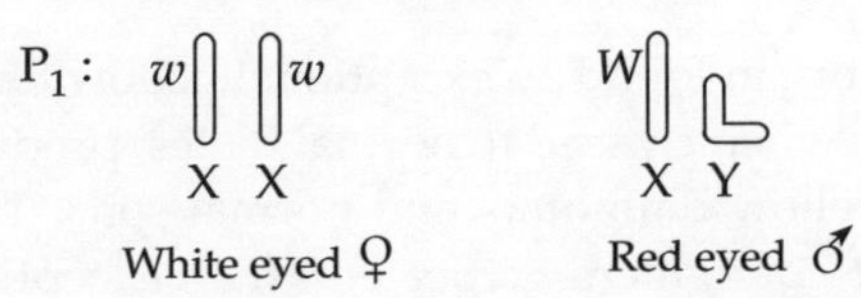


Gametes :

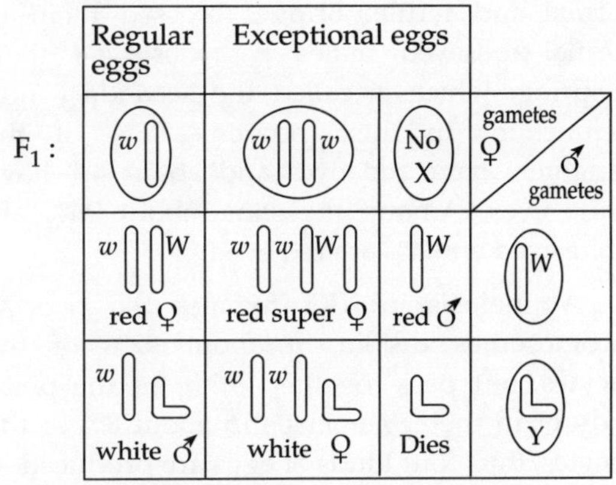


Bridges supposed that the two X-chromosomes present in a female may occasionally fail to disjoin at the meiotic division as they would normally do. This primary non-disjunction leads to production of eggs with two X-chromosomes and of eggs with no X-chromosome.

Such exceptional gametes (eggs) of white females would be fertilized by the normal spermatozoa of red eyed males. This fertilization would give 6 types of zygotes.

(i) Red eyed females (with XX)

(ii) White eyed males (with XY)

(iii) With three X chromosomes red eyed super females, usually dies.

(iv) With two X-chromosomes and a Y-chromosome, white female.

(v) With only one X-chromosome red male.

(vi) With only one Y-chromosome with no X-chromosome, is not viable and dies.

This prediction was also verified by cytological examinations.

### 9.2.5 Secondary Non-disjunction of X-chromosomes in *Drosophila*

The exceptional males without the Y-chromosome are sterile but they are quite normal male in their appearance and in behaviour.

The white eyed XXY females are, however, normal and fertile. Bridges crossed them to normal red-eyed males and observed their offspring, which is called the secondary non disjunction. In their progeny 96% of the daughters have red eyes and about 4% have white eyes. Among the sons, about 96% are white eyed and 4% are red eyed.

At meiosis in XXY females the two X-chromosomes disjoin in about 92% of the oocytes, but pass together either in the polar body or in the egg nucleus in about 8% of the oocytes, thus four kinds of eggs are produced

1. With a single X-chromosome.
2. With an X and a Y-chromosomes.
3. With two X-chromosomes.
4. With a Y-chromosome.

Fertilized by normal X– or Y– containing spermatozoa, 8 kinds of zygotes would be formed.

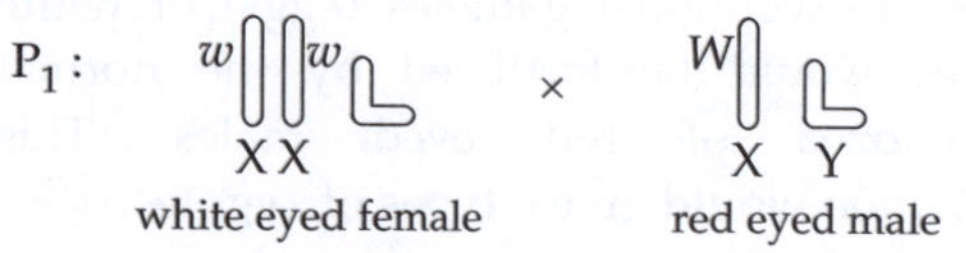


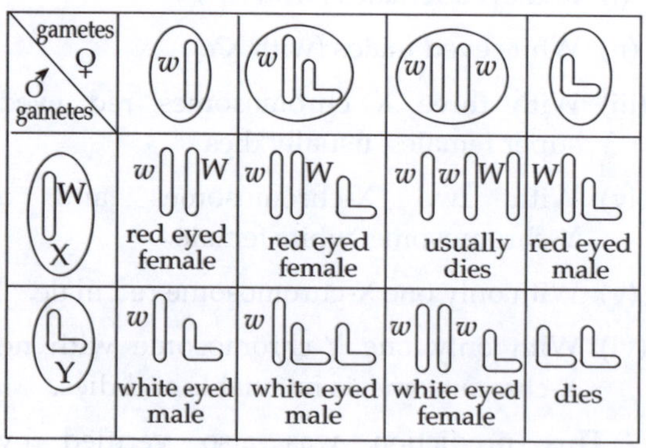


8 kinds of zygotes will not occur with equal frequencies, since at meiosis in XXY females the two X-chromosomes disjoin in about 92% of the oocytes, but pass together either in the polar body or in the egg nucleus in abut 8% of the oocytes.

1. All the white eyed females and some of the red eyed females must carry not only two X-chromosomes but also a Y-chromosome.
2. The red eyed males, in contrast to those arising from primary nondisjunction must have a Y chromosome and accordingly thought to be fertile.
3. Some of the white eyed males must have one X and two Y chromosomes.

Bridges' prediction was verified by cytological examinations.

Non disjunction of sex chromosomes is considered as strong evidence in favour of the **chromosome theory of inheritance**.

### 9.2.6 Attached X-chromosomes in *Drosophila*

In 1922 Morgan found another exceptional case of inheritance of sex linked traits in *Drosophila*.

Yellow body colour in *Drosophila melanogaster* is due to a sex linked recessive gene. Yellow females crossed with normal brownish gray males ordinarily give in $F_1$ all normal daughters and yellow sons in equal number and in $F_2$ equal numbers of yellow and gray in both sexes are observed.

y = Yellow body colour (recessive)

\+ = Gray body colour (dominant)

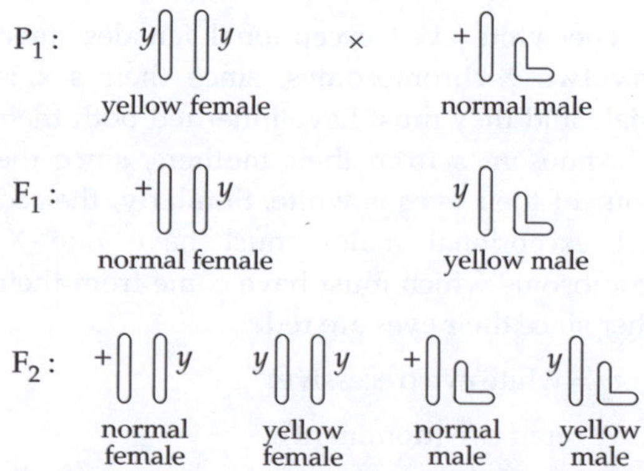


Morgan found an exceptional yellow female which, when crossed to normal males, produced only yellow daughters and normal sons. These yellow daughters repeated the exceptional performance of their mother, the sons of the original exceptional mother were all sterile, but in subsequent generations the normal sons behave like the usual normal flies.

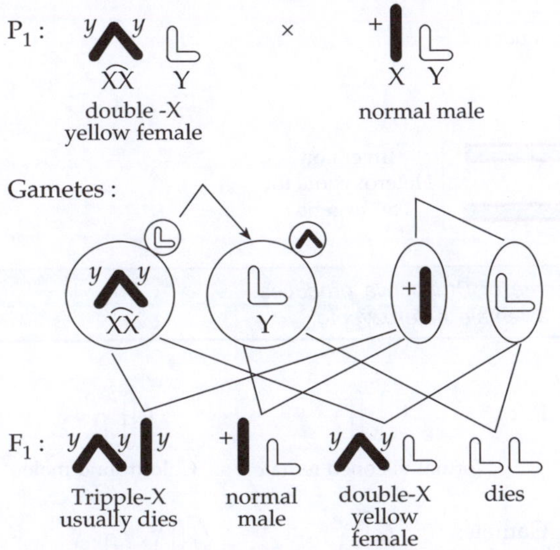


**Explanation :** The exceptional yellow females have X-chromosomes permanently attached to each other so that meiotic disjunction is no longer possible and both Xs either remain in the egg or are extruded in the polar body. Thus have produced two types of eggs, those with attached X chromosomes carrying the yellow genes and those without an X chromosome.

Fertilized by the sperm of normal male, four kinds of zygotes would be formed.

1. With two attached yellow gene containing X-chromosomes and a normal X-chromosome from the male parent.
2. Two attached yellow gene containing X-chromosome and a Y-chromosome.
3. With a normal paternal X– and a Y– chromosome.
4. With two Y-chromosome but no X-chromosomes.

Zygotes of class 2 is observed as yellow daughters and class-3 as normal sons. Zygotes of class-1 and 4 usually die, although class-1 sometimes survives to give so called **super females**.

These predictions of Morgan were tested and found to be valied.

### 9.2.7 Position effect variegation (PEV) in *Drosophila*

Position effects are either stable as in *Bar* eye of *Drosophila* or variegated as with *Drosophila* eye colour.

In *Drosophila,* red eye colour is wild ($x^+$) and dominant over white eye colour mutant, ($x^w$), which is present on their X chromosomes. Therefore, the heterozygous for these genes $X^+X^w$ would have red eyes.

If white locus (*w*) is moved through an inversion so that it comes to lie next heterochromatin, the fly shows a variegation phenotype, *i.e.* white patches of the eyes are white.

This is probably caused by a spread of the tight coiling of the heterochromatin "turning off" the expression of the locus.

In the heterozygote $X^+X^w$, the heterochromatin which comes to lie near the wild red colour gene and turned off its expression. As a result its eye becomes with white patches due to expression of only white (*w*) allele (Fig. 9.1).

## 9.3 SEX LINKED INHERITANCE IN MAN

### 9.3.1 Inheritance of X-linked Genes in Man

In man, more than 50 sex-linked genes have been reported. The most important and common X-linked genes of man are

1. Red-green colour blindness
2. Haemophilia
3. Anhydrotic ectoderma (non functional sweat gland).
4. Night blindness.
5. Myopia (short sightedness)

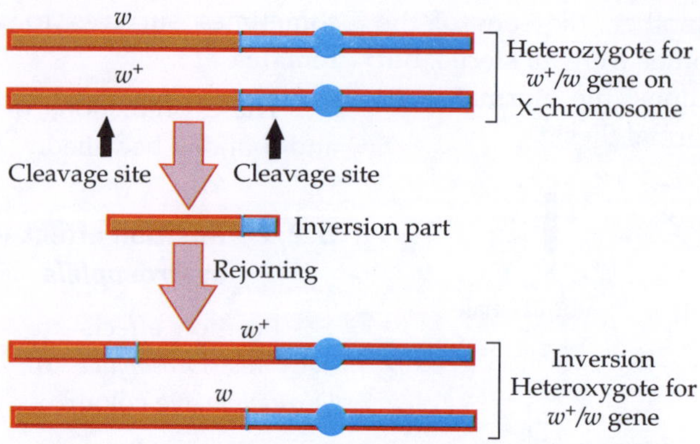


**Fig.9.1 :** *Inversion in X-chromosome of Drosophila produces variegation in eye colour in a female heterozygote.*

6. Juvenile glaucoma (hardness of eyeball)
7. White forked lock etc.

These are associated with X-linked recessive genes and are most common. Certain X-linked diseases such as **defective tooth enamel** (which results in early wearing down of teeth is caused by **dominant genes**.

**A. Inheritance of X-linked gene for colour blindness in man :** The retina of eyes of man contains colour sensitive cells which are necessary for the distinction of red and green colours. These colour sensitive retinal cells are formed and controlled by certain genes which remain located in X-chromosomes. The men having the recessive gene are unable to distinguish the red and green colour so are known as **colour blind** or **red green blind man.**

This X-linked recessive gene is able to express itself in males due to absence its any allelic gene in the Y-chromosome.

The inheritance of colour blindness can be studied in the following two types of marriage.

(a) **Marriage between colour blind man and normal visioned women**

$c$ = Colour blind gene (recessive)

\+ = Normal vision (dominant)

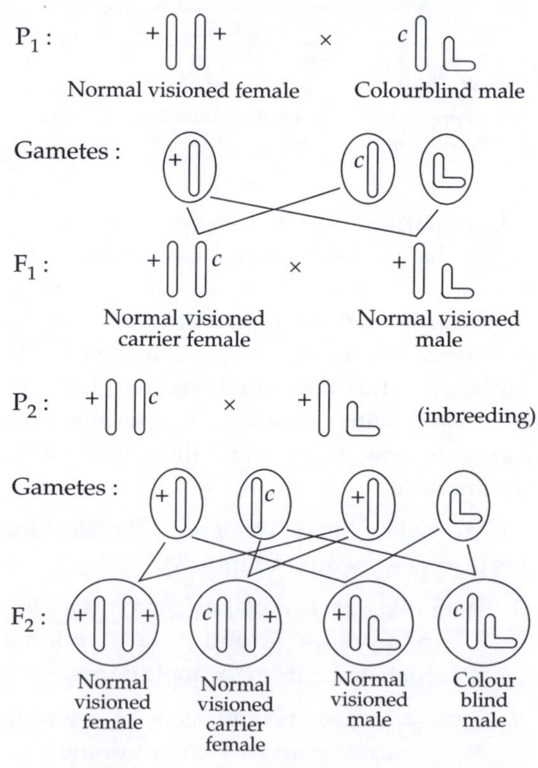


When colour blind man marries with a normal visioned woman, then they produce normal visioned male and female individuals in $F_1$. The marriage between a $F_1$ normal visioned woman and a normal visioned male, will produce in $F_2$, two normal visioned females, one normal visioned male and one colour blind male.

Thus, **criss-cross inheritance** is observed.

(b) **Marriage between normal visioned male and colour blind female.**

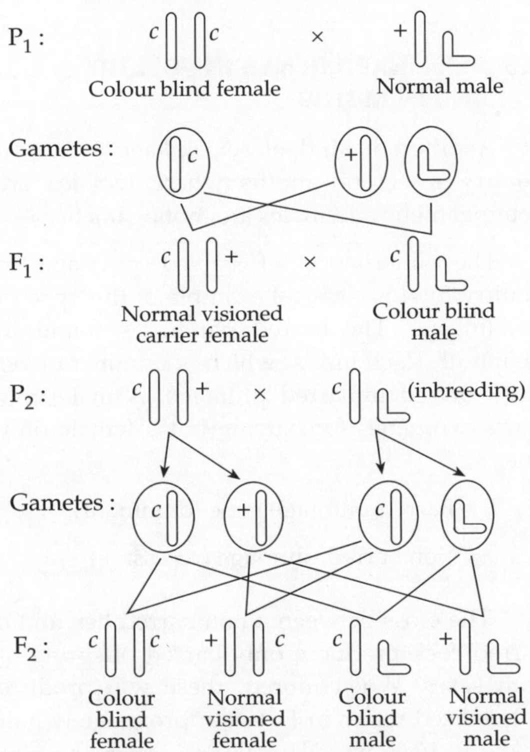


If a woman is colour blind and she happens to marry a normal visioned male, then all $F_1$ sons will be colour blind and daughters will be normal visioned, because, male receives an X-linked recessive gene for colour blindness from colour blind mother. The daughter receives an X-linked dominant gene for normal vision from father and one X-linked recessive gene for colour blindness from the mother.

If the $F_1$ daughter is again married to a colour blind male (inbreeding) then produce a colour blind homozygous daughter, a normal visioned daughter, a normal homozygous son and a homozygous colour blind son.

B. **Sex-Linked Inheritance of Haemophilia in Man :** Haemophilia is the most serious and notorious disease which is more common in men than women. This is also known as **bleeder's disease**. The person who contains the recessive genes for haemophilia lacks in normal clotting substance in blood, so minor injuries cause continuous bleeding and ultimate death of the person due to hemorrhage. This hereditary disease was first reported by John Cotto of Philadelphia in 1803 in man.

The haemophilia had been most common in royal families of Russia and England. e.g., Queen Victoria and her further generations were having the haemophilia disease.

The recessive X-linked gene of haemophilia shows characteristic crisscross inheritance.

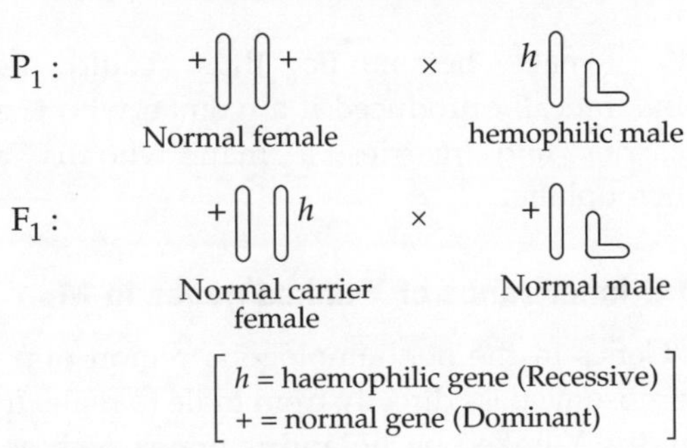


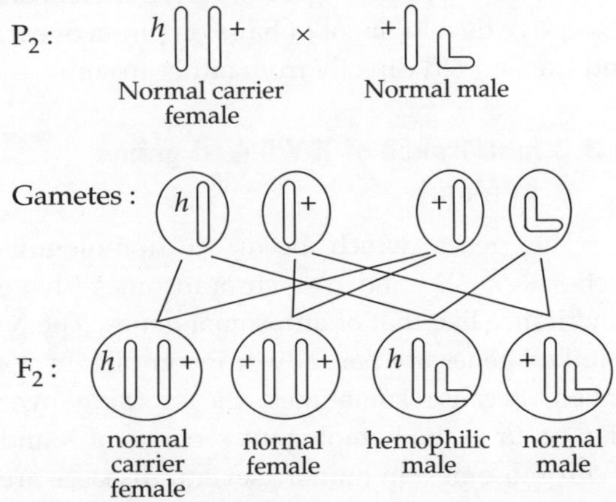


If a haemophilic man survives and reaches the reproductive age and marries a normal female, produce daughters all of whom are normal but are carriers of hemophilia and if this carrier female marries with normal male, the daughter offspring show normal (one half is pure normal and one half is carrier) while the sons will show normal and hemophilic.

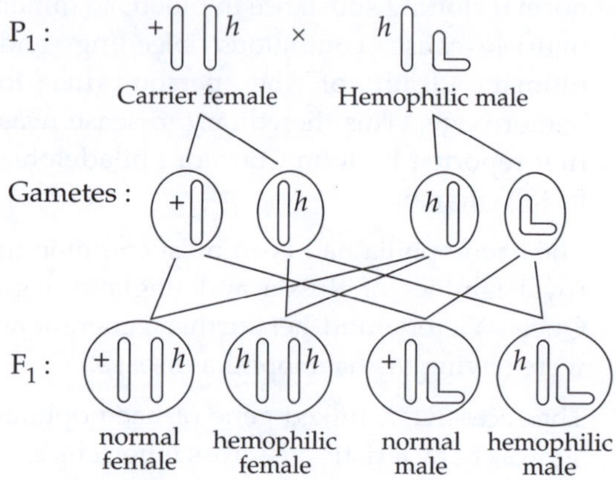


A female hemophilic thus could be theoretically produced if a woman who is a carrier and marries a man who is a hemophilic.

### 9.3.2 Inheritance of Y-linked genes in Man

Genes in the nonhomologous region of Y-chromosome pass directly from male to male. In man, the Y-linked on **holandric genes** such as, **ichthyosis hystrix gravis, hypertrichosis** (excessive development of hairs on pinna of ear) and transmitted directly from father to son.

### 9.3.3 Inheritance of X-Y linked genes in Man.

The genes which occur in homologous section of X and Y chromosomes have inheritance like that of autosomal genes. The X-Y linked genes are partially or incompletely sex linked, because sometimes, the crossing over may occur in the homologous sections of X and Y chromosomes. In human, several diseases are X-Y linked. Certain XY-linked genes of man are **total colour blindness, Xeroderma-pigmentosum, Epiper-molysis bullosa, Retinitis pigmentosa, Spastic paraplegia** etc.

## 9.4 SEX-LINKED LETHALS IN MAN

Certain sex-linked lethal genes are lethal and may cause death from egg upto sexually mature adult stage. The sex linked lethals of man are genes for *haemophilia, pseudohypertrophic muscular dystrophy* etc.

## 9.5 SEX LINKED GENES IN POULTRY AND IN MOTHS

A different kind of sex linkage occurs in poultry fowl and moths where females are heterogametic and males are monogametic.

The inheritance of barred plumage in poultry fowl is classical example of this type of sex linkage. The barred pattern is found in Plymouth Rock breed, which is dominant over black or red unbarred plumage. A male may carry two genes for barring but a female only one.

*B* = Barred plumage gene (dominant)

*b* = Non barred plumage (recessive)

The cross between a non barred hen and a barred cock produces only barred offspring of both sexes. When inbred, these will produce only barred males in $F_2$ but approximately half of the $F_2$ hens were barred and other half non barred.

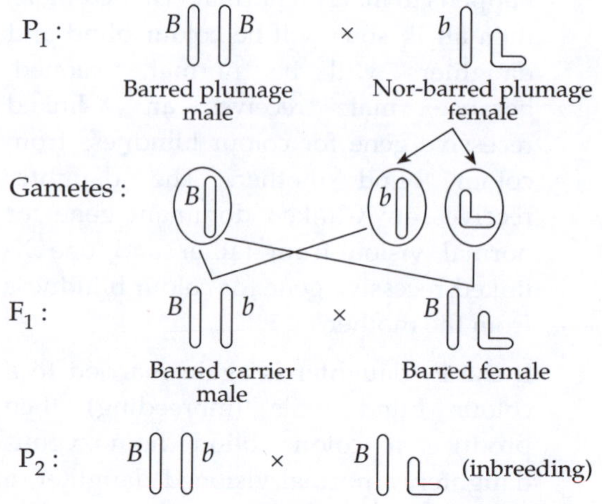

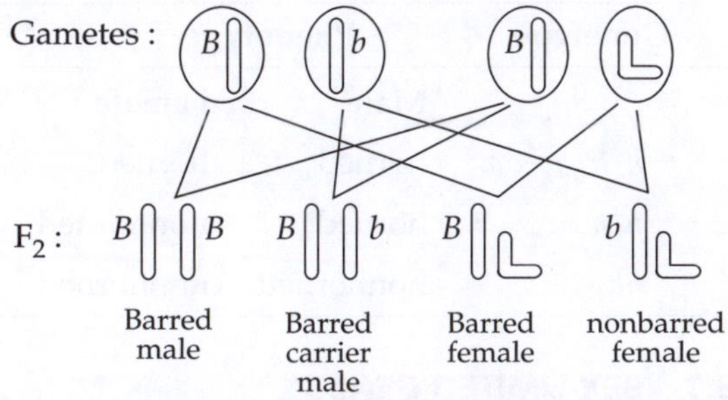


The reciprocal cross of barred hen and non barred cock gives, as might be expected a very different result. Here the $F_1$ males are all barred and the $F_1$ hens are non barred. Whereas, in $F_2$ there are equal numbers of barred and non barred birds in both sexes.

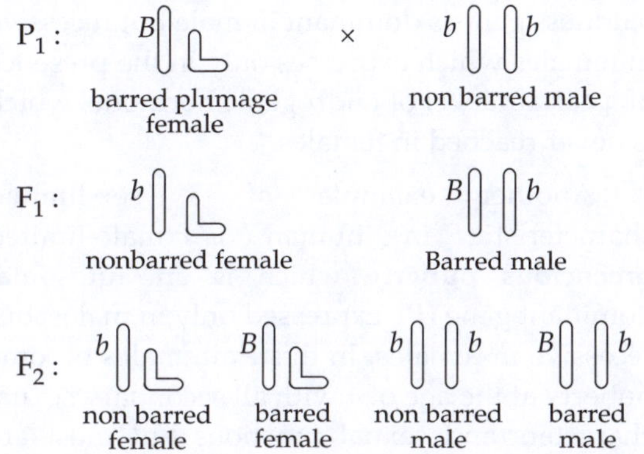


The Barred plumage character thus follows the same **criss-cross mode of inheritance** as white eyes of *Drosophila* except that in the fowl the sex linked gene goes from mother (female parent) to her sons only, whereas the male parent transmits it to both his sons and his daughters.

In fowl, pigeon, duck, several species of moths and one species of fish, sex linked characters have been studied and have found to resemble with the barred plumage in their inheritance.

## 9.6 SEX-INFLUENCED GENES

The expression of certain genes which may reside on any of the autosomes or on the homologous portions of the sex chromosomes as **a dominant trait influenced by the sex** of the bearer is called **sex-influenced gene.** These genes are inherited according to Mendel's principles, but they are expressed in males and females differently. The traits have higher prenetrace in one of the sexes.

In human beings, the pattern baldness, forelock, absence of upper lateral incisor teeth, a type of enlargement of terminal joint finger, harelip, fissure in upper lip, cleft palate (a fissure in the roof of mouth and shuttering) are severely influenced in males.

**The pattern baldness** in humans is characterized by the loss of hair prematurely from the front and top of the head. This is an autosomal trait (*B*), believed to be dominant in males and inherit the trait from either their mother or their father. In heterozygous condition males express its baldness due to presence of one dominant gene, but in females, it is nonbald. Males become nonbald if it is homozygous recessive for *b* genes *i.e. bb*. The females would be bald if only they are homozygous for *B* genes.

| Genetype | Phenotype | |
|---|---|---|
| | **Male** | **Female** |
| *BB* | Bald | Bald |
| *Bb* | Bald | nonbald |
| *bb* | nonbald | nonbald |

**The baldness pattern in humans** is due to the presence of sex hormones. Administration of male hormones may cause *Bb* females into a bald hair condition.

A non-bald mother may have a bald daughter and son.

| | | | | |
|---|---|---|---|---|
| Parent : | *BB* | | *Bb* | |
| | bald ♂ | | non bald ♀ | |
| Offspring : | *BB* | *Bb* | *BB* | *Bb* |
| | bald daughter | non-bald daughter | bald son | bald son |

Nonbald mother and father may have a bald son.

Parent : *bb* × *Bb*
non bald ♂ non bald ♀

Offspring : *Bb* *bb* *Bb* *bb*
bald son, non-bald son, non-bald daughter, non-bald daughter

If mother and father are both bald, their offspring would be bald.

Parent : *BB* *BB*
bald ♀ bald ♂

Offspring : *BB* *BB*
bald son, bald daughter

**The presence of beared of some goats** is determined by an autosomal gene $B^b$, which is dominant in males but recessive in females. In males a single $B^b$ allele causes the beared condition. Thus both $B^bB^b$ homozygotes and $B^bB^+$ heterozygotes have beared and $B^+B^+$ homozygotes are beardless. Females require two $B^b$ genes to have their beared, thus $B^bB^b$ is beared but $B^+B^b$ and $B^+B^+$ are beardless.

| Genetype | Phenotype | |
|---|---|---|
| | **Male** | **Female** |
| $B^bB^b$ | beared | beared |
| $B^+B^b$ | beared | nonbeared |
| $B^+B^+$ | nonbeared | nonbeared |

**Among Dorset sheep**, both sexes are horned and homozygous for $h^+$ gene (i.e. $h^+h^+$).

In Suffolk sheep, both sexes are hornless and homozygous for *h* gene (i.e. *hh*)

When these two breeds are crossed, the $F_1$ offspring $h^+h$ are found to be horned in males but hornless in females. When $F_1$ are intercrossed, among $F_2$ progeny, males were 3 horned : 1 non-horned while in females 3 nonhorned : 1 horned.

It suggests that the expression of $h^+h$ is only influenced by the sex where $h^+h$ is horned in males and hornless in females. So, $h^+$ is dominant in males but *h* is dominant in females.

| Genetype | Phenotype | |
|---|---|---|
| | **Male** | **Female** |
| $h^+h^+$ | horned | horned |
| $h^+h$ | horned | nonhorned |
| $hh$ | nonhorned | nonhorned |

## 9.7 SEX-LIMITED GENES

The sex-limited genes are also autosomal genes, expression of which **occurs only** to a sex. Therefore, the trait appears only in one sex and has zero penetrance in the other sex.

In humans, **premature baldness**, where baldness occurs in twenties or earlier thirty. This baldness gene is dominant in male but recessive in females which expresses only in the presence of a certain level of androgenic hormone, which is never reached in females.

Another example of a sex-limited characteristic in human is male-limited **precocious puberty** which is an autosomal dominant gene (*P*), expressed only in males, but recessive in females. In this trait, males become puberty at the age of 4 with all secondary sexual characters and sexual functions but most are short in height because, the long bones stop growing after puberty. The homozygous or heterozygous for *P* gene, *i.e.*, *PP* and *Pp* are affected males while *pp* homozygous are normal males. Females are not affected ever with *PP* homozygous condition.

| Genetype | Phenotype | |
|---|---|---|
| | **Male** | **Female** |
| *PP* | Affected | Not affected |
| *Pp* | Affected | Not affected |
| *pp* | Not affected | Not affected |

The precocious puberty is a genetic defect which affects the LH-receptor on the testis follicle. The *P* allele for precocious puberty codes for a defective LH receptor which stimulates testosterone production even in absence of LH. The LH receptors are also found in females who carry the precocious puberty genes, but their presence does not result in precocious puberty because additonal hormones are required along with LH to induce puberty in them.

Another example in human sex-limited trait is **breast development**, which is normally limited to females whereas beared growth is limited to males.

**Milk production in cattle** is controlled by the gene which is carried by both females and males, but in females, this gene is expressed only because of the presence of prolactin and LTH as well as other female hormones.

**The plumage character**, cock-feathering ie long pointed tail is never in females, although hen-feathering is common among hens. The Sebright bantams breeds of poultry, both sexes are hen-feathered, while in Hamburgh breed, the males may be either cock-feathered or hen-feathered.

It has been shown that, hen-feathering $h^+$ is a dominant character, so that both males and females are with genotypes $h^+h^+$ and $h^+h$ would be hen-feathered.

The only with genotype *hh* would be cock-feathered in males but hen-feathered in females. Such an expression of gene is due to the presence of female hormone, and therefore, in females, *hh* can not be expressed into cock-feathering character. In an experiment, if gonad is removed from female, *hh* female is resulted into cock-feathering. Similarly if testis is removed from the males, *hh* would not be cock-feathered.

| **Genetype** | **Phenotype** | |
|---|---|---|
| | **Male** | **Female** |
| $h^+h^+$ | hen-feathered | hen-feathered |
| $h^+h$ | hen-feathered | hen-feathered |
| $hh$ | cock-feathered | hen-feathered |

## 9.8 SOLVED PROBLEMS ON SEX-LINKED INHERITANCE

### Problem 1

In *Drosophila*, if a white eyed female is crossed with a red eyed male and if an $F_1$ female from this cross is mated with her father and $F_1$ male with his mother, what will be the appearance of the eye colour of the offspring of these last two crosses?

**Solution :**

1ST CROSS

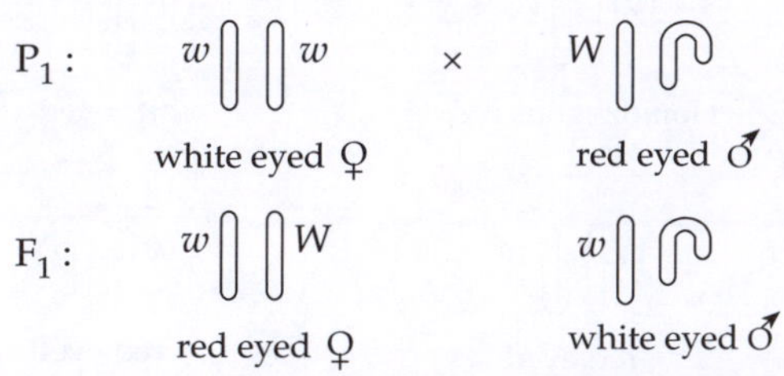

When $F_1$ ♀ is crossed with father

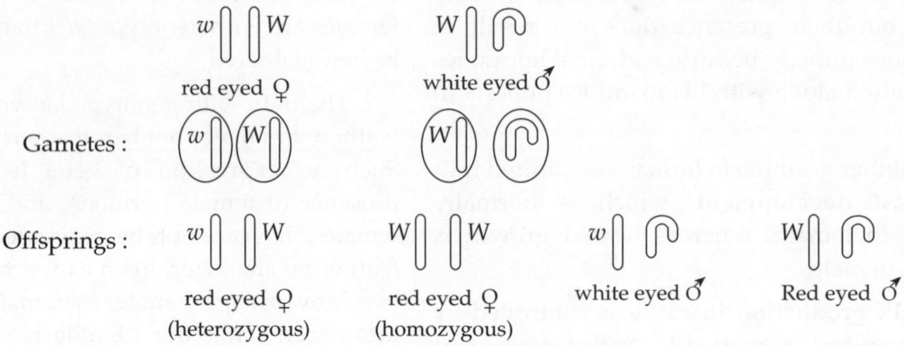


When mother is crossed with $F_1$ son.

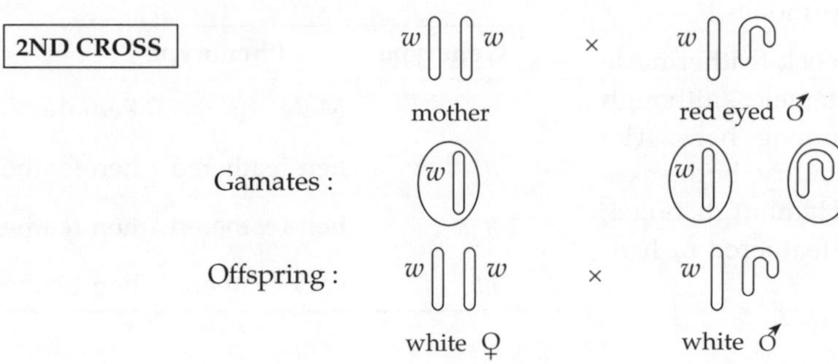


All the male and female offspring would be white eyed.

### Problem 2

In *Drosophila*, if a homozygous red eyed female is crossed with a white eyed male and if an $F_1$ female from this cross is mated with her father and an $F_1$ male with his mother. What will be the appearance of the offspring of these last two crosses as to eye colour?

**Solution :**

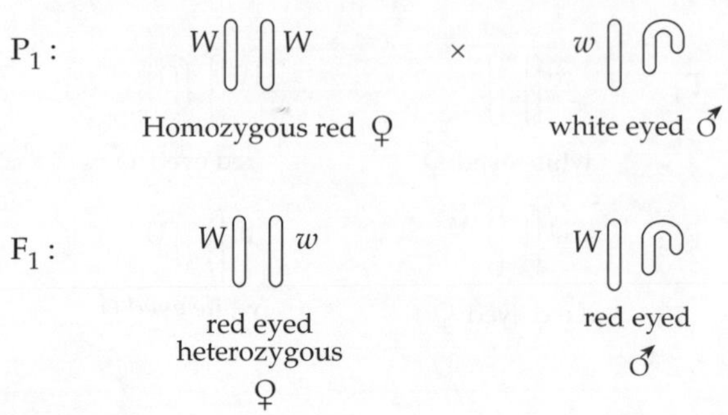


When $F_1$ ♀ crossed with father

**1ST CROSS**

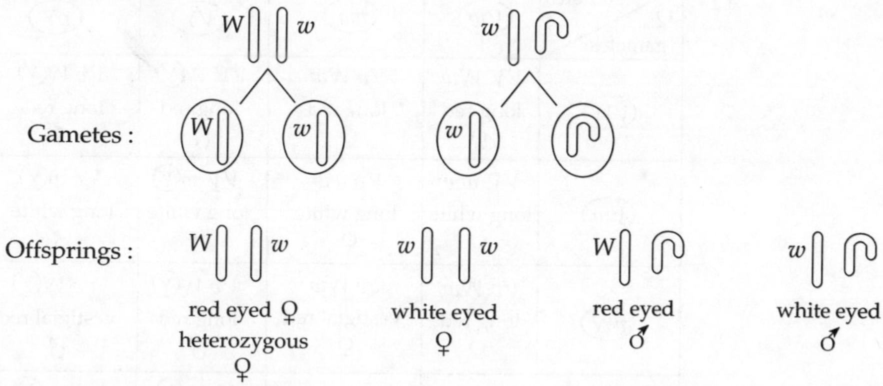


Mother is crossed with $F_1$ male.

**2ND CROSS**

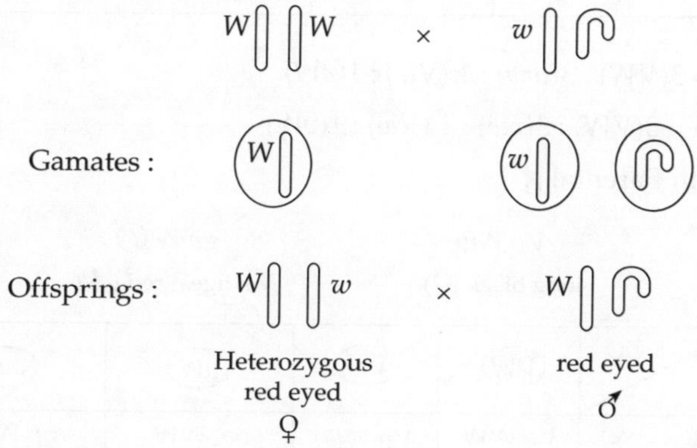


### ➧ Problem 3

In *Drosophila*, vestigial wings($v$) are recessive to the normal long wings ($V$) and the gene for this trait is not sex linked. If a homozygous white eyed long winged female is crossed with a homozygous red eyed vestigial male, what will be the appearance of $F_1$ and $F_2$; and the offspring of $F_1$ crossed with each parental type.

**Solution :**

$P_1$ : *VVww* (white long) × *vv* W(Y) (red vestigeal)

Gametes : (*Vw*) (*vW*) (*vY*) (Y symbolizes Y chromosome in ♂)

$F_1$ : *VvWw* ♀ (Red long) and *Vv wY* ♂ (white long)

$F_2$ :

| ♀ gametes \ gametes ♂ | (Vw) | (vw) | (VY) | (vY) |
|---|---|---|---|---|
| (VW) | VV Ww long red ♀ | Vv Ww long red ♀ | VV W(Y) long red ♂ | Vv W(Y) long red ♂ |
| (Vw) | VV ww long white ♀ | Vv ww long white ♀ | VV w(Y) long white ♂ | Vv w(Y) long white ♂ |
| (vW) | Vv Ww long red ♀ | vv Ww vestigial red ♀ | Vv W(Y) long red ♂ | vv W(Y) vestigial red ♂ |
| (vw) | Vv ww long white ♀ | vv ww vestigial white ♀ | Vv w(Y) long white ♂ | vv w(Y) vestigial white ♂ |

Among males the ratio = 3(*VW*) : 3(*ww*) : 1 (*Vw*) : 1(*vW*)

Among females the ratio = 3(*VW*) : 3(*vw*) : 1 (*Vw*) : 1(*vW*)

When $F_1$ ♀ is crossed with Parental ♂

*Vv Ww* × *vv W*(Y)

long black (♀) Vestigeal red (♂)

Offspring :

| ♂ \ ♀ | (VW) | (Vw) | (vW) | (vw) |
|---|---|---|---|---|
| (vW) | Vv WW long red ♀ | Vv Ww long red ♀ | vv WW Vestigial red ♀ | vv Ww vestigial red ♀ |
| (vY) | Vv W(Y) long red ♂ | Vv w(Y) long white ♂ | vv W(Y) vestigial red ♂ | vv w(Y) vestigial white ♂ |

Ratio in male phenotypes : 1(*VW*) : 1(*Vw*) : 1 (*vW*) : 1(*vw*)

Ratio in female phenotypes : 2(*VW*) : 2(*vW*)

When Parental ♀ is crossed with $F_1$ ♂

*VV ww* × *Vv w*(Y)

long white ♀ long white ♂

Offspring :

| ♀ \ ♂ | (Vw) | (vw) | (VY) | (vY) |
|---|---|---|---|---|
| (Vw) | VV ww long white ♀ | Vv ww long white ♀ | VV w(Y) long white ♂ | Vv w(Y) long white ♂ |

All the males and female offsprings are long white in phenotype.

### Problem 4

In *Drosophila*, what will be appearance of the offspring of the following crosses?

(a) *Ww Vv* × *w*Ⓨ *vv*

(b) *ww Vv* × *W*Ⓨ *Vv*

### Solution :

**(a)**

$P_1$ : *Ww Vv* (red long ♀) × *w*Ⓨ *vv* (white-vestigial ♂)

$F_1$ :

| ♂ \ ♀ | *WV* | *Wv* | *wV* | *wv* |
|---|---|---|---|---|
| *wv* | *Wv Vv*<br>red long<br>♀ | *Ww vv*<br>red vestigial<br>♀ | *ww Vv*<br>White long<br>♀ | *ww vv*<br>white vestigial<br>♀ |
| *Yv* | *W*Ⓨ*Vv*<br>red long<br>♂ | *W*Ⓨ*vv*<br>red vestigial<br>♂ | *w*Ⓨ*Vv*<br>white long<br>♂ | *w*Ⓨ*vv*<br>whtie vestigial<br>♂ |

Here, phenotypic ratio of males = 1(*WV*) : 1(*wV*) : 1(*Wv*) : 1(*wv*)

ratio of females = 1(*WV*) : 1(*wV*) : 1(*Wv*) : 1(*wv*)

**(b)**

$P_1$ : *ww Vv* (white long) × *W*Ⓨ *Vv* (red long)

$F_1$ :

| ♀ \ ♂ | *WV* | *Wv* | *YV* | *Yv* |
|---|---|---|---|---|
| *wV* | *Ww VV*<br>red long<br>♀ | *Ww Vv*<br>red long<br>♀ | *w*Ⓨ *VV*<br>white long<br>♂ | *W*Ⓨ *Vv*<br>white long<br>♂ |
| *wv* | *Ww Vv*<br>red long<br>♀ | *Ww vv*<br>red vestigial<br>♀ | *w*Ⓨ *Vv*<br>white long<br>♂ | *w*Ⓨ *vv*<br>whtie vestigial<br>♂ |

Here, phenotypic ratio of males = 3(*WV*) : 1(*Wv*)

ratio of females = 3(*WV*) : 1(*Wv*)

### Problem 5

In *Drosophila,* two red eyed long winged flies breed together produce following offspring. Female : $\frac{3}{4}$ red long : $\frac{1}{4}$ red vestigial.

Male : $\frac{3}{8}$ red long : $\frac{1}{8}$ white vestigial, $\frac{3}{8}$ white long and $\frac{1}{8}$ red vestigial . What are the genotypes of parent?

**Solution :**

These are the genotypes of two parents.

$P_1$ : *Vv Ww* (red eyed long winged ♀) × *Vv W Y* (red eyed long winged ♂)

$F_1$ :

| ♀ / ♂ | (VW) | (Vw) | (vW) | (vw) |
|---|---|---|---|---|
| (VW) | *VV WW* long red ♀ | *VV Ww* long red ♀ | *Vv WW* long red ♀ | *Vv Ww* long red ♀ |
| (vW) | *Vv WW* long red ♀ | *Vv Ww* long red ♀ | *vv WW* vestigial red ♀ | *vv Ww* vestigial red ♀ |
| (VY) | *VV W*(Y) long red ♂ | *VV w*(Y) long white ♂ | *Vv W*(Y) long red ♂ | *Vv w*(Y) long white ♂ |
| (vY) | *Vv W*(Y) long red ♂ | *Vv w*(Y) long white ♂ | *vv W*(Y) vestigial red ♂ | *vv w*(Y) vestigial white ♂ |

Phenotypic ratio of females = $\frac{3}{4}$ long red : $\frac{1}{4}$ vestigial red.

Phenotypic ratio of males = $\frac{3}{8}$ long red : $\frac{3}{8}$ long white : $\frac{1}{8}$ vestigial red : $\frac{1}{8}$ vestigial white.

### Problem 6

In *Drosophila*, a cross between Bar eyed female and wild type (round eyed) male produces only Bar eyed male and females in the $F_1$. Wild type ♀ × Bar eyed ♂ produces bar eyed females and wild type males.

Explain the inheritance of Bar eye and predict the appearance of the $F_2$ from each of these crosses.

**Solution :**

1ST CROSS

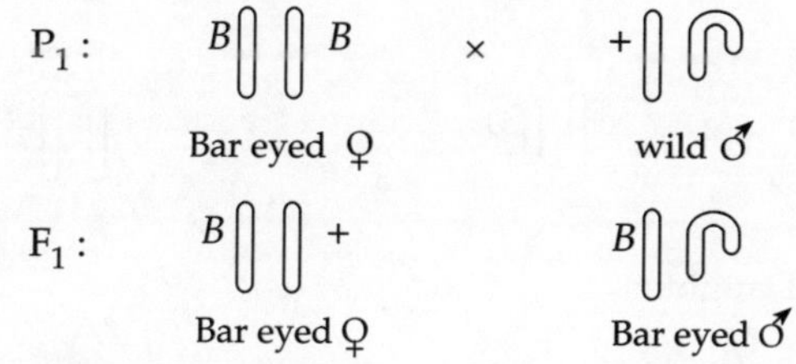


At the males and females are Bar eyed.

2ND CROSS

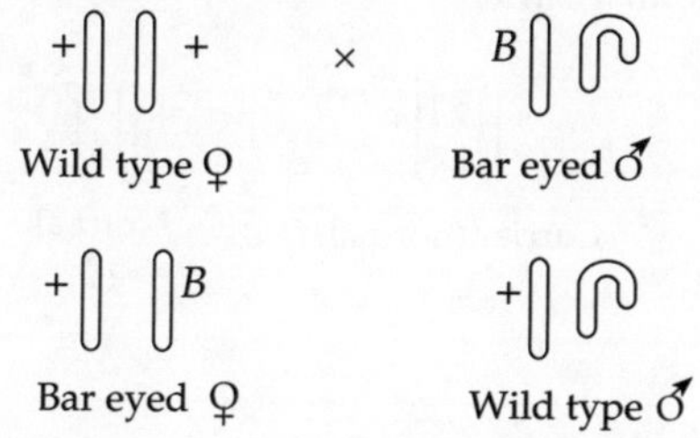


**Again from the first cross**

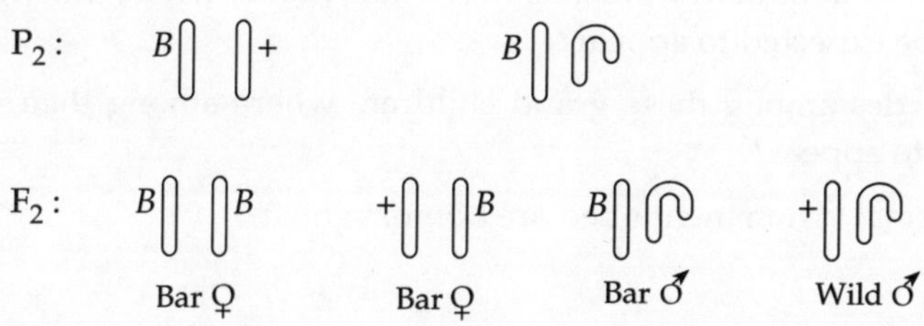


All the males and females are Bar eyed. Whereas, 50% of males are Bar eyed and 50% wild type.

**Again from the second cross**

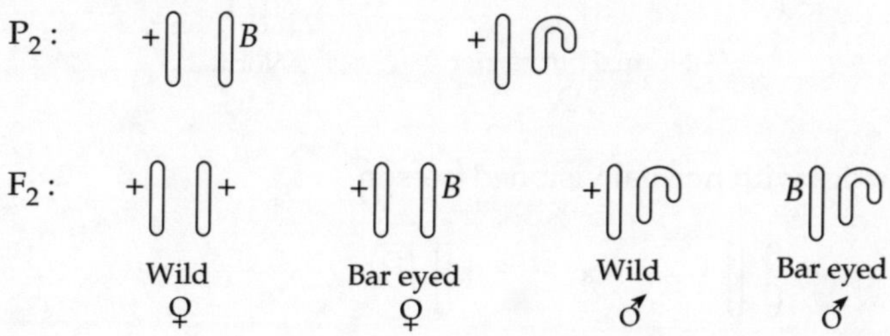


50% of the females are Bar eyed and 50% are wild type.

Among males 50% are also Bar eyed and 50% are wild type.

### Problem 7

A girl of normal vision whose father was colour blind, marries a male of normal vision, whose father was also color blind. What type of vision can be expected in their offspring?

**Solution :**

**Grand father and mother :**

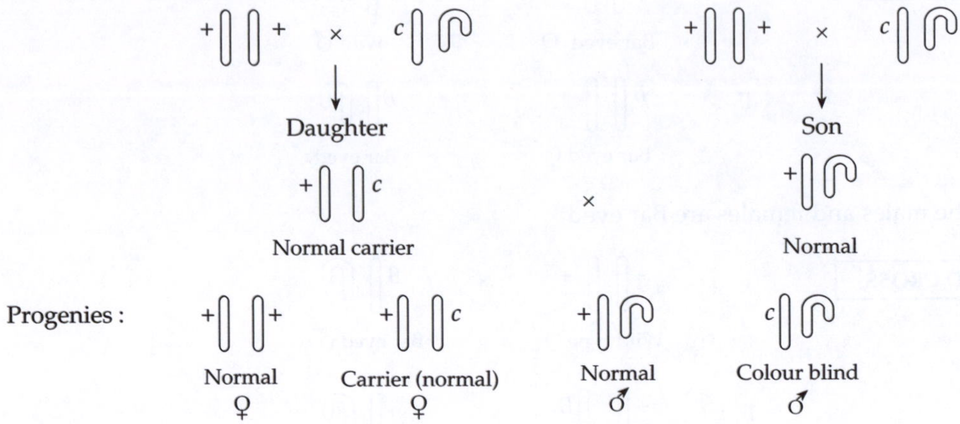


## Problem 8

A color blind man marries a woman of normal vision. They have sons and daughters, all of normal vision and all of whom marry persons of normal vision, where among the grand children may colour blindness be expected to appear?

If their cousin marries among these grand children, where among their offspring may color blindness be expected to appear?

(All persons of normal vision mentioned are homozygous)

**Solution :**

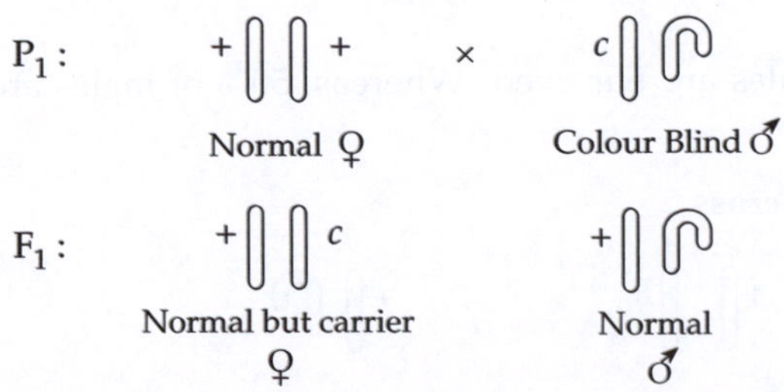


When a carrier marries with normal visioned person.

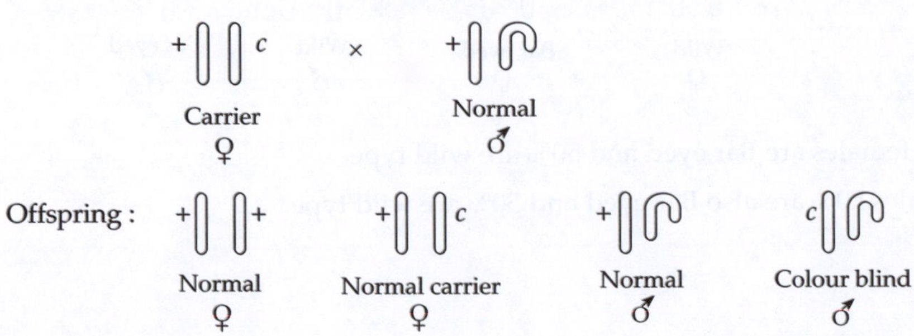

Again, when normal ♀ marries with normal ♂

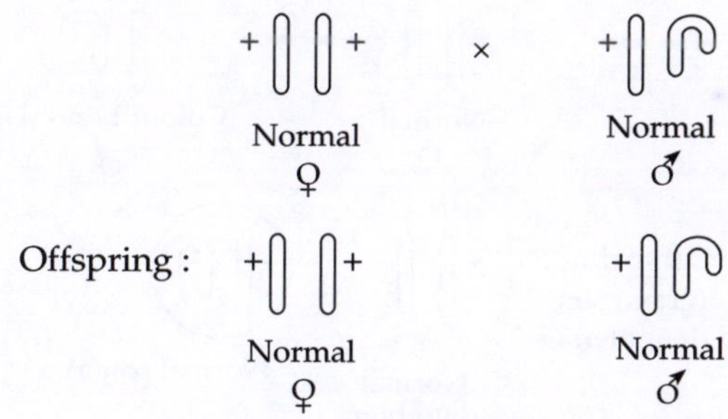


All the males & females are normal

If their cousin marries

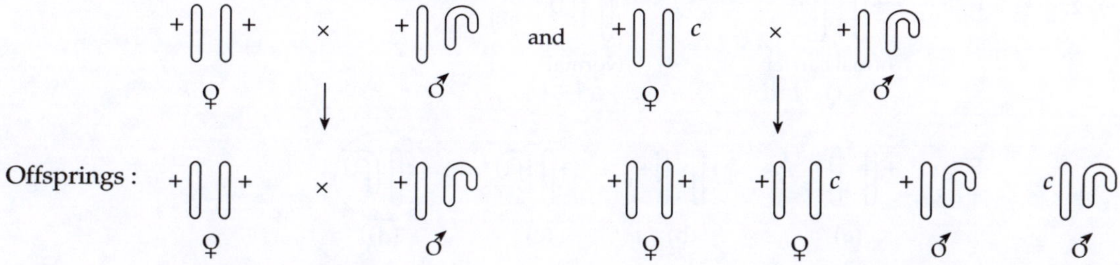


All males and females would be normal

Among females 50% normal and 50% normal carrier

Among males 50% normal and 50% color blind.

### Problem 9

A man and a woman, both of normal vision have

1. A color blind son who has a daughter of normal vision.
2. A daughter of normal vision who has one color blind and one normal son.
3. Another daughter of normal vision who has five sons all normal. What are the probable genotypes of the grand parent, children and grand children?

**Solution :**

1. $P_1$ : grand father & mother

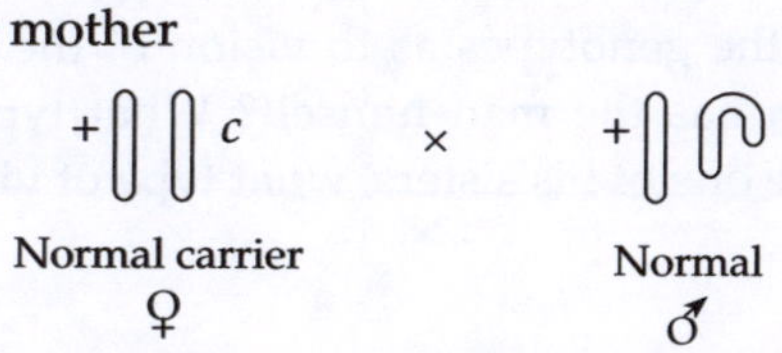


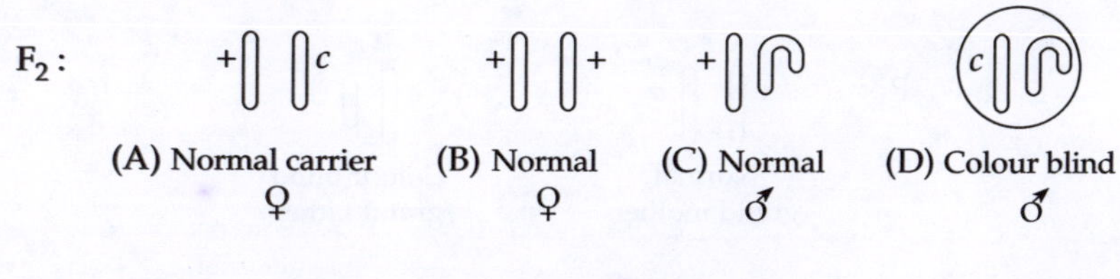

This colour blind (D) male marries with normal ♀

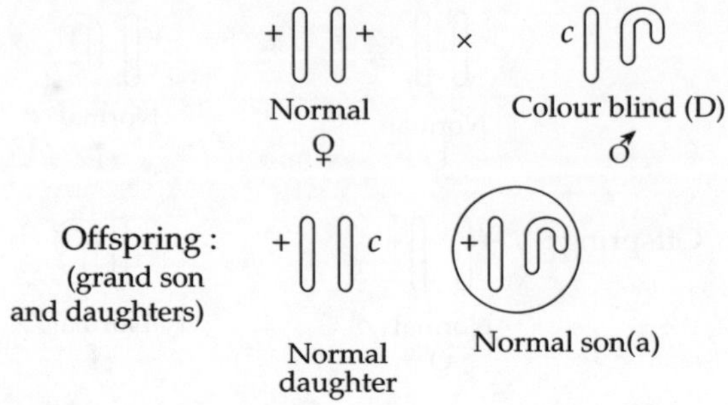


All the grand daughters are normal carrier but all the grand sons are normal.

2.

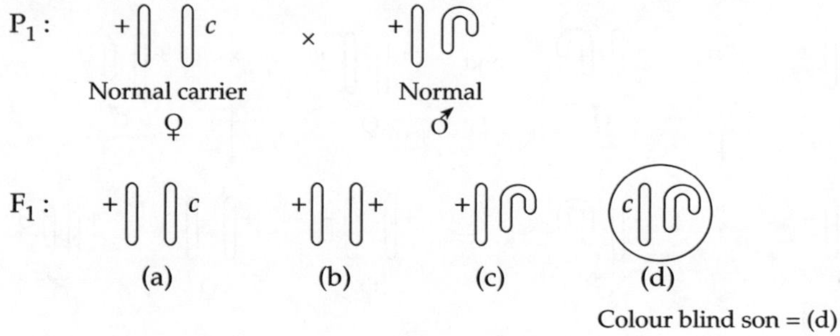


3.

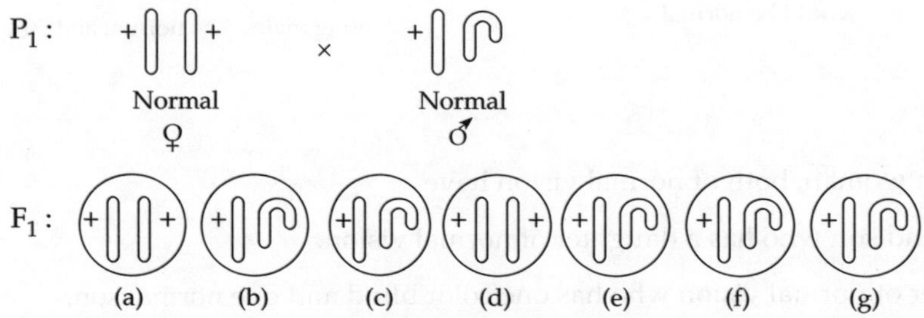


All the five sons are normal.

### Problem 10

A man's maternal grand mother had normal vision, his maternal grand father was colour blind, his father is of normal vision. What are the genotypes as to vision of the two parents and grand parents mentioned? What type of vision has the man himself? What type has his sisters? If he should marry a woman genotypically like one of his sisters, what type of vision would be expected in the offspring?

**Solution :**

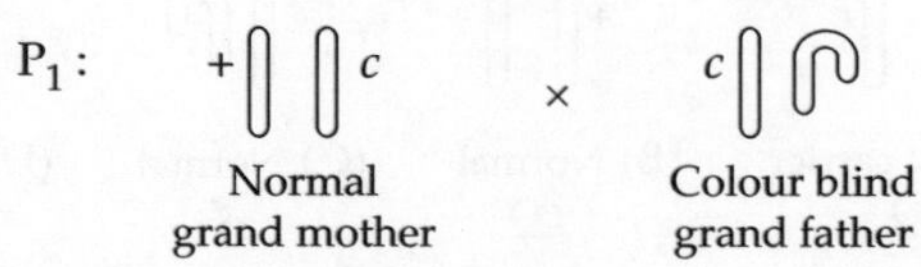

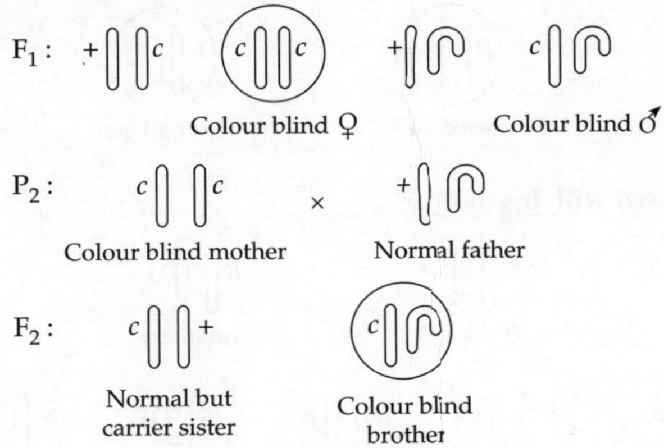


The genotype of the man is c, *i.e.* colour blind

The genotype of grand parent + c and c *i.e.* normal carrier grand mother and colour blind grand father.

The genotype of Parent is c c and + *i.e.,* colour blind mother and normal father

The genotype of his sister is + c *i.e.* normal in vision but carrier

If this man marries with the girl, the genotype is like his sister, and then their offspring would be.

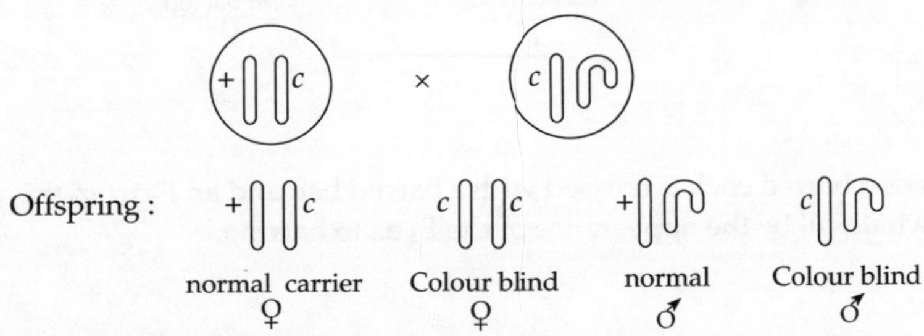


Among daughter, 50% is color blind and 50% is carrier.

Among sons 50% normal and 50% color blind.

### Problem 11

In poultry, if a non barred cock is crossed with a barred hen and an $F_1$ female from the cross is mated with her father and $F_1$ male with his mother, what would be the appearance of the offspring of these last two crosses as to barring?

**Solution :**

Barred feather is dominant over normal. Hen is heterozygote while cock is homozygote.

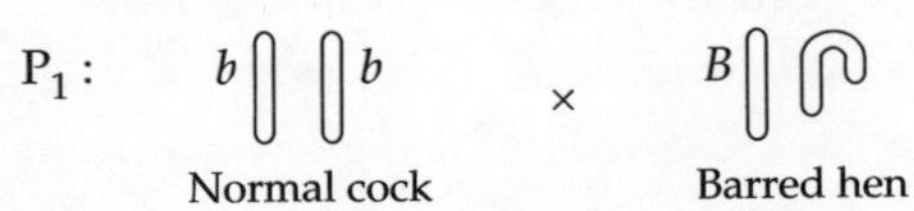

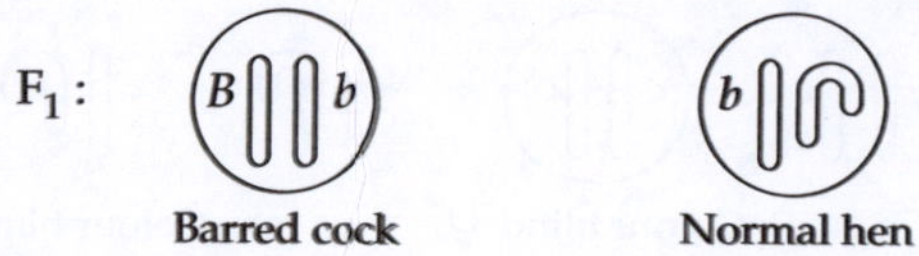


When $F_1$ male in crossed with his mother:

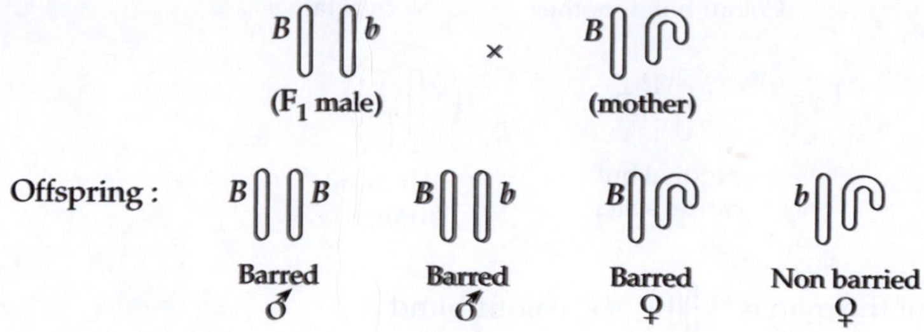


When $F_1$ female in crossed with her father:

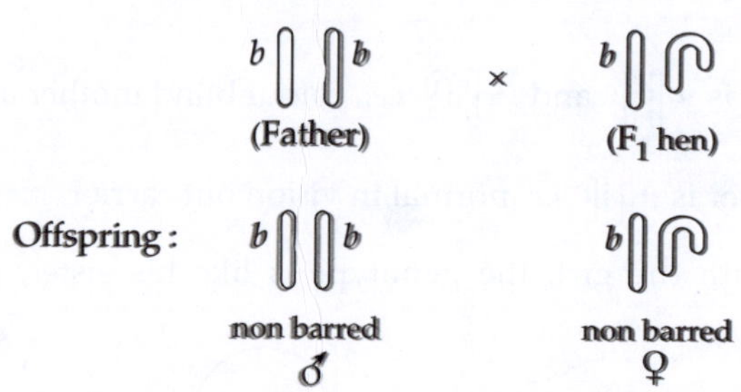


**Problem 12**

**In poultry, if a non barred cock is crossed with a barred hen and an $F_2$ from this cross is allowed to inbreed freely, what will be the appearance of the $F_3$ as to barring.**

**Solution :**

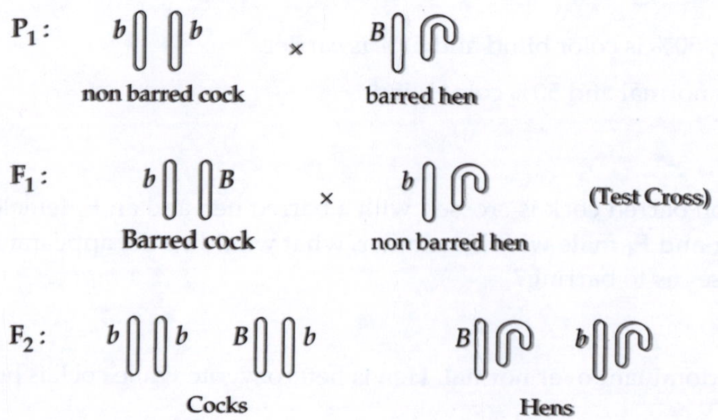

$F_3$ (inbreeding) :

| (b) | (b) | (B) | (b) | ♂ / ♀ |
|---|---|---|---|---|
| *Bb* ♂ barred | *Bb* ♂ barred | *BB* ♂ barred | *Bb* ♂ barred | (B) |
| *bb* ♂ non barred | *bb* ♂ non barred | *Bb* ♂ barred | *bb* ♂ non barred | (b) |
| *bY* ♀ non barred | *bY* ♀ non barred | *BY* ♀ barred | *bY* ♀ non barred | (Y) |
| *bY* ♀ non barred | *bY* ♀ non barred | *BY* ♀ barred | *bY* ♀ non barred | (Y) |

Among males 5 barred and 3 non-barred.

Among females 2 barred and 6 non-barred.

### Problem 13

In *Drosophila*, vermilion eye colour is recessive and sex-linked. In exceptional cases vermilion female × normal male produces in addition to the usual vermilion males and red eyed female, a few vermilion females and red males. Explain this result, and predict what classes of offspring should appear when the vermilion $F_1$ females from the above are crossed with red eyed males?

**Solution :**

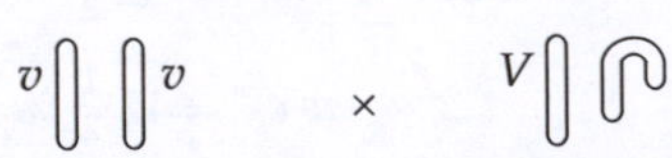

Vermilion ♀ normal ♂

Offspring : Normal Due to non disjunction

| (v) | (vv) | – | Gametes ♀ / ♂ Gametes |
|---|---|---|---|
| *vV* ♀ | *vv V* dies, super ♀ | *V* Red eyed ♂ | (V) |
| *vY* vermilion ♂ | *vv Y* vermilion ♀ | Y dies | (Y) |

### Problem 14

In *Drosophila,* white eye colour and club wing are both sex linked with a cross over value of about 15%. If a wild type female (red long) is crossed with a white club male, what will be the appearance of the offspring? If both male and females of the $F_1$ are crossed back to pure white club stock, what will be the offspring in each case?

**Solution :**

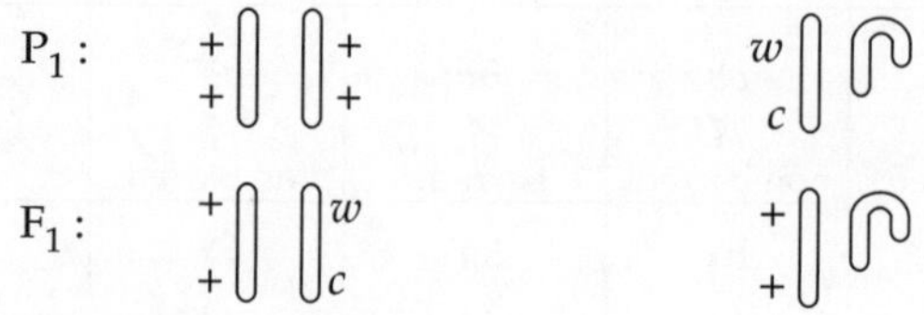


normal long red (hybrid) ♀ normal long red ♂

When this female is crossed with pure club white

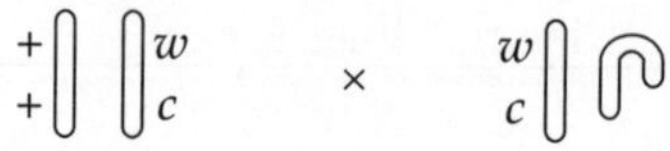


Offspring :

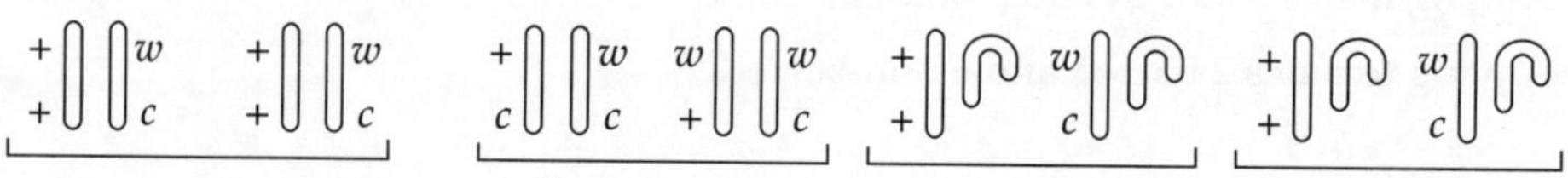


non crossover type ♀ Crossover type ♀ non crossover type ♂ crossover type ♂

Here the crossover value is 15%

Non-crossover value is 85%.

The genotypes belongs to

| | | | |
|---|---|---|---|
| + + / w c | 85% | So, + + | $= 42\frac{1}{2}$ % |
| | | w c | $= 42\frac{1}{2}$ % |
| + c / w + | 15% | + c | $= 7\frac{1}{2}$ % |
| | | w+ | $= 7\frac{1}{2}$ % |

The ratio is $42\frac{1}{2} : 42\frac{1}{2} : 7\frac{1}{2} : 7\frac{1}{2} = 17 : 17 : 3 : 3$

Again, the $F_1$ male is crossed with female which is double recessive.

Offspring :

The ratio is 1 : 1

# Chapter Glossary/Key Terms

**Criscross pattern of inheritance :** The phenotypic pattern of inheritance controlled by X-linked recessive alleles.

**Holandric trait :** Trait controlled by a locus found only on the Y chromosome. Involves father-to-son transmission.

**Nondisjunction :** The failure of a pair of homologous chromosomes to separate properly during meiosis.

**Position effect :** An alteration of phenotype caused by a change in the relative arrangement of the genetic material.

**Sex-limited traits :** Traits that occur in only one of the two sexes.

**Sex-linkage :** The phenormenon that cerain genes are found on one of the two types of sex chromosomes.

# Exercise

**A. Long answer type questions :**

1. What do you mean by sex-linked inheritance and sex-linked genes? Classify sex-linked genes.
2. Describe inheritance of sex-liniked gene for eye colour in *Drosophila*.
3. What is criss-cross inheritance? Describe criss-cross type of inheritance in *Drosophila* and human.
4. What is X-Y linked gene? Give an example and mode of inheritance in *Drosophila*.
5. Describe the inheritance of sex-linked lethals in *Drosophila*. What is its characteristics?
6. What is primary non-disjunction? Give the example and pattern of inheritance of an X-linked gene where the eggs are produced by primary non-disjunction. What is the difference in observation from normal disjunction of X-chromosomes?
7. What is secondary non-disjunction? Give the example and inheritance pattern of X-linked gene where eggs are produced by secondary non-disjunction.
8. Describe Morgan's experiment on the attached X-chromosome inheritance in *Drosophila*.
9. Describe position effect variegation in *Drosophila*.
10. Give the inheritance pattern of color-blind genes in human beings. Why such mode of inheritance is a criss-cross type?
11. Describe the inheritance pattern of hemophilia in human beings.

12. Describe the inheritance pattern of sex-linked pattern in poultry and in moth? What is the difference of inheritance from *Drosophila*.
13. What is sex-influenced gene? Give an example in human and also its inheritance pattern.
14. What is sex-limited gene? Give an example in human and also its inheritance pattern. What is the cause of such sex-limitedness?
15. In human, red-green color blindness is recessive and X-linked, whereas albinism is recessive and autosomal. What types of children can be produced as the result of marriage between two homozygous parents — a normal visioned albino woman and a color-blind, normally pigmented man?
16. In man (A) suffering from defective tooth enamel, which results in brown-coloured teeth, marries a normal woman. All their daughters have brown teeth but the sons are normal. The sons of man-A marry normal woman, and all their children are normal. The daughters of man-A marry normal men and 50% of their children have brown teeth. Explain these facts genetically.
17. A black and orange female cat is crossed with a black male and the progeny are as follows females : two black, three orange and black Males : two black, two orange. Explain the result.

**B. Short answer type questions.**

1. What is sex-linked inheritance?
2. What are sex-linked genes?
3. What are sex-linked lethal, semi-lethal and non-lethal genes?
4. What is X-linked gene?
5. What is Y-linked gene?
6. What is holandric gene?
7. What is X-Y-linked gene?
8. Waht criss-cross inheritance? Give example.
9. Name a gene which is X-linked and also its counterpart is present in the Y-chromosome in *Drosophila*.
10. What would be the cause when half of the sons in a family are missing.
11. What is non-disjunction?
12. What is primary non-disjunction?
13. What would be the cause of the appearance of red-eyed males and white eyed males in $F_1$ when white eyed female *Drosophila* is crossed with red-eyed male?
14. What kinds of eggs would be produced due to non-disjunction of X-chromosomes in *Drosophila* during meiosis?
15. What is secondary non-disjunction of X-chromosome?
16. How you can establish the chromosome theory of inheritance.
17. Yellow female when crossed with normal male of *Drosophila* produced yellow daughters and normal sons. Explain it.
18. What is position effect?
19. Give the example of position effect variegation in *Drosophila*.
20. Give the examples of X-linked recessive genes in man.
21. Give the examples of X-linked dominant genes in man.
22. What is red-green color-blind in man?
23. Why do males are more prone to color blind?
24. What is bleeder's desease?
25. Why do males are more prone to hemophilia?
26. How theoritically a female hemophilic can be produced?
27. Give the examples of Y-linked genes in man. What is its inheritance characteristics?
28. Give the examples of X-Y linked genes of man? What is its inheritance characteristics?
29. Give the examples of sex-linked lethal genes in man.
30. What is the difference between the X-linked inheritance in *Drosophila* with fowl? Whether it shows any kinds of cris-cross inheritance?
31. What is sex-influenced gene? Give example in human beings? What is the cause of such inheritance?
32. "Non-bald mother and father may have a bald son" -explain.

33. "Non bald mother may have bald son" – explain.
34. "If mother and father are both bald, their offspring would be bald" – explain
35. Distinguish between sex-limited and sex-influenced inheritance.
36. What is premature baldness? explain its inheritance?
37. Why heterozygous male is premature bald but females are not?
38. What is the cause of precocious puberty? Why this gene is expressed in males but not in females even in homozygous condition? Describe its physiological causes?
39. How the milk production gene is inherited in cattle? What is the cause?
40. Give the reason of feathering patterns in fowl.

**Write short notes on :**

Holandric genes, Cress-cross inheritance, Sex-linked lethals, primary non-disjunction of X-chromosome, Secondary non-disjunction of X-chromosomes, Attached X-chromosome, Positional effect variegation in *Drosophila,* Haemophilia, Red-green color-blindness, Sex-limited genes, X-Y-linked genes, Sex-influenced genes.

10

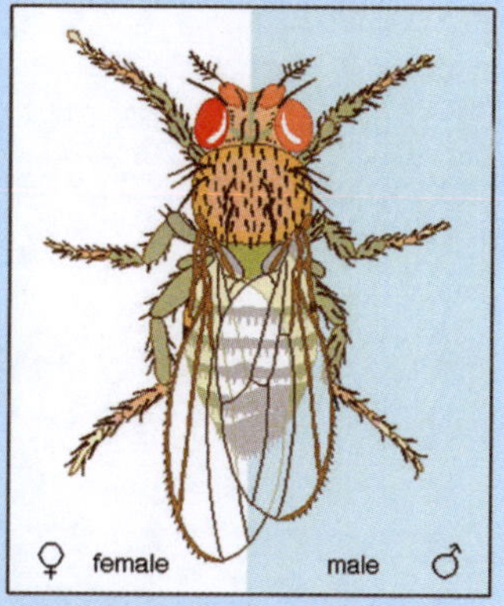


# Determination of Sex

**CHAPTER AGENDA**

**10.1** Concept; **10.2** Chromosomal determination of sex; **10.3** Intersex and Environment; **10.4** Sex determination in Gypsy moth (*Lymantria dispar*); **10.5** Sex determination in Hymenoptera; **10.6** Environmental Sex-determination; **10.7** Sex determination in *Drosophila*; **10.8** Sex determination in Caenorhabditis elegans; Chapter Glossary/Key Terms; Exercise

## 10.1 CONCEPT

Six kinds of sexes in animal kingdom, *viz.*, male, female, intersex, hermaphrodite, gynandromorph and super sexes.

The sex is determined not in the adult but in zygote condition.

Sex differentiation occurs after sex determination at the embryonic differentiation.

Sex determination depends upon the process of fertilization, what type of ovum and what type of sperms are used.

Sex is determined by the composition of chromosomes in the zygote. When the sex is determined by the sex chromosome, is called **sex chromosomal determination of sex** but when the sex is determined by autosomes is called **genetically determination of sex.**

## 10.2 CHROMOSOMAL DETERMINATION OF SEX

Males and females can be differentiated by their composition of chromosomes in the zygote. Usually the males have an odd pair of chromosomes and the females have even paired. In males two types of gametes are produced where each would bear one chromosome from the odd pair. But in females, one type of gametes are produced. The two gametes of opposite sexes are fused, male and female offspring are produced according to their odd paired chromosome constitution or even paired chromosome constitution.

### 10.2.1 Chromosomal Sex determination in Man and *Drosophia*

In man and *Drosophila,* females are homogametic while males are heterogametic. Males contain two sets (diploid number) of autosomes along with X and Y sex chromosomes. Females contain two sets of autosomes and two X chromosomes.

Females produce only one kind of gametes (ovum) having haploid set of autosomes and one X-chromosome, while males produce two kinds of sperms having haploid set of autosomes and either X or Y sex chromosomes.

After fertilization, two kinds of zygotes 2AXX and 2AXY would be produced. The former will be developed into females and the later into males.

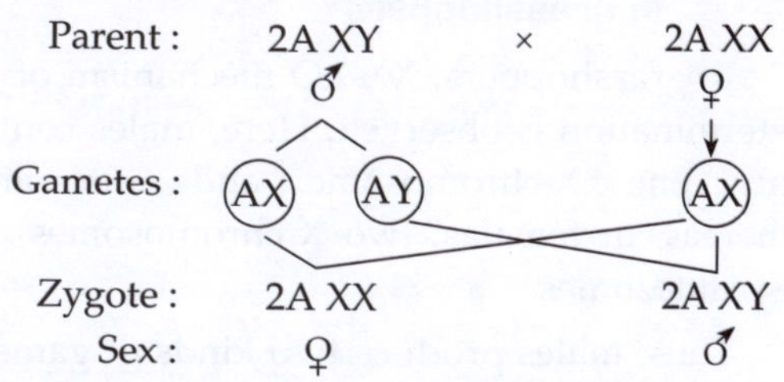


### 10.2.2 Chromosomal Sex determination in butterfly, reptiles and birds

In these animals, females are heterogametic sex, which contain two sets of autosomes along with X and Y sex chromosomes. While the males are homogametic, contain two X-chromosomes alongwith two sets of autosomes.

Females produce two classes of gametes containing either X or Y and males produce one class of gamete containing only X-chromosome and also haploid set of autosomes in both males and females.

After fertilization, two types of zygotes would be resulted. Males would be developed from zygotes containing two X-chromosomes and females from the zygotes containing one-X and one-Y sex-chromosomes.

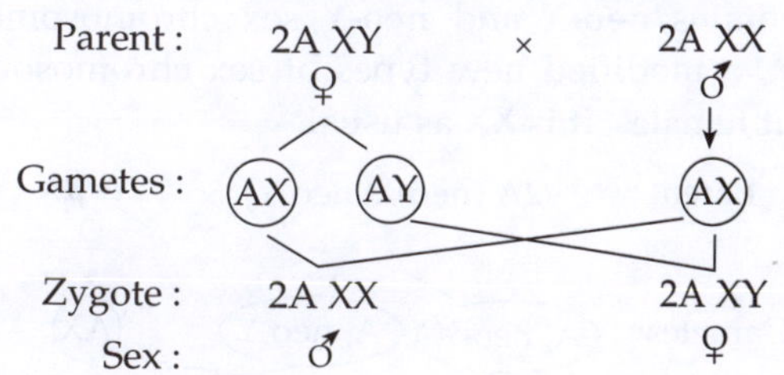

To prevent confusion with the XX-XY system, sexchromosomes in this system are labeled Z and W. Female in the system is ZW. Male is ZZ. Females produce two kinds of ovum containing either Z or W sex chromosomes, while males produce one kind of sperm, containing only Z sex chromosome. This is ZZ-ZW system of sex determination.

### 10.2.3 Chromosomal sex determination in grasshoppers

In grasshoppers, XX-XO mechanism of sex determination is observed. Here, males contain only one X-chromosome and autosomes, whereas, in females, two X-chromosomes and also autosomes.

Thus, males produce two kinds of gametes one of which contains haploid set of autosomes and one X-chromosome, and another will have only haploid sets of autosomes and no sex chromosomes.

After fertilization, two types of zygotes would be produced from which males and females are developed as follows.

Parent : 2A XX ♀ × 2A XO ♂

Gametes : (AX) (AX) (AO)

Zygote : 2A XX 2A XO

Sex : ♀ ♂

### 10.2.4 Neo-XY mechanism of Sex determination in grasshopper

In some particular grasshoppers, the male contains **neo-X** and **neo-Y** sex chromosomes, i.e., a modified new types of sex chromosome but females, it is XX as usual.

Parent : 2A (neo-X, neo Y) ♂ × 2A XX ♀

Gametes : (A, neo-X) (A, neo Y) (AX)

Zygote : 2AX, neo-X 2A X, neo-Y

Sex : New type ♂ New type ♀

Male produces two kinds of gametes which contain either neo-X or neo-Y. But female produces only one kind containing X-chromosome.

After fertilization, two classes of zygotes would be produced, one contains neo X and X chromosome, develops into new type of female and other would contain X and neo-Y would be developed into new kind of male.

### 10.2.5 Multiple sex chromosome method of sex determination in mantids

1. In some mantids, female is homo-gametic but sex chromosomes do not separate *i.e.*, 100% non-disjunction during meiosis. The males are heterogametic with paired X-chromosomes and one Y chromosome.

   If a cross involves between these two races, following results are obtained :

Parent : $\widehat{X_1X_2}$ Y ♂ × $\widehat{X_1X_2}$ $\widehat{X_1X_2}$ ♀

Gametes : ($\widehat{X_1X_2}$) (Y) ($\widehat{X_1X_2}$)

Zygote : $\widehat{X_1X_2}$ $\widehat{X_1X_2}$ $\widehat{X_1X_2}$ Y

Sex : ♀ ♂

Here, males produce two classes of gametes, one containing $\widehat{X_1X_2}$ which are due to 100% non-disjunction and the other with Y.

Females produce one class of non-disjunction chromosome containing gametes.

After fertilization, two kinds of zygotes would be produced. One of which contains $\widehat{X_1X_2}$ $\widehat{X_1X_2}$ which would be developed into females and the other which contains $\widehat{X_1X_2}$Y would develop into males. They will produce sex trivalent during meiosis.

2. In gryllids, this is like as mantids, i.e., the male contains $\widehat{X_1X_2}Y$ and the females $\widehat{X_1X_2}$ $\widehat{X_1X_2}$, but sex trivalent would not be formed in males. It is known as **pseudo trivalent**.

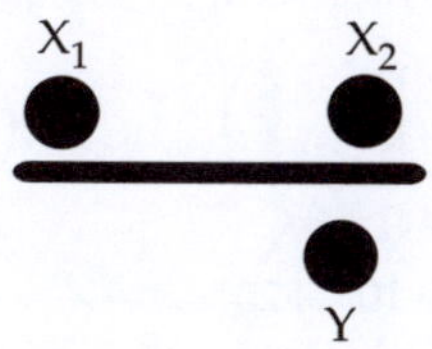


3. In bugs, females contain $\widehat{X_1X_2X_3}$ $\widehat{X_1X_2X_3}$ and males contain $\widehat{X_1X_2X_3}$ Y. Here $\widehat{X_1X_2X_3}$ are non-disjunctions.

### 10.2.6 Compound chromosomes in the sex determination

X-chromosome is most commonly found as single chromosome or single homologous pair of chromosomes. Some species maintain **compounds** of more than one kind of X-chromosome that act together as a sex-determining group. In such species males and females may have large differences in their chromosome numbers.

For example, in *Ascaris incurva,* there are 13 pairs of autosomes and a compound of 8 X-chromosomes. Thus a male produces two types of gametes : (8X and 13 autosomes) and (one Y and 13 autosomes) while female produces only one kind of eggs : 8X and 13 autosomes.

Thus chromosome number in female is (16X + 13 pairs of autosomes), and in male is (8X + Y + 13 pairs of autosomes)

In the beetle *Blaps polychresta,* the male has 12X chromosomes and 6Y chromosomes in addition to 18 autosomes.

## 10.3 INTERSEX AND ENVIRONMENT

In *Drosophila*, all the intersexes have two X-chromosomes and three sets of autosomes. The sexual characters of intersex vary by attaining from a normal male to a normal female through various intermediate situations.

Triploid females are when allowed to produce offspring at different temperatures. At high temperature, the intersexes are shifted to the female direction, i.e., high temperature has a feminizing, while low temperature has a masculinizing effects in *Drosophila*. Possibly this is due to the interactions of the genetic environment or modifiers.

## 10.4 SEX DETERMINATION IN GYPSY MOTH *(LYMANTRIA DISPAR)*

In *Lymantria dispar*, the males contain XX sex chromosomes and females contain XY. Normally, the sex is determined as follows.

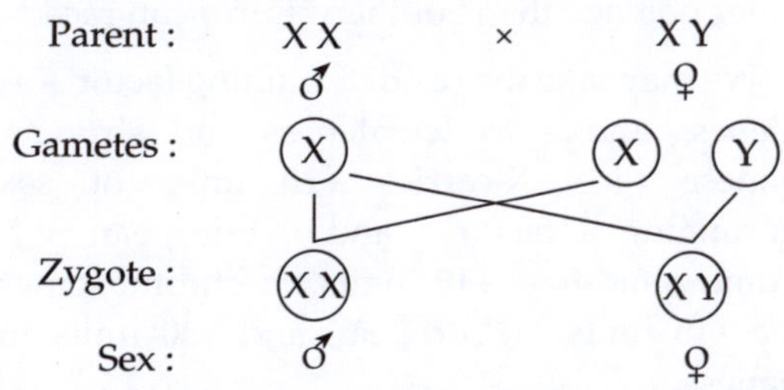


The resulting zygote would be XX and XY and they would be developed into males and females respectively.

Here, Y is responsible for femaleness and X is responsible for maleness characters.

Richard Goldschmidt found that, it is possible to produce intersexes by crossing Gypsy moths from different parts of the world.

For example :

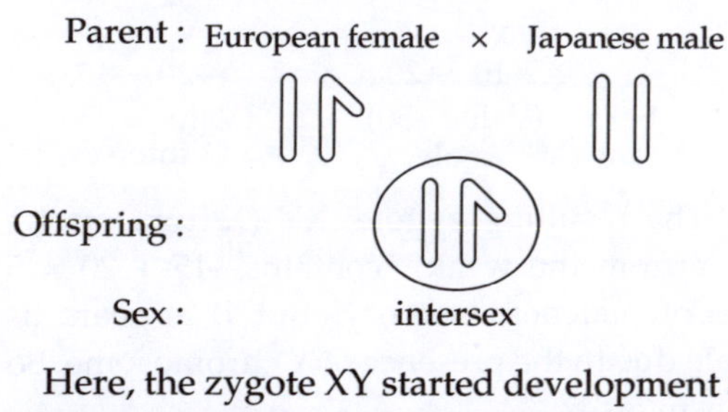


Here, the zygote XY started development as females but later developed into males.

Richard Goldchmidt placed a theory that in the case of moth, the cytoplasm carries the femaleness determining characters and X-chromosome for the maleness. The intersexes are produced due to **combination of weak cytoplasm and strong X-chromosome.** Y chromosome is not important.

When a week European female crossed with strong Japanese male produces a certain number of strong females. Here, the cytoplasmic theory is not improbable, therefore considered another factors. Here, Y-chromosome takes an important sex determining factor, represents by femaleness characters.

Japanese moth develops sexual maturity more rapidly than the European moth. We might express this factor by saying that the sex genes of the Northern Japanese race have greater potency than Southern European race.

We may take the sex determining factor + as maleness and – as femaleness and stronger Japanese race, X-carries +20 units of sex determining factor and European X chromosome has +10 units, Y-chromosomes have –15 units in European and –30 units in Japanese.

If a cross between weak European female with strong Japanese male occurs then the result would be as follows :

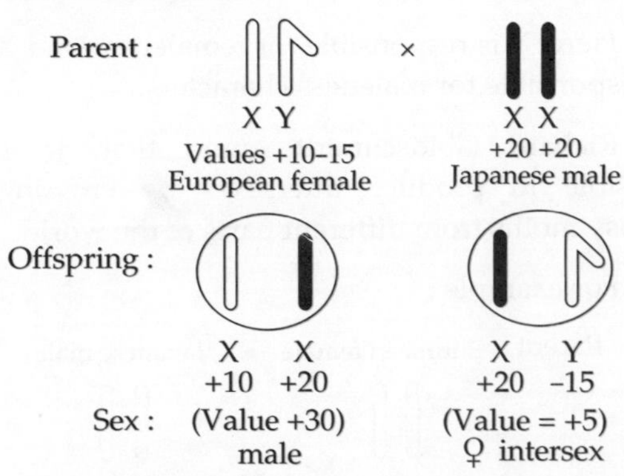


The resulting zygote, XY (X-from strong and Y from the weak) contains –15 + 20 = 5 units of maleness potency. But it appears as female due to the presence of Y chromosome. So this is intersex.

When the cross involves between weak European males and strong Japanese females, the zygote of XY would be –30+10 = –20 units. Therefore, it would be normal females.

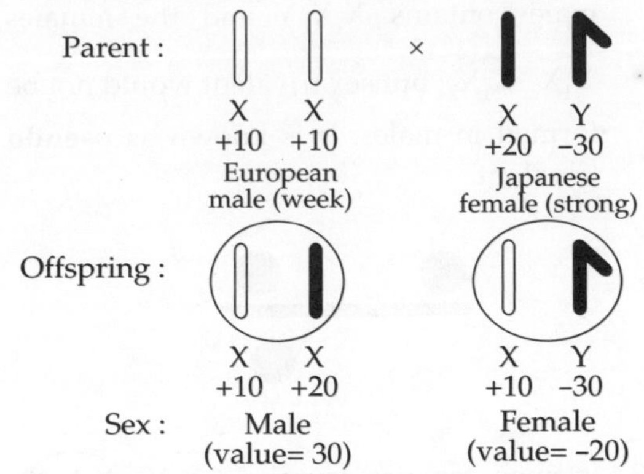


Cytoplasmic factors of sex determination cannot be accepted when a Japanese male containing XXY sex chromosomes is crossed with an European female with XY sex chromosomes.

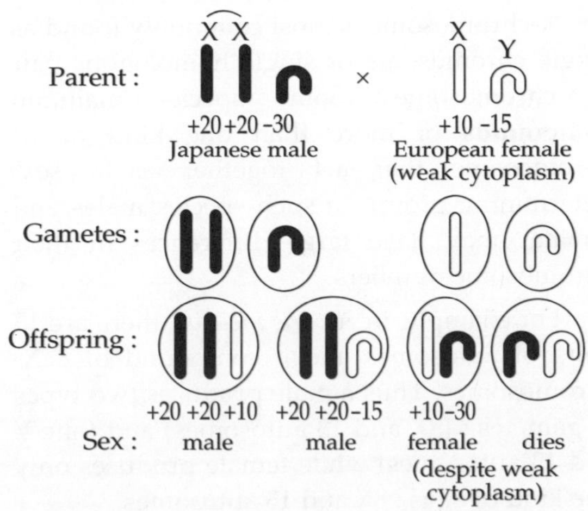


$\widehat{XX}$Y males during spermatogenesis two X chromosomes would not separate from each other. When cross involves, the Japanese males produce two types of gametes containing XX and other only Y with strong cytoplasmic factors. The European females produce weak cytoplasmic factors containing X and Y gametes.

They produce the zygote XY, where X from weak female and Y from strong male, which would develop into females despite weak cytoplasmic factor. So, in this case the cytoplasmic factors for sex determination are not applicable.

## 10.5 SEX DETERMINATION IN HYMENOPTERA

A peculiar method of sex determination has been found in the Hymenoptera (bees, ants, wasps etc.). The method in question has been found by P. W. Whiting and A R Whiting in *Habrobracon*, a wasp, that is parasitic on meal worm. The eggs of *Habrobracon* may develop either with or without fertilization. The unfertilized eggs develop into males. Accordingly, the males are either haploid or diploid depending on weather they develop from unfertilized egg or from fertilized egg. The females are however always diploid.

Whiting has found that, in *Habrobracon*, there is a series of genes that act as though they are alleles (*a*, *b*, *c*, *d* etc.). A given individual might contain any one member of the series in question or if heterozygous, any two of them. Whiting found that females are always heterozygous for the genes (*a/b*). Diploid males on the other hand are homozygous (*a/a*) or (*b/b*). In a sense, haploid males are the equivalent of homozygous diploid, since both have only one kind of allele (*a* or *b*). If the genes under discussion actually are alleles, they all occupy the same locus. This might then be referred to as the **sex locus**.

Inbreeding would often produce homozygous diploids. Thus, suppose that a female is (*a/b*). If she received (*a*) from her mother, some of her brothers would also have (*a*), since, they have the same mother and the mating (+/*a*) × *a* would produce some males. On the other hand if a female of composition (*a/b*) was mated with unrelated male, say, with (*c*) in the sex locus, all the fertilized eggs would be heterozygous (*a/c*) (*b/c*) and they would all develop into females. Thus, in *Habrobracon*, sex is determined by homozygosis or heterozygosis at the specific sex locus.

Whiting has suggested that the locus in question is really a small segment of a chromosome (the x-segment) is at different but closely adjacent loci within the x-segment. If we confine ourselves to just two loci (*a* and *b*), then an x-segment with (*a*) would be normal at the (*b*) locus i.e., (*a*+) and one with (*b*) would be normal at the (*a*) locus, ie., (+*b*). The combination of the two segments would be $\frac{a+}{+b}$, the (+) alleles are dominant and it takes to produce a female. Hence, $\frac{a+}{+b}$ is a female. But either mutant genes (a or b) produce a male. Thus, (*a*+) is a male (haploid) and $\frac{a+}{+b}$ is diploid female.

It is being assumed that in a female, say of genotype $\frac{a+}{+b}$, no recombination of genes takes place at the reduction division, so that the one segment would always remain (*a*+) from one generation to the next, the other segment be always (+*b*).

Sex determination in wasps is somewhat comparable to the production of flower colour in sweet peas. The female would correspond to a purple hybrid genotype $\frac{a+}{+b}$ and males to the mutant white races homozygous for either (*a*+) or (+*b*). In other words, femaleness in wasps depends in part at least, on the complementary action of "normal" genes in x-segments and maleness depends on recessiveness.

It is conceivable that the sex genes are not limited to the x-segment in *Habrobracon*. If genes at loci outside the x-segment were predominantly for maleness, these would cause the haploid egg to develop into a male. They also cause homozygous diploid egg $\left(\frac{a+}{a+}\right)$ to be a male, since the relative proportions of male and female genes would be the same as in the haploid egg.

However, if the diploid egg is heterozygous (as it is in the absence of inbreeding), then the complementary genes for femaleness in the x-segment become effective and they might over balance the genes for maleness outside the x-segment. Thus, sex would be determined in wasps by the interaction of male- and female-genes in different proportions, just as in most other organisms. But the genes for femaleness in the x-segment can express themselves only in the hybrid because of their complementary action and therefore only in an egg, which is fertilized.

It has long been known that, in bees, the fertilized eggs develop into females (either workers or queens depending upon the feeding) and the unfertilized eggs into males (the drones). Sex is determined in bees in essentially the same way as in *Habrobracon*. But diploid males are inviable in bees and so are not found in the adult stage.

## 10.6 ENVIRONMENTAL SEX-DETERMINATION

**(a) Temperature-dependent Sex determination in reptiles**

Recently, it has been shown that the sex of the alligators, crocodiles and many other reptiles depends not on chromosomes but on temperature. Ferguson and Joanen (1982) has concluded that sex in alligators both in the laboratory and in the field condition is determined by the temperature of the egg during the second and third weeks of incubation. When eggs are incubated at 30°C or below during this period, produce female sex, whereas at 34°C produce males.

There is only a small range of temperatures that permits both males and females to hatch from the same brood of eggs.

In read eared slider turtles, it has been found that, if eggs are incubated below 28°C, all the turtles hatching from them will be males. Above 31°C every eggs gives rise to a female. In between this temperature range, the broods will give rise to individuals of both sexes.

In snapping turtle, *Macroclemys*, females are produced from the eggs below 22°C or above 28°C. But between this range males predominate.

The European pond turtle, *Emys obicularis*, has been shown to produce all females above 30°C and all males below 25°C.

Actually, the sex determination in reptiles is hormone dependent. The oestogen is essential for ovarian development. Estrogen can override temperature and induce ovarian differentiation even in masculinizing temperature. On the other hand testosterone is essential for testis development. The enzyme "aromatase", which can convert testosterone into estrogen, is important in temperature dependent sex determination. In *Emys* aromatase activity is very low at 25°C causing the embryos into males, whereas, at 30°C the enzyme activity is increased, oestrogen synthesis is also increased to cause the embryos to develop into females.

Possibly, the genes that encode the enzyme aromatase and other required proteins for sex determination are certainly sensitive to temperature. The neurons of central nervous system sensed the environmental temperature and are transduced to the bipotential gonads by nerve fibres.

Another possible thought is that aromatase activity may be regulated by *Sox-9* gene product, which is raised at the time of production of testes. *Sox 9* expression is retained in the medullary sex cords destined to become Sertoli cells (Spotila *et al* 1998, Moreno-Mendoza *et al* 1999). Recent studies by Bergeron *et al.* (1994, 1999) have shown that polychlorinated biphenyl compounds (PCBs) can act like estrogen and are able to reverse the sex of turtles at "male" temperature.

Thermal pollution, either localy or due to global warming can eliminate a species in a given area. Ferguson and Joanen (1982) speculated that dinosaurs may have had a temperature dependent sex determination. The disappearance of dinosaurs may be linked to temperature dependent sex determination and

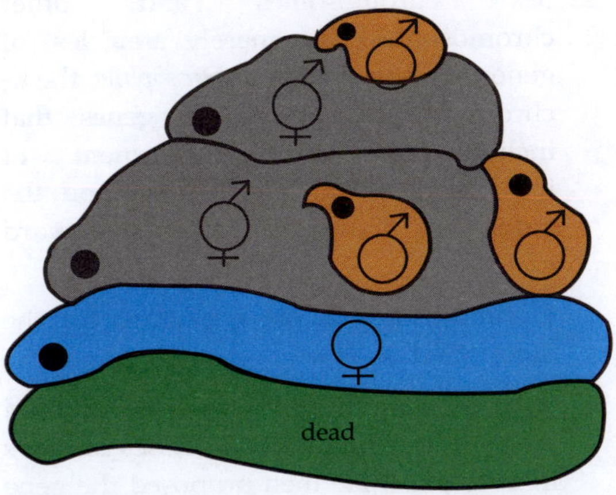


**Fig.10.1 :** *Dueter of Cripidula snails. Two individuals are changing from male to female. Then the molluscs become female and are fertilized by male above them.*

rapid climate change. Slight change in temperature may cause the eggs to hatch only males or females.

### (b) Location-dependent sex determination in *Bonellia* and *Crepidula*

Baltzer (1914) showed that the sex of the echiuroid worm *Bonellia viridis* depends on where the larva settled. The female is marine or rock dwelling animal. Its body is about 10 cm long. She has a proboscis, which can extend up to a metre long. The males are very small about 1-3 mm in length and reside within the uterus of the females. The larvae, which are landed on the sea floor, become females and if they settle on the proboscis become males.

The slipper snail *Crepidula fornicate*, young individuals are always male. The next phase is the degeneration of the male reproductive system. The next phase can be either male or female depending upon the position of the animal on the mound. If the snail is attached to the female becomes male. If the snail is removed from the mound it becomes female. Presence of large numbers of males may cause some males to become female. It is fact that once the individual becomes female, never reversed back to males (Fig. 10.1).

### (c) Adaptive Sex determination in blue-headed wrasse

The blue-headed wrasse is a Panamanian reef fish where temperature is not the only environmental factor that can affect sex determination. It has been found that if wrasse larva reaches a reef, where male lives with many females, it develops into a female. When the male dies; one of the females (usually the largest one) becomes a male. Their ovaries shrink and testes grow within a day, (Warner 1984).

## 10.7 SEX-DETERMINATION IN *DROSOPHILA*

### 10.7.1 Chromosome theory of sex-determination

According to chromosome theory of sex determination, male and female individuals would differ in their chromosome constitution. There may be two types of chromosomes present in individuals : autosomes and sex chromosomes.

The sexchromosomes may be homomorphic *i.e.* XX or heteromorphic *i.e.*, XY.

Role of sex chromosomes in determination of sex becomes evident for the first time due to discovery of sex-linked genes, whose interitance does not follow the expected segregation pattern in both sexes but follows a **cris-cross type of interitance.**

In *Drosophila*, normal females contain two sets of autosomes and two X-chromosomes whereas, males contain two sets of autosomes and one X- and one Y chromosomes.

Females are homogemetic, *i.e.* produce only one kind of gametes containing autosomes and one X-chromosome *i.e.* (AX). Males are heterogamatic, *i.e.*, two kinds of gametes, one containing autosome and one X-chromosome while the other containing autosome and one Y-chrosomosome. (*i.e.* AX and AY)

The sex is determined by the following ways :

Parent : 2A XX (♀) × 2A XY (♂)

Gametes : AX AX and AY

Zygote : 2A XX ♀ 2A XY ♂

C.B. Bridges on nondisjunction of X-chromosomes proved that a diploid set of autosomes with two X chromosomes will always give rise to a female individual irrespective of whether the two X-chromosomes came from the same parent or from the different parents. Y-chromosome does not carry any sex determining factor. Presence of one or two X-chromosomes is more important than the presence or absence of Y-chromosome.

Parent : 2A XX (♀) × 2A XY (♂)

Gametes : (AX) normal, (AXX) (A) Due to non-disjunction; (AX) normal, (AY) normal

Offsprings :

| AX | AXX | AO | ♀ / ♂ |
|---|---|---|---|
| 2A XX ♀ | 2A XXX ♀ | 2AX ♂ | AX |
| 2A XY ♂ | 2A XXY ♀ | 2AY Dies | AY |

### 10.7.2 Gene-balance theory of sex-determination

The gene balance theory of sex-determination in *Drosophila* was proposed by C.B.Bridges. According to this theory.

1. Every individual has in its genotype both female and male potentialities. Which sex would be actually developed, is decided by the balance that is by the preponderance of the female tendency or of the male tendency genes.
2. Sex chromosomes and other chromosomes are merely vehicles of genes. It happens that in *Drosophila*, the X-chromosomes carry more genes that inclined to the development of individuals toward femaleness and the autosomes more that inclined toward maleness.
3. Y-chromosome is not important for the determination of sex.
4. After crossing Triploid female and diploid males, C.B. Bridges got 5 classes of sexes in *Drosophila.* He then proposed the gene balance theory. According to this theory **ratios between the number of X-chromosomes and number of complete sets of autosomes will determine the sex.** The X-chromosome is believed to carry femaleness tendency genes and autosomes carry maleness tentency genes. Both these sets of genes start functioning and there has to be balanced between them for an individual to become male or female. Sex is determined by the ratio of number of X-chromosome and sets of autosomes in their zygote and the different sexes are determined by the different values of the ratio which is described as follows :

| *Ratio* $\frac{\textit{No. of X-chromosomes}}{\textit{No of Sets of autosomes}}$ | *Sex* |
|---|---|
| 1. More than 1.00 | Metafemale |
| 2. Equal to 1.00 | Normal female |
| 3. Equal to 0.5 | Normal male |
| 4. Less than 0.5 | Metamale |
| 5. Less than 1.00 but more than 0.5 | Intersex |

**Diploid-Triploid cross in *Drosphila***

Triploid females contain three sets of autosomes and three Xchromosomes. Bridges obtains 5 classes of sexes by crossing between triploid female with diploid males.

Parent : 3 A XXX × 2 A XY dead
Triploid female Diploid male

Gametes : 2AXX, AX, 2AX, AXX AX, AY

Offsprings :

| 2AXX | AX | 2AX | AXX | ♀ / ♂ |
|---|---|---|---|---|
| 3A XXX | 2A XX | 3 A XX | 2A XXX | AX |
| 3A XXY | 2A XY | 3 A XY | 2A XXY | AY |

| *Zygote* | *No. of X-chromosome* | *Sets of Autosome* | *Ratio* | *Sex* |
|---|---|---|---|---|
| 3 A XXX | 3 | 3 | 1 | Triploid female |
| 2 A XX | 2 | 2 | 1 | Diploid female |
| 3 A XX | 2 | 3 | 0.66 | Intersex (femaleness) |
| 2 A XXX | 3 | 2 | 1.5 | Metafemale |
| 3 A XXY | 2 | 3 | 0.66 | Intersex (maleness) |
| 2 A XY | 1 | 2 | 0.5 | Diploid male |
| 3 A XY | 1 | 3 | 0.33 | Metamale |
| 2 A XXY | 2 | 2 | 1 | Diploid female (exceptional) |

### 10.7.3 Gynanders in *Drosophila*

Sometimes, one region of a fly is male and the rest is female, for example, the left half of the body might be female and the right half male, such flies are known as gynanders or gynandromorphs (Fig. 10.2)

In a gynander, the line of divisions between male and female tissue need not necessarily be through the middle of the body. Sometimes just a quarter of the body is male and the rest as female, or just a small island of tissue might be male.

A gynander begins its development with two Xs. But in course of cell division an X

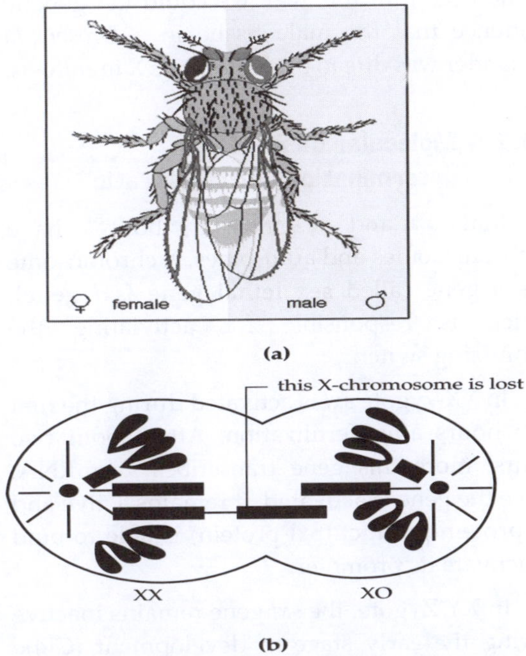


**Fig.10.2 :** *(a) A gynandromorph, left half is female, right half is male ; (b) Loss of an X-chromosome during meiosis.*

chromosome gets lost from one of the products of cell division. In case, this should happen during first cell division, then half of the animal body would develop from the cell with 2Xs, this half would be female $\left(\frac{X}{A}=1\right)$, the other half with one X $\left(\frac{X}{A}=0.5\right)$ would become male. The irregular cell division might occur later, rather than, at the first cell division. In this event, the cell that got just one X, would give rise to less than half the body. It might give rise to only a small patch of cells and then only this small patch would be male tissue.

Suppose a gynander, developed from a fertilized egg which has the recessive gene singed bristle (*sn*) in one X and the normal allele (+) in the other X. Further suppose that, the X that got lost happened to be the one that contained the normal allele. Then the female tissue would be normal (*sn*/+) and the male tissue (*sn*/ ). In this way we could get genetic evidence that the male tissue in a *Drosophila* gynander was due to the loss of one X in mitosis.

### 10.7.4 Molecular basis of sex determination and X : A ratio

Males and females, both have X-chromosomes and autosomes. X chromosome has a gene called **sex lethal gene (*sxl* gene)**, which is responsible for activiating the feminizing switch.

In XX-zygote *sxl* is activated during the first two hours after fertilization. After about two hours, more this gene transcribes *sxl*-mRNA. Once the gene is activated, it remains active and its protein product (Sxl protein) is able to bind to activate its promoter.

In XY Zygote, the *sxl* gene remains inactive during the early stage of development (Cline 1983, Salz *et al* 1987).

This *sxl* gene is thought to be stimulated by numerator proteins, **Sisterless-a** and **Sisterless-b**, encoded by *sis*-a and *sis-b genes of the X-chromosome.* These proteins try to bind to early promoters of *sxl*-gene shortly after fertilization in both males and females.

The autosomes encoded proteins such as **Deadpan** and **Extramacrochaetae** which are called denominator proteins (Van Doren *et at* 1991; Younger -Shepherd *et at* 1992). These proteins inactivate the **Sis-a** and **Sis-b** proteins by forming heterodimers and thus it acts as a repressor of *sxl* gene.

The determination and differentiation of sex in *Drosophila* might be described by following X:A ratio of C.B. Bridges gene balance theory, *i.e.* the ratio of numerator proteins (Sis a and Sis-b) and the denominator proteins (Deadpan, Extramacrochaetal etc.).

**In wild XX-*Drosophila*** (Fig. 10.3)

1. the numerator proteins (Sis a, Sis b) are not all bound by the demominator (repressor) proteins (Deadpan etc.)
2. the excess of Sis a and Sis b proteins bind to the early promoters (PE) of *sxl* gene.
3. Sxl transcribes a pre-*sxl*-mRNA, male exon is spliced and translates into Sxl proteins.
4. Sxl protein has two definite functions. It binds to late promoter maintains the *sxl*-gene expression and secondly, it acts as a self splicing factor to remove male exon from transcript.
5. The *sxl* gene consists of 8 exons but during the *sxl*-mRNA processing yields only seven exons (devoid of 3rd exon) and encodes Sxl-proteins with 354 amino acids in the females.
6. Sxl protein also regulates the splicing and processing of the mRNA of *transformer* (*tra*) genes. The *tra*-gene transcript actually has four exons. but in females after splicing second exon is not utilized (which bears stop coden) and it is spliced out possibly by binding with and blocking a splicing factor called U2AF to the nonspecific splice site. Thus a female specific **Tra** product is produced. (Valcarcel *et al* 1993).
7. This Tra-product then acts in concert with the product of another *tra*-2 gene to help generate the female genotype.
8. A gene *double sex (dsx)* is transcribed into *dsx* transcript which consists of 6 exons.If *tra*-gene product and *tra*-2 gene product is present, the *dsx*-transcript is processed in a female specific manner (Ryner and Baker 1991). The mRNA which is produced after such splicing lacks 5th and 6th exons. After translation, the female specific proteins are produced which

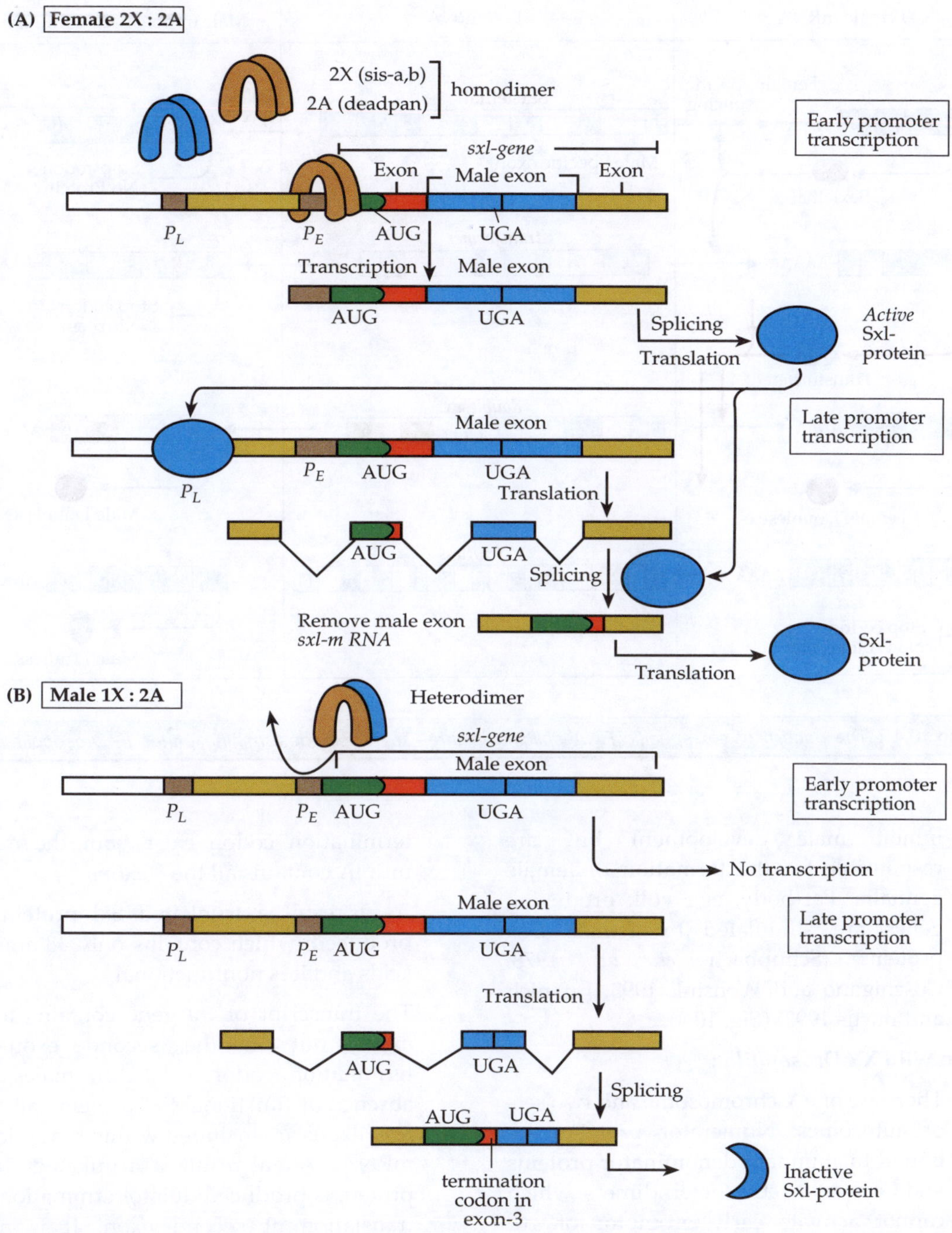


**Fig.10.3 :** *Differential activation of sxl-gene in females and males.*

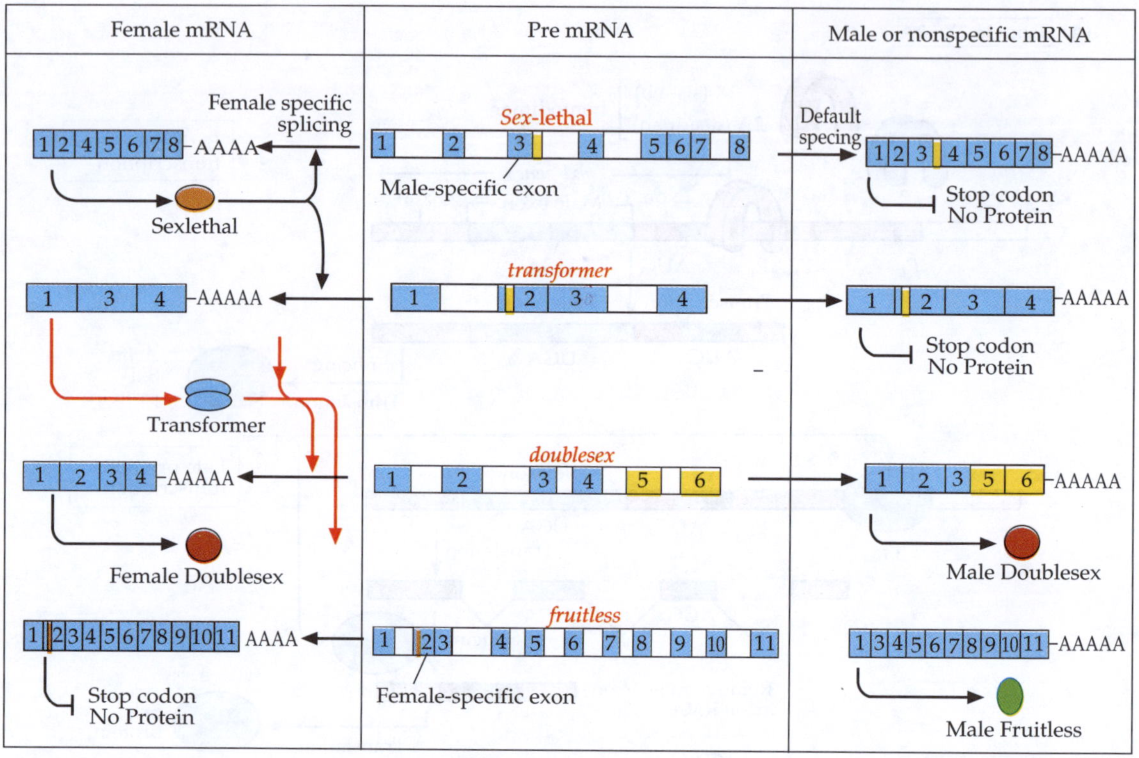


**Fig.10.4 :** *The pattern of sex-specific RNA splicing in three major sex-determining genes in Drosophila.*

inhibit male development but are responsible for the formation of female genitalia. Fat body, egg yolk producing genes are stimulated by female Dsx protein. (Schupbach *et. at.* 1978, Coschigano and Wensink 1993, Jursnich and Burtis 1993) (Fig. 10.4).

**In wild XY *Drosophila* :**

1. There are one X-chromosome and two sets of autosomes. Numerator proteins are bound to abundant denominator proteins and form an inactive heterodimers, which cannot activate early promotor of *sxl.* gene.
2. When *sxl* genes are transcribed from the late promotor, RNA splicing does not exclude the male exon (3rd exon) where termination codon exists, but the male mRNA contains all the 8 exons.

   As a result a trunkated Sxl protein is produced, which contains only 48 amino acids and it is nonfunctional.
3. The transcript of *tra* gene contains four exons but in the second exon a termination codon exists. In males, in absence of functional Sxl proteins all the four exons are included within the spliced mRNA. As a result a trunkated Tra-protein is produced due to termination of translation at second exon. It is non functional.
4. Tra protein is not produced in these Zygotes, therefore, *dsx* gene transcript is spliced normally and the 4th exon is

excluded in such mRNA. After translation a male specific Dsx product is produced, that promotes male primordium to express. Ultimately male sex organs are developed in XY flies.

### 10.7.5 Other genes active in *Drosophila* sex determination

1. **Groucho**, a bHLH transcription regulator, binds to **deadpan**. In females *Groucho* gene (*gro*) is absent. It appears that maternally encoded groucho protein is needed by deadpan as a corepresor (Paroush *et. al.* 1994).
2. The *hermaphrodite* gene (*her*) is required for the normal female development. When mother cannot synthesize the **Her**-protein, their daughters fail to activate the *sxl* early promotoer (Pultz and Baker, 1995).
3. There are four male-specific lethal (*msl*) genes, their proteins form a complex that bind to hundreds of sites along the X-chromosome. Msl-2 proteins is absent in female embryos but amount of *msl-2* pre-mRNA is same in both sexes. It is throught that, in females Sxl-proteins can bind to the *msl*-2-pre mRNA and prevents it from proper splicing. Thus Msl-2 protein only exists in males.
4. The *liz*-gene (stands for Elizabeth-1 of England, who shares some of the mutant character) is a maternal effect gene whose product positively regulates the late *sxl*-mRNAs and proteins.
5. The *fl(2)d* gene may also be involved in the regulation of late *sxl* mRNA. Mutant of this gene in females expresses male spliced *sxl* transcript.

Mutants of *virilizer* gene (*vir*) fail to have female specific splicing of the *sxl* and *tra*-pre-mRNAs (Hilfiker *et. al.* 1995). Possibly *vir* and *fl(2)d* genes encode protein cofactors for Sxl proteins and work with it during female-specific splicing.

### 10.7.6 Causes of Intersex phenotypes

In *Drosophila,* several genes have been identified those have specefic roles in the sex determination and differentiation. Loss-of function mutation of *sxl, tra, tra-2* genes transforms XX individidual into males. But such mutations have no effects on sex determination in XY males.

Homozygosity of the *intersex* (*ix*) gene causes XX to develop into an intersex phenotype having portions of male and female tissues in the same organ.

The *dsx* gene is important for the sexual differentiation of both sexes. If *dsx* is absent both XX and XY flies turn into intersexes (Braker and Ridge 1980, Belote *et al* 1995). In such case, both the male and female primordia develop and intersexual genitalia are produced.

### 10.7.7 Regulatory cascade for *Drosophila* somatic sex determination

1. Transcription factors from the X chromosomes activate the *Sxl* gene in females (XX) but not in males (XY). The Sex-lethal protein(Sxl) performs main three functions (Fig. 10.5).
   a) It activates own transcription, ensuring further Sxl production.
   b) It represses the *msl2* mRNA, the product of which is a factor that facilitates transcription from X-chromosome. This equalizes the amount of transcription from the two X-chromosomes in females with that of the single X chromosome in males.
   c) Sxl enables the splicing of *transformer-1* (*tra-1*) pre-mRNA into functional proteins.
2. The Tra proteins process *doublesex*(*dsx*) pre-mRNA in a female-specific manner that provides most of the female body with its sexual fate. They also process the *fruitless* pre-mRNA in a female-specific

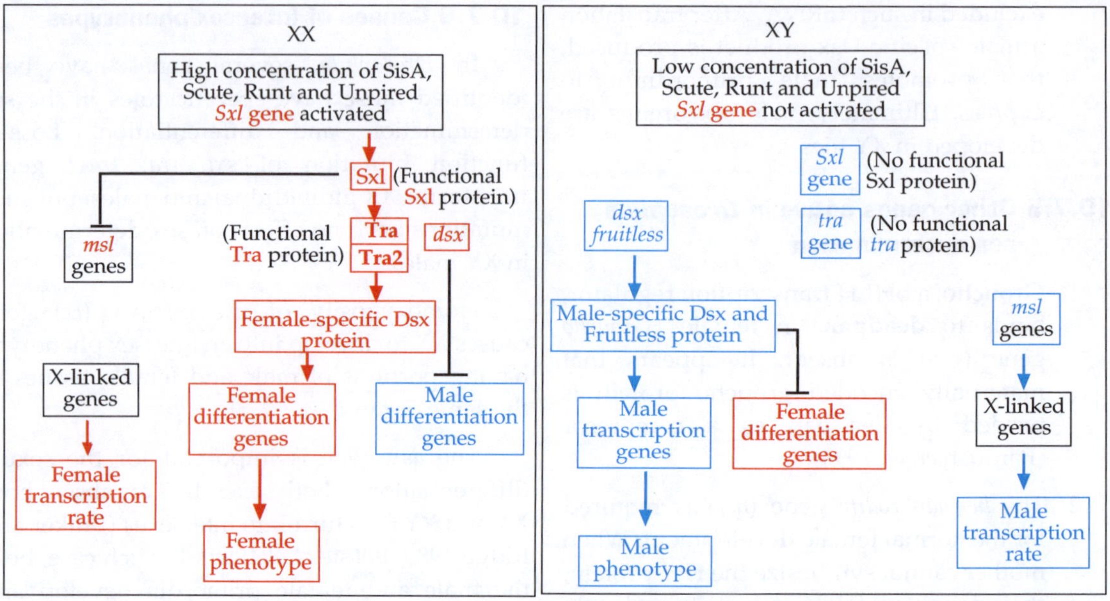


**Fig.10.5 :** *Proposed regulatory cascade for Drosophila somatic sex determination.*

manner, giving fly female-specific behaviour.

3. In absence of Sxl (and thus the Tra proteins), *dsx* and *fruitless* pre-mRNAs are processed in a male-specific manner.

## 10.8 SEX DETERMINATION IN *COENOHABDITIS ELEGANS*

The primary signals for chromosomal sex determination in *C. elegans* are determined by the balance between *the number of X-chromosomes and number of sets of autosomes* (Nigon 1952). They do not have Y chromosome. Therefore, XO leads to males and XX females.

Again, XX-females are protandric hermaphrodites studies by Madl and Herman (1979) determined that X:A ratio of 0.67, leads to males, while the ratio higher than 0.75 results in female development. The signals from X-chromosome correspond to *fox-1*, *sex-1* from autosomes *sea* genes.

*xol-1* gene (XO-lethal) is the master switch of the male or female development. X:A ratio equals to or below 0.75 results in activation of *xol-1* and leads to male switch. XX genotype leads to inactivation of *xol-1* (Fig. 10.6 and 10.7).

*xol-1* inhibits dosage compensation in males by repressing *sdc* gene, *xol-1* is regulated transcriptionally by SEA protein from autosome and SEX-1 protein while post -transcriptionally by RNA-binding protein FOX. *xol-1* is also transcriptionally regulated by femainizing protein TRA-1.

**Mechanism of male and female development :**

1. SDC-2 (sex determining and dosage compensation) recognizes elements on X-chromosome and SDC-3 recognizes *her-1* gene on autosome. In XX-hermaphrodites, transcription rate of *her-1* is reduced by 20-fold (not by 2-fold).

2. In XO males, HER-1 acts as ligand by inhibiting transmembrane receptor TRA-2A. But in XX-animals, in absence of HER-1 protein TRA-2A represses FEM

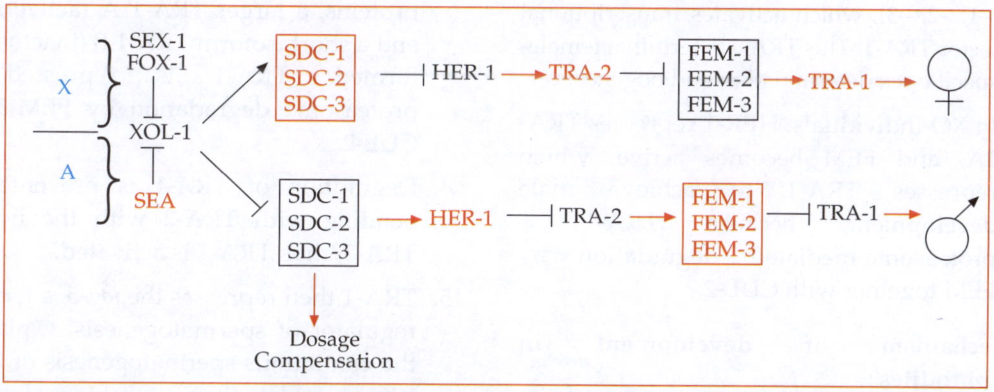


**Fig.10.6 :** *Sex determination in C. elegans by the X: Y ratio*

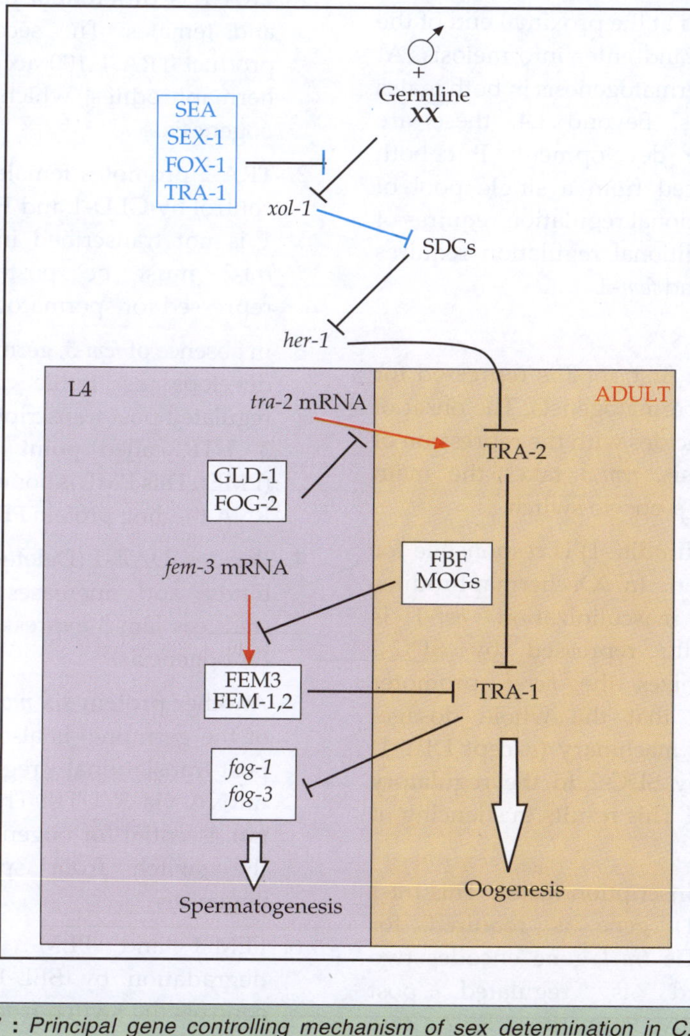


**Fig.10.7 :** *Principal gene controlling mechanism of sex determination in C. elegans*

(–1, –2, –3), which activates transcriptional factor TRA-1. This TRA-1 is terminal female-specific sex determination and oogenesis.

3. In XO-individuals, HER-1 represses TRA-2A, and FEM becomes active, which represses TRA-1 to achieve male development, because TRA-1 is proteasome-mediated degradation by FEM together with CUL-2.

**Mechanism of development in hermaphrodites :**

XX-hermaphrodites develop either male or female depending upon the worm's developmental stages. During L3 stage, the germ cells are located at the proximal end of the gonod, differentiate and enter into meiosis. At L4, they undergo spermatogenesis in both males and hermaphrodites. Beyond L4, these are destined to female development. But both gametes are produced from a single pool of germ line. This additional regulation requires of germ line. This additional regulation requires the control of *tra-2* and *fem-3*.

**Male Switch :**

1. In L3 stage, at first, *tra-2* is repressed for the onset of spermatogensis. The onset of oogenesis coincides with the repression of spermatogenesis. *fem-3* takes the main role of sperm → oocyte switch.
2. *her-1* (hermaphrodite-1) is responsible for masculinization. In XX hermaphrodites after partial masculinization, *her-1* is transcriptionally repressed by SDC-3 which recognizes the *her-1* promoter region. After that the whole dosage-compensation machinary (except DPY-1) is recruited by SDC-2 to the regulatory region of *her-1* This results in silencing of *her-1* gene.
3. TRA-1 is a transcription factor. This *tra-1* (transformer-1) gene is required for female fate. Tis *tra-1* gene encodes two mRNAs and is regulated post transcriptionally. From those RNAs two proteins, a larger TRA-1 A (active form) and a short isoform TRA-1 B (inactive) are formed. TRA-1 is repressed by proteasome degradation by FEM-3 and CUL-2.
4. Degradtion of TRA-1 is prevented by bending with TRA-2 with the help of TRA-3, thus TRA-1 is activated.
5. TRA-1 then represses the *fog-3*, a terminal regulator of spermatogenesis, explaining the continuous spermatogenesis of XO or XX hermaphrodites.

**Female Switch :**

1. TRA-1 is differentially cleaved in males and females. The second *tra-1* shorter product TRA-1 100 accumulates in adult hermaphrodites which is required for oogenesis.
2. TRA-2 promotes females by translational control by GLD-1 and FOG-2. Since HER-1 is not transcribed in hermaphrodites, *tra-2* must be post transcriptionally repressed for spermatogenesis.
3. In absence of *fem-3*, germline of XX-animals develops as fertile female, which is regulated post-transcriptionally through its 3′ UTR called **point mutation element** (PME), This PME is bound by the conserved RNA-binding protein **FBF-1 and 2**.
4. Besides, DAZ-1 (Deleted in Azoospermia) binds and increases FBF translation (reduces fem-3 express)which is required for oogenesis.
5. Another protein six *mog* (mascularization of the germline) is also implicated in the post-translational regulation of *fem-3* mRNA via 3′ UTR. These *mog* genes are not essential for oogenesis, but rather for the switch from spermatogenesis to oogenesis.
6. FEM-1 and FEM-3 are proteasomic degradation by SEL-10. Besides, *larp-1* controls the switch from spermatogenesis to cocyte.

**Role of maternal RNAs in sex determination**

In *C. elegans* few genes control sexual fate by the maternal mRNAs and/or proteins through the oocyte for zygotic sex determination. Some maternal mRNAs are translocated upon fertilization and permit protein synthesis before zygotic transcription sets in.

The heterozygous females (O/+) for *fem-1* gene can be obtained by crossing *fem-1* null mutant female with wild male. Such progenies are expected to be phenotypically wild type. But Andrew Spence's group found that these females produce no *fem-1* mRNA and totally lacking maternal *fem-1* mRNA and are also unable to use paternal wild *fem-1*. Thus their germlines are feminized because of the absence of *fem-1*, which is essential for male development.

The epigenetic control of the expression of *fem1* uses a mechanism of sense RNA, which is independent of *rde-1*, indicating this is distinct from RNA interferance.

## Chapter Glossary/Key Terms

**Genetically determination of sex :** Sex is determined by the autosomes.

**Gynandromorphs :** Mosaic individuals having simultaneous aspects of both the male and the female phenotype.

**Homogametic sex :** Due to similar identical sex-chromosomes, the individual produces same kinds of gametes with identical chromosomes.

**Heterogametic sex :** Due to dissimilar sex-chromosome constitution, the individual produces two different kinds of gametes with different sex chromosomes.

**Intersex :** An organism with external sexual characteristics of both sexes.

**Pseudotrivalent :** In Mantids, three sex-chromosomes X, X, Y during meiotic prophase form a trivalent with dissimillar chromosomes.

**Sex chromosomal sex determination :** Sex is determined by the sex-chromosomes.

**Sex-lethal gene :** A gene in *Drosophila,* located on X-chromosome, that is a sex switch directing development toward femaleness when in the "on" state. It is regulated by numerator and denominator elements that act to influence the genic balance ratio.

**Supersex :** Individual with extra male or female sex-determining factors.

# EXERCISE

**A. Long answer type questions :**

1. Briefly describe the chromosomal sex determination in man and *Drosophila*.
2. Describe the chromosomal sex determination of butterfly, birds and reptiles.
3. Describe chromosomal sex determination in grasshoppers.
4. Describe neo-XY mechanism of sex determination in grasshopper.
5. Describe the multiple sexchromosome method of sex determination in mantids.
6. Describe compound chromosomes in the sex determination in *Ascaris incurva* and *Blaps polychresta*.
7. Describe the role of environment of sex determination in *Drosophila*.
8. Describe Richard Goldchmidt's theory of sex determination in gypsy moth .
9. Describe sex determination in hymenoptera.
10. Briefly describe temperature – dependent sex determination.
11. Describe sex determination in *Bonellia* and *Crepidula*.
12. Describe sex determination in blue-headed wrasse.
13. Describe the chromosomal basis of sex determination in *Drosophila* .
14. Describe gene-balance theory by C.B.Bridges in *Drosophila*. Briefly determine the sexes when diplolid *Drosophila* is crossed with a triploid one.
15. What are gynanders? How do they produce?
16. What are the . numerator genes and denominator genes that are involved in sex-determination in *Drosophila*. Describe the role of denominator and numerator proteins in the sex determination of XX and XY *Drosophila*.
17. Describe the roles of other genes in *Drosophila* sex determination.
18. What are the causes of intersex phenotypes in *Drosophila*.
19. Transformer (*tra*) is an autosomal recessive gene that converts normal females into sterile males. A female *Drosophila* heterozygous for the transformer allele (*tra*) is mated with a normal male homozygous for transformer. What is the sex ratio of their offspring? What is the sex ratio of their offspring's offspring?
20. The autosomal recessive double sex (dsx) gene converts males and females into developmental intersexes. Two fruit flies, both heterozygous for the doublesex (*dsx*) allele, are mated. What are the sexes of the offspring?
21. What is a sex switch? Which gene serves as sex switch in *Drosophila* sex determination.

**B. Short answer type questions.**

1. What kinds of sexes are found in animal kingdoms?
2. What are sex chromosomal determination of sex and genetically determination of sex?
3. What is the difference between X and Z chromsomes?
4. What do you mean by homogametic and heterogametic sex.
5. What is the distinction between the sex determination in *Drosophila* and *butterfly* and also human and birds?
6. What kinds of gametes and formed in male grasshopper? Why so formed?
7. What do you mean by neo-XY mechanism of sex determination? Where does it found?
8. What kinds of sex chromosomes are found in mantids? How their sexes are determined?
9. What is compound chromosome in sex determination?
10. How sex is determined in *Ascaris incurva*?

11. How sex is determined in the *beetle, Blaps polychresta?*
12. How high termperature influences sexes in *Drosophila*.
13. How normally sex in determined in Gypsy moths?
14. What is the result of cross between European female moth and Japanese male? Explain it.
15. What is the result of cross between European male and Japanese female? Explain it.
16. What is Goldchmidt's cytoplasmic theory of sex determination in gypsy moth?
17. "Cytoplasmic theory of sex determination in gypsy moth is not true" — explain with illustration.
18. What is the principle of sex determination in *Habrobracon*?
19. Diploid males are not found — why?
20. How sexes of crocodiles are dependent on temperature?
21. How sexes are dependent on turtles? Explain the mechanism.
22. What is the effect of PCBs on sex determination in turtles.
23. What is the cause of extinction of dinosaurs?
24. How the larva of *Bonellia* transform into males or females?
25. What is the factor that regulates sex determination in *Crepidula*?
26. What is adaptive sex determination? Give example.
27. What is the role of Y chromosome is sex determination in *Drosophila.*
28. Why XXY is female but XO is male in *Drosophila*?
29. What is gynander? How it occurs in *Drosophila*. How the gynander phenotypes can be identified?
30. What is sex switch? Which gene is responsible in *Drosophila*.
31. What are the numerator and denominator genes and proteins in *Drosophila* sex determination?
32. What are *sxl, dsx* and *tra* genes? Explain their roles in the sex specific sex determination of *Drosophila*.
33. What are groucho an deadpan proteins? What are their roles?
34. What is *her* gene? What is its role in sex determination?
35. What are the male-specific lethal genes in *Drosophila?* What are their functions?
36. What is the function of *liz* gene in the sex determination of *Drosophila*.
37. What is the role of *vir* gene and fl(z)d gene in the sex determination of *Drosophila*.
38. What is the cause of intersexes in *Drosophila?*
39. What is the role of aromatase enzyme in sex-determination of *Drosophila* and others?

**Write short notes on :**

Chromosomal sex determination; XX-XY and XX-XO system of sex determination; ZZ-ZW system of sex determination; Compound chromosomes in sex determination; Intersex and supersexes; Temperature dependent sex determination in reptiles; Location dependent sex determination; Adaptive sex determination; Gene balance theory; Gynanders; X: A ratio and its molecular biology; Sex-switch; Role of aromatase enzyme.

# 11

# Extranuclear and Epigenetic Inheritance

**CHAPTER AGENDA**

## 11.1 CONCEPT

The mode of inheritance of a particular character is tied to the behaviour of the nucleus or more specifically to the chromosomes. The transmission of a character and its appearance in individuals can be predicted from knowledge Mendelian chromosome segregation and assortment. Thus, we assumed and considered DNA as the basis of genetic material and practically all the DNAs in the cell are localized in the chromosomes.

Sporadic reports have indicated that extra—nuclear or some cytoplasmic elements were found to act as the hereditary transmission. The immediate environment of the nucleus *i.e.*, the cytoplasm of the zygote may considerably modify the genotypic effect of the developing individual. Such type of inheritance which is controlled by the cytoplasm of the zygote rather than the genotypes (genes in the nucleus) is known as *extra-chromosomal inheritance*.

The genetic component in the cytoplasm or in the cytoplasmic organelles like mitochondria chloroplast etc. are involved in the hereditary transmission rather than the mechanism of segregation or assortment of the chromosomes, therefore, such a type of inheritance is known as **non-Mendelian inheritance**.

## 11.2 CRITERIA FOR EXTRA-CHROMOSOMAL INHERITANCE

1. When a reciprocal cross is made, *i.e.*, a female of strain A is mated with a male of strain B or vice versa, a different result is obtained, suggesting the influence of the egg cytoplasm exerting an influence on a particular trait.
2. Sometimes, eggs (female reproductive cells) carry more cytoplasm along with cytoplasmic organelles than the male reproductive cells. These cytoplasmic organelles or symbionts are analyzed and isolated and have been found to contain some DNA molecules within them, which are associated with the transmission of hereditary traits.
3. Lack of Mendelian segregation and departure from the characteristic Mendelian ratios suggest the extra–chromosomal inheritance.
4. Transmission of the traits without transmission of nuclear genes would suggest the extra-chromosomal transmission.
5. Failure of linkage data may rules out the location of genes (chromosome map) on the chromosome suggesting the extra–chromosomal transmission.

## 11.3 MATERNAL EFFECT

Trait controlled by a gene of the mother but expressed in the progeny is called **maternal effect**.

If a maternal effect is involved, results from reciprocal crosses will be different from each other, with genes of mother being expressed.

### 11.3.1 Maternal effect in snail

The snail *Limnaea peregra*, in which the direction of coiling is determined by a single pair of genes. The allele for dextral coiling is determined by the dominant gene (*R*) and the recessive allele is the sinistral coiling (*r*).

When, dextral (*RR*) female is crossed with sinistral (*rr*) male, all the $F_1$ heterozygotes (*Rr*) would be dextral coiling.

But it is interesting that, if, sinistral female (*rr*) is crossed with dextral male, the $F_1$ hybrid is sinistral rather than dextral.

The snail is hermaphroditic and may reproduce either by crossing or by self fertilization.

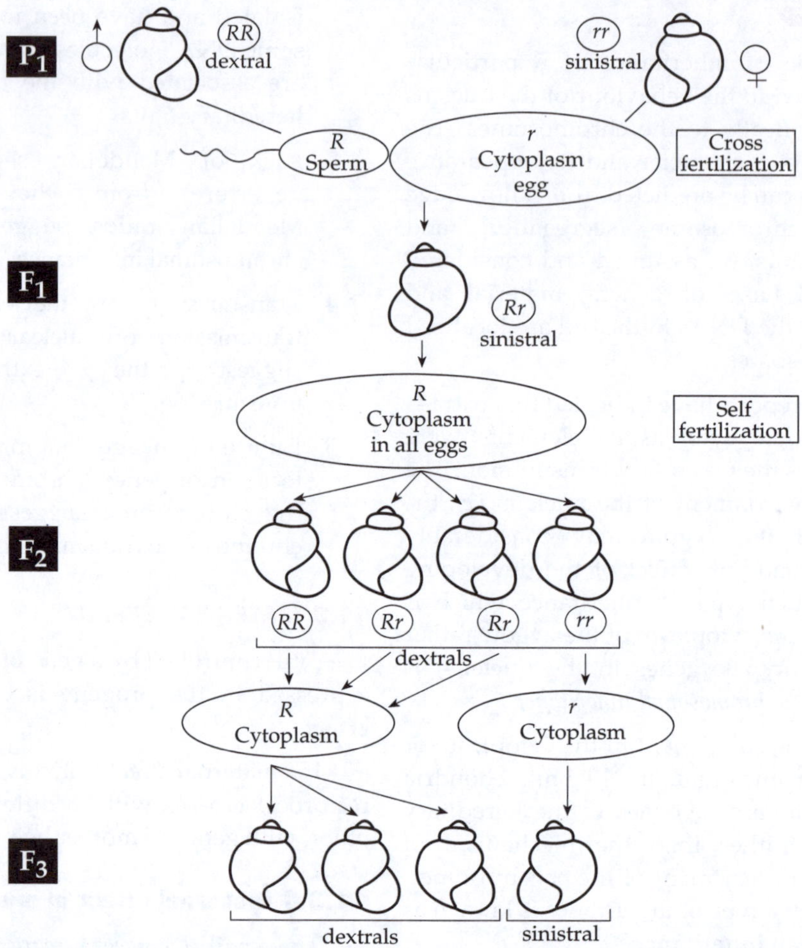


**Fig.11.1 :** *Maternal effect in Limnaea pelegra, results in $F_1$, $F_2$ and $F_3$ from a cross between dextral (RR) male and sinistral (rr) female*

Thus, when dextrally coiled heterozygotes are self fertilized, the eggs will contain *R* or *r* genes but the development occurs within the cytoplasm of dextral hybrid thus all the offspring would be dextral even the genotype is (*rr*).

Similarly, the products of a self-fertilized sinistrally coiled heterozygote (heterozygous offspring of an *rr* mother) will all be dextrally coiled even though some eggs are homozygous (*rr*).

This maternal effect lasts only one generation. These dextrally coiled homozygous (*rr*) snails again when self-fertilized, in the next generation, again sinistral coiled snails are produced (Fig. 11.1 and 11.2).

According to Conklin and others, the cause of the direction of coiling is determined embryologically by the cleavage pattern and the arrangement of spindle in the second cleavage division.

In the sinistral type, the spindle is tipped toward the left of the median line while in the dextral type, it is tipped toward the right. This is determined by some relationship of the egg to the mother before maturation. In the ovary, this

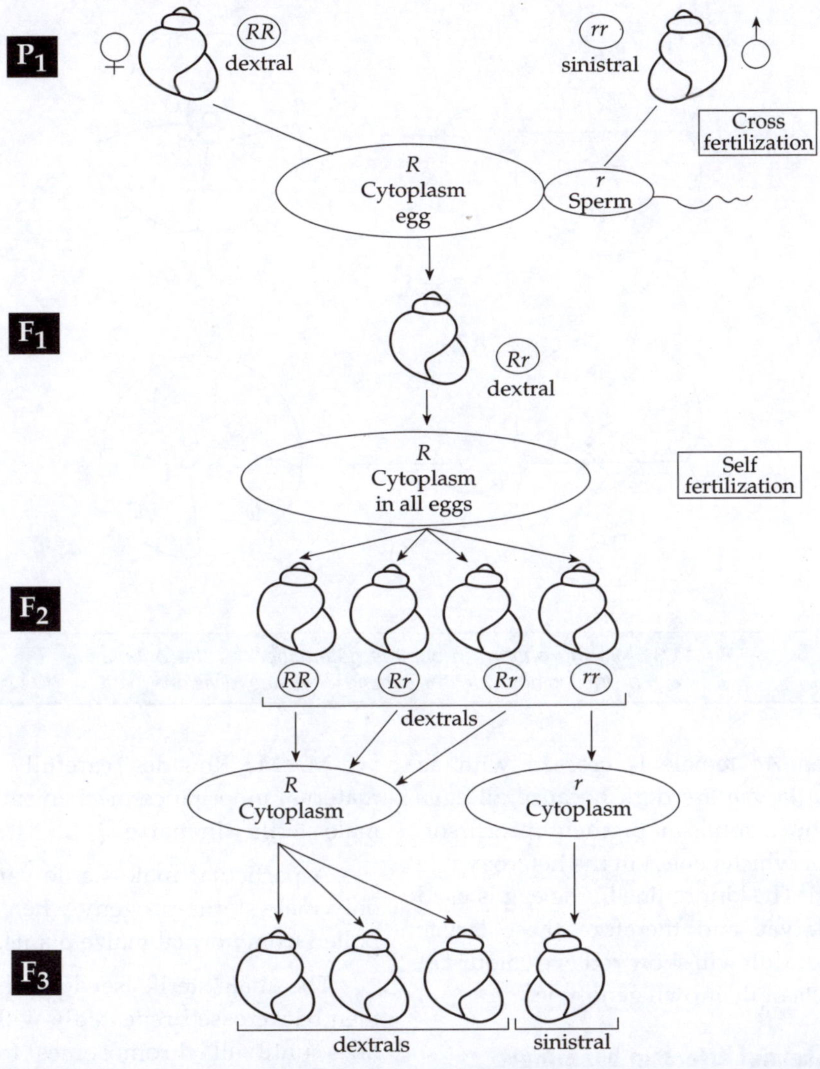


**Fig.11.2 :** *Maternal effect in Limnaea pelegra, results in $F_1$, $F_2$ and $F_3$ from a cross between dextral (RR) female and sinistral (rr) male.*

maternal gene acts on the eggs for predetermining the direction of an early cell division. This maternal effect is transmitted through the egg cytoplasm for only one generation. In the next generation new egg cytoplasm will be formed according to the pattern of new maternal genotype (Fig. 11.3).

### 11.3.2 Maternal effect in Flour moth

Caspari illustrated the maternal effect in flour moth, *Ephestia kiihniella*. This moth has dark-brown eyes and various pigments in larval skin due to a precursor **kinurenine**, produced by a dominant gene (*A*), the recessive allele is (*a*), when present in homozygous condition, lacks kinurenine causing red eye and a lack of larval pigmentation.

If an (*aa*) homozygous female is crossed with (*Aa*) heterozygous male, produce larvae only half of which show the darkening effect of the allele *A*.

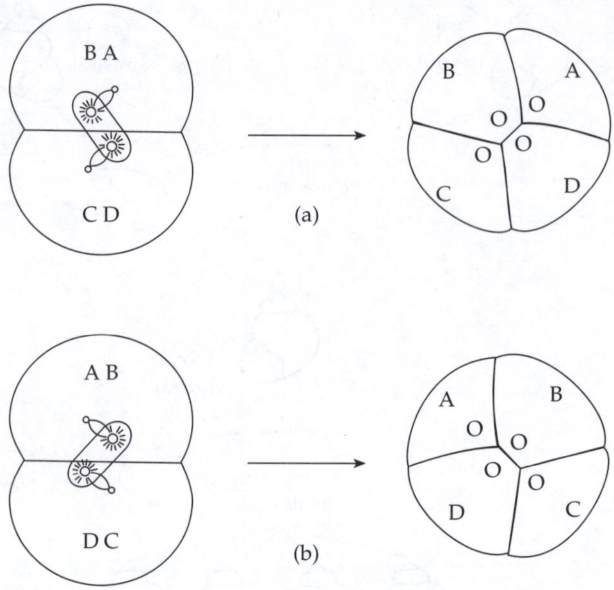


**Fig.11.3 :** *Coiling pattern in snail is determined by the orientation of the spindle for the second cleavage division.*

But when *Aa* female is crossed with aa males, all the larvae are dark because all eggs contain in the cytoplasm pigment precursor, kinurenine for which gene *A* in the heterozygote is responsible. The kinurenine in the egg is used up by the larvae and therefore these larvae when become adult will show red eye colour *i.e.*, only the effects of their own genotype.

### 11.3.3 Maternal effect in Mammals

Certain maternal effects are known among human beings, such as the embryonic defects caused by maternal diabetes and maternal phenylketonuria, left or right handedness etc.

In mice, the induction of mammary gland tumors in strains was found to be caused by an RNA retrovirus, transmitted through the milk of mother which is highly susceptible to cancer.

## 11.4 CYTOPLASMIC MALE STERILITY IN PLANTS

In maize, wheat, sugar beets, onions and some other crops, fertility is controlled partly by cytoplasmic factors (Fig. 11.4).

M. M. Rhoades carefully analyzed the maternal inheritance mechanism that transmits male sterility in maize.

A particular male-sterile variety produced only male sterile-progeny when fertilized with pollen from normal maize plants.

The male-sterile seed-parent plants were then backcrossed repeatedly with pollen-fertile lines until all chromosomes from the male-sterile line had been exchanged by the male-fertile line still the male sterility is persisted. Thus it may be concluded that inheritance is maternal, the nuclear genes do not control this type of sterility.

If a very small amount of such rare pollen obtained from male-sterile plants and reciprocal cross is performed, then it is found that male-sterile line becomes male-fertile line (Fig. 10.4).

Male sterility is thought to be attributed to cytoplasmic genes called **plasmagenes**, which is transmitted by the female gametes, possibly to the failure of function of mitochondria.

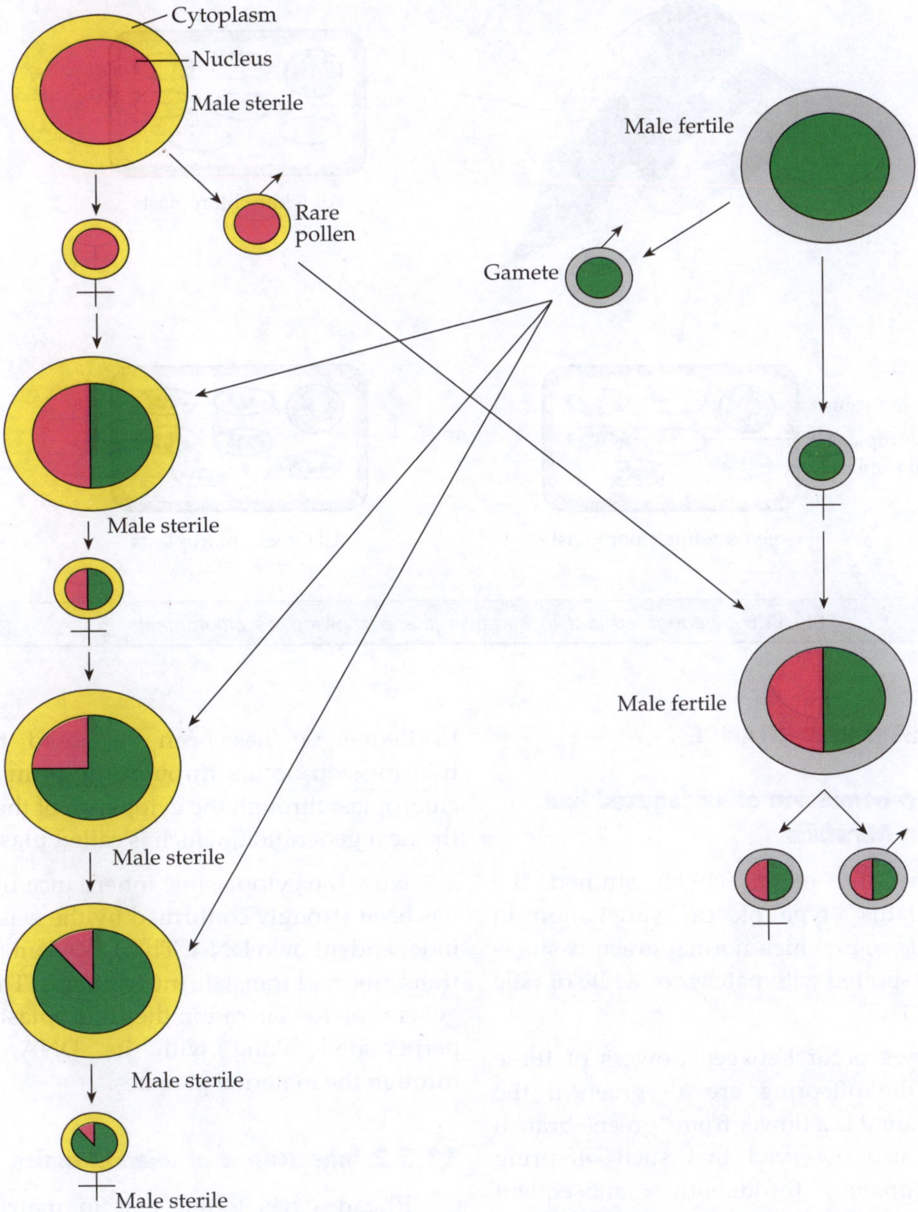


**Fig.11.4 :** *Maternal inheritance of male sterility in maize.*

Now, it is discovered that certain nuclear genes which are known to suppress maternally inherited sterility in maize. This dominant gene can restore pollen fertility in the presence of cytoplasm that usually causes sterility. The pollen abortion occurred only when the cytoplasm consists of dominant male-sterility gene and homozygous recessive allele in the suppressor locus in the chromosome.

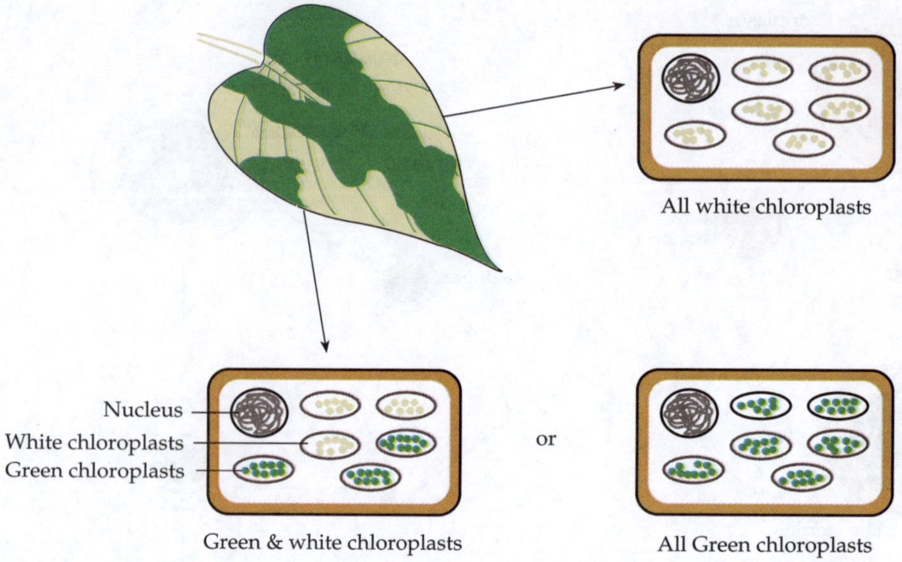


**Fig.11.5 :** *Variegated leaf in Mirabilis jalapa showing it's chloroplasts.*

## 11.5 PLASTID INHERITANCE

### 11.5.1 Transmission of variegated leaf in *Mirabilis*

Correns and others (1909) studied the "albomaculatus" type of leaf variegation in *Mirabilis jalapa*, in which normal green tissue is irregularly spotted with patches of white or pale green (Fig. 11.5).

If crosses occur between flowers of these branches, the offspring are all green if the maternal parent is a flower from "green" branch and it is also observed that such offspring remain green throughout subsequent generations as long as the maternal plant is green.

Similarly, all the offspring would be white if the maternal plant is white (*i.e.*, lack of chloroplast). Again, if the maternal plant is variegated then the offspring are similarly variegated.

Therefore, variegation seems clearly to be determined by cytoplasmic agencies. According to Renner, it has been supposed that the transmission occurs through the primordial of chloroplast through the cytoplasm of the eggs to the next generation, which is called **plastome**.

Now the cytoplasmic inheritance of plastid has been strongly confirmed by the existence of independent own DNA. This DNA can replicate transcribe and translate into proteins. Thus from generation to generation the chloroplasts can be perpetuated along with its DNA, mainly through the maternal gametes.

### 11.5.2 Inheritance of *iojap* in maize

Rhoades has found that in maize plants homozygous for a recessive gene *ij (iojap* in chromosome VII, may be variegated with yellow or white "japonica" striping, where the chloroplasts are in some way affected.

Once formed by this nuclear process, these striping characteristics are not affected by nuclear genotypes, since when *ij/ij* double recessive is crossed with *Ij/Ij* double dominant give different results in reciprocal crosses.

**Cross-1**

Parent : *ij/ij* ♀ × *Ij/Ij* ♂

striped Green

Offspring : *Ij/ij* *Ij/ij* *Ij/ij*

green white striped

Backcross : *Ij/ij* ♀ × *Ij/Ij* ♂

striped green

Offspring :

| *Ij/Ij* | *Ij/Ij* | *Ij/Ij* | *Ij/ij* | *Ij/ij* | *Ij/ij* |
|---|---|---|---|---|---|
| green | striped | white | green | striped | white |

**Cross-2**

Parent : *Ij/Ij* ♀ × *ij/ij* ♂

green striped

Offspring : *Ij/ij*

All green

1. When normal *Ij/Ij* green female plant is pollinated by pollens from *ij/ij* striped plants, $F_1$ plants (*Ij/ij*) are wholly green.
2. When *ij/ij* striped ♀ plants are pollinated by pollens from (*Ij/Ij*) green plants, the $F_1$ plants (*Ij/ij*) will show three different kinds, such as normal-green, striped and nonviable-white seedlings. Though, they have same genotypes but the development depends variously on the ovules from which they arose, *i.e.*, the embryo got the cytoplasm of the egg.
3. When $F_1$ striped plant is used as female and was back crossed with green (*Ij/Ij*) as males, they will produce all the three types of seedlings such as, normal-green, striped and white even which *ij* alleles are lacking in the genotype.

Rhoades concluded that under the influence of the (*ij/ij*) genotype, plastids became permanently changed to a colorless state. This change is perpetuated even if the (*ij*) is replaced by its normal allele.

### 11.5.3 Inheritance of Chloroplast in *Chlamydomonas*

The single-celled green algae, *Chlamydomonas reinhardtii* has a single chloroplast, that occupies approximately 40% of the cell volume.

Ruth Sagar (1954) identified a mutant strain of *Chlamydomonas* with resistance to the antibiotic streptomycin ($sm^r$). The most strains ($sm^s$) are sensitive to this antibiotic. She showed that the mutant gene $sm^r$ is not inherited in a Mendelian manner.

*Chlamydomonas* also found to have two mating types which are designated as $mt^+$ and $mt^-$. Mating type is due to nuclear inheritance, segregates in a 1:1 ratio.

She discovered that $sm^r$ trait is inherited from the $mt^+$ parent but not from the $mt^-$ parent. It is as if the $mt^+$ parent are contributing the cytoplasm to the zygote in a manner similar to maternal plastid inheritance in plants. The $mt^-$ parent acts like a pollen parent by making a contribution of only chromosome not the cytoplasm.

Again, it has been shown that $mt^+$ inheritance is only 99.98% effective. The 0.02% of the offspring in crosses of the type have the streptomycin resistance phenotype of the $mt^-$ parent. Thus, it assumes that recombination in chloroplast may occur between these two genes (Fig. 11.6).

## 11.6 MITOCHONDRIAL INHERITANCE

### 11.6.1 Paternal inheritance of mitochondria

The mitochrondria are generally inherited in a maternal fashion, *ie*, the male gamete usually does not contribute mitrochondria to the zygogte.

But a small amount of "leakiness" may occur in certain instances. It has been shown

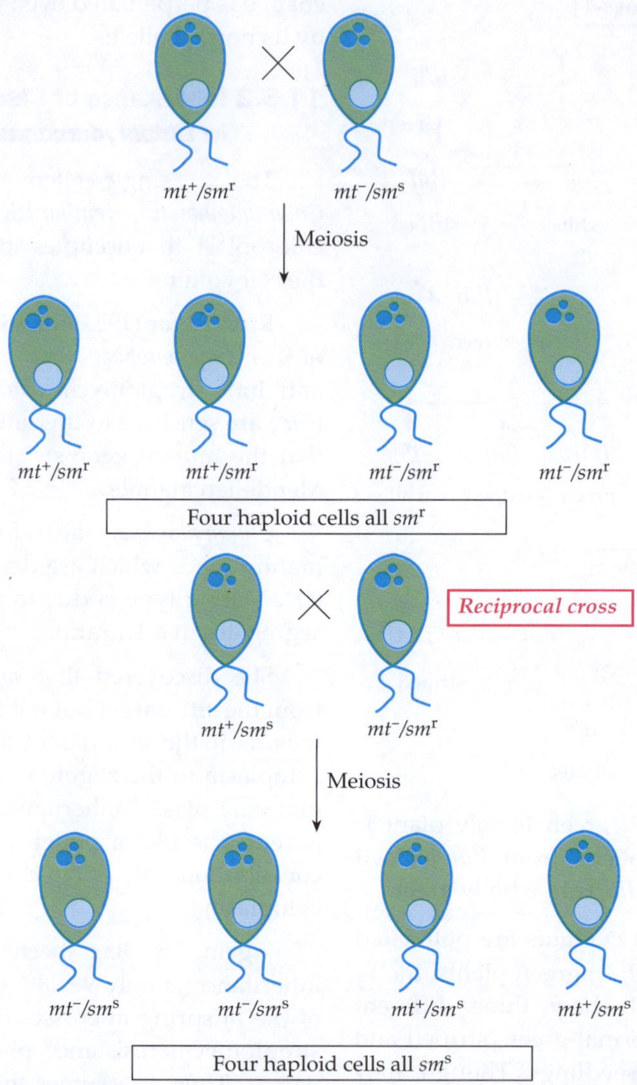


**Fig.11.6 :** *Chloroplast inheritance in Chlamydomonas*

that about one mitochondrion per thousand is of paternal origin in mice. It is also fact that in mussels, the inheritane of mitochondria is biparental, their offspring derives both maternal and paternal mitochondria almost equally. In some gymnosperm plants such as coastal redwoods, mitochondria are inherited only from male parent to the zygote.

### 11.6.2 Homoplasmy and heteroplasmy in mitochondria

Within an organism, uniform population of mitochondria is observed which are genetically identical. Such general pattern of mitochondrial inheritance results in homoplasmy.

In the case of biparental inheritance and leakiness of paternal mitochondria resulting heterogenecity of mitochondria within the cell or organism. Such type of inheritance results in heteroplasmy.

### 11.6.3 Metabolic defects in Yeast (mitochondrial inheritance)

Mitochondria are essential for aerobic respiration of the cell. In anaerobic conditions, the mitochondria have been found to become smaller and the structures are reduced in yeast, *Saccharomyces cerevissiae.*

Occasionally, it is found that in aerobic colony, small anaerobic-like colonies appear. But in these anaerobic colonies, the mitochondria appear perfectly normal. Boris Ephrussi and his colleages identified mutations and called them as *petite mutations.*

Biochemical and physiological evidence indicated that petite mutations are due to defective mitochondria, where they can not produce energy which is required for their metabolic activities. They form small colonies when grown on sugars that are metabolized by glycolytic pathway which occurs outside the mitochondria.

Genetic analyses showed that petite mutants are inherited in different ways.

1. The **segregational petite** mutations are located in the nuclear genes and exhibit Mendelian inheritance. These mutations affect genes encoding proteins necessary for mitochondrial functions.
2. The second category petites are called **vegetative petites**. They do not seggregate in Mendelian inheritance. These petites involve mutations in the mitochondrial genomes itself.

Two types of vegetative petites have been identified by him, viz. *neutral petites* and *suppressive petites.*

The cross between a wild type strain and a neutral strain, resulted all four progenies with wild type. On the other hand, a cross between a wild type strain and a suppresssive petite yields all petite colonies. Therefore, the inheritance of vegetative petites is non-Mendelian type.

The inheritance pattern of vegetative petites can be explained as follows :

Neutral petites lack most of their mitochodrial DNA, whereas, suppressive petites usually lack small segments of mito-DNA.

1. When wild-type is crossed with neutral petite strain, the progeny inherits both types of mitochondria. Since, the offspring cells receive both wild and neutral petite types, the wild normal phenotype is displayed.
2. When wild type is crossed with suppressive petite type, the offspring cells receive both wild and suppressive petite mitochondria. But suppressive petite mitochondria replicate more rapidly so that the wild type mitochondria are not maintained in the cytoplasm. Another experimental evidence suggested that genetic exchange between them may ultimately make them defective population of mitochondria (Fig. 11.7).

## 11.7 CYTOPLASMIC HEREDITY IN *PARAMOECIUM*

Sonneborn (1943) demonstrated the infectious heredity and transmission of some cytoplasmic particles in *Paramecium aurelia* (Fig. 11.8 and 11.9).

Certain strains of *Paramecium aurelia* known as **"Killer strains"** which secrete a substance **"paramecin"** into the environment and kill another strain called sensitive strain of the same species. It is found that the killer strains contain a piece of DNA in the cytoplasm, called the **kappa particle**, which is not found in the sensitive strain.

Production of "paramecin" depends upon the presence of a dominant nuclear gene "*K*" and kappa particle is found to be transmitted through the cytoplasm. The sensitives are usually (*kk*) and killers are (*KK*).

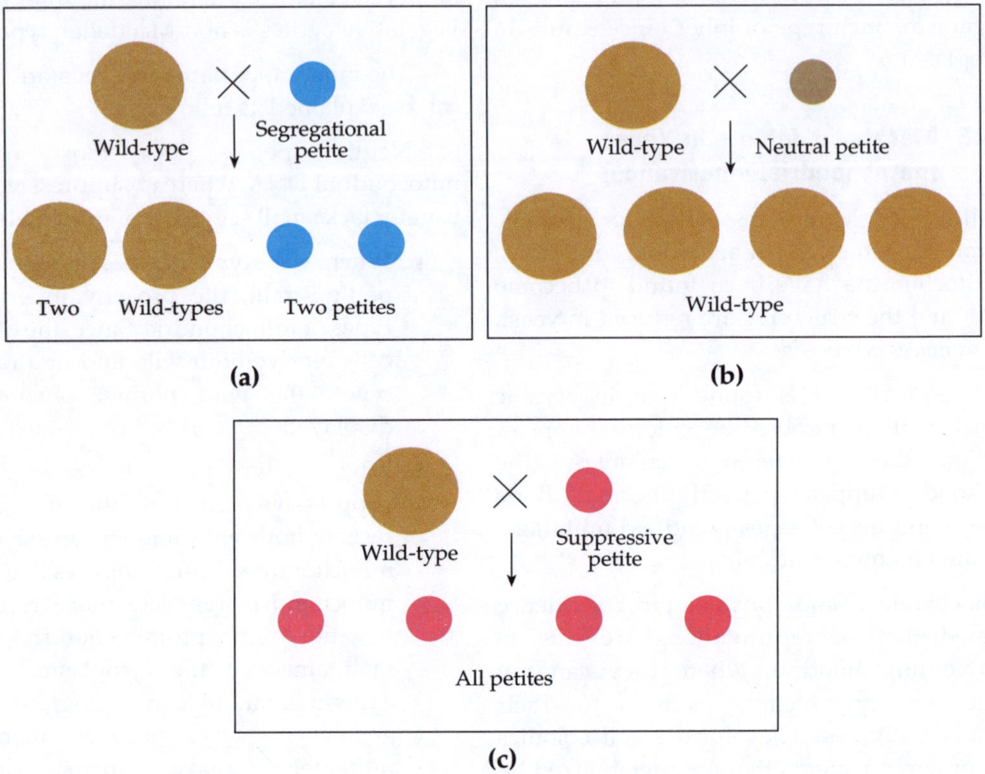


**Fig.10.7 :** *a–c : Crosses between wild type and different petites.*

When killer (*KK*) conjugates with sensitive (*kk*) the exconjugants (*Kk*) would be a killer.

But if the conjugation is brief and little or no cytoplasm is exchanged, then a killer clone and a sensitive clone are produced.

Again, if the conjugation is prolonged and the exchange of cytoplasm is allowed, then all the descendants become killers, which have kappa particles.

Therefore, it has been observed that *Kk* individual may be either a killer or a sensitive, depending upon whether it has kappa particles or not.

It has been evidenced that *KK* or *Kk* can be converted to sensitive by making them undergo very rapid fission during which kappa particles fail to keep pace with the cell division. It has also been found that when kappa is removed by high temperature, X rays or other techniques, *KK* strain may be transformed into sensitive strain. Thus it seemed that kappa particle is an infective particle with a hereditary continuity of its own.

## 11.8 CYTOPLASMIC TRANSMISSION OF SYMBIONTS

Unusual endosymbiotic relationships have been identified in eukaryotic organisms. There are few cases, infectious particles establish a symbiotic relationship with their host. In some cases, research indicates that symbiotic infectious particles are bacteria that exist in the cytoplasm of eukaryotic cells.

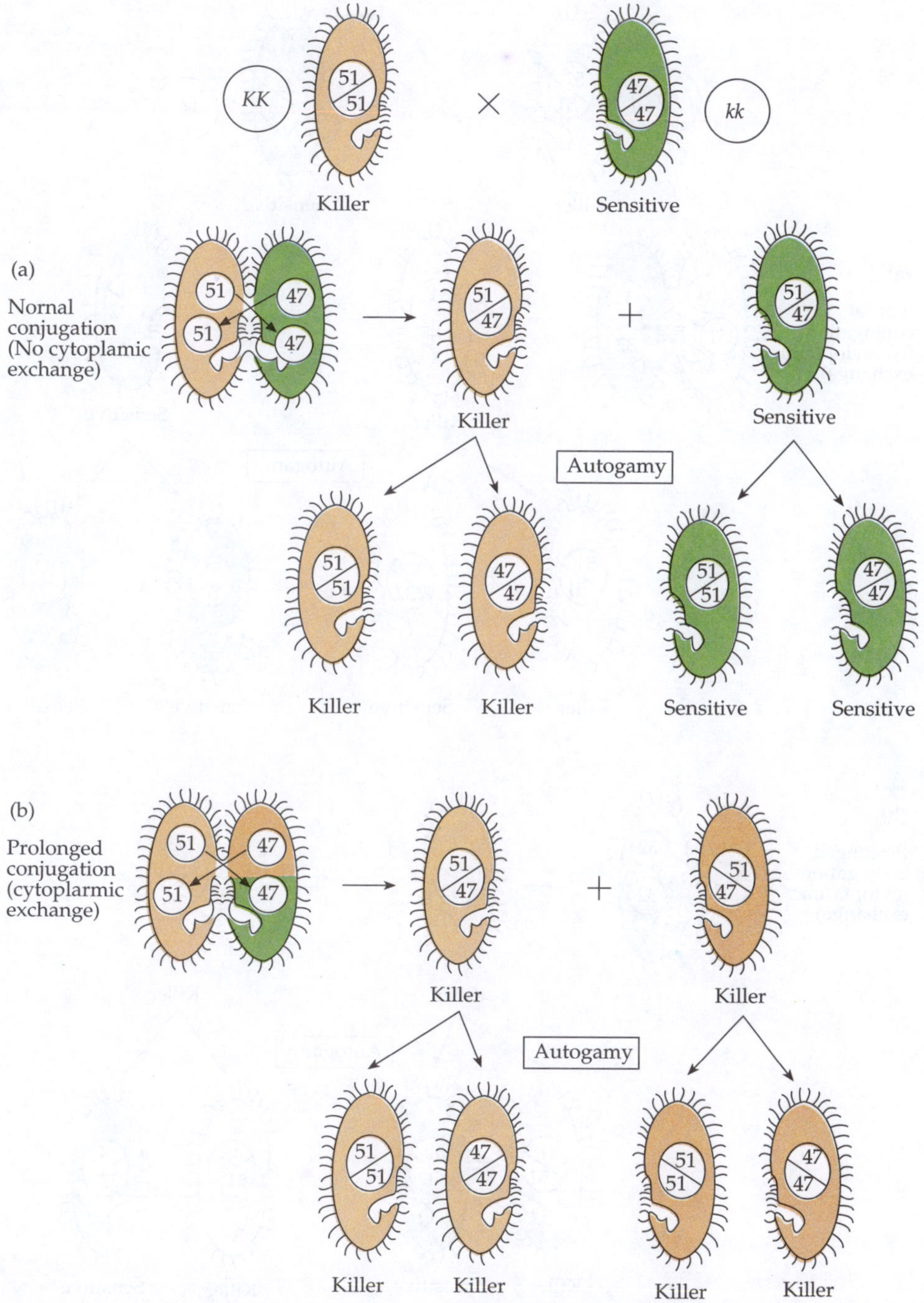


**Fig.11.8 :** *Results of crosses between Killer (51) and sensitive (47) strains of Paramoecium and inhentance of Kappa particles*

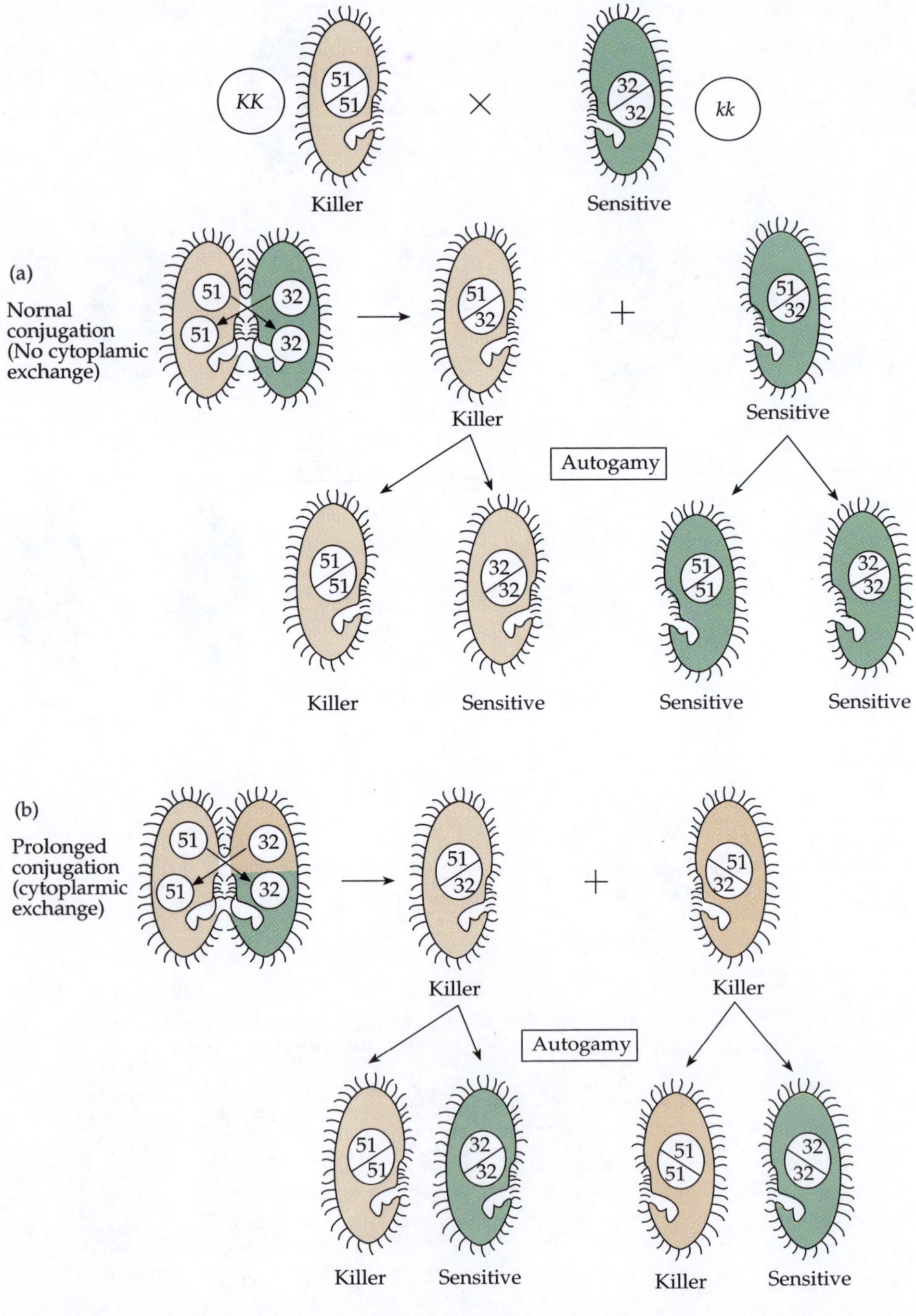


**Fig.11.9 :** *Inheritance of Kappa particle. Results showing crosses between Killer (51) and sensitive (32) strains in Paramoecium.*

### 11.8.1 Killer trait in *Paramecium aurelia*

Sonneborn (1940) found that killer strains contain particles in their cytoplsm, known as **kappa particle** (0.4 μm long) and has its own DNA that can encode the **paramecin toxin**. In addition to that kappa particle can produce another substance that confer resistance to paramecin. If kappa particle is transferred to nonkiller strains, they convert them into killer strains.

Kappa is presumably a bacterium because it has many bacterial characteristics such as, size, cell wall, presence of DNA etc. J. Preer and his colleagues studied kappa and named it as *Caedobacter taeniospiralis.* Kappa occurs in at least two forms.

1. **N-form**, is the infective form that passes from one *Paramecium* to another and does not confer killer specificity to the host cells. The N-form has been found to be attacked by bacteriophage that induces inclusions called **R-bodies** inside the Kappa particles and converts it into B-form.
2. **B-form** of Kappa cannot raplicate and may be lysed in the cell. It confers killer specificity on the host cell.

The sensitives are killed by the toxin paramecin which is released by the killer strain. It is not clearly known whether the viral DNA or the Kappa DNA codes the toxin.

### 11.8.2 Male Killer infection and *mu* Particles

Peer and his colleages observed a bacteria-like particle in certain strain of *Paramecium* which does not release the toxin but kills its mates during conjugation, this is *mu* particle. He named the symbolic bacteria-like particle as *Caedobacter conjugatus*.

One of the two unlinked dominant genes, $M_1$ and $M_2$ is required for the presence of *mu* particles. When the killer $(M_1m_1M_2m_2)$ individuals become $m_1m_1m_2m_2$ by autogamy, eventually lose their *mu* particles but they still remain killer-properties upto eighth generation. In the 15th generation only about 7% cells still have killer-properties.

The diluting out of such killer properties is possibly due to a factor called **metagon** which is necessary for the maintenance of *mu* in the cell. When it is homozygous $(m_1m_1m_2m_2)$ recessive, metagon is not produced but it remains present in the cell cytoplasm upto 15th generation at the time of their successive fissions. But later on it is expected to one daugher to have this **metagon** but other daughter would not during their fission.

Actually the metagon appears to be the mRNA molecules which are present in a number of thousand per cell of a killer *Paramecium.* In homozygous recessive individuals, their mRNAs are not produced but are destroyed by the enzyme RNase and are gradually diluted as they undergo binary fissions.

### 11.8.3 Sex-ratio phenotype in *Drosophila*

An infectious particle in fruit flies involves a trait, known as *sex ratio*, discovered by Chana Malogolowkin and D. Paulson, in one strain of *Drosophila willistoni,* where most of the offspring are female and nearly all male offspring died. This sex ratio trait is transmitted from mother to offspring. The rare survival males do not transmit this trait to their offspring. This indicates a maternal inheritance pattern of this trait.

In addition, it has been found that half of the eggs of a sex ratio female fail to develop. Cytoplasm can be withdrawn from undeveloped egg and used to infect other females and have shown to cause death of such developing female. So it is proved that it is a cytoplasmic factor that causes such death of the egg.

Detailed cytological examination of the cytoplasm of sex ratio females has revealed a symbiotic microorganism, the **spirochaete** that has been isolated and used to infect other female *Drosophila* with sex ratio trait. The presence of this microorganism is lethal to males but not to females.

## 11.9 EPIGENETIC INHERITANCE

Epigenetic inheritance is a pattern in which a modification occurs to a nuclear gene or chromosome, but the expression is not permanently changed over the course of many generations.

Such DNA and chromosomal modifications occur during oogenesis, spermatogenesis or in the early embryonic development. Thus, epigenetic changes can permanently affect the phenotype of the individual but are not permannent over the course of many generations, because they are not caused due to change in the DNA sequence.

There are two such types of epigenetic inheritance *viz.* dosage compensation and genomic imprinting.

### 11.9.1 Dosage compensation

#### Concept

The homogametic sex has two X-chromosomes, while heterogametic sex has only one X and one Y-chromosomes. In most species (plants and animals) homogametic sex XX is female and heterogametic sex XY is male. The exceptions to this rule are the lepidopterans and the birds, where male is homogametic (zz) and female is heterogametic (zw). It is thus obvious that in the homogametic sex, there will be two X-or two Z-chromosomes carrying two sets of identical genes. In the heterogametic sex, there will be only one set of these genes. If both sets of genes are expressed in the homogametic sex, there will be twice as much X-coded gene products in the homogametic sex, as in the heterogametic sex. This would be abnormal situation. Therefore, a machanism had to be evolved to bring about parity in the quantity of X-coded gene products in the two sexes. This phenomenon of bringing about equality in the products synthesized under that control of genes carried on X-chromesomes, was termed as DOSAGE COMPENSATION by Muller (1932).

This compensation in dosage of genes is achieved either by hypoproduction due to inactivation of the one X-chromosome in homogametic sex (*eg.* mammals) or hyperproduction due to hyperactivity of X-chromosome in the heterogametic sex (*eg. Drosophila*).

#### Mechanism of dosage Compensation

**Mechanism of dosage compensation** is different in different species (Table 11.1).

#### X-chromosome inactivation in Mammals

In mammals, it has been demonstrated that in the homogametic XX-female individuals, one X-chromosome gets characteristically condensed and inactivated to form **facultative heterochromatin**, since it becomes inactive in certain part of the life cycle and resumes activity before entering into the germ line. [But in **constitutive heterochromatin** found near the centromere or some other part of the chromosome which is permanently heterochromatic and inactive]. This phenomenon of inactivation was first observed as *barr body* by Barr and Bertram (1949) and was identified by Ohno (1959). Later M.F. Lyon (1972) confirmed the existence in normal females, super females and Kleinfelter males. The number of bar bodies is equals to the number of X-chromosomes minus one. Thus she proposed the famous **Lyon's hypothesis**;

1. Which of the two X-chromosomes remain active in females, is determined at the early stage of development.
2. X-chromosome inactivation is a random process, *i.e.*, paternal and maternal X-chromosomes each has 50–50 chance of inactivation. For example, the mice which is heterozygous for coat colour, some cells carring the X-chromosome with normal allele which becomes inactivated,. The

**TABLE 11.1**
**Mechanism of dosage compensation in different animals**

| Species | Sex chromosomes | | | Mechanism of Compensation |
|---|---|---|---|---|
| | ♀ | ♂ | ♀ | |
| 1. Placental mammals | XX | XY | — | One of the X chromosomes in the somatic cells of females is inactivated in certain species. The paternal X-chromosome is usually inactivated, while in other species, such as human, either the maternal or paternal X-chromosome is randomly inactivated throughout the female's body as sex chromatin body or Barr-body in each cell. |
| 2. Marsupial mammals | XX | XY | — | The paternally derived X-chromosome is inactivated in the somatic cells of females. |
| 3. *Drosophila melanogaster* | XX | XY | — | The level of expression of genes on the X-chromosome in male is increased by two folds. |
| 4. *C. elegans* | — | XO | XX | The level of expression of genes on the both chromosomes in hermaphrodites is decreased to 50% levels compared to males. |

mutant recessive allele is variegated phenotypes expressed in some cells, which is present on the other X-chromosome (Fig. 11.10).

3. There is no general rule for the time at which the inactivation will take place leading to the formation of facultative heterochromatin. Inactivation usually takes place in early embryogenesis in the mammals. In mouse, X-chromosome inactivation is observed in late blastocyst stage.

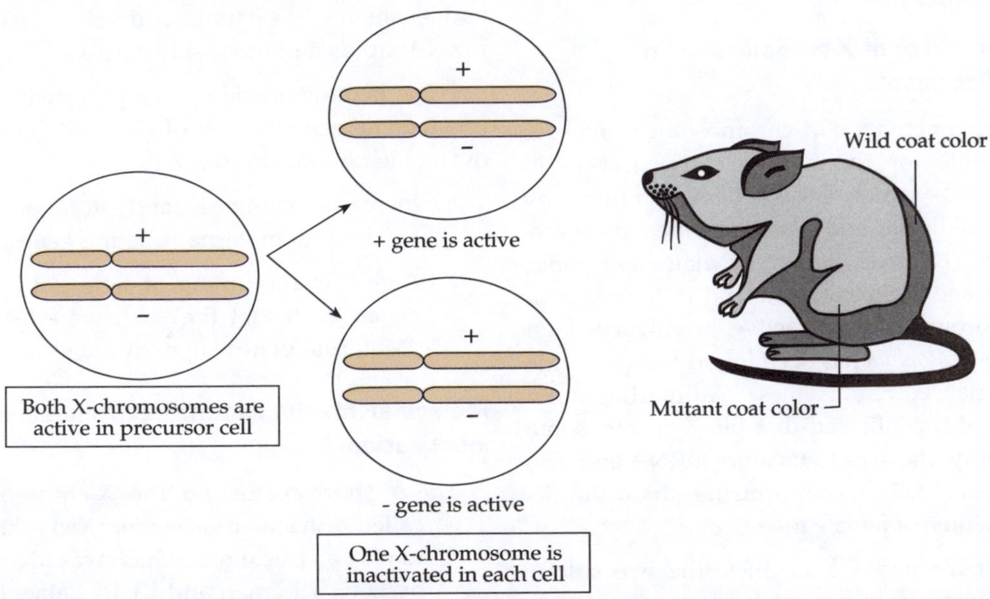


**Fig.11.10 :** *X-linked variegation caused by random inactivation of one X-chromosome*

4. The process of inactivation which is called **lyonization** seems to be reversed in the grem cells and in all germ cells or in eggs both the X-chromosomes will be active. Thus, the condensed **Barr body** is absent in the premeiotic oocytes. The fate of the X-chromosome depends upon whether it goes to the male or to the female individuals. In males it becomes active whether it was active or inactive in the previous generation. In the females any one of them may be active or inactive.

## Position effect

If a translocation occurs from euchromatin segment of an autosome to an X-chromosome, the inactivation of X-chromosome may spread over the translocated autosome segment and thus the genes which were present in the autosome would be suppressed simultaneously by the X-chromosome inactivation. Variegation coat colour may be found in heterozygote mouse where the wild gene in autosome has become translocated to an inactive X-chromosome and the mutant gene is expressed in such heterozygotes. This is **position effect variegation**.

## Hyper-activity of X-chromosome in male *Drosophila*

Hyper-activity of X-chromosome is males is responsible for the dosage compensation in *Drosophila*, which was demonstrated by A. S. Mukherjee and was confirmed by many workers (Lucchesi 1973). In male *Drosophila*, there is one X-chromosome and in female both the X-chromosomes are active. In salivary gland of male *Drosophila* has been found twice as wide as asynapsed autosomes. Autoradiography studies also confirmed that the X-chromosome in male, synthesizes 100% more mRNA and also translates 100% more proteins than the X-chromosome of female insects.

In male and female flies, the eye colour shows same intensity and the enzyme levels such as 6-phosphogluconate dehydrogenase, glucose-6-phosphate dehydrogenase etc. also were found to be similar in the cells of both female and male in insects.

The early replication in X-chromosome in male *Drosophila* also possibly due to its hyper-functional activity.

## Lack of dosage compensation in heterogametic females

In birds, butterflies, moths, some reptilies and amphibians, the female is heterogametic (Zw) and there is no evidence of dosage compensation. This can be proved by following conclusions.

During oogenesis, the heterogametic females synthesize and store morephogenetically essential gene products including those encoded by Z-linked genes in large quantities. These gene products enable the heterogametic females to overcome the monosomic state of Z-chromosome in the zw embroys. The heterogametic females produce more yolk and RNA containing megalecithal eggs than the eggs where male is heterogametic eg. In a frog, *Xenopus laevis* the egg is 4000 times greater in size than the mouse and human ovum and it contains 10000 times as much more stored mRNA, lipids and other substances.

The heterogametic female (ZW) which has unadequate gene, dosage of Z-linked genes can overcome possibly in two way.

1. Increased synthesis and storage of the products of maternally acting genes.
2. A shift in the timing of action of zygotic genes, such that they become effectively **"Maternal genes"** in early stages.

## Molecular Mechanism of X-chromosome inactivation

1. A short region on the X-chromosome called X-inactivation center (*Xic*) is known to play a critical role which was identified by Eeva Therman and Klaus Patae. If one of the X-chromosome is missing *Xic* due to a chromosome mutation, neither

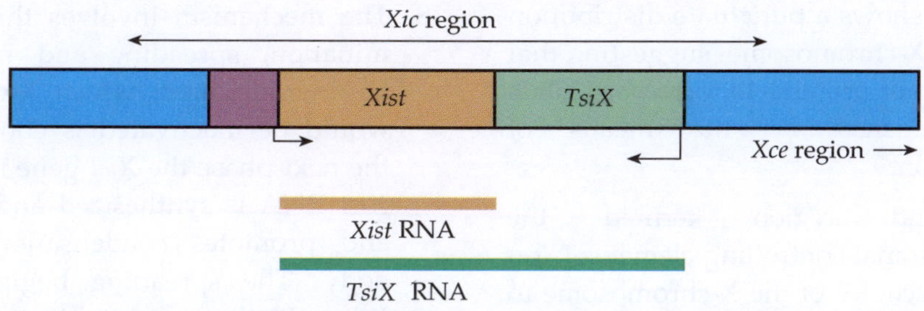


**Fig.11.11 :** *The Xic region of the X chromosome*

X-chromosome will be inactivated. This is lethal condition for a human female embryo.

2. Brown *et al* (1991) discovered the *Xist* (X-inactive specific transcript) gene which is present in the *Xic* region of X-chromosome. They found that *Xist* RNA transcript is made solely from the inactive X-chromosome, but it does not encode a protein, because it lacks open reading frame. It stays in the nucleus and interacts with the inactive X-chromosome to transform into *Xist-Barr body* complex. (Fig. 11.11 and Fig. 11.12).

3. The *Xist* RNA works only in *cis* i.e., on the chromosome that made it. In the pre-implantation mouse embryo, both X-chromosomes synthesize *Xist* RNA but this RNA is quickly degraded. When the cells are differentiated, *Xist* RNA is stabilized on one of the two X-chromosomes (Sheardown *et al.* 1997). The

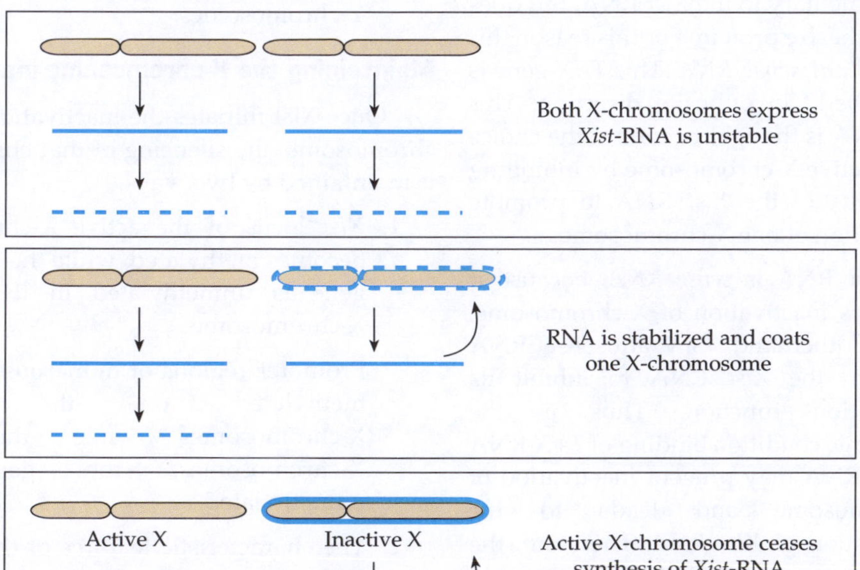


**Fig.11.12 :** *X-inactivation involves inactivation of Xist-RNA which coats the inactive X-chromosome.*

*Xist* RNA shows a punctuate distribution along the X-chromosome, suggesting that association of proteins to form particulate structures may be the means of stabilization.

4. A second region termed the X-chromosomal controlling elements (*Xce*) affects the choice of the X-chromosome to be inactivated. The choice occurs during embryonic development and is maintained in all subsequent cell divisions.
5. The heterozygous females, where two X-chromosomes are present, two different *Xce* alleles are present : one X-chromosome carries stronger *Xce* alleles than the allele present in the other X-chromosome. The stronger *Xce* allele more likely remains active, thereby leading to skewed X-inactivation. The *Xce* region is very close to the end of the Xic region.
6. A gene designated *TsiX* which is regulated by *Xce* region and is expressed only during early embryonic development. It encodes an RNAwhich is complementary to the *Xist* RNA, but does not synthesize protein. For this reason this is called ***antisense RNA***. This *TsiX* gene is transcribed in opposite direction. This *TsiX* RNA is thought to control the choice of the active X-chromosome by inhibiting the ability of the *Xist* RNA to promote compaction of one X-chromosome.
7. The *Xist* RNA is *sense RNA*, because it promotes inactivation of X-chromosome, on the otherhand *TsiX* antisense RNA binds to the *Xist* RNA to inhibit its inactivation function. Thus in the embryonic condition binding of *TsiX* RNA to *Xist* RNA may prevent inactivation of X-chromosome and leads to the degradation of *Xist RNA*. Therefore, the expression of *TsiX* during early embryonic development may play an important role in choosing the active X-chromosome.
8. The mechanism involves three phases : initiation, spreading and maintenance. During initiation, which X-chromosome would be inactivated is chosen. During the next phase the *Xist* gene is expressed, *Xist* RNA is synthesized and coats itself and promotes condensation into Barr body. The spreading begins near the X-inactivation center (*Xic*) region and spreads in both directions along the X-chromosome during embryonic development. In the final phase the inactivated X-chmosome is maintained as such during future cell divisions.

   Though, the X-chromosome is inactivated, but a few genes are expressed in the somatic cells of the adult female mammals. It is thought that these genes escape the effects of X-inactivation. The *Xist* gene and few **pseudoautosomal** genes have been found to express from the highly condensed Barr body. The pseudoautosomal genes are so called because of the autosomal nature of inheritance but are located on both X and Y-chromosomes.

## Maintaining the X-chromosome inactivation

Once Xist initiates the inactivation of an X-chromosome, the silencing of that chromosome is maintained by two ways.

1. *Xist* locus of the active X-chromosome becomes methylated, while the active *Xist* gene is unmethylated in the inactive X-chromosome.

   Promoter regions of numerous genes are methylated on the inactive X-chromosomes while the active X-chromosomes, the genes are unmethylated.
2. The characteristic features of the inactive X-chromosome which include a lack of acetylation of histone H4, conversely the inactive X-chromosome becomes associated with a higher concentration of the histone 2A variant macro H2A1.

Recently Lee and Lu (1999) provide a clue that regulates *Xist* transcription. They have shown that *Xist* may be regulated by a natural antisense RNA that binds to it. This RNA is called *TsiX*, which is trnascribed from the active X-chromosome.

### The Medical Importance of X-chromosome Inactivation and Transmission

There are over 120 human genes located on the X-chromosome, that have no counter part on the Y-chromosome. The trait governed by these genes thus show sex-linked inheritance. This type of inheritance has certain unique characteristics.

1. Most sex-linked traits are recessively inherited. Therefore, females heterozygous for a mutant gene on the X-chromosome will usually not be symptomatic since the other chromosome has the wild type allele. Even though X-chromosome inactivation occurs, the passage of substrates from one cell to the other (either through solutions or through gap junctions) equalizes the material. So in females, a recessive mutation on the X-chromosome can be masked by a dominant wild type allele.

2. Males have only one X-chromosome per cell, a mutant gene on an X-chromosome will not be masked. Males are called hemizygous for these X-linked genes. Thus males with a mutant X-linked gene will express the diseased condition, while females with a mutant X-linked gene usually will not.

3. There is no male to male transmission. If a man has a disease due to a mutation on the X-chromosome, he cannot transmit it to his sons, since any male child of his will have inherited his Y-chromosome, not his X.

4. A female heterozygote is called a "carrier" because she does not express the mutant X-linked gene even though she has it. The carrier has a 50% chance of passing the gene to each of her children. Sons who receive the gene will be hemizygons and will manifest the trait. Daughter who receives the gene will be heterozygous or carrier.

5. A man who has the trait, caused by a mutant X-chromosome, gene will pass the mutant gene to his daughters. They will most likely be carriers unless their mother is a carrier, in which case they have a 50% chance of manifesting the disease.

6. Occassionally, carriers will show mild symptoms of the trait due to inactivation of the wild-type X-chromosome significantly more than the mutant chromosome. The pattern of X-chromosome inactivation is random, which means that certain percentage of heterozygous women who inactivate the wild-type X-chromosome in their large percentage of cells. For instance, at the time of X-chromosome inactivation, which occurs at about the 10th day of embryogenesis in humans, there may only be ten cells that form the liver. Some of these cells, there is a chance for inactivation of wild genes leaving the active mutant genes (such as genes encoding clotting factor VIII is mutant). Such a carrier female will have a very low level of factor VIII and as a result will show symptoms of hemophilia.

7. Y chromosomes does not have genes that are important to the vital body functions. It contains genes for testis formation and sperm maturation. Every one has at least one X-chromosome, which contains many genes that are essential for normal development. For examples : genes encoding **dystrophin** (loss of function causes Duchenne's or Becker's muscular distrophy), factor VIII (whose loss of function results in hemophilia), Ornithine transcarboxylase (whose deficiency causes excess ammonia in the blood) and

hypoxanthine phosphoribosyl transferase (whose deficiency causes mental retardation, uric acid stones etc.).

8. The receptors for testosterone and DHT are also encoded by X-chromosome. The **androgen insensitivity syndrome** is an X-linked recessive condition. Barbara Migeon and Claude Migeon studied on X-chromosome inactivation. They figured that if the transmission is autosomal, each cell from heterozygous (cloning experiment) would have about 50% the amount of androgen receptors. However, if the transmission is X-linked, then some cells of the heterozygous would have 100% of the normal level of testosterone receptors (these would have inactivated the mutant allele), while other cells (which had inactivated the wild type allele) would have 0%. The cells from the heterozygous women were cultured and separated cells were isolated. When these individual cells are divided, it was found that about half the cells have not testosterone receptors, the other half has normal levels. Thus testosterone receptors are X-linked.

## 11.9.2 Genomic imprinting

### Concept

Genomic imprinting is a pattern of inheritance that involves a change in a single gene or chromosome during gametogenesis. Depending upon whether the modification occurs during oogenesis or spermatogenesis, imprinting governs whether an offspring will express a gene that has been inherited from its mother or father.

The term imprinting implies a type of marking process that has a memory. For example, newly hatched birds identify marks on their parents, allowing to distinguish their parents from other individuals. Similarly, genomic imprinting implies the situation in which a segment of DNA is marked and that mark is retained and recognised throughout the life of the organism inheriting the marked DNA.

The phenotype, caused by the imprinted genes, follows a non-Mendetian pattern of inheritance. Thus the marking process causes the offspring to distinguish between maternally and paternally inherited alleles. This is also called **nonallelic expression**, because the offspring expresses only one of the two alleles.

*Example :*

In mouse, a gene *Igf-2* encodes insulin-like growth factor, which is essential for the normal growth. This gene is present is both males and females but imprinting occurs in a way that results in the expression of paternal *Igf-2* allele but not the maternal allele. Here maternal gene is kept silent while paternal gene is transcribed into mRNA and finally into hormone for normal growth.

The mutant allele is designated as *Igf*-2m which yields defective proteins that causes the mouse dwarf. But it depends upon whether the mutant allele is inherited from male or female parent.

**Cross-1**

*Igf*-2m/*Igf*-2m (Mother) × *Igf*-2/*Igf*-2 (Father)

↓

*Igf*-2/*Igf*-2m

normal offspring

(Where Igf-2 allele is expressed due to imprinting in somatic cells of normal heterozygous individual)

**Cross-2**

*Igf*-2m/*Igf*-2m (Father) × *Igf*-2/*Igf*-2 (Mother)

↓

*Igf*-2/*Igf*-2m

Dwarf offspring

(where *Igf*-2m allele is expressed due to imprinting in somatic cells of dwarf heterozygous individual)

### Establishment and maintenance of genomic imprinting

The achievement of genomic imprinting is an epigenetic process. It occurs in three stages.

1. *Establishment phase* : This phase occurs at the time of fertilization when two alleles come from each parent through their gametes, imprinting is established in the allele which is present in the sperm. The same allele in the ovum is kept silent or inactivated.
2. *Maintenance of the imprint* : Throughout the development and in the adult stage, the imprinted allele which comes from father is expressed in their life-time, but the alleles which come from the mother will remain inactive.
3. *Erasure and reestablishment phase* : During gametogenesis, the imprint of the allele is erased. The two alleles of the female during oogenesis which would be silenced but two alleles present in the male, during spermatogenis would be imprinted. In this way the imprinted allele of the female is erased, on the other hand silenced allele of the male is now reimprinted. The mechanism of inheritance is given below :

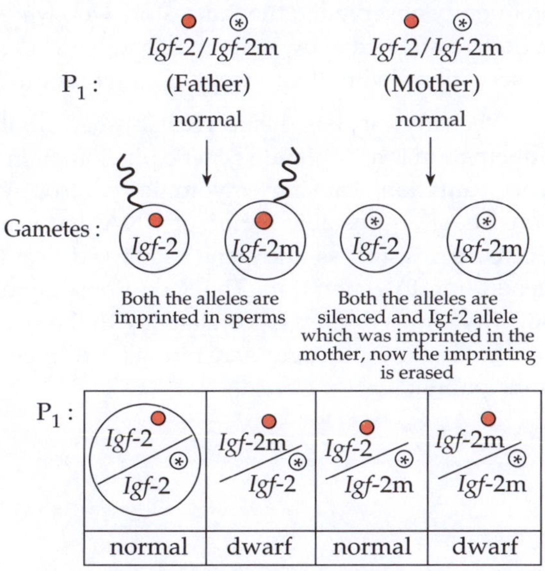


### Molecular mechanism of genomic imprinting

Genomic imprinting occurs in a few gene during oogenesis or spermatogenesis. After fertilization such differential marking affects the expression of that particular genes. There are several genes which are associated with the human diseases that involve imprinting.

**TABLE 11.2**
**Some genes that cause diseases associated with imprinting**

| *Gene* | *Allele expressed* | *Function* |
|---|---|---|
| *WTI* | Maternal | Wilms tumor – suppressor gene — suppresses uncontrollable cell growth |
| *INS* | Paternal | Insulin – Cell growth and metabolism |
| *Igf-2* | Paternal | Insulin – like growth factor - II |
| *Igf-2 R* | Maternal | Receptor for *Igf II* |
| *H19* | Maternal | Unknown |
| *SNRPN* | Paternal | Splicing factor |
| *Gabrb* | Maternal | Neurotransmitter receptor |

1. Nearer to the imprinted genes, there are some regions called **differentially methylated regions** (DMRs). The DMRs contain binding sites for one or more proteins to regulate transcription of nearby genes. If this region is methylated, enhances the binding of proteins that inhibit transcription. This is called **marking process**.
2. Most of the methyl groups are found in CG-doublets (CpG island) Usually the C-residues on both strands of short palindrome sequence are methylated giving the structure.

$$5' \ {}^{m}C\,p\,G \ \ 3'$$
$$3' \ \ G\,p\,C^{m} \ 5'$$

3. When this fully methylated strand is replicated, one methylated and one unmethylated strands are produced first. If the methylation of the unmethylated strand occurs then it restores fully methylated condition. On the otherhand, if methylation does not occur, then hemimethylated condition is perpetuated (Fig. 11.13).
4. Methylation of DNA is controlled by the enzyme "methylase", which adds methyl group to the 5′ position of Cytosine. The enzyme "demethylase" removes the methyl group.
5. The state of methylation is controlled by three enzymes. These are two methylases and one demethylase.

   The first one methylase is known as *de novo* methylase which recognizes unmethylated DNA at the region of DMRs to make it hemimethylated state.

   The second one is a maintanance methylase or perpetuation methylase, which acts constitutively on hemimethylated sites to convert fully methylated form.

   The third enzyme is demethylase which eliminates methyl group from the methylated portion of cytosine in DNA (Fig. 11.14).
6. Both methylation and demethylation occur during embryogenesis. In males, the pattern develops in two stages. Spermatocytes display the methylation pattern that is characteristic of mature sperm, so no further changes occur during spermatogenesis. But further changes are made in this pattern after fertilization.

   In females, maternal pattern is imposed during oogenesis, when oocytes mature through meiosis after birth.

   Thus in two sexes, the paternal and maternal alleles have different patterns of methylation.
7. All allelic differences are lost when primordial germ cells develop in the embryo, irrespective of sex. The previous patterns of methylation is erased and the typical gene is then unmethylated.
8. The specific pattern of methyl group in germ cells is responsible for genomic imprinting. The expression of gene in mouse embryos depends upon the sex of the parent from which they were inherited.

   For example, *Igf-2* gene of oocytes is methylated but this gene of sperm is not methylated, so the genes behave differently in the zygote. The opposite pattern is found is *Igf-2R* gene.

### 11.9.3 Concept of Anticipation

A genetic trait becomes more strongly expressed or is expressed at an earlier age as it is passed from generation to generation.

A disease, patients with moderate to **severe myotonic dystrophy**, caused by an autosomal dominant gene. This muscle disorder were frequently observed in their ancestors who were mildly affected by the disease. These observations led to the concept of **anticipation**.

Recently, it has been reestablished that anticipation is a legitimate genetic phenomenon. The mutation causing myotonic dystrophy consists of an unstable region of DNA that can decrease in size as the gene is passed from generation to generation. The age of onset and severity of this disease is correlated with the size of the region through generations produces anticipation.

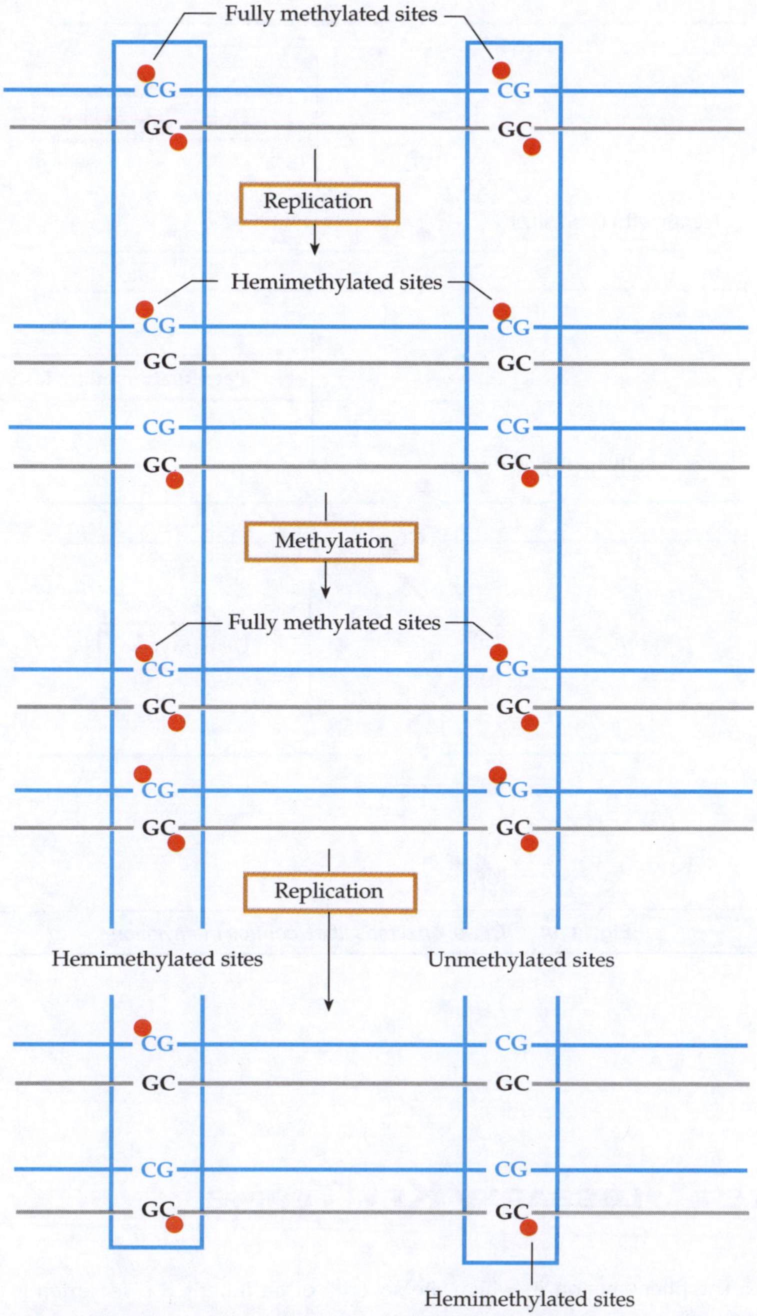


**Fig.11.13 :** *The methylated sites are perpetuated by an enzyme that can recognize only the hemimethylated state of substrate.*

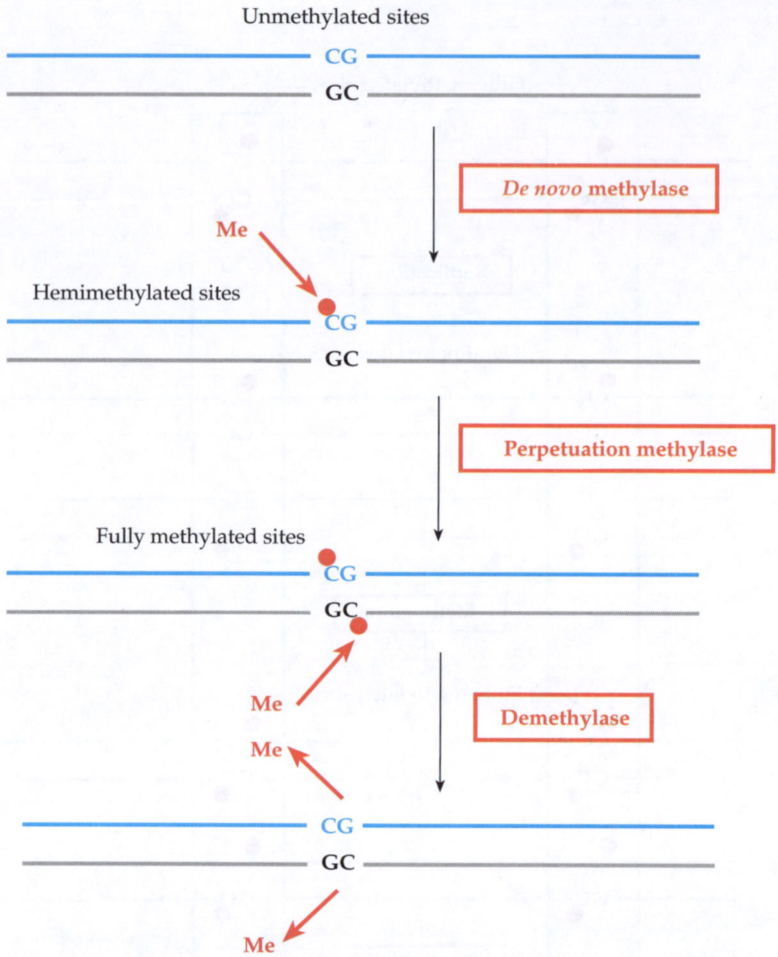


**Fig.11.14 :** *Three enzymes that control methylation.*

## Chapter Glossary/Key Terms

**Anticipation :** The phenomenon in which the severity of an inherited disease tends to get worse in future generation.

**Antisense - RNA :** An RNA strand that is complementary to a strand of mRNA.

**Constitutive heterochromatin :** The regions of chromosomes that are always heterochromatic and are permanently transcriptionally inactive.

*Contd.*

**Dosage compensation :** It refers to the phenomenon that in species with sex-chromosomes, one of the sex chromosomes is altered so that males and females will have similar livels of gene expression, even though they do not contain the same complement of sex chromsomes.

**Epigenetic inheritance :** An inheritance pattern in which a modification to a nuclear gene or chromosome alters gene expressions in an organism, but the expression is not changed permanently over the course of many generations.

**Extrachromosomal inheritance :** The inheritance which is controlled by the cytoplasm of the zygote rather than the genotypes.

**Facultative heterochromatin :** Heterochromatin that is derived from the conversion of euchromatin to heterochromatin.

**Genomic imprinting :** A pattern of inheritance that involves a change in single gene or chromosome during gamete formation. Depending on whether the modification occurs during spermatogenesis or oogenesis, imprinting governs whether an offspring will express a gene that has been inherited from its mother or father.

**Heteropasmy :** The existence within an organism of genetic heterogenecity within the populations of mitochondria or chloroplasts.

**Homoplasmy :** The existance within an organism of only one type of plastid, usually referring to the genetic identity of mitochondria or chloroplasts.

**Kappa particle :** The bacteria-like particles that give a *Paramoecium* the killer phenotype.

**Maternal effect genes :** A gene expressed in maternal tissue that influences a developing embryo.

**Metagon :** An RNA necessary for the maintenance of *mu* particles in *Paramoeciums*.

**Meternal effect :** The effect of the maternal parent's ganotype on the phenotype of her offspring.

***mu*-particles :** Bacteria-like particles found in the cytoplasm of *Paramoecium* that impart the mate-killer phenotype.

**Non-Mendelian inheritance :** The genetic components of cytoplasm and mitochondria are inherited not by the mechanism of segregation or assortment of the chromosomes.

**Paramecin :** A toxin liberated by a "killer" *Paramoecium*

**Petites :** Mutant strains of yeast that form small colonics due to defects in mitochondrial function.

**Plasmagenes :** The genes which are transmitted by the female gametes.

**Plastomes :** The variegation in chloroplast of *Mirabilis* is seemed to be transmitted through the primordial of chloroplast through the cytoplasm of the eggs to the next generation .

**Spirochaete :** A spiral bacterium.

# Exercise

**A. Long answer type questions :**

1. Define extra-chromosomal inheritance. What are the criteria for extra-chromosomal inheritance?
2. What do you mean by maternal effect? How the direction coiling is determined by the genes in the snail?
3. Describe the genetic control of pigmentation of flour moth.
4. What are plasmagenes? Describe the control of male sterility in maize.
5. What is plastome? Describe the genetic mechanism and inheritance of variegated leaf characters in *Mirabilis*.
6. Describe the inheritance pattern of *iojap* in maize.
7. Describe the antibiotic streptomycin resistant and sensitive characteristics inherited in *Chlamydomonas*.
8. What is paternal inheritance? Give example.
9. Describe mitochondrial inheritance in yeast.
10. What is Killer strain of *Paramecium*? Describe the mode of inheritance of Killer characteristics in *Paramecium*.
11. Describe endosymbiont inheritance in *Paramecium*.
12. What is *mu* particle? Give details on its inheritance in *Paramoecium*.
13. What is the cause of death of male progeny in certain strain of *Drosophila willistoni*?
14. What do you mean by dosage compensation? Give the mechanism of dosage compensation in details.
15. Briefly describe the Lyon hypothesis.
16. In heterogametic females, there is no dosage compensation — justify.
17. Describe molecular mechanism of X-chromosome inactivation.
18. How does the inactivation of X-chromosome is maintained?
19. Briefly describe the medical importance of X-chromosome inactivation and transmission.
20. What do you mean by genomic imprinting? Briefly describe the genomic imprinting in *Igf-2* gene in mouse.
21. Briefly describe the establishment and maintenance of genomic imprinting.
22. Describe the molecular mechanism of genomic imprinting.
23. Reciprocal crosses between two types of the evening primrose, *Oenothera hookeri* and *O. muricata* produce following effects on the plastids :

    *O. hookeri* ♀ × *O. muricata* ♂ → Yellow plastids

    *O. hookeri* ♂ × *O. muricata* ♀ → Green plastids

    Explain the difference between these results, noting that the chromosome constitution is same in both types.
24. A form of male sterility in corn is maternally inherited. Plants of a male-sterile line crossed with normal pollen give male sterile plants. Some lines of corn carry a dominant, so called restorer (*Rf*) gene that restores pollen fertility in male-sterile lines.

    (a) If a male-sterile plant is crossed with pollen from a plant homozygous for gene *Rf*, what will be the genotype and phenotype of the $F_1$?

    (b) If the $F_1$ plants of (a) are used as females in the test-cross with pollen from a normal plant (*rf/rf*), what would be the result? Give genotypes and phenotypes and designate the type of cytoplasm?

**Solution :**

(a) If the normal cytoplasm is [N] and the male-sterile cytoplasm is [Ms], the cross is [Ms] *rf/rf* ♀ ×[N]*Rf/Rf* ♂ and $F_1$ would be [Ms] *rf/Rf* and male is sterile.

(b) The cross [Ms] *Rf/rf* ♀ × [N]*rf/rf* ♂ Half of the progeny would be [Ms]*Rf/rf* and be male fertile and half would be [Ms]*rf/rf* and be male sterile.

25. Receprocal crosses between two *Drosophila* species *D. melanogaster* and *D. simulans* produce the following results.

*melanogaster* ♀ × *simulans* ♂ → Females only

*melanogastes* ♂ × *simulans* ♀ → Males with few or no females

Propose a possible explanation for these results.

26. When females of a particular mutant strain of *Drosophila melanogaster* are crossed to wild type males, all the viable progeny flies are females. Hypothetically, this result could be the cousequence of either a sex-lined, male specific lethal mutation or a maternally inherited factor that is lethal to males. What crosses would you perform to distinguish between these alternatives?

**Solution :**

If male lethality is caused by a sex-linked, male-specific lethal mutation (l) then the cross is as follows :

$P_1$ : *l/l* (♀) × +/Y (♂)

$F_1$ : *l*/+ (♀) and *l*/Y (♂ dies)

$P_2$ : *l*/+ (♀) × +/Y (♂)

$F_1$ : *l*/+ (♀), +/+ (♀), +/Y (♂), *l*/Y (♂ dies)

*i.e,* 2 (♀) : 1 (♂)

If the male lethality is caused by a maternally inherited cytoplasmic factor lethal to males then the result is as follows :

$F_1$ females will receive this factor in the cytoplasm from her mother but survive. On the otherhand $F_1$ males will receive this factor from their mother and due to the male specific lethality, they will die. Thus only female offspring will survive.

27. Distinguish between nuclear (segregational) neutral and suppressive petite mutants in yeast.

28. What genetic tests could you conduct to show that mate-killer phenotype in *Paramecium* requires a dominant allele at any one of two loci?

29. In *Paramecium,* the maintenance of Kappa particles requires the dominant nuclear gen-*K*. A *Kk* killer cell conjugates with a sensitive cell of the same genotype without cytoplasmic exchange. Predict the genotypes and phenotypes that result if each exconjugant then undergoes autogamy.

30. In *Paramecium,* heterozygous for both genes involved in the maintenance of the mate-killer trait are forced to undergo autogamy, what phenotypic ratios do you expect?

31. A petite yeast strain is crossed with a wild type. What phenotypic ratio do you expect after meiosis if the petite is

(a) nuclear?

(b) suppressive?

(c) neutral?

32. Discuss the role of *Xist* gene in the spreading stage of X-inactivation.

**B. Short answer type questions.**

1. What is extra-chromosomal inheritance? Why this is called non-Mendelian inheritance?
2. How could you determine the extra-chromosomal inheritance?
3. What do you mean by maternal effect?
4. Why maternal effect lasts only for one generation?
5. How the direction of coiling of snail is determined embryologically?
6. When an (*aa*) female is crossed with (*Aa*) male of flour moth, what will be the darkening effects on the reciprocal cross? Why the results are so?
7. How it can be concluded that male-sterility in maize is due to maternal inheritance?
8. How the male-sterile lines in maize can be transformed into male-fertile line?

9. What are plasmagenes?
10. What is the genetic cause of male sterility in maize?
11. What is albomaculatus type of leaf variefation in *Mirabilis jalapa*?
12. What would be the results when crosses occur between.

    (i) ♀flower from the green branch × ♂ flower of albomaculatous branch

    (ii) ♀flower from the white branch × ♂ flower of albomaculatous branch

    (iii) ♀flower from the albomaculatous branch × ♂ of the same branch

    (iv) What is the genetic cause of such results?
13. *ij*. gene is receissive variegated leaf phenotype of maize against is normal dominant *Ij* gene. What would be results of the following crosses.

    (i) *Ij Ij* green ♀ × *ij ij* striped ♂

    (ii) *Ij ij* green ♀ × *ij ij* striped ♂

    (i) *Ij ij* striped ♀ × *Ij ij* green ♂

    (i) *ij ij* striped ♀ × *Ij Ij* green ♂
14. In *Chlamydomonas* 0.02% of the meiotic products are of the $mt^-$ parental type. How can you use this information in mapping? Use streptomycin sensitivity, $str^s$ and resistance, $str^r$ as an example.
15. An ornamental spider plant has green and white spriped leaves. How can you determine whether cytoplasmic inheritance is responsible for the striping and whether there is interaction with as *iojap*-type chromosomal gene.
16. Snail coiling is called maternal trail. Is it possible that it is caused by an allele at a sex-linked locus?
17. Give genotypes involved when a sinistral female snail produces dextral offspring. What genotypes could the male parent of the sinistral female have?
18. What is paternal inheritance of mitochondria? What is the cause of such inheritance?
19. What is bipaternal mitochondrial inheritance? Give examples.
20. What are homoplasmy and heteroplasmy in mitochondria?
21. What is petite mutation? What is the cause of such mutation?
22. What are segregational and vegetative petites?
23. Distinguish segregational and vegetative petites.
24. How can you say that vegetative petite inheritance in non-Mendelian?
25. What would be the results of the following crosses :

    (i) Wild type vegetative petite × neutral petite strains

    (ii) Wild type vegetative petite × suppressive petite strains

    Give reasons of the results.
26. What is the Killer strain of *Paramecium?* Why it is called so? What is the cuase of such chracteristics?
27. If Killer *KK* and sensitive *kk* strains are conjugated, what would be the results of the descendants, if the conjungation period is brief or the period is prolonged? Explain the causes of the results.
28. How you can assume that Kappa particles are infective?
29. A dextral snail is self-fertilized and produces any sinistral progeny. What is the probable genotype of the snail and its parents?
30. What is *mu* particle in *Paramecium*?
31. What do you mean by matagon? Why this is necessary for the maintaince of *mu* in the cell? What is molecular basis of metagons?

32. What do you mean by sex-ratio trait in *Drosophila*? Why males are rarely survived in this case? Give reason.
33. What do you mean by epigenetic inheritance?
34. Define dosage compensation.
35. What is facultative heterochromatin? What is its significance?
36. What is constitutive heterochromatin? What it its significance?
37. When the inactivation and reactivation of X-chromosome in Man and mice take place during dosage compensation?
38. What is Barr body? In which cells these are found? In which stage these are absent in the cell?
39. What is position effect variegation in *Drosophila*? How can you obtain such effect?
40. What do you mean by hyper-activity of X-chromosome in *Drosophila*? How you can confirm such hyperactive condition of X-chromosome in *Drosophila?*
41. The genes for the enzyme 6-phosphogluconate and glucose-6-phosphate dehydrogenase are X-linked. Still in males and females, the concentration is same in *Drosophila* — explain why?
42. Heterogametic females lack dosage compensation. But how do they overcome such situation?
43. What is the role of *Xist* in X-chromosome inactivation?
44. What is *Xce*? What is its role in X-chromosome inactivation?
45. What is the function of *TsiX*? When this gene is expressed?
46. How *Xist* RNA and *TsiX*-RNA interact and how this interaction becomes essential for choosing the active X-chromosome?
47. Some genes may be expressed in the inactive X-chromosome, Give their names?
48. What are pseudoautosomal genes? Why they are called so?
49. How the inactivation of X-chromosome is maintained.
50. What is the role of maternal antisense RNA to regulate *Xist* translation.
51. In a female, one X has hemophilic gene and other X has normal gene. The carrier sometimes shows hemophic symptoms. Explain why?
52. What do you mean by genomic imprinting?
53. How many Barr bodies would you expect to find in humans with the following persons? XXY, XYY, XXX, XO
54. What is spreading stage of X-inactivation? Why do you think it is called a "spreading stage"?
55. In what types of cells would you expect *de novo* methylation to occur? In what cell types would it not occur?
56. What are the stages of genomic inprinting .
57. Give three paternal and three maternal genes which are associated with human diseases that involve genomic imprinting?
58. What is DMR? What is its role in imprinting?
59. What is CpG island? What is its role in imprinting.
60. What enzymes are responsible for methylation states during imprinting? What are their roles?
61. Distinguish the patterns of methylation and demethylation during embryo genesis in males and females?
62. How the expression of *Igf-2* and *Igf-2R* genes in mouse embryo depends upon the sex of the parent from which they were inherited?
63. What is anticipation?

**Write short notes on :**

Extra-chromosomal inheritance

Maternal effect in snail

Male sterility in maize

Plasmagenes

Transmission of variegated leaf in *Mirabilis.*

- Chloroplast inheritance in *Chlamydomonas*
- Paternal inheritance of mitochondria
- Homoplasmy and heteroplasmy
- Petite inheritance in yeast
- Kappa particle and its inheritance
- Transmission of symbionts in *Paramecium*
- *Mu* particle
- Epigenetic inheritance
- Dosage compensation
- Barr body
- Position effect
- Hyperactivity of X-chromosome
- Absence of dosage compensation in heterozygous females
- Xist Bar body complex
- Anticipation
- Genomic imprinting
- CpG island
- Differentially methylated region.

12

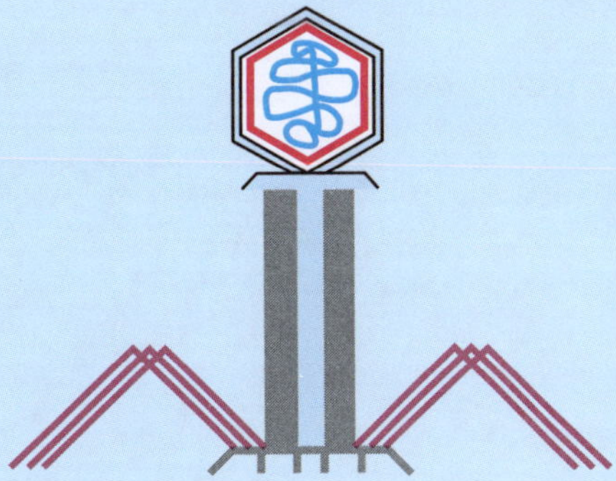

# Genetics of Viral and Sub-viral particles

**CHAPTER AGENDA**

## 12.1 CONCEPT

The entire genetic complement of a living organism is defined as *genome.* The organisms posses a genome that contains the biological informations needed to construct and maintain a living example of that organism.

The genomes are usually made up of DNA, but a few viruses have RNA and these are composed of a chain of monomeric subunits, called nucleotides.

The genomes of the organism consists of two distinct parts

1. Nuclear genome, contained in chromosomes.
2. Extranuclear genome is located in mitochondria, chloroplast etc.

Genomes can replicate, dictate the functions of the body and also the shaping of the body. It can undergo mutation, recombination and gradual evolution over times.

Genomes can inherit through the formation of gametes to the next generations.

## 12.2 GENOME OF PRION

### 12.2.1 Introduction

A disease, *Creutzfeldt-Jakob Disease (CJD)*, which is a neurological disorder, was first clinically described in human in 1972 in Neurology Division of University of California, School of Medicine at Sanfransisco. The disease affects the brain cells and makes the brain porous. But the scientists could not find the reason for this disease and was unable to characterize the nature of the pathogen. In 1982 Dr. Stanley B Prusiner discoverd this new disease-causing agent and characterised it as a proteinaceous infectious particle which is called by him as 'prions', (pronounced as *preeons*). He then established the "**prion theory**" which led him to get the Nobel Prize in Physiology and Medicine in 1997. A very peculiar feature of prion is that this pathogen is infectious as well as heritable and causes a number of diseases in man and also in animals. The common feature of this disease is that the brain is with microscopic holes in its substance. Therefore, the term "**spongiform encephalopathy**" is used for them. This pathogen was first described by Dr. Gajdusek when he reported this fatal neurodegenerative disease in a tribe of Papua New Guinea as "unconventional slow virus" because of its very long incubation, slow course, absence of immune response and genetic predisposition. The route of transmission of the disease was achieved by eating the brain of dead relatives. Dr. Gajdusek was also awarded Nobel Prize in 1976 for his discovery of "**unconventional slow virus**" hypothesis.

### 12.2.2 Prion diseases in man

1. **Kuru :** This is also known as "laughing death" which has been reported in a tribe of Papua New Guinea. The mode of transmission is peculiar where the tribal people in their ritual function eat the brain of dead relatives. This is a fatal neurodegenerative disease occurs in four different stages.

   In the first stage, there is clumsiness in walking and emotional euphoria.

   The second stage is that laughter is inordinate and walking is possible only on stick.

   The third stage is that walking is fully stopped and balance is lost even while sitting.

   Final stage is fatal, the patient cannot sit; lie on the ground, suffocates and dies on account of pneumonia.

2. **Creutzfeldt-Jakob Disease (CJD) :** The symptoms are childish behaviour, very poor short term memory, drowsiness and

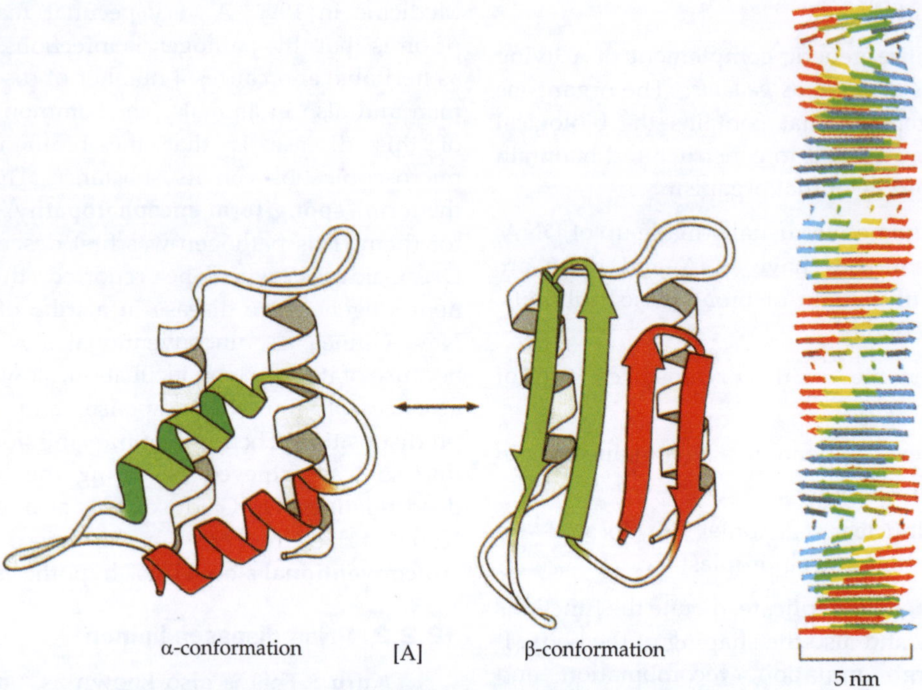


**Fig.12.1 :** *[A] Interconversion of α and β conformations of PrP* protein; [B] Protein aggregates in human neurological diseases (Redrawn from Mol. Biol. of The Cell Alberts et. al. 4th edn.)*

incoordination of movement. It affects the brain cells and makes it porous and spongy. This disease strikes one man in a million around 60 years of age. The disease appears to be heritable and infection is also associated with introduction of extraneous matters like corneal transplantation or use of electrode in brain. About 10% infections of CJD occur as inherited disorders associated with mutation or insertion in human gene on chromosome -20. CJD is world wide in distribution and more than one million persons are affected.

3. **Gerstman-Straussler-Scheinker syndrome (GSS)** : This is an inherited human transmissible spongiform encephalopathy transmitted as an autosomal dominant trait. It usually affects middle-aged adults. This disease is associated with mutation in *PrP* gene, a codon 109 *proline* into *leucine* mutation. The clinical symptoms include cerebellar ataxia, nystagmus and finally dementia.

4. **Fatal familial insomnia (FFI)** : This is a heritable disease occurs in the middle age. due to neuropathological changes in the thalamus. The clinical features are progressive insomnia, disturbance of autonomic function, myoclonus and the same clinical features resembling CJD, FFI is associated with a unique *PrP* genotype (codon 178 *asparagine*, 129 *methonine*).

### 12.2.3 Routes of entry of human Prion disease

A numbers of central nervous system disorders in the humans were shown to have similar symptoms and progression and to share the spongiform pathology of the brain eg Creutzfeldt Jacob disease, Gerstmann

Straussler-Scheinker syndrome and fatal familial insomnia. Many of them are linked to autosomal dominant genes and inheritable. Other cases may be **sporadic** and have no obvious genetic component. CJD was shown to be transmitted by

1. Corneal allograft.
2. Reusable intracerebral electrodes used for electroencephalogram.
3. Grafts of duramater from cavaders.
4. Human growth hormone purified from pituitary glands of cavaders.

### 12.2.4 Pathway from infection to disease

There are four steps in prion infection : penetration, translocation, multiplication and pathogenesis. Although, penetration and multiplication in the periphery occur rapidly (within days to weeks in a mouse), disease symptoms are only apparent after months in the mouse and years to decades in man.

Mammalian prions are usually taken up orally. After penetrating the lining of the gut they enter the lymphatic system, invade the peripheral nervous system and reach the central nervous system. In some hosts they remain in the spleen at lower levels.

Prion multiplication requires expression of *PrP*$^c$ in the tissues involved and while prions have been detected in blood, the role of circulation in spreading infection is not clear. The way by which they elude the immune system and invade the nervous system and damage the brain remain unclear.

### 12.2.5 Diseases in Other Animals

1. **Scrapie :** This is an incurable disease of sheep in England. Affected sheep die within a year. This disease is considered to be heritable. Transmission may occur vertically from ewe to lamb. Nutural transmission is believed to occur during parturition. Its incubation period is about 2 years. The affected animals are unable to stand, become irritable and suffer intense itching and scrape their bodies against trees and rocks, hence the name. Loss of hair, development of paralysis and dies.

   The scrapie causes the neuronal degeneration, loss of myelin, neuronal proliferation and perivascular intrusions as well as plaque-like bodies.

2. **Mad Cow Disease or Bovine Spongiform Encephalopathy :** This was first noted in England in 1986. In 1995 it spreads rapidly throughout the cattle population and affects more than a lac of cases. The cows were received a diet mixed with meat, brain, spinal cord and bone meal from dead sheep who apparently suffered from scrapie. It is quite amazing that the disease which existed in sheep for 250 years or more, made a comeback in another species. Things became worse as reports of 12 persons afflicted with CJD came in. It was reported that these new cases occurred due to consumption of BSE infected beef.

### 12.2.6 Molecular structure of PrP$^C$

Uninfected animals express a cellular isoform PrP$^c$ of the prion protein.

PrP$^c$ is a 208-amino acid glycoprotein normally expressed on the surface of neurons, lymphocytes, follicular dendritic cells. During synthesis and transport to the plasma membrane via endoplasmic reticulum and the Golgi membranes, a 22-amino acid N-terminal signal peptide and 24 C-terminal amino acids are cleaved from the precursor 253 amino acid polypeptide. Thus the mature protein begins at amino acid 23 and ends at amino acid 231. Oligosaccharide chains are added at one or two *asparagine* residues towards the carboxy terminal end of the protein. A carboxy-terminal phosphatidyl inositol glycolipid (GPI) anchors PrP$^c$ in the plasma membrane. A number of octapeptide amino acid repeats in the N-terminal region bind to copper ion via *histidine* (Fig. 12.2 & 12.3).

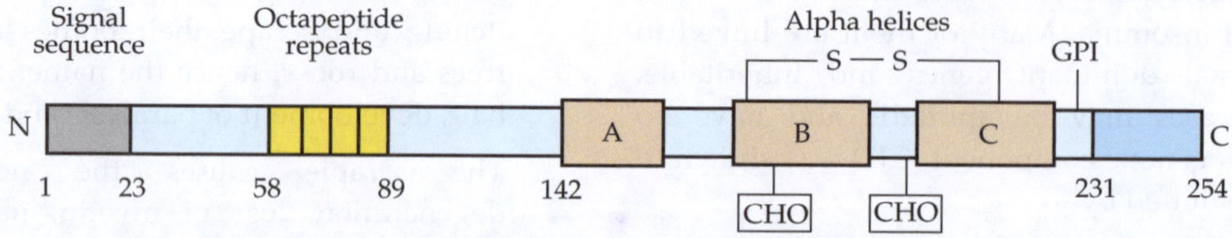


**Fig.12.2 :** *Domains and modifications of prion protein*
CHO = *Carbohydrate residues*
GPI = *Glycophosphatidyl inositol membrane anchor*
S–S = *Pupative disulfide bond*
A, B, C = *Alpha helical regions in PrP^c^*

### 12.2.7 Molecular Biology of Prion

Stanley B Prusiner was not convinced about the nature of the infectious agent, "unconventional slow virus", which was described by Gajdusek (1976). He was against the virus theory, because.

1. This infective agent is extremely resistant to UV or ionizing radiation whereas all viruses are sensitive;
2. The infectivity of the scrapie agent is not altered by treatment with nucleases, *ie*, DNase and RNase enzymes. That means the infective agent does not carry the genetic material as DNA or RNA.
3. Absence of any agent-specific antibody titre, strong tendency to aggregate, hydrophobicity etc.

In 1982 Prusiner and his colleagues extracted the infectious material from hamstar brain. He suggested that the disease–causing agent is a small single protein and named it as *prion* and this protein is designated as PrP (Prion protein).

Of the several routes of inoculation of infected brain tissue brings about most rapid onset of disease in experimental animals. The scrapie agent (prion) appears to enter to the body through skin and in sheep intact intestinal tract may be another portal of entry. The prion first replicates in regional lymph node and later it replicates in brain and other lymphoid organs all over the body. B-lymphocytes are probably required for the spread through the circulation to the brain. The agent may also ascend peripheral nerves to enter the spinal cord directly without involvement of lymphoid tissue.

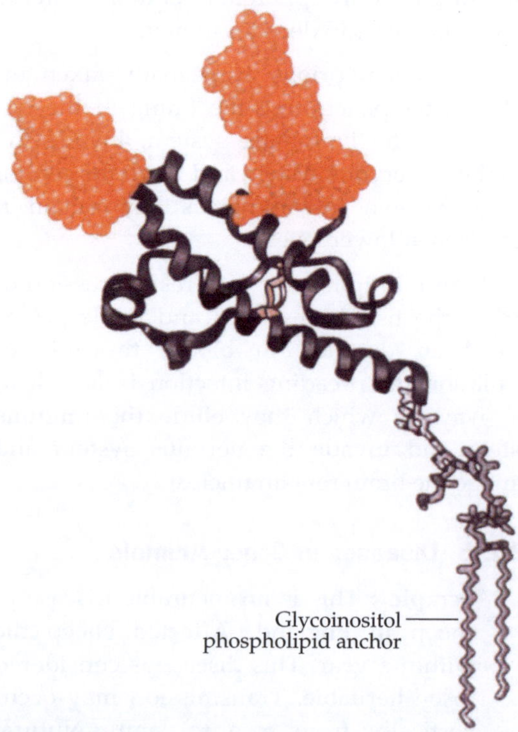


**Fig.12.3 :** *NMR structure of the PrP^c^ protein (Redrawn from Fundamentals of Molecular Virology by N.A.Acheson, 1st edn. 2007)*

When the protein quality control of the cell fails, the protein aggregates tend to accumulate in the affected cells and some critical macro-molecules are adsorbed to it causing severe damage and cell death. The protein aggregates are released from the dead cells and accumulate in the extracellular matrix that surrounds the cells in a tissue and damages the tissue. The nerve cells in the brain are highly organized and are mostly vulnerable. These aggregates then cause neurodegeneration diseases. Some protein aggregates become highly resistant to proteolysis and form fibrils of polypeptide as a continuous stack of β sheets. These β-sheets show abnormally staining deposits known as *amyloid*.

The PrP is normally located on the outer surface of the plasma membrane, most prominently in neurons. It's normal function is not known. But the diseases like Scrapie or CJD or Mad Cow etc all are caused due to abnormal folding of PrP. This abnormal configuration not only resistant to proteases but also infectious. By positive feed back mechanism the conversion of PrP to a mutated PrP (PrP*) allows the PrP* to spread rapidly from cell to cell in the brain. There are several possible models for conversion of PrP to PrP* where two or more α–helices change into four β–strands.

### 12.2.8 Differences between $PrP^{C}$ and $PrP^{SC}$

Proteinase K treatment to $PrP^{c}$ present in the brain of normal animals results in complete digestion of the protein but $PrP^{sc}$ from the diseased animals gives a proteinase-resistant 27-30 kD core fragment that retains infectivity. This fragment is missing N-terminal amino acids 23 to 89 but otherwise is identical. $PrP^{c}$ is a soluble protein but $PrP^{sc}$ tends to form oligomers and aggregates as forming fibrils.

X-ray crystallography and NMR studies showed that $PrP^{c}$ contains three α-helical structures at the C-terminal half of the molecule and the N-terminal region contains octapeptide repeats that binds to copper ions.

$PrP^{sc}$ protein contains less α-helical structures but substantial amounts of β-strands. N-terminal region of $PrP^{sc}$ is folded into a highly stable parallel β-helix.

### 12.2.9 Genetics of Prion

In 1984, a 15-amino acid sequence at amino terminal end of the PrP protein was identified. This sequence helped to construct a molecular probe. Probe is a defined RNA or DNA fragment, radioactively or chemically labeled, that is used to detect specific nucleic acid sequences by hybridization. With the help of this probe Bruno Oesch at University of Zurich showed that hamster cells do contain a gene for PrP. Almost at the same time, Bruce Chesebro of National Institute of Health, USA made his own probes and established that mouse cells harbour this gene. Finally it has been proved that the gene responsible for PrP resides in the chromosomes of hamsters, mice, humans and many other mammals.

There are two isoforms of PrP. The first one is the normal cellular membrane protein $PrP^{c}$. The function of this normal $PrP^{c}$ is not yet clearly understood, although it is suggested that $PrP^{c}$ may act as an acetyl-choline receptor inducer and may be playing an important role in transmission of nerve signal. The Second isoform, is the infective form of prion protein $PrP^{sc}$ (sc-denotes scrapie -like disease). Later on, it was found that $PrP^{c}$ and $PrP^{sc}$ are only due to its difference in conformations (Fig. 12.1).

This discovery of the *PrP* gene and its linkage to scrapie in sheep and their varying degree of susceptibility raised the possibilty of hereditary nature of prion disease.

In 1988, Prusiner and his team reported that human prion diseases can certainly be inherited *i.e.* they could be heritable as well as communicable.

In 1994, in an experiment, when the researchers tried to infect transgenic mice, carrying the human *PrP* gene, with human prion, there was no development of central nervous system dysfunction as expected. The mice could become susceptible to human prions only after removal of mouse *PrP* gene which is called "gene knockout" in genetics.

### 12.2.10 The Prion hypothesis

**Model for the conformational conversion of $PrP^{C}$ to $PrP^{Sc}$.**

While the investigators began trying to isolate the infectious agent for transmissible spongiform encephalopathies, they noted a number of unusual characteristics. viz.

1. Lack of immune response which is characteristic of infectious disease .
2. A long incubation time (upto 40 years)
3. Resistant to radiation
4. Resistant to proteases and heat
5. Can survive standard sterilization techniques
6. Most importantly $PrP^{Sc}$ is infectious and can convert endogenous $PrP^{C}$ to $PrP^{Sc}$ in the host.

These characteristics of prion proteins make them dangerous and difficult to work with them.

The '**prion only**' or '**protein only**' model for infection was proposed by Prusiner that a misfold form of a protein $PrP^{Sc}$ can catalyze the refolding of properly folded native form molecule ($PrP^{C}$) into a similar misfold conformation.

In one model, (**seeding model**) formation of $PrP^{Sc}$ is a nucleation - dependent oligomerization process, which states that the conformational change leading to $PrP^{C}$ into $PrP^{Sc}$ in a reversible thermodynamic equilibrium $PrP^{Sc}$ monomers are less stable, resulting in little or no accumulation of $PrP^{Sc}$. Aggregation of $PrP^{Sc}$ would promote the conversion of $PrP^{C}$ by binding to and stabilizing the otherwise $PrP^{Sc}$ conformation. Thus massive conversion of $PrP^{C}$ to $PrP^{Sc}$ would require initial nucleation process. The exogenous $PrP^{Sc}$ would introduce a "seed" that initiates aggregation. The aggregates clump together into amyloid plaques that surround brain cells and cause them to collapse, creating a characteristic holes in the brain (Fig. 12.4).

An alternative model, the **refolding model**, stated that $PrP^{Sc}$ is a more stable than $PrP^{C}$. But a high energy barrier prevents spontaneous conversion of $PrP^{C}$ to $PrP^{Sc}$. The $PrP^{C}$ is in equilibrium with an intermediate form $PrP^{*}$. This $PrP^{*}$ can bind to exogenously introduced $PrP^{Sc}$ in association with protein "X", a hypothetical factor. The heterodimer is then converted to a $PrP^{Sc}$ homodimer and forms a large aggregate. The **autoinfection process** is maintained by recycling of **protein-X** and breaking off of $PrP^{Sc}$ monomer and oligomers from aggregates to form a new heterodimer.

Prion proteins can be produced by recombinant DNA technology in bacteria. These proteins can be folded into states that resemble the native $PrP^{C}$ and the altered $PrP^{Sc}$ conformations. However, it has not yet been possible to generate infectivity from purified recombinant prion proteins. This confirms that other cellular proteins are required to help catalyze the conformational switch. Success in this kind of experiment might constitute definite proof of the prion hypothesis.

### 12.2.11 Prion gene

$PrP^{C}$ is encoded by a single exon of a unique gene (*prnp* gene), which is highly conserved in the genome of many animals including humans. There are about 20 known mutations in the *prnp* gene that are associated with prion diseases, presumably because of a high rate of spontaneous $PrP^{Sc}$ formation. The *prnp* gene encodes a 35 kD.

1. A number of families with Gerstmann - Straussler-Scheinker-syndrome have a common double mutation in $PrP^{C}$ at amino acid 178 and 200 (D178N, E200K) Some other families with this disease have only one mutation at amino acids 102 (P102L) as *leucine* to *proline*.Thus, in mice

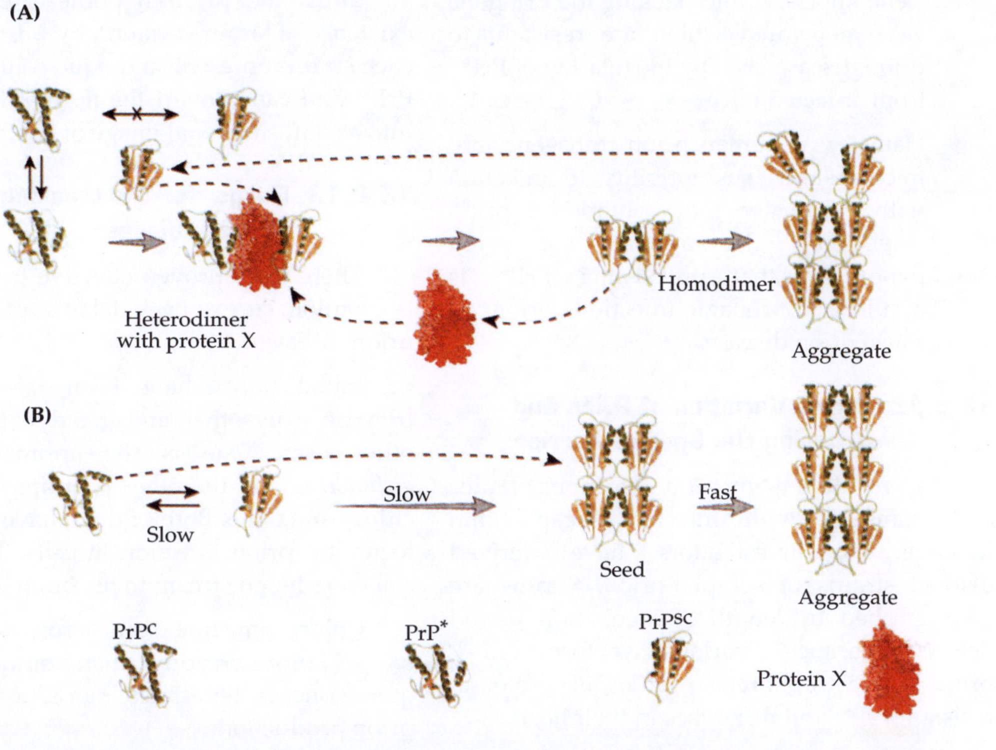


**Fig.12.4 :** *Model for the conformational conversion of $PrP^c$ into $PrP^{sc}$ (A) The refolding model (B) The seeding model (Redrawn from Fundamental Molecular Biology, L.A.Allison, 1st edn. 2007).*

P102L mutation spontaneously develop scrapie-like syndrome.

2. In sheep, homozygous mutation at codon 171 (R171Q) causes substitution of *arginine* for *glutamine* making them entirely resistant to scrapie.
3. Both acquired and sporadic CJD in humans are due to homozygous for *valine* at position 129. But in UK, victims of a new variant have found to be homozygous for *methionine* at position 129.
4. In fact heterozygosity in *prnp* gene particularly at position 129 is present at unexpectedly high levels in human world. Heterozygosity protects against both infected and sporadic prion diseases.
5. Sheep are susceptible to infection with bovine spongiform encephatitis at the same ferquency and incubation time as scrapie, although sheep PrP differs from bovine PrP at amino acids 98, 100, 143, 146 155, 168, 198 and 218.
6. Cattles are very resistant to infection with sheep scrapie, but are susciptible to BSE. It is thought that during epidemic in cattle, BSE was acquired by ingestion of remains not of scrapie-infected sheep but of cattle that had been infected by a rare, spontaneous case of BSE sometime in the past.
7. Mice are resistant to infection with hamster prions, which have 16 differences in amino acid sequences from mouse PrP.

8. Gene knockout mice lacking the PrP gene were generated which are resistant to prion disease even by inoculation of $PrP^{sc}$ from infected mice.

9. Hamster or human prion transgene into mice restores susceptibility to infection with hamster or human prion respectively. It supports the prion hypothesis that preexisting $PrP^{sc}$ is required to propagte infections prions to cause prion disease.

### 12.2.12 Strain Variation of Prion and Crossing the Species barrier

As a result of many serial infections of mice and hamsters with infected sheep brain homogenates, investigators have derived distinct strains of scrapie prion. Strains are distinguished by length of incubation period before appearance of various glycoforms of PrP proteins, electrophoretic profiles of protease-resistant $PrP^{sc}$ and difference in their hosts.

It is observed that a single amino acid substitution in the hamster protein enables it to be converted efficiently by mouse $PrP^{sc}$ into hamster $PrP^{sc}$. Therefore, barrier to interspecific transmission is in the sequence of the PrP protein. On the other hand bovine spongiform encephalopathy prions have an unusually broad host range, infecting a number of meat-eating animals including domestic or wild cats and humans. Two strains of transmissible mink encephalopathy exist as hyper (HY) and drowsy (DY) strains. They transmit different behavioral changes with different neuropathology and incubation period. Protease-K digestion gives rise different protein fragments.

A new strain of CJD (nv CJD) in humans appears to be linked to BSE epidemic in United Kingdom, which is sporadic CJD having distinct pathology, and onsets in a far younger age with different initial symptoms. This nvCJD shows different proteinase K resistant $PrP^{sc}$ species and different patterns of di-mono- and nonglycosylated $PrP^{sc}$ are revealed by electrophoresis but similar to BSE.

Thus, the prion hypothesis explains the existence of strain variation by postulating that each strain represents a unique conformation of $PrP^{sc}$ and can convert the normal $PrP^{c}$ protein into a conformational image of itself.

### 12.2.13 Durgs for the treatment of Prion disease

There is no proven effective treatments for prevention, cure or even delay of progression of prion diseases.

Initial hopes have been raised for two tricyclic drugs that are already approved for other uses. One is the antimalarial drug ***quinacrine*** and the other is antipsychotic drug **chlorpromazine.** Both of them have been found to inhibit prion infection in cells. These drugs can cross blood stream to the brain.

Chlorpromazine can cross blood-brain barrier more readily then quinacrine, but quinacrine is ten times more potent against prion production.

Antibodies and antibody fragments are tried to produce which can bind to prion protein and block prion formation in the cell.

Vaccination and gene therapy and other possible solutions to curing and preventing prion disease may be the tools to fight against prion disease.

### 12.2.14 Prion in Yeast

An epigenetic effect is found in yeast where two different states can be inherited that map to a single genetic locus, although the sequence of the gene is the same in both states. The two different states are [*psi*$^-$] and [*PSI*$^+$], though switch on condition occurs at a low fequency.

The [*psi*$^-$] state maps to the locus *SUP35*, which codes a translation termination factor. When [*psi*$^-$] gene is active, the Sup 35 protein terminates protein synthesis.

The mutant of this is *[PSI*$^+$*]* state, where Sup 35 does not function properly termination of protein synthesis, causing lethal effects.

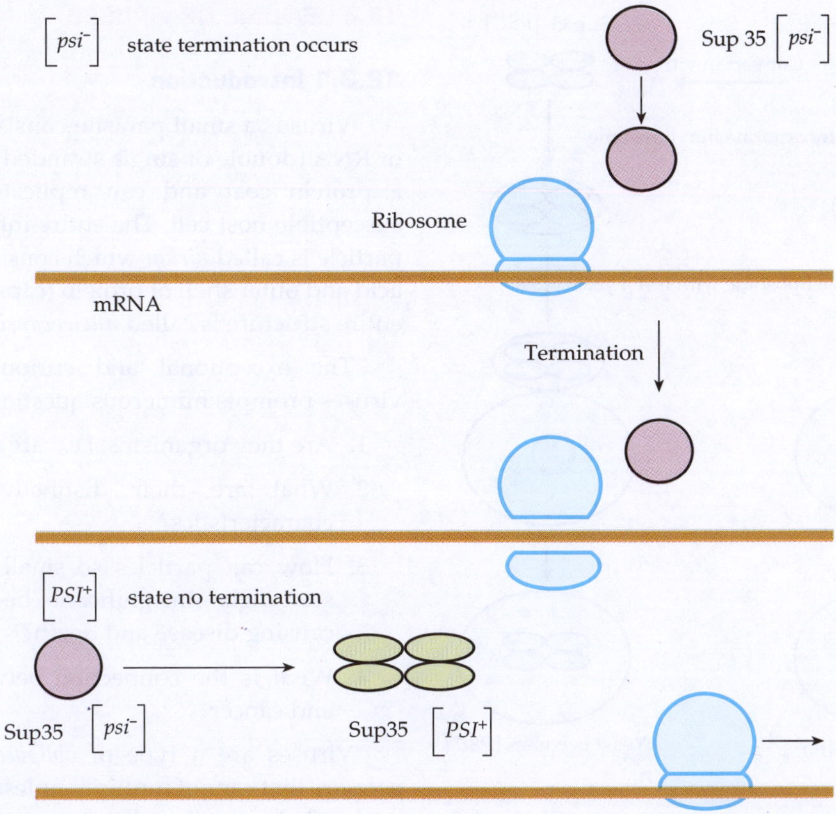


**Fig.12.5 :** *State of the Sup 35 protein determines whether termination of translation occurs or not.*

If [$PSI^+$] strain is crossed with [$psi^-$] strain, all the progeny are [$PSI^+$], but [$PSI^+$] trait can not be mapped to any such nucleic acids. Therefore, it seems to be an *extra chromosomal inheritance.*

In the wild-type [$psi^-$] cell, the protein displays its normal function. The [$PSI^+$] state is determined by the conformation of Sup35 protein. In this [$PSI^+$] state the conformation of Sup 35 is amyloid fibres with a characteristic of high content of β–sheet. Presence of protein in [$PSI^+$] state causes all the Sup35 proteins in the cell into [$PSI^+$] state, by the interaction between the [$PSI^+$] protein and newly synthesized Sup-35 protein and also it has a nucleating role.

If the N-terminal domain of Sup-35 is deleted, [$PSI^+$] state is not formed. Therefore it is seemed that the N-terminal domain is essential for [$PSI^+$] state, this is rich in *Gln* and *Asn* residues.

Chaperon Hsp104 is involved in the inheritance of [$PSI^+$] again, overexpression of Hsp 104 causes loss of [$PSI^+$] state (Fig. 12.5).

If the [$psi^-$] state of Sup 35 is put into the liposome and fused *in vtro* with [$psi^-$] yeast, no change would occur. But if it is fused with [$PSI^+$] yeast, the yeast will be tranformed into [$PSI^+$] state.

On the other hand, if [$PSI^+$] state of Sup-35 is put into liposome and fused *in vitro* with the [$psi^-$] yeast, it will transform into [$PSI^+$] state (Fig. 12.6).

The experiment suggests that there is a common model for the formation of *prion state* that involves aggregation of the *Gln/Asn*

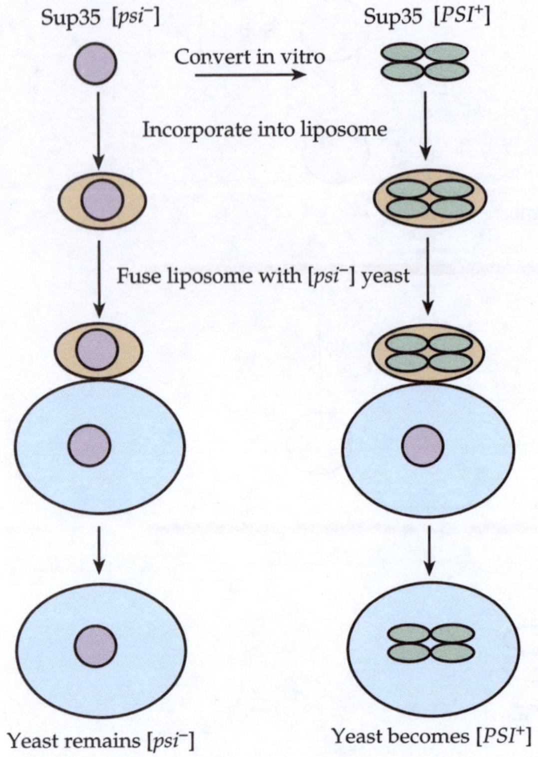


**Fig.12.6 :** *Purified protein can convert the [psi⁻] state of yeast to [PSI⁺].*

domains into a self propagating amyloid structure. The yeast cell may contain soluble protein that antagonize prion formation. The introduction of any *Gln/Asn* domain protein interacts with these proteins and reduces the concentration and allows other *Gln/Asn* proteins to aggregate more easily.

Another locus *URE2* has been shown in the yeast which codes for a protein required for $N_2$-mediated repression of certain catabolic enzymes. When a yeast strain is converted to an alternative state called [*URE2*], Ure2 protein is no longer functional. Ure2 protein has a similar feature with Sup35 is that it consists of two domains that function independently and N-terminal domain is sufficient for formation of the structures that make the protien inactive. It also seems to be a prion protein in yeast.

## 12.3 GENOME OF VIRUSES

### 12.3.1 Introduction

Virus is a small parasite consisting of DNA or RNA (double or single stranded), enclosed in a protein coat and can replicate only in a susceptible host cell. The entire infectious virus particle is called *virion* which consists of nucleic acid and outer shell of protein (capsid). Thus the entire structure is called *nucleocapsid.*

The exceptional and curious nature of viruses prompts numerous questions :

1. Are they organisms, *i.e.,* are they alive?
2. What are their distinctive biological characteristics?
3. How can particles so small, simple and seemingly insignificant be capable of causing disease and death?
4. What is the connection between viruses and cancer?

Viruses are a type of *obligate intracellular parasites* that cannot multiply unless they invade a specific host cell and instruct its genetic and metabolic machinery to make and release new viruses. Therefore, viruses are capable of causing serious damage and disease to living organisms.

### 12.3.2 Unique properties of Viruses

1. Obligate intracellular parasites of bacteria, protozoa, fungi, plants and animals.
2. Ultramicroscopic, ranging from 20 nm to 450 nm.
3. Are not cells, no cellular components and cytoplasm.
4. Do not independently fulfill the characteristics of life.
5. Inactive outside the host cell.
6. Genetic component is DNA or RNA, but not both
7. Nucleic acids are double stranded or single stranded

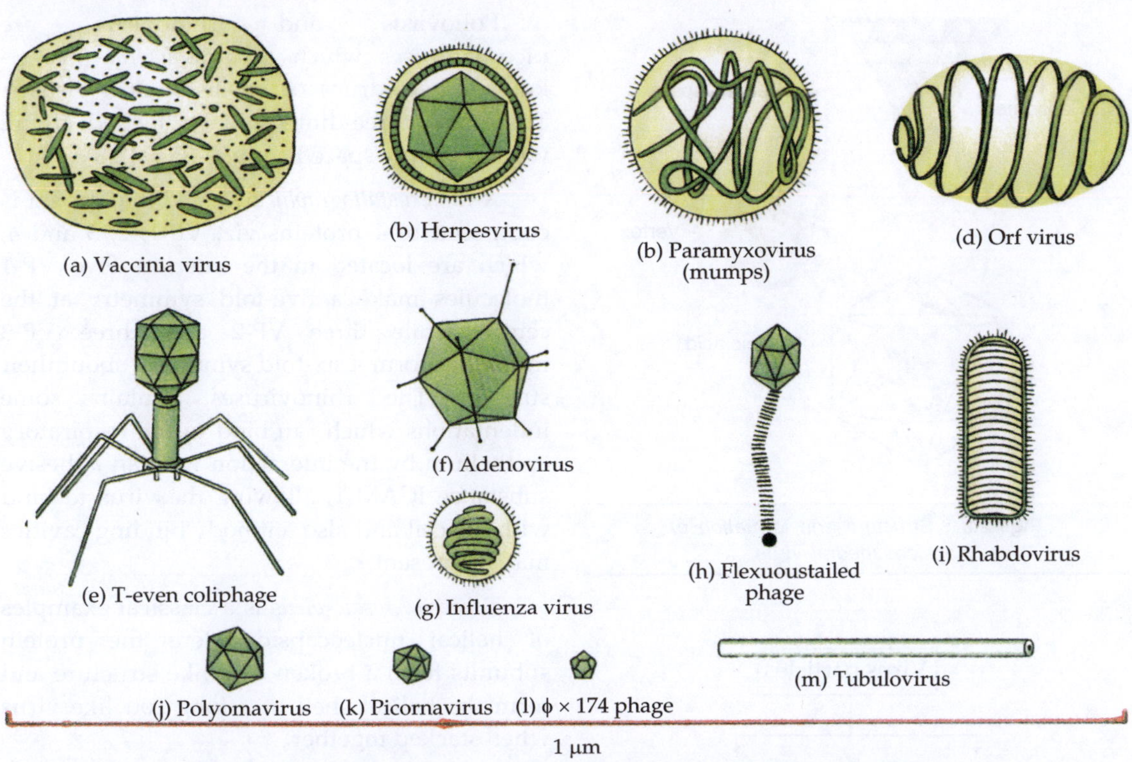


**Fig.12.7 :** *The Size and Morphology of Selected Viruses are drawn to scale. A 1 μm line is provided at the bottom of the figure.*

8. Highly specific to the host.
9. Lack enzymes and machinary for protein synthesis
10. Multiply by taking control of host cell's genetic material and regulating the synthesis and assembly of new viruses.

### 12.3.3 General Structure of Viruses

Viruses represent the smallest infectious agents. They are actually dwarfed by their host cells. Poxviruses are larger (250 nm diameter), while parvoviruses are as small as 20 nm in diameter. Some cylindrical viruses are relatively long (800 nm in length) but are narrow in diameter (15 nm) (Fig. 12.7).

**TABLE 12.1**
**Size of some viruses**

| | |
|---|---|
| **Poxvirus** | 250 nm |
| **Herpes simplex** | 150 nm |
| **Rabies** | 125 nm |
| **HIV** | 110 nm |
| **Influenza** | 100 nm |
| **Adenovirus** | 75 nm |
| **$T_2$ phage** | 65 nm |
| **Poliomyelitis** | 30 nm |
| **Yellow fever** | 22 nm |

**Viral components :** The molecular structure of virus is composed of regular repeating subunits that give rise to a crystalline appearance. They contain only those parts needed to invade and control a host cell. The pattern of organization of viruses is as follows :

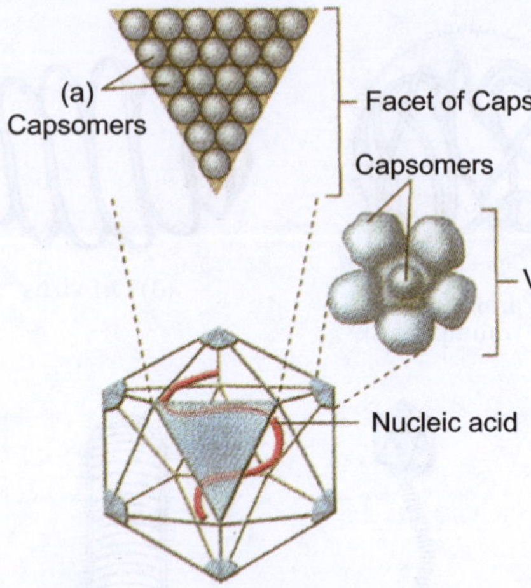


**Fig.12.8 :** *Structure and formation of an icosahedral virus*

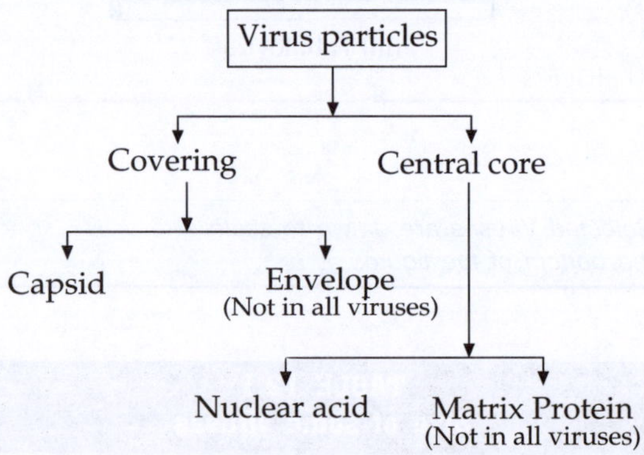


**Capsid :** This is the protective outer shell of the virus particle. It occurs in three main shapes : polyhedral, helical and complex.

Polyhedral capsids have three possible symmetry, viz. tetrahedral, octahedral and icosahedral. Each capsid consists of many *capsomeres*. Each capsomere is composed of a few monomers forming polygonal rings, each with a central space of upto 40A. The capsomeres may be pentameres or hexameres. The minimum number of capsomeres can theoritically be 12 followed by 32, 42, 72, 92, 162, 252, 362, 492, 642 and 812. Of these capsomers, 12 are pentameres occupying the 12 corners, while rest and hexamers.

Poliovirus and rhinovirus are picornaviruses which are *icosahedral* (eye" – koh-suh-hee"-drun) or quasispherical viruses. These are three-dimensional 20-sided figure with 12 evenly spaced corners (Fig. 12.8).

*X-ray crystallography* revealed that capsid is composed of 4 proteins viz. VP-1, 2, 3 and 4, which are located in the interior. Five VP-1 molecules make a five-fold symmetry at the centre while three VP-2 and three VP-3 molecules form a six-fold symmetry about their surface. The rhinoviruses contain some indentations which can bind to the respiratory epithelium by the interaction with an adhesive substance ICAM-1, allowing the virus to bind with the cell and also antibody binding cavities may be present.

*Tobacco Mosaic virus* is a classical examples of helical nucleocapsid. Here the protein subunits form a broken disk-like structure and form the helical shell of a long rod like virus when stacked together.

**Complex viruses** are divided into two groups :

1. Without a definite capsid, the nucleic acid, is surrounded by several coats eg *Vaccinia* virus.
2. With a definite complex capsid eg., phage viruses.

**Phage viruses** are with complex structure. T4 phage of *E. coli* bacterium is tadpole shaped with head and tail regions. The head capsid is 95 nm × 65 nm and has the form of a prolate icosahedron. It is made up of about 2000 similar subunits and is packed with circular dsDNA of 500 μm long. The head capsid consists of two 10-faceted equatorial bands, with a pyramidal vertex at either end. The *tail* has helical symmetry. Thus the bacteriophage shows a combination of icosahedral symmetry and helical symmetry, i.e, binary symmetry. The *tail* consists of a core tube 80Å in diameter, through which DNA passes out, surrounded by a protein tail sheath. The sheath consists of 144 subunits arranged in 24 rings of 6 subunits each.

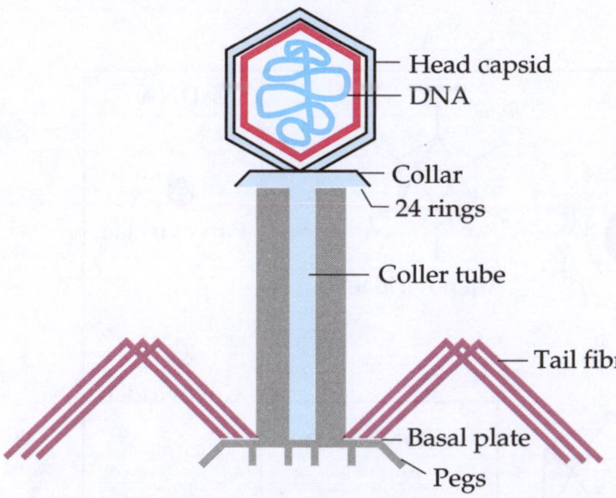


**Fig.12.9 :** *Diagram of T4 phage*

The sheath is connected to a thin disc, called the *collar*, at the upper end and a *base plate* at the lower end. The base plate is hexagonal and has a pin or spike at each corner. From each of the six corners is also given off a long, thin tail fibre, 1300 Å long which serves for the attachment of the phage to the host cell (Fig. 12.9).

**Envelope :** Many animal viruses and some plant viruses are bounded by an outer membraneous layer called an *envelope.* The envelope of animal viruses consists mainly of phospholipid bilayer as it is orginated from the plasma membrane of the host cell. It also contains two types of virus-encoded glycoproteins, which remain exposed on the outside of the envelope. These protruding molecules are called *spikes* or *peplomers,* are essential for the atachment of viruses to the next host cell. Because the envelope is more supple than the capsid. Enveloped viruses are pleomorphic and range from spherical to filamentous in their shape.

Influenza virus has spikes which project about 10 nm from the surface at 7–8 nm intervals. Some spikes possess the enzyme *neuraminidase* which may aid the virus in penetrating mucous layers of the respiratory epithelium to reach the host. Other spikes have hemagglutinin proteins as they bind to RBC with these proteins. Besides, a nonglycosylate protein, the M or matrix protein is found on the inner surface of envelope and helps to stabilize it (Fig. 12.10).

**Nucleic Acids :** Viruses employ all four possible nucleic acid types viz. ssDNA, dsDNA, ssRNA and also dsRNA. These can be linear or circular (Fig. 12.11).

The size of viral genetic material also varies greatly. The smallest genomes (those of MS2 and Qβ viruses) are around $1\times10^6$ daltons, just large enough to code for three to four proteins. T-even bacteriophages, herpes virus and vaccinia virus have genomes of 1.0 to $1.6\times10^8$ daltons and may be able to synthesize over 100 proteins.

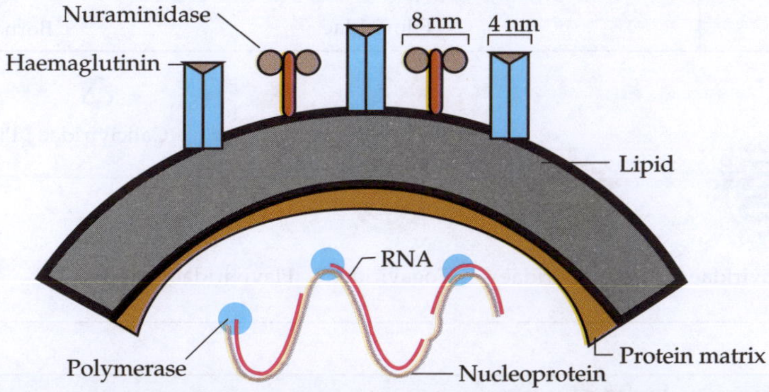


**Fig.12.10 :** *Structure of influenza viral particle*

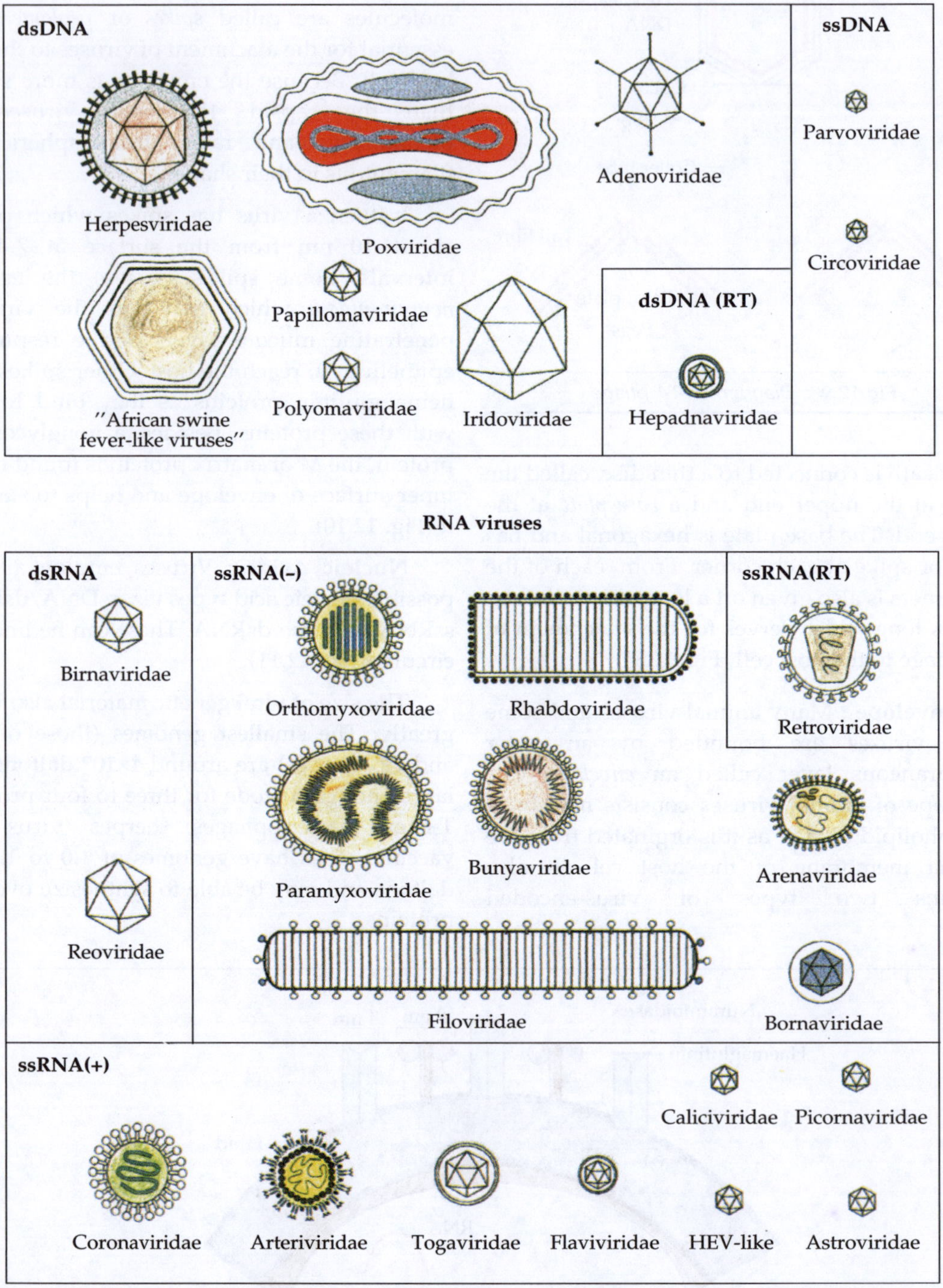


**Fig.12.11 :** *Different types of viruses and their sizes.*

Most ssRNA viruses employ its RNA as their genetic material. These are identical with that of viral mRNA, which are called *positive (+ve) strands.* Some viruses may have the viral genome complementary to mRNA, called negative (–ve) strands.

Just like eukaryotic mRNA, viral mRNA is also capped at 5′ end with 7-methyl guanosine and at 3′ end with a poly A tail. Therefore they can be used to synthesize proteins in the host cell.

### 12.3.4 Tobacco Mosaic Virus

In 1892, Dimitri Iwanowski reported that the organism which caused mosaic disease of tobacco was so smsll that it can pass through filters fine enough to stop all known bacteria. In 1935, Wendell Stanley demonstrated that the organism, called Tobacco Mosaic Virus (TMV) is so simple and homogenous that it could be crystallized like a chemical compound.

**Structure :**

1. Electron microscopic structure of TMV showed a shape much like hollow tubes with protein walls (Table 12.2).
2. A single type of **protomer** (the macromolecular structure to construct the capsid of a virus) associates together in a helical or spiral arrangement to produce a long rigid tube, 15 to 18 nm in diameter by 300 nm long.
3. The RNA genetic material is wound in a spiral and positioned toward the inside of the capsid where a groove is formed by the protein subunits.
4. It's capsid contains a single type of small subunit possessing 158 amino acids.
5. Total number of nucleotide is about 6000.
6. Once the protomer is formed and exposed to the proper condition, they usually interact specifically with each other and spontaneously associate to form the capsid. The process is called self assembly (Fig. 12.12).

**TABLE 12.2**
**Some examples of Viruses and their nucleic acids**

| *Virus* | *Example* |
|---|---|
| 1. Linear ssDNA | Parvoviruses |
| 2. Circular ssDNA | $\phi \times 174$ |
| 3. Linear dsDNA with single chain breaks | T 7 |
| 4. Linear dsDNA with closed ends | Vaccinia |
| 5. Closed circular dsDNA | Papovaviruses and XXPM2 phage |
| 6. Linear ssRNA (+ve strand infectious –ve strand non infectious) | Picornaviruses, Togaviruses and most plant viruses |
| 7. Linear ssRNA (–ve strand non infectious) | Rhabdoviruses, Paramyxoviruses |
| 8. Segmented ssRNA (–ve strand) | Myxoviruses |
| 9. Segmented dsRNA | Reoviruses |
| 10. Diploid ssRNA plus small RNA from host. | Retroviruses |
| 11. Inverted terminal repetitions | Sindbis viruses. |

### 12.3.5 Polyomavirus genome

It belongs to the family Polyomaviridae.

1. These are small viruses with a diameter of 45 nm.
2. It possesses a dsDNA, with a mw. $3\times10^6$ and 5 kbp.
3. It is enclosed in a nonenveloped capsid exhibiting iscosahedral symmetry with 72 capsomeres.
4. Cellular histones are used to condense viral DNA inside the virus particles.

It includes SV 40 from monkey and two human viruses — JC virus and BK virus.

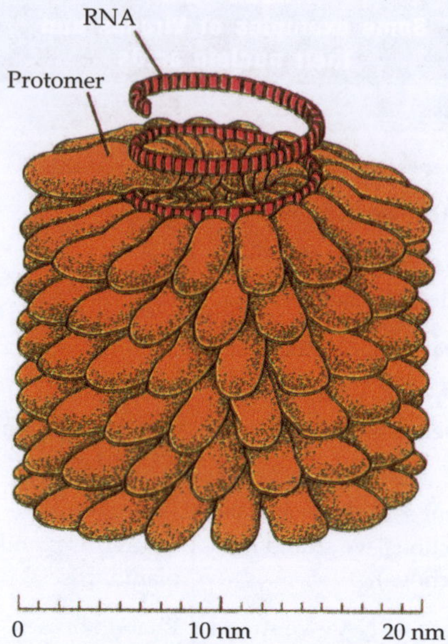


Fig.12.12 : *Structure of TMV*

It is widespread in rabbit. It produces a variety of malignant tumors in newborn mice, hamstars and guineapigs, hence the name polyoma (poly = many, oma = tumor).

JC and BK viruses were recorded from brain of child with Hodgkin's disease.

**Genetics of SV 40**

1. Polyomavirus genome contains "early" and "late" regions (Fig. 12.13).
2. The early region is expressed after infection of cells in the transformed cells. It contains genes that code for "early proteins" which is necessary for the replication of viral DNA in permissive cells and a small tumor (t) antigen.
3. The genome encodes three early proteins viz. small, middle and large T antigens. This one or two such antigens are required for the transformation of the cell. These transforming proteins are required

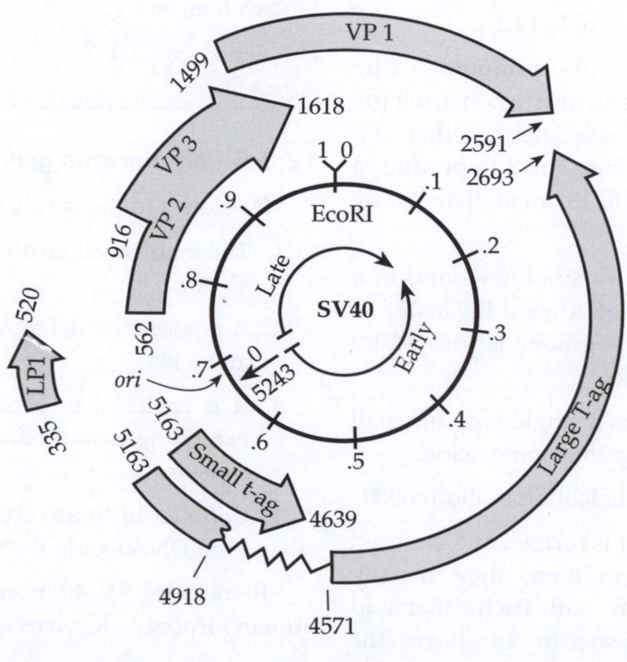


Fig.12.13 : *Genetic map of the polyomavirus SV40. The thick circle represents the circular SV40 DNA.*

continuously to be synthesized to maintain transformed condition of the cell.

4. The late regions consist of genes that code for the synthesis of coat proteins which are not actually synthesized in the transformed cells.

5. T antigen of SV 40 interacts with the cellular tumor suppressor proteins $p^{53}$ and $p^{rb}$ and inactivates the growth inhibitory properties. Thus it allows the cells to enter S-phase so that the viral DNA starts replication. The $p^{53}$ gene product actually senses the DNA damage at $G_1$, either blocks cell cycle progression or initiates apoptosis; abolishing its function would lead to accumulation of T-antigen expressing cells with genomic mutation that might promote tumorigenic growth.

**Pathogenesis :**

SV40 DNA has been detected in selected types of human tumors, including brain tumors, mesotheliomas, bone tumors and lymphomas.

**BK virus** causes cystitis, nephropathy and severe renal allograft dysfunction. The cause of allograft renal transplant failure, at 50% of cases may be due to polyomavirus associated nephropathy. This BK virus appears to be associated with untreated stenosis observed in renal transplants and also in haemorrhagic cystitis observed in bone marrow transplants.

**JC virus** causes the progessive multifocal leukoencephalopathy, a fatal brain disease occurs in some immunocompromised persons. After asymptomatic primary infection, JCV establishes latent infection in the kidneys in B cells and in monocyte-lineage cells. Reactivation in immunocompromized patients may result in illness. Occassional clinical disease is observed e.g. progressive multifocal leuko-encephalopathy (PMLE). It is a subacute demyelinating disease.

BK and JC viruses are widely distributed in human populations in about 70-80% of adult sera. Infection usually occurs during childhood and persists in the kidneys of healthy individuals after primary infection. It may be reactivated during renal transplantation or during preganancy.

### 12.3.6 Hepatitis B Genome

Hepatitis means inflammation of liver and the most common cause is infection with one of the five viruses, called A, B, C, D and E. All of these viruses can cause an acute disease with symptoms lasting several weeks including yellowing of the skin and eyes (jaundice), dark urine, extreme fatigue, nausea, vomiting and abdominal pain. It can take several months to a year to feel fit again.

Hepatitis B virus can cause chronic infection in which the patient never gets rid of the virus and many years later develops cirrhosis of the liver or liver cancer.

Hepatitis B virus is transmitted by contact with blood or body fluid of an infected person. The main ways of getting infected with HBV are

- Perinatal (from mother to baby at the time of birth)
- Child - to - child transmission
- Unsafe injections and transfusions
- Sexual contact.

HBV is not spread by contaminated food or water and cannot be spread casually in the workplace.

**Genome Structure :**

1. The HBV belongs to the family : Hepadnaviridae; genus : *Orthohepadnavirus.*

2. This is a DNA virus, usually spherical, 22 nm diameter or may be about 200 nm long filamentous form due to presence of overesxpression of 'S'-antigens on its envelope or may be larger 42 nm diameter called *Dane particles,*which are less frequently observed (Fig. 12.14 and 12.15).

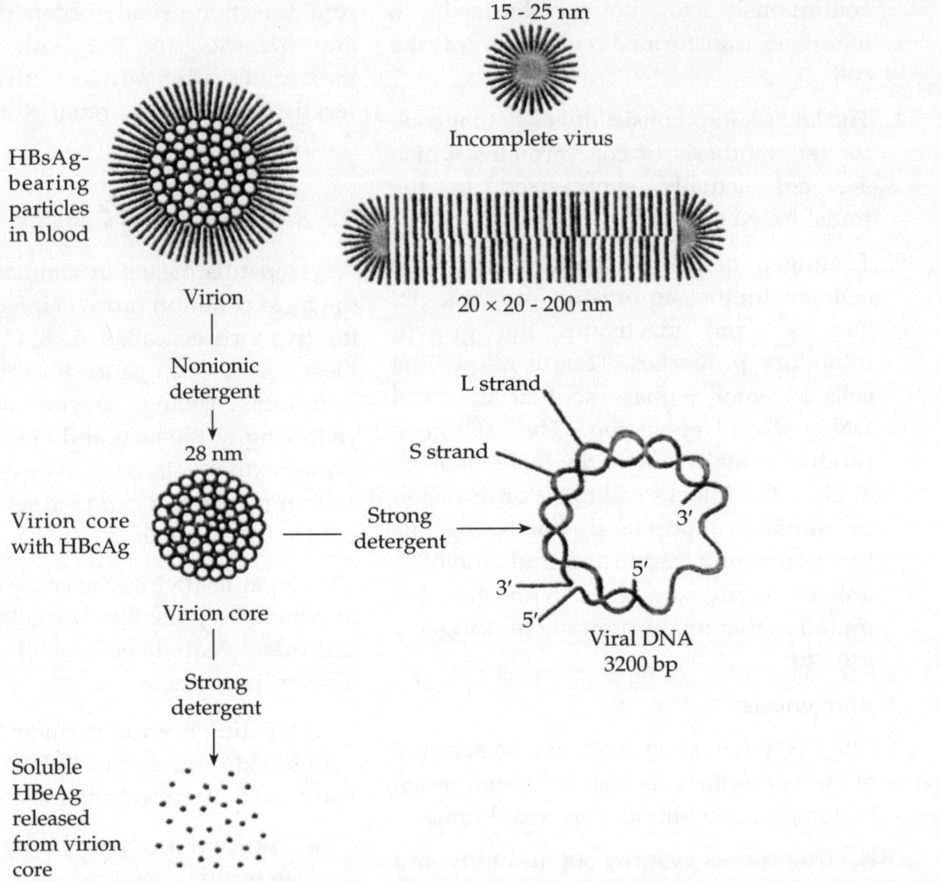


**Fig.12.14 :** *Hepatitis B viral and subviral forms*

3. Outer surface or envelope contains HBsAg and lipid and surrounds a 27 nm inner nucleocapsid core which contains HBcAg.
4. Viral genome is circular partial dsDNA, 3200 bp in length. The full length DNA minus strand (L or long strand) is complementary to all HBV mRNAs. The plus strand (S or short strand) is variable (50–80% of the full length.)
5. There are four ORFs that code seven polypeptides, these include
   (i) Structural proteins of virion surface
   (ii) Structural proteins of virion core.
   (iii) A small transcriptional *trans*-activator (X)
   (iv) A large polymerase protein (P) which includes DNA polymerase, reverse transcriptase and RNase-H activities.
   (v) Regulatory sequences are promoters, enhancers, and glucocorticoid responsive elements (GRE).
6. The '*S*' gene has three in-frame initiation codons and encodes the major HBsAg as well as polypeptides containing in addtion pre-S2 or pre-S1 and pre-S2 sequences.
7. The '*C*' gene has two in-frame initiation codons and encodes HBcAg plus the HBe protein, which is processed to produce soluble HBeAg.

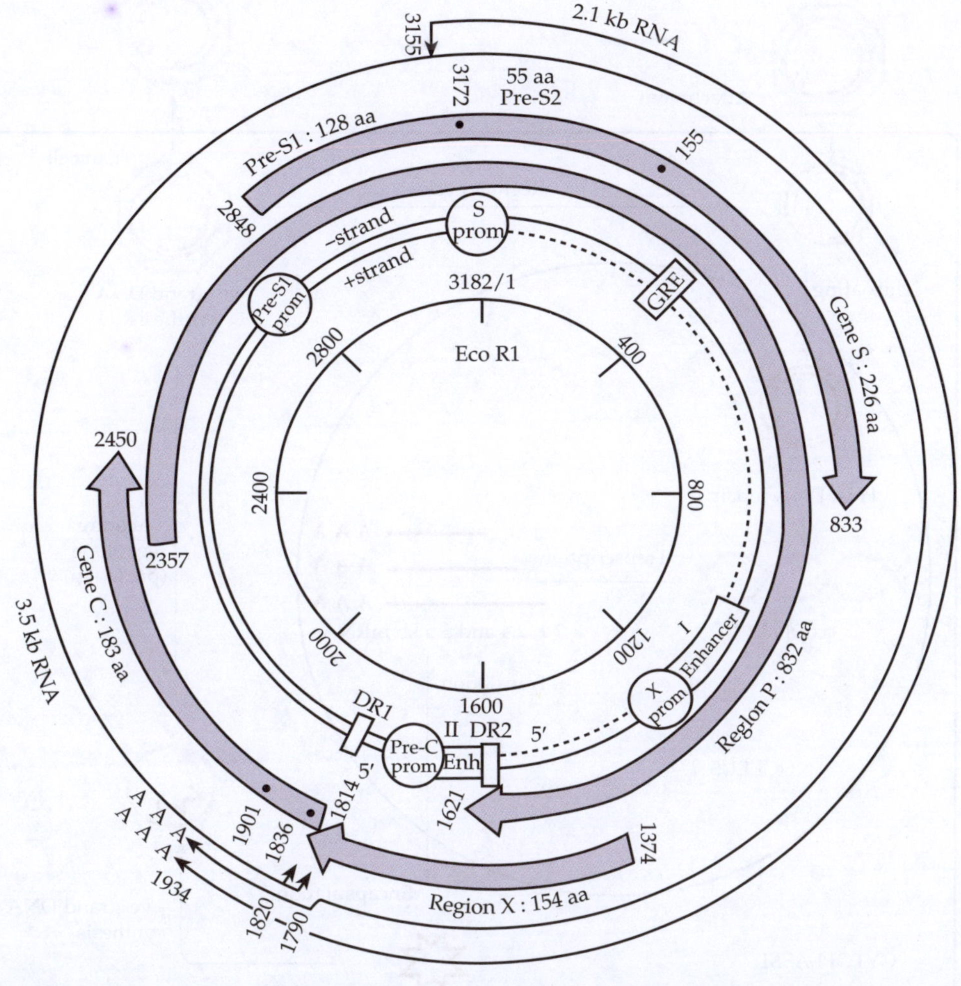


**Fig.12.15 :** *Genetic organization of HBV genome, showing + and – strands and Seven ORFs, Promoters (prom), enhancer and (enh) glucocorticoid responsive elements (GRE)*

8. HBsAg contains a group-specific antigen "a", in addition to two pairs of mutually exclusive subdeterminants *d/y* and *w/r*. Thus four phenotypes of HBsAg have been observed : *adw, ayw, adr* and *ayr*. These virus-specific markers are useful in epidemiologic investigations.

**HBV replication Cycle**

1. HBV attachment to a receptor on the surface of hepatocytes occurs via a portion of the pre-S region of HBsAg (Fig. 12.16).
2. After uncoating the virus, unidentified cellular enzymes convert the partially dsDNA to covalent closed circular DNA (cccDNA), which can be detected in the host nucleus.
3. cccDNA serves as the template for the production of HBV mRNAs and the 3.5 kb RNA pregenome.
4. This **pregenome** is encapsidated by a packaging signal located near the 5′ end of the RNA into newly synthesized core

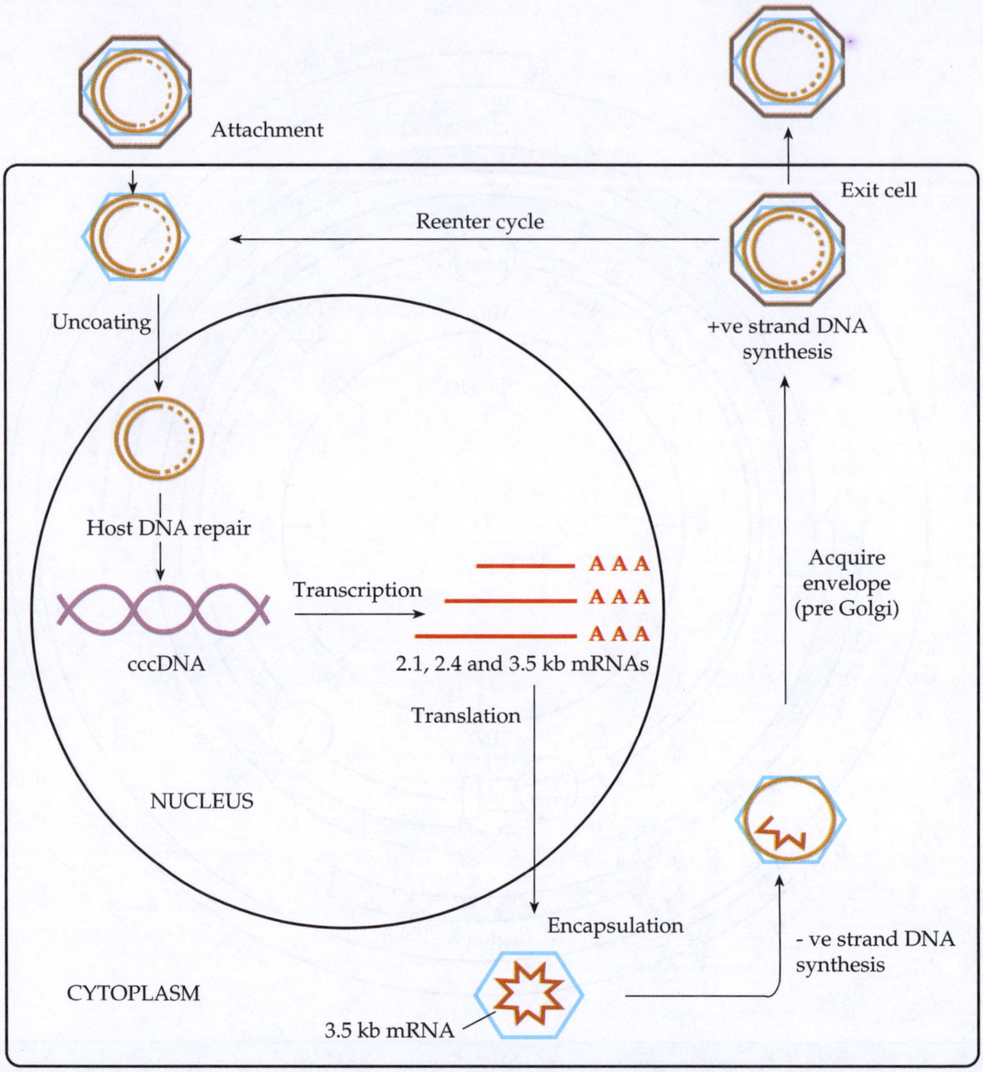


**Fig.12.16 :** *HBV replicative cycle [cccDNA) = covalent closed circular DNA]*

particles, where it serves as the template for HBV reverse transcriptase (encoded within the polymerase gene). RNase H activity of the polymerase removes the RNA template as the negative strand DNA is being synthesized.

5. Positive-strand DNA synthesis does not proceed to complete within the core, resulting in replicative intermediates containing a full length negative strand DNA and a variable-length (20–80%) positive strand DNA. This replication occurs in Golgi bodies and budded off from the Golgi bodies.

6. This may exit from the cell or reenter intracellular infection cycle.

### 12.3.7 Human Immuno-deficiency Virus (HIV)

HIV is believed to cause the dreadful disease AIDS (Acquired Immuno-Deficiency Syndrome.

AIDS is a serious and potentially fatal disease acquired through infection with a virus, was variously called HTLV-III (Human T-cell Lymphotrophic Virus, type-III) or LAV (Lymphadenopathy Associated Virus) or ARV (AIDS related virus). The victim may suffer from irrepairable damage to the body's immune system and becomes susceptible to unusual cancer (Kaposi's sarcoma) and severe infections.

LAV was first isolated and identified in 1983 by Luc Montagnier of France from lymph of a homosexual. HTLV-III was identified in 1980 by Robert Gallo of USA. ARV was isolated by Levy in Sanfransisco.

In 1983, in the Pasteur Institute, Paris and then in 1985, in the National Cancer Institute, Bethesda, USA, the HIV was believed to cause this dreadful disease and currently it's name has adopted as HIV-1.

The HIV-1 is now well characterised and it has been established that this virus is notoriously heterogeneous. The DNA sequences of virus isolated from different patients often vary by as much as 10%. The viruses, originally reported in 1983 compatibility. LAV is now recognized to be an early stage in the development of AIDS.

Another HIV, called HIV-2 was isolated, which has showed much homology with SIV (Simian Immunodeficiency Virus), was originally called STLV from African Green monkey and is thought to be an intermediate stage in the evolution of SIV to HIV-1.

AIDS may remain dormant for years after infection. Usually, it takes 10 years, before a person with HIV infection shows full signs and symptoms of the illness. AIDS does not kill by itself but by breaking down the body's natural biological immune system it allows ordinary diseases, like diarrhoea, fever, pneumonia, tuberculosis, cancer etc. to manifest and kill the patient with impunity.

**Spread of HIV-1**

1. Sexual contact
2. Direct entry into the blood during blood transfusion or through wounds (blood transfusion instruments and collecting instruments) and also through antiserum which is used for the treatment or vaccination.
3. Intravenous drug users who normally share hypodermic needles.
4. Infants born to mothers who are infected with HIV-1 are at high risk of infection.
5. Feeding milk to her baby if the mother is infected. Such transmission of disease is likely to be due to HIV-infected macrophages, dendritic cells and lymphocytes.

**Structure of HIV-1**

HIV-1 is a retrovirus which means that instread of storing its genetic programme in DNA, it uses RNA. It contains an enzyme called reverse transcriptase permitting these RNAs to make their own DNA which then goes to and joins with the chromosomes of the host cell (Fig. 12.27).

1. Diameter of the virus is 100 nm.
2. The outer coat or envelope is a part of the host plasma membrane, is a lipid bilayer and also contains some MHC class-I molecules.
3. The envelope consists of 72 glycoprotein knob-like projections, which is composed of gp 120 and gp 41. Actually these are produced by cleaving a common precursor gp 160. The gp41 is embedded in a envelope (lipid bilayer), while the gp 120 is associated with gp 41, which serves as the viral receptor for CD4 on the host cell.

**TABLE 12.3**
**Genome of HIV-1 and their functions**

| Gene | Protein Products | Functions |
|---|---|---|
| *gag* | 53 KD-*precursor* | Nucleocapsid proteins |
| | p 17 | Outer core-protein layer |
| | p 24 | Inner core-protein layer |
| | p 9 | Component of nucleoid core |
| | p 7 | Directly binds to genomic RNA |
| *env* | 160-KD-*precursor* | Envelope glycoprotein |
| | gp 41 | Assoceates with gp 120 and is required for fusion |
| | gp 120 | Protrudes from envelope and binds to CD4 |
| *pol* | *Precursor* of *enzymes* | Enzymes |
| | p 64 | Reverse transcriptase and RNase activity |
| | p 51 | Reverse transcriptase activity. |
| | p 10 | Cleaves *gag* precursor |
| | p 32 | Integrase function |
| *tat* | p 14 | Activates transcription of Provirus |
| *rev* | p 19 | Splicing of m RNA |
| *nef* | p 27 | Down regulation of host cell class I MHC and CD4 |
| *vpu* | p 16 | Viral assembly, budding and release of viral particles, Degrades CD4 and ER. |
| *vif* | p 23 | Maturation and ineffectivity of viral particles |
| *vpr* | p 15 | Promotes nuclear localization and pre integration complex and also inhibits cell division |

4. Within the envelope is the viral core or nucleocapsid, which is icosahedral and includes a layer of protein called p17 and an inner layer of a protein called p24. The viral genome is enclosed by this nucleocapsid.
5. HIV-1 genome consists of two copies of single stranded RNA.
6. The RNA is associated with some structural proteins, such as, p7, p9, p24 and also some enzymes such as two molecules of reverse transcriptase (p64), nucleoid proteins, a protease (p10) and an integrase enzyme (p32).

**Genetic organization of HIV**

There are nine genes in an HIV. The three major genes are *gag, pol* and *env*, which encode polyproteins and finally it is cleaved to yield nucleo-capsid core protein, enzymes required for replication and envelope core proteins.

Of the remaining six genes, three (*tat, rev* and *nef*) encode regulatory proteins, two (*vif.* and *vpu*) encode virion maturation proteins and one (*vpr*) encodes transcriptional activator. Besides, at the both ends two LTR segments (Fig. 12.18).

HIV-2 and SIV genomes are similar but *vpu* gene is replaced by *vpx*.

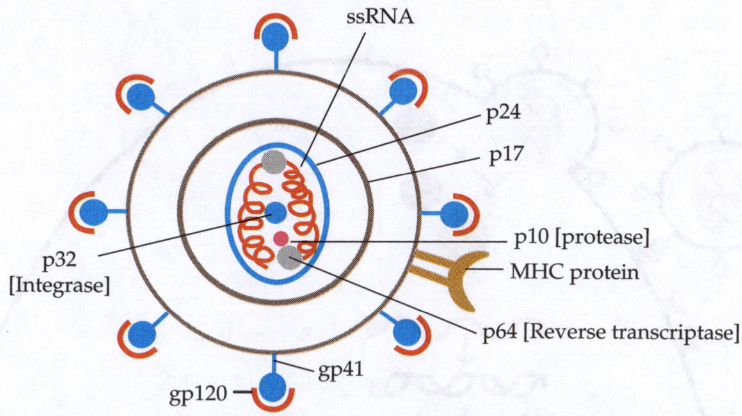


Fig.12.17 : *Structure of HIV*

## HIV-Replication Cycle

**1. Infection to the host cell :** At first, HIV is attached to a molecule called CD4 (cluster differentiation) that is present on the surface of the T-cell. Proteins on the exterior envelope of the virus bind tightly to the CD4 molecules (Klatzmann *et. at* 1984, Maddon *et al* 1986). CD4 is the only receptor for the virus. The viral coat protein gp 120 ($V_3$ loop) recognizes and binds to the N-terminal end of CD4 molecules on the host cell surface (Fig. 12.19).

Althought, the virus binds to CD4 on the cell surface, this interaction is not surfficient for entry and productive infection. The infection of a T-cell is assisted by the T-cell receptor CXCR4 (fusin) and an analogous receptor called CCR5 functions for the monocytes or macrophages. These two serve as coreceptors for HIV-1 on T-cells and macrophages respectively. Some strains of HIV-1 preferentially infect T-cells, called T-tropic strain, uses CXCR 4 while other is M-tropic strain uses CCR5. These two coreceptors function as receptors of chemokines (their normal ligands). These chemokines compete with the virus to bind with these receptors. Thus chemokines can block the viral entry into the host cell. Thus the funsogenic domain of gp 41 and CXCR-4, a G-protein -

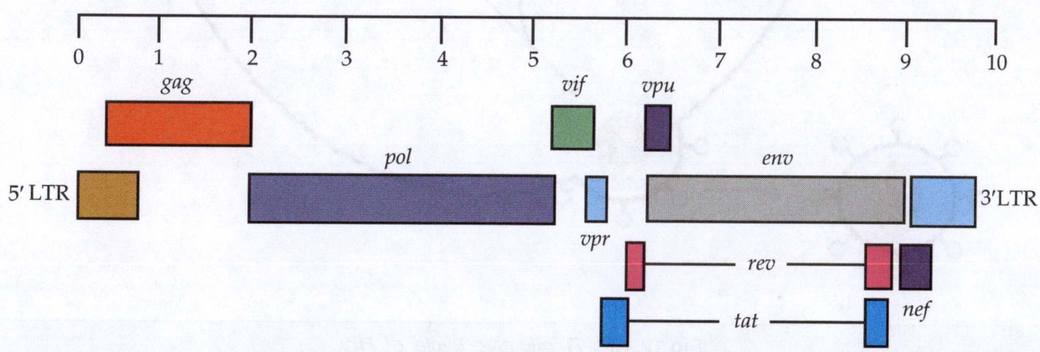


Fig.12.18 : *Genetic organization of HIV-1*

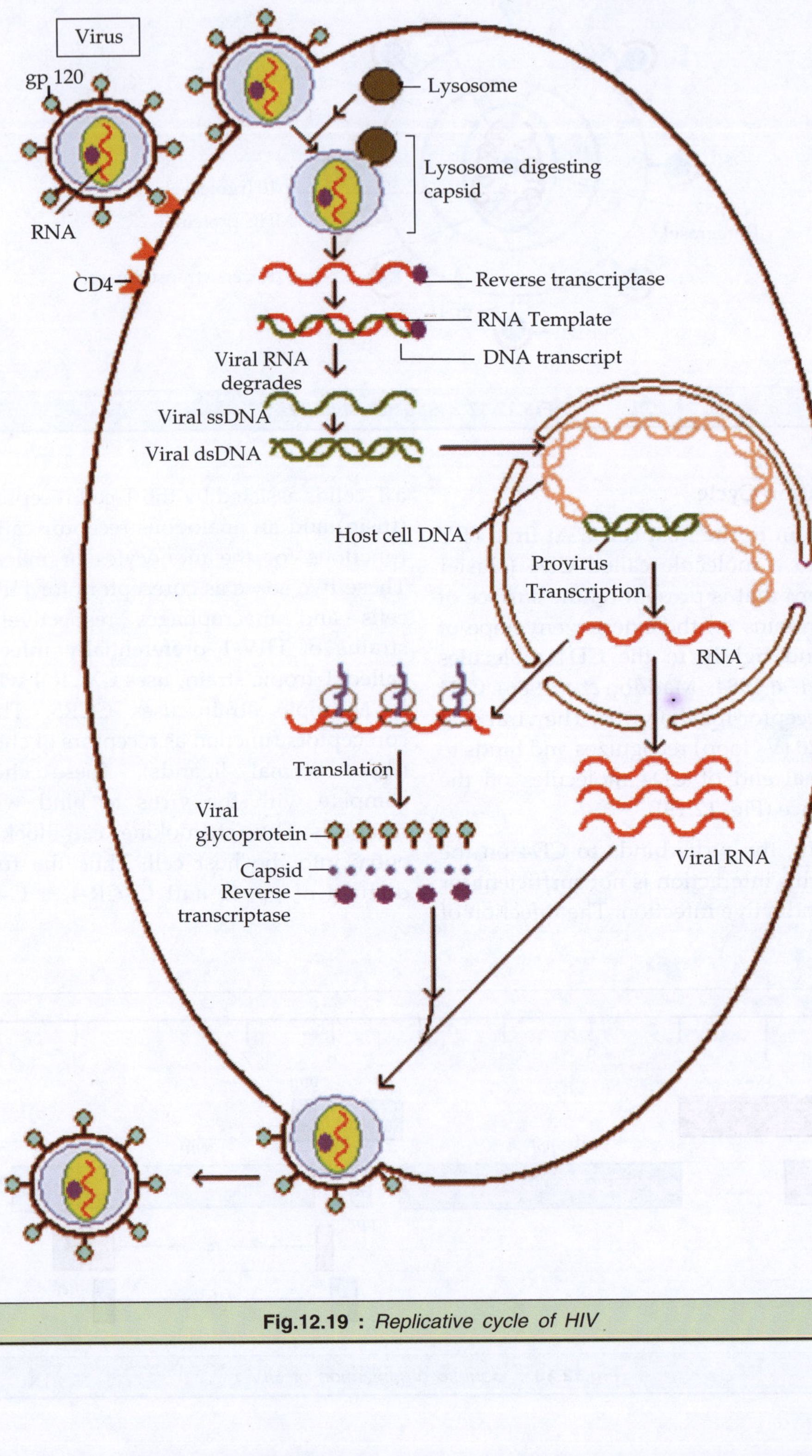


**Fig.12.19 :** *Replicative cycle of HIV*

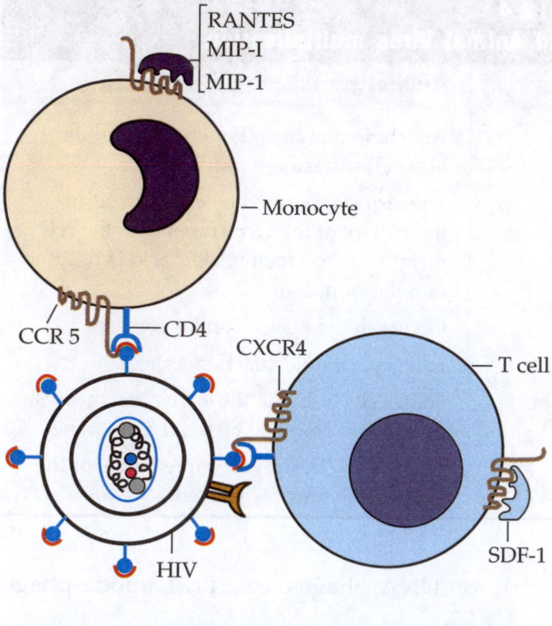


**Fig.12.20 :** *T-cell-topic strain and Macrophage-topic strain of HIV-1 use different coreceptors*

linked receptor in target cell membrane mediate the fusion (Fig. 12.20).

The virus envelope fuses with the T-cell's plasma membrane, releasing the capsid into the cell. A lysosome digests away the capsid and the active RNA core is freed in the cytoplasm along with enzymes.

**2. Reverse transcription :** After entry into the cell, HIV hijacks the cell's genetic machinary. Using this genetic machinery the enzyme reverse transcriptase, HIV transcribes it's own genetic material ssRNA into RNA-DNA hybrid. Original RNA templet is then partially degraded by its own RNase-H component. It is followed by the synthesis of second DNA strand to yield a HIV dsDNA with the same enzyme with its DNA polymerase activity. The viral dsDNA is then translocated to the nucleus and integrated into the host chromosomal DNA by the viral integrase enzyme. This is called *provirus,* which contains the same genetic information as the viral RNA.

**3. Production of new virus particles :** The provirus is now located within the host cell's chromosome, where it may remain dormant for several years. When it is activated, the transcription factors stimulate transcription of proviral DNA into genomic ssRNA and after processing into several RNAs, viral RNA is then transported to the cytoplasm. Host cell ribosomes catalyze synthesis of viral precursor proteins. Viral protease cleaves these precursors into viral proteins.

**4. Release of new virus particles :** The viral proteins are assembled beneath the host cell's plasma membrane. The gp 120 and gp 41 glycoproteins are then inserted into it. The membrane buds out forming viral envelope. The released viral particles complete the maturation process. The incorporated precursor proteins are cleaved by viral protease present in viral particles.

## 12.4 GENOME OF BACTERIOPHAGES

Bacteriophages are viruses that grow in bacterial cells. A bacteriophage is an obligate bacterial parasite. By itself, a phage can persist, but it can not replicate except within a bacterial cell. Most phages possess genes encoding a variety of proteins. All known phages use the protein-synthesizing system, amino acids, an energy-generating systems of the host cell and hence a phage can multiply only in a bacterium (Fig. 12.21).

### 12.4.1 General properties of Phages

1. Protection of it's nucleic acid from environmental chemicals that could alter the molecule (*i.e.* mutation).
2. Delivery of the nucleic acid to the inside of a bacterium.
3. Conversion of an infected bacterium into a phage-producing system, which yields a large number of progeny phage.
4. Release of progeny phage from an infected bacterium.

**Types of Phages :** According to the composition of their nucleic acids as genetic material, phages are of different types.

| TABLE 12.4<br>Comparison of Bacteriophage and Animal Virus multiplication | | |
|---|---|---|
| | *Bacteriophage* | *Animal virus* |
| *Adsorption* | Precise attachment of tail fibre to the bacterial cell wall | Attachment of capsid or envelope to the host cell surface receptors. |
| *Penetration* | No uncoating event. Nucleic acid is directly injected into the host cell cytoplasm. | The virus is engulfed by endocytosis or the surface of the virus fuses with the cell membrane and then nucleic acid is released into the cytoplasm. |
| *Synthesis* | Occurs in the cytoplasm. | Occurs in the nucleus and cytoplasm. |
| *Viral persistence* | Lysogeny | Latency, chronic infection, cancer. |
| *Release from the host cell* | Viral enzymes weaken the wall of the host cell and then it releases. | Some cells lyse. But the enveloped viruses budded off from the host cell membrane. |
| *Cell destruction* | Cell is destroyed immediately | Cell may be destroyed immediately or the destruction may be delayed. |

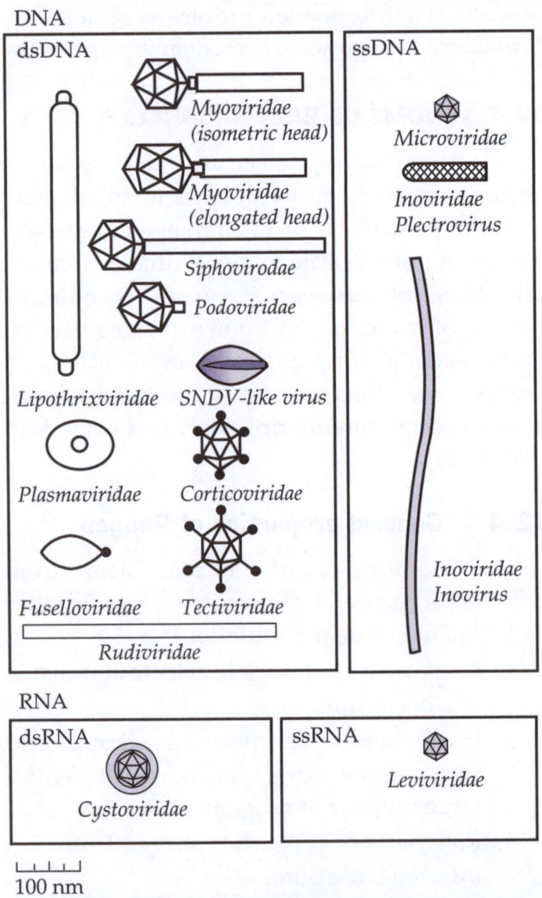


**Fig.12.21 :** *Different types of bacteriophages and their structure*

1. ds DNA phages. eg., T1, Lambda-phage, L2
2. ss DNA phages, eg. MV-L51, M13, fd
3. ss RNA phages, eg. R17, MS2, Qβ
4. dsRNA phages, eg. ϕ6 phage (Table 12.4)

## 12.4.2 dsDNA Phages

- **T4 Genome Organization and replication**

In T4 phage, 200 genes have been identified which accounts for 90% of the DNA.

T4 genes can be divided into two classes : 82 metabolic genes and 53 particle-assembly genes.

(a) Only 22 metabolic genes are involved in DNA synthesis, transcription and lysis. The remaining 60 metabolic genes duplicate bacterial genes.

(b) 34 assembly genes code for structural proteins and 19 code for the synthesis of enzymes and protein factors which are required catalytically for assembly (Fig. 12.22).

T4 DNA differs from typical DNA molecules in that it contains no cytosine. Instead a modified base, 5, hydroxymethylcytosine (HMC) pairs with guanine. Various glucose-like

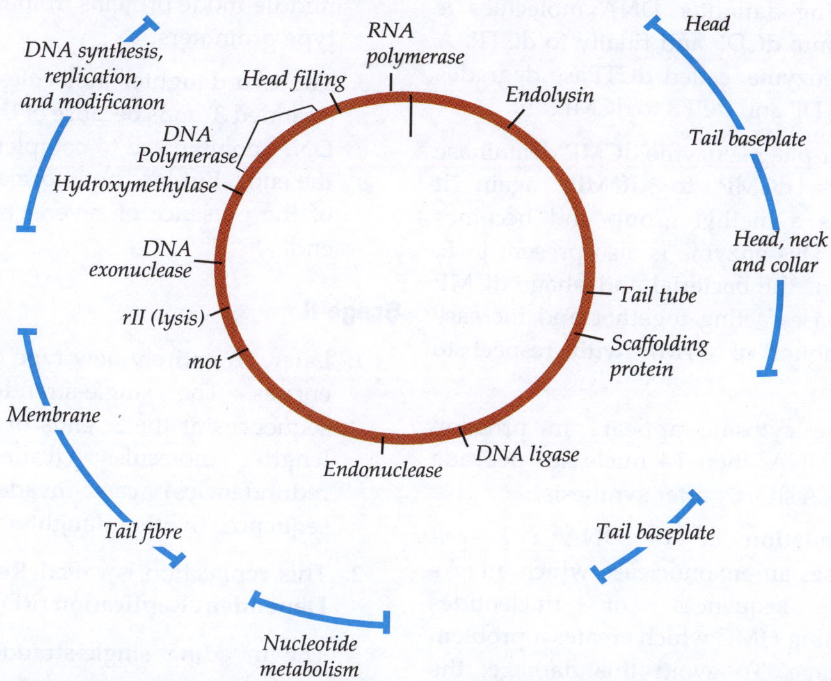


**Fig.12.22 :** *A map of T4 phage genome*

sugars covalently linked to it, so T4 is covered with sugar chain. Therefore glucosylation of HMC is essential for its life cycle (Fig. 12.23).

**Characteristics of Replication in T4 phage**

1. **Degradation of host DNA :** At first host DNA is degraded into deoxynucleotide monophosphates (dNMP). The enzyme is active only on cytosine-containing DNA. These are then degradeed to dNMP by phage coded exonuclease. These are then utilized for the synthesis of dNTPs by *E. coli* enzymes.
2. **Synthesis of HMC :** Two phage enzymes convert dCMP to dHDP. Then the *E. coli* enzymes nucleotide triphosphate kinases convert dHDPs into dHTPs, the immediate precursor of the HMC in the DNA.
3. **Prevention of incorporation of cytosine to T4 DNA :** T4 DNA polymerase cannot distinguish dCTP from dHTP. Therefore both dCTP and dHTP are incorporated into daughter T4 DNAs. But the T4 phage enzymes nuclease degrades cytosine

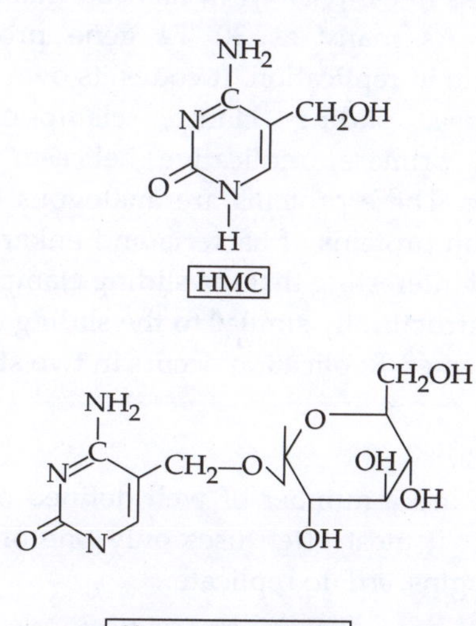


**Fig.12.23 :** *Structure of HMC and glucosylated HMC.*

containing daughter DNA molecules *ie* dCMP into dCDP and finally to dCTP. A phage enzyme, called dCTPase degrades both dCDP and dCTP to dCMP.

Another phage enzyme dCMP deaminase converts dCMP to dUMP; again it acquires a methyl group and becomes dTMP. This enzyme is also present in *E. coli.* Thus the bacterial and phage dCMP deaminases acting together and increase the amount of dTMP with respect to dCMP.

If some cytosine appears in progeny phage DNA, then T4 nucleases degrade this DNA shortly after synthesis.

4. **Glucosylation of T4 DNA :** *E. coli* possesses an enxonuclease which attacks certain sequences of nucleotides containing HMC which creates a problem for phage. To avoid this damage, the HMC residues in T4 DNA are glucosylated and two glucoses are added to HMC in the DNA by two *E. coli* enzymes. Thus T4 DNA becomes protected.

**Mechanism of Replication in T4 phage**

T4 has linear dsDNA in its head that never cyclizes. As many as 30 T4 gene products participate in replication. It codes its own DNA polymerase, sliding clamp, clamp-loading proteins, primase, replicative helicase, DNA ligase etc. These proteins are analogous to the replication proteins of bacteria and eukaryotes. It is most interesting that the sliding clamp of T4 is more structurally similar to the sliding clamp of eukaryotes. Replication occurs in two stages.

### Stage I

1. T4 has a number of well defined origins but it most often uses only one of these origins, *oriE* to replicate.
2. An RNA primer is synthesized on the origin using the host RNA polymerase. These primer RNAs may synthesize middle-mode proteins from middle-mode type promoters.
3. The two daughter molecules have single stranded 3′ ends because of the inability of DNA polymerase to completely replicate the ends. But lose no information because of the presence of several repeats at the end.

### Stage II

1. Later, an entirely new type of replication ensues. The single-stranded repeated sequences at the 3′ ends of the genome-length molecules (called terminal redundancies) can invade the same sequences in other daughter DNAs.
2. This replication is called **Recombination Dependent Replication** (RDR).
3. The invading single-stranded 3′ end is created and invaded into the complementary double stranded DNA forming a three-stranded D-loop. This pairing of the invading strand with complementary strand is promoted by the T4 *uvs* X gene product which is analogous to RecA of *E.coli.*
4. The single stranded T4 DNA coated with gp32.
5. The UvsX protein might be needed a protein UvsY to displace gp32 protein.
6. Once D-loop is formed, gp41 helicase is loaded on the DNA by gp59.
7. The invading 3′ end of DNA now acts as the primer end for the extension and synthesis of DNA as loading strand synthesis. The displaced strand is loaded by primase gp62 and undergone lagging strand synthesis.
8. When replication from defined origins has ceased, there are no double-stranded ends, the recombination is initiated by other proteins gp17 and gp49, that break the DNA and create ends of single-

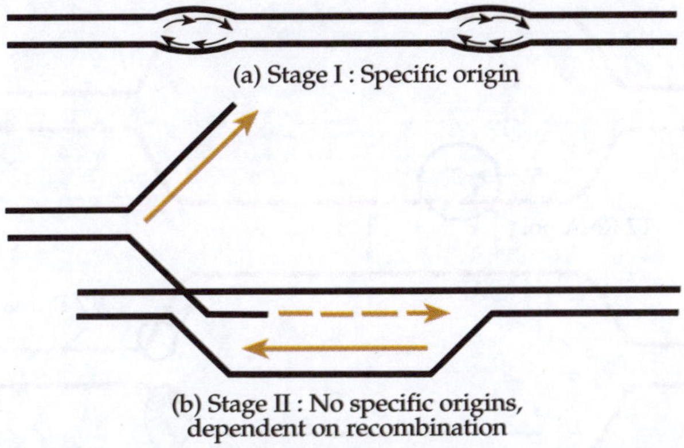


**Fig.12.24 :** *Initiation of replication of T4 phage DNA.*

stranded invasion and the process is continued.

Thus, a very branched concatemer is produced after replication.

**Packaging of DNA from Concatemers**

1. Packaging is initiated by cutting the DNA by a terminase complex which remains attached to the end.
2. This complex is then bound to the head at the opening called the portal and the DNA begins to be sucked into the head.
3. As the concatemer is a branched structure, the problem arises during the process. This is solved by the gp 49 which is an X-phile capable of cutting Holliday junctions and the DNA with branches.

The details of RDR are still being uncovered (Fig. 12.24).

**●● T7 genome organization and replication**

1. T7 phage has a simple programme of gene expression after infection with only two classes of genes, the early and late genes.
2. The phage has about 50 genes. After infection, expression of genes proceeds from left to right, with the genes on the extreme left of the genetic map, up to and including gene 1.3 expressed first. These are the early genes.
3. The genes to the right of the 1.3, the middle, DNA metabolism and late phage assembly genes are transcribed (Fig. 12.25).
4. The early gene products are responsible for turning on the late genes.
5. Product of gene-1 is an RNA polymerase that recognizes the promoters used to transcribe the late genes. The promoter

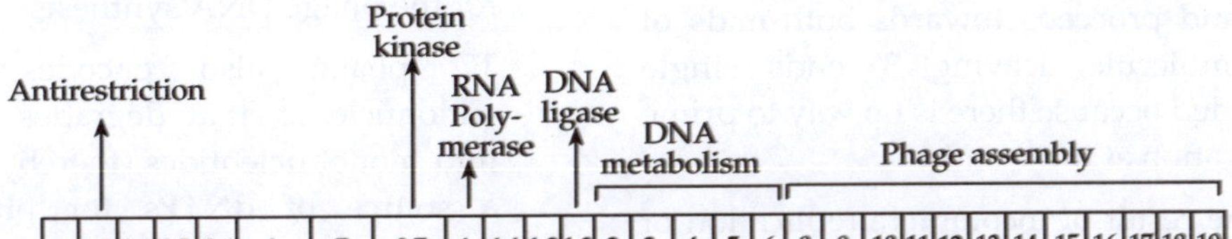


**Fig.12.25 :** *Genetic map of phage T7*

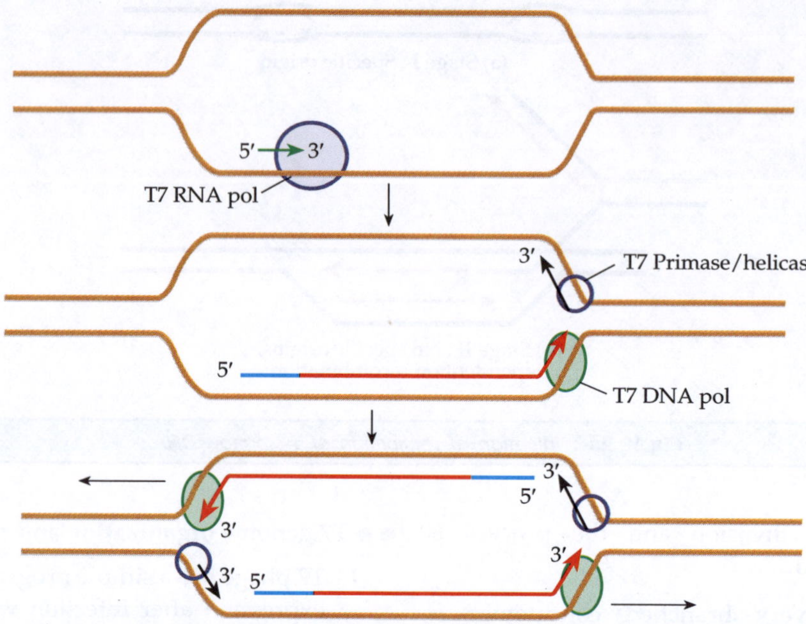


**Fig.12.26 :** *Initiaiton of DNA replication at the left-ward T7 promoter.*

sequences differ greatly from those recognised by bacterial RNA polymerases and so these phage promoters are recognised only by this T7 specific RNA polymerase.

6. Like T4 phage, T7 phage never cyclizes their DNA but forms concatemer, composed of individual genome-length DNAs linked end to end. The phage DNA then be cut out of these concatemers so that no information is lost when the phage DNA is packaged (Fig. 12.26 & 12.27).

**Replication :**

1. Replication of T7 begins at a unique *ori* site and proceeds towards both ends of the molecule, leaving 3′ ends single stranded because there is no way to prime replication at these ends.
2. As the result of incomplete replication of the 3′ ends and complete replication of 5′ end of the other daughter DNA molecule, and due to possession of same sequences at both ends, these single strands are complementary to each other and so can pair, forming a concatemer with the genomes linked end to end.
3. Individual molecules are then cut out of the concatemers at the unique *pac* sites at the ends of the T7 DNA and packaged into phage heads.
4. T7 encodes many of its own replication functions, including DNA polymerase, DNA ligase, DNA helicase and primase.
5. T7 phage RNA polymerase is also required to synthesize the initial primer for the phage DNA synthesis.
6. T7 phage also encodes a DNA endonuclease, that degrades host DNA into mononucleotides, thereby providing a source of dNTPs for phage DNA replication.
7. Host enzyme DNA ligase can substitute the phage DNA ligase.

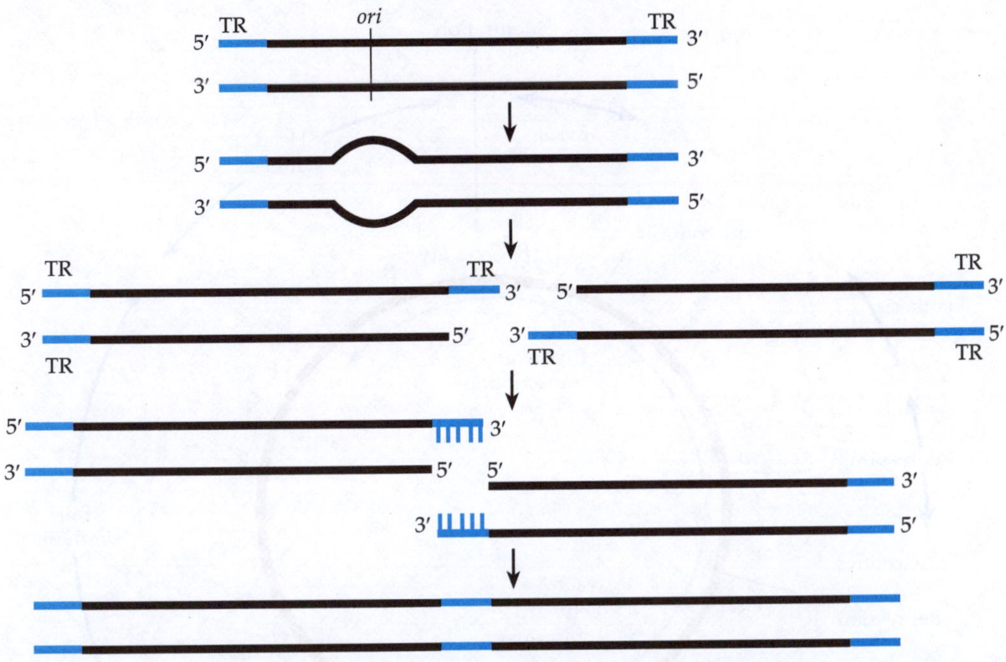


**Fig.12.27 :** *Replication of phage T7 DNA*
*ori = origin of replication ; TR = Terminally repeated end*

### ●●● Lambda Phage genome organization :

Lambda phage belongs to the family Siphoviridae, is a temperate phage uses the K12 strain of *E. coli* as its host (Fig. 12.28).

1. Lambda phage is a double-stranded DNA phage possessing an icosahedral head 55 nm in diameter and a non-contractile tail with a thin tail fibre at its end.
2. DNA is a linear molecule with two cohesive ends having a stretch of 12 nucleotides long single stranded 5′ overhang. The two ends are so complementary that, the linear genome cyclizes immediately just after infection.
3. The genome of lambda phage has been mapped to have 40 genes and most genes are clustered to function for the synthesis of head, tail and also for replication and cell lysis.
4. *pL* and *pR* are the two promoters where RNA polymerase can bind to transcribe leftward and rightward directions respectively.
5. Lytic cycle is controlled by two regulatory proteins coded by leftward gene *N* and rightward genes *cII* and *cro*.
6. The *lambda repressor* coded by *cI* is synthesized continuously and binds to the operators *oL* and *oR* and thereby blocking RNA polymerse activity and then mRNA synthesis is inhibited.

### Genetics of lytic-lysogenic pathway in lambda phage

The Lambha phage makes a decession to follow either the lytic or the lysogenic pathway.

If the lysogenic state continues over a long time, a stable lysogen is established and the prophage is integrated to the host genome. It turns off the expression of the lytic genes.

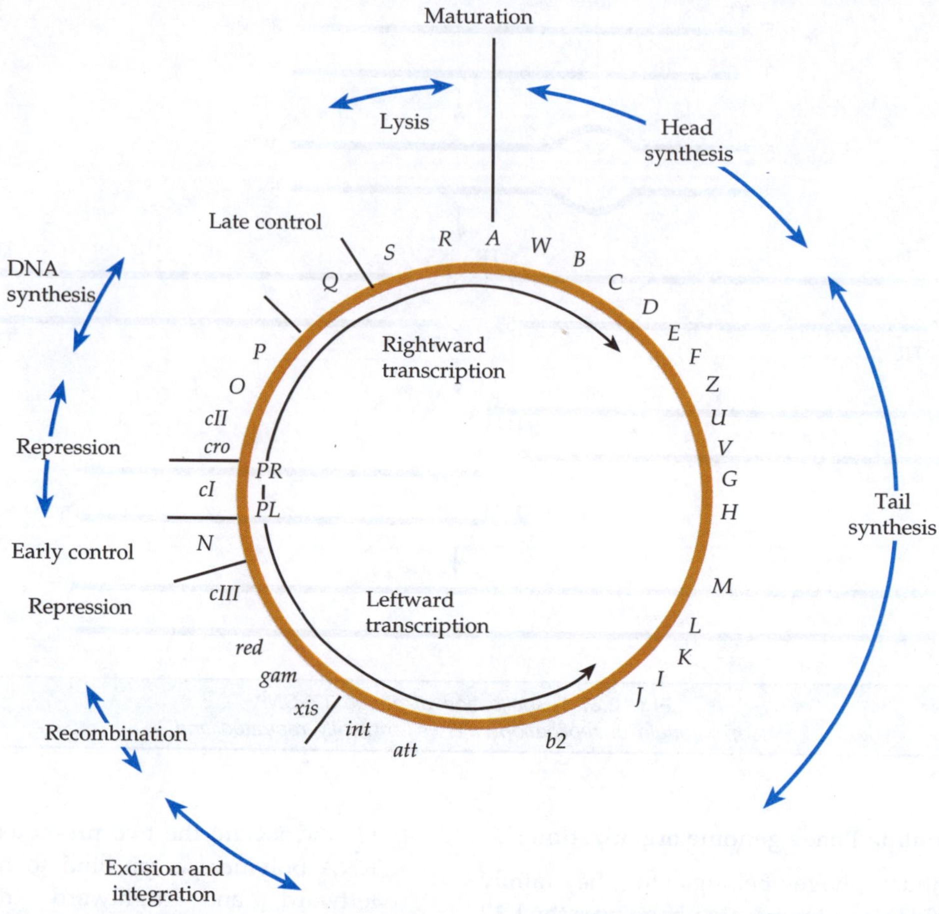


Fig.12.28 : *A map of Lambda phage genome.*

Inducing signals, like UV light that damage the DNA, force the lambda phage to a SOS response and the lysogenic state switches irreversively to the lytic phage. It replicates its DNA automatically, expresses a set of genes and assembles the virion resulting in lysis of the host.

A number of genes ***cl, cll, clll*** and ***cro***; a number of operators ***oL*** (*left-ward*), ***oR*** (*right-ward*) and a number of promoters $P_L$, $P_R$, $R_{RE}$ and $P_{RM}$ are responsible for lytic-lysogenic states of the lambda phage cycle.

The operators ***oL*** and ***oR*** can be subdivided into ***oL1, oL2, oL3*** and ***oR1, oR2, oR3***. Affinity of binding **CI** repressor protein to ***oL1>oL2*** and ***oR1>oR2*** is cooperative, but binding to ***oL3*** and ***oR3*** is noncooperative. On the other hand, affinity of **CRO** repressor to ***oL*** and ***oR*** is opposite to that of **Cl**.

The promoter $P_R$ drives to transcription of lytic genes and relative excess of **CRO** produces right-ward transcription. The promoter $P_{RM}$ drives trasnscription of ***cl*** gene and excess **Cl** repressor, represses the right-ward transcription of lytic gene.

$P_R$ is stronger than $P_{RM}$ (Fig. 12.29).

**A. Mechanism of Establishment of Lysogeny**

1. Infection of the cell by the phage
2. Lysogeney is dependent partly by nutritional states.

   When starved, phage has made enough Cll, activates $P_{RE}$ and $P_{int}$.
3. Cll induces Cl synthesis by $P_{RE}$. Cl favours lysogenic path and turns off *cro* gene to prevent lytic cycle.
4. Cll induces $P_{int}$ for *INT* and *XIS* gene transcription and synthesis of INT and XIS. INT induces integration of phage genome
5. At high multiplicity of infection, Clll is made from leftward transcript. Clll prevents degradation of Cll by FtsH.

**B. Maintenance of lysogeny :**

1. Synthesis of $P_{RM}$ mRNA continues throughout successive generations and translates sufficient Cl repressor protein to repress prophage.
2. Cl binds to *oL1, oR1,* then to *oL2, oR2* and its concentration reaches too high to bind *oL3, oR3,* repressing $P_L$ *and* $P_R$ completely (Fig. 12.30).
3. Thus Cl repressor synthesis is maintained and stable lysogeny is established.

**C. Entry into Lytic cycle :**

1. Entry into lytic cycle requires the CRO protein, which is a repressor synthesised by *cro* gene from right-ward $P_R$ promotor.
2. Once the CRO protein is synthesised, it binds to *oL3* preventing activation of $P_{RM}$ shuts off Cl synthesis but allows more $P_L$ and $P_R$ transcription.
3. It causes excision of viral DNA from bacetrial chromosome and a lytic cycle yields.

**TABLE 12.4**
**Regulatory proteins and their functions in lytic-lysogenic cycle of lambda phage**

| *Protein* | *Function* |
|---|---|
| Cl | At low concentrations a repressor of $P_L$ *and* $P_R$, an activator of $P_{RM}$<br>At low concentrations also represses $P_{RM}$ |
| Cll | An activator of $P_{RM}$ and $P_{int}$ |
| Clll | Prevents degradation of Cll by the enzyme FstH |
| CRO | At low concentrations a repessor of $P_{RM}$ |
| | At high concentrations also represses $P_L$ and $P_R$ |
| $P_L$ | Major leftward transcription |
| $P_R$ | Major rightward transcription |
| $P_{RE}$ | Transcription for repressor establishment |
| $P_{RM}$ | Transcription of repressor maintenance |
| $P_{int}$ | Transcription of genes for integration and excision. |

### 12.4.3 ssDNA Phages

- **ϕ × 174 genome organization and replication**

The ϕ (Greek letter *phi*) in ϕ × 174 refers to phage; the X is the Roman numerical 10; race 'X' bacteriophage was unusually small, as determined by ultrafiltration, and the first isolate was placed in a test tube labeled 174.

The genome consisted of ssDNA. F. Sanger *et. al.* (1978) were the first to determine the nucleotide sequence of the entire genome of ϕ × 174. More recently, the atomic structure of the ϕ × 174 procapsid, an assembly intermediate containing a full complement of scaffolding proteins was solved in 1997 by collaborative effort of the laboratories of Michael Rossmann, Bently Fane and Nino Incardona.

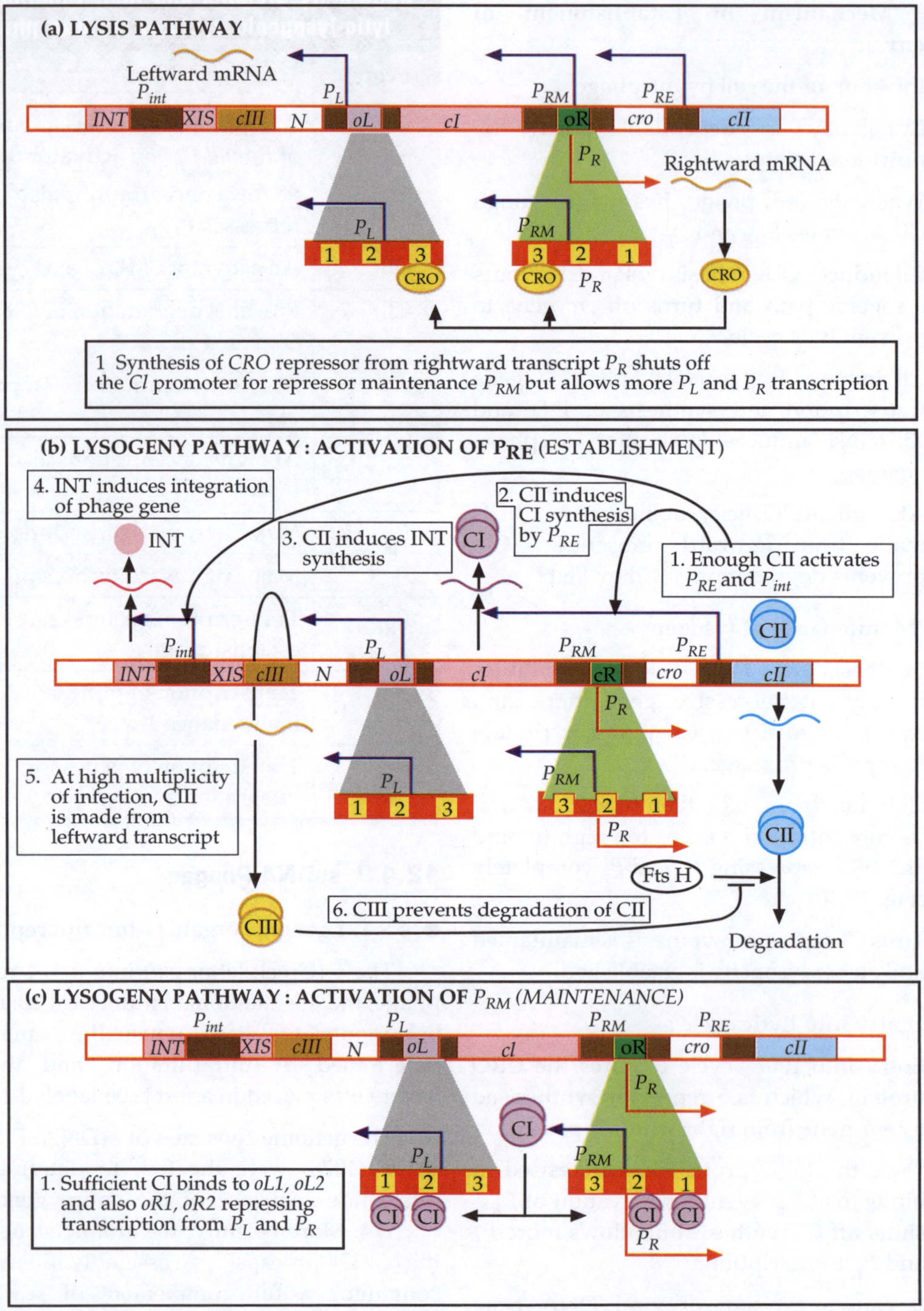


**Fig.12.29 :** *Lytic pathway and Lysogenic pathway in Lamda-phage.*

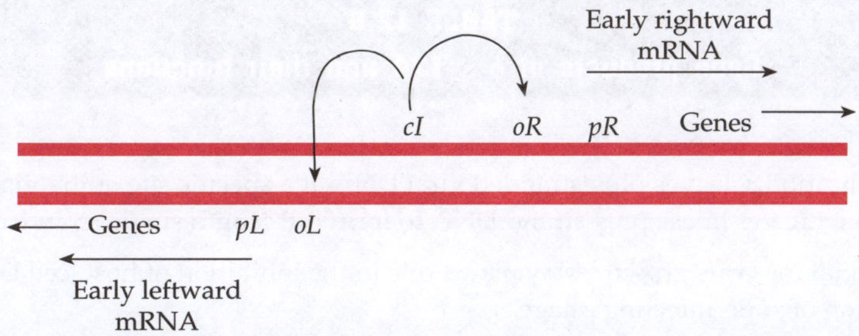


**Fig.12.30 :** *The repressor-operator system of λ-phage showing the early two mRNA molecules cl = repressor gene, p = promoter, o= operator, L = left , R= right.*

**TABLE 12.5**
**Selected Class I, II and III genes and their products of T7 phage**

| Gene | Function |
|---|---|
| **(a) Selected** | **Class I gene Products :** |
| 0.3 | Inhibits host type I restriction endonuclease |
| 0.7 | Inhibits *E. coli* RNA polymerase |
| 1.0 | T7 specific RNA polymerase |
| **(b) Selected** | **Class II gene products :** |
| 1.3 | DNA ligase, joins lagging-strand DNAs |
| 2. | Inhibits *E. coli* RNA polymerase |
| 2.5 | ssDNA binding protein |
| 3 | Endonuclease degrades host cell DNA and also cleaves T7 concatemers. |
| 3.5 | Lysozyme, inhibits T7 RNA polymerase |
| 4 | RNA primase/helicase, initiates lagging strand DNA synthesis |
| 5 | DNA polymerase |
| 6 | Exonuclease, degrades host cell DNA |
| **Selected** | **Class III gene products** |
| 8 | Portal transport, connector for tail |
| 9 | Scaffolding protein for formation of capsid |
| 10 | Capsid protein |
| 11 | Tail protein |
| 12 | Tail protein |
| 14, 15, 16 | Core protein, form channel for DNA |
| 17 | Tain fibre |
| 17.5 | Holin, access of lysozyme to cell wall for lysis |
| 18, 19 | Muturation proteins, DNA packaging |

**Structure :**

1. The icosahedral capsid contains 60 copies of viral capsid protein-F. Each large protrusion found at the 12 icosahedral vertices is composed of 5 copies of major spike protein-G and one copy of DNA pilot protein-H. Besides, there are 60 copies of DNA binding protein-J within virion.
2. $\phi \times 174$ phage DNA consists of 5386 nts, which can code 1896 amino acids, having a total weight of 200000 Da. But it has been found that DNA codes for the proteins of mol. wt. 250000 Da. The genes and their products are given in the (Table 12.6).
3. $\phi \times 174$ phage has 9 genes arranged *A-B-C-D-E-J-F-G-H* order, which can code 9 proteins.
4. It has been found that gene *B* (360 nts) is completely within gene *A* (1536 nts), Similarly gene *E* (273 nts) contained in gene *D*. Thus two larger genes *A* and *D* can code for four proteins.
5. Again, it has been observed that protein synthesized by gene *B* is not homologous to the proteins of gene *A* or as a shorter version of it, because the mRNAs are translated from different reading frames. Such a case is illustrated in the *D* and *E* genes

| TABLE 12.6<br>Gene products of $\phi \times 174$ and their functions | |
|---|---|
| *Protein* | *Functions* |
| A | DNA replication, Cleaves plus-stranded viral DNA at a specific site, initiating rolling circle replication. Ligates linear plus-strand DNA to form full-length single stranded circles. |
| A* | Not essential for virus growth. May play a role in the inhibition of host cell DNA replication and in exclusion of superinfecting phage. |
| B | Internal scaffolding protein, required for procapsid morphogenesis; 60 copies in procapsid. |
| C | DNA packaging, Binds to Stage II DNA replication complex, detecting commitment stage III replication and entry of plus-strand viral DNA into the procapsid. |
| D | External scaffolding protein, required for procapsid morphogenesis; 240 copies in procapsid. |
| E | Host cell lysis |
| F | Major capsid protein; 60 copies in virion. |
| G | Major spike protein; 60 copies in virion. |
| H | DNA pilot protein, required for DNA delivery; also called the minor spike protein; 12 copies in virion. |
| J | Small DNA-binding protein, needed for DNA packaging ; 60 copies in virion. |
| K | Not essential for virus growth. May play a role in the optimization of burst size in various hosts. |

Met Val Gene E

ooooo G T T T A T G G T A ooooo

Val Tyr Gly Gene D

6. Another interesting fact is that the termination codon of gene *D* and initiation codon of gene *J* overlap by one nucleotide only.

*D*-stop codon

T A A T G

*J*-start codon

7. The gene *A* overlaps with gene *A**, *B* and *K* (Fig. 12.31).

**Infection :**

1. $\phi \times 174$ attaches to host cell via sugar residues, most likely glucose, in the lipopolysaccharide that is the part of the outer membrane of Gram negative bacteria. This glucose is present on the major capsid protein F.
2. Genome DNA may be delivered into the host cell through the spike. Spike proteins G and H are also involved in the attachment to the host.
3. It is not clearly known that whether the second host cell receptor is required for penetration.
4. The tailless $\phi \times 174$ may roll along the cell surface until it finds a second receptor, which leads to delivery of the viral DNA directly into the cytoplasm. Penetration requires viral protein H, which is also called **pilot protein.**

**Replication :**

$\phi \times 174$ depends upon the host RNA polymerase to synthesize their mRNA, they must first make a double-stranded DNA before any viral genes can be transcribed. The dsDNA is called ***replicative form*** **(RF)** DNA, which is synthesized during Stage-I DNA replication. This RF DNA molecules are amplified via rolling circle mechanism during Stage II replication.

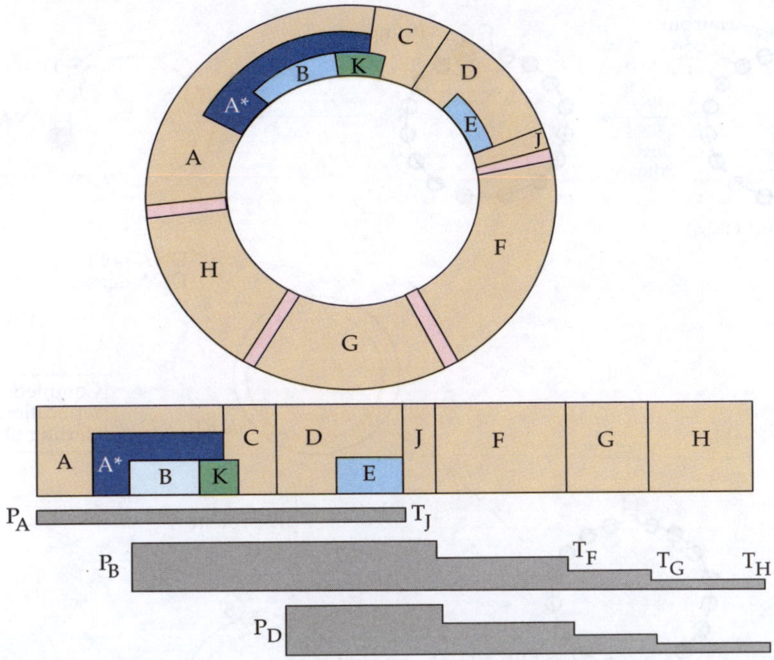


**Fig.12.31 :** *The $\phi \times 174$ genome*
*(a) map of genes on the circular DNA*
*(b) transcriptional map, P = promoter, T= terminator.*

**Stage I replication :**

1. Single-stranded DNA binding protein (SSB) coats the phage DNA except for a specific short highly base-paired hairpin region. This region serves as a signal for the assembly of a **primosome** by seven different host cell proteins called **Pri** .
2. Primosome includes, **DnaB**(helicase), **DnaC**, **Dna G**(primase) and other four proteins viz **PriA, PriB, PriC** and **DnaT.**
3. Helicase is required to open up the hairpin at unique origin of replication of ssDNA and move around the cirucular ssDNA.
4. Primase, one of the component of primosome enables to generate short complementary RNA primers at different locations around the ssDNA.
5. These primers are then extended by cellular DNA polymerase III to make a complete complementary copy of phage DNA. DNA polymerase-I then removes RNA primers and the gaps are filled by DNA ligase. This is RF DNA (Fig. 12.32).

**Stage II replication**

Stage II DNA replication amplifies the number of RF DNA molecules to about 10 per cell. This happens in two distinct steps. Replication occurs by rolling circle method.

1. The viral **"A" protein** cleaves the plus strand or RF DNA at a specific site and is covalently linked to the resulting 5′ end via a *tyrosine* residue in the protein. The host cell **rep** protein acts together with **protein "A"** as helicase and unwinds the dsDNA. Host cell DNA polymerase III extends the DNA and synthesizes more plus-strand DNA and eventually passing through the site where the A-protein originally cleaved the plus strand.

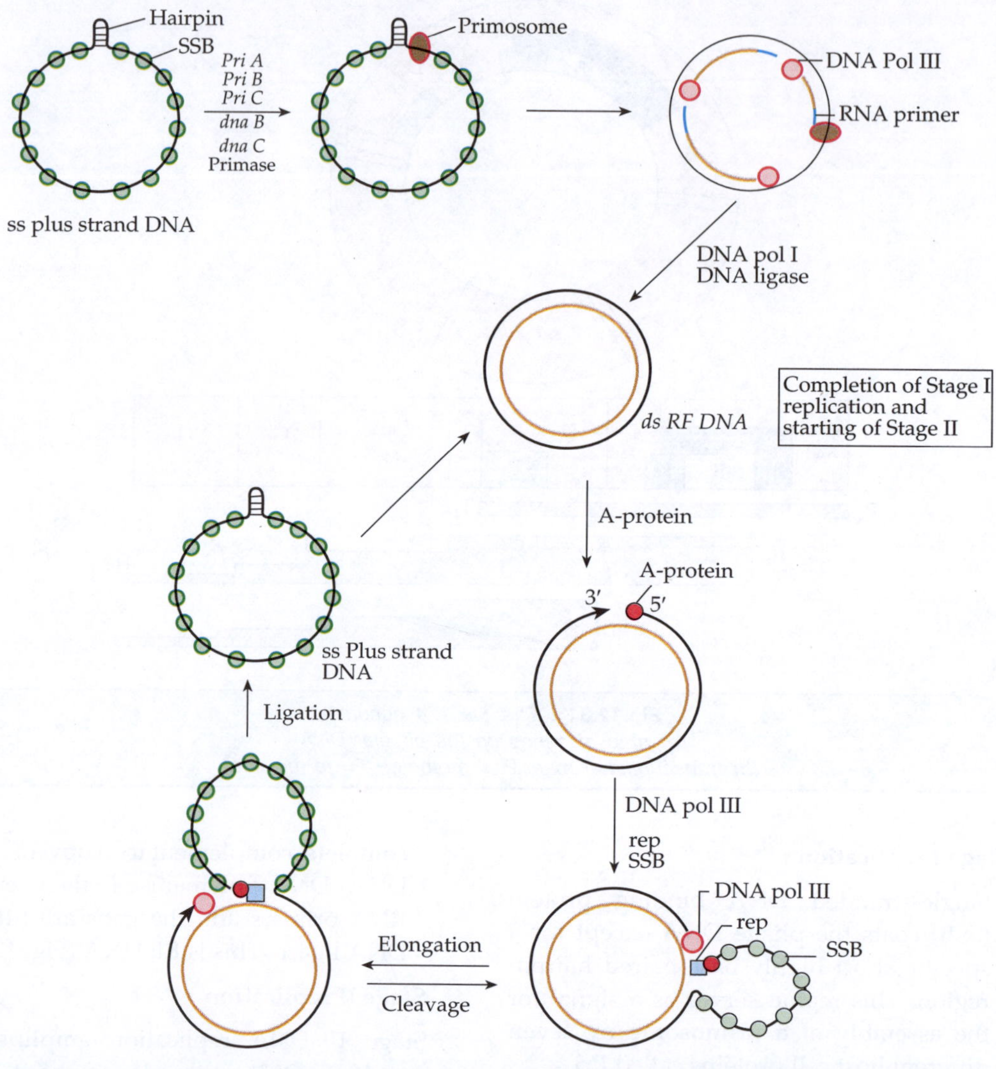


**Fig.12.32 :** *Stage I and stage II DNA replication of $\phi \times 174$*

2. After getting the full length of (+)strand, A-protein cleaves and ligates it to form a new plus (+) strand. This A-protein simultaneously is transferred to the newly formed 5′ end of the (+) strand DNA and starts replication again. Thus minus-strand continuously acts as a template (Fig. 12.33).

**Assembly of viral particle :**

1. The 9S particles are pentamers of the major capsid protein F and the 6S particles are pentamers of the major spike protein G.
2. When the internal scaffolding protein B is present, five copies will bind to the underside of a 9S particle, triggering conformational change on the supper side of the particle.

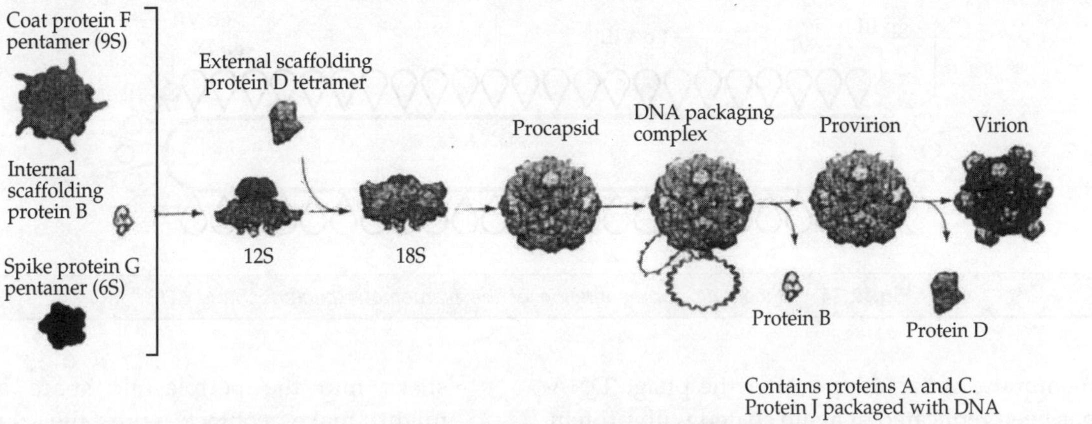


**Fig.12.33 :** *The $\phi \times 174$ morphogenetic pathway.*
*(Redrawn from Fundamentals of Molecular virology, by N.A. Acheson 1st edn. 2007)*

3. Such conformational changes allow the 9S capsid protein pentamers to interact with spike. The two pentamers are brought together forming the 12S particle.
4. The 18S particle results from the addition of 20 copies of the external scaffolding protein D. The scaffolding protein within 18S particles mediate inter-pentamer contacts. Thus 12 pentameric particles are organized into a procapsid.
5. The packaging is sometimes called **Stage III replication.** The viral C-protein redirects plus strand synthesis by binding to the replicative complex consisting a dsDNA.
6. The replication complex (A-protein, the rep preotien and DNA pol III) now associates with preformed procapsid as the DNA is displaced from the double-stranded template.
7. The J-protein binds to phage DNA being packaged and accompanies with it into the procapsid through the pore. During this packaging, B proteins are extruded from the procapsid probably through the same pores.
8. After a round of Stage III replication, viral A-protein cleaves the plus-strand and ligates the 3′ end with the 5′ end. The whole process is occurred in the procapsid.
9. The repication complex now binds another procapsid to synthesize and package another phage DNA. This is provirion.
10. After cell lysis, the influx of divalent cations probably dissociates the protein D yielding the virion.
11. E-protein is responsible for cell lysis, which inhibits the cell **MraY-protein**, which inhibits the the crosslinking of peptidoglycan.

### ●● M13 genome organization and replication

M13 and f1 are referred to as *filamentous phages* as the phages have a single layer of protein, cevering the extended DNA molecule, making the phages filamentous in appearance.

M13 and other filamentous phages are male-specific phages because they specifically adsorb to the sex pilus, encoded by certain plasmids and so infect only "male" strains of bacteria.

The entire phage is ingested by the cell and the protein coat is removed from the DNA as the phage passes through the inner cytoplasmic

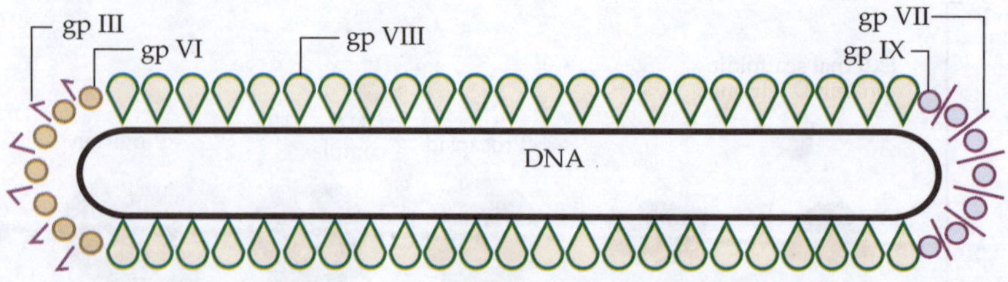


**Fig.12.34 :** *Schematic representation of the filamentous bacteriophage M13*

membrane of bacterium. After the phage DNA has been replicated, it again coated with protein as it leaks back out through the cytoplasmic membrane. These phages do not lyse infected cells and leak out only slowly. The cells infected with M13 or other filamentous phages are "chronically" rather than "acutely" infected. These chronically infected cells grow more slowly than unifected cells (Fig. 12.34).

**Structure :**

M13 phage has a single stranded circular DNA coated with five viral proteins. The gpVIII protein is present at about 2700 copies, while gp III, gp VI, gp VII and gp IX are presents about 5-copies each. All of the coat proteins can be used as platforms for protein display. With the exception of gp III, the capsid proteins are small, with 33 to 112 amino acids. pVII and pIX are located on one end of the phage, and the other two pVI and pIII are on the other end.

**Role of these proteins in infection cycle :**

Infection cycle of M13 is similar to f1 phage.

1. To start the infection, pIII protein on one end of the phage first makes contact with the end of the sex pilus.
2. Sex pilus makes a good contact point because it sticks to the cell and hence is very accessible.
3. The pilus retracts when the phage binds to it, drawing the phage to the cell surface.
4. A different region of the same pIII protein then contacts a host inner membrane proteins called TolA. This TolA protein sticks into the periplasmic space and might make contact with the outer membrane.
5. Phage DNA then enters the cytoplasm while the major coat protein is stripped off into the host inner membrane.
6. Phage is ssDNA, which enters into rolling circle stage of replication. As it rolls off the circle, the newly synthesized ssDNA is coated with pV and waiting in the membrane.
7. The major head protein, gpVII replaces the pV on the DNA as it enters the membrane. Only the DNA containing the *pac* site of the phage is packaged.
8. Other phage proteins gpVII and pIX are then added to the particle.
9. Meanwhile, the phage-encoded secreting protein pIV has formed a channel in the outer membrane, through which the assembled phage can pass (Fig. 12.35).

## Replication of ssDNA Phage M13

1. **Formation of replicative form :** The DNA strand of the phage, encapsidated in the phage head is called (+) stand. Immediately after the single stranded (+) strand DNA enters the cell, a complementary (–) strand is synthesized on the (+) strand to form a double stranded DNA called the **replicative form (RF).** The formation of first RF is dependent entirely on host functions. The synthesis of complementary strand is primed by an RNA

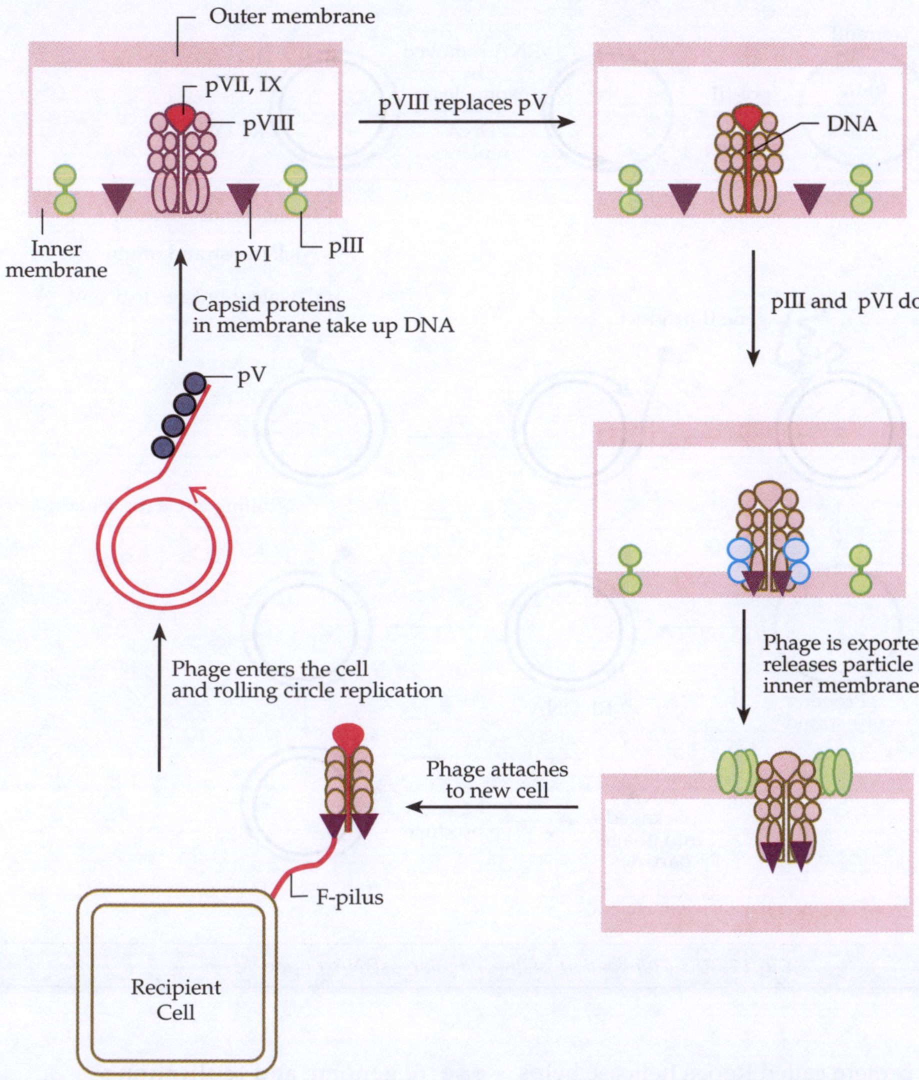


**Fig.12.35 :** *Infection cycle of the ssDNA phage f1 as well as M13 phages.*

made by normal host RNA polymerase. ssDNA forms a hairpin at the origin of replication making a dsDNA strand in that region.

Once the RNA primer is synthesized, the DNA polymerase III and accessory proteins help to synthesize a complementary strand to make a complete circle and encounter the RNA primer.

The 5′ exonuclease activity of DNA polymerase-I then removes the RNA primer. The nick is then sealed by DNA ligase. Thus a double stranded RF is formed.

2. **Synthesis of more RFs :** Once the first RF is synthesized, more RFs are made by semiconservative mode of replication which requires phage proteins.

First a nick is made in the RF at the region of (+) strand by a specific endonuclease synthesized by gene II of M13 and attached to the 5′ end of the DNA at the nick.

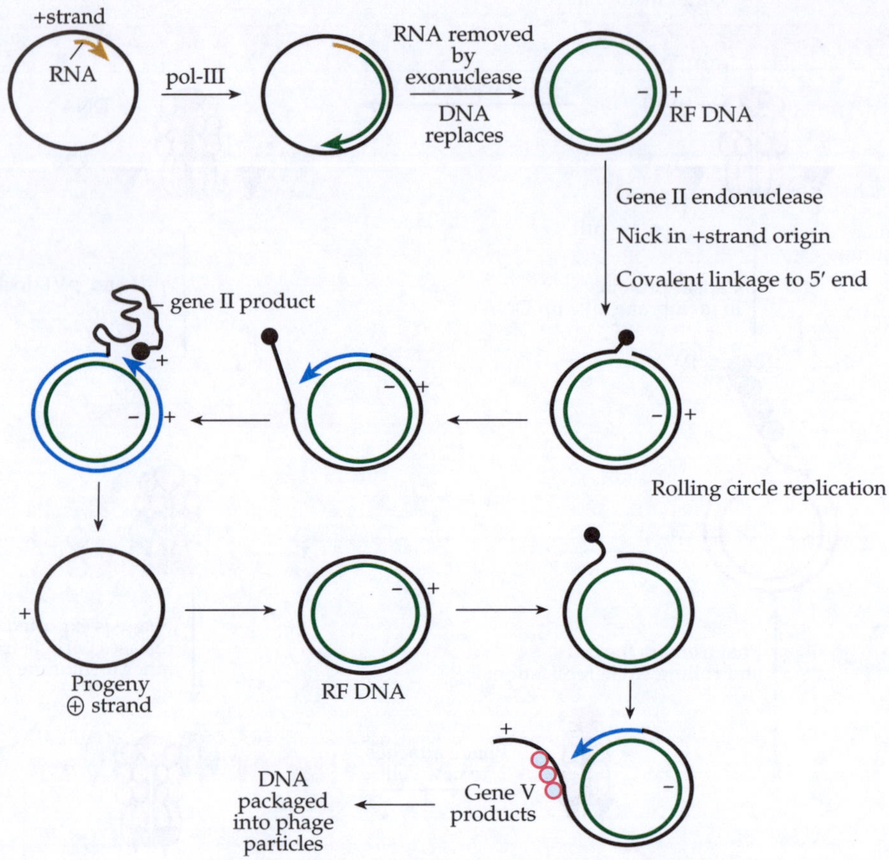


**Fig.12.36 :** *Replication of the circular ssDNA phage M13*

The host protein called Rep, a helicase helps unwind the DNA at the nick.

DNA polymerase III and the accessory proteins extend the 3′ end to synthesize more (+) strands, displacing the old (+) strands.

The gene II protein which is still attached with the 5′ end of the old displaced strand then reseals the ends of the displaced strand by transesterification reaction in which the phosphate attached to its *tyrosine* of gene II product is passed back to the free 3′ end of the old strand. This recyclizes the old (+) end, which can again serve as the template for (–) strand synthesis to create a new RF (Fig. 12.36).

### ●●● *fd* genome and replication :

It belongs to the family Inoviridae. This is filamentous about 6 nm diameter by 900-1900 nm in length.

The circular ssDNA lies in the centre of the filament and it surrounded by a tube made of a small coat protein organized into a helical arrangement.

The phage infects male *E. coli* cells by attaching to the tip of the pilus.

The DNA enters the host along or possibly through pilus with the aid of a special adsorption protein .

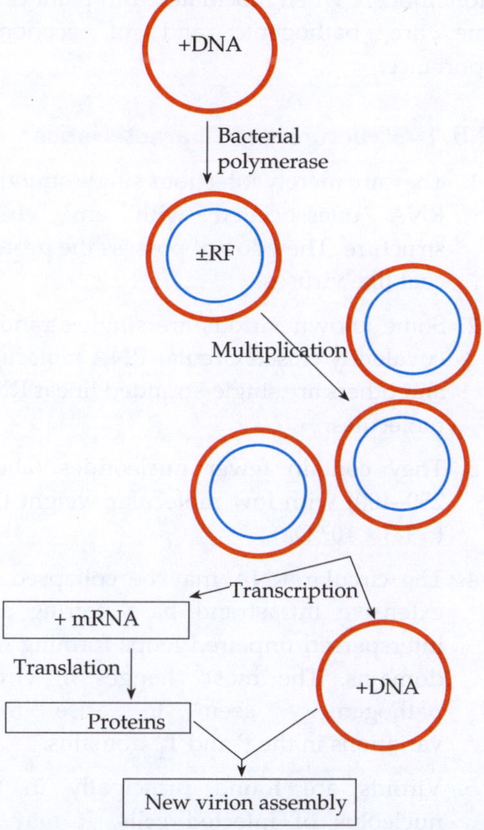


**Fig.12.37 :** *Replicative cycle of ssDNA phages*

A replicative form is synthesized and then transcribed. The phage coated protein then aids in replication of phage DNA by using the rolling circle method.

This phage does not kill the host. Many particles are released as secretory process. The coat protein is first inserted to the membrane of the host cell. The coat is then assembled around the viral +DNA strand and then secreted through the host cell membrane (Fig. 12.37).

### 12.4.4 Reproduction of RNA phages

**• ssRNA phages**

ssRNA phages belong to the family Leviviridae, are small tailless icosahedral structures. They are nonenveloped with 26 nm particles. They have one molecule of linear ssRNA of 3400–4300 nts. Examples MS2 and Qβ. They attach to the F-pilus of their host *E. coli* and enter by an unknown mechanism.

They have only 3–4 genes and are genetically simplest phage known.

MS2 has one protein, which is involved in phage adsorption to the host cell and also for maturation of virion. The other three genes code for a coat protein, RNA replicase and cell lysis protein.

1. The ssRNA genome of phages acts as a messenger RNA which directs the synthesis of phage proteins as well as template for replication.
2. They synthesize first an enzyme called viral RNA replicase which is an RNA dependent RNA polymerase.
3. The ssRNA genome of the phage is termed as + strand. The replicase enzyme then copies the original +RNA strand to produce ±RNA which is called replicative form (RF) (Fig. 12.38)
4. Same replicase then uses this RF to synthesize thousand copies of +RNA molecules.
5. Some of the these + strands are used to made more ±RNA replicative forms in order to accelerate + RNA synthesis.
6. Other +RNA molecules act as mRNAs and direct synthesis of phage proteins.
7. Finally, +RNA strands are incorporated with the phage proteins to produce maturing phages.
8. After lysis of the cell the phages are released.

**• ds RNA phages :**

Till now only one dsRNA phage has been discovered from *Pseudomonas phaseolicola,* called phage f6.

It possesses a membraneous envelope. An icosahedral capsid is present within the

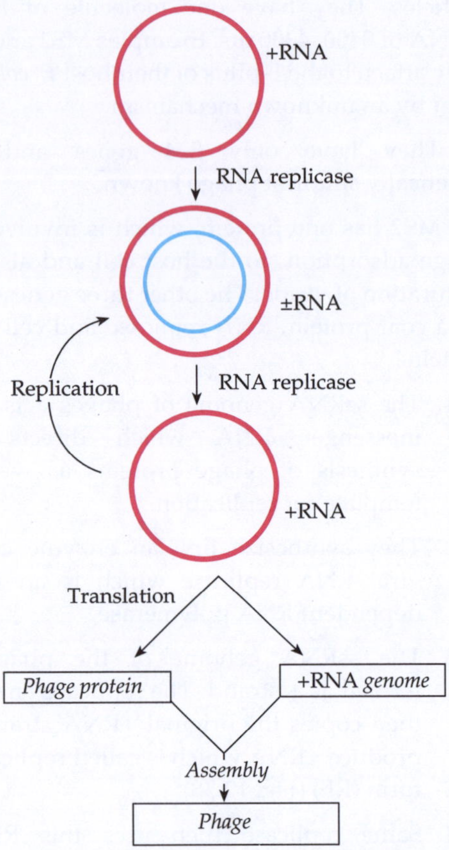


**Fig.12.38 :** *ssRNA phage replicative cycle*

envelope, which also contains an RNA polymerase and three dsRNA segments.

The genome has both + and – strands and directs the synthesis of mRNA. as well as proteins. The mechansim of its replication is not known.

## 12.5 GENOME OF VIROIDS

A class of simple infectious agents, termed as *viroids* were discovered in 1967. They cause 16 different important diseases of cultivated plants. Such diseases include potato spindle tuber, citrus exocortis, chrysanthemum stunt, cucumber pale fruit etc.

Viroids are unencapsidated, small circular, single-stranded RNAs that replicate autonomously when inoculated into plant cells; some are pathogenic and of economic importance.

### 12.5.1 Structure and Characteristics

1. They are merely infectious single stranded RNA unassociated with any virion structure. They do not possess the protein coat like viruses.
2. Some known viriods are single-stranded covalently closed circular RNA molecules and others are single-stranded linear RNA molecules.
3. They contain fewer nucleotides (about 250–400) with low molecular weight (1.1 to $1.3 \times 10^5$ Da)
4. The circular RNA may be collapsed by extensive intrastrand base pairing and interspersed unpaired loops forming five domains. The most changes in viroid pathogenicity seem to arise from variations in the P and $T_L$ domains.
5. Viroids are found principally in the nucleolus of infected cells. It may be present from 200 to 10000 copies. Viroids replicate autonomously in cells of susceptible plant species. Replication occurs by an RNA-dependent RNA polymerase which is synthesized from RNA templates by a host RNA polymerase that mistakes them for a piece of DNA. A rolling circle mechanism is seemed to be involved.
6. Viroids are large enough to encode a single small protein, but it is doubtful that they do, because the RNA of viroids lacks the signals (ribosome – binding sites, start codon and stop codons) that are needed for translation into a protein.
7. It is not known how viroids cause disease. It is thought that their location in the nucleus, association with the cell chromatin material and their apparent inability to act as mRNA suggest that they

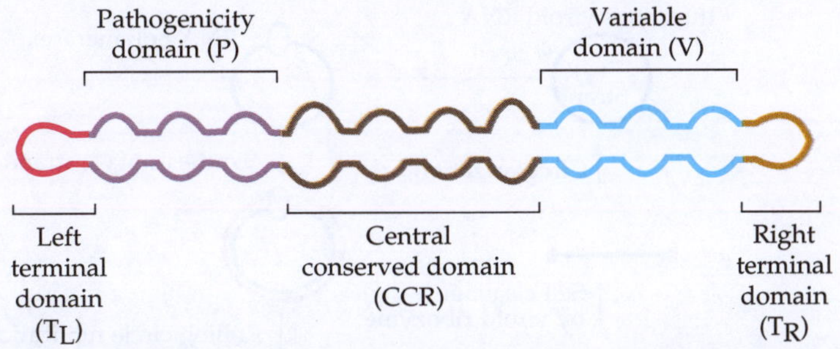


**Fig.12.39 :** *Schematic diagram of a viroid and its general structure*

cause host symptoms by interferance with gene regulation in infected host cells.

Present evidence suggests that viroid-like nucleic acids are also exist in organism other than higher plants (Fig. 12.39).

### 12.5.2 Classification of viroids

Viroids can be classified into two groups based on comparative sequence analysis and whether they possess a central conserved region.

1. Group A or **Avsunviroidae** family : In this group, both plus-and minus stranded viroid RNAs **have the ability to self cleavage** their RNA multimers. Currently only three members have been known. viz. Avocado sunblotch viroid (ABSVd), Pearch latent mosaic viroid and Chrysanthemum chlorotic mottle viroid.

   They replicate in chloroplast. ABSVd is believed to adopt a rod-like secondary structure, while other two members of group-A, have complex secondary structures in which several stem-loops (hairpins) emerge from a central core.

2. Group B or **Pospiviroidae** family : They possess five domains; a highly conserved central reigon (C), the terminal left ($T_L$), pathogenic (P), variable (V) and terminal right ($T_R$). The boundaries between these domains are defined by sharp changes in degree of sequence homology among different viroids. **These are not capable of self cleavage** and replicate in the nucleus. They have high degree of base pairing throughout the molecule. Thus they fold into a rod-like secondary structures that include short double-stranded regions separated by small single stranded loops.

   Group B viruses are divided into five subgroups based mainly on the presence of highly conserved sequences within the C-domains and part on the presence of sequence homologies in the other domains.

   PSTVd (Potato spindle tuber viroid)

   CCCVd (Coconut cadang-cadang viroid)

   HpSVd (Hop stunt viroid)

   ASSVd (Apple scar skin viroid)

   CbVd (Coleus blumei-1 viroid)

### 12.5.3 Replication of Viroids

Viroids are naked molecules of infectious ssRNA, base pairing occurs between bases on opposite halves of the circle to produce rod-like structure. They lack attachment proteins and so cannot recognize and penetrate healthy cells. They can infiltrate a plant cell only when its surrounding membrane is damaged. They may pass from one cell to another cell through cellular junctions.

They do not contain any genes that can encode proteins, merely carry signals for their

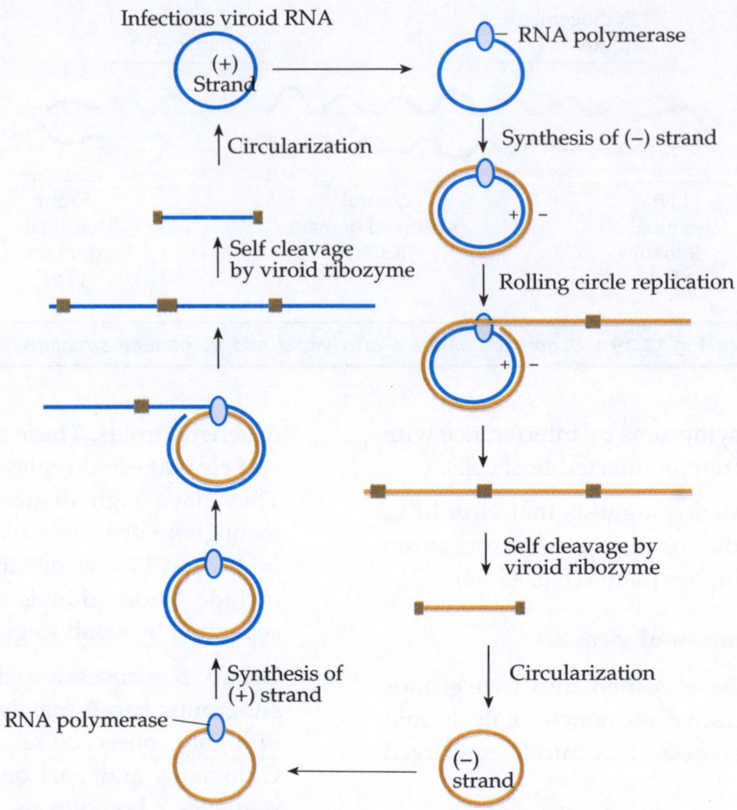


**Fig.12.40 :** *Viroid replication by a rolling circle mechanism.*

own replication by the host machinary. They themselves act as a **ribozyme**.

They replicate by rolling circle mechanism. Two rounds of rolling circle replication are used by viroids to replicate themselves. Upon entry into a plant cell, the circular positive ssRNA uses a plant RNA pol mostly rely on RNA pol-II to make a minus strand. The polymerase continues to make multiple copies using the rolling circle mechansim. The linear negative ssRNA uses its own catalytic activity to cut itself into genome-sized units. These are then circularized to become minus strands. These minus strands then undergo another round of rolling circle replication and then self cleavage to produce multiple copies of the linear plus strands. Finally, these plus strands are circularized to give the infectous circular positive ssRNA viroids (Fig. 12.40).

## 12.5.4 Enzymatic activities during viroid replication

Rolling circle replication requires three distinct enzymatic activities for completion, viz polymerization, cleavage and ligation.

### Polymerization :

**Group A viroids** are found in the chloroplast of the plant cells, chloroplast RNA polymerase resembles bacterial RNA polymerase which is resistant to **α-amanitin.** They use chloroplast RNA polymerase for replication.

**Group B viroids** are found in the nucleus. The cellular DNA-dependent RNA polymerase II appears to be involved in the replication, since, replication can be inhibited by low concentration of α-aminitin, a known inhibitor of the enzyme. It is not clear how viroids recruit these polymerases and induce them to use their ssRNA genome as template to be copied into complementary RNAs Furthermore, the initiation signal and termination signal are not presently known.

### Cleavage :

Group A viroids have the self cleavage property (ribozyme) and can cleavage multimeric linear RNA molecules in absence of any proteins. Self cleavage is carried out by hammerhead or hairpin or delta structures. All these structures align the target cleavage site by base pairing. Self cleavage occurs by the 2′-hydroxyl of the nucleotide at the cleavage site, generating a 2′, 3′-cyclic phosphate at one side of the cleavage and a 5′-hydroxyl terminus at the other side.

Group B viroids have no self cleavage activity. It has been proposed that host cell enzymes carryout cleavage of these RNA molecules (Fig. 12.41 & 12.42).

### Ligation :

Group A viroids do not need host proteins for the ligation of the two ends of linear RNA molecule. The linear monomers resulting from hammer-headed viroid producting 2′-5′-phosphodiester bonds by self-ligation activities.

Group B viroids use cellular enzymes for ligation of 3′- 5′-phosphodiester bond which is an RNA-ligase known to participate in the splicing of tRNA, localized in the nucleus.

## 12.5.5 Subviral infectious agents

Infectious agents that are more primitive than viruses and encode fewer of their own functions. There are several subviral infectious agents.

1. **Satellite virus :** A defective DNA or RNA virus that needs an unaltered helper virus to infect same host cell. The helper virus provides the essential functions that it lacks, such as supplying a replicase, capsid protein or other functions that allow the satellite virus to survive inside the host cell.
2. **Virusoids :** An RNA molecule that does not encode any proteins and depends on a helper virus for replication and capsid formation. The virusoid genome resembles a viroid and consists circular ssRNA with self-cleaving ribozyme activity.
3. **Satellite RNA :** Any small molecules that requires a helper virus for replication and capsid function. Satellite RNAs range from 200 to 1700 nucleotides and the larger ones may encode a protein. Virusoids are sometimes regarded as a subtype of satellite RNA.
4. **Defective interfering RNA (DI-RNA) :** Shorter RNA molecule derived from viral RNA by deletions that remove essential functions. DI-RNA depends on the original parental virus for replication. The presence of DI-RNA usually reduces the yield of the parental virus.
5. **Viroids :** Self replicating pathogen of plants that consists solely of naked single stranded circular RNA. They do not code any proteins. Most viroid RNAs, have self cleaving ribozyme activity.

## 12.5.6 Mode of infection and Cause of diseases

Viroids are transmitted following contact between a wounded uninfected plant and an infected plant, a contaminated agricultural tool or a carrier insects.

Following infection, viroids replicate and propagate in the plant, most likely using cellular junctions to pass from cell to cell.

Symptoms caused by viroid infection include leaf decoloration, dwarfing, enhanced fruit production, organge spotting, decline in fruit yield, stunting etc.

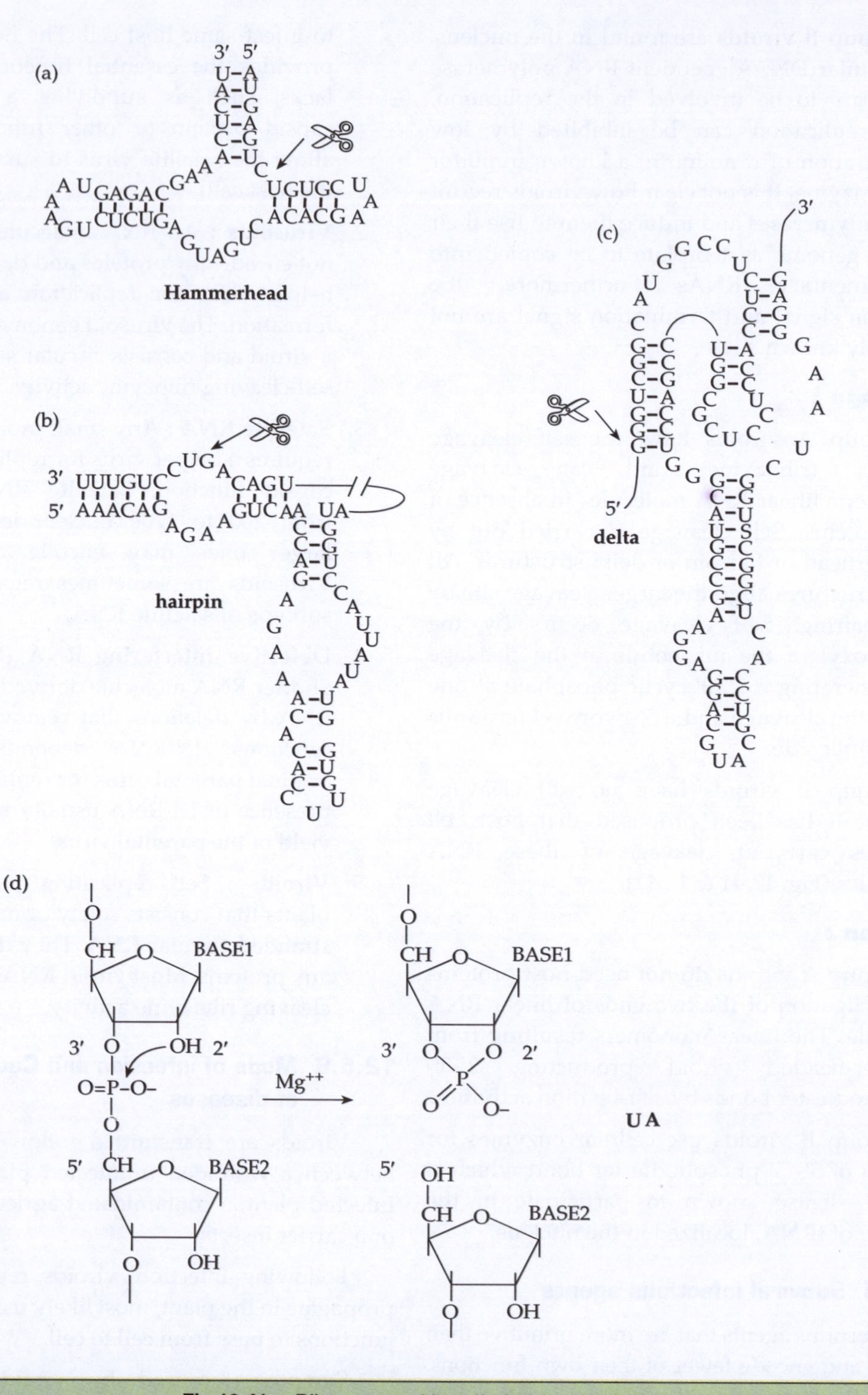


**Fig.12.41 :** *Ribozymes with self cleaving nature*
*(a) Hammerhead structure of peach latent mosaic viroid ; (b) Hairpin structure of satellite tobacco ringspot virus satellite RNA ; (c) Hepatitis delta virus ; (d) Self cleaving reaction*

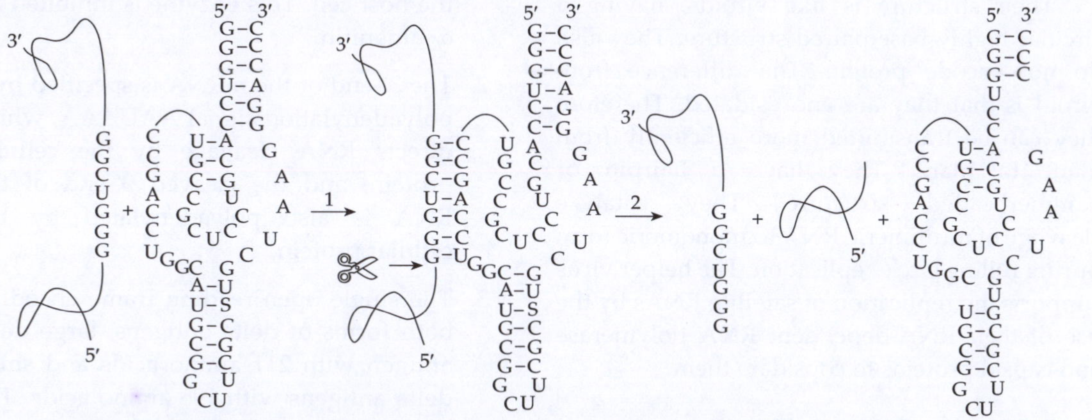


**Fig.12.42 :** *Proposed cleavage of an RNA substrate by a trans-acting delta ribozyme. The target RNA substrate (left) anneals to the ribozyme (step 1) and is cleaved (scissors), producing two products that are released (step2). The ribozyme (right) is then ready to process a new molecule of substrate RNA. (Modified from Fundamentals of Molecular virology by N.H. Acheson 1st edn. 2007*

Because, viroids do not code for any proteins, their effects on plants must be a consequence of direct interactions between the viroid RNA and host constituents. Sequence changes in the P domain (pathogenecity domain) can affect infectivity and severity of the symptoms. Both nucleic acids and proteins have been proposed to be the initial targets of viroids.

1. Some viroids have a region complementary to certain cellular RNA molecules, which are either inhibited or undergo cleavage by the viroids. For example, potato spindle tuber viroid has sequence similarily with U1RNA of mammals (which is involved in RNA splicing).
2. Some viroids contain sequences that could base pair with 7S ribosomal RNA.
3. Host protein, such as, mammalian PKR which is a dsRNA-dependent protein kinase is phosphorylated and activated by PSTVd because its secondary structure resembles, with dsRNA. The activation of PKR then phosphorylates the subumit of eukaryotic eIF2, causing inhibition of protein synthesis.
4. Pathogenecity could also be the result of **molecular mimicry**. Viroid RNA mimics with certain cellular RNAs. For example PSTVd mimics with group I intron as well as U3B RNA which are involved in RNA splicing. Thus the viroid RNA could interfere with splicing events replacing functional RNAs.
5. Another phenomenon is observed in viroid infection, called *cross protection* between strands of same viroids. Actually plants infected with one viroid will not allow replication and pathogenesis by their related viroids. This is like that of **viral interferance.** But this is not clearly known for viroids. Possibly a limiting host factor, which is required for viroid replication, transport or accumulation. Differential affinity for this factor determines which of the two viroids prevails.

### 12.5.7 Plant satellite RNAs

Plant satellite RNAs are small ssRNAs. For their replication and encapsulation, depend on a helper virus. But they show little or no sequence similarity with their helper virus.

Their structure is like viroids, having a circular highly base-paired structure. They also do not encode protein. The difference from viroid is that they are encapsidated. Therefore they can be transmitted more efficiently from plant to plant. They have a hairpin or hammerheaded structure. They catalyze cleavage of multimeric RNA to monomeric form during rolling circle replication. The helper virus supports the replication of satellite RNAs by the use of their RNA-dependent RNA polymerase and capsid proteins to copsidate them.

### 12.5.8 Human RNA-satellite virus

Human delta virus (HDV) is an RNA-satellite virus shares several characteristics with both plant viroids and viroid-like plant satellite RNAs. The virus causes **fulminant hepatitis** in both primates and nonprimates. For their packaging, they use the envelope protein (S-antigen) of another, the hepatitis virus. Therefore, it is considered as an RNA satellite of hepatities B virus.

#### Genome structure of HDV :

1. The HDV is a circular ssRNA molecule with 1682 nucleotides.
2. The ssRNA molecule can be folded into a rod-like structure due to extensive internal base pairing.
3. It has a single protein-coding open reading frame complementary to genome RNA.
4. Transcription is started at 1630 nt site and ends at 956 nt site.
5. There is an editing site at 1014 nt position.
6. Cleavage and polyadenylation site is distinctly located beyond 956 nt site.
7. Two cleavage motifs on the genome RNA at 668-771 nt and antigenome RNA at 819-902 nt indicate the cleavage sites.

#### Transcription and translation :

1. An 800 nucleotide polyadenylated mRNA is synthesized by RNA polymerase II of the host cell. This enzyme is inhibited by α–amanitin.
2. The 3′-end of the mRNA is specified by a polyadenylation signal AAUAAA, which directs RNA cleavage by the cellular protein, and the cleaved 3′-end of the RNA is also polyadenylated by the cellular protein.
3. The single open reading frame encoding both forms of delta antigens, large delta antigen with 211 amino acids and small delta antigens with 195 amino acids. The larger form results from editing (A to G) at 1014 nt position.

#### Replication :

1. HDV replicates in the nucleus via rolling circle mechanism as found in viroids (Fig. 12.43).
2. Production of antigenome RNA from genome RNA templates may use cellular DNA-dependent RNA polymerase I which is resistant to α-amanitin. The multimeric antigenome RNA molecules are generated by rolling circle replication using circular genome RNA as template but are not cleaved at the polyadenylation site.
3. An alternative model on experimental basis suggested that both transcription and replication use RNA polymerase II but the polyadenylation signal is not always recognized by the cellular cleavage factor allowing both 800 nt mRNA and multimeric antigenome template. However, insensitivity to α-amanitin would remain unexplained by this alternative model.

#### RNA editing to generate two forms of hepatitis delta antigen :

1. Antigenome RNAs are edited during replication. Editing occurs at a specific 1014 nt site of a specific A (adenine) into G (guanine); which is carried out by a cellular enzyme *adenosine deaminase*.

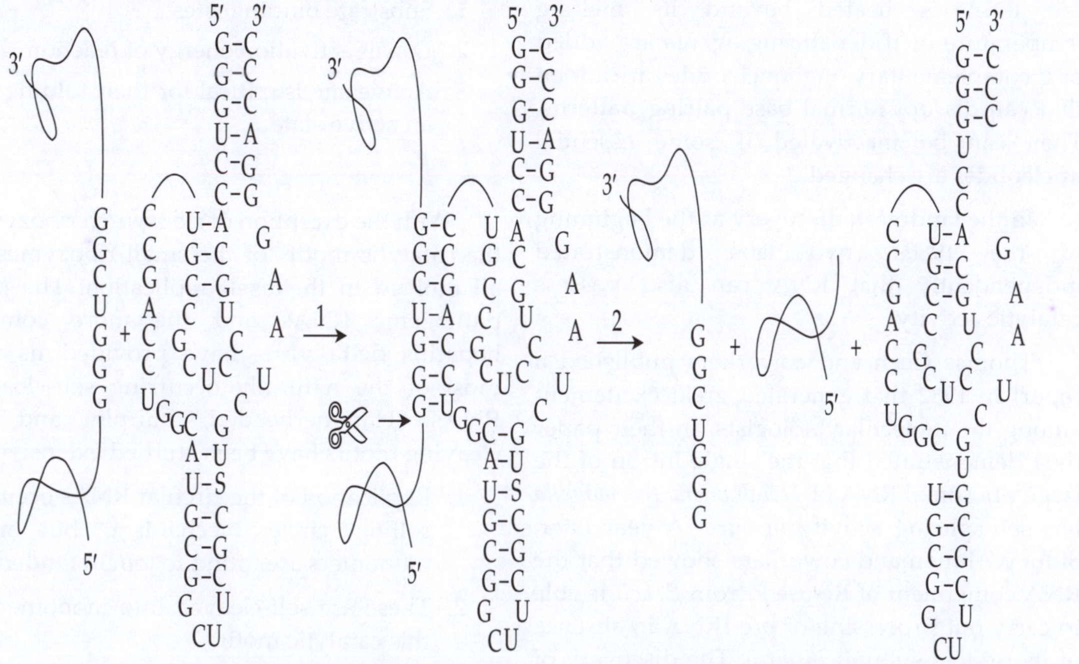

**Fig.12.43** : *Genome of hepatitis delta virus*

2. The enzyme recognizes the specific region of dsRNA but the mechanism how a single "A" residue is selected is not known.
3. As a result of editing, the UAG termination codon is changed to UGG at 195 amino acid position which codes for *tryptophan*. These genome RNAs are with 558 nts (a modified messenger) and 655 nts (normal messenger).
4. After translation of these mRNA molecules two forms of hepatitis delta antigens (proteins) are formed having 195 and 214 amino acids respectively.
5. The exact roles are not clearly known how do they are required for genome packaging.

## 12.6 RIBOZYMES

### 12.6.1 Concept

When the spliceosome was first discovered, it puzzled molecular biologists and thus the study of posttranscriptional processing of RNA molecules has led to one of the most exciting discoveries in the field of biochemistry and molecular biology is the existence of RNA enzymes, called **ribozymes**.

The folded domains of RNA molecules not only are structurally analogous to the α-helices and β-strands found in proteins but in cases also have catalytic capacities that can cut RNA chain. Such catalytic RNAs are called **ribozymes**. It is believed that ribozymes were functioning as catalysts before the occurrence of protein enzymes during evolution of life.

The substrate for ribozymes is often an RNA molecule, sometimes the substrate is itself part of the ribozyme. With an RNA substrate, an RNA catalyst can make use of base-pairing interactions to align the substrate for reaction.

Ribozymes tend to be large. Although the three dimensional structure of these catalytic RNAs is not known, but it is certainly important for it's function. The catalytic activity is lost if the RNA is heated beyond its melting temperature or if denaturing agents are added or if complementary oligonucleotides are added that can disrupt normal base pairing patterns. They can be inactivated if some essential nucleotides are changed.

In the landmark discovery at the beginning of the 1980s, two labs demonstrated independently that RNA can also possess catalytic activity.

Thomas Cech and coworkers published a report in 1982 that generated great excitement among the molecular biologists. In their paper they demonstrated that the single intron of the large ribosomal RNA of *Tetrahymena thermophila* has self-splicing activity *in vitro.* A year later, Sidney Altman and coworkers showed that the RNA component of RNase P from *E. coli* is able to carry out processing of pre-tRNA in absence of its protein subunit *in vitro.* The discovery of self-splicing RNA was completely unexpected. In 1989, Cech and Altman were awarded the Nobel Prize in Chemistry for this revolutionary discovery. It is now believed from this discovery that, four billion year ago, Earth was an ***RNA world*** in which DNA and proteins were not included in the life, they carried out the life processes through RNA.

### 12.6.2 Types of naturally occurring ribozymes

Naturally occurring ribozymes are often autocatalytic, which lead to their own modifications. This contradicts the classic definition of the enzyme, which is "Enzymes increases the rate or velocity of a chemical reaction without itself being changed in the overall process". But it is fact that they often follow Michaelis-Menten kinetics.

Ribozymes are mainly of two types, small and large ribozymes. Their source and function are tabulaled (Table 12.7).

### 12.6.3 Mode of ribozyme action

Like enzymes, ribozymes have

1. Substrate binding sites
2. Lower activation energy of reaction
3. Active site is critical for their folding into an active state.

#### Small ribozymes :

With the exception of riboswitch ribozymes, the catalytic motifs of the small ribozymes are all inolved in their self replication. The plant pathogenic RNAs and the more complex hepatitis delta virus have provided us with most of the naturally occurring self-cleaving RNAs. Hammerheaded, hairpin and self cleaving motifs have been studied extensively.

1. Replication of the circular RNAs occur via rolling circle mechanism, but many monomers are found to join in tandem.
2. These are self-cleaved into monomers by this catalytic motif.
3. The self cleavage of phosphodiester bonds occurs by "in line" nucleophilic reactions.
4. The internal 2′-OH group of the ribose next to the phosphodiester bond to be cleaved, attacks the phosphate, leading to an inversion of the configuration around the phosphorus.
5. The incoming group is "in line" with the –OH group in the transition state leaving the reaction center.
6. The reaction yields a product with a 2′, 3′-cyclic phosphate and a product with a 5′-OH terminus.

The substate is target RNA which can be cleaved by a *trans*-acting delta ribozyme *in vitro.* The target RNA (substrate) anneals to the ribozyme and is cleaved, producing two products that are dissociated from the ribozyme if the complementary region on the two RNAs is short enough, thereby permitting the binding of more substrate molecules for cleavage. Thus a single ribozyme molecule can cleave many substrate molecules and establishing a classic enzyme-substrate relationship.

**TABLE 12.7**
**Types of naturally occurring ribozymes**

| *Ribozyme* | *Source* | *Function* | *Reaction Products* |
|---|---|---|---|
| **Small ribozyme** | | | |
| 1. Hammer-headed | Plant viroids and newt satellite RNA | Replication | 5′-OH; 2′, 3′-cyclic Phosphate |
| 2. Hairpin | Plant satellite RNAs | Replication | 5′-OH; 2′, 3′-cyclic Phosphate |
| 3. HDV | Hepatitis delta virus (human) | Replication | 5′-OH; 2′, 3′-cyclic Phosphate |
| 4. VS | *Neurospora crassa* (mitochondria) | Replication | 5′-OH; 2′, 3′-cyclic Phosphate |
| 5. Riboswitch ribozyme | *Bacillus subtilis* | glm S mRNA self splicing | 5′-OH; 2′, 3′-cyclic Phosphate |
| **Large ribozyme** | | | |
| 1. RNase P | Eukaryotes, prokaryotes | tRNA splicing | 5′phosphate and 3′-OH |
| 2. Group I introns | Eukaryotic cell organelles and Prokaryotes, Bacteriophages | Splicing | Intron with 5′-guanosine and 3′-OH; 5′/3′-ligated exons |
| 3. Group II introns | Eurakyotic organelles and prokaryotes | Splicing | Intron with 2′-5′ lariat and 3′-OH; 5′/3′-ligated exons |
| 4. Spliceosome | Eurkaryote nucleus | Pre mRNA splicing | Intron with 2′-5′-lariat and 3′-OH; 5′/3′-ligated exons |
| 5. Ribosome | Both Prokaryote & eukaryote | Translation | Peptide bond |

Now, the naturally occurring molecules have been engineered by designing oligonucleotides synthesized *in vitro* or by mutagenesis of existing ribozymes. This engineered ribozymes gain an ability to interact directly with RNA. Such ribozymes would be the potential therapeutic weapons of a wide range of diseases, including AIDS, viral hepatitis, cancer, diabetes, cardiovascular disease and osteoporosis.

### Large ribozymes :

The RNA component of RNase P and members of the group I intron family belong to the group of large ribozyme. Most of the activities of these ribozymes are based on two fundamental reactions : transesterification and phosphodiester bond hydrolysis (cleavage).

Group I and group III ribozymes are selfsplicing introns that are discussed in ditail in the chapter on RNA processing. The main differents from the small ribozymes are that in cleavage reactions by large ribozyme generate 3′-OH termini.

RNase P was purified and characterized by Sidny Altman and co-wokers in 1971 in *E. coli* which is involved in the processing of 5′-leader sequence of precursor tRNA. The RNase P is composed of M1 RNA and C5 protein. *In vitro*, the M1RNA alone can process precursor tRNA in the presence of high concentration of monovalent and divalent cations. But *in vivo*, the C5 protein is required to enhance the catalytic activity of M1RNA and increase the substrate versality. This is described in tRNA processing. (See Chapter 15)

The bacterial RNase P is a ribozyme but its eukaryotic counterpart acts as a catalybic ribonucleoprotein.

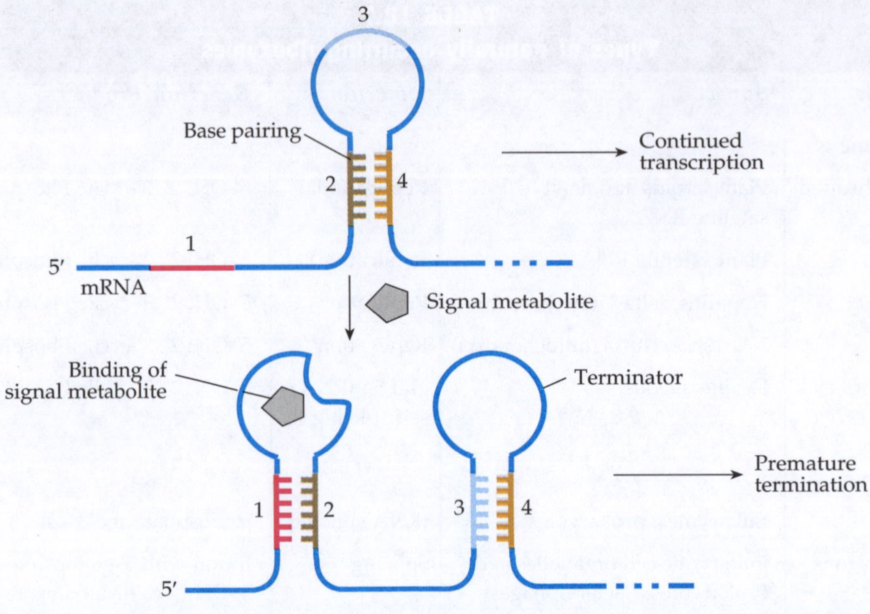


**Fig.12.44 :** *Riboswitch attenuation mechanism.*

### 12.6.4 Riboswitches

Domain of mRNA that directly senses a signal and controls translation by alternating between two structures is referred to *riboswitch.* The riboswitch domain can interact directly with small molecules and controls gene expression at translational level. There are several experimental evidences for riboswitch operation in bacteria. However, sequence analysis has revealed that genomes of certain fungi and plants may contain equivalent sequences.

The biosynthetic pathways that make metabolites such as, amino acids, vitamins etc. are generally induced when the metabolite is in short supply but are shut down when there is plentiful supply of metabolite.

Binding of the metabolite to its **RNA box** changes the conformation of the whole riboswitch system. The riboswitch system exists in two alternative conformations both with different stem and loop foldings of mRNA. There are two mechanisms known which control the gene expression viz, the attenuation mechanism and transcriptional inhibition.

1. In the **attenuation mechanism**, when the metabilite is not present, the riboswitch sequesters the terminator sequences and so the transcription continues. But binding with signal metabolites, the riboswitch changes to a conformation that allows the formation of a terminator stem and loop, which causes premature termination of mRNA. Consequently, the genes are not expressed.

2. In the **translational inhibition** mechanism, when the signal metabolite is not present, the Shine-Dalgarno sequence is free to bind ribosomal RNA and translation proceeds. But binding with signal metabolite, the riboswitch sequesters the Shine-Dalgarno sequence into the loop and stem causing to prevent translation (Fig. 12.44 & 12.45).

The thiamine riboswitch of *E. coli* contains a sequence that binds of thiamine pyrophosphate

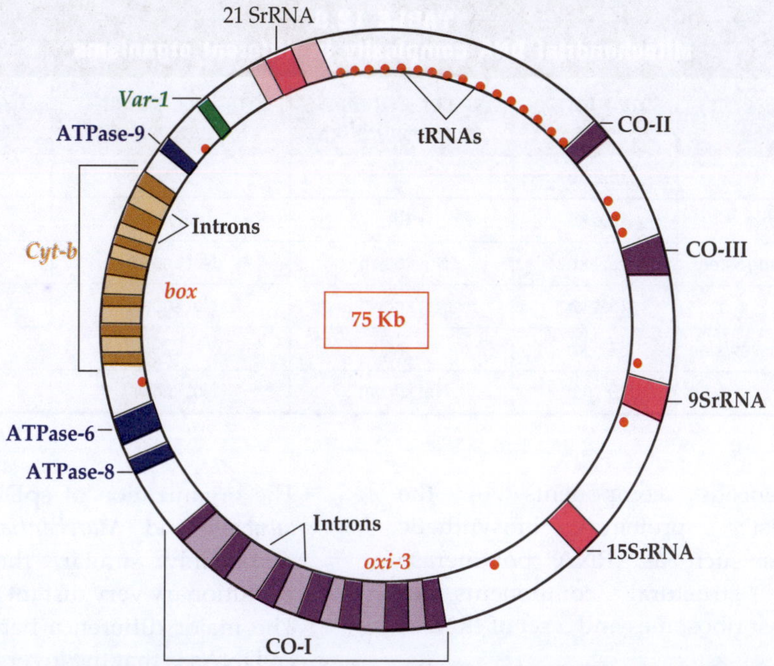


**Fig.12.45 :** *Riboswitch translational inhibition mechansim*

which binds with great specificity to the **THI-box**. Riboflavin riboswitch in *Bacillus subtilis* binds flavin mononucleotide to the **RFN box**.

Riboswitches can also respond to temperature. The **RNA thermosensor** is a special kind of riboswitch which controls mRNA translation by sequestration of Shine-Dalgarno sequence within the newly formed alternative stem and loop structure. For example, the *rpo H* gene of *E. coli* where the translation of mRNA is prevented by RNA thermosensor at low temperature but, in increased temperature, the riboswitch system allows translation. Another examples *Yersinia* and *Listeria* etc. bacteria, where, the virulence genes are switched off by translational inhibition outside the host. But in hot blooded mammalian host, the proteins are expressed causing bacterial virulence.

## 12.7 CHLOROPLAST DNA (CP DNA)

Chloroplasts contain multiple copies of the organellar DNA and ribosomes, which can synthesize some chloroplast-encoded proteins using the *standard* genetic code. Other chloroplast proteins are fabricated on cytosolic ribosomes and are incorporated into the organelle after translations.

cpDNAs are circular molecules have about 120000 to 160000 bp, depending upon the species. For example, in liverwort (*Marchantia polymorpha*) it is 121024 bp., in tobacco (*Nicotiana tabacum*) it is 155844 bp., in rice chloroplast genome it is about 136000 bp., in green algae *Chlamydomonas reinhardtii,* it is 19500 bp.

Chloroplast DNAs often contain multiple copies. A single chloroplast of *Chlamydomonas reihardtii* contains about 100 copies. *Euglena gracilis* contains 15 chloroplasts per cell each with about 40 copies of cpDNA.

Chloroplast genomes contain basically the same set of genes but are arranged in very different ways on the cp DNAs. primarily due to inverted repeats and duplication. These genes are grouped into two major classes.

**TABLE 12.8**
**Mitochondrial DNA complexity in different organisms**

| *Species* | *Complexity* | *No. of genomes per organelle* | *No. of organelle per cell* | *Ratio of MDNA to total DNA* |
|---|---|---|---|---|
| **Mouse** | 16.2 kb | 2 | 500 | 0.2% |
| **Human (Hela)** | 16.6 kb | 10 | 800 | 1% |
| ***Drosophila melanogaster*** | 18.4 kb | Not known | Not known | Not known |
| ***Xenopus laevis*** | 18.4 kb | Not known | Not known | Not known |
| ***Saccharomyces cerevisiae*** | 84 kb | 4 | 22 | 18% |
| ***Pisum sativum*** | 110 kb | Not known | Not known | Not known |

1. Those encode components of the chloroplast protein biosynthetic apparatus such as, RNA polymerase subunits, structural components of chloroplast ribosomes and a set of tRNAs.
2. Those specifying components of the photosynthetic machinery including PS I, PS II and ETC (electron transport chain).
3. Of the ≈120 genes in cpDNA, about 60 are involved in RNA transcription and translation including genes for rRNAs, tRNAs, RNA polymerase subunits and ribosomal proteins. About 20 genes encode subunits of chloroplast photosynthetic electron transport complexes and the $F_0$–$F_1$ ATPase complex. Also encoded in the chloroplast genome is the larger of the two subunits of ribulose – 1, 5-bisphosphate carboxylase which is involved in the fixation of $CO_2$ during photosynthesis.

The rRNA genes are present in duplicate on reverse repeats within the most species. In *Euglena gracilis,* the 16S and 23S rRNA genes are present on three direct tandem repeats, with a separate fourth copy of the 16S rRNA gene located nearby in the genome.

The organization of cpDNA of *Nicotiana tabacum* and *Marchantia polymorpha* is remarkably similar, though they are evolutionary very distant from each other. The major difference between these two cp DNAs is that the inverse repeat regions containing the rRNA genes are considerably larger (150) in tobacco than in *Marchantia* (136). Since two chloroplasts contain virtually the same set of proteins. It is suggested that same genes are present in the cpDNA of one species and in the nuclear DNA of other. It indicates that some exchange of genes between chloroplast and nucleus has occured during evolution.

The regions of cpDNA have been found to be similar to those of the DNA of present day bacteria. For example, cp DNA encodes four subunits of RNA polymerase that are highly homologous to the subunits RNA polymerase that are highly homologous to the subunits of *E.coli* RNA. One segment of cpDNA encodes 8 proteins that are homologous to eight *E. coli* ribosomal proteins. The order of thse genes is the same in two DNAs.

# Chapter Glossary/Key Terms

**"A" Protein :** The viral "A" protein cleaves the plus strand or RF DNA at a specific site and is covalently linked to the resulting 5¢ end. The host cell rep protein acts together with protein 'A' as helicase and unwinds the ds DNA.

**Bacteriocin :** A toxic protein made by bacteria to kill other closely related bacteria.

**Icosahedral symmetry :** Symmetry of a regular icosahedron, with 12 axes of five fold symmetry, 20 axes of two fold symmetry and 30 axes of two fold symmetry.

**Kuru :** Prion disease of the Fore people in Papua New Guinea, caused by ingestion of prions during ritual cannibalism.

**Lysogenic cycle :** The series of events following infection by a bacteriophage and culminating in the formation of a stable prophage.

**Lysogenic phage :** A phage which is known to be capable of entering a prophage state in some host.

**Lytic cycle :** The series of events following infection by a bacteriophage or induction a phophage and culminating in lysis of the bacterium and the release of new phage into the medium.

**Mad Cow disease :** Prion diseases caused to the cow.

**Molecular mimicry :** Viroid RNA mimics with certain cellular RNAs and causing pathogenecity.

**Pilot protein :** This is also known as viral protein H, requires for the delivery of viral DNA directly into the cytoplasm.

**Prion :** Infectious agent responsible for several neurological diseases (scrapie, Kuru, CJD, mad cow disease etc. It is a protein that lacks DNA or RNA.

**Prion only model :** The misfold form PrPsc can catalyze the refolding of properly folded native form PrPc.

**Prophage :** The state of phage DNA in a lysogen in which the phage DNA is integrated into the chromsomes of the bacterium or replicates as a plasmid.

**Proviral DNA :** A DNA copy of a retrovirus genome that is inserted into the chromosome of an infected host cell.

**PrPc :** Normal prion protein found in normal cell this is non pathogenic.

**PrPsc :** Pathogenic conformation of prion protein

**Refolding model :** The PrPsc is more stable than PrPc. High energy barrier prevents spontaneous change from PrPc to PrPsc. An exogenous protein called "X" is involved in the process of conversion.

**Replicative form :** The complementary (–) strand is synthesized on the (+) strand of the ssDNA phage to form a dsDNA.

**Riboswitch :** Domain of mRNA that directly senses a signal and controls translation by alternating between two structures.

**Ribozyme :** RNA molecule acts as an enzyme and catalyzes a specific biochemical reaction.

**Rolling circle replication :** Mechanism or replicating double stranded circular DNA that starts by nicking and uncoiling one strand and using the other, still circular, strand as a template for DNA synthesis. Used by some plasmids and viruses.

*Contd.*

**Satellite virus :** A satellite with a genome that encodes one or two proteins.

**Seeding model :** Formation of PrPsc is a nucleation-dependent oligomerization process the change from PrPc to PrPsc is a reversible thermodynamic equilibrium process.

**Viral interference :** The state of resistance of a cell to virus infection brought about by provirus exposure of the cell to a similar or different virus.

**Virion :** A comple,e inferctious virus particle.

**Viroid :** Small circular DNA that can replicate in absence of a heler virus by reprogramming cellular DNA dependent RNA polymerase to copy its genome RNA.

**Virusoids :** An RNA molecule that does not encode any proteins and depends on the helper virus for replication and capsid formation.

# EXERCISE

**A. Long answer type questions :**

1. Define genome. Where does it occur? Describe the importance of genome.
2. What is Prion? Give some common diseases caused by "Prion" in humans and other animals.
3. What are the routes of entry of human prion disease.
4. Describe molecular structure and molecule biology of prion.
5. Distinguish $PrP^{C}$ and $PrP^{SC}$
6. Describe prion hypothesis
7. Describe the nature of prion gene and how it causes prion disease?
8. How does the disease cross the species barrier.
9. How the prion disease can be treated?
10. Give the nature and evidance of prion genes in yeast.
11. Describe the properties of the virus.
12. Describe the general structure of virus.
13. Describe the structure of TMV.
14. Describe the lytic cycle of dsDNA viruses.
15. Describe the lytic cycle of ssRNA viruses.
16. Describe the lysogeny cycle of Lambda phage.
17. What are the characteristics of polyoma viruses.
18. Describe the genetics of SV40.
19. Briefly describe the genetics and pathogenesis of SV-40 virus.
20. Describe the mode of infection, genome structure, replication cycle of HBV.
21. Describe spread, structure, genetic organization and replicative cycle of HIV-1.
22. Describe the role of nucleic acids in viruses.
23. Describe general properties of bacteriophages.
24. Briefly classify bacteriophages with important characters and examples.

25. Describe organization and replication of T4 phage genome.
26. Describe organization and replication of T7 phage genome.
27. Describe organization of λ-phage genome.
28. Describe the estalishment, maintenance of lysogeny and the entry into lytic cycle in λ-phage.
28. Describe decission between lysis and lysogeny in λ-phage.
30. Describe organization and replication of ϕ ×174 genome.
31. Describe M13 genome organization and replication.
32. Describe fd genome organization and replication.
33. Describe the mechaism of reproduction in ssRNA and dsRNA phages.
34. Describe structure and characteristics of viroids
35. Classify viroids with characters and examples.
36. How replication occurs in viroids?
37. Briefly describe three enzymatic activities during replication of viroids.
38. What are subviral particles? Classify with characters?
39. Describe mode of infection and causing diseases by viroid infection.
40. Give the structure and mode of replication of human RNA satellite virus?
41. How does RNA editing generates two forms of hapatitis delta antigen?
42. What are ribozymes? Give different types of naturally occurring ribozymes.
43. Describe different modes of ribozyme action in both small ribozymes and large ribozymes.
44. What is riboswitch? Give the mechanism of its activity.

**B. Short answer type questions.**

1. What is genome?
2. What are the components of the genome?
3. What are the characteristics of genome?
4. What is prion?
5. What is CJD?
6. Why prion was described as "unconvensional slow virus"?
7. What is kuru disease? What is its causative agent? What are the four stages of the disease?
8. What are the symptoms of CJD?
9. What is GSS syndrome? What is the cause of the disease?
10. What is FFI? What are the clinical symptoms?
11. What are the routes of entry of prion in humans?
12. What are the four steps of prion infection to diseased state?
13. What is the cause of scrapie? What are the symptoms? Why the disease is called so?
14. What is mad cow disease? What are the causes of the disease?
15. What is the chemistry of $PrP^{C}$? How this $PrP^{C}$ anchors plasma membrane?
16. How $PrP^{C}$ is synthesized in the cell?
17. Why S.B. Prusiner was against the "unconvensional slow virus" hypothesis?
18. What is amyloid?
19. What are the differences between $PrP^{C}$ and $PrP^{SC}$.
20. Where the PrP protein is located?
21. What are the characteristics of PrP*?
22. What is the structural difference between PrP and PrP*?
23. What $PrP^{SC}$ does not digested by proteinase-K?
24. What is the normal function of PrP?
25. What are the important characteristics of $PrP^{SC}$?
26. Why $PrP^{SC}$ is dangerous and is difficult to work with this?
27. What is "prion only" hypothesis?
28. What is seeding model?
29. What is refolding model of prion?

30. What do you mean by strain variation of prion?
31. What is nvCJD?
32. Name some drugs for prion treatment.
33. What is the difference in activities with quinacrine and chlorpromazine drugs against prion?
34. What are the two strains of yeast prion?
35. What will be happened if [psi$^-$] is fused with [PSI$^+$] state in yeast?
36. What is the role of Sup35 in yeast prion?
37. What is the common models for the formation of prion state in yeast?
38. What is the role of *URE2* locus in yeast prion?
39. What is virion?
40. What are the unique properties of viruses?
41. What are the viral components in their sturcture?
42. What are capsid and capsomere?
43. What is the structural specifities in the capsomere?
44. Give an example of icosahedral virus?
45. What are the compositions of capsid? How these components are arranged?
46. How the rhinoviruses attach to the respiratory epithelium?
47. Give an example of helical nucleocapsid containing virus?
48. Give an example of complex virus?
49. How phage viruses have binary symmetry?
50. Why envelope of animal virus consists of phospholipid bilayer? What are the protruding molecules on the envelope and what are their functions?
51. What are the compositions of spike and its functions?
52. Which protein stabilizes envelope of virus.
53. What do you mean by positive and negative viruses?
54. Why viral mRNA can be translated in the eukaryotic host cells?
55. What is protomer?
56. How do the capsids of the TMV associate to form its structure?
57. What is lylic cycle?
58. What is lysogeny?
59. What is prophage?
60. In the lytic cycle, how the receptors on host cell plays an important role in adhesion of virion?
63. What three kinds of viral proteins are synthesized from early genes? What are their functions?
64. What are the roles of virulent and nonvirulent viruses.
65. What are the late viral gene expressed proteins? and what are their functions?
66. Which mechanism is followed for the assembly of dsDNA virion particles?
73. How assembly and release occur in ssRNA virus infection?
74. What are temperate phages?
75. How integration of viral genome occurs with the host cell genome?
76. When lysogeny occurs?
77. In which site insertion occurs?
78. What is provirus?
79. What do you mean by prophage induction?
80. How the prophage is excised from the host genome?
81. What are the characteristics of polyoma virus?
82. Why the viruses are so named as polyoma virus?
83. What are the early proteins in SV-40 genome expression? What are their natures?
84. What are the late protein expressed in SV40?
85. How the T antigens induce tumorigenic growth?
86. What are the pathogenesis of Bk virus infection?
87. What are the pathogenesis of JC virus infection?

88. What are the symptoms of hepatitis B?
89. What are the ways by which a person can be infected with hepatitis B?
90. What are Dane particles?
91. Where HBsAg and HBc Ag are present in HBV?
92. What do you mean by circular particle dsDNA?
93. What kinds of partial dsDNA are found in HBV?
94. How many ORFs are present in HBV genome? What kinds of proteins are formed from their ORFs?
95. What is the characteristics of *S.*gene? and what proteins are formed from this gene?
96. What proteins are produced from *C-gene?*
97. What phenotypes are observed in HBsAg? What is the significance of these different phenotypes?
98. How the attachment of HBV with hepatocytes occurs?
99. What is cccDNA ? Where and how does it formed? What is it's function?
100. What is pregenome? How it is formed?
101. How the positive and negative strands of HBV are formed?
102. What is terminal redundency?
117. Give the abbrevated names into full form : ARV, HTLV, AIDS, HIV-1, LAV, SIV.
118. What are the routes of HIV-1 infection?
119. What are the important characteristics of HIV-1?
120. What proteins are found in the genome of HIV-1 and what are their fucntions?
121. What are the genetic organizations of HIV-1?
122. Distinguish HIV-1 and SIV?
123. What are the steps for HIV-1 replicative cycle?
124. Why HIV-1 can only bind to T-lymphocytes of human being.
125. Which proteins are essential to infect HIV-1 to the T-cells along with CD4 molecules?
126. What is M and T-tropic strains? What are their roles in HIV-1 infections?
127. How chemokines block the HIV-1 entry into the host cell?
128. How the genome of HIV-1 is released into the cytoplasm of the host?
129. How the genome is transcribed in the cell? What is the role of RNase-H component of reverse transcriptase?
130. What are dual functions of reverse transcriptase?
131. How the dsDNA made from HIV-1 is integrated into host genome?
132. What is HIV-1 provirus?
133. How viral procursors and viral proteins are produced in the cytoplasm of infected cells?
134. How do assembly and release of virus particles take place?
135. What are the general properties of baceriophage?
136. Give the examples of ssRNA, dsRNA, ssDNA and dsDNA phages.
137. What kinds of genes are sfound in T4 phage?
138. What is the main difference of T4 DNA from typical DNA?
139. What is HMC? What is its characteristics?
140. Why glycosylation is essential for the T4 life cycle?
141. Which origin is used by T4 to replicate?
142. Why two daughter molecules are produced in T4 replication? But why genomic informations are not lost?
143. What is recombination dependent replication?
144. How invading single-stranded 3′-end is created and invaded into complementary dsDNA to form three stranded DNA?
145. Which gene product is responsible for three strand DNA strand synthesis?
146. Which gene product of T4 is analogous to Rec-A of *E. coli*
147. How a branched concatemer is produced after T4 replication?
148. How concatemers are packaged in T4? What is the problem to such assembly and how this problem is solved by T4?

149. Which are the early expressed genes and late expressed genes in T7 phage?

150. What is the difference between T4 and T7 replication.

151. Why the daughter DNA molecules paired with each other to form concatemer? How do these concatemers are separated?

152. What are the replication enzymes encode by their own genes in T7.

153. How the host DNA is degraded to produce dNTPs in T7 infection?

154. Name the host of Lambda phage.

155. Why Lambda phage cyclizes immediately after replication.

156. What is the function of pL and pR promoters?

157. What are the leftword and rightword genes that code regulatory proteins in lytic cycle/

158. What are the *oL* and *oR* operators and their functions?

159. What is lambda repressor? What is its role?

160. Why lysogen stage cannot transcribe early promoters?

161. Why lysogenic cell grows indefinitely?

162. Why nonlysogenic cells can transcribe early promoters after infection with λ-phage?

163. Why lysogenic cells after infection with λ-phage lytic stage development is prevented?

164. What is the criterion for the estabalishment of lysogeny in λ-phage?

165. What is the establishment promoter? How it functions in the infected cells.

166. What is maintenance promoter? How does it function?

167. Why at low concentration of reprossor $oR_1$ and $oR_2$ are occupied?

168. What is repressor maintenance promoter.

169. How long repressor maintenance promoter continued transcription?

170. How the lysogeny is maintained?

171. What are the roles of Cro protein and CI protein in the entry into lytic cycle?

172. What is the role of intergrase enzyme.

173. What are the factors to initiate lytic cycle?

174. What is the role of *xis* gene and its product to proceed lytic cycle?

175. What is the literal meaning of $\phi \times 174$?

176. What are the compositions of the icosahedral capsid structure of $\phi \times 174$?

177. How many genes and code proteins are found in $\phi \times 174$?

178. How does the $\phi \times 174$ attach to the host cell? and how does the genome DNA released?

179. What is pilot protein? What is its role in the infection of $\phi \times 174$?

180. What is replicative form in $\phi \times 174$?

181. What do you mean by primosome? What are the compositons?

182. What are the events of stage I and stage II replication in $\phi \times 174$?

183. What is the role of viral 'A' protein in the replication of $\phi \times 174$?

184. In $\phi \times 174$ replication, the minus strand continuously acts as a template – explain, why?

185. What do you mean by stage-III replication in $\phi \times 174$? Why it is called so?

186. Why M13 is known as male-spcific phage?

187. Which mechanism is used to come through the cell by M13 phage?

188. Why M13 infection is known as chronically infection?

189. What viral proteins coat the M13 phage DNA?

190. What is host of *fd* phage?

191. Waht is the characteristics of RNA replicase of MS2 phage?

192. Name the known dsRNA phage.

193. What are the compositions of $\phi 6$ phage?

194. What is a viroid?

195. What is the difference between viroid and virus?

196. Which enzymes are used for viroid replication?

197. Why viroid RNAs are insignificant for protein synthesis?
198. What is the probable cause of viroid-infected disease?
199. What are the characteristics is of group-A and group-B viroids? Give their examples>
200. What are the five domains of group B viroids?
201. Why viroids can be compared with ribozymes?
202. What mechanism is used by viroids to replicate?
203. How infectious circular viroids are produced?
204. What kind of RNA polymerase is used by group-A viroids? Why α–amanitin can not prevent its replication?
205. What kind of RNA pol is used by group B virus for replications? Why α–aminitin can prevent such replications?
206. Which sites are cleaved to produce linear molecules from a multimeric forms of viroids?
207. Which process is used by group B viroids to cleave the multimeric forms?
208. Which enzymes or proteins are used by group A and group B viroids to circularize the linear forms?
209. What are subviral particles?
210. What is satellite virus? How do they survive and propagate in the host cell?
211. What are virusoids? What are their characterisics?
212. What is saltellite RNA?
213. What is DI-RNA.
214. How the viroids are transmitted to the plants?
215. What are the symptoms of viroid-infected plants?
216. Which domain of viroid is responsible for disease?
217. How do they produce disease in plants?
218. Wht is molecular mimicry? Give example?
219. What is the differene between satellite RNA and viroids?
220. What is HDV?
221. Which infective particle causes fulminant hepatites in human beings?
222. Why HDV replications in inhibited by α–amanitin?
223. How two kinds of delta-antigens are produced in HDV?
224. What are ribozymes? What are their substrates?
225. How do the catalytic activities of ribozymes can be lost?
226. What is RNA world?
227. What is the similarities and dessimilarities between ribozymes and enzymes.
228. How do small ribozymes replicate?
229. How do the ribozymes are used as therapeutic weapons agains AIDS and other diseases?
230. What are large ribozymes?
231. What is the difference in the cleavage reactions between small and large ribozomes?
232. What are riboswitches? How do they function?
233. Where do they found?
234. How attenuation mechanism of riboswitch controls gene expression?
235. How transitional inhibition mechansim of riboswitch controls gene expression?
236. What is RNA thermosensor? How it controls gene expression? Give with example.
237. How many genes are present in mitogenome?
238. What are the differences between mitogenome, genetic code and universal genetic code.
239. What are L and H strands of mito DNA.
240. What are the causes of LHON and MERRF diseases?
241. What is promiscuous DNA.
242. What are the characteristics of mito DNA.
243. What are the characteristics of cpDNA.

# 13

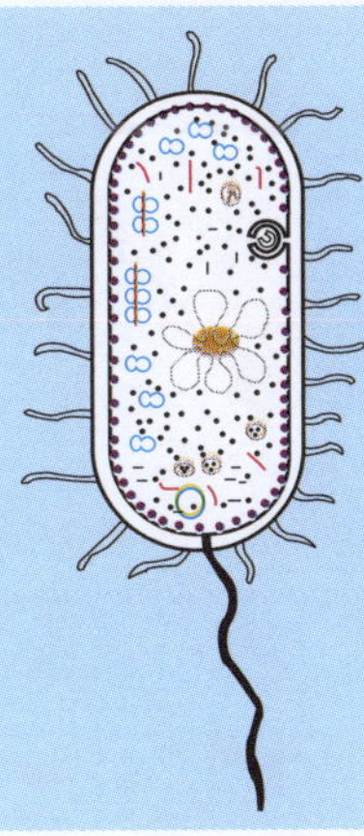

# Bacterial Genetics

**CHAPTER AGENDA**

**13.1** Genome of Bacteria; **13.2** *E. coli* genome; **13.3** Genome of Plasmids; **13.4** Plasmid Replication; **13.5** Plasmid Families and Incomppatibility; **13.6** Partitioning and Par systems of Plasmids; **13.7** Col E plasmid genome; **13.8** F Plasmid genome; **13.9** Plasmid attracting pheromones; **13.10** Control of Copy number of plasmids in the cell by antisense RNA; **13.11** Mobilization of Plasmid; **13.12** Plasmid addiction; **13.13** Integron and Antibiotic resistance; **13.14** Superintegrons and Multiple antibiotic resistant bacteria; **13.15** Bacteriocins; **13.16** Recombination in Bacteria; **13.17** Solved problems on Interrupted mating and Linkage mapping of Bacteria; Chapter Glossary/Key Terms; Exercise

## 13.1 GENOME OF BACTERIA

### 13.1.1 Introduction

Bacteria are the simplest prokaryotic organisms, found in almost all natural environments. These are very small (0.1 to 60 μ in diameter and are visible under the light microscope. They occur in three main shapes — *spherical, rod-like* and *spiral*. Some are free-living or may be parasitic, saprophytic or symbiotic.

### 13.1.2 Structure of Bacteria

1. **Capsule :** Many bacterial species are surrounded by a capsule. This may consist of a loose aggregate of material. Actually it is not a part of the organism and is not essential for the survival of the organisms under favourable conditions. In adverse condition, it is produced around its body and protects itself from the immunogenic reactions of the host. Capsule is secreted by the bacterial cell and is usually composed of polysaccharides or disaccharides or sometimes of polypeptides. Capsulated forms are usually infective and virulent.

2. **Cell Envelope :** Beneath the capsule is cell envelope. On the basis of its chemical composition and structure, it may be divided into Gram positive and Gram negative bacteria (Fig. 13.1).

(a) **Gram negative bacteria :**

(i) *Innermembrane or cytoplamsic membrane* : The inner membrane is a thin (20 – 75Å) membrane. It is semipermeable and made of lipid and protein. The structure of the membrane is typical and is explained by the fluid mosaic model of Singer and Nicolson. The membrane carries out multiple functions which are important for metabolic activities. It contains enzymes required for the synthesis of bacterial cell wall components, such as, phospholipids, pep-tidoglycans, teichoic acids, lipopolysaccharides and simple polysaccharides. It contains many transporter proteins, electron

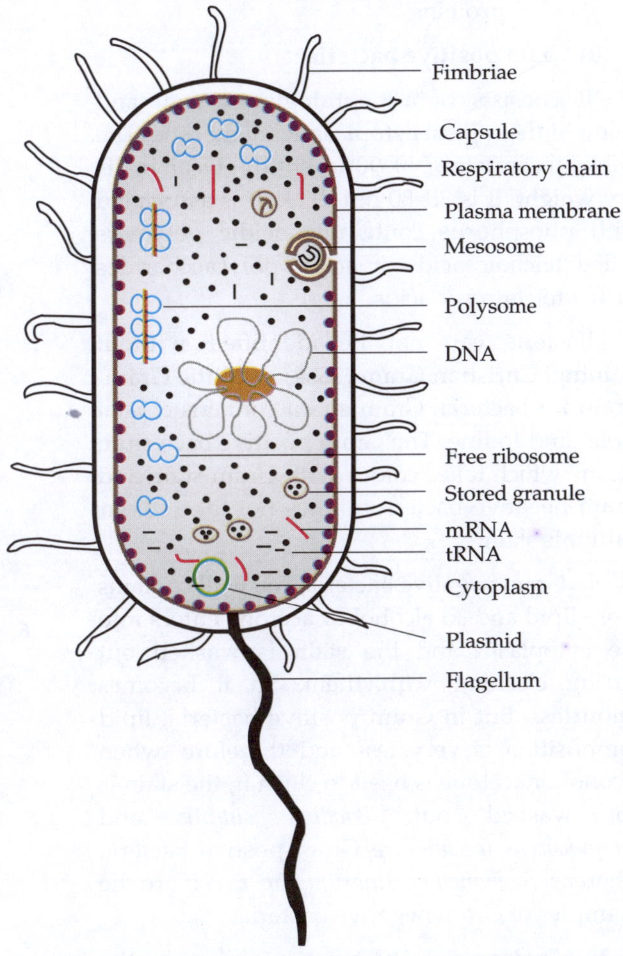


**Fig.13.1 :** *Generalized diagram of a bacterium*

transport chain and oxidative phosphorylation components, photosynthetic apparatus, attachment sites of chromosomes and plasmid DNA etc.

(ii) *Outer membrane or cell wall* : It is similar to the cytoplasmic membrane but contains less phospholipid and fewer proteins. it contains lipopolysaccharides and at least four different major protein components and also certain lipoproteins.

(b) **Gram positive bacteria :**

It consists of a peptidoglycan wall and below it the typical cytoplasmic membrane. The cell wall consists of 40–90% peptidoglycan by its dry weight. It is 30–80 nm thick. It is associated with phosphorus containing acidic polymers called teichoic acids or acidic polysaccharides such a teichuronic acids.

Bacteria can not be identified without staining. Christian Gram (1854) used the Gram-strain for bacteria. Gram strain contains crystal violet and Iodine. The Gram positive bacterium means which takes colour with Gram stain and Gram negative bacterium does not take colour with this stain.

In Gram negative bacteria, cell wall contains more lipid and so alcohol or acetone enters into the cytoplasm and the stain is washed out during cleaning with them. So it becomes colourless. But in Gram positive bacteria, lipid composition is very less and therefore, when alcohol or acetone is used to clean it, the stain is not washed out. *Bacillus subtilis* and *Streptococcus faecalis* are Gram postive bacteria whereas, *Salmonella galinarum* and *E. coli* are the examples of Gram negative bacteria.

3. **Mesosomes :** These are infoldings of the cell membrane, in both Gram positive and negative bacteria, particularly well developed in bacilli. The infoldings form structures with many vesicles, tubules or lamellar whorls. Salton and Owen (1976) have suggested that mesosomes may arise by vesicularization of the outer half of the lipid bilayer. Its function is not clear. It is devoid of enzymes and electron transport components.

4. **Ribosomes :** About 10000 ribosomes are found which remain free in the cytoplasm. It's average size is 70S consists of a larger 50S subunit and a smaller 30S subunit. *E. coli* ribosomes consist three types of RNA (5S, 16S and 23S) and 53 proteins.

5. **Storage granules :** Three different types of storage granules are found in the cytoplasm. viz., polymetaphosphate granules, poly-β–hydroxybutyrate granules and polyglucan granules.

   The polymetaphosphates ($PO^{-}_{3}$) are known as volutin granules, stain reddish violet with methylene blue or toluidine blue, found in *Spirillus volutans*. These are metachromatic because they stain with change in colour.

   Poly-β–hydroxybutyrates are energy reserved compounds, strain with Sudan Black stain. It is formed by the condensation of acetyl-CoA.

   Polyglucan granules conain starch which stain blue, reddish blue or brown with iodine.

6. **Fimbriae or Pili :** Such hair like appendages are called fimbriae or pili found only on the Gram negative bacteria and only one genus of Gram positive bacteria (*Corynebacterium renale*). These are straight, less rigid, 0.2–2.0μ in length and diameter of 250Å.

   Six groups of pili are found in bacteria Group-1 type is adhesive in nature, Group-2 is sex pili, Group-3 is thick and its function is not known. Group-4 is flexible, rod like. Group-5 is contractile tubule, Group-6 is found in Gram positive *Corynebacterium renale*.

   The fimbriae has a protein called **fimbrilin** (Mr 16000)

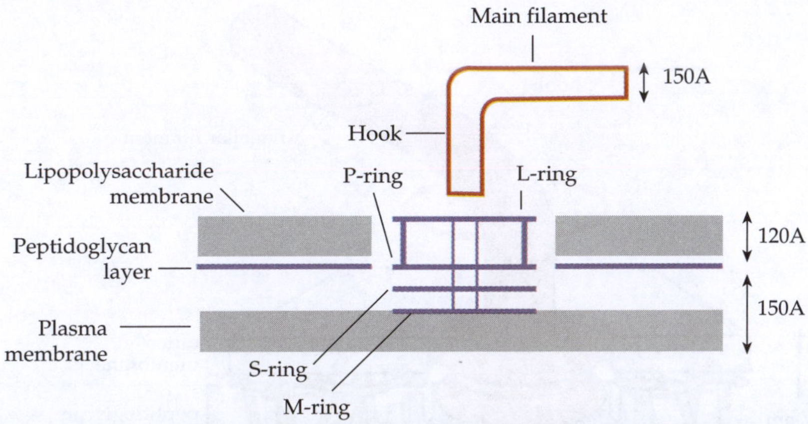


**Fig.13.2 :** *Base of flagellum of a Gram -ve bacterium*

7. **Flagella :** Motile bacteria swim toward higher concentrations to nutrients (attractants) such as sugars, amino acids and small peptides and always from higher concentration of various noxious chemicals (repellents). They swim by means of flagella, each of which is attached by a short flexible hook at its base to a small protein disc embedded in the bacterial membane. This disc is part of tiny motor that uses the energy stored in the transmembrane proton gradient to rotate rapidly and turn the helical flagellum.

The bacterial flagellum of Gram negative has three main parts, a basal body, a hook and a main filament or shaft (Fig. 13.2).

Basal body consists of two sets of rings, a proximal and a distal set, connected by a rod. Each set has two rings. The four rings are called the M (membrane) ring, the S (super membrane) ring, the P (peptidoglycan ring) and the L (lipopolysaccharide) ring, from the inner to the outer sides.

M ring is embedded in the inner membrane. S-ring lies in the periplasmic space between the inner and outer membranes. The P-ring is attached to the peptidoglycan layer of the cell wall and the the L-ring is attached to the lipopolysaccharide layer of the cell wall. The P and L rings form a bearing for the rod to pass through the outer cell wall membrane.

In Gram positive bacteria, the outer set of rings is absent. The M-ring is embedded in the inner membrane. S-ring may be attached to the inside of the thick peptidoglycan layer.

The hook connects the basal body with the shaft. It acts as a bearing. Shaft consists entirely of protein. The protein is *flagellin*. In *Baccillus subtitis* (strain 168), it is a single polypeptide chain of 304 amino acid residues (mol wt 32600). Its N-terminal end is basic, middle is acidic and C-terminal end is weakly acidic. The amino acids *tryptophan* and *cysteine* are absent. There is only one *tyrosine* and two *proline* residues.

Bacterial flagellum is upto 15μ long and 20–30 nm thick.

The shaft and hook are constructed with flagellin subunits about 5 nm in diameter. They are arranged helically to form cylindrical fibrils. Eleven longitudinal rows of subunits form the tube of the shaft.

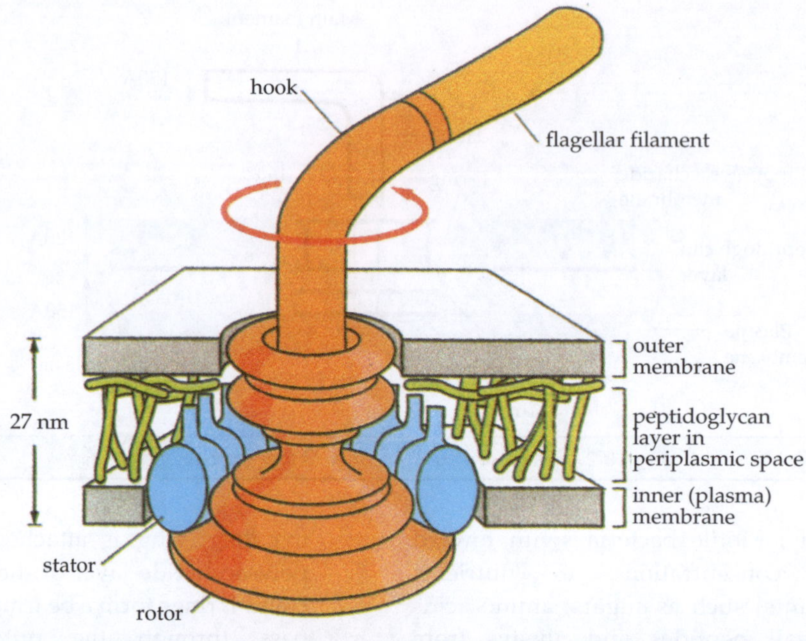


**Fig.13.3 :** *The bacterial flagellar motor. (Redrawn from Mol. Biol. of the Cell by Alberts et. al. 4th edn)*

The rings form a rotor, which rotates with the flagellum at more than 100 revolutions per second. The rotation is driven by a flow of protons through an outer ring of proteins called **stator**, which also contain proteins responsible for switching the direction of rotation(Fig. 13.3).

Counterclock-wise rotation allows all the flagella to draw together into a coherent bundle so that bacterium swims uniformly in one direction. Clockwise rotation causes them to fly apart, so that bacterium tumbles chaotically without moving forward.

8. **Nucleoid :** The nuclear material is prokaryotic type, devoid of nuclear membrane, nucleolus and nuclear reticulum. So this is called **nucleoid**. It is circular RNA at the centre and double helical DNA is present around the centre.

## 13.2 *E. COLI* GENOME

The chromosome of *E. coli* has been thoroughly mapped and the hundreds of identifiable genes have been able to locate in a single circular linkage group. A single cell may have more than one chromosome at a time, this is due to the division of chromosome and division of the cell which are not necessarily coordinated with each other (Fig. 13.4).

The chromosome of *E. coli* is a double helix of DNA, about 11000 μm in length with a diameter of 20 to 40 Å. *E. coli* K12 genome is just 4639 kb and has only 4405 genes (Blattner *et al* 1997) Besides, it may carry additional genes on independent circular or linear DNA molecules called *Plasmids*. These genes coding for properties such as antibiotic resistance or ability to utilize toluene as a carbon source.

*E. coli* genome is compact. It has been observed that a 50 kb segment of the *E. coli* K12 genome, there are more genes and less space between, with 43 genes taking up 85.9% of the segment . Some genes have virtually no space between them. *thr-A* and *thr-B* for example, are separated by a single nucleotide and *thr-C* begins at the nucleotide immediately following the last nucleotide of *thr-B*. These three genes

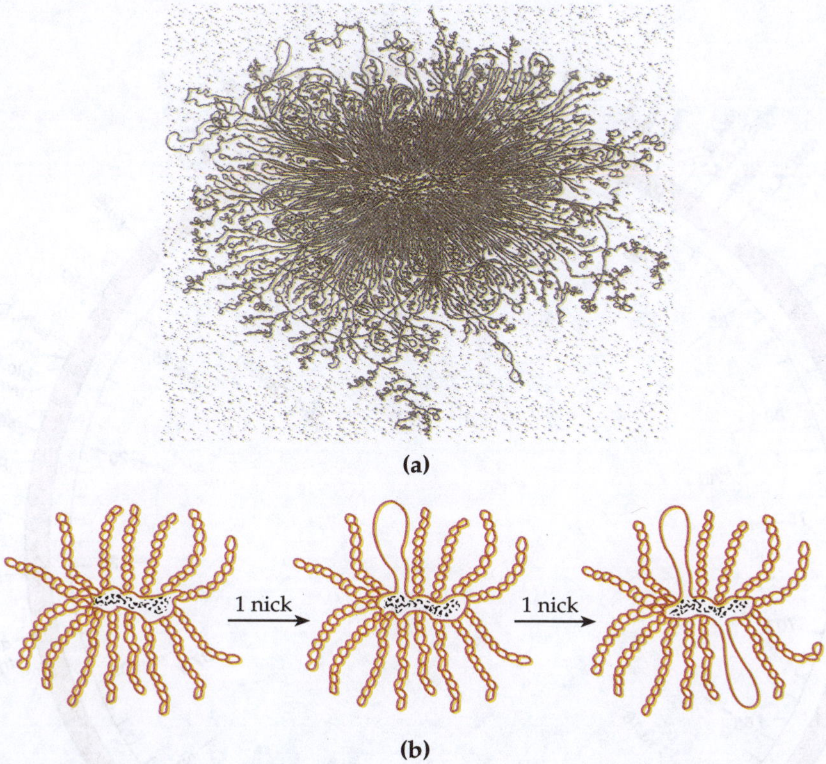


**Fig.13.4 :** *(a) Electron micrograph of E. coli chromosome; (b) Schematic drawing of highly folded supercoiled chromosome*

are the examples of one operon and expressed in conjunction with one another.

*E. coli* genome has no introns *i.e.* there is no discontinuous genes at all and also have no repetitive genes.

They possess certain sequences that might be repeated elsewhere in the genome. These insertion sequences (IS1 and IS186) can be seen in the 50 kb segment, that have an ability to move around the genome. These sequences could be in different position or might be entirely absent from the genome.

The circumference of the circular *E. coli* chromosome is 1.6 mm. The genome is supercoiled. Supercoiling occurs when additional turns are introduced into the DNA double helix (+ve supercoil) or if turns are removed ( –ve supercoiling)

The circular molecule winding around itself to form a more compact structure. *E. coli* super–coiling is thought to be generated and controlled by two enzymes, DNA gyrase and DNA topoisomerase-I.

*E. coli* DNA molecule does not have unlimited freedom to rotate once a break is introduced. This is due to presence of protein into it.

The current model of *E. coli* is that, DNA is attached to a protein core from which 40-50 supercoiled loops radiate out into the cell. Each loop contains approximately 100 kb of supercoiled DNA.

Besides, DNA gyrase and topoisomerase-I which are required for replication, there are at least 4 proteins, have more specific role in packaging the DNA. The most abundant of

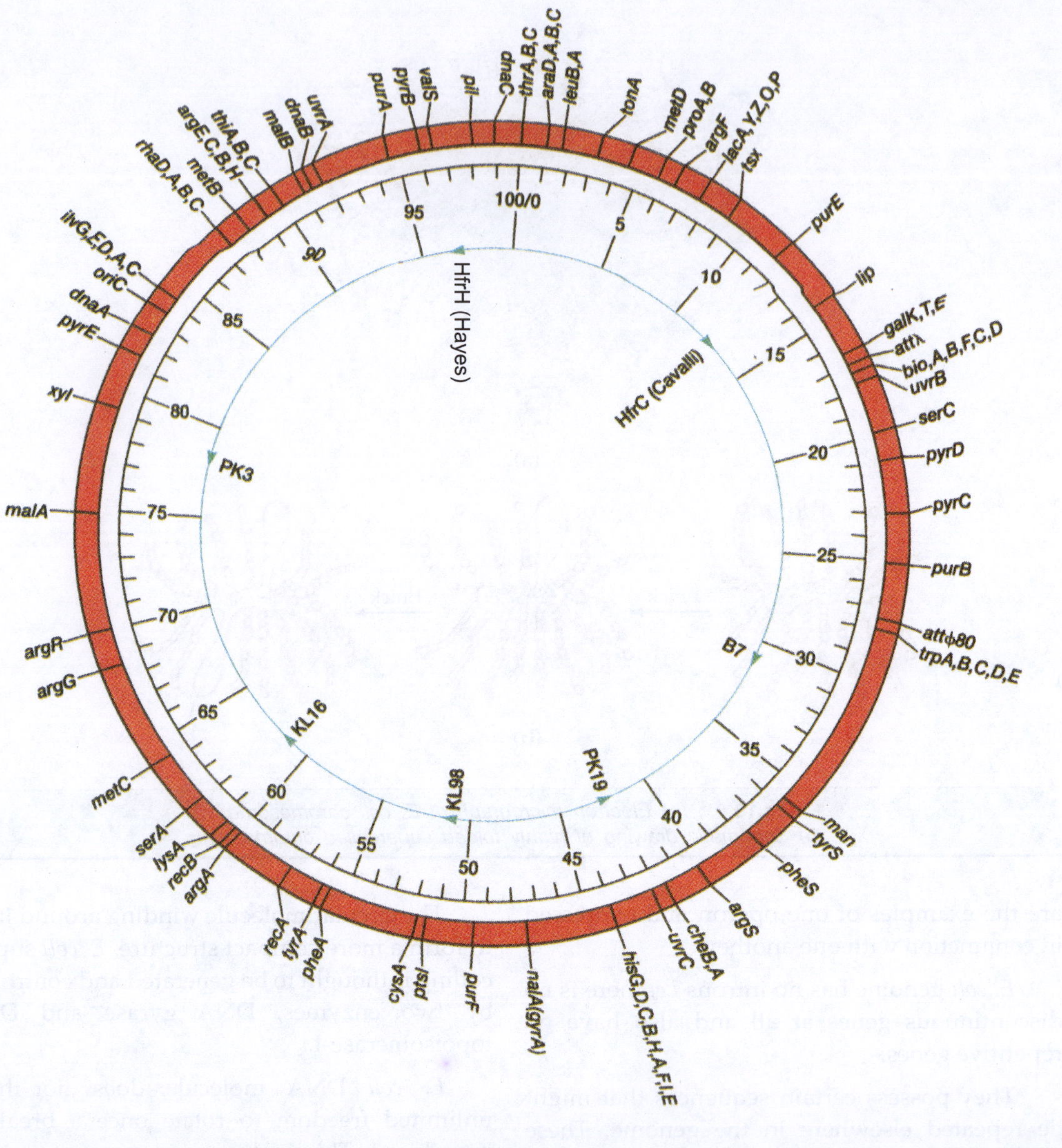


**Fig.13.5 :** *Genome organization of E. coli*

these proteins is HU, forming a tetramer around which 60 bp of DNA becomes wound.

*E. coli.* K12 has a 4.6 Mb chromosome and can harbour various combinations of plasmids, all of which are dispensable, it is acceptable to define the main chromosome as the genome.

The complete genetic map of *E. coli.* K12 genome showed that there is only 11% areas which is non-coding DNA. Over 1500 of the *E. coli.* K12 genes have been assigned their functions and an appreciable number of genes have been known that are involved in their different functions (Fig. 13.5).

**Partial genome analysis of *E. coli* :**

| | |
|---|---|
| Total number of genes | 4405 |
| Total protein coding genes | 4288 |
| Biosynthesis of amino acids | 131 |
| Biosynthesis of cofactors | 103 |
| Biosynthesis of nucleotides | 53 |
| Cell envelope proteins | 237 |
| Energy metabolism | 243 |
| DNA replication, recombination and repair | 115 |
| Protein folding | 9 |
| Regulatory proteins | 178 |
| Transcription | 55 |
| Translation | 182 |
| Uptake of molecules from the environment | 427 |
| Metabolism of lipids and others | 236 |

## 13.3 GENOME OF PLASMIDS

### 13.3.1 Concept

Plasmids are extrachromosomal genetic units. Initially these were termed as **episomes**. These are self replicating. They occur naturally in bacteria and also in yeast and some eukaryotic cells, exist as parasitic or symbiotic relationship with their host cell.

Plasmids are circular, double stranded molecules of DNA. They carry certain genes, inherited to both the daughter cells and carryout a variety of biological functions. They may be conjugating and transmitted from donor to recipient cell by conjugation. The genes on plasmids do not require for the normal viability of the bacteria, but they confer selection advantage to the bacteria. The non-conjugative plasmid is unable to promote its own transfer by conjugation.

### 13.3.2 Types of plasmid

Plasmids are of different classes :

1. **Sex factors :** Some conjugative plasmids can cause the transfer of chromosomal genes during conjugation. Such plasmids are termed as *sex factors*. In *E. coli.* K12, such plasmid is known as sex factor-F which can either exist as an independent or autonomous unit. Sometimes, F-factor is being integrated into their genome. Such a plasmid is called Hfr (high frequency of recombination)

2. **R-plasmids :** They bear antibiotic resistance factor or R-factor, that consists of genes producing resistance to antibiotics and thus the bacteria become antibiotic resistant. Thus the bacteria acquire resistant to gentamycin, chloramphenicol, ampicillin and sulfonamide etc.

   R-plasmids were first discovered in a strain of *Shigella* in the late 1950s during an epidemic of dysentery in Japan. They acquire resistant to four major drugs such as sulphonamides, streptomycin, tetracyline and chloramphenicol. R100 plasmid has been isolated from *S. flexneri* which contains all four resistance genes together with the genes required for transfer in a circular molecule. These are called **cointegrate plasmids**. In the plasmid aggregates, various genes are located at least sometime, on separate molecules. Such a plasmid is found in *Salmonella typhimurium* type 29.

3. **Plasmids that confer pathogenicity to mammals :** Some bacteria are found to be harmless but are found sometimes to be infectious. The enteric plasmids produce heat-stable and heat liable toxins. Hly plasmids code for the production of $\alpha$–haemolysins that cause lysis of RBC.

4. **Col-plasmids :** Certain *E. coli* strains synthesize bacteriocins (colicins) which are active against enteric bacteria.

5. **Tumour inducing plasmids :** In *Agrobacterium tumifacians,* a large plasmid is found to cause the disease crown gall in dicot plants and induces growth of tumor.

### 13.3.3 General Characteristics of Plasmid

Plasmids are autonomous self replicating molecules of DNA or sometimes RNA. These are not regarded as the part of the cell's genome for two reasons.

1. A particular plasmid may be found in cells of different species and may move from one host species to another.
2. A plasmid may sometimes be present and sometimes absent from the cells of a particular host species.

They carry genetic informations that may be expressed in the host cell and these host cells confer these phenotypes.

The general characteristics of plasmid are as follows :

1. These are **replicons**, *i.e.* self-replicating molecules of nucleic acids. The circular plasmids replicate by both replication and rolling circle methods. Linear plasmids replicate by a separate method. Plasmids have distinct *ori* region.
2. The **copy number** is the number of copies of the plasmid in each bacterial cell. For most plasmids, it is one or two copies per bacterium but it may be as many as 50 or more.
3. **Size** of plasmid varies enormously. F-plasmid is 1 percent of the size of *E. coli* chromosome while ColE plasmids are 10% of the size of F-Plasmid. Some plasmids may be as large as 10% of the size of chromosome.
4. Plasmids usually have antibiotic-resistance genes and the cells confer this property. But some plasmids are called **cryptic plasmids**, those confer no identifiable phenotype on the host.
5. The **host range** of plasmids vary widely. Some are restricted to a few closely related bacteria. For example, the F-plasmid only inhabits *E. coli* and related species like *Shigella* and *Salmonella* . Some plasmids have wide range of hosts. For example, plasmids of P-family can live in hundreds of different species. These plasmids are called "**promiscuous**" because of their wide host range.
6. Certain plasmids can move themselves from one bacterial cell to another, a property known as **transferability.** For example, F-Plasmid and P-plamids. They are large plasmids having genes for such property.
7. Small plasmids, such as Col E, do not have enough DNA to accomodate the genes needed. They can be mobilized by self transferable plasmids *i.e.* they are called **Mob$^+$.**

## 13.4 PLASMID REPLICATION

Plasmids encode only a few of the proteins required for their own replication. It encodes only one of the proteins needed for initiation at the *ori* site. All of the other required proteins, including DNA polymerase, ligase, primase, helicase and so on are borrowed from the host.

Plasmid replicates by one of the two general mechanisms. Some plasmids, such as the F-plasmid of *E. coli*, have two separate origins of replication. They divide by bi-directional replication (also known as vegetative replication) when their host cells divide, but use the rolling circle mechanism when they move from one cell to another during conjugation. Bi-directional replication starts are *ori V*, the origin of vegetative replication. But during transfer, they use *ori T*.

**Theta replication :** Just after initiation of replication, the circular DNA creates a structure that looks like the Greek letter θ, hence the name theta replication is given. The theta repliation is the most common form of DNA replication, in the bacteria as well as plasmids like ColE 1, RK2, F and P1 etc.

**Rolling circle replication :** The plasmids which replicate by this mechanism are called RC plasmids. The replication occurs in two stages. In the first stage, the double-stranded circular DNA replicates to form another double stranded circular DNA and a single-stranded circular DNA.

In the second stage, the complementary strand is synthesized on the single-stranded DNA to make another double-stranded DNA. The detailed mechanism is as follows :

1. At the first step, the dimeric **Rep** protein recognizes and binds to a palindromic sequence which contains the double-strand origin (DSO) on the DNA.
2. Binding of dimeric Rep protein allows the formation of a cruciform structure. Rep makes a nick there. and remains convalently attached to the 5′-end of DNA at the nick through a *tyr* in one copy of the Rep protein dimer.
3. DNA polymerase III of the host uses the exposed 3′-OH end of the break as the primer for replication and continues replication on the unnicked strand as a template. The host helicase enzyme or in some cases Rep protein itself acts as the helicase to displace the nicked strand. The SSB proteins are also used to displace the DNA strands.
5. Once the circle is complete, the 5′-phosphate is transferred from *tyr* site on the Rep protein to the 5′-OH on the other end of the displaced strand producing an ssDNA strand. This process is called **phosphotransferase** reaction, requires no energy.
6. Concatemer is not formed here like those in viruses where rolling circle is going on making longer molecules of many times of original length of DNA. Possibly DNA pol-III does keep going past to DSO for a short distance, creating another double-stranded DSO. The other copy of Rep dimer makes a nick at the newly created DSO transferring 5′-end to itself. Thus Rep is being inactivated. Another explanation is that probably involving host DNA ligase causing the nick to be resealed, resulting in a circular dsDNA molecule.
7. The newly synthesized ssDNA molecule is replicated by a different mechanism. The RNA polymerase of host cell makes a short RNA primer at the different origin, called **single stranded origin** (SSO). After making the primer RNA polymerase handed over its 5′-end to the DNA polymerase III to complete the circle. RNA polymerase starts its functions only after the completion of replication, so that the DSO does not appear in the displaced DNA. DNA polymerase-I removes the primer and the nick is sealed by host DNA ligase (Fig. 13.6).
8. The Rep protein is only once for every round of plasmid DNA replication and is destroyed after the round is completed.

**Replication of Linear plasmids :** Linear dsDNA plasmids are found in some bacteria such as *Borrelia* and *Streptomyces,* that also contain linear chromosomes.

Linear plasmids have special structures to protect the end of the DNA. Linear plasmids of *Borrelia* form hairpin loops at the ends, whereas the linear plasmids of *Streptomyces* are coated with proteins that protect the DNA ends (Fig. 13.7).

The linerar DNA faces a problem with replicating the lagging strand, which is called "**primer problem**" because DNA polymerases can not initiate the synthesis of a new DNA strand. Different linear DNAs solve the primer problem in different ways.

Some linear plasmids have hairpin ends. These plasmids replicate from an internal origin of replication to form dimeric circles, composed of two plasmids joined head to tail to form a

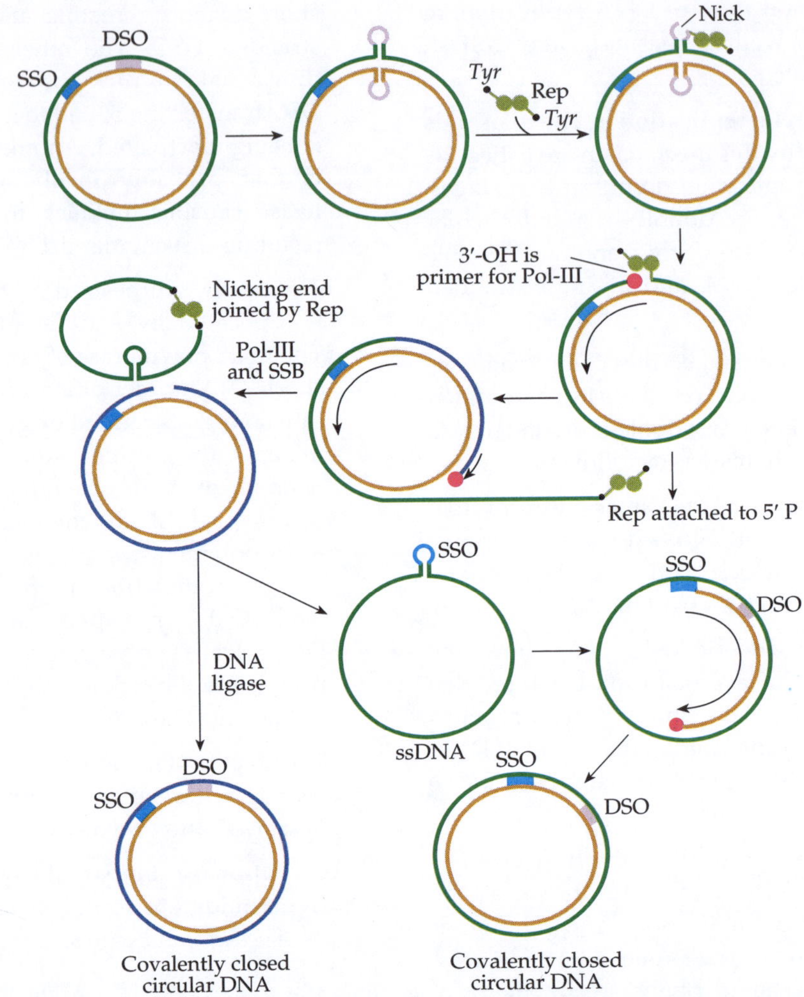


**Fig.13.6 :** *Rolling circle replication of plasmid*
*SSO = Single stranded origin, DSO = Double stranded origin*
*SSB = Single strand binding protein, Pol III = DNA polymerase III*

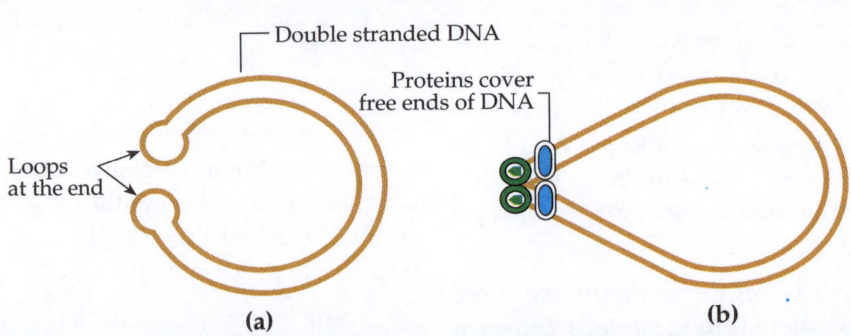


**Fig.13.7 :** *End structures of linear plasmids*
*(a) Hairpin loops of the plasmid of Borrelia*
*(b) Proteins coated to protect the DNA ends in Streptomyces.*

circle. These dimeric circles are then resolved into linear individual linear plasmid DNAs by the enzymes called **prototelomerases** which cut the circle into two linear plasmids and join the ends to each other to form the closed hairpins.

Other linear plasmids have extensive inverted repeated sequences at their ends and a terminal protein attached to their 5′-end. It is not clear how these plasmids replicate, but they might use some sort of **slippage mechansism,** using terminal protein as either a recombinase or a primer or both.

It is fact that bacteria with linear plasmids also often have linear chromosomes and the two DNAs replicate by similar mechanisms.

**Replication of RNA plasmids :** RNA plasmids are rare and most poorly characterized. Some strains of the yeast, *Saccharomyces cerevisiae* contain linear RNA plasmids. RNA plasmids are also found in mitochondria of some varieties of maize plants. These may be ssRNA or dsRNA forms. They replicate in a manner similar to certain RNA viruses. The RNA plasmid encodes RNA-dependent RNA polymerase that directs its own synthesis. But the plasmids do not contain genes for coat proteins. Possibly these RNA plasmids have evolved from RNA viruses that have taken up permanent residence after losing the ability to move from cell to cell as virus particles do.

## 13.5 PLASMID FAMILIES AND INCOMPATIBILITY

Sometimes two different types of plasmid cannot coexist stably in the same cell. This is known as **incompatibility.** In this case one of the other plasmids is lost as the cells multiply. These two plasmids are said to be members of **same incompatibility** (Inc) **groups.**

If two plasmids coesist stably, they are **compatable** or may be said that they belong to **different incompatibility groups.**

The phenomenon of incompatibility can be described by several ways. One way is explained by the **repressor model for initiation of replication** and the other way where they share the **same partitioning functions** which are closely associated with the replication control in the *ori* region.

**Repressor model :** Two plasmids, F and ColE1 may be found in a cell but they have different repressors. Their replication proceeds independently, because repressor of one type does not regulate the repressor of the other type. They belong to the different incompatibility groups. During cell division, both types of plasmid replicate and the daughter cells will inherit both plasmids just like the mother cell but not likely, they will get the same number of each plasmid.

The situation is quite different with two plasmids **A** and **B** are similar enough that repressor of **A** can regulate replication of **B** and vice versa. If a cell having one copy of A and one copy of B, the first replication event results either 1A 2B or 2A1B. When second replication event occurs, each cell would have four plasmids. The plasmid composition has shown to be (1A3B), (2A2B) or (3A1B) depending upon the plasmid that has replicated.

At this point the cell which has twice the initial number of plasmids can divide.

(1A,3B) becomes (1A, 1B) + (1B, 1B)

(2A, 2B) becomes (1A, 1A) + (1B, 1B) or (1A, 1B) + 1A, 1B)

and (3A, 1B) becomes (1A,1A) + (1A, 1B) (Fig. 13.8).

The two possible types of cells (1A1A) and (1B1B) contain only one kind of plasmid. But those have (1A, 1B) both plasmids, 50% of the produced daughter cells would have only one kind of plasmid. Thus with each generation, progeny population with only one plasmid will increase.

Thus incompatibility is the result of two plasmids having a similar repressor and the random selection of plasmids for DNA replication.

**Partitioning model :** Two plasmids can also be incompatible if they share the same **Par**

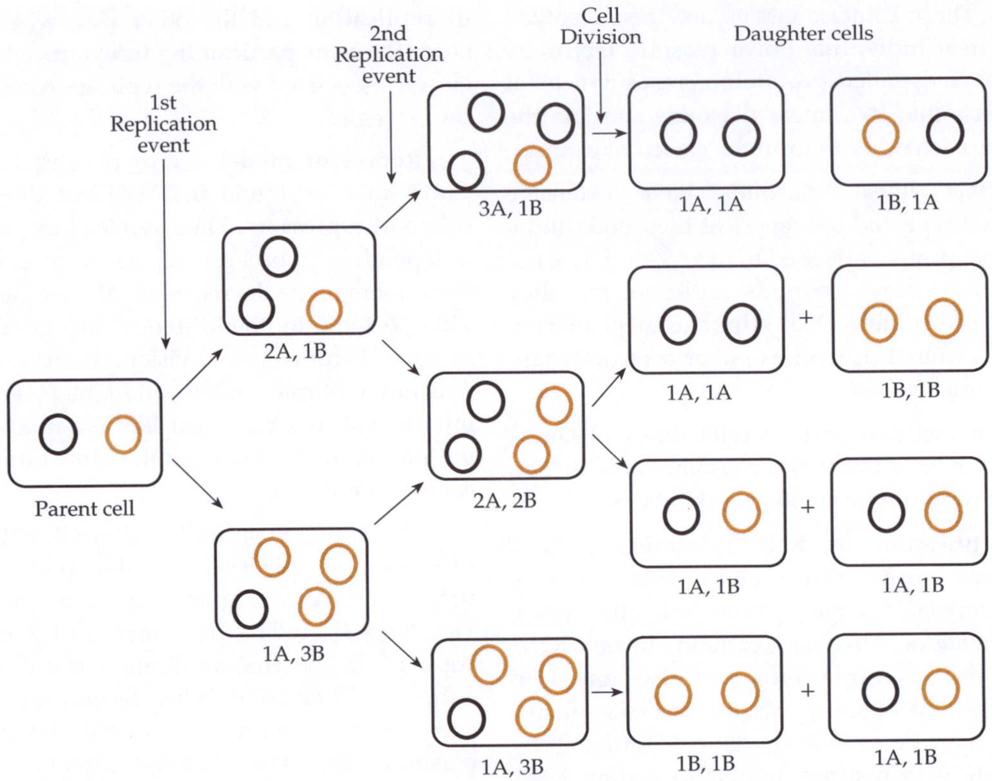


**Fig.13.8 :** *Four possible pairs of daughter cells that can arise from division of a cell containing each copy of the incompatible plasmids A and B.*

(Partitioning) system. Par system helps segregation of plasmids and chromosomes into daughter cells upon cell division. Normally this helps ensure that both daughter cells get at least one copy of the plasmid and neither daughter cell is cured of the plasmid. If coexisting plasmids share the same Par system, one or the other is always distributed into the daughter cells during cell division. However, one daughter cell receives one plasmid type and the other cell gets the other plasmid type, producing cells cured of one or the other plasmid (Fig. 13.9).

## 13.6 PARTITIONING AND THE PAR SYSTEMS OF PLASMIDS

Patitioning is an active process by which at least one copy of replicon (plasmid, chromosome etc.) is distributed into each daughter cell at the time of cell division.

The process of chromosome partitioning is still not understood very well. However, some of the genes whose products play roles in this process are now being identified. This is one of the most exiting areas of current research in bacterial cell biology.

**Par proteins :** The partitioning proteins are the products of *par* genes, which are discovered in plasmids. The **Par** systems of plasmids are known to fall into two families, one represented by the **Par** system of plasmid R1 and the other much larger, represented by plasmids P1, F and many others.

**The R1 plasmid Par system :**

The partitioning system of the R1 plasmid of *E. coli* consists of two protein coding genes *parM* and *parR* as well as a centromere-like *cis*-acting site *par C*.

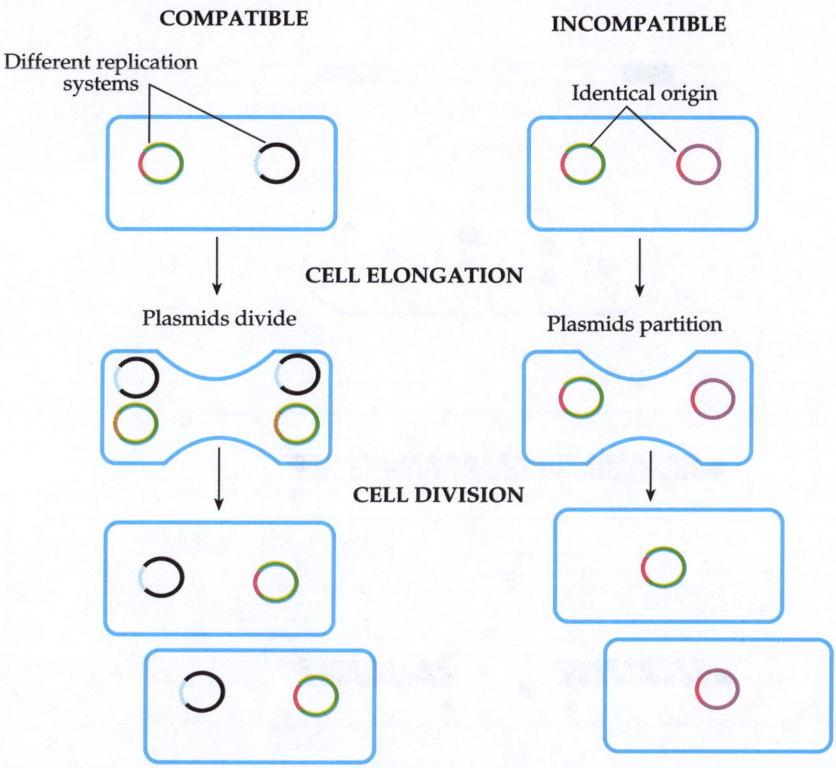


**Fig.13.9 :** *Plasmid incompatibility*

1. A few dimers of the Par R protein bind to the *par C* site.
2. Par R–*par C* complex serves as a nucleation site for the assembly of Par M.
3. Par M protein then can bind to Par R, but if only the latter is already bound to *par C*.
4. While the plasmid is replicating, this complex of the two Par R and Par M proteins is localized to the mid point of the cell and thereby localizes the plasmid to this point.
5. Par M protein begins to polymerize into helical filaments that extend from the center of the cell toward the cell poles. This polymerization might require pairing of the newly synthesized plasmids because it occurs only after plasmid replication is completed. Par M subunit is in the ATP -bound form when it first attaches. ATP is cleaved to ADP when the next subunit is attached. Thus ATP provides energy for the attachment and growth of the filament. Par M is an ATPase similar to actin of eukaryotes. In some species **actin**-like protein **Mre B** has been found which is required for determining cell shape and chromosomal segregation.
6. After the plasmid copies have been pushed to the poles of the cell, the ADP-ParM subunits dissociate from one or both ends and the filaments disappear.
7. Par M can then be recharged with ATP before the plasmids are partitioned again, before the next cell division.

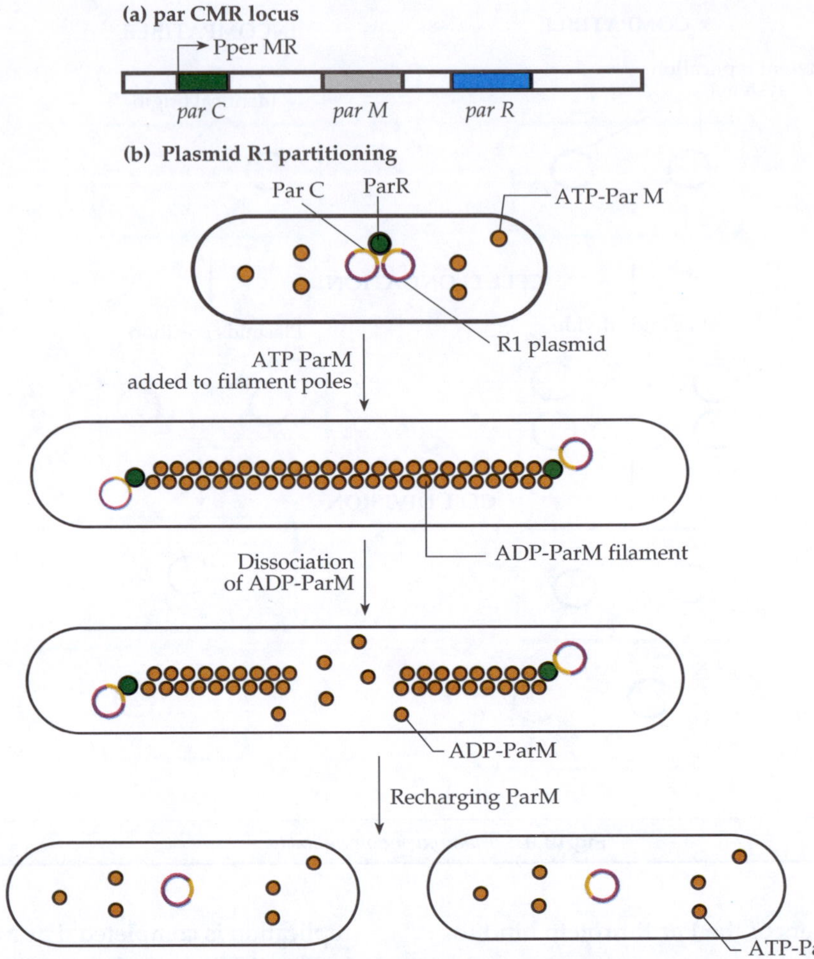


**Fig.13.10 :** *Partitioning of the R1 plasmid*

8. In bacteria, **FtsZ** protein is the homolog of **tubulin** protein of eukaryotes. This protein plays a role in cell division.

This is to be noted that bacterial ParM acts as microtubules of eukaryotes though it is actin-like in structure. Bacterial FtsZ acts as actin of eukaryotes though it is tubulin-like in structure. **Thus the role of actin and tubulin filaments seem to be reversed in the two Kingdoms** (Fig. 13.10).

**The P1 and F plasmid Par systems :**

Such partitioning systems are related to the systems of the P1 plasmid prophage and the F-plasmid and also some bacteria, including *Bacillus subtilis* and *Caulobacter crescentus*.

1. It consists of two proteins Par A and Par B which is similar to Par M and Par B proteins of R1 plasmid par system. The Par A has ATP binding motif but has no homology to actin or any other cytoskeletal proteins. It oscillates in a helical path from one end of the cell to the other during the cell cycle. The *Par S* is the *cis* acting site on which Par B binds.
2. In F plasmid, the corresponding proteins are **SopA** and **SopB** and the site is called ***sop S*** (for stability of plasmid).

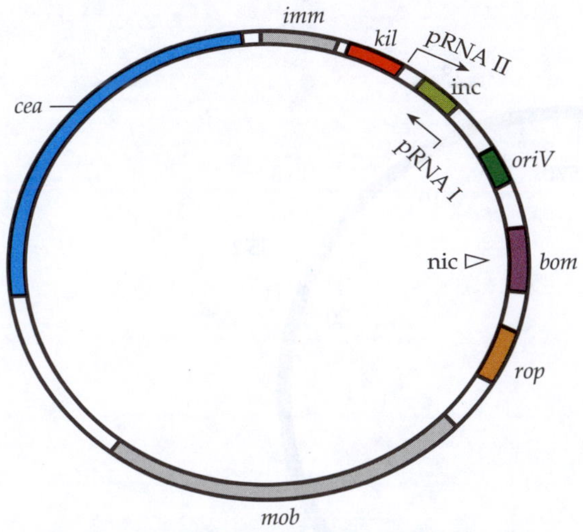


**Fig.13.11 :** *Genetic map of plasmid ColE1*

The mechanism of partitioning is similar to that of R1 plasmid. Rather than forming a single filament, a number of Par A filaments seem to radiate out from the Par B-*par S* complex which are called **radial asters**, like the petals on a daisy flower.

If the two plasmids share the same partitioning system, they will be incompatible, even if their replication control systems are different. If two plasmids that are otherwise different, share the same Par system, they can pair with each other after they replicate. Then one plasmid of each type is directed to opposite ends of the cell before the cell divides. In this way one daughter cell gets one type for plasmid and other cell gets other type of plasmid.

## 13.7 COL E PLASMID GENOME

The colE plasmids of *E. coli* can make bacteriocin. The three related Col E plasmids, Col E1, Col E2 and Col E3 are small plasmids exist in 50 or more copies per cell and have been used to derive many of the cloning vectors used in genetic engineering. A variety of other colicin plasmids also occur, including the Col I and Col IV. These are large single-copy plasmids and usually transferable from one strain to another strain of *E. coli*. Some of them also carry antibiotic resistance genes. Col E1 plasmid has been put to use in numerous molecular biology studies and many vectors have been derived from it or its close relative pMB1. These vectors include pBR322, pUC, pBAD, pACYC 184 etc.

All Col E bacteria are self transmissible. Genome size of ColE1, ColE2 and ColE3 is 6.6 kb, 7.6 kb and 7.6kb respectively. Colicin E1 disrupts energy gradient, colicin E2 is a DNase and colicin E3 is a ribosomal RNase.

Col E1 plasmid is 6646 bp long. It has several sites

1. *ori V* is the origin of replication
2. *cea* is the gene for colicin E1
3. *imm* gene is for immunity to colicin E1
4. *kil* gene required for the liberation of colicin from the producer cell
5. *Rom* gene is involved in copy number control
6. *pRNAII* is the promoter for the primer RNA II.
7. *inc* codes RNA I
8. *rop* encodes a protein which regulates copy number
9. *bom* is a site that is nicked at *nic*
10. *mob* encodes proteins required for mobilization (Fig. 13.11).

## 13.8 F PLASMID GENOME

F-plasmid genome is 94.5 kb size, present in *E. coli*. Number of copies is 1-2 per cell. This plasmid is self transmissible. The phenotypic features of F plasmid-bearing cells are presence of F-pilus and conjugation. The genetic map of the F-plasmid displays several genes and insertion segments (Fig. 13.12).

1. Different *tra* genes with different functions
2. *Ori T* and *ori V* genes
3. *fin O* and *fin P* genes

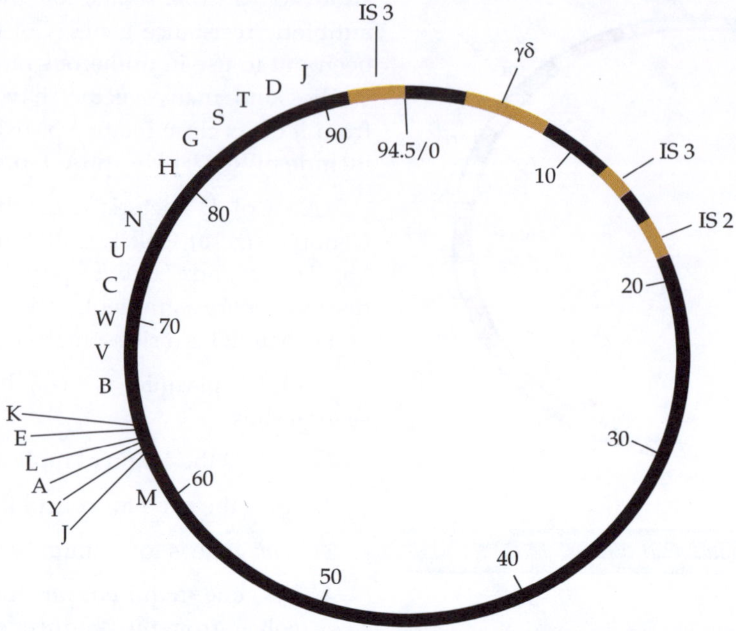


**Fig.13.12 :** *A map of the F-plasmid*

4. *inc B, inc C* and *inc E* genes.
5. IS2, IS3 and γδ transposons

The functions of these sequences and genes are given in the table (Table 13.1)

### 13.8.1 *tra* Genes of F-plasmid

Effectual transfer (*tra*) functions of F- plasmid are encoded in an operon. *Tra* genes encode different proteins which are essential for pili synthesis, assembly of functional pilus, transfer and nicking at the origin of transfer. Several other genes are also found to control other functions during conjugation. These genes are listed in the table 13.1.

**TABLE 13.1**
**Some F-plasmid genes and sites of their functions**

| Gene | Function |
|---|---|
| *tra A* | Pilin, major subunit of pilus |
| *tra B, C, E, F, G, H, K, L, Q, U, V, W* | Biosynthesis and assembly of pilus |
| *tra G, N* | Stabilization of mating pairs |
| *tra H* | DNA helicase |
| *tra J* | Regulation of *tra* operon |
| *tra M* | Initiation of plasmid transfer |
| *tra S, T* | Surface exclusion, Inhibition of mating between F containing cells. |
| *tra Y* | Nicking at *Ori T* |
| *Ori T* | Site nicked to initiate rolling circle replication and DNA transfer |
| *Ori V* | Origin of circular DNA replication |
| *fin O, P* | Fertility inhibition |
| *inc B, C, E* | Plasmid incompatibility |
| *IS2, IS3 and γδ* | Provide a mechanism for integration of F into the chromosome. |

### 13.8.2 Transfer of plasmid DNA

Recombination between donor and recipient cells requires cell to cell contact. The plasmid transfer can be divided into four stages.

1. Effective contact between specific-recipient pair.

2. Preparation of DNA transfer (mobilization)
3. DNA transfer
4. Formation of a replicative functional plasmid in the recipient.

Usually, when F or F′ plasmids come in contact with a recipient, all four steps occur. Based on these properties plasmids fall into 4 groups.

1. **A nontransmissible plasmid**, which lacks genes necessary for effective contact and DNA transfer.
2. **A conjugative plasmid** which carries genes that determine the effective contact function.
3. **A mobilizable plasmid** which can prepare its DNA for transfer.
4. **A self-transmissible plasmid** which is both conjugative and mobiliazable.

The cells which contain F, are mobilizable and conjugative, whereas the cells which contain ColE1, are mobilizable but nonconjugative. Therefore, if a bacterium contains only ColE1, cannot transfer its plasmid. If both F and ColE1 are present in the cell, F can provide missing conjugative function to ColE1. The process in which nonconjugative plasmid is transferred via effective contact provided by a conjugative plasmid is called **donation**. The efficiency of transfer of such nonconjugative plasmid is 10–100%. The *mob* (mobilization) gene for ColE plasmid is responsible for making nick at the origin for the transfer of ColE and unwinding the strand to be transferred.

A self transmissible plasmid cannot enable a nonmobilizable plasmids to be trnasferred by simple complementation. But transfer can still occur in some cases, although at low frequency. The transfer requires recombination between the two plasmids to form a single DNA molecule. The process is **conduction.** In the F-mediated transfer of the chromosome, the chromosome is mobilized by conduction.

**Mobilization of conjugative bacteria :** Transferability is the ability of certain plasmids to move themselves from one bacterial cell to another. Many medium sized plasmids, such as F-type and P-type plasmids can do this and are referred to as **Tra** (transfer positive).

1. **Effective contact :** For transfer to occur the two bacterial cells must come into physical contact. DNA is transferred in one direction only from the plasmid carrying donor to the recipient. Donor cell manufactures a *sex pilus* that binds to suitable recipient and draws the cells together.

   F-Pilus consists of a single hydrophobic protein called *pilin* which forms a hollow tubular structure, which suggested that plasmid DNA is transferred through the core of the pilus. Other experiments indicate that pili retract into the donor cell after pairing and more likely that the pilus serves first to bring the pair into initial contact and then to draw the cells together into close contact (Fig. 13.13).

2. **Mobilization :** Mobilization begins when a plasmid-encoded protein, which is probably the nicking protein of the relaxation complex, makes single-strand break in a unique base sequence called the **transfer origin** or *ori T*. This nick initiates rolling circle replication and the linear branch of the rolling circle is then transferred. The nicking protein remains bound to the 5′end of the nick.

3. **Transfer of DNA :** Transfer of DNA from donor to recipient requires 30 genes. The plasmids that enable a cell to donate DNA are called *fertility plasmids*. F-plasmid of *E. coli* is one of such fertility plasmids, approximately 100kb long. When a recipient (female) cell receives the F-plasmid becomes $F^+$ (i.e. male).

4. **Formation of a replicative functional plasmid in the recepient :** During

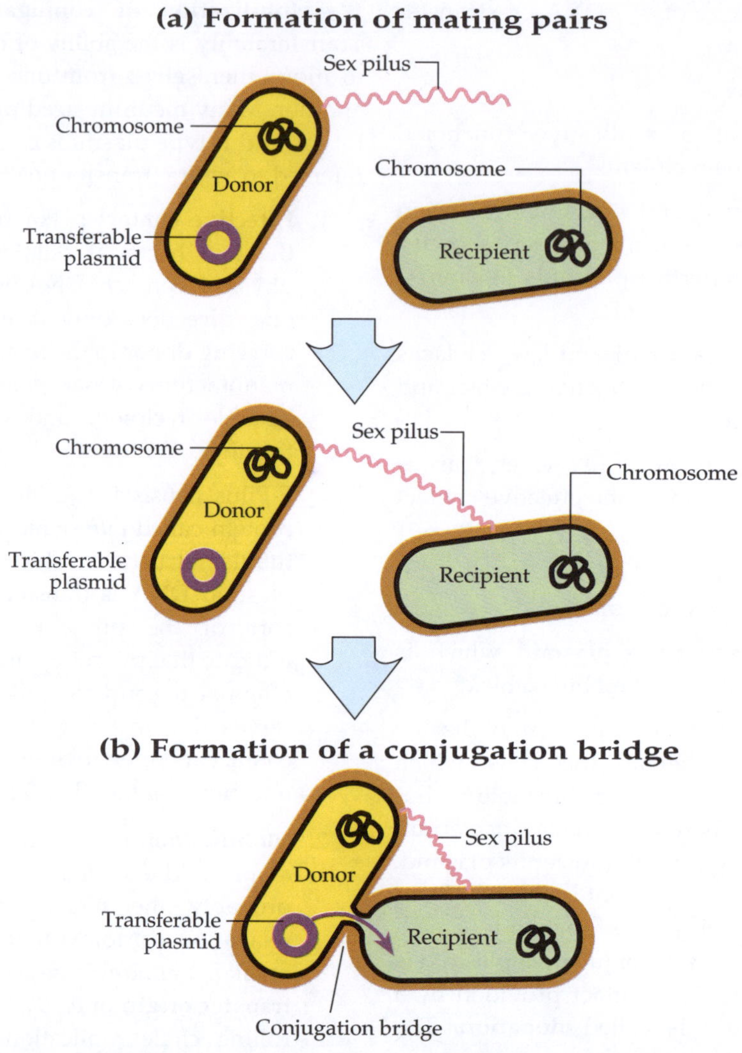


**Fig.13.13 :** *Mobilization of Conjugative bacteria. Modified from, Molecular Biology by Clark, 1st edn., 2005)*

transfer both the donor and recipient cells simultaneously synthesize DNA to make them double stranded, which are known as **donor conjugal DNA synthesis** and **recipient conjugal DNA synthesis.** The synthesis of DNA *i.e.* replication occurs through rolling circle mechanism.

## 13.9 PLASMID ATTRACTING PHEROMONES

Some strains of *Enterococcus faecalis* (gram +ve bacterium) excrete pheromone-like compounds that can stimulate mating with donor cells. These pheromones are small peptides, each of which stimulates mating with cells containing a particular plasmid. The pheromone stimulates the expression of *tra* gene in the plasmids of neighbouring bacteria, inducing aggregtion as well as mating. Once the cell has acquired a plasmid, it no longer excretes other peptides that stimulate mating with cells containing other plasmid types.

**Mechanism :**

1. The recipient cell has the chromosome, which has pheromone genes *cAD1* and *cCF10*. These two genes encodes two propheromone peptides **cAD1** and **cCF10**. These are processed, the signal peptides are cut off and pheromones are then released from the cell.
2. The donor cell which carrying the plasmid, expresses *traA* but product TraA represses transcription of other *tra* genes except *tra C* and *tra B*, which encode two surface proteins **TraC** and **TraB**. The **TraC** can sense pheromone.
3. During induction of mating, *cAD1* pheromone from recipient cell binds TraC on the cell surface of a donor cell in close proximity and enters into the donor cell via the **oligopeptide polymerase system.** The pheromone binds to **TraA** (a repressor), releasing it from DNA, *traE* gene is on and encodes **TraE** protein. Then **TraE** activates the expression of other *tra* gene including the genes encoding the **aggregation substance (Asa).**
4. The next step is plasmid transfer where donor cell establishes direct contact with the recipient cell, producing a transconjugant, and the plasmid is transferred.
5. The transcojugant then shuts down the pheromone. The *iad1* gene is on, encoded a **pro-iAD1** and it is processed to form **iAD1** and secretes. It binds to **TraC** and prevents autoinduction or pheromone induction of mating with other donor cells. **TraB** is an inhibitor protein, may prevent the induction by preventing the excretion of pheromone **cAD1**, but cCF 10 is still continued to be expressed (Fig. 13.14).

## 13.10 CONTROL OF COPY NUMBER OF PLASMIDS IN THE CELL BY ANTISENSE RNA

In bacteria, where multicopy plasmids present, the copy number is limited by themselves when the number of plasmid reaches to a cerain level. These plasmids are sometimes said to have "relaxed" copy number control. The single copy plasmids have "stringent" copy number control because the division is more tightly regulated and they replicate once during the cell cycle.

The initiation of plasmid replication is controlled by the involvement of *antisense-RNA*.

The initiation of ColE1 replication occurs with the transcription of an RNA molecule of 555 bases that acts as a primer for DNA synthesis. This preprimer RNA is called RNA II. This is then cleaved by ribonuclease H to generate a primer with a free 3′-OH group, which can be used by DNA polymerase-I to start DNA synthesis (Fig. 13.15).

If ribonuclease H fails to cleave the preprimer RNA II, no free 3′ end is made, the replication is prevented. Ribonuclease H is specific for DNA-RNA hybrid.

A second transcript RNA I (108 bases long) is also made from the same region of Col E1 as RNA II, but it is trancribed from the opposite strand of DNA and therefore this is complementary to RNA II. The RNA I and RNA II start to base pair forming a region of bubble, no cut is made by ribonuclease-H, then the RNA II transcription continues but DNA synthesis fails to start. The copy number is determined by the relative strengths of binding of RNA I and RNA II (Fig. 13.16).

A protein called **Rom**, which is also encoded by a gene of ColE1 also increases binding between RNA I and RNA II. If the gene for Rom is inactivated, copy number may be increased by it, still controlled.

If an inhibitor of protein synthesis, such as chloramphenicol is added to the culture of

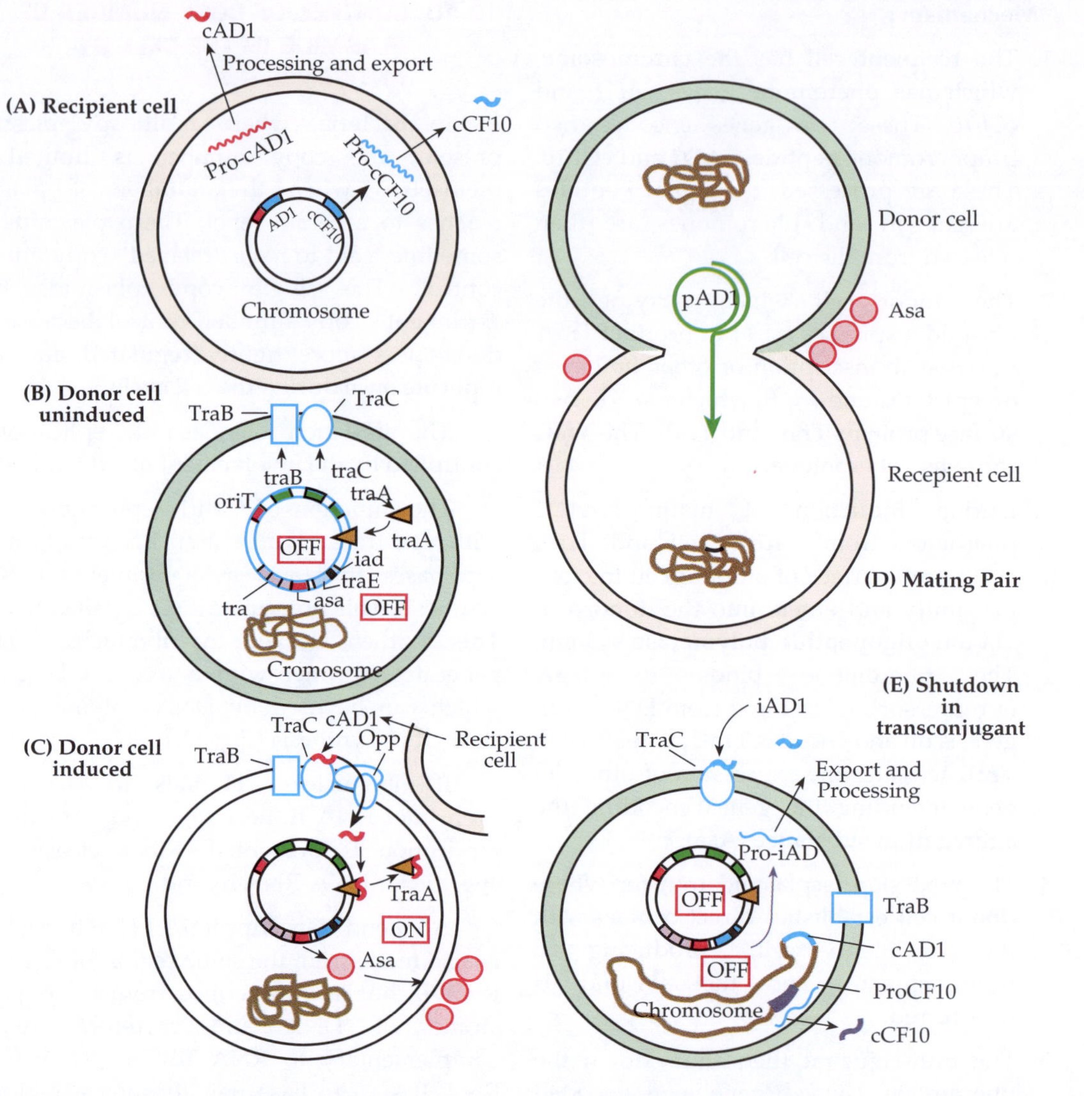


**Fig.13.14 :** *Role of Pheromones in plasmid transfer. (Redrawn from Molecular genetics of bacteria by L. Snyder and W Champners, 3rd edn. 2007)*

plasmid containing bacteria, initiation of bacterial genome replication is inhibited but plasmid replication continues until the number is increased to 1000. This is **plasmid amplification** because plasmid copy number repressor is concentration-dependent inhibitor and the repressor can not accumulate in absence of protein synthesis and plasmid replication will continue unregulated.

## 13.11 MOBILIZATION OF PLASMID

Some plasmids are not self-trasmissible but can be transferred by another self-transmissible plasmid sharing the same cell. *The plasmids that cannot transfer themselves but can be transferred by other plasmids are said to be mobilizable, and the process by which they are transferred is called mobilization.*

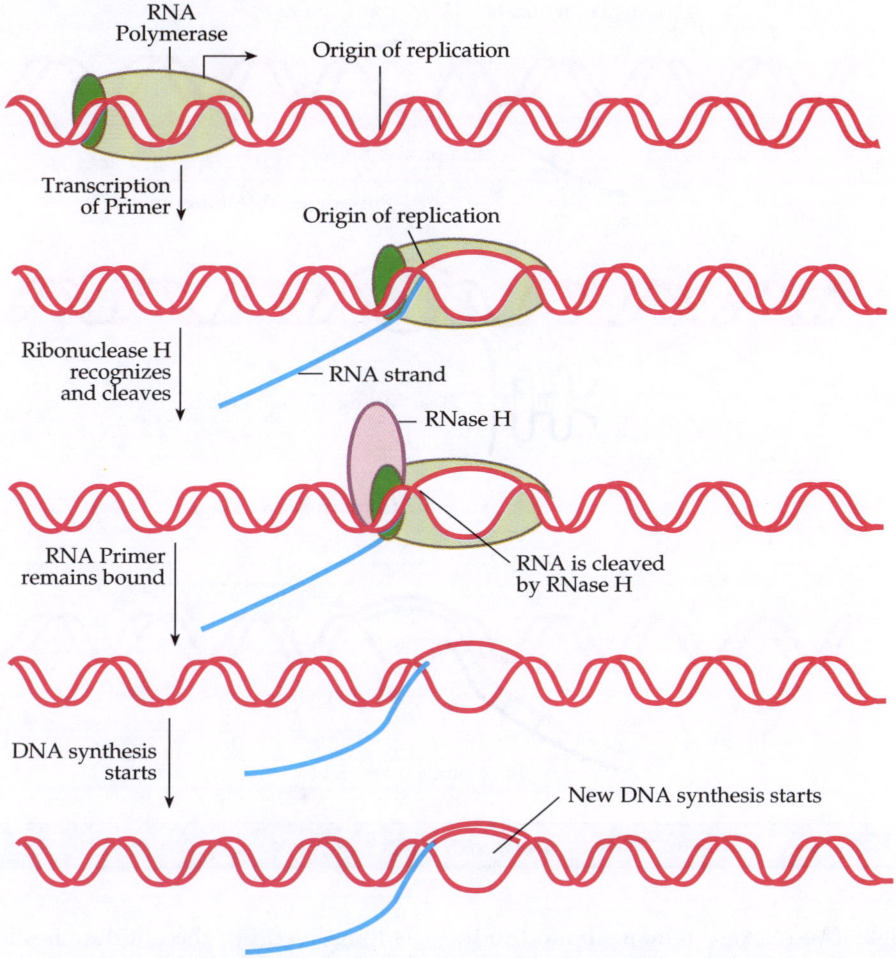


**Fig.13.15 :** *Priming of ColE1 plasmid replication.*

The mobilizable plasmids merely contain the *ori T* sequence of a self-transmissible plasmid.

All mobilizable plasmids encode their own Dtr systems (DNA transfer components). The ***mob* gene** is involved in this process.The system includes their own relaxase and helicase.

The **Mpf system** (Mating pair formation) of self transmissible plasmid is acting not only on its Dtr system but also to the **Dtr system** of the mobilizable plasmids. Therefore, mobilizable plasmid (Col E1) requires a self-transmissible plasmid (F) to ensure the pairing, nicking and transfer of DNA. The mechanism is as follows :

**Step 1 :** Self transmissible plasmid encodes the Mpf component. This component is made up of *tra* gene products, which is involved in making the contact with other cell with coupling proteins. Thus, self-transmissible plasmid forms a mating bridge with the recipient cell.

**Step 2 :** The coupling protein signals to relaxase not only to self-transmissible plasmid but also to mobilizable plasmid.

**Step 3 :** The relaxase of mobilizable plasmid then makes a single stranded break at *ori T* in the *mob* region of mobilizable plasmid and the helicase separates the strands.

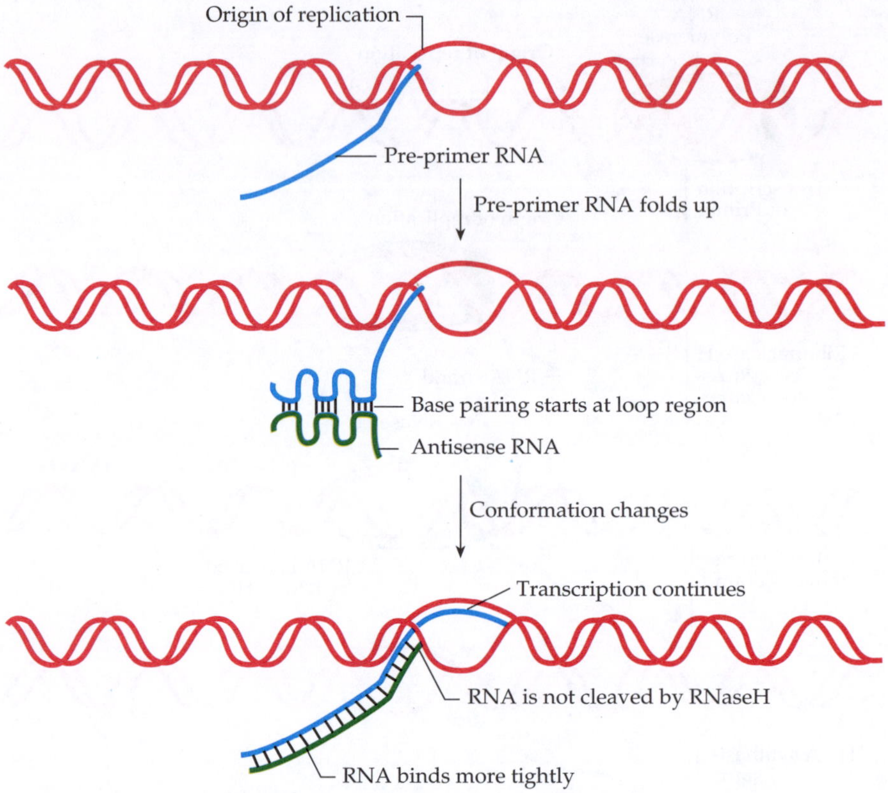


**Fig.13.16 :** *Antisense RNA prevents primer formation.*

**Step 4 :** The relaxase remains bound to the 5′-end of the single-stranded DNA and is transferred into the recipient cell, dragging the ssDNA of the mobilizable plasmid with it.

**Step 5 :** The self-transmissible plasmid is also often transferred at the same time. The mobilizable plasmid is replicated in the recipient (Fig. 13.17).

## 13.12 PLASMID ADDICTION

The plasmid addiction system kills the bacterial cell if the plasmid, is lost. So only cells that retain the plasmid, survive. Thus the plasmids possess gene whose function is to ensure that the host cell does not lose them.

Plasmids made two components, one is lethal to the host and the other is its antidote. The toxin is produced in the cell by them which is long-lived but the antidote is short-lived. As long as the antidote is synthesized in the cell, the effect of toxin is neutralized and the cell survive. But if the cell lost the plasmid, the short-lived antidotes decay but long-lived toxin is still remained present and kills the cell.

There are two different systems for killing the cells.

F-plasmid has the **protein-based host killing operon**, where two genes are operated *ccd A* gene produces CcdA, which is an antidote protein, continuously synthesized and destroyed by host cell protease. But due to its fresh supply it remains attached with the CcdB protein (the *ccdB* gene product). and blocks its action. CcdB is a toxin, blocks DNA gyrase and genererates double stranded breaks in the bacterial chromosome.

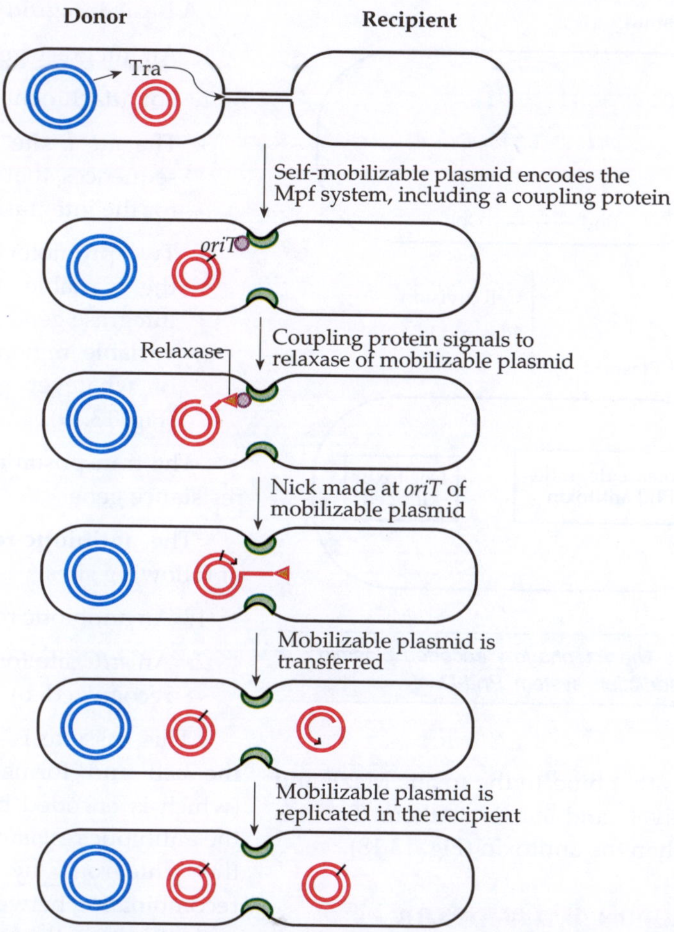


**Fig.13.17 :** *Mechanism of plasmid mobilization.*

F-plasmid and R-plasmids have an antisense-RNA-mediated host survival mechanism and prevent the translation of host killing protein (Hok) as long as the antisense-RNA (Sok) is present in the cell. Sok RNA binds to Hok-mRNA to prevent binding with ribosome, which in turn promotes degradation of mRNA by ribonuclease III. If the cell lost plasmids, the short lived Sok RNA decays and the *hok* mRNA lets free to translate the Hok protein. This toxic protein damages cell wall to kill them.

The another plasmid addiction system is called **PhD-Doc** system found in P1 phage plasmid cells containing the plasmid both Phd and Doc. Phd is the antidote to Doc, binding to it and inactivating it. If the cell is cured of the plasmid, neither PhD nor Doc is made, but Doc is more stable than Phd and outlives it. Once Phd is degraded by a protease, Doc kills the cell. Actually Doc only inhibits translation and seems to work indirectly through another addiction system **MazEF**, encoded in the chromosome, that kills the cells in which translation has been blocked.

MazEF and Rel BE systems both are found in *E. coli* K-12, which are mostly similar. MazF and RelE are the toxins that are ribonucleases which cleave mRNA in the ribosome and block translation, killing the cell. MazE and RelB are

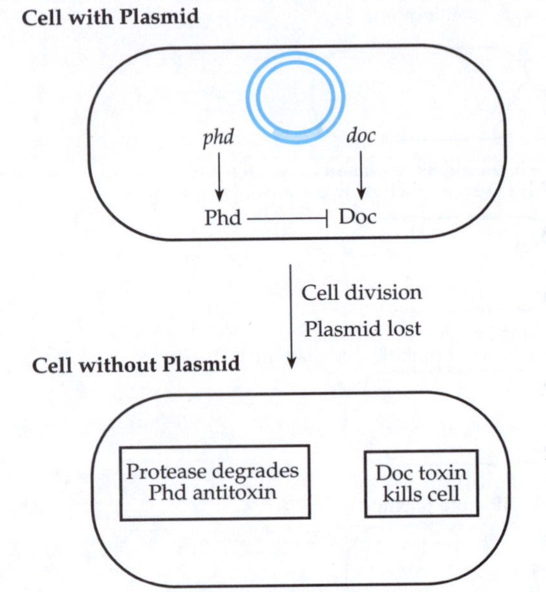


**Fig.13.18 :** *The P1 phage - encoded plasmid addiction system Phd-Doc.*

the antitoxins that bind to the toxins MazF and Rel E respectively and inactivate them. Toxin is more stable than the antitoxin (Fig. 13.18).

## 13.13 INTEGRON AND ANTIBIOTIC - RESISTANCE CASSETTES

Integron is a DNA-integration element, that is able to aquire additional genes by site-specific integration, *i.e.*, it enables the plasmids to capture genes from bacteriophages and other plasmids.

A **basic integron** consists of following sites

1. An integrase gene called *intI 1*
2. For attachment site region called *att I*
3. The *att I* site is flanked by two 7 bp sequences that acts as a recognition site for the integrase.
4. Two promoters are situated upstream of the variable region. One is for the integrase gene and the other faces into the variable region and drives transcription of whatever gene has been integrated (Fig. 13.19).

The transposon originally has no antibiotic resistance gene.

The **antibiotic-resistance cassette** consists of following sites

1. An antibiotic resistance gene.
2. An *attC* site for the attachment of cassette recognized by the integrase.

This cassette is excised from elsewhere in the cell and formed a circle. The integrase (which is encoded by integron) then integrate the antibiotic resistance gene into the *att I* site on the integron by promoting site-specific recombination between *att C* site on the cassette and *att I* site in the integron.

At another time, in another cell, a similar cassette with another antibiotic resistance gene could be integrateed next to the first one. The process may be carried on.

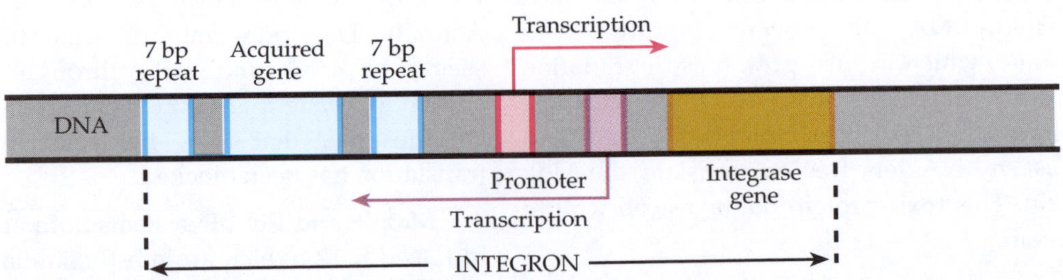


**Fig.13.19 :** *Integrons collect antibiotic resistance genes.*

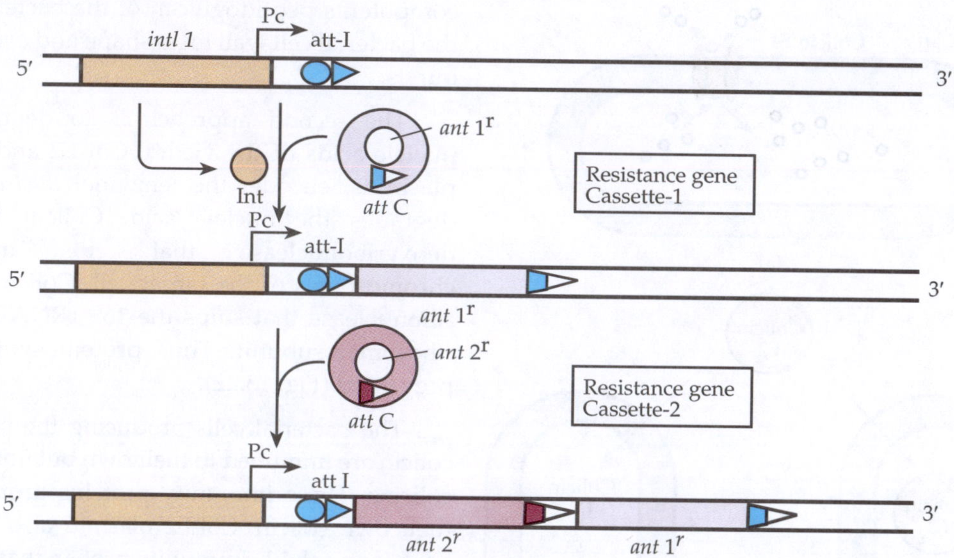


**Fig.13.20 :** *Assembly of integrons.*

The advantages of this system are that, the transposon can carry different antibiotic resistance genes and allows the cell and itself to survive in environments containing various toxic chemicals. But how these antibiotic resistance gene cassettes originically came from remains mystery (Fig. 13.20).

## 13.14 SUPERINTEGRONS AND MULTIPLE ANTIBIOTIC RESISTANT BACTERIA

*Vibrio cholerae* consists of as many as 179 different antibiotic resistant genes on its chromosomes called chromosomal superintegron. These genes are present in a series associated with partially homologous *attC* site next to an integrase gene *intA* and an *attI* attachment site. The *attC* sites contain conserved regions related to the *attC* sites between the cassettes of superintegrons, which is of unknown function (Fig. 13.21).

## 13.15 BACTERIOCINS

Many bacteria make toxic proteins to kill closely related bacteria that compete for the same resources. These toxins are called *bacteriocins*. Particular bacteriocins are named after the species that makes them. For example, **colicins**, produced by *E. coli*, **pesticins**, produced by *Yersinia pestis*. The bacteriocins are encoded by plasmids.

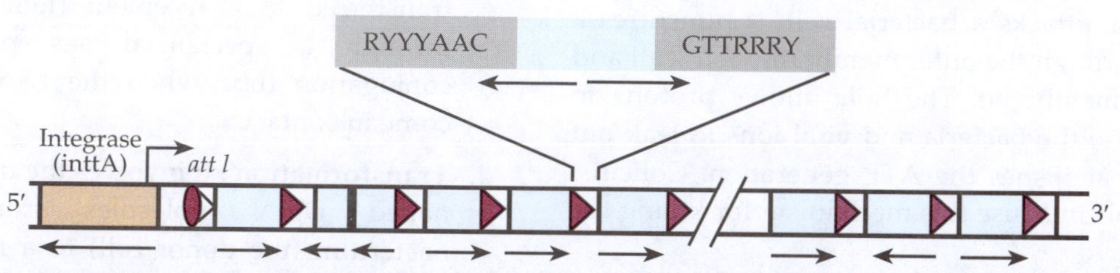


**Fig.13.21 :** *A superintegron from Vibrio cholerae*

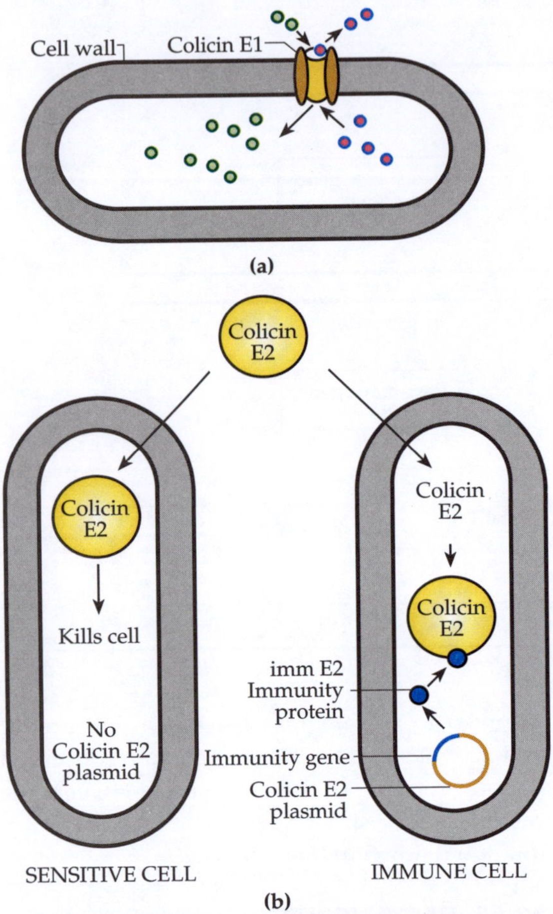


**Fig.13.22 :** *(a) Colicin damages the cell membrane; (b) Colicin immunity system*

Col plasmids allow the strains of *E. coli* that possess them to kill other related bacteria. There are two different mechanisms that can kill their relatives.

Col E1 plasmid encodes the colicin E1 protein, attacks a bacterial cell; it punctures a hole through the outer membrane, cell wall and inner membrane. The hole allows protons to leak into the bacteria and vital ions to leak out which abolishes the ATP generation. Colicin I and colicin V use this mechanism for killing the cell.

Colicin M and Pesticin A1122 utilize another mechanism to destroy the cell wall compotents peptidoglycan of the bacteria, thus the bacterial cell wall loses shape and eventually bursts.

The second approach is to degrade the nucleic acids of the victim. Col E2 and Col E3 plasmids encode the enzyme *nuclease* that degrades the nucleic acid. Colicin E2 is a deoxyribonuclease that cuts up the chromosomes of the target cell. Colicin E3 is a ribonuclease that snips the 16S rRNA of small ribosomal subunit. Thus protein synthesis is prevented (Fig. 13.22).

The bacterial cells producing the particular colicin are immuned to their own but not to other colicins. These immunity proteins protect from their own colicin. CoLE2 plasmid also carries a gene for a soluble immunity protein that binds to colicin E2 and neutralizes this. Immunity to membrane-active colicins is due to a plasmid-encoded inner membrane protein that blocks the colicin from forming pores in the host cell.

The **Ia** immunity protein protects membranes against colicin Ia but not against the closely related colicin **Ib**, though **Ia** and **Ib** share the same receptor and have same mode of action and extensive sequence homology.

## 13.16 RECOMBINATION IN BACTERIA

### 13.16.1 Concept

Sexuality and recombination in bacteria involve transfer of genetic material from one bacterium to the other. There are three modes of transfer of DNA.

1. **Conjugation :** This is the process during which DNA from a donor (male cell) is transferred to a recepient (female cell) through a specialized sex pilus or conjugation tube when the two strains come in contact.
2. **Transformation :** It involves the uptake of naked DNA molecules from one bacterium (the donor cell) to a recipient cell without coming in contact with each other.

3. **Transduction :** In this phenomenon the bacterial genes are transferred from one bacterial donor cell to another bacterial recepient cell by a bacteriophage.

### 13.16.2 Culture media and mutant strains of Bacteria

*Escherichia coli* can be grown in the laboratory in the culture medium, which contains glucose and ammonium salts, and from these, it can synthesize vitamins, amino acids and other substances that are required for its growth and reproduction. This is called **minimal medium**.

The strain of bacteria which can grow on this minimal medium, is called *prototroph.*

Some strains of bacteria cannot manufacture a particular substance from these minimal media. They can grow only if this particular substance is added to this minimal medium. These strains are called **auxotrophs**, the medium is called **supplemented medium**. For example, the strain can not grow in minimal medium but can grow when it is supplied with *methionine*, the mutant strain it is designated as $met^-$ and the wild strain is designated as $met^+$.

### 13.16.3 Discovery of gene transfer in *E. coli.*

Lederberg and Tatum took two strains of bacteria, strain A ($met^-$ $bio^-$ $thr^+$ $leu^+$ $thi^+$) which can grow in minimal media supplemented with *methionine* and *biotin* and strain –B ($met^+$ $bio^+$ $thr^-$ $leu^-$ $thi^-$) which can grow in minimal media supplemented with *threonine, leucine* and *thiamine*.

Strain-A and strain-B grown in supplemented medium, both are now transferred to another culture tube with both supplemented medium, mixed them and incubated overnight. Then it is observed that some of the bacterial cells (about 1 in $10^7$ population) can grow in the minimal . It can simply think that this new strain has transformed into $met^+$ $bio^+$ $thr^+$ $leu^+$ $thi^+$ genotype possibly due to recombination between them in the mixed culture.

$met^-$ $bio^-$ $thr^+$ $leu^+$ $thi^+$ × $met^+$ $bio^+$ $thr^-$ $leu^-$ $thi^-$

**auxotroph Strain A** ↓ **auxotroph Strain B**

$met^+$ $bio^+$ $thr^+$ $leu^+$ $thi^+$

**Prototroph after recombination**

It may be thought that it may be due to mutation. But simultaneous mutation of two or more genes to give rise wild type is certainly impossible.

It may also be thought that the growth of the colonies may be attributed to the cross feeding *i.e.* strain A produces *thr, leu & thi* amino acids and the strains B produces *met and bio* and both are utilized by leakage of necessary substances which they cannot manufacture. This suggestion may be discarded by the following experiment.

A U-tube is taken in the experiment. At the bent of U, a glass filter is fitted which allows only the DNA, macromolecules and viruses, but not the cells like bacteria. Two arms are filled with minimal media along with strain A & strain B separately. By alternate sucking and pressure, the macromolecules are allowed to pass through the filter and thus both the strains can survive. But these are taken out from the tube and subjected to culture in minimal midium, they cannot grow. This proves that physical contact is necessary for the generation of wild type.

### 13.16.4 Transduction

Transduction in bacteria was discovered by N. Zinder and J. Lederberg in 1952. In this mechanism, the bacteriophage carries the DNA of a donor bacteria to the another strain of bacteria facilitating subsequent recombination of gene markers of the two cells.

Two different types of transduction are known :

1. **Generalized transduction :** In this phenomenon, nearly random segment of

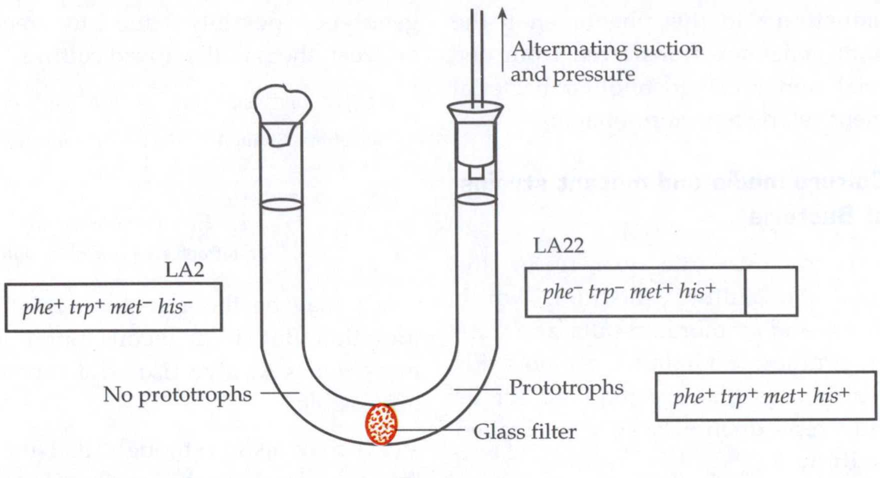


**Fig.13.23 :** *Transduction experiment performed by Zinder and Leaderberg (1962)*

bacterial DNA is wrapped up during phage maturation alongwith or in place of phage chromosome into a few progeny particles (the transducing particles). The transducing particles may contain only bacterial DNA or both phage DNA and bacterial DNA.

2. **Specialized transduction** : In this phenomenon recombination occurs involving the host chromosome and the phage chromosome producing a phage DNA-containing bacterial chromosome.

**Generalized transduction** : Generalized transduction is mediated by some virulent and certain temperate bacteriophages whose chromosomes are not integrated at specified attachment sites on the host chromosome. Generalized transducing particles are produced during the lytic cycle of these phages.

Transduction experiment was performed by Zinder and Lederberg (1972). Two auxotrophic strains of *Salmonella typhimurium* LA 22 and LA2 were placed in the two arms of Davis U-tube. These arms were separated by a glass filter at the bent of U which prevents the movement of bacteria but the DNA or phage particles can easily move. LA22 is a lysogenic strain and the phage P22 is ordinarily associated with it. LA2 is nonlysogenic strain to P22 phage.

Alternate suction and pressure were applied to one arm of the tube during incubation to mix the medium. Occasionally, some prophages were passed into the arm of the U-tube through the glass filter and infected LA2 nonlysogenic strain. Lysis of LA2 then occured and new phage particles are produced which then again passed into the other tube of U and infect LA22. These phage particles carried DNA from LA2, some of which were wild type for mutant genes carried by the LA22 strain, thus LA22 becomes prototroph by recombination, whereas LA2 did not carry the temperate phage and remained as auxotroph.

Here LA22 strain was transduced and the phage particles have transducing activity (Fig. 13.23).

The strain LA2 is *phe*$^+$ *trp*$^+$ *met*$^-$ *his*$^-$ whereas, LA22 is *phe*$^-$ *trp*$^-$ *met*$^+$ *his*$^+$. After transduction, LA2 strain remains as such, whereas LA22 becomes *phe*$^+$ *trp*$^+$ *met*$^+$ *his*$^+$ and transforms into prototrophs.

Zinder and leaderberg therefore proposed that the rare transducing phage particles can carry only a small segment of bacterial chromosomal material.

The DNA fragment of the donor cell may be integrated into the chromosomes of recipient cells. But sometimes it may remain free in the cytoplasm, it will not replicate and will be transmitted to only one progeny cell during each cell division. But genes located on the transduced segment are expressed even if they are not integrated. Cells carrying such nonintegrated transducing DNA segment are called **abortive transductants**.

**Specialized transduction** : Morse and Lederberg (1956) used wild type prototrophs as donors in λ-mediated transduction which could affect mutant recipients only by changing $gal^-$ to $gal^+$ but never transduced various loci such as *thr, trp, lac* etc. This phenomenon is known as **specialized or restricted transduction**.

Specialized transduction involves prophage integration, excision and transduction.

When the λ-chromosome is packed in the phage head, it exists as a linear molecule with gene sequence *A–F–J–pp′–CIII–N–CI–R*,

After infection, it is converted to its circular intracellular form. When λ-phage enters the lysogenic pathway, it undergoes a site-specific recombination event between the *pp′* site on the pahge chromosome and the λ-attachment site, *bb′* on the *E. coli* chromosome. This interaction step is catalyzed by the lambda *int* gene product. In the prophage state, the λ-gene sequence is *p′–cIII–N–cI–R–A–J–p*. This sequence is a circular permutation of the gene sequence in the linear form packaged in the λ-head, which results from a specific endonuclease cut between genes *A* and *R* during phage maturation.

During excision, we can visualize it as a figure - 8, which is followed by a site-specific recombination event between the *bp′* sequence and *pb′* sequence. It requires the *int* gene product and *xis*- λ-gene product.

The excision process is usually very precise but occasionally excision event occurs at a site other than the original attachment site. Thus a portion of the bacterial chromosome is left in the phage chromosome. Such a mistake is required for the specialized transduction. For example, if the excision occurs at a position within the *gal* region of the host chromosome and a position in the gene *F* to gene *J* region of λ–chromosome. Then phage chromosome includes a seqment of host DNA containing *gal* gene wheresas *J*-gene of the phage is left into the host chromosome.

This phage is known as λ–dg, this transducing particle can reproduce only in the presence of a wild type λ-helper phage. The 'g' indicates that the bacterial gene *gal* present in it.

When these λ–dg partcles infect $gal^-$ recipient cells, λ-dg integrates by a recombination event within the *gal* region or at the λ-attachment site. Thus a partially diploid $gal^+/gal^-$ transductant (heterogenote) is formed. Subsequent integration of $\lambda^+$ chromosome (helper phage) to form $\lambda^+/\lambda dg$ double lysogen.

If these double lysogens are induced with UV-light, they will produce lysates containing 50% λ–dg particles and 50% $\lambda^+$ particles. Both prophages will be excised and will replicate with equal efficiency. Such lysates are called Hfr (high frequency transduction) (Fig. 13.24) (Table 13.2).

### 13.16.5 Conjugation

In 1946, Lederberg and Tatum established a process resembling sex.

In conjugation, there is physical contact between two genetically different bacterial cells of the same or closely related species, in which a conjugation tube is established between the conjugants, followed by the transfer of genetic material from the donor cell (male) to the recipient cell (or female) which is formed by special appendages called sex pili.

**Mating types and their surface properties :**

1. Many but not all plasmids of Gram-negative bacteria are conjugative. The plasmids carry "*tra*" genes responsible for their own transfer and also for coding specialized fimbrie (sex pilus). *E. coli* K13 has 1 to 3 pili per cell.

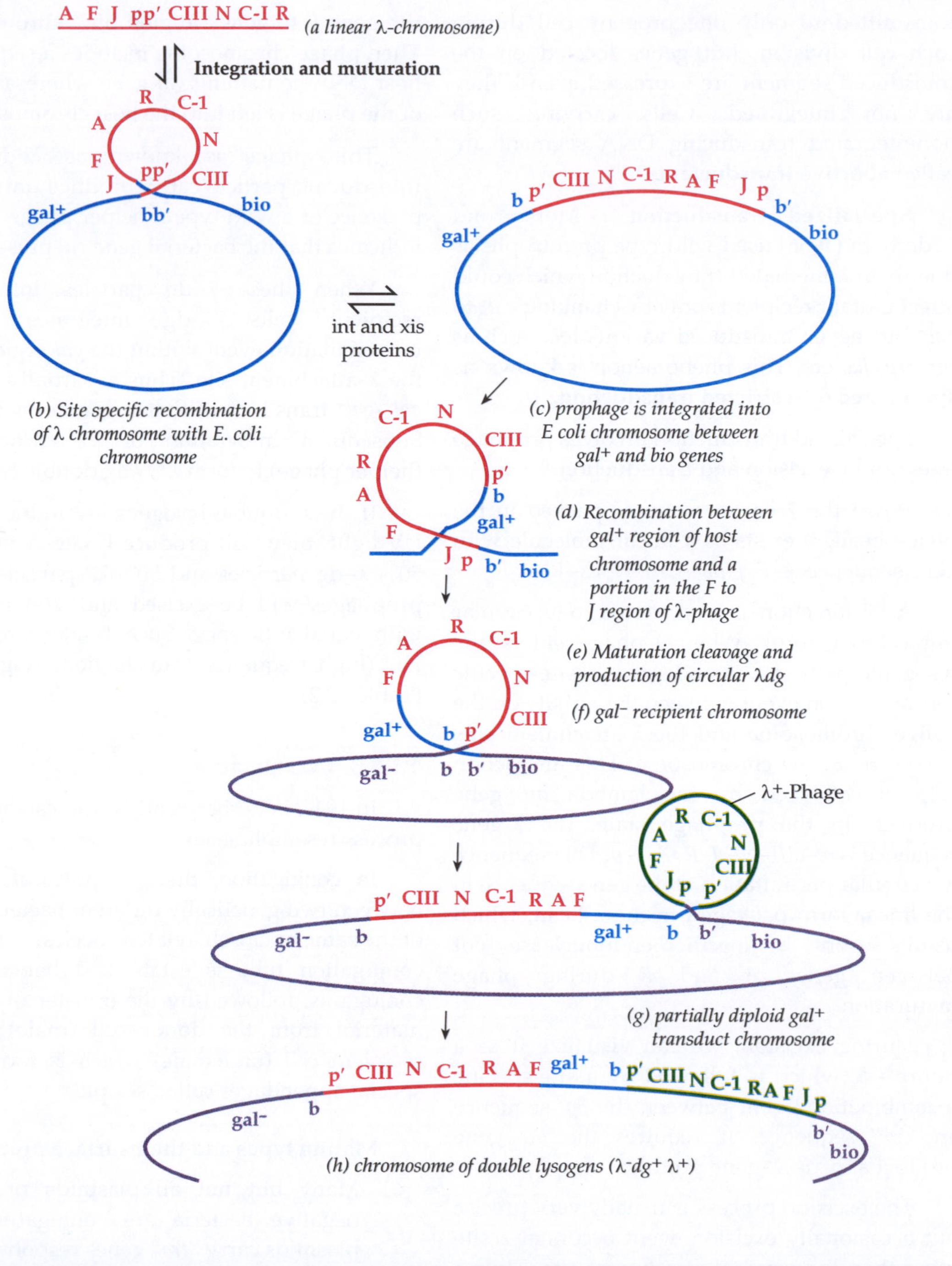


**Fig.13.24 :** *Mechanism of transduction (a) to (c) integration, (d) to (e) excision and formation of λ-dg, (f) and (g) insertion of λ dg with recipient chromosome, (h) subsequent integration of λ+ and formation of double lysogen.*

**TABLE 13.2**
**Distinction between generalized and specialized transduction**

| | *Generalized transduction* | *Specialized transduction* |
|---|---|---|
| *Incidence* | 1 in $10^5$ or $10^6$ | 1 in $10^5$ or $10^6$ |
| *Transfer* | Any genes | Genes immediately adjacent to site of prophage attachment. |
| *Induction* | Transducting phage is produced upon induction of prophage and in infection with virulent phages | Transducing phage is produced upon induction of only prophage |
| *Content in defective transducing phage* | Only bacterial DNA | Hybrid, contain both bacterial and phage DNA |
| *Transducing particles* | Replace recipient gene when integrated in chromosome. | Added to genome of recipient cell |

2. A sex pilus projects from the surface of the donor cell and tip of which attaches to the surface of the recipient cell. The pilus is then retracted into the donor to draw the two cells together until the direct contact is made. It then becomes hollow to form a tube and the DNA passes into the recipient cell through this tube.
3. Conjugation involves two cell types, donor cells are referred to as $F^+$ male cells which posses the F factor and the recipients are called $F^-$ cells as they lack the F factor. F factor is called the *fertility factor* or *transfer factor*, is an extrachromosomal DNA that encodes the information necessary for conjugation.
4. The F factor is infectious and can transfer itself by conjugation. The factor is present as an independent double stranded ring of DNA, distinct from the chromosome. During conjugation, there is a break in one of the two strands of the plasmid. This strand passes into the recipient cell. The donor cell retains one strand. The strands in both donor and recipient cells now synthesize a complementary strand. Thus two intact duplexes are formed, one in each cell. Since the recipient cell now has a copy of the original plasmid, it is potential donor cell. The $F^+$ donor cells converted the $F^-$ recipient cells into $F^+$ cells, while it has itself remained $F^+$, this is called infectious transfer

$$F^+ \times F^- \rightarrow F^+$$

5. When the plasmid containing the F factor, becomes integrated into the bacterial chromosome, the cells are called Hfr (high frequency) recombinant strain cells (Fig. 13.25 and 13.26).
6. When the F-plasmid and bacterial chromosome carry DNA sequences that allow mutual recognition, then two types of DNA can combine. Such integration of F plasmid involves breakage and rejoining of both molecules of DNA. This results from a recombination process between a homologous insertion sequence (IS) on both the F plasmids and the chromosomes.
7. Once F plasmid is integrated with the bacterial chromosome, the whole chromosome acts as a big plasmid. The transfer of chromosomal genes to recipients occur at a relatively high frequencey.
8. Detachment of F takes place 1 per $10^5$ cells at each generation. An endonuclease, may recognize the DNA sequence of the

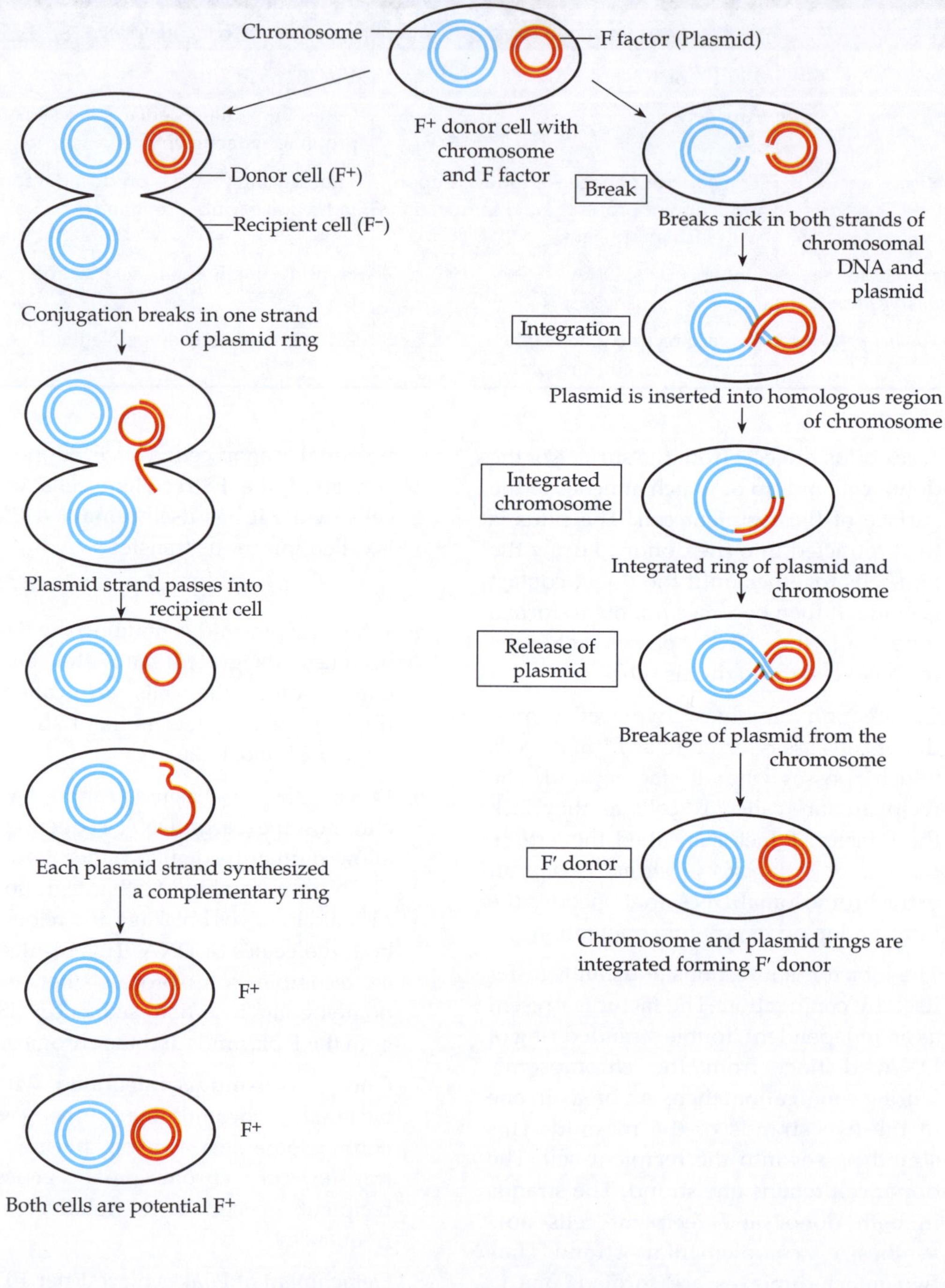


**Fig.13.25 :** *Infectious transfer of plasmid in bacteria*

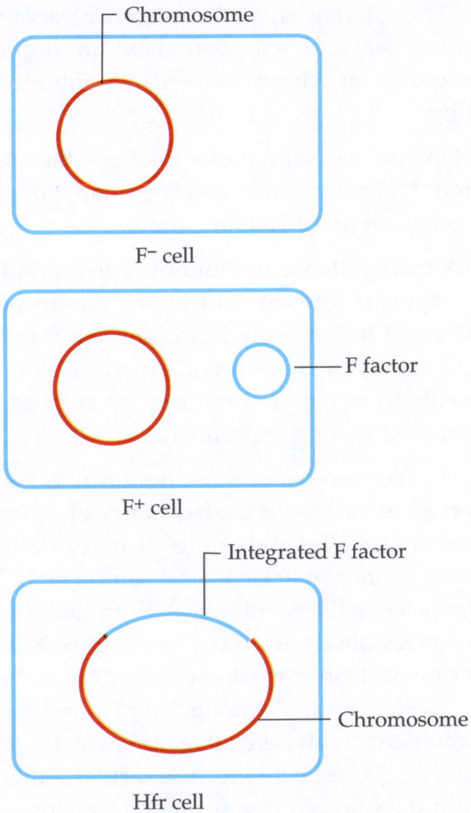


**Fig.13.26 :** *Three strains of E. coli with respect to the F factor*

chromosome-plasmid hybrid and separates the two. Occasionally the endonuclease makes a mistake in such a way that the excised DNA will contain some adjacent chromosomal material in addtion to plasmid DNA. Such a type of hybrid molecule is actually an F factor plasmid with some chromosomal materials, called **F′– factor** or **substituted** F factor. The F′ containing bacteria can conjugate and the recipient bacterium becomes F′. Thus, if an F′ factor containing the lac-operon (*lac*$^+$) is transferred to an F$^-$ lac$^-$ cell, the latter becomes *F lac*$^+$ (the F′ factor carrying the lactose operon is designated as *F lac*$^+$) If the recipient chromosome carries a *lac*$^+$ operon it now would have two *lac*$^+$ operons and is diploid for bacterial genes carried by the episome. The whole transfer sequence is as follows :

$$F' \; lac^+ \quad \times \quad F^- \; lac^-$$
$$\downarrow$$
$$F \; lac^+ \text{ and } \; lac^+$$

This process is called *sexduction* or *F-duction.* which can be defined as the tranmission of bacterial genes to a recipient cell through their incorporation into an **autonomous conjugating plasmid**.

### 13.16.6 Mechanism of DNA transfer during Conjugation in Bacteria

Mechansim of transfer of DNA form donor to recipient cell during conjugation appears to be the same just the F factor is being transferred as in F$^+$ and F$^-$ mating or the chromosome is being transferred as in Hfr and F$^-$ mating.

1. After contact of the cell, a conjugation tube is formed between the two cells.
2. An enzyme endonuclease cleaves one strand of DNA at a unique site, which is called the "origin" of transfer on the F-factor or on the integrated site of Hfr.
3. The 5′ end of the cleaved strand is then displaced as in normal rolling circle replication but the 5′ end moves through the conjugation tube into the recipient cell.
4. The DNA of donor cell undergoes replication by rolling circle, where the intact circular strand serves as template for the synthesis of complementary strand.
5. The linear strand which is gradually entering through the conjugation tube will then undergo replication forming Okazaki fragments, which are then joined by DNA ligase enzyme immediately after transfer.
6. Thus, after mating the conjugants are being separated. The donor cell remains as F$^+$ or Hfr type, whereas, the recipient

cell will have either a F factor or Hfr chromosome along with $F^-$ chromosome. Thus the recipient cell becomes $F^+$ or Hfr after conjugation.

### 13.16.7 Conjugation maping through interrupted mating

F. Jacob and E. Wollman developed a technique called the **interrupted mating** technique for maping the bacterial chromsome . One particular Hfr strain, called Hfr H or Hfr Hayes (isolated by W. Hayes), where F-factor is integrated near the *thr*(threonine) and *leu* loci . They crossed HfrH cells of genotype *thr*$^+$ *leu*$^+$ *azi-s T1-S lac*$^+$ *gal*$^+$ *str-s* with $F^-$ cells of genotype *thr*$^-$ *leu*$^-$ *azi-r T*1-*r lac*$^-$ *gal*$^-$ *str-r*

*thr* and *leu* are two amino acids threonine and leucine and their normal alleles and selectable marker *azi, T1* and *str* alleles with *s* and *r* represent the sensitivity or resistance to sodium azide, T1 bacteriophage and streptomycin respectively. *lac* and *gal,* + or – alleles are represented for ability or inability to utilize lactose and galactose.

In this experiment, Hfr H donor and $F^-$ recipient strains are mixed and allowed to conjungate for a short time. Then the samples are removed at periodic intervals and subjected to violent agitation to break the conjugation tube.

It has been observed that *the number of genes transmitted from donor to recipient is directly proportional to the time interval for which the conjugation was allowed.* Thus the length of donor chromosome transmitted could be determined and mapped in terms of time units required for transfer.

*thr* and *leu* are actually the first of the HfrH genes that have entered the recipient and they produced *thr*$^+$ and *leu*$^+$ recombinants when mating was interrupted within $8\frac{1}{2}$ minutes.

After 9 minutes of mating, the *azi* gene entered the recipient, since some samples of *thr*$^+$ *leu*$^+$ recombinant cells were now also become *azi*$^+$. The *T1* (*ton A*) gene entered at about 11 minutes, *lac* and *gal* were next in order of appearance at about 18 and 25 minutes of mating.

On the basis of these findings the entire bacterial chromosome can be mapped as a complete length of 100 time units.

A map distance of 1 minute corresponds to the length of the segment of the chromosome transferred in 1 minute duration. The standard *E. coli* linkage map is thus divided into minute intervals from 0 to 100 minutes on the basis of interrupted mating experiments.

The frequencies of these donor markers are observed to vary with the frequency of a marker decreasing as a function of its distance from the selected donor markers (*thr*$^+$ and *leu*$^+$). The frequencies will be identical with the plateu frequencies observed in the interrupted mating experiment. Donor markers *azi-s, T1-s, lac*$^+$ and *gal*$^+$ will occur among *thr*$^+$ *leu*$^+$ *str-r* recombinants with percentage frequencies of 90, 80, 40 and 25 respectively. The farther a marker is from the selected donor marker, the lower its frequency among the recombinants (Fig. 13.27 and 13.28).

Such mapping is advantageous, because the relationship between genes is more easily determined as a function of time rather than as the function of recombination frequencies.

### 13.16.8 Transformation

Transformation involves the uptake of naked DNA molecules from one bacterium by another beacterium. This was discovered by Griffith in 1928 in pathogenic strains of *Diplococcus pneumoniae.*

The uptake of DNA molecule by a recipient becterium is an active energy-requiring process. It occurs naturally only those species possessing the enzymatic machinary in an active uptake process as well as the recombination process. Therefore, only competent cells which have a so called "competent factor" are capable as the recepients in transformation.

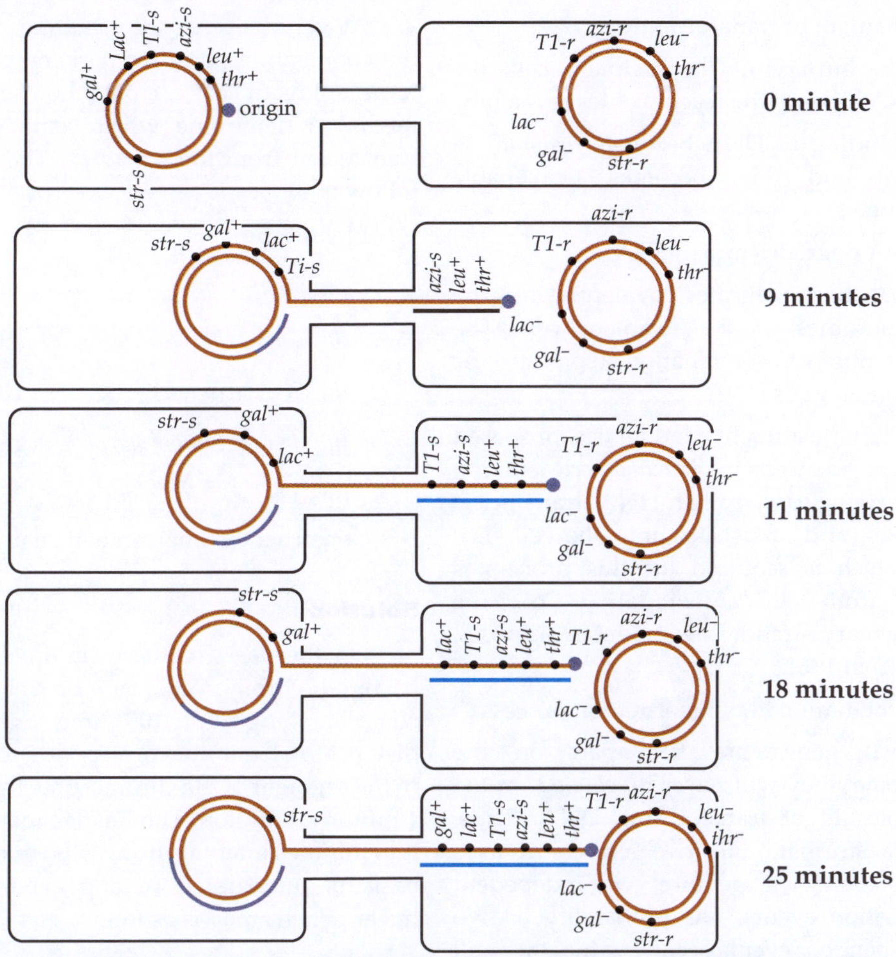


**Fig.13.27 :** *Interpretation of the interrupted mating data of Jacob and Wollman showing linear transfer of Hfr-H chromosomes of $F^+$ bacterium.*

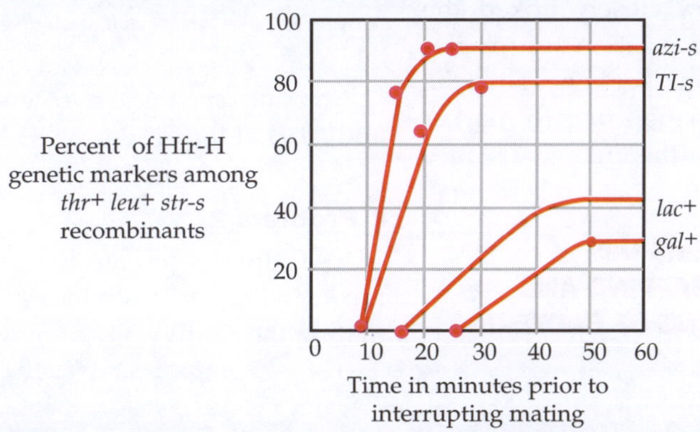


**Fig.13.28 :** *Kinetics of appearance of the unselected Hfr-H azi-s T1-s $lac^+$ $gal^+$ in $thr^+$ $leu^+$ str-s recombinants produced during conjugation.*

**Mechanism of transformation :**

1. On the surface of the recipient cell, the dsDNA binds to the receptor sites reversibly.
2. The binding of DNA becomes resistant to DNase and thus becomes irreversible binding.
3. dsDNA degrades into ssDNA.
4. ssDNA then integrates covalently into the chromosomes of the recipient cell. The integration or recombination step is specific for homologous DNA.

An alternate attractive model was proposed which is evidenced in *Pneumococcus* that a specific exonuclease, called **DNA translocase** pulls one strand of dsDNA into the cell. The energy which is required for this process is derived from the degradation of the complementary strand. This model is proposed by S. Lacks in 1962.

Recombination in transformation process :

If two genes are far apart on the chromosome, they will never be carried on the same molecule of transforming DNA. Thus, double transformation for two genes (such as $a$, $a^+$ and $b$, $b^+$) will require two indepedent transformation events. The probability of two such independent events occurring together will equal to the product of the probability of occurring alone, because transformation of any single marker gene occurs with a low frequency.

If two genes are very closely linked the frequency of double transformation approaches to the frequency of single marker gene. Thus the frequency of co-transformation of two marker genes are used to estimate the linkage distance between them.

## 13.17 SOLVED PROBLEMS ON INTERRUPTED MAPPING AND LINKAGE MAPPING OF BACTERIA

### Problem 1

Interrupted mating experiment involving the cross *HfrH* $thr^+\ leu^+\ azi^R\ ton^R\ lac^+\ gal^+\ str^S \times F^-\ thr^-\ leu^-\ azi^s\ ton^s\ lac^-\ gal^-\ str^R$.

At various times after mating commences, the conjugating pairs are borken apart and the transconjugant cells are plated on selective agar media to determine which genes have been transferred from the *Hfr* to $F^-$. The result is as follow :

| Phenotype | time |
|---|---|
| $thr^+\ leu^+$ | 8 min |
| $thr^+\ leu^+\ azi^R$ | 9 min |
| $thr^+\ leu^+\ azi^R\ ton^R$ | 10 min |
| $thr^+\ leu^+\ azi^R\ ton^R\ lac^+$ | 16 min |
| $thr^+\ leu^+\ azi^R\ lon^R\ lac^+\ gal^+$ | 25 min |

Construct the linear genetic map.

**Solution :**

On the basis of these findings, the entire bacterial chromosome can be mapped as a complete length of 100 time units. A map distance of 1 minute corresponds to the length of the segment of the chromosome transferred in 1 minutes duration. The linkage map is divided into minutes intervals from 0-100 minutes on the basis of interrupted mating experiment. The linear genetic map is as follows.

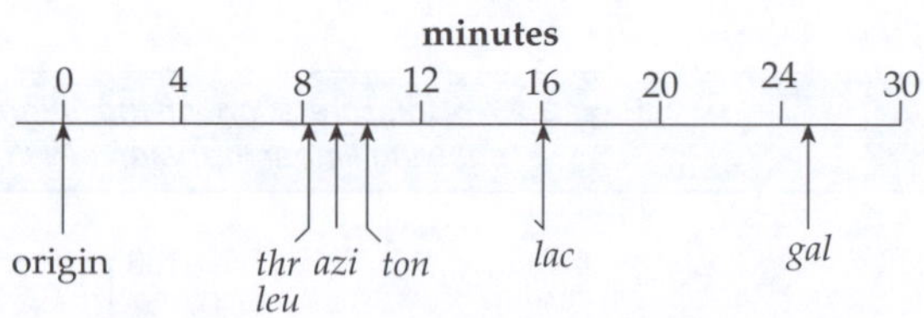


*thr* and *leu,* these two genes are inseparable and *HfrH* at the origin.

### Problem 2

At time zero, an *Hfr* strain (*Hfr-1*) was mixed with an F⁻ strain. After an interrupted mating the result was as follows.

$Hfr\ 1 : a^+\ b^+\ c^+\ d^+\ e^+\ f^+\ g^+\ h^+\ str^S$

$F^- : a\ \ b\ \ c\ \ d\ \ e\ f\ \ g\ \ h\ \ str^R$

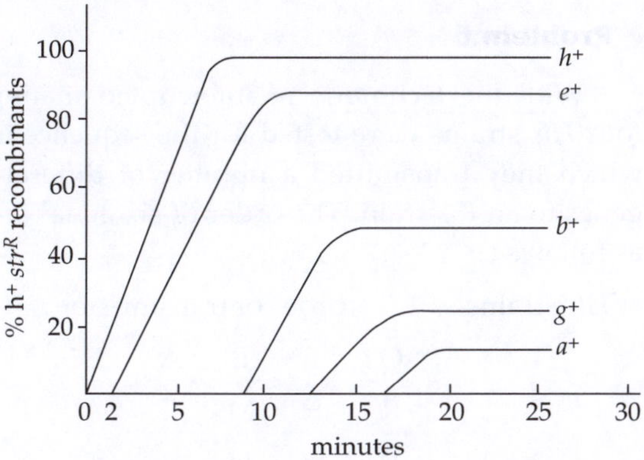


(a) Indicate whether each of the following statements is true or false

(i) All $F^+$ cells that received $a^+$ from *Hfr* in the chromosome fransfer process must also have received $b^+$.

(ii) The order of gene transfer from *Hfr* to $F^-$ was $a^+$ (first) then $g^+$, then $e^+$ and finally $h^+$

(iii) Most $e^+$ $str^R$ recombinants are likely to be *Hfr* cells.

(iv) None of the $b^+$ $str^R$ recombinants plated at 15 minutes are also $a^+$.

(b) Draw a linear map of the Hfr chromosome indicating

(i) The point of origin and the direction of DNA transfer

(ii) The order of genes $a^+$ $b^+$ $c^+$ $e^+$ $g^+$ $h^+$

(iii) The shortest distance between consecutive genes on the chromosomes.

**Solution :**

(a)

(i) False, All $F^+$ cells received $h^+$

(ii) False, order is $h^+e^+b^+g^+a^+$

(iii) False, only about 90%

(iv) False, At 15 min. all are $b^+$ $str^R$ but none are $a^+$.

(b) Linear genetic map is as follows

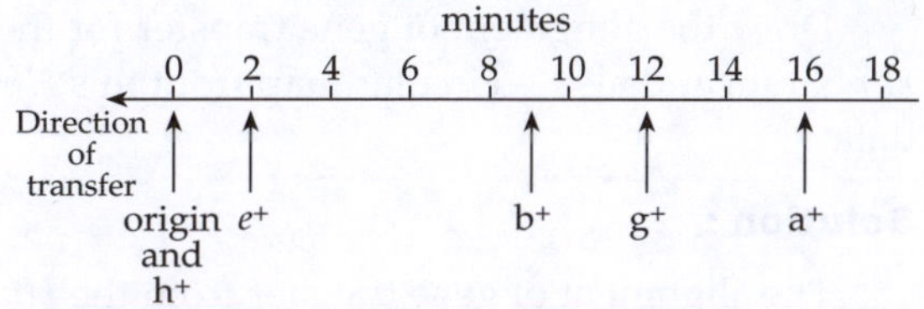


## Problem 3

Time mapping is performed in a cross involving the gene *his*, *leu*, *mal* and *xyl*. The recipient cells were auxotrophic for all four genes. After 25 minutes, mating was interrupted with the following results in recipient cells. Diagram the positions of these genes relative to the origin (O) of the F factor and to one another

(a) 90% were $xyl^+$

(b) 80% were $mal^+$

(c) 20% were $his^+$

(d) none were $leu^+$

**Solution :**

The *xyl* gene was transferred more frequently, which shows closest to origin is "O". The *mal* gene is next closest and reasonably near *xyl*, followed by the more distant *his* gene. The *leu* gene is far beyond these three. The diagram shows these relative locations along a piece of a circular chromosome.

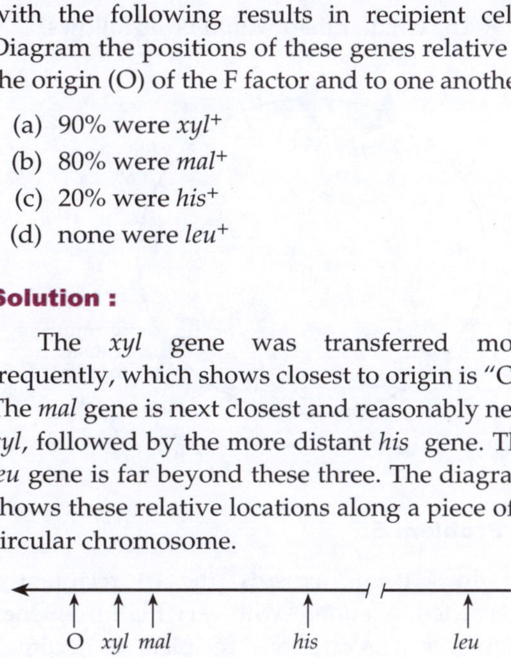


## Problem 4

Interrupted mating experiments with a variety of Hfr strains showing that the *E. coli* linkage map is circular. The order of gene transfer for *Hfr* strain H, 1, 2, 3 are given as follows :

*Hfr* strains

H : Origin – *thr* – *pro* – *lac* – *pur* – *gal*

1 : Origin – *thr* – *thi* – *gly* – *his*

2 : Origin – *his* – *gly* – *thi* – *thr* – *pro* – *lac*

3 : Origin – *gly* – *his* – *gal* – *par* – *lac* – *pro*

Draw the alingment of gene transfer for the *Hfr* strain and also a circular map from this *Hfr* data.

**Solution :**

The alignment of gene transfer from the *Hfr* strain

Strain H : *thr–pro–lac–pur–gal*

1 : *his–gly–thi–thr*

2 : *his–gly–thi–thr–pro–lac*

3 : *pro–lac–pur–gal–his–gly*

The circular map would be as follows.

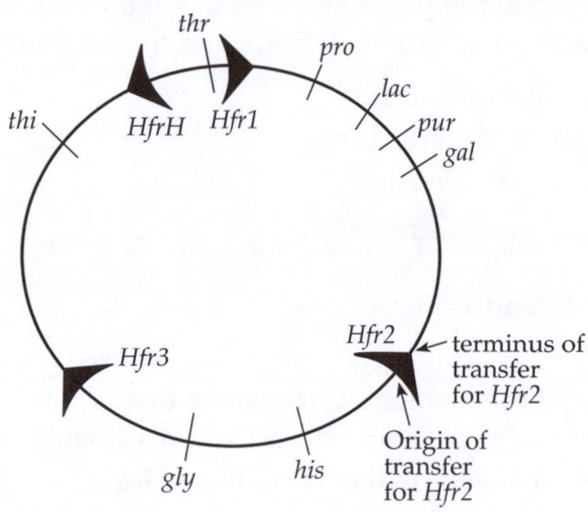


### ➧ Problem 5

In $F^+ \times F^-$ crosses, the $F^-$ recipient is converted to a donor with very high frequency. However, it is rare for a recipient to become a donor in Hfr × $F^-$ crosses; explain why?

**Solution :**

For a recipient to be converted to a donor, a complete *F* factor must be transferred. In $F^+ \times F^-$ crosses only the *F* factor is transferred, and this occurs relatively quickly. In *Hfr* × $F^-$ crosses, transfer starts at the origin within the *F*-element and then must proceed through the bacterial chromosome before reaching the *F* factor. For transfer of the entire *F*-factor, the whole chromosome would have to be transferred. This will take about 100 minutes and usually the conjugal unions break apart before then.

### ➧ Problem 6

With the technique of interrupted mating four *Hfr* strains were tested for the sequence in which they transmitted a number of different genes to an $F^-$ strain. The order of six genes are as follows :

| *Hfr* strains | order of transmission | | | | | |
|---|---|---|---|---|---|---|
| 1 | O | F | B | A | E | M |
| 2 | R | H | M | E | A | B |
| 3 | E | M | H | R | C | X |
| 4 | O | G | X | C | R | H |

What was the gene sequence in the original strain from which these *Hfr* strains derive? Draw the circular map and polarity of the four *Hfr* strains.

**Solution :**

*Hfr* strain

1 O F B A E M→

2 ←B A E M H R

3 E M H R C X →

4 ←H R C X G O

The original gene sequence is GOFBAEMHRCX. The circular map is as follows :

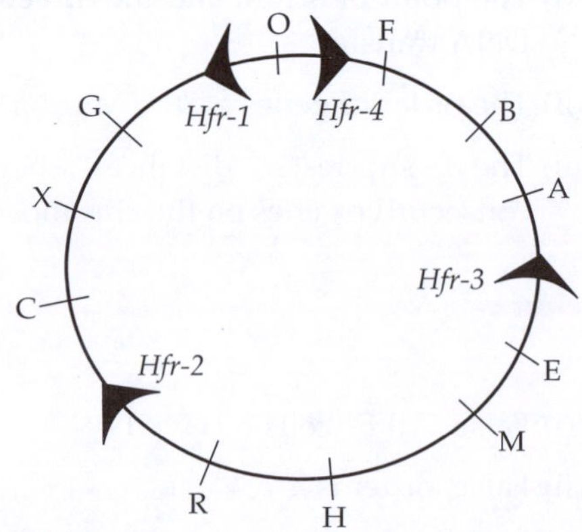


### ➧ Problem 7

Four *Hfr* strains of bacteria, all derived from an original $F^+$ culture grown over several months, a group of hypothetical gene was studied and shown to be transferred in the order shown in the following table :

| *Hfr* strains | order of transfer |
|---|---|
| 1 | *E R I U M B* |
| 2 | *U M B A C T* |
| 3 | *C T E R I U* |
| 4 | *R E T C A B* |

(a) Assuming that B is the first gene determine the sequence of all genes shown.

(b) One strain creates an apparent dilemma. Which one is it? What is the cause?

(c) Draw the circular map.

**Solution :**

(a)

Strain 1 *E R I U M B*

2 *U M B A C T*

3 *C T E R I U M B*

4 *B A C T E R*

Starting with B the gene sequence is *BACTERIUM*.

(b) Strain 4 creates an apparent dilemma in the genes initially apparent to be out of order. The dilemma is resolved when we realize that the *F* factor is integrated in the opposite direction. Thus the gene enter in the opposite sequence, starting with gene *R*.

(c) The circular map is as follows.

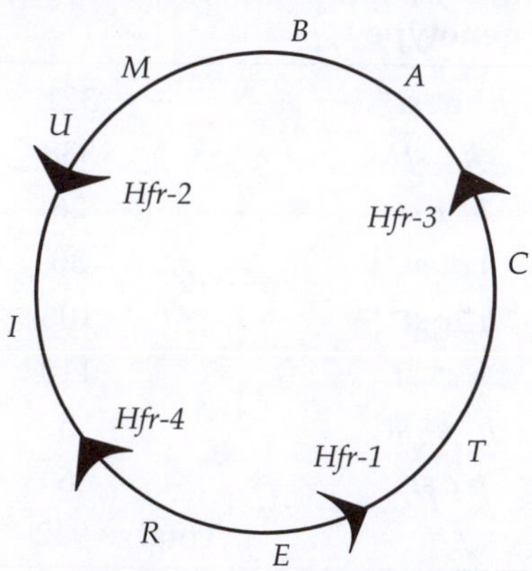


**Problem 8**

Three strains of bacteria each bearing a separate mutation $a^-$, $b^-$, $c^-$, $d^-$ are the sources of donor DNA in the transformation experiment. Recipient cells are wild type for those genes but express the mutation $d^-$.

(a) Based on the following data, and assuming that the location of the *d* gene proceeds *a*, *b* and *c* genes, propose a linkage map for the four genes.

| DNA donor | Recipient | Transformation | Frequency of transformation |
|---|---|---|---|
| $a^-d^+$ | $a^+d^-$ | $a^+d^+$ | 0.21 |
| $b^-d^+$ | $b^+d^-$ | $b^+d^+$ | 0.18 |
| $c^-d^+$ | $c^+d^-$ | $c^+d^+$ | 0.63 |

(b) If the donor DNA were wild type and the recipient cells were either $a^-b^-$, $a^-c^-$ or $b^-c^-$, which of the crosses would be expected to produce the greatest number of wild type transformants?

**Solution :**

(a) The data reflects the relative distance between *a*, *b* and *c* genes, individually, and the *d* gene. The *a* and *b* genes are about the same distance from the *d* gene and are thus tightly linked to one another. The *c* gene is more distant. Assuming that *d* gene precedes the others. The map would be as follows.

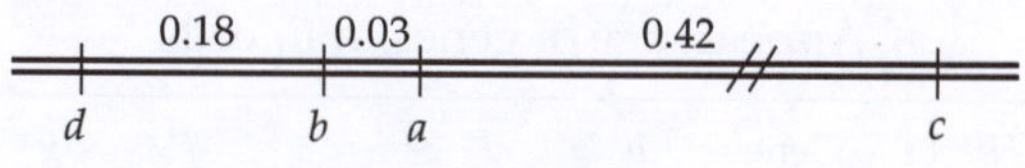


(b) Because *a* and *b* genes are closely linked they most likely co-transform in a single event. Thus recipient cells $a^-b^-$ are most likely to convert to wild type.

**Problem 9**

Consider the following data pertaining to P1 transduction

| Donor | Recipient | Selected marker | unselected marker | % |
|---|---|---|---|---|
| *aro A pyr D*$^+$ | *aro A*$^+$ *pyr D* | *pyr D*$^+$ | *aro A* | 5 |
| *aro A*$^+$ *cml B* | *aro A cml B*$^+$ | *aro A*$^+$ | *cml B* | 26 |
| *cml B pyr D*$^+$ | *cml B*$^+$ *pyr D* | *pyr D*$^+$ | *cml B* | 54 |

Choose the correct order :

(a) *aro A cml B pyr D*

(b) *aro A pyr D cml B*

(c) *cml B aro A pyr D*

**Solution :**

Closer genes have higher **co-transduction** frequency : Therefore *pyr D* and *cml B* genes show the highest co-transduction frequency. Thus these two genes are closest together and the gene arrangement indicated in (c) is eleminated.

The farthest genes have lowest co-transduction frequency. Here *pyr D* and *aro A* genes so lowest frequency. Thus *pyr D* and *aro A* are farthest in position and the gene arrangement indicated in (b) is eliminated

The correct arrangement is

*aro A - cml B - pyr D*

**Problem 10**

Crosses of three different *Hfr* strains with separate samples of an $F^-$ strain are carried out, and the following data are obtained from the studies of interrupted mating

Appearance of genes in $F_1$ cells

| | | | | | | |
|---|---|---|---|---|---|---|
| *Hfr 1* : | Genes | $b^+$ | $d^+$ | $c^+$ | $f^+$ | $g^+$ |
| | time | 3 | 5 | 16 | 27 | 59 |
| *Hfr 2* : | Genes | $e^+$ | $f^+$ | $c^+$ | $d^+$ | $b^+$ |
| | time | 6 | 24 | 35 | 46 | 48 |
| *Hfr 3* : | Genes | $d^+$ | $c^+$ | $f^+$ | $e^+$ | $g^+$ |
| | time | 4 | 15 | 26 | 44 | 58 |

Construct a genetic map of these genes, indicating their order on the bacterial chromosome and the distances between them.

**Solution :**

*F* factor for each *Hfr* strain has been inserted into a different location on the chromosome, and the orientation of the *F* factor varies in the different strain. The relative position of the genes to one another in minutes does not vary So, for the different *Hfr* strains, the distance in minutes between each gene remains constant. The genes and their relative positions are shown in the adjoining diagram. The numbers are minutes.

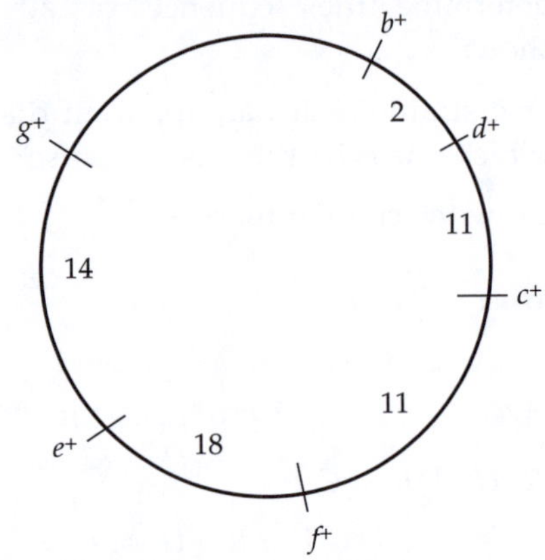


**Problem 11**

*E. coli* cells are simultanceously infected with two strains of Phage-λ. One strain has a mutant host range, is terperature sensitive and produces clear plaques (genotype = *h, st, c*); another strain carries the wild-type alleles (genotype = $h^+$ $st^+$ $c^+$). Progeny phage are collected from the lysed cells and are plated on bacteria. The genotypes of the progeny phage are

| Progeny phage genotype | No. of plaques |
|---|---|
| $h^+ c^+ st^+$ | 321 |
| $h\ c\ st$ | 338 |
| $h^+ c\ st$ | 26 |
| $h\ c^+ st^+$ | 30 |
| $h^+ c\ st^+$ | 106 |
| $h\ c^+ st$ | 110 |
| $h^+ c^+ st$ | 5 |
| $h\ c\ st^+$ | 6 |
| Total | 942 |

(a) Determine the order of genes on the phage chromosome.

(b) Determine the map distances between the genes.

(c) Determine the coefficient of coincidence and interference.

**Solution :**

Linkage between $h^+$ and $c^+$ =

$$\frac{26 + 30 + 106 + 110}{942} \times 100\% = 28.8\%$$

Linkage between $h^+$ and $st^+$ =

$$\frac{26 + 30 + 5 + 6}{942} \times 100\% = 7.1\%$$

Linkage between $c^+$ and $st^+$ =

$$\frac{106 + 110 + 5 + 6}{942} \times 100\% = 24.5\%$$

(a) Therefore the order of the three genes on the phage chromosomes is

$h^+$ ______ $st^+$ ______ $c^+$

(b) The map distance between $h^+$ and $st^+$ is 7.1 mu and between $c^+$ and $st^+$ is 24.5 mu.

(c) The coefficient of coincidence

$$= \frac{\text{Observed double crossing over}}{\text{expected double crossing over}}$$

$$= \frac{(5 + 6)}{0.071 \times 0.245 \times 942} = \frac{11}{16.38} = .67$$

Interference = 1 – 0.67 = 0.33

## Problem 12

A conjugation experiment is set up between $F^+$ $his^+$ $leu^+$ $thr^+$ $pro^+$ bacteria and $F^-$ $his^-$ $leu^-$ $thr^-$ $pro^-$ bacteria and allowed to continue for 25 minutes. At this time, the mating is stopped and the genotypes of the recipient $F^-$ bacteria are determined. The results are shown below :

| Genotype | No. of Colonies |
|---|---|
| $his^+$ | 0 |
| $leu^+$ | 12 |
| $thr^+$ | 27 |
| $pro^+$ | 6 |

(a) What is probability the first gene to enter?

(b) What is the probable order of genes on the bacterial chromosome?

**Solution :**

| Genotypes | No. of Colonies | % |
|---|---|---|
| $his^+$ | 0 | 0 |
| $leu^+$ | 12 | 26.6 |
| $thr^+$ | 27 | 60 |
| $pro^+$ | 6 | 13.3 |
| | Total 45 | |

$thr^+$ gene shows closest to origin which was transformed first, then $leu^+$, then $pro^+$ finally $his^+$

The probable order of genes is

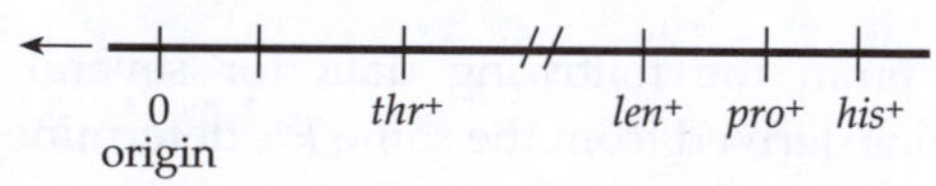


## Problem 13

Three different strains of bacteria are used to conjugate with an $F^-$ strain that is mutant for all of the genes. The time in minutes at which point the wild type genes entered the recipient bacteria are given. Diagram the bacterial chromosome with the arrangement of the genes in their correct order :

| | Hfr P | Hfr K | Hfr R |
|---|---|---|---|
| $gal^+$ | 11 | 67 | 70 |
| $thr^+$ | 94 | 50 | 87 |
| $xyl^+$ | 72 | 29 | 8 |
| $lac^+$ | 2 | 58 | 79 |
| $his^+$ | 38 | 94 | 43 |

**Solution :**

From the results we can assume the sequence of genes in the respective strains and their position of F

Hfr P : F lac$^+$, gal$^+$ his$^+$ xyl$^+$ thr$^+$

Hfr K : F xyl$^+$ thr$^+$ lac$^+$ gal$^+$ his$^+$

Hfr R : thr$^+$ lac$^+$ gal$^+$ his$^+$ xyl$^+$F

The circular $\phi$ map would be as follows :

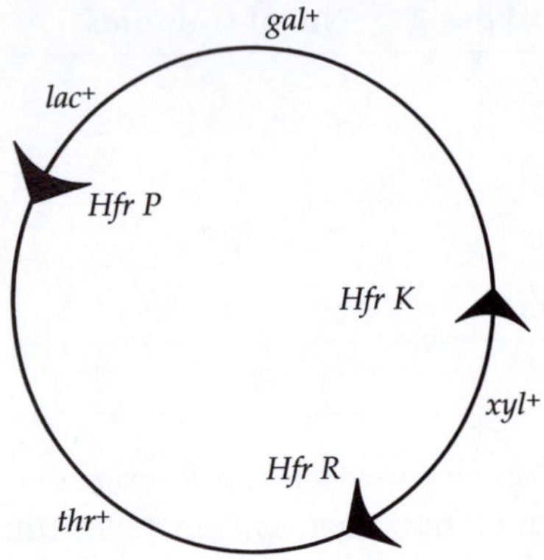


## Problem 14

From the following data for several *Hfr* strains derived from the same $F^+$, determine the order of markers in the $F^+$ strain

| *Hfr* strain | Markers donated in order |
|---|---|
| 1 | – Z – H – E – R → |
| 2 | – O – K – S – R → |
| 3 | – K – O – W – I → |
| 4 | – Z – T – I – W → |
| 5 | – H – Z – T – I → |

**Solution :**

| *Hfr* strain | Order of genes |
|---|---|
| 1 | –Z–H–E–R– |
| 2 | –R–S–K–O– |
| 3 | –K–O–W–I– |
| 4 | –W–I–T–Z– |
| 5 | –I–T–Z–H– |

The order of genes would be

Z–H–E–R–S–K–O–W–I–T–Z–H

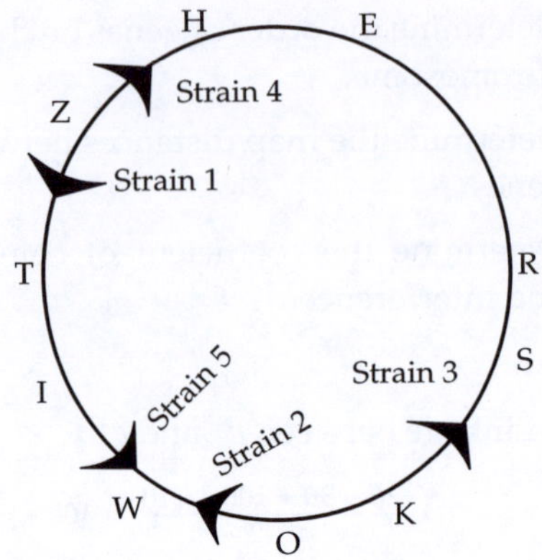


## Problem 15

Following are the number of colonies of different transformant classes from a cross of *trp*$^+$ *his*$^+$ *tyr*$^+$ as the donor with *trp*$^-$ *his*$^-$ *tyr*$^-$ as the recipient.

1. *trp*$^-$ *his*$^-$ *tyr*$^+$ = 685
2. *typ*$^-$ *his*$^+$ *tyr*$^-$ = 418
3. *trp*$^-$ *his*$^+$ *tyr*$^+$ = 3660
4. *typ*$^+$ *his*$^-$ *tyr*$^-$ = 2660
5. *trp*$^+$ *his*$^-$ *tyr*$^+$ = 107
6. *trp*$^+$ *his*$^+$ *tyr*$^-$ = 1180
7. *trp*$^+$ *his*$^+$ *tyr*$^+$ = 11940

Calculate the linkage distance and linkage map between the three loci

**Solution :**

| Distance | Transformant | No. of colonies | Frequency |
|---|---|---|---|
| *trp* and *his* | $trp^+\ his^-$ | 2600+107 = 2707 | $\frac{6785}{19905} = 0.34$ |
| | $trp^-\ his^+$ | 418 + 3660 = 4078 | |
| | $trp^+\ his^+$ | 1180 + 11940 = 13120 | |
| | | Total 19905 | |
| *trp* and *tyr* | $trp^+\ tyr^-$ | 2600 + 1180 = 3780 | $\frac{8125}{20172} = 0.40$ |
| | $trp^-\ tyr^+$ | 685 + 3660 = 4345 | |
| | $trp^+\ tyr^+$ | 107 + 11940 = 12047 | |
| | | Total 20172 | |
| *his* and *tyr* | $his^+\ tyr^-$ | 418 + 1180 = 1598 | $\frac{2390}{17990} = 0.13$ |
| | $his^-\ tyr^+$ | 685 + 107 = 792 | |
| | $his^-\ tyr^+$ | 3660 + 11940 = 15600 | |
| | | Total 17990 | |

Therefore, the linkage distance

*trp* - *his* = 0.34 mu

*trp* – *tyr* = 0.40 mu

*his* – *tyr* = 0.13 mu

The order of genes would be as follows

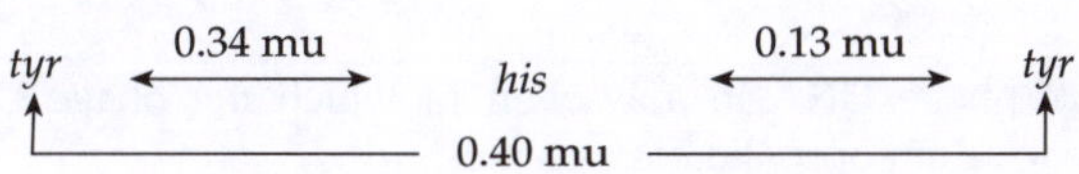


## Chapter Glossary/Key Terms

**"A" Protein :** The viral "A" protein cleaves the plus strand or RF DNA at a specific site and is covalently linked to the resulting 5′ end. The host cell rep protein acts together with protein 'A' as helicase and unwinds the ds DNA.

**Bacteriocin :** A toxic protein made by bacteria to kill other closely related bacteria.

**ColE I plasmid :** Small multicopy plasmid of *E. coli* that forms the basis of many cloning vectors widely used in molecular biology.

*Contd.*

**ColE plasmid :** Small multicopy plasmid that carries genes for colicins of the E group.*Contd.*

**Colicin :** Toxic protein made by *E. coli* to kill closely related bacteria.

**Conjugation :** Process in which genes are transferred by cell to cell contact.

**Copy number :** The number of copies of a gene or plasmid found within a single host cell.

**F-plasmid :** Fertility plasmid that allows *E. coli* to donate DNA by conjugation.

**Generalized transduction :** Type of transduction where fragments of bacterial DNA are packaged at random and all genes have roughly the same chance of being transferred.

**Integron :** A transposon that contains a gene for an integrase and an *att* site for integration of gene cassettes, often for antibiotic resistance. A promoter is also lined up on the transposon to allow transcription of cassette genes inserted into the transposon *att* site.

**Interrupted mating :** A method used in conjugation experiments in which the length of time that the bacteria spend conjugating is stopped by a blender treatment or other a blender treatment or other type of harsh treatment.

**mob gene :** The genes on a mobilizable DNA element that allow it to be mobilized by self-transmissible plasmid.

**mob region :** A region of DNA carrying an origin of transfer (*ori T*) region and often genes whose products allow the plasmid or other DNA element to be mobilized by self-transmissible elements such as self-transmissible plasmid.

**Mobilization :** The process by which a mobilizable DNA element, incapable of self-transmission, is transferred into other cells by the conjugation functions of a self-transmissble element.

**Par function :** A site or gene product that is required for the partitioning of plasmid.

**Partitioning :** The active process by which at least one copy of a replicon (plasmid or chromosome, etc) is distributed into each daughter cell at the time of cell division.

**Plasmid incompatibility :** The inability of two plasmids of the same family to co-exist in the same host cell.

**Prophage :** The state of phage DNA in a lysogen in which the phage DNA is integrated into the chromsomes of the bacterium or replicates as a plasmid.

**Proviral DNA :** A DNA copy of a retrovirus genome that is inserted into the chromosome of an infected host cell.

**Specialized transduction :** Type of transduction where certain regions of the bacterial DNA are carried preferentially.

***Tra*-genes :** Genes needed for Plasmid transfer.

**Transduction :** Process in which genes are transferred inside virus particles.

**Transformation** (in bacterial geneties) The process by which genes are transferred into a cell as free molecules of DNA.

# EXERCISE

## A. Long answer type questions :

1. Define genome. Where does it occur? Describe the importance of genome.
2. Describe the structure of a typical bacteria.
3. Describe *E. coli* genome structure.
4. Classify plasmids with characters and examples.
5. What are the characteristics of plasmids?
6. Describe different modes of plasmid replication.
7. What do you mean by plasmid families and incompatibility of plasmids? Briefly describe repressor model and partitioning models of plasmid incompatibility.
8. What is partitioning? What are the roles of **Par** proteins in partitioning process? Describe different par-systems.
9. Describe Col E plasmid genome.
10. Describe F plasmid genome.
11. What is the role of *tra* gene of F.
12. Briefly describe the mobilization of conjugative bacteria.
13. What is plasmid attracting pheromone? Describe the mechanism of this process.
14. What do you mean by copy number of plasmid in the cell? How does the copy number is regulated.
15. Briefly describe the mobilization of plasmid.
16. What is plasmid addiction? Describe two plasmid addiction systems for killing cells.
17. What are integrons and antibiotic resistant cassettes? Give their different sites.
18. What do you mean by superintegrons?
19. What are bacteriocins? How do these substances kill bacteria?
20. Describe the experiment on recombination in bacteria by leaderberg and Tatum.
21. Describe the mechanism of generalized and specialized transduction in bacteria?
22. What are mating types? Describe the mechanism of conjugation in bacteria and mechanism of DNA transfer during conjugation in bacteria.
23. Describe the method of conjugation mapping of genes in bacteria through interrupted mating.
24. Define transformation and describe the mechanism of transformation in bacteria .

## For practice

1. In *E. coli,* for *Hfr* strains transfer their markers in the order shown below :

| Strain | |
|---|---|
| 1 | A B C D E |
| 2 | G H I E D |
| 3 | J K L G H |
| 4 | J A B C D |

All the *Hfr* strains were derived from the same $F^+$ strain. Arrange the markers on the circular chromosome showing the origin and direction of transfer with an arrow in each case.

2. A cross is made between *Hfr* $met^+$ $thi^+$ $pur^+$ X
$F^-$ $met^-$ $thi^-$ $pur^-$. Interrupted mating studies show the $met^+$ enters the recipient last. So, $met^+$ excongugants are selected on medium containing *thi* and *pur* only. These exconjugants are selected for the presence of the $thi^+$ and $pur^+$. The following number of individuals are found with each genotypes :

| Genotype | Number |
|---|---|
| $met^+$ $thi^+$ $pur^+$ | 280 |
| $met^+$ $thi^+$ $pur^-$ | 0 |
| $met^+$ $thi^-$ $pur^+$ | 6 |
| $met^+$ $thi^-$ $pur^-$ | 52 |

(a) Why was *met* left out of the selection medium?

(b) What is the gene order?

(c) What are the map distances in recombination units?

(d) Why are there no individuals of the $met^+$ $thi^+pur^-$ genotype?

3. In a cross of *E. coli* $F^+$ $trp^+$ $his^+$ $tyr^+ \times F^-$ $trp^-$ $his^-$ $tyr^-$ the following results are obtained.

| | |
|---|---|
| $trp^+$ $his^+$ $tyr^+$ | 11945 |
| $trp^+$ $his^-$ $tyr^-$ | 2700 |
| $trp^+$ $his^+$ $tyr^-$ | 1180 |
| $trp^-$ $his^+$ $tyr^-$ | 400 |
| $trp^-$ $his^+$ $tyr^+$ | 3600 |
| $trp^-$ $his^-$ $tyr^+$ | 600 |
| $trp^+$ $his^-$ $tyr^+$ | 100 |

Calculate the recombination frequencies and draw a genetic map of the region.

## B. Short answer type questions.

1. What is the importance of capsule in bacteria.
2. Distinguish gram +ve and gram –ve bacteria in their membrane composition.
3. What are the compositions of *E. coli* ribosomes?
4. Which Gram +ve bacterium contains pili?
5. What is fimbrilin?
6. Which amino acids are absent in the hook of flagella?
7. What is the length, width and bases in *E. coli* K12 genome?
8. Whether *E. coli* genome has any split genes and repetitive genes or not?
9. What types of overlapping is observed in thr-A, B, C genes in *E. coli* K12.
10. Which two enzymes regulate *E. coli* gene supercoiling?
11. What the current model of *E. coli* DNA?
12. What are plasmids?
13. What is sex factor in plasmid?
14. What is R-plasmids?
15. Why plasmid genome is not regarded as the cell's genome?
16. Why plasmids are replicons?
17. What are cryptic plasmids?
18. What is promiscuous plasmid?
19. What is the transferability of plasmid?
20. What is *mob*$^+$ plasmid?
21. For the replication of plasmids? which enzymes are borrowed from the host cell?
22. When the plasmid replication in the host cell and when moves from one cell to another during conjugation what types of replication take place?
23. What are the origins of replication during bidirectional and transfer?
24. What is theta replication?
25. What is DSO?
26. What is phosphotransferase reaction?
27. What is SSO?
28. Which is primer problem during replication of linear plasmids.
29. How do the two ends of linear plasmids are protected.
30. What is the role of prototelomerase in dimeric circle of plasmid.
31. How the replication occurs in linear plasmids with hairpin structure?
32. What are slippage mechanism in plasmid replication.
33. What are plasmid incompatibility and Inc groups?
34. What is compatible?
35. What is different incompatibility groups?
36. What is repressor model for initiation of replication.
37. What are the genes found in R1 plasmid Par system?
38. How the actin and tubulin proteins seem to be reversed in the two kingdoms, eukarya and prokarya.
39. Which are radial asters?
40. What are the four stages of plasmid transfer?
41. What is conjugative plasmid and non-transmissible plasmid?

42. What is mobilizable plasmid?
43. What is self-transmissible plasmid?
44. Why bacteria containing ColE1 cannot transfer plasmid but if F and Col $E_1$ present can transfer?
45. What is donation?
46. What is conduction?
47. What is plasmid attacting pheromone?
48. What is relaxed copy number control?
49. What is stringent copy number control?
50. What are RNAII and RNA I?
51. What is plasmid amplification?
52. What is the effect of chloramphinicol on copy number of plasmid?
53. What do you mean by plasmid mobilization?
54. What is mobilization plasmid?
55. What is Dtr system? What are their requirements?
56. What is Mpf system of self transmissible plasmid?
57. What is plasmid addiction system?
58. What is lethal-antidote system of plasmid addiction?
59. What is protein based host killing operon?
60. What is Hok-Sok complex to kill host?
61. What is PhD-Doc sytem of plasmid addiction?
62. What are the characteristics of integron?
63. Distinguish transposon and integron?
64. What are the characteristics of antibiotic resistance cassettes?
65. What is the advantage of antibiotic resistance cassettes?
66. What is chromosomal superintegrons? Give example.
67. What is bacteriocin? What is its importance?
68. How do they kill the bacteria? How the bacteria protect themselves from their own bacteriocin?
69 What is minimal medium?
70. Define conjugation, transformation and transduction.
71. What are auxotroph and prototrophs?
72. What is supplemented medium?
73. What do you mean by *met*⁻ and *met*⁺ strains?
74. What is crossfeeding?
75. Compare between generalized and specialized transduction?
76. How can you proof that cross feeding is impossible to produce wild type bacteria?
77. How Zinder and Leaderberg proved the genralized transduction in an experiment?
78. What are abortive transductants?
79. What is restricted transduction?
80. What are the three steps of specialized transduction?
81. What is λdg? What is its literal meaning?
82. What is heterogenote?
83. What is double lysogen?
84. Define conjugation.
85. What do you mean by $F^+$ and $F^-$ cells?
86. What is F-factor?
87. What is infectious transfer?
88. What is Hfr? How this strain is produced?
89. What is F′ or substituted F-factor?
90. What is sex-duction or F-duction? What is the result from F′ *lac*⁺ × F *lac*⁻?
91. What is interrupted mating?
92. What is the principle of conjugation mapping by interrupted mapping?
93. What is competent factor in transformation process?
94. What is the role of DNA translocase in transformation process?
95. What is the literal meaning of chromosome?
96. Who gave the name chromatin and chromosome?
97. What do you mean by chromosome number?
98. What is chromanemata?
99. What is chromomere?

100. What is centromere? Why it is called kinetochore?
101. Classify types of chromosomes according to the position of centromere.
102. What are acentric and dicentric chromosomes? How they are produced?
103. How kinetochore can be traced in $G_1$, S or $G_2$ phases of cell cycle?
104. What is CDE and CDF? How do they interrelated?
105. What is satellite chromosome?
106. What is co-satellite? What is CENP-B box?
107. What are primary and secondary constrictions?
108. In which chromosomes satellites are found?
109. What is NOR? In which arms in human chromosome these are observed?
110. What is telomere? What is its unique feature?
111. What is telomerase? What is its function?
112. What is telomere shortening ? What is its importance?
113. What types of histones are found in chromosomes?
114. What are multistrand and single strand models?
115. What is folded fibre model of Dupraw?
116. What are type-A and type-B fibres?
117. What is nucleosome?
118. What is structural periodicty of DNA in nucleosome?
119. What are core DNA, core particles and linker DNA?
120. What is DNA superhelix?
121. What are histone tetramer and octamers in nucleosome?
122. What is ubiquitin? Where does it occur? What is its function?
123. What is solenoid of nucleosome?
124. What are MAR and SAR?
125. What is the role divalent cations on nucleosome structure?
126. What is the role of HMGs in gene activation?
127. What are G, C, R, T, F and N-banding?
128. How many genes are present in mitogenome?
129. What are the differences between mitogenome, genetic code and universal genetic code.
130. What are L and H strands of mito DNA.
131. What are the causes of LHON and MERRF diseases?
132. What is promiscuous DNA.
133. What are the characteristics of mito DNA.
134. What are the characteristics of cpDNA.

14

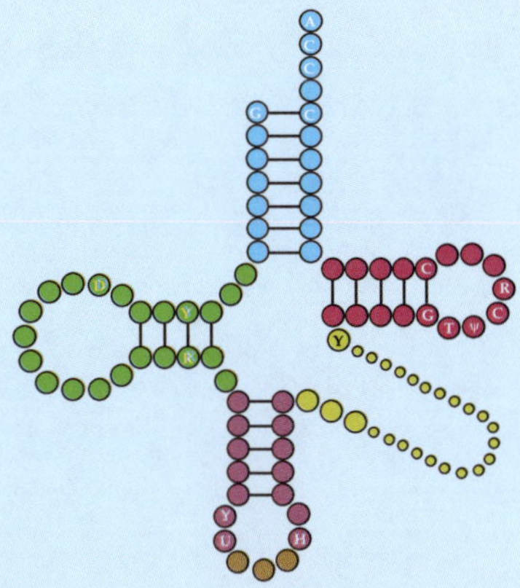

# Organization of Genetic Material

**CHAPTER AGENDA**

## 14.1 INTRODUCTION

After the discovery of Mendelism on 1900, it was concluded that hereditary materials are located within the nuclei of eggs and sperms. This hereditary material is a gene, which is present in the chromosome, not in the blood,. Through the formation of gametes by meiosis and then fertilization, these genes are transmitted from generation to the next generation.

Particulate nature of gene was estiblished and F. Griffith (1928) found that a substance in heat killed bacteria can cause heritable changes in the live bacteria. He called this phenomenon as **transformation**. Oswald Avery, Colin Macleod, and Maclyn McCarty (1944) established the chemical identity of Griffith's transforming principle as DNA and they suggested that it might function as the genetic material.

Soon after this, it has been established that the amino acid suquence of every protein and the nucleotide suquence of every RNA molecule in a cell are specified by that of cell's DNA. *A segment of DNA that contains the information required for the synthesis of a functional product (protein or RNA) is referred to as a* **gene.** The biological informations are stored in the DNA and through replication it is copied itself and through transcription and translation the hereditary traits are expressed by the production of proteins. This one way pathway by which DNA through transcription mRNA and then by translation protein is produced is commonly known as **central dogma.**

In 1953, discovery of the structure of DNA by J. Watson, F. Crick, Rosalind Franklin, Raymond Gosling, M. Wilkin, W. E. Seeds, Alec Stokes, H. Wilson and B. Jacobson opened up our eyes about the nature and role of DNA in heredity. This discovery gave J. Watson, F. Crick and M. Wilkins the Nobel prize in medicine in 1962.

## 14.2 NUCLEOTIDES

Nucleotides are energy-rich compounds that drive all the crucial supporting roles in cell metabolism and polymer of nucleotides provide. The script for everything that occur in a cell the nucleic acids, i.e., deoxyribonucleic acid (DNA) and ribonucleic acid (RNA) are the molecular repositories for genetic information in all living beings from virus to prokaryotes to an algae to human beings. The segment of DNA that contains the information of a functional biological product is referred to as **gene**. mRNA carries information from the gene and tRNA faithfully translate it into a polypeptide within the ribosomes.

Nucleotides have three components : *a nitrogenous base, a sugar* and *a phosphate.*

**Bases :** Bases are of two types : Pyrimidine and Purine

**Pyrimidine bases** are derivatives of parent pyrimidine nucleus which is structurally a 6-membered ring with two nitrogen atoms at 1 and 3 positions and four carbon atoms. Cytosine is 2, oxy, 4 amino pyrimidine, Thymine is 5 methyl, 2, 4, dioxypyrimidine. Uracil is 2, 4 dioxypyrimidine. (Fig. 14.1)

**Purine bases** are derivatives of purine nucleus, which is fused 6 and 5 membered ring, at 4 and 5 carbon positions and have 4 nitrogen atoms at 1, 3, 7 and 9 positions. Adenine is 6, amino purine, Guanine is 2 amino, 6 oxypurine.

**Sugars :** Two types of sugars are found in nucleic acids, viz, *ribose sugar* and 2, *deoxyribose sugars.* These are pentose sugars and have a five membered ring in their structure (Fig. 14.2). When the base condenses with a sugar a **nucleoside** is formed. eg. deoxyadenosine, adenosine guanosine, deoxyguanosine etc. (Fig. 14.3)

In pyrimidine nucleoside, the nitrogen atom at position 1 of the pyrimidine ring is linked to the carbon atom position 1′ of the sugar. But in

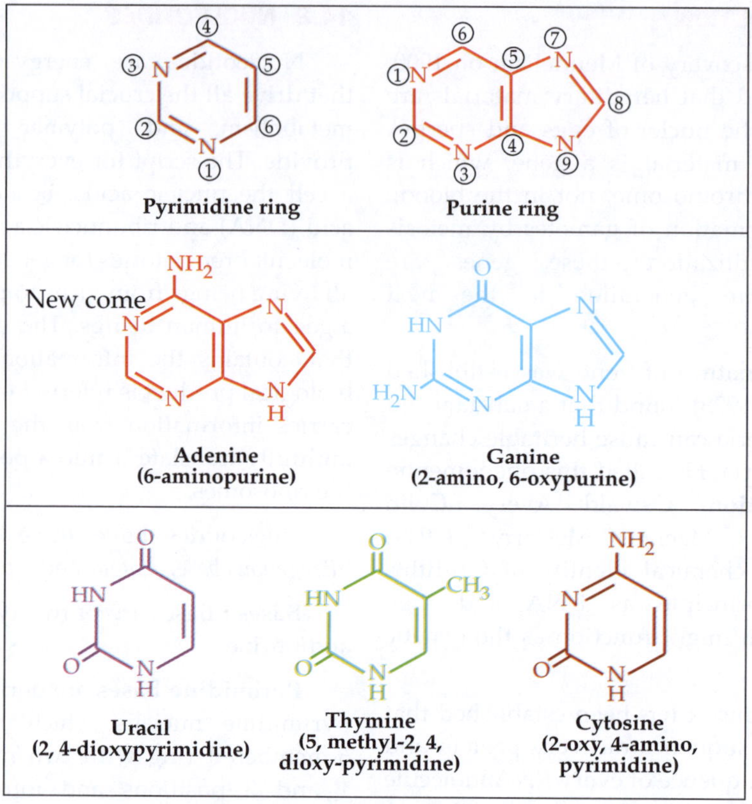


**Fig.14.1 :** *Different types of purine and pyrimidine bases.*

purine nucleoside, the link is between nitrogen, atom 9 of purine and carbon atom of 1′ of the sugar.

When the pentose sugar residue of a nucleoside is esterified with phosphoric acid, a **nucleotide** is formed. Ribose bound in nucleoside, possesses free –OH group in cabon

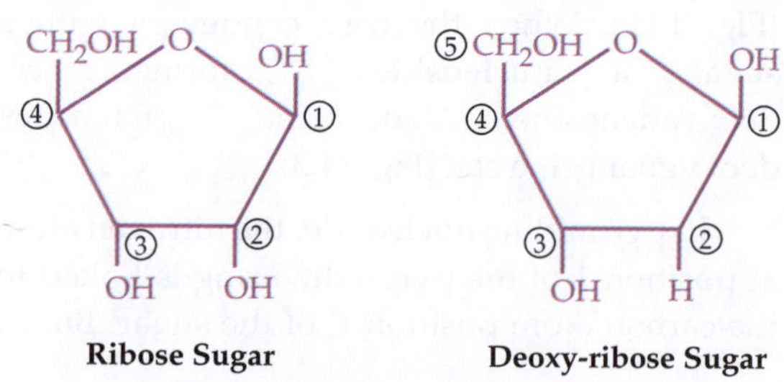


**Fig.14.2 :** *Ribose and deoxyribose Sugars*

2′, 3′ and 5′ and the phosphate residue may be attached to any of the three positions forming nucleoside – 2′ -phosphate or nucleoside – 3′ phosphate or nucleoside – 5′ phosphate or nucleoside 2′, 3′cyclic phosphate.

When 5′ end of a nucleoside is phosphorylated thrice, a 5′, 5′, 5′ triphospho– nucleoside is formed eg. ATP, GTP, UTP, CTP and TTP.

## 14.3 STRUCTURE OF DNA

In the early 1950s Rosalind Franklin and Maurice Wilkins used the powerful method of X-ray diffraction to analyse DNA crystals and shed a light on the structure of DNA.

The epochmaking discovery of the three dimensional structure of DNA by Watson and Crick in 1953 has opened our eyes about the structural and functional aspects of gene and led

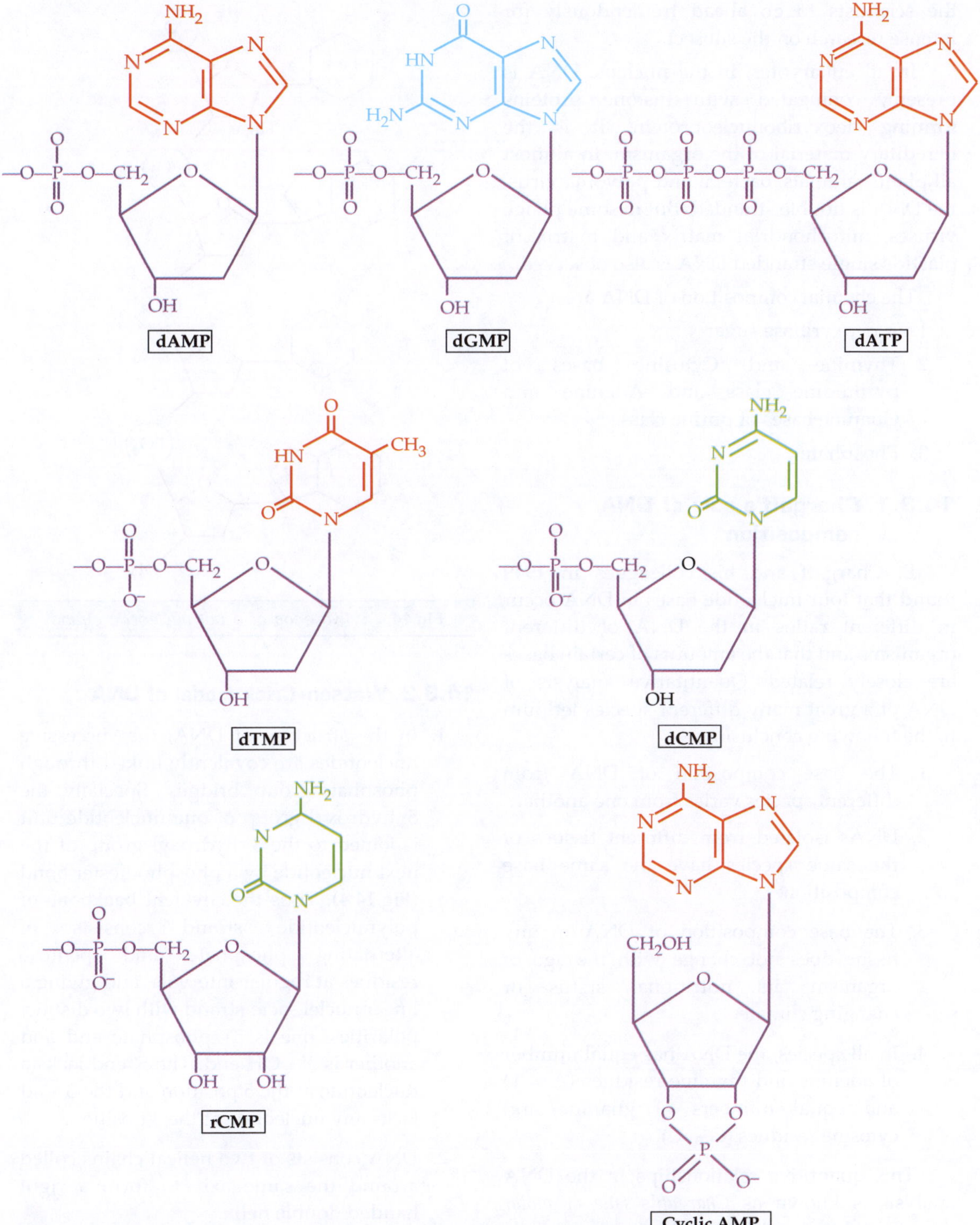


**Fig.14.3 :** *Structure of ribonucleotides and deoxyribonucleotides.*

the scientists to go ahead tremendously for intense research on the subsect.

In all eukaryotes, in the nucleus, DNA is present, conjugated with histone proteins forming deoxyribonucleoprotein. It is the hereditary material of the organism. In allmost all plants, animals, bacteria and polyoma virus, the DNA is double stranded. But in some phage viruses, mitochondrial matrix and matrix of plastids single stranded DNA is also observed.

The chemial composition of DNA are

1. 2, deoxyribose sugar
2. Thymine and Cytosine bases of pyrimidine class and Adenine and Guanine bases of purine class.
3. Phosphate

### 14.3.1 Chargaff's rule of DNA composition

E. Chargaff and his colleagues in 1949 found that four nucleotide bases in DNA occur in different ratios in the DNA of different organisms and that the amounts of certain bases are closely related. Quantitative analysis of DNA of a great many different species led him to the following conclusions.

1. The base compositon of DNA from different species varies from one another.
2. DNAs isolated from different tissues of the same species have the same base composition.
3. The base composition of DNA in any tissue does not change with the age of organism, its nutritional status or changing climate.
4. In all species, the DNA has equal number of adenine and thymine residues (A = T) and equal numbers of guanine and cytosine residues (G—C).

This quantitive relationships in the DNA analysis is known as *Chargaff's rule of molar equivalence between the purines and pyrimidines in DNA.*

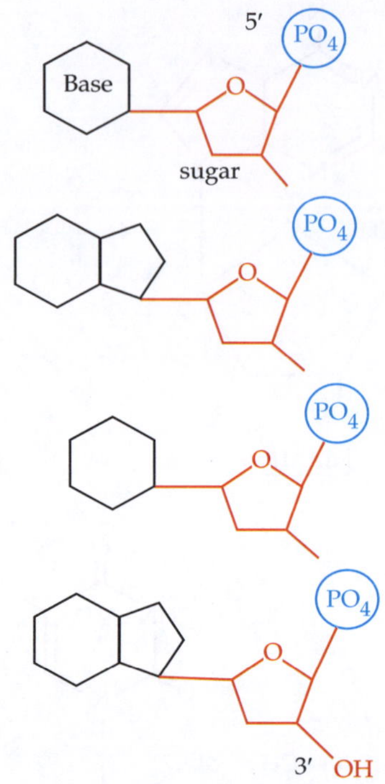


**Fig.14.4 :** *Two ends of a polynucleotide strand*

### 14.3.2 Watson–Crick model of DNA

1. In the structure of DNA, the successive nucleotides are covalently linked through phosphate group 'bridges'. Specially, the 5′ hydroxyl group of one nucleotide unit is joined to the 3′ hydroxyl group of the next nucleotide by a phosphodiester bond (Fig.14.4). Thus the covalent backbone of polynucleotide strand consists of alternating phosphate and pentose residues at regular intervals and giving a linear nucleic acid strand with two distinct polarities, one is 5′ -phosphate end and another is 3′ – OH end. The 5′ end lacks a nucleotide at the 5′position and the 3′ end lacks any nucleotide at the 3′position.
2. DNA consists of two helical chains coiled around the same axis to form a right handed double helix.
3. The hydrophilic backbones of alternating deoxyribose and negatively charged

phosphate groups are on the outside of the double helix. The purine and pyrimidine bases of both strands are stacked inside the double helix with their hydrophobic planar ring structures close together and perpendicular to the long axis of the helix. The spatial ralationship between these strands creates a major groove and minor groove between the two strands.

4. The two polynucleotide strands of the helix are antiparallel, ie, the $5' \rightarrow 3'$ phosphodiester bonds run in opposite direction. Thus, in DNA double helix one strand of polynucleotide runs in $5'P \rightarrow 3'$-OH direction and another $3'$-OH$\rightarrow 5'P$ direction. (Fig.14.4)

5. It is important to note that the two antiparallel strands facing each other are joined with H–bonds between their opposite complementary bases. i.e., the H-bonds are formed between G and C or A and T.

6. When G and C are linked, the H-bonds are formed between their $N_1$–$N_3$, $C_2$–$C_2$ and $C_6$–$C_4$ positions of the respective opposite bases. The lengths of the bonds are 0.292 nm and 0.284 nm, 0.284 nm respectively.

7. When A and T are linked, the H-bonds are formed between $N_1$–$N_3$ and $C_6$–$C_4$ positions of the respective opposite bases. Their bond lengths are 0.291 nm and 0.282 nm respectively.

8. There are three H-bonds between G and C, whereas, two H-bonds between A and T. Although, H-bonds are weak, the fact that there are so many H-bonds which give the stability to the DNA molecule.

9. Watson and Crick model of DNA shows that the vertically stacked bases inside the double helix would be 0.34 nm apart and the distance between the two successive bases i.e. the pitch of helix is 3.4 nm and could be accounted for by the presence of 10 nucleotide residues in each complete turn of the helix. The width of the DNA helix is 20Å (Fig. 14.5)

## 14.4 DNA CONFORMATIONS

DNA can exist in the A, B, C, D usual forms. Sugar puckering is the most important characteristic for distinguishing the DNA forms. The A-form has 3′ endopuckering, B and C forms have 3′ exopuckering and D form has 2′ endopuckering.

The well known Watson-Crick DNA is known as **B-form of DNA**.

D-form of DNA is rare, Another rare form is E-form, found as extreme variants with only b. p. per turn. In some DNA molecules both D and E forms lack Guanine base. D-form to A-transition has been observed at low relative humidity. A-form is metastable and rapidly returns to the D-form. B-form to A-form transition also occurs during transcription because RNA is always in the A-form and thus DNA-RNA hydrid could be formed during transcription.

### 14.4.1 Z-form of DNA

Rich and his group at the MIT, USA have studied the molecular structure of a DNA fragment at atomic resolution and proposed a left handed double helix model with Zigzag sugar phosphate backbone in antiparallel organization and thus it is Z-DNA.

Z-DNA resembles the B-DNA in may respects : both are double helical, two strands of double helices are antiparallel and both exhibit A-T and G-C base pairing .

### 14.4.2 The major differences between Z-DNA and B-DNA

1. Z-DNA has left-handed helical sense as against right-handed helical sense of B-DNA (Fig.14.6).

2. Phosphate backbone follows a zig-zag course, in Z-DNA, while in B-DNA it is regular.

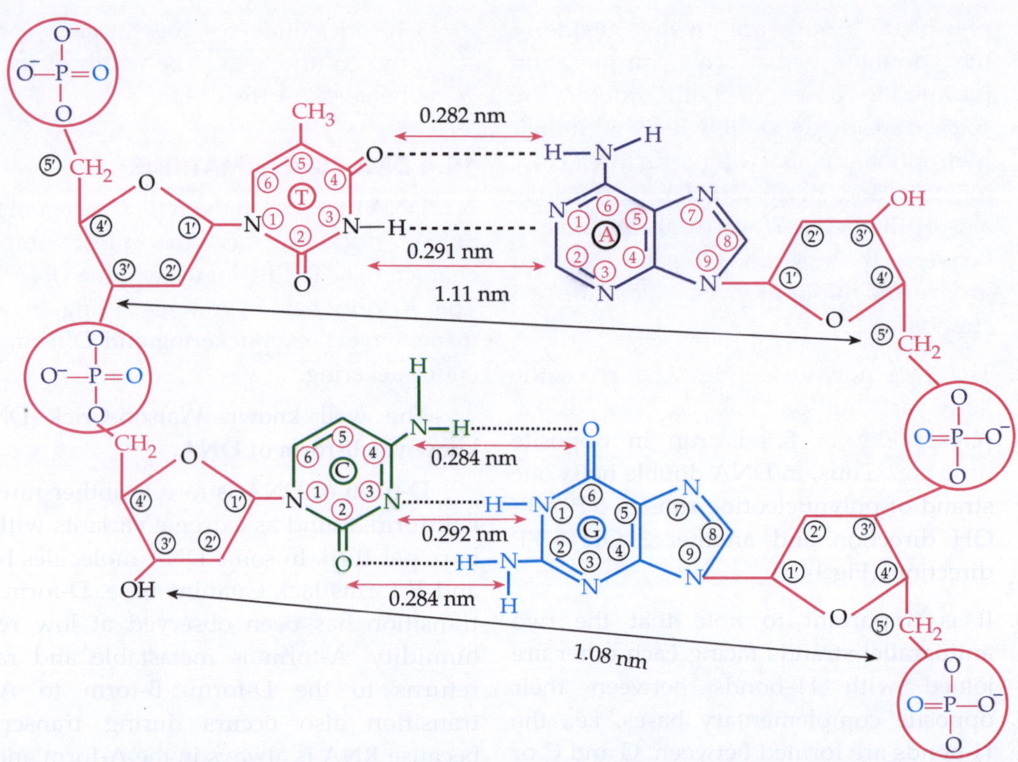


**Fig.14.5 :** *Pairing of complementary bases and antiparallel disposition of polynucleotide strands in the structure of DNA*

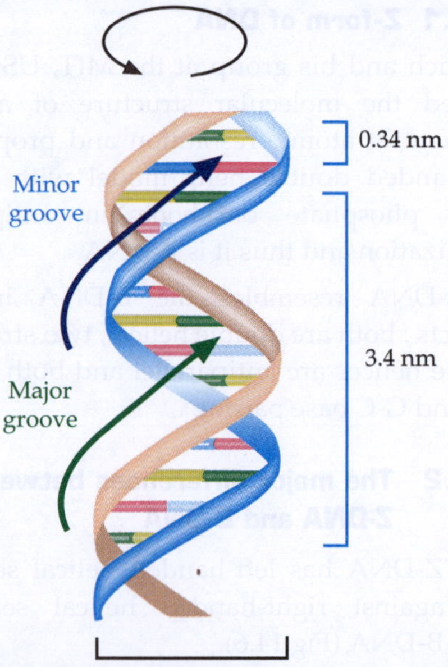


**Fig.14.6 :** *Schematic representation showing the dimensions of the DNA helix*

3. In Z-DNA sugar residues have alternating orientations so that repeating unit is a dinucleotide. In B-DNA repreating unit is mononucleotide. (Fig.14.7)

4. In Z-DNA, 12 bp, per turn, whereas, in B-DNA 10 bp per turn and so angle of twist per repeating unit (dimer) in Z-DNA is 60° as against 36° in B-DNA.

5. One complete helix is 45Å in Z-DNA while 34Å in B-DNA.

6. Angle of tilt in Z-DNA is 60° and diameter is 18Å whereas, tilt in B-DNA is 36° and diameter is 20Å.

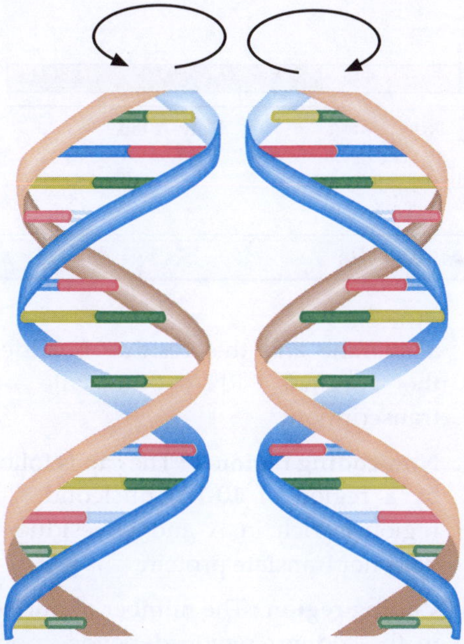

Right-handed B DNA Left-handed B DNA

**Fig.14.7 :** *Two helices one showing right handed B-DNA and other left handed Z-DNA*

### 14.4.3 Role of Z-DNA

Z DNA was thought to be a transient configuration of B-DNA. It was earlier believed and suggested by Alexander Rich, that it plays an important role in the regulation of gene activity, since Z-DNA-specific antibodies bind specifically to the interband region *i.e.,* the inactive region of salivary gland chromosomes. But it was not supported because the result may be due to an artefact of chromosome fixation. However, Willium Holloman and Eric Kmiec suggested that Z-DNA plays a role in genetic recombination or rearrangement of DNA.

### 14.4.4 RL model of DNA

GA Rodley's group in Newzealand and V Sasisekharan (1976-80) and his coworkers of Indian Institute of Science, Bangalore have independently proposed a model which is different from the Watson-Crick B-DNA model.

**TABLE 14.1**
**Comparison between different DNA-conformations**

| *Geometry attribute* | *A form* | *B form* | *Z form* |
|---|---|---|---|
| Helix sense | right-handed | right-handed | left-handed |
| Ropeating unit | 1 bp | 1 bp | 2 bp |
| Rotation/bp | 32.7° | 34.3° | 30° |
| bp/turn | 11 | 10 | 12 |
| Inclination of bp to axis | +19° | – 1.2° | – 9° |
| Rise/bp along axis | 2.3Å (0.23 nm) | 3.32 Å (0.332 nm) | 3.8Å (0.38 nm) |
| Pitch/turn of helix | 28.2Å (2.82 nm) | 33.2Å (3.32 nm) | 45.6Å (4.56 nm) |
| Mean propeller twist | +18° | +16° | 0° |
| Glycosyl angle | anti | anti | C : anti,<br>G : syn |
| Sugar pucker | C3′-endo | C2¢-endo | C : C2′-endo<br>G : C3′-endo |
| Diameter | 23Å (2.3 nm) | 20Å (2.0 nm) | 18Å (1.8 nm) |

According to them, the DNA duplex is formed by alternating right and left handed helices arranged side by side and therefore, this structure is called right-left helix model (R-L helix model) or side by side helix model. Each strand of the DNA duplex has 5 base pairs in the right handed helix alternating with 5 base pairs in the left handed helix.

Sashisekharan and Gupta recently proposed that, the twisting of the helix is uniform and the phosphate groups go round the helix as a zig-zag manner. Right handed helices are produced by purines in the *anti*-conformation and left

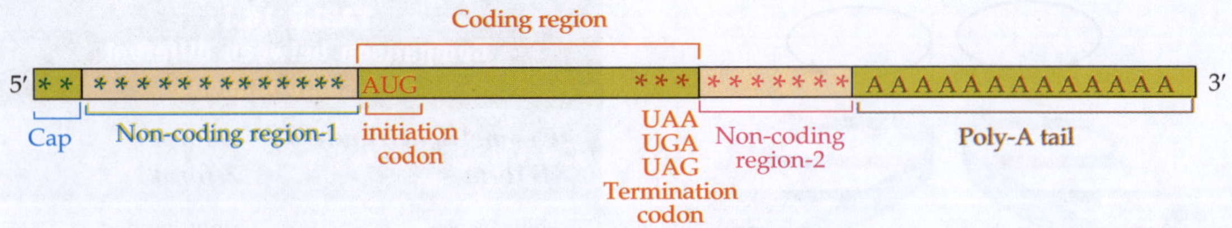


**Fig.14.8 :** *Different regions of mRNA*

handed helices by purines in the *syn* conformation.

The RL helix model can explain the unwinding of DNA duplex during replication without twisting round each other. The model also explains supercoiling of DNA in eukaryotic chromoromes without the presence of the proposed kinks in the regular helix.

## 14.5 mRNA (MESSENGER RNA)

Jacob and Monod (1961) proposed the name mRNA for the RNA carrying informations for protein synthesis from DNA (genes) to the sites of protein synthesis (ribosomes).

Average Mr=500000 and its sedimentation coefficient is about 8S. It would be noted that mRNA varies greatly in length and mol. wt.

It is always single stranded. It contains mostly the bases adenine, guanine, cytosine and uracil. But there are few unusual bases. It's base sequence is complementary to that of the segment of DNA on which it is transcribed.

When one gene codes for a single mRNA strand, the mRNA is called to be a monocistronic. Several adjacent genes may transcribe one mRNA which is called to be polycistronic (Fig. 14.8).

The mRNA molecule has the following structural features :

1. **Cap :** At the 5′ end of the mRNA molecule in most eukaryote cells and animal virus molecules is found a cap. It contains two nucleotides, connected by a 5′, 5′ triphosphate linkage and also bearing methyl group. The terminal base is always a guanine and this residue is added to the orginal RNA molecule after transcription.
2. **Non-coding region-1 :** The cap is followed by a region of 10-100 nucleotides. This region is rich in A and U residues and does not translate protein.
3. **Coding region :** The number of nucleodes in the coding region depends upon the number of amino acids in the polypeptide chain. The initiation codon is AUG in both prokaryotes and eukaryotes but sometimes GUG may be the initiation codon. Termination of translation on mRNA is brought about by a terminating codon. In eukaryotes the termination codon is UAA, UAG and UGA.
4. **Non coding region -2 :** It consists of 50-150 nucleotides and does not translate protein. This region contains an AAUAAU sequences.
5. **Poly-A-tail :** Most eukaryotic mRNAs have a sequence of poly adenylic acid at the 3′ end. This terminal stretch of A– residues is often described as the poly A– tail and mRNA with this feature is denoted poly $A^+$.

The poly-A sequence is not coded in the DNA but is added to the RNA in the nucleus after transcription. The addition of poly A is catalysed by the enzyme poly-A-polymerase, which recognises the free 3′-OH end of the mRNA and adds about 200 A-residues. The added stretch consists exclusively of A-residues.

**TABLE 14.2**
**Comparison between DNA and RNA**

| *DNA* | *RNA* |
|---|---|
| 1. DNA is usual genetic material although, DNA in mitochondria and chloroplast is nongenetic | 1. RNA is nongenetic although, in some viruses it is genetic material. |
| 2. DNA is double stranded except in some phage viruses it is single eg $\phi$ X 174. | 2. RNA is single stranded except some viruses eg. rheoviruses. |
| 3. Pentose sugar is deoxyribose. | 3. Pentose sugar is ribose. |
| 4. Common bases are Adenine, Guanine, Cytosine and Thymine | 4. Common bases are Adenine, Guanine Cytosine and Uracil, besides there some unusual bases are also present. |
| 5. Base pairing is A with T and G with C | 5. Base pairing is A with U and G with C. |
| 6. Pairing of bases throughout the length of the molecule | 6. Pairing only in the helical regions. |
| 7. DNA is only one type | 7. There are different types of RNA viz mRNA, tRNA, rRNA etc. |
| 8. Denaturation is partially reversible only after slow cooling. | 8. Denaturation is complete. |
| 9. DNA molecules replicate. | 9. Does not replicate except in cartain RNA viruses. |
| 10. DNA transcribes RNA | 10. RNA cannot transcribe except in some viruses. |
| 11. DNA contains large number of nucleotides. | 11. RNA contains small number of nucleotides. |

When mRNA first enters into the cytoplasm it has approximately the same length of poly A tail that was added in the nucleus. The tail is gradually shortened, by endonuclease cleavage. Thus the cellular population of mRNA includes both "New" and "Old" molecules with relatively longer and shorter stretches of poly A. However, the length of the poly A tail present on any particular molecule does not seem to influence its ability to be translated or its stability in the cytoplasm.

The poly A of mammalion mRNA is associated with the common 78000 Dalton protein that is a predominant component of mRNA. This suggests that the structure of the 3′ end of the mRNA consists of a stretch of Poly-A bound to roughly on equal mass of proteins.

**Function :** mRNA combines with ribosomes to form polysomes or polyribosomes. Each polysome contains several ribosomes forming a complex with mRNA. Within the ribsomes mRNA is translated and a polypeptide chain is synthesized.

## 14.6 tRNA (TRANSFER RNA)

tRNA is also called soluble RNA (sRNA) because, it is too small to be precipitated by ultracentrifugation. The mol. wt. is about 30,000 and sedimentation coefficient of mature eukaryotic tRNA is 3.8 S. It is made up of 73-93 nucleotides (Rich and Rajbhandary, 1976).

The function of tRNA is to carry amino acids to mRNA during protein synthesis. Each amino acid is carried by specific. tRNA, since 20 amino acids are coded to synthesize proteins. tRNA is synthesised in the nucleus on a DNA template.

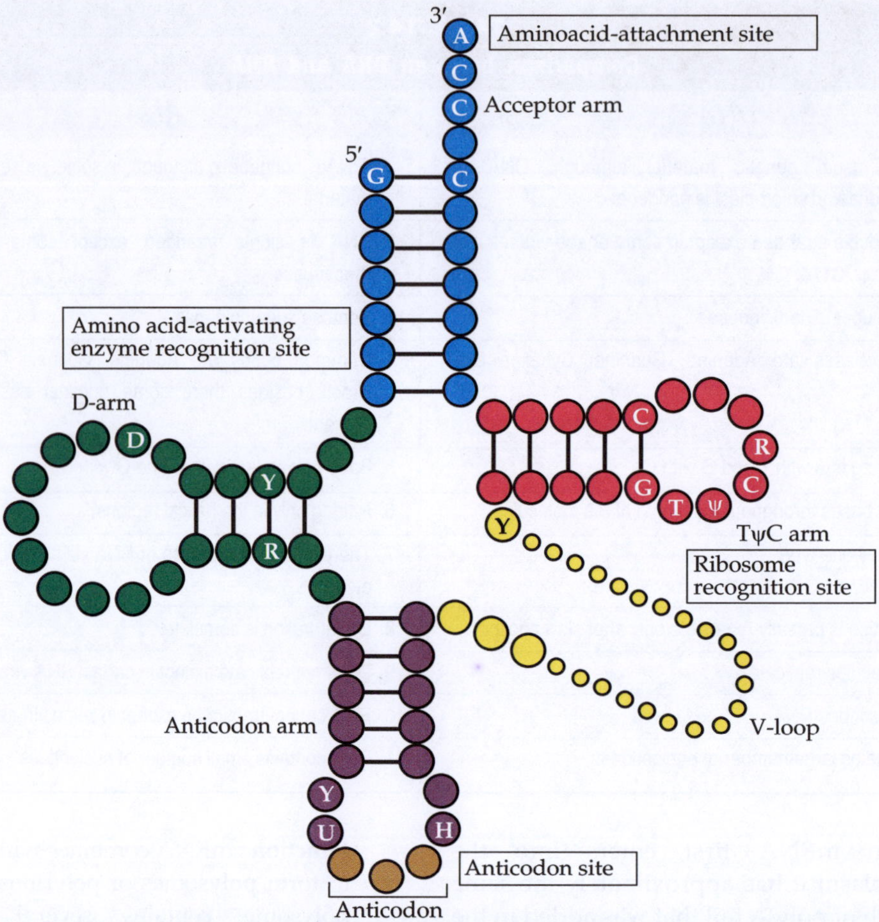


**Fig.14.9 :** *General structure of tRNA*
*O = invariant bases; I = variant bases; Y = Pyrimidine; H = Hypermodified purine*
*T = Ribothymidine; y = Pseudouridine; D = Dihydrouridine*

Structures of different tRNAs for almost all amino acids are now available and fit with the clover leaf model. The first tRNA, for which in 1964 R.W.Holley and his colleagues gave detailed structure, was alanyl tRNA from yeast and received Nobel prize for this work along with Khorana and Nirenberg in 1968.

**Detailed structure :** According to **clover leaf** model, the single polynucleotide chain of tRNA is folded upon itself to form 5 arms. As a result of folding the 3′end and 5′ end of the chain come to each other. An arm consists of a stem and a loop. In the double helical stem there is no base pairing in the loops.

One of the arms has a stem but not a loop is called the acceptor stem. The other arms are called D-arm, the anticodon arm, the variable arm and the TψC arm. The variable arm may or may not have a stem (Fig.14.9)

1. **The acceptor stem :** It consists of seven base pairs and four unpaired nucleotide units. The later includes a constant 3′-terminal-CCA sequence and a fourth variable purine nucleotide. The amino acid molecule attaches to the 3′ terminal of the CCA sequence, which is known as amino acid binding site. The 5′ P terminal end of tRNA is either G or C.

**TABLE 14.3**
**Three classes of tRNA**

| *Class and symbol* | *basepairs in D-arm* | *bases in V-arm* |
|---|---|---|
| Class I ($D_4-V_{4-5}$) | 4 | 4–5 |
| Class II ($D_3-V_{4-5}$) | 3 | 4–5 |
| Class III ($D_3-V_L$) | 3 | large |

2. **The second arm :** It is called D-arm. It consists of 15-18 nucleotides with 3-4 base pairs and 7-11 unpaired nucleotides in the loop. The loop of D-arm is called loop-1 or Dihydrouridine (DHU) loop or D-loop. It contains two variable regions α and β on either side of the two constant G residues. The synthetase site, which recognises the amino acid activating enzyme is located on the part of the D-loop and a part of the acceptor stem on the 5′ side.
3. **The third arm or anticodon arm :** It consists of an anticodon stem of 5 base pairs and a loop, called loop-II or the anticodon loop. This loop consists of 7 unpaired nucleotides of which the middle three form the anticodon. The anticodon recognizes the three-complementary bases which constitute a codon of mRNA. On the 3′ side of the anticodon is a hypermodified purine (H) while, on the other 5′ side is U and a pyrimidine (Y).
4. **The variable arm or the lump or mini loop or loop-III.** It is of two types . In one type there is a loop containing 4-5 bases but no stem. In the other type, the arm consists of 13-21 residues and both the stem and the loop can be distinguished.
5. **TψC arm :** It consists of a stem having 5 base pairs. The TψC loop contains a constant 5′TψC 3′ sequence. All tRNAs have a ribosomal recognition site on the TψC loop consisting 5′GTψCR 3′ sequence.

**Unusual bases :** In addition to the usual bases (A, U, G and C), tRNA contains a number of unusual bases which account for 15-20% of the total RNAs of the cell. Most of the unusual bases are formed by methylation eg. C and G on methylation yield methyl cytosine and methyl guanine respectively.

These unusual bases are important because they protect the tRNA molecules against degradation by RNAase enzyme. Some unusual bases of tRNA are methyl guanine, dimethyl guanine, methyl cytosine, ribothymidine, pseudouridine dihydrouridine, inosine and methyl inosine. In general, organisms higher in evolutionary scale contain more modified bases than the lower organisms.

**Classification :** The structure of acceptor stem, anticodon arm and TψC are constant in different tRNAs. The differences in the tRNA lie in the D-arm and the variable arm. Based on the differences in these two variable regions three classes of tRNAs have been recognised (Table 14.3).

A similar classification is based only on the variable arm : Class I with 4-5 bases in the variable loop and class-II with a large (13-21) number of bases in the variable loop.

**Recognition sites :** tRNA molecules have four recognition sites.

1. **Amino acid attachment site** which is the 3′ terminal –CCA sequence.
2. **The anticodon site** consisting of the middle three bases on the anticodon loop which form the anticodon. The anticodon recognises the three complementary bases i.e. the codon of the mRNA.
3. **The ribosome recognition site** which is common to all tRNAs and consists the GTψCR sequence on the TψC loop.

4. **The amino acid activating enzyme recognition site** by which the activating enzyme recognizes and charges specific amino acids with tRNA.

**Tertiary structure :** Yeast *phe* tRNA is somewhat flattened L-sphaped molecule, 20-25Å thick with one limb being formed by the acceptor and TψC stem and the other by the D- and the anticodon stems (Fig.14.10) There is a sharp bend near 9, 10 and 11 residues. TψC stem is linear. D-stem and anticodon stem is not in the same straight line and their axis may deviate by as much as 25°. This structure is due to the formation of H-bonds between bases, between bases and ribose phosphates, between their back-bone residues.

**Initiator tRNA :** The starting amino acid in eukaryote protein synthesis is methionine while in prokaryotes it is N-formyl methionine. These RNAs are called initiator tRNAs.

In most prokaryotes, the 5′-terminal nucleoside is C. It has opposite nucleoside A and so there is no Watson-Crick pairing between the two.

D-loop of prokaryotic initiator tRNAs contains $A_{11}$=$U_{24}$ base pairing, but all other tRNAs have $Y_{11}$=$R_{24}$ base pairing.

Eukaryotic cytoplasmic initiator tRNAs have AU instead of Tψ in the TψC loop.

In prokaryotes, the purine nucleotide following C in the TψC loop is A while in eukaryotes it is G.

In tRNA $^{f\text{-}met}$ the nucleotide adjacent to the 3′-side of the anticodon triplet is adenosine while in tRNA$^{met}$, it is an alkylated adenosine.

**Specificity :** Each amino acid has a specific activating enzyme, tRNA amino acyl synthetase. Thus there are 20 different tRNA amino acyl synthetases for 20 common amino acids found in proteins. Some tRNA synthetases can activate more than one amino acids. They show only a limited substrate specificity. thus isoleucine tRNA synthetase can also activate L-valine. The enzymes recognise only a specific set of tRNAs as substrates. eg, *val*-tRNA synthetase recognises only tRNA$^{val}$. Thus specificity is involved at two stages, activation of the amino acid and transfer of amino acid to tRNA.

## 14.7 rNA (RIBOSONAL RNA)

Ribosomal RNA, as the name suggests, is found in the ribosomes. It comprises about 80% of the total RNA of the cell.

All ribosomes can be dissociated into two subunits are roughly twice the size of the other. Each subunit contains a major rRNA component and different protein molecules, almost all present in only one copy per subunit. The larger subunit may contain smaller RNA molecules in addition to the major rRNA (Table 14.4).

In prokaryotes, it is formed on a part of the DNA strand called ribosomal DNA. In eukaryotes, ribosomes are formed on the nucleolus. The nucleolar organizer contains ribosomal DNA which transcribes 45 S RNA. This then gives rise to 28S through a series of intermetiate steps.

**Structure :**

1. The base ratios of rRNA are very similar in ribosomes from many different organisms. This suggests a general structural similarity. Depending upon ionic strength, temperature and pH, the RNA molecule may be a short compact rod, a compact coil or an extended strand.
2. Ribosomal RNA consists of a single strand twisted upon itself in some regions. It has helical regions connected by intervening single strand regions. The helical regions may show presence or absence of +ve interactions. In the helical region most of the base pairs are complementary and are joined by H-bonds. In the unfolded single strand regions, the bases have no complements.
3. r RNA is methylated. In mammalion cells, the 18S and 28 SrRNAs carry 43 and 74

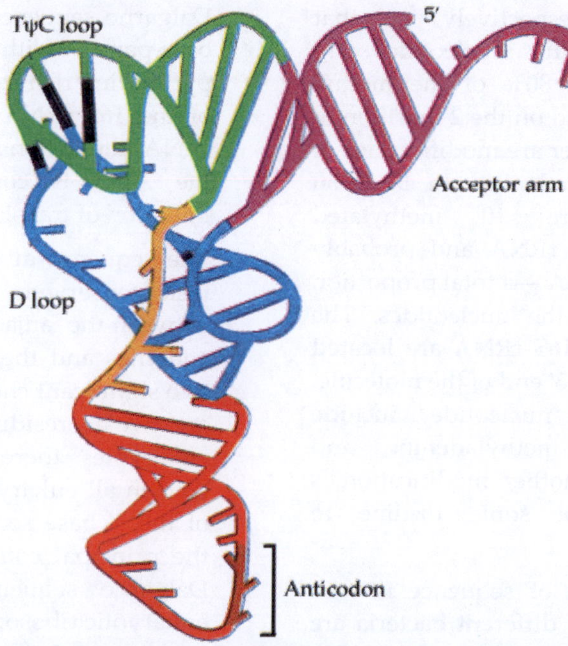


Fig.14.10 : *Three dimensional structure of tRNA.*

**TABLE 14.4**
**RNA and protein components in ribosomes**

| | *Components of* E. coli *ribosome* | | | *Rat liver cytoplasmic ribosome* | | |
|---|---|---|---|---|---|---|
| | *Ribosome* | *Small Subunits* | *Large Subunits* | *Ribosome* | *Small Subunits* | *Large Subunits* |
| **Sedimentation** | 70S | 30S | 50S | 80S | 40S | 60S |
| **Mass (Dalton)** | 2520000 | 930000 | 1590000 | 44200000 | 1400000 | 2820000 |
| **RNA :** | | | | | | |
| **major** | | 16S (1541 b.p.) | 23S (2904 b.p.) | | 18S (1900 b.p.) | 23S (4700 b.p.) |
| **smaller** | | | 5S (120 b.p.) | | | 5.8 S (120 b.p.) |
| **Mass of RNA** | | 560000 | 1104000 | | 700000 | 1820000 |
| **Proportion of mass** | 66% | 60% | 70% | 60% | 50% | 65% |
| **Proteins :** | | 21 polypeptides | 31 polypeptides | | 33 Polypeptides | 49 Polypeptides |
| **Mass** | | 370000 | 487000 | | 700000 | 1000000 |
| **Proportion** | 34% | 40% | 30% | 40% | 50% | 35% |

methyl groups respectively, so that roughly 2% of the nucleotides are methylated. About 80% of the methyl groups are contained on the 2′ position of ribose, the remainder are modifications of the bases mostly adenine. In bacterial rRNA, there are 10 methylated nucleotides in 16S rRNA and probably about 20 in 23S rRNA —a total proportion is about 0.7% of the nucleotides. The methyl groups in 16S rRNA are located mostly towards the 3′ end of the molecule. The methylated nucleotide include dimethyladenine, methyladenine and methylguanine. Another modification is the conversion of some uridine to pseudouridine.

4. Some conservation of sequence is seen when the rRNA of different bacteria are compared and there is some homology with organelle rRNAs. The significance of these relationships is not clear. There is no extensive conservation of sequence with eukaryotic rRNAs, although among eukaryotes conserved regions can be found mostly located in the vicinities of the methylated groups. This is true for species as distant as yeasts and mammals.

5. The current model for *E. coli* 16S rRNA is illustrated (Fig.14.11a). Just under half of the sequence is base paired. The individual double helical regions tend to be short less than eight base pairs long. Often the duplex regions are not perfect, but contain bulges of unpaired bases. The molecule as a whole forms four general domains viz., Central domain, 3′ major domain, 3′ minor domain and 5′ domain.

6. The initiating AUG codon of mRNA in protein synthesis is guided to the correct position on the 30S subunit by an initiating signal called SHINE DALGARNO SEQUENCE, in the mRNA, centered 8 to 13 basepairs to the 5′ side of the initiation codon. Generally, consisting of four to nine purine residues. The Shine-Dalgarno sequence is recognized by and base-pairs with a complementary pyrimidine rich sequence near the 3′ end of the 16S rRNA subunit. This mRNA-rRNA interaction fixes the mRNA so that the AUG is correctly positioned for initiation of translation. (Fig.14.12)

   The sequence at the 3′ end of rRNA is well conserved. In the 20 nucleotides between the adjacent double methylated adenines and the 3′ end, there are only two significant changes. In bacteria, there are two U residues whereas, in higher eukaryotes there are two A-residues. And in all eukaryotes there is a deletion of the 5′ base sequence CCUCC, that is the principal complement to the Shine-Dalgarno sequence. This means that eukaryotic ribosomes could not be able to initiate translation of bacterial mRNA.

   Within the highly conserved 3′ terminal region, both in bacteria and eukaryotes, there is a highly purine-rich sequence. 3′ UAGGAAGGCGU 5′ that in eukaryotes is about the same distance from the 3′ end as the CCUCC sequence in bacteria. It could participate in hairpin formation.

7. In mammalian mitochondrial 12-13S rRNA, the 3′ terminal region does resemble that found in eukaryotic cytoplasm and in bacteria but is less conserved. It may be able to form a terminal hairpin, but no sequence complementary with any region prior to the AUG codons on mRNA has been noticed (Fig. 14.13).

8. In addition to the two major rRNAs, the large subunit also contains a molecule of 5S rRNA (except mitochondria). The 5S rRNA of the prokaryotes shows some conservation of sequence, especially in the regions that bind to ribosomal proteins. Similarly, there is conservation of eukaryotic 5S rRNAs with one sequence predominating in the mammals.

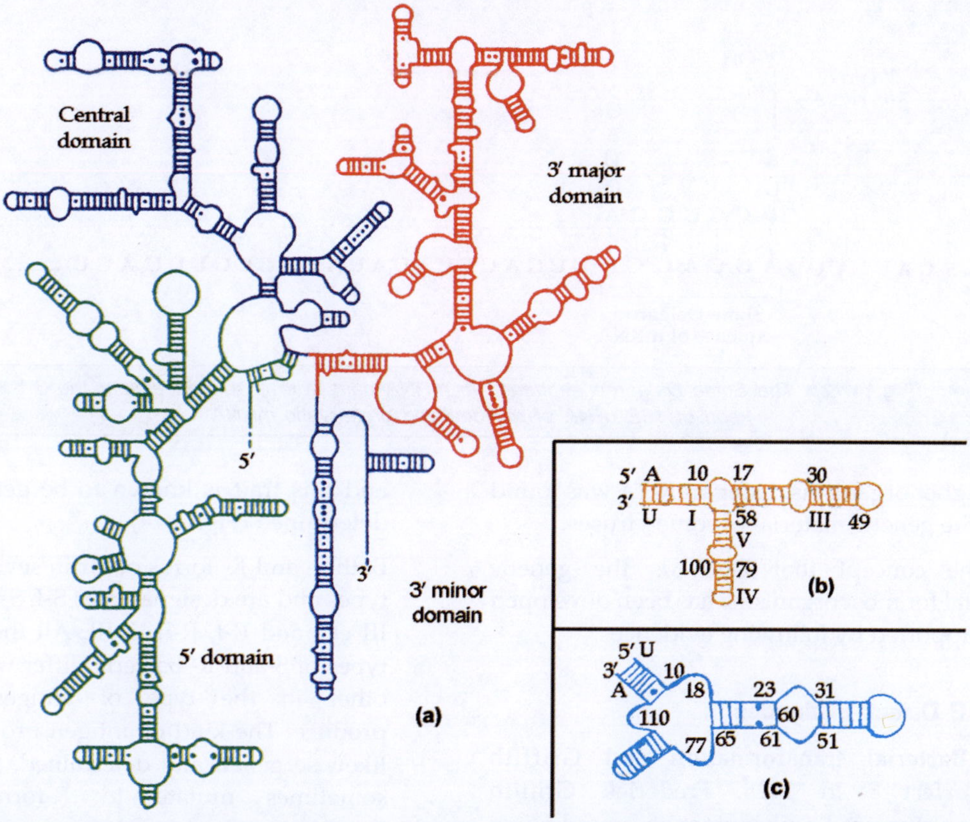


**Fig.14.11 :** *Structure of (a) 16S rRNA in E.coli (predicted folding pattern) (b) 5S rRNA in* Eukaryotic *Chlorella (5 helices structure) (c) 5S rRNA in E.coli (4 helices structure)*

All 5S rRNA molecules display a highly base-paired structure, although there has been some difficulty in settling on an exact model (more than 26 models have been proposed). A current model that fits all known prokaryotic sequences to a structure with 4-base paired regions. As with tRNA the secondary structure is likely to convey the accurate impression of the molecule when viewed in three dimensions. (Fig.14.11b,c)

9. In eukaryotic cytoplasmic ribosomes another small RNA is present in the large subunit. This is the 5.8S rRNA. Its sequence may correspond to the 5′ end of the prokaryotic 23S rRNA.

## 14.8. DNA AS THE GENETIC MATERIAL — EVIDENCES ONLY

### 14.8.1 Concept

When it became evident that the chromosomes were the organelles of heredity, various attempts were made by early molecular geneticists to identify the physical and chemical nature of hereditary materials.

A. Mirsky and H. Ris (1949) found that all the cells of an organism appeared to contain the same amount of DNA, whereas, different cell types contained quite different amounts and kinds of proteins. Its constancy, therefore, favoured DNA as the genetic material. Around 1953, it was universally accepted that DNA is the genetic substance of most microorganisms

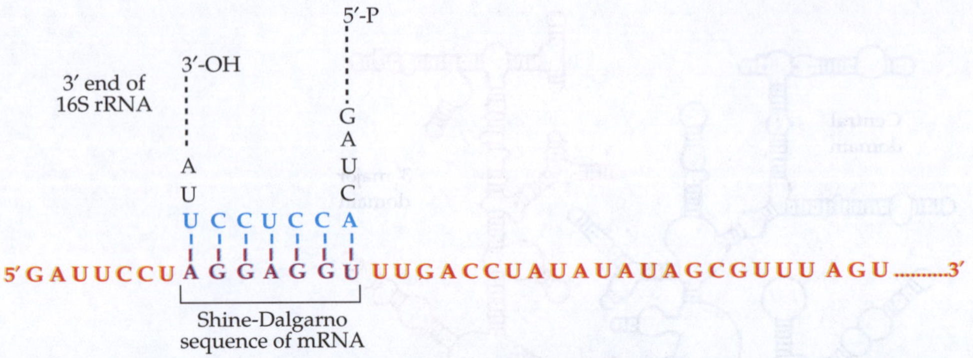


**Fig.14.12 :** *The Shine Dalgarno sequence in mRNA pairs with a sequence near the 3′ end of 16S rRNA of an idealized prokaryotic mRNA.*

and higher organisms. Later on RNA was found to be the genetic material of some viruses.

The concept that DNA is the genetic material for most organisms has been developed and supported by following evidences.

### 14.8.2 Direct Evidences

1. **Bacterial transformation and Griffith effect** : In 1928, Frederick Griffith encountered a phenomenon, now known as *genetic transformation*. Colonies of virulent strain of pneumonia–causing bacterium, *Diplococcus pneumoniae* grown on nutrient agar have a smooth (S) glistering appearance owing to the presence of a type of specific polysaccharide (glucose+ glucuronic acid) capsule. The non-virulent strains, on the other hand, lack this capsule and they produce dull, rough (R) colonies. Smooth and rough characters are directly related to the presence or absence of the capsule and this trait is known to be genetically determined (Fig.14.14).

   Both S- and R- forms occur in several sub-types and are designated as S-I, S-II and S-III etc. and R-I, R-II, R-III. All these sub–types of S-and R- bacteria differ with each other in the type of antigens they produce. The kind of antigen produced is likewise genetically determined. S- forms sometimes mutate to R-forms, but this change has not been found to be reversible.

   (a) Griffith injected laboratory mice with live R-II pneumococci, the mice suffered no illness because, R-II pneumococci were non-virulent.

   (b) When the mice were injected with virulent S-III pneumococci, the mice suffered with pneumonia and died.

   (c) When he injected the heat-killed S-III bacteria to the mice they did not suffer from pneumonia.

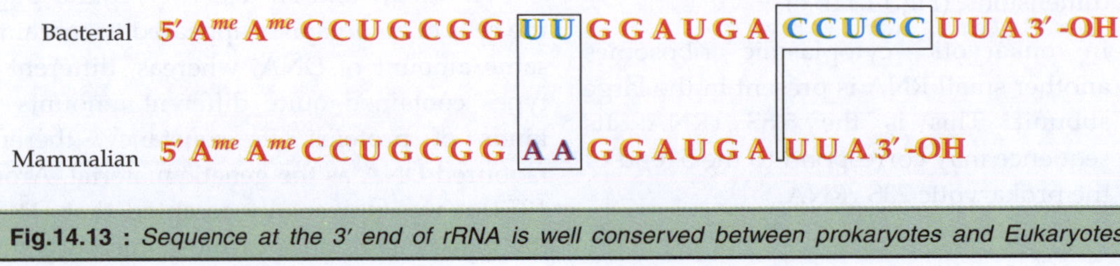


**Fig.14.13 :** *Sequence at the 3′ end of rRNA is well conserved between prokaryotes and Eukaryotes*

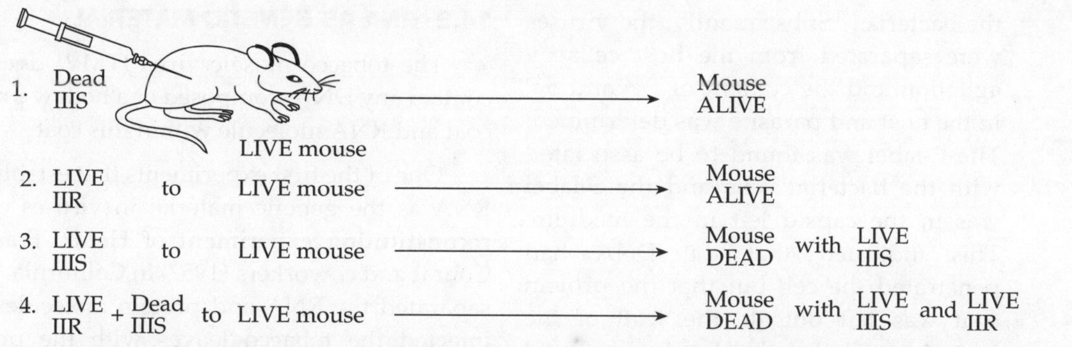


**Fig.14.14** : *Griffith experiment that demonstrated the principle of transformation.*

(d) But when the mice were injected with the mixture of living non-virulent R-II and heat killed S-III virulent, the unexpected symptoms of pneumonia appeared and high mortality was resulted in them. By post-mortoming the dead mice, it was found that their heart and blood had both R-II and S-III pneumococci.

From these results, Griffith concluded that the presence of the heat-killed S-III bacteria must have caused a transformation of the living R-II bacteria, so as to restore them the capacity of capsule formation which they had earlier lost by gene mutation. This was called **Griffith effect** or more popularly as **bacterial transformation**.

Griffith could not understand the cause of bacterial transformation and that was first of all identified by Avery, Macleod and Mc. Carty (1974). They tested a fraction of heat killed S-III bacteria for their transforming ability. They removed proteins, lipids, polysaccharides and RNA from the S-III extract by using a variety of chemicals and enzymatic methods without seriously diminishing its power to transfer R-II mutants into S-III wild type. They concluded that because a cell free and highly purified DNA extract of S-III bacteria could bring about transformation of R-II bacteria into S-III bacteria, therefore, DNA is confirmed as the genetic material of pneumococci.

2. **Mode of infection of bacteriophages and Hershey-Chase experiment** : By using radioactive tracers, A. Hershey and M. Chase (1952) provided further proof that DNA is the genetic material in certain bacteriophages. They prepared a chemically defined culture medium of *E. coli* containing phosphoric acid and sulphuric acid as the only source of P and S. Known quantities of radioactive isotopes of phosphorus ($P^{32}$) and sulphur ($S^{35}$) were added to the culture medium. *E. coli* grown in such a culture medium certainly incorporated the $P^{32}$ and $S^{35}$ into their chemical constituents. When $T_2$ bacteriophage particles were injected to the radioactive bacteria, it was found that phage capsid proteins did not contain appreciable amount of P and only the DNA was labeled with $P^{32}$. The protein envelop around $T_2$ phage was selectively labeled with $S^{35}$. DNA contains virtually no sulphur and was not labeled with $S^{35}$. By this method, it was possible to differentially label the phage DNA and proteins of phage-capsid.

After phage growth, the phage particles were separated from the host cells by centrifugation. The radioactive phages were then introduced to non-radioactive bacterial cultures where they attacked the bacteria. Subsequently, the viruses were separated from the host cells by agitation and the content of $P^{32}$ and $S^{35}$ in the host and parasite was determined. The P-label was found to be associated with the bacterial cells and the S-label was in the capsid left in the medium. This indicated that the DNA had penetrated the cell but that the protein coat was left outside the wall of the bacterium. The labeled DNA was found to reproduce in the host cells.

These experiments clearly demonstrated that genetic information of these bacteriophage is resided in their DNA molecules and not in the protein molecules of their capsid (Fig. 14.15).

3. **Bacterial conjugation** : Another conclusive evidence for DNA as the genetic material came from the phenomenon of conjugation of bacteria. Lederberg and Tatum (1946) found that when a $F^+$ (male) *E. coli* cell conjugating with a $F^-$ (female) *E. coli* cell, a unidirectional transfer of $F^+$ factor of male cell to $F^-$ or female cell has taken place, so that, the later was converted into a $F^+$ or male strain. The $F^+$ factor was found to be a fragment of DNA molecule which occurred in the cytoplasm of the bacterial cell.

### 14.8.3. Indirect Evidences

1. Feulgen technique has shown that DNA entirely remains restricted to the chromosomes and it forms one of the major components of chromosomes.
2. Quantitative measurement of the amount of DNA in different cells has shown that diploid cells contain twice as much DNA as the haploid cells of the same species. For example, mean value of haploid spermatids has 1.68p.g of DNA while diploid and tetrapolid liver cells contain 3.16 and 6.30p.g. respectively.

## 14.9 RNA AS GENETIC MATERIAL

The tobacco mosaic virus (TMV) does not contain any DNA, composed of a hollow protein coat and RNA molecule within this coat.

One of the first experiments that established RNA as the genetic material in viruses called **reconstitution experiment** of Heinz. Fraenhel Conrat and coworkers (1957) in California. They separated the RNA and protein molecules and infected the tobacco leaves with the protein molecules, RNA molecules and combined RNA and protein molecules separately. They observed that the leaves which were infected with only protein coat molecules of TMV do not produce any symptoms of mosaic leaves. But in later two cases mosaic symptoms arise on the leaves.

Different strains of TMV can be identified on the basis of difference in the amino acid sequence of the protein coat and RNA molecule. They made a chimeric TMV by mixing the protein coat of one virus with the RNA of the other virus. When this chimeric virus infected the tobacco leaf, a symptom of mosaic disease is observed in the infected leaves which is similar to the disease infected by the virus from which RNA is taken in the chimera. This is also found that in the leaves, the virus grows and multiplies which have the protein coat of its origin virus from which the virus was taken (Fig. 14.16).

## 14.10. ONE GENE ONE ENZYME (POLYPEPTIDE) CONCEPT

Enzymes bring about numerous chemical processes, which take place in the body. The chemical substances in the body are often complicated and are built up or broken down in a series of steps (such as A→B→C→D etc). As a rule, one enzyme does just one thing, it causes one chemical change or one step (A→B) in a series of reactions. Another enzyme then takes over and brings about the next step (B →C). Thus, if we indicate the enzymes by numbers, we could show their relationship to the chemical

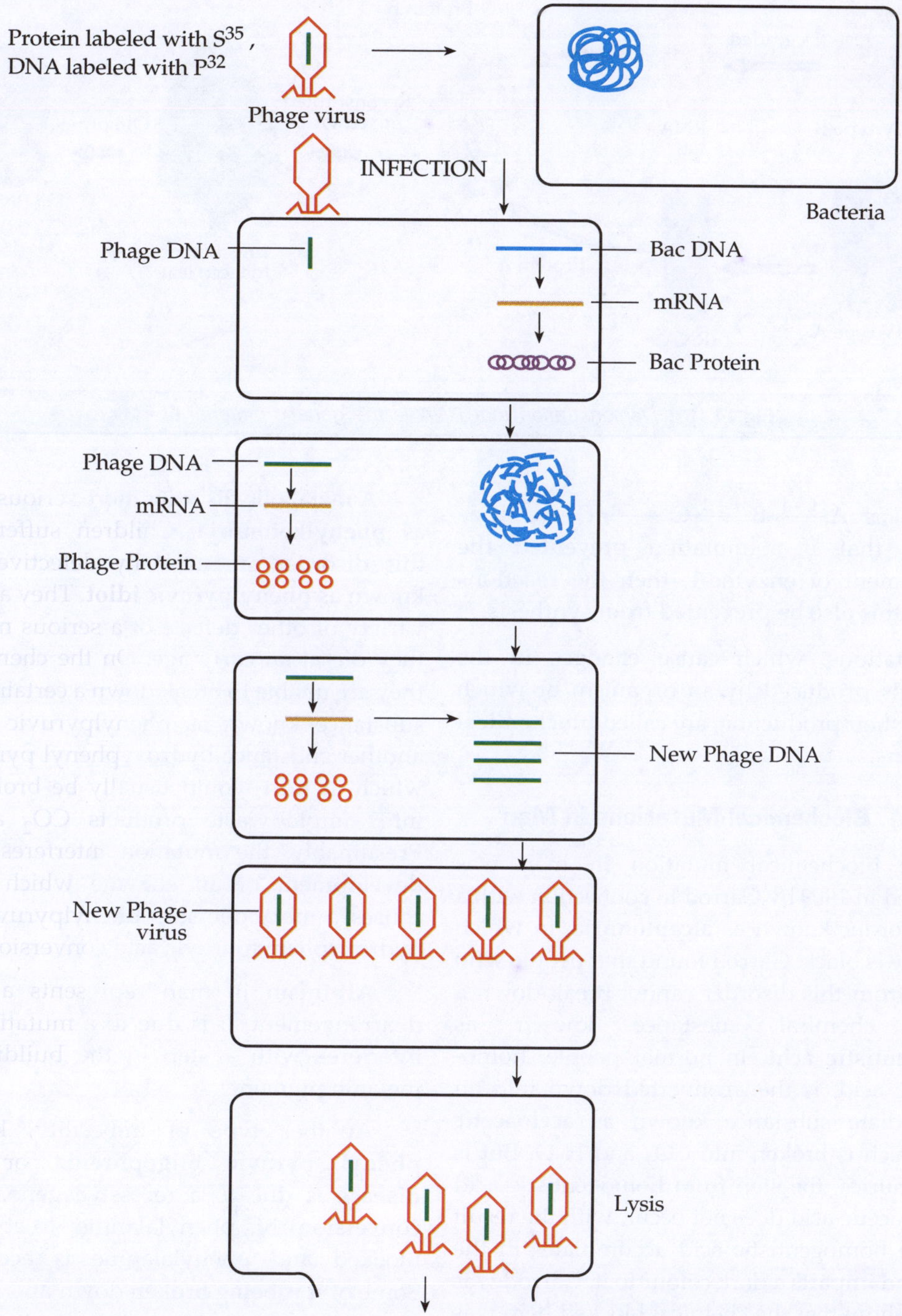


**Fig.14.15 :** *Hershey and Chase experiment.*

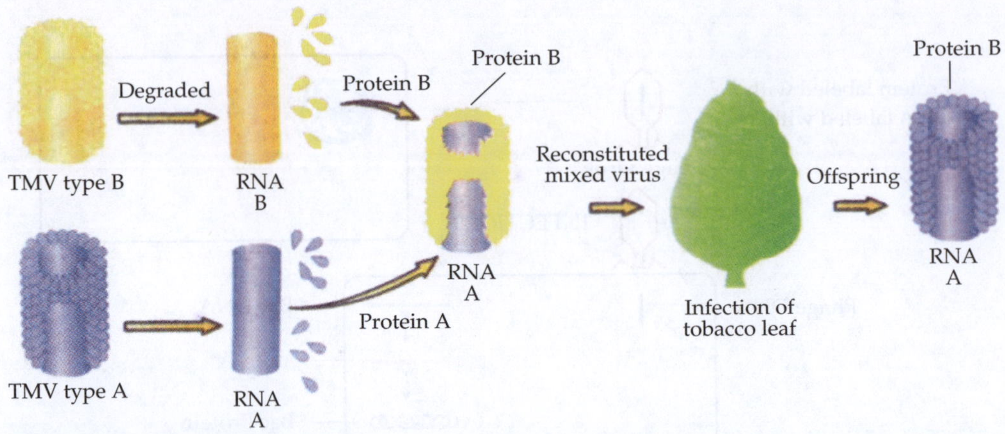


**Fig.14.16 :** *Demonstration that RNA is the genetic material of TMV*

changes as $A \xrightarrow{E-1} B \xrightarrow{E-2} C \xrightarrow{E-3} D$ etc. It is obvious that if a mutation prevented the development of enzyme-1, then the reactions beyond this also be prevented from synthesis.

Mutations, which cause changes in the chemicals produced by an organism or which prevent their production, are called **biochemical mutations**.

### 14.10.1. Biochemical Mutations in Man

The biochemical mutation in man was described in 1909 by Garrod in connection with a rare disorder known as **alcaptonuria**, in which the urine is black. Garrod found that people who suffers from this disorder cannot break down a certain chemical substance known as **homogentistic acid**. In normal people, homogentistic acid, is then converted down into an intermediate substance known as **acetoacetic acid** which is broken into $CO_2$ and $H_2O$. But is alcaptonurics, the step from homogentistic acid to acetoacetic acid does not occur, with the result that the homogentistic acid accumulates in the urine and imparts a dark colour to it. Garrod was able to show that the chemical blocked here was due to a recessive mutation. Presumably, the mutation interferes with the production of an enzyme necessary for the chemical step.

A metabolic disorder more serious is known as **phenylketonuria**. Children suffering from this disorder are mentally defective and are known as **phenylpyruvic idiot**. They also have a variety of other defects of a serious nature and they die at an early age. On the chemical side, they are unable to break down a certain chemical substance known as phenylpyruvic acid into another substance hydroxyphenyl pyruvic acid, which in turn would usually be broken down into simple waste products $CO_2$ and $H_2O$. Presumably, the mutation interferes with the development of an enzyme which normally causes a metabolic step phenylpyruvic acid to hydroxyphenylpyruvic acid conversion.

**Albinism** in man represents a chemical dearrangement. It is due to a mutation, which interferes with a step in the building up of melanin pigment.

Another type of imbecility, known as **phenyl pyruvic oligophrenia** or **Follings disease** is due to a recessive gene, in which conversion of phenylalanine to tyrosine is blocked and phenylalanine is accumulated. Some of it is being broken down and is excreted as phenylpyruvic acid and causes a severe congenital mental impairment (Fig. 14.17).

### 14.10.2. Biochemical Mutations in *Neurospora*

*Neurospora* can readily be grown on agar in the laboratory on a culture medium, which contains a few simple salts, some sugar and biotin. This is called MINIMAL medium. It can manufacture a class of complicated substances, amino acids and can synthesize proteins.

It is possible to produce numerous mutations in *Neurospora* by treating conidia with X-ray. These mutant spores lack the capacity to manufacture a vitamin or an amino acid that is essential for their growth and so they cannot grow in minimal medium. They will grow if they are placed in a medium which supplies the required nutritional element. This is **supplemented medium**.

One irradiated spore is cultured in a complete medium and allowed to grow into mycelium and spores. Then hundreds of such cultures, are made each from a single irradiated spore in a complete medium. They will grow as normal molds.

Then few spores are transferred to a minimal medium for culture in separate dishes, the mutants do not grow, because mutants could not manufacture the required proteins and vitamins.

Numerous media are prepared each of which is a minimal medium, and supplemented with just one of the various nutritional factors. The mutant will grow on a particular single supplemented medium which supplies its deficiency and only on this medium. Thus we came to know what deficiency the mutation has been produced.

There are three arginine requiring mutants, the third can utilize only arginine ie, mutation in gene-3 , the second will grow if supplied with either arginine or citruline ie, mutation in gene-2 and the first will utilize arginine, citruline or ornithine for growth ie, mutation in gene-1. One might guess that second one can produce arginine for itself if it is supplied with the citruline, whereas, the third can also produce arginine from ornithine. The three compounds might thus be arranged in a reaction sequence as follows :

$$\text{Precursor} \xrightarrow{\text{Gene-1}} \text{Ornithine} \xrightarrow{\text{Gene-2}} \text{Citruline} \xrightarrow{\text{Gene-3}} \text{Arginine}$$

A block in the sequence prior to the synthesis of ornithine, by mutation of gene-I could be relieved by supplying ornithine, citruline or arginine itself. If only step-2 was blocked by mutation, the organism could repair the deficiency if given either citruline or arginine, whereas, a block in step-3 could be repaired only by arginine itself. The principal assumption is that different mutants that use the same substance, arginine in this example, will often have blocks at different steps in one chain of reactions leading to the synthesis of that substance. This principle in its simplest form has proved useful not only in identifying gene controlled reaction sequences in micro-organisms but in other developmental sequences in higher organisms as well (Fig. 14.18).

### 14.10.3 Remarks

Most metabolic reactions are catabolized by enzymes and assumed that a gene controls the production of an enzyme or of its specific activity. Mutation could change the gene's activity and impaired the production of specific enzyme. In its specific form this hypothesis was phrased by Beadle in these words :

***A given enzyme will usually have its final specificity set by one and only one gene.*** This *one-gene-one enzyme* hypothesis was subsequently modified by Beadle to read ***one-gene-one function*** in order to include units other than enzymes.

According to Ingram (1957), the normal hemoglobin has two α and two β-chains and more than 300 variants of β-hemoglobin have been discovered including mostly different amino acid substitutions as well as small number of deletions and insertions. In sickle cell

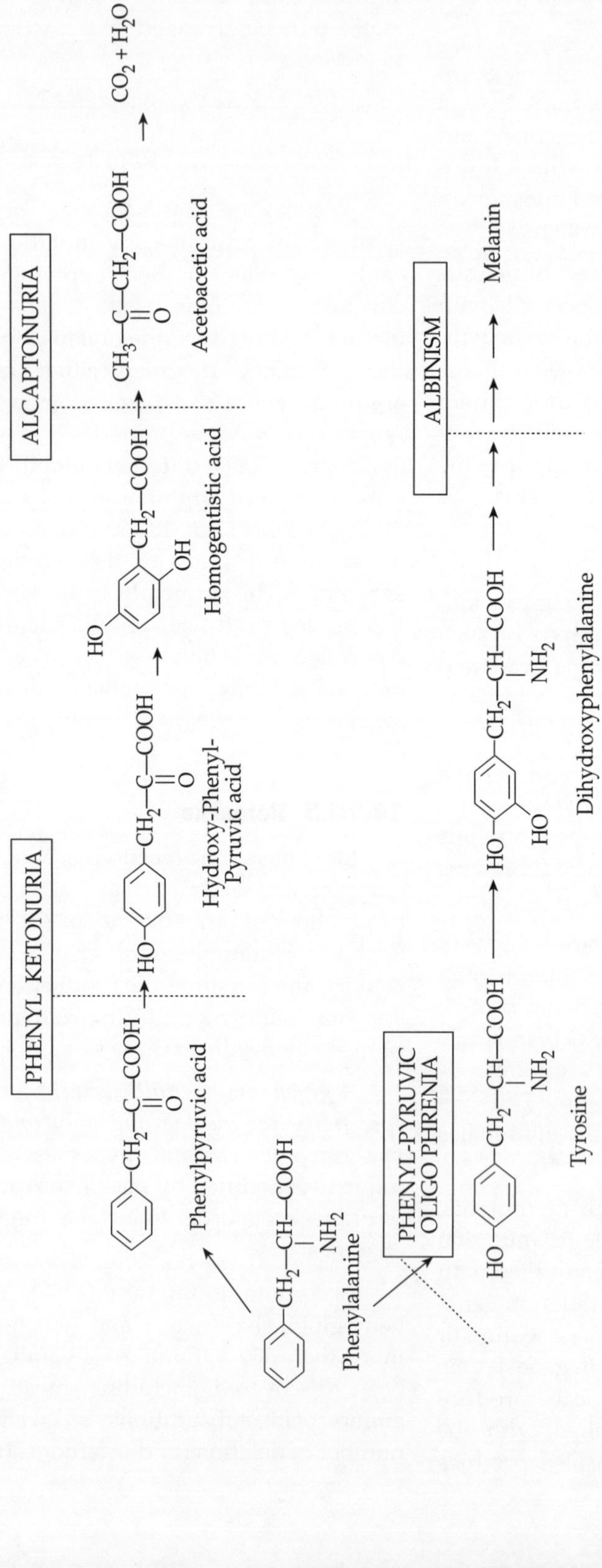


**Fig.14.17 :** *Biochemical mutations in man.*

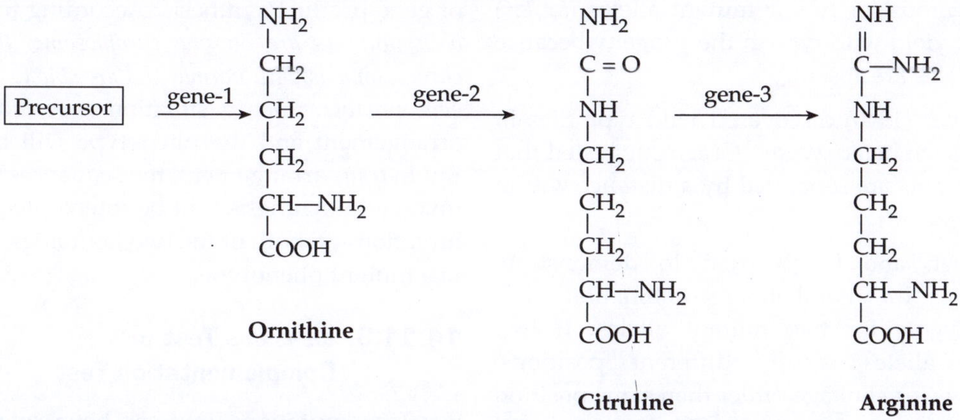


**Fig.14.18 :** *Biochemical reactions in Neurospora.*

anaemia, hemoglobin is symbolized as $\alpha_2\beta_2^{6glu\rightarrow val}$ and $\alpha_2\beta_2^{6glu\rightarrow lys}$, since only β-chains have been modified in each case. The independence of amino acid changes in one chain from amino acid changes in other is evidenced that genes determining the α and β sequences are at different loci. Since, the Hb-protein is so obviously composed of two independent gene products, each as a single polypeptide. Ingram pointed out that it may be appropriate to modify the ***one-gene-one-enzyme*** hypothesis to ***one-gene-one-polypeptide*** hypothesis. Defining the gene as a section of DNA that determines the amino acid sequence of a polypeptide which has the advantage that it relates a unique structural and functional component of a protein to a localized segment of genetic material.

## 14.11. GENE FINE STRUCTURE

### 14.11.1. Multiple Allele

When any one of the three or more allelic forms of a gene occupies the same locus in a given pair of homologus chromosomes, they are said to constitute a series of **multiple alleles**.

Multiple alleles of a series always occupy the same locus in chromosome; no crossing over will occur in between them and always influenced the same character.

When any two of the mutant multiple alleles are crossed, the phenotype is always mutant type but never the wild type.

**Example :** Coat colour of rabbit may have different colours, wild colour is agouti (C). The other three mutants are

Chinchilla ($C^{ch}$)

Himalyan ($C^h$)

and Albino (c)

The dominant series is as follows :

$C > C^{ch} > C^h > c$

The possible phenotypes and genotypes of these multiple alleles could be as follows :

| *Phenotype* | *Genotype* |
|---|---|
| Full color | $CC, CC^{ch}, CC^h, Cc$ |
| Chinchilla | $C^{ch}C^{ch}, C^{ch}C^h, C^{ch}c$ |
| Himalyan | $C^hC^h, C^hc$ |
| Albino | cc |

### 14.11.2. Pseudoallele and Position Effect or *cis-trans* Effect

In *Drosophila*, a sex-linked mutant called lozenge (*lz*) is responsible for smaller darker and more elliptical-shaped eyes. Generally, a fly heterozygous for two *lz* mutant alleles ($lz^1/lz^2$) will not yield wild type in the progeny because wild alleles are absent.

Oliver (1940) discovered wild type flies in case of such heterozygtes. Green suggested that two mutants are separated by a distance within the genes.

Green and Lewis tried to demonstrate intragenic or interallelic recombination of a heterozygote for two mutant alleles. If two mutant alleles occupy different positions, showing close linkage rather than same position then, one may expect that $F_1$ heterozygotes would have a genotype $\left(\frac{lz^1 \quad +}{+ \quad lz^2}\right)$ would express wild phenotype but it is found that $F_1$ did not exhibit wild phenotype.

The absence of complementation is due to the position effect which could be understood by the study of two arrangements of mutant alleles. For instance, in heterozygotes, for $lz^1$ and $lz^2$, two arrangements are possible. One with both mutant alleles on the same chromosome $\left(\text{i.e, } \frac{lz^1 \quad lz^2}{+ \quad +}\right)$, and their counterparts on the other homolog (*cis*-arrangement) and the other with two mutant alleles on two different homologs $\left(\text{i.e, } \frac{lz^1 \quad +}{+ \quad lz^2}\right)$ the *trans*-arrangement.

For lozenge locus $lz^1$ and $lz^2$, the *cis*-and *trans*- arrangements are as follows.

$$\frac{lz^1 \quad lz^2}{+ \quad\quad +} \qquad\qquad \frac{lz^1 \quad\quad +}{+ \quad lz^2}$$

*cis*-arrangement  *trans*-arrangment

It is also indicated that, in *cis* –position, they will express wild phenotype and in *trans*-position, the mutant phenotype. This may be due to the **position effect** where a mutant does not allow adjacent region to express wild phenotype. This difference in phenotype is due to *cis*-and *trans*-arrangement, which is known as ***cis-trans* effect.**

An explanation of *cis-trans* effect was given. E.B. Lewis, who believed the sequential nature of gene product synthesis. According to him, *if both mutants are on one chromosome, the other chromosome is with normal and are able to complete gene product.* Such a situation is found in *cis*-arrangement and the phenotype will be wild. But in *trans* arrangement, the sequences or steps involve in synthesis will be interrupted due to mutations on both of the two homologs, leading to a mutant phenotype.

### 14.11.3. *cis-trans* Test or Complementation Test

Two mutations in *trans* heterozygote are usually allelic, if they produce a mutant phenotype and be non-allelic, if they form wild phenotype.

The alleles of two recessive mutations to restore the wild type phenotype, either partially or completely in the *trans* position has been termed as **complementation.**

The functional allelism of any two recessive mutations is determined experimentally by the *cis-trans* test or complementation test.

***Cis*-test :** The *cis*-test involves putting the two mutations and being examined in a common protoplasm in the *cis*-arrangement. The organism or cell containing two mutations on the same chromosome must have wild phenotype. If the *cis*-heterozygote has the mutant phenotype, then the mutant is dominant.

***Trans*-test :** The *trans*-test is commonly known as **complementation test,** involves putting the two mutations to be tested in a common protoplasm in *trans*-configuration. It simply involves crossing between two homozygotes, one is homozygous for first mutation and other homozygous for second mutation.

$$\left(\frac{+ \quad lz^2}{+ \quad lz^2}\right) \times \left(\frac{lz^1 \quad +}{lz^1 \quad +}\right)$$

In the case of bacteriophage, is involved simultaneous by infecting host cells with two different mutants.

1. If the *trans*-heterozygote has the mutant phenotype, then the two mutations are in the same gene.
2. If the *trans*-heterozygote has the wild phenotype, then the two mutations are on the two different genes.

**Complementation test with *r-II* locus of $T_4$ phage**

Seymur Benzer analyzed the fine structure of *r-II* locus of T4 bacteriophage which infects *E.coli.* Usually mutations of this locus could be distinguished from other loci by inability of the *r-II* to grow in the bacteria *E.coli* K, but produce progeny phage when infects *E.coli* B.

The *r-II* mutant when infects *E.coli* B, then it produces a large round plaque (colony of the phage), while when it infects *E.coli* Kλ, no plaque is formed. The wild gene ($r\text{-}II^+$) also infects *E.coli* B and *E.coli* Kλ and then very small-ragged plaques are formed (Table 14.5).

In order to find out complementation reaction between *r-II* mutant alleles, Benzer used two different *r-II* mutants, arbitrarily designated as $r\text{-}II^x$ and $r\text{-}II^y$. If the two mutants do not form plaques on mixed infection to *E.coli* K λ strains they were placed in the same group. But if plaques are produced, then the two mutants involved were placed in the different groups (Fig. 14.19).

All mutants with the help of complementation test would be classified into two groups in such a manner that two mutants from group-A and one mutant from group-B could not form plaque. But mixed infection by one mutant of group-A and another of group-B could cause plaque formation.

**TABLE 14.5**

| $T_4$ *phage strain* | *E. coli srain* | |
|---|---|---|
| | *E. coli B* | *E. coli Kλ* |
| *rII* (mutant) | large, round plaque is formed | No plaque is formed |
| $rII^+$ (wild) | Small ragged plaque is formed | Small raged plaque is formed |

Since, group-A and group-B are distinguished on the basis of *cis-trans* test. These were termed as cistron-A and cistron-B. Mutants belonging to same cistrons would exhibit *cis-trans* phenomenon and they will give wild phenotype only in *cis*-configuration but not in *trans*-configuration. Two mutants on different cistron would give wild phenotype even in *trans* configuration, which in other words called complementation.

From the complementation test, it is obvious that in *r-II* region, two cistrons, cistron A and cistron B are functionally independent and must be responsible for sequential synthesis of separate products. Therefore, all mutants belonging to same cistron share a common deficiency, which is different from deficiency due to mutants belonging to second cistrons, while two mutants belonging to same cistron both are deficient for same product and therefore, they cannot complement. But when two mutants belonging to two different products and can complement then wild phenotype may be expressed.

### 14.11.4. Cistron Concept

A cistron may be defined as a functional unit of the gene, comprises a sequence of DNA, responsible for the synthesis of a polypeptide chain.

A gene may thus consists of one functional unit, the cistron (where the different mutants affect the different sites of the cistron) called **monocistronic**, or may be consisted of more than one functional units of cistrons (where the mutants affecting different cistrons and will complement with each other but mutants of the same cistron will not complement with each other) are called **polycistronic** i.e., a discrete function of the gene is controlled by the concerted action of this product as a functional unit. The concept of pseudoalleles and complex locus now may be described after *cistron concept*. The different sub-loci of the gene that may be considered as the different mutable sites of the

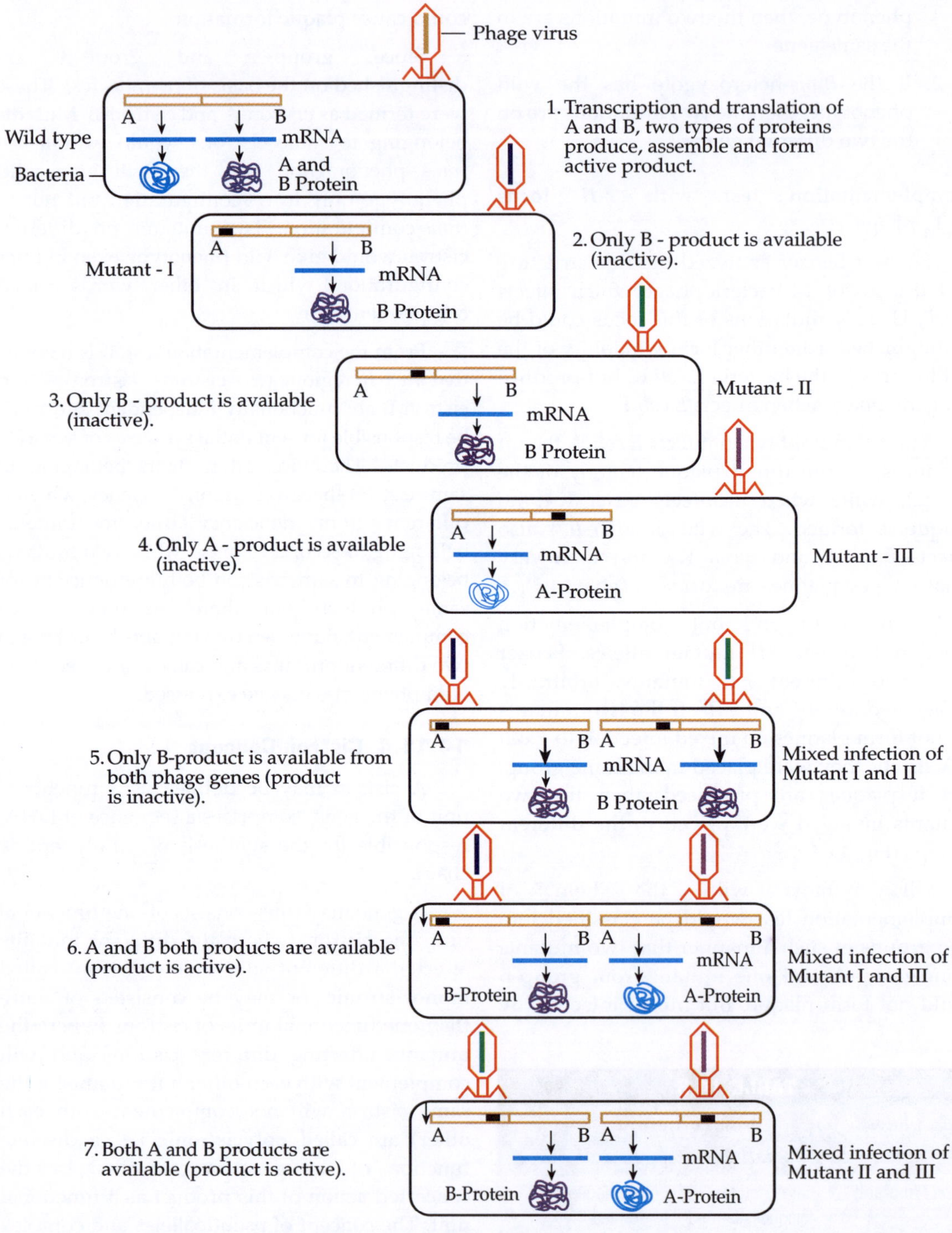


**Fig.14.19 :** *Complementation test taking rII locus of bacteriophage.*

cistron, which can be correlated with the single nucleotide pair of DNA.

Complementation suggests different products or portion of products which are affected by the different alleles, while lack of complementation indicates that both the alleles affect the same gene product or same portion of the gene product. They are therefore assigned to the same complementation group.

A **complementation group** corresponds to a direct genetic unit. This unit is formally called cistron. Two mutations in the same cistron cannot complement in *trans* heterozygote. The occurrence of complementation shows that the mutations lie in different cistron. The products are said to be *trans*-acting.

### 14.11.5 Complementation mapping

The discovery of the *cis-trans* effect enabled a simple functional test for allelism between recessive mutations with similar effects.

Two mutations in *trans*-helerozygote are **usually *allelic* if they produce a mutant phenotype and *non-allelic* if they from a wild type product. The ability of two recessive mutations of restore the wild-type phenotype either partially or completely in the trans position has been termed *complementation.***

Complementation suggests different products or portion of products are affected by different alleles while the lack of complementation indicates that both alleles affect the same gene product or same function. They are therefore assigned to the same **complementation group**.

A complementation group corresponds to a direct genetic unit, this unit is formerly called CISTRON. Two mutations in the same cistron cannot complement in *trans*. The occurrence of complementation shows that the mutations lie in different cistrons. The products are said to be *trans*-acting and they represent diffusible molecules.

In *Neurospora*, many mutations produce strains that lack the ability to synthesize the amono acid *histidine* and such strains will consequently be unable to grow on minimal medium. By introduction of nuclei from each of two such different strains into a heterokaryon, complementation may be observed through the appearance of wild type growth.

We now consider only 5 such *histidine* mutatons that map in the same *his-3* locus on their 1st chromosome; CD16, 245, 261, D-566, and 1438. We draw a complementation matrix using these mutations. The result is as follows :

1. For CD16, the absence of complementations extends also to all other strains.
2. Mutations 245 and 261 complement with all other strains except CD-10.
3. D-566 and 1438 complement with 245 and 261, but not with each other.

Using these data we can draw a complementation map in which the extent on *non complementation* is indicated as a straight line and complementation is indicated by the absence of overlapping between these lines.

1. CD-16 is represented as a single line overlapping (non complementing) all others. CD-16 affects all three functional regions. Its complementation position connot be determined from this data. The CD-16 mutations may be considered as "multisite" mutation or may be a deletion with which no complementation *occurs* due to overlapping of other mutations.
2. Mutation 245 and 261 are represented as small lines that overlap only CD-16, since 245 and 261 complements with each other, they are in different complementation regions.
3. D566 and 1438 overlaps each other and also CD-16, but do not overlap 245 and 261 since D566 and 1438 mutations are in the same complementation region but not in the region of 245 or 261 mutations are located.

4. Additional mutation 430 overlaps 245 and 261 but does not overlap D566 and 1438.
5. Further complementation analysis with additional mutations indicates that the functional order is 245-261-D556-1438.
6. Other data indicate that CD16 extends to the left of 245.

A comparison between the complementation map and the genetic map determined by recombination analysis and the interest is that both are collinear.

**Complementation matrix :**

| | CD 16 | 245 | 261 | D-566 | 1438 |
|---|---|---|---|---|---|
| CD-16 | 0 | 0 | 0 | 0 | 0 |
| 245 | | 0 | + | + | + |
| 261 | | | 0 | + | + |
| D 566 | | | | 0 | 0 |
| 1438 | | | | | 0 |

0 = no complementation

+ = Complementation

**Complementation map :**

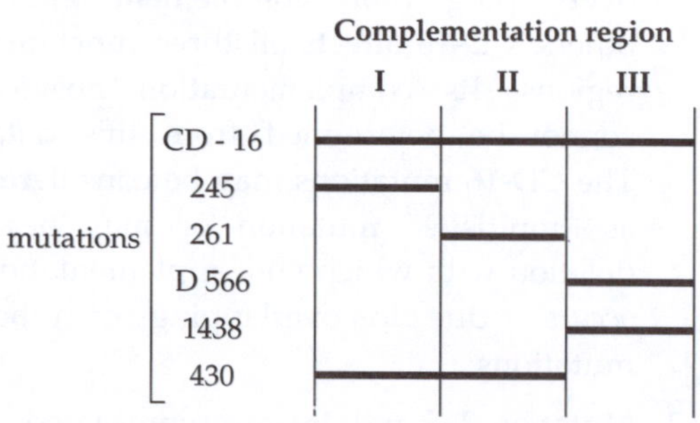


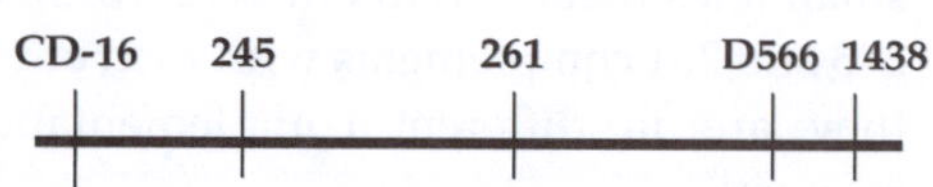


### 14.11.6 Deletion mapping

Most of the *rII* mutants, Benzer isolated were point mutants, their phenotype resulted from an alteration of a single nucleotide pair. A point mutant can revert to the wild-type state spontaneously or after treatment with an appropriate mutagen. However, some of Benzer's *rII* mutants did not revert, nor did they produce $r^+$ recombinants in crosses with a number of *rII* point mutants that were known to be located at different places on the *rII* map. These mutants were **deletion mutants** — the mutants that had lost a segments of DNA.

Benzer devised an analytical approach, known as **deletion testing.** He discovered that some of the *rII* mutations are, in reality, deletions of small parts of both cistrons and when a deletion mutation is tested using simultaneous infection by two phage strains, one having deletion mutation and other having a point mutation located in the deleted part of the same cistron, the test never yields wild type recombinants (Fig. 14.20). By this way, quickly any mutations can be localized, provided. It is contained within a region covered by a deletion.

Thus the deletion mapping is based on the two principles :

1. If two deletion mutants overlap, then no $r^+$ recombinants can be produced.
2. If two deletion mutants not overlap, then $r^+$ recombinants can be produced.

By remembering these principles we can draw the overlapping and nonoverlapping lines (cistron) from the given data.

## 14.12. DENATURATION OF DNA AND MELTING CURVE

Denaturation of DNA means the formation of single stranded from double stranded one by breaking the H-bonds between A=T and G≡C of the double helix. This could be done by the action of alkali (at pH=12) or by heating the solution.

The denaturation of DNA into single stranded one is accompanied with increase in optical density, a phenomenon described as **hyperchromicity** (Fig. 14.21).

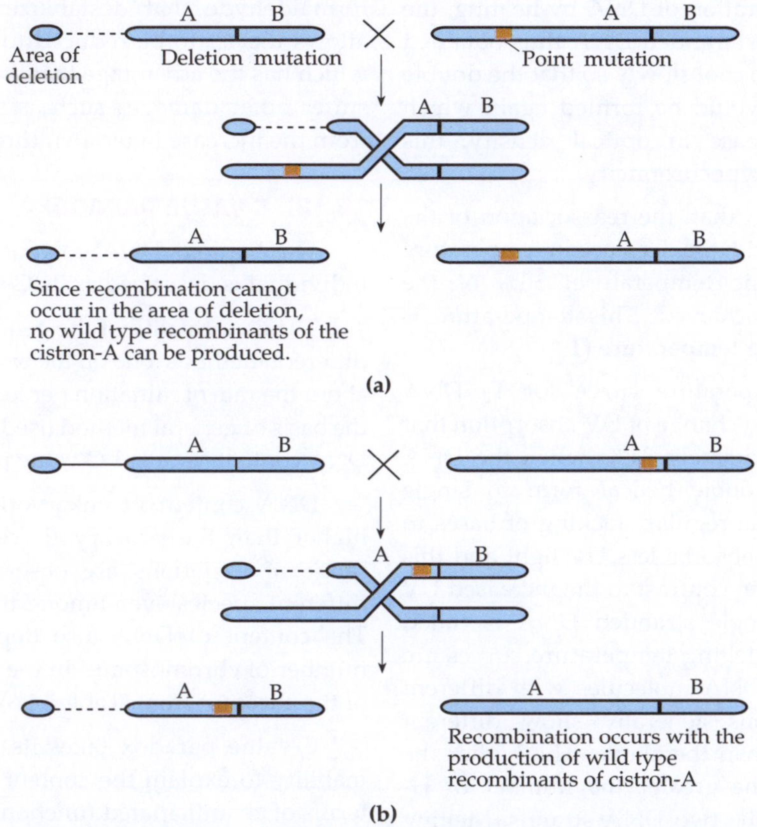


**Fig.14.20 :** *Deletion Test (a) Point mutation at the other homologous region of deletion of other phage chromosome cannot produce wild type recombinants; (b) Point mutation not at the homologous region of deletion of other phage chromosome may produce wild type recombinants.*

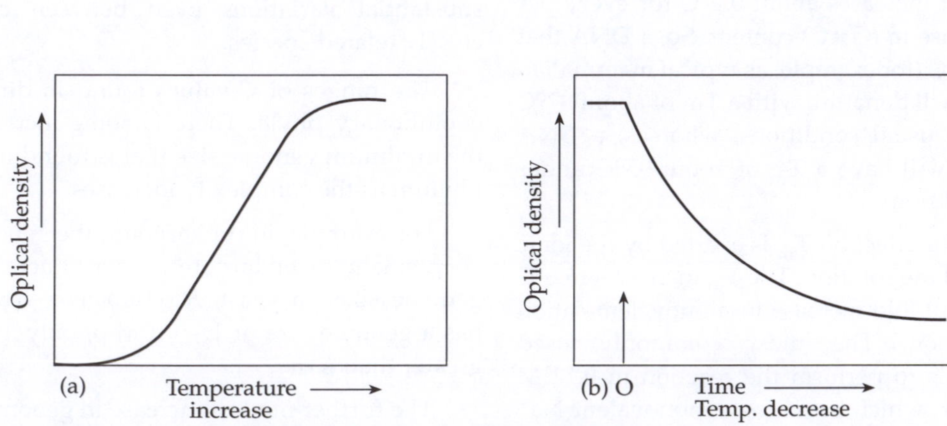


**Fig.14.21 :** *Hyperchromicity (a) and hypochromicity (b) on DNA due to denaturation and reassociation respectively.*

After denaturation of DNA by heating, the solution of single stranded DNA thus obtained is then allowed to cool slowly so that the double stranded DNA would be formed again which will result decrease in optical density, this phenomenon is **hypochromicity**.

It is observed that, the reassociation of the DNA increases with the decrease in temperature and at a specific temperature, 50% of the reassociation is achieved. This temperature is known as **melting temperature** ($T_m$).

Melting temperature curve for $T_4$ DNA shows the marked change of UV absorption that occurs at approximately 84ºC when the DNA changes from double helical form to single strands. Since, the regular stacking of bases in the double helix absorbs less UV light and this is **hypochromic**, in contrast to the increased UV absorption of single stranded DNA is called **hyperchromic**. Melting temperature curves are determined for DNA molecules with different base compositions generally show different melting points than the above. The higher the melting point, the greater the number of H-bonds between the two DNA strands. Melting temperature is therefore associated with the proportion of G and C bases, since these have three H-bonds between them, whereas, each A and T pair has only two such bonds.

The dependence of $\mathbf{T_m}$ on base composition is linear, it increases about 0.4ºC for every per cent increase in (G ≡ C) content. So, a DNA that is 40% G ≡ C (for example, as typical mammalian genome) will denature with a Tm of about 87ºC under the usual conditions, whereas, a DNA with 60% will have a $\mathbf{T_m}$ of about 95ºC under same conditions.

A major effect on $\mathbf{T_m}$ is exerted by the ionic strength of the solution. The $\mathbf{T_m}$ increases 16.6°C for every 10-fold increase in monovalent cation concentration. The most commonly used condition is to perform the reaction in 0.12 M $PO_4$-buffer, which provides a monovalent $Na^+$ concentration of 0.18M.

The $T_m$ can be greatly varied by performing the reaction in the presence of reagents such as formaldehyde that destabilize H-bonds. This allows the $T_m$ to be reduced to as low as 40°C which has the advantage that the DNA does not suffer other damages such as strand breakage from the increase in temperature (Fig. 14.22).

## 14.13. C-VALUE PARADOX

The haploid DNA content in a cell of an individual is described as its **C-value**.

The abnormality of the gene content by two different methods, one on the basis of knowledge about the rate of mutation per locus and other on the basis of general method used for determining DNA content, is called **C-value paradox**.

DNA content in eukaryotic cells is much higher than the prokaryotic cells and a wide range of variations are observed among the different species even among the same species. The content of DNA also depends upon the number of chromosomes in the cells (i.e. ploidy of the chromosome) (Table 14.6).

C-value paradox takes its name from our inability to explain the content of a genome in terms of an anticipated functions.

There are two aspects of the paradox.

**First** aspect is that there are huge variations in C-values between certain species whose apparent complexity does not vary correspondingly. There may be rather substantial variations even between certain closely related species.

The ranges of C-values found in different evolutionary phyla. There is some increase in the minimum genome size that is found in each phylum as the complexity increases.

For example, in prokaryotes, the genome is very small. In eukaryotes, a vast increase in genome size. In yeast, *Saccharomyces cerevisiae* has a genome size of 1.4 $\times 10^7$ bp, only 3 times greater than *E.coli*.

The further modest increase in genome size just over two folds is adequate to support the slime mold, *D. discoideum*, able to live in either unicellular or multicellular modes.

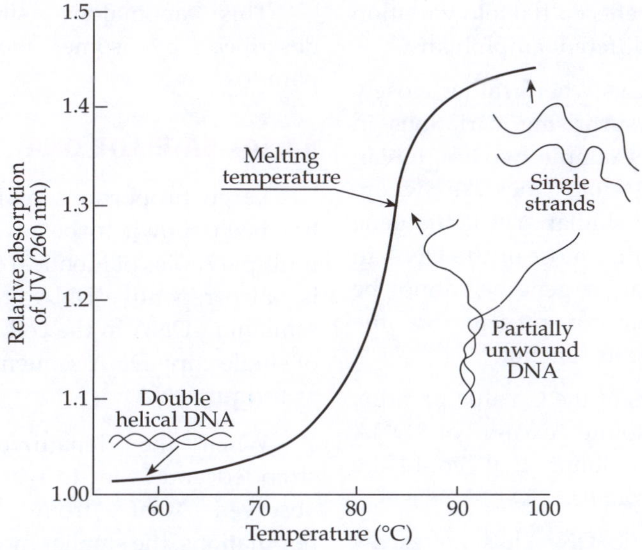


**Fig.14.22 :** *Melting temperature curve for $T_4$ DNA.*

Another increase in complexity is necessary to produce the first fully multi-cellular organisms. For example, *C. elegans* has a DNA content of $8 \times 10^7$ bp. Then any close relationship between complexity of the organism and content of DNA is obscure, although it is necessary to have a genome of more than $10^8$ bp. to make an insect of more than $4 \times 10^8$ bp to assemble an echinoderms, of more than $8 \times 10^8$ bp to produce a bird or amphibians and more than $2 \times 10^9$ bp to develop into a mammal.

In some cases, the spread of genome sizes is quite small. For example, birds, reptiles and mammals all show a little variations within the phylum, with a range of genome size in the case about two folds. But in other cases, there is quite a wide range of values, often more 10 folds. This reflects some surprising discrepancies between genome size and complexity of the organism.

An extraordinary C-value is found in amphibians where the smallest is below $10^9$ bp. while the largest are almost $10^{11}$ bp, it is hard to

**TABLE 14.6**
**DNA content of some organisms**

| *Class of organisms* | *Species* | *Haploid DNA (Picogram)* | *Daltons* | *Base pairs* |
|---|---|---|---|---|
| **Phages** | ø × 174 | $2.6 \times 10^{-6}$ | $1.7 \times 10^6$ | 5400 |
| | $T_4$ | $20.4 \times 10^{-5}$ | $126 \times 10^6$ | 200000 |
| **Animal virus** | adenovirus | $21.7 \times 10^{-6}$ | $13 \times 10^6$ | 21000 |
| **Prokaryotes** | *E. coli* | $4.4 \times 10^{-3}$ | $2.7 \times 10^9$ | $4.2 \times 10^6$ |
| **Unicellular eukaryotes** | *S. cerevisiae* | $14 \times 10^{-3}$ | $8.5 \times 10^9$ | $1.4 \times 10^7$ |
| **Multicellular eukaryotes** | *D. melanogaster* | 0.18 | $0.11 \times 10^{12}$ | $0.17 \times 10^9$ |
| | *Homo sapiens* | 2.8 | $18 \times 10^{12}$ | $2.8 \times 10^9$ |

believe that this could reflect a 100 fold variation in number of genes in different amphibians.

There are some cases where rather closely related species show surprising variations in total genome size. For example two amphibian species may have 10-fold increase where morphologies are very similar. Yet if the gene number is roughly similar most of the DNA in the species with the larger genome cannot be concerned with coding for protein. So, the question, what could be its function?

The **second** aspects of the C-value paradox is the apparent absolute excess of DNA compared with the amount that could be expected to code for proteins.

Actually, eukaryotic DNA has an excess length and the excess is encounted for because genes are much larger than the sequences needed to code for proteins. For example, the human haploid cell has DNA equal to $1.8 \times 10^{12}$ Dalton ≡ 87 cm of DNA, which is equal to $2.8 \times 10^{9}$ base pairs, then this genome could contain approximately as many as $3 \times 10^{6}$ genes assuming 1000 bp per gene coding for nearly 300 amino acids of a polypeptide chain.

However, the number of genes estimated in humans on the basis of knowledge about the rate of mutation per locus. As estimated by Muller (1967), the frequency of deleterious mutations per locus in human is $10^{-5}$ to $10^{-6}$ in each generation. If the number of gene is $3 \times 10^{6}$ (as calculated by general method), then it would yield 30 deleterious mutations in each generation at the rate of $10^{-5}$ mutations per locus. This would be an unbearable genetic load. The actual frequency of deleterious mutations per generation per individual has been estimated to be 0.5 against an expected frequency of 30. This mutation frequency at the rate of $10^{-5}$ per locus would be an estimate of $5 \times 10^{4}$ genes.

Thus it is supposed that the actual number of genes in human should be 50000 and not 3 million as estimated from DNA content.

This anomalous situation has been described by some workers as C-value paradox.

## 14.14. SATELLITE DNA

Large proportions of DNA in eukaryotes has been shown to be present in the form of multiple copies of identical DNA sequences, this is called repetitive DNA or **satellite DNA**. The remaining DNA in the cell is found in the form of single copy DNA sequences, which is known as **unique DNA**.

When the denatured DNA is single stranded and is let to reassociate, then it was observed that from the heterogenous populations, the smaller molecular weight DNA reassociates easily. Britten and his coworkers (1966, 68) have demonstrated that in many vertebrates, DNA reassociates easily when it is broken into small pieces. This observation gives rise to the hypothesis that certain short sequences of bases are repeated hundreds of times in the DNA, this is the satellite DNA.

This repetitive DNA generally contributes at least 20% and can reach up to as much as more than 90% in some cases. It is believed that these repetitive sequences do not carry any genetic informations and therefore do not form genes but play some other structural or regulatory roles.

Repetitive DNA consists of short identical genes which are repeated in tandem, several hundred or thousand times. Such DNA is found in the region of the chromosome adjacent to the centromere. In many cases, the base compositions of the repeating sequences are unlike that of the rest of the DNA. It is therefore easy to separate repetitive DNA by ultra-centrifugation.

The satellite DNA can be isolated by density gradient centrifugation in neutral caesium chloride as they have distinctive bouyant densities. The fraction can be separated as a band from the main band of DNA, this is called **satellite band**.

The satellite band is found on the left of the main band if lighter and on the right if heavier than the DNA of the main band.

In *Drosophila virilis*, there are three highly repetitive DNA and each consists of a repeating sequence of seven nucleotide pairs and about 25% of the DNA is satellite DNA (Table 14.7).

**TABLE 14.7**
**Satellite DNA of *Drosophila virilis* (Gall *et al* 1974)**

| *Repetitive DNA* | *Bouyant density* | *Repeat sequence* |
|---|---|---|
| Sat DNA – I | 1.692 | 5′ A C A A A C T 3′<br>3′ T G T T T G A 5′ |
| Sat DNA – II | 1.688 | 5′ A T A A A C T 3′<br>3′ T A T T T G A 5′ |
| Sat DNA – III | 1.671 | 5′ A C A A A T T 3′<br>3′ T G T T T A A 5′ |

In humans, 30% of DNA is repetitive and is designated as Sat I, II and III.

In mouse, 10% of the DNA is highly repetitive and renaturates within a few second. 20% is moderately repetitive and reassociates at an intermediate rate. 70% is single copy DNA, which renaturates very slowly. There are about a million copies of repetiting sequences of about 300 bp.

In prokaryotes, the repeated base sequence is not observed.

Two striking features of satellite DNA are

1. Remarkable relative uniformity within the same species.
2. Great variability between closely related species.

The satellite DNAs often lies in heterochromatic regions of chromosomes and their location can be demonstrated by cytological hybridization by incubating the cells in the radioactive solution and is determined by autoradiography.

The function of highly repetitive DNA is not known. This can replicate but cannot transcribe RNA for protein synthesis. This is probably because of the short sequences, lack of promoter sites on which RNA chains can be initiated by RNA polymerase. Repetitive DNA is therefore inert and is partly dispensable.

In the African clawed toad *Xenopus laevis*, the genes for 40S precursor RNA which give rise to 28S and 18S ribosomal RNA are repeated about 450 times. The genes are tandemly arranged and are separated by a spacer region of about 5000 bp. Genes for 5S rRNA are also separated by spacer regions and are arranged in clusters of 100 to 1000 repetitive units at the ends of the most of the 18 chromosomes.

## 14.15. COMPLEXITY

*Complexity is the total length of different sequences of DNA present in a given preparation.*

The double stranded DNA is denatured and converted into single stranded by heating the DNA solution. This is accompanied with increase in optical density, which is called hyperchromicity.

Again when it is allowed to cool, the single stranded DNA is transformed into a double stranded DNA, the optical density is decreased, this is called hypochromicity. The 50% resaturation is achieved usually observed at a specific temperature which is called **melting temperature** ($T_m$). The formation of double stranded DNA is actually measured over different values of a parameter which is described as $C_0.t$ (concentration × time). It is the product of DNA concentration and time of incubation in a reassociation reaction.

Complexity of the genome can be described under two aspects.

**Kinetic complexity :** The reassociation of DNA in the solution depends upon the random collisions between the complementary strands, which follows the second order of kinetics, since concentration of both the complementary strands will influence the rate of reaction. The rate of reaction when expressed through differential calculus.

$$\frac{dC}{dt} = -KC^2$$

where, C = Concentration of single stranded DNA at time 't'.
K = Reassociation rate constant.

$$\text{or, } \int \frac{dC}{C^2} = -K \int dt$$

$$\text{or, } -\frac{1}{C} = Kt + A \text{ (A is constant)}$$

$$\frac{1}{C} = Kt - A \quad \text{when } t = 0 \text{ then } C = C_0$$

$$\frac{1}{C_0} = K \times 0 - A$$

$$A = -\frac{1}{C_0}$$

The equation is

$$\frac{1}{C} = Kt + \frac{1}{C_0}$$

When the reaction is half complete then time is $t_{\frac{1}{2}}$ and concentration is C.

$$\frac{1}{C} = Kt_{\frac{1}{2}} + \frac{1}{C_0}$$

$$\frac{C_0}{C} = K.C_0.\, t_{\frac{1}{2}} + 1$$

We know $C = \frac{1}{2} C_0$

Then $1 + K.\, C_0.\, t_{\frac{1}{2}} = 2$

$$\text{or, } K = \frac{1}{C_0.\, t_{\frac{1}{2}}} \quad \text{or, } \boxed{C_0.\, t_{\frac{1}{2}} = \frac{1}{K}}$$

So, during reassociation of DNA occurs at the rate constant K (nt. mole/Lit/Sec) is equal to the reciprocals of $C_0.t_{\frac{1}{2}}$.

***$C_0.t_{\frac{1}{2}}$ is the product of DNA concentration and time (t) required to proceed for half completion of the reaction, it is directly proportional to the unique length of reassociating DNA.***

The $C_0.t_{\frac{1}{2}}$ of a reaction indicates the total length of different sequences that are present. This is described as the complexity. It is usually given in base pairs, but can be expressed in Daltons or any other mass unit.

A higher $C_0.t_{\frac{1}{2}}$ means, slower reaction and lower $C_0.t_{\frac{1}{2}}$ means faster reaction.

If there is no repetitive DNA (because the repetitive DNA reassociates faster), the $C_0.t_{\frac{1}{2}}$ will be directly proportional to the DNA content. In view of this, $C_0.t_{\frac{1}{2}}$ will indicate the length of all the different sequences in a genome, which will be less than the length of the total DNA in a genome when there is repetition. This is called **kinetic complexity**.

***Kinetic complexity is the complexity of a DNA component measured by the kinetics of the DNA association.***

This can be calculated by knowing the $C_0.t_{\frac{1}{2}}$.

For example, *E. coli* has a genome = 0.004 pg DNA = $4.2 \times 10^6$ bp with $C_0.t_{\frac{1}{2}} = 9$.

The kinetic complexity of the genome can be calculated as follows :

$$= \frac{C_0.\, t_{\frac{1}{2}} \text{ of DNA of any genome} \times \text{base pair}}{C_0.\, t_{\frac{1}{2}} \text{ of } E.\ coli \text{ genome}}$$

$$= \frac{4.2 \times 10^6 \times C_0.\, t_{\frac{1}{2}} \text{ of the genome}}{9}$$

In eukaryotes, the genome contains more than one pure component. For example, Calf DNA has two components, each with characteristic $C_0.t_{\frac{1}{2}}$ value. In wheat, more than two such components are found. Proportion of each component is determined by using the formula $(1 - \frac{C}{C_0})$ where C = conc. at $t_{\frac{1}{2}}$ for corresponding components.

From this proportion chemical complexity of the component can be determined.

**Chemical complexity** : Chemical complexity is the amount of a DNA component measured by chemical assay.

For example, if the genome size is $12 \times 10^8$ bp and the component represents 25% of the genome then the chemical complexity of this component is $3 \times 10^8$ bp.

Chemical complexity = Size of the genome × % of the component in this group.

If the kinetic complexity is known from the kinetic equation, then repetition frequency (f) of repetitive DNA component can be determined using the following formula.

$$f = \frac{\text{Chemical complexity}}{\text{Kinetic complexity}} = \frac{C_0 \cdot t_{\frac{1}{2}} \text{ of non repetitive DNA}}{C_0 \cdot t_{\frac{1}{2}} \text{ of repetitive DNA}}$$

Figure 14.23 shows the reasssociation of a (hypothetical) eukaryotic genome starting at a $C_0$.t of $10^{-4}$ and terminating at $C_0$.t of $10^4$. Reaction falls into three types of components and their results are as follows.

| *Properties* | *Fast component* | *Intermediate component* | *Slow component* |
|---|---|---|---|
| % of genome | 25 | 30 | 45 |
| $C_0 \cdot t_{\frac{1}{2}}$ | 0.0014 | 1.9 | 630 |
| Kinetic complexity (bp.) | 340 | $6 \infty 10^5$ | $3 \infty 10^8$ |
| Repetition frequency | 500000 | 350 | 1 |

There is a good relationship between the kinetic complexity and chemical complexity of eukaryotic genome.

Usually *E.coli* is used as a standard. Its components are taken to be identical with the length of the genome. Thus, complexity of any DNA can be determined by comparing its $C_0 \cdot t_{\frac{1}{2}}$ with that of standard DNA of known DNA complexity.

$$\frac{C_0 \cdot t_{\frac{1}{2}} \text{ of DNA of any genome}}{C_0 \cdot t_{\frac{1}{2}} \text{ of } E.coli \text{ DNA}} = \frac{\text{Complexity of any genome}}{4.2 \times 10^6 \text{ bp}}$$

According to the table, the slow component represents 45% of the total DNA, so the concentration in the reassociation reaction is 0.45 of the measured concentration (total amount of DNA).

If DNA is isolated as a pure component, free from other fractions, it would renature with a $C_0 \cdot t_{\frac{1}{2}}$ of $0.45 \times 630 = 283$.

Suppose that, under these conditions *E.coli* DNA reassociates with a $C_0 \cdot t_{\frac{1}{2}}$ of 9.0. Comparing these two clues, we see :

$$\text{The kinetic complexity} = \frac{C_0 \cdot t_{\frac{1}{2}} \text{ (DNA of any genome)} \times 4.2 \times 10^6}{9}$$

$$= \frac{0.45 \times 630 \times 4.2 \times 10^6}{9}$$

$$= 3 \times 10^8 \text{ bp.}$$

Then the whole genome is $3 \times 10^8 \times \frac{1}{0.45}$

$$= 6.6 \times 10^8 \text{ bp.}$$

$$\text{Fast component complexity} = \frac{0.0013 \times 0.25 \times 4.2 \times 10^6}{9} = 340$$

$$\text{Intermediate component complexity} = \frac{1.9 \times 0.30 \times 4.2 \times 10^6}{9} = 6 \times 10^5$$

Reversing the argument, if we take three DNA preparations, each containing a unique sequence of the appropriate length 340 bp, $6 \times 10^5$ bp and $3 \times 10^8$ bp respectively and mix them in the proportions 25 : 30 : 45, each would renature as though it were a single component, together the mixture would display the same kinetics as those determined for the whole genome.

Non-repetitive DNA complexity can estimate the genome size. The complexity of the slow components comprises sequences that are unique in the genome upon denaturation, each single stranded sequence is able to renaturate only with the corresponding complementary sequence. It is usually the major component in eukaryotes. It is called non-repetitive DNA. According to the table, the complexity of non-repetitive DNA is $3 \times 10^8$ bp. If this fraction is unique and represents 45% of the genome, then the whole genome should have a size of

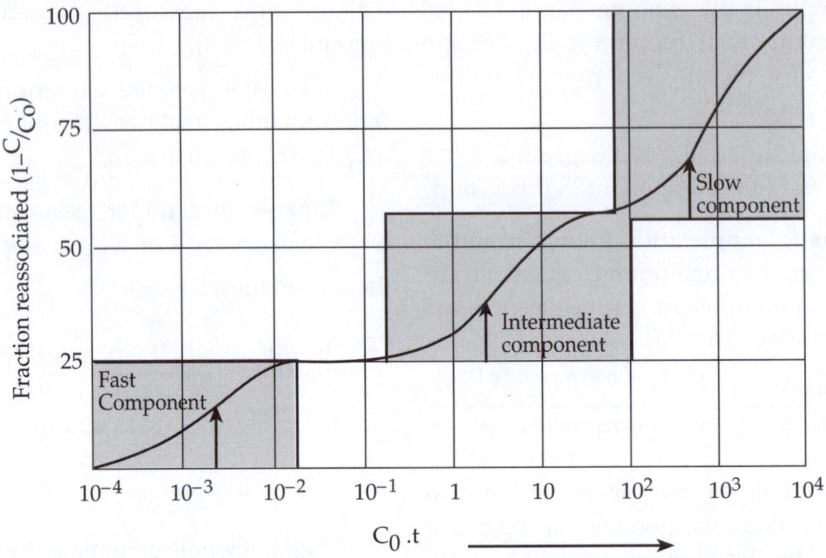


**Fig.14.23 :** *The reassociation kinetics of eukaryotic DNA showing three types of components. Arrow indicates $C_0$. $t_{\frac{1}{2}}$ values of each component.*

$3 \times 10^8 \div 0.45 = 6.6 \times 10^8$ bp. This provides an independent assessment of genome size. The value is approximately $7 \times 10^8$, obtained from the result of chemical complexity.

Eukaryotic genomes certainly contain repetitive sequences. Intermediate component occupies 30% of the genome. According to chemical complexity, the total amount is $0.30 \times 7 \times 10^8 = 2.1 \times 10^8$ bp.

But kinetic complexity of this component is only $6 \times 10^5$ bp.

$$\text{Thus repetition frequency} = \frac{2.1 \times 10^8}{6 \times 10^5} = 350$$

Thus intermediate component behaves as though consisting of a sequence of $6 \times 10^5$ bp. that present in 350 copies in every genome. Repetition frequency (f) is the number of copies present per genome.

Highly repetitive DNA takes the name from the very large number of copies of the basic reassociating sequence present. The fast component consists of 340 bp. long in 500000 copies per genome. Because of the short length of the reassociating unit, sometimes this is also referred to as simple sequence DNA.

$$\text{The repetition frequency (f)} = \frac{C_0 \cdot t_{\frac{1}{2}} \text{ of non repetitive DNA}}{C_0 \cdot t_{\frac{1}{2}} \text{ of repetitive DNA}}$$

$$= \frac{630}{0.0013} = 50{,}0000 \text{ (Approx.)}$$

## 14.16. PSEUDOGENE AND IT'S EVOLUTIONARY SIGNIFICANCE

In multicellular organisms, a wide variety of DNA sequences are found, which are of no apparent use. Some of these sequences are defective copies of functional genes and are therefore called **pseudogenes**.

Pseudogenes have been reported in human beings, mouse and *Drosophila*.

### 14.16.1. α and β Globin Pseudogenes

**In Primates :** The division of globin chains into α-like and β-like is supported by the structure of the protein and by the organization of the genes. The entire β-like family is defined

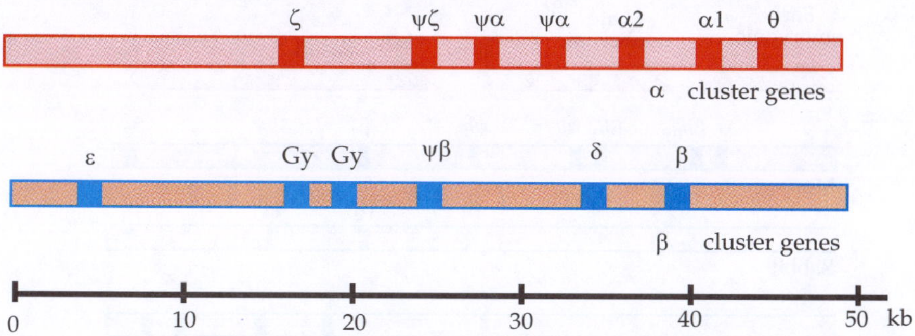


**Fig.14.24 :** *α and β cluster pseudogenes in primates (man).*

by its ability to combine directly with the α–chain. The zeta chain is defined by its ability to combine with the embryonic β-like chains. Each type of globin turns out to be coded by genes organised into a single cluster. In man the α-cluster lies on chromosome no-11 and β-cluster lies on chromosome no-16 (Fig. 14.24).

Each cluster was discovered by the ability of genomic fragments to hybridize with probes representing adult globin mRNA. This analysis led to the discovery of further genes, some representing known or unknown embryonic globins, other comprising non-functional pseudogenes.

The organization of these genes in other higher primates is very similar. For example, the β-clusters of gorilla and baboon are virtually indistinguishable from that of man. All of the genes are transcribed from left to right and they lie in the order of developmental expressions : 5′-embryonic-fetal-adult-3′.

Stretching over 50kb, the β-cluster contains five fundamental genes: ε, Gγ, Aγ, δ and β and one pseudogene ψβ lies between Aγ and δ. The two γ genes differ in their coding sequence in only one amino acid. The G-varient has glycine at position 136, whereas, A-varient has alanine at that position.

The more compact α-cluster extends over 28kb and includes one active ζ (zeta), one nonfunctional ζ -gene, one ψα (pseudo-α-gene), two α-genes and one θ-gene of unknown function. The existence of two α-genes, coding for the identical protein was suspected previously on the basis of genetic evidence.

**In other vertebrates :** A similar general organizations have been found in other vertebrate globin gene clusters, but details of the type of members of genes may vary (Fig. 14.25).

In rabbit, 4 β-like genes have been identified, two embryonic, one pseudogene and one adult gene. Again the functional genes lie in their order of expression 5′ → 3′.

In goat, there are seven β-like globin genes. Two are embryonic, one fetal, two adult and two pseudogenes.

In the mouse, there must be at least nine β-like globin genes. Seven genes so far have been identified. These include the two adult β-genes, the major being expressed at greater level than minor. $\beta h_3$ and $\beta h_2$, whose sequences do not seem to fit with known mouse globin types and these may be pseudogenes.

There may be more members of a gene family, both functional and nonfunctional, then we would suspect on the basis of protein analysis. The extra functional genes may represent duplicates that code for identical peptides or they may be related to proteins.

The pseudogenes show varying relationship with the functional genes and can

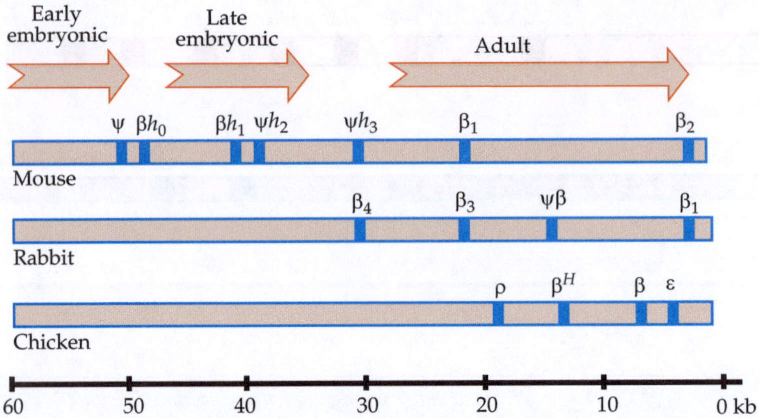


**Fig.14.25 :** *Cluster of β-globin pseudogenes in other vertebrates.*

be analyzed only at the level of DNA sequence.

In the mouse genome, some additional pseudogenes have been found that are not the part of the clusters. The α-cluster consists of one embryonic and two adult genes. Two identified pseudogenes each lie on different chromosomes from the cluster. There may be others. These pseudogenes must have originated by translocation events that moved a gene away from the cluster.

Pseudogenes possess the sequences that are related to those of the functional genes, but that cannot be translated into a functional protein.

Some pseudogenes have the same general structure as functional genes with sequences corresponding to exons and introns in the usual locations. They are rendered inactive by **MUTATIONS** that prevent any or all of the stages of gene expression. The changes can take the form of abolishing the signals for initiating transcription, preventing splicing at the exon-intron junctions or terminating translation prematurely.

Usually, a pseudogene has several deleterious mutations, presumably because once it ceased to be active, there was no impediment to the accumulation of further mutations. Pseudogenes of this type have been found in many systems including globin, immunoglobulins, histocompatibility antigens etc.

A typical example is the rabbit pseudogene $\psi\beta_2$ which has the usual organization of exons and introns and is related most closely to the functional gene $\beta_1$. But there is a deletion of one base pair at codon 20 of $\psi\beta_2$, causing a frame shift that would lead to termination shortly after initiation of translation. Several point mutations have changed later codons representing amino acids that is highly conserved in the β-globins.

Neither of the two introns any longer possess boundary sequences that can form adequately to the GT-AG rule, so probably the introns could not be spliced out even if the gene is transcribed.

The mouse $\psi h_3$ gene has an interesting property. It precisely lacks both introns. Its sequence can be aligned with the α globin mRNA. The apparent tune of inactivation coincides with the original duplication, which suggests that the original inactivating events may have been associated with the loss of introns. Without introns, the gene may have been unable to function and thus will have begun immediately to collect mutations. But how does it occur? This could take the form of insertion of a reverse transcript into the genome, perhaps carried by a retrovirus or of pairing between the mRNA and one strand of DNA at some stage of a recombination process.

In the $\alpha$ globin genes of the goat, there are two adult species $\beta^A$ and $\beta^C$. Each of these has a pseudogene a few kb upstream from it, called $\psi\beta^Z$ and $\psi\beta^X$. The two pseudogenes are better related to each other than to the adult $\beta$-globin genes, in particular, they share several inactivating mutations. Also, the two adult $\beta$-globin genes are better related to each other than to the pseudogenes. This implies that an origin of $\psi\beta \rightarrow \beta$ structure was itself duplicated giving two functional $\beta$ genes, which have diverged further into $\beta^A$ and $\beta^C$ genes and two nonfunctional genes, which have developed into the current pseudogenes.

### 14.16.2. Origin of Pseudogenes

Gene duplication, rearrangement and variation are the important factors for the evolution as the slow accumulation of point mutations in the individual genes.

A gene cluster can expand or contract by unequal crossing over when recombination occurs between nonallelic genes. When two copies of a gene on each chromosome, an occasional misalignment allows pairing between them. Thus generates nonreciprocal recombinant chromosomes one of which has a duplication of gene and other has deletion. The first recombinant can increase the copies of the gene from two to three to more, while the second has a decrease from two to one. The corresponding exons of adjacent gene copies are likely to be well enough related to support pairing. Thalassemias result from the mutations that reduce or prevent synthesis of either $\alpha$ or $\beta$ globin. The occurrence of unique crossing over in the human globin gene cluster is revealed by the nature of certain thalassemias.

One of the possible origin of pseudogenes was based on the assumption that most pseudogenes are flanked by a short repeat of 6-21 bases. It suggests that mRNA or snRNA itself becomes incorporated into DNA or into retrovirus RNA followed by the incorporation of retroviruses.

The reverse transcript of mRNA or snRNA was synthesized as cDNA, which subsequently becomes integrated. The insertion of this cDNA due to staggered cleavage of genomic DNA at a specific site.

### 14.16.3. Evolution of $\beta$-globin Genes

The structural organization of the globin genes in a variety of species highlighted us to trace the evolution of the present globin gene cluster from a single ancestral globin gene.

The mammalian myoglobin gene has a single chain, which has diverged from the globin line of descent about 800 million years ago. The myoglobin gene has the same organization of the globin gene having three exons and is represented as the common ancestor (Fig. 14.26).

The leghemoglobin in plants, which is related to the globin gene, may represent the ancestral form, which has four exons and in between them has three introns.

In some primitive fishes like lamprey and hagfishes, have only one globin chain. That must have arose from the exon fusion of the leghemoglobin. As a result, three exons and in between, two introns resulted. Other view is that by introducing intron into the middle exon, leghemoglobin might have arisen.

The next stage of evolution among vertebrates were found in *Xenopus* where two globin genes $\alpha$ and $\beta$ of both larval and adult types. The cluster must therefore have evolved by duplication of linked $\alpha$ and $\beta$ genes, followed by divergence between the individual copies.

About 350 million years ago separation of $\alpha$ and $\beta$ globin genes must has been resulted from a transposition in the mammalian/avian ancestors. The separate clusters of $\alpha$ and $\beta$ globin genes in both mammals and birds have been physically separated before they have been

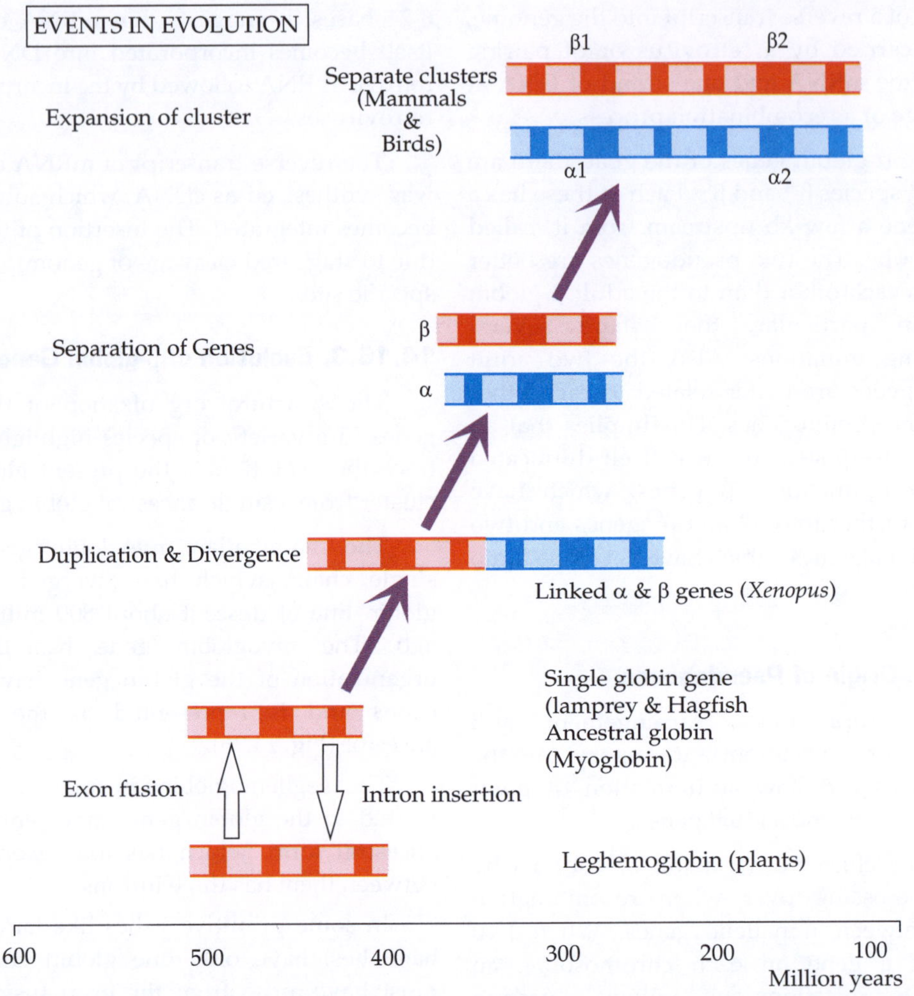


**Fig.14.26 :** *All globin genes have evolved by a series of duplications, transpositions, and mutations from a single ancestral gene.*

diverged from their common ancestors probably 270 millions of years ago.

Now, these two clusters are expanded by further duplication and inactivation by unequal crossing over or by incorporation with retroviruses and established into the separate chromosome.

Most mutations that change the amino acid sequence are deleterious and will be eliminated by natural selection. Few mutations will be advantageous and spread through the population eventually replacing the former sequence. The coding region can be distinguished into potential replacement sites and silent sites. The mutation of the replacement sites alters the amino acid, which may cause deleterious, neutral or advantageous to the organism. The mutations on the silent sites do not change in the proteins.

It is evident that the silent site divergence is much greater than the replacement site divergence. The divergence between any pair of globin sequence is more or less proportional to the time since they are separated. This provides an **evolutionary clock** that measures the accumulation of mutations at an apparently even rate during evolution.

Replacement site divergences between pairs of β-globin genes allow the history of the human cluster to be reconstructed. This tree accounts for the separation of classes of globin genes. Duplications of individual genes are of unknown origin. The time of the α and ζ divergence is not known (Fig. 14.27).

Pseudogenes do not full fill any function and they are present in the genome entirely without any purpose. These genes in the past time in any number may have been eliminated by deletion or by accretion of mutation. Some of them are still present as an unwanted accompaniment with the functional genes and thus it can be said that pseudogenes are **evolutionary dead ends**.

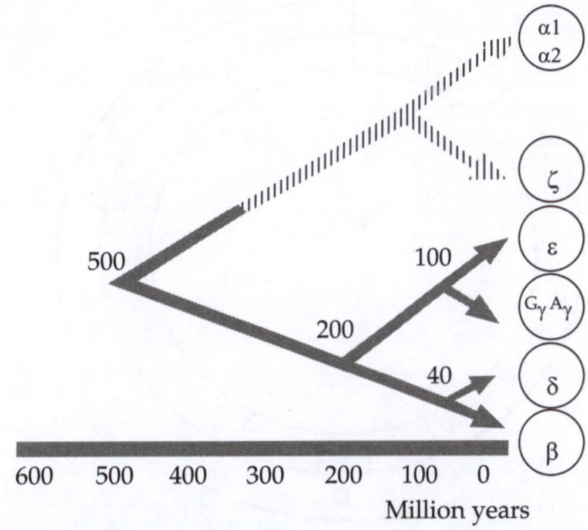


**Fig.14.27 :** *Replacement site divergences between pairs of β-genes allow the history of the human cluster to be reconstructed. The tree accounts for the separation of classes of globin genes. Duplications of in dividual genes are of unknown origin. The time of the α→ζ divergence is not known.*

## 14.17 OVERLAPPING GENES

In the year 1940, Beadle and Tatum proposed the "one gene one protein hyppthesis" and according to them each gene is responsible for coding a protein or polypeptide chain, For example, a DNA segment of 300 bp. can give a protein having not more than 100 amino acids.

In the year 1976-77, Barrell *et. al*(M.R.C. Laboratory of Microbiology, Cambridge, UK) had been able to map the entire base sequence of ϕ × 174 DNA and Phage G4 DNA and got his second Nobel Prize in 1980.

It has been shown that ϕ × 174 hacteriophage has 9 genes arranged in A–B–C–D–E–J–F–G–H order, which can code 9 proteins. Gene-A is coded the proteins for DNA replication, Gene B and D are coded proteins for the assembly of phage particles. F, G, H-genes for structural proteins of the capsid etc.

They gave the evidence that the proteins coded by gene D and E are specified by the same segment of DNA.

ϕ × 174 phage DNA consists of 5386 nts. which can code 1896 amino acids, having a total weight of 200000 Daltons. But it has been found that the DNA codes for the proteins of mol. wt 250000 Daltons. It has also been found that gene-B (360 nts) is completely within gene A (1536 nts). Similarly gene E (273 nts) is contained in gene D (1456 nts). Thus two larger genes A and D can code four proteins. It has been observed that protein synthesized by B is not homologous to the proteins of gene A or as a shorter version of it, because the mRNAs are translated from different reading frames. Such a case is illustrated in the D and E genes of ϕ × 174 as follows.

*Met* *Val* Gene E

• • • • • G T T T A T G G T A • • • • •

*Val* *Tyr* *Gly* Gene D

Thus, if the reading frame is read from one point earlier, the amino acids of the protein are being changed. Thus same gene can code for two different sequences by a frame shift or overlapping codes and produce two different proteins.

Another interesting fact is that the termination codon of gene D and initiation codon of gene-J overlap by one nucleotide only.

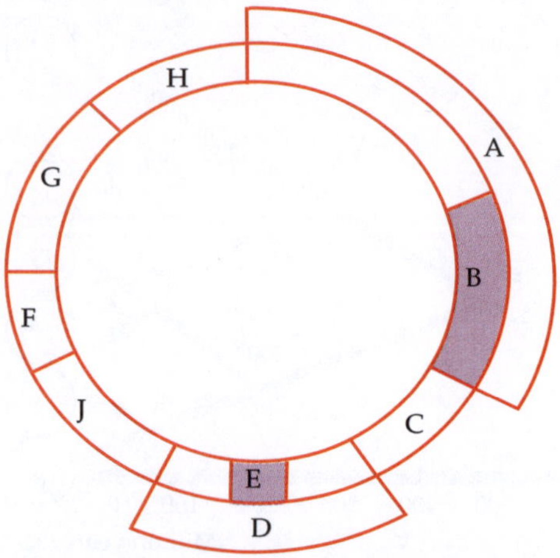


**Fig.14.28 :** *Genetic map of bacteriophage $\phi \times 174$*

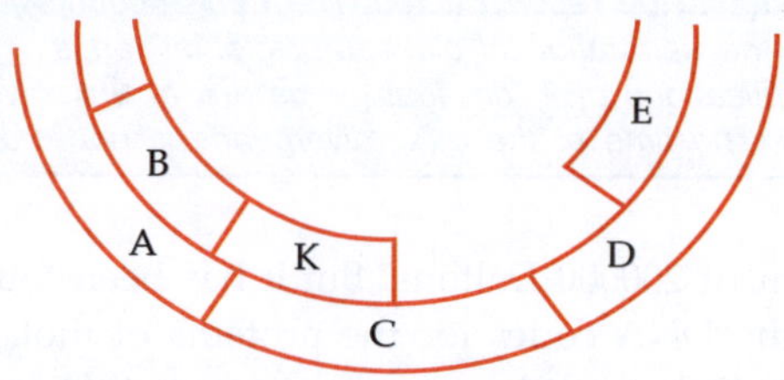


**Fig.14.29 :** *A part of genetic map of G4 virus.*

termination codon of gene D

• • • • • T G A T G • • • • •

initiation codon of gene-J

The G4 bacteriophage has the overlapping genes, where gene-B is completely within gene-A and gene-E within gene-D. Gene K is made up of the last 86 nts of genes (Fig. 14.28/ 14.29).

Sometimes, in the genome, one gene contained within an intron of a second gene. An example in the human genome the neurofibromatosis type-1 gene which has three short genes, called OGMP, EV12A and EV12B, within one of its introns. Each of these internal genes is also splited into exons and introns (Fig. 14.30).

Recently, it has been discovered that many small nucleolar RNAs (snoRNAs) – non-coding RNAs that are involved in chemical modification of other RNAs are specified by genes within genes, snoRNAs are transcribed from and are released by cutting up the intron after splicing. For example, the human U16 snoRNA is specified by a sequence in intron 3 of the gene for ribosomal protein L1 (Fig. 14.31).

The overlapping gene is an economic device to make better use of genetic material through packing the genetic information in less DNA. It has been arisen particularly due to limilations of the quantity of DNA in viruses and also in mitochondrial genome.

## 14.18 SPLIT GENES

We expect the gene to consist of a length of DNA that is colinear with the protein. But a comparison between the structure of DNA and the corresponding mRNA shows a discripancy in many cases. The mRNA has been found to be a nucleotide sequence that corresponds exactly with the protein product according to the genetic code. But the gene includes some additional sequences that lie within the coding region. This is called **split gene** or **interrupted gene**.

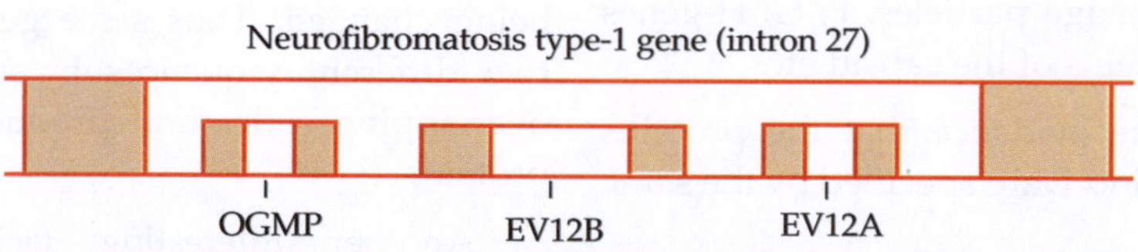


**Fig.14.30 :** *Neurofibromatosis type-1 gene, showing three genes within intron-27.*

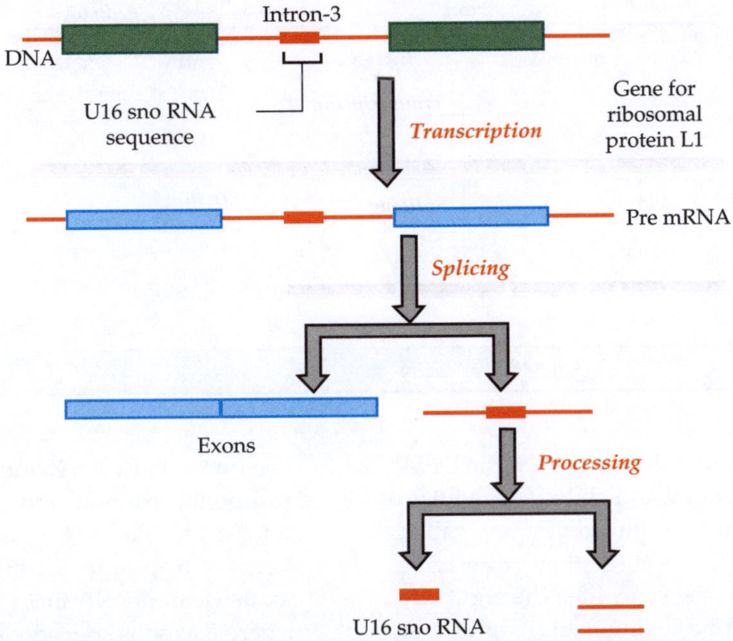


**Fig.14.31 :** *U16 sno RNA synthesized from intron 3 of ribosomal L1 gene.*

The split gene consists of two categories of sequences, (1) The sequences that containing actual information of the gene called **exons**. (2) The intervening sequences that are not coded for proteins and are removed out after transcription from the primary transcripts are called **introns**.

Two research groups headed by Phili. A. Sharp and Richard J. Roberts studied the split genes of adenovirus-2.

Research group of D.S. Hogness, I. B. David and N. Davidson studied split genes of 28S rRNA in *Drosophila.*

Research groups of P. Chambon, P. Leader and R.A. Flavell studed the β-globin split genes, ovalbumin split genes and tRNA split genes.

However, the credit of discovery goes to Philip A Sharp and Richard. J. Roberts and won Nobel Prize in 1993.

The expression of split genes requires additional steps. The transcript from the DNA (which represents the genome sequence) is not the mRNA. This a precursor RNA (pre-mRNA). It does not take part in translation directly. At first, introns are removed from this precursor-mRNA by splicing to give a messenger RNA (mRNA), that consists only of a series of exons tagged together by enzyme ligase. Then this mRNA synthesises proteins.

All the exons are represented on the same molecule of RNA. They are joined together only by intramolecular reaction. Mutations located in different exons of a gene cannot complement one another. Thus they are defined as the members of the same complementation group.

Introns are not a part of the RNA and therefore mutations of intron do not affect the structure of the protein. But sometimes can prevent the splicing. A mutation of this sort acts only on the alleles that carry it, and it fails the complement any other mutation in that allele, and thus constitutes a part of the same complementation group as the exons.

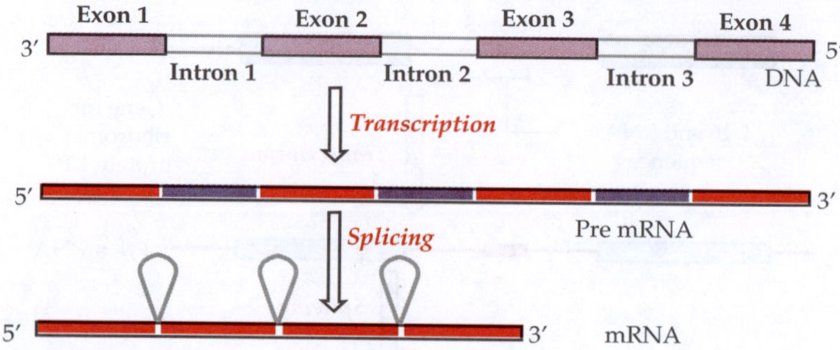


**Fig.14.32 :** *Hexon gene of adenovirus-2*

1. **Hexon genes of Adenovirus-2 :** The DNA is double stranded and codes for about 20 proteins. Eight of the genes are called "Late genes", because they transcribe mRNA late in the virus life. The eight late genes transcribe a single RNA and later cuts into eight mRNAs. The total length of the mRNAs is less than the length of the original transcript.

   When one such gene is paired with the mRNA, the DNA formed three loops indicating the presence of three introns and four exons. These four exon segments will join to produce mRNA (Fig. 14.32).

2. **Ovalbumin genes :** P. Chambons group (France) and W. O′ Malloys group (USA) showed that the ovalbumin gene of chicken is not continuous but is made up of pieces scattered in the chromosome. There are 8 exons and 7 introns. Size of the ovalbumin gene is 7700 bp, although the mature mRNA has only 1872 nts. In pRNA, has a cap of $^{7m}$G is added at 5′ end and a poly A tail at 3′ end. The introns are excised in two instalments. First two at the first step and the remaining six at the second step (Fig. 14.33).

3. **Troponin-T gene :** In troponin-T gene of rat muscles, at the 3′ end, there are five exons of which only four are used to construct an individual mRNA, Three exons, W, X, Z are interrupted by introns. The intron between X and Z there are two additional exons α and β which will be spliced atternately forming two different forms of tropronin-T. In the first form the sequence of mRNA includes WXαZ exons where β exon is spliced, on the other hand in second form the sequence of mRNA WXβZ exons where α exons is spliced (Fig.14.34).

4. **Globin genes :** The components of hemoglobin molecules of mice, rabbits, man, birds and frogs consist of two polypeptide chains, α and β. These two types of globin gene share a common type of structure (Fig. 14.35).

   Interruptions occur at homologous positions in all known active globin genes. The first intron is always fairly short. The second intron is usually longer but the actual length can vary. In mouse, the second intron is the α globin gene is only 150 bp long, so the overall length of the gene is 850 bp. long, whereas, the β-globin gene is 1382 bp in overall length. The length of β–globin mRNA is 585 bases and β-globin mRNA is 620 bases. Thus about two-third of the bases are discarded during splicing.

5. ***DHFR* gene :** The dihydrofolate reductase gene in mammals is organized into six exons that corresponds to total 2000 bases in mRNA. The introns are large, and vary

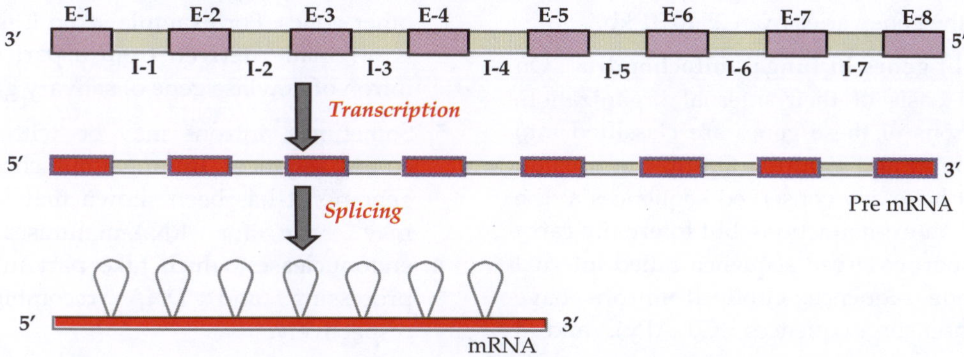


**Fig.14.33 :** *Ovalbumin genes of Chicken.*

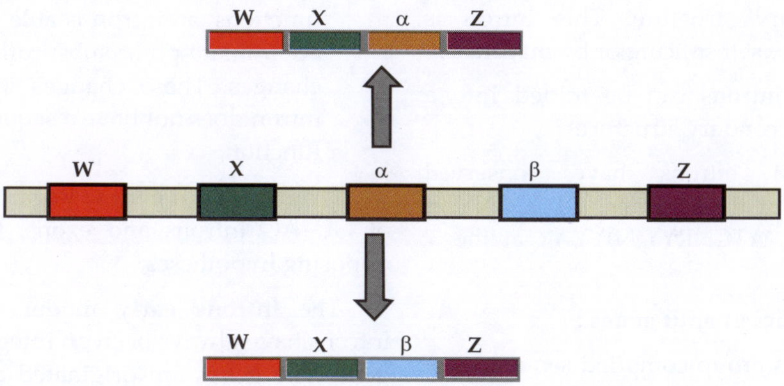


**Fig.14.34 :** *Alternative splicing generates the α and β Troponin-T.*

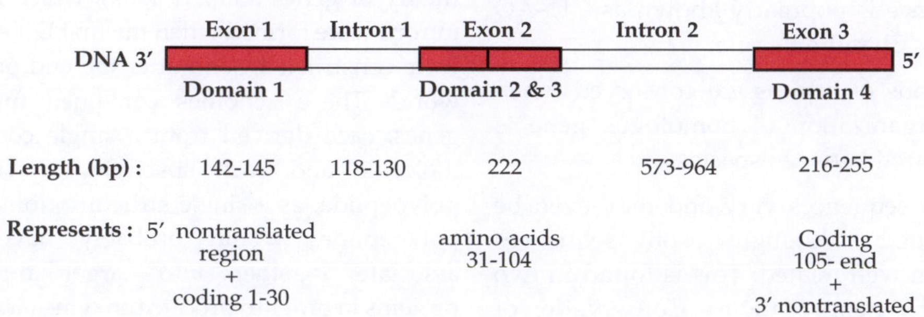


**Fig.14.35 :** *Mammalian β-globin split gene.*

extensively in their lengths thus the length of the gene varies from 25 to 31 kb.

6. **Split genes in fungal mitochondria :** On the basis of their internal organization, introns of these genes are classified into group-I and group-II. Group-I introns do not have any conserved sequences at the intron-exon junctions, but internally carry a short coserved sequence called internal guide sequence. Group-II introns have consensus sequences (GT-APy), and a branch sequence that resembles TACTAAC box. These introns are excised.
7. **Split genes in chloroplasts :** Three classes of introns are found in chloroplast genome. Group-1 introns canbe folded in a secondary structure. This intron is removed by self splicing or by **maturase**.

   Group II introns can be folded into a complex secondary structure.

   Group III introns have conserved sequences at their border, GTGCGNY at the 5′ end, ATCNRYY(N)YYAY at the 3′ end.

**Characteristics of split genes :**

1. Chambon's group compiled sequences of the boundaries of introns from a large number of eukaryotic protein-coding genes and revealed that the intron-exon junction is a conserved sequence. It is always GU at the 5′ end of the intron and AG at the 3′ of its end. This conserved sequence is popularly known as GU–AG rule or **Chambon's rule**.
2. Positions of introns are conserved when the organization of homologus gene is compared between species.
3. Intron sequences vary and may even be unrelated, although exon sequences remain well related. This is found in two β–globin genes of mouse. Conservation of exons can be used to isolate related genes in different species.
4. Introns of one gene may contain exons of other genes. For example, exon L in liver is originally derived from a part of the intron of amylase gene of salivary gland.
5. Sometimes, introns may be with some coding sequnces. In fungal mitochondrial genome, it has been shown that introns may code for RNA-maturases and endonucleases which take part in RNA processing and DNA recombination respectively.
6. Mutations occur at the same rate in both exons and introns, but are removed more efficiently from the exon by adverse selection. However, in the absence of the constraints imposed by a coding functions, an intron is able quite freely to accumulate point substitutions and other changes. These changes imply that the intron does not have a sequence – specific function.

**Origin of split genes :** Regarding the origin of GU–AG introns and exons, there are two opposing hypotheses.

The **introns early** model suggests that, introns have always been an integral part of the gene. The genes are originated as interrupted structures or exons as independent genetic units or microgenes and their association with introns helped generation of diversity in genes through transsplicing and exon suffling.

**Introns early** model is also known as **exon theory of genes** (Gilbert 1987), which holds that introns were formed when the first DNA genomes were constructed, soon after the end of the RNA world. These genomes contained many short genes, each derived from a single coding RNA molecule and each specifying a very small polypeptide, as a single structure domain. These polypeptides would probably have had to associate together into larger multidomain proteins in order to produce enzymes with specific and efficient catalytic mechanisms. To aid the synthesis of such multidomain enzymes it would have been beneficial for enzymes induvidual polypeptides to become linked to a single protein such as we see today. This was achieved by splicing together the transcripts of the relevent **minigenes** and are positioned next to each other. Thus these minigenes became exons and the DNA sequences between them became introns.

The "introns late" model suggests that the ancestral-protein-coding units were consisted as uninterrupted sequences of DNA. The intron evolution is independent. These introns are invaded the genome of eukaryotic ancestor as endosymbionts at the mRNA level, which was followed by reverse transcriptions and recombination with DNA producing split genes.

There are many evidences in support of either hypotheses. The early support for "intron early" model came when four introns in animal and plants genes for triose phosphase isomerase (Glbert *et al* 1986). But later it has been found that introns had been lost in some lineages but gained in others.

Again "introns late" model has come to light when it has been found that in many genes of many organisms, the number of introns has gradually increased during evolution of animal genomes (Palmer and Logsdon, 1991).

Some workers have tried to correlate exons with protein structural domains. A study of vertebrate globin proteins that each comprises four structural domains first corresponding to exon-1, second and third to exon 2 and the fourth to exon-3 (Go, 1981). In the leghemoglobin gene of soybean, the intron has been found exactly at the expected position *i.e.* between exon 2 and 3 (Jansen 1981). But at present more than ten introns have been discovered. Their positions do not correspond to junctions between domains. Therefore, there we find in many cases, no links between gene exons and protein structural domains (Fig. 14.36).

The current evidence disapproves neither hypotheses. Efforts have been made to combine the two hypotheses to formulate a new intermediate hypothesis.

## 14.19 ULTRASTRUCTURE OF EUKARYOTIC CHROMOSOME

Electron microscope cannot give the clear idea about the organization of the chromatin, though such studies demonstrated that the chromosomes have very fine fibrils having a thickness of 2–4 nm. The position of the protein in the chromosome was differently shown in different chromosome models. But now the most accepted model regarding the structure of eukaryotic chromosome is the **nucleosome model**.

- **Structure of Chromosome at Molecular Level (NUCLEOSOME Model)**

In the year 1960 M.F. Wilkins and V. Luzzati, by X-ray diffraction and electron microscopy observed and suggested the patterns of repeating units in the chromatin. Woodcock (1973) showed that under electron microscope chromatin appears to have a string of beads and is made up of a number of repeating units. A.L.Olins and D.E. Olins reported the result of electron microscopy of chromatin obtained from interphase nuclei lysed in water and the chromatin fibres were appeared as arrays of spherical particles about 10 nm in diameter, connected by filaments of 2 nm in diameter. He called these as **nu** bodies. In the year 1975 P.M. Outdet *et al* used the term **nucleosome** for these particles (Fig. 14.37).

Histones were believed to be distributed along DNA in a regular periodicity. When histones were subjected to gel filtration, these are separated into two groups. One consisting of H1, H3 and H4 and the other group consisting of H2A and H2B.

**Chemistry of histones :** Histones are small basic proteins associated with DNA and act as gene repressor. According to Ciba Symposium on Nomenclature, chromatin comprises five principal classes of histones, viz., H1 (H5) H2A; H2B, H3 and H4. These are rich in arginine and lysine but lack tryptophan and are very highly conserved. The size of these histones varies from species to species.

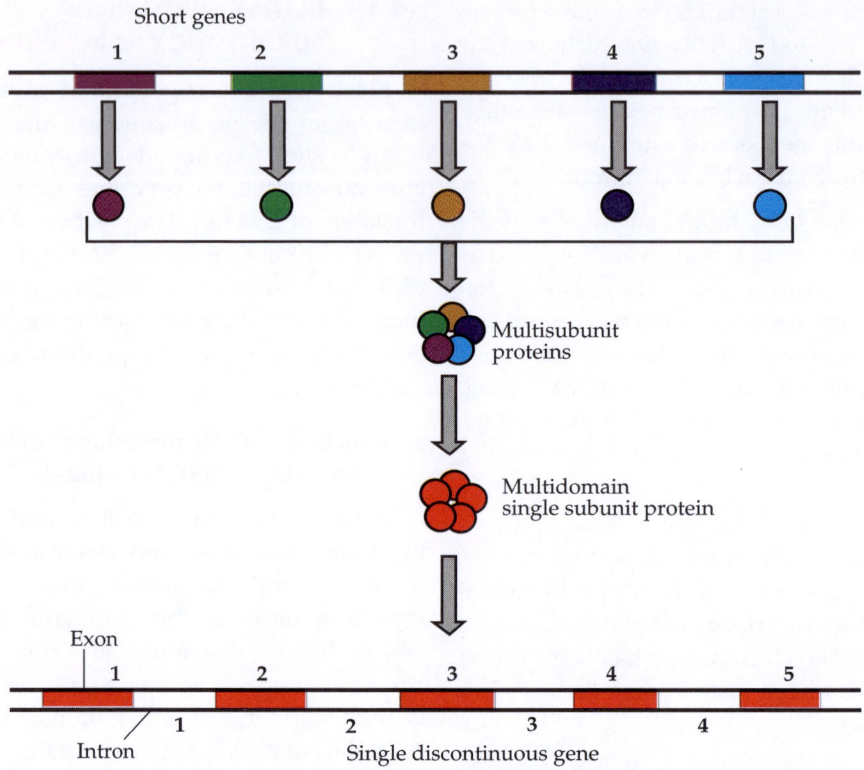


**Fig.14.36 :** *Exon theory of genes.*

H1 is species specific. In avian RBC, a variant from H5 is present in place of H1. H2A and H2B are less conserved while H3 and H4 are highly conserved. Mammalian H3 has two cysteines at 96 and 110 positions while in other eukaryotes only one *cys* at 96 is replaced by *serine*. Histones are not found in association with the DNA of prokaryotes. In slime mould and fungi, there are indications that H1 and H3 are absent.

**Structural periodicity of DNA in the nucleosome :** Treatment with DNAase I and DNAase II makes single-strand nicks in DNA, so after denaturation single stranded fragments are released. It is found that the nicks in DNA occur at 10 bp apart and are designated as S1, S2, ......, S13. S1 is 10 base away from 5′ end; S2 is 20 base away and son on. It was shown that S1 to S4 and S10 to S13 lie 10 bp apart while those from S4 to S10 lie 10.7 bp apart. This result reflects the structural periodicity in core DNA of nucleosome. In the middle, this is close to the value of DNA is solution, but at the ends it is less tightly screwed.

The nucleosome of SV 40 virus has been studied, which is 5200 bp long (15000A). The DNA is packed into the nucleosome in a ratio of about 7. It is called **mini chromosome**.

**Core particles**

1. When nuclease treatment is prolonged and the DNA is removed from both the ends, yielding particles containing only 140–146 nucleotides. This reduced form of nucleosome is called core particle. Core particles contain histone octamers and the core DNAs around it. (Figure of Front page of the book).

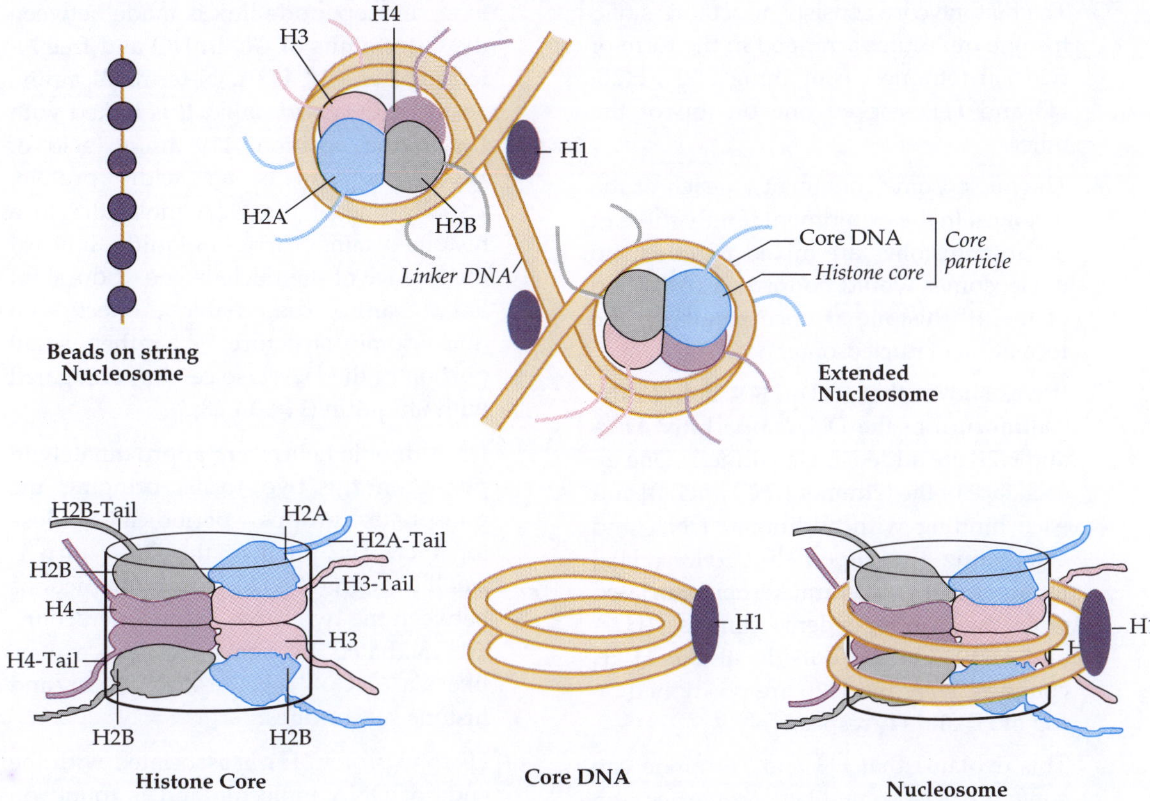


**Fig.14.37 :** *Structure of nucleosome.*

2. Adjacent to core particles, each core DNA is joined with each other though DNA segment called linker DNA. The core DNA has an invariant length of maximum 146 nts but the length of the linker DNA may vary from 8 to 114. Thus accounting for variation in DNA length of nucleosome. By the study with X-ray crystallography, the three dimensional structure of core particle has been revealed. The core particles are not spherical or flat but are wedge-shaped structures, about 100Å in diameter and 60Å high.
3. The DNA (20Å dia) double helix which is coiled around the 60Å particle requires 80 base pairs per turn. Since, the length of the DNA in the core particle is only 146 bp which will occupy only one and three quarter turns. Therefore, the particle is thinner in one side, accounting for its wedge shape. It was also shown that the histone octamer is also bipartite and wedge-shaped structure providing for a short helical ramp on which the DNA is wrapped.

**Arrangement of histones in the histone core**

1. Five classes of histones have been found associated with chromatin, H1, H2A, H2B, H3 and H4. Of these, the location of H1 is believed to be distinct from that of other histones.
2. The histones appear to be arranged in two regions one containing 8 molecules of H2A, H2B, H3 and H4 and other containing only H1.

3. The histone core consists of octamers of 8 histone molecules arranged in the form of two flat tetramers containing H2A, H2B, H3 and H4, stacked one on top of the other.
4. The nucleosome contains two each of the histones. In the experiment if only three of the four histones are mixed together, no nucleosomes would be formed. Addition of the 4th histone at once results in the formation of nucleosome.
5. It was shown that $(H3)_2(H4)_2$ defines the central turn of the DNA superhilix. H2A and H2B are added as two dimers. One on each face of the tetramer $[(H3)_2(H4)_2)]$ and each binding with additional DNA and completing the superhelix. $\{(H3)_2(H4)_2]$ tetramer makes a central kernel associated with two independent dimers (H2A and H2B). On the outside of the $H_3H_4$ complex, H2A and H2B are positioned on top of $H_3$ and $H_4$ respectively.

   This explains that H3 and H4 alone can confer nucleosome-like properties on DNA. But, H2A and H2B cannot confer this property.
6. Nucleosome to nucleosome linkages are formed by histone tails. The tails ae largely unstructured and flexible and may help to pack nucleosomes together into 30 nm fibre. The tails of one histone contact the histone core of an adjacent nucleosome in the crystalline lattice.
7. An extraordinary modification of a histone has been revealed by the characterization of a protein originally found in the non-histone of rat liver chromatin, was known at first as A24. This protein has same C-terminal sequence as H2A but it has two N-terminal sequences.

   This protein is called **Ubiquitin** present in the cells of bacteria to mammals. The H2A-ubiquitin is now known as UH2A. Ubiquitin is itself 76 amino acid residue long, an isopeptide link is made between the C-terminus of *Gly* in UQ and free N-terminal end of H2A. N-terminal amino acid of UQ is *methionine*. It is linked with *Lys* at the position. 119 amino acid of H2A. Ubiquitin is an acidic protein. Usually one of the H2A molecules in a histone octamer carries ubiquitin. It lies at the surface of the nucleosome. It does not have any discernable effect on nucleosome structure. A rather small portion of the H2B also can be conjugated with ubiquitin (Fig. 14.38).

   DNA double helices are approximately in phase on the two turns, bringing the phosphate groups periodically close together. The pitch of the DNA turn is small enough (27Å) to permit interactions between the two turns. These interactions are mediated by some divalent cations like $Ca^{++}$, $Cu^{++}$, $Fe^{++}$, $Zn^{++}$, – or/and histone salt-bridges.
8. Histone protein H1 is associated with the ends of DNA molecule and is found on one side of the nucleosome at the regions of entry and exit of the superhelix. Since H1 is not necessary for coiling of DNA. It is only an accessory protein and may be involved in condensation of chromatin. It was also proved that H1 protein helped in the folding of 100Å fibre into 300Å solenoid, because when H1 was removed, this order of folding was found to be absent and only irregular clumping of nucleosomes could be observed. H1 molecules aggregate by cross linking to form polymers and thus control the formation of solenoid.

**Zig-zag ribbon structure of nucleosomes**

The structure of tetranucleosome, obtained from X-ray crystallography indicated that the 30 nm fibre has a "zig-zag ribbon structure" that is wound into a "two-start" helix made from two strands of nucleosomes stacked on top of each other like coins. These two strands of

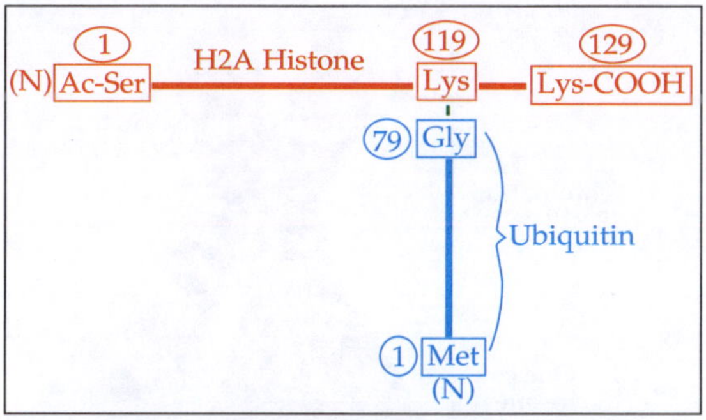


**Fig.14.38 :** *Ubiquitin with H2A protein.*

nucleosomes are then wound into a left-handed double helix. But cryoelectron microscopy of longer strings of nucleosomes supports a very different solenoid structure with intercalated nucleosomes (Fig. 14.39).

**Solenoid structure of nucleosomes**

1. 10 nm fibre of nucleosome gets coiled itself to form 30 nm wide helix with 5 or 6 nucleosomes per helix. In this helix successive turns come close together, so that their centre-to-centre distance is about 10 nm. This 30 nm structure is called **solenoid**. The contraction ratio is 6:1 (Fig. 14.40).

   It was shown that H1 proteins help in folding of 10 nm fibre to 30 nm solenoid because when H1 is removed this ordered folding was found to be absent. H1 molecules aggregate by cross linking to form polymers and thus control the formation of solenoid.

2. The solenoid is further coiled into a super–solenoid structure with a diameter of 400 nm and a wall of 30 nm thick. This super–solenoid structure is the **unit fibre**.

3. The contraction ratio at each level of coiling would be 7 (for the string of nucleosome), 6 (for the solenoid) and 30-

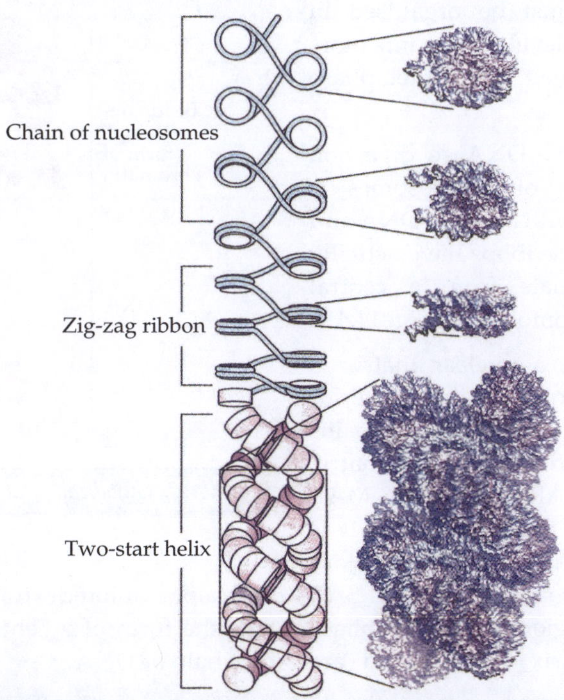


**Fig.14.39 :** *"Zig-zag ribbon" model of nucleosome showing two-strands left-handed double helix structure. (Figure redrawn from "Molecular Cell Biology, Lodish et. al 2008, 6th Edn.)*

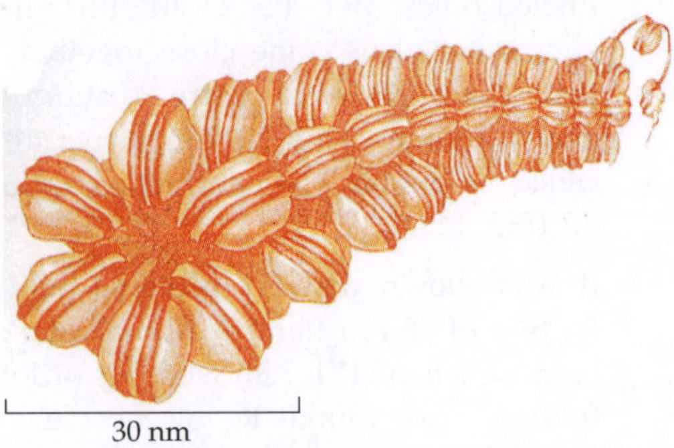


**Fig.14.40 :** *Solenoid structure of nucleosome.*

40 (for the supersolenoid). Thus the overall contraction of DNA within unit fibre would be in the order of 1300 to 1500 fold. This unitfibre or chromonema is further coiled in the chromosome by a factor of about 5. Thus the final contraction of DNA in the chromatin is therefore by a factor of about 7000.

**Scaffolds in chromatin :** The 30 nm fibre in the form of solenoid must be organised in structures at the higher level of organization, which have been examined using metaphase and interphase chromosomes.

It has been shown by DNAase digestion that DNA in the form of nucleosomes is organised in loops, each with 85 kb of DNA and a length of 10-30 nm. These loops have actually been observed to emanate from a central scaffold in metaphase chromosomes (Fig. 14.41).

In interphase nuclei, a nuclear matrix is found as a filamentous structure on the interior of nuclear membrane. Chromatin remains attached to this matrix through matrix attachment regions (MARs). Several MAR sequences have actually been identified. It is believed that the same sequences of DNA work as MAR in interphase nuclei and as SAR (scaffold attachment regions) in metaphase chromosomes. Both matrix and scaffold are proteinaceous in nature.

The histone depleted chromosomes (i.e. when histones are removed by competition

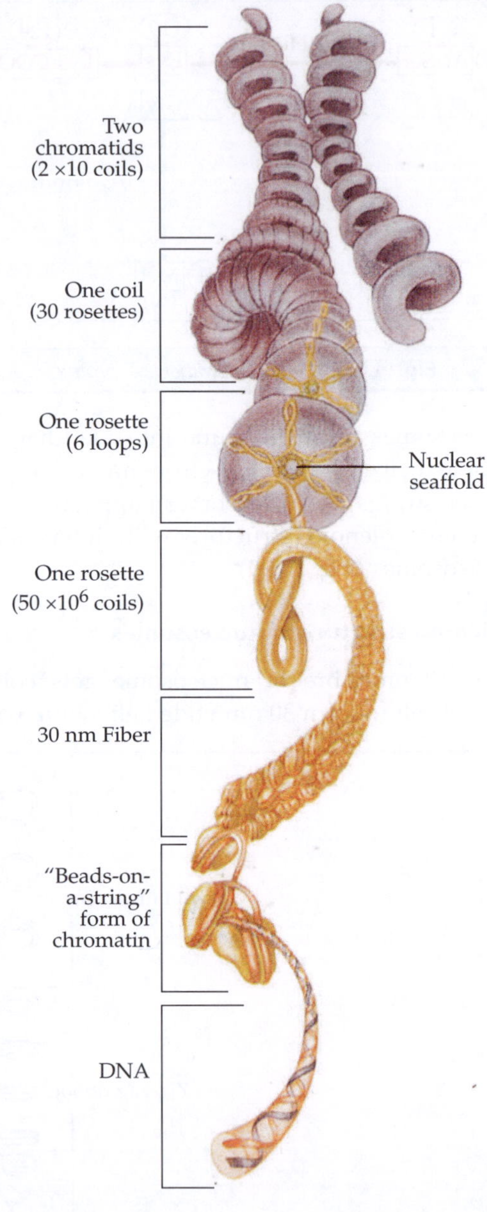


**Fig.14.41 :** *Organization of an eukaryotic chromosome.*

with a polyanion dextran sulphate and heparin) take the form of a central scaffold surrounded by a halo of DNA.

The scaffold consists of a dense network fibre. Threads of DNA emanate apparently as loops of 10 to 30 mm (30-90 kb) DNA of these

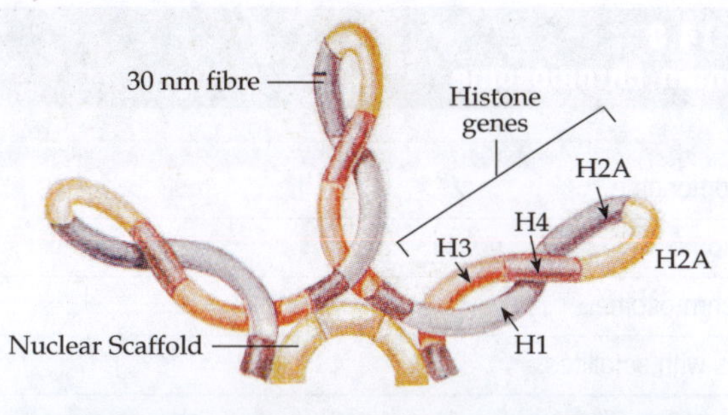


**Fig.14.42 :** *A schematic illustration of loops of chromosomal DNA attached to nuclear scaffold.*

loops may contain a set of histone-coding genes. For example, in *Drosophilla*, complete sets of histone coding genes seem to be clustered together in loops that are bound by scaffold attachment sites.

When divalent cations are removed from chromosomes, cross section shows the loops in the form of radial arrays of the 10 nm fibres and about 60 kb of DNA are anchored in the central proteinaceous scaffold. (Fig. 14.42)

The nonhistone proteins that constitute this scaffold may be metalloprotein. Chelation of metal ions disrupt the scaffold. It can be restored by the addition of $Cu^{++}$ ion and promote scaffold formation. The scaffold may contain several proteins, notably large amount of H1 and topoisomerase II. The latter one is important in DNA unwinding and chromatin assembly.

- **Nucleosome Structure of Active genes**

The exact mechanism involving nucleosome changes during gene activation can not be proposed but some views can be made.

In the tissues such as oviduct in which the globin genes are inactive, the genes are not preferentially digested by the enzyme DNAase-I. Conversely, ovalbumin genes and their surrounding regions are DNAase sensitive in oviduct nuclei but not in RBC. This suggests that the chromatin of active genes is less condensed than that of inactive chromatin, which is presumably under the form of 30 nm fibres.

Acetylation of *lys* group of histone H3 and H4 is more prevalent in active nucleosome.

Another modification is that the histones may have the covalent joining of a small protein called ubiquitin by way of its -COOH end to the free amino group of one *lys* –119 of H2A protein. This bond is although covalent, is reversible, being cleaved during mitosis and rejoined in interphase.

There are evidences of modifications in the DNA due to methylation in inactive genes.

Phosphorylation and dephosphorylation of H1 protein are also important during gene activation.

The nonhistone proteins known as HMGs (High Mobility Group proteins) are present relatively in high amounts in chromatin. About one tenth of all nucleosomes in the cell are associated with this protein. Although their function is not known but may have some role in gene activation.

Nucleosomes also affect the binding of certain transcription factors. In the 5S gene of *Xenopus*, placement of histone octamer blocks the binding of TF IIIA. Actually N-terminal regions of histone molecules are either cleaved or acetylated, which induces changes in the conformation of nucleosome and promotes the binding of TF IIIA with active gene sites.

## 14.20 CHROMOSOME KARYOTYPE AND BANDING PATTERN

The general morphology of a set of chromosomes at the metaphase stage of an individual or species is known as **Karyotype**. It deals mainly with the number of chromosomes in the cell, its relative size, position of the centromere, length of the arms, secondary constrictions and satellites. Karyotype is characteristic of an individual, species, genus or larger grouping and may be represented by a diagram in which the pairs of homologues are ordered in a series of decreasing size, such an arrangement is called **idiogram**. In some species the chromosomes of a set may be of the same

**TABLE 14.8**
**Classification of human chromosome**

| Group | Pairs | Description |
|---|---|---|
| A | 1–3 | Large, alomost metacentric chromosome. |
| B | 4–5 | Large, submetacentric chromosome |
| C | 6–12, X | Medium sized submetacentric chrmosome. |
| D | 13–15 | Large acrocentric chromosomes with satellites. |
| E | 16–18 | No.16 is metacentric, No.-17 and 18 small submetacentric chromosomes. |
| F | 19–20 | Small metacentric chromosome. |
| G | 21–22 and Y | Short, acrocentric chromosomes with satellites, Y-belongs to this group but has no satellites. |

length and have their centromeres located in the same position. In such cases it is not possible to prepare idiograms.

A karyotype of chromosome is usually obtained from microphotographs. The individual chromosomes are cut out of the microphotograph and are then lined up by size with their respective partners. The technique can be improved by determining the so-called **centromeric index**, which is the ratio of the length of the long and the short arms of the chromosome. Recently, a system has been introduced that involves a computer controlled microscope and several accessories that permit the scanning of slides, locating of the cells in metaphase, counting chromosomes and transmission of digitally expressed images for computation and storage. Thus Karyotype could be done easily and rapidly.

By karyotype technique, the chromosomes of a cell can be grouped according to their size and position of the centromere. In this way 23 pairs of human chromosomes are disposed into seven groups (A through G). (Fig. 14.43) and Table 14.8.

Karyotypes of different groups are sometimes compared. Similarities in karyotypes are presumed to represent evolutionary relationship. Karyotype suggests the primitive and advanced feature of an organism. A karyotype showing large differences between smallest and largest chromosome of the set and having fewer metacentric chromosomes, is called **asymmetric karyotype**, which is considered to be a relatively advanced feature when compared with symmetric karyotypes, *i.e.* all the members of the chromosomes are nearly equal in size and the difference in size is little between the larger and smaller chromosomes. G.A. Levitzky (1931) suggested that in flowering plants there is a predominant trend towards karyotype asymmetry. The asymmetry is increased among the most advanced zygomorphic flowering plants.

In some species the chromosome set may be of same length and their centromeric position cannot be distinguished. In these cases the karyotype preparation is not successful for the identification of chromosomes. Development of chromosome banding technique proved very useful for the karyotype preparation. The distinct banding patterns in these chromosomes of same morphology can be easily distinguished. The banding techniques allow detection of GC or AT rich regions or the regions of repetitive DNA. A variety of different kinds of bands namely Q, C, G, R bands have been used in animal materials and Giemsa C bands and N-bands have been utilized in plant materials.

**Q-banding :** In this banding technique a fluorescent dye, quinacrine mustard is used. The bands stained with quinacrine along the length of the chromosome were named Q-

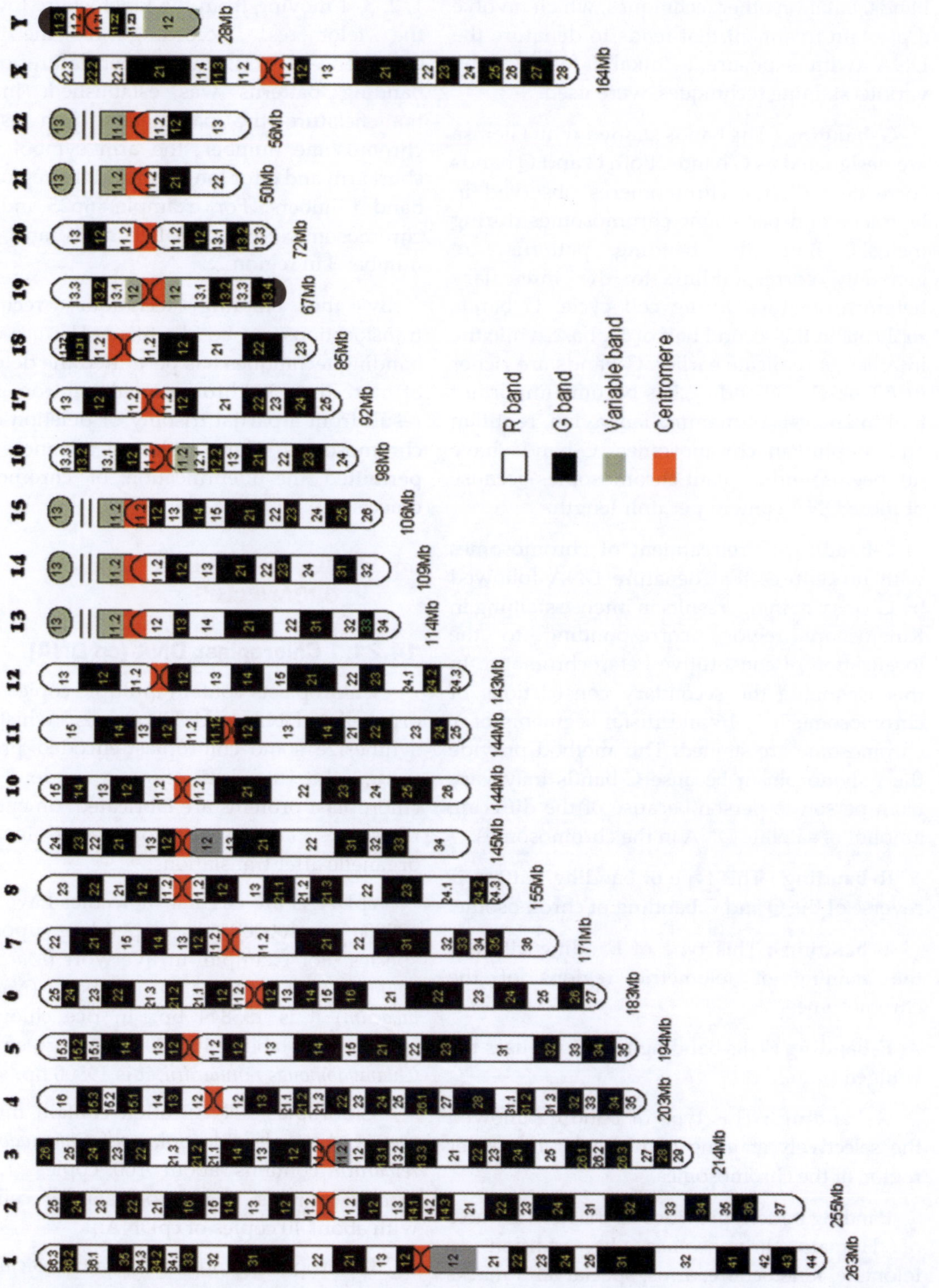


**Fig.14.43 :** *Human chromosome karyotype with the banding technique*

bands. Later on other techniques, which involve a prestain treatment that tends to denature the DNA (with exposure to alkali), followed by various staining techniques, were used.

**G-banding :** The bands stained with Giemsa are designated as G bands. Both G and Q bands correlate with the chromomeres observed in leptolene and pachytene chromosomes during meiosis. Both the banding patterns are generally corresponding to the intercalary heterochromatin. During cell cycle, G bands replicate in the second half of S-phase while the interbands replicate earlier. G-bands are richer in AT bases. G banding has become important tool in analysis of mammalian, avian, reptilian and amphibian chromosomes. G-bands have not been found in plant chromosomes because of more DNA content per unit length.

**C-banding :** Pretreatment of chromosomes with procedures that denature DNA followed by Giemsa staining, results in intense staining in Kinetochore regions corresponding to the localization of constitutive heterochromatin. In this technique the secondary constrictions of chromosome 1, 9, 16 and distal segments of Y chromosome are stained. This method provide the polymorphism because C-bands may vary from person to person because of the differing amount of satellite DNA in the chromosomes.

**R-banding :** This type of banding pattern is reverse of the Q and G banding of chromosome.

**T-banding :** This type of banding allowed the staining of telometric regions of the chromosomes.

**F-banding :** This banding technique uses the Feulgen stain.

**N-banding :** This type of banding allowed the selectively staining of nucleolar organizer region of the chromosomes.

Banding pattern provides us the new features of Human chromosomes. In addition to telomere, kinetochore, arms, special land marks *i.e.* well defined bands were selected to subdivide the arms into regions, designated as 1, 2, 3, 4 moving from the kinetochore towards the telomeres. According to the Paris Conference (1971), the nomenclature of the banding patterns was established. In this nomenclature the parameters such as, the chromosome number, the arm symbol p for short arm and q for long arm and the region and band numbers. For example, 6p23 indicates chromosome No-6, smaller arms and band number 3 in region 2.

By the banding technique, reciprocal translocations can be identified. The use of the banding techniques has permitted the detection of more than 30 chromosomal syndromes that result from a partial trisomy or deletion of the chromosomes. These technical advances have permitted the identification of chromosome defects.

## 14.21 GENOME OF CELLULAR ORGANELLES

### 14.21.1 Chloroplast DNA (cp DNA)

Chloroplasts contain multiple copies of the organellar DNA and ribosomes, which can synthesize some chloroplast-encoded proteins using the *standard* genetic code. Other chloroplast proteins are fabricated on cytosolic ribosomes and are incorporated into the organelle after translations.

cpDNAs are circular molecules have about 120000 to 160000 bp, depending upon the species. For example, in liverwort (*Marchantia polymorpha*) it is 121024 bp., in tobacco (*Nicotiana tabacum*) it is 155844 bp., in rice chloroplast genome it is about 136000 bp., in green algae *Chlamydomonas reinhardtii,* it is 19500 bp.

Chloroplast DNAs often contain multiple copies. A single chloroplast of *Chlamydomonas reihardtii* contains about 100 copies. *Euglena gracilis* contains 15 chloroplasts per cell each with about 40 copies of cpDNA.

Chloroplast genomes contain basically the same set of genes but are arranged in very different ways on the cp DNAs. primarily due to inverted repeats and duplication. These genes are grouped into two major classes.

1. Those encode components of the chloroplast protein biosynthetic apparatus such as, RNA polymerase subunits, structural components of chloroplast ribosomes and a set of tRNAs.
2. Those specifying components of the photosynthetic machinery including PS I, PS II and ETC (electron transport chain).
3. Of the ≈120 genes in cpDNA, about 60 are involved in RNA transcription and translation including genes for rRNAs, tRNAs, RNA polymerase subunits and ribosomal proteins. About 20 genes encode subunits of chloroplast photosynthetic electron transport complexes and the $F_0$–$F_1$ ATPase complex. Also encoded in the chloroplast genome is the larger of the two subunits of ribulose – 1, 5-bisphosphate carboxylase which is involved in the fixation of $CO_2$ during photosynthesis.

   The rRNA genes are present in duplicate on reverse repeats within the most species. In *Euglena gracilis*, the 16S and 23S rRNA genes are present on three direct tandem repeats, with a separate fourth copy of the 16S rRNA gene located nearby in the genome.

   The organization of cpDNA of *Nicotiana tabacum* and *Marchantia polymorpha* is remarkably similar, though they are evolutionary very distant from each other. The major difference between these two cp DNAs is that the inverse repeat regions containing the rRNA genes are considerably larger (150) in tobacco than in *Marchantia* (136). Since two chloroplasts contain virtually the same set of proteins. It is suggested that same genes are present in the cpDNA of one species and in the nuclear DNA of other. It indicates that some exchange of genes between chloroplast and nucleus has occured during evolution.

   The regions of cpDNA have been found to be similar to those of the DNA of present day bacteria. For example, cp DNA encodes four subunits of RNA polymerase that are highly homologous to the subunits RNA polymerase that are highly homologous to the subunits of *E.coli* RNA. One segment of cpDNA encodes 8 proteins that are homologous to eight *E. coli* ribosomal proteins. The order of thse genes is the same in two DNAs.

### 14.21.2 Mitochondrial DNA

Nass, Nass and Afzelius (1965) of Stockholm University demonstrated the occurrence of mitochondrial DNA (MDNA) from a wide variety of cells. Direct biochemical studies confirmed that MDNA is a circular molecule except in some ciliated protozoan and some plants. It may be in a form of ring or may be open or twisted and may form knob. MDNA containing regions of the mitochondria are called nucleoids. Number is usually 2-3 but sometimes may be 6. Average circumference is 5μ, may be attached to the membrane or not.

In addition to normal MDNA monomers, double sized circular dimers, tetramers have also been found.

Mammals have small mitogenome, small enough to have complexity in man, mouse and cow; all are about 16 Kb (Table 4.3). The total amount of MDNA relative to nuclear DNA is less than 1%.

In fruitfly and frog, the size of MDNA is slightly larger but the number of genomes and organelles per cell is not known.

In yeast, actual size varies quite widely among different strains but is about 75 to 84 Kb and about 22 mitochondria per cell and have 4 genomes (DNA) per mitochondria that constitute 18% relative to total DNA.

Plants show a wide range of variations in MDNA size. There is some evidence that the plant mitogenome does not conform to the pattern of a single molecule of DNA but may be more than one.

**TABLE 14.9**
**Difference between universal genetic code anel mitochondrial genetic code**

| | *Universal genetic code* | *Mitochondrial genetic code* |
|---|---|---|
| No. of tRNA | 55 | 22 in mammals and 25 in yeast. |
| Termination codon | UAA, UGA, UAG | UAA, UAG, AGA, AGG |
| UGA | It is a termination codon | It codes for tryptophan |
| AGA, AGG | Both code arginine | Both are termination codons |
| CUN | For Leucine | For threonine |

- **General properties of MDNA**

1. MDNA from a wide variety of species shows great similarities and has a consistent buoyant density.
2. Melting temperature of MDNA differs from nuclear DNA. It has rapid rate of renaturation in contrast to nuclear DNA, which indicates that it has a more homogenous base composition than nuclear DNA. Rabinowitch (1968) has shown that MDNA contains more guanine and cytosine than nuclear DNA.
3. The mitochondrial DNA is shorter than the nuclear DNA, therefore, contains few coded informations.
4. Parson and Simpson (1967) has shown that MDNA contains DNA polymerase, which helps in the duplication of MDNA molecules themselves.
5. Mitochondria are capable to undergo self reproduction by division and they may carry biological information to exhibit a type of cytoplasmic inheritance. This DNA can duplicate 20-66 times more rapidly than that of nuclear DNA.
6. The mitochondrial genetic code and universal genetic code show some major differences in their termination codons. (Table 14.9)
7. Recently in 1983 it was suggested that flow of DNA from mitochondria to nucleus and from nucleus to mitochondria has been taken place in order to function their own biochemical reactions. These transporting DNAs are called **promiscuous DNA**. The *Arabidopsis* mitogenome contains various segments of nuclear DNA as well as 16 fragments of the chloroplast genome including six tRNA genes that have retained their activities after transfer to the mitochondrion. The nuclear genome of this plant includes several segments of chloroplast and mitochondrial genome as well as a 270 kb piece of MDNA located within the centromeric region of chromosome-2.

- **Structure of Yeast MDNA**

Yeast mito DNA is large and with about 84 kb. By recombination technique the genetic map has been possible to construct. This genome has two rRNAs viz. 15S–rRNA and 21S-rRNA which are separated by 25 kb apart. In some strains, the latter gene has a single intron; in other strains it is uninterrupted. The two most prominent loci are the **mosaic genes, box** (coding for cyt-b) and **oxi-3** (coding for subunit I of the cytochrome c oxidase). Many of the long introns in these genes have open reading frames in register with the preceeding exon, at least in some cases there is evidence for translation of the introns. The remaining genes appear to be uninterrupted. They correspond to the other two

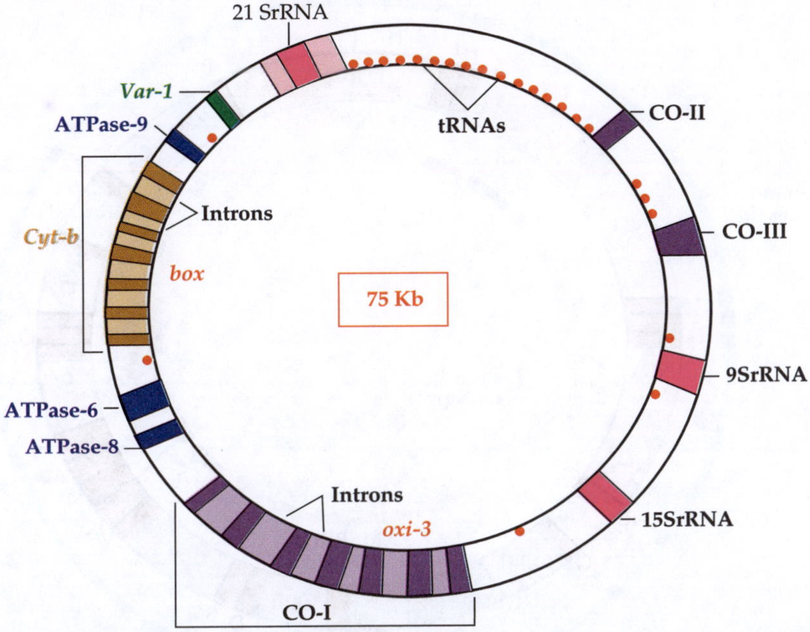


**Fig.14.44 :** *The Saccharomyces cerevisiae mito-genome*

mitochondrially coded subunits of cytochrome c oxidase, to the subunits of the ATPase and to a mitochondrial ribosomal protein (**var**).

Yeast mitogenome consists about 25% of short stretches of A-T rich base pairs, which probably lack any coding function. Total number of genes is unlikely to exceed about 20 (Fig. 14.44).

- **Human mito DNA**

The genome is campact, there is no introns but some genes are overlapping. Human MDNA has 16569 base pairs (Fig. 14.45). There is a D-loop region concerned with the initiation of DNA replication. Not more than 87 base pairs can be regarded as lying intercistronic region.

There are 37 genes including 13 genes that encode proteins of the respiratory chain.

The remaining genes code for ribosomal 12S and 16S rRNA and 22 tRNA species, essential for the protein synthesizing machinery.

Most of the genes are expressed in the same direction and tRNA genes lie between the coding genes for rRNA or proteins. In some case, the last base of one gene is adjacent to the first base of the next gene. Again in some cases the last base of one gene serves as the first base of the next gene. Five of the reading frames lack a termination codon, these end with U or UA and so the ochre codon is created by poly adenylation of the transcript.

The transcription of outer H-strand occurs in the clockwise direction and of the inner L-strand in the counter clockwise direction. Therefore almost all the genes are expressed in the clockwise direction, but 8 out of 22 tRNA genes are coded counter clockwise. ND4 and ATPase8 have an unusually large overlap with their adjacent genes. ND6 is different from the main set of genes that its direction of expression is opposite. ATPase 6 and CO III regions are found in the form of contiguous genes. In other case, at least one tRNA gene separates adjacent

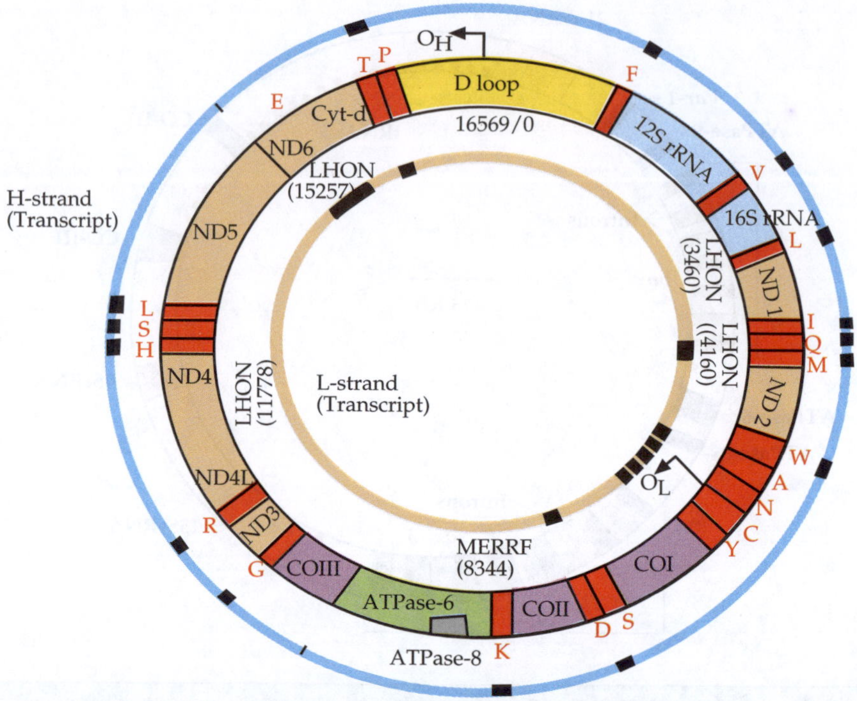


**Fig.14.45 :** *Human mito DNA (the middle circle) : L strand = counter-clockwise transcript; H strand = clockwise transcript; $O_H$ = Origin of replication of heavy chain; $O_L$ = Origin of replication of light chain; Cyt b = cytochrome b of complex-III; ND1-6 = NADH Dehydrogenase; CO I-III = Cytochrome oxidase of complex IV; LHON = Leber's hereditary optic neuropathy; MERRF = Myoclonic epilepsy and ragged red fibre disease.*

**TABLE 14.10**
**Respiratory proteins encoded in human mitogenome**

| *Complexes* | *Total number of subunits* | *Subunits encoded by MDNA* |
|---|---|---|
| NADH dehydrogenase | > 25 | 7 |
| Succinate dehydrogenase | 4 | 0 |
| Ubiquinone-cyto-oxidase | 9 | 1 |
| Cyt-c-oxidase | 13 | 3 |
| ATP synthase | 12 | 2 |
| | > 63 | 13 |

coding regions. An initiation codon lies within 6 bases of the start (AUG, AUA or AUU). The mRNA terminates with nonsense codon or incomplete nonsense codon. So non translated 5′ and 3′ regions are absent from human mito mRNA.

The transcription starts at D loop and continues upto D-loop and a circular mRNA is produced. The strand transcribed is called H-strand, while transcript of inner strand is called L-strand. The cleavage then occurs on the either sides of the tRNA transcripts (except ATPase 6 and CO-III which are monocistronic).

Replication is unidirectional. One starts with D-loop ($O_H$) and other with $O_L$ region, thus produces two strnads, the H-strand and L-strand. The daughter L-strand starts synthesis when two-third of H-strand is already synthesized.

Mutations in MDNA cause the disease called **Leber's hereditary optic neuropathy** (LHON), affects CNS, optic nerve, causing bilateral loss of vision, invariably inherited from the female parent. This is caused by a single base change in ND4 (Base No.11778) that changes *Arg* residue to ***Histidine*** residue of the complex-I protein resulting defective in electron transfer from NADH to UQ. A single base change for ND1 at base 3460 or 4160 of complex I and at 15257 of cyt-b of complex-III also produce LHON.

Another genetic disease **Myoclonic epilepsy and ragged red fiber** (MERRF) is caused by a mutation in the mitogene that encodes tRNA of **Lys** at base No. 8344. This disease is characterised by uncontrollable muscular jerking.

## 14.22. CONCEPT OF TOPOISOMERASES AND TOPOLOGY OF DNA

Molecules of DNA that are the same except for their linking numbers are called **topological isomers**. Enzymes that can interconvert topological isomers are called **DNA topoisomerases**, a name that has replaced a variety of earlier descriptions, such as DNA-relaxing enzyme, swivelase, untwisting enzyme, nicking-closing enzyme etc.

The topoisomerases are divided into two classes according to the nature of the mechanisms they employ.

Type-I enzymes act by making a transient break in one strand of DNA e.g., topoisomerase I and III in *E. coli.* Type-II enzymes act by introducing a transient double strand break e.g., topoisomerase II and IV in *E.coli.*

### 14.22.1. Type-I Topoisomerases

1. The best-characterized type-I topoisomerase is the enzyme of *E.coli* originally called the ω-protein. This enzyme relaxes highly negatively supercoiled DNA with high efficiency. The rate of relaxation becomes slower as the linking number approaches that of completely relaxed DNA. But it does not act on positively supercoiled DNA. It is coded by the gene *top,* whose mutations cause an increase in the level of supercoiling in the nucleoid.
2. *E.coli* topoisomerase-I binds to DNA. It forms a stable complex in which one strand of the DNA has been nicked at its 5′–phosphate end covalently, and linked to a *tyrosine* residue in the enzyme. This suggests a mechanism for the action of the enzyme, it transfers a phosphodiester bond in DNA to the protein, manipulates the structure of the two DNA strands. The two ends of the DNA double helix rotate relative to each other and then rejoin with the original strand. The transfer of bonds from nucleic acid to protein explains how the enzyme can function without requiring any input of energy. There has been no irreversible hydrolysis of bonds. Their energy has been conserved through the transfer of reaction (Fig. 14.46).
3. A model of enzyme action is illustrated in the figure (Fig. 14.47). The enzyme binds to a region in which duplex DNA becomes separated into its single strand, then it breaks one strand, pulls the other strand through a gap and finally seals the gap.
4. The reaction changes the linking number in steps of one. Each time one strand is passed through the break in the other, there is a ΔL of +1. But in a highly supercoiled molecule, the linking number be taken up by a change of ΔW = +1, i.e., by one less turn of negative supercoiling.
5. The type I topoisomerase also can pass one segment of a single stranded DNA through another and renaturation of two single strands complementary circles. It can introduce a knot in single stranded DNA and can act on two circular

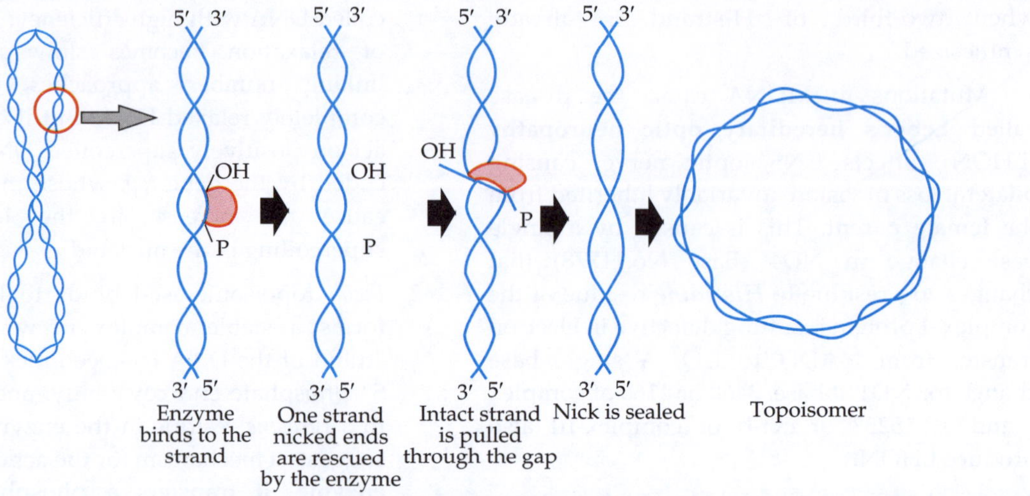


**Fig.14.46 :** *Action of E.coli topoisomerase-I*

duplex molecules of DNA provided that one of them has a nick in one strand. When one circle is passed through another, they become interlocked. This structure is called **Catenane** and the activity is called catenating the DNA (Fig. 14.48).

6. It suggests that in the catenation of double stranded circles, the enzyme binds opposite to the nick, introduces a break in the other strand, passes the duplex of DNA through the break and reseals the break.

7. In eukaryotes, topoisomerase-I is a type-1 topoisomerase, but they can relax positive as well as negative supercoils.

### 14.11.2. Type-II - Topoisomerases

1. Type II topoisomerases have been characterized from both prokaryotes and eukaryotes. and relax both the negative and positive supercoils. The reaction is ATP dependent. Probably one unit of ATP is hydrolyzed for each catalytic event. The reaction is mediated by making a double stranded break in one DNA-duplex and passing another duplex region through it (Fig. 14.49).

2. The formal consequence of two strands transfer is that the linking number is always changed in multiples of two. It can be used also to introduce or resolve catenated duplex circles and knotted molecules.

   The hydrolysis of ATP may be used to drive the enzyme through conformational changes that provide the force-mediated push of one DNA duplex through the break made in the other. Thus the super-coils will be removed from either positively or negatively supercoiled circles. The best example of such enzyme may be the $T_4$ topoisomerase-II, which is the product of three genes and whose activity is essential for replication of phage DNA.

3. Bacterial **DNA gyrase**, best characterized in *E.coli*, is a topoisomerase-II that is able to introduce negative supercoils into a relaxed closed circular molecule. DNA-gyrase binds to a circular DNA duplex and supercoils it processively and catalytically. It continues to introduce supercoils into the same DNA molecule. One molecule of DNA–gyrase can introduce about hundred supercoils per minute.

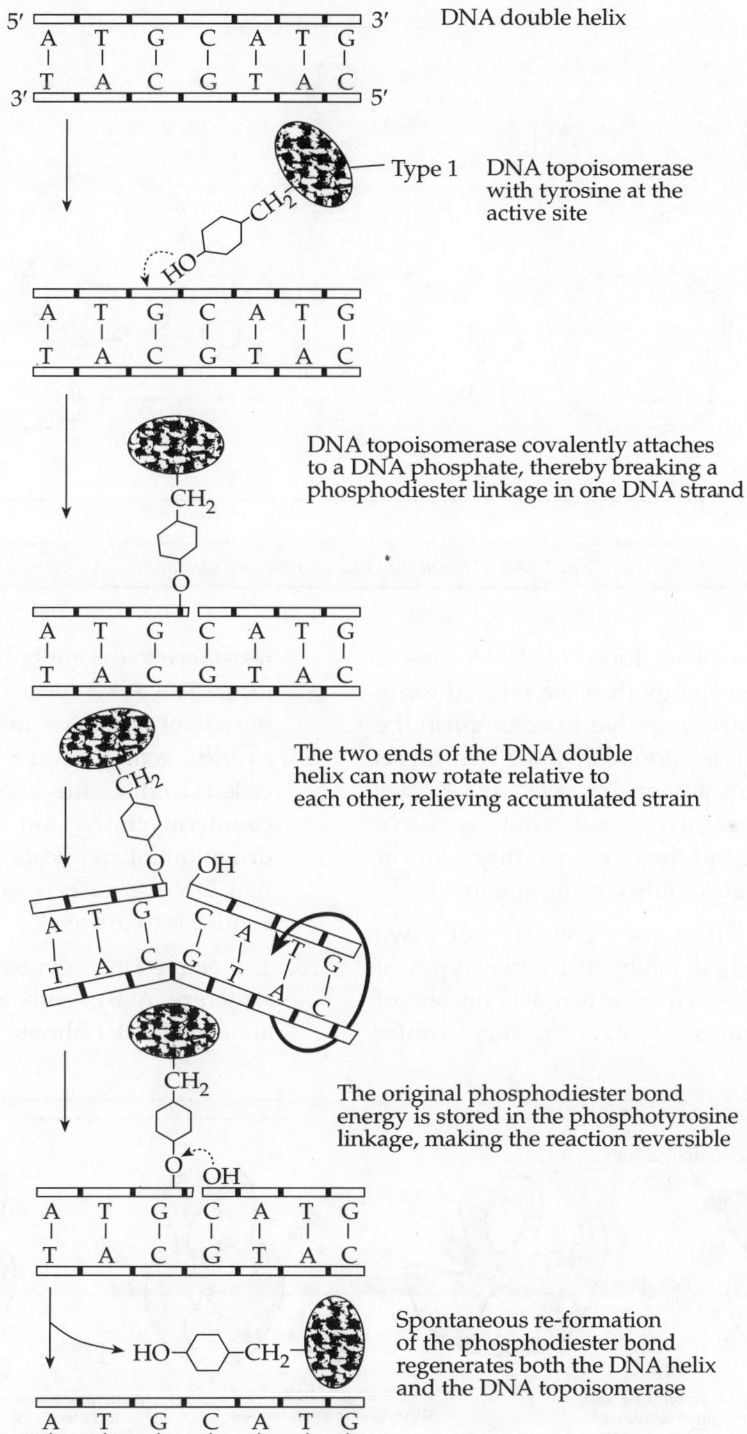


**Fig.14.47 :** *The reversible nicking reaction catalyzed by eukaryotic DNA topoisomerase I enzyme.*

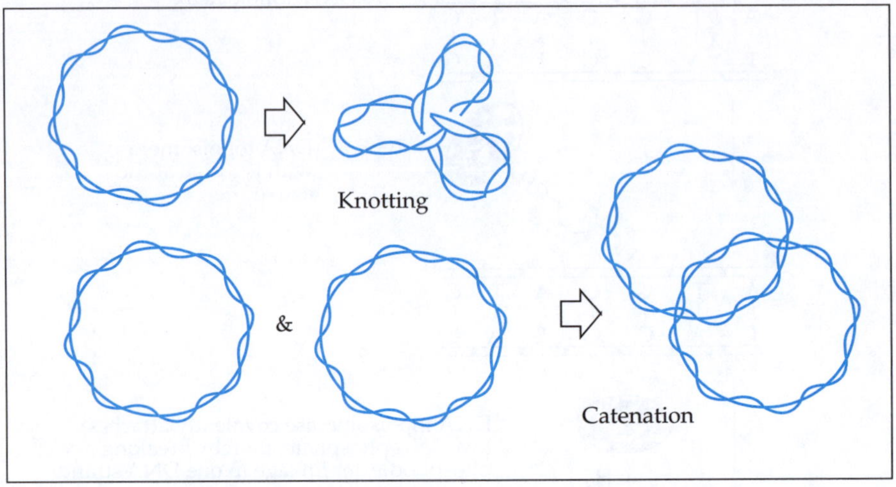


Fig.14.48 : *Knotting and catenation reactions.*

4. The supercoiled form of DNA has a higher free energy than the relaxed form, and the energy needed to accomplish the conversion is supplied by the hydrolysis of ATP. In absence of ATP, the gyrase relaxes negative but not positive supercoils but the rate is ten times slower than the rate of introducing supercoils.
5. *E.coli* DNA-gyrase consists of two subunits. It is inhibited by two types of antibiotics, each of which acts on one of the subunits. Mutations that confer resistance to the antibiotics identifying the locus. The ***gyr A*** locus (formerly ***nal A***) is the site of resistance to ***nalidixic acid*** and ***oxinilic acid***. The ***gyr B*** locus (formerly called ***cou***) is the site of resistance to **coumermycin-$A_1$** and **novobiocin**. These drugs inhibit replication, which suggests that DNA gyrase is necessary for DNA synthesis to proceed.
6. The active DNA gyrase probably has the structure $A_2B_2$, with an overall size of about 400000 Daltons. Gyr A subunit is

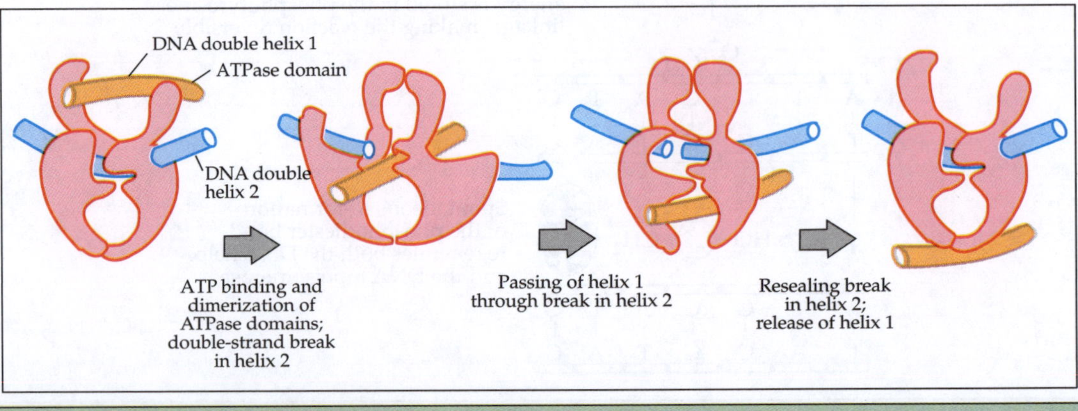


Fig.14.49 : *A model for topoisomerase II action.*

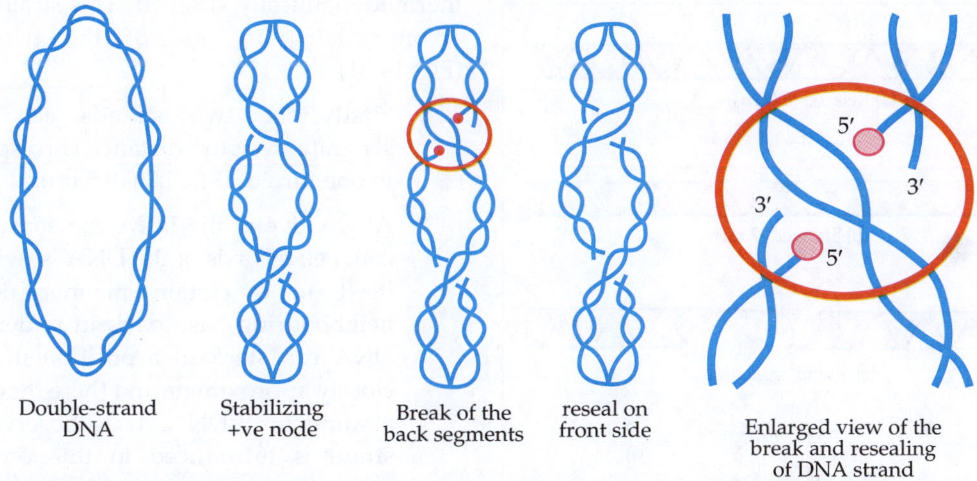


**Fig.14.50 :** *The sign inversion model for the action of DNA gyrase.*

~ 105000 Daltons, the Gyr B subunit is ~ 95000 Daltons, and in *E.coli*, subunit A is 10 times more and it is associated with a 50000 Daltons protein called **U**, which may be a fragment of subunit B.

7. The **sign inversion model** for the action of DNA gyrase is illustrated in the figure 14.50. The enzyme binds the DNA in a crossover configuration, that is equivalent to a positive supercoil. This induces a compensating negative supercoil in the unbound DNA. Then the enzyme breaks double strand at the crossover of the positive supercoil passes the other duplex through and reseals the break. This directly inverts the signs of the supercoil, it has been converted from a +1 turn to a –1 turn. Thus the linking number has changed by $\Delta L = -2$ (Fig. 14.50).
8. When gyrase releases the inverted super coil, its conformation changes. For the enzyme to undertake another cycle of supercoiling, its original configuration must be restored. This process is called **enzyme turnover**, It is thought to be driven by the hydrolysis of ATP, so it does not need ATP for the supercoiling reaction, but does need it to undertake a second cycle. Novobiocin interferes with the ATP-dependent reactions of gyrase by preventing ATP from binding to the B-subunit.
9. The ATP independent relaxation reaction is inhibited by nalidixic acid. This implicates the subunit A in the breakage and reunion reaction. Nalidixic acid allows DNA to be recovered in the form of fragments generated by a staggered cleavage across the duplex. The termini, all possess a free 5′-OH group and a four–base 5′ single strand extension covalently linked to the subunit A. The covalent linkage retains the energy of the phosphate bond, this can be used to drive the releasing reaction, explaining why gyrase can undertake relaxation without ATP.

## 14.23. SUPERCOILING OF DNA

It is fact that cellular DNA must be tightly compacted just to fit into the cell. This implies a high degree of structural organization.

The term **supercoiling** means literally **the coiling of the coil**. An analogy can be made with a telephone cord, which is typically a coiled wire. The twisted path from the base of the

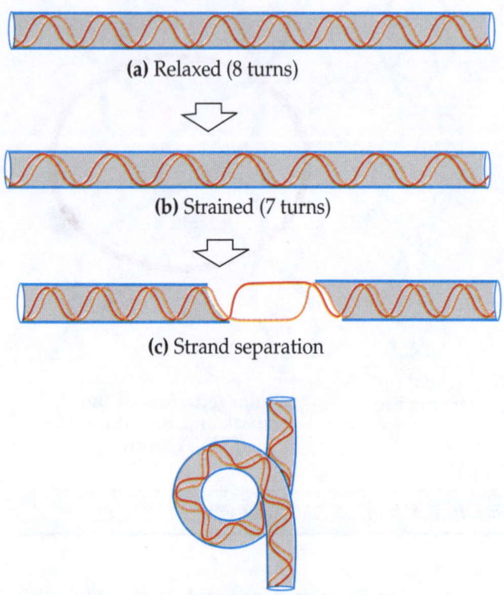


**Fig.14.51 :** *The effects of DNA underwinding. (a) A segment of DNA, 84 base pairs long, in its relaxed form with eight helical turns. (b) Removal of one turn induces structural strain that can be accommodated by (c) strand separation over 10.5 base pairs or by (d) formation of a supercoil.*

phone to the receiver is described as super– coil. DNA is coiled in the twisting of that axis upon itself is referred to as DNA-supercoiling. Thus supercoiling is a structural strain i.e., if there is no net bending of the DNA-axis upon itself, the DNA is said to be relaxed.

The strain is as a result of underwinding of the DNA in the closed circle, i.e., there are fewer helical turns in the DNA than would be expected for the B-form structure. For example, an 84 bp segment of circular DNA, when was relaxed then, the segment would contain eight double helical turns or one for every 10.5 bp. If one of these turns is removed, there will be about 12 bp per turn rather than 10.5, found in B-DNA. Then this DNA molecule is thermodynamically strained. This strain can be accommodated in one of the two ways (Fig. 14.51)

1. Firstly the two strands can simply separate over the distance corresponding to one turn of B-DNA (10.5 bp).
2. Alternatively, the DNA can form super–coil, i.e., the axis of the DNA is twisted on itself in a certain manner that the neighbouring base pairs in underwound DNA can stack in a position that more closely approximate and there they would assume in B-DNA. It is observed that strain is introduced in this process is generally accommodated by supercoiling rather than strand separation, because twisting the axis of the DNA usually requires less energy than breaking the H-bonds that stabilize base pairs.

   The underwound condition of the DNA is maintained by the histone proteins of the chromosome. If there is a break in one of the strand of a histone-free DNA, free rotation at that point will create the underwound DNA to revert spontaneously to the relaxed state.

**Linking number :** Linking number of a DNA molecule specifies the number of helical turns in a closed circular DNA in the absence of any supercoiling. Linking number is a topological property, because it does not vary when double stranded DNA is twisted or deformed in any way as long as both DNA strands remain intact.

By convension, if the interwound of the polynucleotide strand is in right-handed direction, then the linking number is **positive**, while if the interwound is a left handed helix, the linking number is **negative**. The linking number is measured simply the number of base pairs divided by 10.5 (in B-DNA). Thus if in a closed circular DNA with 210 bp in relaxed condition, the linking number (Lk) is 20. The linking number in relaxed DNA is used as a reference and called $Lk_0$ and here $Lk_0 = 20$ (Fig. 14.52).

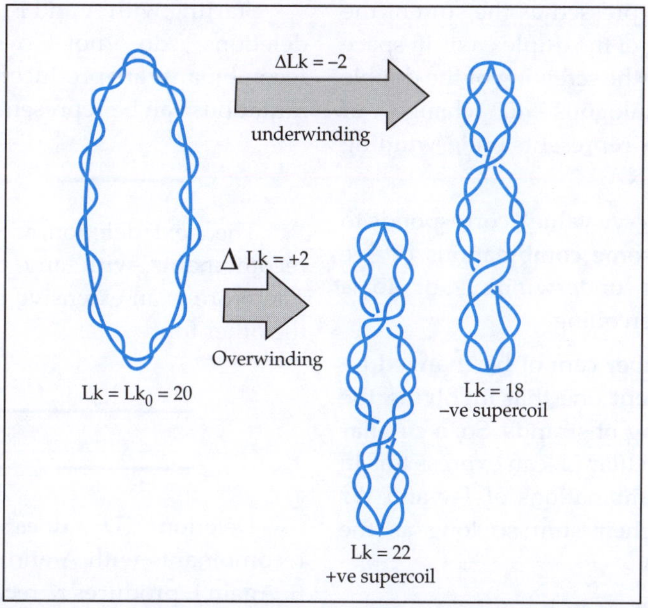


**Fig.14.52 :** *Showing changes in linking number to produce positive and negative supercoils.*

If two turns are removed from this DNA molecule, Lk will be 18. The change in linking number (ΔLk) can be described by the equation.

$$\Delta Lk = Lk - Lk_0 = 18 - 20 = -2$$

**Specific linking difference** (σ) is a measure of the turns removed relative to those present in the relaxed DNA. It is also called **superhelical density** and is defined as $\sigma = \frac{\Delta Lk}{Lk_0}$.

Here $\sigma = \frac{-2}{20} = -0.1$ i.e., 10% of the helical turn present in the B form of DNA has been removed. The –ve sign denotes the changes in linking number comes about as a result of underwinding of DNA and induce –ve supercoil. The overwound results +ve supercoiling.

The linking number can be changed ± 1 by breaking one strand, then forcibly rotating one of the strand 360° about the unbroken strand and rejoining the broken ends. This change has no effect on the numbers of base pairs. Two forms of given circular DNA that differs only in topological property such as linking number are referred to as **topoisomers**.

Linking number can be broken down into two structural components, called Wriths (Wr) and Twist (Tw).

**Wr** may be thought of as a measure of the coiling of the helix axis.

**Tw** is determining the local twisting or spatial relationship of neighbouring base pairs.

When a change in linking number occurs, some of the resulting strain is usually compensated by Writh (supercoiling) and some by change in the twist. Thus the equation becomes :

$$Lk = Tw + Wr$$

For a relaxed molecule (DNA), Wr = 0 and in this case Lk = Tw.

Thus the changes in linking number

$$\Delta Lk = \Delta Tw + \Delta Wr$$

The equation states that any change in the total number of revolutions of the DNA strand to the other can be expressed as the sum of the changes of the coiling of the duplex axis in space (ΔWr) and changes of the screwing of the double helix. ΔWr is analogous to change of supercoiling and ΔTw represents underwinding or over-winding of DNA.

A decrease in Lk (–ve value), corresponds to the introduction of some combinations of –ve supercoiling and/or underwinding or to a reduction in +ve supercoiling.

The linking number cannot be changed by any deformation except one that involving the breaking and rejoining of strands. So, a circular molecule with a particular Lk can express this in terms of different combinations of Tw and Wr but cannot change their sum so long as the strands are unbroken.

## 14.24 SOLVED PROBLEMS ON DELETION AND COMPLEMENTATION MAPPING

### Problem 1

Five different *rII* deletion strains of phage T4 were tested for recombination by pairwise crossing in *E. coli* B. The following results were obtained, where + = $r^+$ recombinants produced or O = no $r^+$ recombinants produced.

| | A | B | C | D | E |
|---|---|---|---|---|---|
| E | 0 | + | 0 | + | 0 |
| D | 0 | 0 | 0 | 0 | |
| C | 0 | 0 | 0 | | |
| B | + | 0 | | | |
| A | 0 | 0 | | | |

Draw a deletion map compatible with these data.

**Solution :**

The principle here is that if two deletion mutants overlap, then no $r^+$ recombinants can be produced. Conversely, if two deletion mutants do not overlap, then $r^+$ recombinants can be produced. To approach a question of this kind, we must draw overlapping and nonoverlapping lines from the given data.

Starting with A and B, we see that these two deletions do not overlap, because $r^+$ recombinants are produced. Therefore these two mutations can be represented as follows

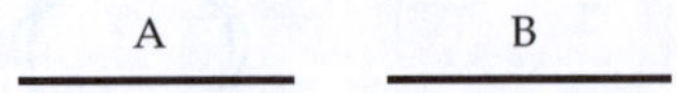


The next deletion, C does not produce $r^+$ recombinants with any other four deletions. Therefore is an extensive deletion and overlaps the other four

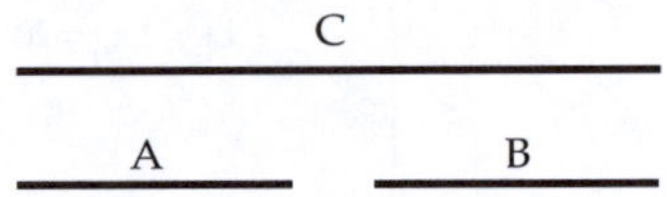


Deletion D does not produce $r^+$ recombinants with A and B or C but does with E. Again E produces $r^+$ recombinants with B and D but not with A or C. Thus D must overlaps both A and B, but not E while E overlaps A and C but not B.

The compatible map for this situation is as follows :

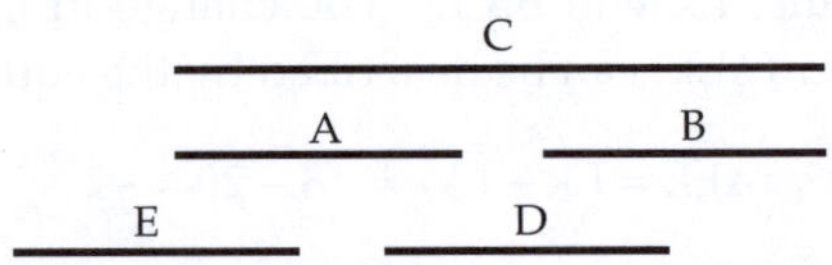


### Problem 2

Seven different *rII* point mutants (1-7) of phage T4 were tested for five deletion strains as described in problem 1. Place the seven point mutations on the map.

| | A | B | C | D | E |
|---|---|---|---|---|---|
| 1 | 0 | + | 0 | + | + |
| 2 | + | 0 | 0 | + | + |
| 3 | 0 | + | 0 | + | 0 |
| 4 | + | + | 0 | + | 0 |
| 5 | + | 0 | 0 | 0 | + |
| 6 | 0 | + | 0 | 0 | + |
| 7 | + | + | 0 | 0 | + |

**Solution :**

The principle is that, if an $r^+$ recombinant is produced, the *rII* point mutation cannot overlap the region missing in the deletion mutation.

Here point mutation 7 produces $r^+$ recombinants with A, B and E but not with D . Therefore mutation 7 is located in the region defined by the part of deletion D and C that is not involved in the overlap of A and B & E

Mutation 6 is located in the region A, C and D but not on B and E.

Mutation 5 is located in the region B, C and D but not on A and E.

Mutation 4 in the region C and E

Mutation 3 in the region A, C and E

Mutation 2 in the region B and C only

Mutation 1 in the region of A and C

The map would be as follows :

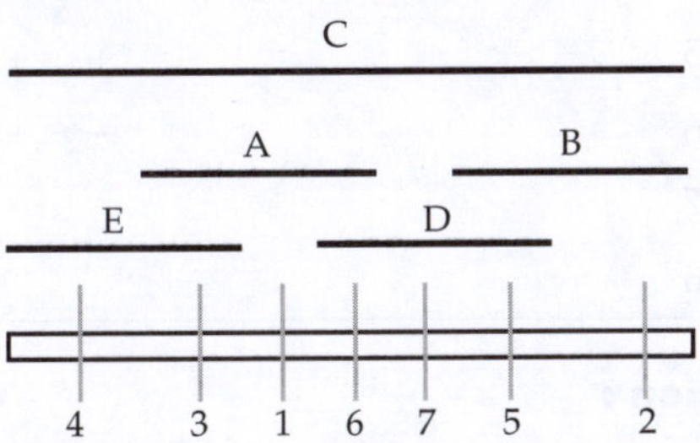


### Problem 3

A map with point mutants and also the data is given. Draw a topological representation of deletion mutants *r21, r22, r23, r24* and *r25*

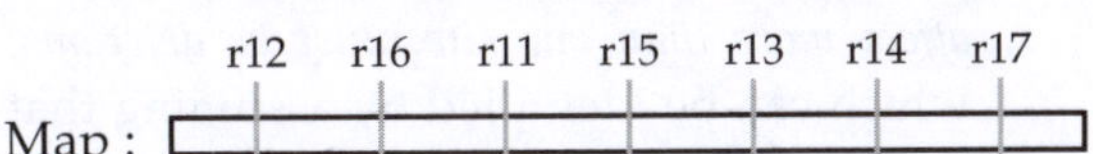


| Deletion mutation | r11 | r12 | r13 | r14 | r15 | r16 | r17 |
|---|---|---|---|---|---|---|---|
| *r21* | 0 | + | 0 | + | 0 | + | + |
| *r22* | + | + | 0 | 0 | + | + | 0 |
| *r23* | 0 | 0 | 0 | + | 0 | 0 | + |
| *r24* | + | + | 0 | 0 | + | + | + |
| *r25* | + | + | 0 | 0 | 0 | + | + |

**Solution :**

The missing region in each deletion mutant is to be identified by applying two principles :

1. If no $r^+$ recombinants are obtained, the deletion removes the site of the point mutant.
2. If $r^+$ recombinants are obtained, the site of point mutation is not within the boundaries of the deletion.

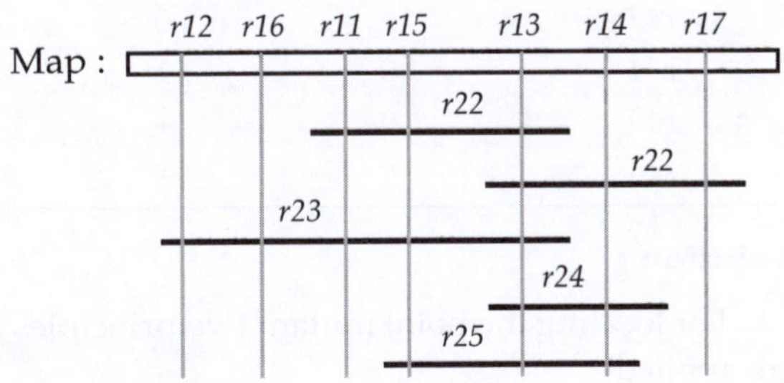


### Problem 4

A deletion map with 6 deletions (*r31, r32,.....*) is given. Place the point mutants *r41, r42,.......* etc on the map.

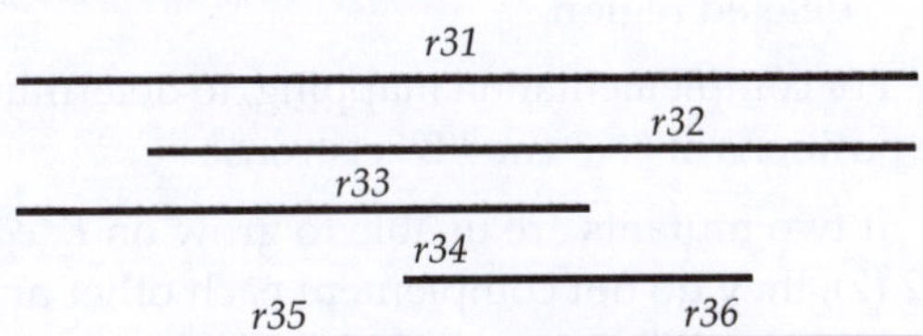


| Point mutation | Deletion mutation *r31* | *r32* | *r33* | *r34* | *r35* | *r36* |
|---|---|---|---|---|---|---|
| *r41* | 0 | 0 | 0 | 0 | + | 0 |
| *r42* | 0 | 0 | 0 | + | 0 | + |
| *r43* | 0 | 0 | + | + | + | 0 |
| *r44* | 0 | 0 | 0 | 0 | + | + |
| *r45* | 0 | + | 0 | + | + | + |
| *r46* | 0 | 0 | + | 0 | + | 0 |

Show the dividing line between the "A" cistron and the "B" cistron on the map from the following data

| Mutant | Complementation with rIIA | rIIB |
|---|---|---|
| r31 | 0 | 0 |
| r32 | 0 | 0 |
| r33 | 0 | + |
| r34 | 0 | 0 |
| r35 | 0 | + |
| r36 | 0 | 0 |
| r41 | 0 | + |
| r42 | 0 | + |
| r43 | + | 0 |
| r44 | 0 | + |
| r45 | 0 | + |
| r46 | 0 | + |

**Solution :**

For locating the point mutant two principles are applied.

1. If point mutant cannot recombine with deletion mutant, it lies within the deleted region.
2. If point mutant can recombine with the deletion mutant, if it lies out side the deleted region.

For complementation mapping, to determine the positions of "A" and "B" cistrons :

If two mutants are unable to grow on *E. coli* K12 (2), they do not complement each other and cannot together provide the functions to complete the *rII* pathway. Both mutants must be defective in the same function and either the rIIA or rIIB function is missing.

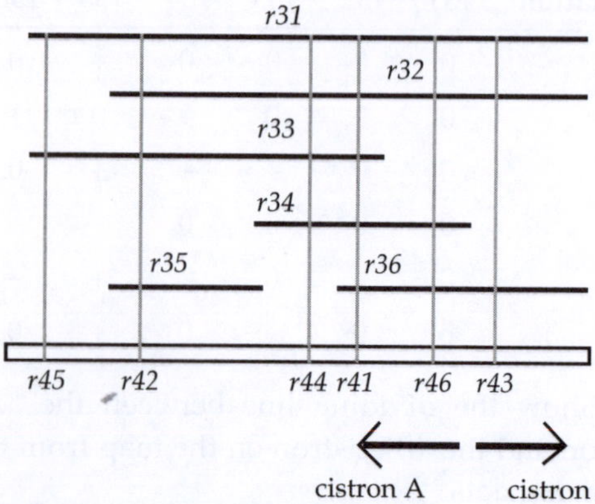


**Problem 5**

Eight mutants were isolated from a parental $F^-$ $str^R$ strain. Each mutant requires supplemental *leucine* to grow but is resistant to *streptomycin*. Interrupted mating was performed with each of the *leu* mutants and a prototrophic *E. coli Hfr* strain sensitive to streptomycin and in each cross $str^R$ $leu^+$ recombinants were recovered after 4 minutes. Each of the eight mutants was individually infected with a generalized transducing phage. The resulting lysate was used to infect the other mutants and $leu^+$ recombinants were selected.

| Leu mutant | 1 | 2 | 3 | 4 | 5 | 6 | 7 | 8 |
|---|---|---|---|---|---|---|---|---|
| 1 | − | − | + | − | + | + | + | + |
| 2 | | − | + | − | + | − | − | + |
| 3 | | | − | + | + | + | − | + |
| 4 | | | | − | − | + | + | + |
| 5 | | | | | − | + | + | + |
| 6 | | | | | | − | + | + |
| 7 | | | | | | | − | − |
| 8 | | | | | | | | − |

**Solution :**

(a) The pairs of mutants that produce $leu^+$ recombinants affect different sites, while pairs of mutants that is unable to produce $leu^+$ recombinants affect one or more common sites. The sites may be single or multiple base-pair regions. *Mutants that affect more than one site must be deletions*, which can be identified by assuming that the mutants unable to produce $leu^+$ recombinants with pairs of mutants that be in different sites.

Here mutants 3 and 8 can recombine to produce $leu^+$ recombinants so they are different sites while mutant 7 recombines with 3 or 8, so it must delete both sites.

Similarly, mutant 2 recombines with 1 or 3 or 6, so it must delete both sides. Mutants-4 recombines with, 1 and 5 so it also must delete both sides. The delection map is like this :

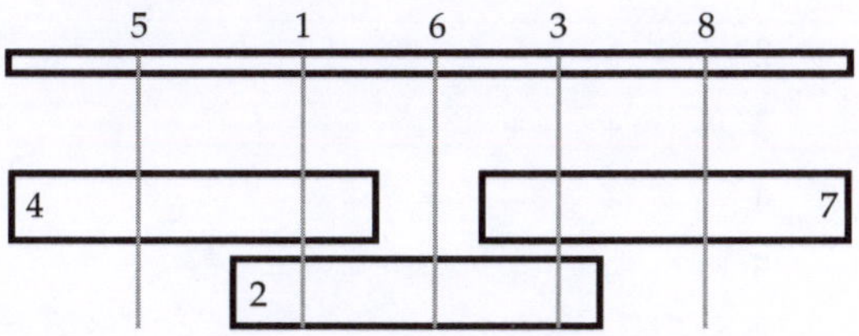


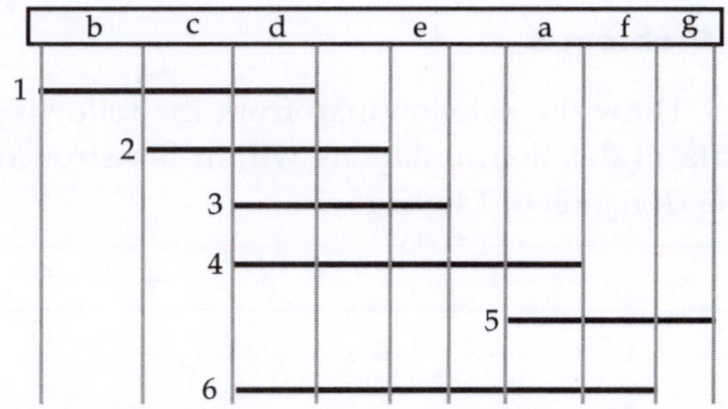


### Problem 6

The house flies homozygous for the recessive mutations (*a*, *b*, *c*, *d*, *e*, *f*, and *g*) are crossed with flies homozygous for the deletions, the following results obtained. m represents mutants phenotype and + as wild type. Determine the relative order of seven mutant genes on the chromosome.

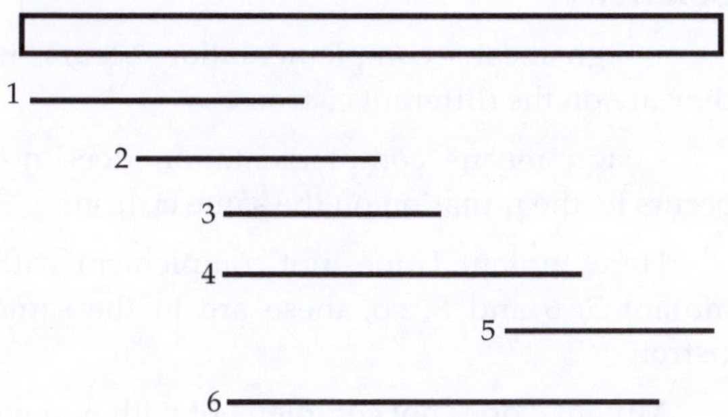


| | Mutations | | | | | | |
|---|---|---|---|---|---|---|---|
| Deletions | *a* | *b* | *c* | *d* | *e* | *f* | *g* |
| 1 | + | m | m | m | + | + | + |
| 2 | + | + | m | m | + | + | + |
| 3 | + | + | + | m | m | + | + |
| 4 | m | + | + | m | m | + | + |
| 5 | m | + | + | + | + | m | m |
| 6 | m | + | + | m | m | m | + |

**Solution :**

Mutation is expressed in flies with deletions 4, 5 and 6 not in other deletions. Therefore, "a" must be in the area that is unique to deletions 4, 5, 6. Using this procedure we can map the remaining mutations.

### Problem 7

Seven deletions within a cistron or rII region of T4 phage were tested and the following result is obtained : Draw a deletion map

| | 1 | 2 | 3 | 4 | 5 | 6 | 7 |
|---|---|---|---|---|---|---|---|
| 1 | – | + | – | – | + | – | – |
| 2 | | – | – | – | + | + | – |
| 3 | | | – | – | + | + | – |
| 4 | | | | – | + | – | – |
| 5 | | | | | – | – | – |
| 6 | | | | | | – | – |
| 7 | | | | | | | – |

**Solution :**

**Conditions** / **Remarks**

1. Deletion-1 overlaps with 3, 4, 6, 7 but not with 2 and 5

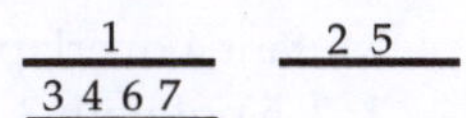


2. Deletion-2 overlaps 3, 4, 7 but not with 5 and 6

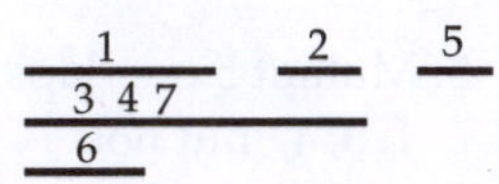


3. Deletion 3 overlaps 1, 2, 4, 7 but not with 5, 6

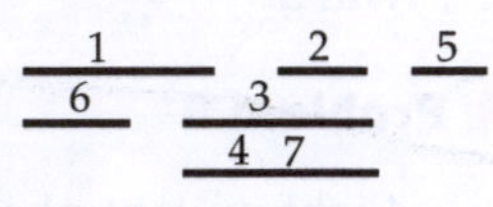


4. Deletion 4 overlaps 1, 2, 3, 6, 7 but not with 5
5. Deletion 5 overlaps with 6, 7 but not with 1, 2, 3, 4, 6

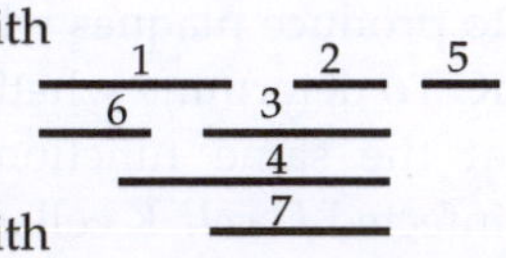


6. Deletion 6 overlaps with 1, 4, 5, 7 but not with 2 and 3
7. Deletion 7 overlaps all.

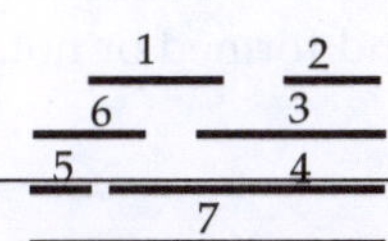

### Problem 8

Draw the deletion map from the following data of deletion mutations within B cistron of the *rII* region of T4 phage.

| | 1 | 2 | 3 | 4 | 5 |
|---|---|---|---|---|---|
| 1 | – | + | + | – | – |
| 2 | | – | + | – | + |
| 3 | | | – | + | – |
| 4 | | | | – | – |
| 5 | | | | | – |

**Solution :**

| Conditions | Remarks |
|---|---|
| 1. Deletion-1 overlaps 4 and 5 but not with 2 and 3. | 1, 4 and 5 in one group, 2 and 3 other group. |
| 2. Mutant 2 overlaps 4 but not with 1, 3, 5 | |
| 3. Mutant 3 overlaps 5 not with 4, 1 and 2 | |
| 4. Mutant 4 overlap 1, 2, 5 not with 3 | |
| 5. Mutant 5 overlaps 1, 3, 4, but not with 2 | |

### Problem 9

Eight mutant phages were isolated that fail to produce plaques when grown in *E. coli* strain K. To determine whether there mutations occur at the same functional gene, simultaneously infected *E. coli* K cells with paired combinations of the mutants and observed whether plaques and formed or not. The data is as follows :

| Mutant | 1 | 2 | 3 | 4 | 5 | 6 | 7 | 8 |
|---|---|---|---|---|---|---|---|---|
| 1 | – | | | | | | | |
| 2 | + | – | | | | | | |
| 3 | + | + | – | | | | | |
| 4 | + | – | + | – | | | | |
| 5 | – | + | + | + | – | | | |
| 6 | – | + | + | + | – | – | | |
| 7 | + | – | + | – | + | + | – | |
| 8 | – | + | + | + | – | – | + | – |

How many functional genes (cistrons) do these mutations belong?

Which mutations belong to the same functional gene?

**Solution :**

+ sign means complementation occurs, ie they are on the different cistrons.

– sign means complementation does not occurs ie, the mutation on the same cistron.

Here, mutant 1 does not complement with mutant 5, 6 and 8, so, these are in the same cistron.

Mutant 2 does not complement with mutant 4 and 7, so there are in the same cistron.

Mutant 3 can complement with all other mutants, so this mutant is in the different cistron.

Thus three cistrons are involved here

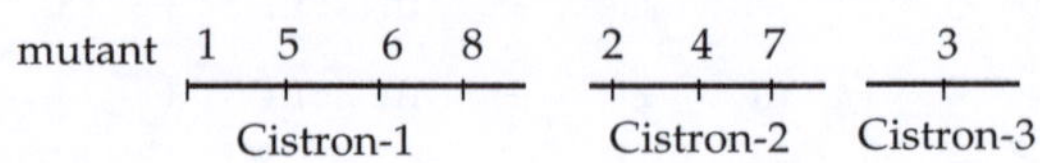


### Problem 10

Eight independently isolated mutants of *E. coli*, all of which are unable to grow in the absence of *histidine*, were examined in all possible *cis* and *trans* heterozygotes.

*Trans*-heterozygotes yielded two different responses as given in the following data. How many genes defined by these eight mutations? Which mutant strains carry mutations in the same gene.

| Mutant | 1 | 2 | 3 | 4 | 5 | 6 | 7 | 8 |
|---|---|---|---|---|---|---|---|---|
| 8 | 0 | 0 | 0 | 0 | 0 | 0 | + | 0 |
| 7 | + | + | + | + | + | + | 0 | |
| 6 | 0 | 0 | 0 | 0 | 0 | 0 | | |
| 5 | 0 | 0 | 0 | 0 | 0 | | | |
| 4 | 0 | 0 | 0 | 0 | | | | |
| 3 | 0 | 0 | 0 | | | | | |
| 2 | 0 | 0 | | | | | | |
| 1 | 0 | | | | | | | |

**Solution :**

Mutant 7 complements with all other mutants and so mutant 7 is in the separate cistron. All the other mutants do not show complementation with each other except mutant 7. Therefore all these are on the separate cistron.

So, there are two cistrons present in these eight mutants.

1 2 3 4 5 6 8 — Cistron-1

7 — Cistron-2

## Problem 11

The complementation data given in the table where the number refers to a particular mutation. + and – signs indicate two mutations do or do not complement respectively. How many cistrons are represented and also assign the mutation to the cistrons.

| Mutant | 1 | 2 | 3 | 4 | 5 | 6 | 7 |
|---|---|---|---|---|---|---|---|
| 1 | – | + | + | + | + | + | – |
| 2 | | – | + | – | + | + | + |
| 3 | | | – | + | + | – | + |
| 4 | | | | – | + | + | + |
| 5 | | | | | – | + | + |
| 6 | | | | | | – | + |
| 7 | | | | | | | – |

**Solution :**

1. Mutant 1 does not complement with mutant 7, so there are on the same cistron.
2. Mutant 2 does not complement with mutant 4, hence these are on the same cistron.
3. Mutant 3 does not complement with mutant 6, hence there are also in the same cistron.
4. Mutant 5 complements with all the other mutants and so this is in a separate cistron.

Therefore, four cistrons are represented and their mutant maps are given below.

1, 7    2, 4    3, 6    5

## Problem 12

The results of all pairwise complement tests for 10 mutations. Assign the mutant strains to complementation group.

| Mutant strain | A11 | A52 | A70 | A71 | B135 | fim2 | L0 | L5 | M1 | S1 |
|---|---|---|---|---|---|---|---|---|---|---|
| A11 | – | | | | | | | | | |
| A52 | + | – | | | | | | | | |
| A70 | + | + | – | | | | | | | |
| A71 | + | + | – | – | | | | | | |
| B135 | – | + | + | + | – | | | | | |
| fim2 | + | + | + | + | + | – | | | | |
| L0 | – | + | + | + | – | + | – | | | |
| L5 | + | + | – | – | + | + | + | – | | |
| M1 | + | – | + | + | + | + | + | + | – | |
| S1 | + | + | + | + | + | + | + | + | + | – |

**Solution :**

1. Mutatant A11 does not complement with B135 and LO, therefore, these are in the same cistron.

2. Mutant A52 does not complement with M1 hence these are in the same cistron.
3. Mutant A70 does not complement with A71 and L5, So, these are in the same cistron.
4. Mutants S1, and fim2 do complement with all others and so these are separate cistrons.

Therefore there are five cistrons.

| A11, B135, L0 | A52, M1 | A70, A71, L5 | S1 | fim-2 |
|---|---|---|---|---|
| Cistron-1 | Cistron-2 | Cistron-3 | Cistron-4 | Cistron-5 |

## Chapter Glossary/Key Terms

**Acceptor arm :** Part of the structure of a tRNA molecule which contains amino acid and acceptor site.

**B-DNA :** The commonest Watson-Crick conformation of the DNA double helix in living cells.

**Cap :** The chemical modification at the 5′ end of most eukaryotic mRNA molecules.

**Capping :** Attachment of a cap to the 5′ end of a eukaryotic mRNA.

**Clover leaf :** A two-dimensional representation of the structure of a tRNA molecule.

**Coding region :** The region of an mRNA molecule that code for a protein.

**Cyclic AMP :** A modified version of AMP in which an intramolecular posphodiester bond links the 5¢ and 3′ carbons.

**D-arm :** Part of the structure of a tRNA molecule which contains a dihydrouridine base.

**Maturase :** A protein, coded by a gene in an intron, thought to be involved in splicing.

**Nucleoside :** A purine or pyrimidine bas attached to a five carbon sugar

**Nucleotide :** A purine or pyrimidine base attached to a five carbon sugar, to which a mono-, di-or triphosphate is also attached.

**Palindrome :** A sequence of DNA that is the same when one strand is read left to right or the other is read right to left consists of adjacent inverted repeats.

**TψC-arm :** Part of the structure of a tRNA molecule which contains a ribothymidine and a pseudouridine bases.

**Z-DNA :** A conformation of DNA in which the two polynucleotides are wound into a left-handed helix.

**"A" Protein :** The viral "A" protein cleaves the plus strand or RF DNA at a specific site and is covalently linked to the resulting 5¢ end. The host cell rep protein acts together with protein 'A' as helicase and unwinds the ds DNA.

**B-chromosme :** A chromosome processed by some invidividuals in a population but not all.

*Contd.*

**Chromatid :** The arm of chromosome.

**Chromatin :** The complexes of DNA and histone proteins found in chromosome.

**Chromosome scaffold :** A compound of the nucelar matrix which change its structure durign cell division, resulting in condensation of the chromosome into their metaphase form.

**Core DNA :** The wound DNA around the nucleosome.

**Core protein :** The central component of nucleosome, made up of two subunits each of histones H2A, H2B, H3 and H4, around which DNA wound.

**Ideogram :** A diagramatic representation of the G-banding pattern of chromosome.

**Interrupted mating :** A method used in conjugation experiments in which the length of time that the bacteria spend conjugating is stopped by a blender treatment or other a blender treatment or other type of harsh treatment.

**Karyogram :** The entire chromosome complement of a cell, with each chromosome described in terms of its appearance at metaphase,

**Solenoid structure of chromatin :** The 10 mn fibre gets coiled itself to form 30 nm wide helix with 5 to 6 nucleosomes per helix.

**$C_0 t_{\frac{1}{2}}$ :** The $c_0$ t required to proceed to half completion of the reaction. It is directly proportional to the unique length of eassociating DNA.

**$C_0$ t :** The product of DNA concentration and time of incubation in a reassociation reaction.

**Catenane :** When one circle is passed through another they become interlocked and form this structure.

***cis*-configuration :** The two sites on the same molecule of DNA

***cis*-trans test :** Assay the effect of relative configuration on expression of two mutations. In double heterozygote, two mutations in the same gene show mutant phenotype in *trans* configuration, wild-type in *cis* configuration.

**Cistron :** The genetic unit defined by the *cis/trans* test, equivalent to gene in comprising a unit of DNA representing a protein.

**Complementation :** The ability of independent (non allelic) genes to provide diffusible products that produce wild phenotype when two mutants are tested in *trans* configuration in a heterozygote.

**Complementation group:** A series of mutations unable to complement when tested in pair wise combination in *trans*, defines a genetic units (cistron).

**C-value :** Total amount of DNA in a haploid genome.

**DNA gyrase :** The type-II topoisomerase of *E.coli* with the ability to introduce negative supercoils into DNA.

**Hyperchromicity :** The increase in optical density that occurs when DNA is denatured.

**Intron :** The segment of DNA that is transcribed, but is removed from within the transcript by splicing together the sequence (exon) on either side of it.

**Kinetic complexity :** The complexity of a DNA component measured by the kinetics of DNA reassociation.

**Linking number :** The number of times the two strands of a closed DNA duplex cross over each other.

**Linking number paradox :** The discrepancy between the existnence of -2 supercoils in the path of DNA on the nucleosome compared with the measurement of –1 supercoil released when histones are removed.

*Contd.*

**Melting temperature (Tm) :** The midpoint of the temperture range over which DNA is denatured.

**Negative supercoiling :** The double helix is itself coiled in the opposite sense from the interwinding of the strands.

**Overwounding :** This is caused by positive supercoiling of DNA.

**Polycistronic mRNA :** It includes coding regions representing more than one gene.

**Positive supercoiling :** Further tension in the direction of winding of the two strands about each other in the duplex.

**Pseudogenes :** The inactive but stable components of the genome derived by mutation of an ancestral active gene.

**Splicing :** The removal of introns from the primary transcript of a discontinuous gene.

**Split gene :** The gene includes some additional non-coding sequences.

**Topoisomerase :** The enzyme that can change the linking number of DNA.

**Topoisomers :** The molecules of DNA that are identical except for a difference in linking number.

**Twisting number :** The number of base pairs in DNA divided by the number of base pairs per turn of the double helix.

**Underwounding :** Caused by negative supercoiling of DNA.

**Writhing number :** The number of times a duplex axis crosses over itself in space.

# EXERCISE

## A. Long answer type questions :

1. Draw and describe the structure of DNA?
2. What do you mean by DNA conformation? Compare between different DNA conformations?
3. What are the major differences between Z-DNA and B-DNA? What is the function of Z-DNA?
4. What do you mean by R-L model of DNA.
5. Describe the structure of mRNA.
6. What are the structural specificities of tRNA? Describe the detailed structure of tRNA?
7. What is rRNA, Describe the structure of rRNAs? Give the details of rRNA processing in prokaryotes as well as eukaryotes.
8. Descuss the Chargaff's rule on DNA composition.
9. Briefly classify bacteriophages with important characters and examples.
10. Describe organization and replication of T4 phage genome.
11. Describe organization and replication of T7 phage genome.
12. Describe organization of λ-phage genome.
13. Describe the estalishment, maintenance of lysogeny and the entry into lytic cycle in λ-phage.

14. Describe decission between lysis and lysogeny in λ-phage.
15. Describe organization and replication of $\phi$ ×174 genome.
16. Describe M13 genome organization and replication.
17. Write a note on chemical composition of chromosome.
18. Draw and describe the nucleosome model of chromosome? Discuss the solenoid structure of the Chromosome. How does nucleosome structure related to the active gene regions on chromosome.
19. What is chromosome Karyotype? How do karyotyping is done? What is its importance?
20. What is banding? How banding is done? Describe diffirent types of chromosome banding in brief. What is its significance?
21. Briefly describe the charactristics of mitochondrial DNA.
22. Briefly describe the structure of yeast MDNA.
23. Briefly describe the structure and characteristics of human mito-DNA.
24. Give direct and indirect evidences that DNA is the genetic material.
25. Describe the "One gene one polypeptide concept" by taking evidences from biochemical mutations in man and *Neurospora*.
26. What is multiple allele? Give examples.
27. What do you mean by pseudoalleles and position effect.
28. What are *cis*-and *trans*-arrangement? Comment on *cis-trans* effect.
29. What are *cis-test* and *trans*-test?
30. What do you mean by complementation? Describe the complementation test with r-II locus of $T_4$-phage.
31. Comment on cistron concept.
32. What are hyperchromicity and hypochromicity Define Tm and mention factors that affect Tm.
33. What is C-value? What is C-value paradox why it is called a paradox? What are the two aspects of paradox? Describe in details.
34. What is statellite DNA? Write a note on satellite DNA.
35. Define complexity. What do you mean by Kinetic complexity? Deduce the formula by which kinetic complexity can be obtained?
36. Define chemical complexity. How do the chemical complexity used to find out the different components of the DNA in the cell?
37. What is pseudagene? Why it is called so? Describe the α and β globin pseudogenes in primates and other vertebrates.
38. How pseudogenes are evolved? Why pseudogenes are evolutionary dead ends?
39. Write a note on the evolution of globin genes from the ancestral gene.
40. What is overlapping gene? Describe its structure and importance.
41. What are split genes? Describe occurrance split genes in different organisms?
42. Describe the characteristies and origin of split genes.
43. What do you mean by topological isomers of DNA? What enzyme is responsible for such interconversion? Describe the mechanism of action of topoisomerase-I in *E. coli*.
44. Describe the mechanism of reaction of eukaryotic topoisomerase-I.
45. Describe the mechanism of catalytic events of typoisomerase-II enzyme.
46. What are twisting number and writhing number? How do they related to linking number?
47. Give the evidence that RNA is genetic material.
48. What is the principle of deletion mapping : Give an example to construct deletion mapping.
49. What is the principle of complementation mapping? Give an example to construct complementation map.

**B. Short answer type questions :**

1. Who discovered transformation?
2. What is a gene?
3. What is a nucleotide?
4. What are bases.
5. What are purines and pyrimidines?
6. What are the components of nucleoside?
7. Distinguish ribose and deoxyribose sugars?
8. Give the IUPAC name of adenine, guanine, cytosine, thymine and uracil? Also give their structure.
9. What is nucleoside?
10. Who discovered the structure of DNA?
11. What was Chargaff's rule on DNA composition?
12. Draw the structure of dATP, dGTP, dTTP, rATP, rGTP, dAMP and rCMP.
13. In DNA what are the lengths of H-bonds between A and T, G and C?
14. What do you mean by DNA conformations?
15. What are the characteristion of A form of DNA?
16. What are the characteristis of C form of DNA?
17. What are the characteristies of Z-DNA?
18. A-form is metastable into D-form in which condition?
19. How you can say that A and B forms are interchangeable?
20. What is RL model of DNA? Why it is also known as Zig-Zag DNA? What is the advantage of this model during replication?
21. How do bending of DNA occur? What is the importance of bending in DNA?
22. What is palindromic DNA? Where does it found?
23. What is H-DNA? What is its importance.
24. What is cruciform structure of DNA?
25. What is hairpin structure of RNA? What is its imporatance?
26. What do you mean by unusual pairing of bases.
27. Distinguish between DNA and RNA.
28. What are genetic and non-genetic RNAs?
29. What is mRNA? Why it is called so?
30. What is a cap of mRNA? Why it is required?
31. What do you mean by $^{7m}$G-capping?
32. What are cap-1, and cap-2?
33. What is cap-0?
34. What are non-coding-1 and noncoding-2 regions in RNA?
35. What is poly-A tail? What is its function?
36. What is the function of mRNA.
37. What is coding region?
38. What is the initiation codon?
39. What are the termination codons?
40. What are the unusual bases in tRNA?
41. What are the roles of TψC loop?
42. What do you mean by invariant and semivariant bases in tRNA?
43. What are the five sites in tRNA?
44. What is the tertiary structure of tRNA?
45. What is 'Shine Dalgarno sequence"? Where does it found?
46. What do you mean by rRNA processing?
47. Distinguish between prokaryotic and eukaryotic rRNA processing.
48. What types of histones are found in chromosomes?
49. What are multistrand and single strand models?
50. What is folded fibre model of Dupraw?
51. What are type-A and type-B fibres?
52. What is nucleosome?
53. What is structural periodicty of DNA in nucleosome?
54. What are core DNA, core particles and linker DNA?
55. What is DNA superhelix?
56. What are histone tetramer and octamers in nucleosome?

57. What is ubiquitin? Where does it occur? What is its function?
58. What is solenoid of nucleosome?
59. What are MAR and SAR?
60. What is the role divalent cations on nucleosome structure?
61. What is the role of HMGs in gene activation?
62. What are G, C, R, T, F and N-banding?
63. How many genes are present in mitogenome?
64. What are the differences between mitogenome, genetic code and universal genetic code.
65. What are L and H strands of mito DNA.
66. What are the causes of LHON and MERRF diseases?
67. What is promiscuous DNA.
68. What are the characteristics of mito DNA.
69. What are the characteristics of cpDNA.
70. What is genetic transformation?
71. What are S and R strains of pneumonia bacteria?
72. What do you mean by bacterial transformation?
73. Why do dead IIIS and live IIR bacteria mixture within the mouse transformed into both live bacteria?
74. How bacterial conjugation experiment proves the DNA as genetic material.
75. What is biochemical mutation?
76. What is the cause of alcaptonuria?
77. What is the cause of phenylketonuria?
78. What is the cause of albinism?
79. Give the causes of phenylpyruvic oligophrenia and Follings disease.
80. What are the minimal and supplimented media?
81. Give the sequence of reaction of ariginine metabolism.
82. Give the sequence of reactions of phenyl–alanine metabolism in man.
83. Why "one gene one enzyme" concept is changed to "one gene one polypeptide" concept.
84. What is multiple allele? What are its characteriistics?
85. Give the example of multiple alleles in the coat colour of rabbit. Note their possible phenotypes and genotypes.
86. What is pseudoallele? Why it is called so?
87. What are *cis-* and *trans-* arrangement of genes?
88. What do you mean by *cis-trans* effect?
89. What do you mean by complementation?
90. What is *cis*-test?
91. What is *trans*-test? What are its criteria?
92. What is r-II locus of $T_4$ phage?
93. What are the two mutants of r-II locus?
94. What is cistron?
95. What are monocistronic and polycistronic genes?
96. How complementation test gives the idea of a cistran.
97. What do you mean by dienaturation and renaturation of DNA?
98. What are hypochromicity and hyper cromicity?
99. What is melting curve? Draw a melting curve of DNA and from this curve determine Tm.
100. What is melting temperature? What factors affect the value of Tm?
101. How Tm is affected by formaldehyde?
102. What is the advantage of using formaldehyde for lowering the Tm?
103. What is C-value?
104. What is C-value paradox? Why it is called so?
105. What are repeated and nonrepeated DNA in the genome?
106. What is satellite band?
107. What are the salellite bands in human genome?
108. What are the remarkable features of salettile DNA?
109. What are the functions of repeated DNA?
110. What do you mean by the complexity of DNA?
111. Define Co.t.
112. What is kinetic complexity?
113. Define $Co.t_{1/2}$. What is its importance?

114. What is chemical complexity?
115. Define repetition frequency? What is its importance?
116. What is pseudogene? What it is named so?
117. Give a sequence of $\alpha$ and $\beta$ globin genes in man.
118. Give the sequenence of globin genes in goat, rabbit and mouse.
119. Give the characteristics of $\psi\beta_2$ in rabbit?
120. What is the interesting property of $\psi h_3$ gene in mouse?
121. How $\beta^A$ and $\beta^C$ genes in goat indicate its origin?
122. What is leghaemoglobin? How does globin gene is originated?
123. Why pseudogenes are the evolutionary dead ends?
124. What are "genes within genes" and "overlapping genes"?
125. What is the importance of overlapping genes?
126. What is split genes? What are exons and introns?
127. What is chambon's rule?
128. What are hexon genes of adenovirus-2?
129. What are the split genes in ovalbumin genes in chicken?
130. What types of split genes found in chloroplast?
131. What are the two hypotheses regarding the origin of split gene?
132. What is topological isomer?
133. What is the function of topoisomerases.
134. What is the functional differences between topoisomerase-I and topoisomerase-II.
135. What is $\omega$-protein? What is its function?
136. Why topoisomerases are called nicking-closing enzymes?
137. Give the synonoyms of topoisomerases.
138. How does reversible nicking reaction catalysed by eukaryotic DNA topoisomerase-I?
139. What is catenane?
140. What are knotting and catenation reactions?
141. What is the source of energy during topoisomerase-II reaction?
142. How does ATP used during topoisomerase-II reaction?
143. What is the function of DNA gyrase in *E.coli*?
144. What are the two subunits of DNA gyrase? Which genes are reaponsible for their production?
145. How does the antibiotics such as nalidixic acid, oxinilic acid, coumermycin-$A_1$ and novobiocin inhibit replication?
146. What is sign invrsion model of DNA gyrase activity?
147. What is supercoiling of DNA?
148. What is positive and negative supercoiling?
149. What is linking number? What do you mean by positive and negative linking numbers?
150. What do you mean by $Lk_0$?
151. What is the change of linking numer equation?
152. What is the change of linking difference?
153. What is superhelical density?
154. What are positive and negative supercoil.
155. How do linking number may be changed?
156. What are topoisomers?
157. What are twists and wriths?
158. How do linking number, twisting number and writhing number interrelated?
159. What is the principle of deletion mapping?
160. What is the principle of complementation mapping.

# 15

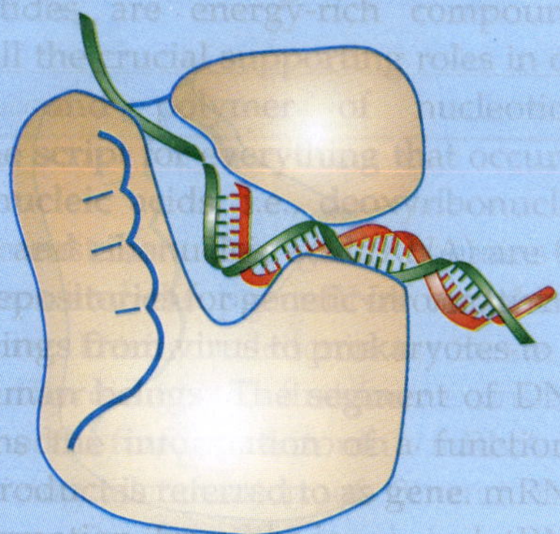

# Replication of Genome

**CHAPTER AGENDA**

**15.1** Concept; **15.2** Experimental proof of Semi-conservative replication; **15.3** Enzymes in DNA replication; **15.4** Replication in *E. coli*; **15.5** Unidirectional and Bidirectional replication; **15.6** DNA replication in Archaea; **15.7** Replication in Eukaryotic DNA; **15.8** Inhibitors of DNA replication; **15.9** Models of Replication; **15.10** Plasmid replication; Chapter Glossary/Key Terms; Exercise

## 15.1. CONCEPT

One of the most important properties of *DNA* is that it *can make exact copies of itself*; this process is called **replication**.

*Replication of DNA takes place during the interphase between the two mitotic cycles.* But no replication of DNA takes place during interkinesis. DNA synthesis does not take place during the entire interphase. It is confined to S-phase. In mitotically inactive cells, $G_1$, S and $G_2$ do not exist. This is called $G_0$ stage.

**Replication is a process in which the DNA copies itself to produce identical daughter molecules of DNA.**

**Delbruk** suggested that *Watson-Crick model of DNA* could theoretically be replicated by three modes: **conservative, semiconservative** and **dispersive** (Fig. 15.1).

According to conservative mode, the double helices formed, one would be entirely of old material and other entirely of new material. The old parent double helix would be unchanged.

According to dispersive method of replication, the DNA helix, would break at several points, forming many pieces, each piece would replicate and then the pieces would join at random. Thus two double helices are formed having a patchwork of old and new pieces.

According to semiconservative mode, proposed by **Watson** and **Crick**, each strand of the two double helices formed, would have one old and one new strand.

## 15.2. EXPERIMENTAL PROOF OF SEMICONSERVATIVE REPLICATION

**Meselson and Stahl's experiment :** The hypothesis of semiconservative replication was proposed by **Watson** and **Crick** soon after publication of their papers on the structure of DNA, the theory was experimentally proved by **Meselson** and **Stahl** in 1957 (Fig. 15.2).

1. They grew *E. coli* cells in a medium in which the sole nitrogen source $NH_4Cl$ contains $N^{15}$, the heavy isotope of nitrogen for many generations. Thus, their DNA becomes heavier than the normal DNA.
2. The DNA isolated from these cells, has a density about 1% greater than that of

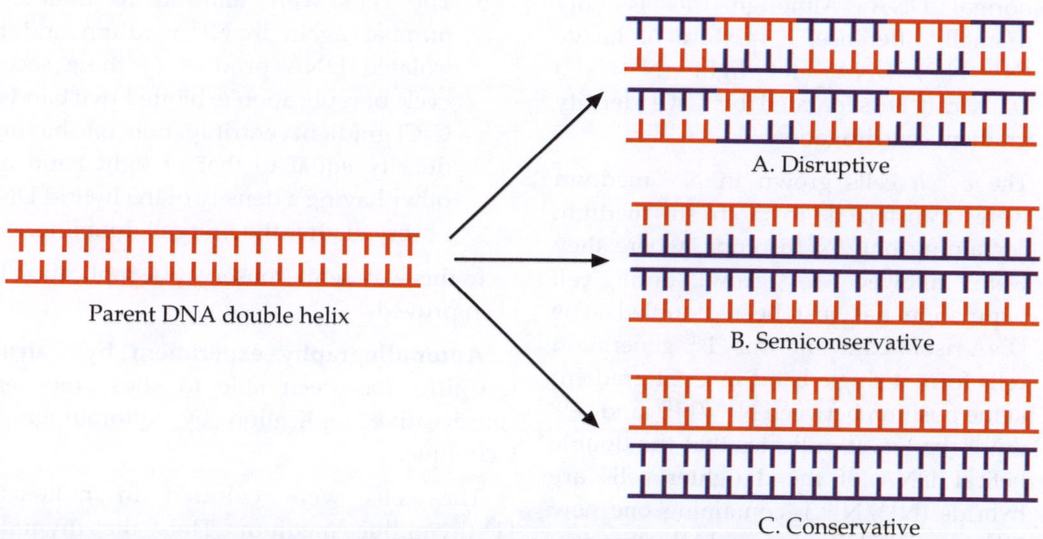


**Fig.15.1 :** *(A–C) Three possible schemes for DNA replication.*

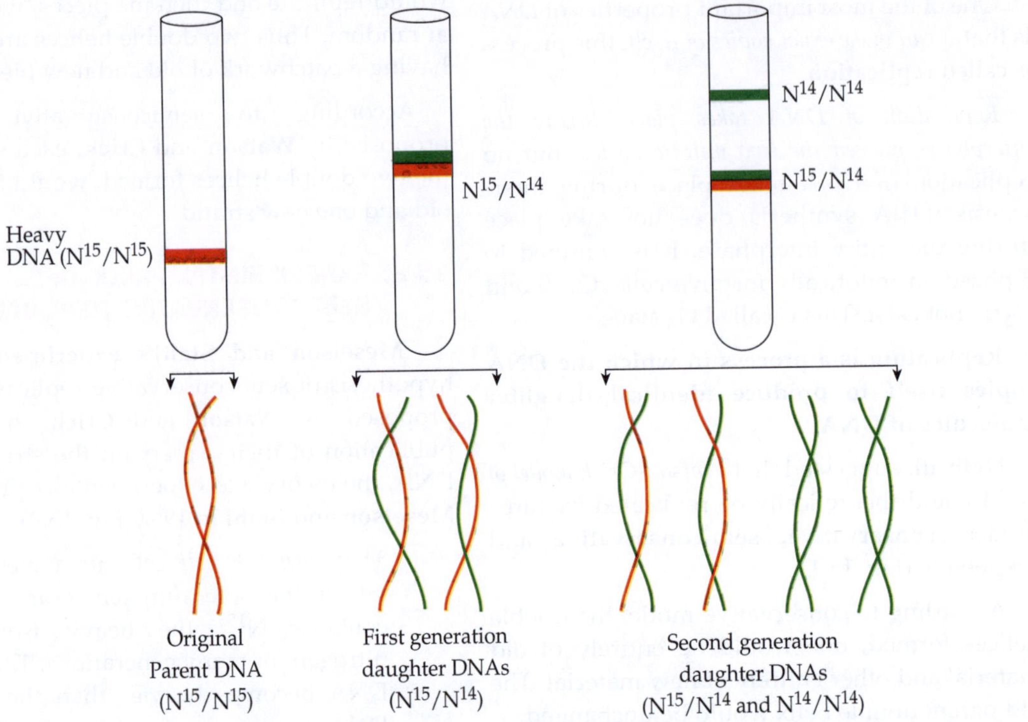


**Fig.15.2 :** *The Meselson-Stahl experiment for the semiconservative replication of DNA.*

normal DNA. Although this is only a small difference, a mixture of heavy ($N^{15}/N^{15}$) DNA and light ($N^{14}/N^{14}$) DNA can be separated by CsCl density gradient centrifugation.

3. The *E. coli* cells grown in $N^{15}$ medium were transferred to a fresh medium containing only $N^{14}$ isotope, where they were allowed to grow until cell population has just been doubled. The DNA isolated from this 1st generation cells form a single band in CsCl gradient at the position between $N^{14}/N^{14}$ and $N^{15}/N^{15}$ bands. It indicates that the double helical DNA of the daughter cells are hybrids ($N^{14}/N^{15}$) containing one new $N^{14}$ strand and one parental $N^{15}$ strand.
4. This result never supports the conservative replication because in this hypothesis, never yield such hybrid DNA molecule.
5. The cells were allowed to double in number again in $N^{14}$ medium and the isolated DNA product of these second cycle of replication exhibited two bands in CsCl gradient centrifugation, one having a density equal to that of light band and other having a density of the hybrid DNA, observed after the first cell doubling.

In this way semi-conservative replication has been proved.

**Autoradiography experiment by Cairns :** J. Cairns has been able to show the semi-conservative replication by autoradiography technique.

The cells were cultured in radioactive $H^3$-thymidine medium. Thus the thymidine bases of the DNA become labeled with $H^3$-thymidine. These cells were processed and in the photographic film, these regions were marked by deposition of Ag-grains.

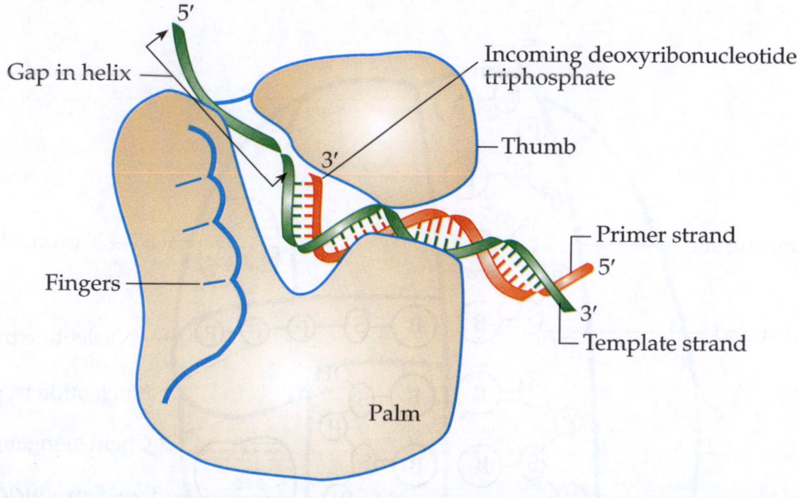


**Fig.15.3 :** *X-ray crystallography of E.coli DNA polymerase resembling right hand in which palm, fingers and thumbs grasp the DNA.*

During incorporation of $H^3$-thymidine autoradiographs can be prepared at regular intervals and semiconservative mode of replication can be demonstrated, because one of the two strands in daughter DNA molecules is derived from the parent molecule and other is synthesized afresh, which is demarketed by dotted deposition of Ag-grains.

## 15.3. ENZYMES IN DNA-REPLICATION

### 15.3.1. Prokaryotic DNA Polymerases

The search for the enzymes that could synthesize DNA was initiated in the mid 1950s as soon as it was realized that DNA synthesis is the key to replication of genes. **Arthur Kornberg** in 1957 for the first time was able to find out, purify and characterize the enzyme DNA polymerase and assumed that this was the main replicating enzyme in *E. coli*. Now this enzyme is called DNA polymerase-I or **Kornberg enzyme**. It has now been found that *E. coli* contains at least two other distinct polymerases. X-ray crystallography structure has been given recently by **Beese** *et al* (1993) (Fig. 15.3).

**DNA polymerase-I :** DNA polymerase-I is not essential enzyme for DNA synthesis. It is a single polypeptide chain (Mw. 109000). There is one atom of $Zn^{++}$ per chain and so this is a metallo-enzyme. This enzyme consists of two fragments, a larger **Klenow fragment** (38kD) and a smaller fragment 35kD.

Electron microscopic studies showed that DNA polymerase is roughly spherical in shape with a diameter of about 65Å; it contains a number of sites, which have functional importance (Fig. 15.4).

1. A template site, which attaches to the DNA template and holds a section of DNA in place.
2. A primer site which contains a primer (60-100 nts.) complementary to the DNA strand. A primer terminus site, at the tip of the primer has a terminal 3′-OH group.
3. A tri-phosphate site where an incoming nucleoside triphosphate matches with a complementary nucleotide on the DNA-template and is bound to the 3′-OH position of the primer.
4. The larger Klenow fragment contains 3′→5′ exonuclease activity with 5′→3′ polymerizing activity while the smaller

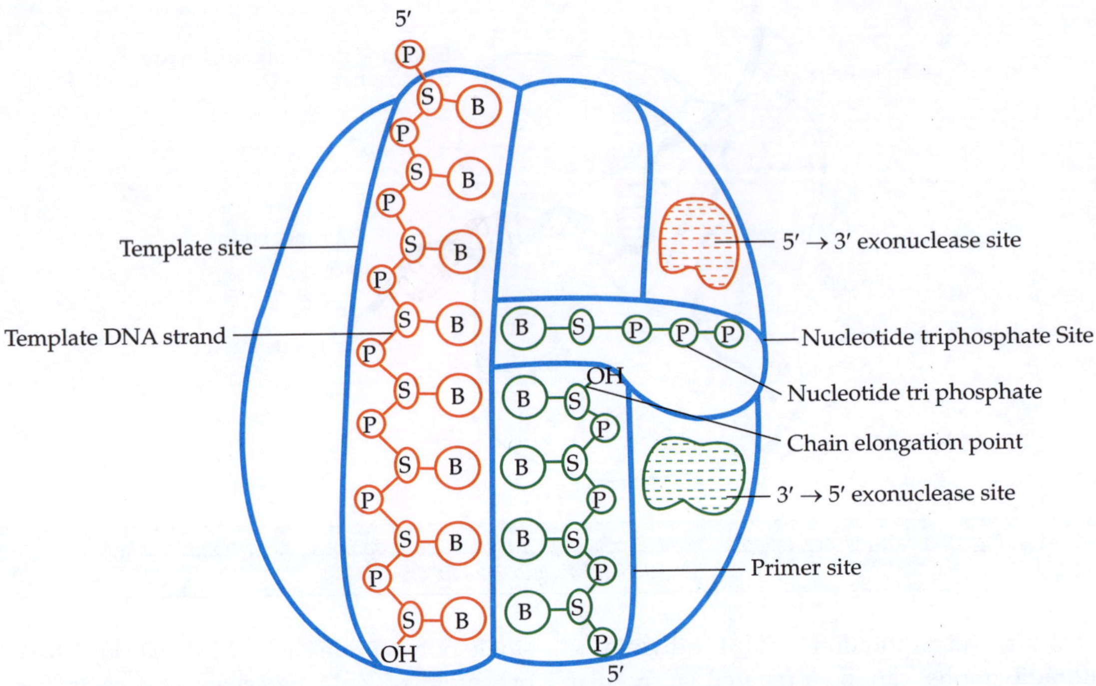


**Fig.15.4 :** *A model of DNA polymerase-I showing its five different sites, with a primer, template DNA and incoming nucleotide triphosphate.*

fragment contains 5′→3′ exonuclease activity.

***Functions of the DNA pol-I are —***

1. Polymerization activity (5′→3′)
2. 5′→3′ exonuclease activity.
3. 3′→5′ exonuclease activity.

DNA pol-I is synthesized under the control of *pol A* gene located at 75 min position of *E.coli*.

**DNA polymerase-III :** It is heteromultimeric enzyme with 10 units, plays an important role in replication. It is present in the cell with a very few molecules (10-20 molecules per cell). It has four components.

1. A polymerase core consisting its α, ε and θ subunits. Its role is to synthesize DNA.
2. A sliding clamp constituting dimer of $\beta_2$ subunits. Its role is to form preinitiation complex accompanied by the ATP-dependent catalysis by γ-complex.
3. γ-complex consisting 6 polypeptides with five subunits viz. $\gamma_2$, $\delta_1$, $\delta'_1$, $\chi_1$, $\psi_1$. It is called matchmaker because it helps in the loading of sliding clamp ($\beta_2$) into the DNA.
4. The τ subunit constituting as a dimer, possibly it has a DNA -dependent ATPase activity.

The DNA pol-III HE has an asymmetric structure consisting 16 polypeptides involving 10 subunits: $\beta_2\,(\alpha\varepsilon\theta)_2\tau_2(\gamma_2\delta_1\delta'_1\chi_1\psi_1)$ (Fig. 15.5).

Pol-III′ consists of two cores and a dimer of $\tau_2$, so that the polymerase acts in pair for coordinated replication of both strands of a DNA duplex.

Pol-III* contains 14 polypeptides but lacking sliding clamp or $\beta_2$.

**Functions :**

1. $\beta_2$ is loaded into DNA in an ATP–dependent reaction catalyzed by γ–complex to form preinitiation complex. $\beta_2$

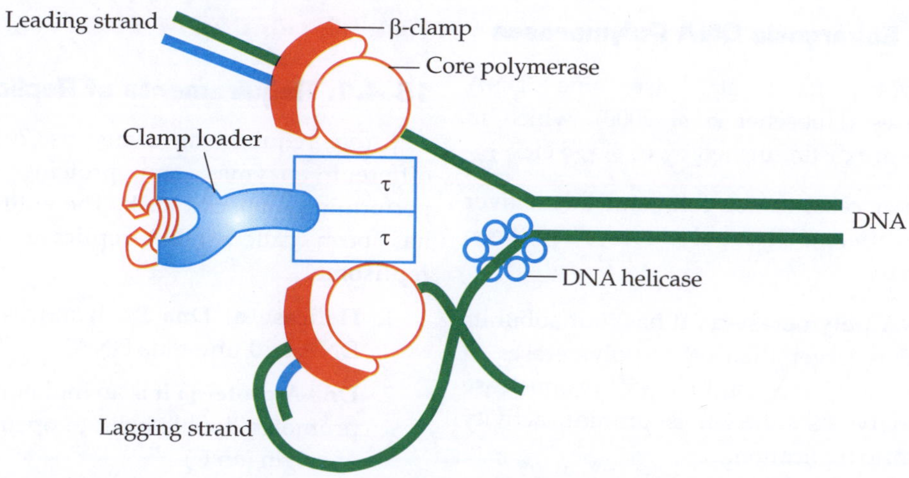


**Fig.15.5 :** *Schematic representation of DNA polymerase -III HE (replisome)*

is a ring shaped, head-to-tail dimer, its central cavity accommodate DNA duplex.

2. Core enzyme is assembled with pre-initiation complex to form initiation complex in an ATP-independent reaction.
3. It has polymerase activity.
4. It has 3′→5′ exonuclease activity.
5. It lacks 5′→3′ exonuclease activity.
6. Different subunits are synthesized by different genes and perform different functions (Table 15.1).

**TABLE 15.1**
***Subunits of DNA Pol III HE***

| *Protein* | | *Genes* | *Functions* |
|---|---|---|---|
| α | Core (Pol III′) | *dna E* | Polymerase |
| ε | Core (Pol III′) | *dna Q* | 3′→5′ exonuclease |
| θ | Core (Pol III′) | *hol E* | Stimulates ε |
| τ | Pol III′ | *dna X* | Dimerization of core, ATPase |
| γ | γ complex | *dna X* | Binds ATP |
| δ | γ complex | *hol A* | Binds to β |
| δ′ | γ complex | *hol B* | Stimulates clamp loading |
| χ | γ complex | *hol C* | Binds SSB |
| ψ | γ complex | *hol D* | Bridges between χ and γ |
| β | γ complex | *dna N* | Processivity factor sliding clamp. |

**DNA Polymerase–II** : It is a single polypeptide chain (Mw. 120000) resembles DNA pol-I in its activity. It is not a replication enzyme. It can brings about 5′→3′ polymerization using free 3'-OH, but mainly uses duplex with short gaps only. It has 3′→5′ exonuclease activity but lacks 5′→3′ exonuclease activity. It is used in repair replication.

*Pol B* gene is responsible for the synthesis of enzyme in *E.coli* (Table 15.2).

**TABLE 15.2**
**Comparison of properties of Pol I, II and III**

| *Properties* | *Pol I* | *Pol II* | *Pol III* |
|---|---|---|---|
| Mol. wt. | 109 000 | 120 000 | 250 000 |
| No. of chain | Single | Single | Hetero multimeric |
| Polymerization (5′→3′) | Yes | Yes | Yes |
| Exonuclease (5′→3′) | Yes | No | No |
| Exonuclease (3′→5′) | Yes | Yes | Yes |
| Molecule per cell | 400 | Not known | 10–12 |
| Use of nicked duplex | No | No | No |
| Rate of polymerization (molecules/min. at 37°C) | Upto 1000 | Upto 50 | Upto 15000 |

### 15.3.2. Eukaryotic DNA Polymerases

Eukaryotes have at least nine DNA polymerases (Hübscher *et al* 2000), which in mammals are distinguished by α, β, γ, δ etc.

In yeast cells, tumor cells and in rat liver cells, five different DNA polymerases have been characterized.

1. **DNA polymerase-α :** It has four subunits and is larger than other polymerases. It has no 5′→3′ and 3′→5′ exonuclease activity. Its function is priming activity during replication.
2. **DNA polymerase-β :** Smaller polymerase found only in vertebrates, not in yeast cell or in lower invertebrates.
3. **DNA polymerase-γ :** Its function is the DNA replication in mitochondria but is encoded in the nucleus. It has two subunits. It has 3′→5′ exonuclease activity but lacks 5′→3′ exonuclease activity.
4. **DNA polymerase-δ :** It is the main replicating enzyme. It has two subunits and it works in conjunction with an accessory protein called PCNA (proliferating cell nuclear antigen), which is a functional equivalent of β subunit of DNA pol III in *E.coli.* It has 3′→5′ exonuclease activity but lacks 5′→3′ exonuclease activity.
5. **DNA polymerase-ε :** It has at least one subunit, has 3′→5′ exonuclease activity but lacks 5′→3′ exonuclease activity. It is required for detection of DNA damage during genome replication.
6. **DNA polymerase-κ :** It has 1 or 2 subunits. Its presence or absence or the direction of exonuclease activity is not known. It is required for attachment of cohesin proteins, which hold sister chromatids together until the anaphase stage of nuclear division.

## 15.4. REPLICATION IN *E.COLI*

### 15.4.1. Requirements of Replication

*E. coli* requires as many as 20 or more different enzymes and proteins and each performing a specific task. The entire complex has been called **DNA–replicase** system or **replisome**.

1. **Helicase or Dna B :** It moves along the DNA and unwinds DNA.
2. **Dna A protein :** It is an initiator protein. It promotes double helix to open at the site of origin (*ori* C).
3. **Dna C protein :** It is an required for Dna B binding at origin.
4. **λP :** Complexes with Dna B, delivers Dna B to *ori-λ* complex.
5. **IHF :** Sequence specific double strand DNA–binding protein binds to *ori C*.
6. **FIS :** Sequence-specific double-strand DNA–binding protein, binds to *ori C*.
7. **HU :** A histone-like protein stimulates initiation.
8. **Dna K :** Heat shock protein, disassembly of *ori λ* protein.
9. **Primase :** Primer synthesis.
10. **SSB :** It binds to single stranded DNA.
11. **RNA polymerase :** Synthesis of RNA.
12. **Ligase :** Joins nascent DNA fragment.
13. **Gyrase or Topoisomerase II or swievel protein :** Holds the replication fork.
14. **Topo IV** : Decatenation
15. **TBP :** *Ter*–binding protein, stalling replication fork.

### 15.4.2. Origin of Replication

Replication starts at a unique site called **origin**. In *E. coli* there is a single replicon with the origin. This genetic locus is *ori C*, other origin site has been found to phage replication

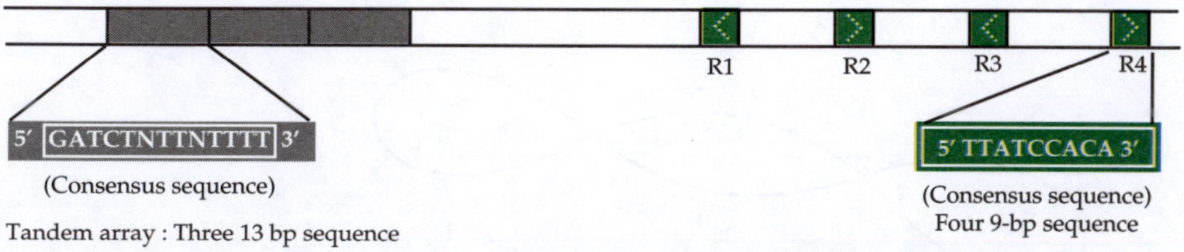


**Fig.15.6 :** *The arrangment of sequences in the E.coli replication origin called ori-c.*

origin *ori λ*, phage PI lysogenic origin *ori PI* and Co1E1 and pBR322 plasmid origin.

### 15.4.3. Initiation of Replication

The event of origin is called **prepriming**.

For the initiation of replication in *ori C*, following steps are involved (Fig. 15.6)

1. *ori C* consists of 245 bp. It has two series of short repeats. Three repeats of 13 bp segments and four repeats of 9 bp sequence. The 13 bp consensus sequence is 5′GATCTNTTNTTTT3′ and four 9 bp consensus sequence ($R_1$, $R_2$, $R_3$, $R_4$) is $\left[\begin{array}{l} 5'\ \text{TT}\underline{\text{A}}\text{T}\underline{\text{C}}\text{CA}\underline{\text{C}}\text{A}\ 3' \\ \quad\ \ \text{T}\ \ \text{A}\quad \text{A} \end{array}\right]$.

2. Dna A–ATP complex, about 20 monomers bind at 9 bp inverted repeat region of *ori C*. It is called *initial complex*.

3. It promotes opening of the DNA in the region of three 13 bp sequence. The opening, i.e., strand separation or melting occurs from right to leftward of the negatively supercoiled DNA and requires HU or IHF protein and ATP. This is *open complex*.

4. Dna B, which contains 6 subunits, is transferred to exposed single stranded DNA with the help of Dna C and ATP. Dna C escorts and helps transfer of Dna B, but Dna C is released. This is *prepriming complex*.

5. Dna B helicase causes unwinding of DNA on addition of ATP. SSB and DNA gyrase then react with this prepriming complex to hold the single strand DNA separate. Dna B complexes are loaded on each strand.

6. Dna B moves along the single stranded DNA to which it binds in the direction of its free 3′ end and unwinds DNA in the 5′→3′ direction. Dna B protein forms a clamp around a single strand DNA. Dna B does not fall off until it reaches the end of that strand or is unloaded from DNA by another protein (Fig. 15.7).

### 15.4.4. Replication Fork Movement

1. Dna B while travelling along 5′→3′ direction generates a Y-shaped replication fork by opening the DNA duplex. At that region about 200 molecules of SSB proteins may be found to bind at the separated single strand DNA upto the replication fork region. Thus the strands remain separated.

2. The binding of SSB protein to single strand of DNA is cooperative. SSB is a tetramer but this may bind to the DNA as a monomer or dimer. Each subunit has 8–10 nucleotide binding sites. Thus 200 molecules of SSB at the replication fork separate about 2000 bp of DNA.

3. As the replication fork moves down the DNA double helix, the parental strands wind. In circular DNA, supertwisting imposes a strain. This strain can be relieved to some extent by supercoiling. But there is a limit of supertwisting and ultimately the replication fork will not be able to move further along the DNA. The strain is relieved by the action of the

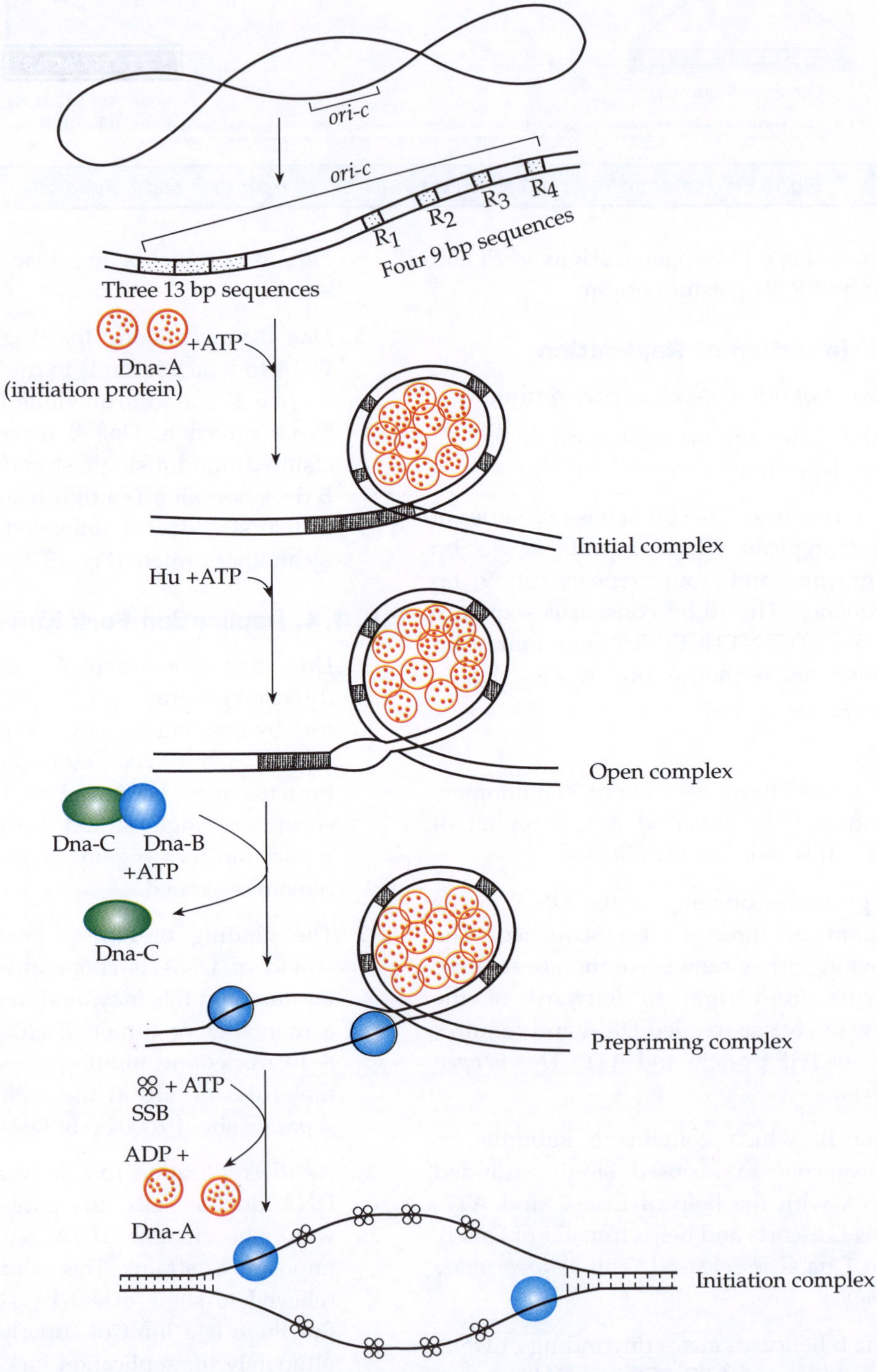


**Fig.15.7 :** *A model for initiation of replication at the E. coli origin, ori-c.*

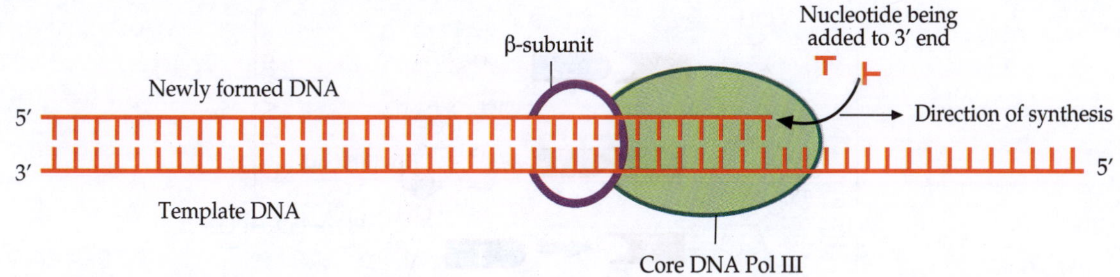


**Fig.15.8 :** *Schematic diagram proposed association of the core polymerase with β subunit clamp at the primer template terminus.*

super- helix relaxing protein. This protein has nicking-closing activity. This protein is known as DNA gyrase or DNA topoisomerase II. By introducing a nick on one region of a DNA strand, the strand rotates upon the other, relieving the strain. The break is then closed by this enzyme.

The fork movement again commences by helicase activity.

### 15.4.5. Formation of Pre-initiation and Initiation Complexes

1. The initiation of replication is brought about by DNA pol III HE, which contains a core enzyme (α, ε, θ subunits) a sliding clamp ($\beta_2$), γ complex of 6 subunits ($\gamma_2\delta_1\delta'_1\chi_1\psi$) and a $\tau_1$ subunit.
2. The initiation complex is formed in two stages, in the first stage, sliding clamp ($\beta_2$) is loaded on DNA in an ATP-dependent reaction, catalyzed by γ-complex to form **preinitiation complex.**
3. The second stage is that the core enzyme is bound to $\beta_2$ to form initiation complex. Simultaneously, γ-complex is released from the sliding clamp. In the HE, $\tau_2$ acts as a bridge between two core enzymes during coordinated replication.
4. β subunits form donut shaped dimer around duplex DNA and hold the catalytic core polymerase near the 3′ terminus of the growing strand and can slide freely along the DNA like a ring on a string. Loading and unloading is done by γ-complex (Fig. 15.8).

### 15.4.6. Elongation of Replication

Dna B (helicase) is a motor protein having 6 subunits. It has two ATP binding sites, two ADP– binding sites and two are empty.

While it is travelling along the 5′→3′ direction generates a replication fork. The strand having Dna B is lagging strand template.

**(A) Lagging Strand synthesis :** Lagging strand synthesis is accomplished by the formation of short fragments called **Okazaki fragments**, synthesized in the direction opposite to fork movement.

1. **Primase activity :** The regulatory apparatus for lagging strand synthesis is a travelling protein machine called **primosome**, which consists of 7 different proteins including Dna B, Dna C, Primase and protein i, n, n′, n″.

   The primosome moves along the lagging strand template in the 5′→3′ direction keeping the pace with the replication fork. As it moves, the primosome at intervals compels primase to synthesize a short RNA primer, to which the DNA is then added and extended by DNA pol III HE

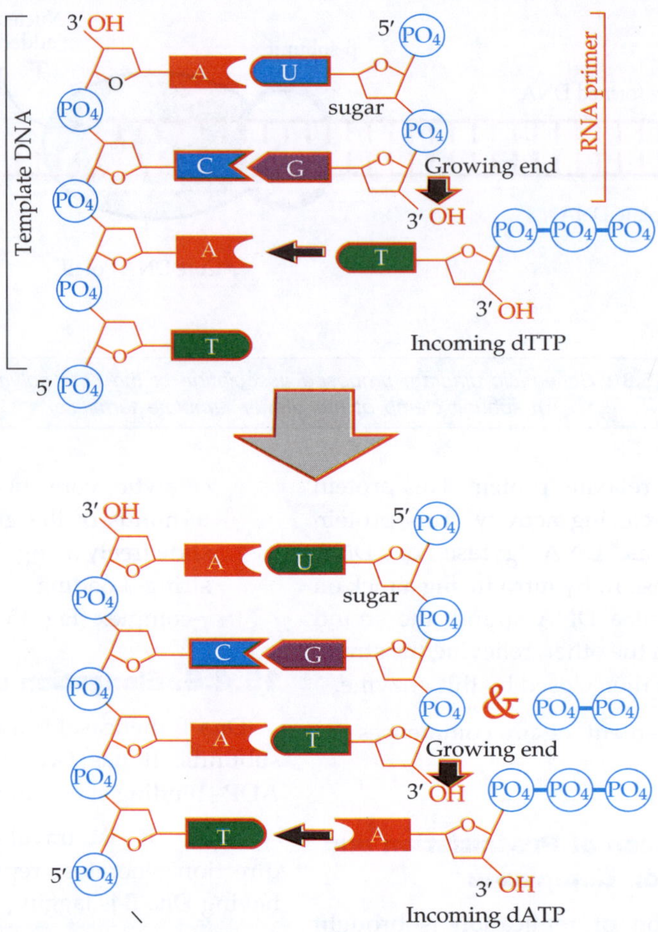


**Fig.15.9 :** *Addition of dNTP at the primer end and elongation of DNA strand during replication.*

The primase synthesizes short primer about 4-15 nucleotides (Frick and Richardson 2001) at 5′→3′ direction on holding an 3′ end of the template as an initiating point.

The direction of synthetic action of primase and DNA pol III HE is opposite to the direction of primosome movement.

DNA Pol-III HE interacts with the primase and provides the signal for primase to dissociate from the fork.

2. **Synthesis of complementary strands :** Dna B, Primase and DNA Pol III HE function together in elongation process.

The core enzyme moves towards the growing chain. The clamp (β) subunit bound tightly to the 3' terminal end of the primer RNA.

The clamp slides freely along the DNA alongwith core enzyme. In this way the active sites of the core enzyme remain near the growing fork and the synthesis of the DNA continues until the primer of the previously added Okazaki fragment is encountered (Fig. 15.9).

The detachment of the SSBs from the template takes place by a protein called replication mediator protein (RMPs, Beernik and Morrrical 1999) during

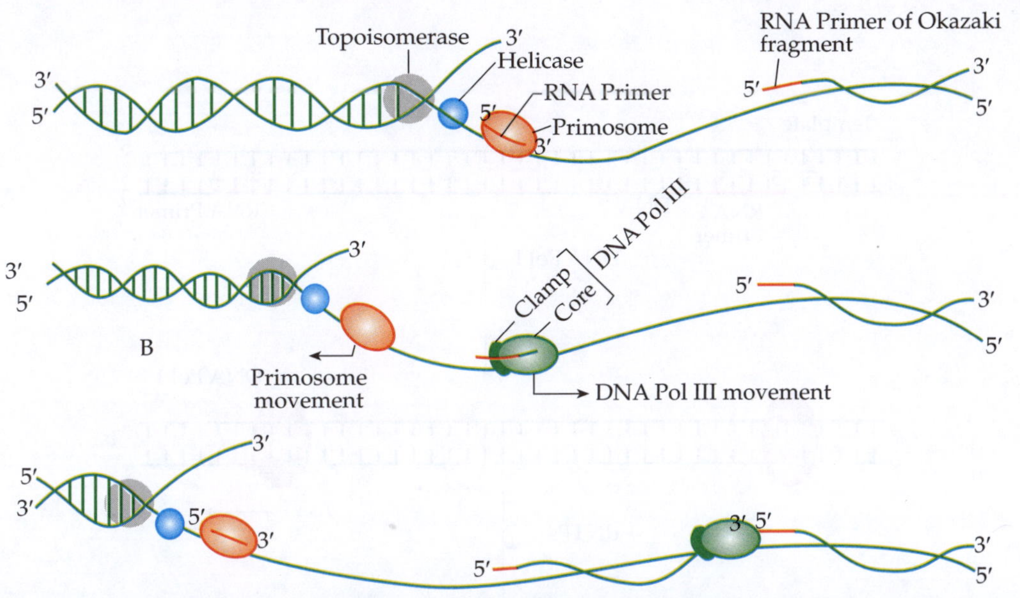


**Fig.15.10 :** *Schemetic diagram of lagging strand synthesis, showing fork movement, primosome movement, RNA primer synthesis, DNA pol III HE movement and DNA strand synthesis.*

copying of the open single strand (Fig. 15.10).

After completing the Okazaki fragment, core enzyme rapidly dissociates leaving $\beta_2$ clamp that may be assembled at another primed site.

3. **Elimination of RNA primer :** When the new Okazaki fragment is complete, the RNA primer is removed by DNA pol-I and using its 5′→3′ exonuclease activity, the nucleotides of the RNA primer is replaced by DNA strand by the same enzyme (Fig. 15.11).

4. **Ligase activity and joining of two DNA fragments :** After elimination of RNA primer a nick is remained between the two DNA fragments. This gap is joined by the enzyme DNA ligase.

   There are three steps during ligase activity. In each step, one phosphodiester bond is formed at the expense of another. The enzyme must be activated using ATP or $NAD^+$ to supply the required chemical energy.

   An AMP is transferred first to the enzyme DNA ligase and then the 5′ phosphate in the nick. The 3′–OH group then attacks this phosphate and displaces AMP leading to the formation of phosphodiester bond and the nick is then sealed (Fig. 15.12).

**(B) Leading strand synthesis :** Leading strand synthesis begins with the synthesis by primase with a short RNA primer at the 3′ – OH end of replication origin. Deoxyribo- nucleotides are then added to this primer by DNA pol III HE. Once begin, leading strand synthesis proceeds continuously on keeping the pace with the replication fork.

The exonuclease activity by DNA pol-I and ligase activity by DNA ligase enzyme take place on that RNA primer and on the nick respectively.

**(C) Coupling synthesis of leading and lagging strands :** In *E. coli*, synthesis of leading and lagging strands may actually be coupled and is accomplished by the dimeric DNA pol-III HE.

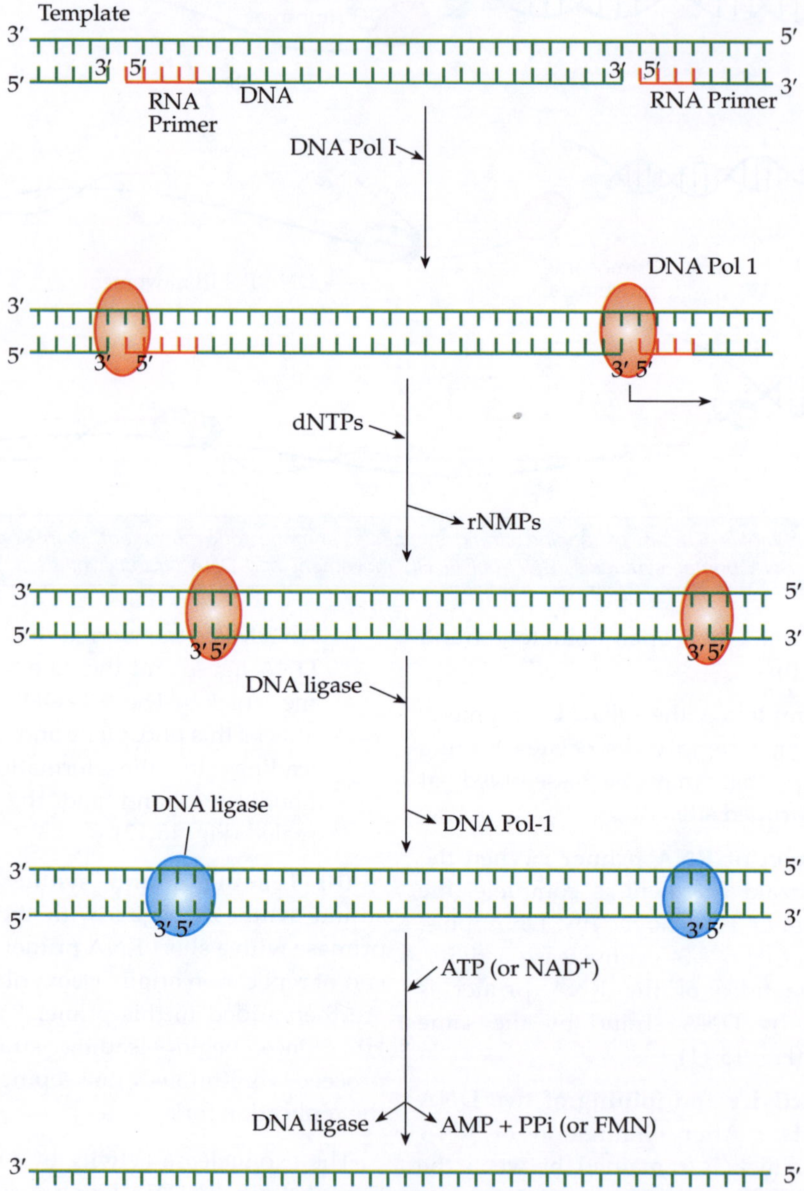


**Fig.15.11 :** *Removal of RNA primer and joining of Okazaki fragments.*

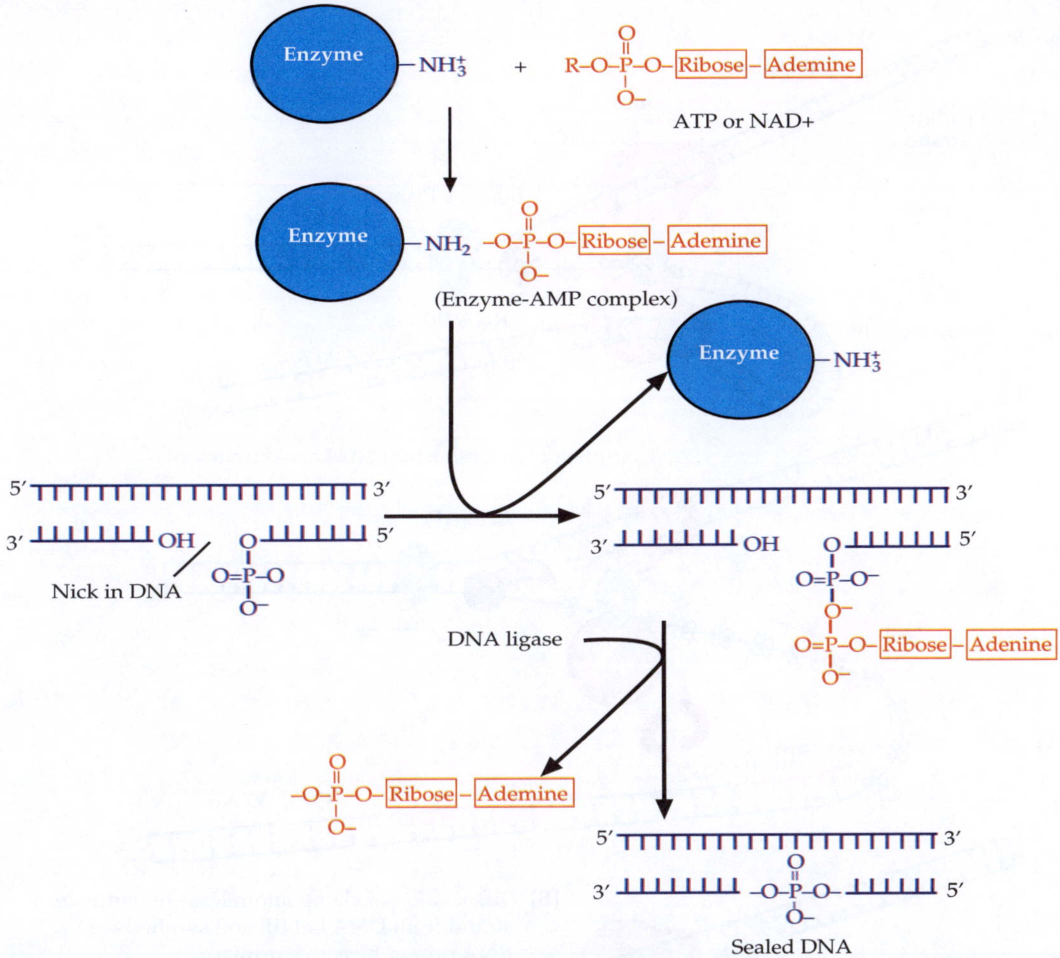


**Fig.15.12 :** *Mechanism of the DNA ligase reaction.*

The template of lagging strand is looped tightly so that the direction of synthesis has the same orientation of the both strands.

The combination of the DNA pol-III dimer and the primosome migrating along the parent DNA and carrying out most of the replicative function is called the **replisome**.

Two DNA polymerases are joined by $\tau$-protein. One core polymerase adds nucleotides to 3′ end of leading strand and another core enzyme adds nucleotides to the lagging strand discontinuously.

The clamp that keeps the DNA pol attached to lagging strand dissociates. The DNA pol temporarily releases the lagging strand template DNA.

As the DNA helicase continues to unwind the parental DNA, the primase becomes activated and synthesizes a short RNA primer on the growing lagging strand.

The DNA pol binds to the DNA again and becomes locked in by the clamp. The polymerase uses the RNA primer, a short copy DNA is synthesized on the lagging strand template DNA.

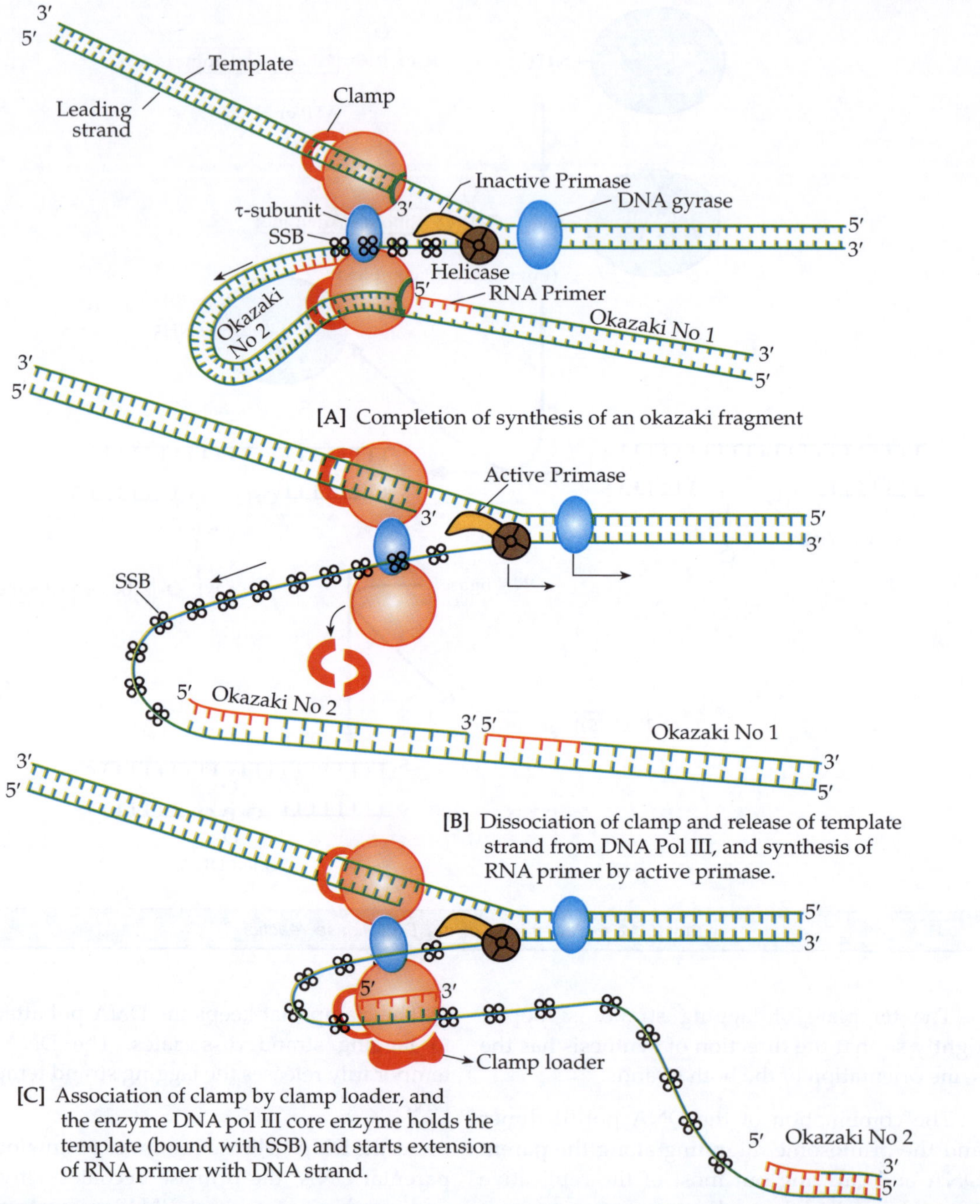


**Fig.15.13 :** *Events of coordinate synthesis of both the leading and lagging strands.*

The polymerase stalls when it reaches the RNA primer of the preceeding Okazaki fragments and the entire cycle is repeated (Fig. 15.13).

### 15.4.7 Termination of Replication

*E.coli* chromosome carries a large termination zone, diametrically opposite to *ori C*, which blocks the progress of replication fork of bi-

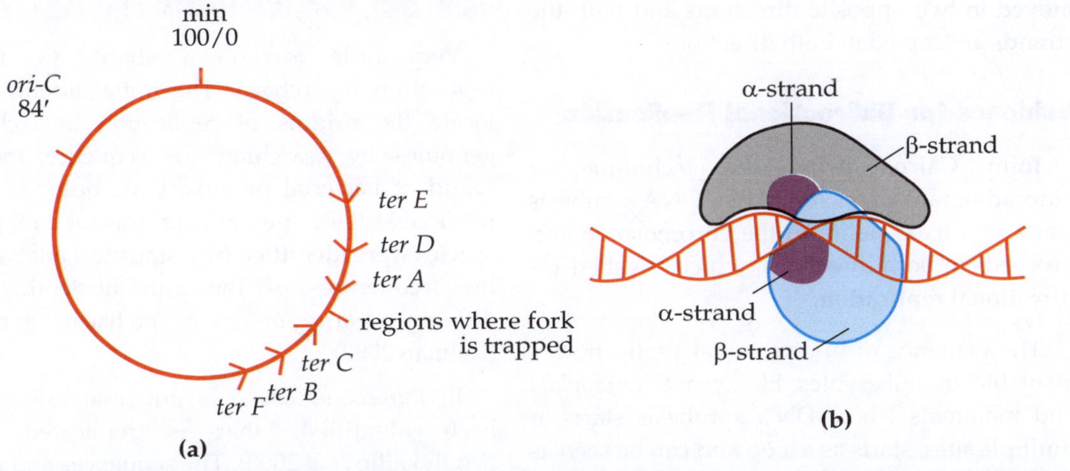


**Fig.15.14 :** *(a) A partial map of E. coli chromosome showing the six ter sites; (b) Interaction of tus protein in ter site for termination of DNA replication.*

directional replication meeting at this region. *E.coli* chromosome carries specific sequences called ***ter***-sites a short sequence of ~23 base pairs. It requires the binding of a product of the ***tus*** gene, which is a 36kD protein (Fig. 15.14).

In the termination zone of *E. coli* there are three *ter* sites (*ter A, ter D, ter E*) for clockwise fork and three *ter* sites (*ter B, ter C* and *ter F*) for anticlockwise fork. These six sites are arranged in overlapping manner leaving no replication free gap. This arrangement creates a **replication trap**, if for some reason one fork is delayed, more rapid fork will be trapped at the ***ter*** region and waits for the arrival of the slow fork.

Tus protein stops the movement of a replication fork in only one direction. The crystal structure of a Tus-*ter* complex shows that the Tus protein binds to DNA asymmetrically, α-helices of the protein is protruded around the double helix at the end that blocks the replication. Presumably a fork proceeding in the opposite direction can displace Tus and then continue.

The Tus–*ter* complex stalls the replication fork by inhibiting Dna B from unwinding the DNA.

When this *ter* sites are deleted, replication stops simply by the meeting of opposite replication forks, thus the mutations in *ter* and *tus* are not lethal.

After replication of circular DNA of *E.coli*, DNA topoisomerase IV is necessary for the final separation of the replicated circular DNA molecules.

## 15.5. UNI-DIRECTIONAL AND BIDIRECTIONAL REPLICATION

There are three possible mechanisms of DNA strand growth which result in semiconservative DNA replication.

In the first, simplest possibility of replication mechanism is that, one new strand derives from one origin and other new strand from the other origin. Each strand has its own growing point. In this mechanism, which operates in linear DNA viruses such as adenoviruses, the ends of the DNA act as a site of origin as well as termination of replication.

The second uni-directional mechanism is that there is one origin and one growing fork but both the strands are being copied. The example of such replication is the plasmids.

The most common in both eukaryotes and prokaryotes is that the synthesis might start from a single origin, two replication forks are moved in two opposite directions and both the strands are copied in both directions.

### Evidence for Bidirectional Replication

**John Cairns** using the technique of autoradiography concluded that DNA synthesis starts at a fixed point on the chromosome and proceeds in both directions, which is called **bi-directional replication**.

The evidence of bi-directional replication is available in eukaryotes like yeast, *Drosophila* and mammals where DNA synthesis starts at multiple sites, starts as a loop and can be seen as expanding bubbles or eyes under electron microscope.

The first experimental supports for bi-directional replication in cultured replicating mammalian cells were obtained by fiber autoradiography of labeled DNA. These cells were exposed first to high and then to low concentrations of $H^3$-thymidine, the resulting DNA will be heavily labeled (Hot) near replication origin and lightly labeled (warm) farther away. When such labeled DNA is dried on a microscopic slide as a long linear molecules (fiber) and then is exposed to a radiation sensitive emulsion, autoradiographic signals would be produced corresponding to the hot-warm-DNA regions.

Bidirectional replication and chain growth from a single origin in viral DNA have been obtained. The replicating viral DNA from SV 40-infected cells were cut by the restriction enzyme Eco R 1, which recognizes a single site, and examined by electron microscopy. The electron micrographs and corresponding diagrams showed a collection of increasingly longer replication bubbles, the center of which is constant distance from each of the cut molecules. Thus indicating that chain growth occurs in two directions from a common origin (Fig. 15.15).

## 15.6. DNA REPLICATION IN ARCHAEA

Very little is known about the DNA replication in archaea. The initial attempts to locate the **origins** of replication in archaeal genomes by searching for sequence motifs, found at bacterial or eukaryotic origins, were unsuccessful. But potential origins for a range of species were identified by a statistical analysis of the frequencies of the four nucleotides in different parts of each archaeal genome (Kelman 2000).

In *Pyrococcus abyssi*, a potential origin has been identified, that is replicated first (Myllykallio *et al* 2000). The sequences and most of the proteins involved in elongation phase in archaeal genome, that have been predicted are similar to the equivalent eukaryotic versions. The protein homologus to eukaryotic RFC PCNA has been found to occur in archaea. The DNA polymerase is peculiar that the synthesis activity is similar to DNA pol-δ of eukaryotes where the proof reading function is conferred by a protein that appears to be a homolog of subunit ε of *E.coli* DNA pol-III.

## 15.7. REPLICATION IN EUKARYOTIC DNA

### 15.7.1. Replication Origin in Yeast

Each yeast chromosome has multiple origin of replication. Cloning experiments indicate that about 400 origins exist in the 17 chromosomes of *S. cerevisceae*.

Each **origin** sequence is called **autonomously replicating sequence (ARS)**. It is less than 200 bp in length.

Detailed analysis of ARS1 (≈180 bp) revealed a 15 bp segment, designated as element A or ACS, stretching from position 114 to 128. Three other short segments are B1, B2 and B3 elements. The 11 bp. consensus sequences of ARS is (5′) $^{A}/_{T}$-T-T-T-A-T-$^{A}/_{G}$-T-T-T-$^{A}/_{T}$ (3′). In element A at 10 of 11, in element B2, 9 of 11 bases are identical.

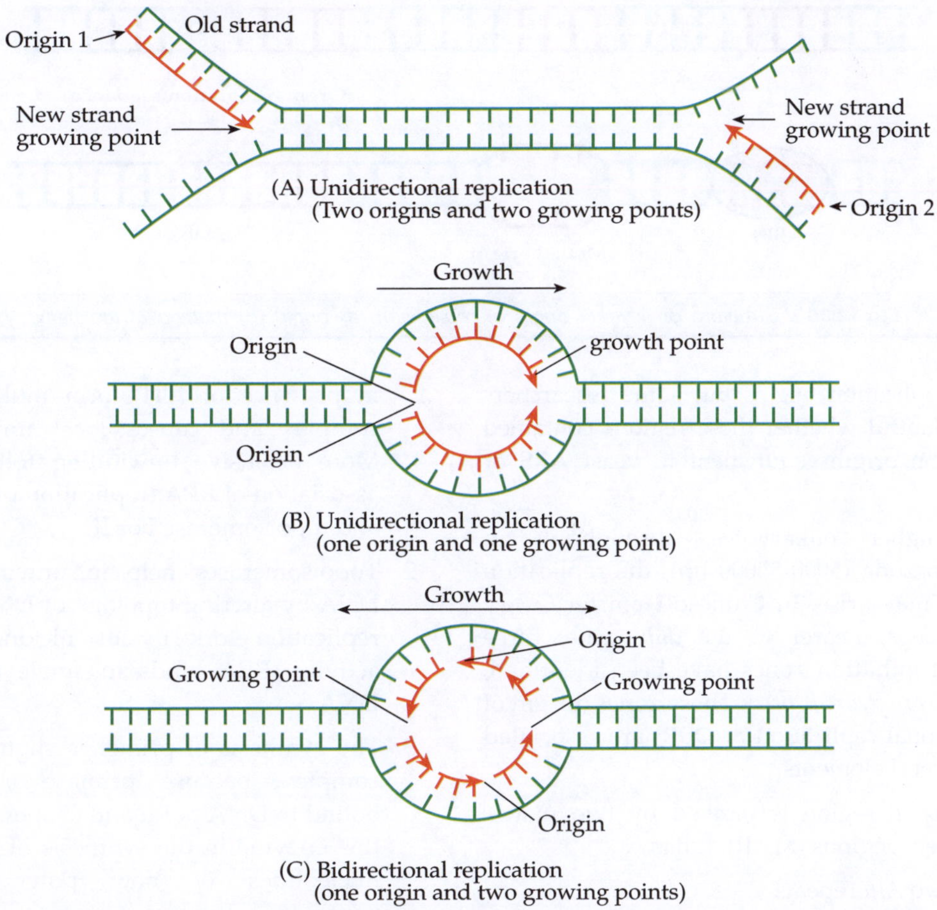


**Fig.15.15 :** *Three mechanisms of DNA strand growth in semiconservative replication.*

Subdomains A and B1 make up the origin–recognition sequence, which is a stretch of about 40 bp in total that is binding site for the origin recognition complex (ORC), a set of six proteins that attach to ARS. ORC is homologus to Dna A of *E.coli* (Kelman 2000) but this interpretation is not strictly correct.

Two other conserved sequences in the ARS are B2 and B3 subdomains, which are functionally homologous with 13 nt, repeat and four-9-nt repeats of *E.coli* respectively.

Element A binds to ORC specifically in an ATP–dependent manner. It has been found that ORC remains bound to ARS throughout the cell cycle and during replication it becomes associated with other proteins and then triggers initiation of DNA synthesis.

The DNA binding protein called ARS binding factor-1 (ABF-1) attaches to subdomain B3. This binding causes a tortional stress and induces the melting at the position of subdomain B2 and at that region two strands are being separated. It is followed by the attachment of the helicase, and other replication enzymes to the DNA and enabling the replication forks to begin their progression along DNA (Fig. 15.16).

### 15.7.2. Replication Origin in Higher Eukaryotes

Several experiments suggested that there are specific regions in mammalian chromosomes

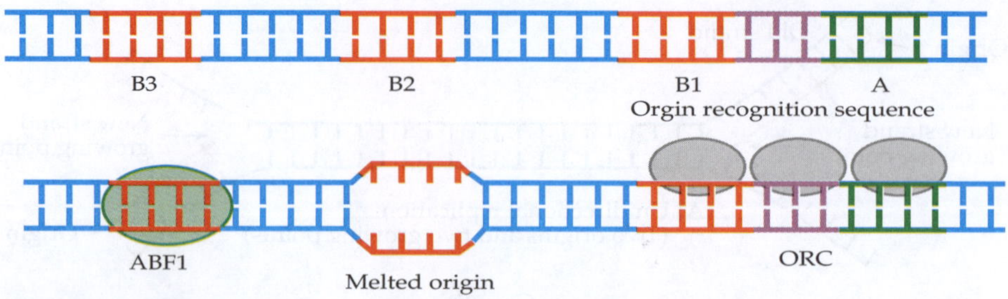


**Fig.14.16 :** *Structure of a yeast origin of replication (a) origin (b) melting of the helix.*

where replication begins but some researchers were doubtful whether these regions contained replication origins equivalent to yeast ARS or not.

In higher eukaryotes, throughout an initiation zone (5000-55000 bp), the replication bubbles may arise. In Chinese Hamster Ovary (CHO) cells, nearer to the *dhfr* gene, three different initiation zones have been identified, these are *ori-α, ori-β, ori-γ*. These zones (origin of bidirectional replication or OBR) are associated with several elements.

The *ori-β* region is flanked by two matrix attachment regions (MAR). It has

1. Two *Alu* repeats
2. Sequences associated with DNA amplification
3. A segment of DNA bent.
4. Autonomously replicating plasmid DNA.
5. ARS sequence
6. Binding sites for proteins (R1P60, PUR, OCT1 and AP1)

### 15.7.3. Elongation Phase

Different proteins have been identified, which are with similar functions at the replication forks in *E.coli* and mammalian system (Table 15.3).

1. *Tag* site I is an imperfectly inverted repeat sequence, *Tag* site II is a 27 bp. binding site for **Tag**. During the formation of unwound DNA complex, Tag (I) and (II), in presence of ATP form multisubunit complex and causes local unwinding. More extensive unwinding follows the association of RPA (replication protein A) and topoisomerase I or II.
2. Topoisomerases help in unwinding of DNA by altering topology of DNA at the replication fork by its nicking-closing activity. RPA binds to single stranded DNA.
3. The synthesis of primer is slightly more complex, because primase is tightly bound to DNA pol-α and cooperates with this enzyme in the synthesis of first few nucleotides of new polynucleotide.

**TABLE 15.3**
**Different proteins required for replication and comparison between *E. coli* and Eukaryotes.**

| *Function* | *E. coli* | *Hela SV40* | *Phage T4* |
|---|---|---|---|
| 1. **Helicase** | Dna B | Tag (I) | g 47p |
| 2. **Leading helicase/Primase** | Dna C | Tag (II) | g 59p |
| 3. **Single strand binding** | SSB | RPA | g 32 p |
| 4. **Priming** | Dna G | Pol a / Primase | g 61 p |
| 5. **Sliding clamp** | $b_2$ | PCNA | g 45 p |
| 6. **Clamp loading (ATPase)** | g-complex | RFC | g 44 or g 62 p |
| 7. **Catalysis** | Pol III core | Pol d | g 43 p |
| 8. **Holoenzyme dimerization** | $t_2$ | ? | g 43 p |
| 9. **RNA removal** | Pol I | MF I | g 43 p |
| 10. **Ligation** | ligase | ligase T | $T_4$ ligase |

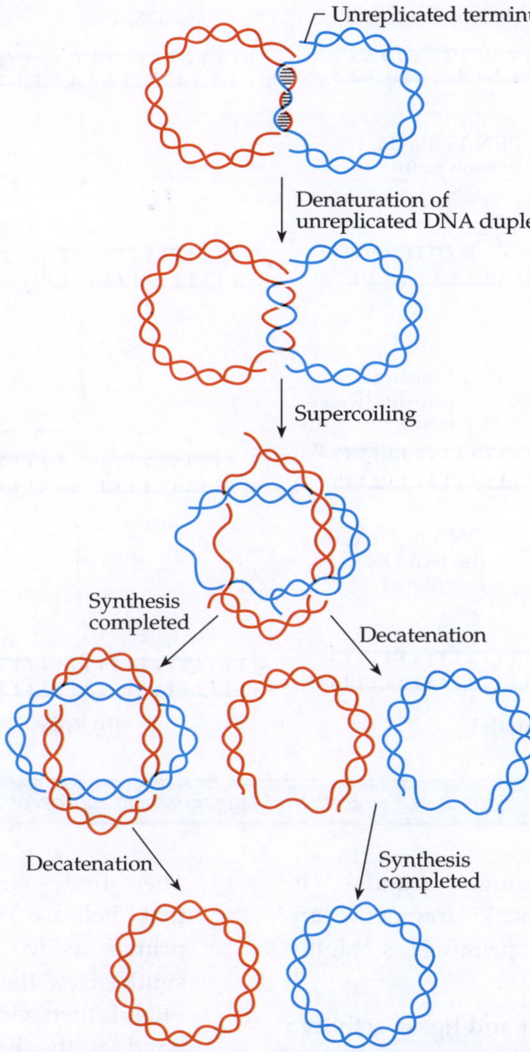


**Fig.15.17 :** *Completion of replication of circular DNA molecules.*

Primase synthesizes 8–12 nucleotides and then hands over to DNA pol-α, which extends the RNA primer by adding about 20 nucleotides of DNA, this is called **iDNA**. This DNA stretch often has a few ribonucleotides mixed in but it is not clear whether these are incorporated by DNA polymerase α or by intermittent activity of the primase. DNA pol α has no 3′→5′ proof reading activity and therefore synthesizes DNA in a relatively error-prone manner.

4. After completion of the RNA-DNA primer, DNA synthesis is continued by the main replicative enzyme, DNA polymerase-δ (Fig. 15.17).

5. RF-C (replication factor C), binds with 3′ end of iDNA and loads DNA pol δ and PCNA (Proliferating cell nuclear antigen), which is functional equivalent of $\beta_2$ clamp of *E.coli*. RF-C and PCNA help in switching of DNA pol-δ replacing DNA pol-α. Then continuously synthesizes

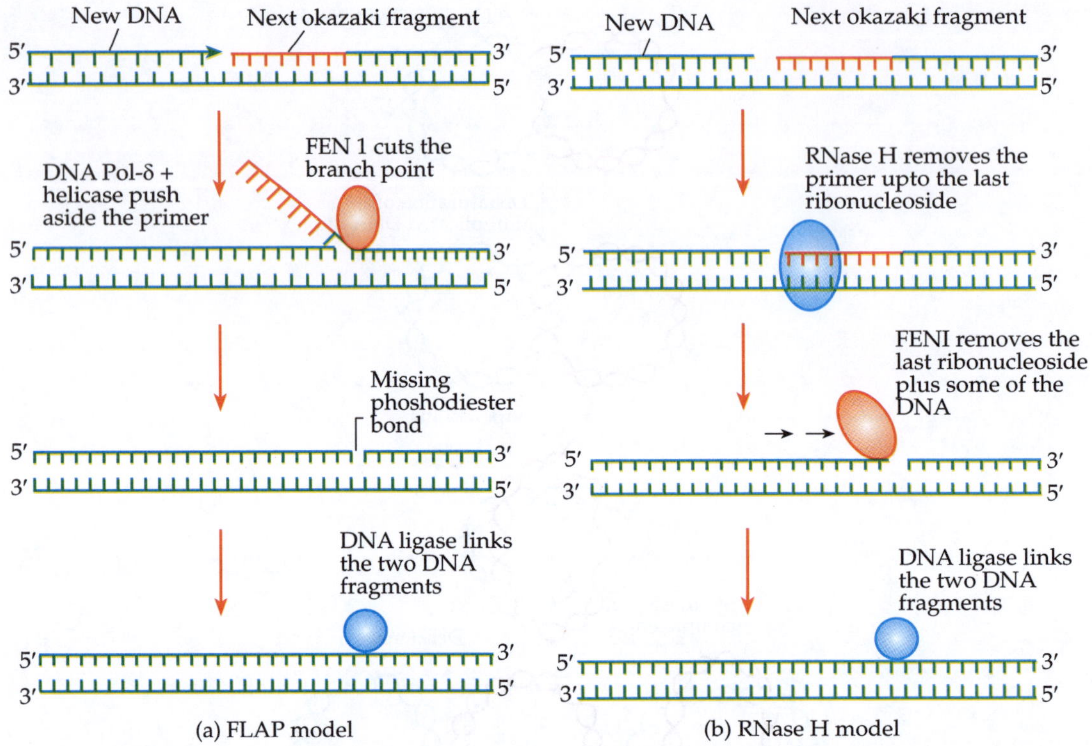


**Fig.15.18 :** *Two models for completion of lagging strand replication in eukaryotes.*

leading and lagging strands. In eukaryotes, the Okazaki fragments are much shorter and priming is highly repetitive event.

**Removal of RNA primer and ligase activity :** There appears to be no eukaryotic DNA–polymerase with 5′→3′ exonuclease needed for the removal of primer.

The central player is the **flap endonuclease** (FEN I previously called MF I), which is associated with the DNA polymerase δ complex at the 3′ end of the Okazaki fragment in order to degrade the primer from the 5′ end of the adjacent fragment, because it cannot remove the ribonucleotide at the extreme 5′ end of the primer, since 5′ end ribonucleotide carries a 5′ triphosphate group, which blocks FEN I activity.

There two models have been proposed (**Waga** and **Stillman**, 1998).

1. The first alternative possibility is that helicase breaks and pushes the primer aside. The DNA pol β then synthesizes the exposed template. The FEN I then cleaves the phosphodiester bond at the branch-point. The missing phosphodiester bond is then ligated by DNA ligase.
2. The second alternative model is that the primer is removed by RNase H, which can degrade RNA-DNA hybrid upto the last ribonucleotide of the primer but cannot remove the phosphodiester bond between last ribonucleotide and first deoxy-ribonucleotide. FEN I then removes the last ribonucleotide plus some of the DNA of Okazaki fragments. DNA ligase then joins the gap between the two DNA fragments (Fig. 15.18).

### 15.7.4. Termination of Replication

Little is known about the termination in eukaryotes and no sequences equivalent to bacterial terminator are known in eukaryotes and proteins similar to **Tus** have not been identified.

It is fact that the replication complexes do not break down. Various models have been proposed about the termination of replication. One of these models was proposed by Cook (1998) and **Wei** *et al* (1998) that the eukaryotic genome is orderly packed into the nucleus and the cohesin proteins attach immediately after passage of the replication fork and hold the daughter DNA molecules together until anaphase. During anaphase, the **cohesins** are cleaved enabling the replicated chromosomes to separate prior to their distribution into daughter nuclei.

The cohesin protein molecules are attached at the replication fork by DNA polymerase K (**Takahashi** and **Yanagida** 2000).

## 15.8. INHIBITORS OF DNA REPLICATION

There are several substances those inhibit the RNA primer synthesis as well as DNA elongation and thus interfere with the DNA replication.

1. **Actinomycin D :** The elongation of RNA chains by RNA polymerase in both bacteria and eukaryotes is specifically inhibited by the antibiotic actinomycin-D. The planar portion of this molecule intercalates into the double helical DNA between successive G ≡ C base pairs, thus deforming the DNA. This local alteration prevents the movement of polymerase along the template. In effect, actinomycin-D jams the zipper because actinomycin-D inhibits RNA elongation in intact as well as in cellular extracts. It has become very useful for identifying cell processes that depend upon RNA synthesis.
2. **Acridin** inhibits RNA synthesis in a similar fashion.
3. **Rifampicin :** It is an antibiotic, inhibitor of RNA synthesis that binds specifically to the β subunits of bacterial RNA polymerase. Thus DNA replication is inhibited by affecting RNA primer synthesis.
4. **Novobiocin** and **nalidixic acid** inhibit elongation by inhibiting DNA gyrase, which functions as a replication swivel.
5. **Aphidicolin** inhibits the activity of DNA pol-I, II and III as well as α, δ and ε of prokaryotes and eukaryotes respectively.
6. **N-ethyl maleimide** inhibits the activity of DNA polymerase I and II and eukaryotic DNA polymerase- γ.
7. **Butyl phenyl dGTP** inhibits DNA pol-I.
8. **Dideoxynucleoside 5′ triphosphate** inhibits DNA polymerase-β.
9. **Carbonyl diphosphonate** inhibits DNA pol-II.

## 15.9. MODELS OF REPLICATION

### 15.9.1 Cairn's model of replication

1. Replication starts at specific origin in the circular duplex DNA.
2. It consists of two strands, H-strand is used as a template for synthesis of new strand. After synthesis of a short distance its original partner, L-strand is displaced. It remains single stranded and forms a D-loop. Sometimes many D-loops may be found due to multiple origins.
3. RNA polymerase transcribes a short primer whose 3′ end is generated by cleavage with an endonuclease at several sites. This endonuclease is specific for it's triple structures, i.e., DNA-RNA hybrid and a displaced DNA single strand.
4. The 3′ end of this RNA is then extended into DNA by DNA polymerase.
5. The displaced L-strand becomes longer and D loop is extended. As the expansion

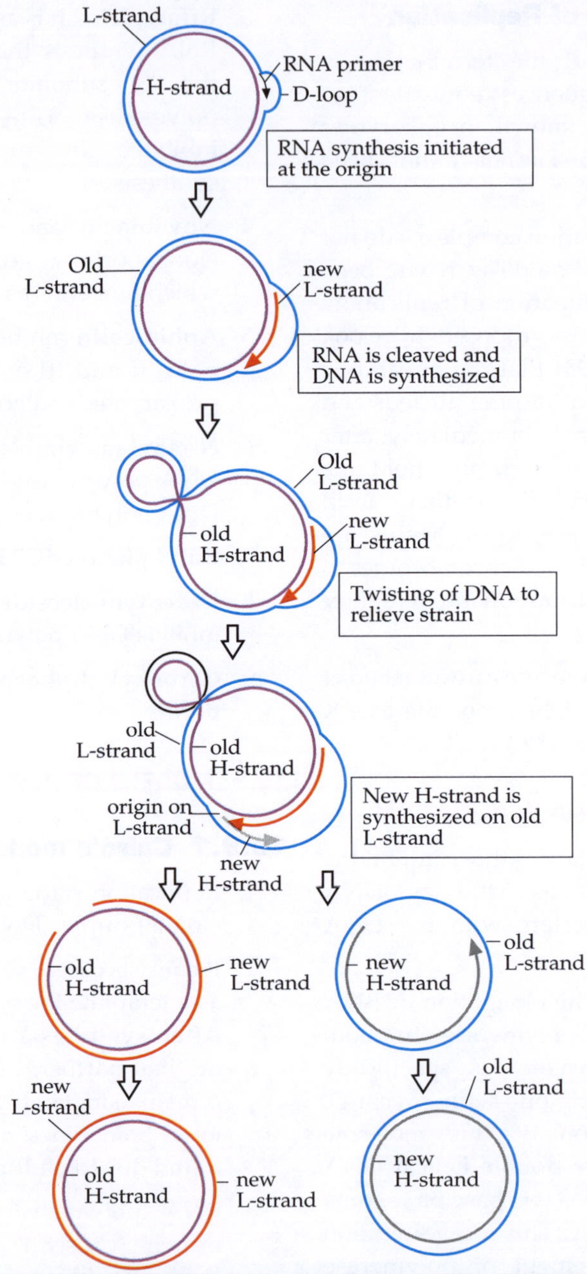


**Fig.15.19 :** *Rplication in mito DNA*

reaches a point about two third of the way round the circle, synthesis of a new H-strand initiates at this site. It uses a special primase that synthesizes a short RNA and then extended into DNA by DNA polymerase. The synthesis of DNA on L-strand and H-strand is in the opposite directions (Fig. 15.19).

6. As the growing points move apart, unwinding of the DNA double strand takes place. The unwinding creates torque

since the parental DNA strands cannot unwind freely. The torque is transmitted to the unreplicated part of the molecule, which consequently becomes super-twisted. Supertwisting brings about a conformational strain on the DNA-molecule and prevents it from replicating further. To counteract this effect, a temporary nick is brought about on one of the strands by topoisomerase. This break permits the parental strands to rotate freely on each other thus releaving the strain. The same topoisomerase then seals the break and replication continues.

7. When the L-strand synthesis is finished, then the H-strand synthesis is about $^1/_3$rd of the circle. After L-strand synthesis, the duplex circle is released and H-strand synthesis continues until the synthesis is completed. The gap is then sealed to become continuous.

This model of replication is called **Crain's model**, proposed by Cairn's (1963). This type of replication has been demonstrated in the bacteria *E.coli* and *Bacillus subtilis*, in several viral and plasmid chromosomes and in mitochondrial and chloroplast DNA replication.

### 15.9.2 Replication in linear DNA

DNA polymerases as well as RNA polymerases proceed only in the 5′→3′ direction. In linear DNA, one strand may synthesize a new strand upto the last base and the polymerase then falls off. But to synthesize the other strand the polymerase has to bind at its last base but how it is possible?

Several solutions have been proposed.

1. It is converted to circular DNA as in $T_4$ or lambda phage.
2. Formation of hairpin at the terminus leaving no free end as in mito-DNA of *Paramoecium*.
3. Presence of a number of copies of short repeating units and a mechanism is involved to add or remove units which makes it unnecessary to replicate right upto the very end as in eukaryotic cells.
4. A special protein, which solves the initiation problem of the actual terminus as found in adenoviral DNA, phage $\phi$14 DNA, polio viral DNA etc.

### 15.9.3 Adenoviral DNA Replication

1. DNA synthesis is initiated at the 5' end, fork proceeds and the homologus strand is displaced. When the replication reaches the other end, the single stranded DNA is displaced.
2. Its two ends form a duplex by some sort of base pairing, which acts as the origin of replication.
3. An adenoviral protein is found to be covalently attached to the 5′ end of mature viral DNA via a phosphodiester bond bound to *serine*.
4. The protein carries a primer cytidine nucleotide, binds to end of the adenovirus and the free 3′-OH end of C-nucleotide is used to prime the elongation reaction by the DNA polymerase. Thus a **new strand** is generated whose 5′ end is covalently linked to the initiating C-nucleotide.
5. This protein is displaced and the DNA synthesis proceeds by DNA polymerase.
6. Terminal protein binds to the region located between 9 and 18 bp from the end of DNA. The adjacent region between position 17 and 48 is essential for binding a host protein. So, the initiation complex may be formed between position 9 and 48, a fixed distance from the actual end of DNA (Figs. 15.20/15.21).

### 15.9.4 Rolling Circle Model

Proposed by **Gilbert** and **Dressler** (1968) **Eisen, Pareira de Silva** and **Jacob** (1968). This is the current model for explaining replication in single strand DNA virus e.g., $\phi \times 174$ and the transfer of *E.coli* sex factor.

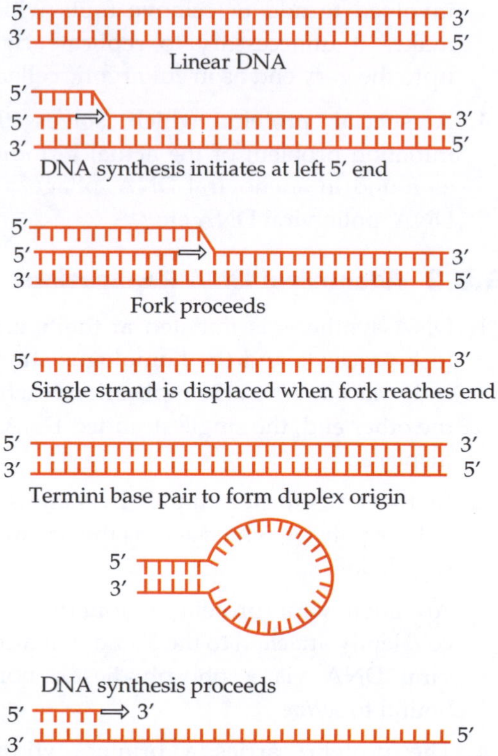


**Fig.15.20 :** *Adenovirus DNA replication is initiated separately at the two ends of the molecule and proceeds by strand displacement.*

The more detailed view of a phage replication cycle that is centered on the rolling circle model.

1. ϕ ×174 phage consists of a single stranded circular DNA known as the plus (+) strand. A complementary strand is called the minus (–), which is synthesized first. Thus a duplex circle is being generated and becomes supercoiled.
2. Phage genome coded an "A"- protein, which creates a nick at the origin of plus strand of the duplex DNA and this protein remains connected to the 5′ end that it generates.
3. The 3′ end serves as a primer for the synthesis of a new DNA strand under the catalytic action of DNA-polymerase. The unbroken strand is used as the template for this purpose and a complementary strand is synthesized. Thus the parental molecule itself is used as a primer for initiating replication.
4. The "A" protein is sometimes called **relaxase**, because, when the tail is displaced and rolling of the circle is completed, then the same "A" protein again recognizes the origin and nicks it. This protein now gets attached to the end, generated by the new nick, and thus the cycle can be repeated indefinitely.

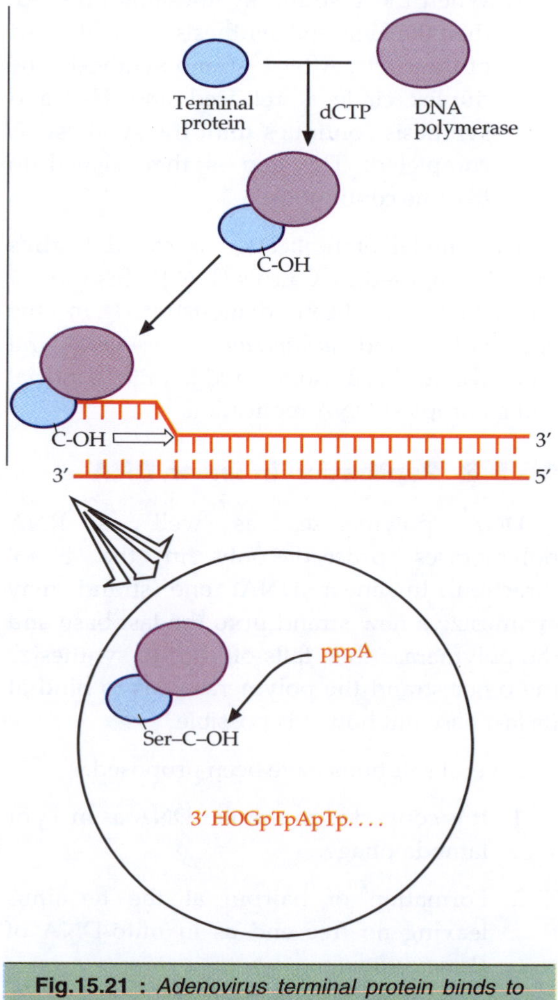


**Fig.15.21 :** *Adenovirus terminal protein binds to the 5′ end of DNA and provides a C–OH end to prime synthesis of a new DNA strand.*

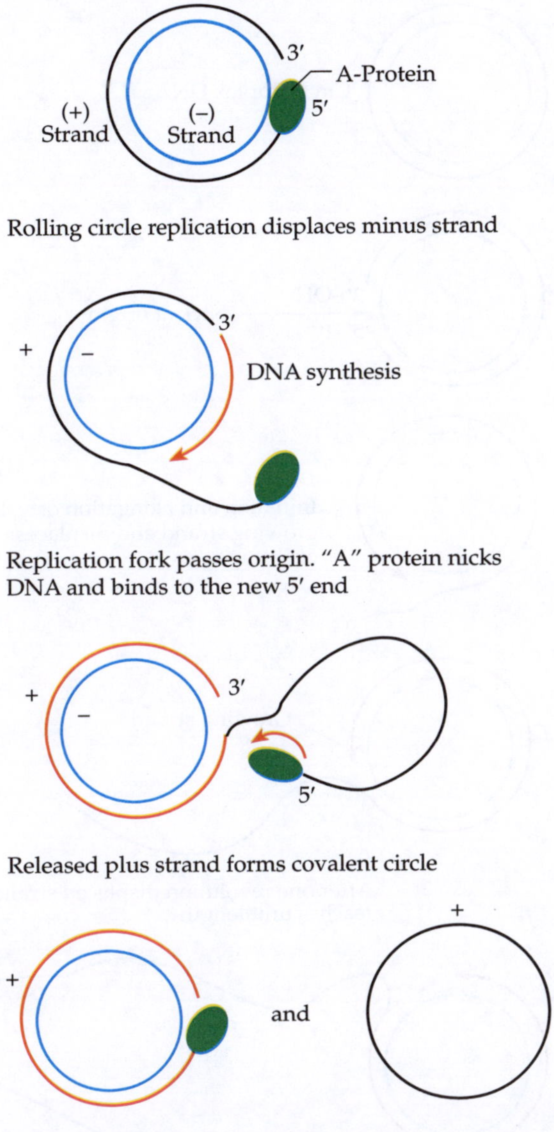


**Fig. 15.22 :** *Replication in φ ×174 RF DNA*

5. As a result a duplex circle and a single (+) strand is released, which then undergoes circularization uniting its 5′ and 3′ ends by "A" protein by its ligase activity. This (+) strand is packaged into the phage again or generates more progeny (Figs. 15.22 and 15.23).

## 15.10 PLASMID REPLICATION

Plasmids encode only a few of the proteins required for their own replication. It encodes only one of the proteins needed for initiation at the *ori* site. All of the other required proteins, including DNA polymerase, ligase, primase, helicase and so on are borrowed from the host.

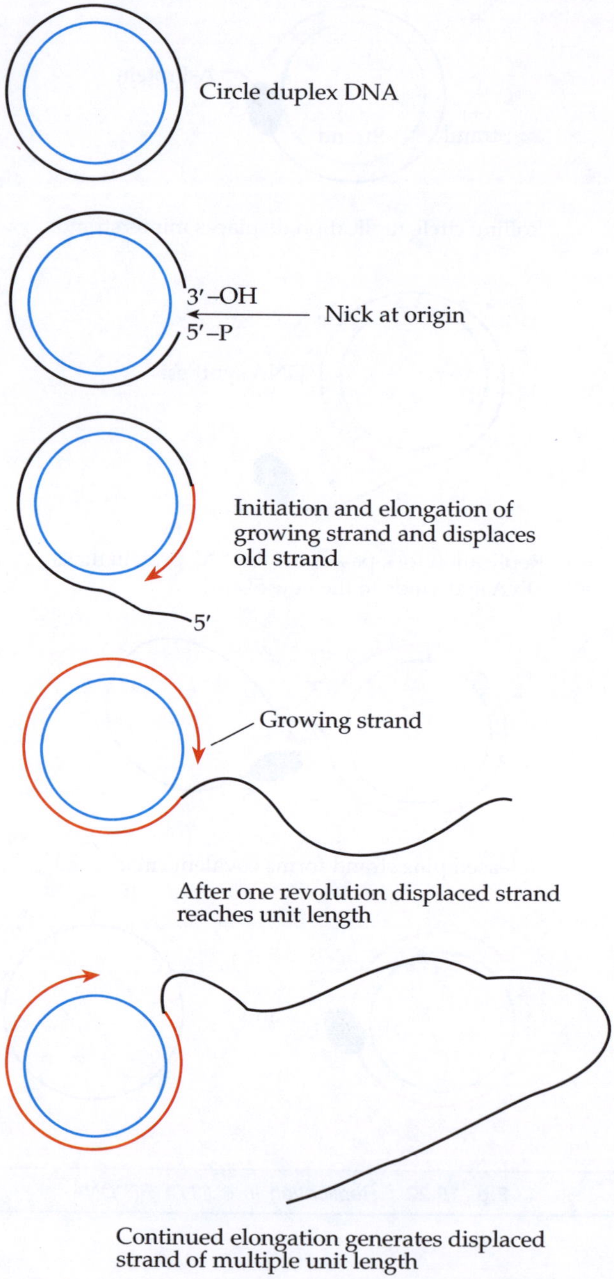


**Fig. 15.23 :** *The rolling circle generates a multimeric single-stranded tail.*

Plasmid replicates by one of the two general mechanisms. Some plasmids, such as the F-plasmid of *E. coli*, have two separate origins of replication. They divide by bi-directional replication (also known as vegetative replication) when their host cells divide, but use the rolling circle mechanism when they move from one cell to another during conjugation. Bidirectional replication starts are *ori V*, the origin of vegetative replication. But during transfer, they use *ori T*.

**Theta replication :** Just after initiation of replication, the circular DNA creates a structure that looks like the Greek letter θ, hence the name theta replication is given. The theta repliation is the most common form of DNA replication, in the bacteria as well as plasmids like ColE 1, RK2, F and P1 etc.

**Rolling circle replication :** The plasmids which replicate by this mechanism are called RC plasmids. The replication occurs in two stages. In the first stage, the double-stranded circular DNA replicates to form another double stranded circular DNA and a single-stranded circular DNA.

In the second stage, the complementary strand is synthesized on the single-stranded DNA to make another double-stranded DNA. The detailed mechanism is as follows :

1. At the first step, the dimeric **Rep** protein recognizes and binds to a palindromic sequence which contains the double-strand origin (DSO) on the DNA.
2. Binding of dimeric Rep protein allows the formation of a cruciform structure. Rep makes a nick there. and remains convalently attached to the 5′-end of DNA at the nick through a *tyr* in one copy of the Rep protein dimer.
3. DNA polymerase III of the host uses the exposed 3′-OH end of the break as the primer for replication and continues replication on the unnicked strand as a template. The host helicase enzyme or in some cases Rep protein itself acts as the helicase to displace the nicked strand. The SSB proteins are also used to displace the DNA strands.
5. Once the circle is complete, the 5′-phosphate is transferred from *tyr* site on the Rep protein to the 5′-OH on the other end of the displaced strand producing an ssDNA strand. This process is called **phsosphotransferase** reaction, requires no energy.
6. Concatemer is not formed here like those in viruses where rolling circle is going on making longer molecules of many times of original length of DNA. Possibly DNA pol-III does keep going past to DSO for a short distance, creating another double-stranded DSO. The other copy of Rep dimer makes a nick at the newly created DSO transferring 5′-end to itself. Thus Rep is being inactivated. Another explanation is that probably involving host DNA ligase causing the nick to be resealed, resulting in a circular dsDNA molecule.
7. The newly synthesized ssDNA molecule is replicated by a different mechanism. The RNA polymerase of host cell makes a short RNA primer at the different origin, called **single stranded origin** (SSO). After making the primer RNA polymerase handed over its 5′-end to the DNA polymerase III to complete the circle. RNA polymerase starts its functions only after the completion of replication, so that the DSO does not appear in the displaced DNA. DNA polymerase-I removes the primer and the nick is sealed by host DNA ligase (Fig. 15.24).
8. The Rep protein is only once for every round of plasmid DNA replication and is destroyed after the round is completed.

**Replication of Linear plasmids :** Linear dsDNA plasmids are found in some bacteria such as *Borrelia* and *Streptomyces,* that also contain linear chromosomes.

Linear plasmids have special structures to protect the end of the DNA. Linear plasmids of *Borrelia* form hairpin loops at the ends, whereas the linear plasmids of *Streptomyces* are coated with proteins that protect the DNA ends (Fig. 15.25).

The linerar DNA faces a problem with replicating the lagging strand, which is called "**primer problem**" because DNA polymerases

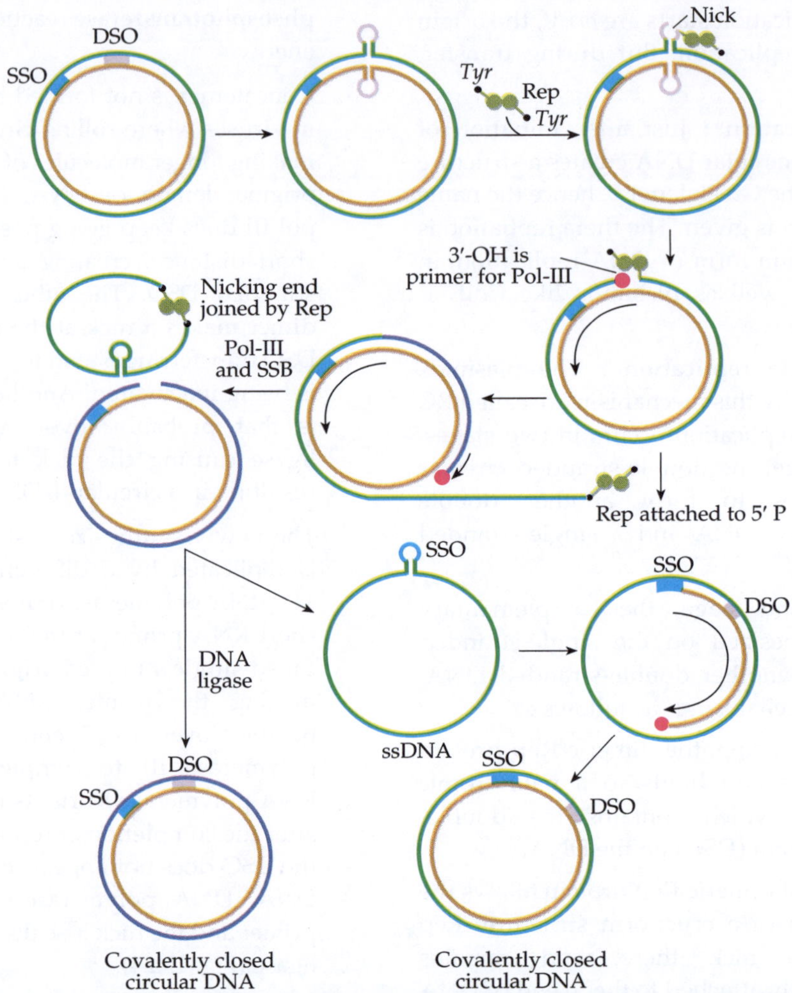


**Fig.15.24:** *Rolling circle replication of plasmid*
*SSO = Single stranded origin, DSO = Double stranded origin*
*SSB = Single strand binding protein, Pol III = DNA polymerase III*

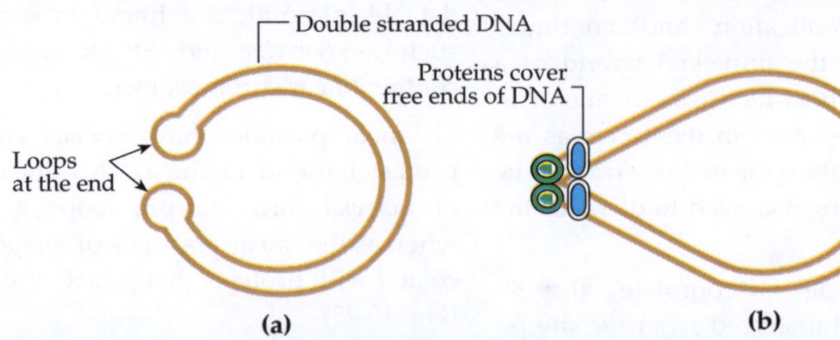


**Fig.15.25 :** *End structures of linear plasmids*
*(a) Hairpin loops of the plasmid of Borrelia*
*(b) Proteins coated to protect the DNA ends in Streptomyces.*

can not initiate the synthsis of a new DNA strand. Different linear DNAs solve the primer problem in different ways.

Some linear plasmids have hairpin ends. These plasmids replicate from an internal origin of replication to form dimeric circles, composed of two plasmids joined head to tail to form a circle. These dimeric circles are then resolved into linear individual linear plasmid DNAs by the enzymes called prototelomerases which cut the circle into two linear plasmid and join the ends to each other to form the closed hairpins.

Other linear plasmids have extensive inverted repeated sequences at their ends and a terminal protein attached to their 5′-end. It is not clear how these plasmids replicate, but they might use some sort of **slippage mechansism,** using terminal protein as either a recombinase or a primer or both.

It is fact that bacteria with linear plasmids also often have linear chromosomes and the two DNAs replicate by similar mechanisms.

**Replication of RNA plasmids :** RNA plasmids are rare and most poorly characterized. Some strains of the yeast, *Saccharomyces cerevisiae* contain linear RNA plasmids. RNA plasmids are also found in mitochondria of some varieties of maize plants. These may be ssRNA or dsRNA forms. They replicate in a manner similar to certain RNA viruses. The RNA plasmid encodes RNA dependent RNA polymerase that directs its own synthesis. But the plasmids do not contain genes for coat proteins. Possibly these RNA plasmids have evolued from RNA viruses that have taken up permanent residence after losing the ability to move from cell to cell as virus particles do.

## Chapter Glossary/Key Terms

**Autonomously replicating sequence (ARS) :** A DNA sequence primarily from yeast, that confers repliative ability on a non replicative plasmid.

**D-loop :** An intermediate structure formed during Meselson-Radding model for homologous recombination. Also an intermediate formed during displacement replication.

**DNA ligase :** An enzyme that synthesizes phosphodiester bonds as part of DNA replication repair and recombination process.

**Klenow polymerase :** A DNA polymerase enzyme, obtained by chemical modification of *E. coli* DNA pol-I, used primarily in chian termination DNA sequencing.

**Kornberg polymerase :** The DNA polymerase-I enzyme of *E. coli.*

**Lagging strand :** The strand of the double helix which is copied in a discontinuous fashion during genome replication.

**Leading strand :** The strand of the double helix which is copied in a continuous fashion during genome replication.

**Okazaki fragment :** One of the short segments of RNA-primed DNA synthesized during replication of the lagging strand of the double helix.

**Origin of replication :** A site of a DNA molecule where replication initiates.

**Origin recognition sequence (ORC) :** A set of proteins that binds to the origin recognition sequence.

**Primase :** The RNA polymerase enzyme that synthesizes RNA primers during bacterial DNA replication.

**Primer :** A short oligonucleotide that is attached to a single-stranded DNA molecule in order to provide a start point for strand synthesis.

**Replication :** The process by which the DNA copies itself to produce identical daughter molecules of DNA.

**Replication eye :** The region in which DNA has been replicated within a longer unreplicated region.

**Replication fork :** The point at which strands of parental duplex DNA are separated so that replication can proceed.

**Replication mediator protein (RMP) :** A protein responsible for detachment of single strand binding proteins during genome replication.

**Replicon :** The unit of genome in which DNA is replicated, contains an orgin for initiation of replication.

**Replisome :** The multiprotein structure that assembles at the bacterial replicating fork to undertake synthesis of DNA, Contains DNA polymerase and other enzymes.

**Rolling circle replication :** A replication process that involves continual synthesis of a polynucleotide which is "rolled off" on a circular template molecule.

**Semiconservative replication :** The mode of DNA replication in which each daughter double helix is made up of one polynucleotide from the parent and one newly synthesized polynucleotide.

**Single strand binding protein :** The protein that attaches to ssDNA in the region of the replication fork, preventing base pairs forming between the two parent strands before they have been copied.

# EXERCISE

## A. Long answer type questions :

1. What is replication? What do you mean by conservative and semiconservative replication? Describe the Meselson and Stahl's experiment on the proof of semiconservative replication.
2. What are the replication enzymes in *E. coli*. Describe their nature and functions in replication process.
3. Describe the functions of different DNA polymerases in eukaryotes.
4. Describe the mechanism of replication in *E. coli.*
5. What are the requirements for replication in *E. coli.*?
6. What do you mean by lagging strand synthesis and leading strand synthesis? Describe these processes?
7. What is coupling synthesis. Describe the mechanism.
8. How the replication in *E. coli* is terminated?
9. What do you mean uni- and bidirectional replication? Give the experimental evidence on bidirectinal replication?
10. Write a note on the replication origin in yeasts and higher eukaryotes.
11. Briefly describe the elongation phase, and termination phase of replication in eukaryotes.

12. Give some examples of inhibition of DNA replication with their role.
13. Shortly, describe the Cairn's model of replication.
14. How linear DNA is replicated?
15. Shortly describe the DNA replication in adenovirus.
16. Describe the Rolling circle model of replication of $\phi \times 174$ phage virus.

**B. Short answer type questions**

1. Define replication.
2. What is $G_0$ stage?
3. Define conservative, semiconservative and dispersive mode of replication.
4. What is Kornberg enzyme?
5. What are the functions of DNA pol-I?
6. Which of the three enzymes in *E. coli* DNA replication possesses proof reading activity?
7. Distinguish between the three *E. coli* replication enzymes.
8. Which eukaryotic DNA pol- has mitochondrial DNA replication activity?
9. What is PCNA?
10. What is replisome?
11. What is the role of DNA gyrase in replication?
12. What is TBP? What is its function?
13. What is the role of SSB in replication?
14. What is DNA helicase? What is its function.
15. What are the components of *ori-C*?
16. What is open complex? How it is formed?
18. What is prepriming complex? How it is formed?
19. What is initial complex? How it is formed?
20. What is fork movement?
21. What is replication fork?
22. Define DNA pol-III HE? What are its constituents?
23. What are DNA Pol III′ and DNA Pol-III*.
24. What are the functions of DNA Pol-III HE.
25. What is the role of β-clamp and clamp loader?
26. How preinitiation complex is formed?
27. What is lagging strand template?
28. How lagging strand synthesis occurs?
29. What is Okazaki fragment?
30. What do you mean by primase activity?
31. What is primosome? What are the components?
32. What is RMP? What is its function?
33. How RNA is eliminated from okazaki fragments and two DNA fragments are joined?
34. What is nicking-closing activity?
35. How the strain due to unwinding of DNA is releived?
36. What do you mean leading strand synthesis?
37. Distinguish leading strand synthesis and lagging strand synthesis?
38. Which enzyme is required for coupling synthesis?
39. What is *ter* sequence for coupling synthesis?
40. What do you mean by unidirectional and bidirectional replication?
41. What are the differces in the replication of archaea from prokaryotes and eukaryotes?
42. What is ARS-1 and ARF-1?
43. What are the characteristics of ori β?
44. What is tag site I and II?
45. What is FEN-I? What is its function.
46. What is the role of RNase H is the remval of RNA?
47. How actinomycin-D inhibit replication?
48. Give the name of some antibiotics which inhibit replication? How they inhibit replication?
49. What are L and H strands in *E. coli*.
50. What is relaxase? Where rolling circle type of replication occur?

16

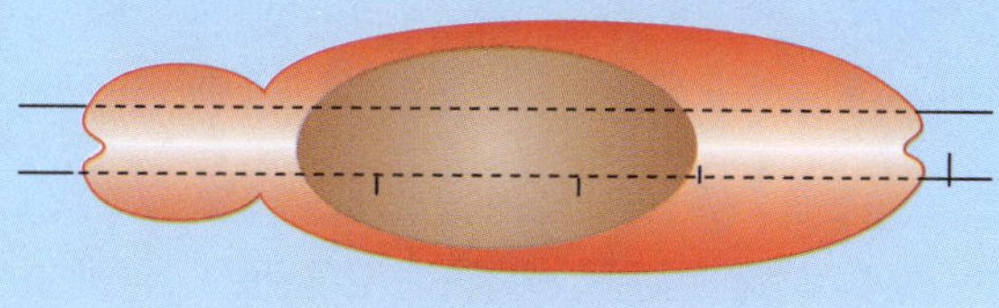

# Transcription of Genome and Processing RNA

**CHAPTER AGENDA**

## 16.1. CONCEPT OF TRANSCRIPTION

Biosynthesis of proteins is under direct control of DNA in most cases or else under the control of genetic RNA where DNA is absent. Information for the structure of a polypeptide is stored in a polynucleotide chain. The sequences of bases in a particular segment of a polynucleotide chain determine the sequence of amino acids in a particular polypeptide. The relationship is popularly known as **CENTRAL DOGMA**. It explains how protein synthesis is directed by the nucleic acids. ***Flow of information is transferred to mRNA by a process of transcription and then to proteins by translation.***

$$\text{DNA} \xrightarrow{\text{Transcription}} \text{mRNA} \xrightarrow{\text{Translation}} \text{Protein}$$

Transcription is an enzymatic process converts the genetic information of a segment of DNA (gene) into mRNA strand, with a base sequence complementary to one of the DNA strands.

The sequences of the two strands of the DNA are different and serve different functions during transcription. The strand that serves as template for RNA synthesis is called **template strand** or **minus strand**. The DNA strand complementary to template strand is called **nontemplate strand** or **plus strand or coding strand.**

The template strand transcribes mRNA while the nontemplate strand has no direct function in transcription. It may serve as regulatory sequences that are needed for transcription. In some bacteria, one strand transcribes clock-wise and another anticlockwise directions.

## 16.2. RNA POLYMERASES

### 16.2.1. Prokaryotic RNA pol

*E. coli* has single DNA – directed RNA – polymerase that synthesizes all types of RNA. It is larger (Mr.=390000) and is a complex enzyme. containing 5 core subunits and a 6th subunit called ó factor (Mr. 70000) that binds transiently to the core and directs the enzyme to specific initiation sites on the DNA. These 6 subunits constitute the RNA polymerase holoenzyme.

The holoenzyme comprises two-α (Mr. 40 K Deach), one-β (Mr. 155 kD), one β′ (Mr.=160 kD), one ω (Mr.=11000) and one σ (Mr. 70000) subunits (Fig. 16.1).

α subunit functions as promoter binding.

β subunit functions as nucleotide binding and binding with σ-subunit.

β′ subunit functions as template binding.

σ subunit functions as initiation of transcription.

ω subunit is required for the assembly of all the subunits to form an RNA polymerase HE.

Three dimensional crystallography structure of RNA polymerase shows that, it has a rudder, that displaces the newly formed RNA, allowing the two strands of DNA behind the polymerase to rewind (its dimension is 90 ×95 ×160Å). A short region of DNA–RNA hybrid of nine nucleotides length is formed transiently and a **window** of DNA/RNA helix therefore moves along the DNA with the polymerase.

RNA polymerase lacks a proof reading 3′→5′ exonuclease activity such as found in many DNA polymerases. As a result, during transcription about one error is made for every $10^4$–$10^5$ nucleotides incorporated into RNA (Fig. 16.2).

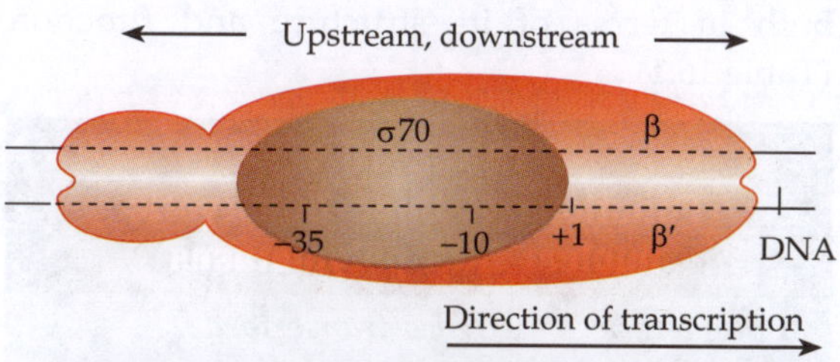


**Fig.16.1 :** *Subunit structure of E.coli. RNA polymerase*

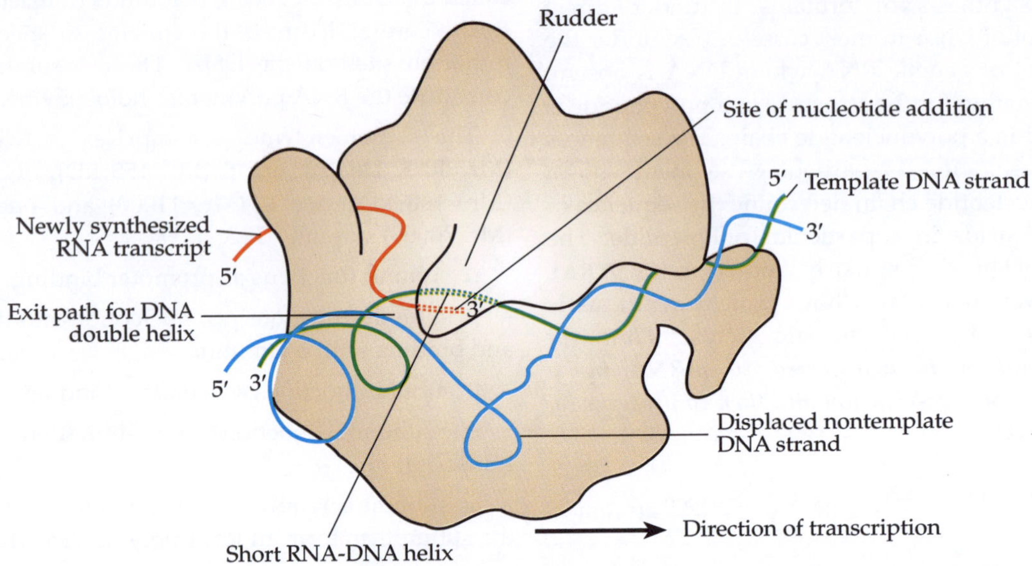


**Fig.16.2 :** *Structure of a bacterial RNA polymerase.*

### 16.2.2. Eukaryotic RNA pol

Eukaryotic cells have 3 kinds of RNA polymerases, designated as I, II and III. Each has specific functions and binds to different promoter sequences. Each is a multisubunit protein (8–12 subunits) with a molecular mass in excess of 500 kDa. Structurally, these polymerases are quite similar to one another. The three largest subunits are closely related and some of the smaller ones are being shared by more than one enzyme, however, functionally they are quite distinct. The 6 subunits have its own special properties both in terms of its structure and function (Table 16.1) .

**TABLE 16.1**
**Functions of three Eukaryotic nuclear RNA polymerases**

| *Polymerase* | *Genes transcribed* |
|---|---|
| RNA Polymerase I | 28S, 5.8S and 18S rRNA genes. |
| RNA Polymerase II | Protein-coding genes, sn RNA genes. |
| RNA Polymerase III | Genes for tRNAs, 5SrRNA, U6-snRNA, small nucleolar (sno) RNAs, small cytoplasmic (sc) RNA. |

RNA pol II has the central function of synthesizing mRNAs as well as some special functions. This enzyme must recognizes thousands of promoters, many of which share some key sequence similarities in most eukaryotes. These sequences are generally binding sites for proteins called **transcription factors**, which modulate the binding of RNA polymerase to the promoter.

### 16.2.3 Archaea RNA pol

Archaea possesses a single RNA polymerase that is very similar to eukaryotic enzymes (Bult *et al.*, 1996). But this is not typical of the prokaryotes in general, because the bacterial polymerase is very different, consisting $\alpha_2 \beta\beta'\sigma$ subunits.

### 16.2.4. Mitochondrial RNA pol

Mitochondrial RNA polymerase consists of a single subunit with a molecular mass of 140kDa. This enzyme is more closely related to the RNA polymerases of certain bacterio-phages than it is to the bacterial RNA polymerase. The polymerase works in conjugation with at least two additional proteins one of which is

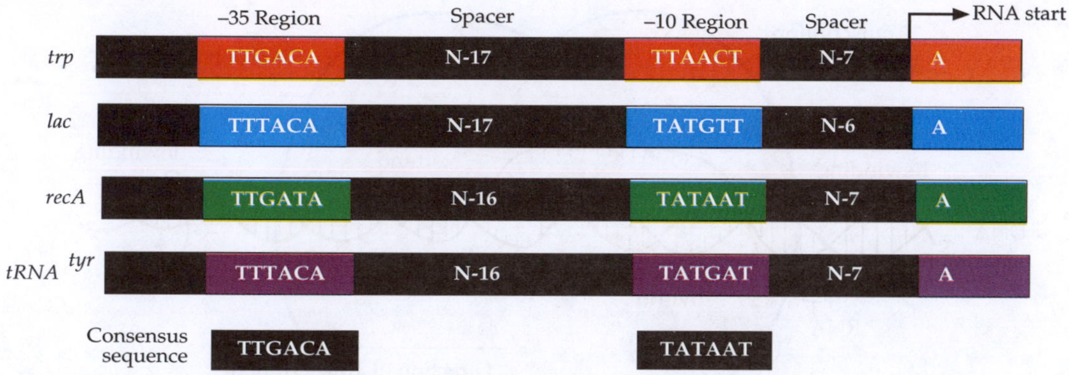


**Fig.16.3 :** *The sequences of four promoters of E.coli and the consensus sequence of –35 region and –10 region.*

transcription factor called mtTF1 in mammals and ABF2 in *Saccharomyces cerevisiae*, which binds to mitochondrial promoters and enhances initiation of transcription.

### 16.2.5. Chloroplast RNA pol

Chloroplast RNA polymerases appear to be much more similar to the bacterial RNA polymerase and their promoters are also like that of *E. coli*.

## 16.3. TRANSCRIPTION IN PROKARYOTES

### 16.3.1. Recognition Sequences for Transcription Initiation

The RNA polymerase binds to specific sequences in the DNA, called **promoters** by cyclic AMP receptor protein (CRP), which directs the transcription of adjacent segments of DNA (gene).

Analysis and comparison of sequences in many different bacterial promoters have revealed similarities in two short sequences located about 10-35 bp. away from the point where RNA synthesis is initiated. By convension the base pair that begins an RNA molecule is given the number +1, so, these sequences are conventionally called the –10 and –35 regions (centre of the consensus sequence).

The sequences are not identical for all bacterial promoters but certain nucleotides are found much more often than other at each position. The most common nucleotides from what are called **consensus sequence**. For most promoters in *E.coli* and related bacteria, the consensus sequence for the –10 region (actually from –8 to –12) is called **Pribnow Box** (after David Pribnow, 1975) is 5′ TATAAT 3′ and the consensus sequence at the –35 region is 5′ TTGACA 3′, **which is present in the coding strand of DNA**.

The conservation of the 6 bases of Pribnow Box varies from 45% to 96% as represented by subscript in the following sequence $T_{80}$ $A_{95}$ $T_{45}$ $A_{60}$ $A_{50}$ $T_{96}$.

The recognition region (–35 region) has the conservation of their bases are represented 5′ $T_{82}$ $T_{84}$ $G_{78}$ $A_{65}$ $C_{54}$ $A_{45}$ 3′ (Fig. 16.3).

### 16.3.2. Recognition and Binding

It has been suggested that –35 sequence provides the signal for recognition by RNA polymerase while, the –10 sequence allows the complex to convert from closed to open form. Thus –35 sequence comprising a **recognition domain** and –10 sequence comprises an **unwinding domain** of the promoter.

The interaction of RNA polymerase with the recognition site requires some ancillary proteins.

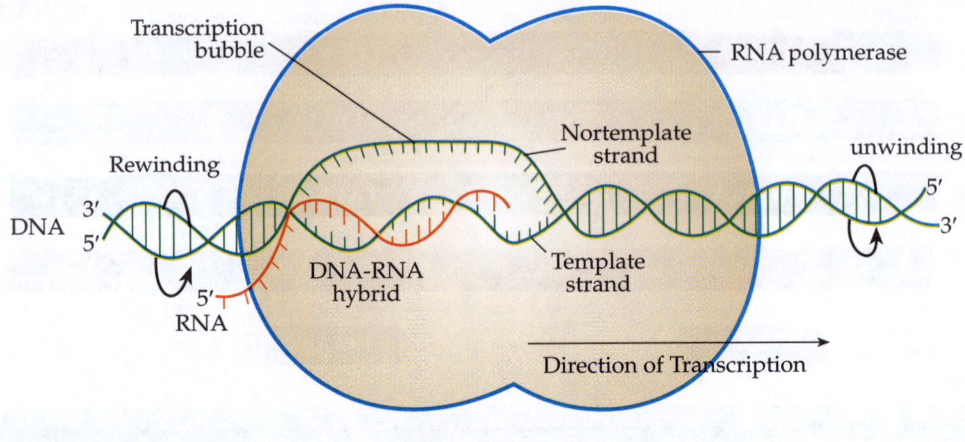


**Fig.16.4 :** *Transcription by RNA polymerase.*

RNA polymerase binds to one face of DNA with the promoter in at least two steps. The holoenzyme first binds to the DNA and then migrates to the –35 region, forming what is called the **closed complex**.

Sigma factor has sequence-specific DNA binding domains that recognizes the promoter DNA. When sigma factor is independent, it does not bind to DNA, but when holozyme forms a tight binding complex sigma factor contacts the DNA in the region upstream of the start point. This difference is due to change in the conformation of sigma factor when it binds to core enzyme. The N-terminal region of free sigma factor suppresses the activity of the DNA binding region. When sigma binds to core, this inhibition is released and it becomes able to bind specifically to the promoter sequences.

Where the recognition of promoter occurs at –35 region and forms a **closed complex**, the RNA polymerase spans some 60 bp from the upstream of the –35 region to the downstream of the –10 box. This is followed by melting of the base pairs within the –10 box to produce the **open complex**. The –10 box comprises mainly or entirely of A=T base pairs which are weaker than G≡C pairs.

**Open complex :** DNA is then unwound for about 17 base pairs beginning at the –10 region exposing the template strand at the initiation site. RNA synthesis then begins. Once a few phosphodiester bonds are formed the sigma subunit dissociates leaving the core polymerase to complete synthesis of the RNA molecule.

*About 17 base pairs are unwound at any given time. A short DNA–RNA hybrid (12bp) is present in the unwound region.* The transcription bubble moves from left to right keeping pace with RNA synthesis. The DNA is unwound ahead and rewound behind as RNA is transcribed.

As the DNA is rewound the DNA–RNA hybrid is displaced and the RNA strand is extruded from the complex via a channel formed partly by the β and partly by β′ subunits (Korzheva *et al* 2000).

As the supercoiling of DNA is brought about by transcription, positive supercoils form ahead of transcription bubble and negative supercoils form behind. The active site for RNA synthesis and the DNA template both lie between β and β′ subunits, while the nontemplate strand of DNA held within the β-subunit (Fig. 16.4).

### 16.3.3. Elongation

Chain elongation takes place by addition of activated ribonucleoside triphosphates (ATP, GTP, CTP and UTP) to one strand of the DNA template. For each nucleotide added to the growing RNA chain, a pyrophosphate (PPi) is given off. This pyrophosphate is rapidly hydrolyzed to Pi. The synthesis of the RNA chain is energized by the expenditure of energy in the form of PPi. The entire reaction is as follows:

$$\text{DNA template + ATP, GTP, CTP, UTP} \xrightarrow{\text{RNA Pol.}} \text{DNA template + P~P + RNA Polymer (AMP, GMP, CMP, UMP)}$$

The first base of RNA synthesized in the transcription is always purine, either pppG or pppA. In *E. coli*, most chains start with pppG (while $\phi \times 174$ and $T_7$ bac-phage, chain starts with pppA).

Growing of RNA chain is always in the $5' \rightarrow 3'$ direction. If RNA chain is synthesized in the $5' \rightarrow 3'$ direction, the first nucleotide would have a triphosphate group. On the other hand, the chain grows in a $3' \rightarrow 5'$ direction; the triphosphate group would be on the nucleotides at the growing end. It has been found that triphosphate group is always attached to the first nucleotide, *which confirmed that RNA chain grows in* $5' \rightarrow 3'$*direction.*

Elongation of the RNA chain takes place by means of the core enzyme, which moves along the DNA template (Fig. 16.5).

1. σ factor and core enzyme join to form RNA polymerase HE. σ factor displaces NusA from $\alpha_2\beta\beta'$ NusA complex of RNA polymerase and attaches to the initiation site.
2. DNA unwinds and core enzyme catalyses the synthesis of mRNA and about 7–10 nucleotides are synthesized.
3. After commencement of chain elongation the sigma factor dissociates from the core enzyme. It can now be used by another polymerase molecule. *The release of sigma factor may be taken place either because it is no longer required or because its presence might hinder the effective movement of the enzyme along the DNA template.* Dissociation of this σ factor marks the entry of **NusA** (N-utilization) protein, which helps elongation and promotes pausing and termination at specific site. NusA protein possibly may be a subunit of RNA polymerase.
4. After the dissociation of sigma factor, the core enzyme now undergoes a major conformational rearrangement and a stable **ternary elongation complex** is formed. This complex moves along DNA, synthesizing RNA all along its path at a rate of about 40 bp/sec at 37°C and the elongation of RNA continues till an unstable termination complex is formed.
5. M. J. Chamberlin (1993) proposed the **Inchworm model** for elongation. RNA polymerase has two sites for DNA binding (leading product site and lagging product site) and also has a catalytic site. When the leading product site gets filled by about 10 nucleotides, in each elongation cycle, the lagging product site goes forward and thus about 2-10 nucleotides of mRNA are being extruded from the lagging product site (Fig. 16.6).

### 16.3.4. Termination of Transcription

The termination of mRNA chain synthesis in prokaryotes is brought about by certain termination signals on the DNA. These DNA sequences providing signal are called **terminators.**

In *E. coli*, there are at least two classes of terminators. One is ρ–dependent and the other is ρ–independent. In both the cases, the polymerase has to reach a position on the template where dissociation is more favourable than RNA synthesis.

**ρ-independent termination** : At the terminator region of *E. coli*, DNA contains an inverted palindrome followed by a run of deoxyadenosine nucleotides. The palindrome region constitutes G≡C rich bases. As the RNA

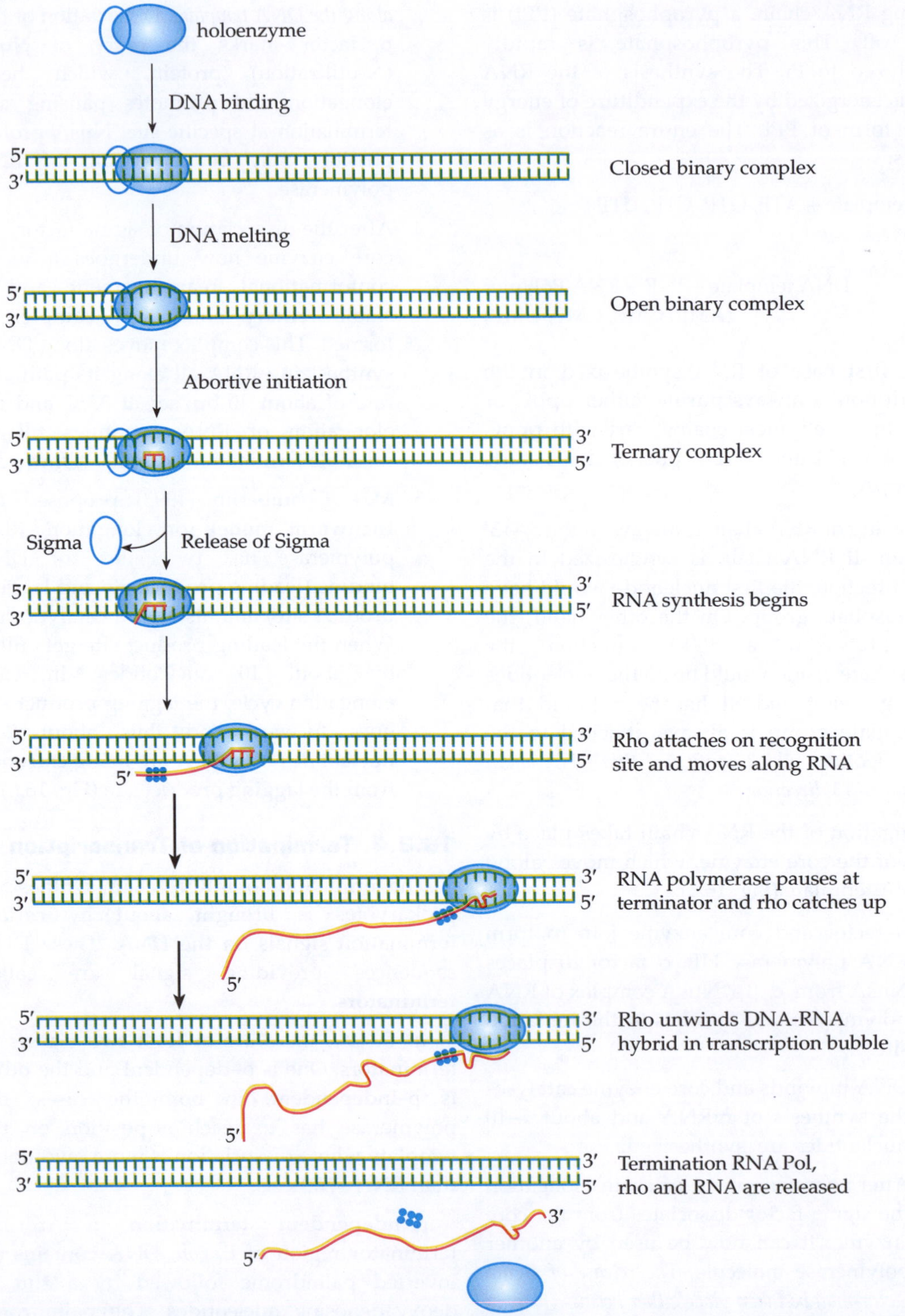


**Fig.16.5 :** *Initiation, elongation and termination of transcription in E.coli.*

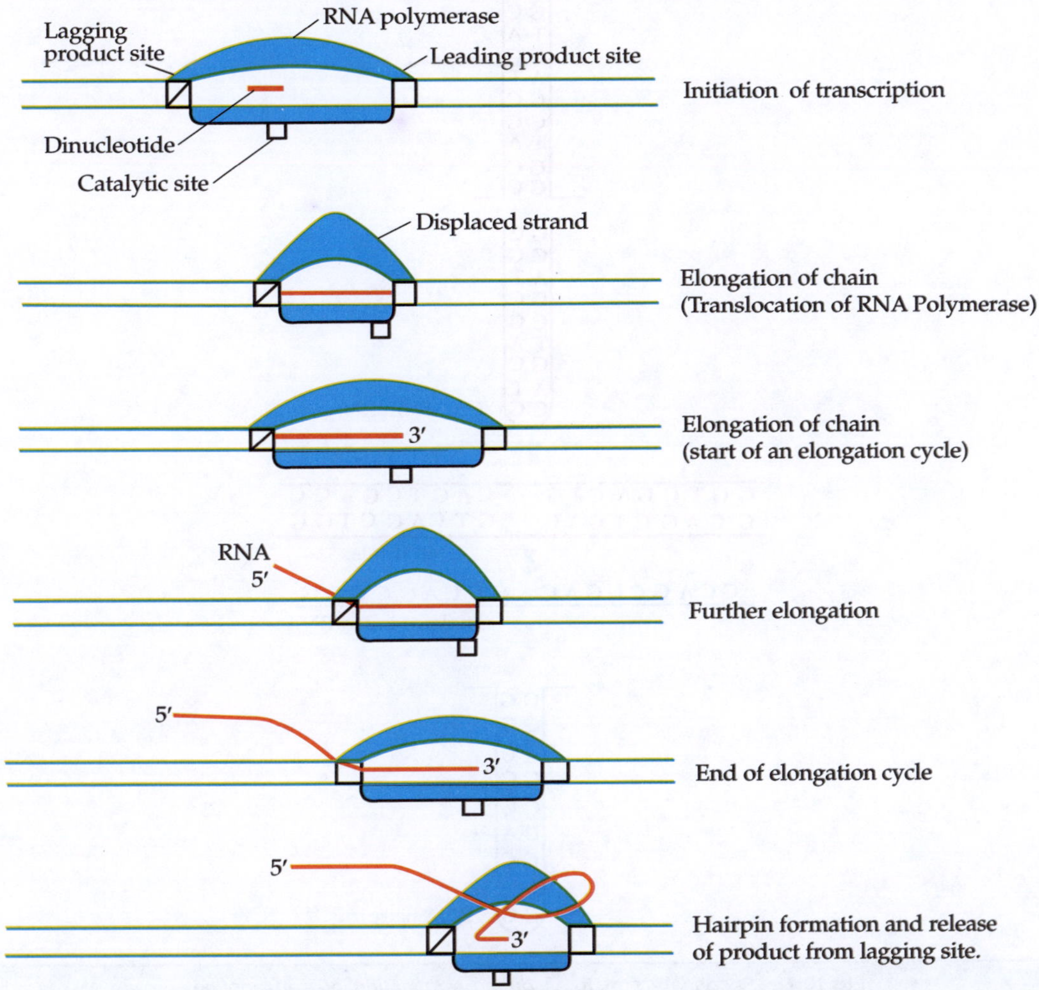


**Fig.16.6 :** *Inchworm model of transcription.*

polymerase reaches to that palindrome region, the RNA transcript is synthesized but DNA forms a cruciform structure and the RNA is folded into a hairpin structure (Fig.16.7).

The RNA polymerase halts there. The hairpin structure (RNA–RNA base pairing), which occurs within the transcription bubble reduces the contacts between the template and the transcript, weakening the overall interaction and favouring dissociation.

The ***long run of A*** and its ***transcript*** U-pairing (A=U) also weakened the interaction, because A=U has two H- bonds, compared to three H-bonds, in between G≡C pair. The net result favours termination over continued elongation. (Hippel, 1998).

Toulokhonov (2001) demonstrated that RNA-hairpin makes contact with a flap structure on the outer surface of the β–subunit of RNA polymerase adjacent to the exit point of the channel through which the RNA emerges out from the point. This interaction between the RNA-hairpin and the flap causes to affect the positioning of amino acids within the active site;

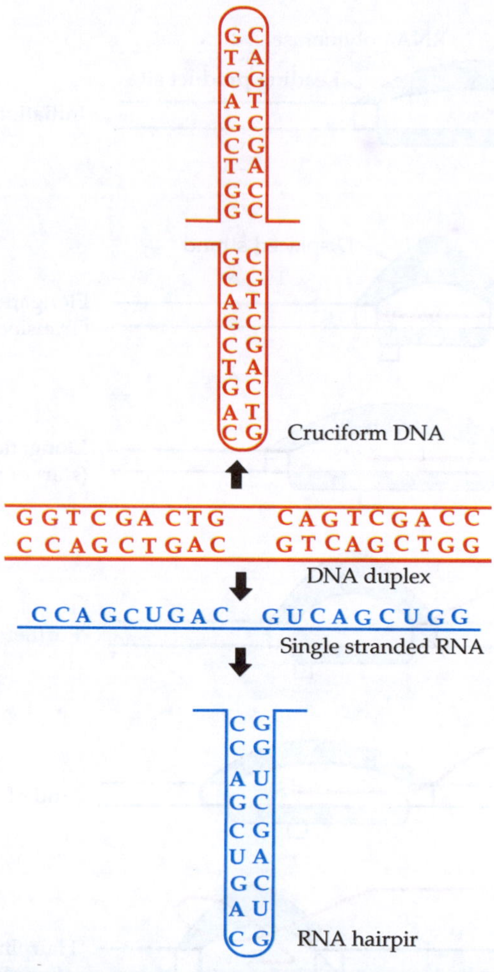


**Fig.16.7 :** *Secondary structures during termination of transcription.*

that possibly causing the break down of DNA-RNA hybrid, leading to termination. The protein NusA, also enhances such interaction between hairpin loop and flap structure and may stabilize the contact between them. Thus hairpin is necessary but not sufficient for termination.

**ρ-dependent termination :** ρ-factor is a protein of ~ 46kD, probably active as a hexamer (275kD).

The sequences required for ρ–dependent terminator are 50-90 bases long, lies upstream of the terminator. The RNA is C-rich and G-poor. It also forms a hairpin due to presence of palindrome sequences on DNA but have no run of dexyribouridine at their 3′ terminal end.

The **Hot pursuit** model for ρ–action described that ρ binds to specific type of sequence, which is present just at the 5′ end of the nascent mRNA. ρ then translocates along the mRNA but moves more rapidly than the movement of RNA polymerase.

The RNA polymerase pauses when it reaches to a terminator, thus ρ catches it there. It may affect on the RNA polymerase causing its release from the DNA-RNA hybrid, but how, it is not known.

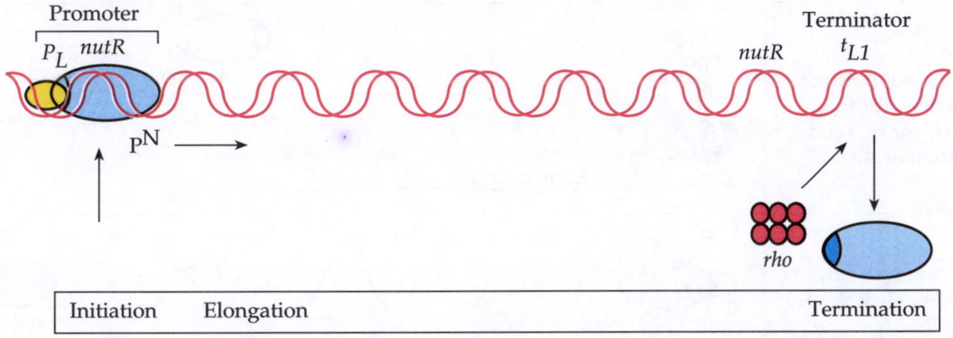


**Fig.16.8 :** *Immediate early transcription is terminated by the rho-factor.*

In absence of RNA polymerase, ρ has an ATP dependent 5′→3′ helicase activity that causes separation of RNA from the hybrid either by unwinding or by the interaction between ρ and RNA polymerase.

### 16.3.5 Molecular mechanism of Termination of Transcription

**NusA, NusB** and **NusG** functions are concerned solely with the termination of transcription. *NusE* codes for ribosomal protein S-10, located in 30S subunit but it's function is not clear.

1. NusA is a general transcription factor, which enhances RNA pol to pause at the termination site (Fig. 16.8).
2. NusB and S-10 form a dimer that binds RNA pol as it elongates *box A*. But in lambda phage RNA, does not bind to Nus B-S10 and is probably enabled to do so by the presence pN and NusA. *Box B* sequence could be required to stabilize the reaction.
3. NusA binds to RNA pol core enzyme but does not bind to holoenzyme. When sigma factor is added to $\alpha_2\beta\beta'$NusA complex, it displaces NusA protein; thus it reconstitutes the αββ′σHE. Again when $\alpha_2\beta\beta'\sigma$ binds to promoter, it releases its sigma factor and thus generates the core enzyme $\alpha_2\beta\beta'$ to synthesize RNA.

Then a NusA protein recognizes the core enzyme and binds to it to generate $\alpha_2\beta\beta'$ NusA-polymerase complex. It binds to DNA. NusA component cannot be displaced. But when termination occurs, the enzyme is released in a state in which the Nus factor either is released or can be displaced by sigma factor.

Thus core enzyme alternates between the association of sigma factor for initiation and association of Nus for termination (Fig. 16.9).

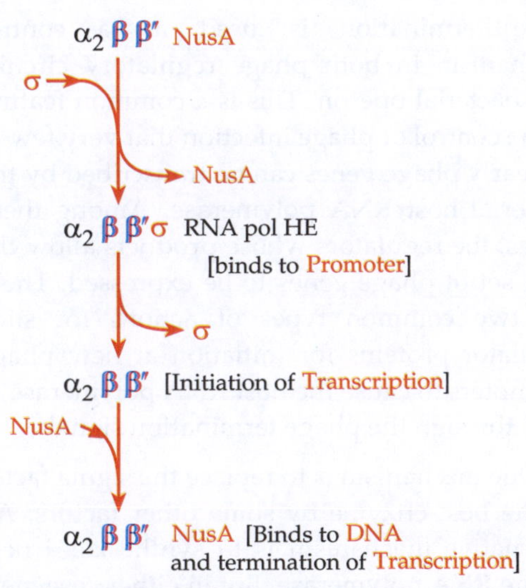


**Fig. 16.9 :** *Mechanism of termination of transcription*

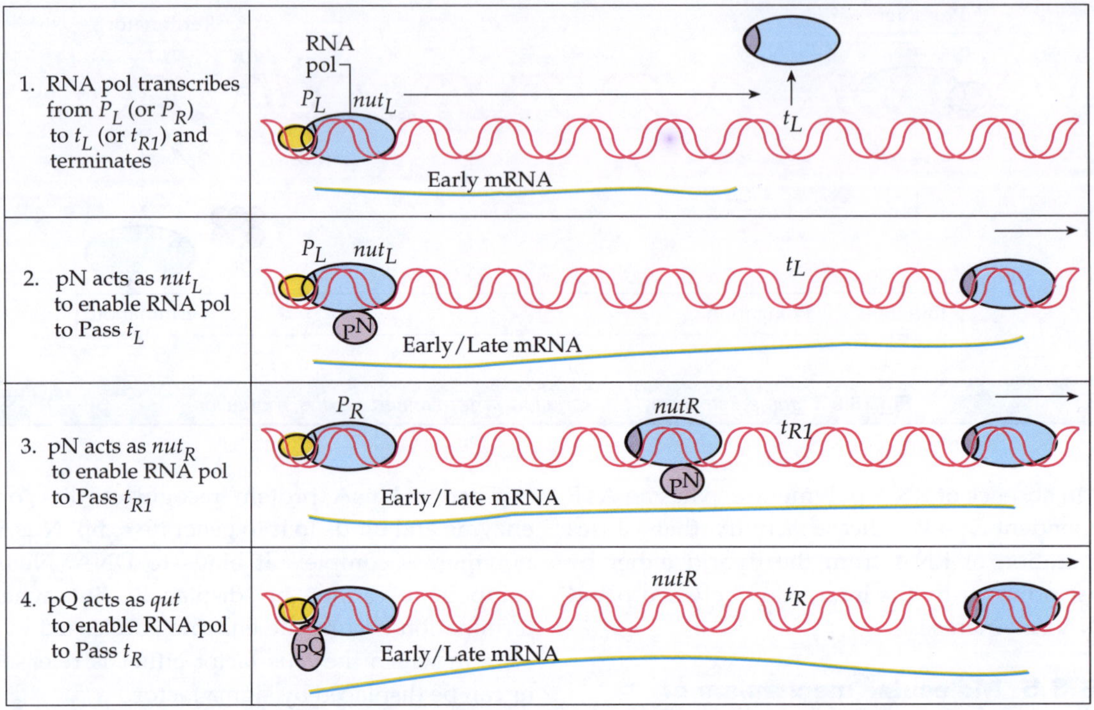


**Fig. 16.10 :** *Mechanisms of antitermination.*

## 16.3.6 Antitermination of Transcription

Antitermination is used as a control mechanism in both phage regulatory circuits and bacterial operon. This is a common feature in the control of phage infection that very few of the early phage genes can be transcribed by the bacterial host RNA polymerase. Among these genes, the regulators whose products allow the next set of phage genes to be expressed. There are two common types of actions for such regulator proteins for initiation at new phage promoters to cause the host RNA polymerase to read through the phage termination signals.

One mechanism is to replace the sigma factor of the host enzyme by some other factors. An alternative mechanism is to synthesize a new phage RNA polymerase. But in either case, new set of genes is distinguished in their possession of different promoters from those originally recognized by host RNA polymerase. The two sets of transcripts are independent. Early expression of gene can be ceased after the new sigma factor or polymerase has been produced.

The antitermination depends on a particular arrangement of genes. The early genes lie just adjacent to the next gene to be produced, but are separated by **terminator site**. If termination prevents at these sites, the polymerase continues to read through the gene. Here same promoter is recognized by the same RNA polymerase. Thus a long mRNA chain is formed (Fig. 16.10).

1. In lambda phage, there are two transcription units of immediate early genes which are transcribed from the promoters $P_L$ and $P_R$. Transcription by *E. coli* RNA plymerase itself stops at $t_L$ and $t_R$ terminators respectively.
2. When *N* gene is expressed, the product pN is an antitermination protein. This

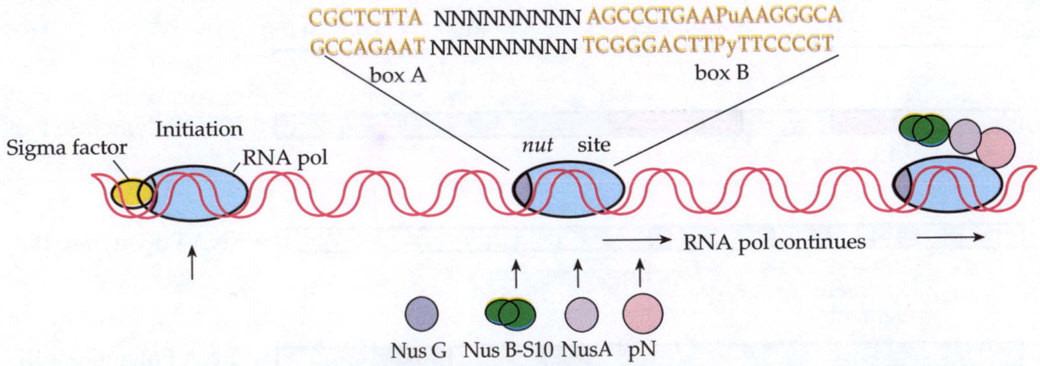


**Fig. 16.11 :** *Delayed early transcription is extended by several factors that act at nut.*

protein allows RNA polymerase to read through $t_{L_1}$ and $t_{R_1}$ to transcribe beyond the early gene next to it.

3. This switch is regulated by gene *Q* (itself a delayed early gene). Its product pQ is also an antitermination protein. It allows RNA polymerase to initiate at another site *pR* (late promoter) to read through a terminator that lies between it and the late gene.
4. The recognition sites required for pN action are called *nut* (Nutilization). The sites determine leftward and rightward antitermination are called *nut L* and *nut R* respectively. The *nut L* is located between the start point of $P_L$ and the beginning of the N coding regions. The *nut R* is located between the end of the *cro* gene and $t_{L1}$. So, *nut L* is nearer to promoter but *nut R* is nearer to terminator. The *qut* lies within promoter.
5. When pN recognizes the *nut* site, it acts on RNA polymerase to ensure the RNA polymerase can no longer respond to the terminator.

The *nut* site consists of two sequences. Nus B S10 joins core enzyme as it passes *box A*. The NusA and pN protein bind as RNA polymearse passes box B. The presence of pN allows the enzyme pass through the terminator. Thus a long mRNA is transcribed containing both early and late genes (Fig. 16.11).

## 16.4. TRANSCRIPTION IN EUKARYOTES

### 16.4.1. Eukaryotic Promoters

The eukaryotic promoters are termed to describe all the sequences those are important in initiation of transcription of a gene. Sometimes the sequences can be numerous. Not only the **core promoter** (sometimes called basal promoter), which is the site at which the initiation complex is assembled, but also there is one or more **upstream promoter elements** (UPE), upstream of the core promoter. These UPEs are required to promote gene expression after binding with activators of transcription.

Each of the three types of eukaryotic RNA polymerase recognizes a different types of promoter sequence (Fig.16.12).

1. RNA polymerase-I transcribes only the genes for rRNA, from a single type of promoter. The promoter has a bipartite sequence. The core promoter spanning the transcription start point between –45 and +20 and an **upstream control element** (UCE) about 100bp farther upstream. Both regions have an unusual composition, being G≡C rich base pairs and these are about 85% identical.

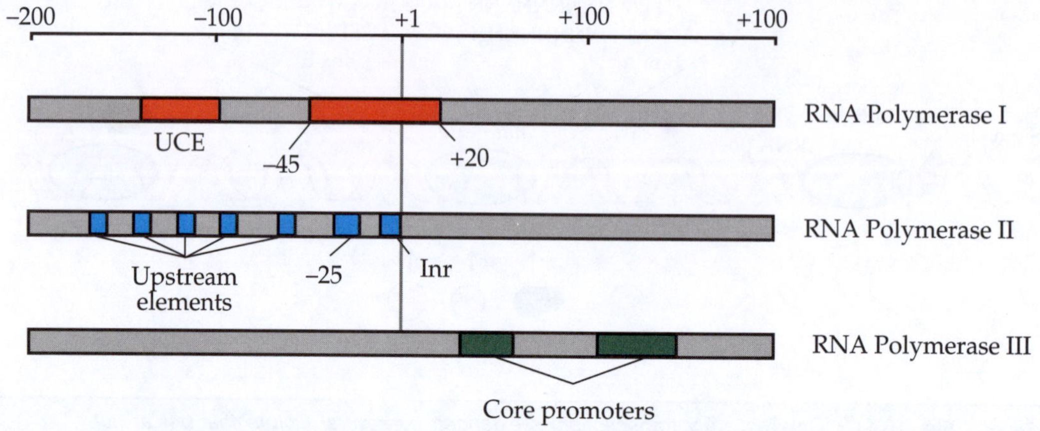


**Fig.16.12 :** *Structure of eukaryotic promoters.*

2. RNA polymerase III promoters are unusual and are located within the genes whose transcription they promote. These promoters are variable.

   Promoters for 5S rRNA and tRNA genes are internal; they lie downstream of the start point and lie between positions +55 and +80 within the gene.

   The structure of RNA polymerase-III falling into three categories. Two types are of internal promoter, each containing a bipartite structure in which two short sequence elements are separated by a variable sequence. Type 1 consists of box-A and box-C. Type 2 consists of a box A sequence separated from a box-B sequence.

   The third class of RNA pol-III promoter has three upstream elements. The TATA element and two upstream elements, PSE and OCT which increase the efficiency of transcription (Fig.16.13).

3. RNA polymerase II promoters are variable and can stretch for several kilobases upstream of the transcription start site and can be looked on as a series of modules.

   (a) The core promoter modules consist of two segments, the –25 or **TATA box** (consensus sequence 5′TATAWAW3′

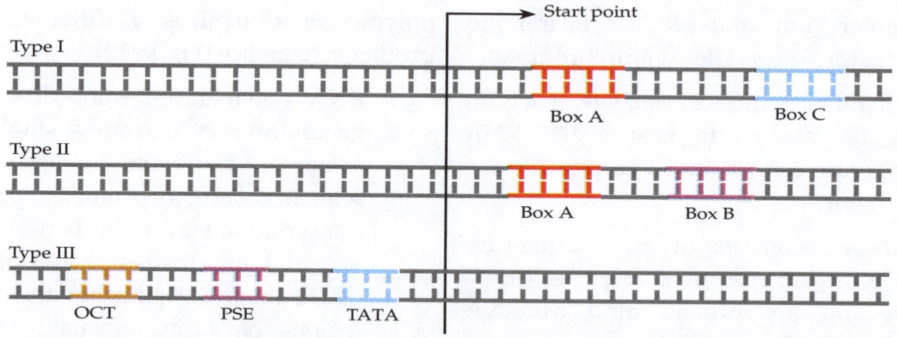


**Fig.16.13 :** *Different promoters of RNA pol III.*

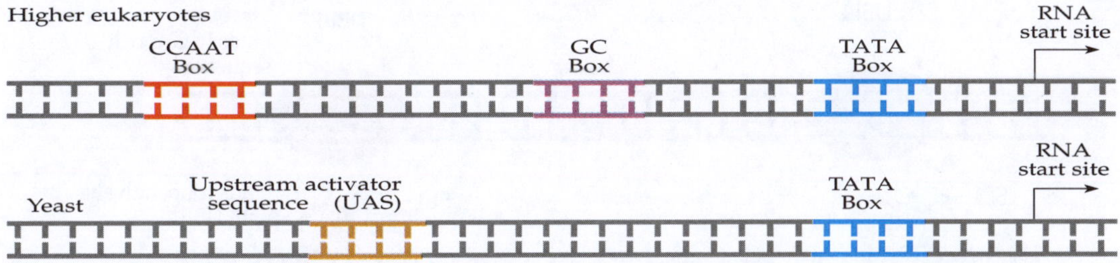


**Fig.16.14 :** *Generalalized eukaryotic promoters with some typical binding sites for regulatory proteins.*

where, W is A or T) and the initiator (**Inr** sequence, consensus, 5′YYCARR3′ where Y is C or T and R is A or G) located around nucleotide +1 position.

Some genes transcribed by RNA pol II have only one of these two components of the core promoter. Again some genes transcribe without having any one of these. They are called **null genes.** A sequence called MED-1 lies within these genes (Novina and Roy 1996).

(b) Basal promoter elements are modules that are present in many promoters and set the basal level of transcription initiation without responding to any tissue specific or developmental signals. These include the **CAAT Box** (consensus 5′-GGCCAATCT-3'), which is recognised by NF-1 & NF-Y. The second one is **GC-Box** (consesus - 5′GGGCGG3′), recognized by Spl activator. The third one is the **octamer module** (consensus 5′ATGCAAAT3′) recognized by Oct-1 (Fig. 16.14).

(c) **Response modules** are found upstream of various genes and transcription is initiated after responding to signals from outside the cell. For example, cAMP response module CRE (consensus 5′-WCGTCA-3′), recognized by CREB activator; **heat –shock module** (consensus 5′CTNGAATNTTCTAGA3') recognized by HSP 70.

(d) Cell specific module located in the promoters of the genes. For example, the thyroid module (consensus 5′ WGATAR 3′), which is a binding site for GATA-1 activator; the pituitary cell module (consensus 5′-ATATTCAT-3′) recognized by Pit-1.

(e) Modules for developmental regulators mediate expression of genes which are active only in the specific stages of the development.

For example, in *Drosophila*, the **bicoid module** (consensus 5′-TCCTAATCCC-3′.

## 16.4.2. Transcription Initiation with RNA Polymerase - I

During initiation of transcription with RNA polymerase-I, UBF1, a single polypeptide binds to G–C rich region in the core promoter and UCE. Once UBF1 has bound, SL1 can bind cooperatively to extend the region of DNA that is covered. After the binding of these two proteins, RNA polymerase can bind to core promoter to initiate transcription. SL1 (in humans) and TIF B in mice consist of 4 proteins, one of them is TBP (TATA binding protein), which does not bind directly to G–C rich region of DNA. SL1 resembles sigma factor of *E coli* (Fig.16.15).

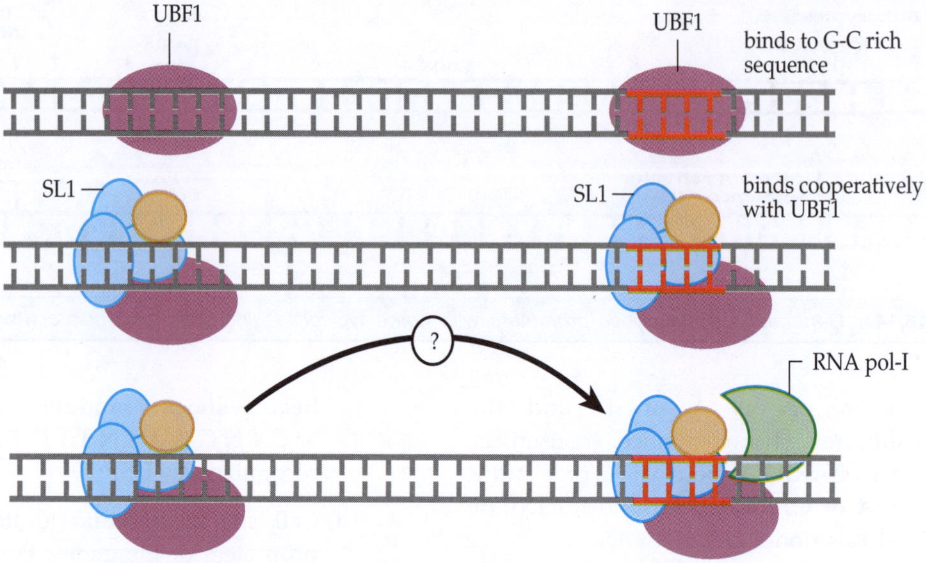


**Fig.16.15 :** *Transcription unit for RNA polymerase-I and assembles of initiation complex.*

### 16.4.3. Transcription Initiation with RNA Polymerase-III

All the reactions that occur at the pol-III promoters are not fully understood but the principle is clear.

At type-1 promoters, TF IIIA binds to a sequence that includes box C and this is required to enable TF III C to bind, whereas , at type-2 promoters TF III C recognizes box-B, but binds to a more extensive region including both boxes A and B.

The TF III C, then in turn enables TF III B to bind to a sequence surrounding the start point. This is **preinitiation complex**. TF III B functions as a **positioning factor**, responsible for localizing the RNA-polymerase correctly. TF IIB resembles sigma factor. It contains TBP and directly interacts with RNA pol-III.

The third class of polymerase III promoter which initiates transcription on a short region that immediately precedes the start point and contains only the TATA element. The crucial TATA element is recognized by a factor, which includes the TBP that actually recognizes the sequence in DNA. The TBP is associated with other proteins some of which are specific for promoters of pol-III. TBP and its associated proteins function to position RNA polymerase – III correctly at the start point (Fig. 16.16).

### 16.4.4. Transcription Initiation with RNA Polymerase-II

RNA pol-II does not bind to naked DNA sequence. It requires additional protein factors to bind efficiently to promoters. At least 6 nuclear proteins have been shown to be necessary for the proper initiation of transcription by RNA pol-II. These proteins are also called **basal transcription factors** (Fig. 16.17).

1. TF II D (Mr. 800 kD), containing TBP (Mr. 15 kD) and 12 TAFs (varying mass from 15-50 kD).

   TBP (TATA binding protein) is the key component for initiation. It is a saddle shaped protein, binds to TATA box, parallel to the DNA axis wrapping around DNA in its minor groove, but also bends

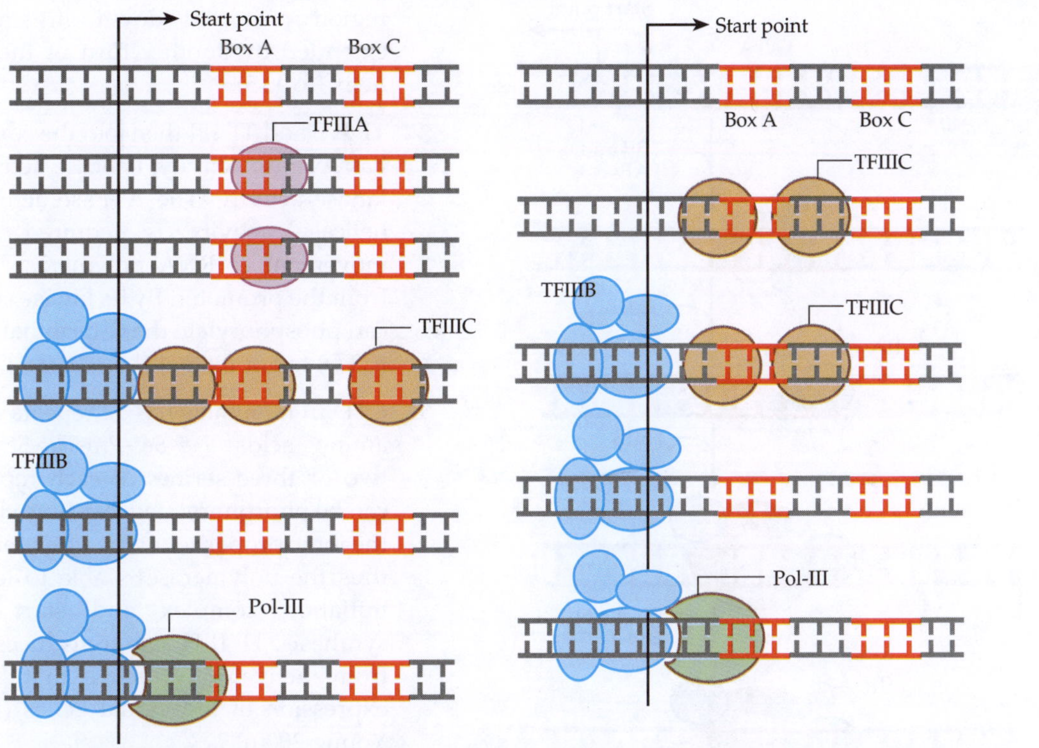


**Fig.16.16 :** *Initiation via the internal pol III promoters.*

the DNA by 80°. *The TATA box bends towards the major groove thus the minor groove widens.*

TAFs (TBP- associated factors) are tissue specific and can recognise different promoters. $TAF_{11}$ 215 binds to TBP, where it occupies the concave DNA binding surface. The only exception is the adeno-associated virus (AAV) P5 promoter, on which transcription can start in absence of TBP, making use of **Inr-binding protein** (IBP), the YYI.

2. Bending of DNA by TBP provides a recognition structure for other transcription factors.
3. TF II A joins the complex and activates TBP relieving the repression that is caused by $TAF_{11}$215.
4. Addition of TF II B gives some partial protection of the region of the template strand in the vicinity of the start point from –10 to +10. It binds adjacent to TBP, extending contacts along one face of DNA. *TF II B has two sites. Its C-terminal domain is necessary for TF II D and TATA complex, N- terminal region is required for the recruitment of RNA pol-II.* That it provides the surface, which would be recognized by RNA polymerase.
5. TF II F consists of two subunits. The larger is RAP 74, which has an ATP-dependent helicase activity that could be involved in melting the DNA at initiation. The smaller subunit is RAP 38, has some homology to bacterial sigma factor, binds to RNA pol-II and thus TF II F brings the pol-II to the transcription complex.

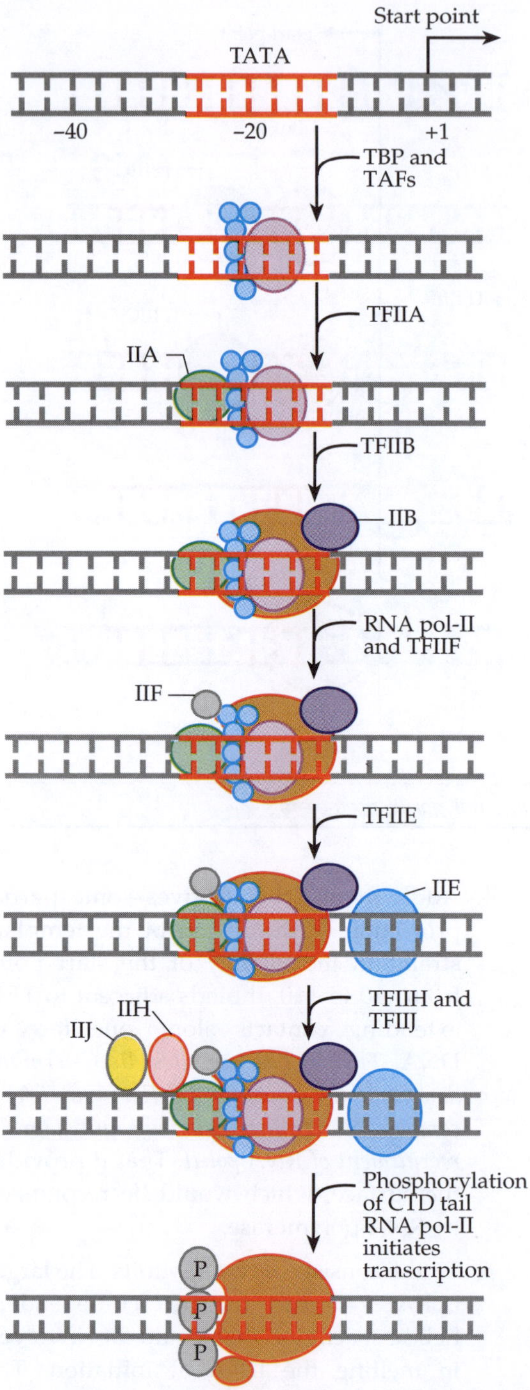


**Fig.16.17 :** *Events in the formation of initiation complex and phorphorylation of the CTD of RNA pol II during transcription.*

6. Binding of TF II E causes the boundary region protected down stream to be extended by another turn of the double helix (to +15).
7. TF II F and TF II J then join the complex. It has ATPase activity, helicase activity and kinase activity. The ATPase activity and helicase activity is required for the movement of RNA polymerase II away from the promoter. By its kinase activity it can phosphorylate the C-terminal domain (CTD) tail of the pol-II.
8. CTD in mammals has 52 repeats of seven amino acids *Tyr-Ser-Pro-Thr-Ser-Pro-Ser* two or three serines in each repeat unit can be phorphorylated, causing change in the ionic properties of the polymerase and thus the polymerase is able to leave the initiation complex and start mRNA synthesis. TF II H also transduces signals from activator proteins that regulate expression of individual genes (Lee and Young 2000).
9. Most of the TF II factors are released before RNA pol-II leaves the promoter (Table 16.2).

### 16.4.5 Elongation of mRNA

At the fundamental level, transcription is similar both in bacteria and eukaryotes. X-ray crystallography and cross-linking studies by Klug (2001) revealed that the contact between eukaryotic RNA pol-II, DNA template and RNA transcript are similar to the interactions described for bacterial transcription.

The most striking dissimilarities are that eukaryotic mRNAs are processed during transcription even just after initiation, whereas, in bacteria, the transcripts of protein-coding genes are not processed at all, these primary transcripts are mature mRNA.

In eukaryotes, **cap** is added at 5′ end and at 3′ end it is polyadenylated and the mRNA has many introns that will undergo splicing.

**TABLE 16.2**
**Functions of general transcription factors (GTFs)**

| GTF | Functions |
|---|---|
| TBP | Recognition of TATA box and possibly Inr sequence, forms a platform for TF IIB binding |
| TFs | Recognition of the core promoter and regulation of TBP binding. |
| TF II A | Stabilizes TBP and TAF binding |
| TF II B | Intermediate in recruitment of RNA pol–II and also influences the selection point for transcription. |
| TF II F | Recruitment of RNA Pol–II |
| TF II E | Intermediate in recruitment of TF II H and modulates various activities of TF II H. |
| TF II H | Helicase activity responsible for the transition from the closed to open promoter complex, possibly influences promoter clearance by phosphorylation of the C-terminal domain of the largest subunit of RNA Pol – II. |

The fundamental aspects of transcript elongation are the same in both bacteria and eukaryotes. But due to the presence of many introns within the genes of eukaryotes, RNA pol-II requires a long time to complete the synthesis of mRNA transcript from a gene.

As many as 13 elongation factors for transcription have been recently known that have specific functions. (Conaway 2000).

CSB, ELL, Elongin etc. elongation factors suppress pausing of RNA pol-II.

S II elongation factor prevents arrest.

FACT, HMG14 have been thought to modify chromatin in order to assist elongation.

Inactivation of CSB, results in **Cockayne syndrome**, a disease characterized by developmental defects, mental retardation. Disruption of ELL causes **acute myeloid leukemia**. FACT has been shown to interact with histones H2A and H2B, possibly influencing nucleosome positioning (Orphanides and Reinberg, 2000).

Yeast possesses an elongation factor called **elongator**, which has a role in chromatin modification (Wittschieben *et al* 1999).

### 16.4.6. Termination of mRNA Synthesis

The termination event of mRNA synthesis is combined with polyadenylation.

At the 3′ end of eukaryotic mRNA about 250 adenosines are added by a template independent RNA polymerase (Bard *et al* 2000). In mammals polyadenylation is directed by a signal sequence in the mRNA 5′ AAUAAA 3′, located 10 and 15 nucleotides upstream of the polyadenylation site. After this there is a dinucleotide 5′-C A–3′ and is followed 10-20 nucleotides later by GU-rich region. The poly A and 'GU' rich regions have the binding sites for CPSF (cleavage and polyadenylation specificity factor) and CstF (cleavage stimulating factor) (Fig. 16.18).

CPSF is known to interact with TF II D and is recruited into the RNA pol-II during initiation stage. CPSF is able to bind to poly A sequence as soon as it is transcribed. Both CPSF and CstF then contact with the CTD of polymerase.The nature of these contacts changes when the poly–A signal sequence is located, and this change alters the properties of the elongation complex and thus termination becomes favoured. Transcription stops soon after the poly A signal sequence has been transcribed (Bentley 1999) (Fig. 16.19).

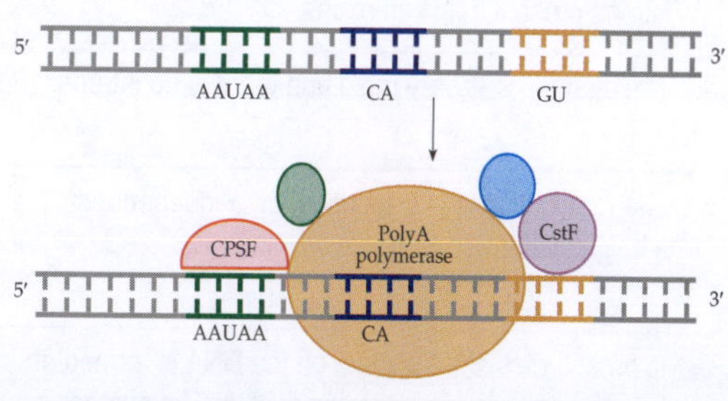


**Fig.16.18 :** *Binding of CPSF and CstF on mRNA.*

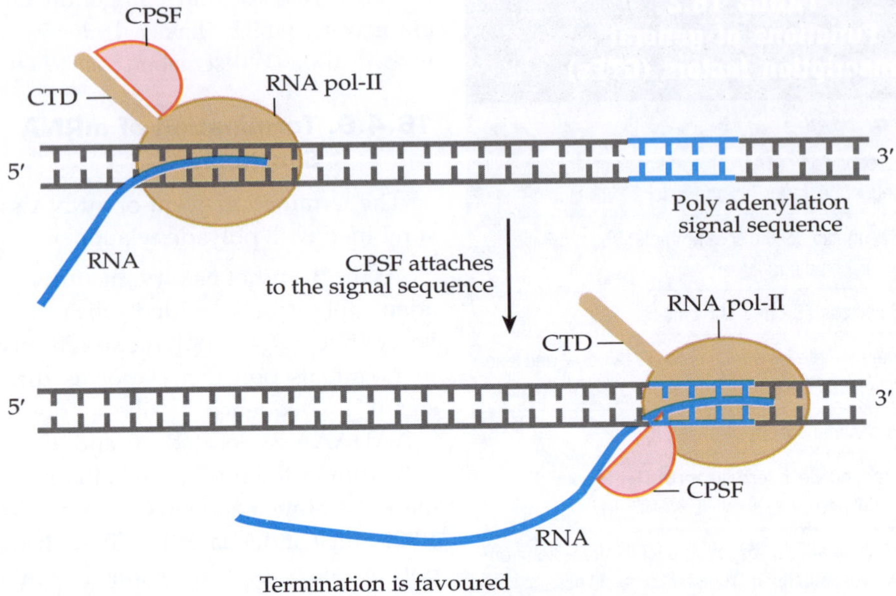


**Fig.16.19 :** *Termination in eukaryotic transcription.*

**TABLE 16.3**
**Distinction between prokaryotic and eukaryotic transcription**

| *Prokaryotic transcription* | *Eukaryotic transcription* |
|---|---|
| 1. The prokaryotes have only one RNA polymerase that synthesizes all types of RNA. | 1. The eukaryotes have three RNA polymerases, viz. pol-I, II and III and they synthesize different types of RNAs such as rRNAs, mRNAs and tRNAs respectively. |
| 2. Prokaryotic promoters are TATA box and the recognition domain. | 2. Three RNA polymerases have three different types of promoters. |
| 3. Protein coding mRNAs are not processed at all, the primary tanscripts are mature RNAs, as they have no introns present between exons. | 3. The eukaryotic mRNAs are processed just after initiation, splicing of introns from exons make the primary transcript into mature transcript. |
| 4. The elongation is very rapid and there is no introns. | 4. The elongation is not so rapid due to presence of introns between exons. |
| 5. The termination is ρ-dependent or ρ-independent, a hairpin is formed to pause termination. | 5. Termination is ρ-independent but no hairpin is formed, only the template independent polyadenylation of long poly-A tail signals to stop the elongation. |
| 6. In prokaryotes, the template on the DNA is formed on both the strands to synthesize mRNA. The synthesis of mRNA is bidirectional. | 6. In eukaryotes, the synthesis of mRNA is only on the template strand. So, the synthesis of mRNA is unidirectional. |

## 16.5 POST TRANSCRIPTIONAL MODIFICATIONS IN mRNA

### 16.5.1 Concept

A newly synthesized RNA molecule is called a **primary transcript**. A primary transcript of an eukaryotic mRNA typically contains sequences encompassing one gene. But in majority of cases the coding sequence is interrupted by non-coding tracts called *introns,* the coding segments are called *exons.* In the process called **splicing,** the introns are removed from the primary transcript and the exons are joined to form a contiguous sequence specifying a functional polypeptide. Eukaryotic mRNAs are also modified to each end. A structure called the *cap* is added at the 5′ end and a polymer containing 20-250 adenylate residues is added to the 3′ end. Besides, some usual bases, such as adenine, guanine, cytosine and uracils are modified in the intrinsic part of the mRNA. As a result an mRNA is produced which becomes functional in the cellular process.

### 16.5.2 Mechanism

**A. Capping :** RNA capping is the first modification of eukaryotic pre mRNAs. As soon as RNA polymerase-II has produced about 25 nucleotides of RNA, the 5′ end of the new RNA molecule is modified by the addition of a "cap" that consists of a modified guanine nucleotide, where two nucleotides are connected by a 5′, 5′ triphosphate linkage and also bearing a methyl group. The terminal base is always a guanine and this residue is added to the original RNA molecule after or during transcription is still continued (Fig. 16.20).

The addition of the 5′ terminal G is catalysed by a nuclear enzyme, *guanylyl transferase.* The reaction occurs soon after transcription has started that it is not possible to detect more than trace amounts of the original 5′ triphosphate end in the nuclear RNA.

**In the first step**, the enzyme becomes covalently linked to the donor GMP moiety, then the GMP is added to RNA, which loses its

3′Gppp5′ + 5′ pppApNpNpNp..........................3′

⇩

3′GpppApNpNpNp...............3′ + ppi + pi

**Fig.16.20 :** *Capping of nascent RNA with $G_{ppp}$.*

terminal γ-phosphate group. The result is that the new G-residue now at the end of the RNA is in the reverse orientation from all the other nucleotides. This structure is called the **cap** of mRNA. It is a substrate for methylations at certain positions that occur in a specific order (Fig. 16.21).

**The second step** is the methylation, which occurs in all eukaryotes and consists of the addition of a methyl group to the 7-position of the newly added terminal guanine. The enzyme responsible for this, *guanine-7-methyl transferase,* is present in the cytoplasm. It uses S-adenosyl-methionine as cofactor to provide the methyl group. A cap that possesses this single methyl group is known as a **cap-O**. This is as far as the reaction proceeds in the unicellular eukaryotes.

**The next step** is the addition of another methyl group to the 2′-O-position of the penultimate base. This reaction is catalysed by another enzyme, **2′-O-methyl transferase**. A cap with the two methyl groups is called **cap-1**. This is the predominant form of all caps in all eukaryotes except the unicellular organisms.

In a small minority of cases in higher eukaryotes, another methyl group is added to the second base. This event happens only when the position is occupied by adenine and the reaction involves the addition of a second methyl group at the $N^6$-position. The enzyme responsible is *2′-O-methyl adenosine transferase* and substrate that already has the methyl group in the 2′-O-position.

In some species, a methyl group may be added to the third base of the capped mRNA. The substrate for the reaction is the cap-1-mRNA that already possesses two methyl groups. The third base modification is always a

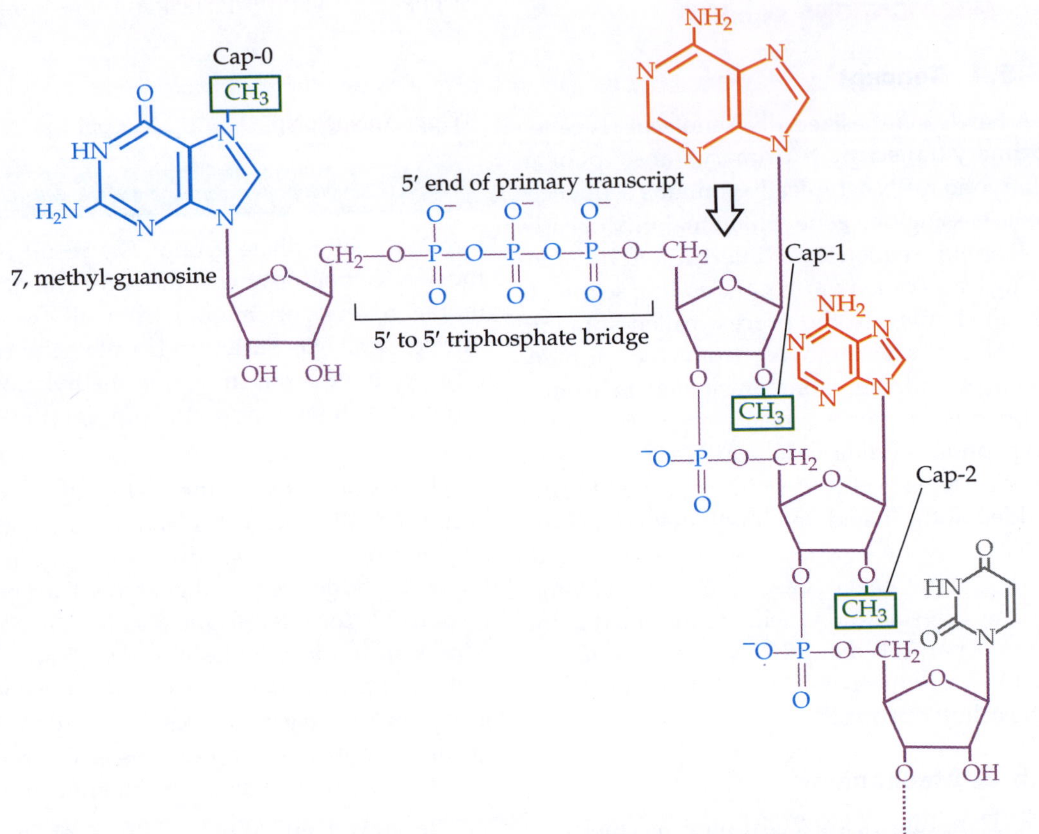


**Fig.16.21 :** *Structure of a cap of eukaryotic pre-mRNA.*

2′-O-ribose methylation. It creates the **Cap-2** type. In cases where this occurs , this cap is usually 10-15% of the total capped population. The rate of protein synthesis depends upon the presence of the cap. Without the cap molecules, mRNA binds very poorly to ribosomes (Fig. 16.22).

B. **Splicing :** A newly synhesized RNA molecule is called a **primary transcript**. A primary transcript for a eukaryotic mRNA typically contains sequences encompassing one gene. The introns transcribed into the pre-RNA are removed by splicing and the exons are joined to form a mature functional RNA (Fig. 16.23).

There are 4 classes of introns :

1. The first one is called *groups-I intron,* which is found in some nuclear, mitochondrial and chloroplast genes coding rRNAs. Groups-I splicing reaction requires a guanine nucleotide or nucleotide co-factor. But this cofactor is not used as a source of energy. The 3′ -OH group of guanosine is used as a nucleophile in the first step of this splicing pathway (Fig. 16.24 and 16.25).

The guanosine 3′ -OH forms a normal 3′, 5′–phosphodiester bond with 5′end of the intron. The 3′–OH of the exon that is displaced in this step then acts as

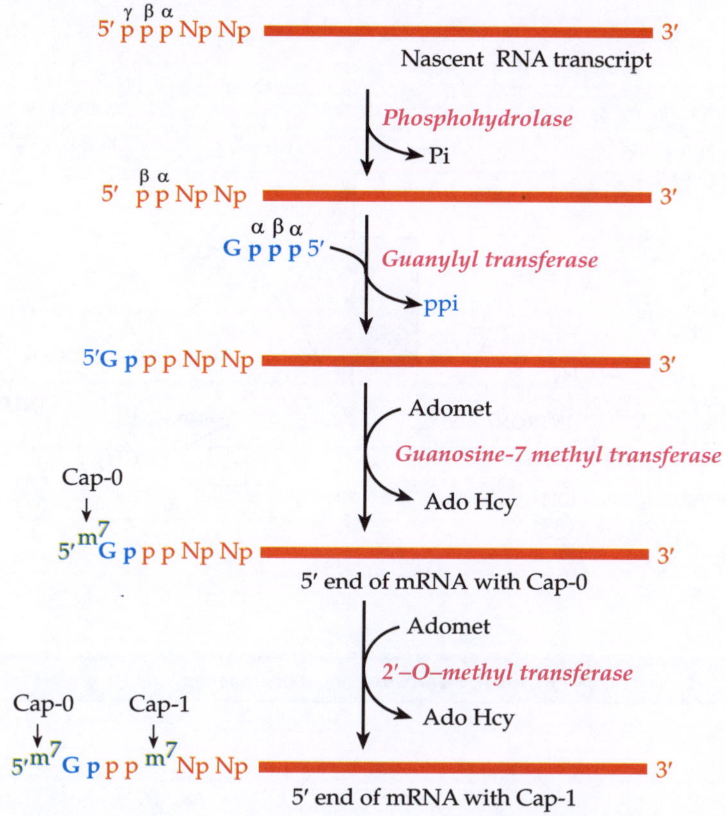


**Fig.16.22 :** *Generation of 5′ cap in pre-mRNA transcript.*

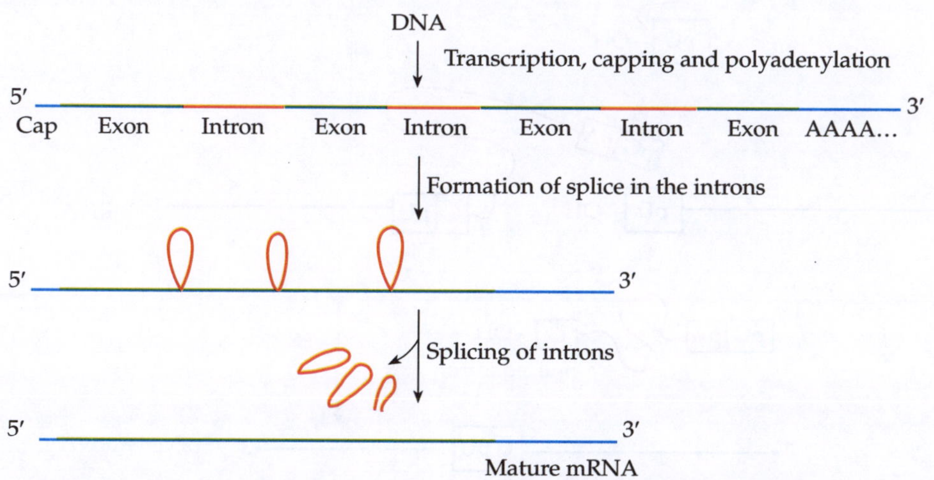


**Fig.16.23 :** *Formation of primary transcript and splicing of introns to form mature mRNA.*

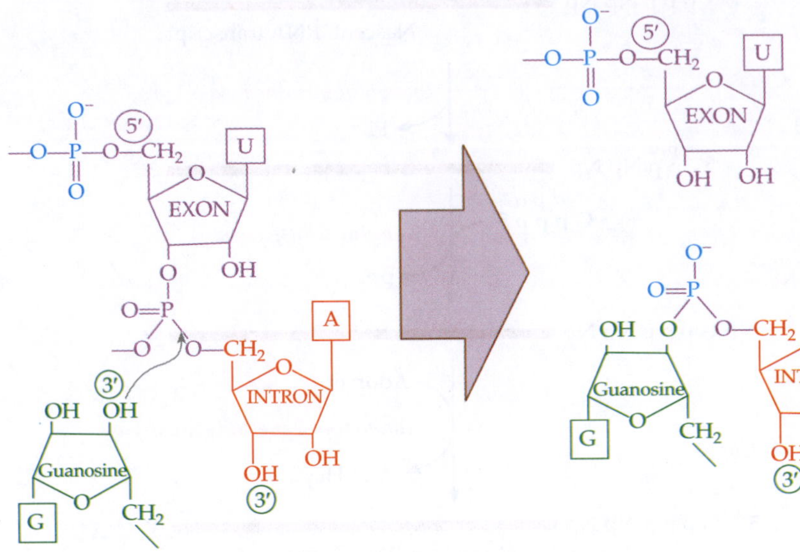


Fig.16.24 : *Transesterification reaction.*

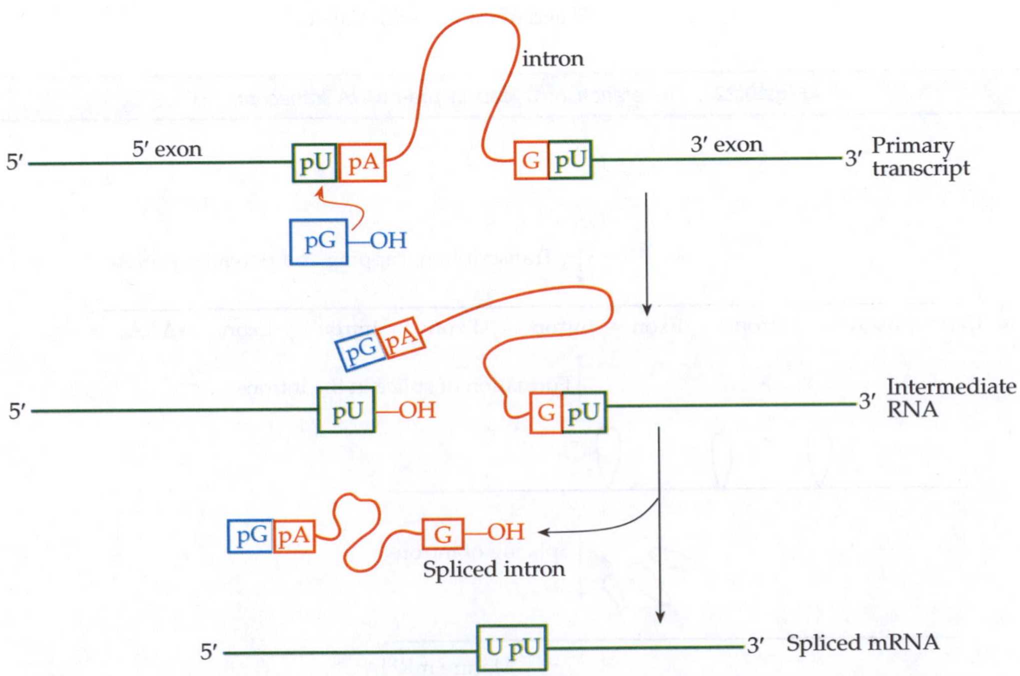


Fig.16.25 : *Splicing mechanism of group-I intron.*

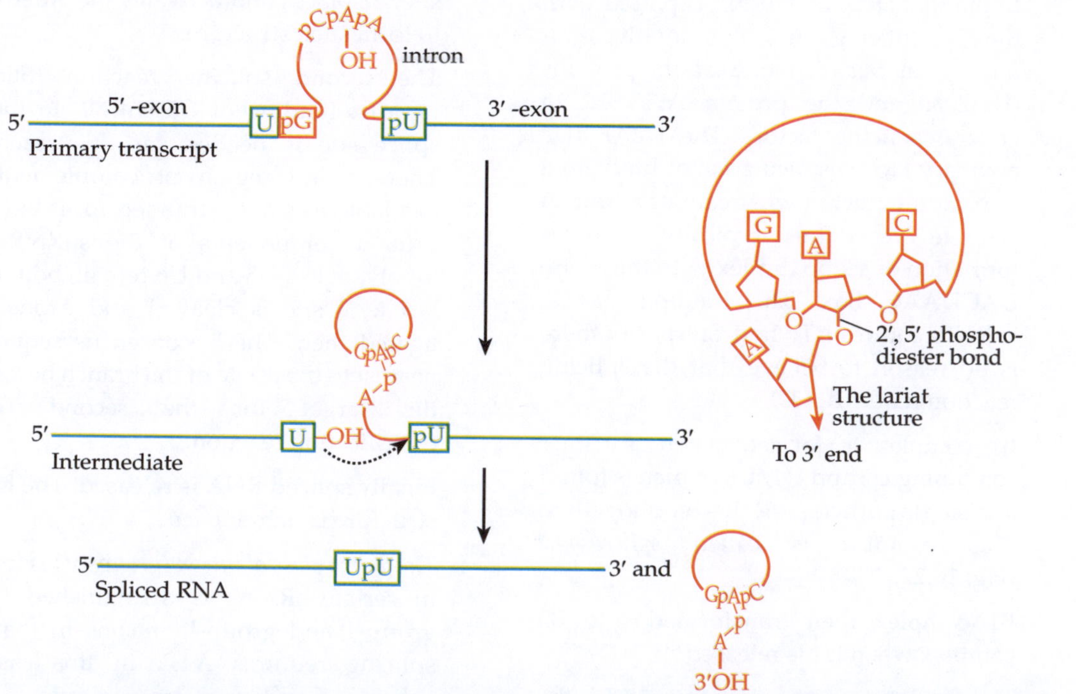


**Fig.16.26 :** *Splicing mehanism of group-II introns and lariat structure.*

nucleophile in a similar reaction at the 3′ end of the intron.

The result is precise excision of the intron and ligation of the exons. Many of these introns are **self splicing, no proteins or enzymes are involved.**

2. *Group II introns* are genenally found in the primary transcript of mitochondrial or chloroplast mRNAs. In group-II introns, the pattern is similar except for the nucleophile in the first step. Instead of an external cofactor, the nucleophile is the 2′-OH group of an adenylate residue within the intron. An unusual branched **lariat structure** is formed as an intermediate. **The mechanism involved self splicing and no protein and enzymes are required.** Here the RNA acts as an enzyme itself i.e, autocatalytic in nature (Fig. 16.26).

3. *The third group of introns ie, group-III introns* are found in nuclear mRNA primary transcript. **They are not self splicing.** Splicing requires the action of spliced RNA-protein complexes containing a class of eukaryotic RNAs called SMALL NUCLEAR RNAs (snRNAs). Five snRNAs, U1, U2, U4, U5 and U6 are involved in splicing reactions, range in size from 106 (U6) to 189 (U2) nucleotides. These are complexed with the proteins to form SMALL NUCLER RIBONUCLEOPROTEINS (snRNPs) often referred to as SNURPS.

U1 snRNA has a single stranded sequence complementary to consensus sequence at the 5′ splice site of the intron. It pairs directly with the 5′ terminal 11 nucleotides of this complementary splice site of intron. Addition of U2, U4, U5 and U6 snRNPs leads to the formation of a complex called SPLICEOSOME. Within this spliceosome, the acual splicing reaction occurs.

In the first step, U1 snRNP is paired with the 5′ -splicing site, this involves an interaction between one of its proteins (U1-70K) and the protein ASF/SF2 (a general splicing factor). The U2AF (U2 auxiliary factor) splicing factor binds to a pyrimidine tract downstream of a branch site. In yeast this typically involves formation of a 7 bp duplex with the entire UACUAAC box. The binding of U2 snRNP requires ATP hydrolysis, but there is no reason to believe that the splicing reaction requires ATP.

B1 complex is formed when a trimer containing U5 and U4/U6 (which is found as a single particle) snRNPs bind together. This complex is called *spliceosome* (Fig. 16.27).

B1 complex then transformed into B2 complex when U1 is released.

The catalytic reaction is triggered by the release of U4 and thus the spliceosome is able to proceed which requires hydrolysis of ATP, When U4 dissociates, the attachment region of U6 becomes free to take up another structure. The first part of it pairs with U2 and the second part forms an intramoleuclar hairpin. The 5′ splice site is actually now close to the U6 sequence immediately on the 5′ side of the stretch bound to U2. This sequence in U6 snRNA contacts the conserved GU at the 5′ splice site.

Base pairing between U2 and U6 creates a structure that resembles the active centre of the group-II introns. U5 shifts from exon to intron and a C1 complex is formed. The U5 snRNA is then immediately adjacent to the first base positions in both exons. *Trans*-esterification is possibly catalysed by U6/U2 components. U5 binds to the exon at 3′ splice site. The 5′ -site is cleaved and a lariat structure is formed through a 2′–5′ phosphodiester bond which is formed by base pairing of U2 snRNA to the branch site, displaces and activates the Adensine to form such structure.

The second splicing reaction follows rapidly. Binding of U5 snRNP to the 3′ splice site is needed for this reaction. There is no region of complementary available in single stranded form but the protein components of the snRNP are involved. U2, U5 and U6 remain bound to lariat. 3′ site is cleaved and exons are ligated then. The 3′ consensus sequence nearest to the 3′ site of the branch becomes the target for the second trans esterification reaction.

Finally spliced RNA is released. The lariat structure is debranched.

4. *The fourth class of intron (group-IV)* is found in certain tRNAs is distnguished from group-1 and group-II introns in that its splicing requires ATP. In this case a splicing endonuclease cleaves the phosphodiester bonds at both ends of introns and the two exons are joined. The joining reaction is similar to the DNA ligase mechanism (Fig. 16.28).

## 16.6 ALTERNATIVE SPLICING AND mRNA PROCESSING

Generally, after transcription of eukaryotic genes, pre-mRNAs undergo processing, so that the noncoding introns are excised and exons are ligated together and thus, without any variation of the mature RNA, the cell produced a specific type of protein. Such splicing is called *constitutive splicing*.

But from virus to mammals; production of two or more mRNAs from a single pre-RNA by joining together different combinations of exons are observed and as a result varieties of mRNA are produced from a single pre-mRNA transcript. Such a phenomenon is called *alternative splicing*. By this method different types of proteins are synthesized from a single pre-mRNA in a cell (Fig. 16.29).

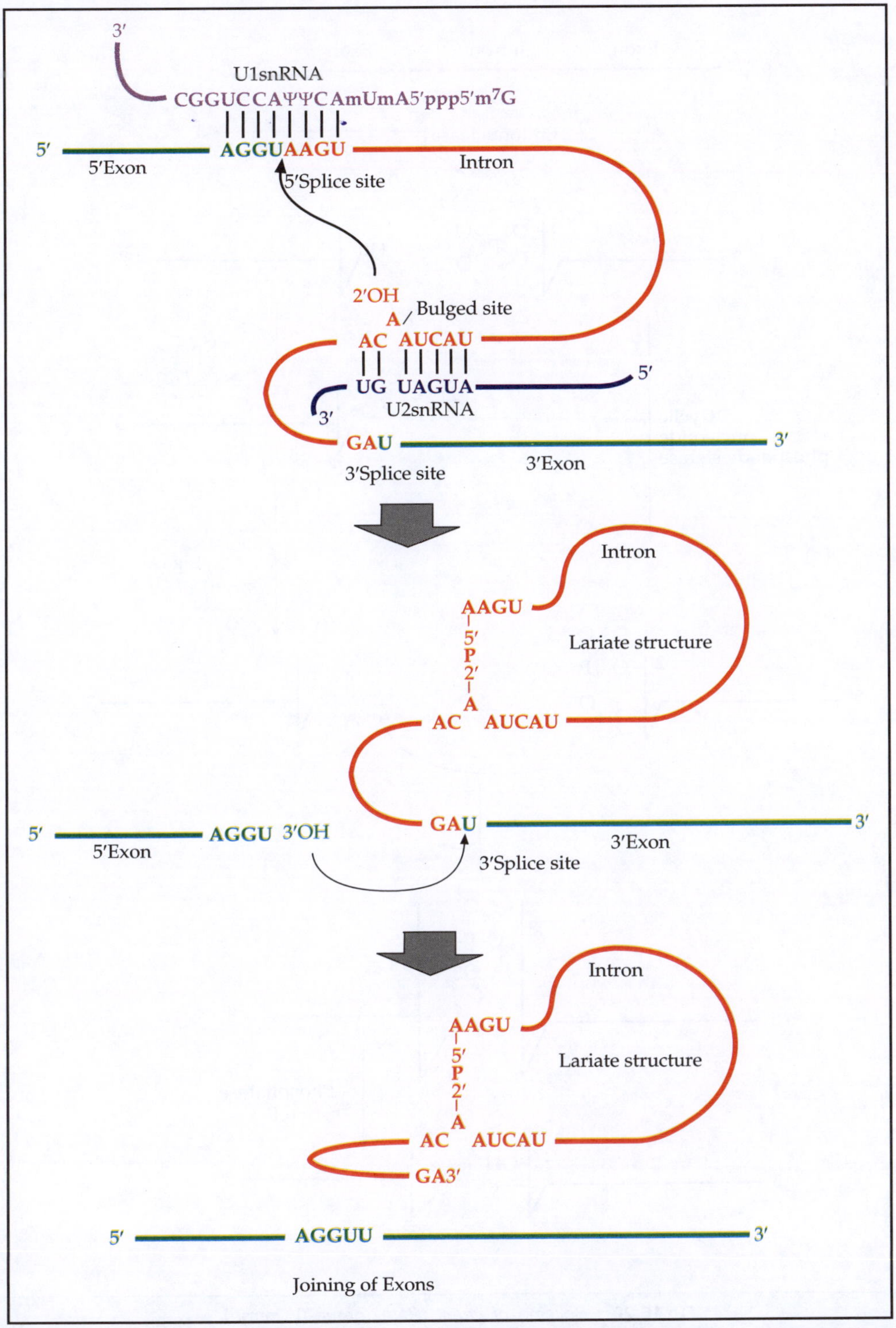


**Fig.16.27 :** *Splicing mechanism of group-III. intron : ψ = pseudouridine; m = methylated residues.*

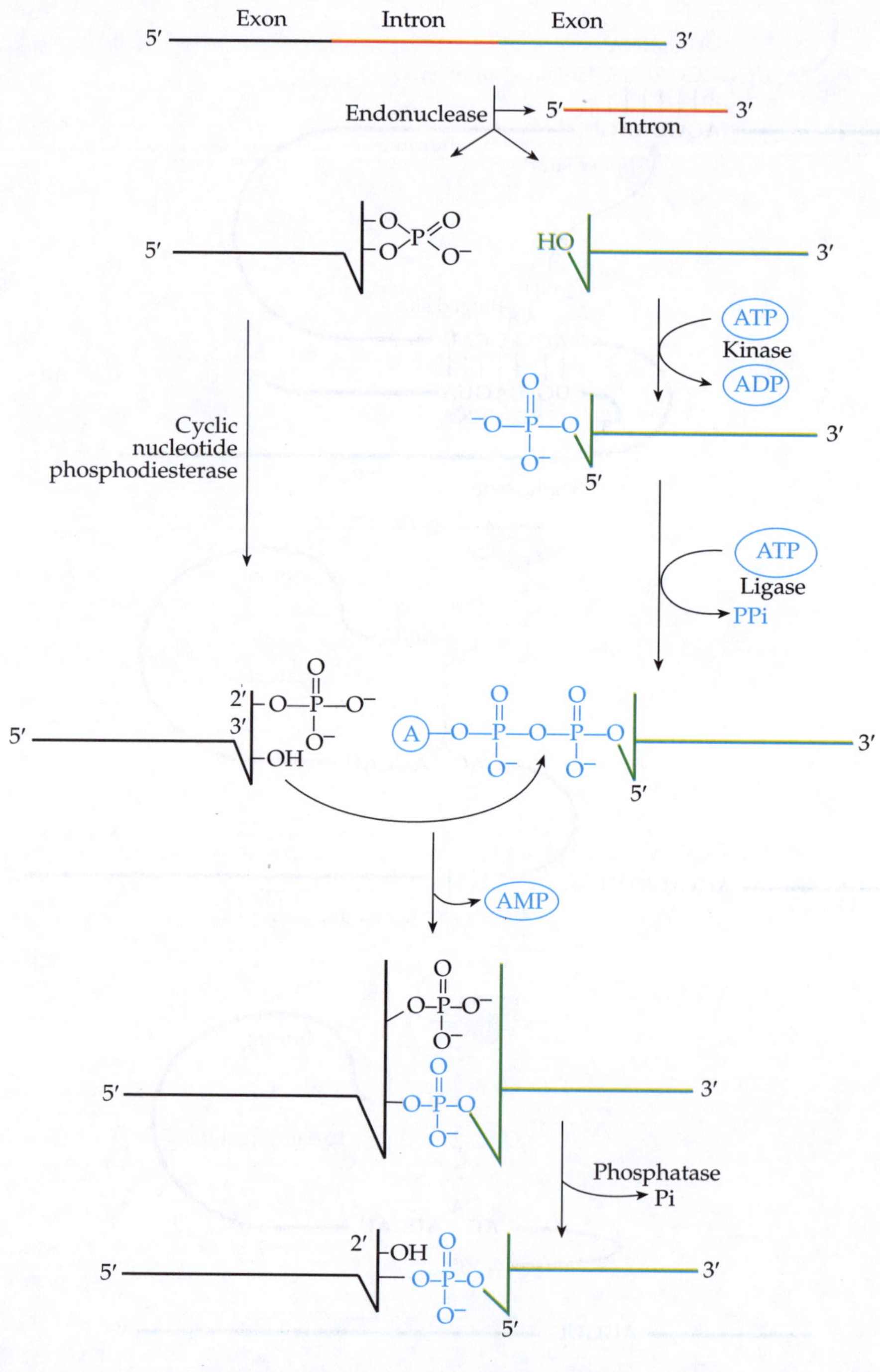


**Fig.16.28 :** *Splicing of yeast tRNA (group-IV intron)*

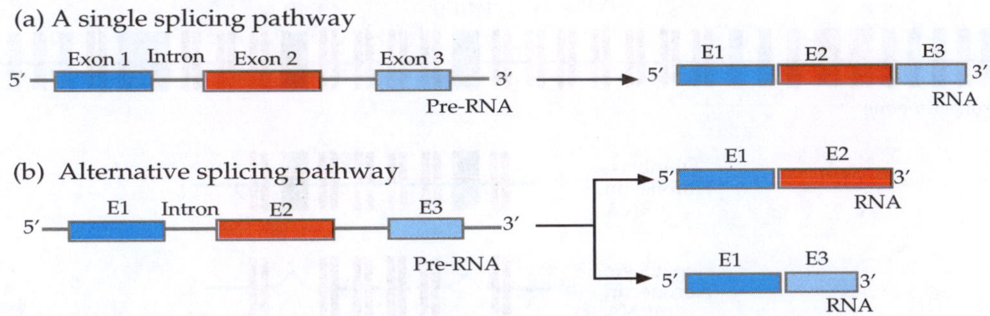


**Fig.16.29 :** *Pre-mRNA follows a single splicing pathway and alternative pathways.*

The primary transcripts produced from complex transcription units can be processed in alternative ways to yield different mRNAs. The expression of both simple and complex transcription units could be controlled by on-off regulation of the cleavage and polyadenylation of their pre-mRNAs.

### 16.6.1 OFF-ON mechanism of Post-transcriptional modification

The off-on regulation of cleavage and polyadenylation step in RNA processing are coordinated by U1A protein with U1 snRNP assembly and they play a crucial role in RNA splicing.

The pre-mRNA encoding U1A itself contains two copies of U1A – binding sites (7—base sequence) just upstrem of its polyadenylation signal).

When a U1A protein binds to each copy of this 7-base sequence in a U1A pre-mRNA, containing poly-A polymerase and other factors, only cleavage occurs but polyadenylation does not occur. Thus a free 3′ end is generated and in absence of polyadenylation, both cleavage products are degraded rapidly by exonuclease and so no U1A-mRNA is produced. As a result U1A protein synthesis is decreased until all the excess is used in formation of new U1 snRNPs.

Once this occurs, no U1A protein is available to bind to newly made U1A premRNA which then can be processed normally.

Therefore, U1A premRNA splicing is autoregulated by its own protein. U1A which inhibits polyadenylation to its cleavage site (Fig. 16.30).

### 16.6.2 Examples of Alternative splicing

1. **Tissue-specific RNA splicing in fibronectin :** The fibronectin, a protein, found in both blood plasma and the extracellular matrix. Fibronectin is produced by fibroblasts and retained in the matrix, contains two extra peptides compared to the version of the proteins produced in the liver cells and secreted in the blood. The extra peptides are retained

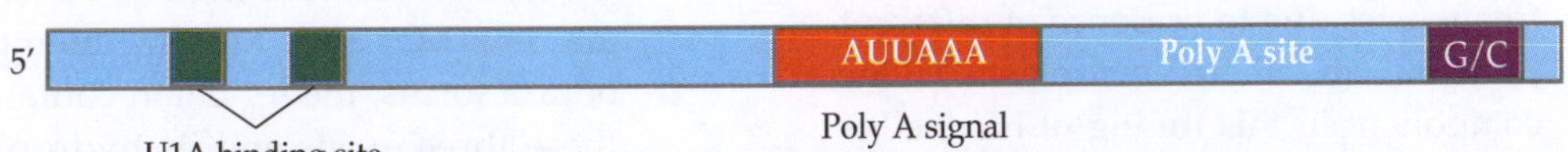


**Fig.16.30 :** *Diagram of 3′ end of the pre mRNA encoding U1A protein.*

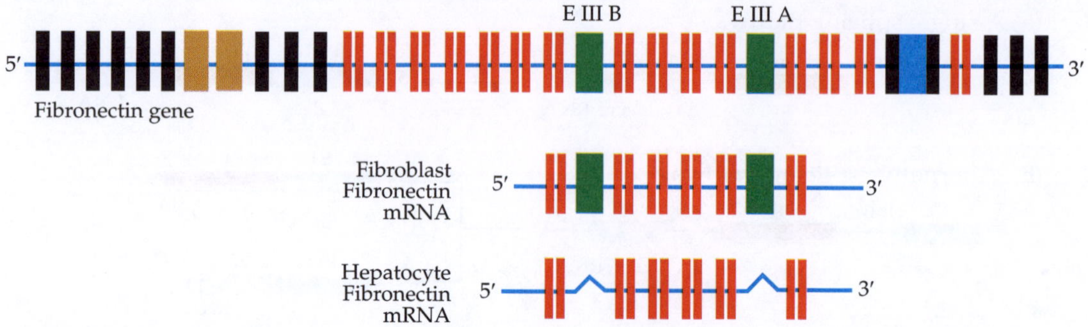


**Fig.16.31 :** *Cell type-specific splicing of fibronectin mRNA in fibroblasts and hepatocytes.*

during processing in the fibroblast but are removed during processing in the liver.

The fibronectin gene consists of a number of exons and introns. Two of these exons encode portions of the polypeptide called E III A and E III B which are included in the protein produced by fibroblasts, But these two are excluded from the protein produced in the liver. The difference is due to alternative splicing, those portions of the pre-mRNA that encode these two exons are excised from the transcript in liver cells (Fig. 16.31).

2. **Multiple protein isoforms in vertebrate nervous system and immunoglobulin diversifications :**

(a) During transmission of impulses through the nerve axons $K^+$ ions and $Ca^{++}$ ions are transported to and from the cell membrane through some channels. The sound sensing inner ear cells of vertebrates are hair cells (ciliated neurons) found in the cochlea which can respond the sound 20–2000 HZ. The cells are so tuned that different hair cells can perceive different sound frequencies due to presence of different proteins in their cytoplasm. One component in this tuning of hair cell is the opening of $K^+$ ion channels in response to increased intracellular $Ca^{++}$ concentrations. The $Ca^{++}$ concentration at which the channel opens determines the frequency with which the membrane potential oscillates, the frequency to which the cell is tuned.

The individual capability of respond is determined by the alternative splicing of *slo* gene transcript. The human *slo* gene comprises 35 exons, eight of which are optional and appear in different combinations in different *slo* mRNA. There are 8! = 40320 possible splicing pathways and hence 40320 possible mRNAs. But only 576 possible isoforms are thought to be synthesized in human cochlea. Thus alternate splicing of *slo* gene in cochlea hair cell determines the auditory range of humans (Fig. 16.32).

(b) **Immunoglobulin-M** (IgM) consists of heavy chain and light chain. IgM is secreted as a pentamerous form with 5 IgM and a J chain which joins them.

The membrane bound heavy chain ($\mu_m$) and secretory heavy chain ($\mu_s$) differ only at their C-terminal ends.

Cμ chain consists of 6 exons viz. μ1, μ2, μ3, μ4, M1 and M2. In membrane bound forms, the $\mu_m$ chain contains all these three exons and its hydrophobic end secures it in the lipid bilayer of the membrane. These hydrophobic exons

**Fig.16.32 :** *Schematic diagram of human slo gene comprising 35 exons.*

M1 and M2 are replaced by a shorter hydrophilic sequence in its secretory chain $\mu_s$. Thus secretory IgM chain consists of only 4 exons. The change of C-terminus is accomplished by an alternative splicing which is controlled by the 3′ end of the nuclear RNA (Fig. 16.33).

(c) **Calcitonin** is secreted by the parafollicular cells of thyroid glands , is a single chain polypeptide hormone containing 32 aminoacids.

CGRP (or Calcitonin gene-related polypeptide) is a peptide hormone, is related to calcitonin but normally it acts only as a neurotransmitter in the CNS — not as an agent of calcium homeostasis. The gene contains 6 exons and the pre mRNA contains 6 exons. During calcitonin synthesis in the thyroid glands first four exons are joined to form a calcitonin – mRNA by splicing elemination of 3′ end two exons. On the other hand during the synthesis of CGRP, the 4th exon is alternatively spliced, as a result 3′ end of 3rd exon is joined with the 5′ end of 5th exon (Fig. 16.34).

3. **Splicing Control of *Drosophila* sex differentiation :** The differentiation of sex is determined by following the X : A ratio. In XX-*Drosophila sxl*-gene transcribes pre sxl-mRNA, male exon in spliced and translates into Sxl-protein. Sxl-proteins

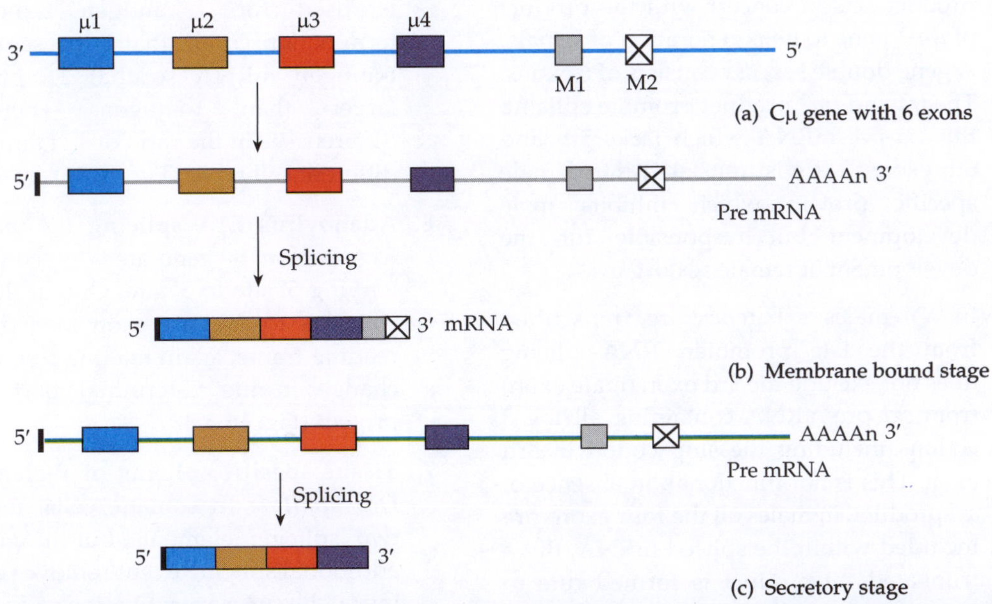


**Fig.16.33 :** *Alternative splicing of Cμ pre-mRNA into membrane bound and secretory stages.*

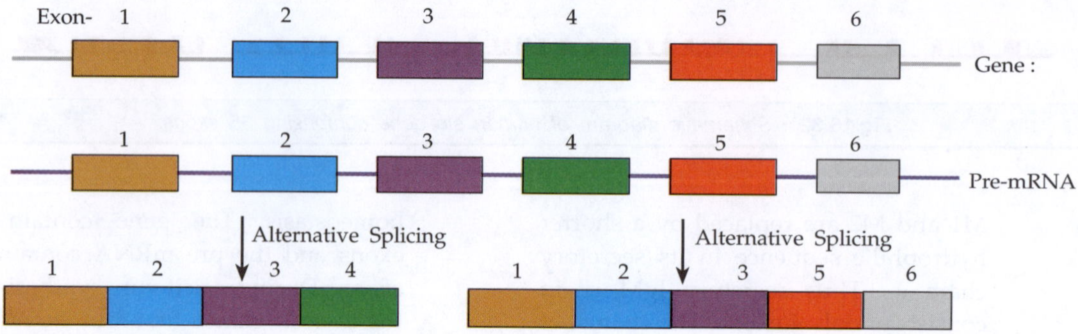


**Fig.16.34 :** *Alternative splicing of Calcitonin and CGRP pre-mRNA.*

have two definite functions. It binds to late promoter to maintain *sxl*-gene expression and secondly, it acts as a self splicing factor to remove male exon from transcripts. The *sxl*-gene consists of 8 exons. 3rd exon is spliced alternatively and such mRNA consists of 7 exons and produces Sxl-protein in females. It regulates the splicing of *tra* gene which has four exons, but in females 2nd exon is not utilized and is spliced out by splicing factor U2AF. This female-specific *tra* product acts in concert with the product of *tra-2* gene to help generation of female. A gene double sex, *dsx* consists of 6 exons. The *tra* and *tra2* product promote splicing the *dsx*-pre mRNA which lacks 5th and 6th exons. Thus is translated into female specific protein which inhibits male development but responsible for the development of female sex organs.

In XY males sxl genes are transcribed from the late promoter. RNA-splicing does not exclude the 3rd exon (male exon) from *sxl* pre-mRNA containing all the 8 codons including the stop codon in 3rd exon. This is not functional. In absence of *sxl* product, in males all the four exons are included within the spliced mRNA. But a trunkated *tra* product is formed due to presence of stop codon in second exon. It is not functional. The *dsx* gene transcript is spliced normally with but skips 4th exon. It promotes development of male *Drosophila*.

4. **Troponin-T in muscle fibres :** Alternative splicing also may be influenced by repression of one site. Exon 2 and 3 of mouse troponin-T gene are mutually exclusive. Exon-2 is used in smooth muscles but exon-3 is used in other tissues (Fig. 16.35).

5. **SV 40 T/t antigen :** In this case, the 5′ site is used for T antigen removes a termination codon that is present in the t-antigen mRNA so that T antigen is larger than t-antigen. There are differencees in the ratio of T/t antigens in different cell types (Fig. 16.36).

6. **Adenovirus E1A splicing :** Adenoviral, E1A region is generated by connecting varying 5′ site to 3′ site. One of the 5′site connects to the last exon in a different reading frame, again making a significant change in the C-terminal part of the protein (Fig. 16.37).

7. **Tissue specific splicing of P-element in *Drosophila* :** In somatic cells, there are two splicing elements but in germline additional splicing event removes another intron. Because a termination codon lies in the germ line-specific intron, a longer

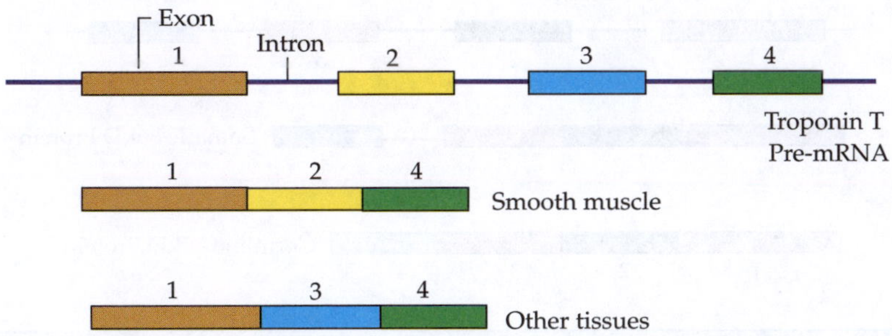


**Fig.16.35 :** *Alternative splicing of pre mRNA Troponin T.*

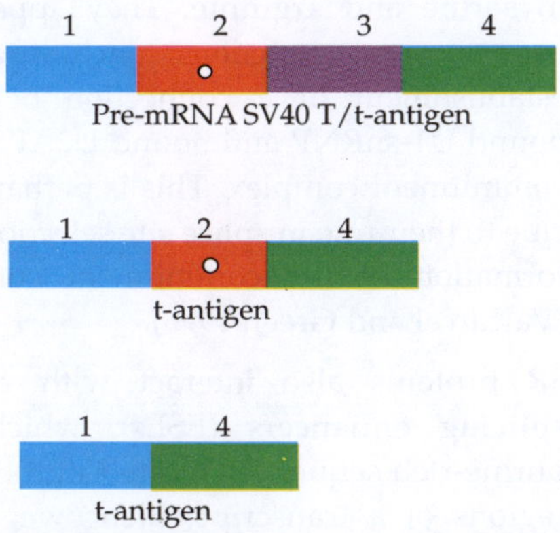


**Fig.16.36 :** *Alternative splicing of pre mRNA SV40 T/t antigen, o – termination codon*

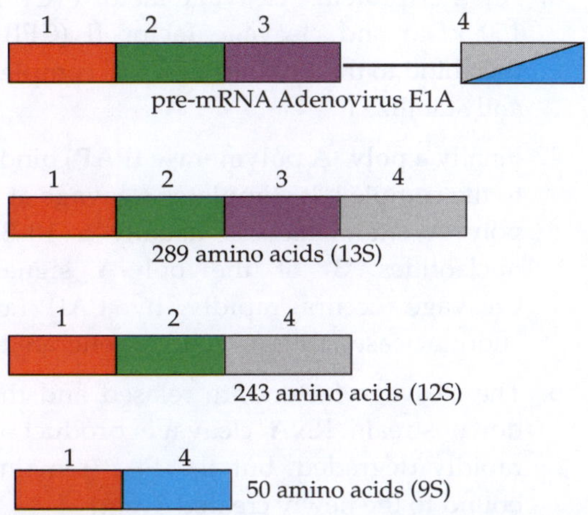


**Fig.16.37 :** *Alternative splicing of Pre-mRNA Adenovirus E1A.*

protein with different properties is produced in the germline (Fig. 16.38).

## 16.6.3 Generation of 3′ end of pre mRNA and Polyadenylation

Pre-mRNAs are cleaved at specific -3′ sites and rapidly polyadenylated. Early sequencing of cDNA clones from animal cells showed that nearly all mRNAs contain the sequence AAUAAA, 10-35 nucleotides upstream from the polyA tail. AAUAAA acts as a poly-A signal. Just after a poly A run there is a GU rich region or simply a U-rich region. The cleavage site is actually located at the poly-A region in between AAUAAA signal and G–U/U-rich region.

According to the model.

1. A 360 kDa protein, called cleavage and plyadenylation specificity factor (CPSF), composed of four different polypeptides, first forms an unstable complex with the upstream AAUAAA – poly A signal.
2. A 200 kDa heterotrimer, called cleavage stimulatory factor (CStF) interacts with a

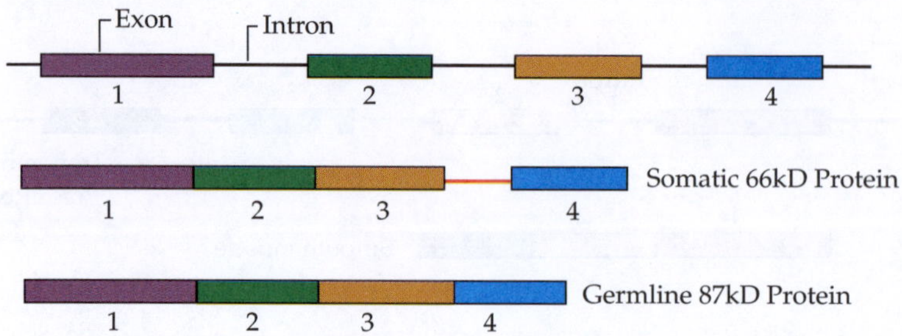


**Fig.16.38 :** *Alternative splicing of P-element in Drosophila.*

down stream GU or U-rich sequence and bound to CPSF forming a loop in the RNA.

3. Another proteins, cleavage factor I (CF 1, 150 kDa) and cleavage factor II (CFII), then bind to the RNA-CPSF-CStF complex and stabilize it.
4. Finally a **poly -A polymerase (PAP)** binds to the complex. It stimulates cleavage at a poly A site, which is usually a 10–35 nucleotides, 3′ of the poly-A signal. Cleavage occurs rapidly by PAP (an endonuclease), thus a 3′ end is generated.
5. The cleavage factors are relased and the down stream RNA cleavage product is rapidly degraded, but the PAP remains bound to the newly created 3′ end .
6. Polyadenylation by PAP at the new 3′ OH end proceeds in two phases. Addition of first few (=12) residues occurs slowly, followed by rapid addition of upto 200–250 or more A residues. The protein called PAB II. **(polyA binding protein)** that binds to initial short poly-A tail, acelerates the rate of addition by PAP. After 200–250 A residues have been added, PAB II signals PAP to stop polyadenylation (Fig. 16.39).

### 16.6.4 Formation of Commitment Complex during Pre-mRNA splicing

The aspect of splicing is still poorly understood, but role of some regulatory proteins is analysed critically.

1. **SR** proteins are known to have an important role in splice-site selection. SR-proteins are so called beacause their C-terminal domains contain a region rich in **serine** and **arginine.** They appear to have several functions, including the establishment of a connection between bound U1-snRNP and bound U2AF in the commitment complex. This is perhaps the clue to their role in splice site selection and formation of the commitment complex (Valcarcel and Green 1996).
2. SR proteins also interact with **exonic splicing enhancers** (ESEs), which are purine-rich sequences located in the exon regions of a transcript (Blencowe, 2000) This is very important to know that **muscular dystrophy disease** in human is caused by the mutation in ESE sequence.
3. ESE and SR protein influence splicing. U4/ U6-snRNP and U5-snRNP which are thought to be taken a critical role. The attraction between U1 snRNP and U2 snRNP brings the exons and three critical parts of the intron (two splice sites and the branch point) into close proximity. Thus **spliceosome** is formed (Fig. 16.40 and 16.41).

### 16.6.5 Role of Exonic Splicing Enhancers (ESEs) in Alternative splicing

Alternative splicing process is very difficult to study, because it requires the preparation of

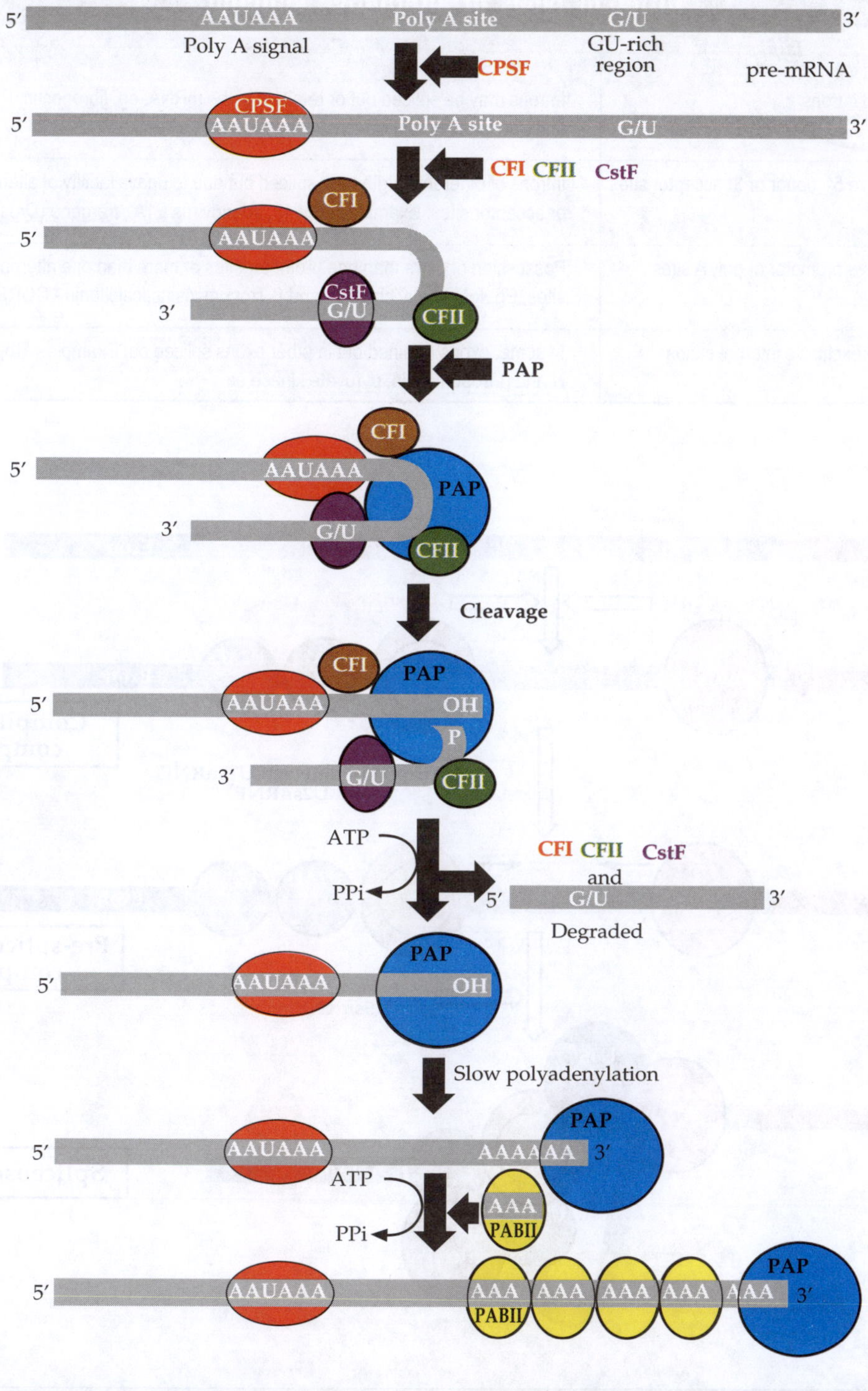


**Fig.16.39 :** *Model for cleavage and polyadenylation of pre mRNA in mammalian cell.*

**TABLE 16.4**
**Different types of alternative splicing**

| *Types* | *Examples* |
|---|---|
| 1. Retained introns | Introns may be spliced out or retained in the mRNA. eg, fibronectin, PDGFA chain and transpoase of P-element in *Drosphila*. |
| 2. Alternative 5′ donor or 3′ acceptor sites | Introns of different lengths are spliced out due to unavailability of alternative donor or acceptor sites. Examples - SV 40, adenovirus E1A , *tra*-gene (*Drosophila*) |
| 3. Alternative promotor or poly A sites | Possession of more than one promoter sites or more than one alternative poly A sites, Eg, IgM heavy chain, $\alpha$ and $\beta$ Tropomyosins, calcitonin - CGRP genes. |
| 4. Mutually exclusive internal exons | In some, exons retained but in other exons spliced out Example - Troponin T, $\alpha$ and $\beta$ tropomyosin, pyruvate kinase etc. |

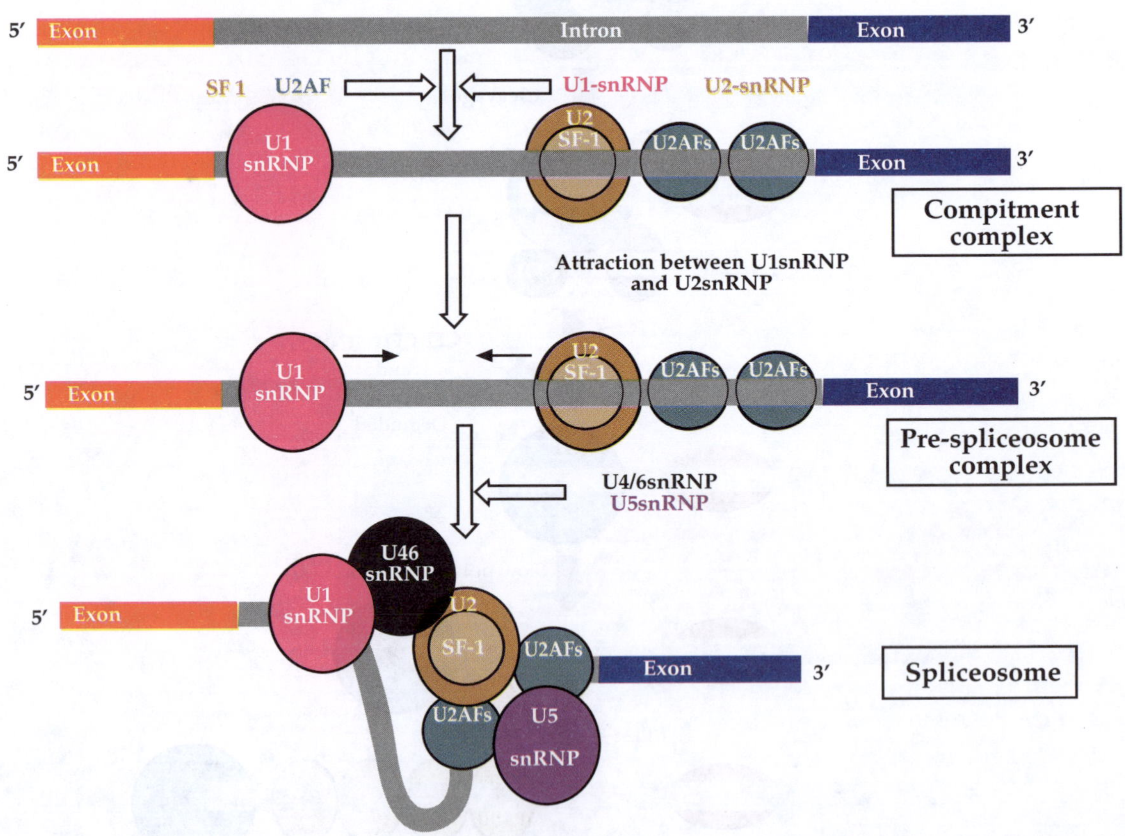


**Fig.16.40 :** *Role of snRNPs and associated proteins during splicing.*

**Fig.16.41 :** *An alternative model for assembly of the commitment complex.*

full length mRNAs from many different tissues and the stages of development. It is fact that 74 percent of human genes are subjected to alternative splicing.

1. The exon may contain several splicing enhancers, each of about 6–8 nucleotides long, that bind to specific regulatory proteins, typically SR proteins.
2. These boud regulatory proteins recruit key splicing factors USAF and U1 snRNP to near by 3′ and 5′ splice sites respectively.
3. U2AF plays a direct role in recruiting U2 snRNP to the branch point site (BPs), which is required for the formation of lariat.
4. If U2AF and U1 snRNP were not recruited to the splice site on each side of exon-2, this exon would not be recognised and would be excised as a part of the intron (Fig. 16.42).

## 16.7 *TRNAS*-SPLICING OF mRNA

In genetic terms, splicing occurs only in *cis*, which means that only sequences on the same molecule of RNA can be spliced together. In this case introns can be removed from each RNA molecule to be spliced together, but there is no intermolecular splicing of exons between different RNA molecules.

A particular variation on splicing, called *trans*-splicing has been discoverd in a few eukaryotic organisms where the splicing occurs in *trans* if complementary sequences are introduced into the introns. of two RNAs. Base pairing between the complements should create an H-shaped molecule and could be spliced by joining of one 5′ exon with the other 3′ exon. As a result, products of *trans*-splicing have the same 5′exons and different 3′ exons.

There is no mechanistic impediment to *trans*-splicing and no models for splicing. It must be possible for the spliceosome to recognise the 5′ and 3′ splice site of different RNAs only when they are in close proximity with their complementary intron sequences. Therefore, in *trans* splicing, exons from two separate RNA transcripts are spliced together to form a mature mRNA molecule (Fig. 16.43).

*Trans*-splicing is rare. But in Trypanosomes, the protozoans that cause African sleeping sickness in humans, produce abundant amounts of a single 140 nts. leader RNA from tandemly repeated transcription units. Here, a 15-nts portion of leader RNA (called a **mini exon**) is spliced to the 5′ end of protein encoding exons in primary transcript, which lack internal introns. The 5′ mini-exon is present in all trypanosome mRNAs, is thought to assists in initiation of transcription. Therefore, from a polycistronic primary transcript, several monocistronic mRNAs can be yielded. In this way trypanosomes produce all their mRNAs by *trans-splicing*.

The model roundworm, *Caenorhabditis elegans* produces 10-15% of their mRNAs by the process of *trans*-splicing. *Trans*-splicing also occurs in chloroplasts.

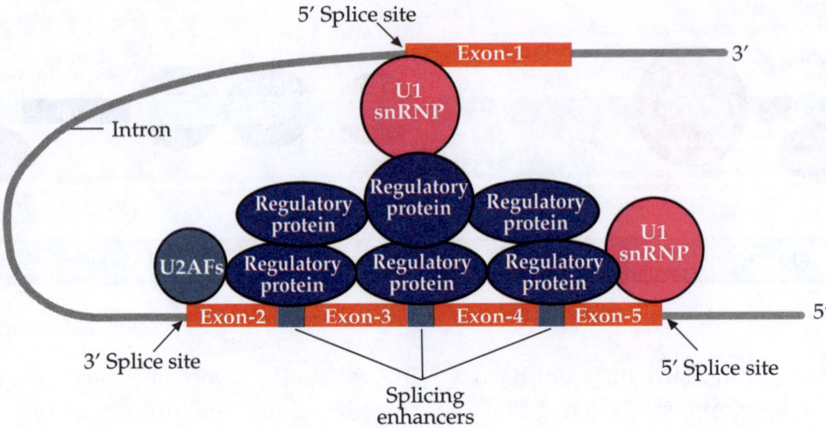


**Fig.16.42 :** *A model for the role of exonic splicing enhancers in regulating alternative splicing.*

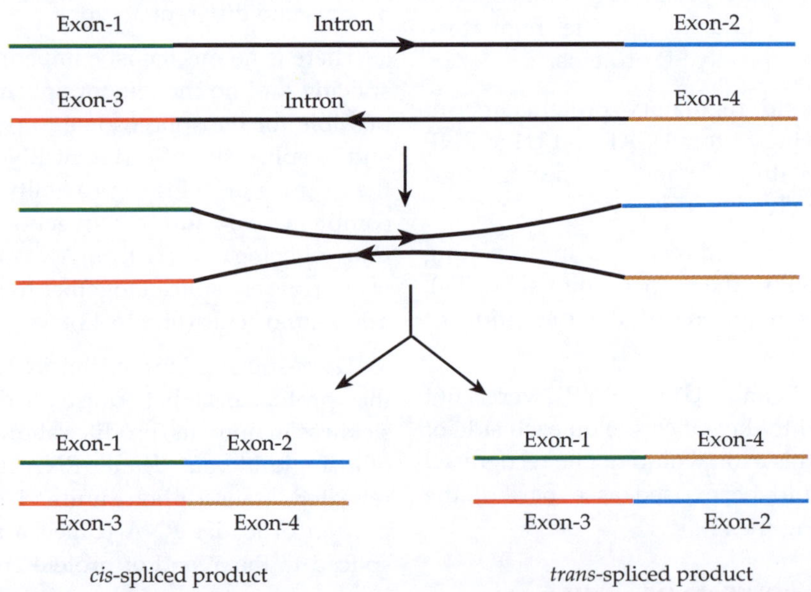


**Fig.16.43 :** *Cis and trans splicing of mRNA.*

*Trans*-splicing uses a unique snRNA called SLRNA (**spliced leader RNA**). The SL RNA provides an exon that is connected to the first exon of an mRNA by *trans*-splicing. The reaction involves the same interactions as nuclear *cis* splicing but generates a Y-shaped RNA instead of a lariat, because the intron is in two seperate parts. Trypanosomes do not have U1 or U5 snRNAs but SL RNA carries out the function of U1 snRNA. SL RNA can function without participation of proteins ie, the recognition of the 5′ splice site, depends diectly on RNA (Fig. 16.44).

## 16.8 PROCESSING OF tRNA

Pre-tRNAs are large precursors of tRNA, synthesized from the tRNA–genes in the

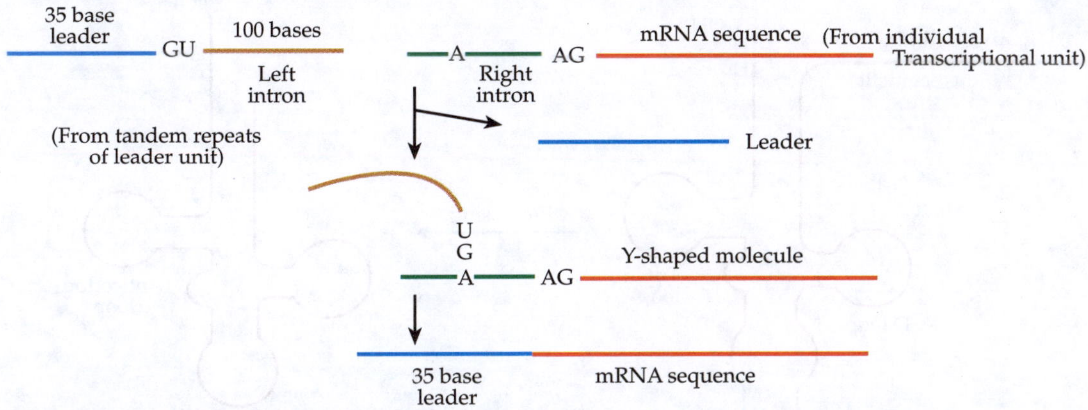


**Fig.16.44 :** *trans-splicing using SL RNA.*

nucleoplasm by RNA polymerase-III. During the processing, mature tRNA is produced by splicing and folding of the RNA chain and simultaneously modification of some bases and replacement of terminal UU residue by CCA.

1. Pre-tRNAs are larger in length than mature tRNA. The 5′ terminal end has a sequence of variable length. In *tyrosine-*tRNA, it is 16 nucleotides in length and does not form any loop or base pairing. This extra nucleotides are removed by RNase P (a ribonucleoprotein endo-nuclease) *E. coli* RNase P is a 14 kD protein with 377 nucleotide RNA, called M1 RNA. At high concentration of $Mg^{++}$ it recognises and cleaves the 5′ terminal nucleotides of pre-tRNA (Fig. 16.45).

2. About 10% of the bases of pre-tRNA are enzymatically modified during processing. Four types of base modifications occur, viz, Two methyl groups are added to guanine to form N, N-dimethyl -Guanine, two hydrogens are added to uridine to form dihydrouridine, deamination of guanine to form inosine and replacement of oxygen by sulfer in uridine to form 4-thiouridine (Fig. 16.46).

3. Replacement of terminal 3′ two-uridine molecules are replaced by CCA sequence which is found in all tRNAs.

4. The trimming and splicing of pre tRNA molcecules occur though a *cut-and-paste* mechanism that is clatalysed by some proteins and enzymes., The splicing process is not similar to that of mRNA splicing. First, the pre-tRNA is cleaved at two places, on each side of the intron. The cleavage generates a 2′, 3′ cyclic - prosphomonoester at the 3′ end of the 5′ exon. Then GTP phosphorylates the 5′ end of 3′ exon. Further phosphorylation by ATP – activated ligase causes the 3′ → 5′ linkage between the two exons. The 2′–phosphate of 5′-exon is then removed by 2′ – phosphotransferase enzyme. In such processing no lariat formation or snRNP are required (Fig. 16.47).

When introns containing yeast tRNA genes are microinjected into *Xenopus* oocyte nuclei, correctly processed tRNA are produced. There is no consensus sequence that could be recognised by the splicing enzymes. The same general rules apply to the nuclear tRNA genes of plants, amphibians and mammals. This finding indicates that enzymatic systems for

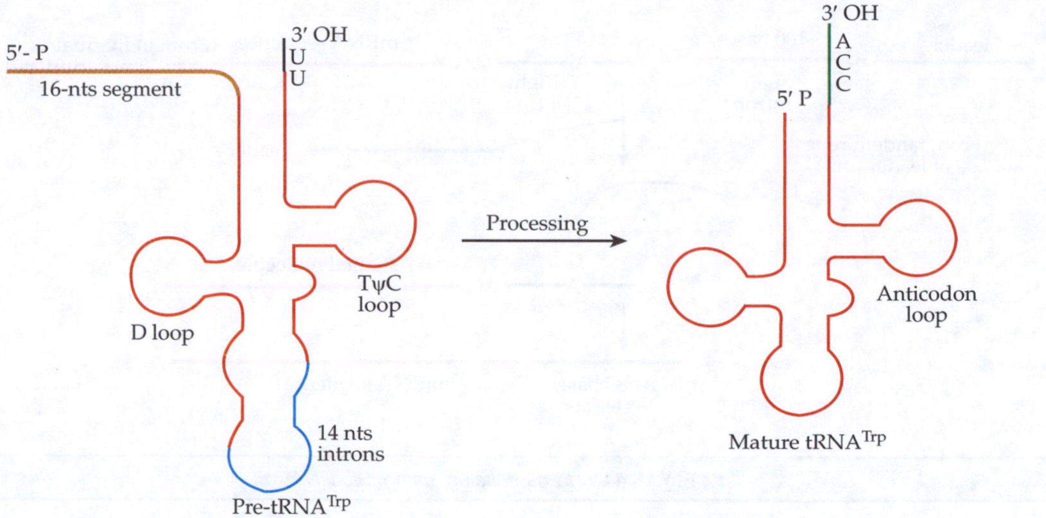


**Fig.16.45 :** *Processing of tyrosine pre-tRNA involves four types of changes.*

cleaving, modifying and splicing pre-tRNA have been conserved over a wide evolutionary range.

5. The yeast endonuclease, which is responsible for the specificity of intron recognition and cleaves precursors at both the ends of the intron, is a multimeric protein. The subunits *Sen 34* and *Sen 2* cleave the 3′ and 5′ splice sites respectively. Subunit **Sen 54** may determine the sites of cleavage by "measuring" distance from the mature domain. The *AI* base pair that forms between the first base in the anticodon loop and the base preceeding the 3′ splice site is required for 3′ splice site cleavage (Fig. 16.48).

6. The endonucleses of tRNA splicing in archaea are homodimers or heteroteramers, in which each subunit has an active site (although only two of the sites function in the tetramer) that cleaves one of the splice sites. The sequence of the subunits is related to the sequence of the

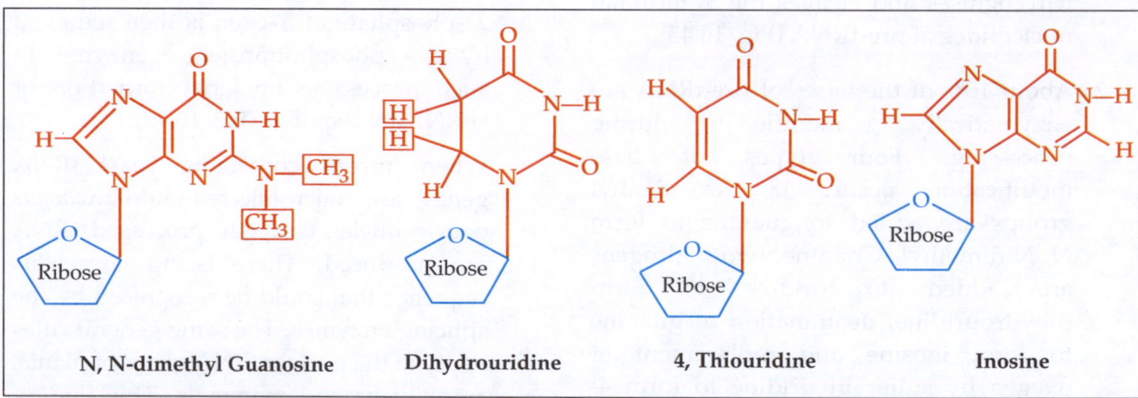


**Fig.16.46 :** *A few of the unusual nucleotides found in tRNA molecules.*

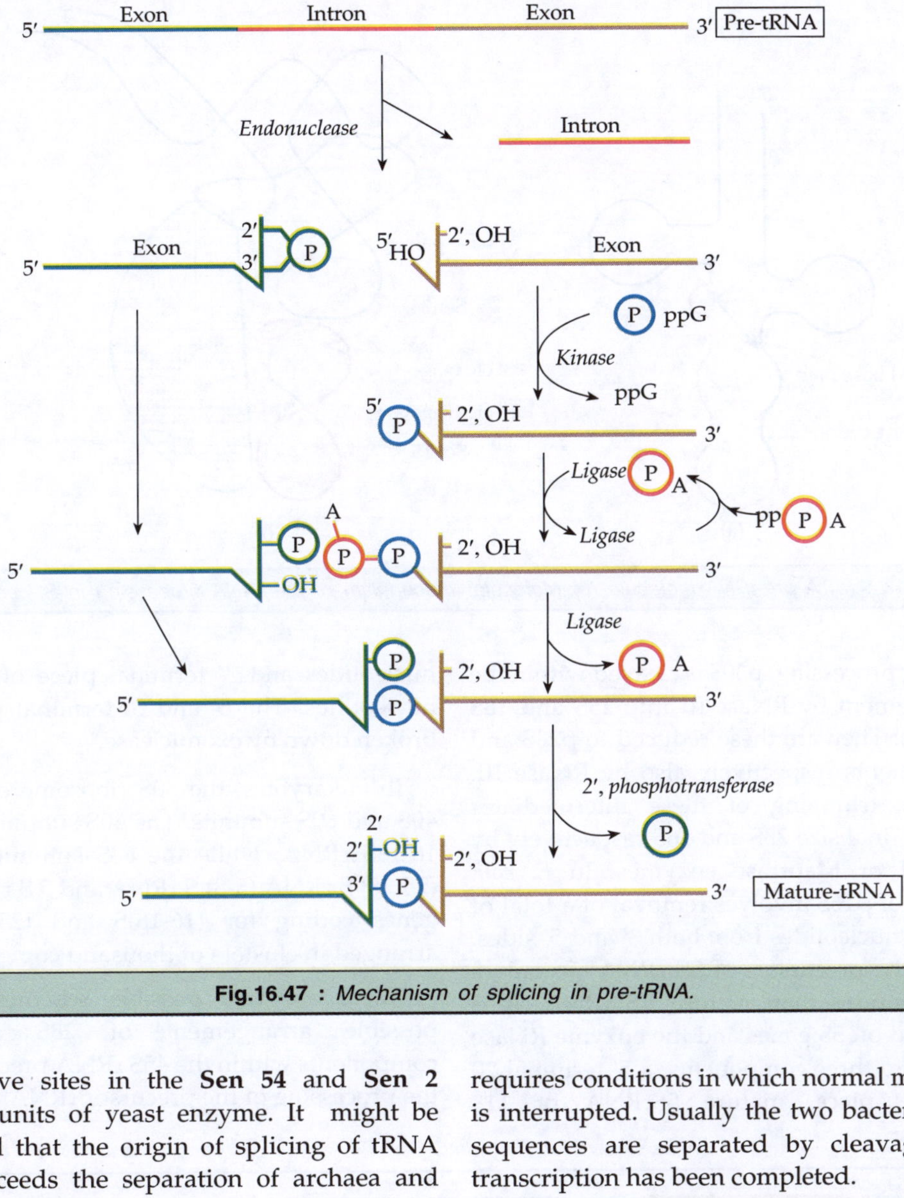


**Fig.16.47 :** *Mechanism of splicing in pre-tRNA.*

active sites in the **Sen 54** and **Sen 2** subunits of yeast enzyme. It might be said that the origin of splicing of tRNA preceeds the separation of archaea and eukaryotes.

## 16.9 SYNTHESIS AND PROCESSING OF rRNA

The major ribosomal RNAs are synthesised in the form of a single precursor molecule that contains both their sequences. In eukaryotes, the joint precursor is sufficiently stable to be isolated. In bacteria, this is more difficult and requires conditions in which normal maturation is interrupted. Usually the two bacterial rRNA sequences are separated by cleavage before transcription has been completed.

In bacterial genes, the sequence specifying 16S, 23S and sometimes 5S RNA are arranged in series. mRNA is trnascribed from DNA as a 30S unit, which has been called p30S. Experimental evidence indicates that the 30S, unit has the 16S component at the 5′ end and 23S component at the 3′ end with a spacer unit between these two components. In some prokaryotes 5S rRNA is also transcribed at or near 3′ end.

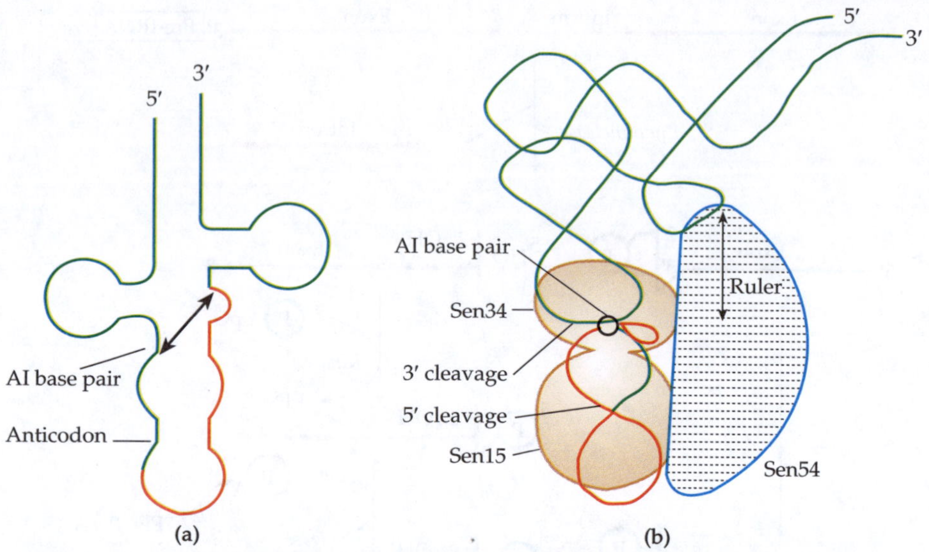


**Fig.16.48 :** *(a) A pre-tRNA molecule (b) Molecular mechanism of pre tRNA processing in S. cerevisiae.*

During processing, p30S is cleaved within the spacer segment by RNase-III into 25S and 18S (Fig.16.49). Then are these reduced to p23S and p16S segments respectively also by RNase III. Secondary trimming of these intermediates yields the final size 23S and 16S respectively by **RNase M** or **Maturase** enzymes. In *E. coli.* trimming of p16S involves removal of a total of about 200 nucleotides from both 3′ and 5′ sides. In *E. coli* the precursors of 5S rRNA are only a few nucleotides than mature 5S rRNA. It is transcribed on 5S genes and the enzyme RNase splits it into three components, a 5′ terminal 20 nucleotide piece, mature 5SrRNA of 118 nucleotides and 3′ terminal piece of about 40 nucleotides. The 5′ and 3′ terminal pieces are broken down by exonuclease.

In eukaryotes, the 80S ribosome consists of 40S and 60S subunits. The 40S subunits contain 16-18S rRNA, while the 60S subunits contain (25-28) S rRNA (5-8) S rRNA and 5 S rRNA. The genes coding for (16-18)S and (25-28)S are arranged in clusters of thousand copies.

There are two possible schemes for the possible arrangement of 28S and 18S components within the 45S rRNA precursor and the processing of the precursor rRNA.

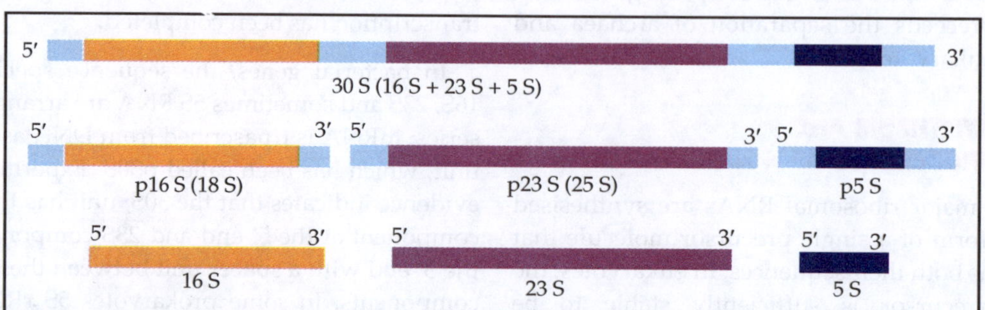


**Fig.16.48A :** *Processessing of Prokaryotic 30S rRNA.*

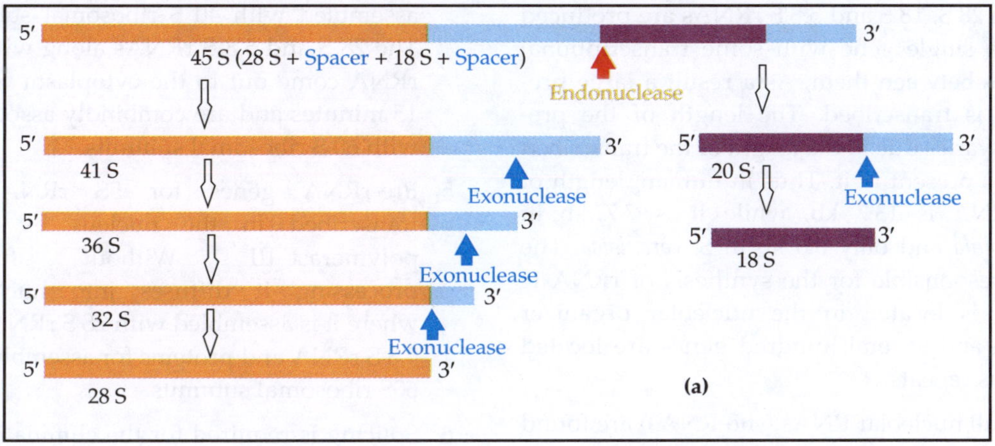


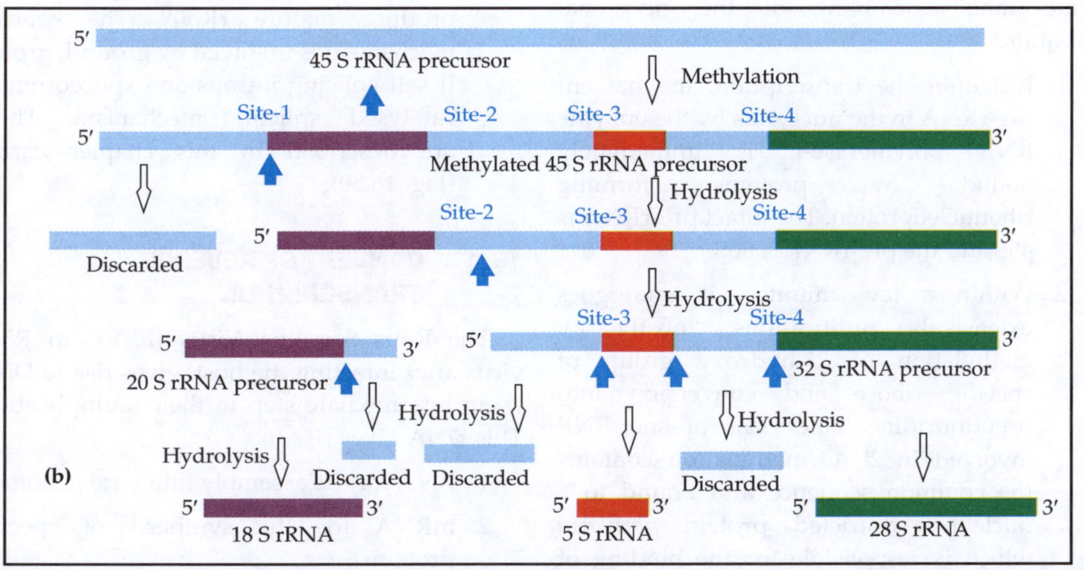


**Fig.16.49 :** *Processing of eukaryotic rRNA (a) first scheme; (b) second scheme.*

1. According to the first scheme 45S rRNA has a general form : **3′ P 28S rRNA-spacer-18S–rRNA-spacer-3′ OH**. The processing of the occurs as follows (Fig. 16.49a).

2. According to the second scheme the spacer sequence is situated at the 5′ P end of the 45S rRNA and the 28S component at the 3′ –OH end. Cleavage occurs at 4 sites. Cleavage at site-1 removes : 5′ P end spacer, cleavage at site 2 separates 18 S rRNA, cleavage at site 3 removes end spacer, and cleavage at site 4 results in final trimming of the large rRNA. 5S rRNA is trimmed separately. The cleavage steps are as follows (Fig. 16.49b).

## 16.10 ASSEMBLY OF rRNA IN THE RIBOSOME

In all eukaryotes, 60S ribosomal subunits consist of 28 S, 5.8 S and 5 S rRNAs while 40 S subunit consists of 18 S rRNA.

The 28 S, 18 S and 5.8 S rRNAs are produced from a single gene with some transcriptional specers between them, As a result a large pre-rRNA is transcribed. The length of the pre-rRNA varies due to the length of the transcribed spacers present in it. Thus in human, length of pre-rRNA is 13.7 kb, while it is 7.7 kb in *Drosophila* and only 6.6 kb in *S. cerevisiae*. The gene responsible for the synthesis of rRNA ie rDNA is located in the nucleolar organizer region and several hundred genes are located there as repeats.

Small nucleolar RNAs (sno RNAs) are found to assists in the processing of rRNAs and at the same time assembling of the ribosomal subunits.

1. Just after the transcription, the nascent pre-rRNA in the nucleolus by the enzyme RNA polymerase-I, is immediately bound by proteins forming ribonucleoprotein. The intact pre-rRNA is 45S and the pre-rRNP is 80S.
2. Within a few minutes, it undergoes extensively mdifications, mostly by methylation of 2′–hydroxy group of specific ribose and conversion into pseudouridine. One class of sno RNP involved in 2′ -O–methylation contains the common sequence and bound to a nucleolus restricted protein *fibrillarin* which is responsible for the binding of methyl transferase enzyme to the ribose moiety. Another class of snoRNP; called RNase MRP, catalyzes the cleavage reaction by which transcribed spacers are removed.
3. Within the nucleolus, 45 S pre-rRNA (80S pre-rRNP) is cleaved into two, one is 20 S and other is 32S rRNA.
4. 20 S rRNA undergoes further processing to become 18 S rRNA. The 32 S rRNA is further cleaved and processed into 28S rRNA and 5.8 S rRNA. 18S rRNA within 5 min comes out of the nucleolus and nucleus to the cytoplasm and are assembled with 40 S ribosomal subunit. The 28 S and 5.8 S rRNAs along with 5 S rRNA come out to the cytoplasm within 15 minutes and are combindly associated with 60 S ribosomal subunits.
5. Pre-rRNA genes for 5S rRNA are transcribed in the nucleus by RNA polymerase-III. Without further processing it diffuses into nucleolus where it is assembled with 28 S rRNA and 5.8 S rRNA and proteins for assembly into 60S ribosomal subunits.
6. Splicing is required for the elimination of transcribed spacers from the pre-rRNA to produce mature rRNA. The splicing mechanism is involved by group-I, group-II self splicing introns and spliceosome – catalysed splicing mechanism. These are described in this chapter earlier (Fig. 16.50).

## 16.11. CONCEPT OF REVERSE TRANSCRIPTION

The Rous Sarcoma Virus (RSV), an RNA virus after infecting the host, gives rise to DNA as an intermediate step in their multiplication. This DNA gives rise to

1. RNA for the assembly into viral genome.
2. mRNA for the synthesis of specific proteins.

In 1960's following experiments were done on RSV and observed the following results:

1. RNA synthesis, but not RNA to RNA synthesis.
2. Amethopterin and flurodeoxyuridine inhibit the synthesis of DNA soon after incubation of RSV with cells.
3. DNA extruded from infected cells, when denatured and hybridized with RNA, DNA-RNA hybrid molecules would be obtained. These informations indicated that, DNA is synthesized on RNA. But no enzymes were discovered then.

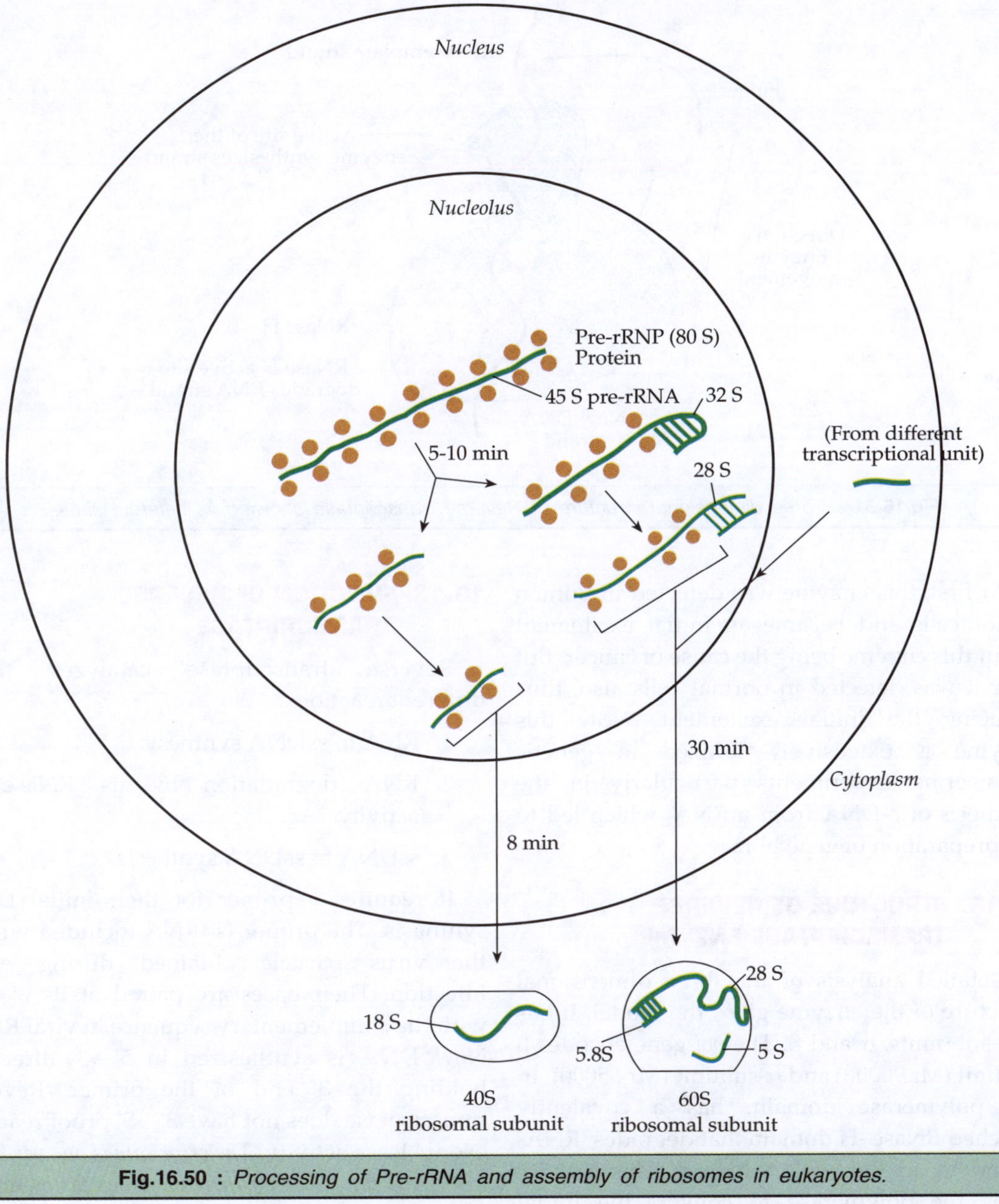


**Fig.16.50 :** *Processing of Pre-rRNA and assembly of ribosomes in eukaryotes.*

From the above experiments, ***Provirus hypothesis*** was proposed. In 1976, Temin and David Baltimore discovered first time this enzyme from RSV and MLV (Mouse leukovirus) respectively and suggested that an enzyme must be existed in the core particle of these viruses, which could stimulate RNA to DNA synthesis. For this work they have been awarded Nobel Prize.

This enzyme was initially called RNA dependent DNA polymerase, but later it was called RNA-directed DNA polymerase. This enzyme was then isolated and was utilized in producing DNA-RNA hybrid in genetic engineering and become popularly known as **reverse transcriptase**.

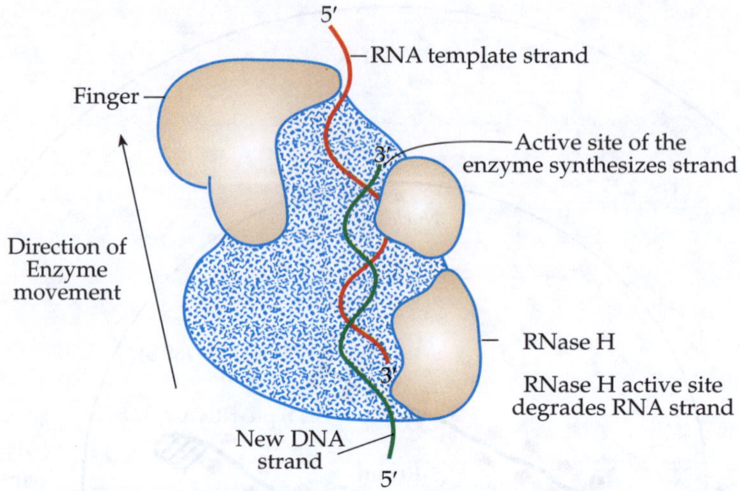


**Fig.16.51 :** *Three dimensional structure of Reverse transcriptase showing its different sites.*

At first, this enzyme was detected in human tumor cells and became an initial excitement about this enzyme being the cause of cancer. But later it was detected in normal cells also, thus reducing the initial excitement. Now this enzyme is extensively utilized in genetic engineering experiments particularly in the synthesis of c-DNA from mRNA, which led to the preparation of gene library.

## 16.12. STRUCTURE OF REVERSE TRANSCRIPTASE ENZYME

Detailed analysis of the three dimensional structure of the enzyme gives the model. It has two sub units, α and β. The *pol* gene encodes β subunit (Mr 90000) and α-subunit (Mr 65000). In the polymerase domain, has a covalently attached RNase–H domain that degrades RNA-strand in an RNA-DNA hybrid. This activity helps the polymerase to convert the initial hybrid helix into DNA double helix.

Viral reverse transcriptase contains $Zn^{++}$. They are mostly active with the RNA of their own type of virus, but can be made DNA experimentally, complementary to a variety of RNAs by these enzymes (Fig. 16.51).

## 16.13. FUNCTION OF REVERSE TRANSCRIPTASE

Reverse transcriptase catalyzes three different reactions.

1. RNA to ssDNA synthesis
2. RNA degradation by its RNase H activity
3. ssDNA to ssDNA synthesis

It requires a primer for their initial DNA synthesis. The primer is tRNA included within the virus particle obtained during early infection. Their bases are paired at its 3′ end with the complementary sequence in viral RNA. New DNA is synthesized in 5′→3′ direction holding the 3′ end of the primer. Reverse transcriptase does not have 3′→5′ proof reading exonuclease activity. *The error rate is one per 2000 nts. Thus the RNA virus genome has faster rate of evolution and appears frequently new strains of disease-causing viruses.*

Specific DNA sequence near the two ends of the dsDNA produced by the enzyme is then held together by a virus encoded **integrase** enzyme. This integrase creates activated 3′-OH viral DNA ends that can attack directly to the target DNA, molecules by a mechanism, called ***cut and paste mechanism***.

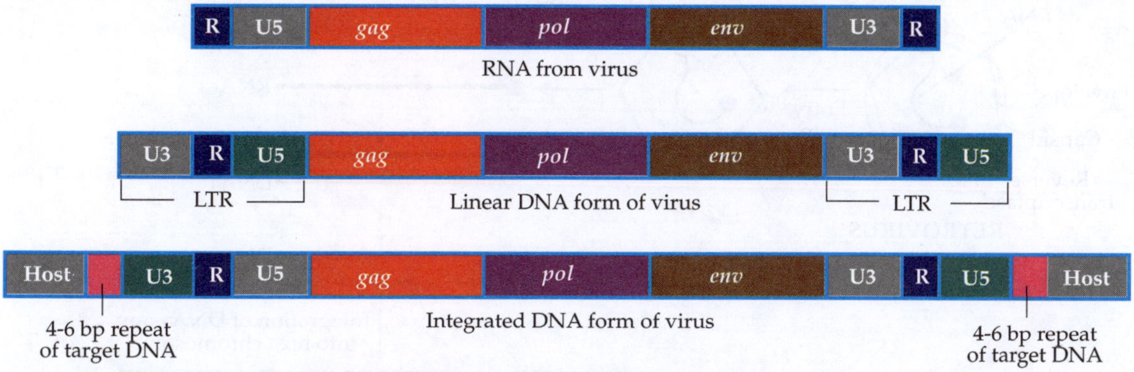


**Fig.16.52 :** *Retroviral RNA ends in direct repeats (R), the free linear DNA ends in LTRs and the provirus ends in LTRs.*

## 16.14. TYPICAL GENOME OF RETROVIRUSES

Two copies of the RNA genome are packed into each virion, making the individual virus particle effectively diploid. A typical retroviral sequence contains three or four genes, is organized in the sequence *gag-pol-env*. It is capped at the 5′ end and polydenylated at the 3' end. At the each end, a long terminal repeat (LTR) is present. It is about 250–1400 bp in length. It is also sub divided into R segment (10-80 nts). At the 5′ end is U5 region (80-100 nts.). Preceding the R-segment at the 3′ terminus is the U3 segment (170-1350 nts), which is unique to the 3′ end.

Gag protein is translated by reading from the initiation codon to the first termination codon. Pol-protein is produced by bypassing this termination. Splicing generates a shorter subgenomic messenger that is translated into the Env product. Gag-protein is a polyprotein, which makes up the interior core of the virus. Pol-protein is reverse transcriptase enzyme while Env-protein is the viral envelop protein (Fig. 16.52)

Retroviruses are called plus strand viruses, because itself codes for proteins. It may be converted into minus complementary strand by reverse transcription. The second strand which is synthesized into duplex is called plus strand DNA.

## 16.15. RETROVIRUS REPLICATIVE CYCLE

During retroviral replicative cycle following events have been found to be taken place (Fig. 16.53).

1. The retroviral replicative cycle takes place in the host cell. The virus is absorbed on the specific receptor on the surface of the host cell and then penetrates through the cell membrane. The virion invades into the cell and the RNA is released into the cytoplasm.

2. The RNA synthesizes proviral DNA in the cytoplasm with the help of primer–dependent reverse transcriptase. **This enzyme cannot synthesise new DNA chains *de novo*. It can only extend the originally existing chain of the primer.** The primer is cellular tRNA a part of which has complementary bases to the sequence in the virion RNA. This complementary sequence on the viral RNA is called **primer-binding site** (PBS).

Synthesis of DNA begins from the 3′ terminal end of the primer tRNA by the enzyme reverse transcriptase and it is extended upto the end of 5′ end of the virus.

Hybrid RNA is removed also by the RNase–H activity of the reverse transcriptase.

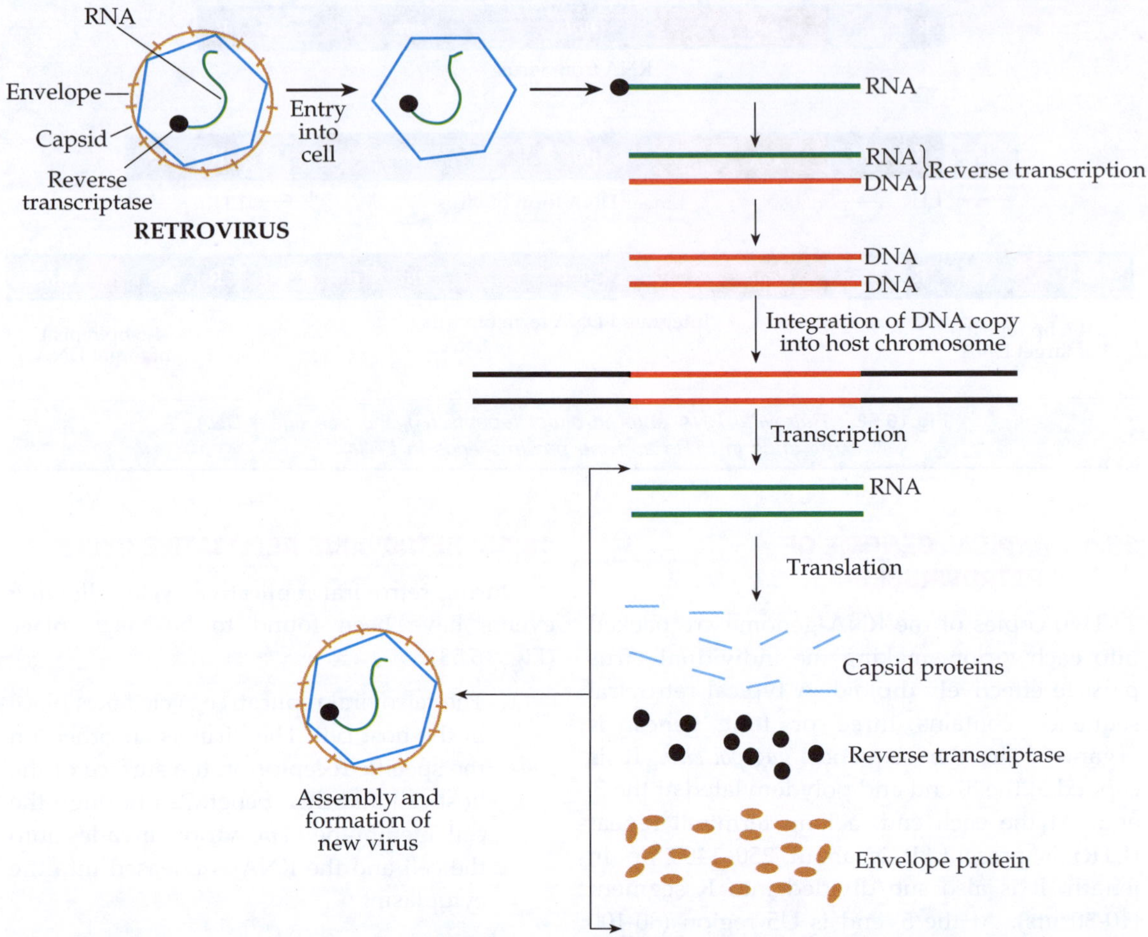


**Fig.16.53 :** *Life cycle of a retrovirus.*

Single stranded DNA R region pairs with the 3′ terminus in FIRST JUMP to another retroviral RNA.

Reverse transcription continues, extended from 3′ end.

Most hybrid RNA is then removed by RNase H activity of the enzyme excepting some region of the coding region at its 3′ end.

The 3′ end of the remaining RNA is extended by the enzyme upto PBS region.

tRNA and the remaining RNA is then removed.

The plus strand DNA is then transferred to other end of minus strand in second jump.

Both strands are completed by the synthesis from their 3′ ends (Fig. 16.54).

## 16.16. INTEGRATION OF dsDNA INTO HOST CHROMOSOME

The provirus is generated by directly inserting a linear DNA into target site. For a long time it was supposed that the intermediate is a circle, but it is now known that the linear form is involved in the integration (Lewin 2000).

The most conserved feature is the presence of the dinucleotide sequence **CA** close to the end of

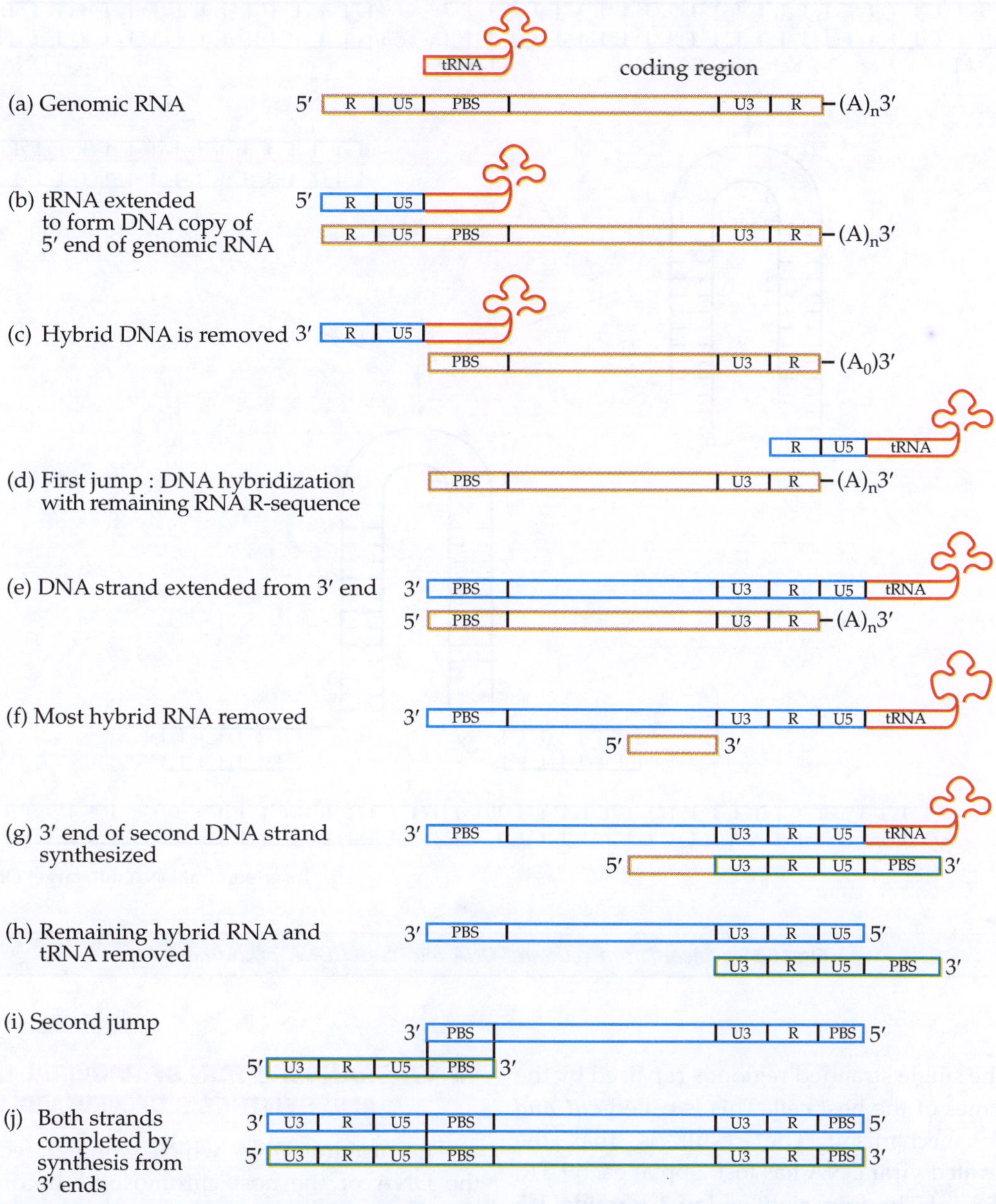


**Fig.16.54 :** *Retroviral DNA synthesis.*

each inverted repeat. The enzyme integrase brings the both ends of the linear DNA together in a form of ribonucleoprotein complex and then it removes two nucleotides beyond the conserved CA at their 3′ ends. Thus the blunt end is transformed into a staggered end (Fig. 16.55).

Target site on the host genome is selected randomly with respect to sequence. Integrase enzyme also cuts at the target site and makes it into staggered ends.

Both termini of the viral DNA are joined by one strand to the target DNA of the host.

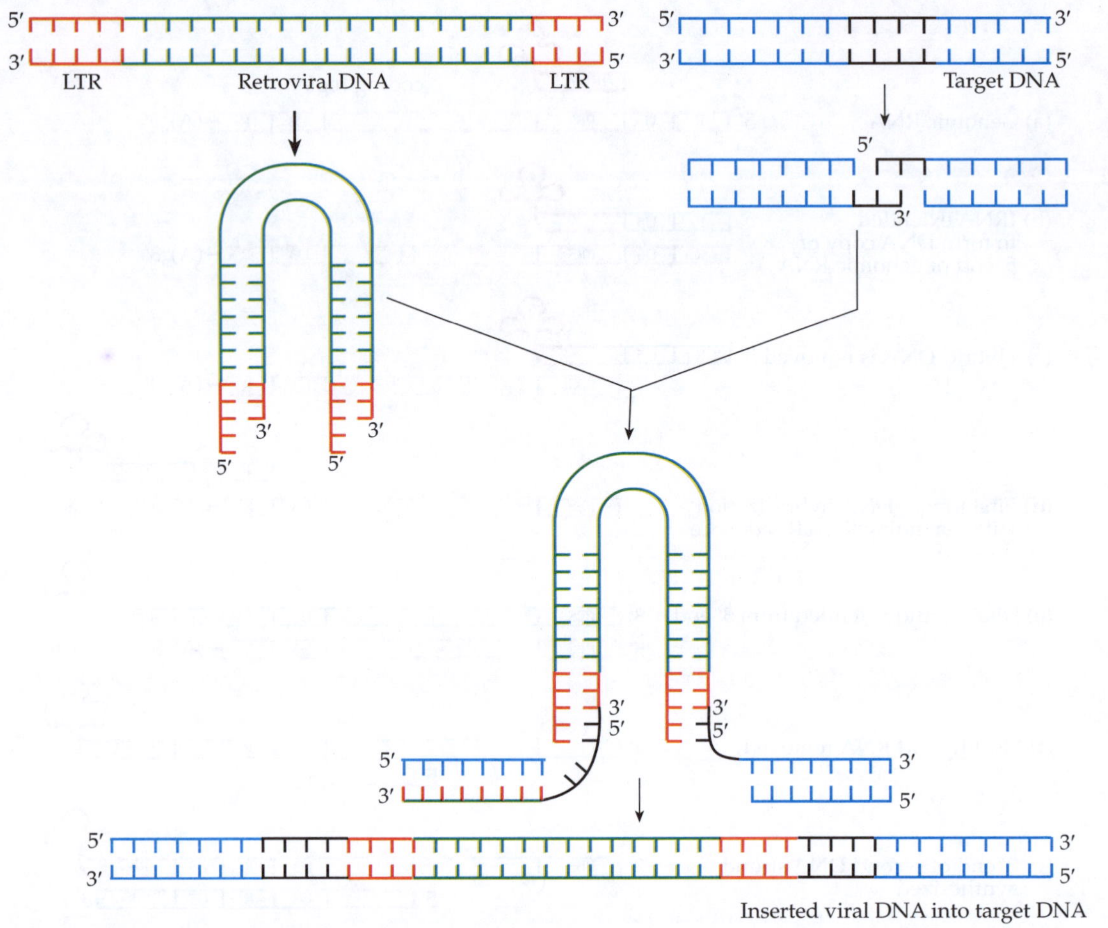


**Fig.16.55 :** *Insertion of retroviral DNA into target DNA of the host.*

The single stranded region is repaired by the enzymes of the host cell. This is called ***cut and paste*** mechanism. The result is that the integrated viral DNA has lost 2 bp at each LTR, i.e., loss of 2 bp from right end of 3' terminal U5 and 2 bp from the left end of the 5' terminal U3. Integration of the retrovirus can be responsible for converting a host cell into a tumorigenic state when certain types of genes are activated, because the promoter in the right LTR sometimes sponsors transcription of the genes of the host adjacent to it.

## 16.17. TRANSCRIPTION OF PROVIRAL DNA AND SYNTHESIS OF NEW VIRUSES

The proviral DNA which is integrated into the DNA of the host chromosome becomes a part of the host genome. This proviral DNA may remain latent or may transcribe RNA. The host cell is not affected by this integrated DNA. Transcription provides RNA for the progeny virus as well as RNA for protein synthesis.

The U3 region of each LTR carries promoter. The promoter in the left LTR is responsible for initiating transcription provirus by the host cell RNA polymerase.

# CHAPTER GLOSSARY/KEY TERMS

**Alternative splicing :** The production of two or more mRNAs from a single pre-mRNA by joining togerther different combinations of exons.

**CAAT box :** A basal promoter element.

**Capping :** Attachment of a cap to the 5¢ end of a eukaryotic mRNA.

**Central dogma :** One way flow of information from DNA to mRNA to protein by transcription and translation respectively in the organism.

**Closed promoter complex :** The structure formed during the initial step in assembly of the transcription initiation complex. The closed promoter complex consists of the RNA polymerase and/or accessory proteins attached to the promoter, before the DNA has been opened up by breakage of base pairs.

**Consensus sequence :** An idealized sequence in which each position represents the base most often found when many actual sequences are compared.

**Cruciforn :** The structure produced at inverted repeats of DNA if the repeated sequence pairs with its complement on the same strand.

**C-terminal domain (CTD) :** A component of the largest subunit of RNA polymerase-II important in activation of the polymerase.

**Elongation factor :** A protein that plays an ancillary role in the elongtion step of transcription or translation.

**Exon :** A coding region within a discontinuous gene.

**Exonic splicing enxhancer (ESC) :** A nucleotide sequence that plays a positive regulatory role during splicing of GU-AG introns.

**Exonic splicing silencer (ESS) :** A nucleotide sequence that plays a negative regulatory role during splicing GU-AG introus.

**Exon-intron boundary :** The nucleotide sequence at the junction between an exon and an intron.

**Exon-skipping :** Aberrant splicing in which one or more exons are omitted from the spliced RNA.

**GC-box :** A type of basal promoter element.

**Hairpin :** A double-helical region formed by base pairing between adjacent (inverted) complementary sequences in a single strand of RNA or DNA.

**Intron :** A non-coding region within a discontinuous gene.

**LTR (Long terminal repeat) :** A sequence directly repeated at both ends of a retroviral DNA.

**Non template strand :** The strand complementary to template strand.

**Open promoter complex :** A structure formed during assembly of the transcription initiation complex, consisting of the RNA polymerase and/or acessory protein attached to the promoter, after the DNA has been opened up by breakage of base pairs.

**Palindrome :** A sequence of DNA that is the same when one strand is read left to right or the other read right to left consists of adjacent inverted repeats.

**Polyadenylation :** The addition of a series of adenines to the 3¢ end of a eukaryotic mRNA.

**Pribnow box :** A component of the bacterial promoter.

**Primary transcript :** The initial product of transcription of a gene or group of genes, subsequently processed to give the mature transcripts.

*Contd.*

**Promoter :** The nucleotide sequences, upstream of a gene to which RNA polymerase binds in order to initiate transcription.

**Provirus :** This is a duplex DNA sequence in the eukaryotc chromosome corresponding to the genome of an mRNA retrovirus.

**Recognition domain :** An a-helix in a DNA binding protein, one that is responsible for recognition of the target nucleotide sequence.

**Retrovirus :** This an RNA virus that propagates via conversion into duplex DNA.

**Reverse transcriptase :** A polymerase that synthesizes DNA on an RNA template.

**Reverse transcription :** Senthesis of DNA on a template of RNA accomplished by reverse transcriptase enzyme.

**Rho :** A protein involved in termination of transcription of some bacterial genes.

**RNA poloymerase :** An enzyme that synthesizes RNA on a DNA or RNA template.

**RNA transcript :** An RNA copy of gene.

**snoRNA :** A type of short eukaryotic RNA molecule involved in chemical modification of rRNA.

**snRNA :** A type of short eukaryotic RNA molecule involved in spling GU-AG and AU-AC introns and in other RNA processing events.

**snRNP :** Structure involved in splicing GU-AG and AU-AG introns and in other RNA processing events comprising one one or two snRNA molecules complexed with proteins.

**Spliceosome :** The protein -RNA complex involved in splicing GU-AG or AU-AC introns.

**Splicing :** The removal of introns from the primary transcript of a discontinuous gene.

**Tandem repeat :** Direct repeats that are adjacent to each other.

**Tanscription :** The synthesis of the RNA copy of a gene.

**TATA binding protein :** A component of the general transcription factor TFIID, the part that recognises the TATA box of the RNA-pol-II promoter.

**TATA box :** A component of the RNA polymerase-II core promoter.

**Template strand :** The strand that serves as template for RNA synthesis.

**Transcription bubble :** The non-base-paired region of the double helix, maintained by RNA pol, within which transcription occurs.

**Trans-splicing :** Exons from two separate RNA molecules are joined together to form an mRNA.

**Upsteam promoter element :** Components of a eukaryotic promoter that lie upstream of the position where the initiation complex is assembled.

**Upstream control element (UCE) :** A component of an RNA polymerase-I promoter.

# EXERCISE

## A. Long answer type questions :

1. What is central dogma?
2. Draw and describe the prokaryotic RNA polymerase. What are the functions of its different subunits.
3. Describe different events in transcription in *E. coli.*
4. How transcription is terminated in *E. coli.* ?
5. Describe the inchworm model of transcription.
6. What are different eukaryotic promoters for RNA pol I, II and III?
7. Describe initiation of transcription by RNA polymerase I, II and III.
8. Describe the eleongation process in eukaryotic mRNA synthesis.
9. What are general transcription factors? What are their functions?
10. Describe the termination of trancription in eukaryotes.
11. Destinguish between prokaryotic and eukaryotic trancription.
12. What do you mean by post transcriptional processing of mRNA. What is capping? How does capping of mRNA occur in eukaryotes?
13. What is polyadenylation? How does poly adenylation occur in mRNA?
14. What are exons and introns? What do you mean by splicing? Describe different types of splicing mechanisms in eukaryotes.
15. What do you mean by alternative splicing?
16. Distinguish between *cis* and *trans* splicing?
17. Describe the OFF-ON mechanism of post transcription regulation.
18. Give some examples of alternative splicing.
19. What is commitment complex? How does it form?
20. Describe tRNA and rRNA processing.
21. Describe the provirus hypothesis, proposed by Temin.
22. What is reverse transcriptase? what is its characteristics?
23. Describe the structure and function of the enzyme reverse transcriptase.
24. Describe the typical genome of a retrovirus.
25. Describe the retrovirus replicative cycle.
26. How the dsDNA, or privirus is integrated into host genome?
27. Describe the molecular mechanism of termination of transcription.
28. Describe antitermination of transcription.

## B. Short answer type questions

1. What is Central Dogma?
2. Why are plus and minus strands?
3. What are template strand and nontemplate strands?
4. What is the function of template and nontemplate strands?
5. What is RNA polymerase holoenzyme? What are their subunits and their roles?
6. What are rudder and window in the molecular structure of RNA polymerase? What are their roles?
7. What the errors during transcription in *E. coli.* are not rectified?
8. What are the roles of three RNA polymerases in eukaryotes?
9. What is transcription factor?
10. Distinguish the RNA pol of archaea with prokaryotes.
11. What is the chracterisitic of mito-RNA pol?
12. What is Pribnow box?
13. What do you meant by consensus sequence?
14. What is a promoter? What are its characteristics?
15. What are the consensus sequences of *E. coli.* promoters and the recognition region?
16. What are the steps of RNA polymerase binding to promoters?
17. What is the role of sigma factor during transcription?
18. What is closed complex? How it is formed?
19. What is open complex? How it is formed?
20. How do you confirm that transcription of mRNA is always $5' \times 3'$ direction?

21. What is the role of Nus A protein during transcription?
22. What is ternary elongation complex?
23. What do you mean by inchworm model for transcription?
24. What is a terminator?
25. What is palindrome sequence in DNA.
26. What is cruciform structure of DNA? How it is formed?
27. What is a hair pin structure? How it is formed?
28. What is ρ-protein? How does it terminate trancription?
29. What do you mean by Hot pursuit model for ρ-action?
30. How does ρ-independent termination occur in transcription?
31. What is core promoter?
32. What is UPE?
33. What are the three types of promoters in different RNA polymerases?
34. What is UCE?
35. What is internal promoter?
36. What are null genes?
37. What are CAAT box and GC box? What are their consensus sequences?
38. What are CRE and CREB?
39. What is the role of HSP 70?
40. What are bicoid module and cell specific module?
41. How transcription is initiated by RNA pol-I in eukaryotes?
42. How transcription is initiated by RNA pol-III in eukaryotes?
43. What do you mean by positioning factor?
44. What is the function of TBP?
45. What is basal transcription factor?
46. What is the role of CPSF in the termination of transcription?
47. Distinguish between eukaryotic and prokaryotic transcription.
48. What are exons and introns?
49. What do you mean by post transtional modification of RNA?
50. Waht is capping? Which enzyme is required for capping?
51. What are Cap-o, Cap 1 and Cap-2?
52. What are the functions of guanylyl transferase and guanine-7-methyl transferase in capping of RNA?
53. What is splicing?
54. What is the characteristics of group I intron splicing?
55. What is self splicing ?
56. What are snRNP or SNURPs?
57. What is SnRNA?
58. What is Spliceosome?
59. What enzymes are required in group IV intron splicing.
60. What do mean by lariat formation?
61. What is spliceosome?
62. What is alternate splicing?
63. What are the roles of *sxl, tra* and *dsx* genes in the sex deffertiation of *Drosophila?*
64. What do you mean by commitment complex?
65. What is *trans* splicing where does it occur?
66. What are the four steps in tRNA processing?
67. What is RSV?
68. What is provirus hypothesis?
69. What are reverse transcriptase and reverse transcription?
70. What is the function of RNAase H of reverse transcriptase?
71. What do you mean by cut and paste mechanism?
72. What are the functions of *gag, pol* and *env* genes.
73. What do you mean by retroviral replicative cycle?
74. What is PBS?
75. What primer is used in the extension by reverse transcription?
76. What is a provirus?
77. What is LTR? What is its function?
78. What proteins are concerned with the termination of transcription?
79. What is the role of NusA in the termination of transcription?
80. What is antitermination?
81. What are the promoters and terminators in *E. coli.*

17

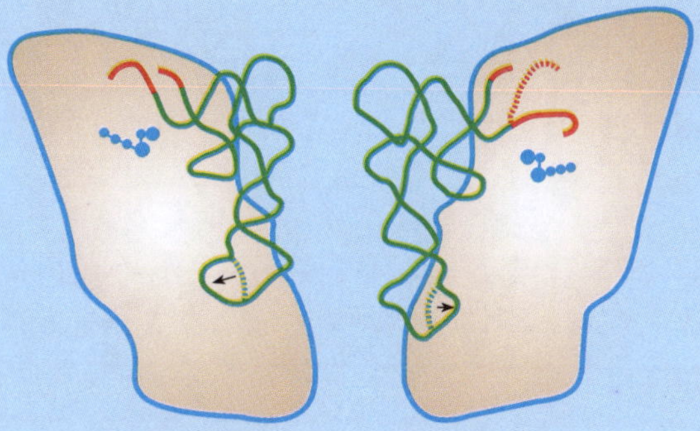

# Translation of Genome

**CHAPTER AGENDA**

**17.1** Concept of Genetic Code; **17.2** Important features of Genetic Code; **17.3** Wobble Hypothesis; **17.4** Reason of Unexpected codon-anticodon pairing; **17.5** Exceptions of the universality of Genetic code; **17.6** Mitochondrial Genetic Codes; **17.7** Origin and Evolution of Genetic Code; **17.8** Selenocysteine and Pyrrolysine : the genetically encoded amino acids; **17.9** Concept of Protein Synthesis; **17.10** Activation of Amino acid; **17.11** Amino acylation of tRNA by aminoacyl tRNA synthatase; **17.12** Mechanism of Protein synthesis; **17.13** Translation in Archaea; Chapter Glossary/Key Terms; Exercise

## 17.1. CONCEPT OF GENETIC CODE

The set of triplet code words in DNA or mRNA coding for the amino acids of a polypeptide chain is called **genetic code**.

It is fact that all genetic informations are stored in the DNA or RNA and the genetic information in the nucleic acids is expressed through synthesis of proteins. There are 20 different kinds of amino acids in the polypeptide chain and only 4 kinds of different bases. It may be realized that 20 amino acids are the alphabets of the language of proteins, 4 bases are the alphabets of the language of nucleic acids.

The problem of genetic code was to prepare a dictionary for translating the language of RNA into the language of protein. If singlet code is used then there would be 4 codons only, which is not able to designate 20 amino acids properly and separately. If a doublet code is used then $2^4$ =16 codes would not also be sufficient to designate all the 20 amino acids separately. A triplet code would have $4^3$=64 codons, which would be enough to designate all the 20 amino acids separately (Table 17.1).

## 17.2. IMPORTANT FEATURES OF GENETIC CODE

The genetic code has several important features.

1. **The code is triplet :** If the code is a triplet then there would be $4^3$=64 possible codes for 20 amino acids. It is then clear that more than one code are present for the same amino acids.
2. **The code is degenerate :** For a particular amino acid more than one triplet code can be used. This phenomenon is described in saying that the code is degenerate. On the contrary, a non-degenerate code would be such that there is one code for one amino acid relationship. If so 44 codons out of 64 would be useless or nonsense. It has been definitely shown that there is no nonsense codon. There is only three stop codons (UAA, UAG and UGA) which were called earlier as nonsense codons.
3. **The code is non-overlapping :** A base in an mRNA is not used for two different codons. If it is overlapping, six bases would represent four amino acids. Actually six bases code for not more than two amino acids.

For example,

(i) If the code is overlapping

**No. of amino acids :** ①②③④

**Bases :** C A T G G T

(ii) If the code is non-overlapping

**No. of amino acids :** ① ②

**Bases :** C A T G G T

4. **The Code is Commaless** : There is no punctuation mark between any two words, i.e., it can be said that after one amino acid is coded, the second amino acid will be automatically coded by the next three letters. Therefore no letters are wasted.
5. **Code is non-ambiguous :** There is no ambiguity about a particular codon. A particular codon will always code for the same amino acid wherever it is found. There some elements of ambiguity when AUG and GUG are considered as *methionine*, although, GUG is meant for *valine* when it is not an initiation codon.
6. **The Code is universal :** Although, the codon-amino acid relationship has been worked out using *in vitro* system prepared usually from microorganisms there is no doubt that in all kinds of living organisms (micro and macro), plants and animals, the same genetic code is used. There are some exceptions, which exist in mitochondria and chloroplast where some

**TABLE 17.1**

**The Genetic Code : Nucleotide Triplets (Codons) Specifying Different Amino Acids in Protein Chains**

| DNA triplet | RNA triplet | Amino acid |
|---|---|---|
| AAA | UUU | Phenylalanine |
| AAG | UUC | |
| AAT | UUA | Leucine |
| AAC | UUG | |
| GAA | CUU | |
| GAG | CUC | |
| GAT | CUA | |
| GAC | CUG | |
| AGA | UCU | serine |
| AGG | UCC | |
| AGT | UCA | |
| AGC | UCG | |
| TCA | AGU | |
| TCG | AGC | |
| GGA | CCU | proline |
| GGG | CCC | |
| GGT | CCA | |
| GGC | CCG | |
| TAA | AUU | isoleucine (Ileu) |
| TAG | AUC | |
| TAT | AUA | |
| TAC | AUG | methionine |
| TGA | ACU | threonine |
| TGG | ACC | |
| TGT | ACA | |
| TGC | ACG | |
| CAA | GUU | valine |
| CAG | GCC | |
| CAT | GUA | |
| CAC | GUG | |
| CGA | GCU | alanine |
| CGG | GCC | |
| CGT | GCA | |
| CGC | GCG | |

| DNA triplet | RNA triplet | Amino acid |
|---|---|---|
| ACA | UGU | cysteine |
| ACG | UGC | |
| ACC | UGG | tryptophan |
| ATA | UAU | tyrosine |
| ATG | UAC | |
| ATT | UAA | (termination : end of specification) |
| ATC | UAG | |
| ACT | UGA | |
| GCA | CGU | arginine |
| GCG | CGC | |
| GCT | CGA | |
| GCC | CGG | |
| TCT | AGA | |
| TCC | AGG | |
| GTA | CAU | histidine |
| GTG | CAC | |
| GTT | CAA | glutamine (GluN) |
| GTC | CAG | |
| TTA | AAU | asparagine (AspN) |
| TTG | AAC | |
| TTT | AAA | lysine |
| TTC | AAG | |
| CCA | GGU | glycine |
| CCG | GGC | |
| CCT | GGA | |
| CCC | GGG | |
| CTA | GAU | aspartic acid |
| CTG | GAC | |
| CTT | GAA | glutamic acid |
| CTC | GAG | |

codons are not similar to that of usual genetic code.

7. **Several Codons serve special functions :** The initiation codon AUG signals the beginning of polypeptide chain. AUG not only is the initiation codon, but also codes for **methionine** residue in the internal position of the polypeptide chain.

UAA (amber). UAG (ochre) and UGA (opal) do not code for amino acids. They are the **termination codons** (previously these were called nonsense codons).

## 17.3. WOBBLE HYPOTHESIS

tRNAs recognize codons by base-pairing between the mRNA codon and the three-base sequence on the tRNA called the **anticodon**. The two RNAs are paired in antiparallel manner the first base of the codon (5′→ 3′) pairing with the third base of the anticodon (Fig. 17.1).

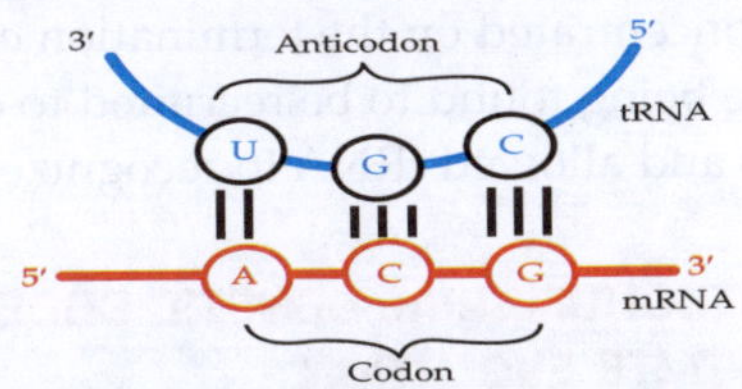


**Fig.17.1 :** *Codon-anticodon pairing.*

One might expect the anticodon triplet of a tRNA to recognize only one codon triplet through Watson- Crick base pairing. So that there would be a different tRNA for each codon of an amino acid. However, the number of different tRNAs for each amino acid is not the same as the number of its codon. Moreover, some of the tRNAs contain the nucleotide *"inosinate"*, which contains an uncommon base *hypoxanthine*. Molecular Model shows that *inosinate* can form hydrogen bonds with U, C, and also with A.

The third base of *arginine* codon (A, U and C) forms rather weak H-bonds with I-residue at the first position of the anticodon.

**Anticodon :** 3′ G C I 5′

**Codons :** 5′ C G A 3′
or 5′ C G U 3′
or 5′ C G C 3′

Examinations of these and other codon – anticodon pairing led Crick to conclude that *"The 3rd base of most codon pairs rather loosely with the corresponding base of its anticodons, to use his picturesque word, the third bases of such codons wobble"*. Crick proposed a set of four relationships called **Wobble hypothesis**.

1. The first two bases of a codon in mRNA always form strong Watson-Crick base pairing with the corresponding bases of the coding specificity.
2. The first base of some anticodons (reads as 5′→3′) determines the number of codons read by a given tRNA. When the first base of the anticodon is C or A, binding is specific and only one codon is read by that tRNA. However, when the first base is U or G, binding is less specific and two different codons may be read. When I is the first or wobble, nucleotide of an anticodon, three different codons can be read by that tRNA. This is the maximum number of codons that can be recognized by a tRNA. This relationship is summarized in the figure (Fig. 17.2).
3. When an amino acid is specified by several different codons, those codons that differ in either of the first two bases require different tRNAs.
4. A minimum of 16 tRNAs are required to translate all 61 codons.

## 17.4. REASON OF UNEXPECTED CODON - ANTICODON PAIRING

The first two bases of a codon confer most of the codon-anticodon specificity. The wobble (or third) base of the codon contributes to specificity but because it pairs only loosely with its corresponding base in the anticodon, it permits rapid dissociation of the tRNA from its codon

**One codon recognised :**

anticodon : 3′ X – Y – C 5′
codon : 5′ Y – X – G 3′

anticodon : 3′ X – Y – A 5′
codon : 5′ Y – X – U 3′

**Two codon recognised :**

anticodon : 3′ X – Y – U 5′
codon : 5′ Y – X – A/G 3′

anticodon : 3′ X – Y – G 5′
codon : 5′ Y – X – C/U 3′

**Three codon recognised :**

anticodon : 3′ X – Y – I 5′
codon : 5′ Y – X – A/U/C 3′

**Fig.17.2 :** *The wobble base of the anticodon determines how many codons of a given amino acids a tRNA can recognise X is complementary to Y.*

during protein synthesis. If all three bases of mRNA codons engaged in strong Watson-Crick pairing with the three bases of the tRNA anticodons, tRNA would dissociate too slowly and severely limit the rate of protein synthesis. Codon-anticodon interactions optimize both accuracy and speed of translation.

## 17.5. EXCEPTIONS OF THE UNIVERSALITY OF GENETIC CODE

1. In *Mycoplasma capricolum* (a prokaryote) UGA is not used for termination codon, but it codes *tryptophan*.
2. In some protozoan ciliates, UAA and UAG read on *glutamine* instead of termination codon. *Tetrahymena thermophila* contains three tRNA$^{glu}$ species. One recognizes CAA and CAG and the other recognizes both UAA and UAG (in accordance with the Wobble hypothesis).
3. In *Euplotes octacarinatus* a protozoan ciliate, UGA codes for *cysteine*. Only UAA is termination codon. UAG is not found.
4. In *Candida* sp (a yeast), CUG means for *serine* instead of *leucine*, UAG is used as a sense codon.

From the above examples it can be assumed that the changes in genetic code are sporadic. They appear to have occurred independently in specific line of evolution. The changes are mainly concentrated on the termination codons, which are being found to be recruited to coding purposes and allowed tRNA to recognize them.

## 17.6. MITOCHONDRIAL GENETIC CODE AND ITS EVOLUTION

Some exceptions to the universal genetic codes also occur in the mitochondria. Changes in the genetic code in mitochondria can also be traced in phylogeny. From this evolution tree it has been supposed that the AUA = *Met* and AAA = *Asn* changes independently twice.

The earliest change was the employment of UGA to code *Trp*, which was common to all mitochondria. In mammalian mitochondria four termination codes are UAA UAG, AGA and AGG. In yeast mitochondria CUN codes for threonine and UAG also codes for *threonine* (Fig. 17.3).

## 17.7. ORIGIN AND EVOLUTION OF GENETIC CODE

Many geneticists support the **"frozen accident"** theory, which suggests that codons

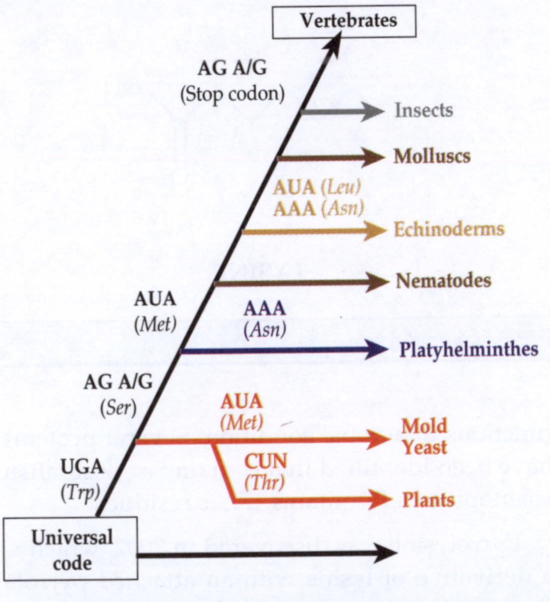


**Fig.17.3 :** *Changes in the genetic code in mitochondria and its phylogeny.*

were randomly allocated to amino acids during earliest stages of evolution, the code subsequently becoming "frozen" because any changes would result in widespread disruption of the amino acid sequences of proteins. The code might have evolved in a less random manner (Knight *et al* 1999, Szathmary 1999).

The experimental results suggest that some amino acids bind to RNA containing the appropriate codons, which suggests that code might have originated from natural interactions between RNA molecules and amino acids. Therefore, there might be some kind of chemical relationship between an amino acid and its codons.

The deviation from the universal codons suggest that the codons were reallocated in the same way on at least three separate occasions e.g., 5′ UAA 3′ and 5′ UAG 3′ is *glutamine* in three unrelated protozoans rather than termination codon. Similarly 5′ UGA 3′ as a *Trp* codon must have evolved twice, once in mitochondria and once in the ancestors of *Mycoplasma*.

If the relationship between codon and amino acid is entirely random, as suggested by the "frozen accident" theory, then we would not expect to see the same codon reallocations recurring on different occasions.

## 17.8 SELENOCYSTEINE AND PYRROLYSINE : THE GENETICALLY ENCODED AMINO ACIDS

There are 20 standard amino acids which are the countituents of synthesized proteins in the cell. They have definite genetic codes and tRNA molecules to carry them during translation of mRNA.

Two unusual amino acids have been discovered recently which are also found to the incorporated into the cellular proteins and they have genetic codes and tRNA molecules to carry them to the ribosomes (Fig. 17.4 and 17.5).

*Selenocysteine (Sec)* is an amino acid, occurs in both prokaryotes as well as eukaryotes including humans. This amino acid is encoded by UGA, usually a stop codon and therefore this is given the honour to be the 21st genetically encoded amino acid. During translation, the choice between "stop" and selenocysteine depends upon the presence of a special recognition sequence in the following part of the gene, called the selenocysteine insertion sequence or SECIS element. Selenocysteine also has its own tRNA and special protein to escort tRNA — *sec* to the ribosome. In fact selenocysteine - RNA is charged with serine and then the attached serine is enzymatically

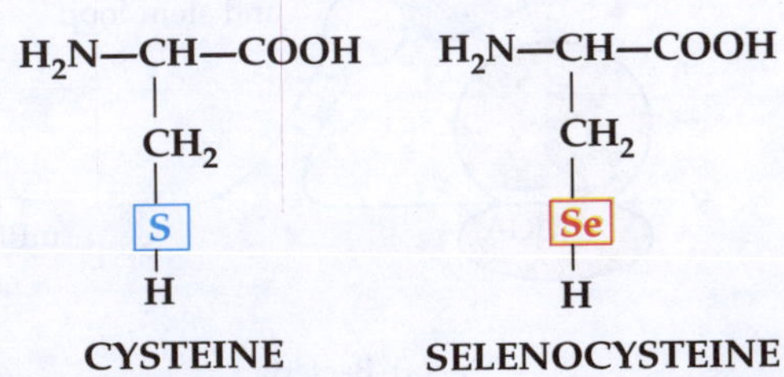


**Fig. 17.4 :** *Structure of pyrrolysine and selenocysteine.*

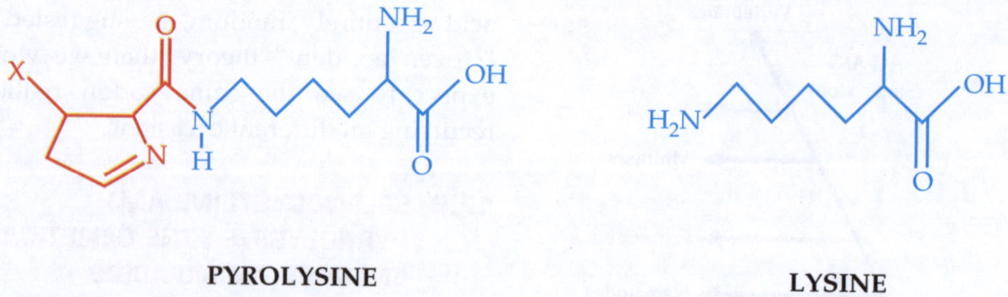


**Fig. 17.5 :** *Structure of pyrrolysine and lysine.*

modified to form selenocysteine. Selenocysteine is an analog of cysteine, but has selenium instead to sulfer.

In bacteria, the tRNA carrying selenocysteine first binds to **SelB** protein and the complex then binds to a stem and loop in the mRNA. This aligns the tRNA-*Sec* with a UGA codon within the coding sequence on the mRNA. Selenocysteine is then inserted as part of the growing polypeptide (Fig. 17.6).

In mammals, the stem and loop-form is found beyond the end of coding sequence *ie* in the 3′-untranslated region next to UGA codon. The protein that binds the stem and loop with tRNA-*Sec* is called eEF*sec*. Somehow the eEF*sec* delivers the tRNA-*Sec* to the correct position for insertion. Selenocysteine is susceptible to oxidation. Therefore, the enzyme formate dehydrogenase in bacteria which contains *Sec* functions in aerobic condition. Several proteins have been identified that contain *Sec*. Zebrafish solenoprotein P contains 17 *Sec* residues.

Pyrrolysine was discovered in 2002, which is a derivative of lysine with an attached pyrrole ring. This was first discovered in archaebacteria *Methanosarcina,* in the active site of the enzyme methylamine methyl transferases used for the production of methane. The stop codon UAG is used occassionally in protein synthesis by a special tRNA and an unusual aminoacyl -tRNA synthase. It is believed that pyrrolysine-tRNA is first charged with lysine, which then modified to form pyrrolysine. This is not known how UAG codons for pyrrolysine are distinguished from those still meaning stop. Genome analysis has revealed that pyrrolysine system may be present in eubacteria but not yet been identified in these organisms.

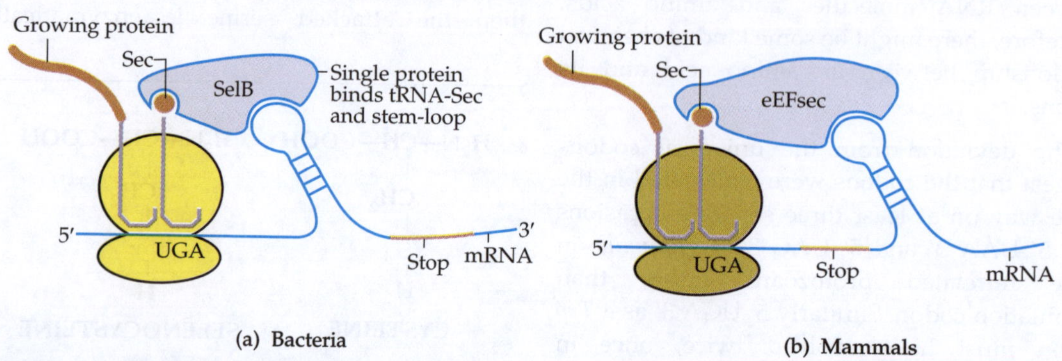


**Fig. 17.6 :** *Delivery of tRNA with Selenocysteine to an internal UGA stop codon.*

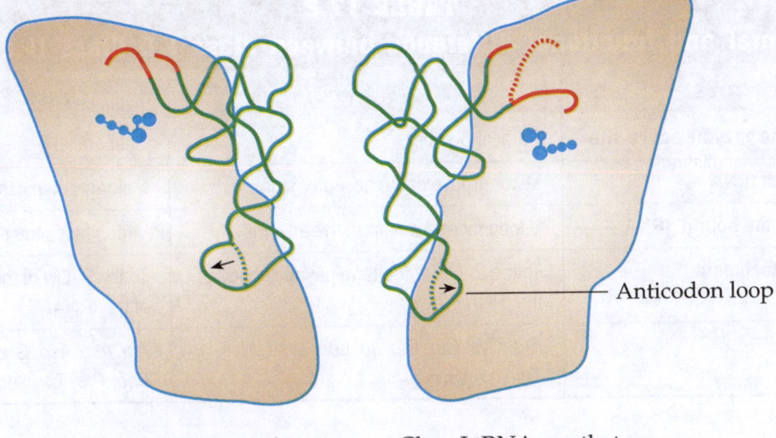


**Fig.17.7 :** *Binding of tRNA with Class I and Class II tRNA synthetases.*

## 17.9 CONCEPT OF TRANSLATION

In the cell, DNA stores the information, which is transcribed into mRNA. It carries genetic information in the form of a series three – base code words, each of which specifies a particular amino acid. On the ribosomes in the cytoplasm, this m RNA is translated into a protein, which is crucial to the proper functioning of cells and organisms.

## 17.10 ACTIVATION OF AMINO ACID

In the first step, an enzyme- bound intermediate; aminoacyladenylate is formed by the reaction with ATP. In this reaction, the carboxyl group of amino acid is bound in anhydrite linkage with 5′- phosphate group of AMP, with displacement of pyrophosphate.

$$\text{Amino acid} + \text{ATP} \rightarrow \text{Aminoacyladenylate} + \text{PPi}$$

## 17.11 AMINOACYLATION OF tRNA BY AMINOACYL tRNA SYNTHETASE

In the second step, aminoacyl group is transferred from enzyme bound aminoacyl–AMP to its corresponding specific tRNA. In the cytosol, the 20 different amino acids are esterified to their corresponding tRNAs by the enzyme aminoacyl tRNA synthetase, each of which is specific for one amino acid and one or more tRNAs. In *E. coli* the exception to this rule is *lysine* for which there are two aminoacyl-tRNA- synthetases. In this process, two high-energy phosphate bonds are ultimately expended for each amino acid activation and the reaction is irreversible.

The enzyme aminoacyl synthetase has a catalytic domain includes the binding sites for ATP and amino acid. It can be recognized as a large region that is interrupted by an insertion of a domain that binds the acceptor helix of the tRNA. This places the terminus of the tRNA in proximity to the catalytic site. A separate domain binds the anticodon region of tRNA (Fig. 17.7).

Two classes of enzymes can be recognized on the basis of the structure of the domain that contains the active site. These are class –I and class-II enzymes (Table 17.2).

For class-I enzymes, the aminoacyl group is transferred initially to the 2′-OH group of 3′-terminal adenylate residue at tRNA and then moved to the 3′-OH by a transesterification reaction.

**TABLE 17.2**
**Structural and functional difference between class I & Class II enzyme.**

| Features | Class I enzymes | Class II enzymes |
|---|---|---|
| 1. Structure of the enzyme active site | Parallel β-sheet | Antiparallel β-sheet |
| 2. Interaction with tRNA | Minor groove of the acceptor stem. | Major groove of the acceptor stem. |
| 3. Orientation of the bound tRNA | V loop faces away from the enzyme. | V-loop faces the enzyme. |
| 4. Amino acid attachment | To the 2′-OH of the terminal nucleotide of the tRNA | To the 3′-OH of the trminal nucleotide of the tRNA. |
| 5. Enzymes for | *Arg, Cys, Gln, Glu, Ile, Leu, Lys-I, Met Trp, Tyr, Val* | *Ala, Asn, Asp, Gly, Lys-II, His, Lys II, Phe, Pro, Thr, Ser.* |

For class- II enzymes, the aminoacyl group is transferred directly to the 3′-OH of the terminal adenylate (Fig. 17.8).

An individual aminoacyl-tRNA-synthetase must be specific not only for a single amino acid but for a certain tRNA as well.

The interaction between aminoacyl-tRNA synthetase and tRNAs has been referred to as the "**second genetic code**" to reflect its critical role in maintaining the accuracy of protein synthesis. Nucleotide positions have been identified which is concerned with the substrate specificity. These interactions seem to be concentrated in the amino acid arm and the anticodon arm, but are also located in many other parts of the molecule.

## 17.12 MECHANISM OF PROTEIN SYNTHESIS

Protein synthesis falls into three stages, viz, initiation, elongation and termination.

### 17.12.1 Initiation of Protein Synthesis

It involves the reactions that precede formation of the peptide bond between the first two amino acids of the protein( Fig. 17.9).

• **IN PROKARYOTES :** Although, there is only one codon (AUG) for *methionine*, there are two tRNAs for *methionine* in all organisms. One tRNA is used exclusively when AUG represents the initiation codon for protein synthesis. The second is used when *methionine* is added to the internal position in a polypeptide. In bacteria, the two separate classes of tRNAs, specific for methionine are designated as $tRNA^{Met}$ and $tRNA^{f\text{-}Met}$. GUG is read as f-met but when it is present within gene, read by $tRNA^{val}$ as *valine*.

The starting amino acid residue at the amino terminal end is N-*formylmethionine*. It enters into the ribosome as N-*formylmethionine* $tRNA^{f\text{-}Met}$ which is formed in two successive reactions.

$$\text{Met} + \text{tRNA}^{f\text{-}Met} + \text{ATP} \rightarrow \text{Met-tRNA}^{f\text{-}Met} + \text{AMP} + \text{PPi}$$

$$\text{Met} - \text{tRNA}^{f\text{-}Met} + \text{N}^{10}\text{- formyl-tetrahydrofolate} \rightarrow \text{tetrahydrofolate} + \text{f-Met-tRNA}^{f\text{-}Met}.$$

**Events on Ribosome :**

**Step-1 :**

1. In the first step, the 30S ribosomal subunit binds to initiation factor-3 or (IF-3), which prevents the 30S and 50S subunits from combining prematurely. The binding is stoichiometric, one molecule of IF-3 per subunit. There is a relatively small amount of IF-3 in a cell.
2. The second function of IF-3 is that it controls the ability of 30S subunits to bind to m RNA.
3. Binding of the mRNA to the 30S subunit then takes place in such a way that the

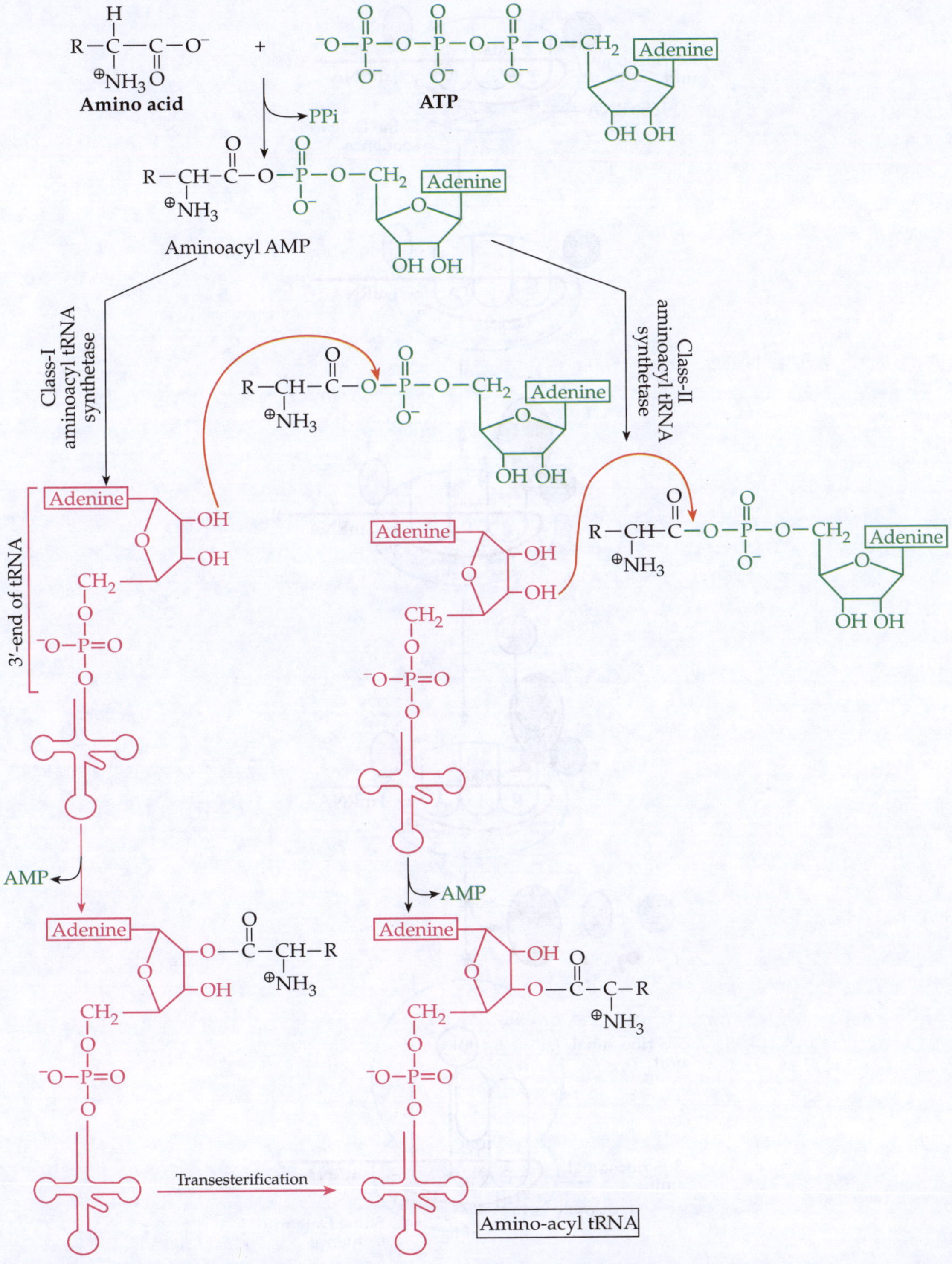


**Fig.17.8 :** *Stepwise aminoacylation of tRNA by aminoacyl tRNA synthetase.*

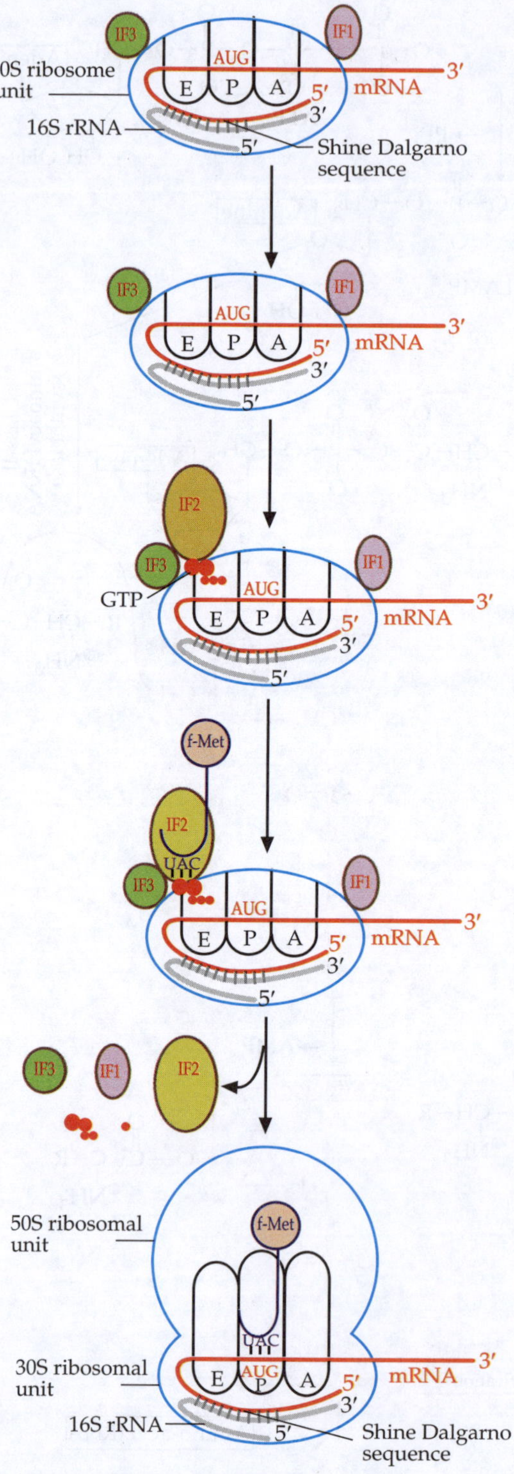


**Fig.17.9 :** *Formation of initiation complex in E. coli.*

initiation codon AUG binds to a precise location on the 30S subunit.

4. The initiation codon AUG is guided to the correct position on the 30S subunit by an initiating signal called SHINE-DALGARNO-SEQUENCE in the mRNA, centered 8-13 bp upstream to the 5′ side of the initiation codon (Fig. 17.10).

5. The Shine-Dalgarno sequence is recognized by the base pairs (anti-parallel) with a complementary pyrimidine-rich sequence near the 3′-end of the 16S rRNA which is present in the 30S subunit of ribosome. This mRNA-rRNA interaction fixes the m RNA so that the AUG is correctly positioned for the initiation of translation.

**Step-2 :**

In the second step, the complex consisting of the 30S subunit, IF-3 and m RNA now forms a larger complex by binding with IF-2, which already is bound to GTP and the initiating fMet-$tRNA^{f\text{-}Met}$. The anticodon of this t RNA pairs correctly with the initiation codon in this step. IF-1 stimulates the activation of IF-2 and IF-3.

**Step-3 :**

1. In this step, this large complex combines with the 50S ribosomal subunit, simultaneously, the GTP molecule bound to IF-2 is hydrolyzed to GDP and Pi. IF-3 and IF-2 also depart from the ribosome.

2. Ribosome has three sites that bind aminoacyl tRNA, these are the aminoacyl or A- site, peptidyl or P-site and exit or E-site. Both 30S and 50S subunits contribute to the characteristic of each site. The AUG is positioned in the P-site, which is the only site to which fMet-t $RNA^{fMet}$ can bind.

3. The resulting functional 70S ribosome is called **initiation complex**, which contains the fMet- t $RNA^{f\text{-}Met}$.

● **IN EUKARYOTES** : First feature to be recognized during translation of a eukaryotic mRNA is the methylated cap that marks the 5′ end. Sometimes the AUG initiation codon lies within 40 bases of the 5′ terminus of the m RNA. But in many mRNAs, the cap and AUG are farther apart in extreme cases ~1000 bp distance.

"**Scanning**" model for initiation of translation has been proposed.

1. 40S subunit initially recognizes the 5′ cap and then "migrates" along the mRNA and scans the m RNA at the leader region.

2. It melts secondary structure hairpins. The migration stops when 40S subunit encounters the AUG initiation codon. The halt of migration requires 5′ GCC (A/G) CCAUGG 3′ sequence at the initiation codon. 5'ACCAUGG3' is called KOZAK CONSENSUS (Fig. 17.11).

3. Initiatior tRNA is a distinct species, but its **methionine** does not become formylated. It is called t $RNAi^{Met}$. In yeast t $RNAi^{Met}$, it has an unusual tertiary structure and it is modified by phorphorylation of the 2′-ribose position on nucleotide 64, but in elongation $tRNA^{Met}$, it is not modified.

4. eIF-2 forms a ternary complex with Met-$tRNAi^{Met}$; The ternary complex binds to free 40S subunits, which attaches to the 5′ end of mRNA. Later in the reaction, GTP is hydrolyzed when eIF-2 is released in the form of eIF2-GDP. eIF-2B regenerates the active form.

5. Little is known about the process how 40S subunit bind to mRNA and migrates along to reach the first AUG codon.

   (a) The eIF-4F factor is multimer that binds at the 5′ end.

   (b) It includes cap-binding subunit eIF-4E, the RNA- dependent ATPase eIF 4A and the "scaffolding" subunit eIF 4G.

   (c) After binding, eIF 4A unwinds the secondary structures that exist in the first 15 bases of the mRNA. ATP is

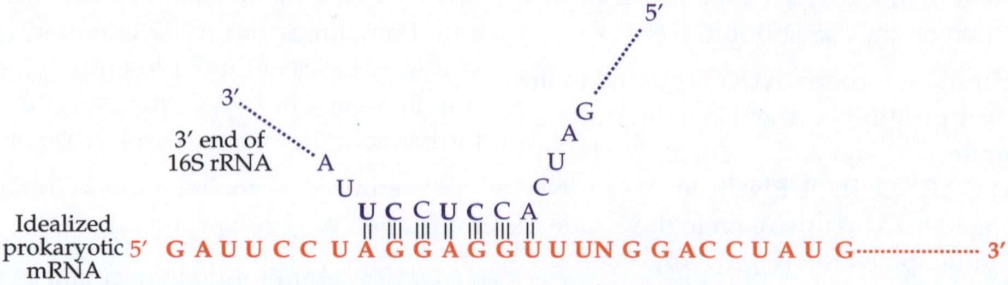


**Fig.17.10 :** *Pairing of Shine-Dalgarno sequence with a sequence near the 3′ end of the 16S rRNA as shown for an idealized prokaryotic mRNA.*

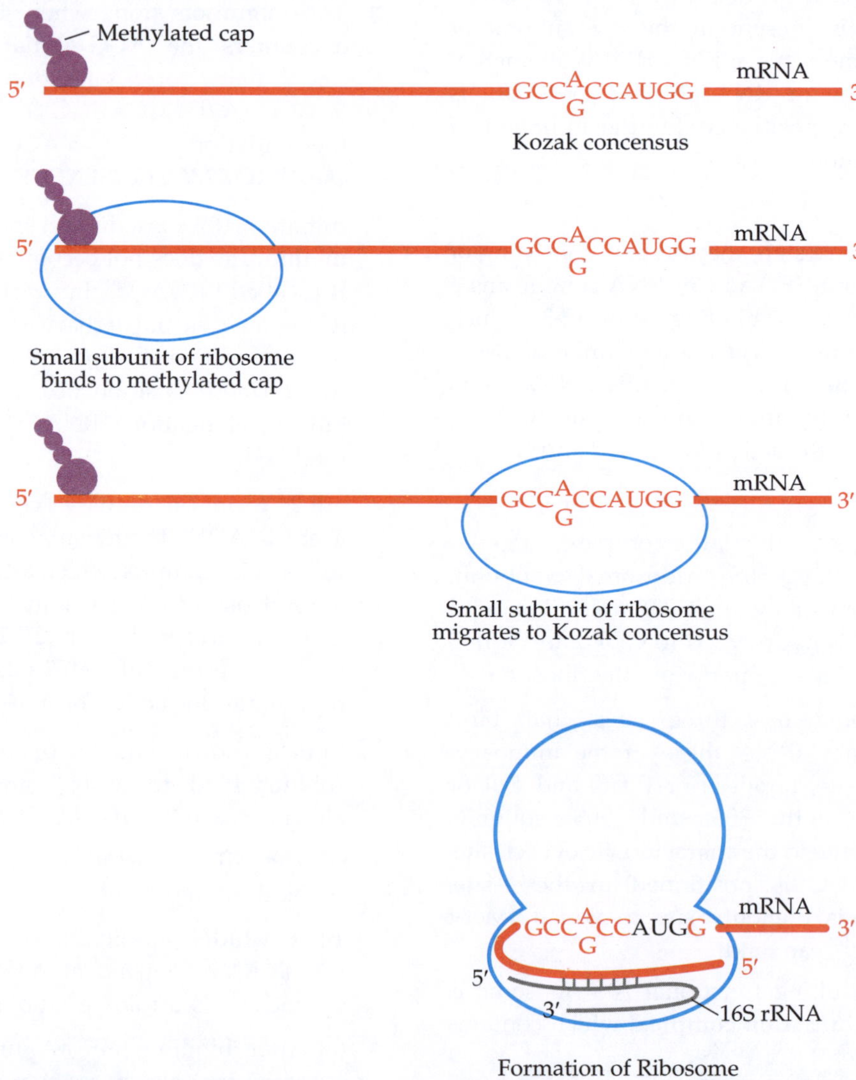


**Fig.17.11 :** *Eukaryotic ribosomes migrate from 5′ end of RNA to Kozak-consensus.*

hydrolyzed for that purpose by eIF 4A and eIF 4B.

(d) eIF 4F contains a subunit (called Mnk-1) which phorphorylates e IF 4E by its kinase activity. It is the main regulator of protein synthesis.

(e) eIF 4G binds to eIF –3, which is associated with 40S subunit. It provides the means by which 40S subunit binds to e IF 4F, which functions to get eIF 4G in place and thus it can attract the 40S ribosomal subunit.

(f) eIF-3 and eIF6 are required to maintain the dissociated state of 40S and 60S unbunits. eIF3 is required for 40S subunit with ternary complex to bind to 5′ end.

(g) eIF2 and eIF3 are released by the GTPase activity of e IF5 and then 60S subunit joins to form a complete 80S ribosome.

(h) Poly A tail of mRNA stimulates the formation of initiation complex at the 5′ end. The *poly-A –binding protein* (pab-1b in yeast) is required which binds to eIF 4G and again eIF 4E transiently to form a circular organization of mRNA where both 5′ and 3′ ends are held together (Fig. 17.12).

## 17.12.2 Elongation process in Protein Synthesis

Elongation includes all the reactions from synthesis of the first peptide bond to the addition of the last amino acid. The elongation process is more or less similar in both prokaryotes and eukaryotes. The entry of activated aminoacylated tRNA into the ribosome is mediated by an elongation factor EF-Tu.

**Step-1 (Loading of aminoacyl tRNA into the A –site of ribosome)**

1. The binary complex of EF –Tu-GTP binds to aminoacyl-tRNA to form a ternary complex of aminoacyl –tRNA- EF-Tu-GTP. This ternary complex binds only to the A site of the 70S ribosome. Its P-site is already occupied by initiator amino-acyl peptidyl tRNA.
2. In the A-site, the aminoacyl- tRNA is loaded in two stages. First the anticodon end binds to A site of the 30S subunit. Then codon-anticodon recognition triggers a conformational change of EF-Tu and GTP is hydrolyzed. The CCA terminal end of tRNA moves into A –site of 50S subunit. Finally EF-Tu-GDP is released (Fig. 17.13).
3. In the cytoplasm, EF-Tu-GDP again becomes active. At first EF-Ts complex displaces GDP to form EF-Ts-EF Tu complex. Then EF-Ts is displaced by GTP, Thus EF-Tu-GTP complex is reformed. **Kirromycin** is an antibiotic that inhibits the function of EF-Tu. It prevents the release of EF-Tu-GDP complex from the ribosome. Thus the protein synthesis is stalled.
4. In eukaryotes, the factor eEF-1$\alpha$ is responsible for bringing aminoacyl tRNA to the ribosome; it is homologus to EF-Tu of prokaryotes. It hydrolyses GTP. The active form of eEF -1$\alpha$ is regenerated by eEF-1$\beta\gamma$, which is homologous to EF-Ts of prokaryotes.

**Step-2 (Formation of peptide bond)**

1. In this step, a new peptide bond is formed between the amino acids bound by their tRNAs to the A-site and P-site on the ribosome. This occurs by the transfer of the initiating N- formyl- methionyl group of t RNA to the second amino acid now in the A-site (Fig.17.14).
2. The $\alpha$ amino group of the amino acid in the A-site acts as nucleophile, displacing the t RNA in the P-site to form the peptide bond between the successive amino acids.
3. This reaction produces a dipeptidyl-tRNA in the A site and the "uncharged" tRNA $^{f\text{-Met}}$ remains bound to the P-site.

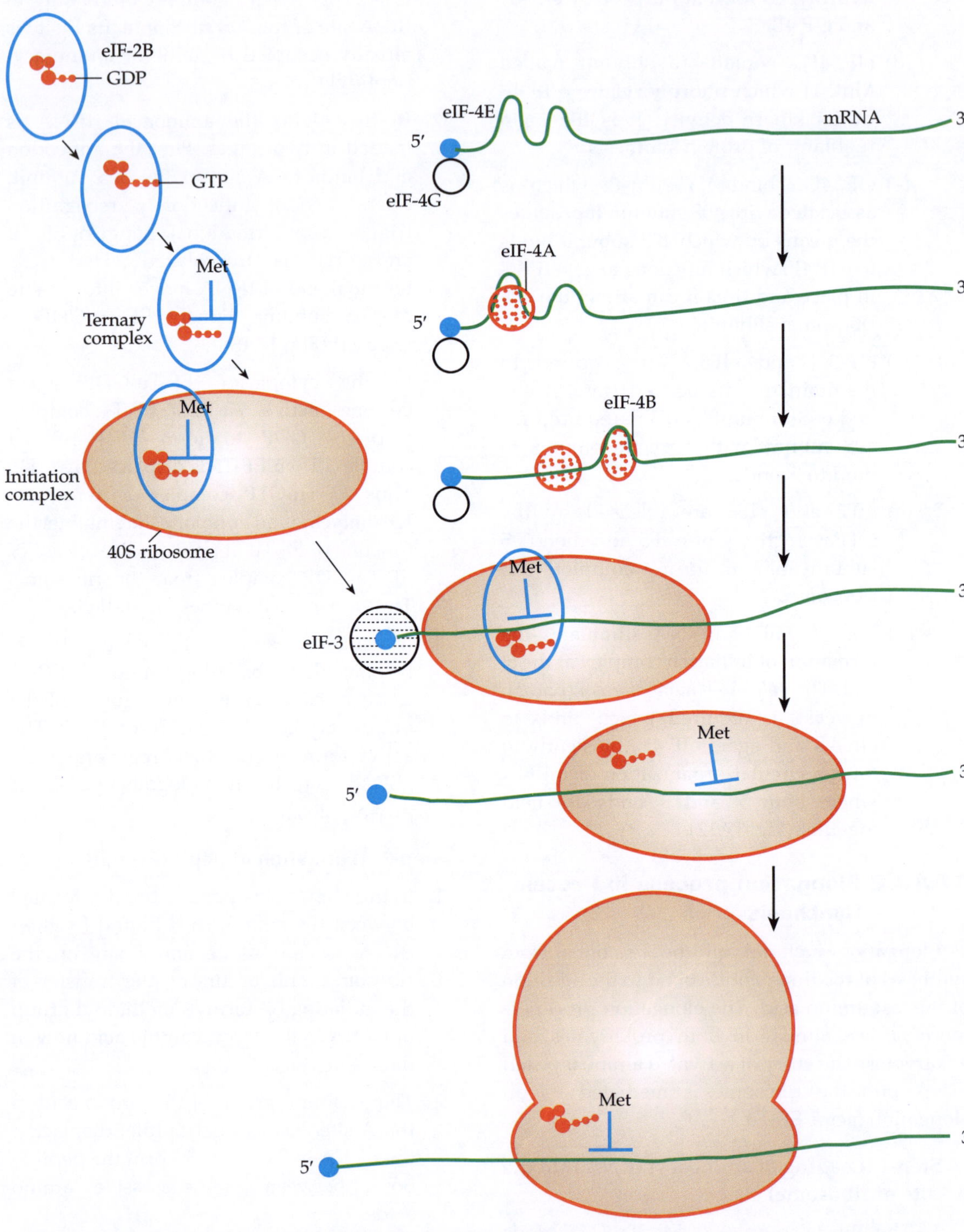


**Fig. 17.12 :** *Eukaryotic initiation of transcription.*

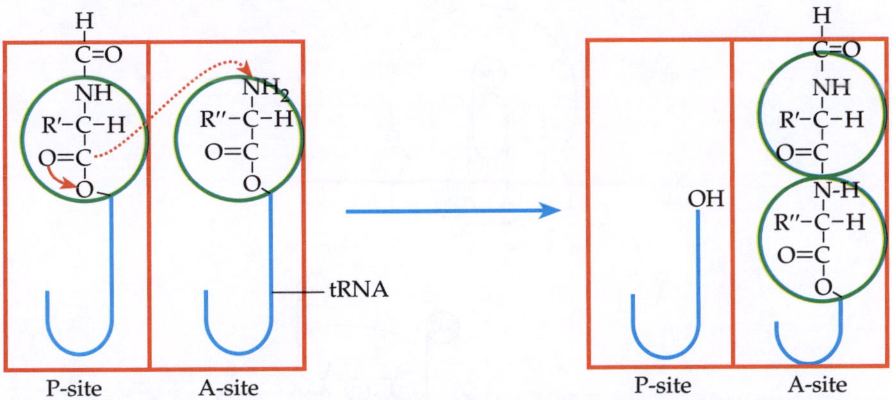


**Fig.17.13 :** *Reaction showing peptide bond formation by the enzyme peptidyl transferase in the P- and A-sites of ribosome.*

4. The catalytic activity responsible for the synthesis of peptide bond is done by the enzyme **peptidyl transferase**.
5. **Puromycin**, an antibiotic, resembles an amino acid attached to the terminal adenosine of tRNA. The polypeptide attached to peptidyl-tRNA is then transferred to the —$NH_2$ group of the puromycin. The puromycin-polypeptidyl complex is then released from the ribosome thus premature termination of the protein synthesis takes place .

**Step-3 (Translocation) :**

1. This step of the elongation cycle is called translocation, the ribosome moves by a distance of one codon towards the 3'-end of the m RNA.
2. Because, the dipeptidyl-tRNA is still attached to the second codon of the mRNA, the movement of the ribosome shifts the dipeptidyl- tRNA from the A-site to the P-site and the deacylated tRNA leaves the ribosome via another site, E- site in bacteria, while in eukaryotes it is directly expelled into the cytosol.
3. The process of relocating the discharged t RNA and peptidyl –t RNA takes place in two stages. First, aminoacyl end of t RNA (located at 50S subunit) moves into new sites. At this stage, the tRNA is effectively bound in hybrid site, consisting of the 50SE/30SP and 50SP/30SA sites. Then movement is extended to the 30S subunit so that the anticodon – codon pairing region finds itself in the right site. This model for two-part movement is called **Hybrid-state Model**.
4. The third codon of m RNA is now in the A- site and the second codon in the P-site. This shift of the ribosome along the mRNA requires EF–G (also called **translocase**) in the bacteria and e EF-2 in eukaryotes. The energy is provided by the hydrolysis of GTP. A change in the three-dimensional configuration of the entire ribosome is believed to be taken place at this step in order to move the ribosome along the m RNA at $5' \rightarrow 3'$ direction.
5. Ribosomes cannot bind to EF-Tu and EF-G simultaneously. Protein synthesis follows the cycle in which these factors are alternatively bound to and released from the ribosome. So EF-Tu—GDP complex must be released before EF–G can bind and then EF–G must be released before aminoacyl tRNA –EF-Tu-GTP can bind.

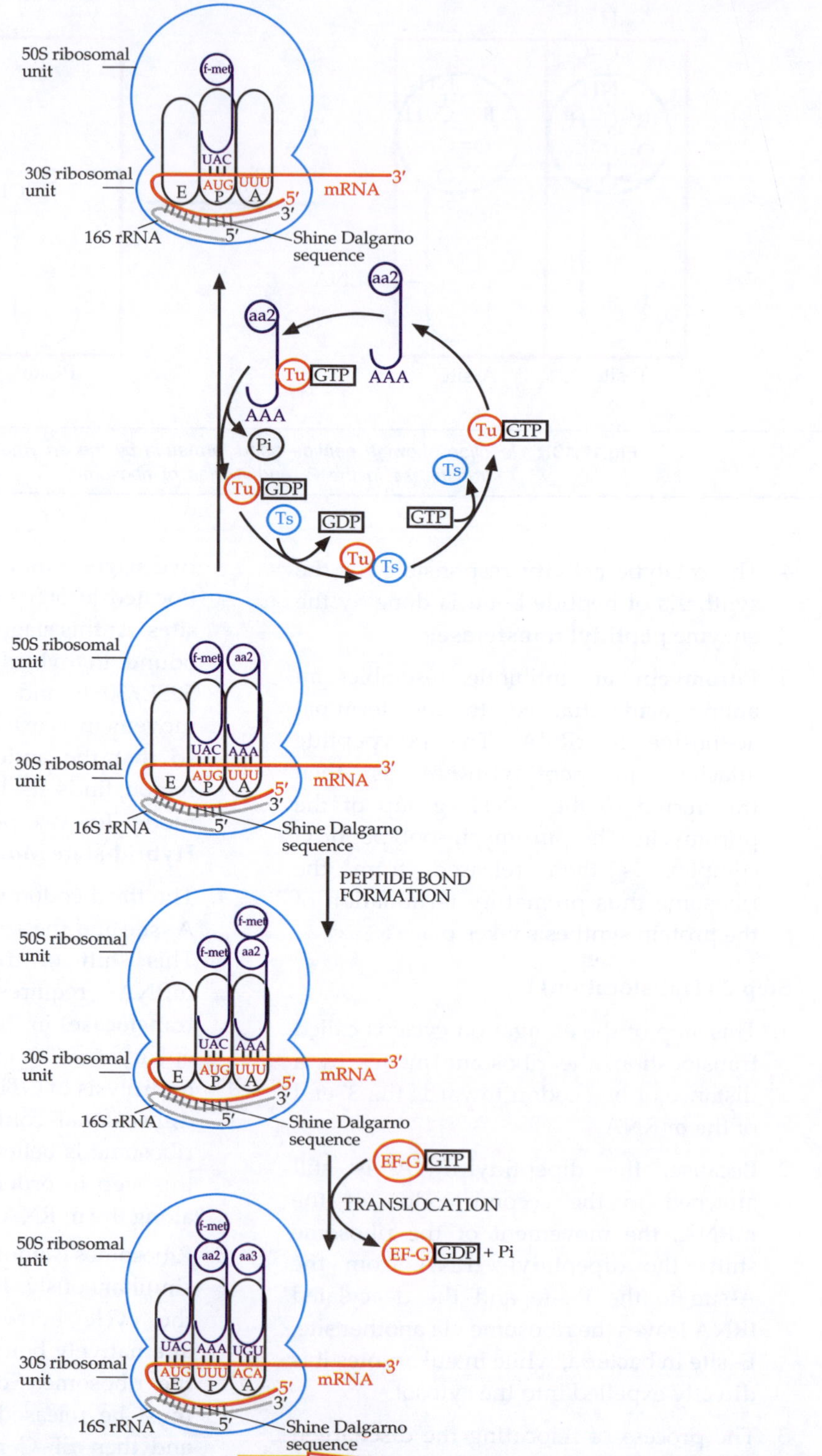


**Fig.17.14 :** *Three steps in elongation of translation in Prokariotes.*

6. The steroid antibiotic **fusidic acid**, which jams the ribosome in the post-translocation state. Fusidic acid stabilized the ribosome. EF- G.GDP complex, so that it remains on the ribosome No further amino acids can be added to the chain.

7. The eukaryotic eEF-2 (homologus to bacterial EF-G) is susceptible to **diphtheria** toxin. The **toxin** uses NAD as co-factor to transfer an adenosine diphosphate ribosyl (ADPR) moiety on the eEF-2. This ADPR-eEF-2 conjugate becomes inactive in protein synthesis.

### 17.12.3 Termination in Protein Synthesis

Elongation continues until the ribosome adds the last amino acid, completing the polypeptide coded by the mRNA. Termination of the polypeptide synthesis is signaled by one of the three termination codons in the mRNA which are UAA (amber), UAG (ochre) and UGA (opal), immediately following the last amino acid codon (Fig. 17.15).

In *E. coli*, two related proteins catalyze termination. They are called release factors (RF) and are specific for different sequences. Once a termination codon occupies the ribosomal A-site, three releasing factors, the RF-1, RF-2, RF-3 contribute to

1. Hydrolysis of the terminal peptidyl-tRNA bond.
2. Release of the free polypeptide and the last t RNA (uncharged) from the P-site.
3. The dissociation of the 70S ribosome into its 30S and 50S subunits.

RF-1 recognizes the termination codon UAG and UAA while RF-2 recognizes UGA and UAA.

Either RF-1 or RF-2 binds at the termination codon and induces peptidyl transferase to transfer growing peptide chain to a water molecule rather than to another amino acid.

RF-1 or RF-2 is released from the ribosome by RF-3, which is a GTP-binding protein resembles with EF-G. It has been suggested that the action of RF3 on RF1/2 utilizes the same site that is used by the elongation factors.

Eukaryotes have just two release factors : eRF-1 recognizes termination codons, and eRF3 which might play the same role as RF3 although it has not been proven (Kisselev and Buckingham 2000).

Dissociation of ribosome subunits is mediated by an additional protein called **ribosome recycling factor** (RRF), which like eRF-1, has a tRNA- like structure (Selmer *et al* 1999), probably enters the P and A site and unlocks the ribosome. Dissociation requires energy, which is released from GTP by EF-G. An eukaryotic equivalent of RRF has not been identified, possibly e RF-3 does such functions.

Polysomes allow rapid translation of a single message. 10-100 ribosomes which can be isolated from either eukaryotes and bacterial cells and that are very active in protein synthesis. Such clusters are known as **polysomes**. A single strand of m RNA is being translated simultaneously by many ribosomes, spaced closely together and allow highly efficient use of the m RNA.

## 17.13 TRANSLATION IN ARCHAEA

The translation in the archaea more closely resembles the equivalent events in the eukaryotic cytoplasm rather than in bacteria. The one apparent exception is that the archaeal ribosome is 70S, is comparable in size to bacterial ribosome and contains 23S, 16S and 5S rRNAs.

The archaeal structures are different from eukaryotic versions but ribosomal proteins that are attached to the r RNA s are homologus with of the eukaryotic proteins. Archaeal mRNAs are capped and polyadenylated and involve in the scanning process similar to eukaryotes. In archaeal tRNA, TψC arm lacks T and are variously modified. Initiator t RNA carries *Met* residue and the elongation factors resemble the eukaryotic molecules.

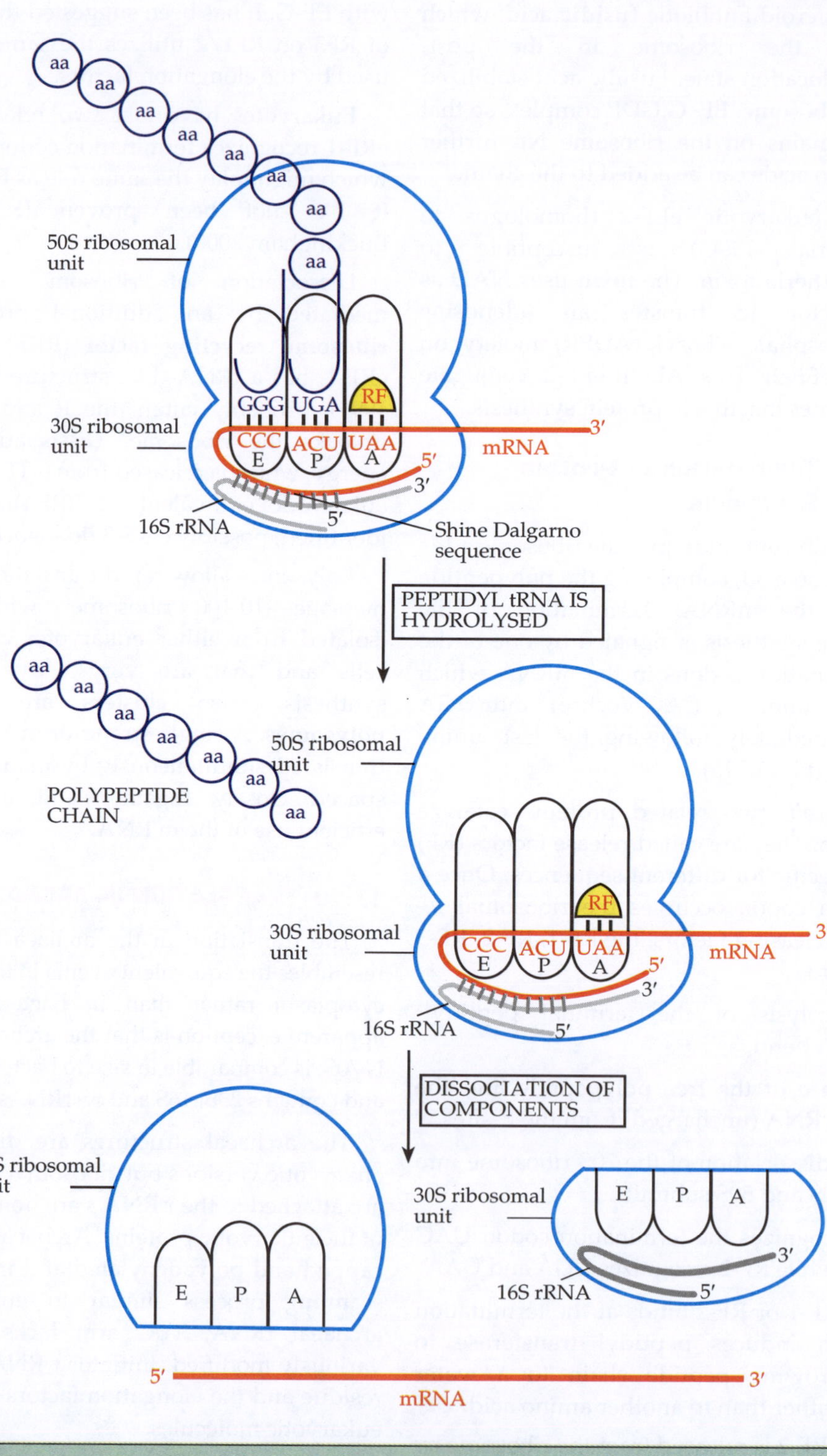


**Fig.17.15 :** *Termination of translation in Prokaryotes.*

**TABLE 17.3**
**Functions of the bacterial translation factors**

| *Factors* | *Functions* |
|---|---|
| **Initiation factors:** | |
| IF - 1 | Binding of IF-1 blocks A site, so its function may be to prevent premature entry of tRNAs into A-site. IF-1 may cause conformational changes that prepare the small submit for attachment to the large subunit. |
| IF - 2 | Directs the initiator tRNA to its correct position in the initiation complex. |
| IF - 3 | Prevents premature reasociation of the large and small subunits of the ribosome. |
| **Elongation Factors :** | |
| EF - Tu | Directs the next tRNA to its correct position on the ribosomes. |
| EF - Ts | Regenerates EF-Tu |
| EF - G | Mediates translocation. |
| **Release Factors :** | |
| RF - 1 | Recognizes the termination codons UAA and UAG |
| RF - 2 | Recognises UAA and UGA |
| RF - 3 | Stimulates dissociation of RF 1 and RF 2 from the ribosome after termination. |
| **Ribosome recycling factor** | |
| RRF | Responsible for dissociating the ribosome subunits after termination of translation. |

**TABLE 17.4**
**Eurakyotic translation factors**

| *Factors* | *Functions* |
|---|---|
| **Initiation factors:** | |
| eIF 1 | Component of preinitiation complex |
| eIF 1A | Component of preinitiation complex |
| eIF 2 | Binds to the initiatior $tRNA^{met}$ within the ternary complex. |
| eIF 3 | Components of the preinitiation complex, makes direct contact with eIF 4G to link with cap binding complex. |
| eIF 4A | Component of the cap binding complex its helicase activity aids scanning by melting secondary structure. |
| eIF 4B | Aids scanning by its helicase activity. |
| eIF 4E | Component of cap binding complex, makes direct contact with the cap of mRNA. |
| eIF 4F | The cap binding complex. |
| eIF 4G | The cap binding complex, forms a bridge between the cap binding complex and eIF 3 in the pre-initiation complex. It also forms an association with the poly A tail via the polyadenylate binding protein. |
| eIF 5 | Aids release of the other initiation complex after completion of initiation. |
| eIF 6 | Associates with the large subunits of the ribosome, prevents large subunit from attachment in the cytoplasm. |
| **Elongation Factors :** | |
| eEF 1 | Complex of four subunits eEF1a, 1b, 1d and 1g), directs next tRNA in its correct position in the ribosome. |
| eEF 2 | Mediates translocations. |
| **Release Factors :** | |
| eRF 1 | Recognises the termination codons. |
| eRF 3 | Stimulates dissociation of eRF 1 from ribosome after termination. |

## Chapter Glossary/Key Terms

**Amino acyl tRNA :** The tRNA carrying an amino acid, covalently linkage between the —NH2 group of amino acid and either 3¢-OH or 2¢-OH group of the terminal base of the tRNA.

**Amino acyl tRNA synthetase :** The enzyme responsible for covalently linking amino acids to the 2¢- or 3¢-OH position of tRNA.

**Codon :** A triplet of nucleotides coding for a single amino acid.

**Codon anticodon-recognition :** The interaction between a codon on an mRNA molecule and the corresponding anticodon on a tRNA.

**Genetic code :** The rules that determine which tripet of nucleotide codes for which amino acid during protein synthesis.

**Initiation factors :** These are proteins that associate with a small subunit of the ribosome specifically at the stage of initiation of protein systhesis .

**Kozak consensus :** The nucleotide sequence surrounding, the initiation codon of a eukaryotic mRNA.

**Peptidyl transferase :** The enzyme activity that synthesizes peptide bonds during translation.

**P-site :** The site in the ribosome occupied by the tRNA attached to the growing polypeptide during protein synthesis.

**Release (termination) factors :** These factors respond to termination codon to cause release of the completed polypeptide chain and the ribosome from mRNA.

**Second genetic code :** The interaction between aminoacyl -tRNA synthetase and tRNAs has a critical role in maintaining the accuracy of protein synthesis. This is second genetic code.

**Shine-Dalgarno sequence :** The sequence AGGAGG located on bacterial mRNA just prior to an AUG initiation codon, is complementary to the sequence at the 3¢ end of 16S rRNA, involved in binding of ribosome to mRNA.

**Super wobble :** The extreme form of wobble that occurs in vertebrate mitochondria.

**Termination codon (stop condon) :** One of the three codons that made the postion where translation of an mRNA should stop.

**Translation :** The synthesis of protein on the mRNA template.

**Translocation of ribosomes :** Movement of ribosome one codon along mRNA after the addition of each amino acid to the polypeptide chain.

**Triplet codon :** The genetic code is represented the abbreviations of three letter code.

**Wobble hypothesis :** The process by which a single tRNA can decode more than one codon.

# EXERCISE

## A. Long answer type questions :

1. What do you mean by a genetic code? Why singlet code and doublet code are not possible?
2. What are the features of genetic code?
3. Describe the wobble hypothesis with examples.
4. Give the reasons of wobble pairing.
5. What are the exceptions of the universality of genetic code?
6. Give the characteristics of mitochondrial genetic code and illustrate the evolution of mito-genetic code.
7. Describe the origin and evolution of genetic code.
8. What do you mean by translation? Where does it occur?
9. Describe the mechanism of the activation of amino acids.
10. How amino acid is tagged into the tRNA.
11. Destinguish between the Class-I and Class-II amino-acyl tRNA synthetase.
12. What are the steps of protein synthesis.
13. Describe the process of the formation of initiation complex in prokaryotes and eukaryotes.
14. Describe the different steps in elongation of protein synthesis in prokaryotes and eukaryotes
15. Briefly describe the process of termination of translation in prokaryotes and eukaryotes.
16. What are the characteristics of translation in archaea.

## B. Short answer type questions

1. Define genetic code.
2. How many codes may be formed from four bases?
3. Why the code is triplet?
4. What do you mean that code is degenerate?
5. What are the stop codons?
6. What do you mean by the non overlapping of codon?
7. What do you meant by the commaless characteristic of codon?
8. How code is non ambiguous?
9. What is Wobble?
10. How codon is anticodon pairing occurs?
11. What do you mean by three codon recognition?
12. Give the plylogeny of mitochondrial genetic code evolution.
13. What is frogen accident theory?
14. What do you mean by translation?
15. How amino acid is activated.
16. What enzyme is required for the activation of amino acids.
17. Why tRNA is called second gnetic code?
18. What is the role of tetrahydrofolate in the production of N-formylmethionine.
19. What is the Shine-Dalgarno sequence? What is its function?
20. What are the functions of IF-1, IF-2 and IF-3 in translation?
21. What are the three sites on ribosomes. What is "scanning model" for initiation of translation?
22. Waht do you mean by Kozak consensus?
23. How does loading of amino acyl tRNA occur in the A-site of ribosome?
24. What are the role of Ts and Tu proteins in translation?
25. What is Ts-Tu cycle?
26. How and where peptide bond is formed during translation?

27. How does puromycin inhibit peptide bond formation?
28. What do you mean by translocation? Which enzyme is required for this?
29. What is Hybrid state model?
30. How does Diphtheria toxin inhibit protein synthesis?
31. What is the role of RF-1, 2 and 3?
32. How does temination of translation occur in eukaryotes?
33. What are the two other genetically encoded amino acids that have no usual genetic codes?
34. What codes are used by selenocysteine and pyrrolysine?
35. What is SECS? What is its function?
36. How the selenocysteine is inserted into the growing polypeptide chain?
37. How pyrrolysine is inserted into the polypeptide chain?

# 18

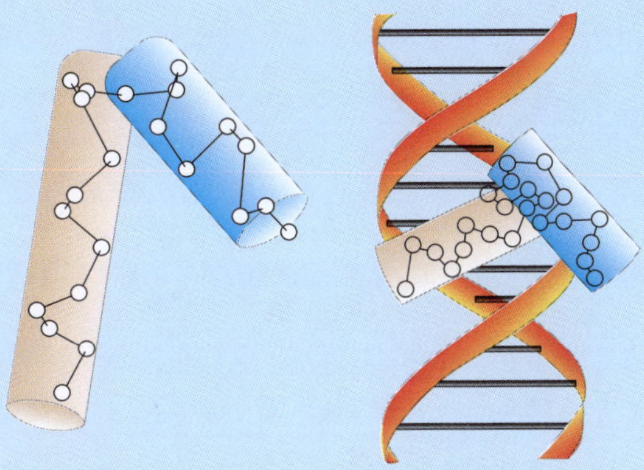

# Regulation & Expression of Genome

**CHAPTER AGENDA**

**18.1** Concept; **18.2** Regulation of Transcription Initiation; **18.3** DNA Footprinting; **18.4** Regulation of Gene-expression in Prokaryotes; **18.5** Regulation of gene expression in Eukaryotes; **18.6** Transport of RNA within the eukaryotic cells; **18.7** Regulation of gene expression at Translational level; **18.8** Trypanosomes change suface proteins to elude Immune system; **18.9** Internal Eliminated Segments (DNA splicing and Role of two nuclei in *Paramoecium*); Chapter Glossary; Exercise

## 18.1 CONCEPT

All the cells in a multicellular organism constitute the same genome as they have originated from a single cell. But these cells become different from one another because, they synthesize and accumulate different sets of RNA and protein molecules. Although, we still do not know the answer to this fundamental question, how different cell types synthesize different sets of proteins? But we can make certain general statements.

1. Many processes are common to all cells and any two cells in a single organism, therefore, have many proteins in common.
2. Some proteins are abundant in the specialized cells in which they function and cannot be detected elsewhere.
3. Although the differences in mRNA among specialized cell types are striking, they nonetheless underestimate the full range of differences in the pattern of protein production.

Some gene products are required all the time and their genes are expressed at a more or less constant level in virtually all the cells of a species or organisms. Many of the genes for the enzymes that catalyze steps in central metabolic pathways, such as, the citric acid cycle fall into this category. These genes are often referred to as **house keeping** genes.

Constant, seemingly unregulated expression of gene is called **constitutive gene expression**.

Most of the specialized cells in multicellular organism are capable of altering their patterns of gene expression in response to extracellular cues. The amounts of gene products rise and fall in response to molecular signals. Gene product that increases in concentration under prescribed molecular circumstances is referred to an **inducible** and the process of increasing the expression of the gene is called **induction**. Conversely, gene products that decrease in concentration in response to a molecular signal are referred to as **repressible** and the decrease in gene expression is called **repression**.

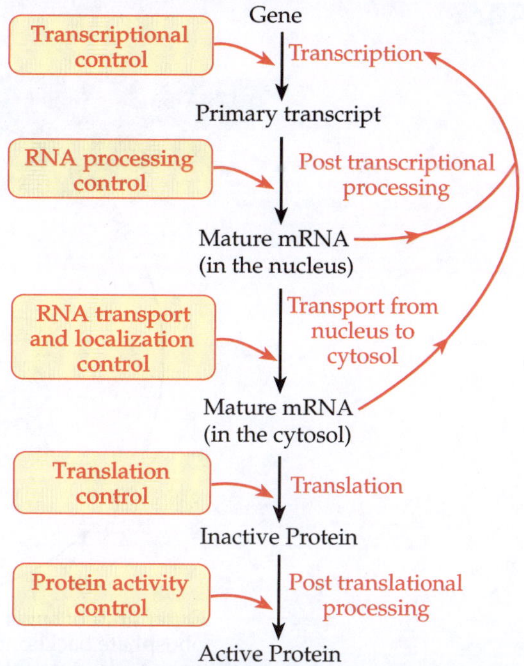


**Fig.18.1 :** *Different steps at which the gene expression can be controlled.*

Gene expression can be regulated at many of the steps in the pathway from DNA to RNA to protein. There are at least six potential points at which the amount of protein can be regulated (Fig. 18.1).

## 18.2 REGULATION OF TRANSCRIPTION INITIATION

Transcription initiation is an excellent point, at which, to coordinate the regulation of multiple genes, different gene products have independent activities.

At least three types of protein, regulate the transcription initiation by RNA-polymerase:

1. **Specificity factors** alter the specificity of RNA polymerase for a given promoter or set of promoters.
2. **Repressors** to bind to a promoter, blocking access of RNA polymerase to a promoter.

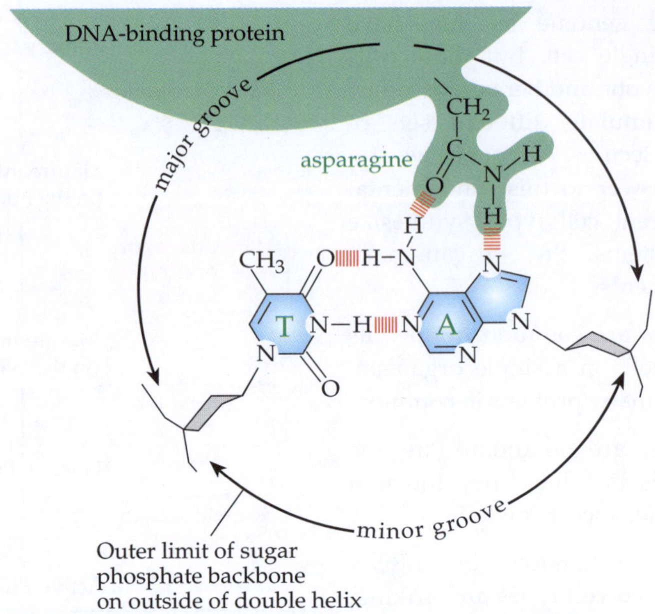


**Fig.18.2 :** *The binding of a gene regulatory protein to the major groove of DNA.*

3. **Activators** bind near to a promoter, enhancing the RNA-promoter interaction.

### Regulatory Proteins

Gene Regulatory proteins contain structural motifs that can read DNA sequences. These molecules are complementary to each other. The surface of these proteins can make contact with the special surface features of the double helix in that region, which involves hydrogen bonds, ionic bonds and hydrophobic bonds. X-ray crystallographic and NMR spectroscopic studies have revealed that many of the proteins contain one or another of a small set of DNA- binding structure motifs. These motifs generally use α helices or β sheets to bind to the major grooves as well as minor grooves of DNA. Regulatory proteins also interact with other proteins (Fig. 18.2).

Regulatory proteins have DNA- binding domains, these proteins tend to be small, 60-90 aminoacid residues. These domains contact with the DNA in a specific way. Two structural motifs that play the major role in DNA binding have been found in numerous regulatory proteins. viz. Helix- turn – helix and Zinc-finger. Other DNA – binding motifs also exist in some proteins

**Helix- turn – helix :** It is the physical basis of protein – DNA interaction for many prokaryotic as well as eukaryotic regulatory proteins. It generally consists of 20 amino acid residues, segment with an α – helix (7-9 amino acids), then a β–turn (8-11 residues) and second α – helix. C–terminal of second α–helix (called recognition helix) participates in sequence specific recognition of DNA and this helix fits into the major groove of DNA. N–terminal of first α –helix functions primarily as a structural component that helps to position the recognition helix (Fig.18.3).

Genetic analysis in ***Drosophila*** led to the characterization of an important class of genes, **the homeotic selector genes**, (that play a critical role in fly development) are found to bind with such motif. It contains an almost identical stretch of 60 amino acids, therefore it is called **homeodomain**. More than 60 homeodomain proteins have been also discovered from yeast to

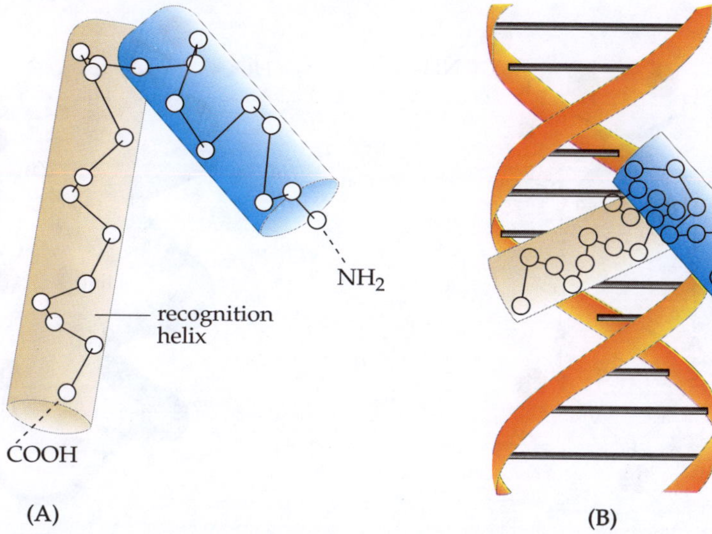


**Fig.18.3 :** *The DNA-binding helix-turn-helix motif.*

plant and humans. The homeodomain is folded into three α–helices, which are packed tightly together by hydrophobic interactions. The part containing helix-2 and helix-3 closely resemble the helix- turn-helix motif. The helix-3 is recognition helix contacts with the major groove of DNA. For example, *Asn* contacts to adenine. Helix-1 is flexible and contacted with minor groove. It bound to a specific consensus sequence of DNA, known as *homeobox* (Fig. 18.4).

**Zinc – finger :** Structure of zinc finger motif is of several types. The initially discovered one activates the transcription of an eukaryotic ribosomal RNA gene. It consists about 30 amino acid residues. Three-dimensional structure of

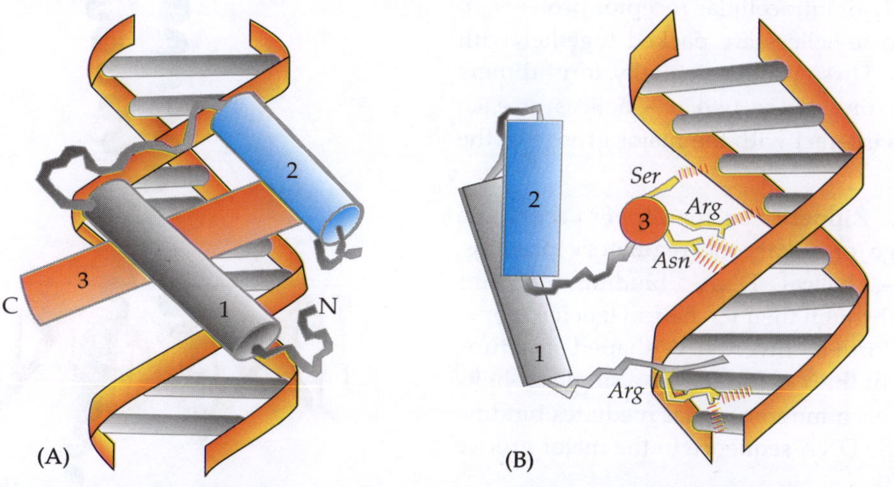


**Fig.18.4 :** *A homoeodomain bound to its specific DNA sequence.*

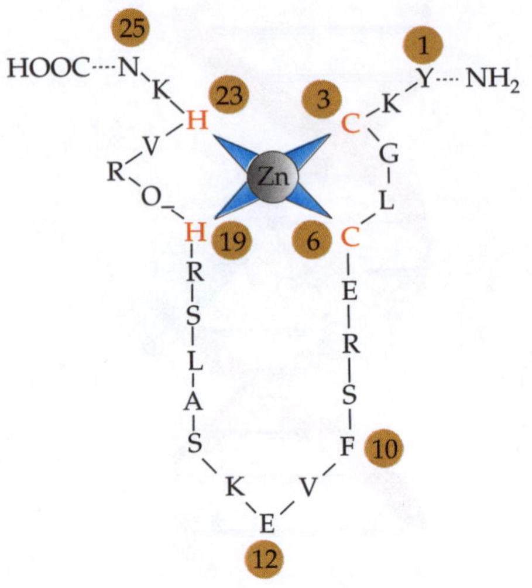


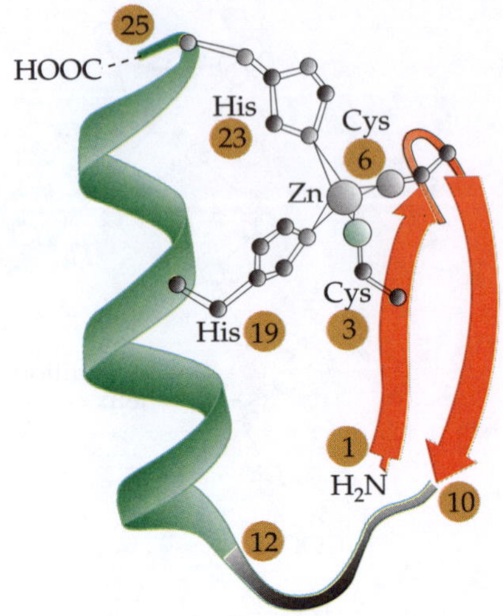


**Fig.18.5 :** *One type of zinc finger protein*

this type of zinc finger is constructed from an antiparallel β –sheet (1-10 amino acids) followed by an α–helix (12-24 amino acids). The four amino acids *Cys-3, Cys-6, His-19* and *His-23* bind to the Zn molecule and hold one end of the α –helix firmly to one end of the β–sheet. The fingers are responsible for DNA binding (Fig. 18.5).

Another type of zinc finger is found in the large family of intracellular receptor proteins, in which two α–helices are packed together with Zn–atoms. These proteins usually form dimers that allow one of the two α – helices of each subunit to interact with the major groove of the DNA.

**Leucine Zipper :** Leucine Zipper occurs in a wide range of eukaryotic regulatory proteins. Two α – helical DNA- binding domains dimerize through their α – helical leucine zipper region to form an inverted Y- shaped structure. Each arm of the Y is formed by a single α –helix one from each monomer that mediates binding to a specific DNA sequence in the major groove of DNA.

Each α–helix binds to one-half of a symmetric DNA structure. The leucine zipper is so named because two interacting α – helices, in which *Leu* residues in every seventh position are prominent features of the interacting surfaces (Fig. 18.6 ).

Heterodimerization of leucine zipper can alter their DNA- binding specifically. Hetero-dimerization, i.e. the combination of two

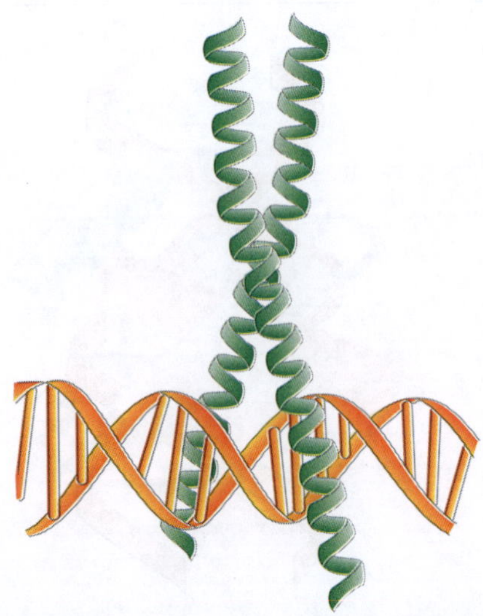

**Fig.18.6 :** *A leucine zipper dimer bound to DNA*

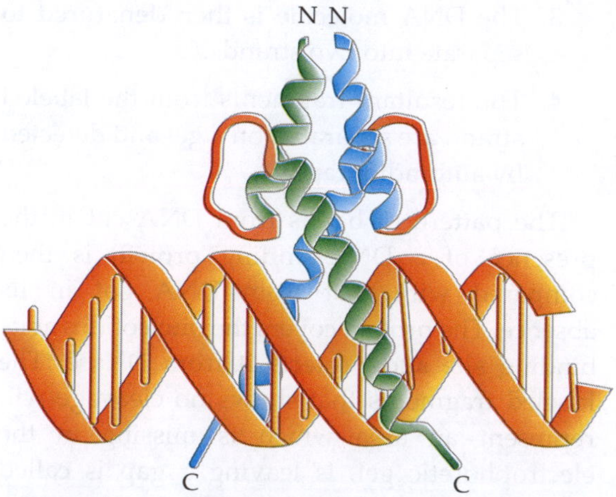


Fig.18.7 : *A helix–loop–helix dimer bound to DNA.*

separate monomers can recognize a hybrid DNA sequence. Heterodimerization is used by eukaryotic cells to control gene expression that occurs in a wide variety of different types of gene regulatory proteins.

**Helix – loop – helix :** These are groups of regulatory proteins, which have been implicated in the control of gene expression that directs the development of multicellular organism. The protein has a basic region those contacts with DNA and a neighbouring region that mediates dimer formation. The dimerization region forms an α –helix, a flexible loop and a second α –helix, DNA binding is mediated by stretch of amino acids, which is rich in basic residues. The truncated motifs can form heterodimer with full-length HLH proteins but it is unable to bind DNA tightly, and acts as an inhibitory regulation.(Fig. 18.7)

**β- sheet motif of repressor protein :** A group of gene regulatory proteins has been identified, in which case the information on the surface of the major groove is read by a two stranded β –sheet, with side chains of amino acids extending from the sheet toward the DNA. The bacterial *Met*-repressor protein is the example, which carries the β–sheet. When this amino acid is abundant, it binds to repressor that enables it to bind DNA tightly, and inhibits the synthesis of enzyme that catalyses methionine synthesis (Fig. 18.8).

## 18.3 DNA FOOTPRINTING

When transcription factor binds to a DNA sequence, it protects that sequence from digestion by nucleases. Researchers take advantage of this property by isolating chromotin from cells and treating it with DNA-digesting enzymes, such as DNase-I, that destroy sections of the DNA that are not

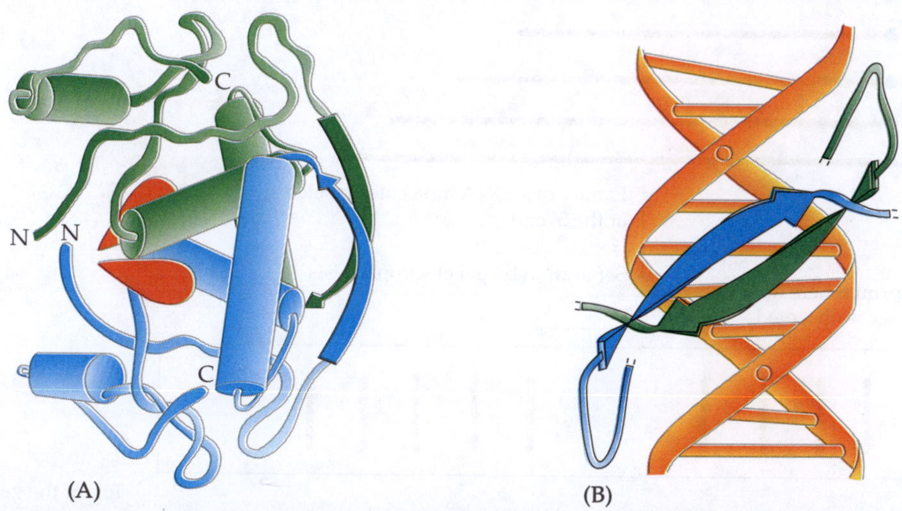


Fig.18.8 : *The bacterial met repressor protein.*

protected by bound transcription factors. Once the chromatin has been digested, the bound protein is removed and the DNA sequences that had been protected are identified. This method is called **DNA footprinting**. This is also used to locate the binding sites of proteins on RNA.

**Method :**

1. A pure DNA fragment that is labeled at one end with $^{32}P$ is isolated.
2. This molecule is then cleaved with a nuclease or a chemical that makes random single-stranded cuts in the DNA.
3. The DNA molecule is then denatured to separate into two strands.
4. The resultant fragments from the labeled strand are separated on a gel and detected by autoradiography.

The pattern of bands from DNA cut in the presence of a DNA-binding protein is then compared with that from DNA cut in its absence. The protein covers the nucleotides at its binding site and protects it from DNase. The labeled fragments that shows no cleavage will represent an area which is missing in the electrophoretic gel, is leaving a gap is called "**footprint**" (Fig. 18.9).

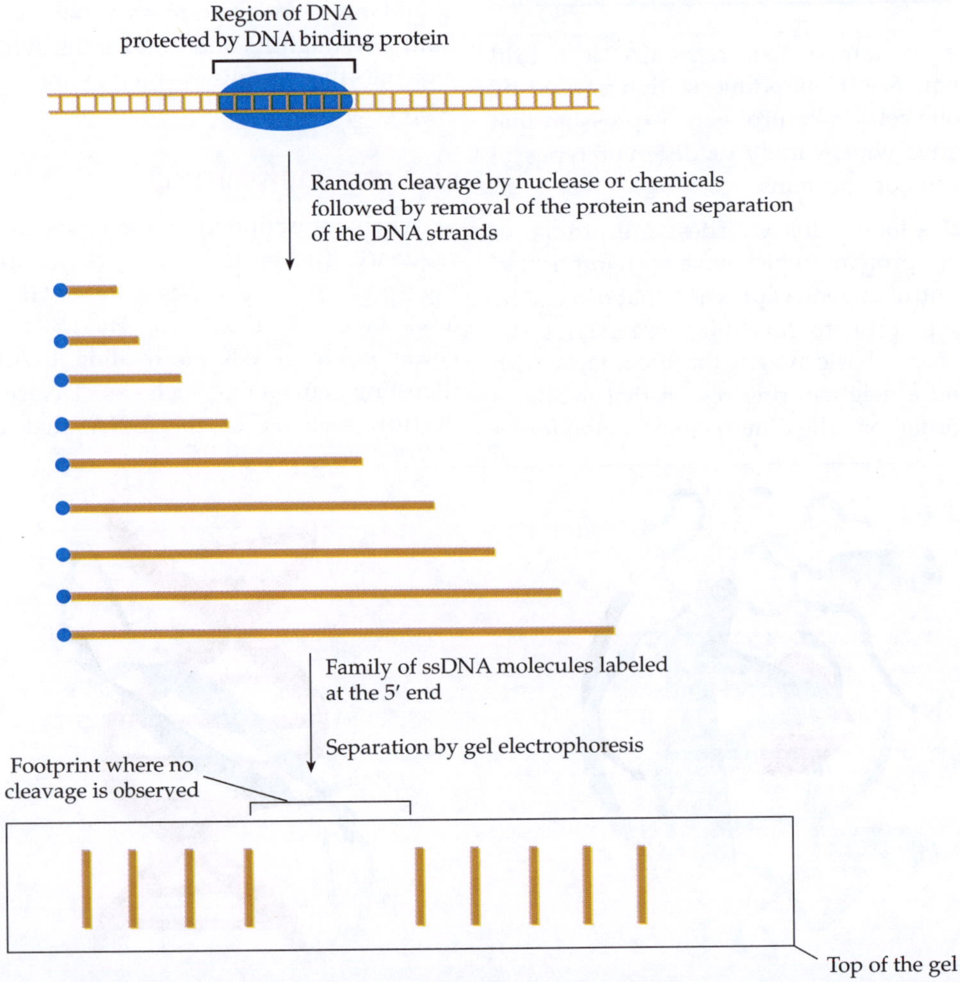


**Fig.18.9 :** *DNA footprinting technique*

## 18.4 REGULATION OF GENE EXPRESSION IN PROKARYOTES

### 18.4.1 Operon Concept

In 1961, Francois Jacob and Jacques Monod published a short paper in the "Proceedings of the French Academy of Sciences" demonstrating that two genes involved in lactose metabolism were coordinately regulated by a genetic element located adjacent to them. The term "**Operon**" and "**Operator**" were first introduced in this paper.

There are two types of sequences in DNA, sequences that code for ***trans*-acting products** and ***cis*-acting sequences** that function exclusively within the DNA. The *trans*-acting product is a protein product or may be RNA, which diffuses away from its site of synthesis to act elsewhere. Any gene product that is free to diffuse to find its target is described as ***trans*-acting**.

***cis*- acting** applies to any sequence of DNA where the *trans*-acting product binds.

**Operon** is defined as a group of contiguous genes in a bacterial chromosome that are transcribed into a single mRNA molecule. It constitutes a repressor gene, promoter, operator gene, leader and the structural gene.

Promoter and terminator are examples of *cis*-acting sites. A promoter serves to initiate transcription only of the gene. Here the *trans*-acting substance that recognizes promoter is RNA polymerase. Terminator can terminate transcription. RNA polymerase is also the *trans*-acting substance in this case. Promoter is located in the immediate vicinity of the start point (structural gene) of m RNA synthesis.

Close to the promoter is another *cis*- acting site called the **operator**, which is the target for the repressor protein. When the repressor binds to operator, RNA polymerase is prevented from initiating transcription and the gene expression is turned off. The repressor protein is produced by a **repressor gene**. Its mode of control is negative.

A transcription factor is required to assist RNA polymerase in initiating at the promoter. *i.e.*, the mode of control is positive. Several *trans*-acting factors have target sites in the vicinity of the promoter and binding of some or all of these factors enable RNA polymerase to initiate transcription.

### 18.4.2 *lac*-operon an Inducible operon in *E. coli*

There are three structural genes in the *lac* operon :

*Lac Z* codes for the enzyme *β –galactosidase*, whose active form is a tetramer of ~ 500KD. This enzyme breaks a β–galactoside into its component sugars. (Disaccharide lactose into monosaccharides, glucose and galactose).

*Lac Y* codes for the *β – galactoside permease,* a 30KD membrane – bound protein constituent of the transport system. This transports β – galactoside into the cell.

*Lac A* codes for *β –galactoside transacetylase*, an enzyme that transfers an acetyl group from acetyl- CoA to β –galactoside.

Because of their close linkage, all the three genes are transcribed as a single unit, resulting in a polycistronic mRNA. A single message serves for the translation of all the three gene products.

• **Negative Control of *lac*-operon :** Jacob and Monod proposed that adjacent to the *lac ZYA* structural genes, there is an operator gene, which interacts with a *trans*-acting gene product called the repressor molecule (that is coded by *lac I*). *lac I* gene product i.e., the repressor protein is allosteric *i.e.*, it reversibly interacts with another molecule causing the conformational change in three-dimensional shape and a change in chemical activity.

This repressor protein normally interacts with the DNA sequences of the operator region and inhibits the action of RNA polymerase. Thus, the transcription of structural genes is repressed. Repressor is a tetramer of identical subunits of 30 kD each. The operator extends from –5 just upstream of the mRNA start point to position +21 within the transcription unit.

When lactose is introduced into the culture medium, lactose binds to the repressor molecule and causes an allosteric conformational change. This change alters the binding site of the repressor rendering it incapable of interacting with operator DNA. Then RNA polymerase transcribes the structural genes. So, when the repressor fails to bind operator, transcription occurs. This is negative control.

● **Genetics of *lac* operon :**

1. In wild type bacteria (genotype is $I^+P^+O^+Z^+Y^+A^+$) if lactose is present, it binds to repressor and inactivates it, promoter is free from repressor, RNA polymerase then transcribes the genes into mRNA and then translates into protein.
2. If in these wild type bacteria, lactose is absent, the repressor binds to the operator. The transcription and translation is inhibited.
3. Constitutive mutation of the *lac I* gene produces a mutant *lac* $I^-$ gene, which will produce a mutant repressor product that cannot bind to operator gene. Thus the constitutive mutant bacteria with genotype $I^-P^+O^+Z^+Y^+A^+$, in presence or absence of lactose, can transcribe *lac ZYA* product (Fig 18.10).
4. Mutation that abolishes the ability of *repressor to bind to inducer* is described as *lac* $I^s$. ($I^sP^+O^+Z^+Y^+A^+$) They are trans-acting. The repressor is "locked in" to the active form that recognizes operator and prevents transcription (Fig. 18.11).
5. Repressor is a multimeric protein. When two different alleles of *lac I* gene are mutant, the subunits are made from each and associate to form a heterotetramer at random It is described as interallelic complementation.
6. Another mutation *Lac* $I^d$ (genotype is $I^dP^+O^+Z^+Y^+A^+$) alone results in a production of a repressor that cannot bind to operator even this is paired with a wild type. This is called *trans*-dominant or dominant negatives. Actually *lac* $I^d$ produces a "bad" subunit which not only itself unable to bind to operator but is also able as a part of the tetramer to prevent any good subunits from binding. This mutation is present extreme left end of *lac I* gene. This identifies the N-terminal end of the repressor protein as the DNA binding site.
7. A second set of constitutive mutations producing identical effects was found in a region immediately adjacent to the structural gene. This class of mutation designated as $O^c$ (operator gene mutation (genotype is $I^+P^+O^cZ^+Y^+A^+$). In this case the operator gene is altered; the repressor cannot bind to the operator and structural genes are always transcribed even in presence of wild *lac I* gene (Fig. 18.12).
8. The F-plasmid may contain the chromosomal gene is designated as $F^+$. A $F^-$ cell may acquire such a plasmid along with its own chromosome. This type of host cell is called **merozygote**, that is diploid for those genes. Jacob-Monod operon model predicts how regulation should be affected in such cells (Table 18.1).

● **Role of Inducer :** The repressor binds to wild type *lac O* but does not bind to *lac* $O^c$ promoter. The addition of chemical analogues of lactose such as Isopropyl–thiogalactoside (IPTG) releases the repressor from the operator *in vitro*.

The operator has palindrome repeats. Repressor is a tetramer of identical subunits, each of which must therefore has the same DNA binding site. Each inverted repeat of the operator is contacted in the same way by a repressor monomer.

It has been suggested that induction results from a reduction in the attraction between

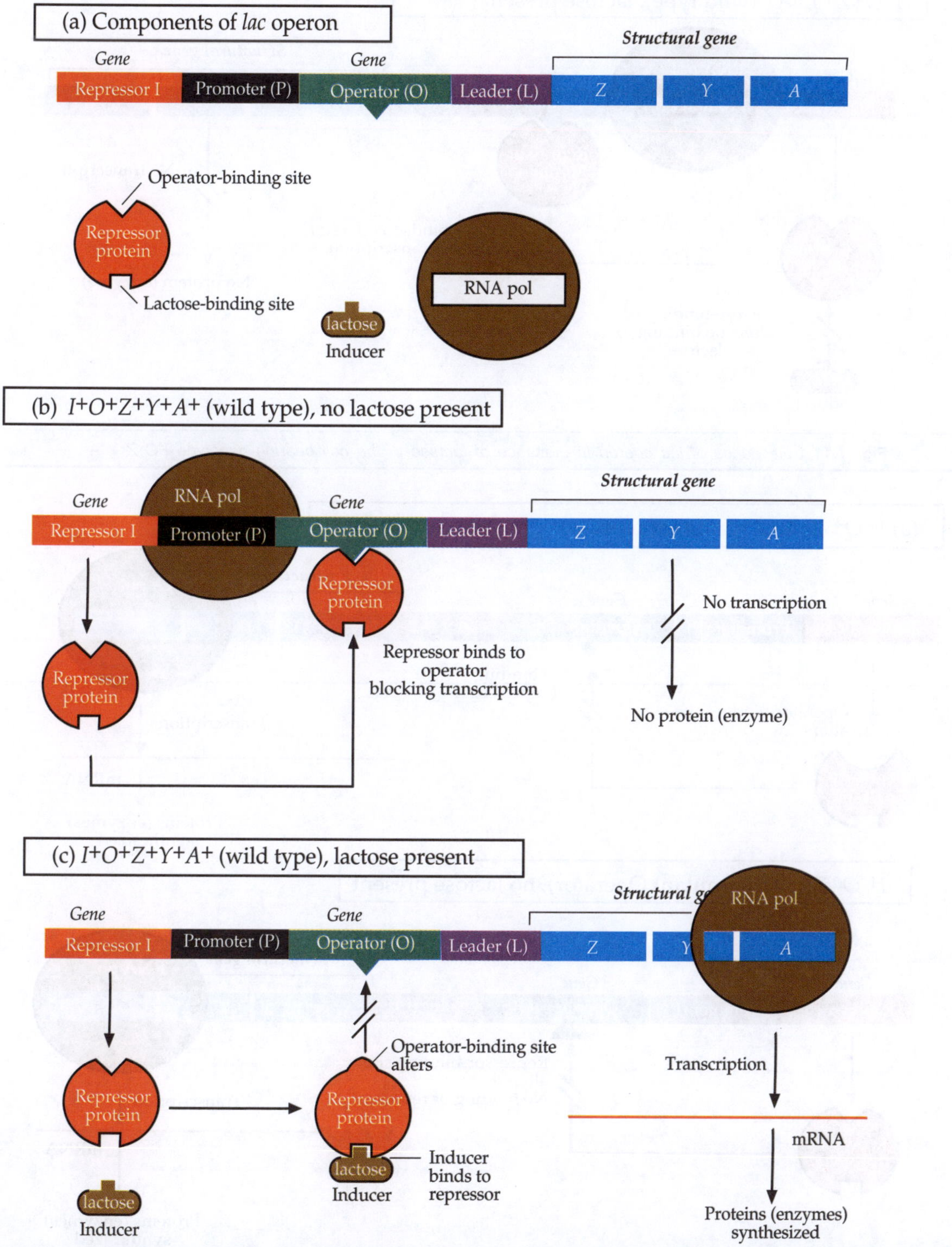


**Fig.18.10 :** *Components and functions of lac operon.*

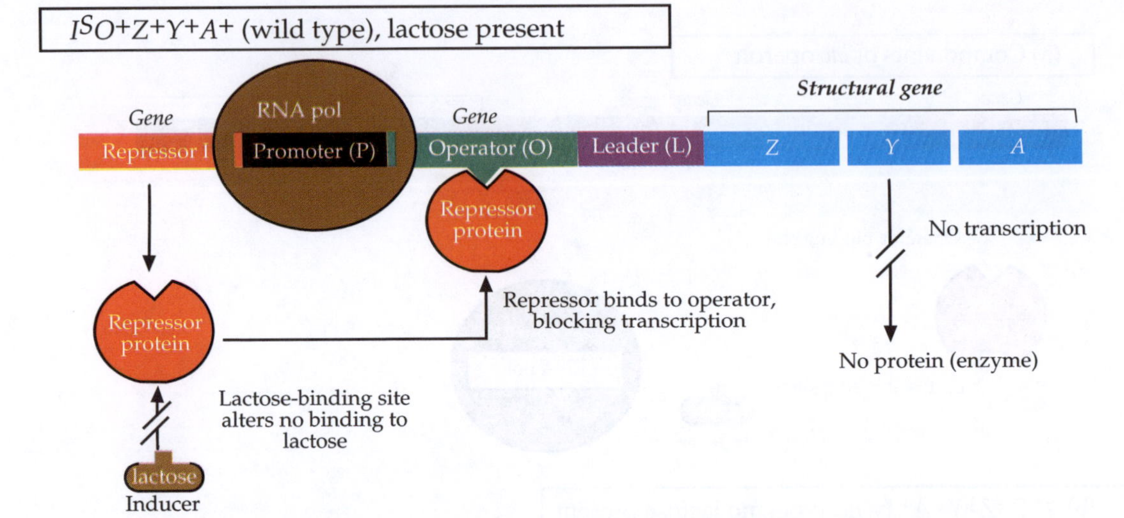


**Fig.17.11 :** *Response of lac operon in presence of lactose in the cell bearing genotype $I^sO^+Z^+Y^+A^+$.*

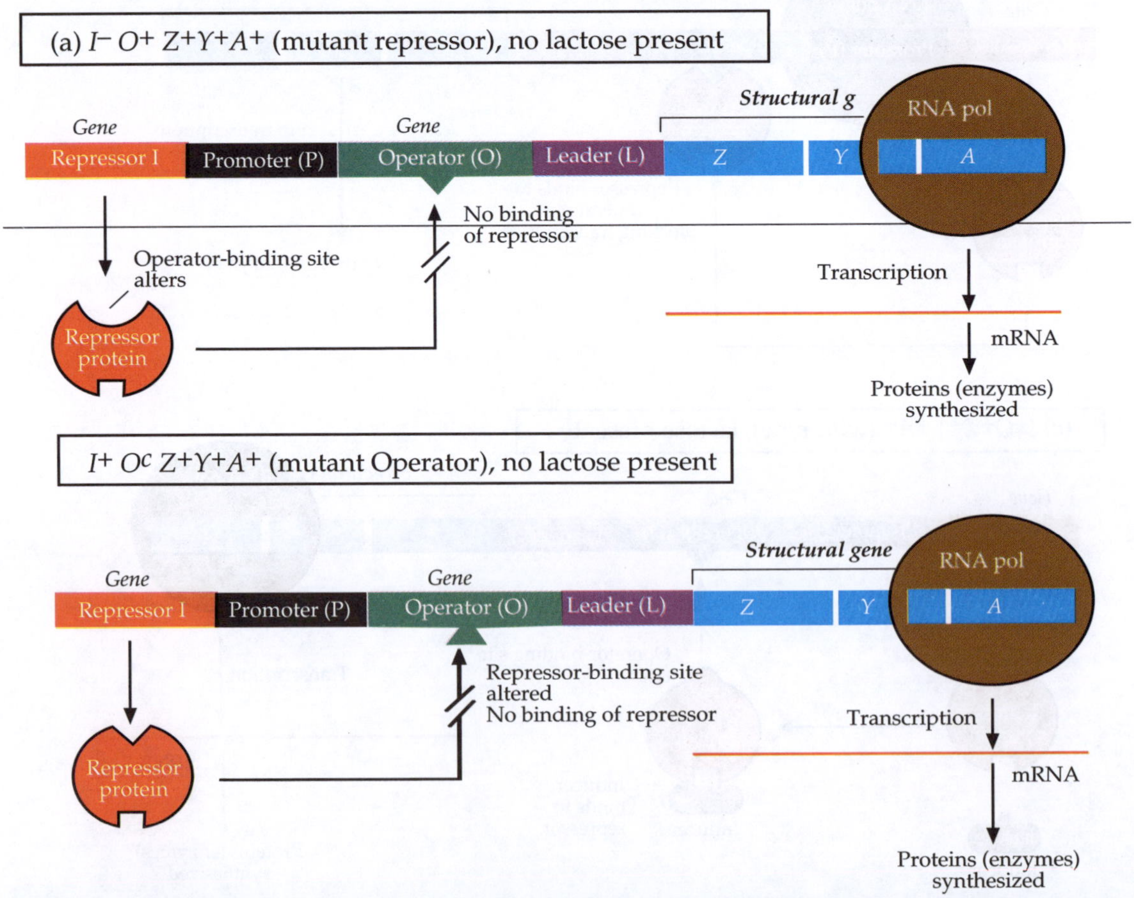


**Fig.17.12 :** *Response of lac operon in absence of lactose in $I^-$ and other $O^c$ mutant forms.*

**TABLE 18.1**
**Showing different mutations in *lac* operon and expresson of *lac* gene in presence or absence of inducer**

| Genotype | Inducer absent | | Inducer present | |
|---|---|---|---|---|
| | *β-galactosidase* | *Permease* | *β–galactosidase* | *Permease* |
| 1. $I^+P^+O^+Z^+Y^+$ | – | – | + | + |
| 2. $I^+P^+O^+Z^-Y^+$ | – | – | – | + |
| 3. $I^+P^+O^+Z^+Y^-$ | – | – | + | – |
| 4. $I^-P^+O^+Z^+Y^+$ | + | + | + | + |
| 5. $I^sP^+O^+Z^+Y^+$ | – | – | – | – |
| 6. $I^+P^+O^cZ^+Y^+$ | + | + | + | + |
| 7. $I^sP^+O^cZ^+Y^+$ | + | + | + | + |
| 8. $I^+P^+O^cZ^+Y^-$ | + | – | + | – |
| 9. $I^{-d}P^+O^+Z^+Y^+$ | + | + | + | + |
| 10. $\frac{I^-P^+O^+Z^+Y^+}{I^+P^+O^+Z^-Y^-}$ | – | – | + | + |
| 11. $\frac{I^-P^+O^+Z^+Y^-}{I^+P^+O^+Z^-Y^+}$ | – | – | + | + |
| 12. $\frac{I^sP^+O^+Z^+Y^-}{I^+P^+O^+Z^-Y^+}$ | – | – | – | – |
| 13. $\frac{I^+P^+O^cZ^-Y^+}{I^+P^+O^+Z^+Y^-}$ | – | + | + | + |
| 14. $\frac{I^-P^+O^cZ^+Y^-}{I^+P^+O^+Z^-Y^+}$ | + | – | + | + |
| 15. $\frac{I^sP^+O^+Z^+Y^+}{I^+P^+O^cZ^+Y^+}$ | + | + | + | + |
| 16. $\frac{I^{-d}P^+O^+Z^+Y^-}{I^+P^+O^+Z^-Y^+}$ | + | + | + | + |
| 17. $\frac{I^+P^-O^cZ^+Y^-}{I^+P^+O^+Z^-Y^+}$ | – | – | – | + |
| 18. $\frac{I^+P^-O^+Z^+Y^-}{I^+P^+O^cZ^-Y^+}$ | – | + | – | + |
| 19. $\frac{I^-P^-O^+Z^+Y^+}{I^+P^+O^+Z^-Y^-}$ | – | – | – | – |
| 20. $\frac{I^-P^+O^+Z^+Y^-}{I^+P^-O^+Z^-Y^+}$ | – | – | + | – |

operator and repressor. So, when inducer enters into the cell, it reduces the affinity for the operator of any repressor to which it binds.

There are two models for the release of repressor from operator by the inducer.

1. The equilibrium model for repressor bound to DNA to be rapid equilibrium with free repressor. Inducers upset the equilibrium, which bind to repressor preventing reassociation with DNA.

$$\text{Operator-Repressor complex} \rightleftharpoons \text{Operator + Repressor} \xrightarrow{\text{+ Inducer}} \text{Inducer-Repressor complex}$$

2. The second model is that inducer must directly bind to repressor, which was complexed with operator; the conformational change of the repressor makes it to release.

$$\text{Operator-Repressor Complex} \xrightarrow{\text{+ Inducer}} \text{Operator + Inducer–Repressor complex}$$

- **Positive control of *lac*-operon :** Another regulatory mechanism, called **catabolic repression**, has evolved to keep the genes for catabolism of lactose, arabinose and other sugars repressed in the presence of glucose even when these secondary sugars are also present. The repressive effect of glucose is mediated by cAMP and the protein is called **catabolite gene activator protein** (CAP).

CAP is a homodimer, with binding sites for DNA and cAMP. The protein is active only in presence of cAMP. When glucose is absent, CAP binds to a specific site near the *lac* promoter and stimulates transcription 50 folds. So CAP is a positive regulatory element in *lac*-operon.

**CAP-DNA- interaction :** CAP is a dimer of two identical subunits of 22.5 KD, which can be activated by a single cAMP molecule; A CAP monomer contains a DNA-binding region and a transcription-activating region. It recognizes the well conserved sequence of $\begin{matrix}\text{TGTGA}\\\text{ACACT}\end{matrix}$ sequence of DNA, and may lie in either orientation. In *lac*-operon, CAP–binding site lies adjacent to the promoter, protected by CAP is centered on –61 regions. CAP binds to DNA on one face of DNA, the same face that is bound to RNA polymerase In *gal* locus it is centered on –41 and in *ara* operon it is centered to –92, here it cannot contact with RNA polymerase).

There may be two ways in which CAP activates transcription: it could interact directly with RNA polymerase or it could act upon DNA to change its structure and in some way that assists RNA polymerase to bind.

The CAP acts directly upon the α– subunits to stimulate RNA polymerase. The CAP dimer has a functional transcription-activating region, which is actually a small exposed loop of CAP.

The CAP-DNA binding region has a bend, because CAP may distort the double helical structure. The bending may be more than $90^0$ to its axis. The mechanism of bending is to introduce a sharp kink within the TGTGA consensus sequence. Such bend may simply allow CAP to contact RNA polymerase at the promoter (Fig.18.13).

- **Mechanism of Positive Regulation**

*Lac*-repressor is negatively regulatory element responsive to lactose, whereas, CAP is a positively regulatory element responsive to glucose.

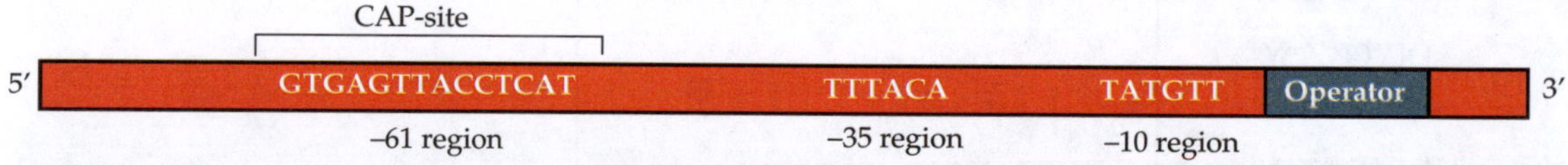


**Fig.18.13 :** *Location of CAP site in relation to operator in lac operon of E.coli.*

Both the elements act in concert.

1. CAP has little effect on the system when the *lac* repressor is blocking transcription and dissociation of the repressor from the operator has little effect unless CAP is present to facilitate transcription (Fig. 18.14b).
2. The effect of glucose on CAP is mediated by cAMP. When cAMP concentration is high and cAMP- binding site of CAP is occupied, the CAP binding to DNA occurs.
3. In presence of glucose, the concentration of cAMP declines, preventing CAP binding to DNA and thereby decreasing the expression of *lac* operon (Fig. 18.14d).
4. When high concentration of lactose present but the glucose is absent or with very low concentration, cAMP concentration is increased and facilitate CAP binding and also transcription (Fig. 18.14C).

Thus CAP and cAMP are involved in the coordinated regulation of many operon (such as galactose, arabinose etc). Such a network of operon with a common regulator is called REGULON.

It provides a mechanism for large concerted changes in cellular functions in response to environmental changes and thus they control hundred of genes (Fig. 18.14)

### 18.3.3 *ara* (arabinose)-operon in *E. coli*

*E. coli* can use arabinose as a carbon source by converting it into xylulose-5-phosphate, an intermediate in the pentose phosphate shunt. It requires three enzymes, *viz*, arabinose isomerase, ribulose kinase and ribulose-5-phosphate epimerase, which are encoded by the genes *ara A*, *ara B* and *ara D* respectively (Fig.18.15).

**Components of *ara*- operon**

1. The *ara* operon constitutes three genes viz *ara B*, *ara A* and *ara D*. Therefore this is collectively called *ara BAD*.
2. There is a regulatory site containing two operators, *ara* $O_1$ and *ara* $O_2$.
3. Besides, it includes another binding site for the *ara C* gene product (**Ara C**) called *ara I* (inducer) and a promoter ($P_{BAD}$) adjacent to *ara I*.
4. The *ara C* gene is present nearby and transcribed from its own promoter (Pc) near *ara* $O_1$, in opposite direction from *ara BAD* gene.
5. There is also a CAP-binding site adjacent to *ara* operon promoter ($P_{BAD}$). The binding site is centered –92 bp away from the start-point (Fig.18.16).

**Mechanism :**

1. One regulatory protein mediates both positive and negative control. The regulatory protein is **Ara C** encoded by *ara C* gene. Binding of a signal molecule (L-arabinose) alters its conformational change from a repressor form to an activator form and binds to a different DNA sequence.
2. The **Ara C** protein regulates its own synthesis by repressing transcription of its gene. This phenomenon is called *auto regulation*. **Ara C** binding at *ara* $O_1$ and repressing the transcription of *ara-C* gene when its concentration exceeds about 40 copies per cell. RNA polymerase synthesizes *ara C* mRNA in a direction opposite to the *araBCD* gene transcription.
3. When arabinose levels are low and glucose levels high, Ara C protein binds to both *ara I* and *ara* $O_2$ and brings these sites together to form a DNA loop of about 210 base pairs. The operon is repressed in this state. Ara C protein also binds to *ara* $O_1$ repressing further synthesis of Ara C.
4. When glucose is absent or its concentration is very low but arabinose concentration is high, **Ara C** protein binds to arabinose, its conformation changes to

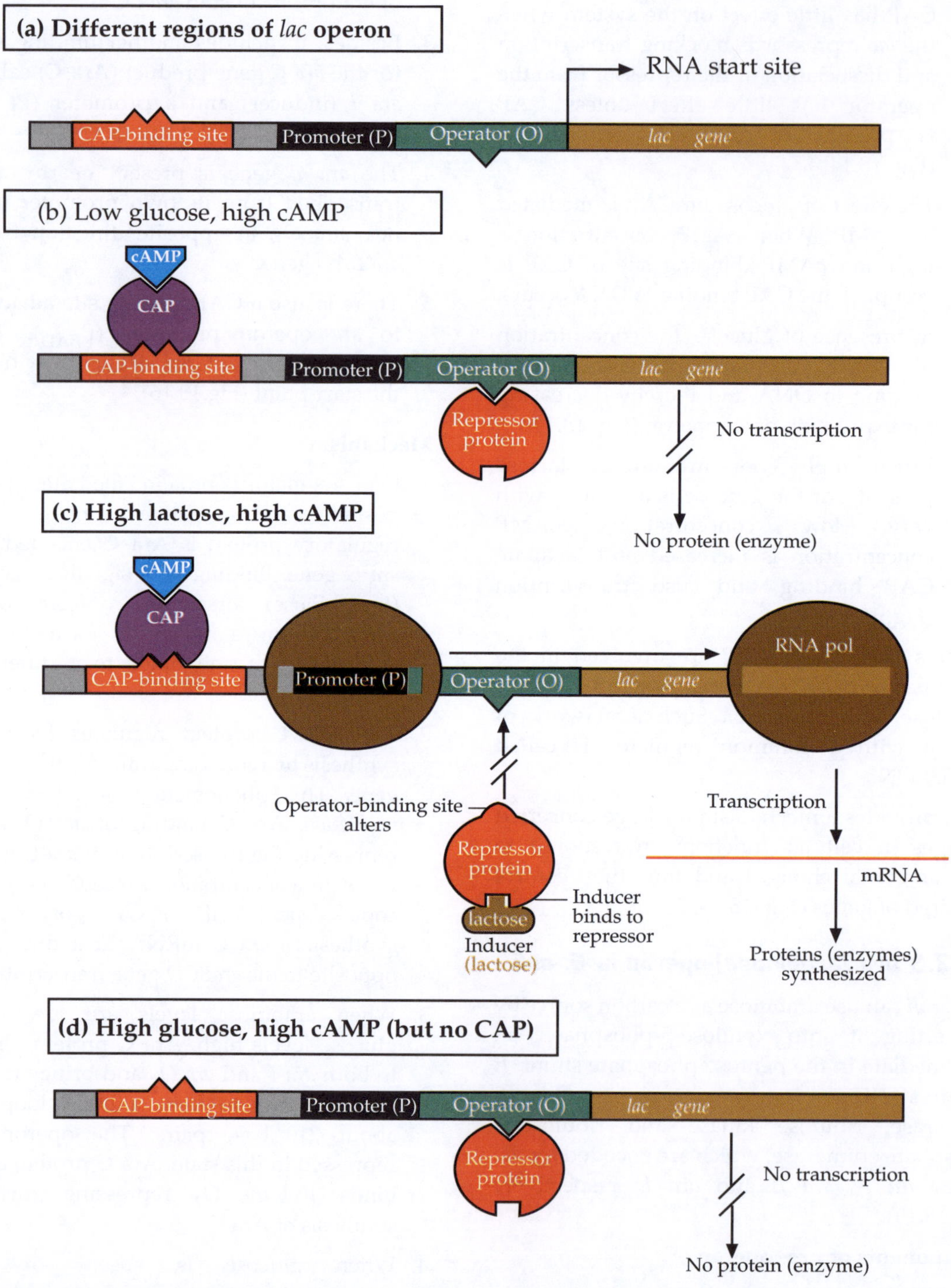


**Fig.18.14 :** *Combined effect of glucose and lactose on the expression of* lac *operon.*

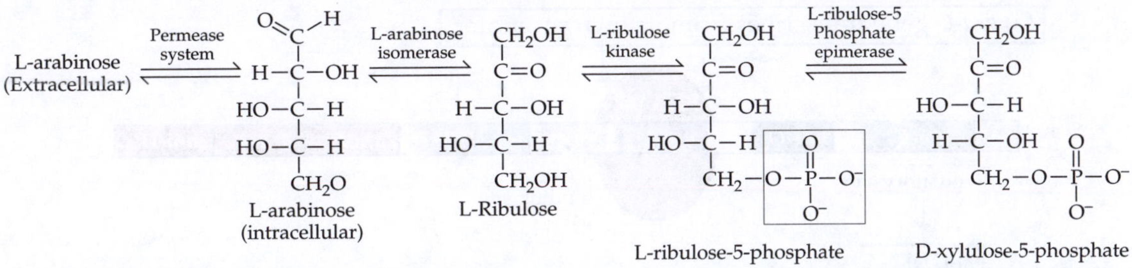


Fig.18.15 : *Metabolism of arabinose.*

an activator. The DNA loop is opened and the **Ara C** protein acts in concert with CAP –cAMP binding to induce transcription of *ara BAD* genes.

5. When arabinose and glucose both are abundant or absent, the *ara BAD* transcription remains inhibited. The exact system is not clear (Fig. 18.17).

### 18.4.4 *trp* (a repressible) operon in *E coli*

Amino acids are required in large amounts for protein synthesis, and wild-type *E. coli* has enzymes for synthesizing all of them. Jacob and Monod discovered that if tryptophan amino-acid is present in sufficient quantity in the growth medium, the enzymes necessary for its synthesis are not produced. Energetically, repression of the genes involved in the production of these enzymes is highly economical for the cell.

*E coli trp*-operon consists of five contiguous genes, *trp* E, *trp* D, *trp* C, *trp* B and *trp* A, transcribe a polycistronic message that directs translation of enzymes which catalyse biosynthesis of tryptophan (Fig. 18.18).

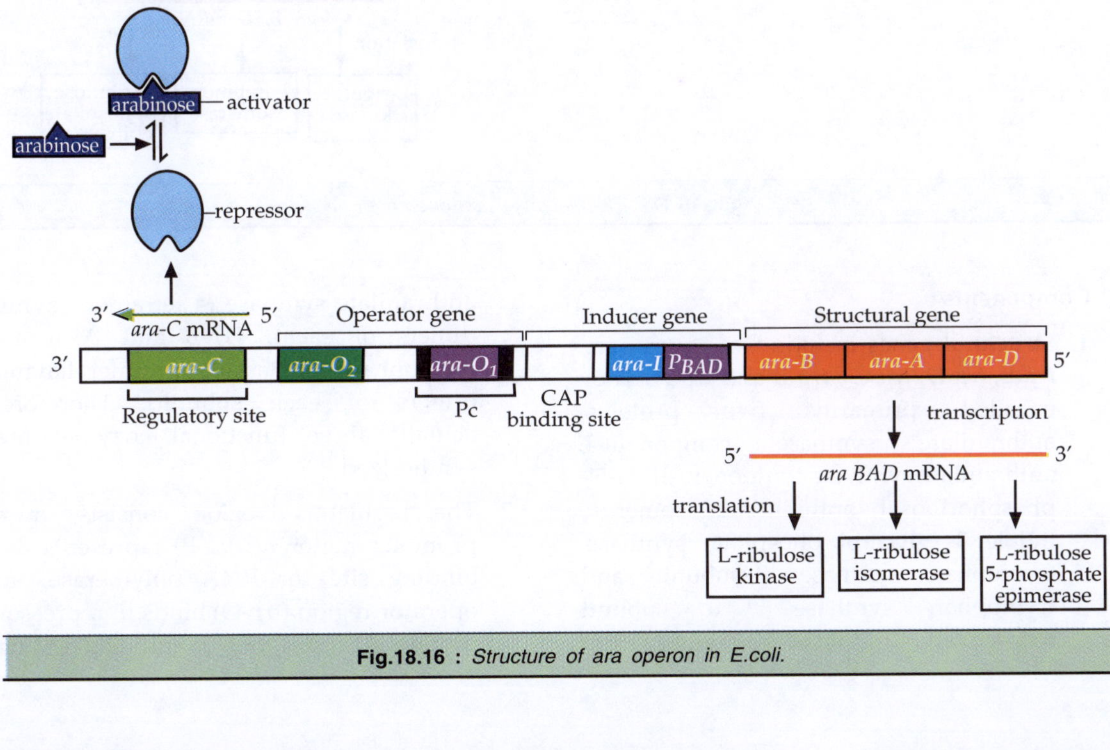


Fig.18.16 : *Structure of ara operon in E.coli.*

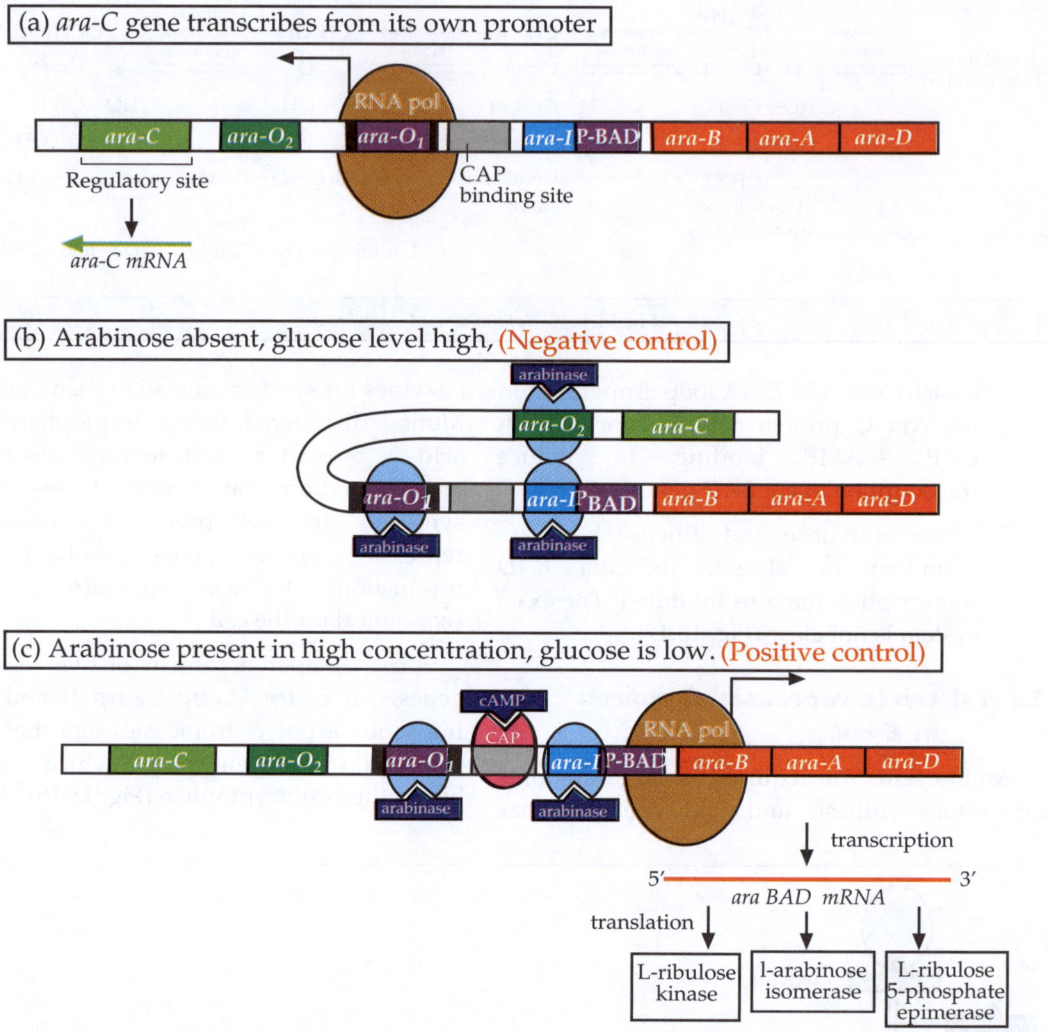


**Fig.18.17 :** *Regulation of ara-operon.*

**Components :**

1. Structural genes include five genes , *viz*, *trp* E, *trp* D, *trp* C , *trp* B and *trp* A. They encoded primarily five proteins, anthranilate synthase component-I, anthranilate synthase component-II, N-5′-phosphoribosyl anthranilate isomerase indole 3- glycerol phosphate synthase, tryptophan synthase β–subunit and tryptophan synthase α subunit respectively. Product of *trp E* and *D* form anthranilate synthase (a tetramer having dimers of each). *Trp-B* and A forms tryptophan synthase (a tetramer having dimers of each subunit). Therefore, actually three functional enzymes are synthesized.

2. The regulatory region consists of a promoter region (*trp* –P) represents the binding site for RNA polymerase, an operator region (*trp*-O) binds to repressor protein. Transcription is initiated within

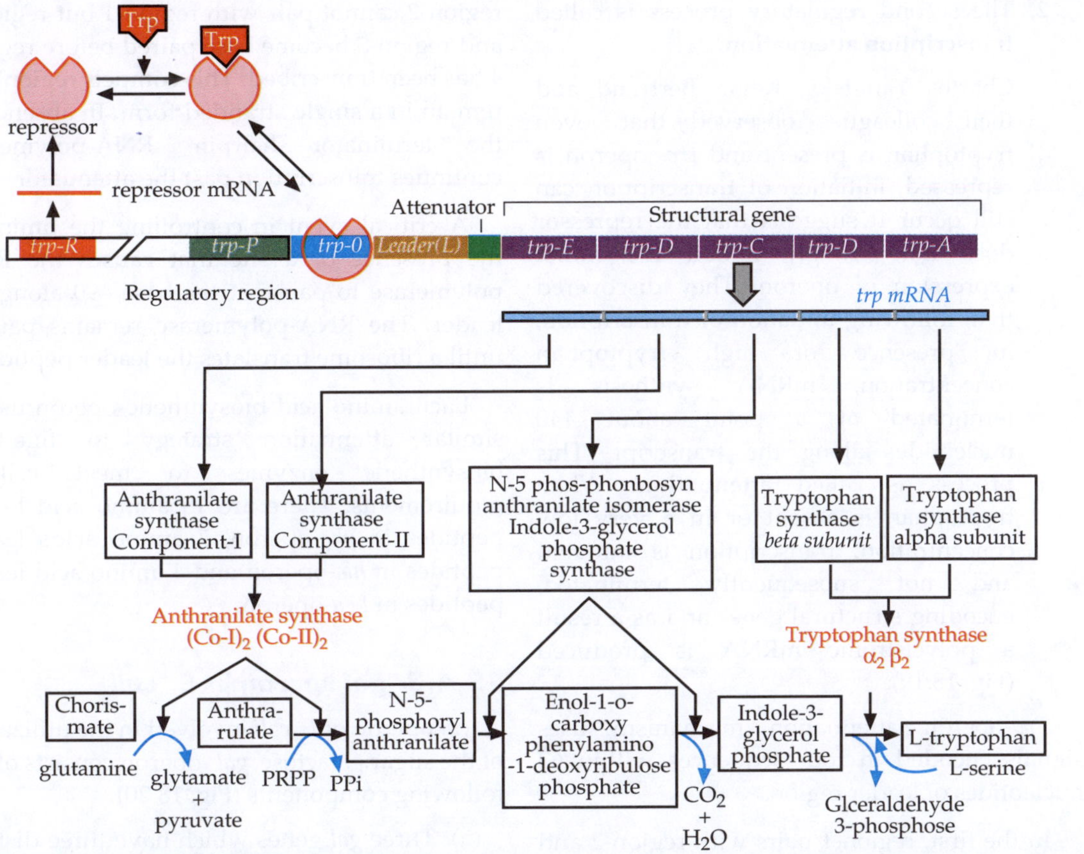


**Fig.18.18 :** *Diagram of a trp operon and tryptophan biosynthesis.*

the overlapping *trp*-P and *trp*-O regions and proceeds along a leader sequence, 162 nucleotides prior to the first structural gene *trp* E leader sequence represents a leader peptide of 14 amino acids. Within the leader sequence, there is another regulatory site, called attenuator (or intrinsic terminator), which provides a barrier for transcription of the structural genes. The mRNA transcript is terminated here producing a 140-base transcript. It is the integral part of the control mechanism of the operon.

3. Repression of expression is exercised by a repressor protein (**Trp-R**), coded by the unlinked gene *trp*-R. **Trp- R**-repressor is a homodimer with each subunit containing 107 amino acids.

**Mechanism of regulation** : When the enzymes are required, the operon corresponding to an amino acid is expressed. When the amino acid tryptophan is in abundant supply, the biosynthetic enzymes are no longer needed and the operon is repressed.

1. The mRNA from the *trp* operon has a half-life of only about 3 min, allowing the cell to respond rapidly for changing requirements of this amino acid. When tryptophan is abundant, it binds to the **Trp**-R repressor protein that causes the conformational change and now the repressor binds to its operator. The *trp*-O gene overlaps *trp*-P gene. Thus binding of the repressor blocks the binding of RNA polymerase to the promoter.

2. The second regulatory process is called **transcription attenuation.**

   Charles Yanofsky, Kevin Bertrand and their colleagues observed that, even tryptophan is present and *trp-* operon is repressed, initiation of transcription can still occur It suggests that the repressor does not strongly inhibit the initial expression of operon. They discovered that, following initiation of transcription, in presence of high tryptophan concentration, mRNA synthesis is terminated at a point about 140 nucleotides along the transcript. This process is called **attenuation**. When tryptophan is absent or in a very low concentration, transcription is initiated and not subsequently terminated, encoding structural genes and as a result a polycistronic mRNA is produced (Fig. 18.19).

*Trp*-operon attenuation mechanism uses signals encoded in four sequences within 62 nucleotides of leader region.

In the first, region-1 pairs with region-2 and region-3 pairs with region-4. The pairing of region 3 and 4 generates a hairpin that precedes the $U_8$ sequence. This is essential signal for **intrinsic termination**.

When tryptophan is present in high concentration, *Trp-* $tRNA^{Trp}$ concentration (charged tRNA carrying Tryptophan) also becomes high; ribosomes are able to synthesize leader peptide. They continue along the leader section of the m RNA rapidly past *Trp* codon to UGA codon, which is present between region-1 and region-2 by progressing this point, ribosomes extend over region-2 and prevent them from base pairing. Now the region-3 is available to base pair with region-4, generating a terminator hairpin. Under these conditions RNA polymerase terminates at the attenuator.

When there is no tryptophan, charged t $RNA^{Trp}$ is unavailable, ribosomes stall at a *Trp* codon, which is the part of region-1. Then region-2 cannot pair with region-1 but region-2 and region-3 become base paired before region-4 has been transcribed. This compels region-4 to remain in a single stranded form. In absence of the terminator hairpin, RNA-polymerase continues transcription past the attenuator.

A critical event in controlling the timing is the presence of a site that causes the RNA polymerase to pause at the base –90 along the leader. The RNA-polymerase remains paused until a ribosome translates the leader peptide.

Each amino acid biosynthetic operon uses a similar attenuation strategy to fine-tune biosynthetic enzymes to meet cellular requirements. There are 15 amino acid leader peptides in *phe*-operon, 7 amino acids leader peptides in *his*-operon and 4 amino acid leader peptides in *Leu*-operon.

### 18.4.5 *gal* operon in *E. coli*

*gal* operon of *E. coli* involved in the utilization of the sugar galactose. *gal* -operon consists of the following components (Fig. 18.20).

(a) Three *gal* genes which have three distinct functions.

   1. *gal K* gene, the product is galactokinase that phosphorylates galactose into galactose-1-phosphate.
   2. *gal T* gene, the product is transesterase that transfers the galactose-1-phosphate to UDP glucose.
   3. *gal E* gene, the product is phosphoglucomutase (epimerase) that converts UDP galactose into UDP glucose.

(b) Two promoters which are overlapping $P_{G1}$ and $P_{G2}$ upstream from *gal E*.

(c) Two operators, one is upstream of the promoter and the other is internal to the first gene *gal E*. These are therefore named as $O_E$ and $O_I$ for external and internal to gene *gal E*. These are located (–) 60 and (+)50 from the start point.

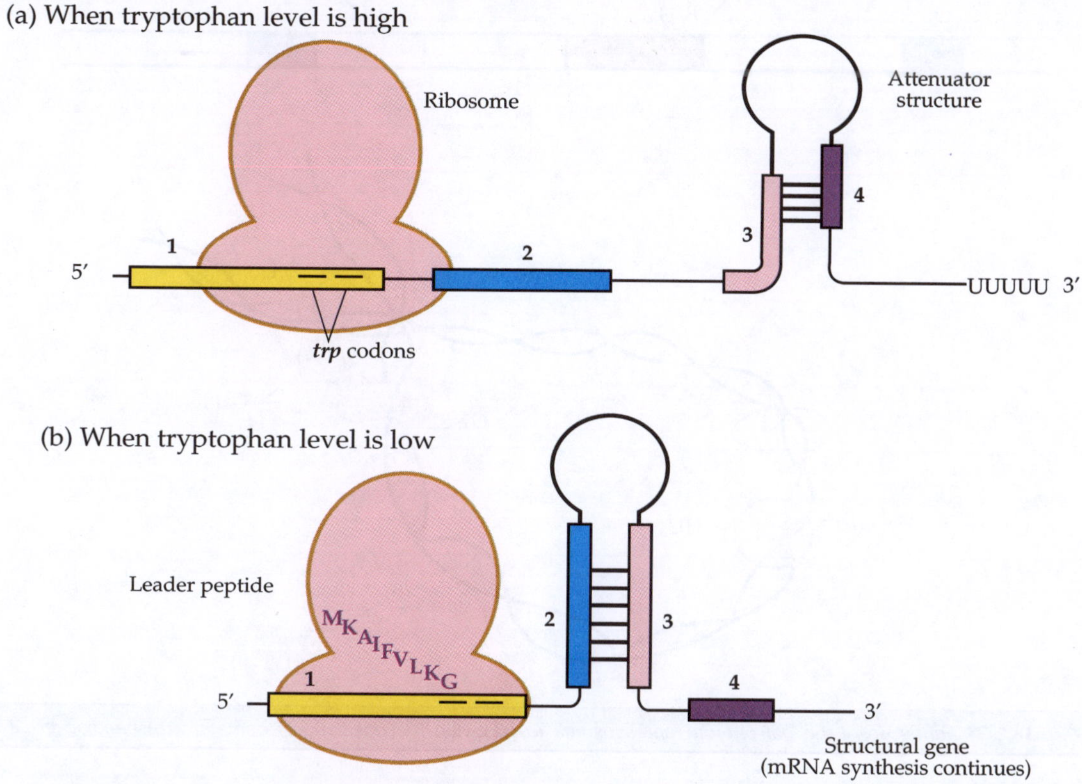


**Fig.18.19 :** *Attenuation mechanism in trp operon.*

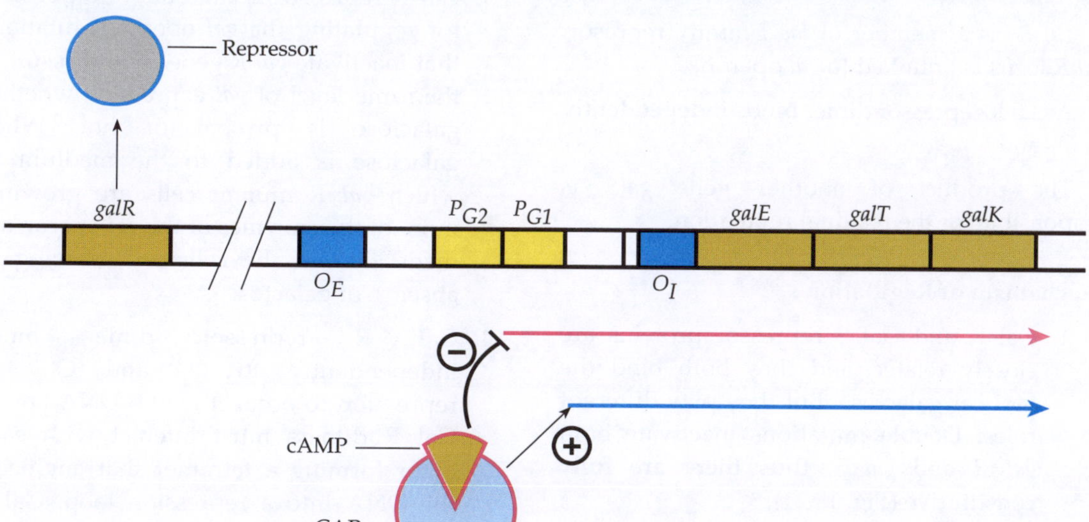


**Fig. 18.20 :** *Structure of galactose operon of E. coli.*

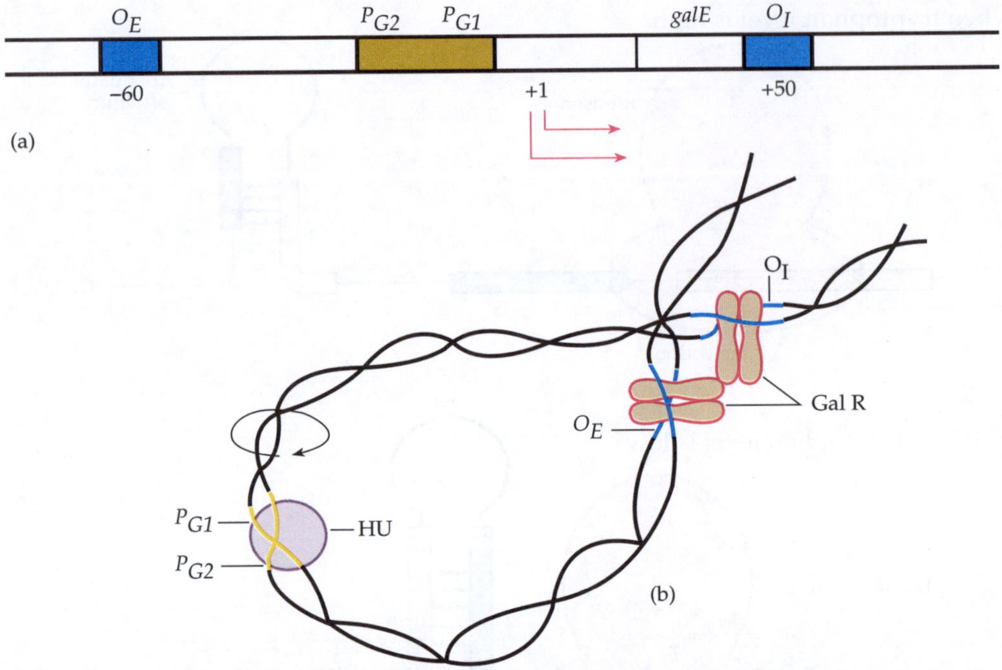


**Fig. 18.21 :** *Formation of the gal operon repressosome (a) showing the positions of operators (b) bending of DNA.*

(d) Two repressors that control *gal* operon. Gal R and Gal S are encoded by *gal R* and *gal S* genes respectively.

*gal R* is a member of *lac I* family represor, *gal R* locus is unlinked to *gal* operon.

A Gal R repressor dimer binds independently to $O_E$ and $O_I$.

The product of another gene *galS* is responsible for the residual regulation.

**Mechanism of Regulation :**

1. Gal R and Gal S repressor proteins are closely related and they both bind the inducer galactose. But they play different roles. Double mutations inactivate both *gal R* and *gal S*, thus there are fully constitutive (Fig. 18.21).
2. Gal R is a repressor protein, represses *gal* operaon in absence of galactose but Gal S repressor plays a minor role in regulating the *gal* operon. It controls the genes of galactose transport system into the cell.
3. Gal R repressor is not solely responsible for regulating the *gal* operon. Mutations that inactivate *gal R* gene should result in the same level of *gal* expression whether galactose is present or not. When galactose is added to the medium in which *gal R* mutant cells are growing, more of the enzymes of the *gal* operon are made than if the cells are growing in absence of galactose.
4. Gal R repressor dimer binds independently to $O_E$ and $O_I$. For repression to occur, the two DNA bound Gal R dimers must interact with each other forming a tetramer that engineers the DNA into a repression loop. Gal R dimers interact weakly. In order to stabilize that interaction, the histone-like protein **Hu** binds to a specific site *hbs* between the two operators introducing a

180° loop. The DNA loop sequesters $P_{G1}$ and $P_{G2}$ from RNA polymerase access.

Inspite of this, some access must occur because basal level of the *gal* enzymes are synthesized even under repressed conditions.

5. *gal* operon is also a catabolite-repressible operon. When cAMP levels high, the CRP-AMP complex binds to the *cat* site (at -35 region) promoting $P_{G1}$ transcription but inhibiting transcription from $P_{G2}$. When grown on glucose, cAMP level is low, transcription can occur from $P_{G2}$ assuming a basal level of *gal* enzymes.

## 18.5 REGULATION OF GENE EXPRESSION IN EUKARYOTES

The regulation of gene expression in eukaryotes differs in three important ways from that typically found in bacteria.

1. The eukaryotes make use of gene regulatory proteins that can act even when they are bound to DNA, thousands of nucleotides away from the promoter that they influence and a single promoter can be controlled by an almost unlimited number of regulatory sequences scattered along the DNA.
2. Only the eukaryotic RNA polymerase-II transcribes all protein coding genes, cannot initiate transcription on its own. It requires a set of proteins called **general transcription factors**, which must be assembled at the promoter before starting the transcription.
3. The packing of eukaryotic DNA into chromatin provides opportunities for regulation of transcription.

Though, the control of gene expression can occur at multiple stages, but it is clear that in eukaryotes the majority of regulatory events occur in the initiation of transcription. Regulation of tissue-specific gene transcription lies at the heart of eukaryotic differentiation. The regulatory transcription factor serves to provide common control of a large number of target genes but the mechanism how does this transcription factor identify its group of target genes? And how the activity of these transcription factors are regulated in response to external or internal signal? are the major questions regarding the tissue specific gene activation.

### 18.5.1 Response Elements

It is fact that, groups of eukaryotic genes are under common control and they share a promoter (or enhancer) element that is recognized by a regulatory transcription factors. An element that causes a gene to respond to such a regulatory transcription factor is called a **response element**. They have the same general characteristics as upstream elements of promoters or enhancers, contain short consensus sequences. The response elements found in different genes are closely related but not may be identical.

For example, HSE (heat shock response element), GRE (glucocorticoid response element), SRE (serum response element) etc. The response elements may be present < 200bp upstream, are sufficiently to confer the regulatory response, but sometimes there may be multiple copies.

The DNA sites to which the eukaryotic gene activators bound were originally termed as **enhancers**, since their presence enhance or increase the rate of transcription dramatically. **Promoter** is a region where RNA polymerase and transcription factors are assembled.

The response elements may be located in promoters or in enhancers. *e.g.*, an HSE is found in promoter, while a GRE is found in an enhancers. A gene is regulated by a sequence at promoter or enhancer that is recognized by a specific protein. The protein functions as a transcription factor needed for RNA polymerase to initiate transcription. Active protein is available only under conditions when the gene is to be expressed.

For example, heat shock genes also possess a common consensus sequence (HSE), but are located at various positions relative to start point and are recognized by an independent transcription factor HSTF. Both HSE and HSTF have been conserved in evolution. It is striking that a heat shock gene from *Drosophila melanogaster* can be activated in species as distant as mammals or sea urchin. The HSTF protein of fruit fly and yeast appears to be similar.

### 18.5.2 Differential Gene Expression

Seven generalizations that emphasize their importance for differential gene expression have been made.

1. Most genes require enhancers for their transcription.
2. Enhancers are the major determinants of differential transcription in cell types and time.
3. The enhancer functions by providing multiple signals to the promoters whether a given gene is transcribed. One given gene can have several enhancer sites and each enhancer can be bound by more than one transcription factors.
4. The interaction between proteins bound to enhancer sites and transcription initiation complex assembled at the promoter is thought to regulate transcription.
5. Enhancers are modulators, there are various DNA elements that regulate temporal and spatial gene expression and these can be mixed and matched. For example, insulin and lens-specific crystalline both have sites that bind **Pax 6** protein. But Pax 6 does not tell the lens to make insulin or endocrine pancreas to make crystalline; because there are other transcription factors that must bind. Thus combination of transcription factors causes particular genes to be transcribed.
6. A gene can have several enhancer elements and each turning it on in a different sets of cells.
7. Enhancers can also be used to inhibit transcription. In some cases, the same transcription factors that activate the transcription of one gene can be used to repress the transcription of other genes. These are called **negative enhancers** or **silencers**.

### 18.5.3 Positively regulated Eukaryotic Promoters

Two types of generalized RNA polymerase II promoters and regulatory regions can be recognized in eukaryotes. The first of these regulatory elements is a TATA-box (consensus sequence is TATAAAA). It is located 25-30 base pairs upstream from the initiation site, although it may be more variable. These sequences appear to be the binding sites for TF II D, which is required for the recruitment of RNA polymerase.

A variety of short regulatory sequences may be found which are located few hundred base pairs away from the start site. GC-box is one of them found in many genes of higher eukaryotes. The consensus sequence is GGGCGG. Another CCAAT box is also found in some higher eukaryotic genes. Its consensus sequence is GCCAAT. Additional regulatory sequences called enhancers have also been encountered in higher eukaryotes.

In yeast, in addition to TATA-box, there is a regulatory sequence element, which is more complex structure called the **upstream activator sequences** (UASs). They are present few hundred base pairs upstream away from the start point (Fig. 18.22/23).

Regulation of transcription initiation involves protein-protein interactions between different proteins or between proteins and RNA polymerase. The regulatory sites are located far away upstream from the RNA start site. Therefore, DNA–looping is essential for the protein- protein contact.

A number of transcription factors are required for the recruitment of RNA polymerase

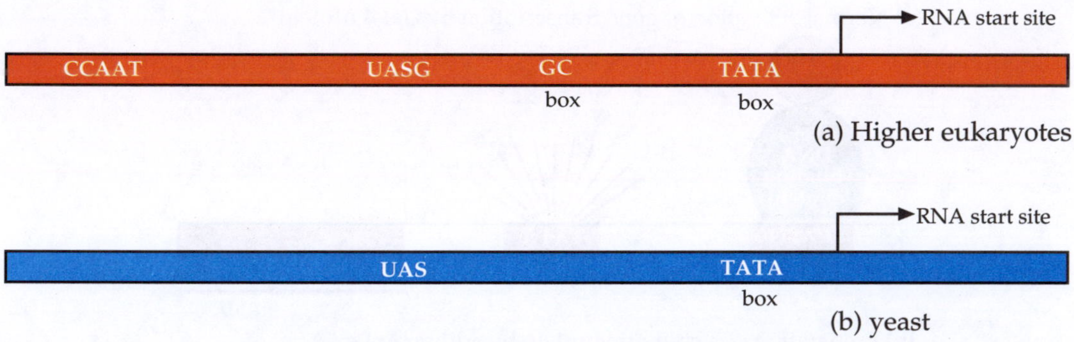


**Fig.18.22 :** *Generalised eukaryotic promotoers*

and to start RNA synthesis. The first of all transcription factors, TF II D is essential to recognize TATA-box. Then other TFs are serially bound to complete the complex. TF II D is a general transcription factor.

Other regulatory sequences are bound generally by transcriptional regulatory factors with their distinct DNA- binding motifs such as Leucine Zippers, HTH, HLH, and ZF etc.

In the vertebrates, the protein called SP–1 (80KD) essentially binds to GC-box. The binding domain of SP–1 is located at its C- terminal domain and contains three zinc fingers. Its 25% of the amino acids are *Gln.* (*glutamin*-rich domain)

The CCAAT-. box is bound by a specific class of proteins, one of which is CTF 1 (55KD). It has no zinc finger or helix-turn-helix domains. Its

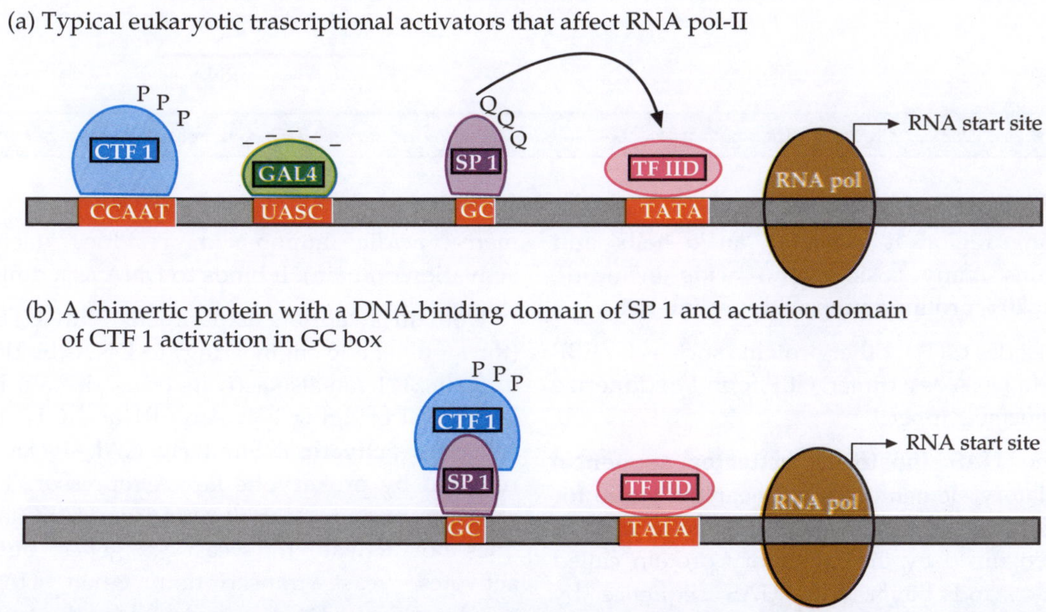


**Fig.18.23 :** *Regulation of initiation of transcription in higher eukaryotes.*

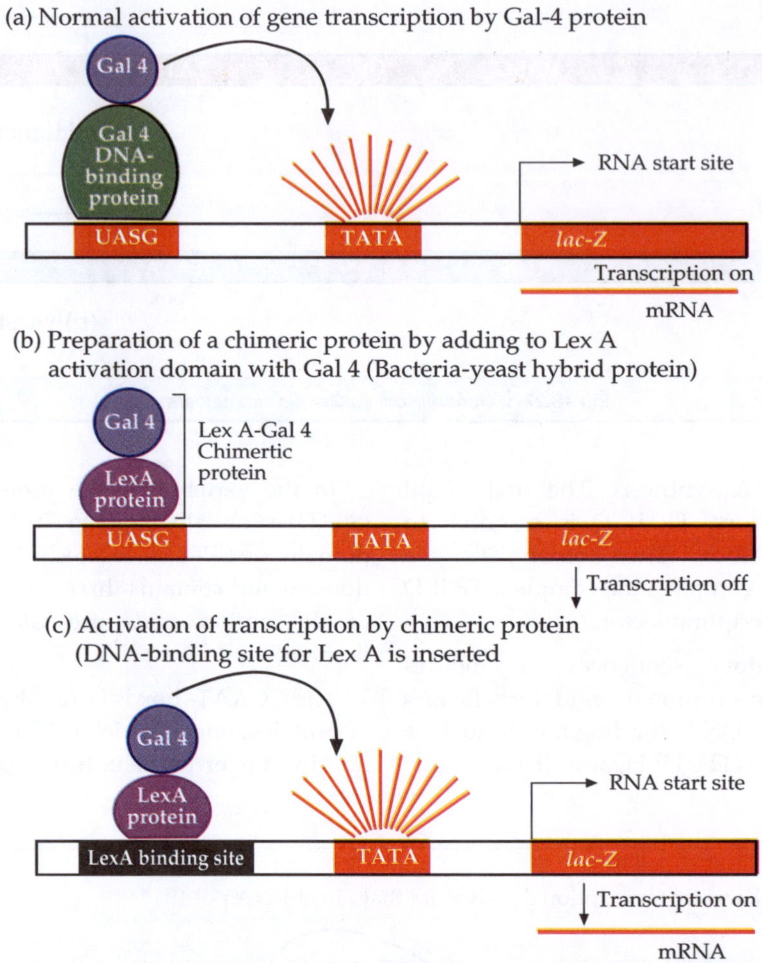


**Fig.18.24 :** *Domain swapping experiment where GAL-4 is replaced by prokaryotic LEX-A repressor in Yeast genome.*

binding region is probably an α–helix and contains many basic amino acids including about 20% proline amino acid (proline-rich).

Besides CTF 1, other proteins such as C/EBP bind to DNA as a dimer. CBP found to dimerize by Leucine-Zipper.

The UAS (**upstream activator sequence**) regulatory element is found near the genes for the enzymes of galactose metabolism in yeast. It is recognized by the regulatory protein called GAL-4, and binds with UAS sequence by several zinc fingers, which is present at its C-terminal end. The activation domain contains many acidic amino-acid residues (acidic activation domain). It binds to DNA as a dimer.

Domain swapping experiment with CTF 1 (through genetic engineering) to DNA- binding domain SP 1 can also activate transcription. The additional bridging between SP1 and CTF 1 is called **co–activation**. Similarly GAL–4 can be replaced by prokaryotic Lex-A repressor. This chimeric protein does not bind as UASG and does not activate the yeast *gal* genes, but it activates yeast transcription when UASG sequence of the DNA is replaced by the Lex A recognition site of prokaryotes (Fig. 18.24).

Gal 4 is normally responsible for activating the transcription of yeast genes that code for the enzymes which convert galactose to glucose. In the experiment shown here, the control region for one of the genes was fused to the *E. coli lac Z* gene, which codes for the enzyme β– galactosidase. Thus **lac Z** serves as a **reporter gene** since it reports the activity of a gene control region.

### 18.5.4 Remodelling of Chromatin Structure during Gene Activation

Both the histone-DNA interactions within the nucleosome core particle and histone tail interactions in the chromatin fiber contribute to repression. This repression can be counteracted by "chromatin remodeling protein" DNA-histone interactions involving the histone tail is abrogated by histone–acetyl–1–transferase (HATS), enzymes that acetylate histones.

The normal ground state for eukaryotic chromatin is nonpermissive to transcription. Normal chromatin blocks the association of TF II D and RNA polymerase II with the DNA. However, it does allow various modulators of transcription to bind (Kornberg and Lorch, 1999; Struhl 1999). The restrictive ground state can be modified such that the chromatin can enter a highly repressed **'silent'** state or can be converted to a transcriptionally "**poised**" state that is able to bind the TF II D and RNA polymerase II.

The connection between histone acetylation and DNA transcription was confirmed from the experiments in yeast and mammals and showed that the nucleosomes containing promoters and enhancer elements were acetylated in those genes that were transcriptionally active. **Gen 5**, a transcriptional activator in yeast, was shown to have histone-acetyl-transferase activity (Brownell *et al*1996; Kuo *et al* 1998). At the same time, the **p300/CBP** mammalian coactivator was found also to be a HAT (Bannister and Kouzarides 1996; Ograyko *et al* 1996; Grusntein 1997). Many transcriptional activators (such as MITF, microphthalmia proteins) bind this co activator. The acetylation of the histones by promoter-associated factors is localized to the nucleosomes around the promoter region (Parekh and Maniatis 1999).

The acetylation of the histone tail is probably necessary to *decondense* the chromatin in the region of promoters. Indeed, promoters and enhancers of active genes are usually seen in regions devoid of nucleosomes. It is thought that nucleosomes are displaced from the enhancer and promoter regions by chromatin remodeling complexes.

There are two main types of chromatin remodeling complexes. The first type is called SWI/SNF complex. These proteins were discovered in yeast genes, whose protein products were opposed to the repression of transcription (Cairns *et al* 1994; Cote *et al* 1994). These two proteins form a complex that has an ATPase activity. Homologous protein has also found in mammals (Imbalzano *et al* 1994). The second family of chromatin remodeling complexes is called either the ISW1 or NURF family. SWI/SNF proteins disrupt DNA histone contacts and releasing the histones, while, the NURF family of nucleosome remodelers merely slides the nucleosomes along the DNA (Hamiche *et al* 1999, Langst *et al* 1999) (Fig. 18.25). Another SWR1 is involved in depositionof H2AZ in active chromatin.

Eukaryotic gene activator proteins can influence several different steps in transcription initiation and this property has important consequences when different activator proteins work together. In general, where several factors work together to enhance a reaction rate, the joint effect is generally not merely the sum of the enhancements caused by each factor alone, but the product. Therefore, it may be said that the gene activator proteins exhibit transcriptional synergy.

### 18.5.5 Inhibition of gene expression by gene repressors

In addition to activator proteins, eukaryotes use gene repressor proteins to regulate transcription of their genes. There are five ways

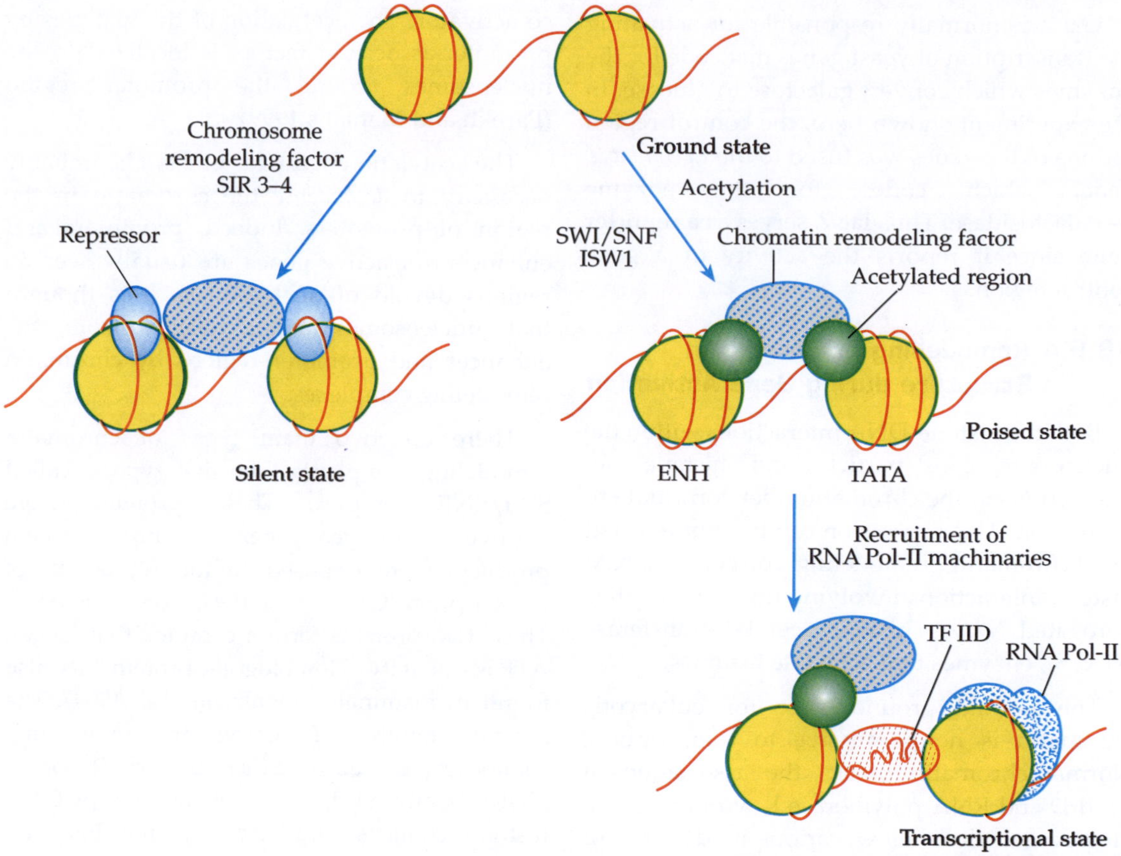


**Fig.18.25 :** *Transcriptional states of eukaryotic chromosome. ENH is enhancer and TATA is promoter.*

by which eukaryotic gene repressor protein can operate (Fig. 18.26).

1. **Competitive binding :** The repressor proteins bind replacing the activators on the same regulatory DNA sequence.
2. **Masking the activator surface :** Repressor protein binds to the activation domain of the activator protein, thereby preventing it from carrying out its activation functions.
3. **Direct interaction with the general transcription factors :** Before binding of activator, general transcription factor TF IID binds to their repressor and thus preventing the binding to activator.
4. **Recruitment of repressive chromatin remodeling complex :** Certain types of remodeling complexes are engaged in restoring the repressed nucleosomal state of the promoters and thus ground state of the chromatin remains as the silent state. SIR 3-4 proteins are found to do so. These two proteins interact with the tails of H3 and H4 along the entire length of the silenced region. They cause aggregation of nucleosomes to form a heterochromatic and transcriptionally inert region e.g. the X-chromosomal inactivation in mammalian cells particularly in females of human beings.

5. **Recruitment of histone deacetylation :** Deacetylation means the removal of acetyl group from the nucleosomes, which causes repression of gene expression. This connection was demonstrated by the finding that two yeast and human repressor proteins Rpd3 and HDAC, respectively, were histone deacetylases (Grozinger *et al* 1999). Histone deacetylases often form complexes that can be bound by transcriptional repressors (*e.g.* Sin 3) that bind to DNA. Sin 3 can interact with repressive transcription factors such as Mad or unbound nuclear hormone receptors to bring the Rpd3/HDAC histone deacetylases to a particular region. Sin 3 can bind to a methyl CpG-binding protein and thereby recruits these histone deacetylases to methylated DNA regions, thereby repressing their transcription.

### 18.5.6 Co-activators, Co-repressors and Enhanceosome

Gene regulatory proteins that do not themselves bind DNA but assemble on DNA-bound gene regulatory proteins are often termed **co-activators** or **co-repressors**, depending on their effect on transcription initiation. The same co-repressor or co-activators can assemble on different DNA binding proteins. They typically carry out multiple functions. They can interact with chromatin remodeling complexes histone modifying enzymes, RNA polymerase HE and several general transcription factors.

Typically, the assembly of a group of regulatory proteins on DNA is guided by a few relatively short stretches of nucleotide sequence.

The term enhanceosome is a more elaborate protein-DNA structure. Formation of the enhanceosome requires the presence of many gene regulatory proteins. The protein surfaces of the enhanceosome interact with a co-activator which activates transcription at a nearby promoter (Fig. 18.26 and 18.27).

### 18.5.7 Enhancer elements

Enhancer element is a *cis*-acting sequence that increases the utilization of some eukaryotic promoters and can function in either orientation (bidirectional) and in any loaction (upstream or downstream) relative to the promoter. It is involved in the initiation of transcription and it is identified by sequences that stimulate initiation but are located in a considerable distance from the start point. The components of enhancer elements resemble those of promoters as they consists of a variety of modulator elements and are closely organized in a closely packed array.

The element in an enhancer functions like that in a promoter but the enhancer does not need to be nearer to the start point. However protein bound to enhancer elements interact with protein bound at promoter elements. The distinction between promoter and enhancer is operational. A promoter contains only elements recognised by general and upstream factors should be transcribed in any cell type and located vicinity of the start point. Enhancer can move from one place to another place but promoters can not. It can stimulate transcription by its inverted state without affecting its ability.

The activity of the promoter is enormously increased by the presence of an enhancer and is located at a variable distance from those regarded as comprising part of the promoter itself.

An enhancer in the virus SV 40 is located in the region of the genome that contains two identical sequences of 72 bp each, repeated in tandem ~200 bp upstream of the start point of transcription unit. Each 72 bp repeat contains a copy of enhancer. The enhancers often show redundency in function, ie. they are more active when they are separated by introducing sequeces between them.

An enhancer works upon the promoter that is nearer to it. Sometimes, promoter lacks specific regulation but become active only when

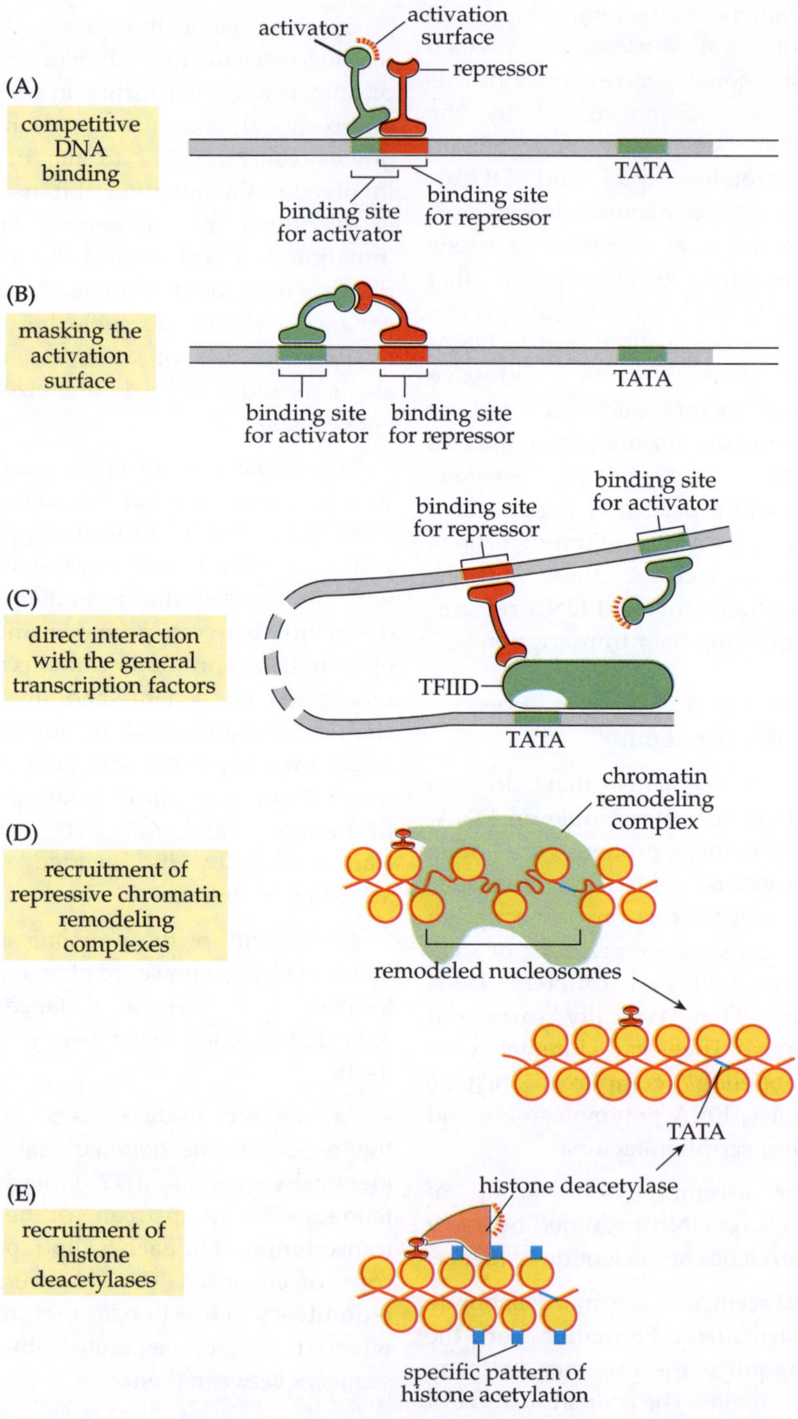


**Fig.18.26 :** *Five ways in which eukaryotic gene repressor proteins can operate.*

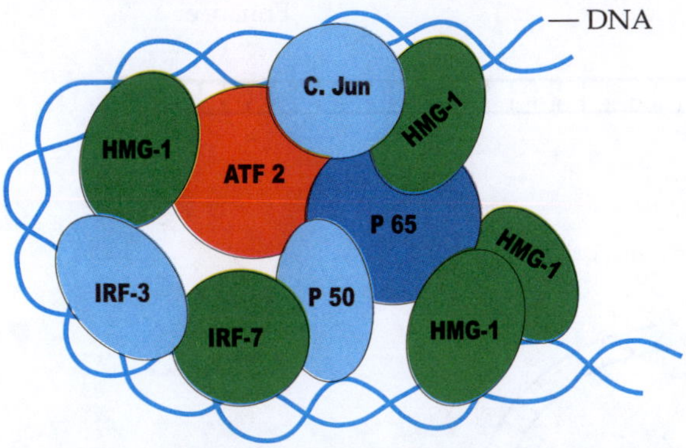


**Fig.18.27 :** *Model of the enhanceosome that forms on the β-interferon enhancer.*

a nearby enhancer is specifically activate. For example, Ig-enhancers appear to be active only in the B-lymphocytes in which Ig genes are expressed. Such enhancers provide part of the regulatory network by which gene expression is controlled.

It was thought previously that the functions of enhancer are

1. Changing in the overall structure of the template, for example, by influencing the density of supercoiling.
2. It could be responsible for locating the template at a particular place within the cells, for example, attaching it to the nuclear matrix.
3. An enhancer could provide an "entry site" a point at which RNA polymerase associates with chromation.

But now it was clearly demonstrated that its functions are :

1. Enhancers are modulators like promoters.
2. The function of enhancer involved the same sort of interaction with the basal apparatus as the interactions sponsored by upstream promoter elements.
3. Some elements are found in both enhancers and promoters. Some individual elements found in promoters share with enhancers the ability to function at variable distance and in either upstream.

   Enhancers might be viewed as containing promoter elements that are grouped closely together with the ability to function at increased distances from the start point.
4. The essential role of enhancer may be to increase the concertration of transcription factors in the vicinity of the promoter.
5. If proteins bound at an enhancer several kb. distance from a promoter interact directly with proteins bound in the vicinity of the start point. Formation of a large loop allows the enhancer and promoter to be closely located. Such loop is formed in bacterial enhancers (Fig 18.28).
6. Some enhancers are activated only in the tissues in which their genes function, but others could be active in all cells.

Cooperative binding of different proteins (transcription factors) on enhancer DNA produces a multiprotein complex that is assembled during initiation of transcription. This is called *enhanceosome*.

## 18.6 TRANSPORT OF RNA WITHIN THE EUKARYOTIC CELLS

About 80% of RNA is processed in the nucleus before leaving for the cytoplasm. The other 20% *i.e.* snRNAs and snoRNAs are coated with protein molecules and are then transported from cytoplasm to nucleus for the processing of mRNA, tRNA and rRNAs. Thus RNAs are continuously moved from nucleus to cytoplasm and back to nucleus.

RNA molecules are too large to diffuse through the nuclear pore complexes that is present in the nuclear membrane. So, they have to be transported across the membrane by an energy yielding process, particulary by

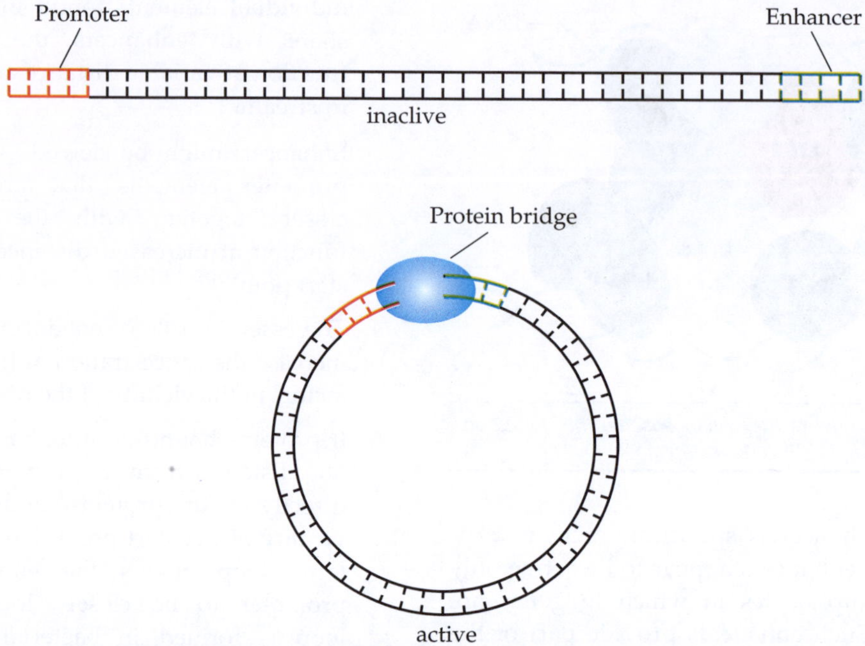


**Fig.18.28 :** *An enhancer functions by bringing proteins into the vicinity of the promoter.*

breaking down of ATP to ADP or GTP to GDP. The energy generation is carried out by a protein called ***Ran*** which requires a receptor protein ***Karyopherins*** (or **exportins** and **importins**) depending upon the direction of their movement. There are at least 20 different karyopherins, Exportin-t has been identified for export of tRNAs in yeast and mammals. Other types of RNA are probably exported by protein-specific karyopherins which recognize the proteins bound to the RNA.

Importin-β has been found to import snRNA from cytoplasm to nucleus.

After completion of splicing, mRNA is transported to the cytoplasm by the action of a protein called ***Yra1p*** in yeast and ***Aly*** in animals.

mRNAs are translated in different places such as on the ribosomes located on the endoplasmic reticulum or in the mitochondria. It is assumed that protein "address tags or signal seuences" are present at the mRNA in order to direct them to their correct destinations in the cytoplasm.

## 18.7 REGULATION OF GENE EXPRESSION AT TRANSLATIONAL LEVEL

### 18.7.1 RNA Editing

A process by which nucleotides not coded by a gene are introduced at specific positions in an RNA molecule after transcription is called *RNA editing*.

Chemical modification of nucleotides of rRNAs and tRNAs affects only their structures, and only catabolic activities, But chemical modification of nucleotides of mRNA has the potential to change the coding properties of the transcript, resulting in an alternation in the amino acid sequence of the protein that is specified. This is known as RNA editing.

The phenomenon of RNA editing was first identified in *Trypanosoma,* the protozoa that causes sleeping sickness. Since that time, how ever, RNA editing has been shown to occur in various organisms and in a variety of ways.

A notable example of RNA editing has been found to occur in human RNA for apolipoprotein B. The gene codes a polypeptide of 4563 amino acids called applipoprotein B 100, which is synthesized in the liver cell. In the intestinal cell, same gene codes another lipoprotein containing only 2153 amino acids and is found to be very similar in their N-terminal amino acids. This is because of the changes in the codon CAA into a termination codon UAA due to a process of deamination of cytosine converting into uracil. Such an RNA editing causes the translation of a trunkated polypeptide. The deamination is carried out by an RNA-binding enzyme along with some auxiliary factors.

In humans, RNA editing is responsible for the generation of antibody diversity and also has been implicated in the control of the HIV-1 infection cycle by changing C→A and C→U.

The enzyme adenosine deaminase acting on RNA (ADAR) selectively edited at a limited number of positions and converts adenosine into inosine. This occurs during the processing of the mRNA for mammalian glutamate receptors.

Extensive deamination by ADAR, is observed in the viral RNA, for example the measles virus which undergoes **hyperediting**. Thus hyperediting has an important role in the etiology of the diease, caused by them.

More complex types of RNA editing may be found.

1. **Pan-editing :** It involves the extensive insertion of nucleotides into RNAs in order to produce functional molecules. It occurs in the mitochondria of Trypanosomes and the editing process involves the participation of a *guide RNA* (gRNA), a short RNA that can base pair to the pre-RNA and can insert one or more U-residues into an RNA or deletion of one or more U-residues. The guide RNA, first with it's 5′ anchor is complementary to the RNA that is to be edited and binds to the target RNA and is cleaved at a defined location by an nuclease. The 3′ end of guide RNA becomes displaced from the target RNA. The enzymes, called the terminal U-transferase then attaches to U-containing nucleotides. For deletions, the enzyme called 3′ -U-exonuclease removes one or more unacils. Finally, RNA ligase rejoins the two pieces of RNA (Fig. 18.29).
2. **Insertional editing :** This insertion is not specified by guide RNAs or by RNA polymerase activity, occurs in some viral RNAs. For example, the paramyxovirus P gene gives rise to at least two different proteins because of the insertion of G nucleotide specific positions in the mRNA.
3. **Polyadenylation editing :** Few mRNAs transcribed from the human mitogenome end with just a U or UA. Polyadenylation converts it into UAA..., a termination codon.

### 18.7.2 Degradation of eukaryotic RNA

The half life of eukaryotic RNA varies from 10–20 min for yeast to several hours for mammals. The mRNA degradation is controlled by several processes.

1. **Exosome–mediated degradation :** The multiprotein complex called exosome degrades transcription in the 3′→5′ direction in yeast and contains nucleases related to the enzymes of the bacterial degradosome. Exosomes are probably also present in mammalian cells and are clearly important but they are not particularly well studied. Their role may be in the monitoring polyadenylation and ensuing that transcripts that are about to leave the nucleus which have an appropriate poly-A tail.
2. **Deadenylation-dependent capping :** The poly A tail of mRNA is recognised by the poly–A–binding protein. This binding enhances the RNA stability.

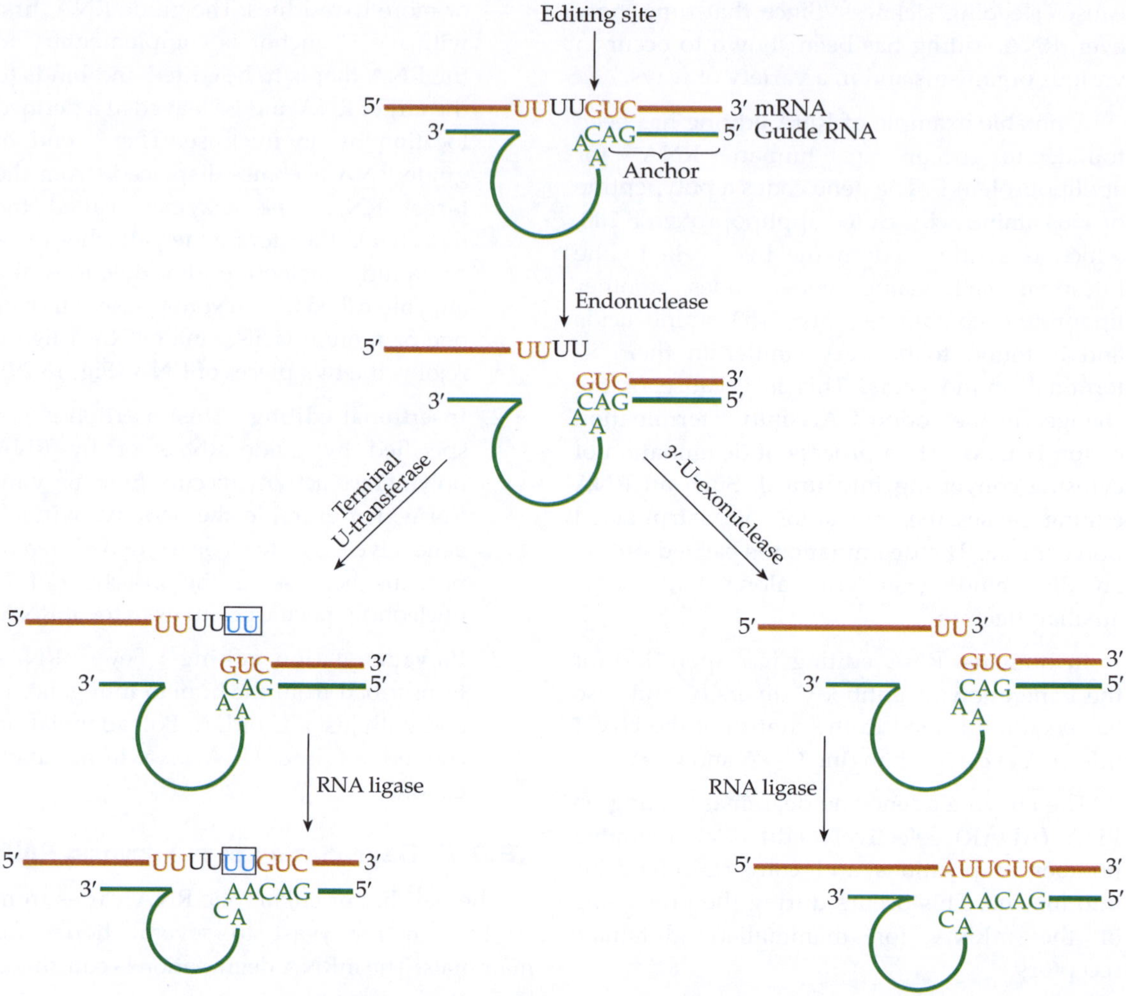


**Fig.18.29 :** *RNA editing in Trypanosomes.*

As an mRNA ages, its polyA tail tends to be shortened by the action of cellular exonucleases. Once it becomes less than 10–30 adenosines in length, the poly-A-binding protein can no longer bind and the mRNA is rapidly degraded by exo-and endonucleases.

Pdy-A tail removal is followed by the cleavage of the 5′ cap by the decapping enzyme **Dcp1p**. Decapping prevents the mRNA from being translated and so ends its functional life, Then mRNA undergoes rapid exonuclease digestion from it's 5′ end.

Degradation is also influenced at least with some yeast mRNAs by sequences called instability elements located within the transcript, which leads to increased degradation of mRNA (Fig. 18.30).

3. **Nonsense-mediated RNA decay (NMD) or mRNA surveillance :** As a result of mutation or incorrect splicing, production of the

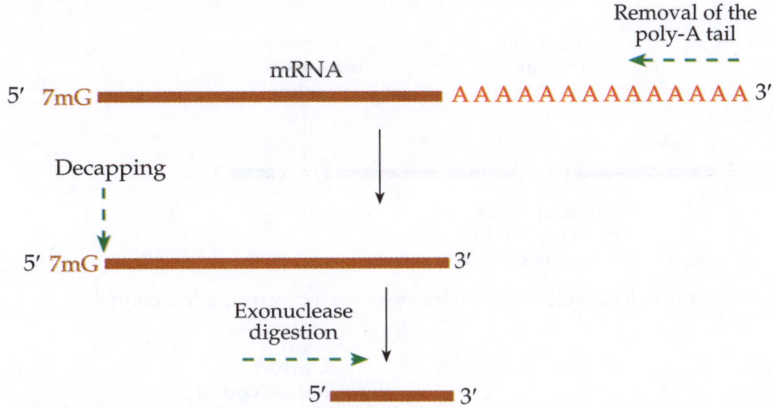


**Fig.18.30 :** *The deadenylation-dependent decapping pathway for degradation of an mRNA.*

termination codon in incorrect position causes the degradation of mRNA. This incorrect codon is thought to be detected by a *surveillance* mechanism that involves a complex protein which scans the mRNA and somehow is able to distinguish between the correct termination codon located at the end of the coding regions of the transcript and one that is in the wrong position.

Current hypotheses are based on the demonstration that the correct termination codon is recognized as aberrant so that the intron-exon boundary is placed down stream of the termination codon. The surveillance enzymes then identified it as incorrect termination codon and induces cap cleavage by 5′→3′ exonuclease degradation without prior removal of poly A tail (Fig. 18.30).

4. **Regulation of translation by antisense RNA** : The antisense RNA, which contains sequences complementary to the region of mRNA containing an initiation codon. It occurs naturally in bacterial cells, hybridization of the complementary antisense RNA to an mRNA blocks recognition of the intiation codon and binding of 30S ribosomal subunit to the Shine-Dalgarno seqauence. Thereby initiation of translation is inhibited.

The strategy of antisense control has been adapted to inhibit gene expression experimentally in eukaryotic cells. By use of genetic engineering, a complementary DNA strand of a gene can be inserted in reverse orientation (3′→5′). This is referred to an antisense gene. The mRNA produced by antisense gene is complementary to the mRNA synthesized by normal gene. As a result, both these mRNAs hybridize and thus the normal translation of mRNA is blocked.

It has been found that certain plant viruses produce dsRNA as part of their life cycle. In addition, these plant viruses may carry genes that are very similar to genes that already exist in the genome of the plant cell. When the virus infects plant cells, they silence the expression of the plant gene by hydridizing with the mRNA.

When the cloned genes are introduced randomly in multiple copies, then expression of the gene has been found to be silenced, because some of the cloned genes are randomly inserted by chance next to a plant gene promoter that is oriented in the opposite direction, both strands of the cloned

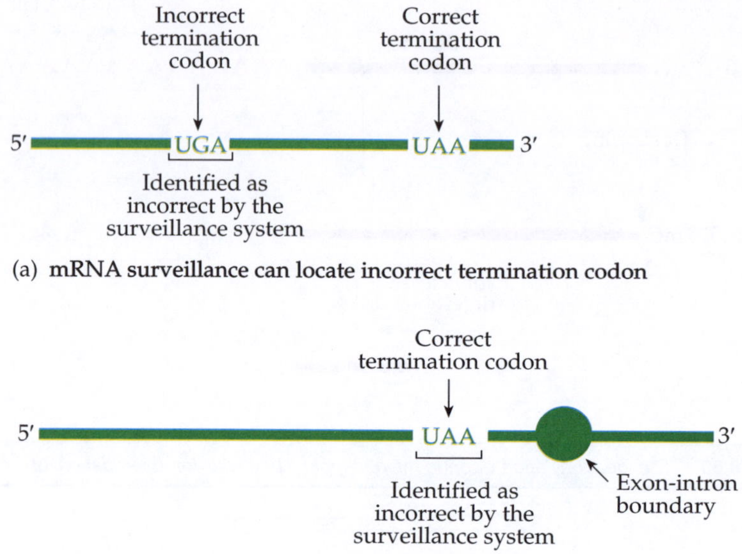


(a) mRNA surveillance can locate incorrect termination codon

(b) The influence of an exon-intron boundary

**Fig.18.31 :** *The mechanism of mRNA surveillance.*

gene would be transcribed, thereby generating a dsRNA. Thus led to the silencing of the gene (Fig. 18.32).

Gene silencing by injecting antisense RNA into oocytes of *C.elegans* proved that the mechanism is not only in plants but also happened in animals.

The surprising discovery came when Andrew Fire and Craig Mello and their colleagues injected dsRNA into oocytes, shockingly, the dsRNA was 10 times more potent in inhibiting the expression of the corresponding mRNA compared to the injection of anti-sense RNA. They coined the term RNA interference (RNAi) to describe the phenomenon. This sensational discovery led them Nobel Prize in Physiology and medicine in the year 2006.

**Mechanism :**

a) The dsRNA is first recognised by binding proteins that form an attachment site for an ATP dependent ribonuclease (endonuclease), called **dicer**, which cleaves the dsRNA molecules into short interferring RNAs (siRNAs) of 21-28 nucleotides in length.

b) These short RNAs then associate with cellular proteins to become part of a complex called the *RNA-induced silencing complex* (**RISC**).

c) The short RNA strands that were part of the antisense strand will specifically bind to mRNAs that are complementary to its sequence. Therefore, the short antisense RNA directs **RISC** to specific mRNA in the cell.

d) After the **RISC** binds to an mRNA, endonucleases within the complex cut the RNA and inactivate it. In this way the expression of the gene that encodes this mRNA is silenced (Fig. 18.33).

The **RNAi** mechanism is found widely in eukariyotic species and it is believed to offer a host defensive mechanism against certain

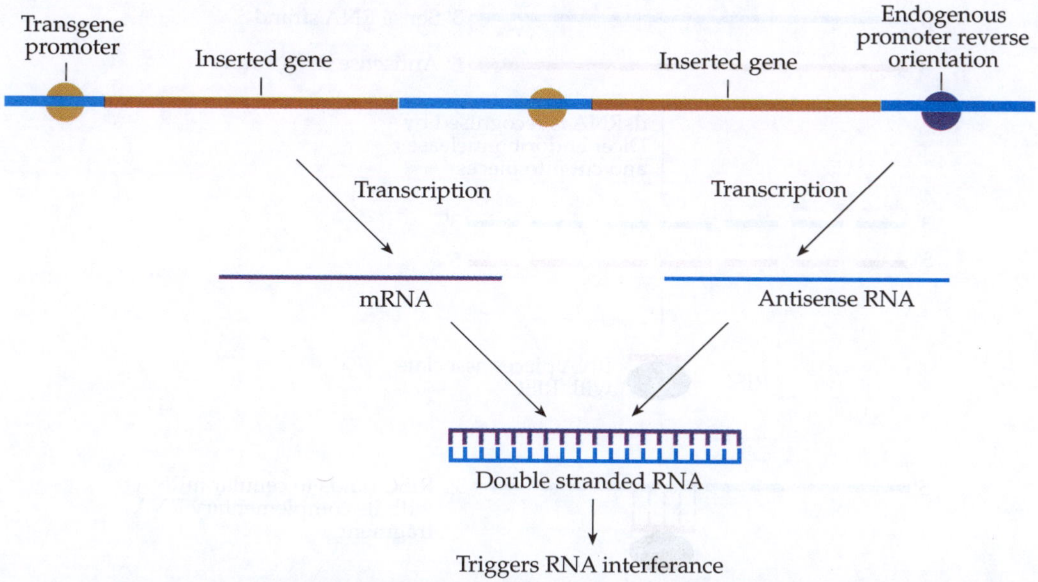


**Fig.18.32 :** *RNA interference explains how transgenes are sometimes become inactive.*

viruses and can inhibit the proliferation of viruses that have dsRNA genome or produce dsRNA as a part of their life cycle. This mechanism would help to produce antisense RNA drugs against HIV and certain cancer causing viruses.

RNAi may also play a role in the silencing of certain transposable elements. Certain transposable elements produce dsRNA intermediates as part of the transposition process. RNAi may inhibit their ability to move. Silencing of genes within transposable elements via RNAi protects the organism against the potentially harmful effects of the transposition process.

If a synthetic oligonucleotide (DNA or RNA) is introduced into the cytoplasm, that is complementary to the mRNA, it will form a duplex with the mRNA at the complementary site and will block its translation. Since the sequence of oligonucleotide is complementary to that of the mRNA, it is called **antisense oligonucleotide**. If the antisense molecule thus introduced is a DNA, the RNA part of the DNA-RNA hybrid will then be degraded by RNAase H that specifically acts on the RNA-DNA duplex. On the other hand, if the antisense molecule is RNA, the dsRNA will degrade by the mechanism as described earlier.

Synthetic oligonucleotides are charged molecules and are not easily absorbed by the cells and are rapidly degraded. Therefore, these are chemically modified as phosphorothioate derivatives to enhance their stability. Initially a number of antisense drugs against cancer, viral and respiratory diseases were developed. But later it has shown certain non-specific effects of antisense oligonucleotides (such as boosting of the immune respone). Now one antisense drug named **vitravene** for treating cytomegalo-virus–induced retinitis has been successfully marketed. It has low toxicity low cost and easy to design. It is likely that in near future a number of effective antisense drugs treating cancer, immune disorder, viral infection etc. will be available in the market.

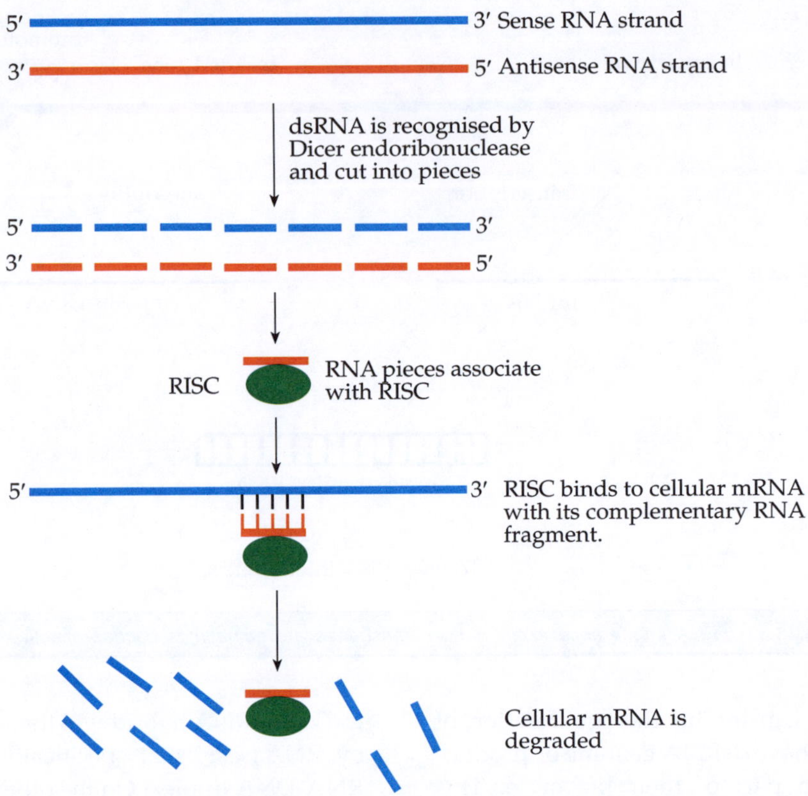


**Fig.18.33 :** *Mechanism of RNA interference.*

5. **Regulation of gene expression by micro RNAs :** More than one type of **Dicer** protein has been identified in many organisms. For example, in *Drosophila melanogaster* and *Arabidopsis thaliana*, two and four such Dicers have been recognized respectively.

   These dicers differ slightly and therefore it has been assumed that there are alternative RNA degradation proceses, by synthesizing microRNAs (miRNAs). The mechanism is as follows :

   a) The microRNAs are synthesized by RNA polymerase II by the fruit fly genome and is initially as precursor molecules called **foldback RNAs**. The RNAs can form a series of intrastrand base pairs forming one or more internal hairpin structures.

   b) Within the nucleus, these foldback RNAs are cut into individual hairpins by the enzyme **Drosha**. These are then transported to the cytosol.

   c) The dsRNA then stimulates the RNA interference pathway with the second Dicer proteins in *Drosophila* and cuts into smaller pieces of RNAs approximately of 21 nucleotides length.

   d) These miRNAs are complementary to part of the cellular mRNA and therefore they base pairs with the target mRNA.

   e) These miRNA then assembled with the protein to form microribonucleoprotein (miRNP) which is identical to the RISC. This leads to the degradation of mRNA (Fig. 18.34).

The main feature of this pathway is that cleavage by miRNP does not disrupt the coding region of the mRNA, it leads to the

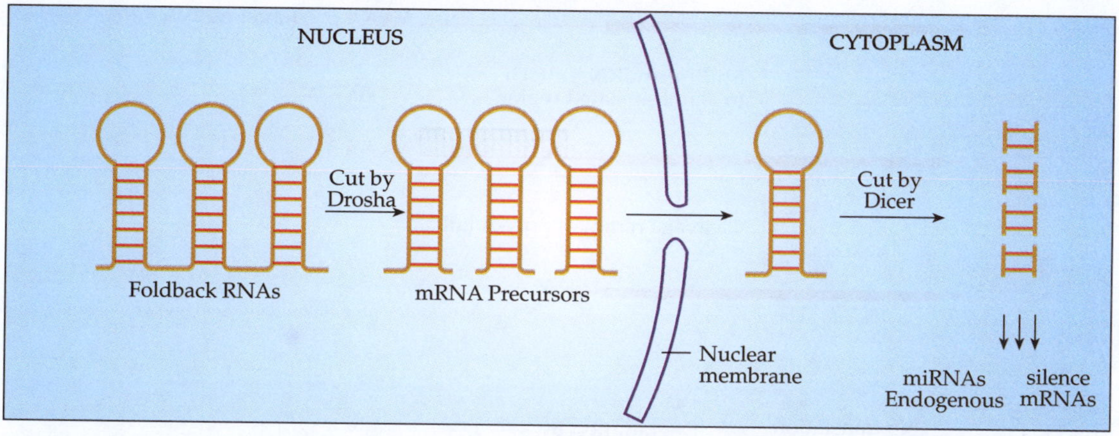


Fig.18.34 : *The microRNA interference pathway.*

detachment of the poly A tail. Thus it might interfere with the process of translation initiation, which insolves poly A tail or target mRNA degradation by deadenylation– dependent decapping pathway. Thus leads to the silencing of gene expression (Fig. 18.35).

In (*C. elegans,* two genes *lin-4* an *let-7* have been found to code fold back RNAs. It is very important to note that it not only degrades the unwanted mRNAs, but it also regulates the normal regulation of gene expression and is involved in selveral biological events such as apoptosis, specification of neuron cell types and control of fat storage. Thus it seems that gene expression at translational level is also controlled by miRNA for normal growth process of the eukaryotic bodies.

### 18.7.3 Regulation of translation by Ribosomal Initiation Factors

In eukaryotes two translation initiation factors, eIF2 and eIF4F appear to play a central role in controlling the initiation of translation. The functions of these two factors are modulated by phosphorylation in opposite ways. When the α–subunit of eIF2 ie eIF2α is phosphorylated, then translation is inhibited, on the other hand phosphorylation of eIF4F increases the rate of translation.

A variety of conditions such as viral infection, nutrient deprivation, heat shock and presence of toxic heavy metals can lead to the shutdown the synthesis of proteins in a specific way.

1. These conditions promote the activation of a protein kinase, eIF2α protein kinase first. A number of eIF2α protein kinases have been identified.
2. Once activated, this protein kinase phosphorylates the α–subunit of eIF2 ie eIF2α.
3. Phosphorylation of eIF2α causes it to bind tightly to another initiation factor, eIF2B.
4. This functional eIF2B is necessary so that eIF2 can promote binding of the initiator $tRNA^{met}$ to the 40S subunit of ribosome. But when phosphorylated eIF2α binds to eIF2B, then it prevents eIF2B from functioning and then the initiator $tRNA^{met}$ does not able to bind to 40S subunit of ribosome. Thus the protein systhesis is controlled.

Another translation initiation factor called eIF4F molulates the binding of mRNA to the ribosomal initiation complex.

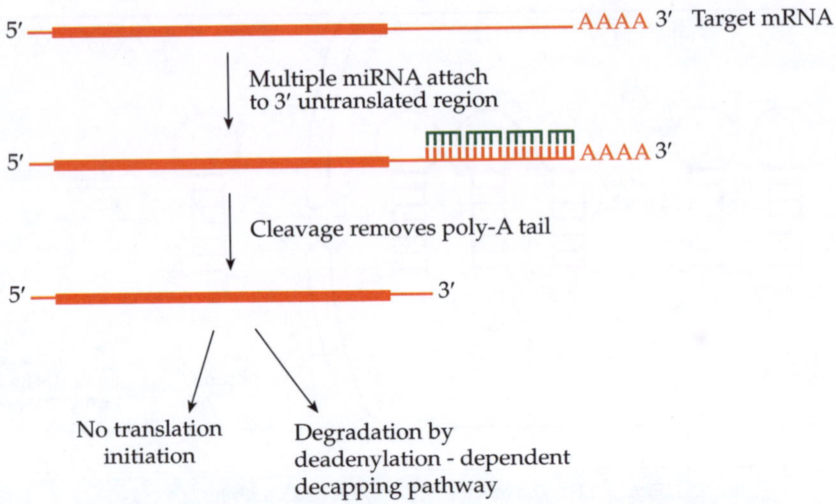


**Fig.18.35 :** *Micro RNA target sites are showing in the 3′* untranslated region of the target mRNA.

Viral infection, heat shock etc conditions decrease the level of phosphorylation of eIF4F and thereby inhibit translation. On the contrary a variety of conditions such as presence of growth factors, insulin etc. have been found to cause phosphorylation and promote the synthesis of proteins (Fig. 18.36).

### 18.7.4 Sumoylation and Gene expression

SUMO is a polypeptide of 101 amino acid residues. Sumoylation is the addition of one or more copies of this polypeptide (sumo) to the *lysine* residues on the (activator) protein. The process is similar to ubiquitination but instead of being destroyed, sumoylated activators appear to be targeted to a specific nuclear compartment that keeps them stable but unstable to reach their target genes.

For example, the activator for promyelocytic leukemia, PML is normally sumoylated and sequestered in the nuclear bodies PML oncogenic domains (PODs), with no signs of leukemic state. But, in leukemic state, PODs are disrupted and PML is released as transcription factor and reaches to and activates target genes to become leukemic.

## 18.8 TRYPANOSOMES CHANGE SURFACE PROTEINS TO ELUDE IMMUNE SYSTEM

Sleeping sickness in Africa, and the rare. Chagas' disease of South America, are both caused by **trypanosomes**. These are flagellates, swim around the blood. Tsetse fly is its carrier. While growing and multiplying in the gut of the insect, the trypanosomes are covered with a protein, called "**Procyclin**" which protects them from the digestion by insect. While waiting in the saliva for infection to human host, they cover their surface layer by **variant surface glycoprotein** (VSG) which is designed to protect from the hosts immune system.

VSG protein is a dimer has two domains, the conserved region anchors the protein in the membrane which does not change. The second domain is variable region extends to the outside of the membrane which undergoes changes to avoid the immune system (Fig. 18.37).

After entering into the human body, trypanosomes grow and divide until the immune sytem kills most of them. A few of the trypanosomes switch their VSG shape and escape recognition by the immune sytem. They multiply and 2nd wave of the parasite is

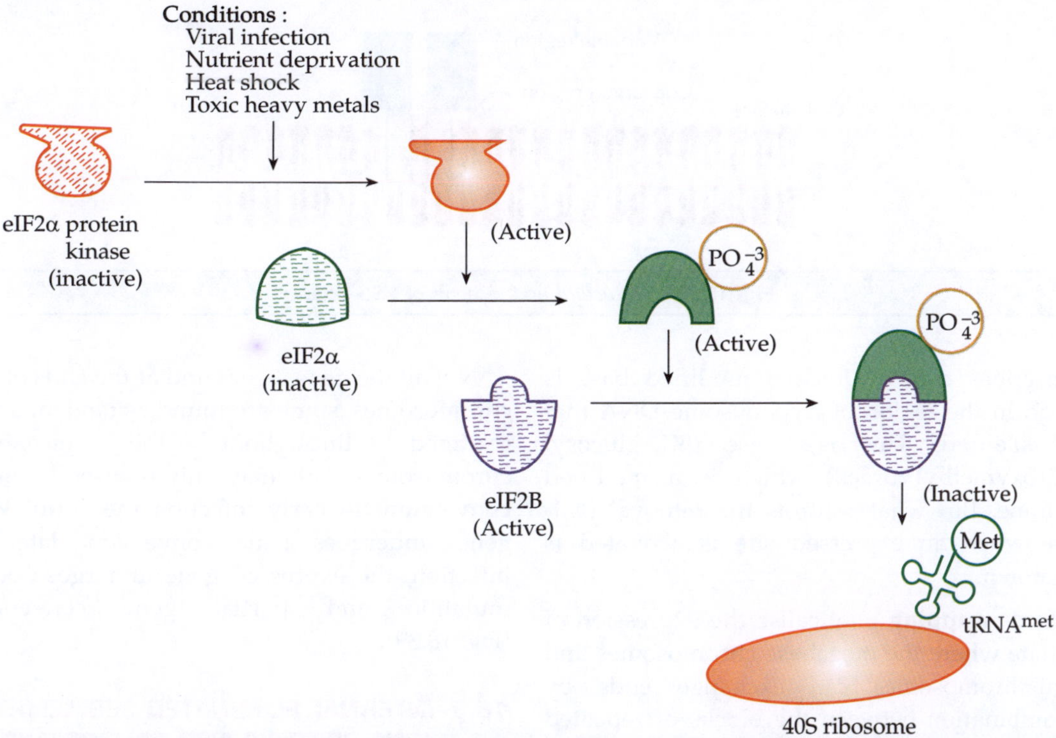


**Fig.18.36** : *The pathway that leads to the phosphorylation of eIF2α and inhibition of translation.*

observed in the patient body. Eventually, the immue system learns about the new surface protein and kills off most of the parasites. But some of them again switched their another VSG type again. In this way they continuously elude the host's immune sytem and spread further inside the human victim. The immune system never catches up with the constantly changing VSG, thus it results to the death of the victim.

Both nuclear and mitochondrial genomes of trypanosomes are divided up in a peculiar manner. Besides, there is also *trans*-splicing of many genes at RNA level as well as **RNA** editing.

The mito-genome comprises 50 copies of large circular DNA and 10000 copies of minicircles (encode **guide RNA** for RNA editing).

Nuclear genome is divided into 11 large "normal" or "megabase" chromosomes and also 100 minichromosomes. The minichromosomes have one silent copy of VSG gene located close to the two ends of the chromosome. The VSG genes are found at the ends to the megabase chromosome. It possesses over 1000 slightly different copies of the gene for the variant surface glycoprotein. Among 1000 *VSG* genes, there are only about 200 that can actually be expressed. These genes have special expression sites located just inside the telomeres. **Only one expression site is acitve at any given time and the others are in standby mode. The trypanosome switches from one expression site to another, which results in a different VSG being expressed.**

There are three mechanisms for VSG-switching *viz.* expression site activation, chromosome end-swapping and gene conversion.

The expression site promoters are unusual, recognised by RNA pol-I which normally

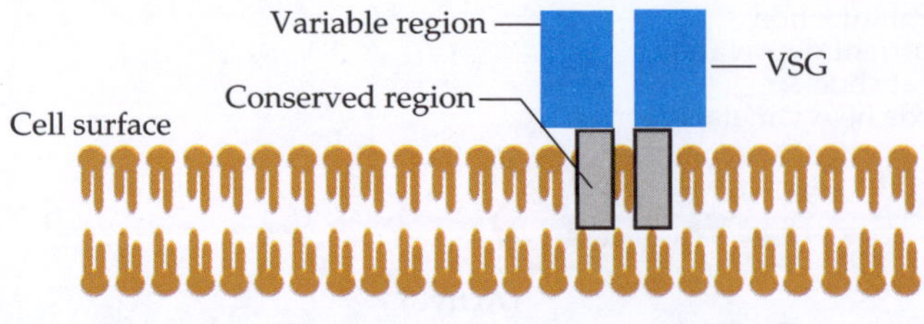


Fig. 18.37 : *Structure and location of VSG protein*

transcribes rRNA. Unusual modified base is found in the region of trypanosome DNA that are silenced. This is J-base (β-D-glucosyl hydroxymethyl uracil) which is a modified thymine. But what controls the removal of J-base when an expressed site is activated is unknown.

**End-swapping** may cause the expression of the site where the megabase chromosomes and mini-chromosomes can exchange ends by recombination between the blocks of repeated sequences just to the inside of the *VSG* genes. This may allow 200 alternative *VSG* genes to be exchanged into the telomeric expression sites of the megabase chromosomes (Fig. 18.38).

Not all the genes are found at the ends of the chromosomes, some are found as tandem array scattered throughout the megabase chromosomes. This may only be used by **gene conversion**. In early infection the entire *VSG* gene undergoes gene conversion. later in infection, the expressed gene undergoes point mutation and partial gene conversion (Fig. 18.39).

## 18.9 INTERNAL ELIMINATED SEGMENTS (DNA SPLICING AND ROLE OF TWO NUCLEI IN *PARAMOECIUM*)

Ciliates contain two types of nuclei, a micronucleus and a macronucleus within the

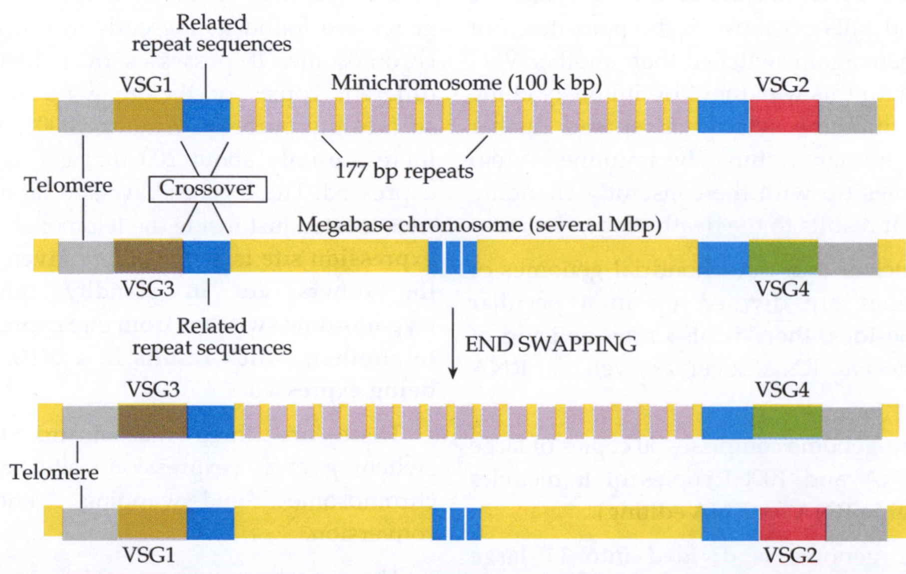


Fig. 18.38 : *VSG genes are transferred between Mini- and Megabase chromosomes.*

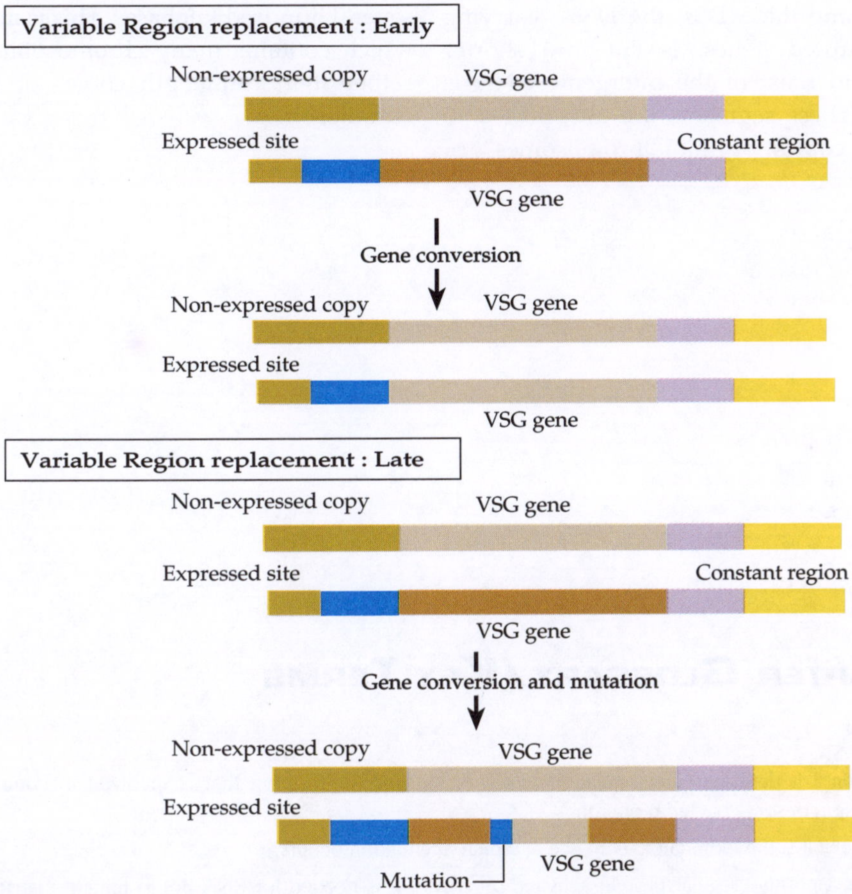


**Fig. 18.39 :** *Variation of VSG by Gene Conversion.*

same cell. Numer of macronucleus is single while micronucleus may be one, two or more in *Paramoecium*. Micronucleus is diploid and is regarded as the germline nucleus, used for the sexual exchange of DNA. The genes of micronucleus are silent and not expressed. But the genes of macronucleus are transcribed to mRNA the component of macronucleus is polyploid. It contains about 50-1000 copies of the genome. During conjugation micronucleus undergoes meiosis and they exchange haploid micronucleus and fuse to give diploid micronucleus. It divides and one of them is converted to new macronucleus after DNA processing.

The DNA of micronucleus contains many extrasequences that interrupt the germline genes, which are known as **internal eliminated segments** (IESs). These are about 5-900 bp in length and very A-T rich. After removal of IES, the remaining segments are called **macronucleus-destined segments** (MDCs) are spliced to form uninterrupted genes, that can be expressed. Each IES is flanked by a repeats of 2–4 bp that lie within the MDS sequence on either side. After splicing, the IES and one of the two repeats are removed. **IES sequences are not introns because they are removed from DNA, not from RNA.**

After joining the MDSs, the DNA, carrying the reconstituted genes, is cut into shorter segments and most of the intergenic DNA is eliminated. These segments are durplicated to give many copies of mini-chromosomes" of several hundred kilobases. This is macronucleus which contains many chromosomal fragments rather than full-length copies of the original chromosomes.

## Chapter Glossary/Key Terms

**Attenuation :** It describes the regulation of termination of transcripton that is involved in controlling the expression of some bacterial operon.

**Atternuator :** It is the terminator sequence at which attenuation occurs.

**CAP :** It is a positive regular protein activaed by cAMP. It is needed for RNA pol to initiate ftranscription of certain (catabolic – sensitive) operons of *E. coli.*

***Cis*-acting locus :** It affects the activity only of DNA sequences on its own molecule of DNA, this property usually implies that the locus does not code for protein .

***Cis*-acting protein :** It has the exceptional property of acting only on the molecule of DNA from which it was expressed.

**Co-activator :** A protein that works in conjunction with an activator to stabilize construction of the RNA polymerase-II transcription initiation complex.

**Co-repressor :** It is a small molecule that triggers reprssion of transcription by binding to a regulator protein.

**Constitutive gene expression :** Constant, seemingly unregulated expression of gene.

**DNA binding motif :** The part of a DNA -binding protein that makes contact with the double helix.

**DNA binding protein :** A protein that attaches to a DNA molecule.

**Enhanceosome :** A stucture formed by DNA bending that comprises a collection of proteins involved in activaton of the RNA polymerase-II transcription initiation complex.

**Enhancer element :** This is a *cis*-acting sequence that increases the utilization of (some) eukaryotic promoters and confunction in either orientation and in any location (upstream or down stream) relative to the promoter.

**F-plasmid :** A fertility plasmid directs conjugal transfer of DNA between bacteria.

*Contd.*

**Homeobox :** The conserved sequence that is part of the coding region of *D. melanogaster* homeotic genes. It is also found in amphibian and mammalian genes expressed in embryonic development.

**Homeodomain :** A DNA binding motif found in many protein involved in developmental regulation of gene expresion.

**Homeotic gene :** Mutations that convert one body part into another, for example, an insect leg may replace an antenna.

**Housekeeping genes :** Those genes are expressed at more or less constant levels in all the cells of the organisms.

**HRE :** The nucleotide sequence upsteam of a gene that mediates the regulatory effect of a steroid hormone.

**Inducer :** The molecule that triggers gene transcription by binding to a regulator protein.

**Inducible substances :** The amount of gene products are increased considerably in presence of these substances.

**Induction :** Switching on transcription as a result of interaction of the inducer with the regulator protein.

**Intrinsic terminator :** A position in bacteial DNA where termination of trnascription occurs without the involement of Rho.

**IES :** Internal eliminated segments, which are not introns, removed from DNA by splicing not from RNA. These sequences are found in the nucleus of *Paramoecium.*

**Operator :** The site on DNA at which a repressor protein binds to prevent transcription from initiating at the adjacent promoter.

**Operon :** A unit of bacterial gene expression and regulation, including structural genes and control elements in DNA recognised by regulator gene products.

**Promoter :** This is a region of DNA involved in binding of RNA pol to initiate trnascription.

**Repression :** Inhibition of transcription by binding of repressor proteins to a specific site on DNA or mRNA.

**Repressor protein :** It binds to operator on DNA or RNA to prevent transcription or translation.

**Response module :** A sequence molif found upstream of various genes that enables transcription initiation by RNA polymerase-II to respond to general signals from outside of the cell.

**Silencer :** A regulatory sequence that reduces the rate of transcription of a gene or genes located some distance away in either direction.

***Trans*-acting :** Any gene product that is free to diffuse to find its target.

***Trans*-acting product :** It is a protein product or may be RNA whch diffuses away form its site of synthesis to act elsewhere.

**URF :** This is an open (unidenlified) reading frame presumed to code for protein but for which no product has been found.

**VSG :** Variant surface glycorprotein whcih covers the surface layer of the protozoa, *Trypanosoma,* which undergoes changes to avoid body's immune systems.

**Zinc finger protein :** The repeated motif of amino acids with chracteristic spacing of cysteins that may be involved in binding zinc, is characteristic of some proteins that bind DNA and/or RNA.

# Exercise

**A. Long answer type questions :**

1. Describe the six potential regulatory points for proteins synthesis.
2. What do you mean by regulatorty DNA-binding proteins? Describe the structure and functions of such regulatory DNA-binding proteins.
3. Write a note on operon concept.
4. What are the constituents of *lac*-operon? Describe the negative and positive control mechanism of *lac*-operon. Write down the role of inducer in *lac* operaon.
5. Briefly describe the genetics of *lac* operon.
6. What are the constituents of *ara*-operon?
7. What are the constituents of *trp*-operon?
8. How eukaryotic gene expression is regulated.
9. What do you mean by differential gene expression? Briefly describe the mechanism.
10. Briefly describe the mechanism of regulation of eukaryotic promoters.
11. Describe the remodeling of chromatin structure during gene activation.
12. Briefly describe the inhibition of gene expression by gene repressors.
13. What are coactivators, repressors and enhancers. How they regulate the expression of genes.
14. Describe different RNA editing mechanisms.
15. Describe different eukaryotic RNA degradation mechanisms.
16. What is antisense RNA? Describe the mechanism by which it regulates eukaryotic translation.
17. Describe the mechanism of regulation of translation by ribosomal initiation factors.
18. Describe the role and importance of RNAi.
19. Describe the composition of *gal* operon in *E. coli*.
20. Describe the mechanism of regulation of *gal* operon in *E. coli*.
21. What is sumoylation? How it regulates gene expression?
22. How trypanosomes elude immune system of the body?
23. Describe the role of micro and macro nuclei.

**B. Short answer type questions :**

1. Define house keeping genes.
2. What do you mean by constitutive gene expression?
3. What do you mean by inducible substance, induction, repressible substance and repression?
4. What are the six points at which the protein synthesis is regulated?
5. What types of protein regulate transcription initiation?
6. What do you mean by regulatory proteins? What is their role?
7. What is homeotic selector gene?
8. What is homeodomain?
9. What is homeobox?
10. What is zinc finger motif? What is its role?
11. What is leucine zipper, How it regulates gene expression?
12. What is HLH? What is its role in gene expression?
13. What is an operon?
14. What do you mean by *trans* acting and *cis* acting?
15. What are the contituents of *lac* operon?
16. How does lactose control the *lac* gene expression?
17. What is the genotype of *lac*- wild type bacteria?

18. What is the role of repressor protein in *lac* gene expression.
19. What is *lac* $I^d$? How does such mutation affect on the *lac*-gene expression?
20. What is lac $O^c$? How such mutation affects on the *lac* gene expression?
21. What are $F^-$ and $F^+$ plasmid?
22. How does *lac* $I^-$ gene mutation affect on *lac* gene expression?
23. What is IPTG? How it affects lac gene expression in lac I and lac $O^c$ mutants?
24. What are the two modes regarding the role of inducer in *lac* gene expression.
25. What is catabolic repression?
26. What is CAP?
27. How does CAP–DNA interaction occur?
28. Waht is regulon?
29. What is the effect of glucose on CAP and cAMP?
30. What is the effect of lactose on CAP and cAMP?
31. What are the components of *ara*-operon?
32. What are the components of *trp*-operon?
33. What is transcription attenuation?
34. What types of attenuation take place in the *trp* operon expression?
35. What is intrinsic termination?
36. What is the role of leader region.
37. What do you mean by general transcription factor?
38. What is response element?
39. What is the difference between promoter and enhancer?
40. What do you mean by differential gene expression.
41. What do you mean by positively regulated eukaryotic promoters?
42. What is upstream activator elements?
43. What are chromatin remodeling proteins?
44. What are the roles of acetylation process in chromatin remodeling?
45. What are the ways that the repressor proteins can operate?
46. What are coactivators?
47. What are co-repressors?
48. What is enhanceosome?
49. What is RNA editing?
50. What is pan-editing?
51. What is mRNA surveillance?
52. What is interference RNA?
53. Waht is antisense RNA?
54. What is antisense oligonuleotide?
55. What do you mean by microRNAs.
56. What are the components of *gal* operon?
57. What are the functions of three *gal* genes?
58. What are the *gal* promoters?
59. What are the *gal* operators?
60. What are *gal* repressor?
61. What are the functions of Gal R and Gal S.
62. Why *gal* operon is termed as catabolite repressible operon?
63. What is Sumo?
64. What do you mean by sumoylation?
65. How sumoylation is related to leukemia?
66. What is procyclin?
67. What is VSG?
68. What is the mechanism to change VSG?
69. What is end swapping?
70. What is IES?
71. What is MDC?
72. Why IES is not an intron?
73. What is composition of macronucleus?

## C. Problems on gene Expression :

### Problem 1

In a hypothetical *E. coli* operon the regulator gene is closely linked to a region containing two structural genes and an operator. In the table, regulator, operator and structural genes are listed in correct sequence. Which of these genes is the regulator, the operator and the structural gene? Explain the reasons for your selection. S= enzyme synthesized in normal quantities; s = Little or no synthesis.

**TABLE : Phenotype**

| Genotype | Inducer absent | Inducer present |
|---|---|---|
| $a^-b^+c^+$ | S | S |
| $a^+b^+c^-$ | S | S |
| $a^+b^-c^-$ | s | s |
| $a^+b^-c^+/a^-b^+c^-$ | S | S |
| $a^+b^+c^+/a^-b^-c^-$ | s | S |
| $a^+b^+c^-/a^-b^-c^+$ | s | S |
| $a^-b^+c^+/a^+b^-c^-$ | s | s |

### Problem 2

$I^s$ (super repressor), $I^+$ (inducible) and $I^-$ (constitutive) repressor genes; $O^C$ (constitutive, *cis* dominant) and $O^+$ (inducible, *cis* dominant) operators; $Z^+$ and $Z^-$ are structural genes.

(a) Which of the following genotypes will produce b-galactosidase and permease if lactose is present and lactose is absent

(i) $I^- O^C Z^+ Y^+$

(ii) $I^s O^C Z^+ Y^+$

(iii) $I^- O^+ Z^+ Y^+$

(b) For each of the following partial diploids indicate whether enzyme formation is constitutive or inducible.

(i) $I^+ O^+ Z^+ Y^+/I^+ O^C Z^+ Y^+$

(ii) $I^+ O^C Z^+ Y^+/I^+ O^C Z^+ Y^+$

(iii) $I^- O^+ Z^+ Y^+/I^- O^+ Z^+ Y^+$

### Problem 3

In a series of experiments the following results are obtained.

$Z_1^-$, $Z_2^-$, $Z_3^-$ are three different mutant alleles of Z gene.

(a) Complete the table for expt. 5 to 10 and write the expected missing numbers.

(b) Compare expt. 1 and 4. Why do the values for induced β-galactosidase differ?

(c) Compare expt. 5 and 8 with expt. 1. Can you think of any explanation for the low values obtained in expt. 5 and 8 in the induced state?

(d) How could you prove that lactose is not the real inducer of *lac* operon?

| Expt. : | Genotype | observed β-galactosidase activity | | Expected β-galactosidase activity | |
|---|---|---|---|---|---|
| | | Induced | Uninduced | Induced | Uninduced |
| 1. | $I^+ O^+ Z^+$ | 100 | 0.1 | 100 | 0.1 |
| 2. | $I^- O^C Z^+$ | 100 | 100 | 100 | 100 |
| 3. | $I^- O^C Z_1^-$ | 0.1 | 0.1 | 0.1 | 0.1 |
| 4. | $I^-O^+Z^+/I^+O^+Z^+$ | 200 | 0.1 | 200 | 0.1 |
| 5. | $I^-O^cZ_1^-/I^+O^+Z^+$ | 10 | 0.1 | | |
| 6. | $I^+O^cZ_1^-/I^-O^+Z^+$ | 10 | 0.1 | | |
| 7. | $I^-O^+Z_1^-/I^+O^cZ^+$ | 10 | 100 | | |
| 8. | $I^+O^cZ^+/I^-O^-Z_1^-$ | 10 | 100 | | |
| 9. | $I^-O^+Z_2^-/I^+O^cZ_3^-$ | 40 | 0.1 | | |
| 10. | $I^-O^+Z_3^-/I^+O^cZ_2^-$ | 40 | 0.1 | | |

19

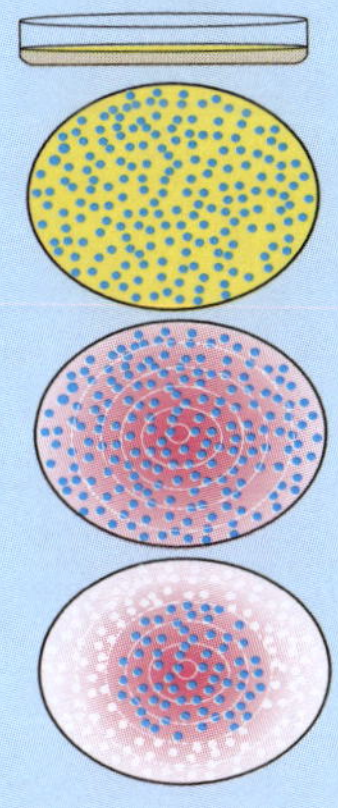

# Mutation and Repair of Genome

**CHAPTER AGENDA**

**19.1** Mutation : Concept; **19.2** Mutation : Types; **19.3** Biochemical mutations in man; **19.4** Mutagens and Mutagenesis; **19.5** Reverse genetics; **19.6** Site-directed mutagenesis; **19.7** Detection of mutation; **19.8** Reversions; **19.9** Repair of DNA; Chapter Glossary/Key Terms; Exercise

## 19.1. MUTATION : CONCEPT

In DNA molecules, genetic information is stored in the form of genetic code and sequence of amino acids in the protein is determined by base sequences in one strand of a DNA.

Genetic code consists of three bases known as triplet. The process of DNA replication is very accurate but mistakes may occur during replication. The chance of error during replication can be increased considerably if DNA has been damaged before replication due to exposure to environmental agents, which may be physical or chemical. The environmental agents that cause damages to living cells are categorized as follows:

1. **Carcinogens:** Cause cancer, the neoplastic transformation of eukaryotic cells.
2. **Clastogens :** Cause fragmentation of chromosomes.
3. **Mutagens :** Cause mutations.
4. **Oncogens :** Induce tumor and cancer formation.
5. **Teratogens :** Result in developmental abnormalities.

## 19.2. MUTATION : TYPES

The term **Mutation** was first used by **Hugo de Vries** to describe the heritable phenotypic changes of *Oenothera lamarckiana*.

The term **mutation** is defined *to all hereditary changes in the genome excluding those resulting from incorporation of genetic material from other organisms*.

Diploid organisms carry two copies (alleles) of each gene. Recessive mutation leads to a loss of function of wild gene, which is masked if a normal copy of the gene is present. For the mutant phenotype to occur, both alleles must carry the mutation. Dominant mutation leads to a mutant phenotype even in the presence of a normal copy of the gene. The phenotypes associated with dominant mutations may represent either a loss or a gain of function.

A mutation involving a change in a single base pair often called a **point mutation** or a deletion of a few base pairs generally affects the function of a single gene.

The second major type of mutation involves large-scale changes in chromosome structure and can affect the functioning of numerous genes resulting in major phenotypic consequences. Such **chromosomal mutations** (or abnormalities) can involve deletion or insertion of several contiguous genes, inversions of genes on a chromosome or the exchange of large segments of DNA between non-homologous chromosomes.

### ☆ Gene Mutation or Point Mutation

Point mutation involves alteration in a single base pair and small deletions which generally directly affect the function of only one gene.

Point mutations are of two main types viz, base pair substitutions and frame–shift mutations.

**A. Base Pair Substitutions**

Base pair substitutions result in the incorporation of wrong bases during replication or repair of replication.

The base pair substitution may result in different types of mutations (Fig. 19.1).

A **mis-sense mutation** results in the replacement of one amino acid in a polypeptide chain. For example, if the sense strand is changed from 3′ AAA 5′ to 3′ AAT 5′. The codon of mRNA may be changed from UUU (codes for phenylalanine) to UUA (codes for leucine).

If a single base substitution modifies a codon to a termination codon the chain may be terminated at the point of mutation. For example, If the codon of a sense strand of a gene is changed from 3′ ACC 5′ to 3′ ATC 5′, the codon for the mRNA is changed from 5′ UGG 3′ to a nonsense codon 5′ UAG 3′. Then the synthesis of polypeptide is terminated prematurely. Such mutations are called **nonsense mutations**.

ds DNA
Coding strand : 5′T T T C G A T G G A T A..........3′
Sense strand : 3′A A A G C T A C C T A T..........5′

mRNA : 5′U U U C G A U G G A U A..........3′

Amino acid sequence : N - *Phe* - *Arg* - *Trp* - *Ile* - C

**Missence Mutation :**

Coding strand : 5′T T A C G A T G G A T A.........3′
Sense strand : 3′A A T G C T A C C T A T..........3′

mRNA : 5′U U A C G A U G G A U A..........3′

Amino acid sequence : N - *Leu* - *Arg* - *Trp* - *Ile* - C

**Non-sense mutation :**

Coding strand : 5′T T T C G A T A G A T A.........3′
Sense strand : 3′A A A G C T A T C T A T.........5′

mRNA : 5′U U U C G A U A G A U A..........3′

Amino acid sequence : N - *Phe* - *Arg* - Stop

**Fig.19.1 :** *Different types of base pair substitutions.*

Sometimes a mutation can convert a termination codon to a sense codon. For example, the α-chain of hemoglobin is normally 141 amino acid residues long. A mutation U to C converts the termination codon into a sense codon i.e., UAA to CAA and thus the chain synthesis proceeds beyond the normal termination point producing a long polypeptide until and unless it reaches to a termination codon and thus 172 amino acids containing polypeptide is synthesized.

Base pair substitution may occur by different ways

1. **Transition :** If a purine base is replaced by another purine or a pyrimidine by another pyrimidine, the substitution is called transition *i.e.,*

$$A \rightleftharpoons G \text{ and } T \rightleftharpoons C$$

Therefore, each base pair can undergo one kind of transition.

The transitional substitution mutations may occur due to tautomerization.

In a DNA molecule, normally the purine, adenine is linked to the pyrimidine, thymine by two hydrogen bonds while

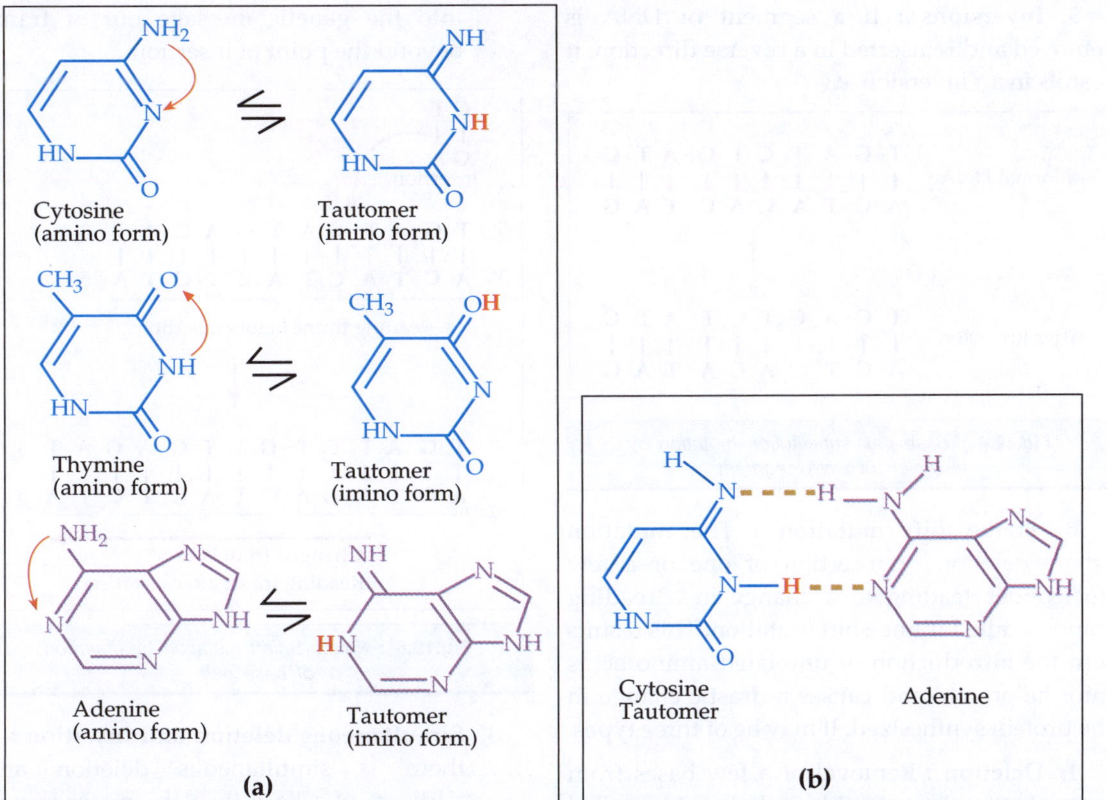


**Fig.19.2 :** *(a) Tautomers of Cytosine, Thymine and Aden ine, (b) Base pairing of Adenine with cytosine tautomer*

guanine is linked to cytosine by three hydrogen bonds. Each DNA base may have some altered uncommon molecular configuration. Some uncommon forms of DNA bases are generated by single proton shift are called rare states or **tautomers**. The –$NH_2$ form of a adenine is changed to =NH (imino). Similarly a **tautomeric shift** may occur in thymine changing form =CO form to the rare –COH enol form. Thus adenine can form a bond with cytosine or thymine with guanine.

2. **Transversions** : If a purine base is substituted by a pyrimidine or vice versa the substitution is called transversion.

   Adenine is replaced by thymine and cytosine is replaced by adenine or guanine. So, each base pair can undergo two kinds of transversions.

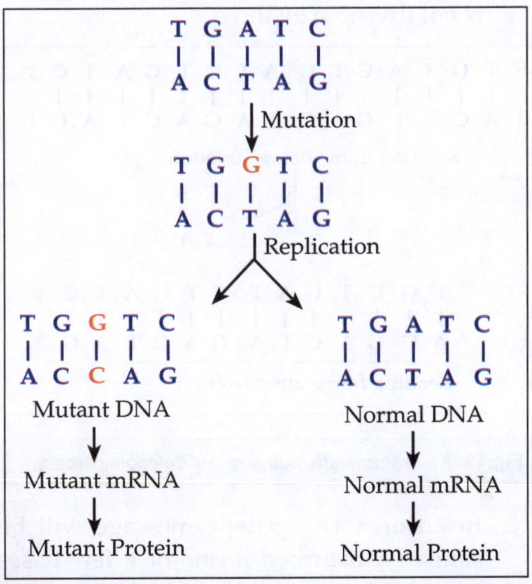


**Fig.19.3 :** *Base pair substitution mutation by transition.*

**3. Inversions :** If a segment of DNA is removed and reinserted in a reverse direction, it results in an inversion. *e.g.*

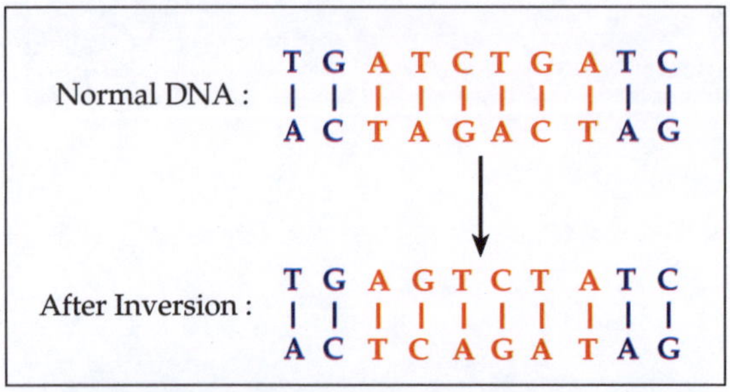


**Fig.19.4 :** *Base pair substitution mutation by inversion of DNA segment.*

**B. Frame-shift mutation :** The mutation where deletion or insertion of one or a few nucleotides leading to a change in a reading frame is called frame-shift mutation. This results into the introduction of unrelated amino acids into the protein and causes a drastic change in the protein synthesized. It may be of three types:

1. **Deletion :** Removal of a few bases from the polynucleotide chain is called deletion. It leads into the genetic message out of frame beyond the point of deletion. The number of bases in the deleted region is not divisible by three.

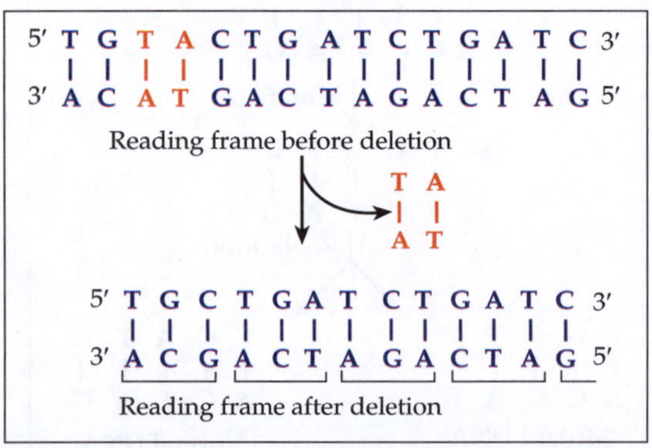


**Fig.19.5 :** *Frame-shift mutation by deletion of base.*

2. **Insertion :** The genetic message will be similarly disturbed if one or a few bases are added (the number of such inserted bases is not divisible by three). It leads into the genetic message out of frame beyond the point of insertion.

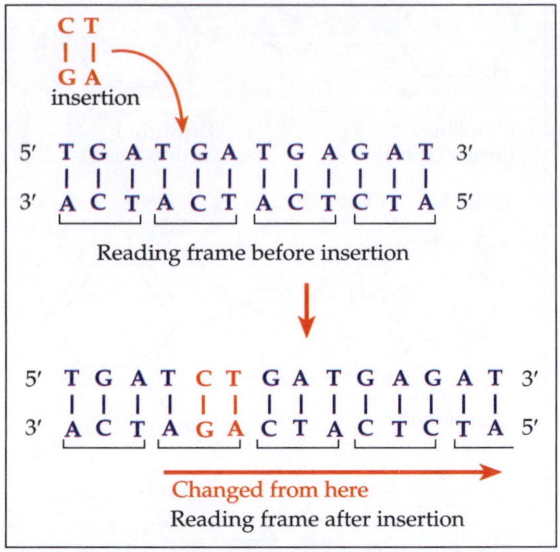


**Fig.19.6 :** *Frame-Shieft mutation by insertion of base pair*

3. **Simultaneous deletion and insertion :** If there is simultaneous deletion and addition of a base then the message will be out of frame.

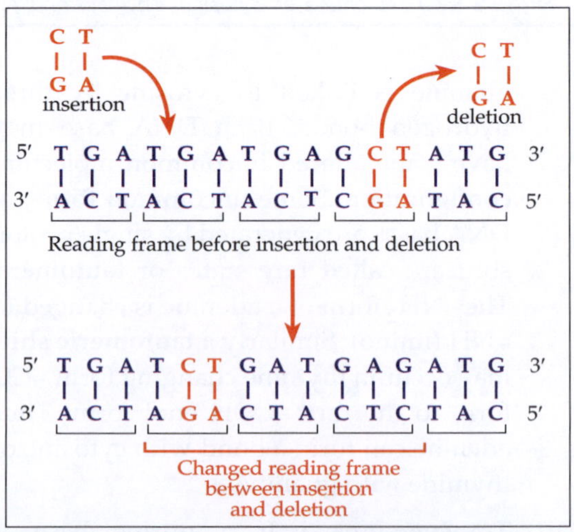


**Fig.19.7 :** *Frme-Shieft mutation by insertion and deletion of base pair*

**C. Other types of mutations**

1. **Silent mutation :** The gene mutation, which does not result in phenotypic

expression is called silent mutation. Silent mutations are of several types :

(a) The genetic code is degenerative i.e., more than one codon may specify an amino acid *e.g.*, AAA and AAG specify *lysine*. If AAA undergoes mutation to AAG still it will specify the same amino acid. Thus it is a silent mutation.

(b) The mutation sometimes changes the amino acid but the function of the protein is not modified, then it would be a silent mutation.

(c) Sometimes the gene undergoes mutation but their product is no more required for the function of the body.

(d) Some times a mutation is neutralized by a second mutation, which is called genetic supression.

Genetic suppression may be of two types : Intragenic and intergenic.

(i) **Intragenic suppression :** When the mutation of a gene is suppressed by another mutation of the same gene is called intragenic suppression.

A codon that has undergone a change as a result of mutation may undergo another mutation to a codon that is less harmful to function and restore the function partially.

Due to mutation by deletion the altered protein, which differs from the wild type. The second mutation few bases away from the first mutation may change the frame-shift in such a way that the changed mutated product becomes inactive.

Sometimes first mutation can be suppressed by an amino acid substitution with a second substitution mutation *e.g.*, *tryptophan synthetase gene* of *E.coli* by primary mutation *gly* → *glu*, resulted non-functional. This is corrected by a second mutation *tyr* → *cys* and restore the enzyme activity.

(ii) **Extragenic or intergenic suppression :** Sometimes the deleterious effect of a mutation is overcome by mutation of another gene, which is called intergenic mutation.

Sometimes the 1st mutation converts a codon nonsense, the effect of nonsense codon can be suppressed by altering the anticodon of tRNA due to its mutation. For example, if a codon is UAC mutated to UAA (stop codon). The tRNA, which has an anticodon AUG mutated to AUU can recognize and pair with the mRNA bearing UAA and the protein synthesis is continued.

2. **Lethal mutation :** Mutation causes the developing organism to die prematurely.

3. **Conditional mutation :** Mutation produces its phenotypic effect only under certain conditions called restrictive conditions. Under other conditions the permissive conditions, the effect is not seen. For a temperature sensitive mutation the restrictive condition typically is high temperature, while the permissive condition is low temperature.

4. **Loss of function mutation :** Mutation reduces or abolishes the activity of the gene. This is commonest class of mutation. This is usually a recessive mutation.

5. **Gain-in-function mutation :** Mutation increases the activity of the gene or makes it active in inappropriate circumstances. These are usually dominant mutations.

6. **Null mutation :** The loss of function mutation that completely abolishes the activity of the gene.

7. **Dominant negative mutation :** The dominant acting mutation that blocks the gene activity causing loss-of function phenotype even in the presence of a normal copy of gene.

## 19.3. BIOCHEMICAL MUTATIONS IN MAN

Earliest cases of biochemical mutations were described in man by A.E.Garrod (1909) in his book "Inborn Errors of Metabolism". These are important diseases associated with metabolic break down of *phenylalanine* (Fig. 19.2).

Sequences of biochemical reactions in human beings with the metabolism of *phenylalanine* and various metabolic blocks are shown, which are believed to be caused by the effect of a separately inherited genetic defects on a specific enzyme. For example, in the classic form of phenylketoneuria, a defect in phenylalanine hydroxylase, prevents the hydroxylation of *phenylalanine*, thereby leading to the accumulation of *phenylalanine* and subsequent neurological damage caused high concentrations of this amino acid. This disease is called as **Follings disease**. Some of the *phenylalanine* also undergoes transamination to phenyl pyruvic acid, which is then excreted with the urine.

Block in **alkaptoneuria** leads to the accumulation of homogentistic acid, which is oxidized readily to benzoquinone acetic acid. This then is polymerized into the visible pigment in alkaptonuric urine and also deposited in connective tissues of the body.

**Albinism** may be caused by the absence of the enzyme tyrosinase, which metabolizes tyrosine to DOPA. This albinism might be caused by the absence of another tyrosinase enzyme, which catabolizes DOPA into melanin.

Another diseases **Tyrosinosis**, **Tyrosinemia** are also associated with the disturbance of the same metabolic pathway.

In combination with other studies, these findings indicate that the action of a mutation appears as a metabolic "block" usually affecting only on a single step of a chemical reaction. The cause of the block has been localized in most investigated cases to an impaired function of the enzyme that is usually active at the particular metabolic step. The genetic control of phenotypes through rate of metabolic reactions had long been traced by Goldchmidt possessed neither detailed biochemical information of the reactions nor of the enzymes involved. Beadle and Tatum's contribution, therefore not only related to genes of metabolism but also led to more precise investigations of the relationship between genes and enzymes.

As much as 170 human hereditary conditions are known so far to show a loss of enzymatic activity of some of them are listed here in Table 19.1.

## 19.4. MUTAGENS AND MUTAGENESIS

A chemical, physical or biological agent that induces mutations is called **mutagen**.

In 1927 **H. J. Muller** (Animal Institute of Genetics, Edinburg, UK) was first to show that X-ray could induce mutations in the fruit fly, *Drosophila melanogaster*. At the same time L. J. Stadler (University of Missouri, Missouri, USA) also demonstrated that radiation could produce mutations in plants. Thus it was demonstrated that genetic changes could be produced by external agents and such chemicals produced the same kind of effects that X-ray produces and so the name **radiomimetic** agent has been given them to denote that they mimic the radiation effect. Apart from the physical and chemical agents various microbes have also been proved to be mutagenic.

Mutations could be brought about by Physical agents Chemical agents and Living or Biological agents.

### 19.4.1. Physical Agents

1. **Ionizing radiations** (X-rays, β-rays, α-particles, protons and neutrons) : Timofeeff Ressovsky *et al* (1935) interpreted the relationship between the number of gene mutation induced and the X-ray treatment given. The frequency of mutation is proved simply proportional to the amount of X-rays. The same amount of X-rays may, however, given in a few seconds or minutes, if the organism is treated by placing it to a powerful source of radiation

**TABLE 19.1**
**Some biochemical mutations in human beings**

| *Conditions* | *Phenotypic effect* | *Enzymes* | *Normal enzyme activity* |
|---|---|---|---|
| **Acatalasia** | Oral gangrene | Catalase | Acts in decomposition of $H_2O_2$. |
| **Alkaptonuria** | Darkening of urine and Arthritis | Homogentistic acid – oxidase | Catalyses transformation of homogentistic acid into Maleylacetoacetic acid |
| **Cretinism** | Thyroid mal-function, mental retardation | Iodotyrosine – deiodinase | Catalyses transformation of tyrosine into thyroxine |
| **Galactosemia** | Liver-enlargement, galactose in urine and blood, Cataracts, mentel deficiency | Galactose – 1 – phophatase, Uridyl–transferase | Catalyses transformation of galactose to glucose |
| **Gaucher's disease** | Presence of Gaucher's cells causing enlargement and destruction of tissues viz. spleen, liver bonemarrow and brain. | Glucocerebrosidase | Catalyses the cleavage of glucose from glucocerebroside. |
| **Glycogen-storage disease** | Liver enlargement caused by accumulation of glycogen | Glucose –6–phosphatase, Branching enzyme, Muscle and liver phosphorylases; Debranching enzymes. | Catalyses transformation of glycogen to glucose. |
| **Huntingtons Chorea** | Progressive mental diterioration | Glutamic acid – decarboxylase | Catalyses synthesis of Gama-amino-butyric acid. |
| **Hypophosphatasis** | Deficient calcification | Alkaline phosphatase | Catalyses hydrolysis of phosphoryl ethanolamine. |
| **Jaundice (congenital non-hemolytic, Crigler Najjar syndrome** | Presence of bile in various tissues | Glucouronyl-transferase | Catalyses transfer of glucouronic acid from uridine diphosphate to bilirubin receptors. |
| **Liesch-Nyhan Syndrome** | Mental retardation, self mutilation spasticity, increased uric acid production. | Hypoxanthineguanine phosphoribosyl transferase | Purine metabolism |
| **Metachromatic Leukodystrophy** | Neurological changes mental regression, Urinary incontinence, death usually by age of 10 yrs. | Arylsulfatase-A | Catabolises sulfatids in normal tissues. |
| **Methmoglobinemia** | Increased proportion of oxidized hemoglobin | NAD-methaemoglobin – reductase | Catalyses the reduction of methaemoglobin into normal hemoglobin. |
| **Nemann-Pick disease** | Accumulation of lipids in reticulo–endothelial cells and destructive changes in nervous system. | Sphingomyelinase | Catalyses hydrolysis of phosphorylcholine from sphingomyelin. |
| **Phenylketonuria** | Mental retardation, excretion of phenylalanine | Phenylalanine-hydroxylase | Converts phenylalanine into tyrosine. |
| **Primaquine — synsitivity (FAVISM)** | Haemolytic anemia | Glucose–6–phorphate – dehydrogenase | Oxidises glucose permitting accumulation of protective levels of glutathione. |
| **Tay-Saches disease** | Mental and motor retardations, death by the age of 2–4 years. | β–D-N-acetyl – hexosaminidase-A | Cleaves the terminal residue from a stored ganglioside (Brain lipid). |

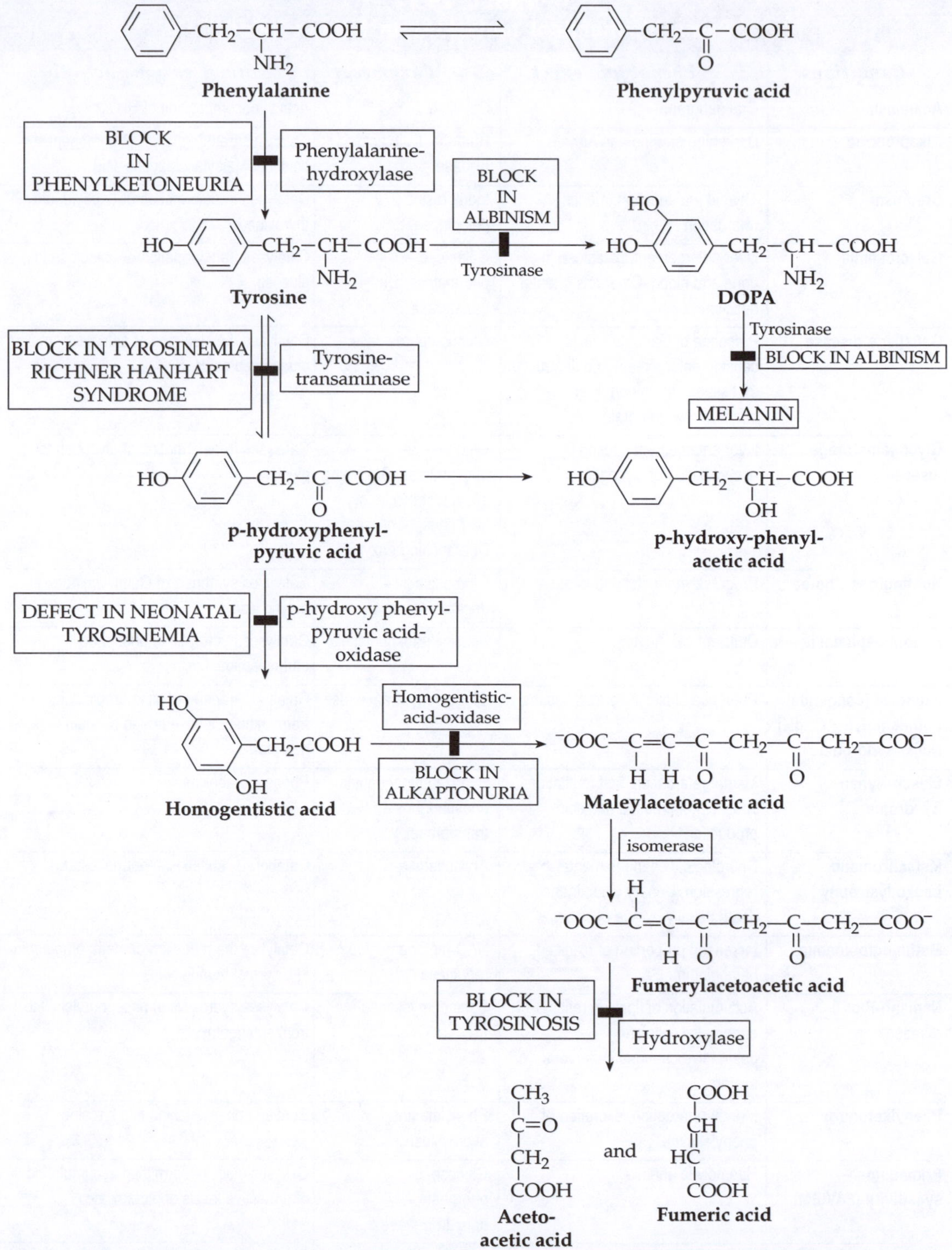


**Fig.19.8 :** *Metabolic pathway in phenylalanine metabolism and some biochemical diseases.*

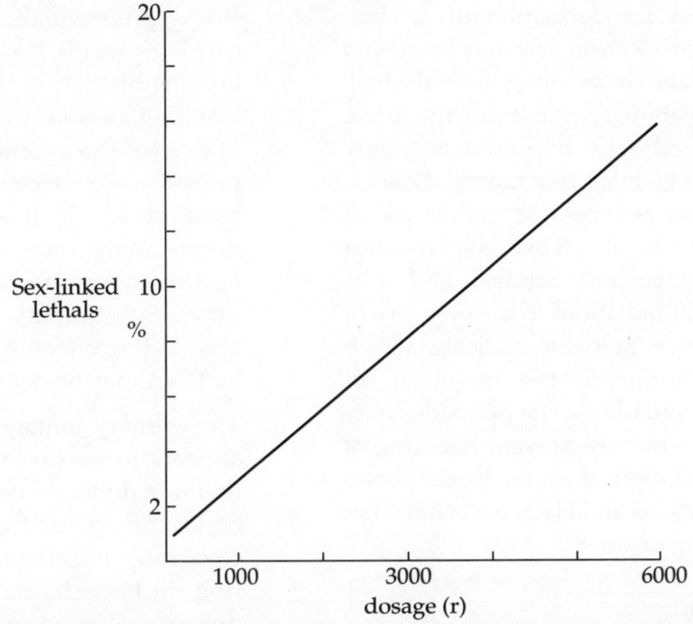


**Fig.19.9 :** *Relationship between percentage of sex-linked lethals in Drosophila and X-ray dose measured in Roentgens.*

or in days, weeks and even years if the intensity is low. The number of gene mutations produced is constant and independent both of the time and of the intensity of treatment remain the same.

Muller (1927) showed that the X-ray produces changes in the structure of chromosomes *i.e.,* breakage and loss of parts lead to deficiency, duplication, translocation, inversion etc. Sometimes, the broken ends of a chromosome may rejoin the "heal" in old position, so that the chromosome structure is restituted or a broken end of one chromosome may rejoin with a broken end of another chromosome giving rise to translocations, inversions, deficiency, duplications etc.

**Target Theory :** Timofeeff-Ressovsky, Zimmer and Delbruck (1935), Lea (1936) Catcheside (1948) and others have proposed the so called "Target theory" of induction of gene mutation by high energy radiation. According to this theory the particles of the X-ray directly hitting the genes, which is regarded as the target struck by the X-ray photon. The theory assumes that mutations caused by a single ionization or atomic excitation within a certain volume of matter called the **target** or **sensitive volume**. *A single radiation hits anywhere in a sensitive volume will always produce a given kind of mutation* (Fig. 19.3).

$$\textbf{Sensitive volume} = \frac{\text{Frequency of given kind of mutation per r unit (m)}}{\text{Change of ionization of an atom in the organic material (i)}}$$

But this theory meets difficulties that mutagenic effectiveness of radiation is not independent of the physiological state of the organism.

It is found that X-ray induced more mutations in Oxygen-atmosphere and some chemicals were found to protect the organisms from radiation.

**Biochemical Theory :** The ionizing radiations can change the atomic structure of a substance by causing the loss of an electron and the formation of an ion. Sometimes an electron pair may be moved from an inner to an outer orbital shell. This brings about excitation of the atom. In the excited state the atom is highly reactive and is called **free radical**. Low $O_2$ concentration reduces the frequency of chromosome breaks. This oxygen effect has been extensively studied and it is probable that radiations in the presence of $O_2$ form some peroxide radicals, which may then influence the frequency of breaks and mutations. The peroxides may cause breaks or may prevent rejoining of breaks. Ionization of water in cells may give free radicals and $H_2O_2$ is produced in the following manner.

**In absence of Oxygen :**

$$H_2O + \text{Ionizing radiation} \longrightarrow H_2O^- + H_2O^+$$

$$H_2O^+ \longrightarrow OH^{\bullet} + H^+$$

$$H_2O^- \longrightarrow OH^- + H^{\bullet}$$

$$OH^{\bullet} + H^{\bullet} \longrightarrow H_2O$$

$$OH^{\bullet} + OH^{\bullet} \longrightarrow H_2O_2 \longrightarrow H_2O + \tfrac{1}{2}O_2$$

$$H^{\bullet} + H^{\bullet} \longrightarrow H_2$$

$$OH^{\bullet} + H_2 \longrightarrow H_2O + H^{\bullet}$$

$$H^{\bullet} + H_2O_2 \longrightarrow H_2O + OH^{\bullet}$$

**In presence of Oxygen :**

$$H^{\bullet} + O_2 \longrightarrow HO_2^{\bullet} \text{ (Hydroperoxyl radical)}$$

$$HO_2^{\bullet} + H^{\bullet} \longrightarrow H_2O_2$$

$$2HO_2^{\bullet} + H^{\bullet} \longrightarrow H_2O_2 + O_2$$

[Unpaired electron of the radical is shown as a dot]

**Fig.19.10 :** *Mechanism of DNA mutation by ionizing radiation*

2. **Non-ionizing radiations (U-V-rays) :** UV absorption is limited to molecules carrying conjugated double bonds and each molecule has a special absorption spectrum with maximum at certain specific wave–lengths. Both DNA and RNA preferentially absorb UV light causing their N-containing bases to become highly reactive free radicals. The resulting instability caused the conversion of one base to another (Purine to another purine or pyrimidine to another pyrimidine). If this change occurs in mRNA, only a few inactive proteins will be formed, because mRNA is soon broken down. Substitutions in DNA may have a long lasting effect. All the proteins coded by DNA may be defective.

The primary mutagenic effect of UV-ray appears to be due to the production of thymine-dimer. The 5, 6 unsaturated bonds of adjacent pyrimidines become covalently linked to form a cyclobutane ring. In bacteria, three possible types of dimers are found in DNA *e.g.,* T-T , T-C and C–C. Pyrimidine dimers can also be formed between double helix and cause distortion of the molecule.

In RNA, dimers can be formed between adjacent uracil and cytosine rings.

UV-radiations also cause addition of water molecules to pyrimidines in both DNA and RNA resulting in the formation of **photohydrates**. The water molecule is added across the C5–C6 double bond.

UV effect can be reversed by exposing the cells to visible light containing wave-lengths in the blue region of the spectrum. This phenomenon is known as **photoreactivation**. It indicates that the damage caused by UV radiation may be reversed before genetic material is permanently affected. In *E.coli* photo-reactivation is caused by the activity of an enzyme (DNA pol-I), which splits the thymine dimer and repairs DNA molecule. In human beings also sunlight (UV component) causes DNA damage, producing dimer and repair system is impaired, the patient suffering from **Xeroderma-pigmentosum**. The patient becomes susceptible to sunlight because

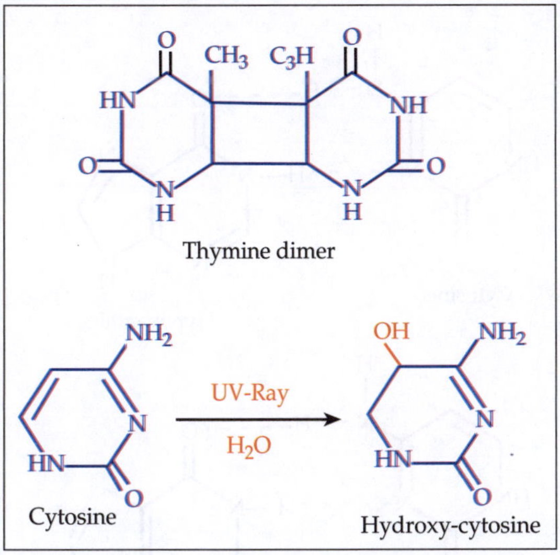


**Fig.19.11 :** *Effects of UV-Ray on Thymine and Cytosine*

now it does not have the functional enzyme required for removing thymine dimers produced due to UV damage.

3. **Exposure to low pH :** At low pH some bases become positively charged and strand separation occurs, which may be lethal. At pH = 4 or above, this effect is negligible. Complete removal of A or G (depurination) at low pH has been reported. G is more readily than A. This will lead to base pair substitutions either transversions or transitions.

   At low pH, backbone breakage also occurs whenever the sugar phosphate backbone breaks, it could be lethal.

4. **Exposure to high temperature :** High temperature causes strand separation and could be lethal. Besides this, it also causes some depurination.

## 19.4.2. Chemical Mutagens

1. **Alteration during replication of nucleic acids :**

   (a) **Incorporation of base analogues**

   (i) **5-bromouracil (BU) or 5-bromodeoxyuridine (BUdr) :** BU

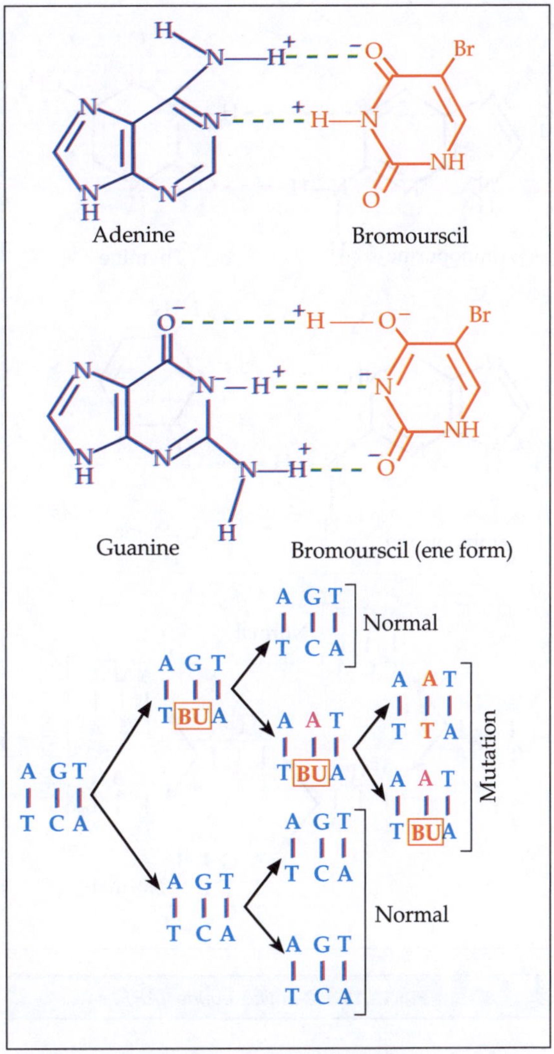


**Fig.19.12 :** *Mistake in G-BU pairing.*

can pair with adenine just like thymine. Occasionally, 5-BU loses a hydrogen atom in position-1 and pairs with guanine instead of adenine. This pairing – mistake may occur at the time of incorporation or after incorporation during replication (Fig. 19.12).

BUdr is more effective mutagen probably because it is more easily converted to deoxyribonucleoside-

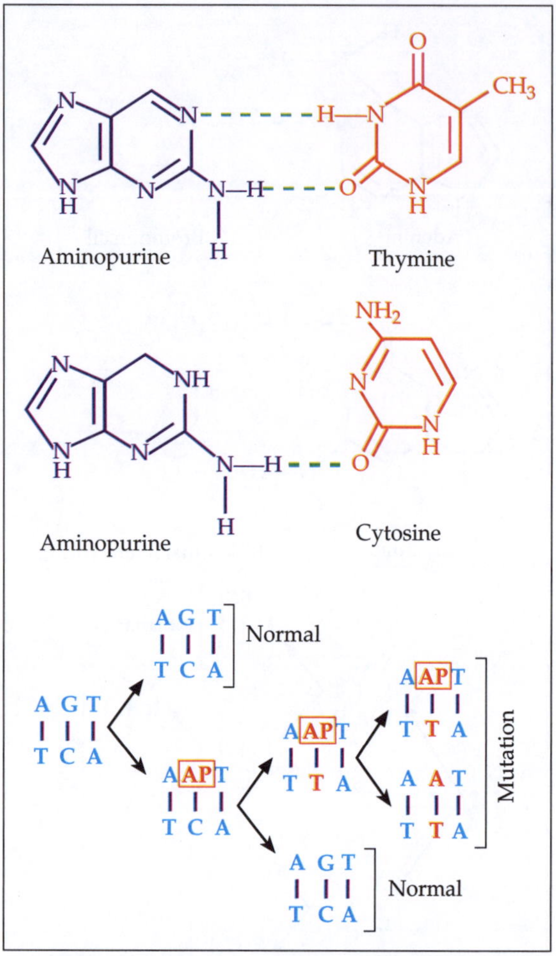


Fig.19.13 : *2-amino purine (AP)*

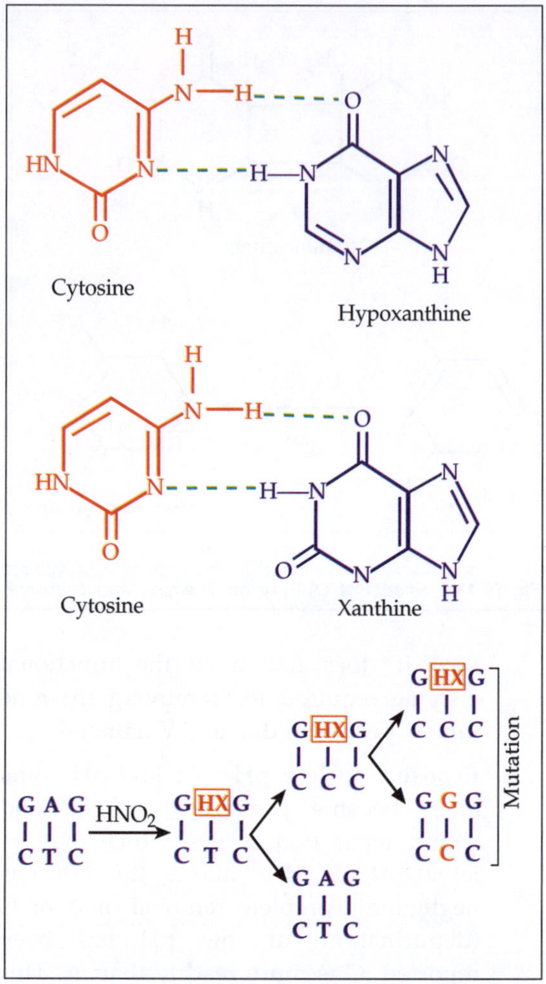


Fig.19.14 : *Mistake in H—T pairing.*

triphosphate. Both BU and BUdr induce point mutations.

(ii) **2- amino purine (AP) :** AP can pair with thymine by two hydrogen bonds and with cytosine by one hydrogen bond. N- in AP and N-in cytosine repel each other and cause their separation AP-C base pair and cause mutation in subsequent generations. Similarly, formation of AP–T base pair may lead to a mutation (Fig. 19.13).

**(b) Inhibition of nucleic acid precursor** : There are several agents, which interfere with normal synthesis of nucleic acid precursors. **Azaserine** is one of the strongest mutagen, inhibiting purine synthesis; its mutagenecity may be due to its alkylating ability rather than its inhibitory action.

**Urathane** is an inhibitor of pyrimidine synthesis and also a mild alkylating agent.

It is surprising that adenine also shared mutagenic effect, though, normal purine nucleosides have an

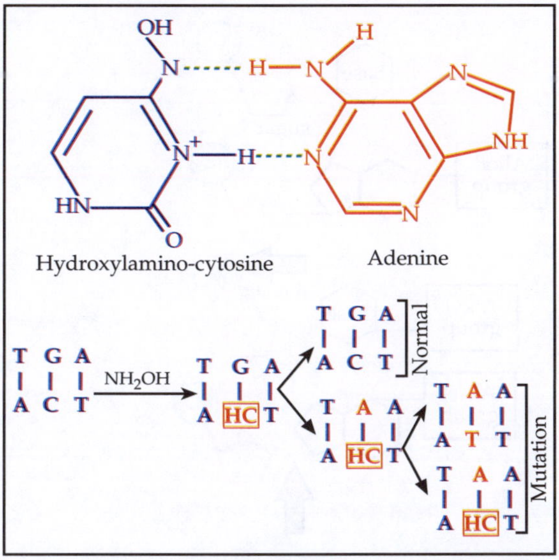


**Fig.19.15 :** *Mistake in G—HC pairing.*

antimutagenic effect. It is possible that lack of one base either causes breaks or causes pairing mistakes.

2. **Aberration in resting nucleic acid :**

(a) **$HNO_2$ :** It deaminates Adenine (A) into Hypoxanthine (H), Cytosine (C) to Uracil (U) and Guanine (G) to Xanthine (X). 'H' pairs with 'C' and 'U' pairs with 'A" and 'X' pairs with 'C'. Thus $HNO_2$ may bring about changes like A–T to G–C and G–C to A–T. But no change is brought about when G is deaminated to Xanthine (Fig. 19.6).

(b) **$NH_2OH$ and $NH_2$–$NH_2$ :** Hydroxylamine probably causes hydroxylation of cytosine at amino group giving rise to hydroxyl cytosine, which then subsequently pairs with adenine. This is because of hydroxyl amino group would be more electro-negative than amino group and hence this hydroxylated molecule could be more frequently in the tautomeric form having a hydrogen atom in place of nitrogen at position –3. Thus tautomeric form can pair with A but cannot pair with G (Fig. 19.15).

The effect of $NH_2$-$NH_2$ lies in breaking the rings of uracil and cytosine giving rise to Parazolone and 3-amino pyrasole respectively. Treatment of RNA by anhydrous hydrazine produces ribo-apyrimidic acid, free of pyrimidines and the treatment of DNA produces the corresponding apyrimidinic acid.

(c) **Alkylating agents :** Many mutagenic agents carry one or two or more alkyl groups in the reactive forms. These are called mono-bi-or poly-functional alkylating agents eg., Diethyl-sulphonate (DES), Dimethyl sulphonate (DMS), Methyl methane-sulphonate (MMS), Ethyl ethane sulphonate (EES) etc. DNA can be changed by alkylating agents in four different ways.

(i) **Alkylation of phosphate groups of nucleic acids :** When phosphate group is alkylated, unstable phosphate triester is formed, which hydrolyzes to return the alkyl group. It remains attached till the time of duplication. The duplication may be inhibited or the non-complementary bases may be incorporated [Fig. 19.16(a)].

(ii) **Hydrolysis of Triester between sugar and phosphates :** Hydrolysis of phosphate triester may take place between sugar and phosphate and thus causes the breakage of the backbone. This may be lethal or may cause larger alterations but will not cause point mutation [Fig. 19.16(a)].

(iii) **Alkylation of bases :** Some of the bases are also alkylated. Thus, 1-methyl adenine; 2-methyl adenine; 1,3 dimethyl adenine and

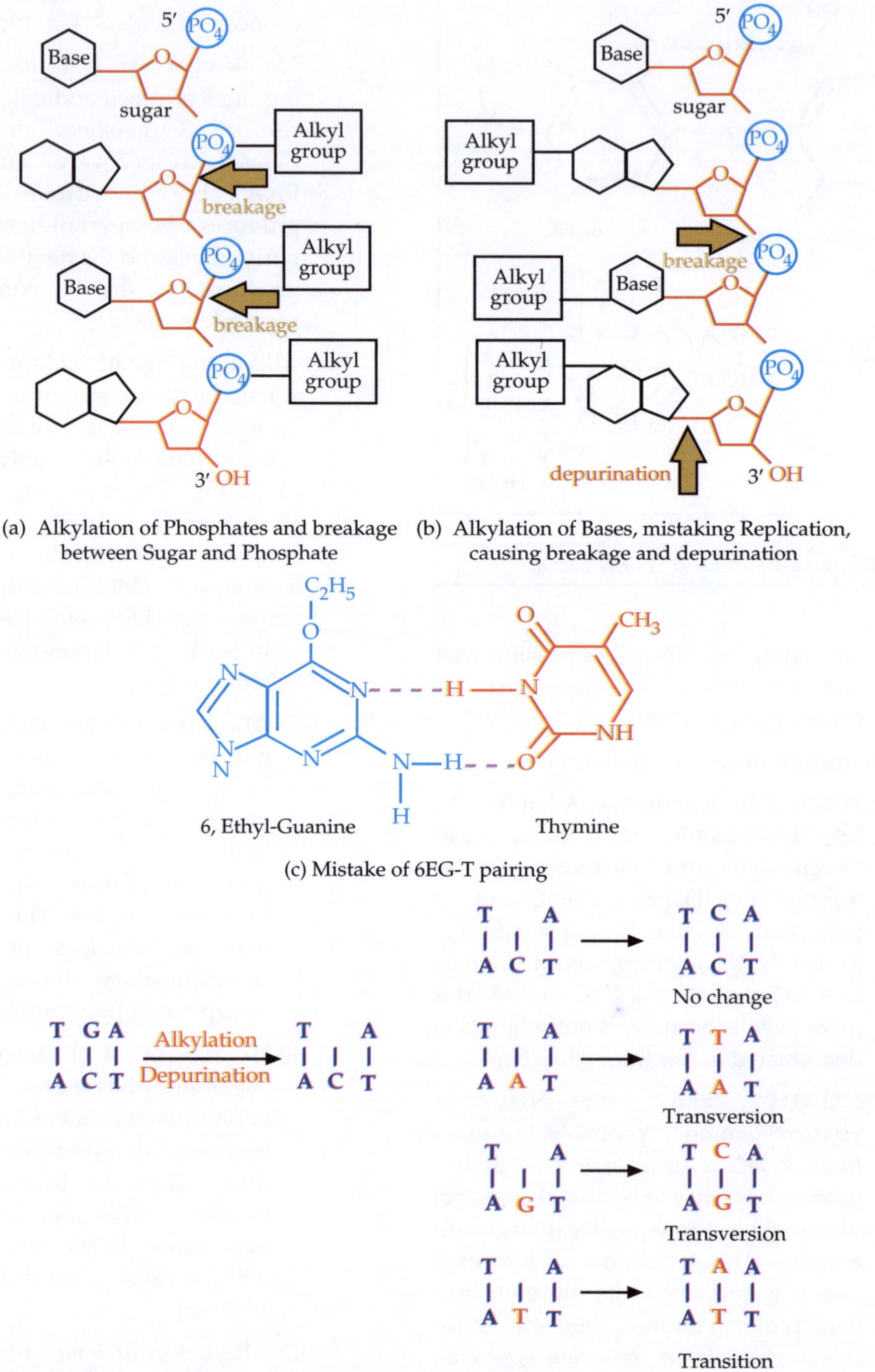


(a) Alkylation of Phosphates and breakage between Sugar and Phosphate

(b) Alkylation of Bases, mistaking Replication, causing breakage and depurination

(c) Mistake of 6EG-T pairing

(d) Depurination and Mutation

**Fig.19.16 :** *(a)-(d) Effects of alkylation DNA*

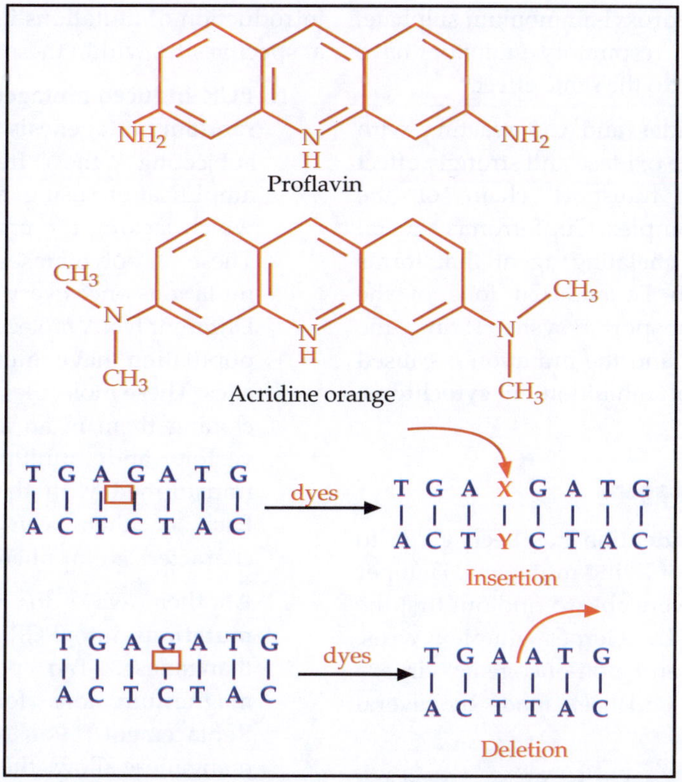


**Fig.19.17** : *Effects of Dyes on DNA*

cytosine derivatives can also be obtained (see figure 19.32).

6– alkyl guanine derivative is the common form that can pair with thymine instead of pairing with cytosine. The alkylated base may inhibit DNA-replication or cause base-pair mistakes during DNA replication [Fig. 19.16(c)].

(iv) **Depurination** : Alkylation at 7th position gives rise to quarternary nitrogen, which is unstable. This either hydrolyses away the alkyl group or separates from deoxy ribose sugar leaving it depurinated. The gap may then interfere with DNA duplication or incorporation of wrong bases. This may undergo breakage in the backbone and induce large alterations or may be lethal but will not cause point mutation [Fig. 19.16(d)].

3. **Effect of dyes on nucleic acid sequence :** Certain fluorescent acridine dyes such as pro-flavin and acridine – orange cause mutations by insertion and deletion of bases. The acridines are flat planar molecules like purine bases. And can be inserted between the bases of the DNA helix. This distorts the structure of DNA and results in deletion or insertion of bases during recombination (Fig. 19.17).

4. **Respiratory Inhibitors :** Intense work has been done on the mutagenic and clastogenic effect of inhibitors of oxidative phosphorylation. KCN, Na-azide, Maleic

hydrazide, Hydroxyl-ammonium sulphate, Cupferron etc. respiratory inhibitors have been found to do the same effect.

Cyanides, azides and CO reacting with Fe-cytochrome oxidase and strongly affect the electron transport chain of the respiratory complex. Cupferron is a metal (Cu and Fe) chelating agent that forms complex with Fe and Cu ions of the electron transport system in the mitochondria and the mutation is caused as a result of inhibition in cytochrome system.

### 19.4.3. Living Mutagens

Recently much attention has been given to study on the effect of living mutagens. Hamper and Ellison (1961) were able to find out first the mutation induced by Herpes simplex virus. Several oncogenic and non-oncogenic virus – induced mutations had been made by several workers.

Nicols (1966) suggested that virus affect the DNA by direct action or indirectly due to chemical action mediated through the cytoplasmic organelles like lysosomes.

Besides viruses, bacteria and spores and hyphae of fungi, even protozoa can induce DNA mutation. This is possibly due to the effect of toxins produced in the cytoplasm of the cell.

## 19.5 REVERSE GENETICS

The term "reverse genetics" reflects the idea that in the experimental steps occur in an order opposite to that in the conventional approach used to study the function of a gene.

*"The reverse genetics is an experimental strategy in which the researchers first identify the wild type gene using cloning method. The next step is to make a mutant version of the wild type gene, introduce it into an organism, and see how the mutant gene affects the phenotype of the organism".*

Genetic engineering and genomics have contributed many new techniques for introduction of mutations into specific genes or at specific sites within these genes.

1. **PCR-induced mutagenesis :** PCR-induced **random mutagenesis** can be generated by subjecting the fragment to PCR amplification using a DNA polymerase which lacking the proof-reading activity. These polymerases can produce mutations once every few hundred bases. Different DNA molecules in the amplified population have mutations in different sites. These molecules can be separated by cloning them in an appropriate plasmid vector and multiplying in a cell transformed with the cloned molecules. Each of them can be sequenced an characterised for phenotypic effects.

   Another way to introduce **random mutations** into PCR products is to use manganese. Taq polymerase requires magnesium ions for proper fucntion. Replacement of magnesium by manganese allows the enzyme to continue synthesize DNA, but the accuracy is greatly reduced. Thus random changes greatly reduced. Thus random changes in bases occur and yield a mixture of different mutations from a single PCR reaction. The error rate depends upon the manganese concentration. In this way single or multiple random mutations are possible to obtain.

2. **Site–directed mutagenesis :** Mutations may be inserted artificially into DNA by altering a few bases in a PCR. The most obvious way of *directed mutagenesis*, to change one or two bases in a segment of DNA is to synthesize a PCR primer that carries the required alterations. Consider the sequence AAGC**C**GGAGCCA. Suppose, we wish to alter the middle base of second genetic code "C" into "G". Then we make a PCR -primer with required base alteration, that is, AAG C**G**G. This mutant primer is used as one of pair of PCR primer to amplify the appropriate

segment of DNA using wild type DNA as template. The PCR-product will contain the desired mutation.

3. **Knock-out mutation :** Such mutation can be obtained by inactivation of a specific gene by *in vivo* digestion of the DNA containing this gene and inserting a foreign DNA cassette containing a selectable gene. It can also be done *in vivo* in certain organisms.

The constructs thus obtained can be transferred to a recepient cell by transformation where it can undergo homologous recombination with the resident wild type allele of the gene which is inactivated.

## 19.6 SITE DIRECTED MUTAGENESIS

Site-directed mutagenesis is the technique for generating amino acid coding changes in the gene. In this way the enzymes which are synthesized by the gene become more efficient and more suitable than naturally occurring counterparts.

Different methods of site-directed mutagenesis are employed.

### 19.6.1 Oligonucleotide-directed mutagenesis

1. The ssDNA, which is targeted for site directed mutagenesis is to be carried in M13 phage vector.
2. It is then mixed with a DNA-primer (oligonucleotides) which has been made artificially and is complementary to the target DNA except a point of mismatched sequence. Therefore, it hybridizes with the target DNA except the single base mismatch region at low temperature (Fig. 19.18).
3. DNA polymerase along with all four dNTPs are added to enhance replication utilizing the complementary strands of target DNA and M13 phage DNA.

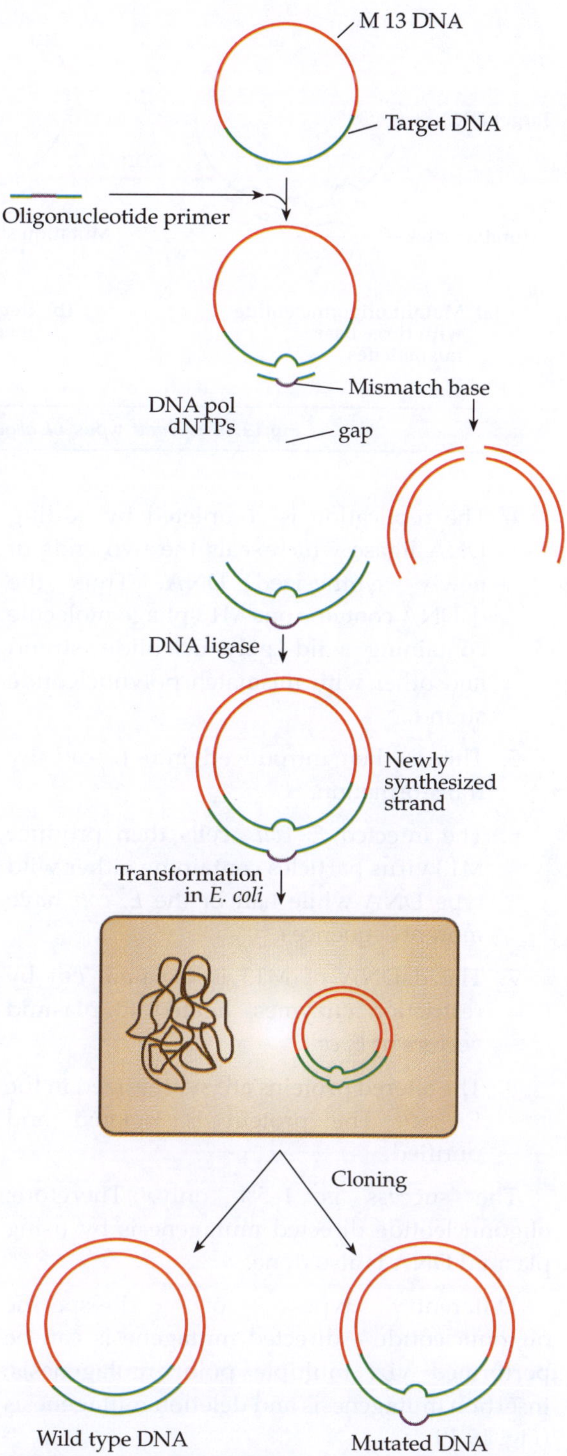


**Fig.19.18 :** *Mechanism of Site specific oligonucleotide - directed mutagenesis.*

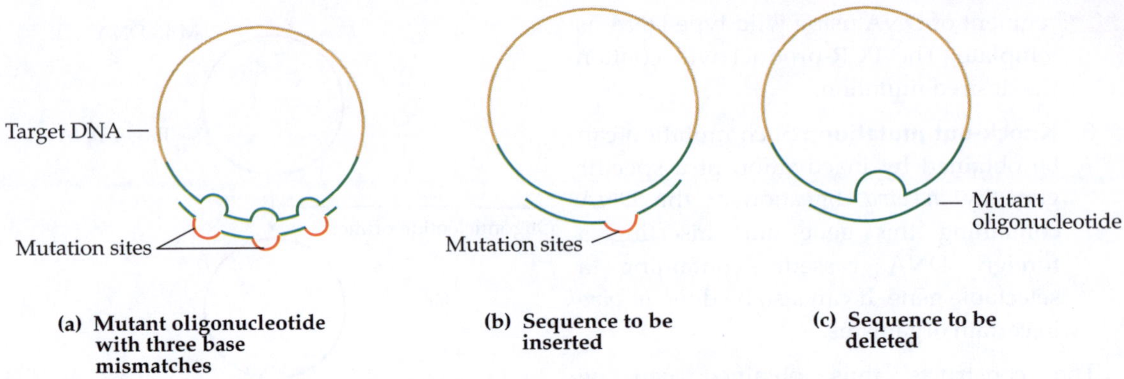


**Fig.19.19 :** *Three types of oligonucleotide directed mutagenesis.*

4. The replication is completed by adding DNA ligase which seals the two ends of newly synthesized DNA. Thus the dsDNA contains one M13 phage molecule containing wild polynucleotide strand and other with mismatch polynucleotide strand.
5. This is then introduced into *E. coli.* by transformation.
6. The infected *E. coli* cells then produce M13 virus particles containing either wild type DNA while half of the *E. coli* have mutant sequences.
7. The dsDNA of M13 is isolated, cut by restriction enzymes, ligated to plasmid vectors of *E. coli.*
8. The altered proteins are synthesized in the *E. coli.* The protein is isolated and purified.

The success is 1–5% only. Therefore, oligonucleotide directed mutagenesis by using plasmid DNA is also done.

Different types of site-specific oligonucleotide – directed mutagenesis can be performed viz. multiple point mutagenesis, insertion mutagenesis and deletion mutagenesis (Fig. 19.19).

### 19.6.2 Cassette mutagenesis

1. A synthetic dsDNA segment similar to the target gene is made in which the mutated portion lies between two restriction sites.
2. The recombinant plasmid in which the target gene is present, is cut by restriction enzymes (such as *EcoRI* and *HindIII*) in the target gene region.
3. Simultaneously the dsDNA is also cut by the same enzymes.
4. The piece is then ligated into the cut recombinant DNA by DNA ligase (Fig. 19.20).
5. The piece is then ligated into *E. coli.* for cloning.
6. This technique is called casette mutagenesis with 100% efficiency. It is important to note that restriction sites are essential to be present within the target gene.

### 19.6.3 PCR – amplified oligonucleotide – directed mutagenesis

PCR is an important tool for the amplification of genes. This technique is also used in the creation of site-directed mutagenesis. In this technique M13 bacteriophage is not utilized. The mechanism is as follows.

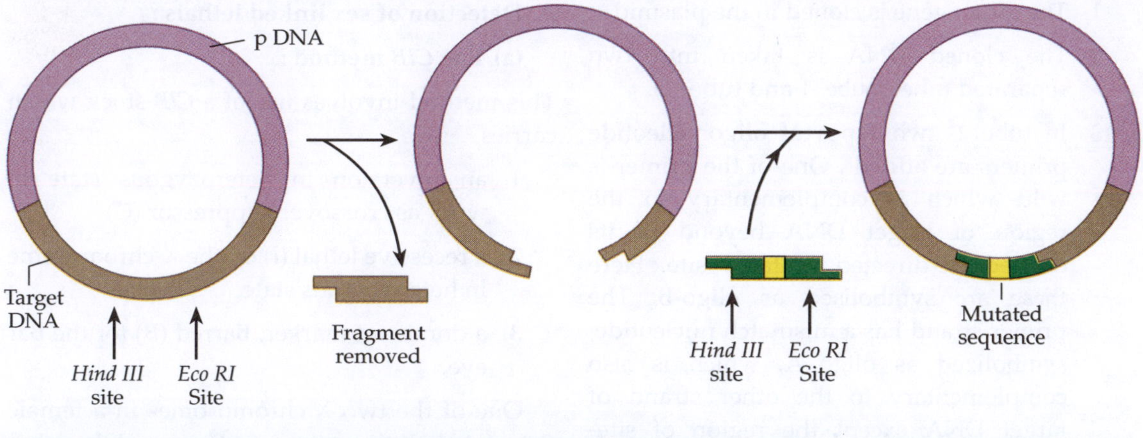


**Fig.19.20:** *Casette mutagenesis.*

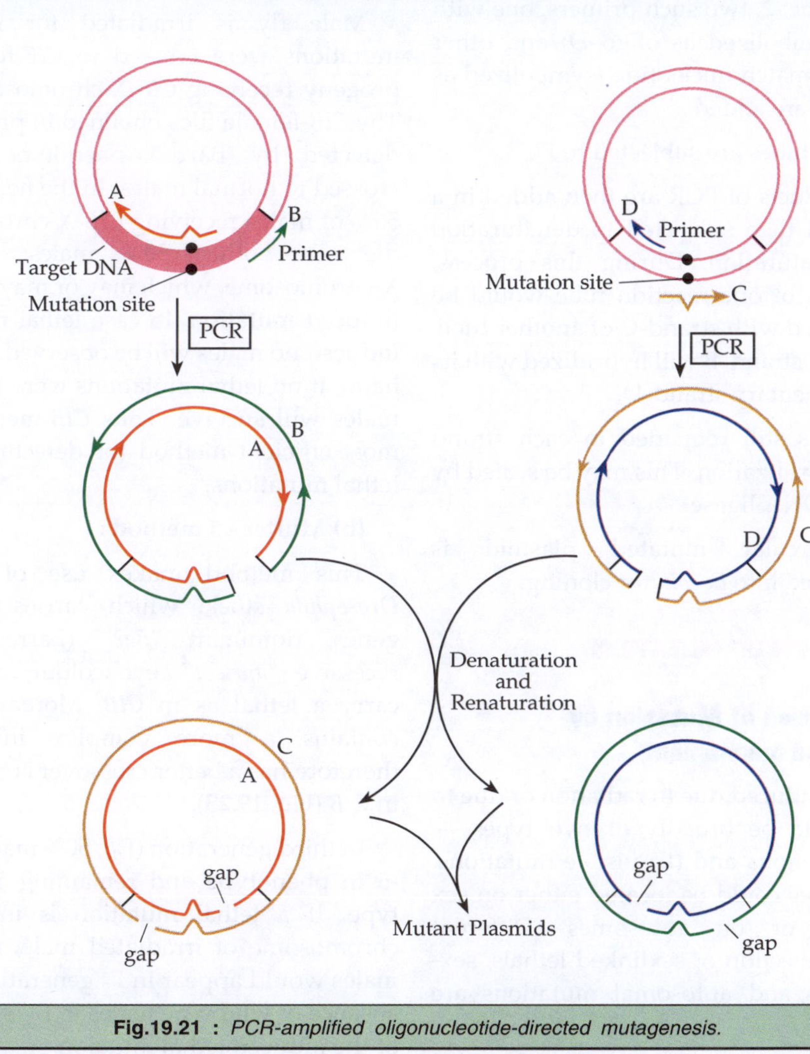


**Fig.19.21 :** *PCR-amplified oligonucleotide-directed mutagenesis.*

1. The target gene is cloned in the plasmid.
2. The cloned DNA is taken into two separated tubes (tube-1 and tube-2).
3. In tube 1, two types of oligonucleotide primers are added . One of the primer is wild which is complementary to the region of target DNA beyond of its desired sie-directed mutated site. Here these are symbolised as oligo-B. The primer strand has a mismatch nucleotide, symbolized as oligo-A, which is also complementary to the other strand of target DNA except the region of site-directed mutagenesis.
4. In the tube-2, two such primers, one with wild (symbolized as oligo-D) and other with mismatch nucleotide (symbolized as oligo-C) are added.
5. Both the tubes are subjected to PCR.
6. The products of PCR are then added in a tube and then subjected to denaturation and renaturation. During this process, strand-A of one reaction tube would be hybridized with strand-C of another tube. Similarly strand-B will hybridized with its complementary strand-D.
7. A nick is still remained in each strand after hybridization. This may be sealed by adding DNA ligase.
8. This circular mutated plasmid is introduced into *E. coli* for cloning.

## 19.7 DETECTION OF MUTATION

### 19.7.1 Detection of Mutation by genetic mechanism

Mutations induced due to radiation or due to chemicals could be broadly of two types — (I) Lethal mutations and (II) visible mutations. Both these types could be located either on sex chromosomes or on autosomes. Different methods for detection of sexlinked lethals, sex-linked visibles and autosomal mutations are available.

**A. Detection of sex linked lethals :**

**(a) The *ClB* method :**

This method involves use of a *ClB*-stock which carries

1. an inversion in heterozygous state to work as crossover suppressor (C)
2. a recessive lethal (*l*) on the X-chromosome in heterozygous state.
3. a dominant marker, Barred (*B*) for the Bar eye.

One of the two X chromosomes in a female fly carried all these three features and the other X-chromosome is normal (Fig. 19.22).

Male fly is irradiated for induction of mutations were crossed to *ClB*-females. Male progeny receiving *ClB*-X-chromosome will die. The *ClB*-female flies obtained in progeny can be detected by Barred phenotype. These are crossed to normal males. In the next generation, 50% of males receiving *ClB*-X-chromosome will die. The other 50% males will receive X-chromosome, which may or may not carry the induced mutation. In case lethal mutation was induced no males will be observed. On the other hand, if no lethal mutations were induced, 50% males will survive. Thus *ClB*-method was the most efficient method for detecting sex-linked lethal mutations.

**(b) Muller - 5 method :**

This method makes use of a Muller-5 *Drosophila* stock, which carries two marker genes, dominant *"Bar"* (Barred eye) and recessive *"apricot"*, eye colour, but does not carry a lethal as in *ClB*. Moreover Muller-5-contains a more complex inversion and therefore has a better crossover suppressor than in *ClB* (Fig. 19.23).

In third generation ($F_2$), 50% males are Muller -5 in phenotype and remaining 50% are wild type. If a lethal mutation is induced in X-chromosome of irradiated male, no wild type males would appear in $F_2$ generation. Therefore absence of wild type males in $F_2$ is an indication of the induced lethal mutaion.

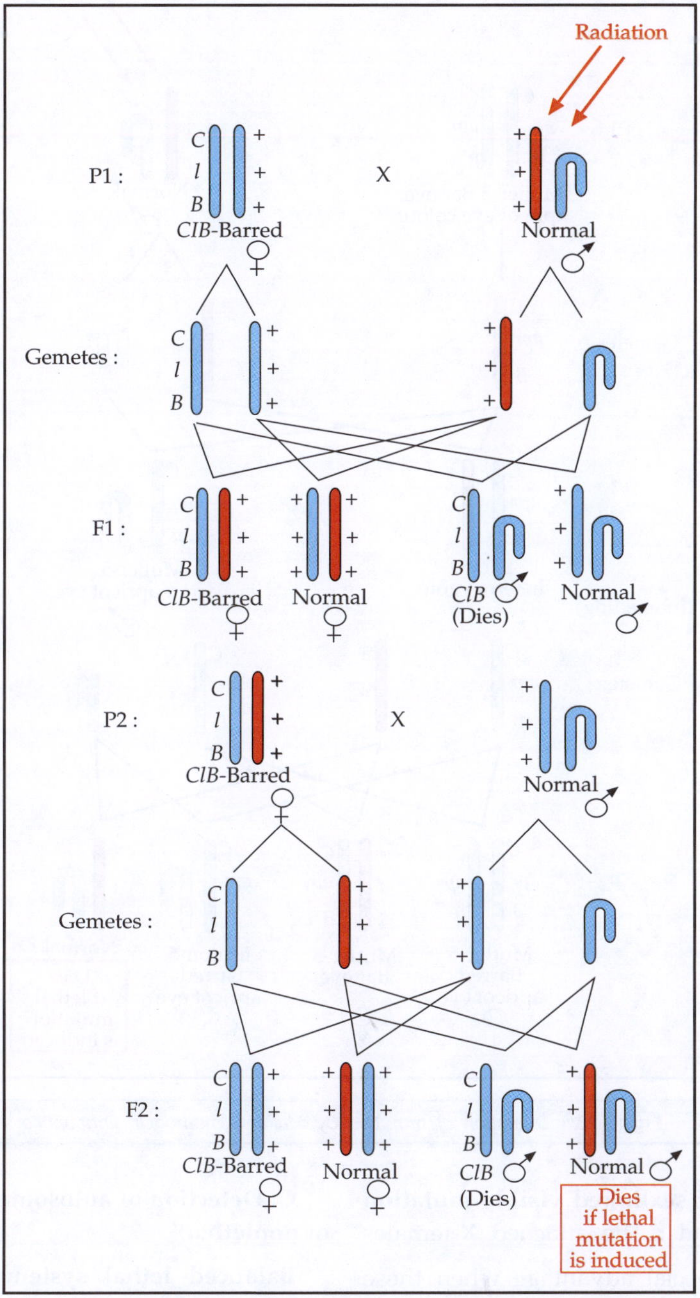


**Fig.19.22 :** *Detection of sex-linked lethals by* ClB*-method in Drosophila.*

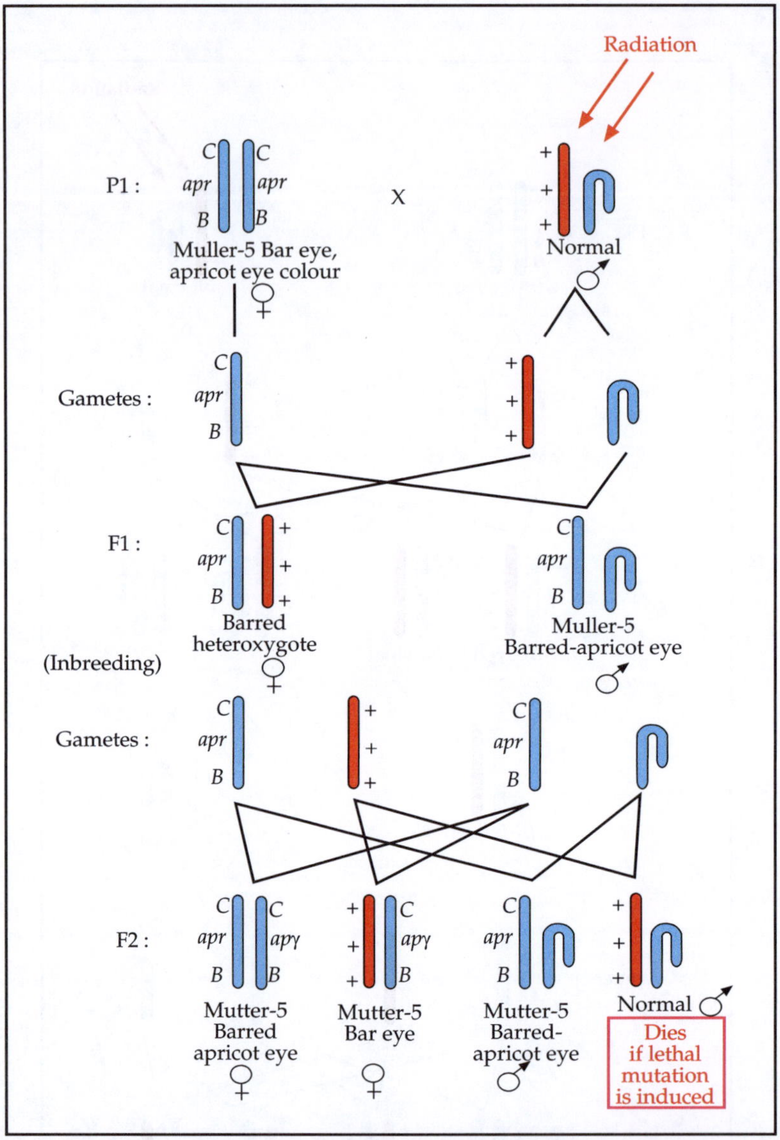


**Fig.19.23 :** *Detection of mutation by Muller-5 method in Drosophila.*

B. **Detection of sexlinked visible mutation Attached X-method :** The attached X-females ($\widehat{XX}Y$) have a special advantage when these females are crossed to an irradiated male.X-chromosome of irradiated male goes either to superfemale daughters or to the sons. Since, in sons, there is a single X-chromosome any visible induced mutation will immediately express itself and can be easily scored (Fig. 19.24).

**C. Detection of autosomal mutations (lethal or nonlethal)**

**Balanced lethal system :** Balanced lethal stock is one which carries mutant lethal marker alleles on specific homologous chromosomes, their normal allele being present on its homologue, consequently, homozygous individuals will not survive.

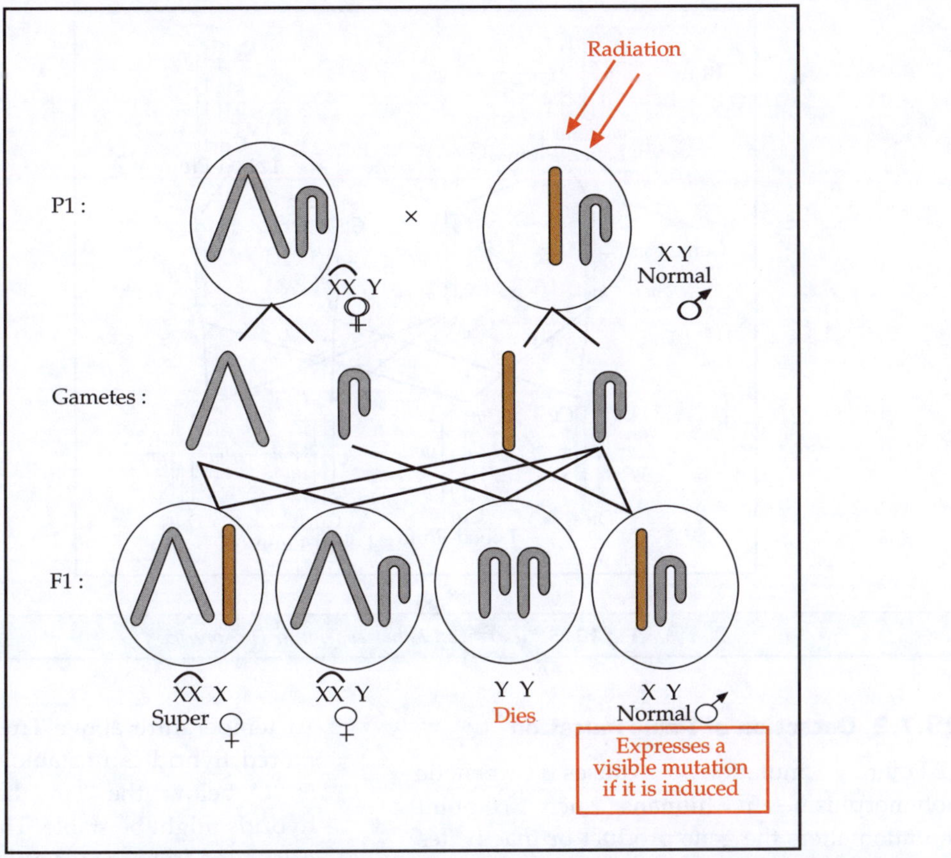


**Fig.19.24 :** *Detection of sex-linked visible mutation by attached X-chromosome method in Drosophilla*

In *Drosophila,* a stock carried the dominant genes *Cy* (curly wing) and *L* (lobed eye) on one chromosome and *Pm* (plum) eye, *i.e.* brownish eye on the other homologue so that the organism can be designated as *Cy* + *L*/+ *Pm* +. Phenotype of the stock which is heterozygous for *Cy, L* and *Pm* was curly, lobe and plum. If such individuals are crossed among themselves, progeny is always heterozygous, because, each of the two homologous chromosomes carried lethal mutant genes. Through the presence of inversion, crossing over was also suppressed, so that, *Cy* and /or *L* may not be transferred to the chromosome carrying *Pm* and vice versa (Fig. 19.25).

For detection of an autosomal mutations, *Cy* + *L*/+ *Pm* + stock is crossed to irradiated fly. From $F_1$, $\frac{Cy + L}{+ + +}$ flies were again back-crossed to *Cy* + *L*/+ *Pm* + in order to obtain curly lobe (heterozygous) male and female flies carrying the same autosome to be tested. Such $\frac{Cy + L}{+ + +}$ heterozygote when crossed among themselves would give one (*Cy* + *L*/*Cy* + *L*) : Two (*Cy* + *L*/ + + +) and one (+ + +/+ + +). Since $\frac{Cy + L}{Cy + L}$ homozygotes are lethal, phenotypic ratio will be 2 : 1. However, if lethal mutation was induced, only curly lobe will appear. If a recessive visible mutation was induced this will appear in homozygous state in one-third of the progenies (Fig. 19.26).

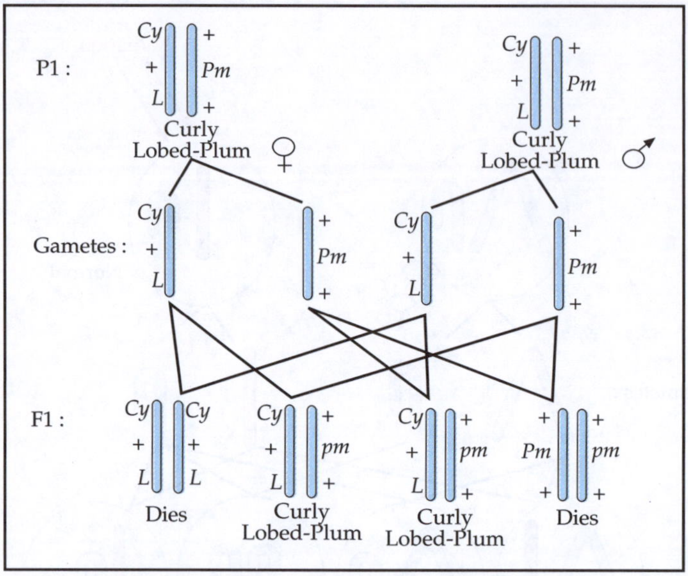


**Fig.19.25 :** *Balanced lethal system in Drosophilla.*

### 19.7.2 Detection of Point mutation

Point mutation causes genetic polymorphism. In humans such a point mutation alters the gene product or inactivates it, which may result in genetic diseases. Therefore, detection of mutation is very important to examine different versions of that gene from different individuals which is responsible for different disease states. Point mutations can be detected by several ways.

1. Any mutation can be identified by direct **DNA sequencing.** But the process is slow and laborious, because large number of samples have to be screened. Therefore this method is inappropriate.

2. By using **DNA chips,** point mutation can be detected and screened. If there is a single mismatch between the ssDNA strand on the chip and the mutaled ssDNA, then hybrid in the microarray chip does not form. To achieve this level of stringency, the incubation temparature must be just below the melting temperature (Tm) of the oligonucleotide. At temperature above Tm the fully base paired hybrid is unstable. At more than 5° C below the Tm the mismatched hybrids might be stable. The Tm in "C" is calculated from the formula.

$$Tm = (4 \times \text{number of G + C nucleotides}) \times 2 \text{ (numbers of A+T nucleotides)}$$

By comparing the presence and absence of bands far below the Tm and nearer Tm would indicate the presence of SNPs in the genome.

This technique could be employed for the detection of mutation, but this is not yet a widely available option.

3. **Mutation scanning technique** is employed for the detection of mutation. Here the mutated strand is first hybridized with complementary strand of unmutated control sequence. If the test DNA contains a point mutation, there will be a single mismatched position in this heteroduplex DNA where base pairing has not formed. This mismatch DNA can be detected by electrophoresis or HPLC or

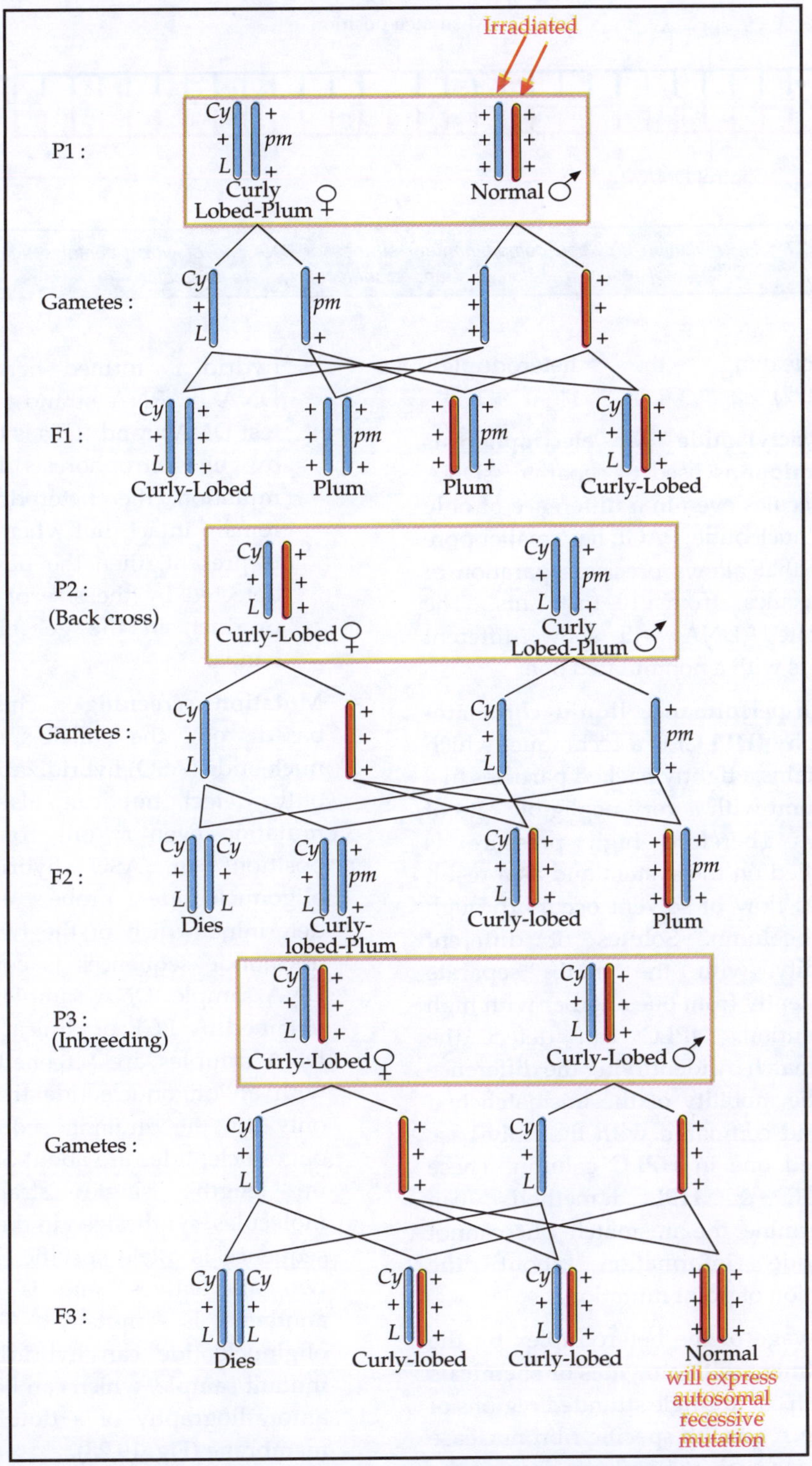


**Fig.19.26 :** *Detection of autosomal mutation by balanced-lethal system in Drosohilia.*

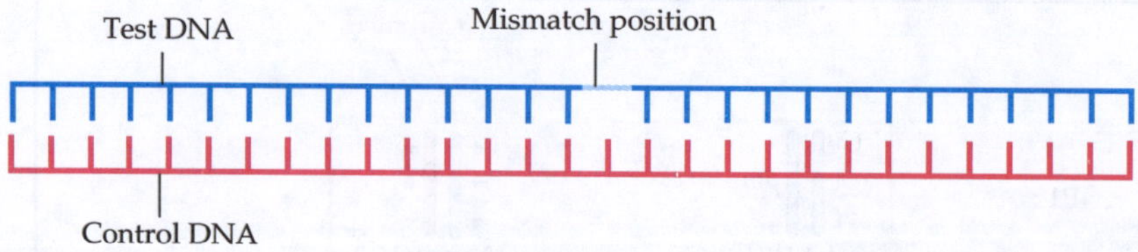


**Fig. 19.27 :** *Hybridization between complementary strands of DNA,one of which contains a mutation, will result in a double-stranded molecule with a mismatch.*

by cleaving the heteroduplex. (Fig. 19.27)

(a) **Polyacrylamide gel electrophoresis technique** is used to separate ssDNA molecules even in a difference of only one nucleotide. PAGE has smaller pore size that allows precise separation of molecules from 10–1500 nts. The mutated DNA will show different bands with a nonmutated one.

(b) **High-performance liquid chromatography (HPLC)** is a technique, which contains a tightly packed particles in a column with a very negligible rate of flow. Therefore high pressure is applied on the system and as a result rapid flow of solvent occurs through the column. Solutes of different affinity with the matix separate efficiently from one another with high resolution. HPLC can detect the mismatch by identifying the difference in the mobility of the mismatchched hybrid compared with the fully base paired one in HPLC column. These PAGE & HPLC methods can determine the mismatch but cannot provide information about the location of point mutation.

(c) Cleavage of the heteroduplex by the **treatment with enzymes or chemicals** which cut at single stranded regions of dsDNA or with specific ribronuclease enzyme such as S1-ribonuclease if the hydrid is formed between control DNA or RNA strand with mutated test DNAstrand. This is then followed by gel electrophoresis. If there is no mutation the heteroduplex would remain intact. But when such mutant is present, then the position can be detected by the size of the cleavage product, in the gel electrophoretic bands.

4. **Mutation screening :** This method is based on the allele-specific oligonucleotide (ASO) hybridization. It can not only detect but can also locate the mutation even at only one nucleotide position. In ASO hybridization an oligonucleotide probe is used to determine which of the two alternative nucleotide sequences is contained in a DNA sample. DNA samples are usually obtained by PCR of clinical isolates. The DNA samples are screened by probing with an oligonucleotide that hybridizes only to the mutant sequence. These oligonucleotides are about 50 nucleotides in length, single stranded DNA molecules, synthesized in the test tube. Its sequence is allele specific, i.e. there are two alternatives, one is normal and another is mutant. The mutant oliginucleotide can hybridize with the mutant sample, which can be detected by autoradiography of a dotblot on nylon membrane (Fig. 19.28).

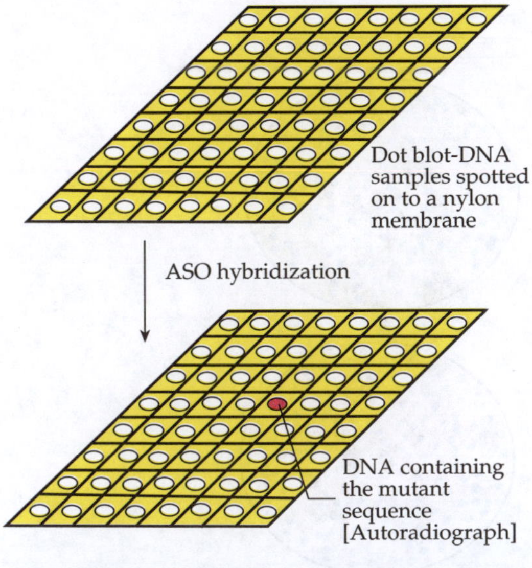


**Fig. 19.28 :** *Allele-specific oligonucleotide (ASO) hybridization.*

## 19.8 REVERSIONS

Due to mutation, a change from wild type to mutant state takes place.

The process by which the wild-type phenotype is regained from the mutated state is called **back mutation** or **reversion.** This resulting mutatnt is called a **reverent.**

Reversion may occur in two ways :

1. A **true reversion** is due to a back mutation that exactly restores the original DNA sequence.
2. A **pseudoreversion** or **suppressor mutation** is due to an additional mutation at a second site that restores the original phenotype.

**Reversion a mean of detecting Mutagens and Carcinogens :**

Most carcinogens are also mutagens, so assaying mutagenecity can be used for the initial screening of these hazardous agents. One simple method of screening large numbers of substances for mutagenecity is a REVERSION TEST using auxotrophic mutants of bacteria (the mutant bacteria having a growth requirement of specific nutrient.). For this purpose, a compound that is a potential mutagen is added to solid growth media, known numbers of a mutant reverent colonies that arise are counted. A significant increase in the reversion frequency above that obtained in the absence of the compound tested would identify the substance as a mutagen. This test is simple but may fail to demonstrate the mutagenecity of a number of potent carcinogens because some carcinogens are not directly mutagenic, they become so after certain enzymatic metabolism in the liver of the animals and are transformed into nontoxic substances. These enzymes are present in the liver as microsomes. Addition of rat liver microsomes to the growth medium has been used to extend the sensitivity and usefulness of the reversion test system.

Ames used this microsomal fraction for the carcinogens, called as **Ames test**. In this test, histidine requiring mutants ($His^-$) of *Salmonella typhimurium* is used (which is produced due to a base substitution or a frameshift mutation) for reversion to $His^+$. This strain also contains a plasmid that enhances SOS repair of DNA as well as sensitive to mutagenesis by the incorporation of mutations that inactivate the excision repair system and make the cell more permeable to foreign molecules. A solid agar medium is used, which contains enough *histidine* to support only few rounds of replication, but not enough to permit formation of a colony.

The liver microsomal fraction is spread on the agar surface. Then mutated bacteria are plated. A paper disc., saturated either with distilled water (as a control) or a solution of the compound being tested is placed in the center of the plate. The test compound would diffuse outward from the disc, forming a concentration gradient. If the substance is a mutagen or if it is converted into a mutagen, colonies form. With a highly effective mutagen, colonies will be present all over the surface of the medium including far from the disc where the concentration is low. With a weak mutagen, colonies will form only very near the disc where

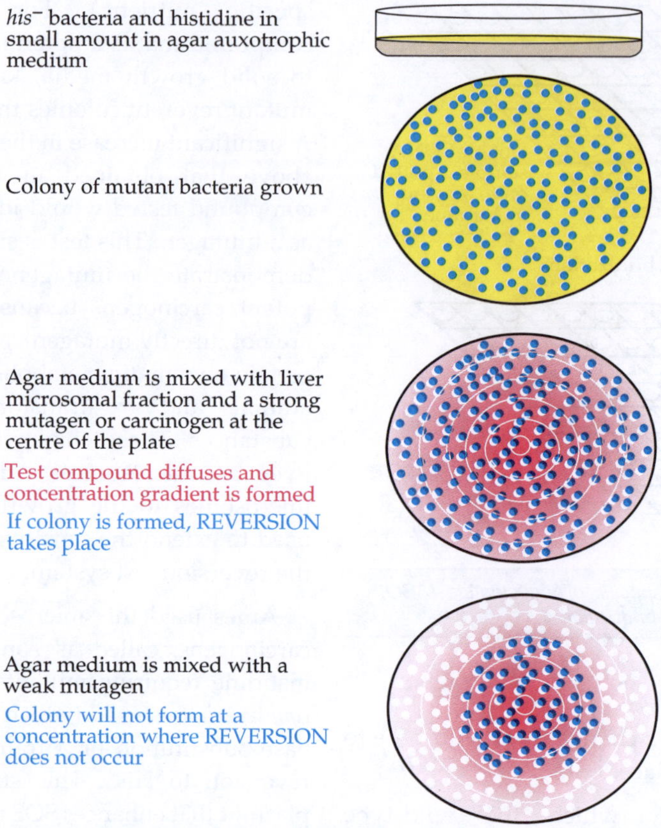


**Fig.19.29 :** *Ames test.*

the concertration is high. This **Ames test** is highly sensitive and also permits the detection of weak mutagens (Fig. 19.29).

At present, Ames test is used with thousands of substances and mixtures such as industrial chemicals, food additives, pesticides, hair dyes and cosmetics as well as many suspected substances. This is used for the formulation of cosmetics, hair dyes to render them non mutagenic and to determine its carcinogenecity *i.e.* tumor formation in laboratory animals.

## 19.9 REPAIR OF DNA

### 19.9.1 Concept

Every day our genome is undergoing thousands of damages during replication or mutation by physical and chemical mutagens or by other means. The cell certainly contains the repair systems so that the damaged genome can be repaired and would become functional again.

Most cells possess *four* different categories of DNA repair system (**Lindahl and Wood 1999**).

*Direct repair system, Excision repair, Mismatch repair* and *Recombination repair*. Defects in DNA repair system result in certain diseases (Fig. 19.30).

### 19.9.2 Direct repair systems

The damages of DNA caused by chemical and physical mutagens can be repaired by excision of the damaged nucleotides followed by resynthesis of a new stretch of DNA. This is direct repair of DNA.

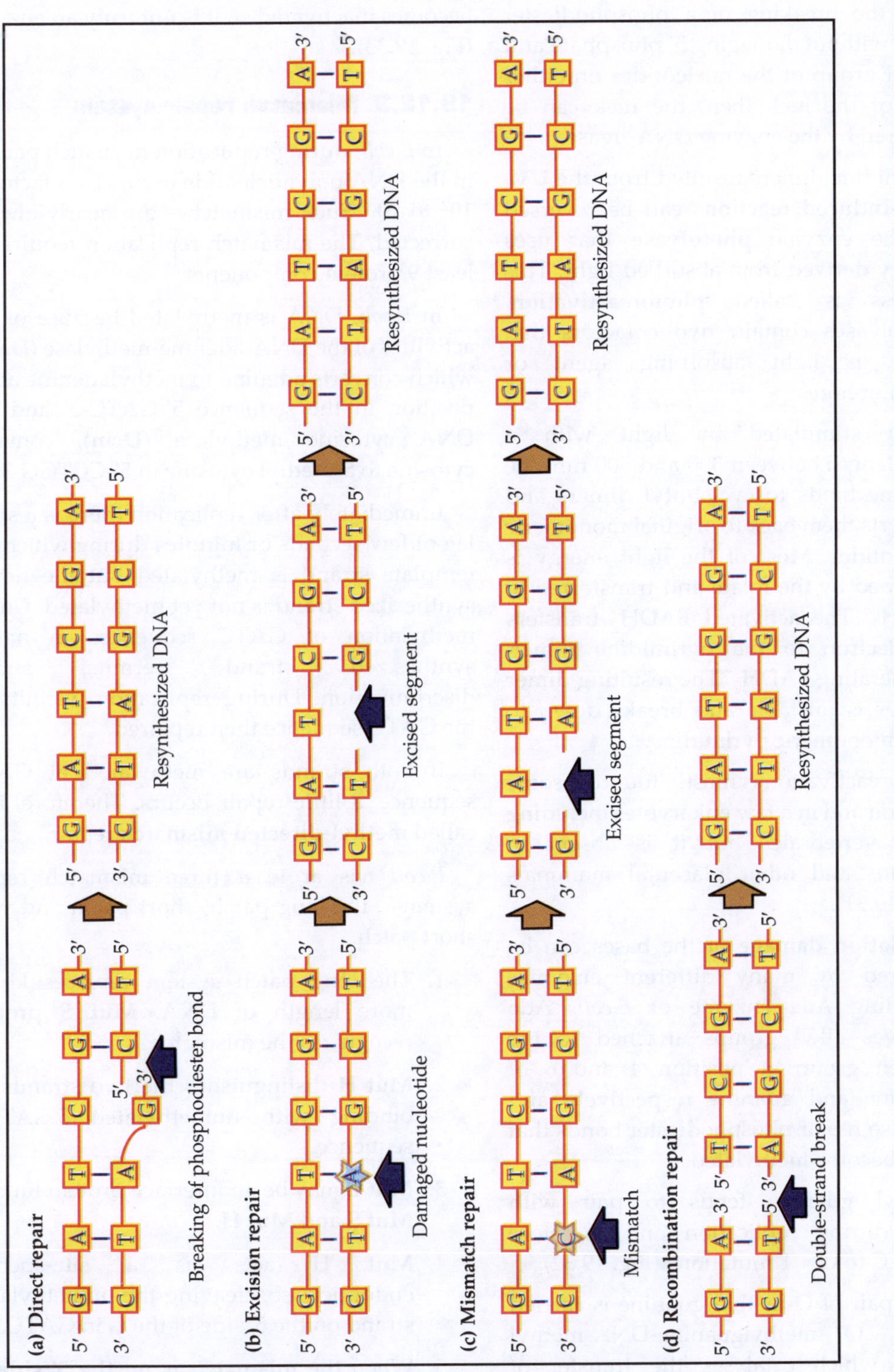


**Fig.19.30 : *Four catagotries of DNA repair system***

1. If nick is produced by **ionizing radiation** with the breaking of a phosphodiester bond without damaging 5′ phosphate and 3′-OH group of the nucleotides on either side of the nick then, the nick can be repaired by the enzyme DNA-ligase.
2. Pyrimidine dimers resulted from the **UV-light-induced reactions** can be reversed by the enzyme **photolyase** that uses energy derived from absorbed light. This process is called **photoreactivation**. Photolyases contain two cofactors that serve as light absorbing agent or chromophores.

   When stimulated by light with a wavelength between 300 and 500 nm, the enzyme binds to cyclobutyl dimers and converts them back to original monomeric nucleotides. Most of the light energy is absorbed by the folate and transferred to $FADH_2$. The activated $FADH_2$ transfers an electron to the pyrimidine dimer, regenerating $FADH_2$. The resulting dimer species is unstable and breaks down to form monomeric pyrimidine.

   Photoreactivation is mostly found in some bacteria and in a few eukaryotes including some vertebrates but it is absent in humans and other placental mammals (Fig. 19.31).
3. **Alkylation damage** of the bases can be repaired by many different enzymes including **Ada** enzyme of *E.coli.* Ada removes alkyl groups attached to the oxygen group at position 4 and 6 of thymine and guanine respectively and can also repair phosphodiester bonds that have become methylated.

$O^6$-methyl guanine tends to pair with thymidine during replication and therefore causes G — C to G = T mutations (Fig. 19.32).

Direct repair of O-methyl guanine is carried out by $O^6$–methylguanine-DNA-methyl transferase, which catalyses the transfer of —$CH_3$ group to a specific *Cys* residue of the same protein (enzyme). This enzyme then becomes inactivated so it is not truly an enzyme (Fig. 19.33).

### 19.12.3 Mismatch repair system

In *E.coli,* during replication mismatch pairing in the DNA polynucleotide occurs by a factor of $10^2$ to $10^3$. Such mismatches are nearly always corrected. The mismatch replication requires at least 9 protein components.

In *E.coli,* DNA is methylated because of the activities of the DNA-adenine-methylase (**Dam**), which converts adenine to methyladenine at $N^5$ position in the sequence 5′-GATC-3′ and the DNA cytosine methylase (**Dcm**), converts cytosine to 5-methyl cytosine in 5′-CCTGG-3′.

Immediately after replication there is a short lag of few seconds or minutes during which the template strand is methylated but the newly synthesized strand is not yet methylated. Under methylation of GATC sequences in newly synthesized strand permits strand discrimination. During replication, vicinity of the GATC sequence then repaired.

If both strands are methylated at GATC sequence, a little repair occurs. Therefore, it is called **methyl-directed mismatch** repair.

*E.coli* has at least three mismatch repair systems : the long patch, short patch and very short patch.

1. The long patch system replaces kb or more length of DNA. **Mut S** protein recognizes the mismatch.
2. **Mut H** distinguishes the two strands by binding with unmethylated 5′GATC3′ sequence.
3. **Mut L** may be an interface protein linking **Mut S** and **Mut H**.
4. **Mut H** acts as a site-specific endonuclease, cleaving the unmethylated strand on the 5' side of the G in GATC.
5. When the **mismatch is on the 5′ side** of the cleavage site, the unmethylated strand

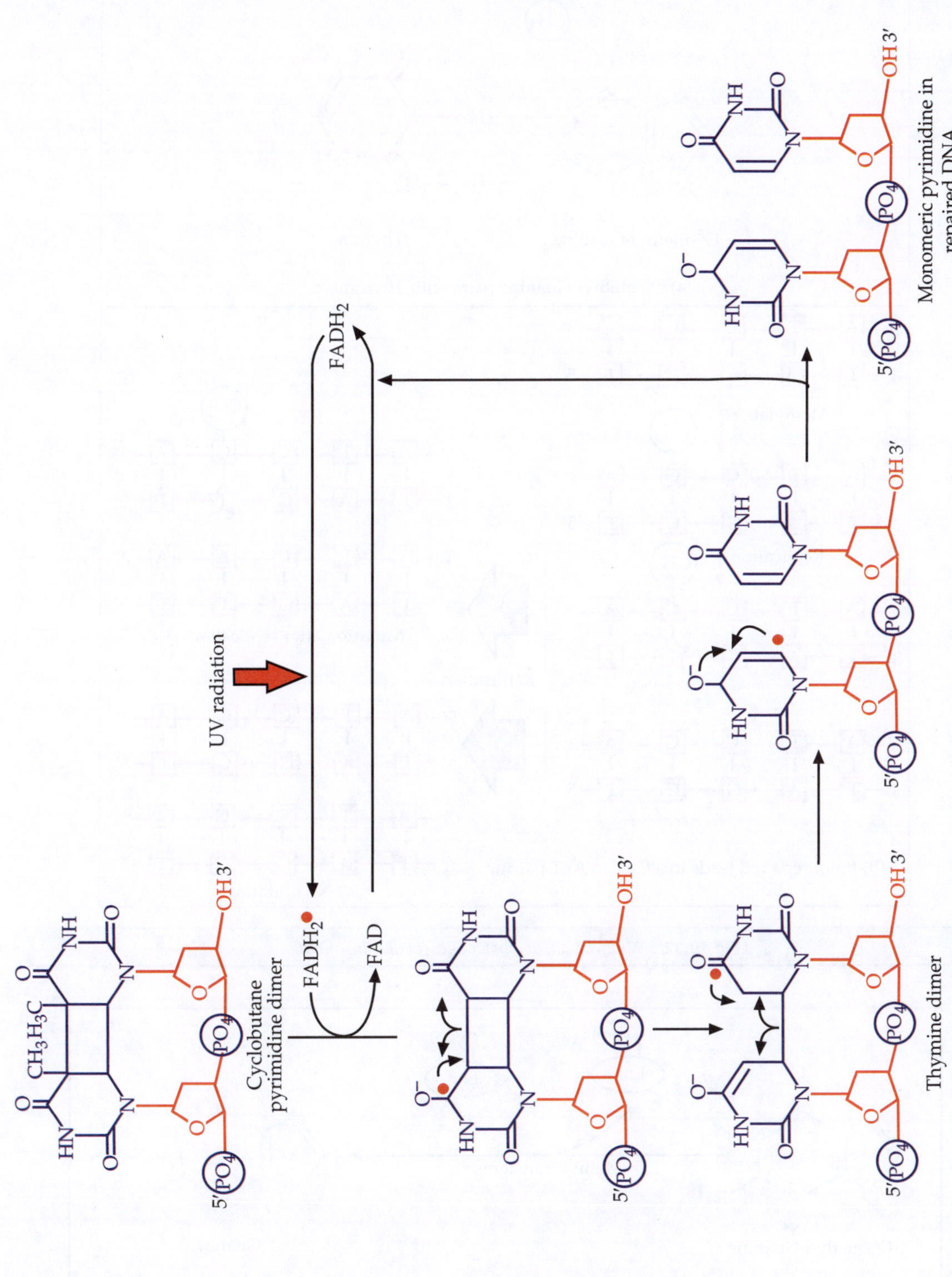


**Fig.19.31:** *Repair of pyrimidine dimers with photolyase.*

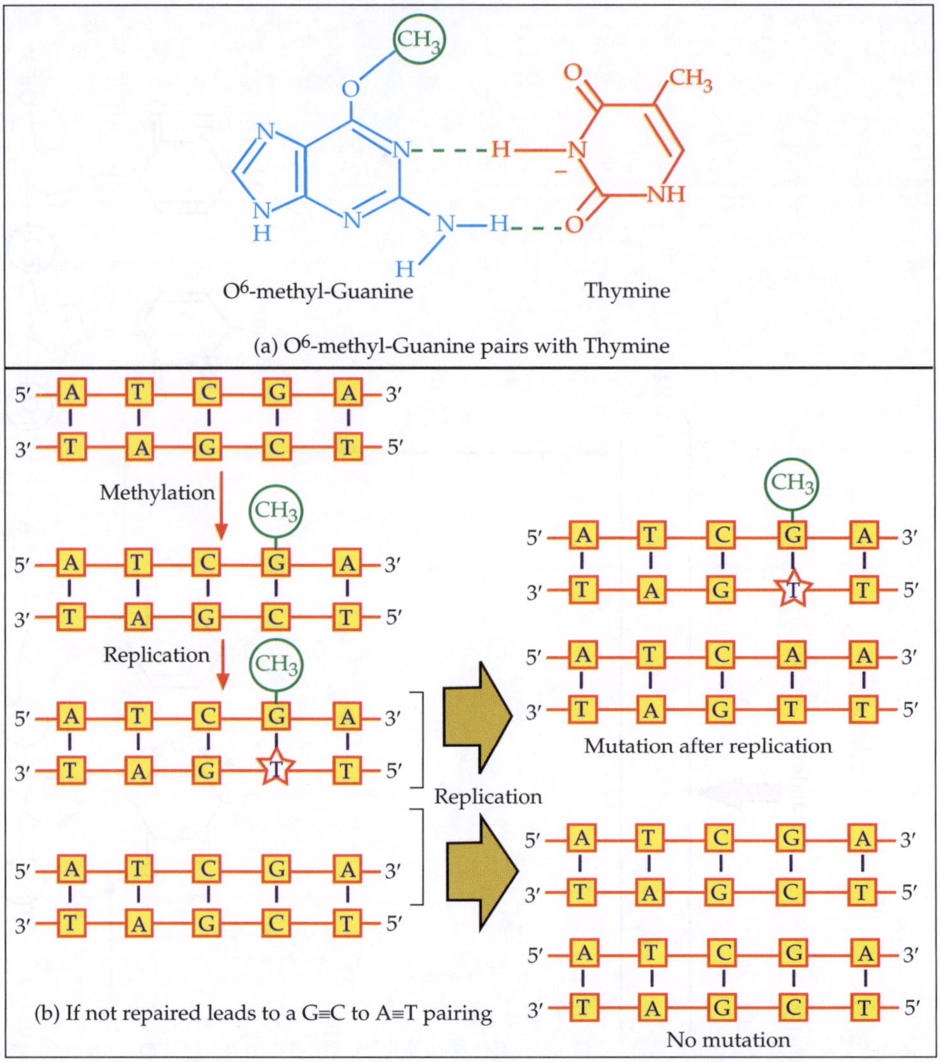


(a) $O^6$-methyl-Guanine pairs with Thymine

(b) If not repaired leads to a G≡C to A≡T pairing

**Fig.19.32 :** *Methylation of nucleotide results in mutation.*

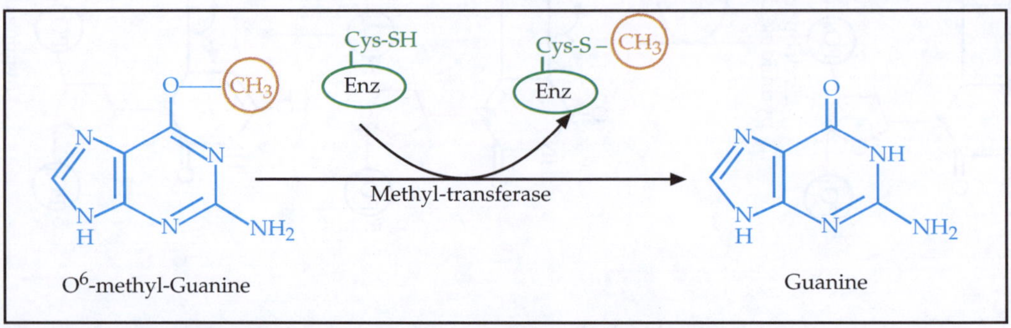


**Fig.19.33 :** *Direct repair by* Methyl-transferase.

is unwound and degraded in 3′∅5′ direction from the cleavage site through the mismatch and this is then replaced with new DNA. This process requires combined action of DNA helicase-II, SSB exonuclease-I, DNA polymerase-III and then ligase.

6. When the *mismatches are on the 3′ side* of the cleavage site, the process is mostly similar except that exonuclease-VII or **Rec J** protein (which degrades ssDNA in 5′→3′ direction) replaces exonuclease-I (Fig. 19.34).
7. Similar events are thought to occur during short and very short mismatch repair. The differences are that the recognition protein and the length of the excision segment. **Mut Y** recognizes in A—G or A—C mismatch with an excision of 10 nucleotides length. Vsr–endonuclease recognizes G—T mismatches in the very short repair system.
8. Some eukaryotes including fruit fly and yeast, the methylation does not occur but in mammals methylation has been implicated. The mismatch repair is mostly similar process (Kolodner 2000).
9. The *msh* repair system of *S.cerevisiae* is homologus to **MSH2** provides a scaffold for the apparatus that recognizes mismatches. **MSH3** and **MSH6** provide specificity factors. The MSH2-MSH3 complex binds to mismatched loops of two or four nucleotides and MSH2-MSH6 complex to single base mismatches or insertions or deletions. The other proteins are then required for completing the reaction.
10. Mismatch repair system is an expensive process. Degradation and replacement of strand segment of a kilo base length is invested. Besides, G–T mismatches are replacing well whereas C–C mismatches are poorly replaced.

**TABLE 19.3**
**Examples for human DNA glycosylases**

| *DNA glycosylase* | *Specific for* |
|---|---|
| MBD4 | Uracil |
| MPG | Ethenoadenine, hypoxanthine, 3 methyladenine |
| NTH 1 | Cytosine glycol, dihydrouracil, formamidopyrimidine, thymine glycol. |
| OGG 1 | Fomamidopyrimidine and 8 - oxoguanine |
| SMUG 1 | Uracil |
| TDG | Ethenocytosine, uracil |
| UNG | Uracil, 5-hydroxyuracil |

* Based on Lindahl and Wood (1999) and Wood et at (2001)

### 19.9.4 Base Excision Repair

Every cell has a class of enzymes called **DNA glycosylases** that recognize particularly common DNA lesions such as the product of deamination of adenine and guanine and remove the affected bases by cleaving the β- N-glycosyl bond. Each DNA glycosylase has a limited specificity.

DNA glycosylase first removes a damaged base by flipping the structure to a position outside of the helix and then detaching it from the polynucleotide (Kunkel *et al* 1996, Roberts *et al* 1998).

Excision creates a baseless or AP-site (Apurinic or apyrimidinic site).

A single nucleotide gap is produced at the AP site by an AP endonuclease such as endonuclease III or endonuclease IV of *E.coli* or human APE1, which cuts the phosphodiester bond on 5′ side of the AP site. Some AP nucleases can also remove the sugar from the nucleotide with a separate phosphodiesterase.

An alternative path is that a gap in the AP site is produced utilizing the endonuclease activity of some DNA glycosylases, which can make a cut at 3'-side of the AP site.

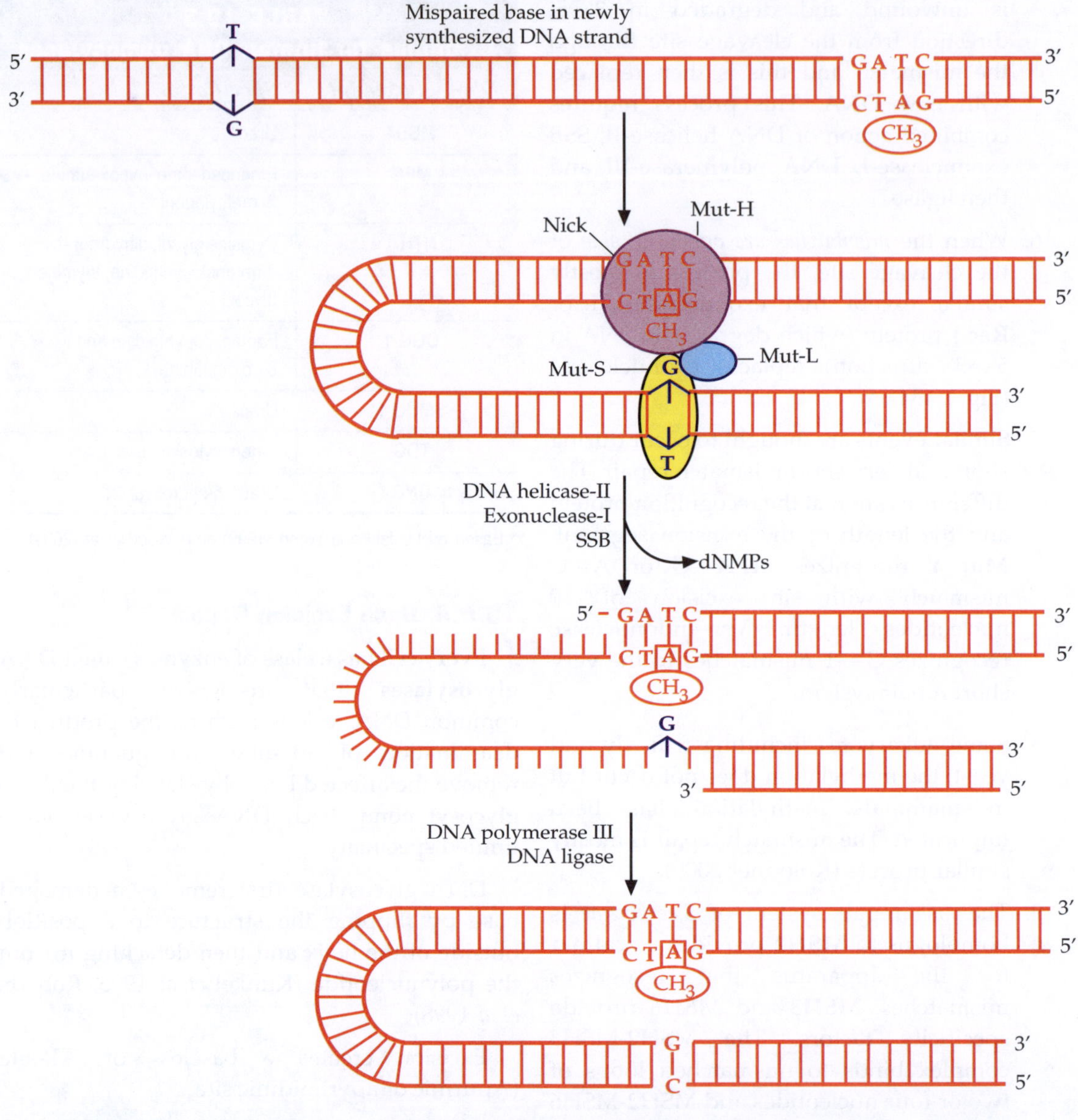


**Fig.19.34 :** *A model for methyl directed mismatch repair.*

This gap is then filled up by DNA polymerase-I in *E.coli* and DNA polymerase-β in mammals. Yeast uses DNA-polymerase δ for this purpose.

The gap is then joined by forming the phosphodiester bond by DNA-ligase (Fig. 19.35).

### 19.9.5 Nucleotide Excision Repair

In *E. coli* the key enzyme for nucleotide excision repair consists of three subunits, Uvr A, Uvr B and Uvr C and thus this multienzyme complex is known as Uvr ABC endonuclease or **ABC excinuclease** (Mr 246000). The term excinuclease is used because of its nucleolytic

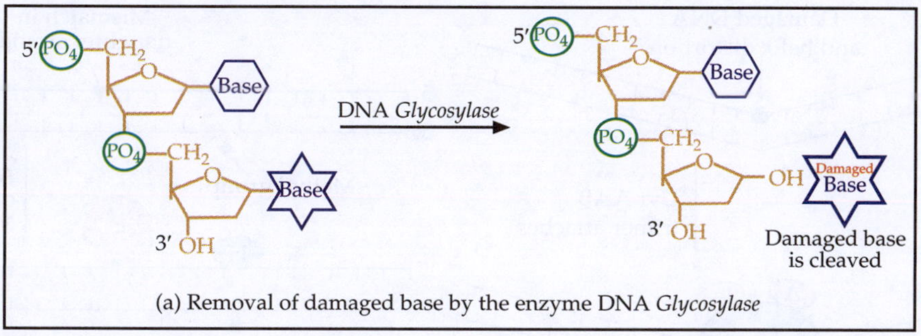

(a) Removal of damaged base by the enzyme DNA *Glycosylase*

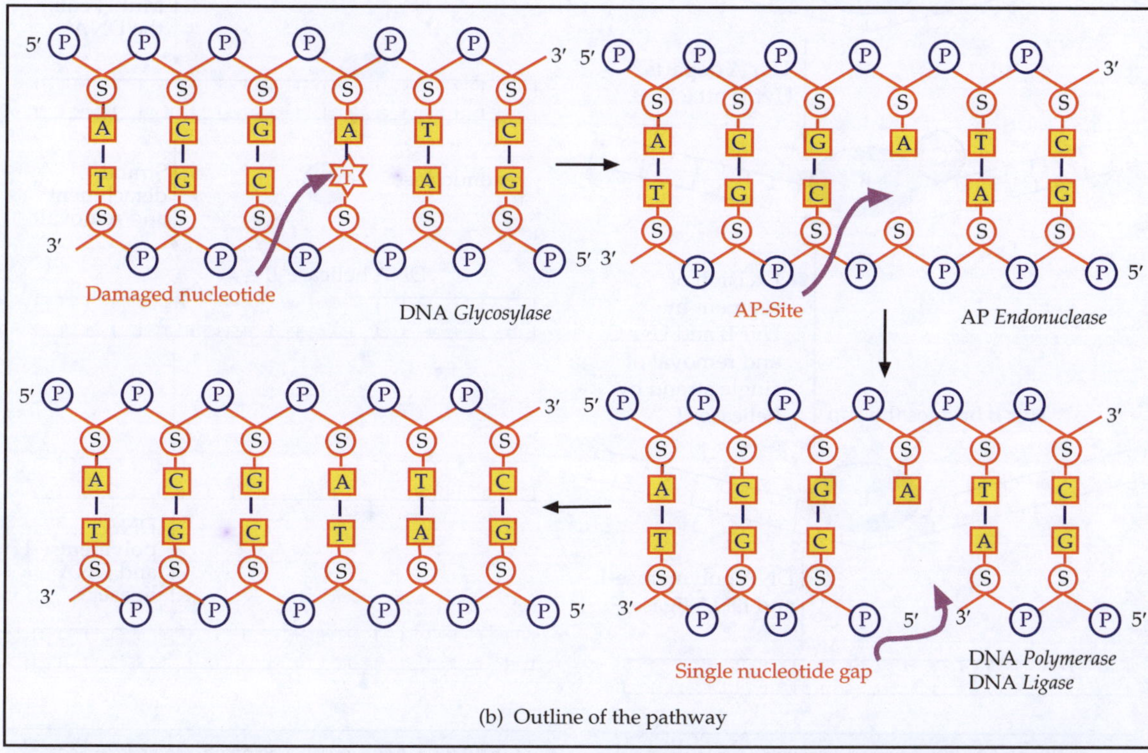

(b) Outline of the pathway

**Fig.19.35 :** *Base excision repair*

activity is novel in the sense that two cuts are made in the DNA.

The enzyme recognizes many types of lesions including cyclobutane pyrimidine dimers, 6–4 photoproducts and several other types of base adducts. Those organisms that do not have photoreactivation system such as humans, by this type of **dark repair process** the damage is corrected.

1. In the first stage, a trimer comprising two Uvr A and one copy of Uvr B attaches to the damaged site of DNA possibly recognizing the area of distortion of the double helix.
2. After recognition of DNA, the UvrA subunit leaves the complex and it allows Uvr C to bind forming Uvr BC-complex.
3. This Uvr-BC complex thus cuts the polynucleotide either sides of the

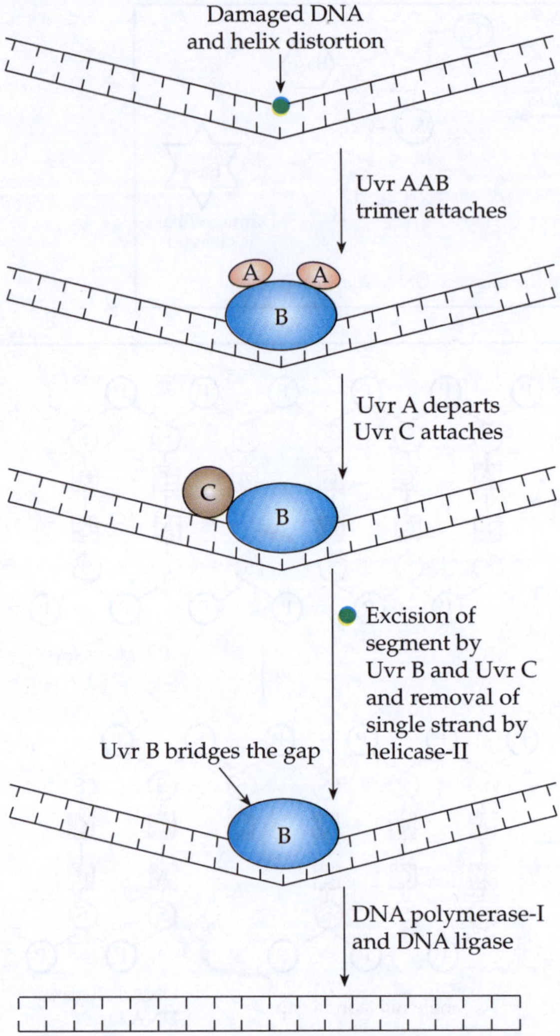


**Fig.19.36 :** *Short patch nucleotide excision repair in E. coli.*

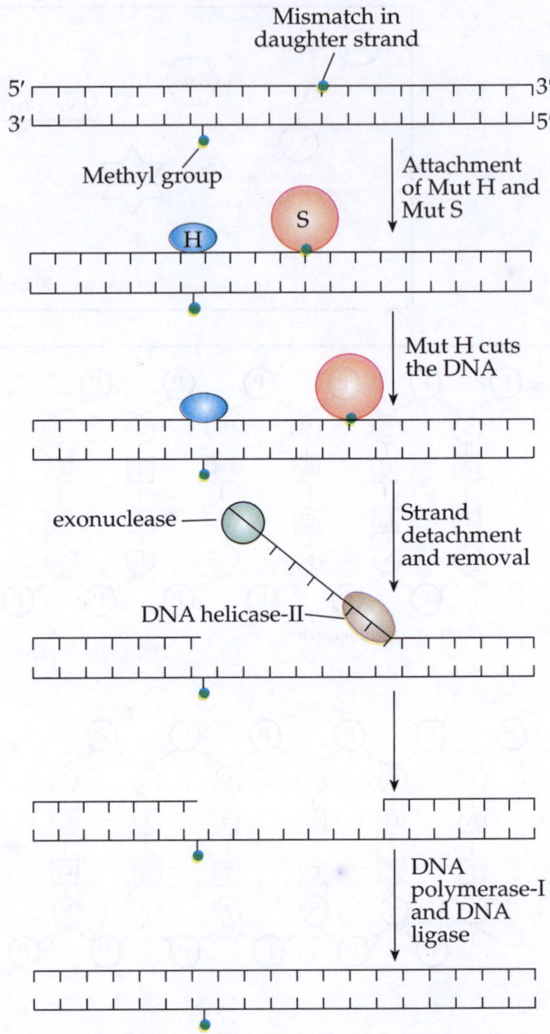


**Fig.19.37 :** *Long patch mismatch repair in E. coli.*

damaged site. At first Uvr B cuts the DNA at 5$^{th}$ phosphodiester bond down stream of the damaged nucleotide. The second cut is made by Uvr C at the 8th phosphodiester bond upstream, resulting 12-nucleotide excision.

4. The excised site is removed. DNA helicase -II presumably detaches the segment breaking the base pairs holding it to the second strand.

5. Thus Uvr C detaches from the complex. Only Uvr B remains in place and prevents pairing of single stranded region.

6. The gap is now filled by DNA polymerase-I and the phosphodiester bond is formed by DNA ligase to close the nick (Fig. 19.36).

*E.coli* has a long patch nucleotide excision repair system that involves Uvr proteins but differ is that, excision of about 2 kb length of DNA occurs (Fig. 19.37).

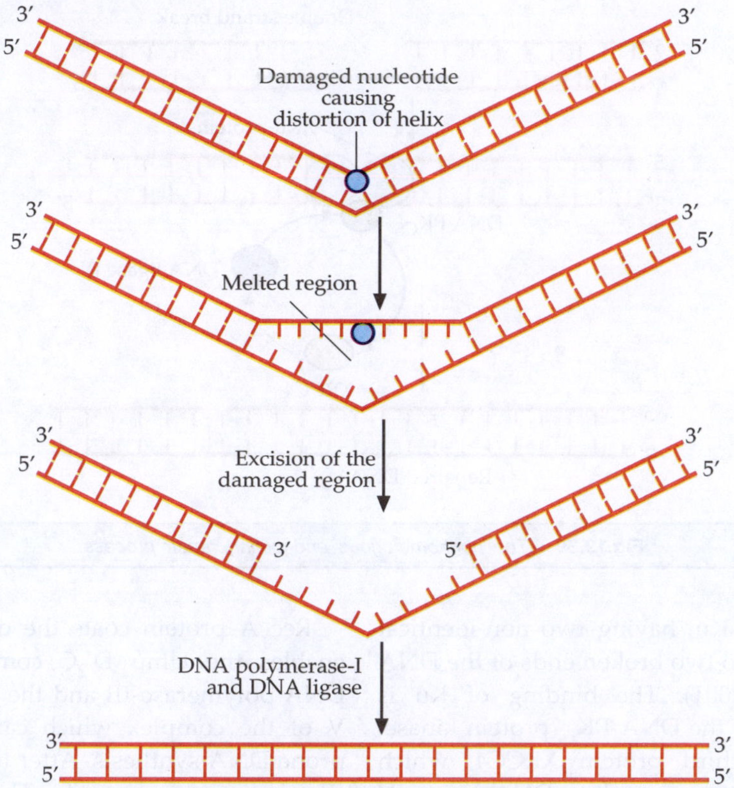


**Fig.19.38 :** *An outline of the events involved during nucleotide excision repair in eukaryotes.*

In eukaryotes the replacement of only 24–29 nucleotides of DNA takes place. In human at least 16 proteins are involved with downstream cut at 5th phosphodiester bond but with a more distance upstream cut, resulting in the longer excision (Fig. 19.38).

The damaged region causing helix distortion and helicase activity of TF II H causing melting at that region. Endonuclease removes the damaged region making cuts specifically at the junction between single stranded and double-stranded regions of the DNA-molecule DNA-polymerase-I and DNA ligase then take part in DNA synthesis and closing the nicks respectively.

Thus TF II H components of RNA polymerase-II have a dual role in the cell functioning separately in both transcription and repair. This view is supported by the discovery of **transcription couple repair**, which repairs some forms of damages in the template strands that are transcribed.

### 19.9.6. Recombination Repair

It is also called double-stranded DNA repair because in this phenomenon repair of the two broken ends of the DNA takes place and protects the genome from further degradation. Possibly the presence of special telomere-bindng proteins mark the natural ends of the chromosome.

Double strand breaks are generated by exposure to ionizing radiations or chemical mutagens or during recombination events.

A multi-component protein complex directs a DNA ligase to the break. The complex contains

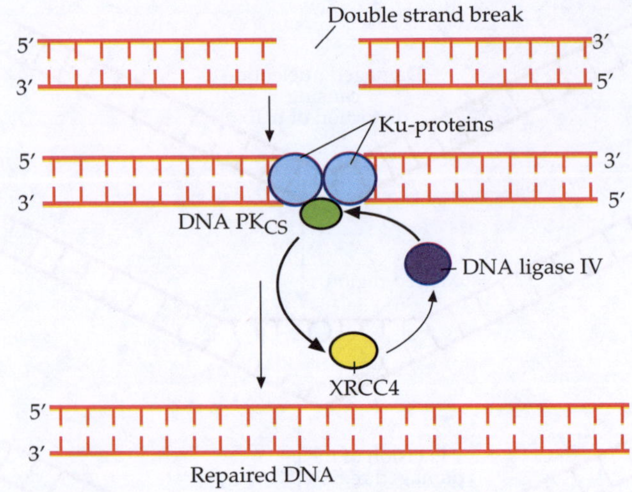


**Fig.19.39 :** *The nonhomologous end-joining repair process.*

a protein called **Ku**, having two non-identical subunits, binds to two broken ends of the DNA (Walker *et al* 2001). The binding of Ku is accomplished by the DNA-$PK_{cs}$ protein kinase. It activates a third protein XRCC4, which interacts with the mammalian DNA ligase-IV directing this repair protein to join the double strands broken ends. Like recombination, non-homologus ends are joined by this process. Therefore, this type of repair process is also called non-homologus end joining repair process (Fig. 19.39).

### 19.9.7 Repair of DNA when damage is extensive

When the damage of DNA is extensive then the DNA-repair is significantly less accurate. It simply allows a damaged region to be replicated. Therefore, this is called **error-prone repair** also called **translesion synthesis**. It only maintains the structural integrity of the cellular DNA.

This type of bypass process is best studied is the **SOS response**. Bypass of the damaged sites required construction of a "mutasome" comprising Umu $D'_2C$ complex, DNA polymerase-V and several copies of Rec A protein (Goodman 2000).

Rec A protein coats the damaged DNA. It enables the Umu $D'_2C$ complex to displace DNA polymerase-III and the DNA polymerase V of the complex which carry out the error prone DNA synthesis. After this, the DNA pol-III takes over once again. The two other DNA polymerases in *E.coli* also act in a similar way. These are DNA polymerase-II which can do bypass repair bound to mutagenic chemical, N-2 acetyl-amino-fluorine. DNA polymerese IV which can synthesize DNA in which two parent polynucleotides have become misaligned (Lindahl and Wood, 1999; Hanaoka 2001) (Fig. 19.40).

In Eukaryotic cells, such bypass repair has also been discovered. The DNA polymerase-η can bypass cyclobutyl dimers (Johnson *et al* 1999), DNA polymerase-ι and ζ, which work together to replicate through photoproducts and AP sites (Johnson et al 2000).

### 19.9.8 DNA repair and Cancer

Loss of DNA repair mechanism causing DNA damage and become permanent changes in the base sequence, which is called mutation. Sometimes this damage affects non-essential function of the gene it is called *silent mutation*. But sometimes it becomes **lethal** and

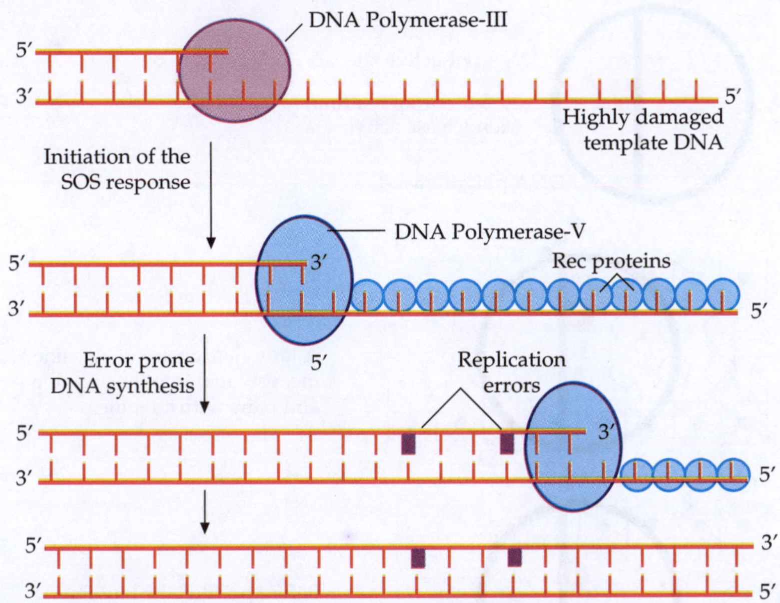


**Fig.19.40 :** *The SOS response of E. coli.*

**deleterious mutation**. The accumulation of several mutations can led to the **cancer**.

A rare human genetic disease called **xeroderma pigmentosum** is caused by a defect in the multienzyme process by which pyrimidine dimers and other bulky lesions in DNA are repaired. Many of these lesions are induced by UV-light and patients with this disease rapidly develop multiple skin cancers if exposed to sunlight.

Trichothiodistrophy is also caused by defects in nucleotide excision repair.

The breast and ovarian cancers are due to transcription-coupled defects in BRCA-1 gene.

Cockayne syndrome, a complex disease manifested by growth and neurologic disorder (Hanawatt 2000).

The cancer susceptibility syndrome, (hereditary nonpolyposis colorectal cancer) has been identified, which is actually due to a deficiency in transcription- coupled repair.

**Ataxia telangiectasia**, the symptoms of which are including sensitivity to ionizing radiation results from defects in the *ATX*-gene which is involved in the damaged detection process.

Bloom's and Werner's syndrome may be caused by inactivation of DNA helicase and has a role in non-homologus end joining disease. (Shen and Loeb 2000 Wu and Hickson 2001) and Fanconi's anemia.

### 19.12.9 Error Correction in Replication by DNA polymerase-I

In *E. coli,* during replication a mistake is made only once for every $10^9$ to $10^{10}$ nucleotides added. Thus from $4.7 \times 10^6$ base pairs about 1000 to 10000 errors may be taken place. Incorrect nucleotides in polynucleotide chains will not form correct hydrogen bonds.

The DNA polymerase I has both $3' \rightarrow 5'$ exonuclease activity and $5' \rightarrow 3'$ polymerization activity and therefore, it can remove the mismatched base pairs and simultaneously begins DNA polymerization. This activity is called **proof reading** activity.

1. Cytosine may undergo a rare tautomeric form that pairs with adenine and is incorporated into the growing strand.

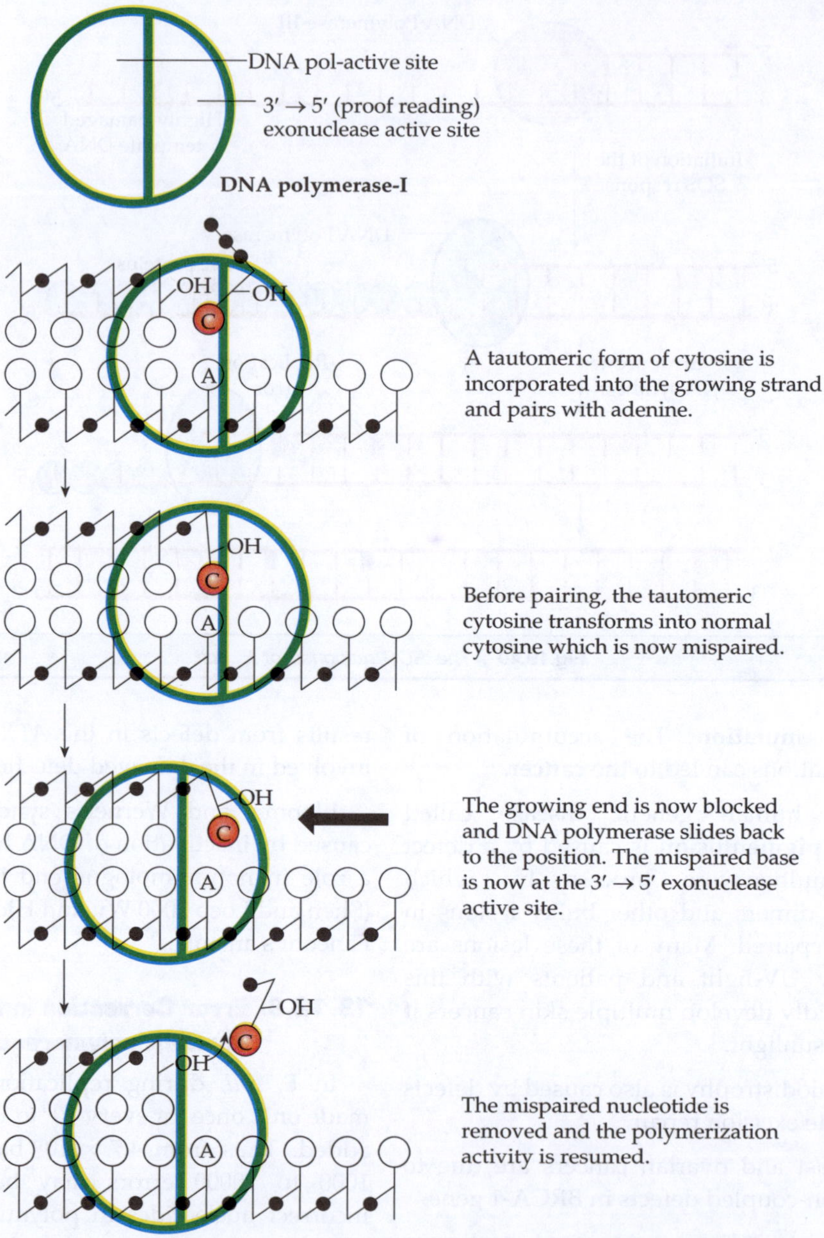


**Fig.19.41 :** *Error correction by DNA polymerase-I with its 3′ →5′ exonuclease activity.*

2. Before the polymerase moves on, the cytosine undergoes a tautomeric shift and now the cytosine is misplaced.
3. The misplaced 3′-OH end of the growing strand blocks further elongation. DNA polymerase slides back to position the mispaired base in the 3′→5′ exonuclease active site.
4. The mispaired nucleotide is removed.
5. Then the DNA polymerase-I slides forward and resumes it polymerization activity (Fig. 19.41).

## Chapter Glossary/Key Terms

**Ada enzyme :** This enzyme can repair alkylation damage of DNA in *E. coli.*

**Albinism :** A genetic disease where the melanin synthesis in the body in impeded.

**AP endonuclease :** An enzyme involved in base excision repair.

**AP site :** A position in a DNA molecule where the base component of the nucleotide is missing.

**Base excision repair :** A cut and patch mochanism of the removal from the DNA of altered nucleotides.

**Clastogen :** The agents that cause various types of cellular anomalies and cytological changes in the chromosome morphologies.

**Fetal alcohol syndrome :** Birth defect in the children of an alcoholic mother.

**Frame-shift mutation :** It arises by deletions or insertions that are not a multiple of 3 bp; they change the frame in which triplets are translated into protein.

**Heinz-Bodies :** Abnormal denaturation of Hb and forming precipitation in the cell and are demonstrable by supravital stain.

**Methyl transferase enzyme :** Catalyses the transfer of methyl group to specific *cys* residue.

**Minamata disease :** Mercury readily penetrates the central nervous system causing teratogenic effect among the children born in Minamata area.

**Mismatch :** A position in a double stranded DNA molecule where base-pairing does not occur because the nucleotides are not complementary in particular, a non-base paired position resulting from an error in replication.

**Mismatch repir :** A DNA repair process that corrects mismatched nucleotide pairs by replacing the incorrect nucleotide in the daughter polynucleotide.

**Mutagen :** The agents that cause mutation to the living cells and organisms.

**Mutagenesis :** Induction of mutation by any chemical, physical or biological agents.

**Mutasome :** A protein complex that in constructed during the SOS response in *E. coli.*

**Mutation :** Any change in the squences of genomic DNA.

**Null mutation :** The loss of function mutation that completely abolishes the actvity of the gene.

**Oncogens :** The agents that induce cancer and tumor formation.

**Photolyse :** The enzyme in *E. coli.* involved in photoreactivation.

**Photoreactivation :** A DNA repair process is which cyclobutyl dimers and (6–4) photoproducts are corrected by light activation enzyme.

**Photoreactivation :** Damage caused by UV-radiation in DNA can be reversed by exposing to visible light.

**Point mutation :** Change involving single base-pairs.

**Proof reading :** It refers to any mechanism for correcting errors in protein or nucleic acid synthesis that involves scrutiny of individual units after they have been added to the chain.

**Radiomimetic agents :** The agents viz. some chemicals produce same kinds of mutagenic effect that X-ray produce.

**Recombination repair :** This is a mode of filling a gap in one strand of duplex DNA by retrieving a homologus single strand from another duplex.

*Contd.*

**Reverent :** The resulting mutant from a mutant by reversiom process.

**Reverse genetics :** The process by which gene is identified primarily by its map position or the sequence cloned for getting the information about the gene, whose products are not known.

**Reversion :** The process by which wild type phenotype is regained from the mutated state.

**Silent mutation :** The mutation that does not change the product of the gene.

**Site-directed mutagenesis :** The technique for generating artificially amino acid coding changes in the target gene a target site.

**SOS response :** A series of biochemical changes that occur in *E. coli* in response to damage to the genome and other stimuli.

**Target theory :** A single radiation his anywhere in a sensitive volume will always produce a given kind of mutation.

**Target volume :** The mutation caused by a single ionization or atomic excitation within a certain volume of matter is target volume.

**Teratogen :** The exogenous agent causes congenital abnormalities of the fetus in the womb.

**Thymine dimer :** The chemically cross-linked pair of adjacent thymine residues in DNA, a result of damage induced by UV-radiation.

**Transition :** A mutation in which one pyrimidine is substituted by the other or in which one purine is substituted for the other.

**Transversion :** A mutation in which a purine is replaced by a pyrimidine or vice versa.

**Xeroderma pigmentosum :** Absence of functional DNA pot-I, in human beins UV caused DNA damage is impaired causing this disease.

# Exercise

### A. Long answer type questions :

1. What types of chemical or physical agents that cause damage to living organisms.
2. What is mutation? Describe different types of mutations.
3. What do you mean by point mutation? Describe different types of gene mutations.
4. Give different biochemical mutations in man.
5. What do you mean by mutagens? What are these mutagens.
6. Describe the mechanism of mutations by ionizing radiations.
7. Describe the mechanism of mutations by nonionizing radiations.
8. Give details about the mechanism of action of chemical mutagens.

13. What do you mean by DNA repair? What are the four categories of DNA repair system?
14. Write a note on direct DNA repair systems.

15. What is mismatch repair? How does the mismatch repair take place in *E. coli*?
16. What do you mean by Base excision repair? Give some examples of human DNA glycosylases. How does base pair excision repair occur?
17. Waht do you mean by nucleotide excision repair? Describe the mechanism of nucleotide excision repair mechanism in *E. coli*.
18. What is recombination repair? How does it occur?
19. Describe the mechanism of repair when damage is extensive.
20. Give a not on the relationship between DNA repair and cancer.
21. How DNA polymerase-I is engaged in repair in replication errors.
22. What are means of reverse genetics? Briefly describe.
23. How oligoneucleotide directed mutagenesis is used for site directed mutagenesis?
24. What is cassette mutagenesis? How it is used for the site-directed mutagenesis?
25. Describe the principle and method of PCR-amplified oligonucleotide directed mutagenesis.
26. Describe ClB method of detection of X-linked mutation in *Drosophila*.
27. Describe Muller-S method of detection of mutaiton in *Drosophila*.
28. Describe autosomal lethal or nonlethal mutation detection in *Drosophila*.
29. Describe different techniques of detection of point mutation.
30. What is reversion? How this mechanism is used to detect mutagens or carcinogens?

### B. Short answer type questions :

1. What are the damages in the living cells caused by the environmental agents?
2. What is mutation?
3. What do you mean by loss of function and gain -in function mutation?
4. What is point mutation?
5. What is chromosome mutation?
6. Define base pair substitution.
7. What is non-sense mutation?
8. What is missense mutation?
9. What is termination mutation?
10. Define transition and transversion.
11. What do you mean by tautomers?
12. How C–A base pairing occurs?
13. Define inversions?
14. What do you mean by frame-shift mutation?
15. What are the causes of frame-shift mutation?
16. Define deletion and insersion.
17. What is simultaneous deletion and insertion?
18. What is silent mutation? How does it occur?
19. Define intragenic and intergenic suppressions?
20. What is lethal mutation? Give example.
21. What is conditional mutation? Give example.
22. What is null mutation?
23. What do you mean by biochemical mutation?
24. What is phenylketoneuria?
25. What Follings disease?
26. What is alkaptoneuria?
27. What do you mean by radiomimetic effects?
28. What is target theory of radiation effect?
29. What is sensitive volume?
30. Describe the biochemical effect of ionizing mutation?
31. What do you mean by oxygen effect.
32. What are free radicals? How does it affect the cell?
33. What are non ionizing radiations.
34. What is the effect of UV rays on DNA.
35. Why UV ray does not usually affect on RNAs?
36. How thymine and cytosine are affected by UV-ray.
37. What is photoreactivation?
38. How xerodermapigmentosum is caused?
39. Give some example base analogues?

40. How base analogues cause mutation?
41. How BU, BUdr and AP cause mutation?
42. Give some chemicals that inhibit the synthesis of nucleic acid precursors?
43. How $HNO_2$ causes mutation?
44. How $NH_2OH$ and $NH_2–NH_2$ cause mutation?
45. What are alkylating agents?
46. How alkylating agents cause mutation.
47. How acridine dyes cause mutation?
48. What do you mean by depurination?
49. What are respiratory inhibitors that cause mutation?
50. What do you mean by living mutagens?
51. What are clastogens? How do they cause demage?
52. What are delayed and non-delayed types of effects?
53. What is the cause of polyploidy?
54. What is the cause of lagging of chromosomes?
55. How clastogens act on the cell?
56. What is cytotoxicity?
57. What do you mean by disruptions?
58. What are teratogens?
59. What is the molecular cause of sickle cell condition.
60. Why DNA repair is required?
61. What are the different categories of DNA repair system?
62. What do you mean by direct DNA repair? Which enzymes are required for this purpose?
63. What is photoreactivation?
64. What is the role of Ada enzyme in DNA repair?
65. What is the role of O-methyl guanine-DNA methyltransferase enzyme in DNA repair?
66. What is mismatch repair? Which proteins are required for this purpose?
67. What are the roles of *Mut-S, Mut-H* and *Mut L* in DNA repair.
68. What is the role of Rec-J?
69. What is the role of Mut-Y.
70. What do you mean by *msh* repair system.
71. What is the role of MSH-2, MSH-3 and MSH-6?
72. What do you mean by base excision repair?
73. What are the roles of DNA pol-I and ligase in DNA repair?
74. What are the roles of Uvr-A, B and C in DNA repair of *E. coli*?
75. What is recombination repair? How does it occur?
76. What is mutasome?
77. What is error-prone repair?
78. What are the roles of DNA pol-$\delta$ and $\zeta$?
79. How Xerodermapigmentosum is resulted?
80. How BRCA-1 gene causes cancer?
81. What is Ataxiatelangiectasia?
82. How DNA pol-I repairs DNA?
83. What is the characteristic of exinuclease?
84. What is reverse genetics?
85. What is site-directed mutagenesis?
86. How oligonucleotide - directed mutagenesis is used for site directed mutagenesis.
87. What is casette mutagenesis?
88. What is the principle of PCR amplified oligonucleotide directed mutagenesis?
89. What is ClB stock? What are the characteristics?
90. What is the principle of ClB method for the detection of sex linked mutation in *Drosophila?*
91. What are the characteristics of Muller's stock? Why it is advantageous than ClB method?
92. What is balanced lethal? Give example?
93. What are the techniques for the detection of point mutation?
94. What is mutation scanning technique?
95. What do you mean by mutation screening?
96. What is reversion of mutation? What are the ways for reversion?
97. What is the principle of Ames test?
98. What are the applications of Ames test?

# 20

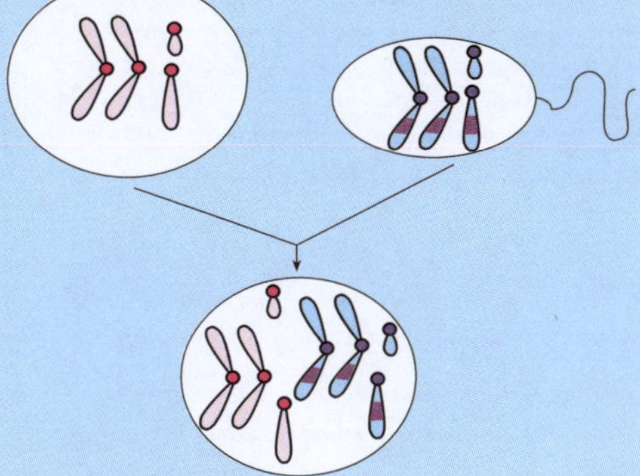

# Recombination of Genome

**CHAPTER AGENDA**

## 20.1 CONCEPT OF RECOMBINATION

*Crossing over* or *recombination* actually results from *exchange of chromosome segments,* which is believed to have taken place during prophase I of meiosis.

***Recombination is a process in which chromosomes or DNA molecules are cleaved and the fragments are rejoined to give new combinations.*** It occurs naturally in cells as the result of the exchange of DNA sequences on maternal and paternal chromosomes during meiosis.

The *DNA rearrangements* are caused by a set of mechanisms that are called *genetic recombinations*. Two broad classes are commonly recognized viz, **general recombination** and **site specific recombination**.

The *general recombination* is (also known as homologous recombination) is the genetic exchange taken place between a pair of homologous identical or similar chromosomes (DNA sequences). These are located usually on two copies of the same chromosome.

The *site-specific recombination* can alter gene order and also add new informations to the genome. Site-specific recombination moves specialized nucleotide sequences called *mobile genetic elements* between non-homologue sites within a genome. The movement can occur between two different positions in a single chromosome as well as between different chromosomes.

## 20.2. RELATION BETWEEN CROSSING OVER AND CHIASMA

The physical crossing over may or may not be identical with the chiasma observed during meiotic prophase. To explain the relationship between *crossing over* and *cytological chiasmata, the following two main theories* have been proposed (Fig 20.1).

1. **Classical theory or two-point theory :** This theory was proposed by L.W. Sharp (1935). According to this theory, when the chiasmata are formed then they each signifies an accident al arrangement of homologous chromatids. When a chiasma is ruptured then a reunion of broken ends brings about recombination. Therefore, according to this theory *a chiasma does not represent a recombination rather than recombination results when a chiasma is ruptured and a reunion of broken ends has been taken place.* At diplonema the loops of each bivalent are considered to be alternately reductional (sister chromatids are not separating) and equational (sister chromatids are separating). As chromosome contracts due to strain imposed by chiasma formation, the two chromatids are ruptured at the point of chiasma. It is assumed that adjacent loops would be present in different planes at right angles to each other. Therefore this is also known as **two-plane** theory.

2. **Chiasmatype theory or one point theory :** This theory was proposed by F.A Janssen (1909, 1924) and was developed by J.Belling and C.D.Darlington.

   This theory proposed that crossing over occurs sometimes during the early meiotic stages, perhaps pachytene, when homologous chromatids are closely paired. As the meiotic cell moves toward metaphase a chiasma is formed at the point where crossing over has occurred. Thus according to this theory *each chiasma represents one prior genetic crossing over and chiasma is the result of crossing over*. There is always reductional separation (sister chromatids not separating) on both sides of a chiasma.

   The two-plane theory i.e., the classical theory is now of only historical importance since all available experimental evidences have gone in favour of chiasmatype theory.

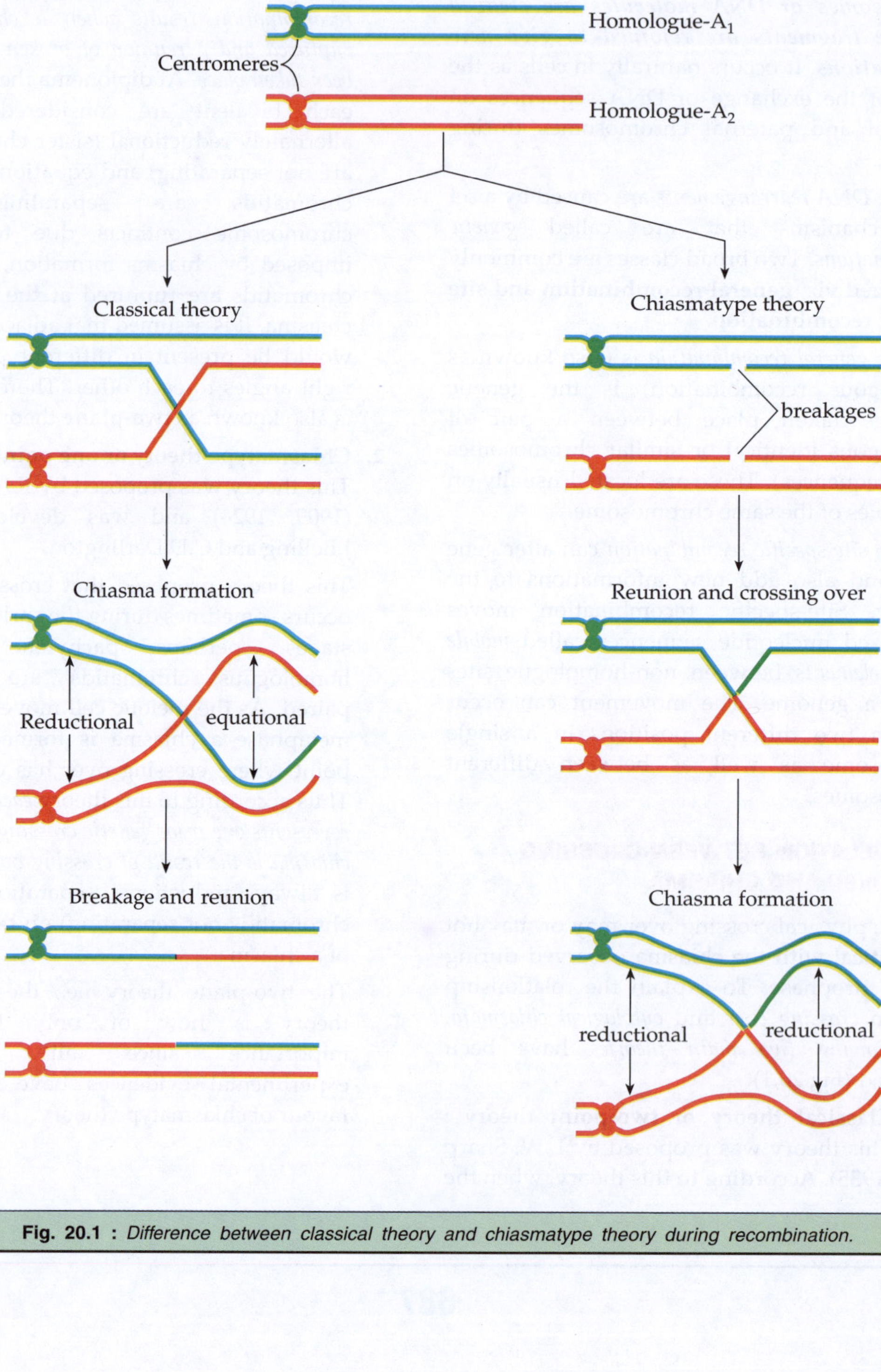


**Fig. 20.1 :** *Difference between classical theory and chiasmatype theory during recombination.*

## 20.3. MOLECULAR MODELS OF RECOMBINATION

### 20.3.1. Hybrid DNA Models involving single strand break

Several hybrid DNA models have been proposed regarding the molecular mechanism of recombination, which assume breaks in only one of the two strands on each of the two DNA molecules belonging to two non-sister chromatids. Two such models have been suggested, one by H.L.K Whitehouse (1963) of Cambridge and the other by Robin Holliday of London (1964).

1. **Whitehouse Model :** The salient features of this model are :

   (a) It assumes that each chromatid is thought to be a single double helical DNA and two of the non-sister chromatids are involved in recombination.

   (b) Breakage of a single nucleotide chain of each homologous DNA takes place at the same locus. The breakage of nucleotide chains would be of opposite polarity.

   (c) Rejoining of the breakage points will take place with the other homologous DNA but it would be of same polarity.

   (d) Synthesis of two new strands will be taken place over a short segment.

   (e) Formation of hybrid (new and old) unpaired nucleotide segments over the same segment will occur, simultaneously unpaired old chain break down takes place.

   Whitehouse model is applicable to fungi but it is yet to show in diploid organisms (Fig 20.2).

2. **Holliday Model :** This model (proposed by Holliday in 1964) is commonest among the homologous recombination models and is visualized under the electron microscope This model has received wide support and has been accepted for both eukaryotes and prokaryotes. The difference from the Whitehouse model is that in this model the breakage that takes place on the DNA polynucleotide strand has the same polarity. According to this model (Fig. 20.3).

   (a) A paired bivalent in meiosis consists of four chromatids at a particular location, two of them take part in recombination although for double and multiple crossing overs three or all the four chromatids may be involved.

   (b) The process starts with breakage at corresponding points of the homologus strands of two paired DNA duplex. Other two chromatids are being not involved.

   (c) The breakage allows movement of the free ends created by the nicks. Each strand at the broken end leaves its partner, crosses over, by displacing the broken strand of the other non sister molecule and it pairs with its complement into the other DNA duplex. Thus it creates a connection between the two DNA duplexes.

   (d) Initially this connection is sustained by hydrogen bonding but at some points branch migration takes place and the nicks at the sites of exchange are sealed with the help of ligase enzyme. The connected pair of duplex is called a **joint molecule** and the point at which an individual strand of DNA crosses from one duplex to the other is called the **recombinant joint**.

   (e) At the site of recombination, each duplex has a region consisting of one strand from each of the two parental DNA molecules. This region is called **hybrid DNA** or **heteroduplex DNA**.

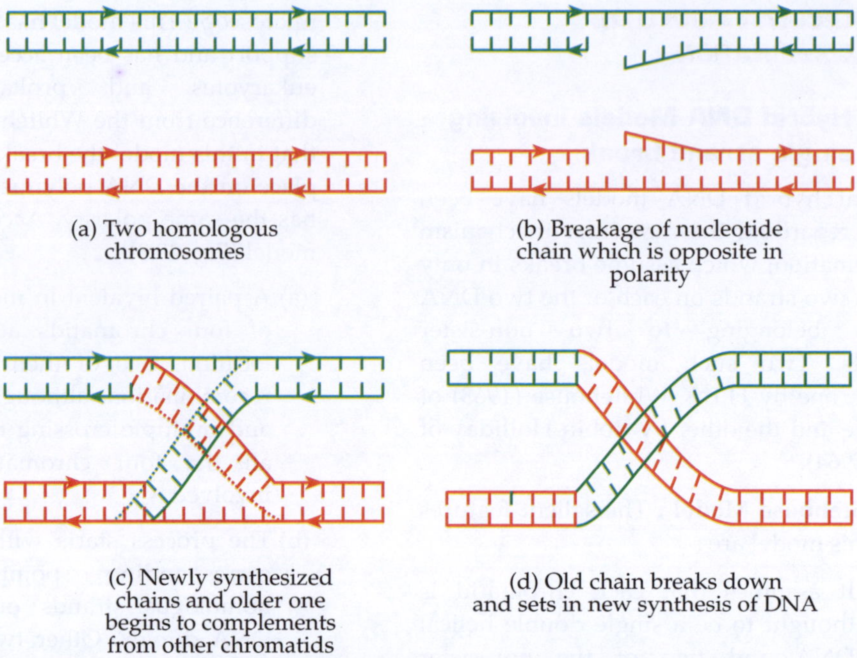


**Fig.20.2 :** *Whitehouse model of recombination.*

(f) Now the structure is formed by the repulsion of the chromatids (DNA strands) called the "**Chi**" structure.

(g) One of the two DNA duplexes in the joint molecule undergoes rotation giving rise to a **planar molecule**. In planar molecules there are four strands and two of them are nicked.

(h) The consequences of nicking will depend upon, which pair of strand is being nicked?

- If the nicks are made in the pair of strands that are not originally nicked, leads to release of recombinant DNA molecules. The DNA duplex segment of one parent is covalently linked to the DNA duplex segment of the other parent via a stretch of hetero-duplex DNA. This means that conventional recombination has taken place between markers located on either sides of the heteroduplex region.
- If the two strands involved in the original nicking are nicked again, then only original parental duplexes with heteroduplex segments with no recombinant DNA molecules are released between the marker genes (Fig. 20.3).

**Molecular Mechanism of initiation of Recombination :** The molecular mechanism of initiation of recombination can be established by **Rec BCD** enzyme in *E.coli*, which generates a recombinogenic single stranded region of DNA.

Rec BCD is a multifunction enzyme, which binds to free blunt ends of DNA, acts as a helicase, 3′→5′ exonuclease and 5′→3′ exonuclease activity both. This enzyme complex is composed of proteins, encoded by the *rec B, C*

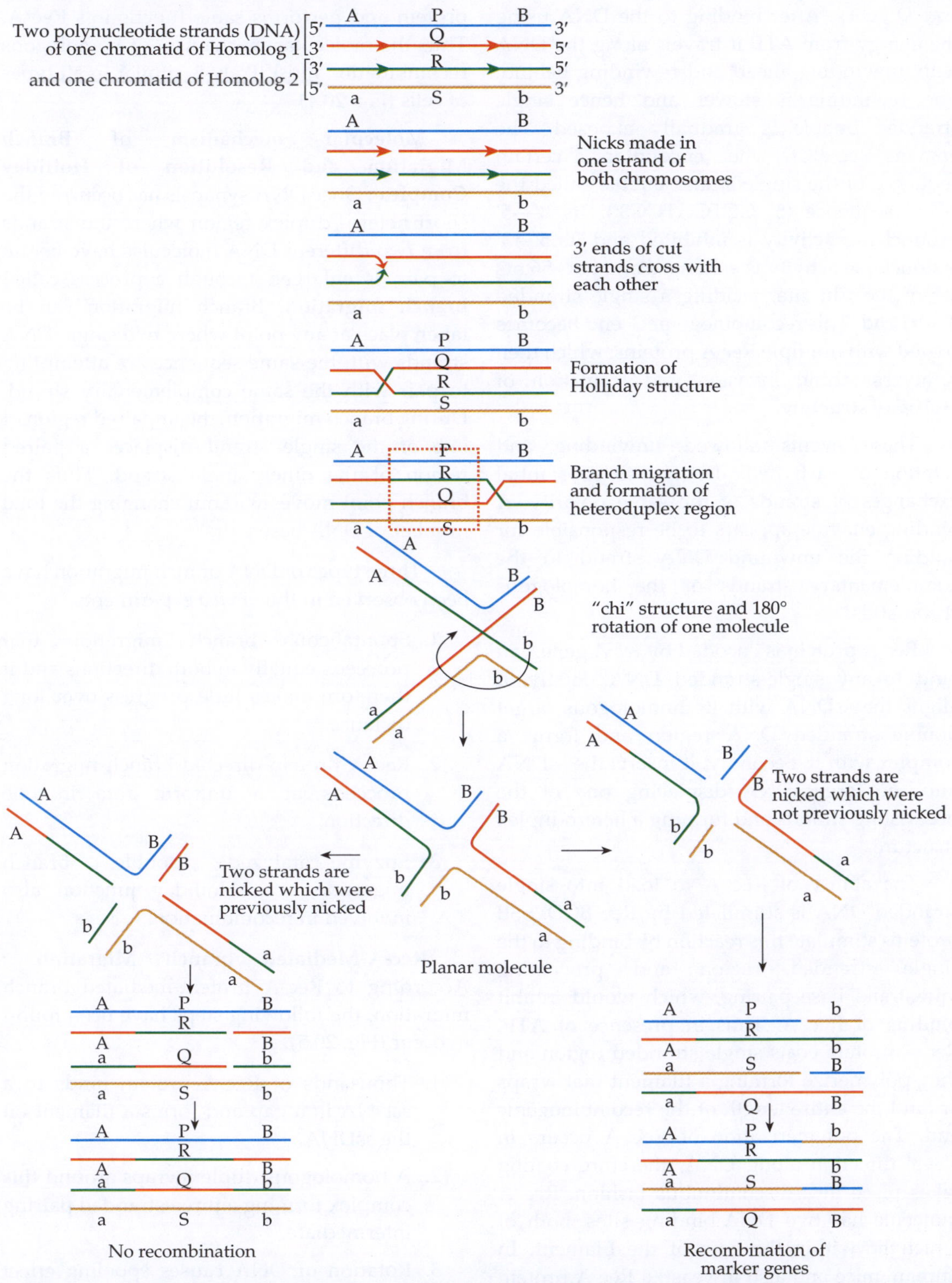


Fig.20.3 : *Molecular mechanism of recombination, Holliday model.*

and *D* genes. After binding to the DNA using the energy from ATP it travels along the DNA helix unwinding ahead and rewinding behind. The rewinding is slower and hence single stranded bubble is gradually exposed. The enzyme Rec BCD when encounters a certain sequence of the single strand bubble called the *"Chi"* sequence (5′ GCTGGTGG3′). Its 3′→5′ exonuclease activity is inhibited and its 5′→3′ exonuclease activity is enhanced and cuts 56 nts 3′ of the Chi site, yielding a single stranded 3′-OH end. This recombinogenic 3′ end becomes coated with multiple Rec A proteins, which then catalyzes strand invasion and formation of **Holliday structure**.

These events allowed unwinding and rotation of each helix leading to substantial exchanges of strands of the same polarity. A binding enzyme appears to be responsible for holding the unwound DNA strand to the complementary strands of the homologous chromatids.

Rec A protein is encoded by *rec A* gene, can bind to any single-stranded DNA. Firstly, it aligns the ssDNA with its homologous target double stranded DNA region and forms a complex with it. Secondly, it inserts the ssDNA into the target DNA displacing one of the preexisting strands and forming a heteroduplex structure.

The ability of Rec A to load into single stranded DNA is stimulated by Rec BCD. SSB proteins stimulate this reaction by binding to the single stranded region and preventing intrastrand base pairing, which would inhibit binding of Rec A. Thus in presence of ATP, Rec A protein coats single stranded region and they polymerize forming a filament that wraps around the entire length of the recombinogenic end. The polymerization of Rec A occurs in 5′→3′ direction along DNA, therefore coating takes place in a discontinuous fashion. Rec A molecule has two DNA-binding sites, both of which lie within the core of the filament. In human, mice and also in yeast, a Rec A protein homolog has been found, which is called Rad 51 protein and performs same function as Rec A. Thus the molecular mechanism of homologous recombination most likely is similar in all types of cells (Fig. 20.4).

**Molecular mechanism of Branch Migration and Resolution of Holliday Complex :** Once DNA synapsis has occurred the short hetero- duplex region where the strands from two different DNA molecules have begun to pair, is enlarged through a process called **branch migration**. Branch migration can be taken place at any point where two single DNA strands with the same sequence are attempting to pair with the same complementary strand. During branch migration, the unpaired region of one of the single strand displaces a paired region of the other single strand. Thus the branch point moves without changing the total number of DNA base pairs.

Three types of DNA branch migration have been observed in the *in vivo* experiments.

1. Spontaneous branch migration that proceeds equally in both directions and it therefore makes little progress over long distance.
2. Rec A protein-directed branch migration proceeds at a uniform rate in one direction.
3. Enzyme–catalyzed double branch migration at a Holliday junction also involved in recombination.

**Rec-A-Mediated branch Migration :** According to Rec-A protein-mediated branch migration, the following steps have been found to occur (Fig. 20.5).

1. Thousands of Rec-A protein binds to a ssDNA in a gap and forms a filament on the ssDNA.
2. A homologous duplex wraps around this complex forming a three-stranded pairing intermediate.
3. Rotation of DNA causes spooling effect that moves the three-stranded region from

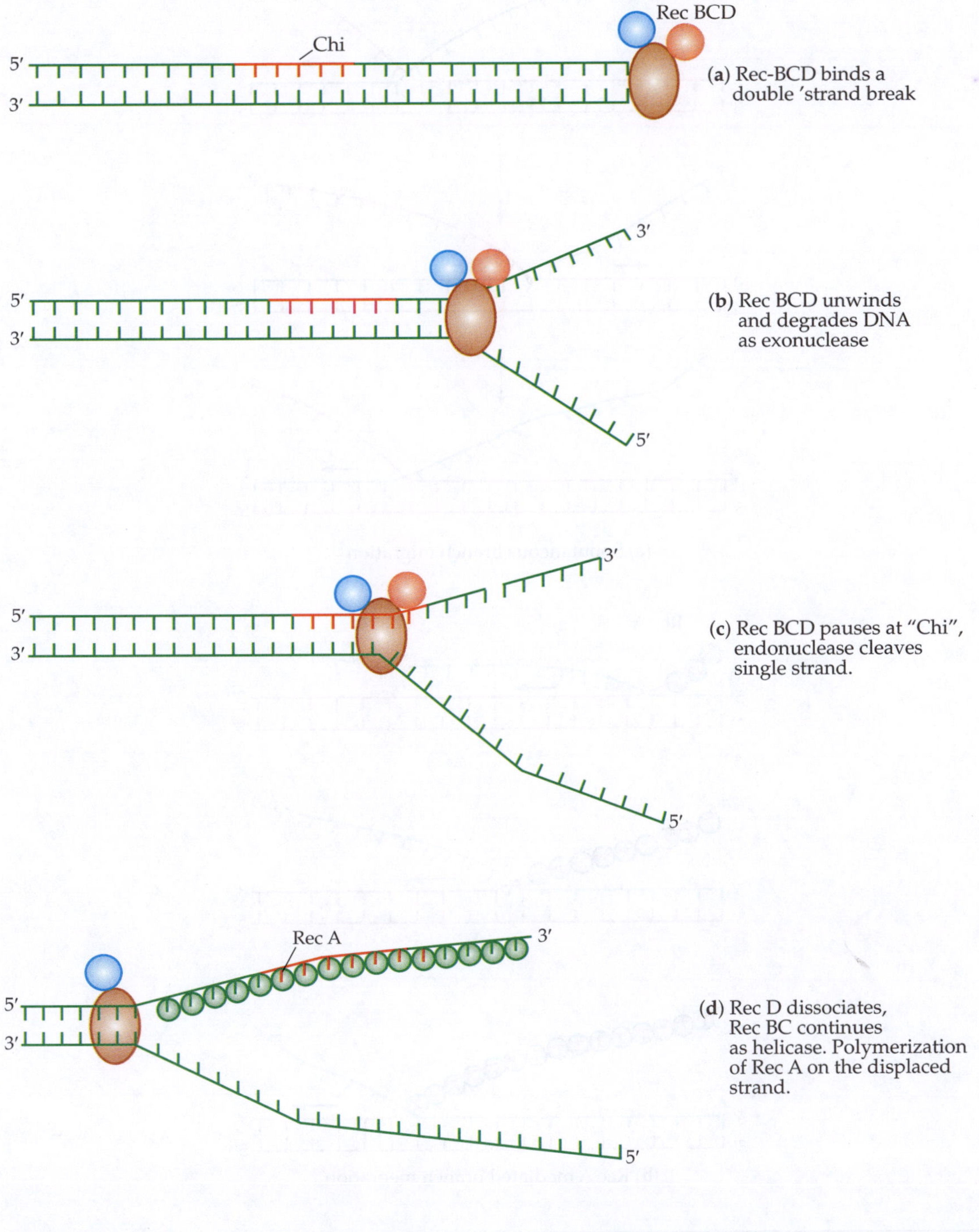


**Fig.20.4 :** *Initiation of recombination*

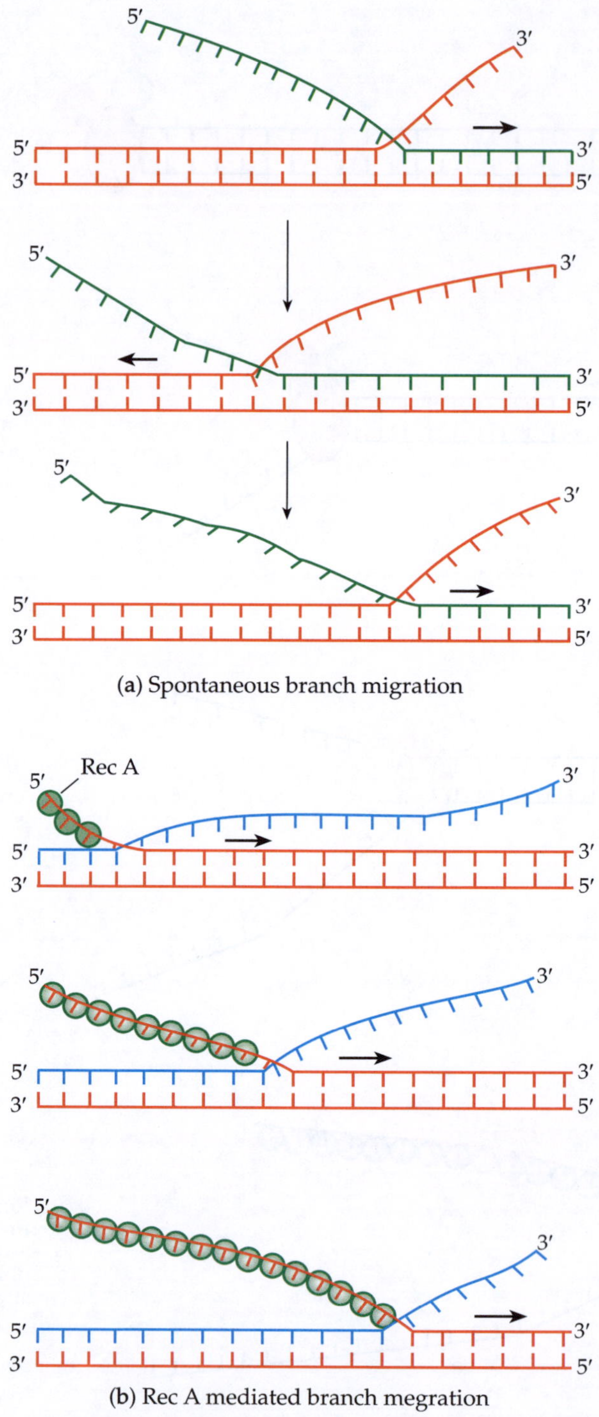


**Fig.19.7 :** *Two types of DNA branch migration observed in vitro experiment.*

left to right within the three-stranded region, one of the strand incoming duplex switches pairing with partners and its original complement is displaced.

4. Rotation continues and displaced strand is eventually being separated entirely.
5. In addition to DNA binding sites, the Rec A protein has a DNA dependent ATPase activity with an additional site for binding and hydrolysing ATP. The new Rec A molecule bound with ATP which is added to one end of the Rec A protein filament and ATP is then hydrolyzed to ADP.

**Enzyme-catalyzed double branch migration :** Enzyme-catalyzed double branch migration at Holliday junction may occur in *E.coli* with the help of two proteins Ruv A and Ruv B, which have helicase property. Ruv A protein is a tetramer and Ruv B protein is a hexamer (Fig. 20.6).

1. Ruv A protein binds to the centre of a Holliday junction, unfolding the junction into a square planer configuration and keeping the four single stranded segments apart (Fig. 20.6).
2. This induces binding of two ring-like hexameric Ruv B proteins, which surround the double stranded DNA like a ring, exting from opposite sides of the Ruv A complex.
3. Ruv B hydrolyses ATP.
4. It rotates like a screw inside the nut and pulling the two double stranded DNAs into the Ruv A complex separating the strands and then extruding two double-stranded hetero-duplex out of the Ruv A complex.

**Resolution of Holliday's structure :** After branch migration, two Ruv C proteins bind to the Ruv A-Ruv B complex. They cut the DNA intermediate at two sites 180° apart by its endonuclease activity. Subsequent ligation generates recombinant molecules of hetero-duplex DNA.

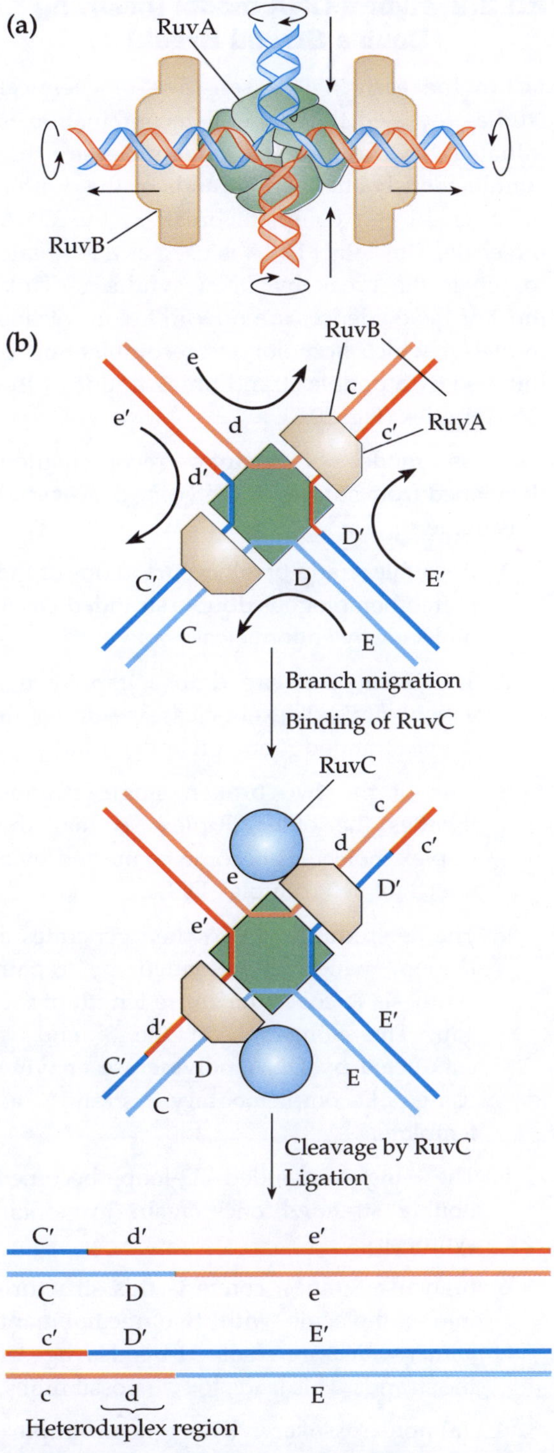


**Fig.20.6 :** *Action for E. coli proteins in branch migration and resolutioin of Holliday junctions.*

### 20.3.2. Hybrid DNA model (Involving Double Strand Break)

In the early 1990's sensitive biochemical studies revealed that general recombination is initiated by a special endonuclease that simultaneously cuts both strands of the double helix, creating a complete break in the DNA molecule. This intact DNA is used as a template to repair the break by DNA synthesis. Thus most of the evidences are now in favour of this model in which homologous recombination is initiated by a double strand break in one of the DNA duplex (Fig. 20.7).

This model of meiotic recombination developed from studies in the yeast, S. *cerevisiae* is as follows :

1. A double strand break occurs in one of the paired homologous double stranded DNA molecule by endonuclease enzyme.
2. The break is enlarged to a gap by the action of 5′→3′ exonuclease resulting in single stranded 3′ end on both strands.
3. One of the two broken single strands invades the other duplex so that the duplex molecules become connected by a stretch of heteroduplex DNA.
4. The heteroduplex DNA then generates a D-loop, which is extended by repair synthesis to cover the entire length of the gap. The elongation at the 3′ end is conducted by DNA polymerase enzyme using D-complementary strand as template.
5. The single stranded D-loop becomes double stranded once again by repair synthesis.
6. Branch migration converts this structure into a molecule with two recombinant joints, which are resolved by cleavage of the strands. This leads to two possibilities.
   (a) non-crossover with heteroduplex DNA.
   (b) crossing over with heteroduplex DNA.

Therefore according to this model there is an initial loss of nucleotides, which is recovered by resynthesis of DNA.

This model can account for nonMendelian segregation of certain markers that have been observed during meiotic recombination. In a cross of multiple marker yeast strains most allelic markers segregate according to the Mendelian ratio 2:1 but those located near the crossover point exhibit 3:1 segregation. Such non-reciprocal event is called **gene conversion** because one allele is apparently converted to another.

The gene conversion mechanism has been depicted in the (**Fig**) where ***P*** and ***p*** markers lie between two crossovers in the intermediate. Of the two recombinant DNA duplexes, one contains the ***P***-marker in one strand and the complementary ***P′*** in the other, whereas the other is a heteroduplex with ***P′*** in one strand and the allele ***p*** in the other.

Similarly, two nonrecombinant DNAs that would result from cleavage of the intermediate at different sites. One is also heteroduplex in the ***p*/*P*** segment. This mismatched duplex may repair and will convert into ***P′* / *P*** or **p / p′**. The former indicates gene conversion whereas the later as no gene conversion.

## 20.4 GENE CONVERSION

Recombination and repair of DNA during meiosis that lead to replacement of one allele by another is called *gene conversion*.This may result in a non-Mendelian ratio among the progeny of a genetic cross.

Crossing over between two DNA molecules creates a short region of heteroduplex, very close to the Holliday junction. Sometimes, this heteroduplex lies with a gene with two different alleles. The two DNA molecules that are about to cross over each carry different alleles (*r* or *R*) (Fig. 20.8) of the same gene. Crossing over occurs within the gene and a short region of heteroduplex that contains one strand of allele *r* and other strand of allele *R* is generated in one of the daughter DNA molecules (Fig. 20.9).

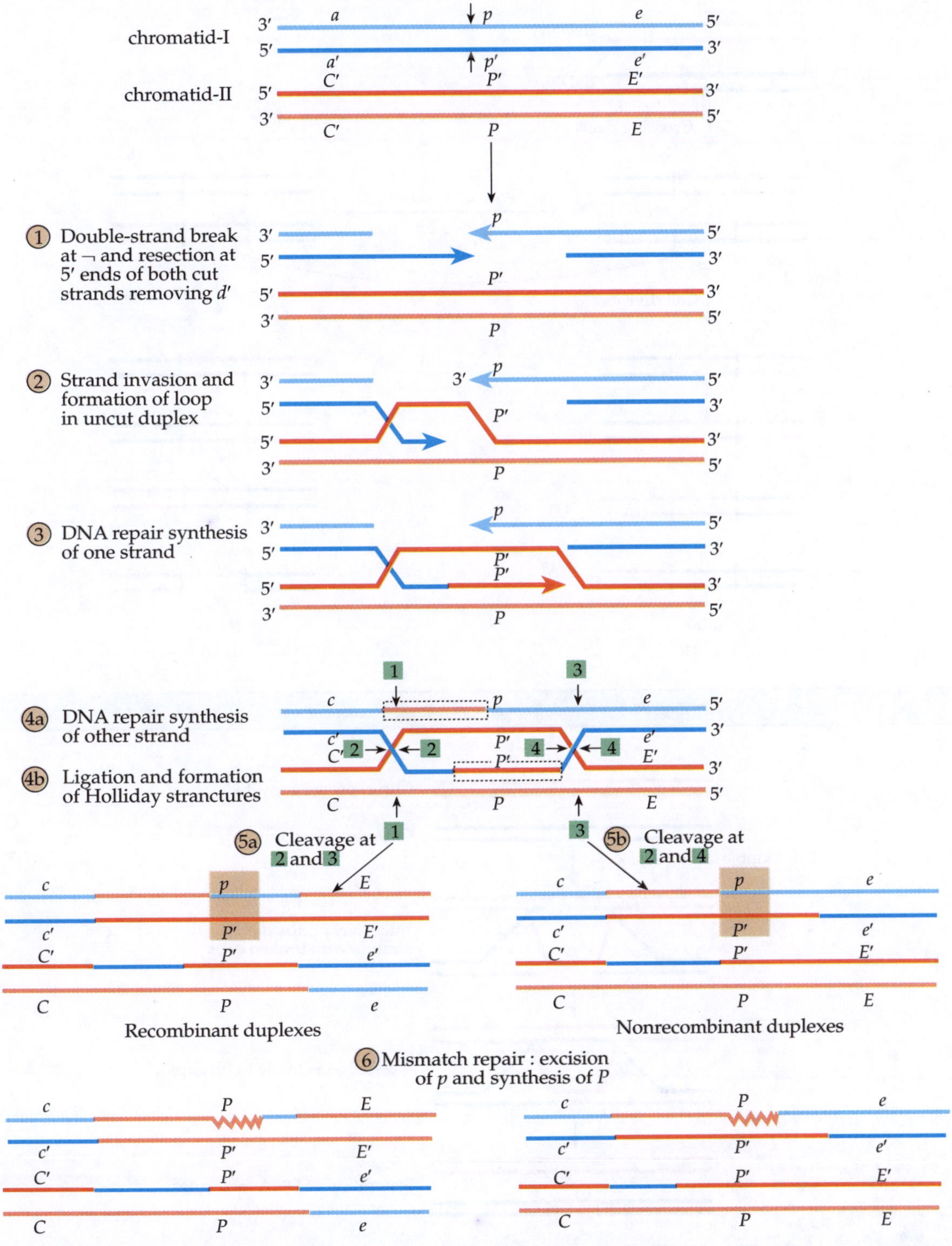


**Fig.20.7 :** *A hybrid DNA model for recombination involving double strand breaks.*

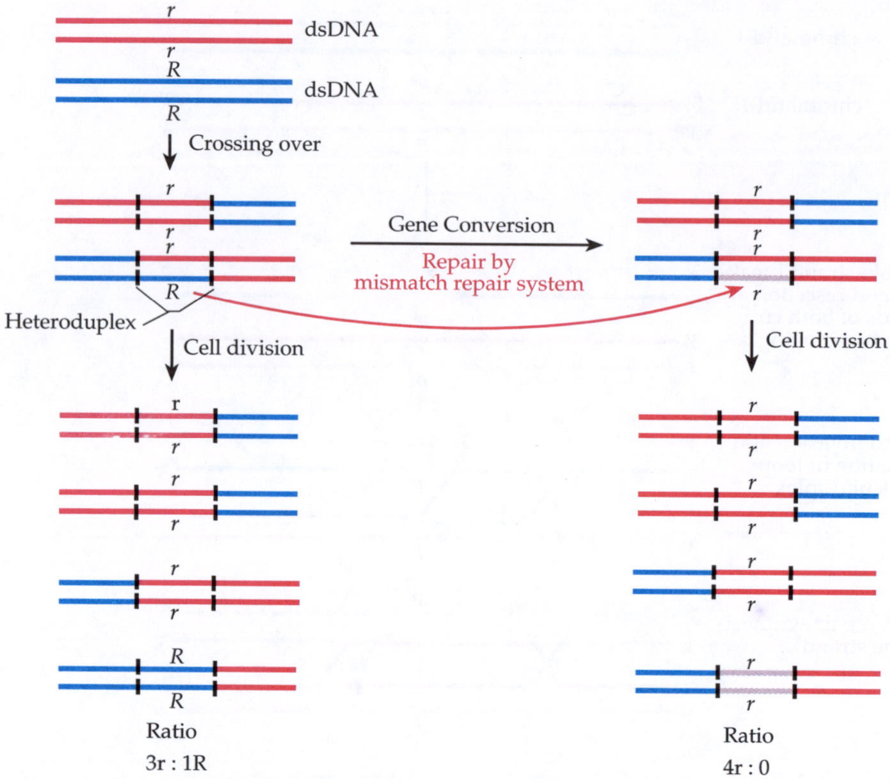


**Fig. 20.8 :** *Gene Conversion following crossing over.*

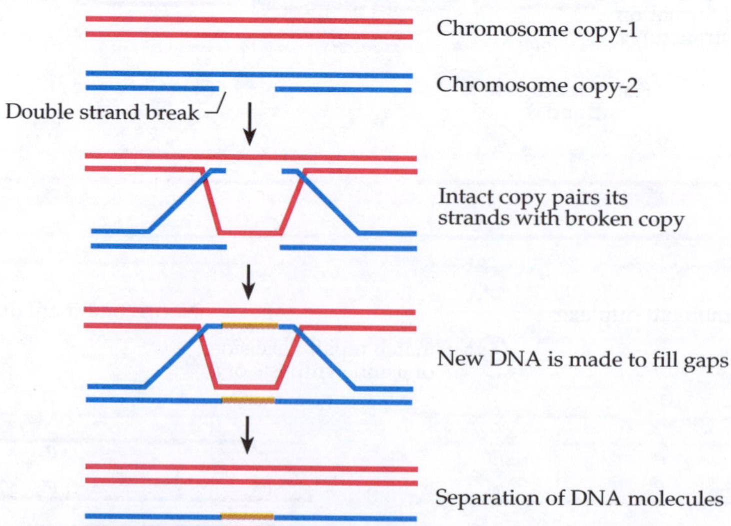


**Fig. 20.9 :** *Gene Conversion repairs broken chromosomes in eukaryotes.*

When the mismatch repair system corrects the heteroduplex, giving a molecule with r allele in both strands. Gene conversion then purturbs the final ratio of the two alleles following cell division. If no heteroduplexes were formed between *r* and *R*, a ratio of *2r* : *2R* would be obtained. But if the heteroduplex is formed, the gene conversion does not occcur, which results *3r* : *1R* ratio, whereas heteroduplex formation followed by gene conversion gives *4r* : *0R* ratio.

Such occasional deviations are difficult to detect, but it is thought to occur in all or most organisms and is only detectable under special circumstances. In yeast and *Neurospora*, sexual reproduction results in the formation of zygote from egg and sperm. Meiosis in these fungi then produces 4 spores all derived from the same zygote and then they may undergo mitosis in *Neurospora* to produce 8 spores.The ascospores stay together inside a special bag called ascus. It is thus possible to count the Medalian ratio separately for each group of 4 or 8 offspring derived from the same zygote.

## 20.5 NICK TRANSLATION

The term "nick" refers to a break in the nucleic acid backbone with missing no nucleotides. When Pol-I binds a nick, it cuts out a small stretch of DNA or RNA, approximately 10 bases long. It then fills in the gap with new DNA or RNA.

This property of Pol I is used in the laboratory for labeling small fragments of DNA with radioactive nucleotides by a procedure called "nick translation" "Nicks are introduced into one strand by DNase I. Then DNA pol-I starts at the nick and moves along the DNA removing the nucleotides ahead of it and replacing them with the radioactive nucleotides provided.

## 20.6. SIGNIFICANCE OF GENETIC RECOMBINATION

The significances of genetic recombination system are as varied as their mechanisms.

1. The process involves a breakage and rejoining of DNA. This exchange is called crossing over or recombination and can be observed cytologically as chiasmata. Crossing over links together all four homologous chromatids and this linkage is essential for the proper segregation of chromosomes during meiosis. Recombination can occur with equal probability at almost any point along the length of two homologous chromosomes. The frequency of crossing over in a region separating the two points on a chromosome is therefore proportional to the distance between the points. By using the fact, geneticists had tried to map the relative positions and distances between genes on the chromosomes.
2. In bacteria, which do not of course undergo meiosis, homologous genetic recombination occurs in the processes such as conjugation, a mating in which chromosomal DNA is transferred between two closely linked bacterial cells or it can occur within a single cell between the two homologous chromosomes present during or immediately after replication.
3. Recombination is described as a source of genetic diversity. Recombination during meiosis in the germ cells provides an opportunity for the exchange of genes and thus causes the genetical variations among the species. The variations are the raw materials for the evolutionary process. It is necessary for the natural selection.
4. Recombination provides an avenue for accurate DNA repair. In certain types of DNA lesions, such as double strand breaks, double strand cross links or lesions left behind in single strands during replication, the complementary strand is itself damaged. These kinds of damage commonly result from ionizing radiations and oxidative reactions and their repair is critical to the

production of viable gametes in eukaryotes and to the everyday existence of bacteria. Repair that is mediated by homologous genetic recombination is simply known as **recombinational repair.**

## 20.7. SITE-SPECIFIC RECOMBINATION

***Site-specific recombination is a genetic recombination where exchange occurs only at a defined DNA sequence.*** It occurs virtually in all cells but their functions are specialized including the regulation of expression of certain genes, the promotion of programmed DNA rearrangement that occurs during development of many organisms and also recombination, tied with the replication system in viral or plasmid DNA. It requires an *enzyme* called **recombinase** and a ***short unique DNA sequence*** called ***recombination site***. It also requires some other auxiliary proteins.

Site specific recombination can proceed via two distinct mechanisms, each of which requires specialised recombination enzymes and specific DNA sites.

1. **Transpositional site-specific recombination** or DNA transposition usually involves breakage reaction at the end of the mobile DNA segment embedded in chromosomes at the attachment of those ends at one or many different nonhomologous target DNA sites. It does not involve the formation of heteroduplex DNA.
2. **Conservative site-specific recombination** involves the production of a very short heteroduplex joint and it therefore requires a short DNA sequence that is the same on both donor and recipient DNA molecules.

## 20.8. REACTION PATHWAYS OF SITE-SPECIFIC RECOMBINATION

1. A recombinase enzyme recognizes and binds to each of the two recombination sites of the different DNA molecules or within the same DNA.
2. One DNA strand in each site is cleaved at a specific point within the site. The recombinase is covalently linked to DNA at the cleavage site through a phosphotyrosine or phosphoserine bond. This transient protein-DNA linkage preserves the phosphodiester bond.
3. The cleaved DNA strands are rejoined with two new partners by new phosphodiester bonds created at the expense of the protein DNA linkage. Thus a Holliday intermediate is produced.
4. The process is then repeated at a second point within each of the two-recombination sites and completes the reaction.

   In some systems, both strands of each recombination site may be cut concurrently and rejoined to new partners without the Holliday intermediate (Fig.20.10).

## 20.9. CONSERVATIVE SITE – SPECIFIC RECOMBINATION IN BACTERIOPHAGE-λ

In the lytic cycle, lambda (λ)DNA exists as an independent circular molecule in the infected bacterium. In the lysogenic state, the phage DNA is an integral part of the bacterial chromosome called **prophage**. Transition between these states involves site-specific recombination.

To enter into the lysogenic condition, free lambda DNA must be integrated into the host DNA. Again the prophage DNA is excised and released from the chromosome from lysogeny to lytic cycle.

1. The specific integration and excision site on the bacterial and phage DNA are known as **attachment** (*att*) sites.
2. The bacterial attachment site is called *att*-B consisting of the sequence component BOB′.

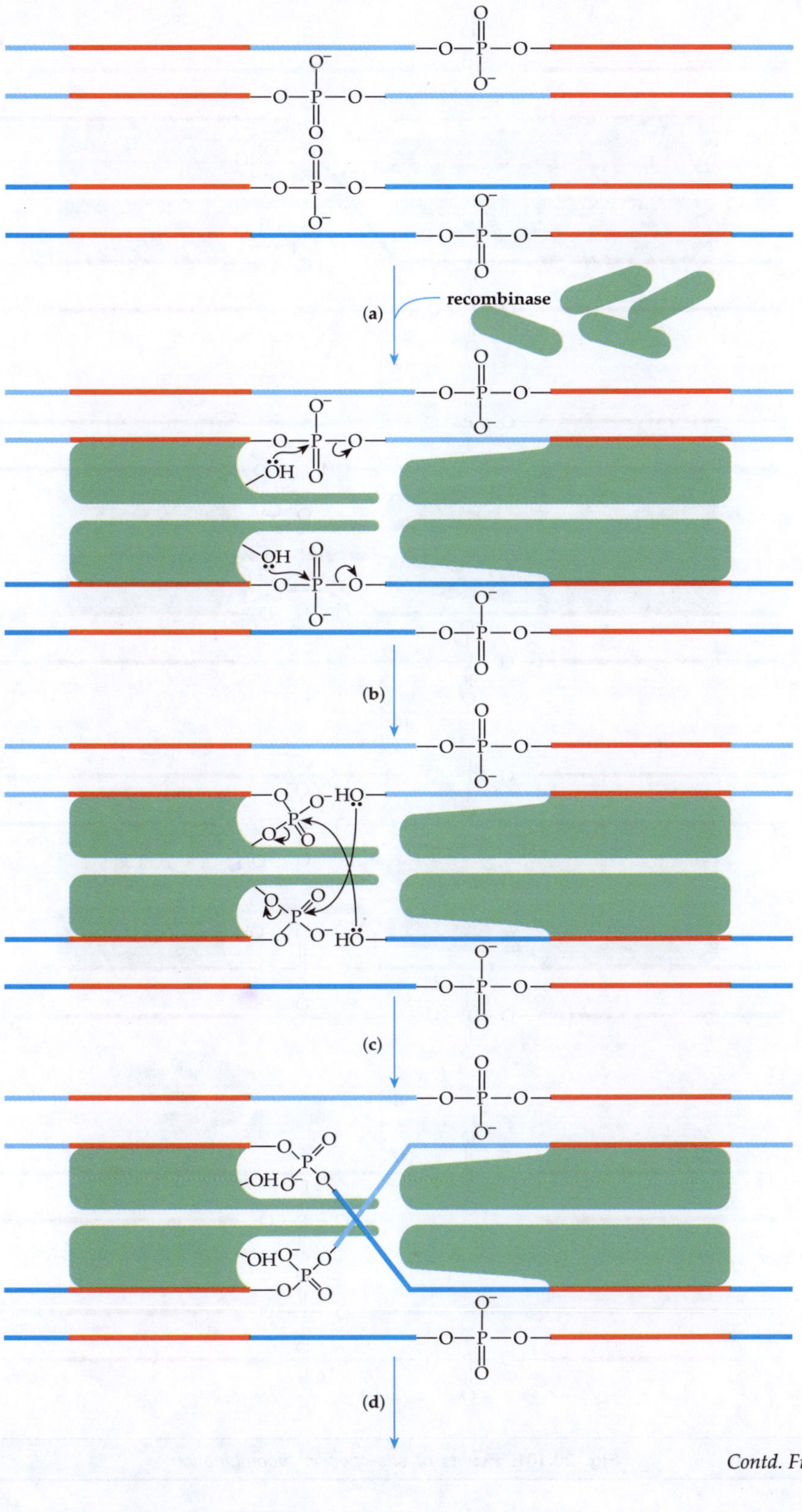


Contd. Fig. in next page

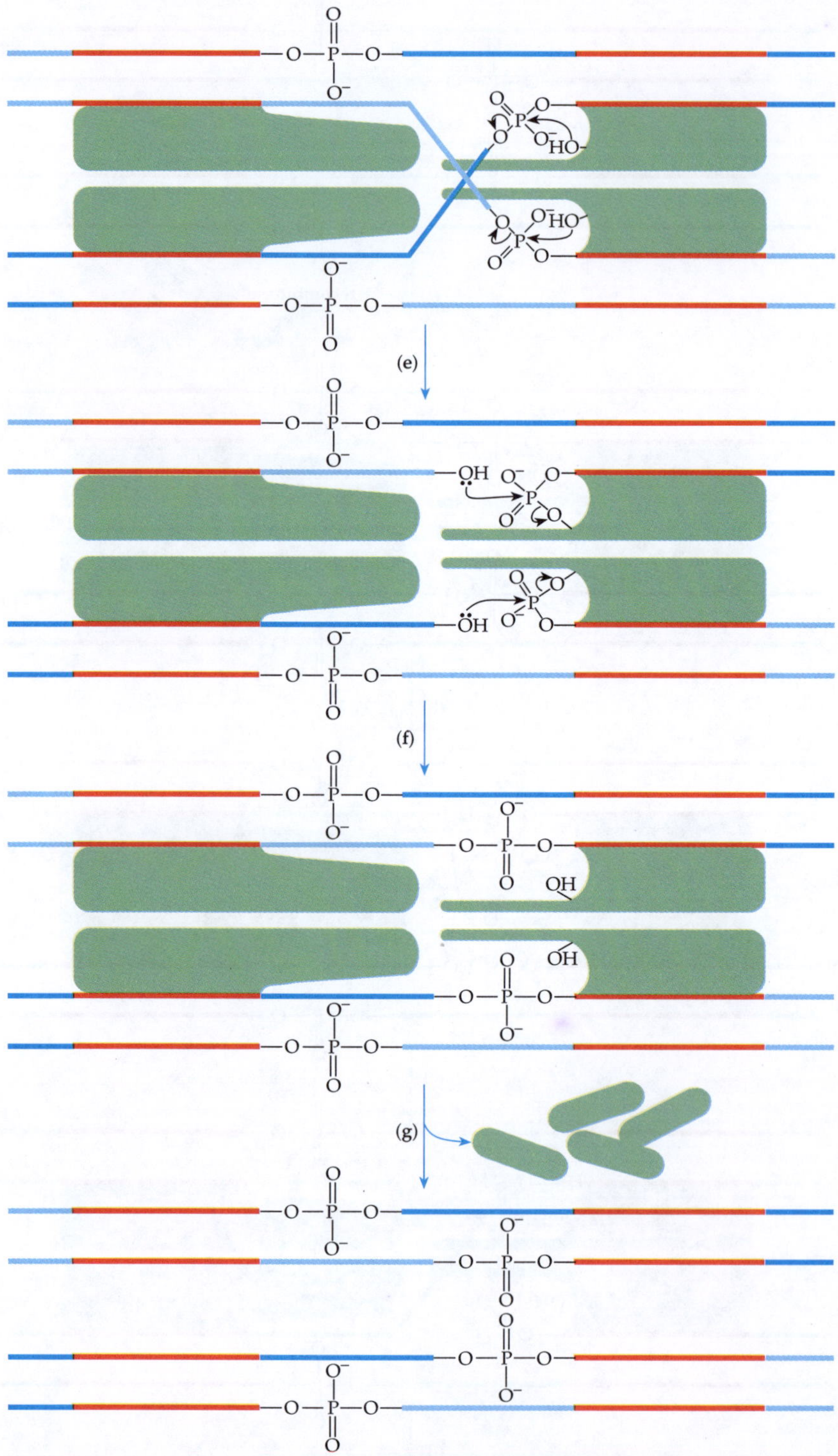

**Fig. 20.10 :** *Events of site-specific recombination.*

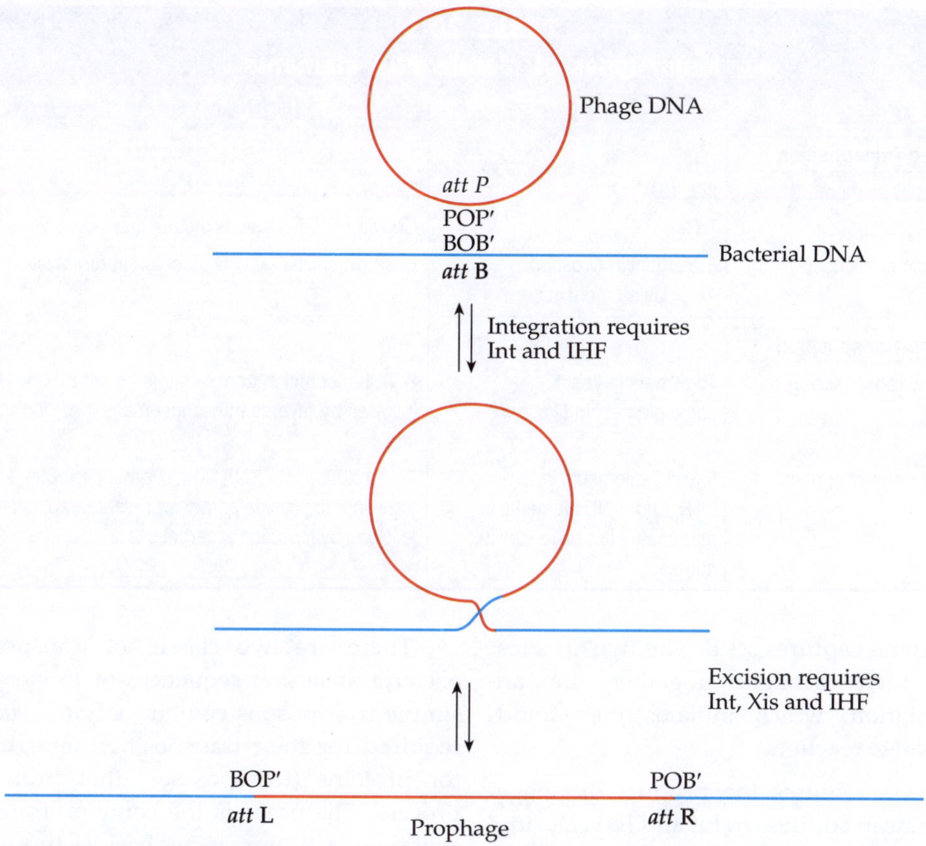


**Fig.20.11 :** *Phage DNA is converted to an integrated prophage by a reciprocal recombination.*

3. The attachment site on the phage, *att-P* consists of the component POP′.
4. The sequence 'O' is common to *att B* and *att-P*. This is called **core sequence**.
5. The recombination occurs within the core sequence. The flanking **region B, B′** and **P,** P′ are called **arms** (Fig. 20.11).
6. After recombination, circular phage DNA is inserted into the bacterial chromosome as a linear sequence. The prophage is bounded by two new *att* sites called *att L* and *att R*.
7. The integration requires recognition between *att P* and *att B* while excision requires recognition between *att L* and *att R*.
8. During integration of lambda phage requires **Int** and **IHF** (integration host factor) proteins. Int protein is *int*-gene product and IHF is a dimeric protein coded by two genes, *him A* and *him D*. Int and IHF bind cooperatively to *att P* and their affinity for the site is enhanced by supercoiling. Int binds to inverted sites at the core sequence positioning itself to make cuts on each strand. These sites share a consensus sequence. IHF binds to sequences of –20 bp in *att P*, the IHF binding sites are approximately adjacent to sites where Int binds. Multiple copies of Int protein may organize *att P* into an **intasome**, which initiates site-specific recombination by recognizing *att B* on free DNA.

**TABLE 20.1**
**Major types of Mobile DNA elements**

| *Type* | *Examples* | *Mechanism of movement* |
|---|---|---|
| **DNA mediated Transposition** | | |
| Bacterial IS element | *IS1, IS10* | Excision or copying of DNA and its insertion of target site |
| Bacterial transposon | Tn 9 | Copying of DNA and its insertion at target site |
| Eukaryotic transposon | P-element in *Drosophila*<br>Ac or Ds element in corn | Excision of DNA and its insertion at target site. |
| **RNA mediated Transposition** | | |
| Viral retrotransposon | Ty-eliment in yeast<br>*copia*-element in *Drosophila* | RNA transcription from promoter in left LTR by RNA pol-II followed by reverse transcription and insertion at target site. |
| Nonviral retrotransposon | F and G-elements in *Drosophila*<br>LINE and SINE elements in mammals Alu sequences in human. | Transcription into RNA from internal promoter, folding of transcript to provide primer for reverse transcription followed by insertion at target site. |

9. Intasome captures *att B*. The two *att* sites are then brought together in an orientation, which initiates the strand exchange reaction.
10. Excision requires the product of phage gene *xis* in addition to Int and IHF. During excision Int forms a similar complex with *att R* only if Xis is added. This complex can pair with a condensed complex that Int forms at *att L*.

## 20.10. TRANSPOSITIONAL SITE-SPECIFIC RECOMBINATION OR DNA TRANSPOSITION

DNA transposition is a distinct type of genetic recombination which usually involves a short segment of DNA with the remarkable capacity to move from one location in the chromosome to another. These genes are called "**hopping genes**" or 'jumping genes' and were first observed by Barbara Mc Clintock in maize in 1950.

The transposable elements are called **transposons** or **Mobile DNA**, which are actually segments of DNA, found in all cells that can move or hop from one place on a chromosome (the donor site) to another on the same or different chromosome (the target site).

There are two classes of transposons in bacteria. Insertion sequences or IS elements or simple transposons contain only the sequences required for their transposition and the genes for proteins (transposases) that promote the process. The other is the complex transposons contain one or more genes besides those needed for transpositions. These additional genes often confer resistance to antibiotics.

There are two major classes of transposons the DNA mediated transposons and RNA mediated transposons.

The DNA mediated transposons are bacterial insertion sequences (IS elements), bacterial transposons and eukaryotic transposons.

The RNA mediated transposons are viral retrotransposons and nonviral retrotransposons (Table 20.1/Fig. 20.12).

## 20.11 DNA-MEDIATED TRANSPOSITION

### 20.11.1 General Characteristics of Transposable elements

Transposable elements (TEs) are mobile DNA sequences found in the genome of all organisms. Most transposable elements are able

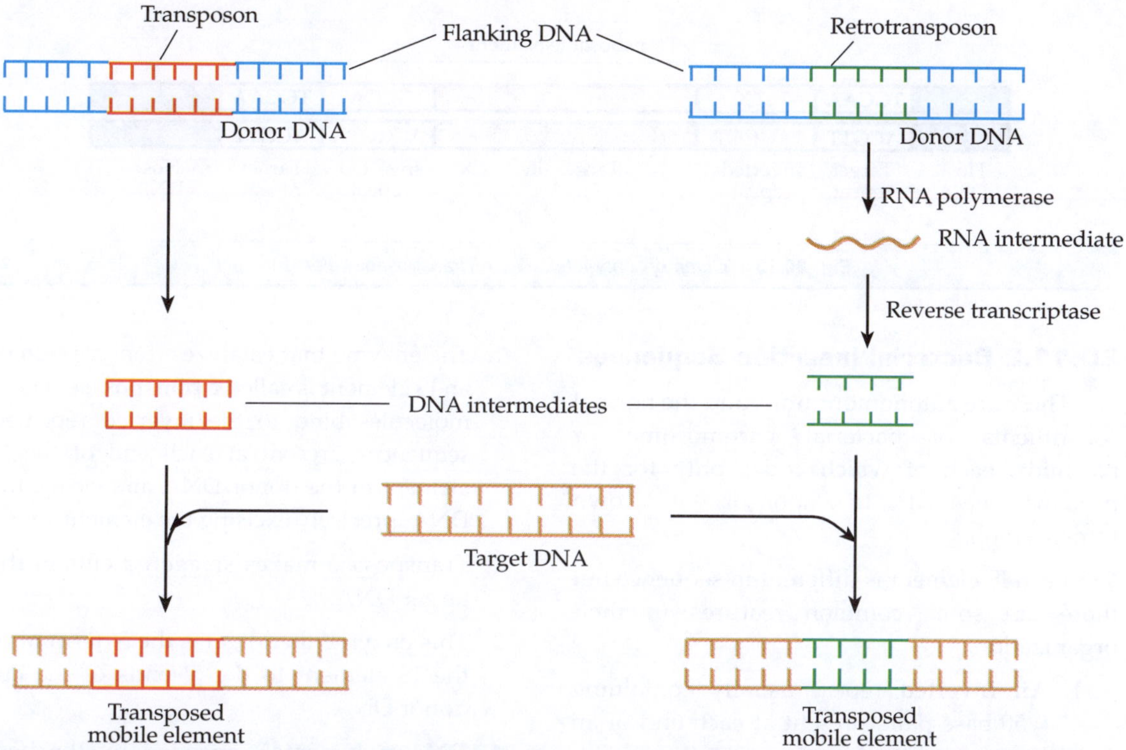


**Fig.20.12 :** *Classification of mobile elements into two major classes viz. transposons and retrotransposons.*

to insert at the many different locations, relying on mechanisms that are distinct from homologous recombinations. There are many different types of transposable elements, some have simple structures encompassing only those sequences necessary for their own transposition, whereas, others have complex structures and encode a number of functions not directly related to transposition. Despite this variation, many transposable elements have certain features in common.

1. *Short flanking direct repeats* : These are 3-12 bp long, are present on both sides of the TEs. These are not the part of the TE, and also do not travel with it. These are generated in the process of transposition at the point of insertion. The length is specific and constant for each type of transposable element.

2. *Terminal inverted repeats* : At the end of many but not all transposable elements possess terminal inverted repeats on two ends. These are 9 to 40 bp in length but inverted to one another. The two sequences are not simply inverted on the same strand. They are both inverted but complementary, *ie*, the sequence from left to right in the top strand is the same at the sequence from right to left in the bottom strand. These terminal inverted repeats are recognized by the enzymes that catalyze transposition.

3. None of these elements have their own origin of replication, except for conjugative transposons, which has an origin of transfer, but not of vegetative replication (Fig. 20.13)

4. Transposons must have at least one gene that encodes the enzyme *transposase* which recognizes the inverted repeats and moves the segment of DNA from one site to another.

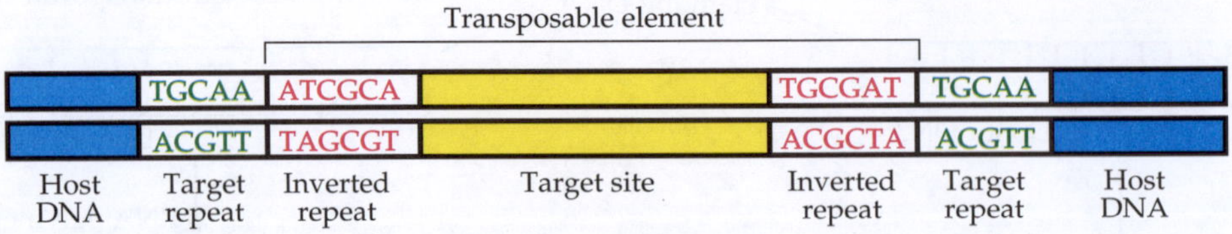


**Fig. 20.13 :** *Common characteristics of transposable element.*

## 20.11.2 Bacterial Insertion Sequences

These are autonomous units and the normal constituents of bacterial chromosome or plasmids, each of which codes only for the proteins needed to sponsor its own transposition.

Each IS element is different in sequence but there are some common features in their organization.

1. **An inverted** repeat usually containing ≈ 50 base pairs present at each end of an IS sequence.
2. Between the inverted repeats is a **protein coding region**, which encodes one or two enzymes required for transposition of its own to a new site. IS encoded proteins are expressed at a very low rate.
3. The **direct repeat** is the another important characteristic of the IS sequence whose 5′ and 3′ short repeats of 5-11 base pairs have been generated from the target site DNA during insertion of a mobile element. The sequence depends upon the site of insertion. Only one copy of direct repeat is found in the wild type gene. During insertion process a second direct repeat adjacent to the IS sequence is created on the other end (Fig. 20.16).

Simplest mechanism of IS insertion is that the IS element is excised and then is inserted to a new position in bacterial chromosome by a non-replicative process. i.e., the transposing element moves as a physical entity directly from one site to another and is conserved.

1. The enzyme that catalyzes transcription of an IS element is called a **transposase**. These molecules bind to the inverted repeated sequences present at each end of the IS element in the donor DNA and cleave the DNA, precisely excising the element.
2. Transposase makes staggered cuts in the target DNA.
3. This enzyme then ligates the 3′ termini of the IS element to the 5′ ends of the cut donor DNA.
4. DNA polymerase, encoded by the host cell then extends the 3′ end of the target site and the gap is filled in forming a 3′×5′ phosphodiester bond. Thus an another short repeat is generated and two short direct repeats are observed on the two ends of IS element after insertion into bacteria (Fig. 20.15).

## 20.11.3 Bacterial Transposons

A genetic element that can move from one position to another position of a DNA molecule is "transposon". Copying of DNA and its insertion at target site are involved in bacterial transposition mechanism. It may be replicative or non-replicative transposition.

(a) **Replicative transposition :** In replicative transposition, *the element is duplicated during the reaction, so that the transposing entity is a copy of the original element* (Fig. 20.16). These are also called *Complex transposons.*

In this mechanism the transposon is copied as part of its movement. One copy

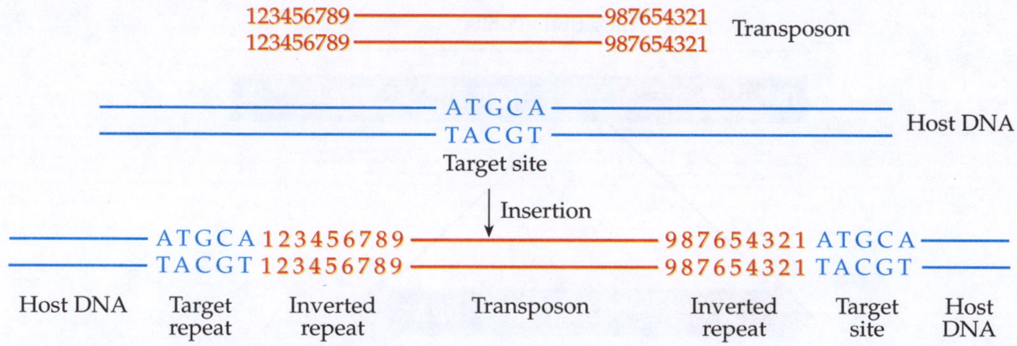


**Fig.20.14 :** *Structure of a genetic transposon before and after insertion at the target site.*

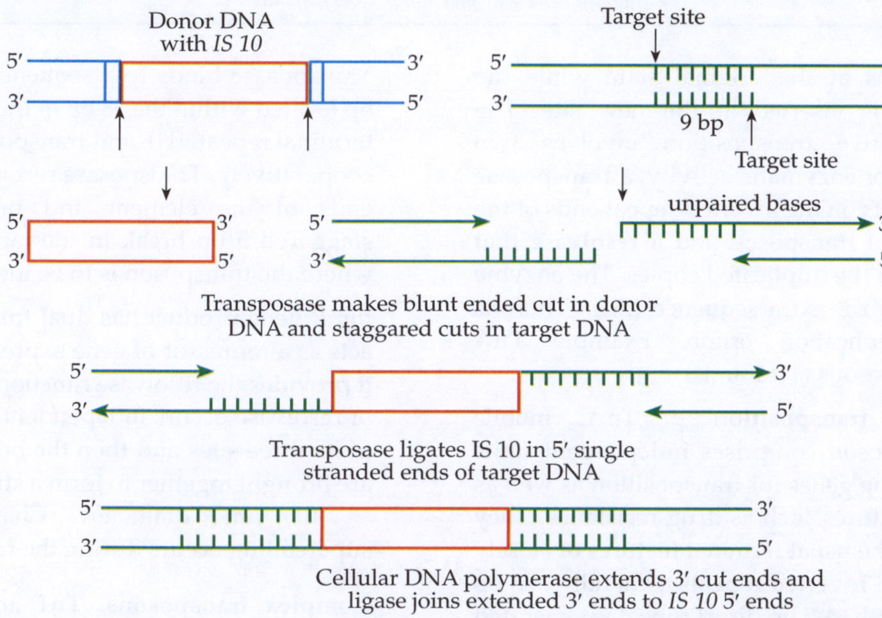


**Fig.20.15 :** *Model for non replicative transposition of bacterial insertion sequences.*

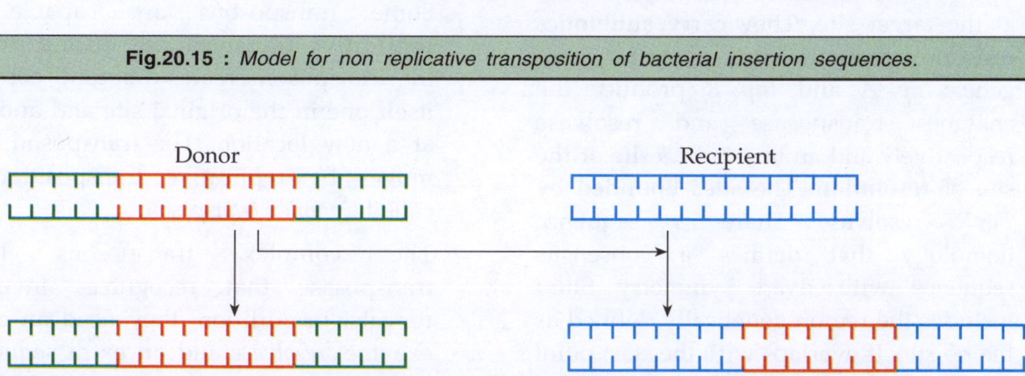


**Fig.20.16 :** *Replicative transposition*

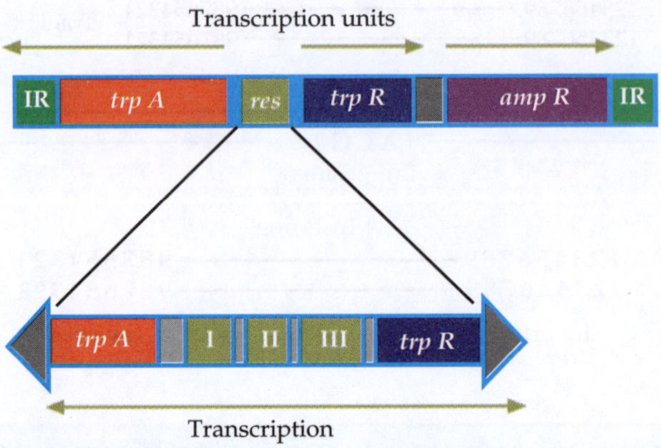


**Fig.20.17 :** *Transposons of the Tn A family have inverted terminal repeats (IR), an internal res site and three known genes.*

remains at the original state while the other is inserted at the new site. The replicative transposition involves two types of enzymatic activity, a **transposase** that acts on the inverted repeat ends of the original transposon and a **resolvase** that acts on the duplicated copies. The enzyme recognizes extra sequence (IRS). There is no replication origin. Example **TnA** transposons (Tn 1 and Tn 3).

**TnA transposition :** TnA mobile transposon comprises independent units carrying genes for transposition as well as for features such as drug resistance. They have the usual terminal features of closely related **inverted repeats**, generally ~38 bp in length. A 5 bp direct repeat is generated at the target site. They carry antibiotics resistance markers such as $amp^R$. Two genes *tnp A* and *tnp R* produce the enzymes transposase and resolvase respectively and an internal *res* site or the site of resolution. The sites bounded by *TnpR* resolvase share a sequence homology that defines a consensus sequence with dyad symmetry Site-I includes the region genetically defined as the *res* site. It overlaps with the start point for tnp-A transcription Site II overlaps with start point for *tnp R* transcription (Fig. 20.17).

Transposase binds to a sequence of ~ 25 bp located within the 38 bp of the inverted terminal repeat. IHF and transposase bind cooperatively. Transposase recognizes the ends of the element and makes the staggered 5 bp break in the target DNA where the transposon is to be inserted.

*tnp R* gene product has dual functions. It acts as a repressor of gene expression and it provides the resolvase function. Binding of resolvase occurs independently at each of its three sites and then the bound sites are brought together to form a structure of ~ 10 nm diameter. Changes in supercoiling occurs during the reaction.

**Complex transposons, Tn1 and Tn3 :** Some transposons are capable of **replicative transposition**, during which the transposon creates a second copy of itself one in the original site and another at a new location. The transposon that moves by replicative transposition is called *Complex transposon*.

The complex transposons have transposase that recognizes inverted repeats. In addition, they need an extra exzyme, *resolvase* and an extra sequence IRS (internal resolution site) which is recognized by *resolvase* (Fig. 20.18)

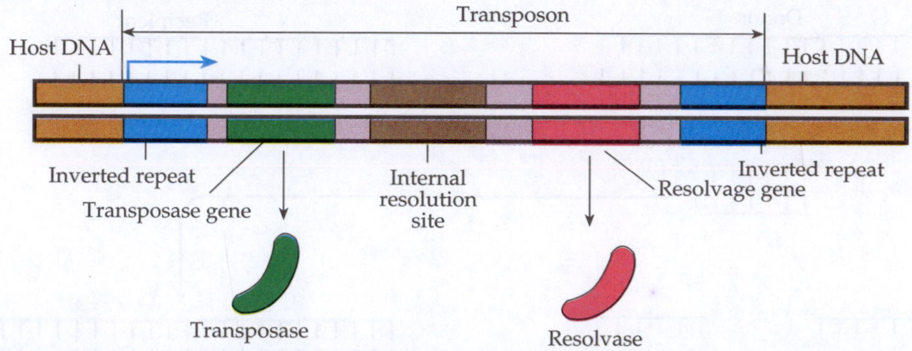


**Fig. 20.18 :** *Components of Complex Transposon.*

**Tn 1 and Tn 3 Transposition :** These transposons are replicated but are not replicons, no origin of replication.

1. At first transposase makes single stranded nicks at the end of both the transposons and the target sequence.
2. It joins the free ends to create a **cointegrate** in which both DNA molecules are linked together via a single strand of transposon DNA.
3. The presence of single stranded DNA alerts the host cell repair system and synthesizes the complementary strands, thus duplicating the transposon. Thus two double-stranded DNA molecules linked by two transposons.
4. The resolvase then resolves the cointegrate and separates the two DNA molecules. The resolvase recognizes the two IRS sequences in the middle of the two copies of transposon and carried out recombination between them (Fig. 20.19).

(b) **Nonreplicative transposition :** The transposing element moves as a physical entity directly from one site to another and is conserved. This occurs by either of two types of mechanism. One utilizes the connection of donor and target DNA sequences and shares some steps with

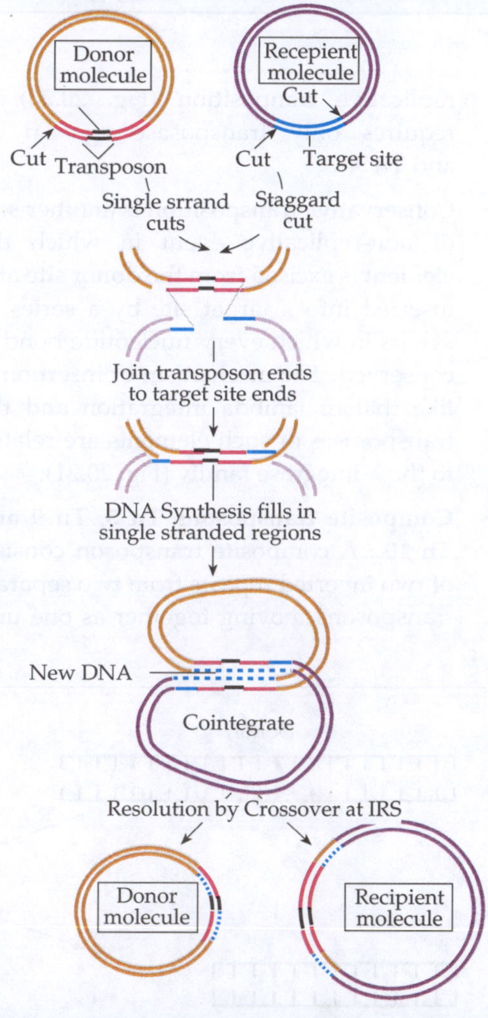


**Fig. 20.19 :** *Replicative transposition forms a Cointegrate.*

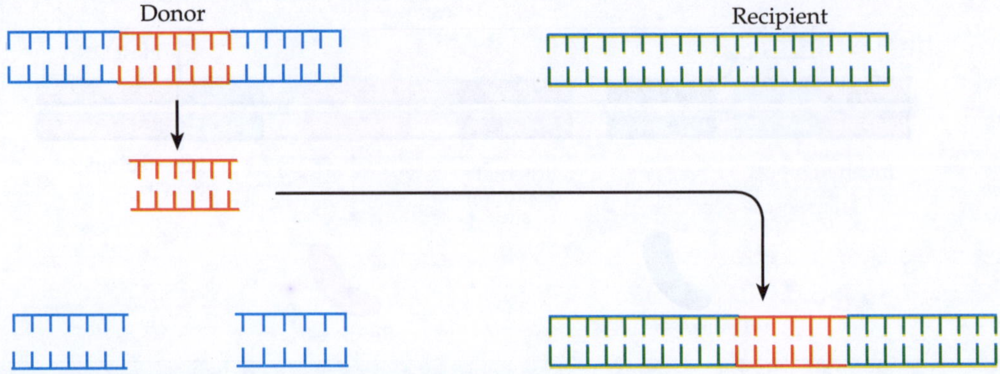


Fig.20.20 : *Norreplicative transposition.*

replicative tranposition (Fig. 20.20). It requires only transposase eg. Tn 10 and Tn 5.

Conservative transposition is another sort of non-replicative event in which the element is excised from the donor site and inserted into a target site by a series of events in which every nucleotide bond is conserved. The mechanism of insertion is like that of lambda integration and the transposases of such elements are related to the λ-integrase family (Fig. 20.21).

**Composite transposons Tn 5, Tn 9 and Tn 10 :** A composite transposon consists of two inverted repeats from two separate transposons moving together as one unit carrying the DNA bewteen them. For example, if a segment of DNA is flanked, at both ends by two identical insertion sequences, the transposase will move any segment of DNA surrounded by a pair of inverted repeats that it recognizes. Each insertion sequence may move independently or the whole sequence between two outermost inverted repeats as a unit. Therefore, this is a composite transposon. For example, Tn 5 (Kanamycin resistance), Tn 9 (chloramphenicol resistance) and Tn 10 (tetracycline resistance). The IS elements of Tn 5 and Tn 10 are named as IS-5 and IS-10 respectively (Fig. 20.22).

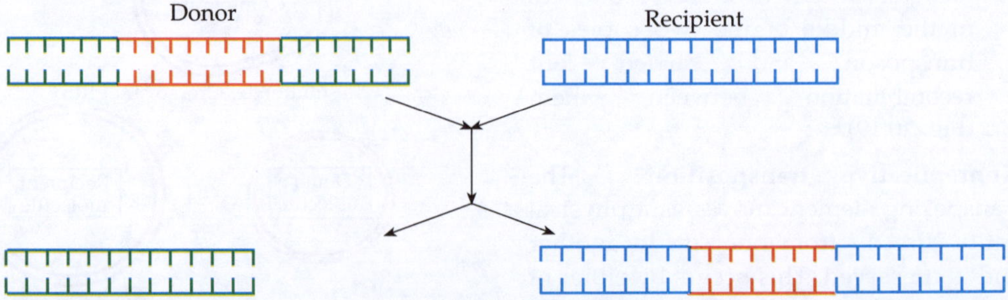


Fig.20.21 : *Conservative tansposition.*

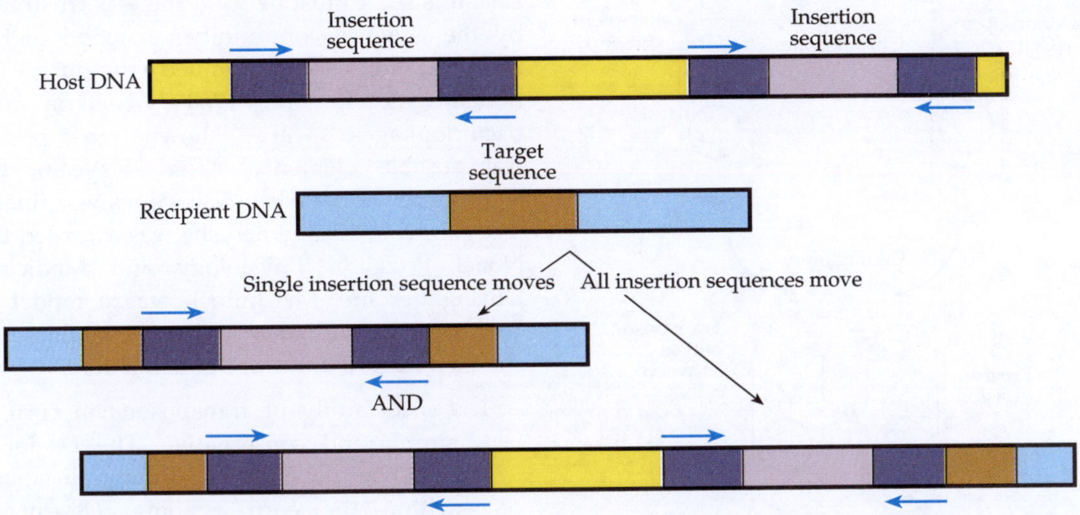


**Fig. 20.22 :** *Principle of the Composite Transposon.*

### 20.11.4 Conjugative Transposons

These transposons are found in bacteria, the hybrid elements that can transpose and also can move from cell to cell like a transmissible plasmid. Example Tn916 which can confer tetracycline resistance gene, found in *Enterococcus faecalis*.

It moves from cell to cell during bacterial conjugation. It can excise precisely and leaves the donor bacterium to host bacterium. It then transposes into the DNA of the host cell. The transposon does not duplicate their sequence. In this way the host bacterium becomes tetracycline resistant (Fig. 20.23).

### 20.11.5 Bacteriophage μ–Transposon

The bacteriophage Mu is both a virus and a transposon. When it enters into *E. coli*, its bacterial host, it integrates at random as multiple copies into the host chromosome and acts as a transposon. Even when it inserts into the middle of the host gene, this gene is inactivated. Therefore, it causes mutation to the host which makes its names **mutator gene or Mu**.

Again, when it integrates into the chromosome of the host, it remains dormant as prophage or may go to lytic cycle, then it is a bacterial virus.

Mu is never replicated as the independent molecule when freed from the host chromosome.

When DNA segment is packed into bacteriophage, it contains the whole Mu genome and small stretches of DNA on it's two ends. When it infects the new host cell, the Mu genome transposes out the tiny fragment of host DNA that is brought with it. Thus Mu is a true transposon (Fig. 20.24).

## 20.12 TRANSPOSITION IN EUKARYOTES

### 20.12.1 *Ds* and *Ac* Elements in Maize

Original discovery of mobile DNA by Barbara McClintock came from the observation of certain spontaneous mutations in maize. During her long carrier as a scientist, McClintock identified many unusual features in corn chromosomes. She was succeeded in identifying each of the 10 maize chromosomes. She noticed that one strain of corn had the

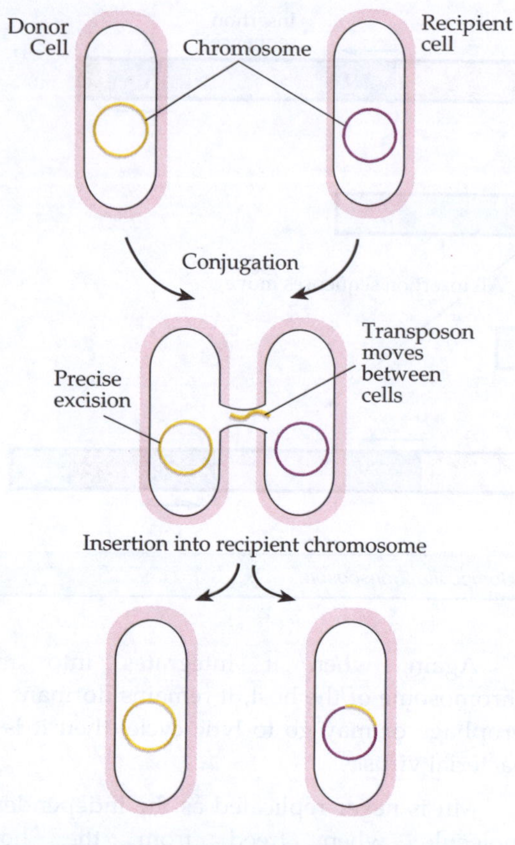


Fig. 20.23 : *Conjugative Transposon.*

strange characteristic, that a particular chromosome, number 9, tended to break at a fairly high rate at the same site. She termed this a *mutable site* or *locus*. She proposed that these mutable sites are actually locations where transposable elements have been inserted into the chromosomes. She published her first report about transposable elements in 1948. In the year 1951, major paper was published in *Cold Spring Harbour Symposium on Quantitative Biology*. Some geneticists of that time were unable to accept the idea that the genetic material can move from one place to another place. Instead they wanted to believe that the genetic material was always very stable and permanent in a structure. Of her work, Alfred Sturtevant, the famous geneticist remarked. "I didnt understand one word she said, but if she says it is so, it must be so!". She was frustrated by the genetics community's reaction to her research, but she continued to pursue it nonetheless. In the 1960's, bacteria and bacteriophages were shown to posses transposable elements. After 35 years, the significance of her early discoveries was finally recognized in 1983, when she was awarded the Nobel Prize in Physiology and Medicine. During her life, McClintock was a model of "adamant individuality and self containment" she died in 1992 at the age of about 90.

1. *Ds/Ac* family of transposons in corn is simple and conservative. The *Ds* locus could be transposed to different locations within the corn genome. *Ds* means **dissociation element** because the locus

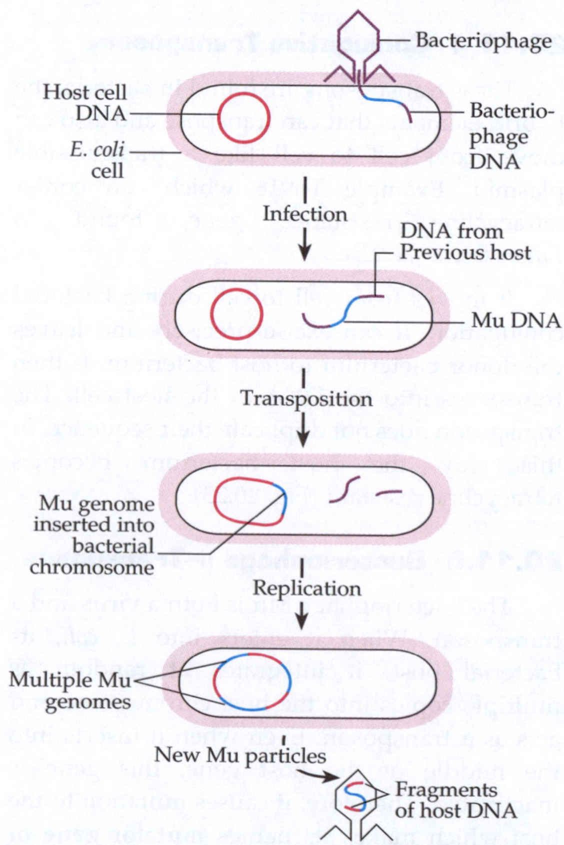


Fig. 20.24 : *Bacteriophage Mu Transposition*

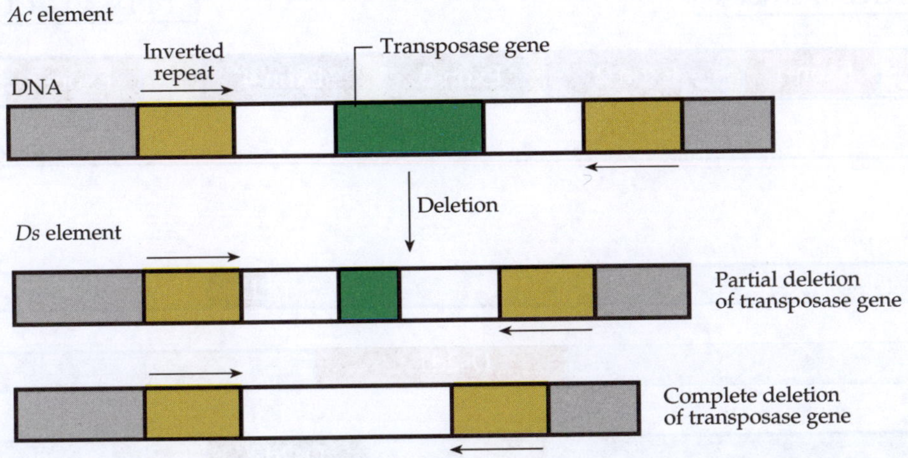


**Fig. 20.25 :** *Ac/Ds element of maize showing formation of Ds from Ac elements by partial or complete deletion*

was known to frequently cause chromosomal breaks. The *Ds* elements vary in size and are defective, which are derived from *Ac* (activator) element by deletion of all or part of the transposase enzyme (which is essential for transposition). Therefore, *Ds* element cannot move without *Ac* element. The *Ac* and *Ds* elements do not need to be on the same chromosome for transposition to occur (Fig. 20.25).

2. The *Ac* element consists of 5 exons but is actually a single gene. the product is transposase. On the two sides have the inverted 11 bp repeats like a typical transposon and target sequence of 8 bp is duplicated at the site of insertion. It has two ORFs. This is **autonomous element**.
3. *Ds* element vary in length and sequence but related to *Ac*. The ends are with same inverted repeats as that of *Ac* element. This is non-autonomous element (Fig. 20.26).
4. Each kernel in an ear of corn is a separate individual originating from the two haploid maternal nuclei and a haploid pollen grain *ie.* triploid in nature.
4. The pigment (anthocyanin) encoding allele can be designated as "*C*" which is dominant over colourless allele "c". Therefore, *CC* and *Cc* are purple while *cc* is colourless. When *Ds* is transposed into the *C* allele, the $C^tc$ genotype would be colourless. If $C^t$ allele moves to a new location, the "*C*" allele becomes functional again. All cells will have the genotype *Cc* will be purple. The presence of these pigmented cells surrounded by colourless cells produce a purple spot or streak on the kernel to become **variegated** appearance or **sectoring** phenotype.

**Explanation :** McClintock took seveal genes on a single chromosome that could be used as chromosomal marker genes and all the genes affect the phenotype of corn kernel . The marker genes are

1. "*C*", and *c* for purple colour (dominant) and colourless (recessive) alleles respectively. $C^t$ is designated as the third allele causing colourless kernel, also dominant to other two alleles "*C*" and "*c*".
2. "*Sh*" is an allele produces normal endosperm, while *sh* is its recessive allele for shunken kernel.

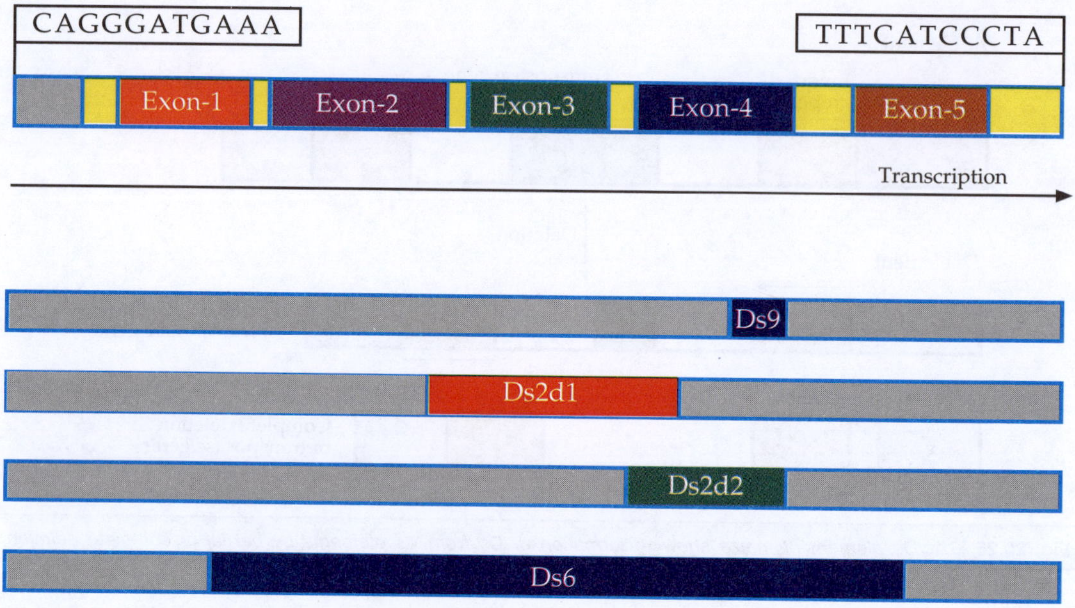


**Fig.20.26 :** *The Ac element and the molecular information.*

3. *Wx* is allele that produces normal starch in the endosperm, while its recessive allele is *"wx"* produces waxy starch in the endosperm.

McClinktock produces strains of corn which demonstrated that transposition of *Ds* locus and how the variegated appearance is produced on the maize kernel (Fig. 20.27).

1. One of the chromosome (comming from pollen) has $C^t$, *Sh* and *Wx* all the dominant alleles and then *Ds* element. The Kernel is expected to be colourless, because $C^t$ allele (dominant) is presenent in one chromosome.

   *Ds* locus may break and then it loses the terminal part of the chromosome alongwith $C^t$, *Sh* and *Wx* dominant alleles. Other two chromosomes have "*C*" allele would produce purple, shunken, waxy phenotype as some patches on the kernel.

2. She was also able to identify cases in which *Ds* has moved to a new location.

   If *Ds* is moved out of its original location and inserted between *Sh* and *Wx*, a break at *Ds* would produce a new phenotype which would be purple, shunken but the kernel would be normal nonwaxy. She also found that *Ac* locus is necessary for the *Ds* site to move.

3. She obtained an exciting result and unusual event. The tripple recessive gene (*c sh wx*) containing ovule is fertilized with purple, full kernel but waxy endosperm containg (*C, Sh, wx*) pollen. The kermel is expected to be red. The chromosome of the pollen has a *Ds* as well as *Ac* loci. Among 4000 kernels, one is noticed to be colourless background with purple patches. It suggested that the background genotype is due to recessive "*c*" and the wild "*C*" allele on the chromosome is mutable to become $C^t$ ie, *Ds* element is transposed into the *C* gene.

Mc Clintack postulated that the colourless phenotype was due to a transposition of *Ds* into the *C* gene and inactivated the "*C*" gene, causing colourless patches on the purple kernel.

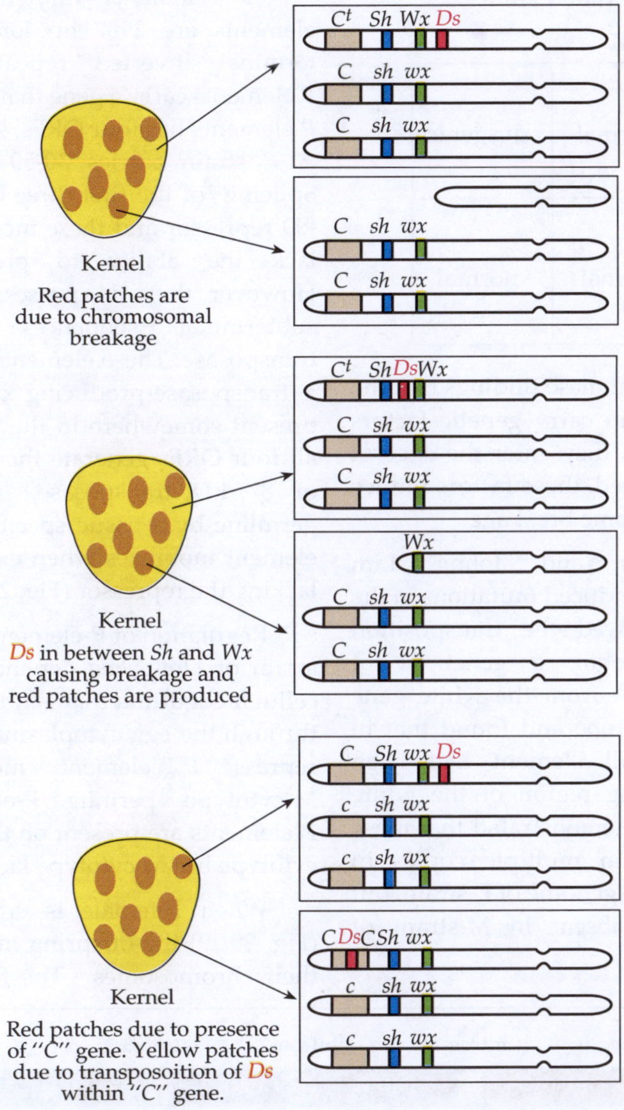


**Fig. 20.27 :** *The Sectoring trait in corn kernel.*

## 20.12.2 P-elements and Hybrid dysgenesis is *Drosophila*

In 1977 , Margeret and James Kidwell discovered that crosses between certain strains of *Drosphila melanogaster* produce hybrids which showed frequent mutation, chromosome breakage and sterility. The term **hybrid dysgenesis** was used to denote this abnormalities.

Kidwell and her colleagues classified this *Drosophila* strain as "P" and "M". Crosses between two different "P"-strains or between two different M strains produce normal hybrids. But when males of P-strain is crossed with M-strain females, produce hybrid dysgenesis.

| | | Male Parent | |
|---|---|---|---|
| | | M | P |
| Female Parent | M | normal | dysgenic |
| | P | normal | normal |

They suggested from these findings that the chromosomes of P-strain carry genetic factors that are activated when they enter the eggs of M-females. Once activated, these factors induce mutations and chromosome breakage.

Mitchel Simmons and Johng Lim discovered dysgenesis-induced mutations in the *white gene* which allowed the transposition hypothesis. Gerald Robin, a geneticist of Maryland isolated DNA from the white gene which was used as a probe and found that in each mutation a small element had been inserted into the coding region of the white gene. Later it has been demonstrated that these elements are present in multiple copies in different locations of the genome of P-strain, but these are completely absent in M-strain of *Drosophila melanogaster*.

"P" elements vary in size. The largest elements are 2907 bp long including 30 bp terminal inverted repeats. These *complete P* elements carry a gene that encode transposase. *P* elements has four ORFs, separated by introns. A *P* strain carries 30-50 copies of P-factor. Splicing of the first three ORFs generates a 66 kD repressor and these incomplete *P* -elements lack the ability to produce transposase. However they do possess the terminal and subterminal sequences that bind the transposase. These elements can be mobilized if a transposase-producing complete element is present somewhere in the genome. Splicing of all four ORFs generate the complete P element of 87 kD transposase, occurs only in the germline by a tissue specific splicing event. *P*-element mobilizes when exposed to cytoplasm lacking the repressor (Fig. 20.28).

Regulation of P-element movement in some strain of *Drosophila* depends upon *Cytotype,* a cellular condition that is transmitted maternally through the egg cytoplasm. The P-cytotype can repress *P* element movement whereas, M-cytotype permits *P*-element movement. *P*-elements are present on the chromosome of P cytotype but M cytotype lacks *P*-element.

When P-female is crosed with M male (Fig. 20.29) the offspring inherit P elements on their chromosomes. The female transmits the

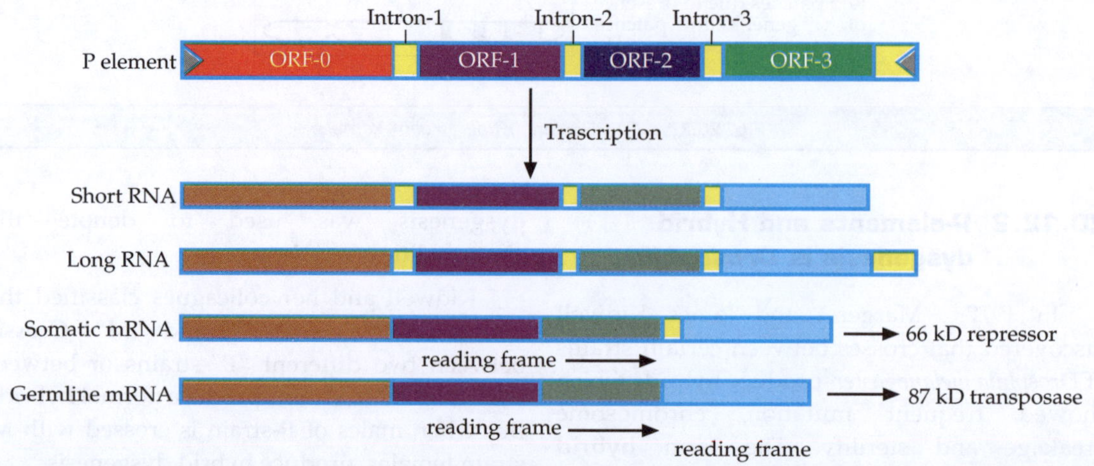


**Fig.20.28 :** *P-element in Drosophila.*

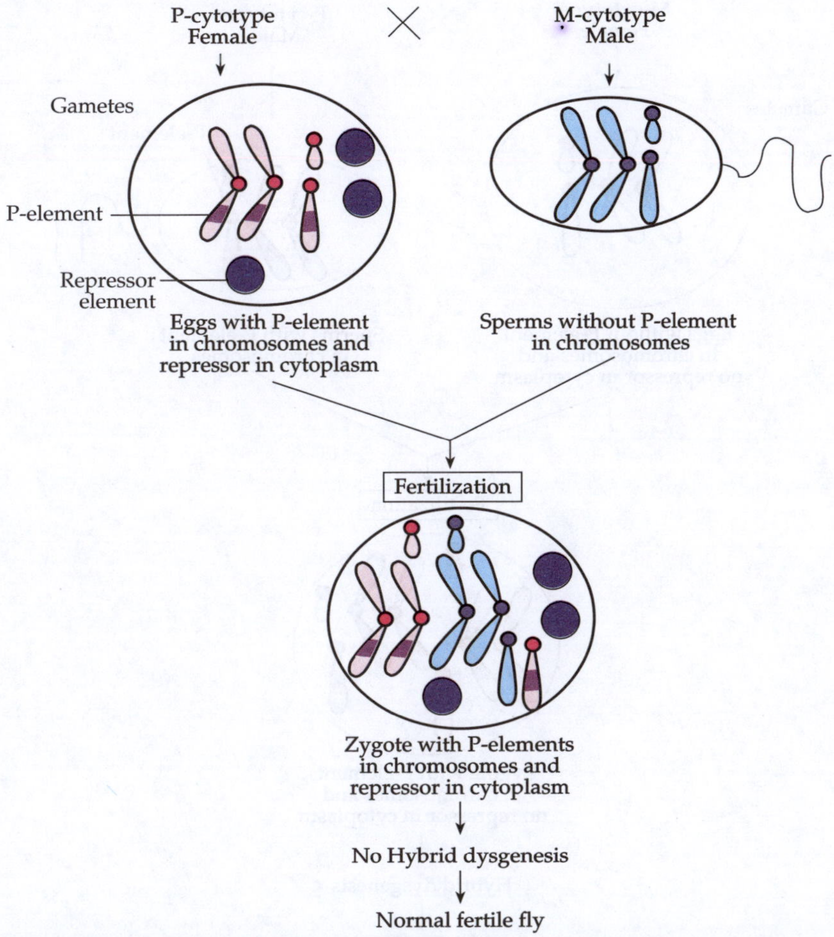


**Fig. 20.29 :** *Production of normal fertile files when P-cytotype female is crossed with M-cytotype male.*

P-cytotype to their progeny which then represses P movement The hybrid is normal (Fig. 20.30)

When M female is crossed with P male, . The zygote carrying P element in their chromosome and are healthy, because *P* elements move only in the germline.

In the somatic tissues, where P element movement would cause serious problems, but P-transposase is not synthesized there. The metabolic block occurs at the RNA-splicing level, one intron remains in the transcript of the transposase and synthesizes shorter 66 kD repressor protein and P-element is unable to move.

But in the germ line, the cell contains P element in their chromosome which is inherited from the male parent, but in the cytoplasm repressor is not present because the female parent is M type, lacks repressor. As a result, germ cells have no repressor to prevent transposition of P elements and the fly is subjected to massive damage in their germ cells. The fly becomes sterile.

P elements appear to have invaded *D.melanogaster* within the past 50 years. Today

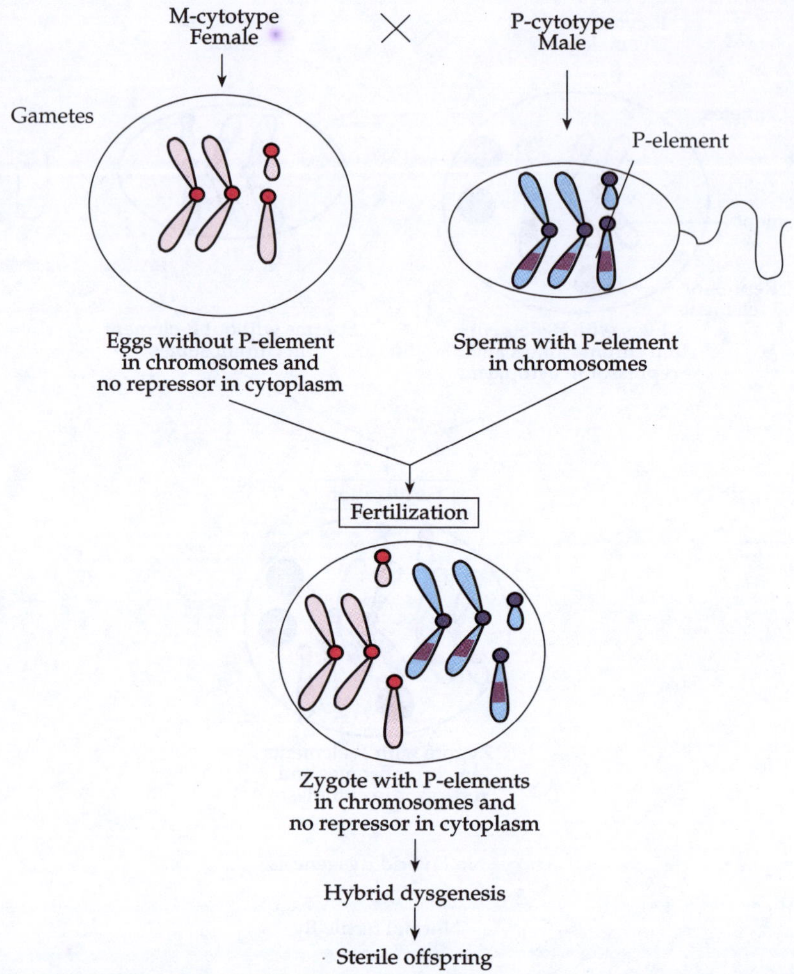


**Fig. 20.30 :** *Production of Sterile files when M-cytotype female is crossed with P-cytotype male.*

almost all *D. malanogaster* caught in the P element but these transposable elements are uncommon in laboratory colonies of flies that were established more than 30 years ago. A likely source is *D. willistoni* which possessed P elements and the P elements made the leap from *D. willistons* to *D. melanogaster* by hitching a ride on a mite, possibly the mite is *Proctolaelaps regalis* which infest both *D. millistoni* and *D. melanogaster*. Houck and Kidwell suggested that while feeding on *D. willistoni* larvae or egg, the mite picks the DNA with P element and later it injected it into the developing *D. melanogaster*. Thus, the P-element becomes identical to these two *Drosophila* species.

## 20.13 RNA-MEDIATED TRANSPOSITION AND RETROTRANSPOSONS

Retrotransposons are those transpose through an RNA intermediate utilizing a reverse transcriptase enzyme. All eukaryotes studied so far from yeast to humans contain such mobile elements.

These may be of viral or nonviral retrotransposons.

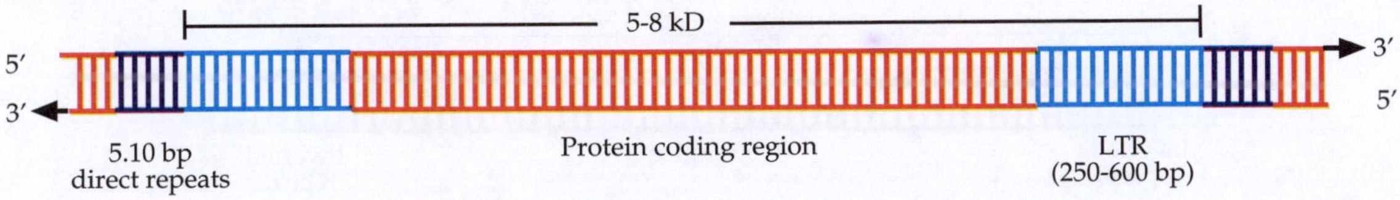


**Fig.20.31** : *General structure of eukaryotic viral retro-transposon.*

## 20.13.1. Viral retro-transposons

The viral retro-transposons are estimated to account for ~4% of human DNA. **Ty**-elements in yeast and **Copia** in *Drosophila* are the examples of viral retrotransposons (Fig. 20.31).

The general structure of viral retro-transposons has a central protein coding region is flanked by two long terminal repeats (LTRs) of 250-600 bp. which are element –specific direct repeats. It has also a short target site direct repeat (5 to 10 bp) at their 3′ and 5′ ends.

### Ty elements in yeast

Ty elements (transposon yeast) comprise a family of dispersed repetitive DNA sequences that are found at different sites of different strains of yeast.

Most Ty elements fall into two major classes called Ty 1 and Ty 917. Each element is 6.3 kb long, last 330 bp at each end constitute direct repeats called δ. Individual Ty elements of each type have many changes due to base pair substitutions, insertions and deletions etc.

In typical yeast genome, there are ~30 copies of the Ty 1 and ~6 of Ty 917 type. In addition, there are ~100 independent delta elements called **solo δs.**

The Ty element has two open reading frames, expressed in the same direction having an overlapping by 13 amino acids. The sequences of *TyA* codes DNA—binding protein, TyB codes reverse transcriptase, protease and integrase proteins like retroviruses.

Ty element is transcribed into an RNA that is recognized by the splicing apparatus. The spliced RNA is then recognized by a reverse transcriptase and generates a duplex DNA. It does not give rise to infectious particles but it is transposed by a mechanism, which is similar to the integration of retroviral DNA.

### Copia in *Drosophila*

Besides P-element, in *Drosophila* there are two types of retrotransposons viz, Copia retrotransposon and FB (fold back) family of unknown type.

The *Copia* element is ~ 5000 bp long with identical direct terminal repeats of 276 bp. Each direct repeat ends in related inverted repeats. At the site of insertion a direct repeat of 5 bp of target DNA is generated. There is about 20-60 copies and sometimes it is found in the form of free circular DNA like retroviral DNA circles. *Copia* is unlikely able to generate virus – like particles as it has no envelope coding genes and has no infectious properties (Fig. 20.32).

### FB elements in *Drosophila*

FB is abbreviated for "fold back" has inverted terminal repeats of variable length. Some FB elements consist solely of juxtaposed inverted repeats but the two copies in a single FB element are not identical. Length of the element varies from 500 to 5000 bp. can be greater upto 200kb. There is no knowledge of what confers their ability to transpose (Fig. 20.32).

## 20.13.2 Non-viral Retrotransposons

Non-viral retrotranspons are also mobile DNA in mammals. With the sequencing of the

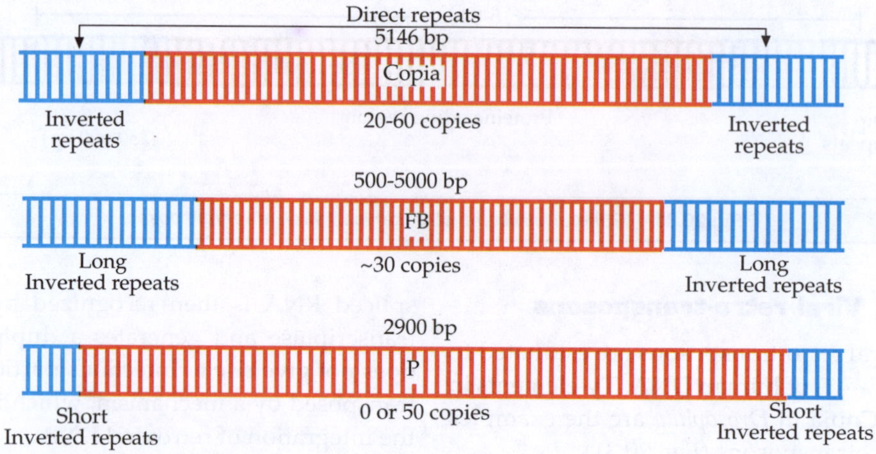


**Fig.20.32 :** *Three types of transposable elements in D. melanogaster.*

human genome, it is now possible to assess the significance of transposable elements in our own species. At least 44% of human DNA is derived from transposable elements, including retro-transposons (33%) and several families of DNA transposons that transpose by a *cut-and - paste* mechanism (3%). These are described as long interspersed elements (LINEs) and short interspersed elements (SINEs). Full lengths of LINE are 6-7 kb long and SINEs are 300 bp long in human.

### *L1* (LINE) element

About 600000 copies of L1 elements occur in the human genome. Its general structure constitutes the length of the flanking direct repeats ( target site) varies among copies of the element at different sites in the genome. Full length of L1 sequence is ~ 6 kb long. The consensus sequence contains two long open reading frames (ORFs) one is ~ 1 kb long or ORF 1 and the other is ~ 4 kb long or ORF2. ORF 1 encodes an RNA binding protein, whereas, ORF2 encodes reverse transcriptase, like retroviruses. It does not contain LTR but there is A-T rich region at the right end, which is thought to function in retrotransposition (Fig. 20.33).

Transcription of *L1* is directed by promoter sequences located within the left end of the element. *L1* element also contains A-T rich region near the right end, which generates a stretch of RNA transcript. The RNA folds back on itself with U=A hybridization. 3' end of RNA acts as primer and DNA is synthesized on the RNA by *L1* reverse transcriptase. The cDNA then serves as a template and *L1* is transformed into a double stranded DNA. By unknown mechanism *L1* element is inserted into cellular DNA. Sometimes, the 5′ region of the *L1* RNA is not copied into DNA. When this happens the resulting *L1* insertion will lack 5′ sequences, *i.e.*, it will be an incomplete *L1* element.

Only a small number of the complete *L1* element in the human genome appears to be transpositionally active. Transposed copies of these elements have been discovered through the analysis of genetic diseases in a small number of individuals. To date, 14 disease-causing *L1* insertion mutations have been identified, including mutations in the *factor VIII* gene, (the cause of hemophila), and the *dystrophin* gene (the cause of muscular dystrophy) and in the *APC* gene, helping to cause **adenomatous polyposis coli**, a kind of colon cancer. In the case, the patient's cancer

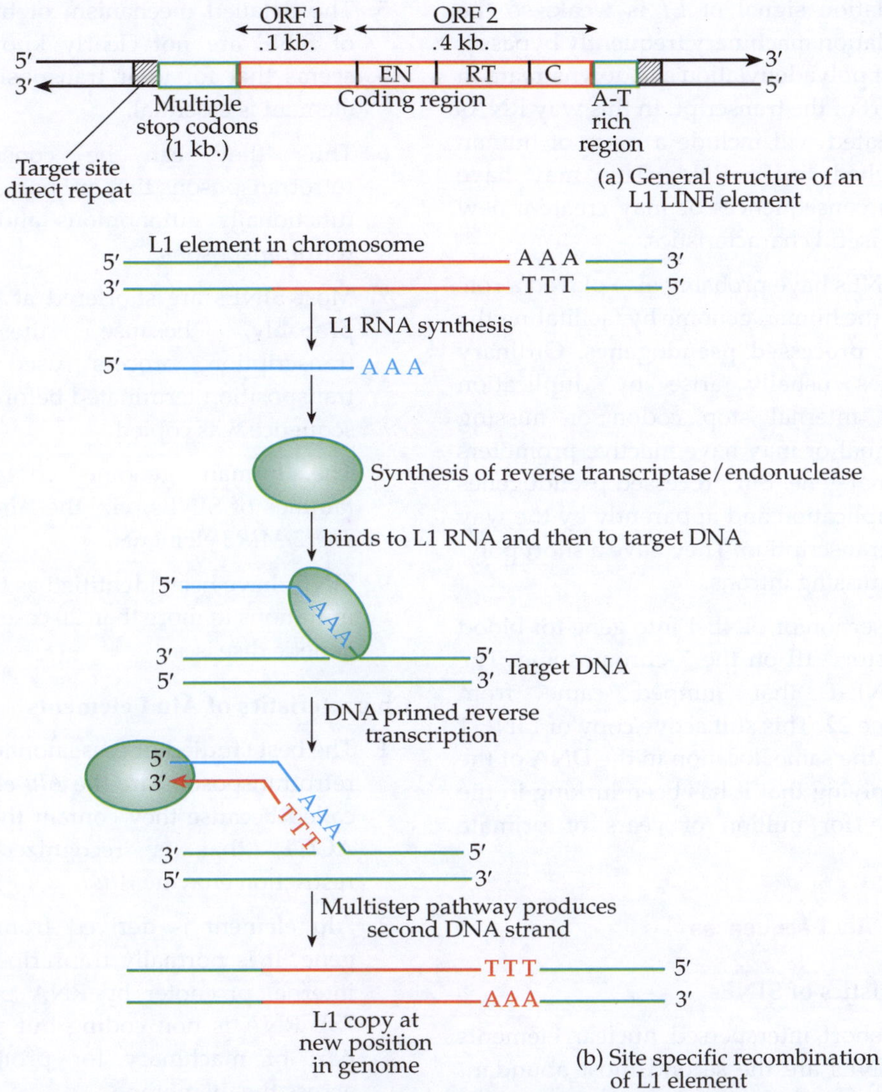


**Fig.20.33 :** *Non-retroviral transposable element (L1 LINE) and site speicific recombination. EN = endonuclease RT = Reverse transcriptase and C = Cysterine run.*

cells had the *L1* element in their *APC* gene but the normal cells did not. Thus this transposition had occurred during the patient's lifetime as a somatic mutation.

The transposition of *L1* elements, therefore seems to be rare event. The human genome contains two other types of LINE sequences, viz. *L2* (315000 copies) and *L3* (37000 copies), however, neither is transpositonally active.

There is a significant homology between the reverse transcriptase of *L1* and human telomerase, suggesting that *L1* may have been the origin of the enzyme that maintains the end of the chromosome, which is an example of beneficial consequence of *L1* transposons. Another beneficial aspect of *L1* is that it may facilitate *exon suffling* and exchange of exons among genes. This happens because the polyadenylation signal of *L1* is weak, so the polyadenylation machinary frequently bypass it in favour of polyadenylation site downstream in the host part of the transcript. In this way RNAs polyedenylated will include a piece of human RNA attached to *L1* RNA. This may have deleterious consequences or may create a new gene with useful characteristics.

The LINEs have probably also played a role in shaping the human genome by facilitating the creation of **processed pseudogenes**. Ordinary pseudogenes usually arise by duplication having an internal stop codon or missing splicing signal or may have inactive promoters of the normal gene. But processed pseudogenes arise by duplication and apparently by the way of reverse transcription. They have a short poly-A tail and missing introns.

The insertion of LINE-1 into gene for blood clotting factor VIII on the X-chromosome. The intact LINE-1 that jumped came from chromosome 22. This still active copy of LINE-1 is found in the same, location in the DNA of the gorilla, implying that it has been lurking in the same place for million of years of primate evolution.

## SINEs and Alu I sequences

### Characteristics of SINEs

1. The short interspersed nuclear elements or SINEs are the second most abundant class of transposable elements (about 11% of the human genome). These elements are usually range from about 200-400 bp in length.
2. They do not encode proteins and enzymes.
3. Like all the retrotransposons, they have a sequence of A-T base pairs at one end.
4. SINEs transpose through a process that involves reverse transription of an RNA that has transcribed from an internal promoter.
5. The detailed mechanism of transpostion of SINE are not clearly known. But it seems that for their transposition, LINE element is essential.
6. Thus they can be considered as retrotransposons that are parasites on the functionally autonomous and authentic retrotransposons.
7. Most SINEs are shortered at the 5′ end, probably, because the reverse transcription process used in their transposition terminated before the entire sequence was copied.
8. The human genome contains three families of SINEs, viz, the *Alu, MIR* and *Ther2/MIR3* elements.
9. SINEs have been identified as the cuase of mutations in more than 20 cases of human genetic diseases.

### Characteristics of Alu I elements

1. The best studied of these nonautonomous retrotransposons are the *Alu* elements, so called because they contain the sequence AGCT, that is recognized by the restriction enzyme *Alu I.*
2. Alu element is derived from *7SL-RNA* gene. It is normally transcribed from an internal promoter by RNA pol-III. This 7SL RNA is non coding but serves as a part of machinary for protein export across the membrane.
3. These are about 300 bp long, made up of two similar but nonidentical DNA sequences and are present upto a millon copies in the human genome.
4. The *Alu* sequences are similar to that of 7SLRNA molecules and it has been proposed that these were independently derived from 7SLRNA some 100 million years ago in a common ancestor of primates and rodents.
5. The 7S L RNA is a core component of the signal recognition particle which interacts

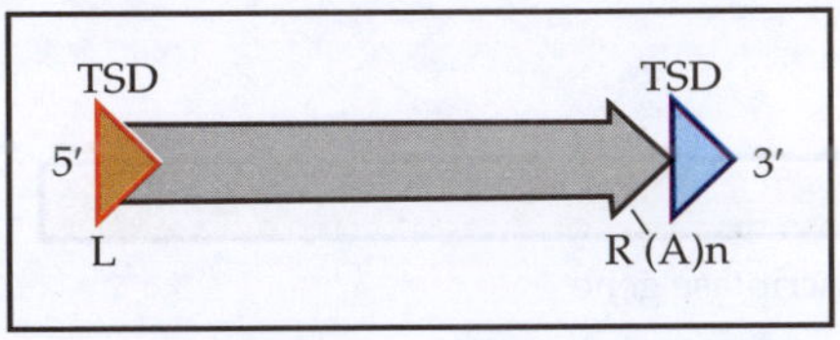


**Fig. 20.34 :** *Alu element*

with ribosomes and transports newly synthesized proteins across the endoplasmic reticulum.

6. *Alu* elements contian two similar monomers, the left, the right and poly A tail .
7. *Alu* elements do not encode any proteins or enzymes required for transposition, but they actively move throughout the genome.
8. *Alu* elements are flanked by 7-20 bp target site duplications (TSD) that share homology with *L1* element.
9. The reverse transcriptase encoded by some LINEs is proposed to interact with the shared 3′ end of the sequence to mobilize *Alu* element in *trans*.
10. *Alu* repeats and other mammalian SINEs preferably insert at DNA target sites of about 15 bp that contain a conserved consensus sequence 5′-TTAAAA-3′ (Fig. 20.34 and 20.35).

### 20.13.3 Retrons

Retrons are found in bacteria but are relatives of the retrotransposons of higher cells. They have only one gene that is transcribed into RNA molecule consisting of a large non translated region and then the coding region for reverse transcriptase. This noncoding region is used by reverse transcriptase as template and also as primer to make a branched molecule of DNA and RNA.

The non-translated region has a 5′ and a 3′ ends. It folds to form a hairpin structure so that 5′ end meets with 3′ end. Reverse transcriptase recognizes a specific guanine residue near the front of the hairpin and begins to synthesize DNA holding the 2′ -OH end to start. The RNA is then partly degraded resulting in a strange RNA/DNA hybrid. The ssDNA may be cleaved off from RNA or remain attached with. Retron DNA has not been found to reintegrate into the chromosomes.

Some strains of myxobacteria have such repeated sequences related to retrons. How they move around is unknown. Retrons are often found to insert into phages that have inserted in turn into the bacterial chromosome. But how and where the phages picked them up remain obscure (Fig. 20.36 and 20.37).

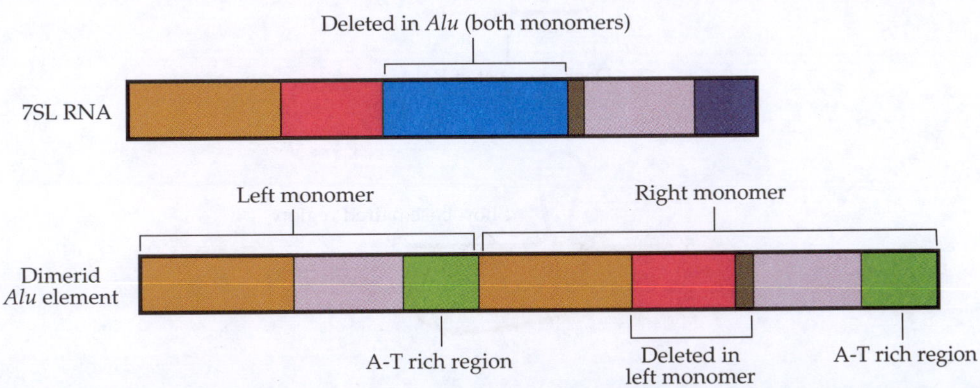


**Fig. 20.35 :** *Origin of the Alu element from 7SL RNA*

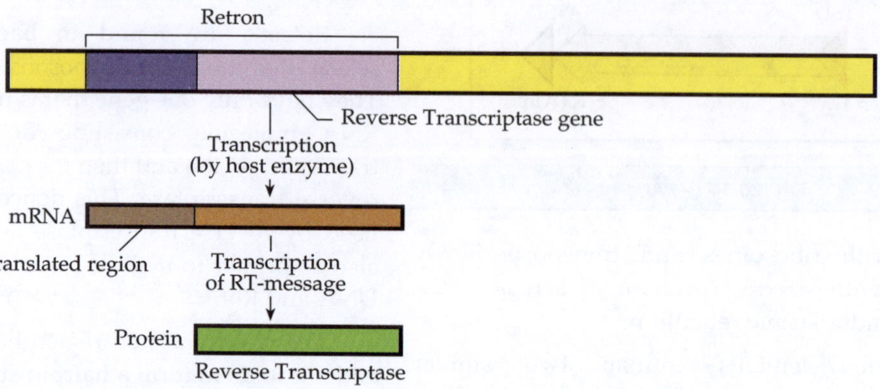


**Fig. 20.36 :** *Structure of a Retron and its Gene Products.*

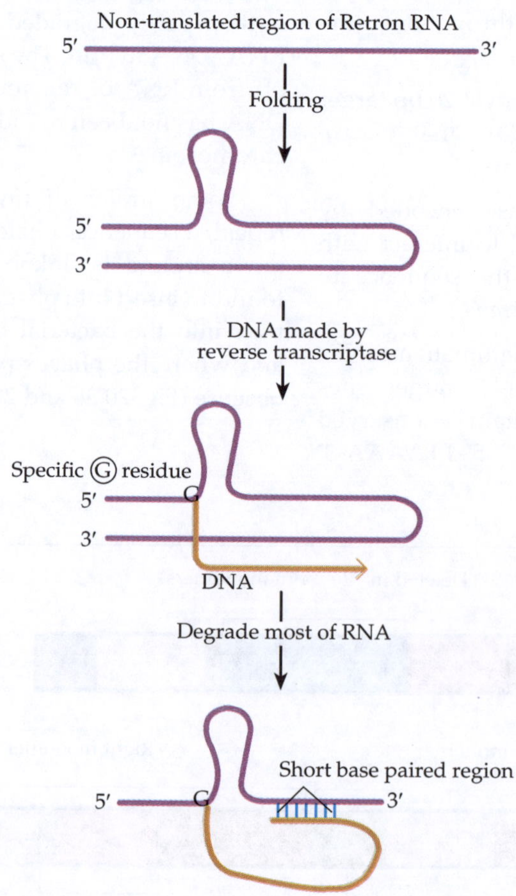


**Fig. 20.37 :** *Retron RNA and DNA/RNA hybrid*

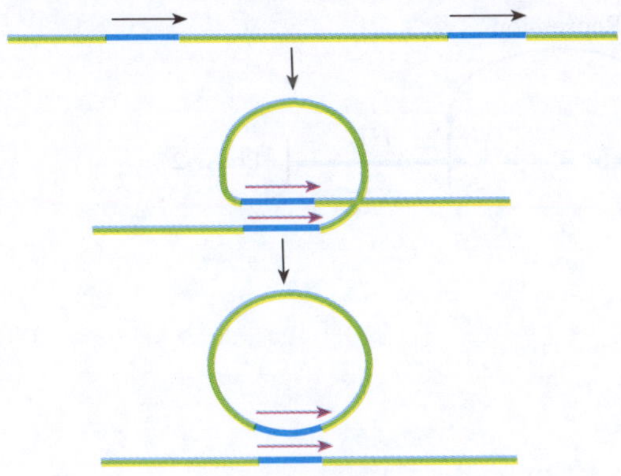


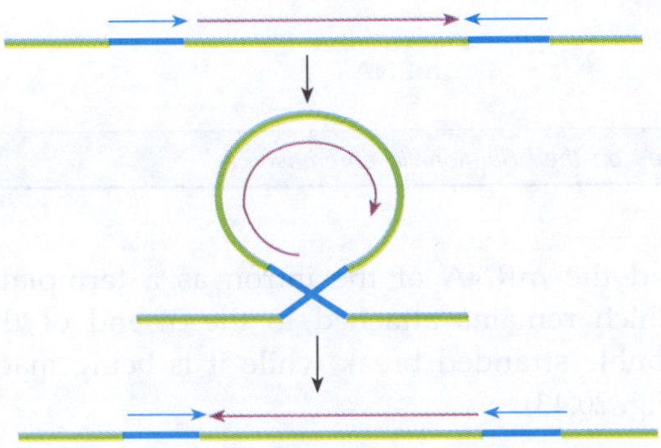


**Fig. 20.38 :** *Pairing and recombination in DNA repeats (a) Direct repeats can result in deletion ; (b) inverted repeats can result in inversion of the region between the repeats due to a crossing over*

## 20.14 PHENOTYPIC AND GENOTYPIC EFFECTS OF TRANSPOSITION AND DNA REARRANGEMENT IN *SALMONELLA*

If transposition takes place into a gene or its promoter, it can disrupt the expression of that gene. Transposon can also cause deletions and inversions.

For example, the sequential transposition of same transposon of same orientation may cause **deletion** following pairing and recombination. Similarly same transposon of opposite orientation may cause **inversion** following pairing and recombination (Fig. 20.40).

Orientation of transposon controls the phenotype in *Salmonella typhimurium* (a bacterium). It's flagella occur in two types : type-1 and type-2. The difference is due to the presence of a protein called **flagellin.** The flagellin of type-1 is determined by *H1* gene while type-2 is by *H2* gene. The change from one type to another type may occur at the rate of about $10^{-4}$ per cell division.

By extensive studies using recombinant DNA techniques, it has been suggested that *H1* and *H2* genes are located at separate loci. *H2* is a part of an operon which contains rH1 (the repressor of *H1* gene). The promotor lies within a transposon upstream of this operon. When this promoter is in proper orientation, *H2* operon is expressed resulting type-2 flagella but *H1* is gene is repressed due to the synthesis of rH1 repressor (Fig. 20.39)

If the inverted repeat ends of the transposon undergo recombination, the transposon is inverted, promoter is oriented incorrectly for the transcription of *H2* operon. Then repressor of *H1* gene is not produced. Therefore *H1* gene is expressed to make type-1 flagellum.

Thus transposon orientation has an effect on the phenotype which is also valuable for the cells. But usually they exist without an noticeable consequences. Therefore some evolutionary geneticists suggested that transposons are *evolutionary accidents* and that once created are self maintaining. Therefore transposons are referred to an **selfish DNA.**

## 20.15 HOMING INTRON

**Homing intron is a mobile intron that encodes a protein enabling it to insert itself into a recognition sequence within a target gene.** As its name, homing intron is intervening sequence that is inserted into gene between two exons. This target gene can thus exist in two versions, with or without the inserted homing intron. The homing intron will then insert itself into the target gene that lacks a copy of the intron. In eukaryotes, this situation may occur during zygote formation but in bacteria it may

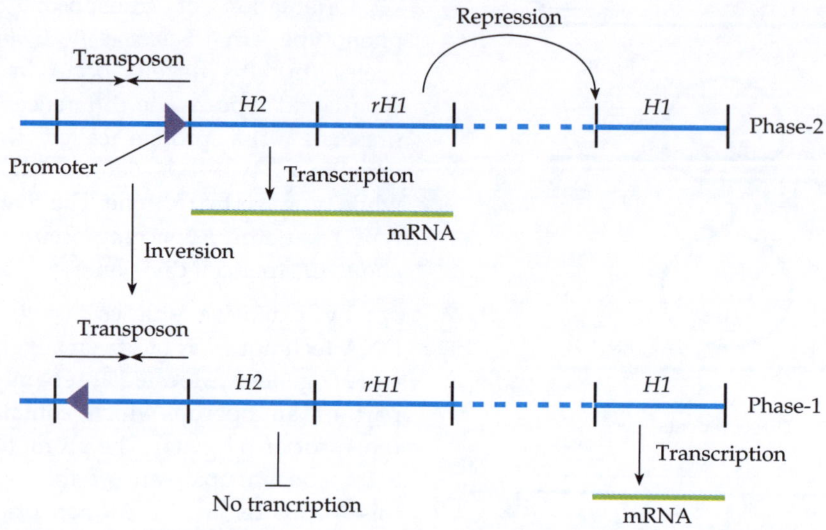


**Fig. 20.39 :** *Arrangement of flagellin genes on the Salmonella chromosome*

occur during conjugation or other mechanisms when DNA enters a recepient cells.

**Homing introns of group-I** use simple endonucleases. A homing intron contains a single gene for an endonuclease. This enzyme cleaves a very specific short target site of 18 to 20 bp length, to make staggard ends whch is only found in a copy of the target gene not containing the homing intron. This situation occurs only when two copies of the target gene are present in a cell, one with the homing intron and one without. This double-stranded break triggers a gene conversion, thus duplicating the homing intron. These are found in various bacteria and lower eukaryotes (Fig. 20.40).

**Homing introns of group-II** are found in bacteria and organelles of lower eukaryotes. These homing introns are retro-elements that use an RNA intermediate not via gene conversion. The homing intron expresses an enzyme with both reverse transcriptase and endonuclease activity. The endonuclease generates a double strand break at the specific target site. The reverse-trancriptase generates a DNA copy of the intron using the 3′ -OH of the double stranded break as a primer for synthesis and the mRNA of the intron as a termplate, which remains attached to the 3′ end of the double stranded break while it is being made (Fig. 20.43).

## 20.16 SELFISH DNA AND JUNK DNA

The coding DNA makes up only 1.5% of the human genome. Presence of extensive amounts of noncoding DNA in eukaryotic genomes is a puzzle for molecular biologists. There are three alternatives about the functions of such noncoding DNAs : These are involved in the genome organization; might have a broad-ranging control function that so far has eluted discovery by the molecular biologists or having no function but is tolerated by the genome because there is no selective pressure to get rid of it. This non coding DNA is **Selfish DNA.**

According to **selfish DNA hypothesis**, the posession of noncoding DNA is neither an advantage nor a disadvantage and so this is simply propagated with coding DNA. These are regarded as the *genetic parasites* of a very degenerate kind. If the host DNA is degraded, the parasite dies with it. Thus the spread of selfish DNA is limited by the need to avoid

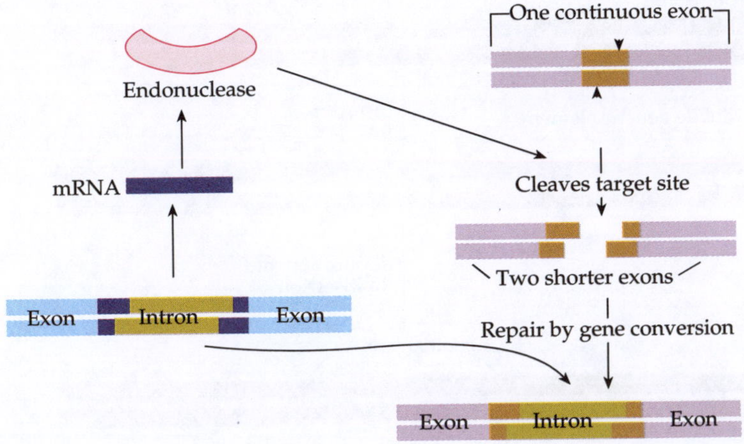


**Fig. 20.40 :** *Homing Intron inserts in a Unique location*

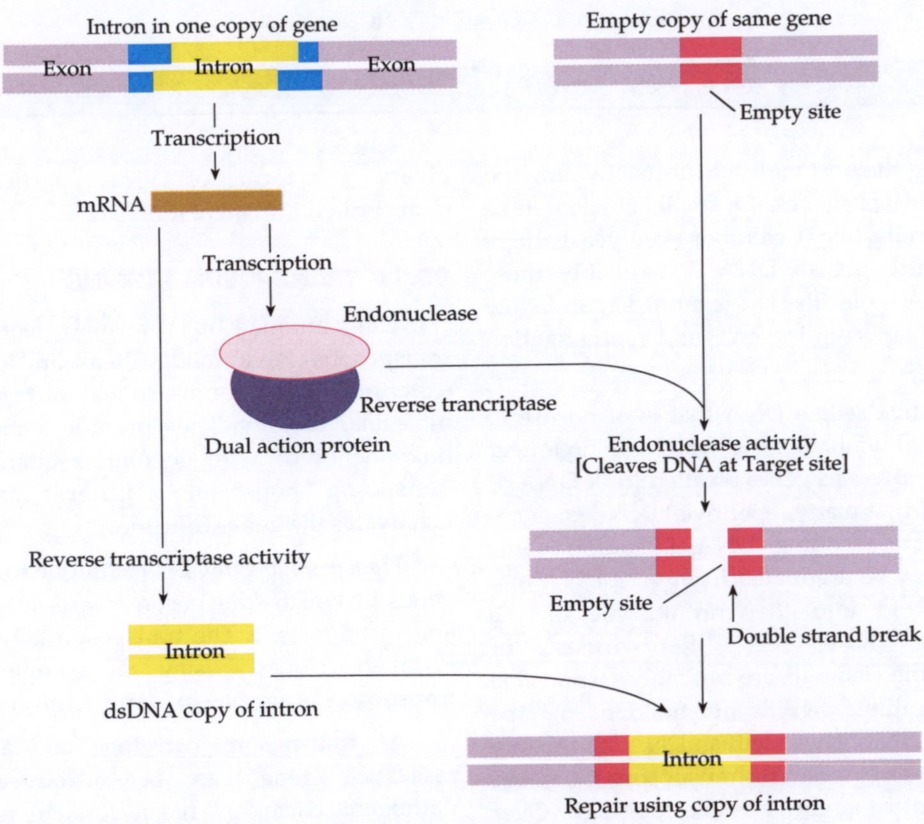


**Fig. 20.41 :** *Homing Retro-intron inserts via RNA Intermediate*

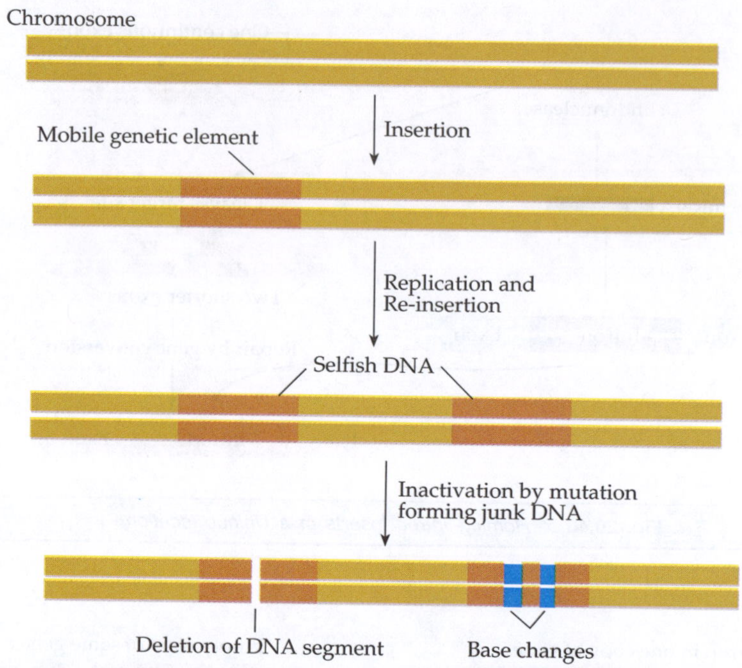


**Fig. 20.42 :** *Origins of Selfish DNA and Junk DNA*

destroying the host molecule or inactivating too many host cell genes. In small, efficient fast-growing cells, like bacteria or even yeasts there is very little selfish DNA. Presumably these extra DNA molecules cause a burden and slow down their replication and propagation (Fig. 20.42).

Defective selfish DNA that is of no use to the host cell it inhabits and which can no longer move or express its genes is called **junk DNA**. It is thought that many repetitive DNA sequences and other noncoding DNA including some introns may be originated from viral DNA that was inserted into the chromosome of the eukaryotic host cells. Retroviruses or transposable elements are probably responsible for generating significant fraction of the repetitive DNA. These selffish DNA is probably the remains of viruses or transposons that were inserted into the chromosome long ago. Over long periods of time of copies diverge both by single base mutation or by deletion and eventually become defective and lose their ability to form of virus particles and degenerated into mere junk DNA.

## 20.17 TRANSPOSON TAGGING

The unique an unusual features of transposons have made them an important experimental tool for insertional mutagenesis in molecular biology. They provide a method to link phenotype with genomic sequences. If a transposon "hops" into a gene, it may likely inactivates the genes function.

*Transposon tagging* is a technique for cloning genes in which transposon inserts into a gene and inactivates it. The transposon-tagged gene is then cloned using a complementary transposon as a probe to identify the gene.

A transposon carrying an antibiotic resistance gene can be introduced into pathogenic bacteria. If the bacteria are no longer pathagenic, this indicates that insertion of the transposon disrupted a gene important in pathogenicity. The disease gene which is tagged by antibiotic-resistant phenotype can then be cloned.

In 1981, Paul Bingham, in collaboration with Robert Levis and Gerald Rubin used transposon tagging to clone the *Drosophila* X-linked eye color gene, where red eye is dominant and loss-of-function allele (recessive) is white eye.

1. At first, a wild type red eyed strain of *Drosophila* has been characteriszed that it carries a transposable element called *copia.*
2. The individuals of this strain is inbred to obtain a rare white eyed strain. In this white *Drosophila*, the transposable element *copia* has been transposed to the X-chromosome within the red eye gene and inactivates it.
3. The chromosomal DNA from this white-type strain was isolated and digested with restriction enzymes and inserted it into viral vectors to construct a DNA library.
4. Each vector is introduced into the bacterial cells and ultimately produces viral plaques.
5. If transposon has jumped into the wild eye colour gene, the gene will tagged with transposable elements. Therefore, radioactive probe made with the complementary DNA sequence of *copia* can be detected by autoradiography to screen DNA library.
6. In this way transposon tagging became successful at cloning an eye color gene in *Drosophila* (Fig. 20.43).

## 20.18 EPIGENETIC CONTROL OF TRANSPOSABLE ELEMENTS

Although, transposable elements are continuously entering into the genomic sites and causing mutations and alterations of chromosomes, but the frequency is lesser than that of point mutations in all organisms, because these elements remain resonably stable. To keep them silence, there are two control mechanisms *viz* methylation of transposable elements and formation of heterochromatin by RNAi.

1. **Methylation of transposable elements :** Methylation of cytosine in transposable elements is a mechanism of host defense against its insertion, inactivation and also its transcriptional activity.

   (a) Inactive elements of *Ac* and *Spm* elements in maize were found to have methylated cytosine, whereas active elements are nonmethylated. These changes in methylation pattern is heritable. Varigated mutant of *Ipomoea tricolor* results from insertion of 0.4 kb Mu-related transposable elements in the promoter region of *DFR-B* gene about upsteam of the strart of transcription. *DFR-B* encodes dihydroflavonol-4-reductase involved in anthocyanin pigment biosynthesis in wild type morning glory. When the transposon is heavily methylated and spreads into the adjacent promoter region, blocking *DFR-B* transcription causing variegated flower, which is a heritable change.

   (b) Mammalian retrotranspons have been found to become active by its demethylation. On the other hand hypermethylated state in the somatic cells renders its immobilization. For example, a particular strain of agauti mice with $A^{vy}$ allele (agouti variable yellow) has LTR retrotransposon insertion (IAP) upstream of the agouti gene. $C_pG$ methylation in the inserted retrotransposon varies dramatically among individual $A^{vy}$ mice. This epigenetic variability causes a wide variation in individual coat colour. Normally the fur of $A^{vy}$ mice is yellow, brown or calico-like colour depending upon the number of attached methyl group in the 5′ LTR promoter. Increase in the methylation of LTR causing gradually them into slightly mottled,

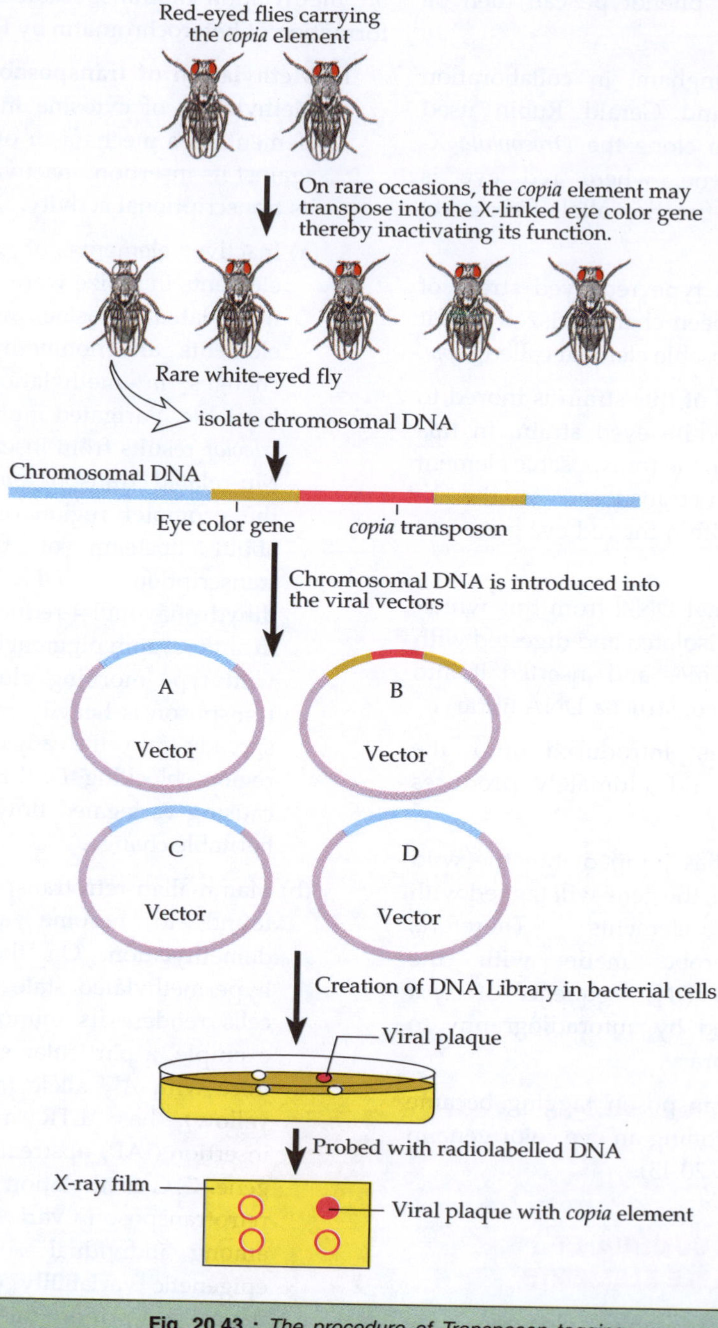


**Fig. 20.43 :** *The procedure of Transposon tagging*

mottled, heavily mottled and pseudo agouti. Robert A. Waterland and Randy L. Jirtle fed folic acid and other methyl rich supplements to pregnant agouti mice with the $A^{vy}$ allele, the mice gave birth to offspring with mostly brown fur (pseudoagouti) by maximum methylation of retro-

**TABLE 20.2**
**Possible Consequences of transposition**

| *Consequence* | *Cause* |
|---|---|
| 1. Chromosomal breakage | Excision of transposable elements. |
| 2. Chromosomal rearrangement | Homologous recombination between transposable elements located at different positions in the genome. |
| 3. Mutataion | Incorrect excision of transposable elements. |
| 4. Gene activation | Insertion of a transposon into a gene |
| 5. Alteration in gene regulation | Transposition of a gene next to or prior to a regulatory sequence. |
| 6. Alteration in the exon | Insertion of exons into the coding sequence via transposons. |
| 7. Gene duplication | Creation of composite transposons and its transposition in the genome. |

transposons. This is peculiar that, these mice were found to be hyper-methylated retrotransposon and it has also found that these mice inherit this methylation to their offspring. Mother mice those are feed without methyl-rich supplements gave mostly yellow pups with high susceptibility to obesity, diabetes and cancer. In these mice retrotransposons and active.

2. **Heterochromatin formation by RNAi mediated DNA methylation** : Hetero-chromatin domain is inaccessible to DNA-binding factors and become trancrip-tionally inactive. These hetero-chromatins are inherited through many cell divisions. In addition to histone modification, DNA methylation also contributes to the stability of reterochromatin. Usually transposable elements and satellite bodies are heterochromatinized.

In plants, heterochromatin-targeting involves RNA-directed DNA methylation which is linked to RNAi.

The dsRNA or siRNA derived from transcripts generated by transposable elements can direct DNA methylation. These RNAs are called small heterochromatic RNAs (shRNAs). This shRNA triggers RNA dependent RNA polymerase **Dicer** and **Argonaute** proteins. Methylation occurs at $C_pG$ as well as non $C_pG$ cytosines in the target region by specific DNA methyltransferases.

## 20.19 SIGNIFICANCE OF MOBILE DNA

**Consequeuces of transposition** : Transposable elememts have a variety of effects on chromosome structure and gene expression (Table 20.2). Though, transposition is usually a highly regulated phenomenon and occurs in a few individuals under certain conditions. Radiation, chemical mutagens and hormones stimulate the movement of transposable elements. Sometimes trans-positions may cause detrimental to the living organisms.

Most of the insertions of transposable elements into the genome in higher organisms occur in the noncoding regions. Therefore, it is usually not harmful to them. Occasional insertion of retrotransposons may inactivate the normal gene causing hereditary defects.

1. **Medical significance** : **Neurofibro-matosis**, a genetic disorder marked by the occurrence of multiple neuronal tumors called neurofibromas is caused by the mutation in the NF1 gene. It develops only when both NF1 alleles carry a mutation. In some neurofibromatosis one NF1 allele contains an inactivating *Alu* sequence. In the other NF1 allele, it is inactivating by somatic mutation.

Several other inherited recessive mutations causing diseases in humans also have been found to result from insertion of *Alu* sequences in their exons thereby disrupting its protein coding region. A form of muscular dystrophy, known of Fukuyama type Congenital Muscular Dystrophy (FCMD), is an autosomal recessive disorder in Japan, occurrying 0.7–1.2 per ten thousand births and with a carrier frequency 1 in 80. A retrotransposon is inserted into the 3′ end of *FCMD* gene. The mRNA is unstable and so, is not detectable in the affected cells. Normal *FCMD* gene encodes a protein with 461 amino acid residues and expressed in brain, skeletal muscles and heart.

Possibly the insertion of retrotransposon in *FCMD* gene could have been derived from a single ancester who lived 2000-2500 years ago. The Yayoi people of Korea and China were migrated to Japan and brought the defective *FCMD* allele to the Japanese poulation.

2. **Evolutionary significance** : Mobile elements appear to have no direct function but their existence probably has an important role in the evolution of modern-day individuals.

Many spontaneous mutations in *Drosophila* and man have been found, which are resulted from insertion of mobile DNA into or near the transcription unit.

Homologous recombinations between mobile DNA, which are dispersed throughout the ancestral genome may have an important role in generating gene duplication and arrangement of genes during evolution. The evolution of β-globin gene cluster in primates have provided an important evidence that human $G\gamma$ and $A\gamma$ genes have been arose due to unequal homologous crossing over between two L1 sequences. There is a surprizing ability of transposons to infiltrate a popultion of organism. For example, the *P*-element was probably introduced into *Drosophila melanogaster* from *D. willistoni* in the 1950s and now the *P*. element has expanded throughout the *D. melanogaster* populations world-wide. There is no evidence the presence of *P* elements prior to 1950s.

Transposable elements may cause greater genetic variability by promoting recombination. Bacterial transposable elements often may carry antibiotic resistance gene that provides the organism with survival advantage.

Homologous recombination between mobile elements inserted into introns probably contributed to the duplication of introns within genes. Thus multiple copies of similar exons have been generated that encode similar protein domain (e.g., fibronectin gene). This suggests that new genes are generated from the novel preexisting exons during the course of evolution in higher organisms. The term exon shuffling has been coined to refer to this type of evolutionary process.

Eukaryotic genes have transcription control regions called enhancers that are operated over a long distance from the location of the gene. Recombination between mobile elements inserted randomly near enhancers probably contributed to the evolution of such enhancers, which control the gene expression in modern organisms.

## CHAPTER GLOSSARY/KEY TERMS

**Alu :** A type of SINE found in the genome of human and related mammals.

***att* sites :** These are the loci on a phage and the bacterial chromosome at which recombination integrates the phage into or excises it from the bacterial chromosome.

**Branch migration :** A step in Holliday model for homologous recombining double-stranded DNA molecules.

**Chiasma :** The site at which two homologous chromosomes appear to have exchanged material during meiosis and formed an X-structure.

***Chi*-sequence :** A repeated nucleotide sequence in *E. coli* genome that is involved in the initiation of homologous recombination.

***Chi*-structure :** This is a joint between two duplex molecules of DNA revealed by cleaving an intermediate of two joint circles to generate linear ends in each circle.

**Crossing over :** The reciprocal exchange of material between chromosomes that occurs during meiosis and is responsible for genetic recombination.

**Gene conversion :** This is the alteration of one strand of a heteroduplex DNA to make a complementary with the other strand at any positions where there were mispaired bases.

**Heteroduplex :** DNA-DNA or DNA-RNA hybrid.

**Heteroduplex DNA :** Base pairing between complementary single strands derived from the different parental duplex molecules. It occurs during genetic recombination.

**Holliday structure :** An intermediate structure formed during recombination between two DNA molecules.

**Homologous recombination :** Recombination between two homologous dsDNA molecules *i.e.* ones which share extensive nucleotide sequence similarity.

**Insertion sequene :** It is a small bacterial transposon that carries only the genes needed for its own transposition.

**LINE :** A type of genome-wide repeat, often with transposable activity.

**Planar molecules :** One of the two DNA duplexes in the joint molecule undergoes rotation giving rise to a planar molecule.

**RecBCD :** The protein present in *E. coli* involved in homologous recombination.

**Recombinant joint :** The dense object present on the synaptonemal complex could be involved in crossing over.

**Recombinant nodule :** The dense object present on the synaptonemal complex could be involved in homologous recombination.

**Recombinase :** A diverse family of enzymes that catalyze site-specific recombination.

**Retrotransposition :** Transposition via an RNA intermediate.

**Retrotransposon :** A genome-wide repeat with a sequence similar to an integrated retroviral genome and possibly with retrotransposition activity.

**SINE :** A type of genome wide repeat typified by the Alu sequences found in human genome.

*Contd.*

**Transpoase :** An enzyme that catalyses transposition of a transposable genetic element.

**Transposable element :** A genetic element that can move from one postion to another in a DNA molecule.

**Transposition :** The movement of a genetic element from one site to another in a DNA molecule.

**Transposon :** A DNA sequence able to insert itself at a new location in the genome.

**Zyg-DNA :** A very small fraction of DNA synthesis is delayed during replication till zygotene, this fraction of DNA is Zyg DNA.

# Exercise

## A. Long answer type questions :

1. Define recombination and genetic recombination.
2. Establish a relatonship between crossing over and chiasma.
3. What are one-point and two-point theories regarding crossing over.
4. Describe the procosity theory of crossing over
5. Describe the Bellings hypothesis of crossing war. Why it is called copy choice model? What are the objections against this hypothesis?
6. Draw and describe the Uhls model of crossing over.
7. Briefly describe the Whitehouse model of crossing over.
8. Draw and describe the Hollidays model of recombination. What is the main difference from Whitehouse model?
9. How recombination is initiated? Describe the molecular mechanishm.
10. Describe the role of Rec-BCD and Chi sequence in the initiation of recombination.
11. What do you mean by branch migration? What are the three types of branch migration?
12. Briefly describe Rec A mediated branch migration.
13. Describe the enzyme catalyzed double branch migration.
14. How resolution of Holliday structure is involved.
15. Describe the Hybrid DNA model involving double strand break.
16. Briefly describe the significance of genetic recombination.
17. What is site specific recombination? Where does it occur? Shortly describe the mechanism of pathways of site specific recombination.
18. Briefly describe the mechanism of site specific recombination in bacteriophage.
19. What are the major types of mobile DNA
20. What do you mean by DNA transposition? What do you mean by mobile DNA. Name two types of transposons in bacteria.
21. What do you mean by bacterial insertion sequence. What are their common features? How does IS element inserted into bacterial chromosomes?
22. What are bacterial transposons? Describe the Tn A transposition mechanism.

23. Describe the transposons in maize.
24. Describe the transposons in *Drosophila.*
25. What is retrotransposons? Describe the viral retrotransposons.
26. Write notes on Ty element in yeast, Copia in *Drosophila* and FB elements in *Drosophila*.
27. What are nonviral transposons? Give notes on L1 LINE elements are SINES and *Alu* sequences in human genome.
28. Discuss about the significance of mobile DNA.
29. Write a short note on gene conversion.
30. What are the general characeritics of transposable elements?
31. What do you mean by complex transposons? What are their requirements for transposition? Give the mechanism of Tri-1 and Tn-3 transposition.
32. What is composite transposon? What are their characteristics?
33. What is the characteristics of conjugative transposon?
34. Describe mutator gene transposition by bacetriophage.
35. Describe *Ac/Ds* transposition in corn.
36. Describe P-elements and hybrid dysgenesis in *rosophila*.
37. What are the characeristics of LINEs and SINEs?
38. Waht are the characteristics of Alu elements?
39. What are retrons? What are the characteristics?
40. Describe transposition and DNA rearrangement in *Salmonella*.
41. What do you mean by homing introns? What are the characteristics of two different types of homing introns?
42. Write short notes on selfish DNA and junk DNA?
43. What do youl mean by transposontagging give the mechanism in brief.
43. Describe the epoigenetic control of transposable elements.

## B. Short answer type questions

1. What is genetic recombination?
2. What is homologous recombination?
3. Distinguish chiasma and crossing over?
4. Why classical theory is regarded as two-point theory and chiasma type theory is called one point theory?
5. What is zyg DNA?
6. Why Belling recombination hypothesis is called copy choice or switch synthesis theory?
7. What are the demerits of Bellings hypothesis?
8. What is the difference between Bellings hypothesis and Uhls hypothesis?
9. What is the difference between Holliday model and Whitehouse model of recombination?
10. Define branch migration, Holliday intermediate, joint molecule, planar molecule, hetero-duplex DNA and recombinant joint.
11. What is the role of Rec BCD and Rec A in recombination?
12. What is the role of Rec BCD and Rec A in recombination?
13. What is gene conversion? What do you mean by recombination repair?
14. Define site specific recombination.
15. What is the function of recombinase?
16. What is prophage?
17. What is the bacterial attachment site?
18. What is the phage attachment site?
19. What is the role of *att R* and *all P*? What are the roles of IHF and Int proteins.
20. Give The examples of DNA mediated transpositions and RNA mediated transpositions?
21. What is intasome?
22. What is hopping gene?
23. What is mobile DNA?
24. What is transposons?

25. What are the two classes of mobile DNA?
26. What is IS element?
27. What is transposase? What is its function?
28. What is the function of resolvase?
29. What is the characteristics of Tn A?
30. What is activator element?
31. What is dissociation element?
32. What are autonomous and non autonomous elements in maize?
33. How does P-element movement occurs in *Drosophila*?
34. What is cut and paste mechanism?
35. What do you mean by retrotransposons?
36. What is delta element?
37. What is Ty B?
38. What do you mean by FB element?
39. What do you mean by copia in *Drosophila*?
40. Waht is the characteristic of L1 LINE element?
41. What is the characteristics of SINES element?
42. What do you mean by *Alu* family and *Alu* sequence?
43. What are the medical significance of mobile DNA?
44. What is the evolutionary significance of mobile DNA?
45. What gene conversion? What are the results of gene conversion when heteroduplexes are formed or not formed?
46. What are nick and nick translation?
47. What is complex transposon? Give example What are their requirement for transposition?
48. What is complex transposon? Give example.
49. What is conjugative transposition?
50. What do you mean by mutor gene?
51. What do you mean by *Ac* and *Ds* elements?
52. What do you mean by autonomous elemens?
53. What is P-element?
54. How P-element is related to hybrid dysgenesis?
55. What are the causes of P-element related hybrid dysgenesis in *Drosophila*?
56. What are the homologies between L1 reverse transcriptase and human telomerase?
57. What are the characteristics of LINEs and SINEs?
58. What are the examples of SINEs in human genome?
59. What is the ancestor of Alu element?
60. What are retrons?
61. What are the causes of differences in the flagellin in *Salmonella*?
62. Why transposons are regarded as evolutionary accidents?
63. Define homing introns?
64. What is selfish DNA?
65. Why selfish DNA is regarded as genetic parasite?
66. What is junk DNA?
67. What is transposon tagging?
68. What are the two control mechanisms of epigenetic control of transposable elements?
69. What is shRNA? What are the roles?

# 21

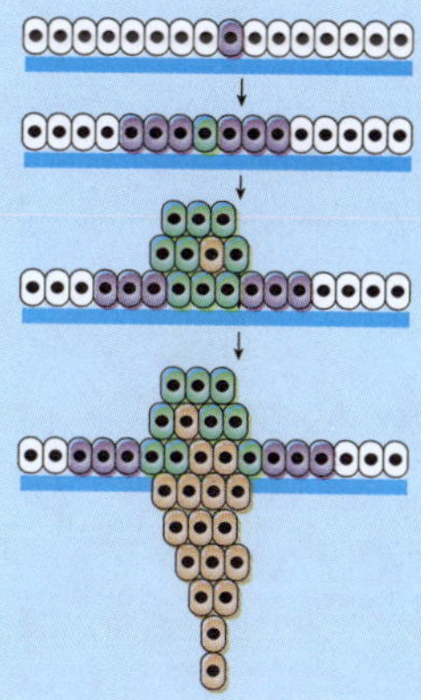

# Genetics of Cell Division, Cancer, Apoptosis and Aging

**CHAPTER AGENDA**

**21.1** Cell division Cycle; **21.2** Regulation of Cell cycle progression; **21.3** Genetics of Cell Cycle; **21.4** Molecular basis of Cellular check points; **21.5** Benign and Malignant tumors; **21.6** Several and Successive Mutations are involved in Tumor genesis and Progression; **21.7** Genetics of Colorectal cancer; **21.8** Genes and Cancer; **21.9** Mutations causing loss of Cell cycle control and induction of Cancer Genesis; **21.10** Role of Carcinogens in inducing Cancer; **21.11** Molecular designing of Cancer treatment; **21.12** Cancer and Epigenesis; **21.13** Apoptosis; **21.14** Aging and Senescence; Chapter Glossary/Key Terms; Exercise

## 21.1 CELL DIVISION CYCLE

### 21.1.1 Introduction

Dividing cells have a definite life cycle. In a growing tissue, it divides in such a manner that the two daughter cells are similar to each other.

Primarily cell divisions are of two kinds: **mitosis** i.e., the divided cells have the same chromosome number as it's original cell and **meiosis**, i.e., the divided cells have a half the number of the chromosome of the original cell.

The cell cycle mainly consists of interphase and dividing phase. Again the dividing phase has karyokinesis (nuclear division) and cytokinesis (cytoplasmic division) whereas, interphase has $G_1$ (presynthetic gap), S (synthesis) and $G_2$ (postsynthetic gap) phases.

The period between the two successive dividing phases is called **interphase**. It is a critical time in terms of preparation of the next cell division. The interphase occupies the time between the end of cytokinesis and the beginning of the next prophase.

A typical cell cycle including interphase lasts from 20 to 24 hours (Table 21.1).

Usually in higher eukaryotes, during M-phase nuclear envelope breaks down into small vesicles. Golgi bodies, endoplasmic reticulum also vesiculate during M-phase but at the end of the mitosis they reform into two daughter cells. In yeast and some fungi, the nuclear envelope does not break down; the mitotic spindle is formed within the nuclear envelope which then pinches off, forming two nuclei at the time of cytokinesis.

After M-phase the $G_1$ or pre-synthesis phase of the interphase starts and then each chromosome usually appears as a single strand. In synthesis phase the DNA-replication takes place and ultimately two chromatids are formed in a chromosome. $G_2$ is the preceeding stage of the mitosis and after proper stimulation; the cell starts to divide and enters again into mitosis (M-phase).

Most postmitotic cells exist in $G_1$ and not entering into the S phase they enter into a phase called $G_0$. The $G_0$ cells normally do not divide. But after proper stimulation it again returns to the cell cycle and through S-phase and $G_2$ it divides (Table 21.2).

### 21.1.2 Cdk and Cyclins

The main controlling mechanism in the cell cycle progression is made through a family of protein kinases known as **Cyclin-dependent kinases** (Cdks). The activity of these kinases rises and falls as the cell progresses through the cycle. The cyclical changes in the phosphorylation of intracellular proteins initiate and regulate the major events in the cell

**TABLE 21.1**
**Different phases of mitotic cell cycle**

| *Phases* | *Duration in hour* | | |
|---|---|---|---|
| | *Vicia faba* | *Mouse Liver cells* | *Human Hela cells* |
| $G_1$ | 12 | 12 | 12 |
| S | 6 | 6 – 8 | 10 |
| $G_2$ | 12 | 3 – 6 | 3 |
| M | 1 | 1 | 1 |

**TABLE 21.2**
**Duration of different stages of mitosis in different materials**

| *Material* | *Duration in minutes* | | | |
|---|---|---|---|---|
| | *Prophase* | *Metaphase* | *Anaphase* | *Telophase* |
| Mouse spleen | 21 | 13 | 5 | 4 |
| Grashopper neuroblast | 102 | 13 | 9 | 57 |
| Onion root tip | 71 | 6.5 | 2.4 | 3.8 |
| Pea root tip | 78 | 14.4 | 4.2 | 13.2 |
| Pea endosperm | 40 | 20 | 12 | 110 |

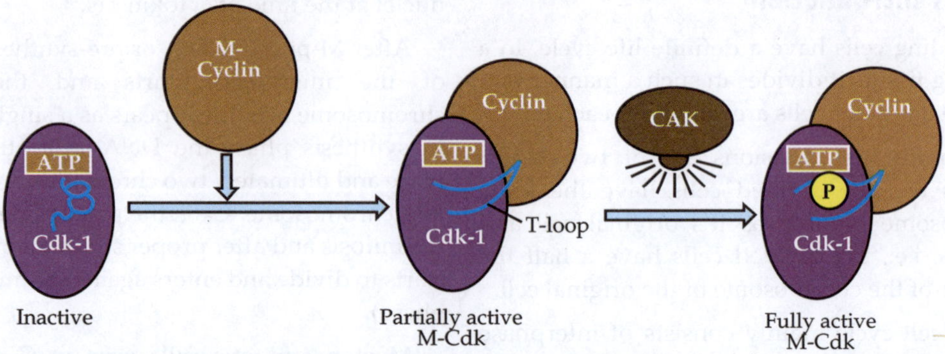


**Fig.21.1 :** *The structural basis of Cdk activation.*

cycle such as, DNA-replication, mitosis or cytokinesis etc.

Cyclical changes in Cdk-activity are controlled by a complex arrangement of enzymes and proteins. The most important of this Cdk regulatory protein is **cyclin**. The tightly binding and formation of Cyclin-Cdk complex triggers cell cycle events.

Three types of cyclins are found in all eukaryotic cells that bind Cdk.

1. $G_1$ /S cyclins bind to Cdk at the end of $G_1$ and commit the cell to DNA replication.
2. S-cyclins bind to Cdk during S-phase and are required for the initiation of DNA replication.
3. M-cyclins promote the events of mitosis.

In most cells another class of cyclin, the $G_1$-cyclin helps to promote passage through **start** in late $G_1$.

In the yeast cell only one Cdk binds to all classes of cyclins, whereas, in vertebrates, $G_1$-cyclin interacts with two Cdk partners whereas $G_1$/S cyclin and S-cyclin with one common type of Cdk and M Cyclin with one Cdk partner (Table 21.3).

Each Cyclin-Cdk complex phosphorylates a different set of substrate proteins. The same Cyclin-Cdk complex can also induce different effects at different times in the cycle.

The three-dimensional structures of Cdk and Cyclin proteins revealed that "Cyclin binding with Cdk protein", remove the protein (blocking slab) called T-loop and the active site is being opened resulting in partial activation of Cdk enzyme. Later on another enzyme, Cdk-activating kinase (CAK) phosphorylates the *threonine* residue in the T-loop further activates the enzyme by changing the shape of the T-loop and Cdk becomes fully active (Fig. 21.1).

**TABLE 21.3**
**Major cyclins and Cdks of Vertebrates and Budding yeast**

| *Cyclin-Cdk complex* | *Vertebrates* | | *Budding yeast* | |
|---|---|---|---|---|
| | *Cyclin* | *Cdk-Partner* | *Cyclin* | *Cdk-Partner* |
| $G_1$-Cdk | Cyclin D | Cdk 4, Cdk 6 | Cln 3 | Cdk 1 |
| $G_1$/S-Cdk | Cyclin E | Cdk-2 | Cln 1, 2 | Cdk 1 |
| S-Cdk | Cyclin A | Cdk-2 | Clb 5, 6 | Cdk 1 |
| M-Cdk | Cyclin B | Cdk 1 | Clb 1, 2, 3, 4 | Cdk 1 |

The Cyclin-Cdk complex activity can be inhibited by phosphorylation at a pair of amino acids just above the active site by another protein kinase **Wee-1**, Dephosphorylation of these sites by a phosphatase called Cdc25 returns back its activity.

Another protein, Cdk-inhibitor protein (CKI) binds with the Cyclin-Cdk complexes rendering it inactive.

## 21.2 REGULATION OF CELL CYCLE PROGRESSION

**Entry into mitosis :**

1. After completion of DNA synthesis in S-phage, *M-cyclin* gene is transcribed and M-cyclin is synthesized. Then M-cyclin is gradually accumulated at the end of $G_2$.
2. Cdk-1 in this complex is phosphorylated at *Thr-14* and *Tyr-15* by wee-1 (an inactivating kinase) and at *Thr-161* by CAK (Cdk-activating Kinase). Thus large amount of M-Cdk remains in inactive state.
3. At late $G_2$, Cdc-25 (a phosphatase) removes the inhibitory phosphates *Thr-14* and *Tyr15*. Thus M-Cdk becomes active. This is MPF. Actually inactive Cdc-25 is activated by polokinase and M-Cdk itself by +ve feedback.
4. Wee-1 is inhibited by M-Cdk and also by nim-I.

When MPF reaches to a threshold concentration the cell enters into M-phase in an all-or-none phenomenon.

**Inactivation of M-Cdk and exit from mitosis and entry into $G_1$**

1. MPF controls all the events in M-phase.
2. Exit from mitosis requires inactivation of M-Cdk.
3. Inactivation takes place by ubiquitin-dependent proteolysis of M-cyclin which is triggered by Cdc-20-APC (which promotes destruction of securin at metaphase-anaphase transition), to activate separase, which then promotes dissociation of cohesin at anaphase.
4. Another APC-activating protein called Hct-1 binds to APC and inactivates M-cyclin.
5. Another protein CKI (Cdk inhibitor) binds directly to M-Cdk rendering it inactive. Sic-1 is a CKI protein.

**Escape from stable $G_1$ to initiate S-phase**

1. In early $G_1$, the $G_1$-cyclin is accumulated, which is not destroyed by Hct-APC or not inhibited by Sic-1.
2. In $G_0$ stage, $G_1$ cyclin does not accumutate. Then Rb (retinoblastoma protein) binds to E2F and blocks further transcription of $G_1$/S-cyclin or S-cyclin.
3. In presence of extracellular signals, $G_1$cyclin is accumulated. It becomes activated to form $G_1$-Cdk which phosphorylates Rb protein. Thus, E2F becomes active and allows the transcription of $G_1$/S-cyclin and S-cyclin genes. Thus $G_1$-S-Cdk and S-Cdk are synthesized. $G_1$/S-Cdk inturn activates Rb phosphorylation and E2F activation by +ve feedback. Therefore, at $G_1$/S transition, E2F and $G_1$-S-Cdk concentrations are increased rapidly.

**DNA synthesis in S-phase**

1. As the cell approaches to S, S-Cdk is immediately transported to nucleus and DNA replication starts at the origin of replication (ORC).
2. In S, ORC is associated with Cdc-6. The Mcm protein complexes are assembled on the adjacent region. This is prereplication complex.
3. S-Cdk induces the assembly of DNA polymerase and other replication proteins to trigger replication.
4. The replication occurs only once, because, S-Cdk causing dissociation of Cdc-6 from

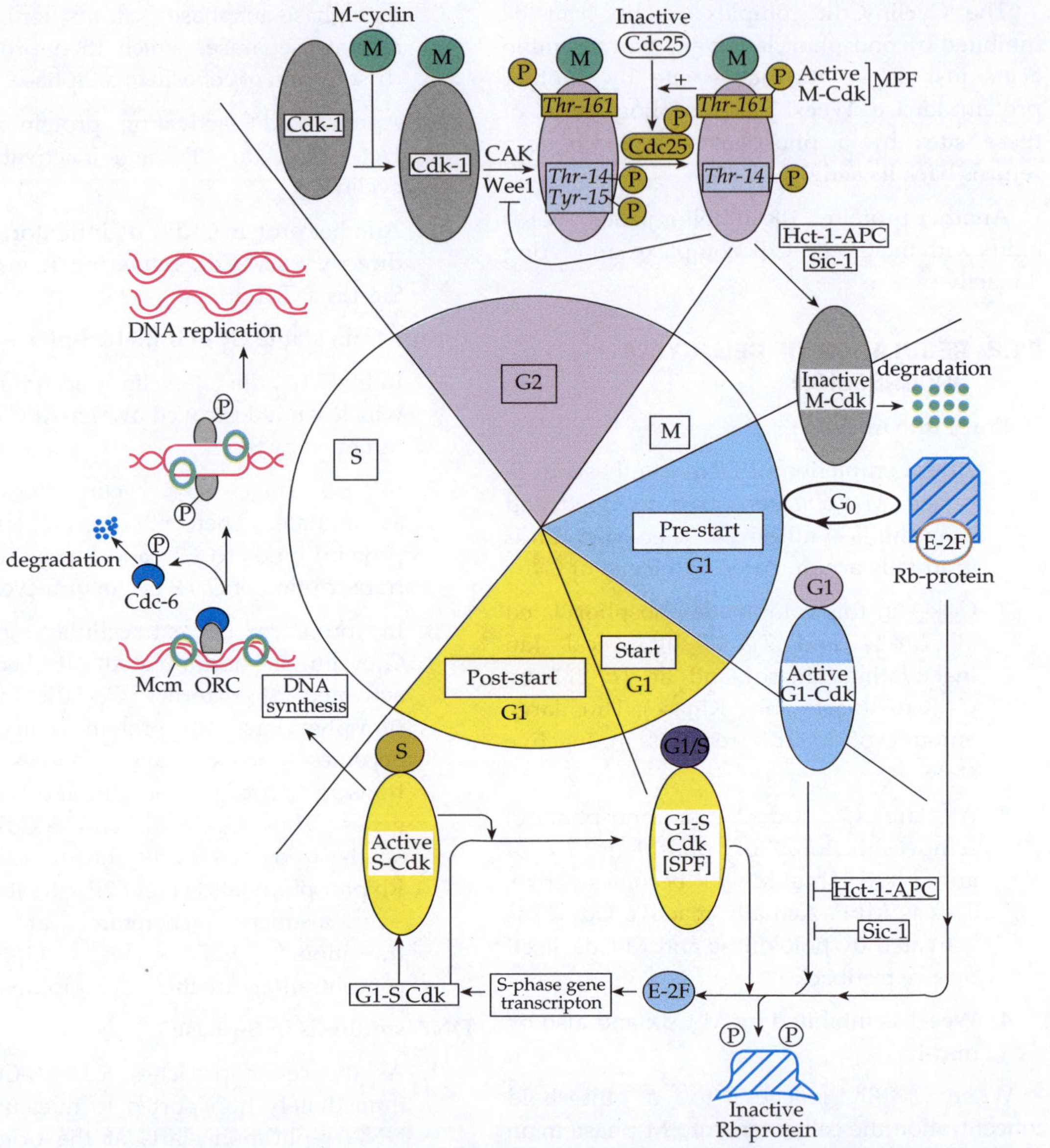


**Fig. 21.2 :** *Regulation of cell cycle progression in vertebrates.*

the origin and degradation of Mcm and thus Cdc-6 and Mcm can not return to the origin to replicate further.

## 21.3 GENETICS OF CELL CYCLE

A cell reproduces by performing an orderly sequence of events in which it duplicates its contents and then divides into two. This cycle of duplication and division is known as the cell cycle. The basic organization of the cell cycle and its control system are essentially the same in all eukaryotic cells. Three eukaryotic systems in which cell cycle control are commonly studied- yeasts, frog embryo and cultured mammalian cells.

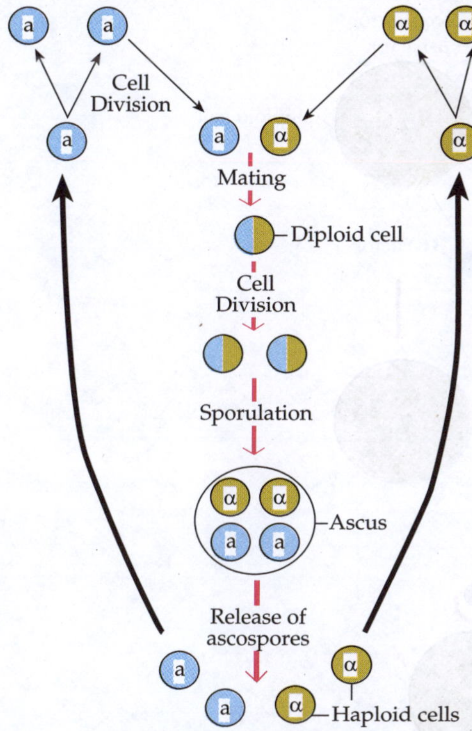


**Fig.21.3 :** *Alternating haploid and diploid phases of Yeast.*

Yeasts are tiny, single celled fungi. Two species are generally used in the studies of cell cycle. The fission yeast, *Schizosaccharomyces pombe*, is a rod shaped cell, that grows by elongation at its ends. Division occurs by the formation of a septum or cell plate in the center of the rod. It has a typical eukaryotic cell cycle with $G_1$, S, $G_2$ and M phases. In contrast with that happens in higher eukaryotic cells, the nuclear envelope of the yeast cell does not break down during M-phase. The microtubules of the mitotic spindle form inside the nucleus and are attached to spindle pole bodies at its periphery. The cell divides by forming a partition (cell plate) and splitting into two. The mitotic chromosomes are readily visible.

The budding yeast *Saccharomyces cerevisiae* also called baker's yeast. It is oval cell and divides by forming buds which first appears during $G_1$ and grows until it separates from the mother cell after mitosis. It has normal $G_1$ and S-phase but does not have a normal $G_2$. The microtubule based spindle begins to form inside the nucleus early in the cycle during S-phase. Nuclear envelope remains intact during mitosis and the spindle forms within the nucleus.

### 21.3.1 Pheromones in Yeast and determination of Mating types

Yeast can live either in the haploid or the diploid state. Both types of cell are structurally and metabolically similar and grow by budding but belong to one of the two mating types known as **a** and **α**. During mating, two haploid cells of different mating types fuse to give a diploid cell. These diploid cells grow and divide until poor environmental conditions and trigger spore formation and then form ascus, inside of which meiosis occurs to form four spores (Fig. 21.3).

Mating type is controlled by the *MAT* locus which exists in two alternative states, *MATa* and *MATα*. Both states contain two genes that are transcribed divergently *ie*, either *MATa1*, *MATa2* or *MATα1*, *MATα2* and their gene products are MATa1, MATa2, MATα1 and MATα2 respectively. These gene products activate specific **pheromones** (or mating factors) and their corresponding receptors.

α -mating type cells express the genes for α-pheromone and a-pheromone receptor. Similarly, a-mating type cell express a-pheromone and α-pheromome receptor. Therefore, during mating pheromones bind to their corresponding receptors and they form a mating pair (Fig. 21.4).

The haploid α cell produces two proteins from it's *MAT* locus, α1 and α2. α1 protein activates transcription of "α" factor gene and "a" factor receptor gene. At the same time α2 protein repress "a" factor gene and "α" factor receptor gene. Both α1 and α2 act as homodimers.

The haploid "a" cell also produces two MAT proteins a1 and a2. The a1 protein turns on the

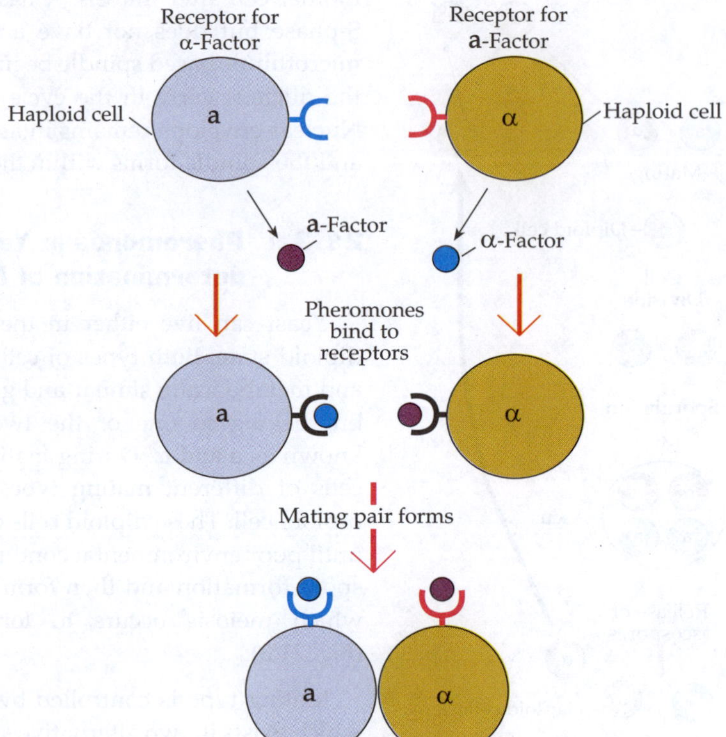


**Fig.21.4** : *Pheromones and Receptors in Mating Yeast.*

gene for "**a**" factor and the α receptors. Here **a1** works as a homodimer (Fig. 21.5).

In the diploid cell, a heterodimer **a2-a1** is produced which represses the expression of *HO*-locus expression of mating types switching.

Actually active mating type locus is flanked by two loci called *HML* and *HMR* which contain silent version of *MAT*α and *MAT a* genes respectively. Yeast cells replace the *MAT* gene at active *MAT* locus with a copy of DNA from either *HML* or *HMR* for its switching on. For example, *MATa* gene at the active locus is replaced with the *MAT*α gene from the *HML* site, switching the phenotype of the yeast cell from an "a" to an "α". After a while, the *MAT*α gene at the active locus is replaced with *MATa* gene from *HMR*, thus changing, the yeast back to an "a" type. The replacement of such DNA is controlled by HO-endonuclease in both 'a' and "α" mating types, while in diploid cells, mating type switching does not occur because transcription of *HO*-gene is repressed by $\mathbf{a_1\alpha_2}$ heterodimer (Fig. 21.6).

It is to be noted that the first generation yeast cells cannot switch mating type, because HO-endonuclease is not expressed. HO-endonuclease is required only in $G_1$ for its activity. HO-endonuclease gene expression required a protein SWI 5 which is expressed in $G_2$ phase. Therefore, haploid yeast cells must complete at least one cell division before it can switch mating types.

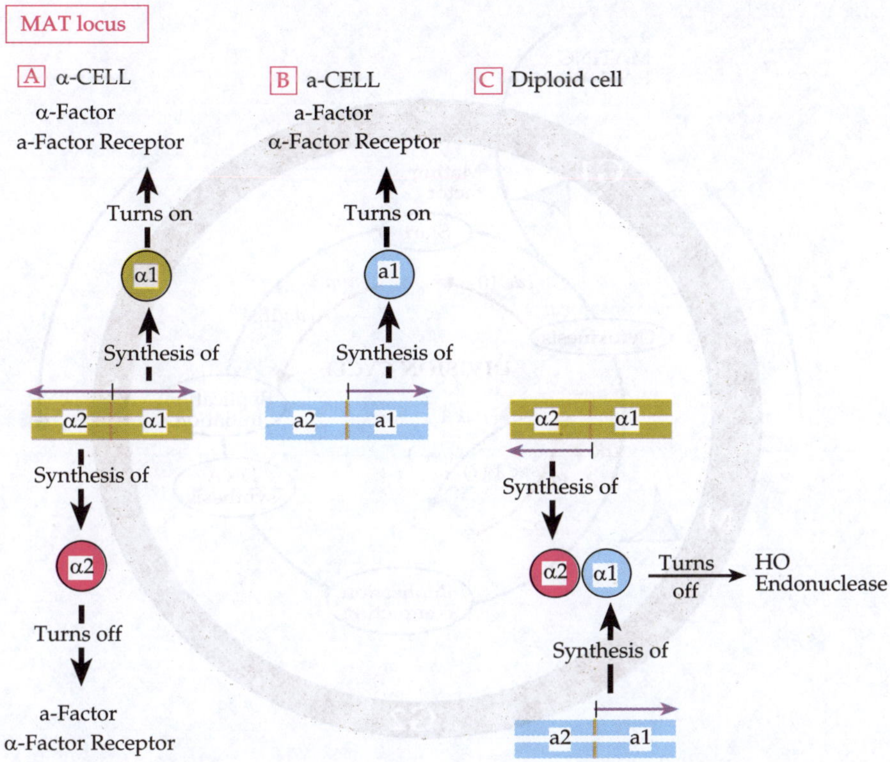


**Fig.21.5 :** *MAT a and MAT α Proteins are Transcriptional Regulators.*

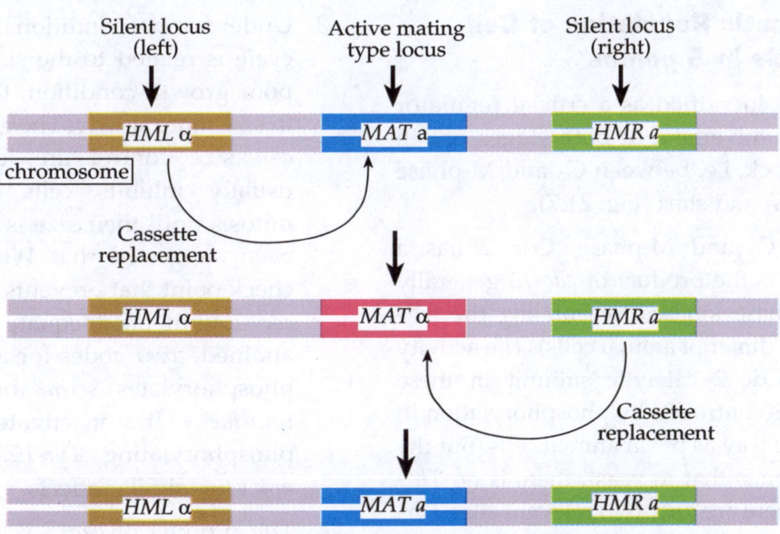


**Fig.21.6 :** *Switching the Mating type in Yeast.*

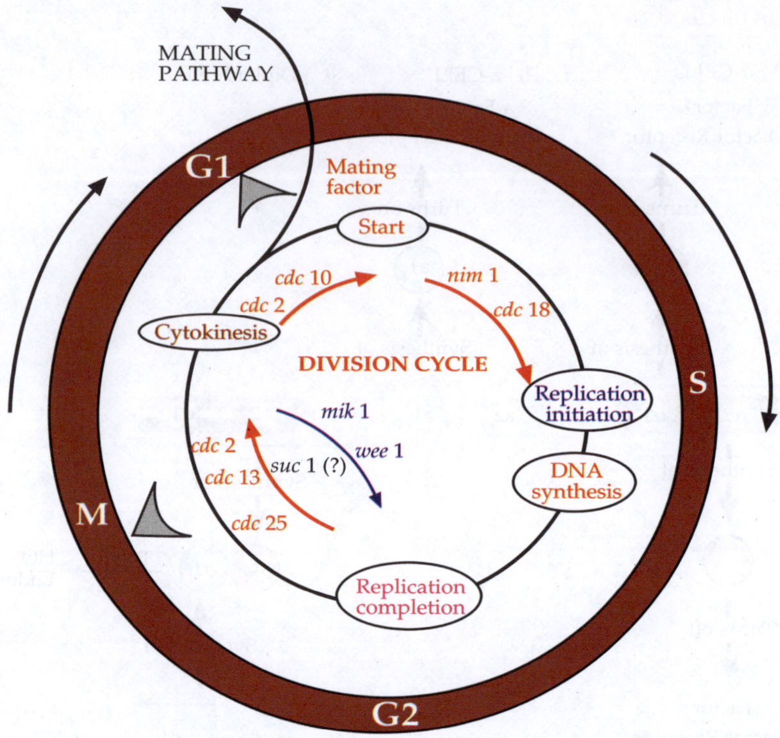


**Fig.21.7 :** *The cell cycle in S.pombe requires cdc genes to pass specific stages, but may be retarded by genes that respond to cell size (wee 1). Cells may be diverted into the mating pathway early in G1.*

### 21.3.2 Genetic Regulation of Cell Cycle in *S.pombe*

1. **Cdc 2** is identified as a crucial regulator by its involvement at both stages of cell cycle block, i.e. between $G_2$ and M-phase and in $G_1$ and start (Fig. 21.7).
2. During $G_2$ and M-phase, Cdc 2 has a partner, is the product of *cdc 13* generally an M phase kinases (resembling the $p^{34}$-B–cyclin dimer of animal cells). The activity of the Cdc 2 catalytic subunit in these dimers is controlled by phosphorylation in the same way as $p^{34}$ in animal cells. But the difference is that in yeast, there is no *Thr-14*, so, there are only two relevant sites *Tyr-15*, where phosphorylation is inhibitory and *Thr-161*, where phosphorylation is essentially required.
3. Under normal conditions, the cell division cycle is related to the size of the cell. In poor growth condition, the cells increase in size more slowly. The genes involved in cell size control are identified. **Wee1** usually inhibits cells from initiating mitosis until their size is adequate. It has been suggested that **Wee1** is part of a check point that prevents the activation of *cdc 2* until an adequate mass has been attained. *wee1* codes for a kinase and can phosphorylates *serine* or *threonine* and *tyrosine*. It inactivates *Cdc 2* by phosphorylating *Tyr-15*. Another gene *mik 1* has similar effects.
4. The product of *cdc25* is required for the dephosphorylation of Cdc2 in the Cdc 2/ Cdc13 dimer. It is probably responsible

for the key-dephosphorylating event in activating the M phase kinase. The level of Cdc25 increases at mitosis and its accumulation over a threshold level could be important. Cdc25 executes the check point that ensures S-phase is completed before M-phase can be activated.

5. The products of *wee1* and *cdc25* play antagonistic roles. The kinase activity of **Wee1** acts on *Tyr-15* to inhibit Cdc2 function. The phosphatase activity of **Cdc25** acts on the same site to activate Cdc2.
6. During mitosis the Cdc2 of Cdc2 – Cdc13 dimer is in the active state that lacks the phosphate at *Tyr-15* and has the phosphate at *Tyr-161*. At the end of mitosis, kinase activity is lost and Cdc13 is degraded. Cdc2 does not change at this point.
7. During $G_1$ the active form of Cdc2 has a different partner, the B-like cyclin, Cig2 encoded by *cig2* gene. The dimer is converted from inactive state to active state by dephosphorylation of *Tyr-15* residue of Cdc2.
8. Progression of $G_1$ into S is controlled by Cdc2-$G_1$ cyclin. In ***S. pombe*** it is Cdc2/Cig2.
9. Transcription of ***cdc18*** is activated as a consequence of passing START and Cdc18 is required to enter S-phase. Over expression of *cdc18* allows multiple cycle of DNA replication without mitosis.
10. For Cdc18 to become active, Cdc2/Cdc13 must be inactive. Again when M-phase kinase is active, causes Cdc18 to be inactive possibly by phosphorylating it and prevents initiation of another S-phase.
11. Activity of Cdc2/Cdc13 M phase kinase is influenced itself by a factor **Rum-1**, which controls entry into S-phase. When **Rum-1** is depleted, premature entrance into mitosis occurs and overexpression causes cells fail to enter mitosis. This suggests that **Rum-1** is an inhibitor of the M-phase kinase. It is expressed between $G_1$ and $G_2$ and keeps M-phase kinase in an inactive state.

### 21.3.3 Genetic Regulation of Cell Cycle in *S. cerevisiae*

Cell cycle in *S. cerevisiae* consists of three cycles that separate after START and join before cytokinesis. The cells may be diverted into the mating pathway early in $G_1$ (Fig. 21.8).

**Chromosome cycle :** In this event, the duplication of chromosome, separation of chromosome, completion of S-phase and nuclear division take place. Mutation of *cdc8* stops this cycle in S-phase. Mutations in the chromosome cycle do not stop the cytoplasmic cycle.

**Cytoplasmic cycle :** It consists of bud emergence and nuclear migration into the buds. *cdc24* mutation does not prevent chromosome replication but this cycle can be halted before bud emergence.

**Centrosome cycle :** In this event, duplication and separation of spindle polar body take place and microtubules are formed, which allow chromosome segregation within the nucleus. *cdc31* mutant does not prevent S-phase or bud emergence but blocks spindle formation.

Nuclear division requires in chromosome cycle and centrosome cycle, whereas, cytokinesis requires in these and the cytoplasmic cycle. Therefore, completion of entire cell cycle requires all three constituent cycles to be functional.

1. ***S. cerevisiae*** expresses a single cyclin–dependent protein kinase (**Cdk**) encoded by ***CDC28*** gene, which interacts with several different cyclins during different phases of the cell cycle.
2. Just after cytokinesis, the decision on whether to initiate a division cycle is made before the START. The cells can be diverted into mating type pathway by mating factors and *cdc36* and *cdc39*, which appear to block the cycle before START,

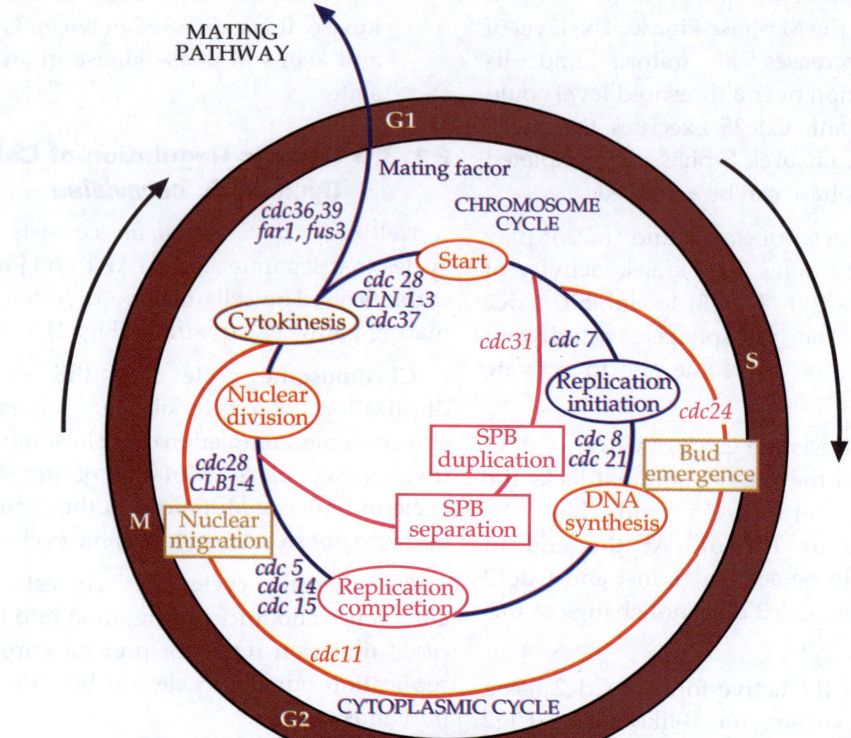


**Fig.21.8 :** *The cell cycle in S. cerevisiae consists of three cycles that separate after START and join before cytokinesis. Cell may be diverted into the mating pathway early in G1.*

and really function in the mating type pathway. Mutants block cell cycle by diverting cells into mating even in absence of the mating gene.

3. After cytokinesis the mother cell and the bud both the cells remain in the $G_1$ period of the cell cycle. The ability to pass START is determined by environmental conditions. Prior to bud formation, spindle body duplication and DNA replication, the yeast exhausts their nutrients. When *S. cerevisiae* cells in $G_1$ have grown sufficiently in the growth medium they begin a program of gene expression that leads to entry into mitosis. Once $G_1$ cells reach the critical size, they become committed to complete cell cycle even if they are shifted to the low nutrient medium.

4. The crucial gene in passing START is ***CDC-28***, which is homologous to *cdc2* in ***S. pombe***. Three cyclins are active in $G_1$. Cln-1, Cln 2, Cln 3 etc are encoded by *CLN-1*, *CLN-2* and *CLN-3* respectively. Mutations in any one or even any two of these genes fail to block the cell cycle, thus the *CLN* genes are functionally redundant.

5. The complexes formed between Cdc 28 and the three $G_1$-cyclins (Cln1, Cln 2 and Cln 3) have protein kinase activity and constitute the hypothesized S-phase promoting factors (SPFs). In wild type yeast cells, Cln 3 is expressed at a nearly constant level throughout the cell cycle.

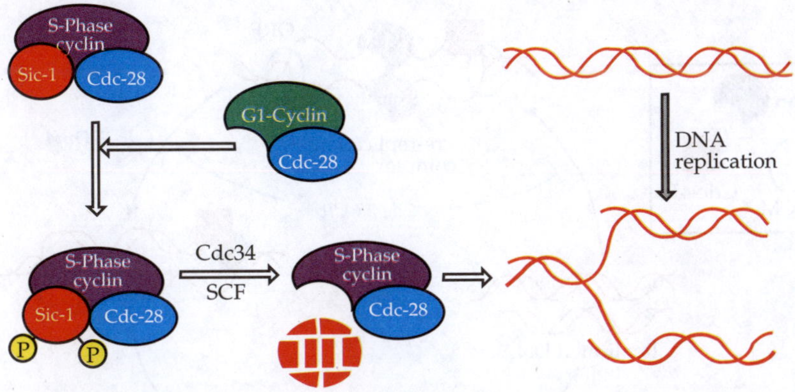


**Fig.21.9 :** *Control of the G1→ S phase transition in S. cerevisiae by regulated proteolysis of Sic1.*

Cln 1 and Cln 2 are expressed during the second half of $G_1$ and they increase in rapidly and when their accumulation is exceeded to a critical threshold level, trigger the passage of start into S-phase. After that, its concentration declines gradually and is eliminated by the time of mitosis.

6. Cdc28-Cln 3 phosphorylates and activates SPF and MPF. These induce transcription of *CLN1* and *CLN2* genes as well as several other genes required for DNA replication, including genes encoding DNA polymerase, RPA (ssDNA binding proteins), DNA ligase and certain enzymes are required for deoxy ribonucleoside triphosphate synthesis.
7. Cdc 28-Cln 1 and Cdc 28 –Cln 2 phosphorylate APC in late G1 and inactivate it.
8. Two B-type cyclin genes *CLB 5* and *CLB 6* are also regulated by MBF and transcribed in late $G_1$. The corresponding proteins Clb 5 and Clb 6 accumulate because of the inactivation of APC.
9. At late $G_1$, Cdc28- Clb 5 and Cdc-28-Clb6 heterodimers accumulate and they are inactivated by Sic-1, which is an S-phase inhibitor, but it has no effect on Cdc28-Cln complexes. When Sic 1 is being degraded following polyubiquitination by E2 associated with E3, then Cdc28-Clb5 and Cdc-Clb 6 kinases induce DNA replication (Fig. 21.9).
10. Initiation of DNA replication requires both assembly of pre-replication complex and an active Cdc28-Cln complex. A second heterodimeric protein kinase Cdc7-Dbf 4, which is expressed in $G_1$, is also required to trigger initiation. Once replication has initiated, Mcm proteins and Cdc 45 move away from the origin along with DNA polymerases. Mcm proteins are homologus to helicase, associated with replication fork movement (Fig. 21.10).
11. Later in S-phase, transcription begins of the genes *CLB3* and ***CLB4***, encoding two additional B-type cyclins, Clb 3 and Clb 4, which also form hetrodimeric protein kinases with Cdc28. These two Cdc28-Clb 3 and Cdc28-Clb 4 complexes also initiate the formation of mitotic spindle at the beginning of mitosis.
12. As cells complete chromosome replication and enter $G_2$, two more B-cyclins are expressed. These are Clb 1 and Clb2 encoded by *CLB 1* and *CLB 2*. These

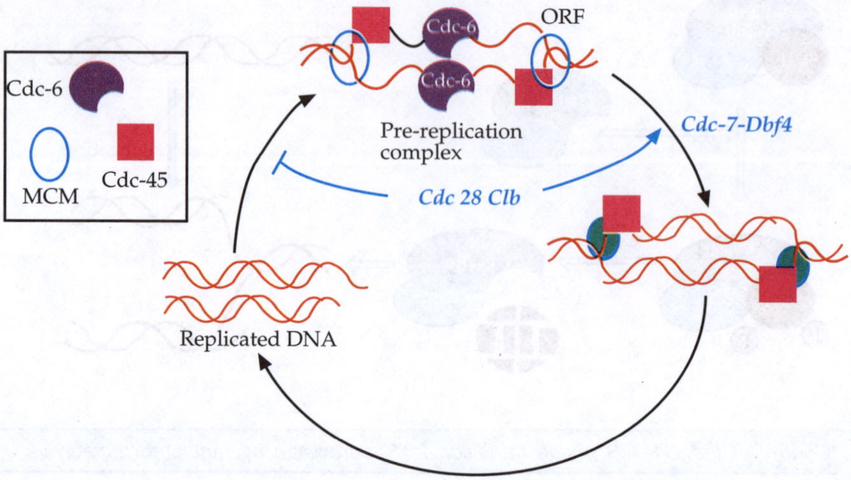


**Fig.21.10 :** *Assembly of pre-replication complex and its regulation by* **Cdc 28-Clb** *(Cdk-Cyclin B) complex in S. cerevisiae.*

function as mitotic cyclins, associating with Cdc28 to form complexes that are required for chromosome segregation and nuclear division. All the B-cyclins are degraded in late anaphase by activated APC.

## 21.4 MOLECULAR BASIS OF CELLULAR CHECKPOINTS

In most cells there are several points in the cell cycle, called **checkpoints**, at which the cycle can be arrested if previous events have not been completed. Four such checkpoint controls can arrest the passage through cell cycle. These are (a) $G_1$-arrest due to DNA damage, (b) S-arrest due to unreplicated DNA, (c) $G_2$-arrest due to DNA damage, (d) M-arrest due to improper spindle formation (Fig. 21.11).

In the checkpoints, the control system can be regulated by extracellular signals from other cells. These signals either promote or inhibit cell proliferation. Checkpoints generally operate through negative intracellular signals.

### 21.4.1 The DNA Replication Checkpoint

Most of the cells by a DNA replication checkpoint mechanism avoid entry into cell division until the last nucleotide in the genome has been copied. The molecular mechanism has not been discovered but **any signal from unreplicated DNA or unfinished replication fork sends a negative signal to the cell cycle control system that blocks the activation of M-Cdk.** Thus normal cells treated with chemical inhibitors of DNA synthesis such as hydroxyurea, do not progress into mitosis. This block activates a checkpoint mechanism that arrests the cells in S-phase, delaying mitosis. But if caffeine is added along with hydroxyurea, checkpoint mechanism fails, and the cells proceed into mitosis according to their normal schedule with incompletely replicated DNA. As a result, the cells die.

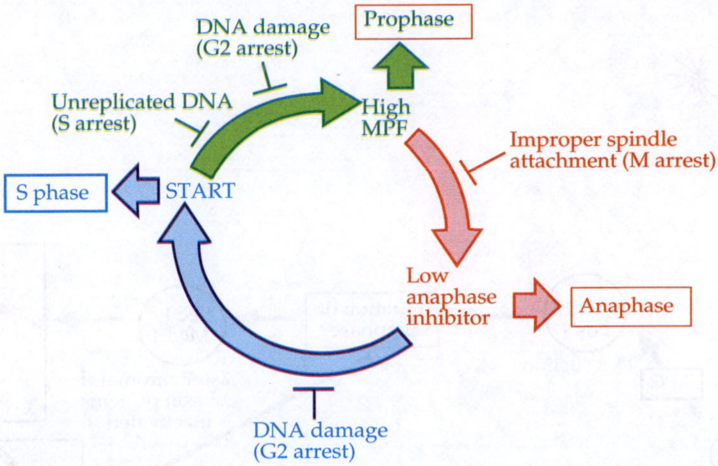


**Fig.21.11 :** *Stages at which checkpoint controls can arrest passage through the cell cycle.*

### 21.4.2 The Spindle Attachment Checkpoint

The effect of colchicine, which inhibits spindle assembly demonstrates the presence of this checkpoint. In most cell types, a spindle-attachment checkpoint mechanism operates to ensure that all chromosomes are properly attached to the spindle before sister chromatid separation occurs. During metaphase, kinetochore regions of the chromosomes are attached to microtubules and any kinetochore that is not properly attached to the spindle, sends out a negative wait signal to the cell cycle control system that blocks Cdc20-APC activation, which is required for sister chromatid separation. The nature of signal is not clear. But it has been observed that several proteins, including Mad2 are recruited to unattached kinetochores, which are required for spindle attachment checkpoint to function. Even a single unattached kinetochore results in inhibition of Cdc20-APC by binding with Mad2. There may be some other mechanisms normally determine the timing of the anaphase in yeast and frog embryo. Since defective checkpoints undergo anaphase with normal timings. Mutants, defective in this cell cycle checkpoint proceed through anaphase before assembly of spindle and attachment of kinetochore is complete, they mis-segregate their chromosomes, producing abnormal daughter cells that die. Analysis of these mutants in yeasts two such mechanisms, called *bub* (budding uninhibited by benomyl) and *mad* (mitotic arrest deficient) by which the mitotic checkpoint operates. *BUB* gene codes a protein kinase, which influences the activation of other essential, multiple proteins of the cell cycle control system.

In mice *MAD2* and *BUB1* and in human *MAD2* genes have been recently identified. MAD2 protein remains concentrated at the kinetochore until microtubule attachment is completed. This protein is continuously migrating into the cytoplasm and broadcasting signal throughout the cytoplasm. In mammals *MAD2* is associated with $P^{55}$ *CDC* while in budding yeast *MAD2* is with *CDC20* and in fission yeast Mad2-Slp1 (slp=sleepy) form a large complex with APC. APC is kept in check by MAD2 and when APC is active, the cell initiates anaphase by catalyzing degradation of its two proteins with the help of Hct1 and CDC20.

CDC20/Slp1 promotes degradation of CUT2 but the activity of CDC20/Slp1, which is inhibited by MAD2. Hct1 promotes degradation

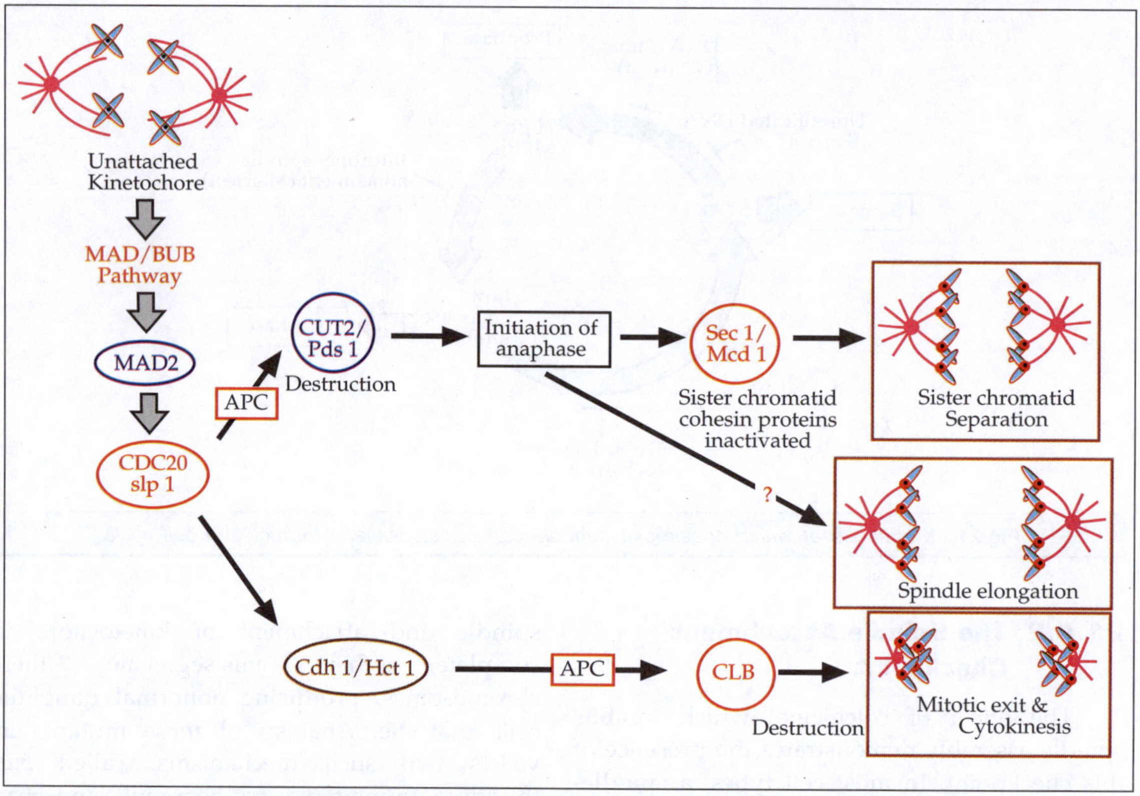


**Fig.21.12 :** *A model showing the role of CDC20 and Hct 1 in the degradation of CUT2/Pds1 and CLB2/Ase1; these degradations are necessary for the success of anaphase.*

of CLB-1. APC catalyzes this degradation by ubiquitination. This ubiquitination is inhibited by spindle checkpoints (Fig. 21.12).

In mammals BUB1, BUB3 proteins along with CMEP-E protein induce changes that ultimately shut down the transmission of wait signal. MAD2 dissociates from p[55] CDC and loses its control on APC. APC is being activated and catalyzes breaking down of cyclines and facilitates anaphase separation of chromatids.

### 21.4.3 DNA Damage Checkpoints

The cell cycle control system can readily detect DNA damage and arrest the cell cycle at DNA damage checkpoints. These two such checkpoints : one is in late $G_1$, which prevents entry into S-phase and the other is in late $G_2$, which prevents entry into mitosis.

1. $G_2$-checkpoint depends on a similar mechanism that delays entry into mitosis in response to incomplete DNA replication. The damaged DNA sends a signal to a series of protein kinases that phosphorylate and inactivate the phosphatase Cdc25. This blocks the dephosphorylation and activation of M-Cdk, thereby blocking entry into mitosis. When the damaged DNA is repaired, the inhibitory signal is turned off and the cell division continues.

In the yeast *S. pombe*, the checkpoints sense the DNA damage and transduce inhibitory signal. Four genes including *RAD9*, *RAD17*, *RAD24* and *MEC3* will sense this damage. The model proposed that DNA damage activates a protein

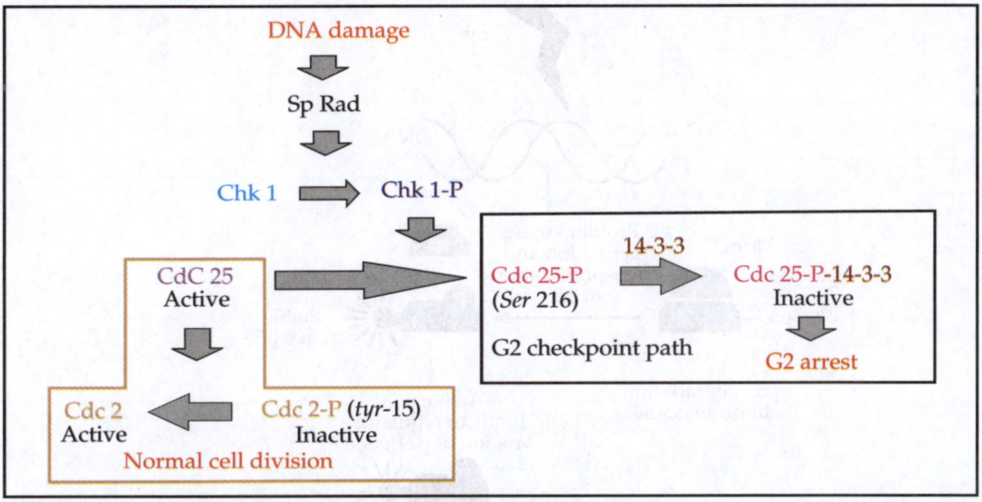


**Fig.21.13 :** *Model showing the operation of DNA damage check point at $G_2$.*

spRad3 (sp prefix means ***S. pombe***). It brings about phosphorylation of Chk1 and Chk1-P, functions as a kinase, which brings about phosphorylation at $Ser^{216}$ of Cdc25. It then promotes binding of Cdc25 to a protein **14-3-3**; coded by *rad24* and *rad25*, leading to sequestration of Cdc25. Then Cdc25 is not available for activation of Cdc2-P ($tyr^{15}$) and the cell division is arrested at $G_2$-M transition (Fig. 21.13).

2. $G_1$ checkpoint blocks progression into S-phase by inhibition of $G_1$/S-Cdk and S-Cdk complex.

   (a) In mammalian cells a gene regulatory protein $\mathbf{p^{53}}$ is being activated by DNA damage and it stimulates transcription of many genes.

   (b) A CKI protein called $\mathbf{p^{21}}$ is encoded by such activated genes, which binds to $G_1$/S-Cdk and S-Cdk and inhibits their activity and thus blocks entry into mitosis.

   (c) Actually in an undamaged cells, $\mathbf{p^{53}}$ is very unstable and is present at a very low concentration. It interacts with another protein Mdm2, that causes destruction of $p^{53}$ by ubiquitination mechanism. Damaged DNA activates protein kinase, phosphorylates $p^{53}$ and reduces the binding of Mdm2, and degradation of $p^{53}$; as a result $p^{53}$ concentration rises and stimulates gene transcription of $p^{21}$, which inactivates $G_1$S-Cdk and S-Cdk activity (Fig. 21.14).

   (d) A rare genetic disease **ataxia telangiectasia** is caused by a defect in one of the protein kinases that phosphorylates and activates p53 in response to radiation and due to the loss of the DNA damage checkpoints; they suffer from increased rate of cancer.

## 21.5 BENIGN AND MALIGNANT TUMORS

Cancer cells are defined by two heritable properties : they and their progeny (1) reproduce in defiance of the normal restraints on cell division and (2) invade and colonize territories normally reserved for other cells.

The controlling mechanism in cell proliferation is maintained by a chain of events. Very occasionally, this control breaks down. A cell then begins to grow and divide in an unregulated fashion without regarding the

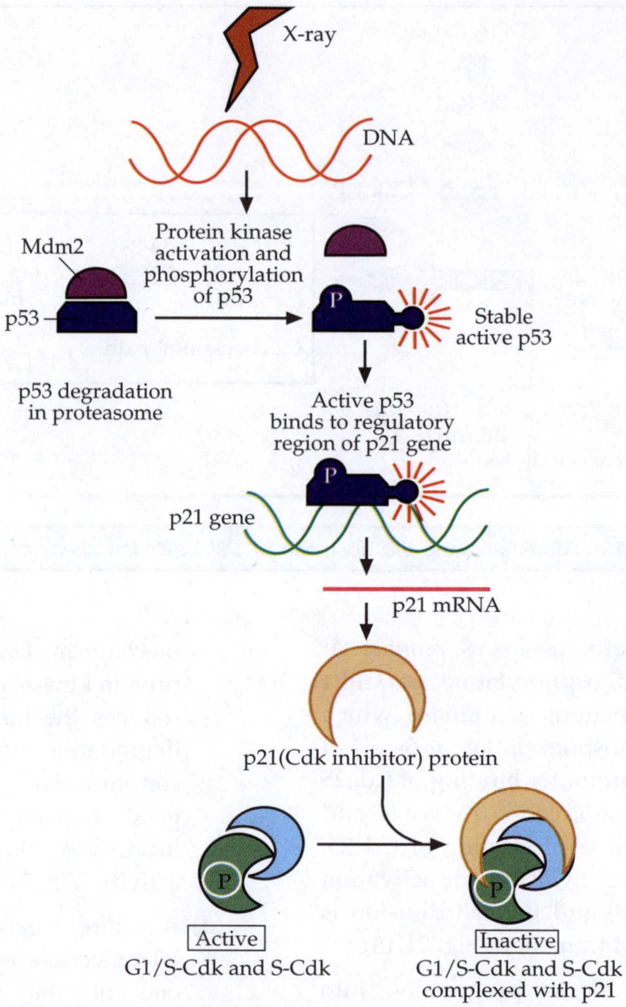


**Fig.21.14 :** *DNA damages arrests the cell cycle in $G_1$.*

body's need. The descendent cells also proliferate without responding the regulation, as a result a clone of cells will be able to expand indefinitely, and will give rise to a tumor or **neoplasm**.

Normally, the neoplastic cells remain clustered together in a single mass, which is called a **benign** tumor. By removing the mass of tissue surgically one can achieve a complete cure from the tumor. A tumor can be transformed into a cancer, if it is malignant, i.e., if cells acquire an ability to invade the surrounding tissue and then through circulation these loose cells form there a secondary tumor. The process of spreading of cancer cells through circulation and invading into a new location is called **metastasis** (Table 21.4).

The fibronectin molecules which increase the cell adhesion to the substratum and other cells. This protein is drastically absent in cancerous transformation. The breaking up of fibronectin protein causes the cell to invade tissues locally to metastasize. Cancer cells produce an elevated level of cell surface receptor specific proteins, carbohydrates composing the basal lamina. They

**TABLE 21.4**
**Distinction between benign tumor and cncerous tumour**

| *Benign tumour* | *Cancerous tumour* |
|---|---|
| 1. Nucleocytoplasmic ratio is more or less normal and the nucleus stains normally with appropriate dyes. | 1. Nucleus becomes large and therefore, nucleo-cytoplasmic ratio is abnormally high. The nucleus stains deeply and its DNA content is greatly increased. |
| 2. Cytoskeleton remains normal as the normal cells. | 2. Cytoplasm is disorganized. |
| 3. The cells remain clustered in a single mass. By removing the mass of tissue surgically one can achieve a complete cure from tumor. | 3. These cells acquire an ability to invade the surrounding tissue and through circulation these loose cells form a secondary tumour at a distance place. This spreading process of is called metastasis. |
| 4. The cell division becomes normal after few rapid divisions and remains controlled. | 4. Unregulated, uncontrolled and continuous division takes place without following the normal principle of cell division. |
| 5. Structural or numerical changes in chromosome is rarely found. | 5. Various types of chromosomal abnormalities are observed. |
| 6. The principles of apoptosis is obeyed by the cell. | 6. Cells of cancerous tumours are immortal, they disobey the rules and principles of apoptosis. |

also secrete a protease, called plasminogen activator, which converts plasminogen to plasmin. This active plasmin digests and penetrates basal lamina and promotes metastasis by degenerating the basal lamina of the cell.

Cancer may be classified according to the cell or tissue types. The cancer arising from epithelial cells is termed as **carcinoma**, those arising from connective tissues or muscle cells are termed as **sarcomas**.

At present, the set of names for malignant tumors and benign tumors have been given. For example, a benign epithelial tumor with glandular organization is known as **adenoma**; the same type of tumor with malignant form is known as **adenocarcinoma**. Similarly **chondroma** and **chondrosarcoma** are termed for benign and malignant tumors of cartilages respectively.

The ***basal cell carcinoma*** is derived from the keratinocyte stem cell of the skin and which will generally continue to synthesize cytokeratin intermediate filaments, this is only locally invasive and rarely metastatic. **Melanoma** is derived from pigment cells of the skin, continue to make pigment granules, if not removed properly, is much more malignant and rapidly gives rise to many metastases. Malignant cells are certainly different from normal cells (Table 21.5).

## 21.6 SEVERAL AND SUCCESSIVE MUTATIONS ARE INVOLVED IN TUMOR GENESIS AND PROGRESSION

Carcinogenesis appears to be linked with autogenesis, because, the aberrations in the cancer cell is heritable and have shown to share abnormality in their DNA sequences. The chemical mutagen and X-ray induce aberrations and local changes in DNA that led into cancer.

In normal human beings, in their lifetime, an estimated $10^{16}$ cell divisions take place. In a mutagen free environment, a single gene is likely to have undergone mutation on about $10^{10}$ separate occasions. Mutation rate has been calculated to be about $10^{-6}$ mutations per gene per cell division. If a single mutation causes the cell cancer then we would not be viable organisms.

From epidemiological studies it has been observed that the incidence of most types of cancers in human beings increases markedly and exponentially with age.

**TABLE 21.5**
**Difference between cancer cell and normal cell.**

| *Cancer Cell* | *Normal Cell* |
|---|---|
| **A. Cytological Differences** | |
| 1. Cancer cells are much rounded in shape, smaller in size, mitochondrial swelling appears, growth granules are sometimes found, Golgi apparatus are reduced in size, usually multipolar, larger nucleus, larger nucleolus, altered nucleocytoplasmic ratio. | 1. Not much rounded in shape, larger in size, no mitochondrial swelling and growth granules, well organised Golgi apparatus, unipolar during division, smaller nucleus and nucleolus. Same and unaltered nucleocytoplasmic ratio. |
| **B. Chromosomal Differences** | |
| 1. These cells have abnormal number and structure of chromosomes. Sometimes localized reduplication of DNA may be observed and thus some homogenously staining regions are observed. | 1. Chromosome number and structure would be normal. No reduplication of DNA and no HSR is observed. |
| **C. Differences in Molecular organization** | |
| 1. More glycosyltransferase enzymes in Golgi complexes. | 1. Less glycosyltransferase in Golgi complex. |
| 2. Defective glycolysis and TCA cycle, utilize more blood glucose. Cannot oxidise excessive pyruvic acid and is reduced to lactic acid, overproduction of hexokinase. | 2. Normal glycolysis, oxidation of pyruvic acid and TCA cycle. |
| 3. Aldolase A type is present. | 3. Aldolase enzyme is B-type. |
| 4. $\alpha$–fetoprotein and carcinogen embryonic antigen etc. fetal proteins are synthesized. | 4. AFP and CEA are not synthesized. |
| 5. Plasminogen activator is secreted by cells which causes digestion of basal lamina and leads to metastasis. | 5. No plasminogen activator and therefore basal lamina is intact and no metastasis. |
| 6. Receptor molecules are diffused. | 6. Receptor molecules are not diffused. |
| 7. GM3 type of ganglicides are present on the cell membrane. | 7. GM1, GM2 etc gangliosides are on the cell membrane. |
| 8. Fibronectin molecule is drastically absent. | 8. Fibronectin is normal. |
| 9. Ctoskeleton is disonganized and as a result the cytoplasmic organelles are disorganised. | 9. Well organized cytoskeleton and therefore, cytoplasmic organelles are correctly distributed. |
| 10. Loss of inhibition contact is mostly observed, as a result cancer cells form multilayered structure in culture medium. | 10. Some electron dense plaques are formed and so in culture medium they form a monolayer. |
| **D. Difference in genetic organization** | |
| 1. Becomes immortal and overcome apoptosis. | 1. All the cells undergo apoptosis. |
| 2. oncogenic mutation occurs that leads to homozygous mutants. | 2. Genetically these cells are homozygous or heterozygous for normal genes. |
| 3. Cancer cells are genetically unstable, i.e., DNA repair mechanism is failed. | 3. Genetically stable and DNA repair mechanism is perfect. |
| 4. Display abnormal Karyotype . | 4. Display abnormal Karyotype. |
| 5. Loss of tumor suppressor genes. | 5. Tumor suppressor genes are active. |

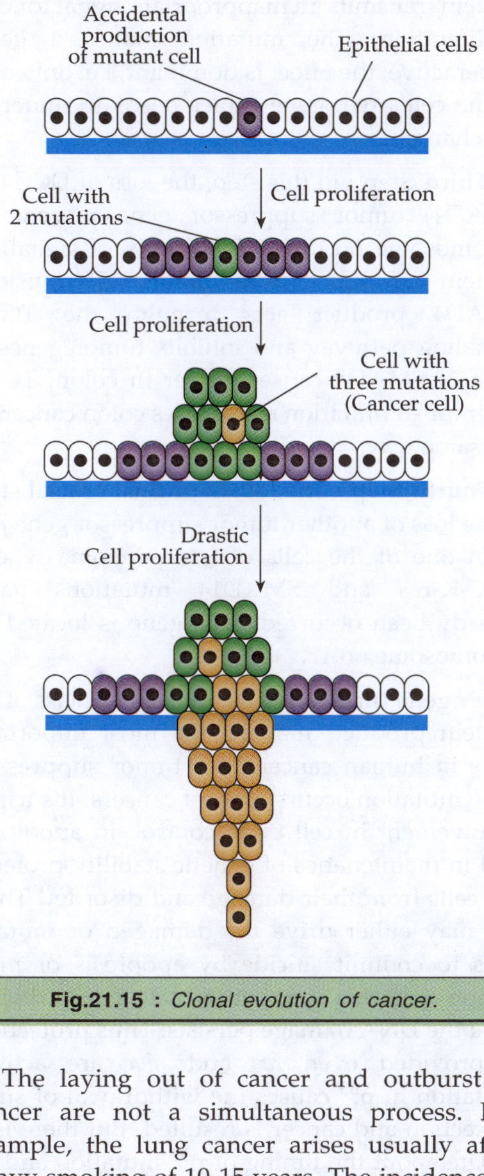


**Fig.21.15 :** *Clonal evolution of cancer.*

The laying out of cancer and outburst of cancer are not a simultaneous process. For example, the lung cancer arises usually after heavy smoking of 10-15 years. The incidence of leukemia in Hiroshima and Nagasaki did not show a marked rise until 5 years after the atomic bomb explosion. So, during this long incubation period the prospective cancer cells undergo successive changes.

According to **multihit model**, cancer arises by a process of clonal selection. The cancers in general seem to arise by a process in which an initial population of the cell or a single cell undergoes mutation and gives it a slight growth advantage. One of the progeny cells would then undergoes a second mutation and that would allow its descendants to give more selective advantage over its neighbours, they become adapted themselves and will continue to divide. Thus a benign tumor may be formed. The third mutation within such tumors would allow it to outgrow the others and progeny would form a mass of cells. All the previous three mutations are remained in these cells and would allow their descendants to escape from their original location to the other tissues through circulation (Fig. 21.15).

Now, many of the specific mutations responsible for the development of cancer have been identified. The concept that the development of a cancer requires mutations in many genes-perhaps ten or more –fits with a large body of information, dating back over many years, concerning the phenomenon of tumor progression. **Initial mild disorder of cell in course of time evolves gradually into a full-grown cancer.**

## 21.7 GENETICS OF COLORECTAL CANCER GENESIS

The detailed molecular basis of colon cancer genesis has been carefully studied *in vivo*. The cancer arises from the epithelial lining of the colon and rectum and USA has recorded 11% of the total deaths from this type of cancer. It is diagnosed mostly after the age of 55.

The colorectal cancer evolves through distinct well-characterized morphological stages. A small polyp which has been arisen in the initial step and through certain intermediate stages, becomes cancerous. To become such carcinoma from the polyp it requires 10-35 years.

The studies have identified a series of mutations that commonly arise in a well-defined order. These studies provide strong support for the multihit model of cancer genesis.

**First Step :** The first step of colon cancer is the precancerous growth on the inside of the colon wall, which is called **polyp**. Hundreds of polyps can be seen on the wall of that region. Most of the cells in the polyp contain the same one or two mutations or deletion of *APC* gene present on the long arm of chromosome-5. APC is one of the tumor suppression genes, which encodes a protein that inhibits the progression of some types of cells. APC does so by inhibiting the ability of the **Wnt** protein to activate expression of *myc* gene. *myc*-gene product is ***Myc***-protein which is a transcription factor required for expression of many genes during transition from $G_1$ to S-phase of the cell cycle. For polyp formation both the chromosomes must carry mutant APC genes or deletion of this normal gene.

APC protein is known to be an inhibitory component of **Wnt-signaling pathway**. It acts by binding to β-catenin, preventing activation of *TCF-4* gene regulartory protein that stimulates growth of colon epithelium. So lack of APC may cause overgrowth by opposite effect. Only β- catenin mutation can cause so, even that did not have APC mutation.

The individuals who inherit a germline mutation in one APC allele only the one remaining functional APC allele. There requires only one mutation in APC allele to form a polyp in colon. These individuals have a greatly increased risk for developing colon cancer before the age of 50.

**Second Step :** In the second steps of the molecular mechanism of colon cancer formation, one of the cells in a polyp undergoes another mutation, which activates the *k-ras* oncogene. Its progeny divide in an uncontrolled fashion forming a large adenoma. *k-ras* gene is present in chromosome no.-2. Overexpression of *myc* gene is insufficient to induce tumor in transgenic mice. *$Ras^D$* gene expression can cause mammary cancer but slowly. When *myc* and *$ras^D$* both are present, tumors arise rapidly and all animals succumb to cancer. *K-ras* gene is effected through the **receptor tyrosine kinase** signaling. **Ras** proteins are monomeric GTPase that help to transmit signals from growth factor receptor on the cell surface. Hyperactive Ras-protein transmits an inappropriate signal for cell proliferation. The mutation makes a gene hyperactive, the effect is dominant, i.e. only one of the cell's two gene copies needs to undergo the change.

**Third Step :** in this step, the loss of DCC (or SMAD4) tumor suppressor gene present in chromosome no.18. **TGF β** family of signaling protein can function to inhibit cell division. SMAD4 product acts through the TGFβ signaling pathway and inhibits tumor genesis. Loss of SMAD4 causes cancer in colon. TGFβ receptor -II mutation also causes colon cancer in the same way.

**Fourth Step :** The fourth or final crucial step is the loss of another tumor suppressor gene ***$p^{53}$*** from one of the cells of late adenoma where **APC-K-ras** and SMAD14 mutations have already been occurred. This gene is located in chromosome no.17.

*$p^{53}$* gene-(named for the molecular mass of its protein product) may be the most important gene in human cancer. This tumor suppressor gene mutation occurs in most cancers. It's triple involvement in cell cycle control, in apoptosis and in maintenance of genetic stability protects the cells from their damage and disorder. Thus **$p^{53}$** may either drive the damaged or mutant cells to commit suicide by apoptosis or may trigger a mechanism that the cells not to divide until the DNA damage persists. Thus protection is provided even *ras* and *myc* are active. Mutation in **$p^{53}$** causes the withdrawal of such protection and cancer is resulted. But there is a debate about the timing of **$p^{53}$** mutation and of genetic instability (Fig. 21.16).

## 21.8 GENES AND CANCER

The genes whose mutation contribute to the causation of cancer are known as ***cancer critical genes***. These genes are grouped into two broad classes according to their mode of activity. For example, the genes that, after their mutation, gain hyperactivity of the gene product to cause cancer is **protooncogene**; their mutant, over-active form is called oncogene. The genes,

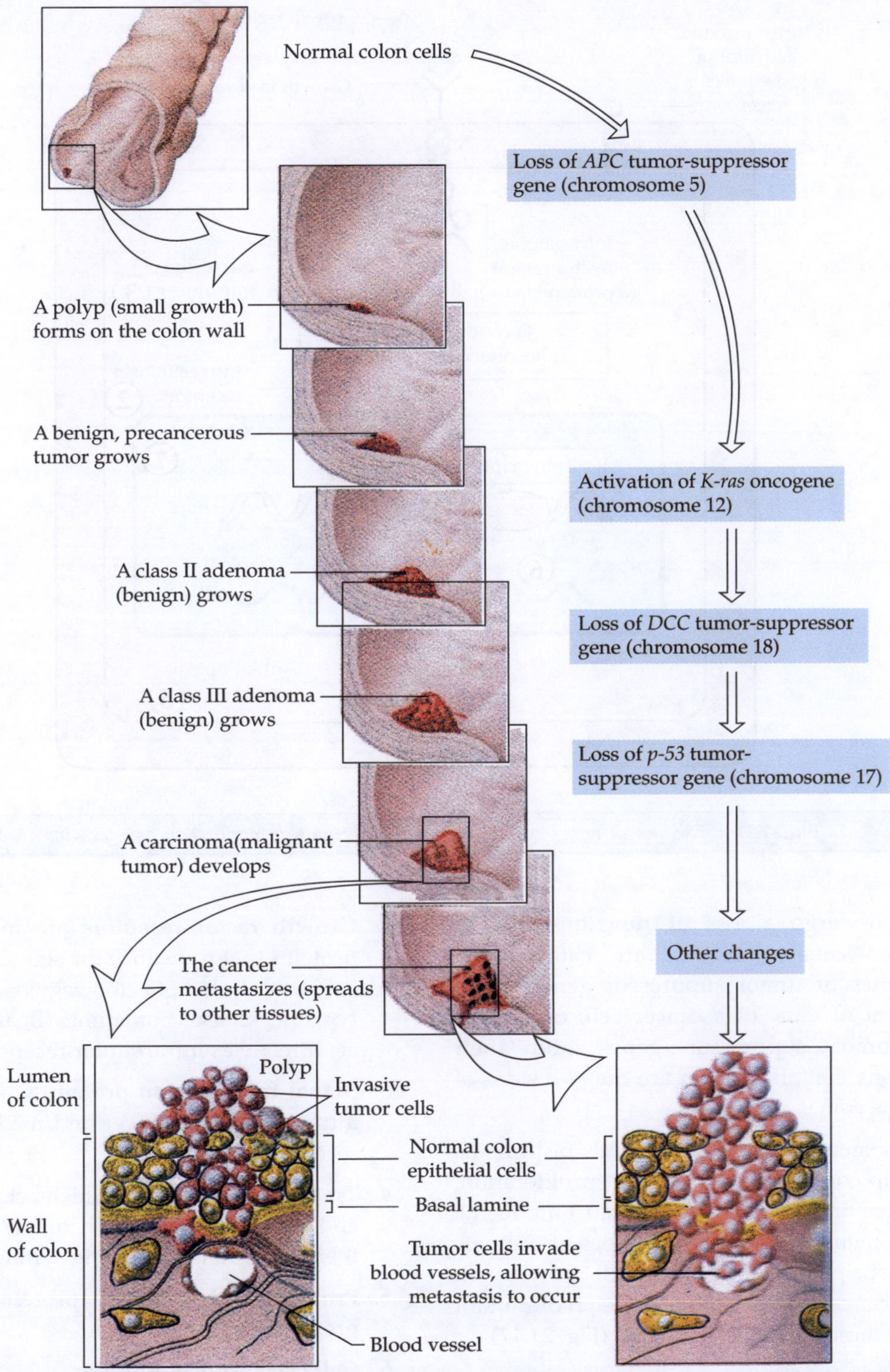


**Fig.21.16 :** *The development and metastasis of human colorectal cancer and its genetic basis.*

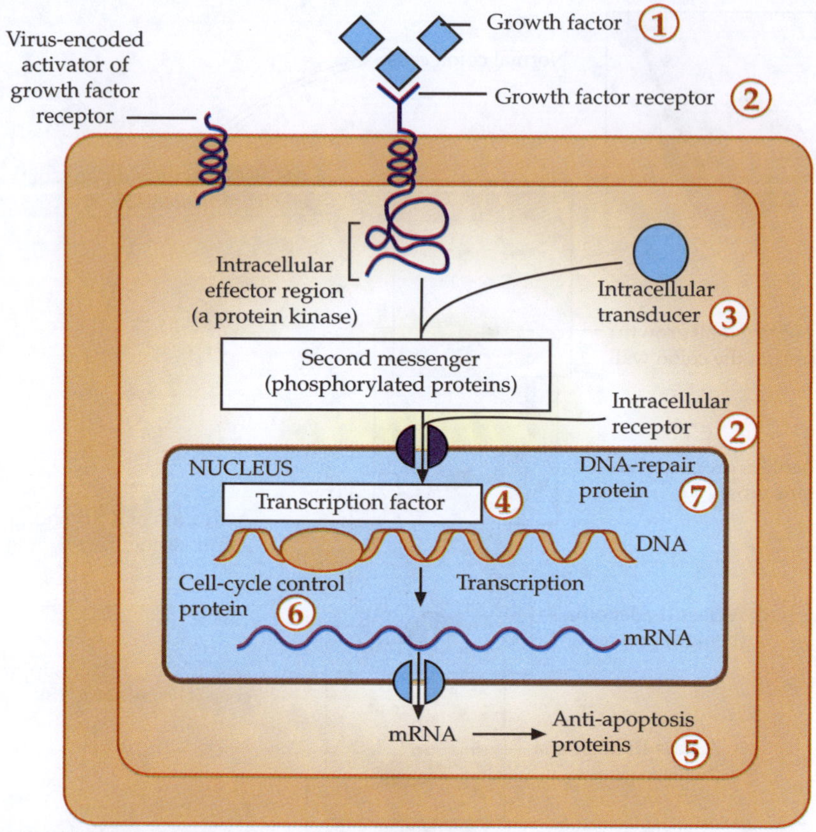


**Fig.21.17 :** *The seven types of proteins that participate in controlling cell growth.*

which undergo a loss of functions due to mutation causing cancer, are called **anti-oncogenes** or tumor suppressor genes. From the point of view of a cancer cell; oncogenes and tumor suppressor genes and their mutations that affect them are the two sides of the same coin.

These genes encode many kinds of proteins that help control cell growth and proliferation. Mutations in these genes can contribute to the development of cancer. Seven types of proteins that participate in controlling cell growth and the cancer can result from expression of mutant form of these proteins. These are (Fig. 21.17)

1. **Growth factors,** which function as ligands.
2. **Growth factor receptors** are membrane proteins that transduce the signal through its intracellular effector regions, often a tyrosine kinase. Sometimes ligands may act directly as intracellular receptors.
3. **Signal transduction protein,** which is an intracellular transducer and mediated by second messengers.
4. **Transcription factors,** which act on DNA and initiate transcription of mRNA and then the proteins are being synthesized.
5. **Pro-and anti-apoptotic proteins** direct programmed cell death.
6. **Cell cycle control proteins.**
7. **DNA repair proteins,** those are required for mismatch repair replication.

**TABLE 21.6**

**Some retroviruses that carry oncogene derived from a cellular gene.**

| *Virus* | *Oncogene* | *Species* | *Tumor* |
|---|---|---|---|
| ***Rous Sarcoma (RSV)*** | *src* | Chicken | Sarcoma |
| ***Harvey murine sarcoma (Ha-MuSV)*** | *H-ras* | Rat | Sarcoma |
| ***Kirsten murine sarcoma (Ki-MuSV)*** | *K-ras* | Rat | Sarcoma |
| ***Melony murine sarcoma (Mo-MuSV)*** | *mos* | Mouse | Sarcoma |
| ***Simian Sarcoma (SSV)*** | *sis* | Monkey | Sarcoma |
| ***Avian myelocytomatosis (MC29)*** | *myc* | Chicken | Sarcoma, carcinoma and myelocytoma |
| ***Abelson Leukemia (MuLV)*** | *abl* | Mouse | B-Cell lymphoma |
| ***FBJ murine osteosarcoma (FBJ-MuSV)*** | *fos* | Mouse | Chondrosarcoma |
| ***Fujinami sarcoma (FuSV)*** | *fps* | Chicken | Sarcoma |

The mutations changing the structure or expression of proteins belonging to 1st-4th group generally give rise to dominantly active oncogenes. The protein belonging to 5th group acts as a tumor suppression, recessive mutation of these genes encoding proteins increase the surveillance of the cell and causing tumorous growth. Mutations in 7th group genes greatly increase the probability of mutations of the other groups. A virus encoded growth receptor which is a miniature form of normal ligand receptor, also can induce cancer.

### 21.8.1 Oncogenes

The oncogenes are described as viral or ***v-onc genes*** present in the host cells. The ***c-onc* genes** are not oncogenic and are described as proto oncogenes, which have the potentials of becoming oncogenes.

Oncogenes may be of DNA ***v-onc* genes** and RNA-***v-onc* genes.**

**RNA v-oncogenes :** RNA v-oncogenes were first discovered by Peyton Rouse in 1911 in fibrosarcoma in chicken and called the virus as Rous Sarcoma Virus (RSV) and was awarded Nobel prize in the year 1966. Later it was shown that RSV is a retrovirus whose RNA genome is reversely transcribed into DNA and this DNA is incorporated into the host cell genome. The genes ***gag; pol*** and ***env*** are non transforming genes, whereas, *v-src* is the transforming gene, required for cancer induction. In 1977 Mitchell Bishop and Harold Varmus showed that a gene very closely related to RSV *v-src* is present in the normal cellular gene of chicken. Then this cellular gene is designated as *c-src* gene. Later on a large number of *c-onc* genes have been identified by their representation in retroviruses. Some *c-onc* genes may be found in more than one retroviruses and more than one c-onc genes may be present in different strains of the same retroviruses (Table 21.6).

*v-onc* gene is actually derived from mRNA so that it contains uninterrupted sequence or sequence missing at one or both ends, while the corresponding *c-onc* may be a split gene with exons and introns.

In some, *v-onc* sequence is expressed as a part of a fusion product and their boundaries can be defined by comparing with the corresponding *c-onc.*

**TABLE 21.7**
**Some DNA n-onc genes**

| *Virus* | *Oncogenes* | *Sources of tumor* |
|---|---|---|
| **Papova virus** | T-antigens | SV 40 induces solid tumor in hamster and polyoma virus in mice. |
| **Adenoviruses** | EIA and EIB | Induce malignancy in hamster and rats |
| **Epstein Barr** | BNLF-1 | Causes mononucleosis in children |

For example :

*gag-abl, gag-myc, gag-fos* etc. while the *v-onc* of *mos, ras, sis* and *myc* genes having no missing region comparing with its *c-onc* counterparts.

**DNA *v-onc* genes :** SV40 DNA viruses also integrate the small part of their genome into the host cell and the cells become transformed because such viral DNA contains one or more oncogenes. Human genital warts are caused by virus (Table 21.7).

In culture, DNA tumor viruses are of two types

(a) **Permissive cells :** It can be productively infected, virus components are produced, replication and assembly of particles occur and ultimately cell death, lysis and release of virus particles.

(b) **Non permissive cells :** It is not productively infected but get transformed by becoming the part of the host genome.

Most oncogenes in these viruses are expressed by altenative splicing.

Papillomaviruses have double stranded circular DNA. In a wart or other benign infections these chromosomes are maintained in the basal cells of the epithelium as plasmids, replicate in parallel with the host cells DNA in the course of ordinary cell division cycles. They remain latent and harmless. Rare genetic accidents can cause the integration of a fragment of such a plasmid into a chromosome of the host altering the environment of the viral genes causing unbalanced production of viral replication protein, which interferes the control of cell division, and thus causing cancer induction.

In papillomavirus, two viral genes ***E6*** and ***E7*** encode the product that interact with many host cell proteins, particularly to two key tumor suppressor proteins $p^{53}$ and RB proteins respectively. Thus RB protein is inactivated by binding with E7 while E6 protein binding leads to ubiquitilation of $p^{53}$ inducing $p^{53}$ proteolysis (Fig. 21.18).

A papillomavirus protein designated E5, which contains only 44 amino acids, spans the plasma membrane and forms a dimer or trimer. Each E5 polypeptide can form a stable complex with one endogenous receptor for PDGF, thereby aggregating two or more PDGF receptors within the plane of the plasma membrane. This mimics hormone mediated receptor dimerization and activation, causing sustained receptor activation and leading to cell proliferation.

### 21.8.2 Activation of Proto-oncogenes

Proto-oncogenes (*c-onc* genes) are present in the host and are not oncogenic. Most of them are basic to animal life; they have been highly conserved over eons of evolutionary time. Activation (or conversion) of a proto-oncogene into an oncogene generally involves a gain of function mutation. There are at least three mechanisms that a proto-oncogene can be made overactive to convert it into an oncogene.

1. **Deletions or point mutations** in coding sequence of a proto-oncogene that result in a hyperactive protein product made in normal amount. Here the oncoprotein is slightly differ from normal protein.
2. **Localised reduplication** (gene amplification) of a DNA segment that includes a proto-oncogene leading to over expression of the genes those code normal proteins greatly overproduced.

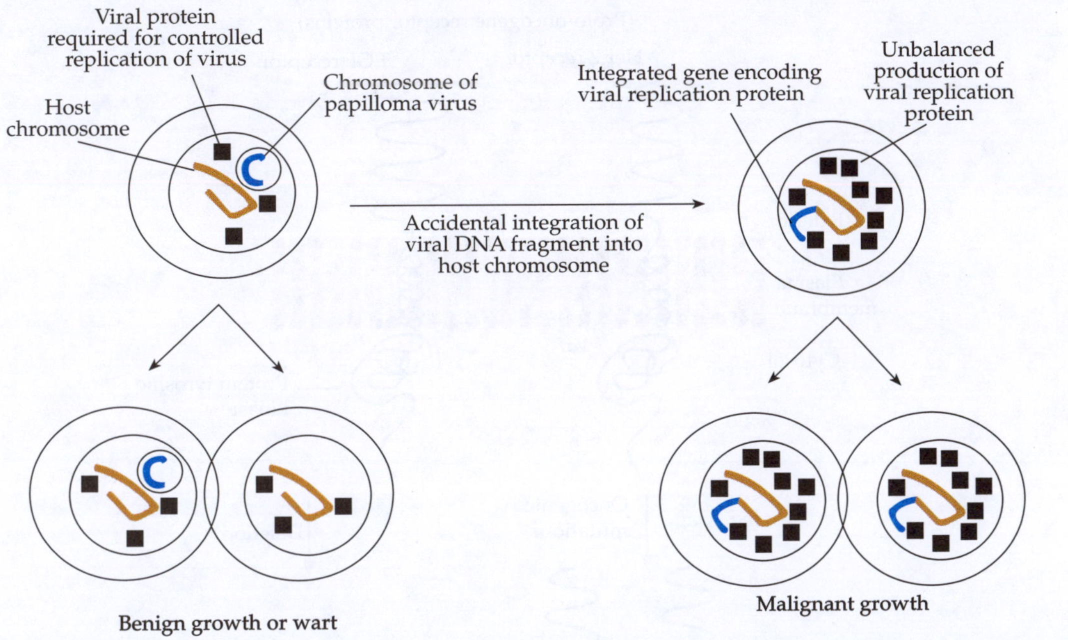


**Fig. 21.18 :** *Cancer induction by papilloma viruses in uterine cervix.*

3. **Chromosome rearrangement** causing either insertion of a regulatory DNA sequence nearby causing overproduction of normal proto-oncoprotein or fusion of actively transcribed genes that greatly overproduce fusion proteins, which may be hyperactive.

In the latter two mechanisms, the oncoproteins are identical with normal proteins but are expressed higher than the normal level and oncogenes act dominantly i.e., mutation in one of the two alleles is sufficient to induce cancer.

### A. Activation of proto-oncogene by mutation

1. **Virus encoded oncoprotein activates the growth factor receptors :** The proliferation and differentiation of RBC requires a protein **Epo** which is made by the cells in the kidney. Binding of the natural ligand Epo, dimerizes the Epo-receptors and induces formation of RBC from erythroid progenitor.

Progenitor cells infected by spleen focus-forming virus (SFFV), a retrovirus, that encodes a mutant glycoprotein gp55, which is missing much of the normal extra-cellular domain and all the cytosolic domain. This protein has an ability to bind to and activate the Epo receptors leading to inappropriate proliferation of erythroid progenitor leading to the induction of erythroleukemia.

2. **Mutations causing overexpression of growth factor receptor :** A single mutation that alters a single amino acid, *valine* to *glutamine* in the transmembrane region of **Her2** receptor into **Neu** oncoprotein which is found in certain mouse cancers. Such mutation causing demerization of two receptor proteins in the absence of the normal EGF-related ligand, making the protein continuously active as a kinase.

A deletion that causes loss of the extra cellular ligand-binding domain in the EGF receptor leads to an oncoprotein **ErbB** which also activates the protein kinase.

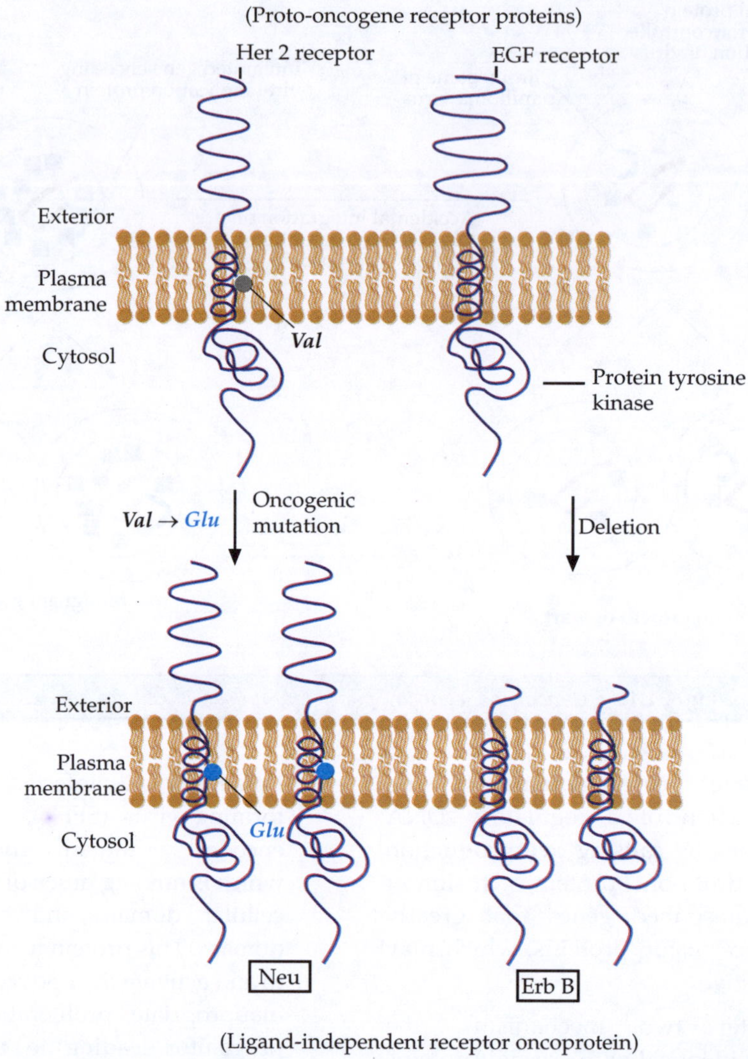


**Fig.21.19 :** *Effects of oncogenic mutations of protooncogenes that encode cell-surface receptors.*

Normal **Trk** protein, which is localized to the plasma membrane and is activated by a nerve growth factor (NGF). In the **Trk** oncoprotein most of the extracellular domain in the normal human **Trk** receptor tyrosin kinase is replaced with the 221 N-terminal amino acids of non-muscle tropomyosin. The recetors are dimerized by tropomyosin segment and thus the Trk oncoprotein protein kinase becomes constitutively active (Fig. 21.19).

3. **Mutations causing active signal transduction proteins encoded by many oncogenes:** *v–H-ras* and *v-K-ras* differ from corresponding *c-ras* genes by alterations of 3 and 7 amino acids respectively.

Usually a mutation of a single amino acid at position 12 or 61 in the *ras* proteins by a single base substitution, a *c-ras* protooncogene can giverise to an oncogene. In a patient of lung carcinoma, it has been shown the presence of mutant *c-ras* gene while in normal tissue it is wild type *c-ras*. Thus it has been assumed that spontaneous mutation leading the cells to be cancerous.

**Ras** proteins are anchored to the inner side of the plasma membrane by a farnesyl group covalent bonding. This attachment is essential for signal transduction from activated receptor tyrosine kinase via two proteins GRB2 and SOS and then to Ras, converting it to active GTP bound form. This activated Ras then transmits signal via two intermediate protein kinases and then to MAP kinases, eventually leading to the alteration of cell growth and differentiation. Activating Ras mutations short circuit the first part of this pathway and without binding of ligand to the receptor this pathway continuously triggers cell growth and differentiation leading to cancer.

A recessive loss of function mutation in the *NF 1* leads to constitutive Ras activation. *NF 1* encodes the enzyme called GTPase activating enzyme (GAP) which is required for conversion from active GTP bound Ras to inactive GDP bound Ras. *NF 1* mutation causes loss of GAP, then constantly sustained GTP bound Ras passes transduction signal, leading to continuous abnormal cell growth and differentiation. This mutation is also inherited as an autosomal dominant trait.

Another oncogene *src* encodes cytosolic protein kinase. The *c-src* contains an SH2, SH3 and tyrosine kinase domain. The kinase activity is normally inactivated by phorphorylation of *tyr* residue at position 527 which is six residues far from C-terminus. Hydrolysis of this phosphate, it becomes activated. The transforming *v-src* oncoprotein encoded by RSV is missing the c-terminal 18 amino acids and thus the *tyr* residue is missing in *v-src*, continuously becomes active causing abnormal proliferation of many types of cells.

4. **Mutation causing inappropriate expression of transcription factors:** *c-jun* and *c-fos* protooncogenes encode proteins that sometimes associate to form a heterodimeric transcription factor AP1. This binds to a sequence of a promoter and enhances many genes. *Fos* and *Jun* can also act independently. ***c Fos*** and ***c Myc*** stimulate transcription of genes encoding proteins that promote progression through $G_1$ to S transition. Inappropriate expression of nuclear transcription factors such as **Fos, Jun** and **Myc** that can induce transformation. In several tumors *c-myc* has been translocated to a position juxtaposition with enhancer of the antibody genes and is continually expressed causing the cell to become cancerous.

### B. Activation of proto-oncogene by insertion

**c-Myc** is a transcription factor, which is essential for transcription of many genes required for encoding cell cycle proteins. The **c-myc** gene has three exons E1, E2 and E3 of which E1 is not translated but transcribed. In some tumors, the avian leucosis proviral DNA is found at the 5′ end of the *c-myc* gene in the same transcription orientation. This retrovirus has right-handed LTR, which serves as a terminator as well as is believed to act as a promoter, initiating synthesis of mRNA transcript from *c-myc* gene. There may be three classes of insertions of DNA provirus to the *c-myc* genes (Fig. 21.20).

1. The promoter can be activated when the defective retrovirus is inserted upstream 5′ of the **c-myc** exons. The right-handed LTR (long terminal repeat) may then act as promoter if the provirus has a defect preventing transcription through the right handed LTR.

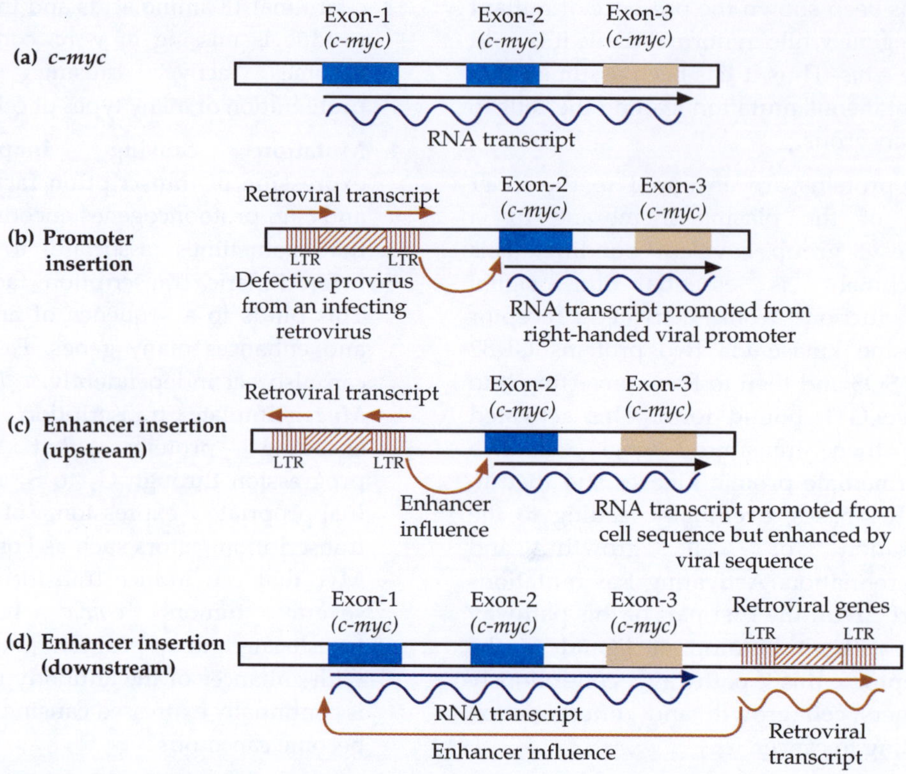


**Fig.21.20 :** *c-myc gene (A) and three different kinds of retroviral insertions (B, C and D) leading to activation of c-myc gene.*

2. If the proviral DNA is inserted in opposite transcriptional orientation, then it is thought to exert an indirect enhancer activity, activating transcription from the *c-myc* promoter sequence.
3. The retroviral genome may also be inserted down stream of *c-myc* gene and LTR may work as an enhancer.

   These mechanisms of oncogene activation are called promoter insertions and enhancer insertions.

## C. Activation of protoongene by chromosome translocation

It has been found that a protooncogene, *c-myc* which is located on chromosome-8 in man and chromosome-15 in mouse, translocated into the proximity of the Ig locus in B cells and TCRα locus in T cells on another chromosome-14 in man and chromosome 12 in mouse results in activation of this protooncogene and causes cancer, which is commonly known as **plasmacytoma** in mouse and **Burkitt lymphoma** in man.

Another such chromosomal translocation that results in fusion of a portion of *bcr* gene locus (breakpoint cluster region) of chromosome-22 (whose function is unknown but N-terminal segment form a coiled-coil domain that links several *bcr* polypeptides together) with 5000 kb region from the end of chromosome-9 carrying *c-abl* gene which encodes a protein tyrosine kinase whose normal substrate is also unknown. The chimeric polypeptide expressed from the resulting *bcr-abl* oncogene forms a tetramer (mr. 210000 dalton) that exhibits constitutive Abl kinase activity.

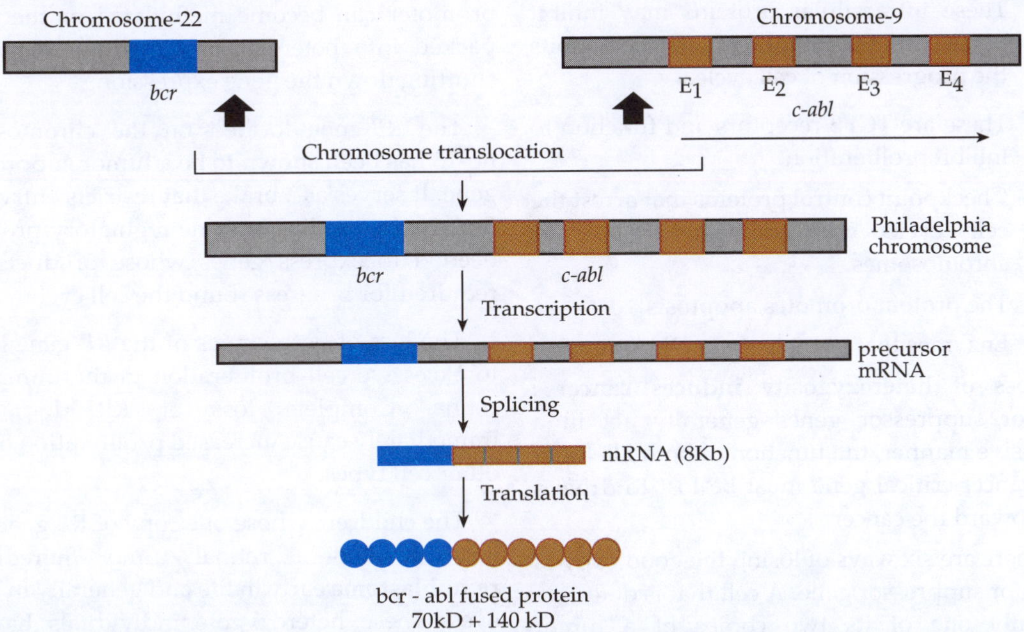


**Fig.21.21 :** *A translocation between chromosome 22 and chromosome 9 generating Philadelphia chromosome associated with chronic myelogenous leukemia.*

**Bcr-Abl** binds to many other signal transducing proteins and phosphorylates them, which were not normally activated by **Abl**. **Jak-2 protein kinase, Stat 5-transcription factor** and **$PI_3$ kinase** are also being activated in absence of growth factor. This translocation is responsible for **chronic myelogenous leukemia**. The smaller of the two resulting abnormal chromosomes is called **Philadelphia chromosome**, after the city where the abnormality was first recorded (Fig. 21.21).

A synthetic drug has been discovered called STI – 571 (now renamed Gleevec) that can inhibit the activity of protein kinase and also blocks **Bcr–Abl** by preventing transfer of ATP to kinase. This drug was given to a series of 54 patients with chronic myeloid leukemia. All but one of them showed excellent response with return of their normal WBC count. After one year 51 of them were still well. But the patients had already progressed through further mutations, genetic instability has set in and the cancer cells were able to evolve a resistance to the Gleevec. It now seems that if such drugs are designed properly with effective rational method, some hopeful result should be obtained in future.

### 21.8.3 Tumor Suppressor Genes or Antioncogenes

Tumor suppressor genes generally encode proteins that inhibit cell proliferation. As the formation of cancerous tissue is regulated by growth promoting proto-oncogenes and are counter balanced by growth suppressing factor, these genes are known as tumor suppressor genes and these are also commonly called anti-oncogenes because it's function is likely to be of opposite to the oncogenes. Loss of the one or more controls of the tumor suppressor genes contribute to the development of cancer.

Tumor suppressor genes encode different types of proteins and these proteins function in different ways during induction of cancer.

1. These intracellular proteins may inhibit $p^{16}$ cyclin-kinase that regulates or inhibits the progression of cell cycle.
2. These are TGFβ receptors and function to inhibit proliferation.
3. Checkpoint control proteins that arrest the cell cycle with damaged DNA or chromosomes.
4. The protein promotes apoptosis.
5. Enzymes that participate in DNA repair.

**Loss of heterozygosity induces cancer :** Tumor suppressor genes generally act in a recessive manner, the function of both alleles of the cancer-critical gene must be lost to drive a cell toward the cancer.

There are six ways of losing the good copy of a tumor suppressor gene. A cell that is defective in only one of its two copies of a tumor suppressor gene (*eg*, *Rb*–gene ) which usually behaves normally in healthy cell,. it may come to lose in function of the normal gene copy as well and thereby progress towards cancer.

1. Loss of normal copy of the gene due to non-disjunction of chromosome during mitosis and one mutant gene is remained.
2. After nondisjunction the single copy of the mutant gene containing single chromosome may be duplicated.
3. Due to mitotic recombination the normal gene can be replaced by a mutant version.
4. By the mechanism of gene conversion the normal gene can be replaced by mutant gene.
5. Deletion of the normal gene from the chromosome and expression of mutant without opposing by its normal counter part.
6. Due to point mutation of the normal gene.

The seventh possibility encountered with some tumor suppressor is that the gene may be inactivated by an epigenetic changes without altering the DNA damage. For example, its promoter can become methylated or the gene packed into heterochromatin, thus effectively shutting down the gene expression.

The *RB*-gene located on the chromosome no-13 has been shown to be a tumor suppressor gene. It serves as a brake that restricts entry into S-phase by binding to gene regulatory proteins needed to express genes whose products are required for progress round the cell cycle.

The loss of both copies of the *RB*-gene leads to excessive cell proliferation in the immature retina. Complete loss of *RB* does not immediately cause increased proliferation of the other cell types.

The children, whose one copy of *RB* gene has lost, develop a retinal tumor **hereditary reinoblastoma** early in life and generally in both eyes. These heterozygote individuals have 4 $\infty 10^6$ cells in the retina and about one in $10^6$ cells actually give rise to a tumor cell. The loss of *RB* gene in the normal chromosome certainly have undergone deletion or mutation and thus become homozygous for defective recessive *RB* genes.

Individuals with **sporadic retinoblastoma** have two normal *RB*-genes in two chromosomes. Each of which has undergone somatic loss of function mutation in a single retinal cell. This type of retinal cancer develops late in life and usually affects only one eye.

If the tumor in early stage is removed in hereditary retinoblastoma then the child would survive but inherits one mutant *RB* gene to their offspring. While in sporadic retinoblastoma the child would inherit only normal *RB* genes in future.

***BRCA 1*** is tumor suppressor gene. Women who inherit one mutant ***BRCA-1*** allele have a 60% probability of developing breast cancer by age 50. The normal two ***BRCA-1*** allele-containing female has 2% probability. The heterozygous women would certainly have to be a second ***BRCA-1*** gene mutation on the normal chromosome which is required for a breast duct cell to become malignant.

### 21.8.4 $P^{53}$ : the Guardian of the Genome

$P^{53}$ is known as a **tumor suppressor protein**. It is named so, because of its molecular size of 53 kDa. The gene for this protein is $p^{53}$ lies on chromosome no 17. which is found to be mutated in about half of all human cancers.

$p^{53}$ protein is a transcription factor and can activate or repress over 100 target genes which have been identified so far. Bioinformatic studies predict that the number may be much greater and more than 4000 human genes contain pupative $p^{53}$ binding sites in their promoters. Mutation of this gene and the production of cancer are due to their involvement in cell-cycle control, in apoptosis and in maintenance of genetic stability.

In almost all cells, $p^{53}$ protein is found very little quantity, because in normal cells this protein is not required and this is constantly turning over. The expression level of $p^{53}$ is regulated both by treanscriptional and translational levels.

Under normal circumstances, $p^{53}$ is targeted to proteasomal degradation by the binding of MDM2 (mouse double minute-2) a ubiquitin ligase. The process is enhanced by the transcription factor **YY1** (Yin Yang 1). Various inhibitory proteins may prevent $p^{53}$ degradation eg. $p^{14\ Arf}$ binds to MDM2 to inhibit its $E_3$ ligase activity. PML (Promyelocytic leukemia) protein binds to MDM2 and sequesters it to the nucleolus.

**$p^{53}$ and Cell cycle :** DNA damage at early $G_1$ of cell cycle activates a protein kinase, which phosphorylates $p^{53}$ and reduces the binding of MDM2 and degradation of $p^{53}$. Then it activates $p^{21}$ gene transcription which encodes $p^{21}$ protein. This is a CDK-inhibitor, inactivates $G_1$/S-Cdk and S-Cdk activity and causes $G_1$ arrest. The cell resumes division after the repairing of DNA damage.

**$p^{53}$ and apoptosis :** The ability of $p^{53}$ to promote apoptosis is less well understood, although it is known to play a role in both mitochondrial mediated and death receptor-mediated apoptotic pathways. DNA damage at $G_2$ triggers apoptosis by $p^{53}$ which can activate the transcription of genes tht encode proteins that promote the release of cytochrome-C from mitochondria. These proteins belong to Bel-2 family.

**$p^{53}$ and cancer :** Many cancer cells contain large quantities of mutant $p^{53}$ proteins. Cancers including cervix, breast, bladder, prostrate, liver, lung, skin and colon have been found to have mutant version of $p^{53}$. The hereditary cancer syndrome, Li-Fraumeni syndrome has been discovered in 1969, which predisposes patients to brain tumors, sarcoma, leukemia and breast cancer, where $p^{53}$ gene is defective.

$p^{53}$ is a tumor suppressor gene. Wild type $p^{53}$ allele produces homotetramers and functions as tumor suppressor. But a missense point mutation in one of the two alleles may cause the production of dominant negative mutant protein. Such behaviour is like that of oncogenes which may lead to confusion wheather it is an oncogene or a tumor suppressor gene. The dominant negative mutation of $p^{53}$ inhibits wild type $p^{53}$ activity as it is formed a heterotetramer and leads to unrestrained cell growth.

Majority of $p^{53}$ mutation is located in the central region of this protein, the region which actually mediates DNA binding and also interaction with ASPP (apoptosis stimulating protein of $p^{53}$), BAK (BCl-2 antagonist Killer-1) and BCl-2 (B cell chronic lymphocytic leukemia), those regulate the apoptotic function of $p^{53}$. Mutations in $p^{53}$ prevents binding to and expression of $p^{53}$ gene.

## 21.9 MUTATIONS CAUSING LOSS OF CELL CYCLE CONTROL AND INDUCTION OF CANCER

### 21.9.1 Controlling the Passage from $G_1$ to S-phase by Tumor Suppressor genes

Cyclins, cyclin-dependent kinases (Cdks) and **Rb** proteins are elements of control system that regulate passage through $G_1$ to S restriction point.

Overexpression or loss of the cell cycle control proteins commonly takes place in human cancers.

Expression of cyclin-D in mammals is induced by many extracellular substances, called growth factors or mitogens. These cyclins ($D_1$, $D_2$, $D_3$) assemble with their partners Cdk-4 and Cdk-6 to generate catalytically active kinase ($G_1$ – Cdk).

Stimulation of $G_0$ cells with mitogen induces expression of Cdk-4 and Cdk-6. D-type cyclins and E2F transcription factors (E2Fs), all are encoded by delayed response genes. Interaction of E2Fs with hypophosphorylated Rb protein initially inhibits E2F activity. When signaling from mitogen is sustained, the resulting Cdk-4-Cyclin D and Cdk-6-Cycin D complexes initiate the phorphorylation of **Rb**, converting some E2F to the active form. Active E2F then stimulates its own synthesis and the synthesis of Cdk-2 and Cyclin E. Cdk2-Cyclin E further stimulates Rb phosphorylation increasing more E2F, activity. These processes result in positive feed back loop leading to a rapid rise in both E2F and Cdk-Cyclin E activity as the cell approaches the $G_1 \rightarrow S$ transition.

Withdrawal of mitogen prior to passage through the restriction point leads to accumulation of $\mathbf{P^{27}}$ or $\mathbf{P^{16}}$, which bind to and inhibit Cyclin D- dependent kinase activity thus causing $G_1$-arrest.

**Rb** binds to transcription factor E2F and thereby prevents E2F – mediated transcriptional activation of many genes that produces DNA polymerase. Rb-E2F complex acts as a transcriptional repressor for many of these genes.

1. Overproduction of Cyclin $D_1$ may be caused by chromosome translocation and initiate human cancer, indicating that it can function as an oncoprotein. In certain tumors, *Cyclin $D_1$* gene is translocated to the B cells in such a way that the $D_1$-Cyclin production is enhanced throughout the cell cycle irrespective of extracellular signals. Overexpression of $D_1$ cyclin is common in human breast cancer.
2. Loss of $p^{16}$ function can be achieved by deletion of the *$p^{16}$* gene, that inhibits $D_1$-cyclin activity. Loss of $p^{16}$ would cause overexpression of $D_1$ cyclin, leading to Rb hyperphosphorylation and release E2F transcription factor, causing tumor.
3. Loss of Rb function whether by inherited or by somatic mutation leads to induction of many types of cancers, including childhood retinoblastoma with normal $D_1$-cyclin and $p^{16}$ protein, Rb-protein normally acts as a brake in $G_1$ progression and entry into S-phase. It binds to E2F and transcription factors as well as the proteins required for DNA synthesis. In absence of Rb protein, E2F protein is continuously being active and cell proliferation continues leading to cancer.

### 21.9.2 Abnormal Cell Proliferation Due to Loss of TGF-β Signalling Pathway

Tumor-derived growth factor β (TGF-β) is secreted by most body cells. It inhibits the growth of many types of cells including most epithelial and immune system cells. Loss of TGF-β mediated growth inhibition contributes to the development and progression of varieties of tumors.

TGF-β signals through heteromeric complexes type–I and type II receptors on the cell membrane surface, which are serine/threonine kinases, induce the formation of multimeric receptors. Type–II phosphorylates type–I receptors in the juxtamembrane region. Activated type–I receptors specifically phorphorylate receptor regulated Smads (Smad-3), which then dimerize to Co-Smad complex (Smad-4) in the cytosol. This Smad-3/Smad-3 complex is tranlocated to the nucleus, where it binds to regulatory sequences in combination with specific transcription factors to activate transcription of a variety of genes. Expression of $p^{15}$ causes cells to arrest in $G_1$.

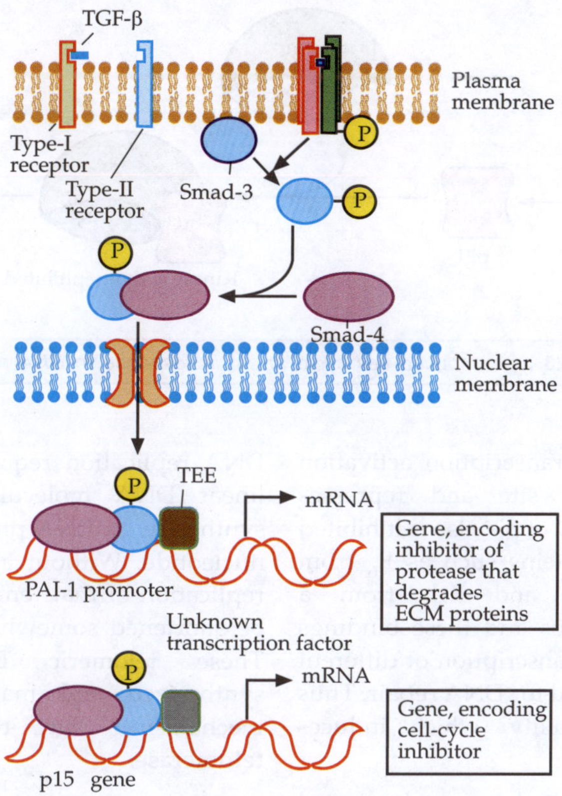


**Fig.21.22 :** *TGFβ signaling pathway.*

Many tumors contain inactivating mutations in either the TGF-β receptors or the Smad proteins, and thus are resistant to growth inhibition by TGF-β. Most of the human pancreatic cancers contain a deletion in the gene encoding Smad-4. Most of the cancers in colon, gastric cancer, T-and B-cell cancer, hepatoma, retinoblastoma are unresponsive to TGF-β growth inhibition probably due to the loss of type-I or type- II receptors (Fig. 21.22).

### 21.9.3 Abolishing $G_1$ Checkpoint Control by Inactivating $P^{53}$.

Mutations in the $p^{53}$ gene occur in more than 50% of human cancers. Normally an unstable $p^{53}$ protein is stabilized by damaged DNA and its concentration increases. It acts as a transcription factors. $p^{53}$ induces $p21^{cip}$ protein, a Cyclin-kinase inhibitor that inhibits all Cdk-1, Cdk 2, Cdk4 and Cdk6-Cyclin complexes. Binding of $p21^{cip}$ to these Cdk- cyclin complexes leads to cell cycle arrest in $G_1$ and $G_2$ (Fig. 21.23).

$p^{53}$ is expressed at a very low levels in normal cells because it is extremely unstable. $p^{53}$ is activated only in stressful situation like γ-irradiation, low oxygen etc. DNA damage stress somehow leads to the activation of certain kinases, that phosphoylates $p^{53}$ and results in its stabilization.

The active $p^{53}$ is a tetramer of four identical subumts. A missence mutation can inactivate $p^{53}$ tetramer and cannot function as a transcription factor and thus oncogenic mutation of $p^{53}$ acts as ***dominant negatives***.

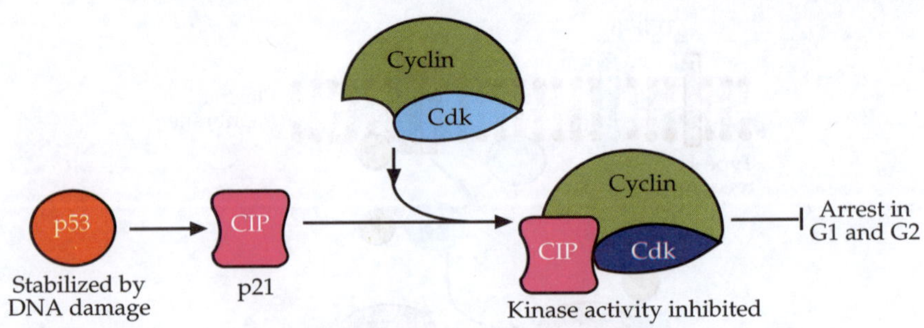


**Fig.21.23 :** *$p^{53}$ induced cell cycle arrest in response to DNA damage.*

MDM2 binds to its transcription activation domain at N-terminal site and represses transcription. The activity of $p^{53}$ also is inhibited by binding of viral proteins such as $E_6$ from human papillomavirus and E1b from a adenovirus or SV40 virus and these bindings lead to inactivation of transcription of different enzymes that are required for DNA repair. Thus causing genome instability, which induces cancer.

The chemical carcinogen **benzopyrine** found in cigarette smoke, undergoes metabolic activation in liver to a potent mutagen that causing mainly G to T transversion mutations. In bronchial epithelial cells it induces inactivation of $p^{53}$ by mutations at codon position 175, 248 and 273. These are the hot spot mutation causing **lung cancer**.

**Aflatoxin**, a fungal protein induces G to T transversion at codon 249 of $p^{53}$ leading to inactivation that causes liver cancer.

Mutation of $p^{53}$ causes failure of DNA mismatch repair replication which causing colorectal and many other types of human cancers (Table 21.8).

### 21.9.4 Mutant Telomerase Induces Cancer

The unique feature of the telomere is that the DNA repeat of G-rich sequence (TTAGGG) having a single stranded 3′-OH overhang which creates a particular biological problem. DNA replication requires a primer, but in a linear DNA molecule it is impossible to synthesize an RNA primer starting at the end nucleotide. Without a special mechanism for replication of that ends, chromosomes would be shortened somewhat in each cell division. These telomeric DNA sequences are synthesized and maintained by a special mechanism that requires the enzyme **telomerase**.

**TABLE 21.8**
**Some hereditary diseases with DNA repair defects**

| *Disease* | *Sensitivity* | *Cancer susceptibility* |
|---|---|---|
| **Ataxia telangiectasia** | γ-irradiation | Lymphoma |
| **Bloom's syndrome** | Mild alkylating agents | Carcinomas, Leukemias and Lymphomas. |
| **Fanconi's anemia** | Cross-linking agents | Leukemia |
| **Hereditary nonpolyposis colorectal cancer** | UV-radiation and chemical mutagens | Colon, ovary cancer |
| **Xeroderma pigmentosum** | UV radiation, chemical mutagens | Skin cancer and melanomas. |

Because most human somatic cells lack telomerase, telomere shortens with each cell cycle. Complete loss of telomeres leads to end-to-end chromosome fusions and cell death.

After many divisions, the telomeres become so short that they cease to function correctly, and the inadequately capped chromosome ends produce an intracellular signal similar to that produced by double-strand breaks.

In the normal cell $p^{53}$ is functional and their cell cycle cheque points remain intact, this triggers an arrest of cell division.

But a rare cell within the cell population that has acquired a mutation in $p^{53}$ gene that it may ignore this signal in its cell cycle checkpoint, and continues to divide. It enters into the breakage– fusion cycle that causes massive chromosomal damage and ultimately death due to genetic-instability. But some of these damaged cells then may survive and by the telomerase activity. It accumulates further additional mutations needed to produce a cancer. In breast and colorectal cancers, gross chromosomal abnormalities appear to occur in early tumor development, before telomerase is reactivated (Fig. 21.24).

## 21.10 ROLE OF CARCINOGENS IN INDUCING CANCER

We cannot avoid mutations absolutely because there are fundamental limitations on the accuracy of replication. In the long enough human life time, accumulation of a set of mutations at least at one of his cell is enough to develop cancer.

The risk factors of the cancer depend upon the genetic constitutions and environmental conditions such as food habits exposure to certain carcinogenic chemicals and radioactive irradiations etc. The environmental factors that induce cancer have been estimated to be 80-90% of the cancers, which are certainly be avoidable or at least postponable.

Most of the carcinogens cause cancer by inducing damage to DNA but some others do not alter cell's DNA sequence, do some other biochemical defects that induce cancer.

The cancer–causing DNA damage — inducing substances include some chemical carcinogens, viruses and various forms of radiations UV light and ionizing radiations such as gamma rays and alpha particles from radioactive substances. The chemical carcinogens cause cancer when these are fed or painted repeatedly on the skin of the experimental animals. These chemicals are mostly of aromatic hydrocarbons, alkylating agents (mustard gas), aromatic amines and nitrosamines. They cause chromosome aberrations, DNA damage and mutation.

Some chemicals usually act directly to DNA, causing mutations. But generally, the relatively inert chemicals become active forms by the metabolic process, possibly by a set of intracellular enzymes known like the cytochrome P-450 oxidises them and become highly mutagenic. For example, aflatoxin B1, a toxin produced by *Aspergillus flavus oryzae* which grows on grains and peanuts, when they are stored under humid tropical condition. It is thought to be a contributory cause of liver cancer in the tropics and is associated with characteristic mutations of the $p^{53}$ gene (Fig.21.25).

Benzopyrine, a cancer causing chemical present in coal tar and tobacco smoke or its related compound dimethyl benza-anthranene (DMBA) also cause cancer by latent genetic damage. A single application of the carcinogen usually does not itself giverise to a tumor but sow a seed of cancer. A further exposure to the same substance or certain other substance may induce cancer.

The carcinogen, which sows the seeds of cancer, is called **tumor initiator.** The substance that accelerates the development of cancer, which was already exposed to tumor initiator substance previously, is known as **tumor promoter**. Tumor promoter is not mutagenic. Immediate effect of tumor promoters is to stimulate cell division. It can induce the growth

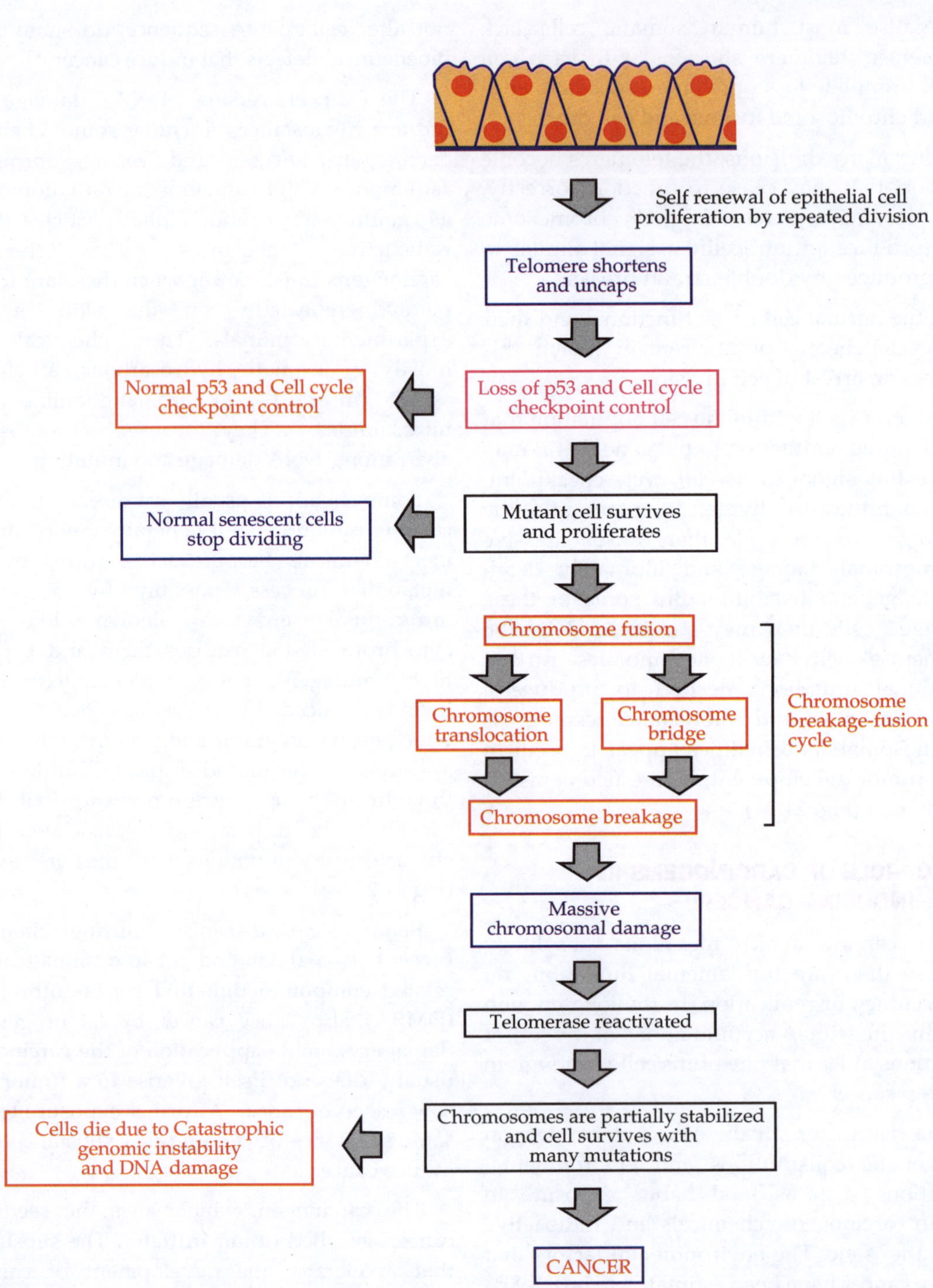


**Fig.21.24 :** *A view of how shortened telomere may lead to chromosomal instability and cancer.*

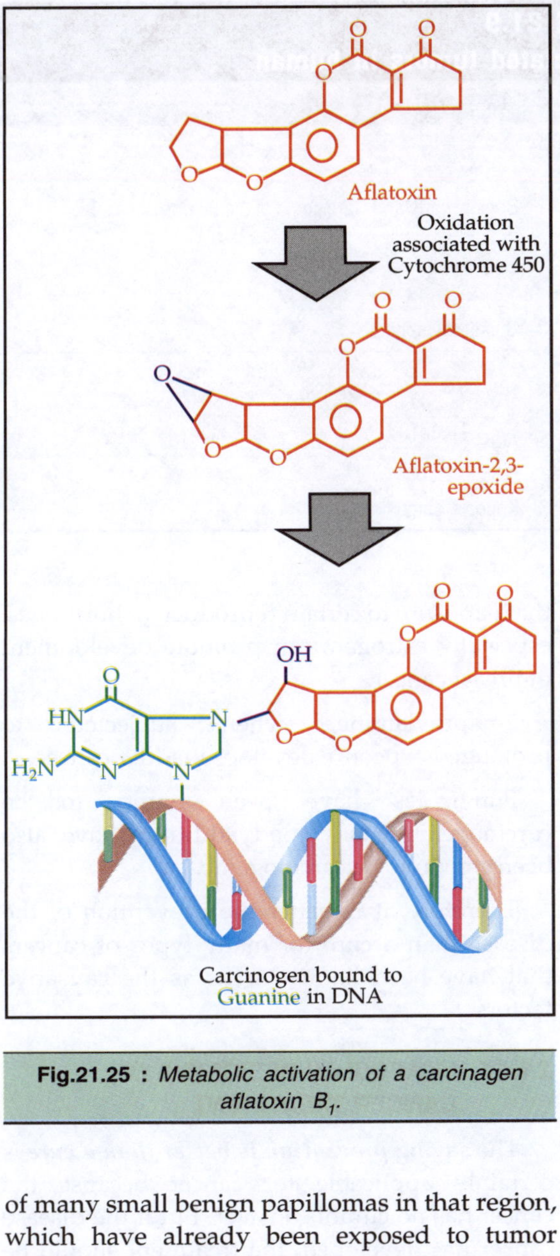


**Fig.21.25 :** *Metabolic activation of a carcinagen aflatoxin $B_1$.*

of many small benign papillomas in that region, which have already been exposed to tumor initiator. The mechanism how tumor promoters work is not certain but probably different tumor promoters work in different ways. One possibility is that it simply induces the expression of growth controlling genes that have already been mutated. The mutation makes a gene product hyperactive.

Another possibility is that the tumor promoters temporarily release the cell from the inhibitory influence of which normally overrides the proliferation inducing effect of the mutation. Thus the cells divide drastically into a large cluster of cells. Therefore the tumor promoters apparently favour the development of cancer by expanding the population of cells that carry an initial mutation.

**Viruses as carcinogens :** About 15% of the human cancer is caused due to viral infection. The main culprits are the DNA viruses and also some RNA viruses which have been shown to cause cancer (Table 21.9).

Like cancer-causing chemicals, viruses can either alter a cell's DNA directly or act as tumor promoters. DNA viruses frequently carry genes that can subvert the control of cell division in the host cell, causing uncontrolled proliferation. Human papilloma virus follows this mechanism to produce warts.

Some viruses, like the hepatitis-B-virus seem to have additional indirect tumor promoting action and favour the development of liver cancer by doing damage which provoke cell division.

The HIV promotes Kaposis' sarcoma by destroying immune system, permitting a secondary infection with a human herpes virus (HHV-B), which has a direct carcinogenic action.

**Other Parasites as Carcinogen :** Chronic infection of a bacterium, ***Helicobacter pylori*** causes ulcers to stomach and induces stomach cancer. The bacterium produces several cytotoxins that destroy the stomach epithelical cells creating painful ulcers. The resulting chronic inflammation promotes cell proliferation leading to stomach cancer.

The flat worm, ***Schistosoma haematobium*** has been found to induce bladder cancer in some parts of the world.

**Risk factors of cancer :** A number of physical and chemical agents have been identified which can cause cancer. These agents are thought to be the main environmental causes of cancer when the human beings are exposed to them.

**TABLE 21.9**
**Some viruses and associated tumors in human**

| *Virus* | *Associated Tumors* |
|---|---|
| 1. ***DNA Viruses*** | |
| (i) ***Papovavirus family*** | |
| Papilloma virus | Benign warts and Carcinoma of the uterine cervix |
| (ii) ***Hepadnavirus family*** | |
| Hepatitis-B virus | Liver cancer |
| (iii) ***Herpesvirus family*** | |
| Epstein-Barr virus | Burkitt's lymphoma |
| 2. ***RNA Viruses*** | |
| (i) **Retrovirus family** | |
| Human T-Cell leukemia virus type-I (HTLV-1) | Adult T- cell leukemia |
| (ii) **Human immunodeficiency virus** (HIV) | Kaposis' sarcoma |

Industrialization, rise in pollution and use of food additives are such environmental hazards that increase the risk of cancer. In USA from 1930 to 1996, the incidence of different types of common cancers like colorectal, stomach, breast (female) and prostrate (males) cancers are almost uniform, while, the incidence of lung cancer is gradually increased after 1960 in both sexes. In males the dramatic rise in lung cancer is mostly due to cigarette smoking, which becomes the common cancer in the twentieth century.

In Africa and Asia, the most potent known carcinogen is aflatoxin-B1, produced by a fungi that naturally contaminates foods such as tropical peanuts.

The risk of cancer in women is influenced by reproductive hormones that secrete at different stages of life. Usually breast cancer is caused by such hormonal activity.

The longer the period of exposure to reproductive hormones up to birth of the first child, the risk of breast cancer is greater. It is thought that the first full-term pregnancy may result in a permanent change in the state of differentiation of the cells of the breast, altering their subsequent responses to hormones. Several other evidences also support the view that exposure to certain reproductive hormones, especially estrogen, can promote development of breast cancer.

2-napthylamine, when subjected to prolonged exposure develops bladder cancer.

Fungicides have been found to be carcinogenic. Many food additives have also been shown to be carcinogenic.

Therefore, it is better the prevention of the disease than a cure for many types of cancers that have been known to us as the causative factors.

## 21.11 MOLECULAR DESIGNING OF CANCER TREATMENT

The saying ***prevention is better than a cure*** is certainly applicable for cancer because the cancer has no curable answer. But if the disease cancer has developed, the treatment should be done as soon as possible. Usually surgical operation is beneficial for benign tumors or the stage before their metastasis, that can cure cancer completely. Sometimes the tumor cells can be removed or destroyed with chemical treatment or irradiations. But these can do harm to the normal cells and if a few cancerous cells remain, they can proliferate and produce a resurgence of the disease and sometimes they

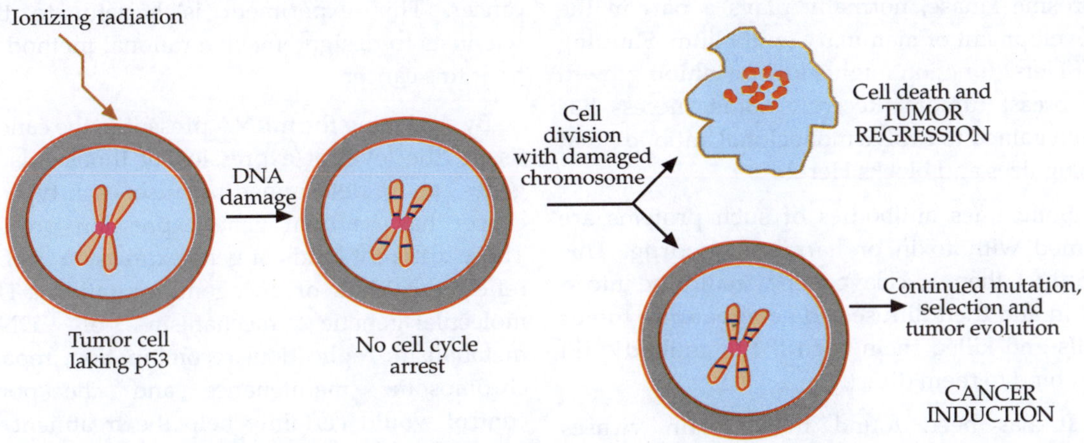


**Fig.21.26 :** *Effect of ionizing radiation on normal cell.*

become resistance against these poisons. In spite of these difficulties many attempts have been made and different chemicals have been used for the treatment of such dreadful disease. But still the cure seems to be beyond our reach. The existing cures can only prolong life or at least relieve distress. Scientists are trying to find out the answer by designing drugs at molecular level of some forms of cancer diseases.

**Irradiation :** Anticancer therapeutic agents mostly used as certain chemicals and ionizing radiations that can cause DNA damage. Cancer cells tend to be more susceptible than normal cells to the damaging effects of ionizing radiation because they lack an ability to arrest the cell cycle. The damage may cause catastrophic chromosome damage and almost all the cells may die after a few days. Thus the tumor can be regressed. Unfortunately, the some genetic defects may render some cancer cells to become resistant to radiation treatment and may lose the ability to arrest cell cycle and continue to multiply immediately after irradiation (Fig. 21.26).

**Resistance to drugs :** The main problem of the chemotherapy of malignant tumor is that the cancer cells have the abnormally high mutability and thus the tumor cell populations have heterogeneous characters in many respects, which may make them difficult to target with a single type of treatment. This mutability sometimes allows many cancers to gain resistance to therapeutic drugs.

Cells that are exposed to one anticancer drug often develop a resistance not only to that drug but also to other drugs to which they have never been exposed. This phenomenon is called **multidrug resistance**. The gene *Mdr-1* codes for a plasma membrane – bound transport ATPase belonging to ABC transporter super family. The overproduction of this protein can prevent the intracellular accumulation of lipophilic drugs by pumping them out of the cell.

**Molecular designing :** A drug, **tamoxifen**, an antagonist to estrogen, has been widely used in patients to prevent or delay recurrence of breast cancer. It blocks the estrogen synthesis. It does not kill the tumor cells but improves the patient's prospects of survival.

Some tumor cells dependent on a particular protein that they overproduce. Molecular designing for blocking the activity of this protein may be an effective mean of cancer treatment, if it is not harmful to normal cells. For example, **Her-2** protein is usually at high level in majority of breast tumors. It is a receptor-tyrosine kinase, normally plays a part in the development of mammary epithelium. Shutting off Her-2 function might slow or inhibit growth of breast tumors. Recently some success has been gained to evolve monoclonal antibody that recognizes and blocks Her-2.

Sometimes antibodies of such proteins are armed with toxin or harmless prodrug. This product then is cleaved enzymatically into a toxin and then diffused to neighbouring tumor cells and killed them even if the antibody did not bind to them directly.

It has been found that certain viruses including the papilloma viruses and adenoviruses encode proteins that bind to and inactivate the host cell's **$p^{53}$**. The virus replicates continuously inside the undefended cells. Now an adenovirus has been constructed that lacks the gene that encodes the **$p^{53}$ blocking protein**. This virus can replicate in the cell in which $p^{53}$ is already inactivated in many types of cancer and kills only the cancer cells that lack $p^{53}$ leaving normal cells unharmed.

Recently a drug has been tried to design, which can block the angiogenesis process in tumor cells because new local signals are required for angiogenesis in tumor cells.

Chronic myelogenous leukemia is associated with chromosomal translocation and two genes, *abl* and *bcr* are fused to create a hybrid gene that codes a chimeric protein consisting of N-terminal fragment of **Bcr** fused with C-terminal portion of **Abl**. **Abl** is a protein tyrosine kinase involved in cell signaling and **Bcr** fragment at N-terminal end makes it hyper active. Thus haemopoietic precursor cells undergo rapid proliferation.

At present a drug has been discovered, which is known as STI-571 that blocks **Bcr-Abl** protein. Now this is renamed as **Gleevec**. It was applied to 54 patients, 53 of them showed excellent response and 51 patients survive for one year (Fig. 21.27).

But after that the cells become resistant to that drug and they die after relapse of the cancer. This experiment is hopeful to the scientists to design effective rational method to treat this cancer.

By analyzing the mRNA present in the cancer tissue, the level of expression of thousands of genes can be determined because; each type of cancer has its own gene expression profile. These different kinds of gene expression profile reflect the ideas of oncogenic mutations. The molecular-genetic mechanism of DNA metabolism, replication, recombination, repair, chromosome maintenance and checkpoint control would certainly help the treatment of cancer in near future. The molecular mechanism of drug designing is the only path to find out the answer of the cancer in future.

**Topoisomerase - targeted anticancer drug**

Cancer cells are rapidly growing and usually contain higher levels of topoisomerases than the normal cells. A number of anticancer drugs are now used where topoisomerases are the targets.

A drugs **camptothecin**, derived from the bark of *Camptotheca acuminate* a Chinese yew tree. This is a poison to topoisomerase I. The drug acts in one of the two ways, either as an inhibitor of at least one step of the calalytic cycle or as poisons *i.e*, the transient broken DNA is trapped as a stable intermediate bound to topoisomerase. Thus the break becomes permanent. Now this chemical is used for the treatment of ovarian and colon cancers. The drug also affects normal fast growing cells such as WBC, lining of gastrointestinal tract, hair follicle etc. Therefore, it causes diarrhoea, fall of hair and loss of immunity against infectious diseases.

Topoisomerase II-targeted drugs are used tremendously for the chemotherapeutic agents on cancer.

## 21.12 CANCER AND EPIGENESIS

$C_pG$ islands are small regions of CG-rich DNA (1-2kb). In human genome, approximately 50000 $C_pG$ islands are observed, 40-50% of them are associated with the *housekeeping genes* (the

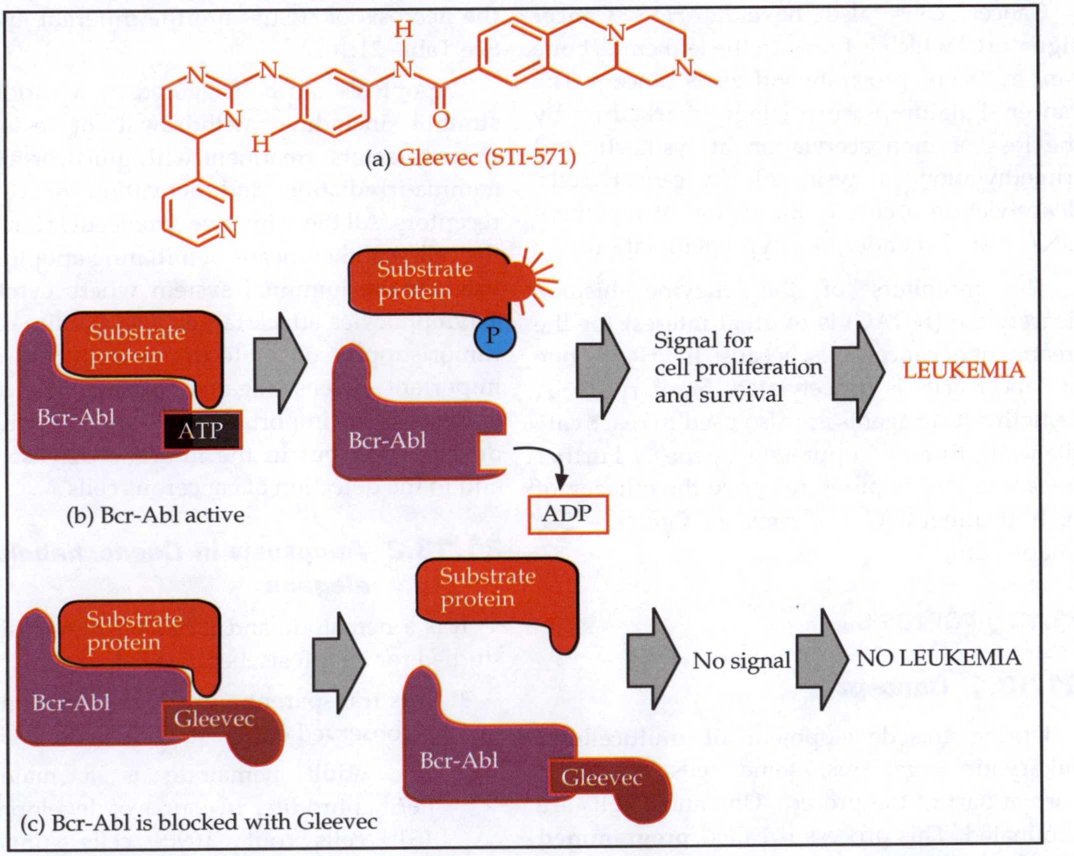


**Fig.21.27 :** *(a) Structure of Gleevec, (b) Activation of Bcr-Abl protein and leukemia (c) Inactivation of Bcr-abl protein and preventation of Chronic Myeloid Leukemia*

genes that code for proteins needed for basic processes in all kinds of cells. This is sensitive to *Hpa II* restriction endonuclease which cuts only unmethylated CCGG. The 5-methyl cytosine is highly susceptible to spontaneous deamination to transform C→T, thus TG dinucleotide is produced. In the mammalian genome $C_pG$ island is protected from spontaneous deamination because they are normally unmethylated.

$C_pG$ hypermethylation and genome-wide hypomethylation are common features of cancer cells.Too little methylation causing activation of near by oncogenes, on the contrary too much methylation of $C_pG$ islands can cause the silencing of tumor suppressor genes.

Genome – wide demethylation *ie*, loss of methylation appears to progress with age, which explains the incidence of cancer among elderly. Loss of methylation has also been linked to poor nutrition.

S-adenosylmethionine, a derivative of folic acid (a vitamin-B) is the primary methyl donor in the cell. Lack of folic acid in the food may cause a cell of organism to become cancer. A diet lacking folic acid has been found to activate a retrotransposon in mice. If the retrotransposons are methylated, they cannot be mobilized. Extensive human epidemiological data have indicated that prenatal and early post natal nutrition influence adult susceptibility to diet – related chronic diseases, including cardiovascular disease, type-2 diabetes, obesity and cancer.

Cancer cells also have a H4 "**Cancer signature**" which is found in the leukemia, bone cancer, cervix, prostrate and testis cancers. The cancer signature is surprizingly marked on by the loss of monoacetylation at lysine-16 and trimethylation at lysine-20. In cancer cells, deacetylation occurs in the region of repetitive DNA that also undergoes hypomethylation.

The inhibitors of the enzyme histone deacetylase (HDAC) is of great interest for the treatment of cancer cells, because the H4 histone of cancer cells is deacetylated. Similary, DNA demethylating agents are also used to reactivate silenced tumor suppressor genes. Further researches are required to prove the efficacy of such treatment (*Gene therapy in Cancer* – See Chapter 26).

## 21.13 APOPTOSIS

### 21.13.1 Concept

During the development of multicellular eukaryotic organisms, some cells die as a normal part of the process. Unwanted cells are eliminated. This process is called **programmed cell death** or **apoptosis**.

In this process unwanted cells are eliminated during embryogenesis, metamorphosis and tissue turnover. It provides a crucial control over the total cell number. Cell death occurs during vertebrate development, the prominent locations are the immune system and nervous system.

Apoptosis involves the activation of a pathway that leads to suicide of the cell by a characteristic process in which the cell becomes more compact, blebbing occurs at the membranes, chromatin becomes condensed and DNA is fragmented. The pathway is an active process that depends on RNA and protein synthesis by the dying cells. It becomes hyper-pycnotic (condensed with small fragmented nucleus) and the fragmentation of DNA. Ultimately the dead cells become fragmented into membrane bound pieces and are engulfed by surrounding cells (Fig. 21.28). Apoptosis and the necrosis of tissues are the different events. See Table 21.10.

Apoptosis can be triggered by a variety of stimulii including withdrawal of essential growth factors, treatment with glucocorticoids, gamma-irradiation and activation of certain receptors. All these involve a molecular insult to the cell. Another means of initiating apoptosis is used in the immunal system where cytotoxic T-lymphocytes attack target cells. Ability of the tumor suppressor $p^{53}$ to trigger apoptosis is an important defense against cancer. Therefore, apoptosis is important not only in tissue development but in the immune defense also and in the detection of cancerous cells.

### 21.13.2 Apoptosis in *Caenorhabditis elegans*

It is a nematode and it has been extensively studied for apoptosis, because,

1. It is transparent and it's cell division can be observed easily.
2. The adult nematode is a male or hermaphrodite. In course of development 131 cells out 1090 cells undergo programmed cell death and the cells die predictably at a defined time and place in each animal.

   The programmed cell death in *C. elegans* can be described and analyzed in four stages (Fig. 21.29).

**Stage-I : Specificity of cell death**

Three genes ***ces1*** and ***ces2*** (*ces* = cell death specificity) and *egl-1* (egg lying) are responsible for the specification of the cell which will die. Dominant mutations in *ces-1* gene prevent death of four neurons in the pharynx. *ces-2* mutant prevents two of these cell death by regulating *ces1* negatively. *egl1* gene causes death of two neurons in males but not in hermaphrodites. These neurons control egg laying but mutation of this gene causes death of these two neurons in hermaphrodites.

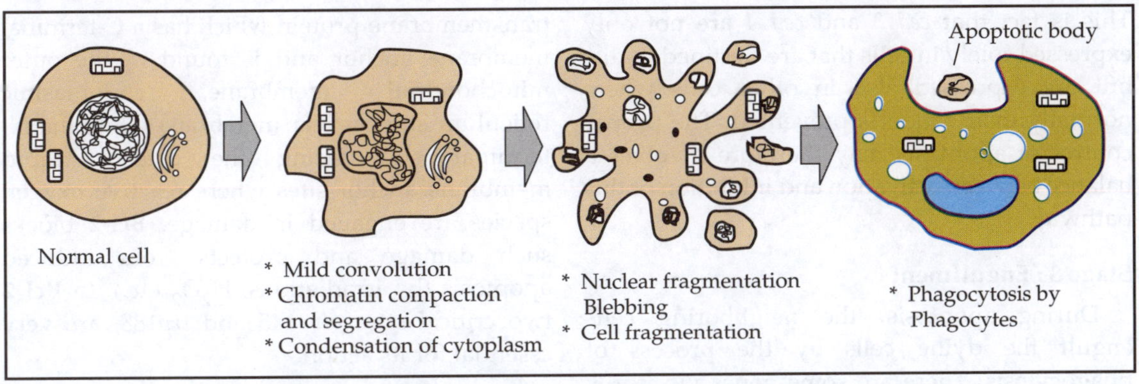


**Fig.21.28 :** *Ultrastructural features of cell death by apoptosis.*

**Stage 2 : Execution of death**

Two genes *ced 3* and *ced 4* (cell death abnormal) are responsible for apoptosis. Mutations in *ced 3* and *ced 4* cause the survival of cells that usually die, demonstrating that these genes are essential for cell death. *ced-3* codes for protease (cysteine protease) activity with phosphorylation site. *ced-4* codes protein with $Ca^{++}$ binding sites. Possibly cell death is mediated by $Ca^{++}$ binding and by the phosphorylation of protein.

*ced-9* is another gene inhibits apoptosis. A mutation causes death of cells that should survive. This process requires *ced 3* and *ced 4*.

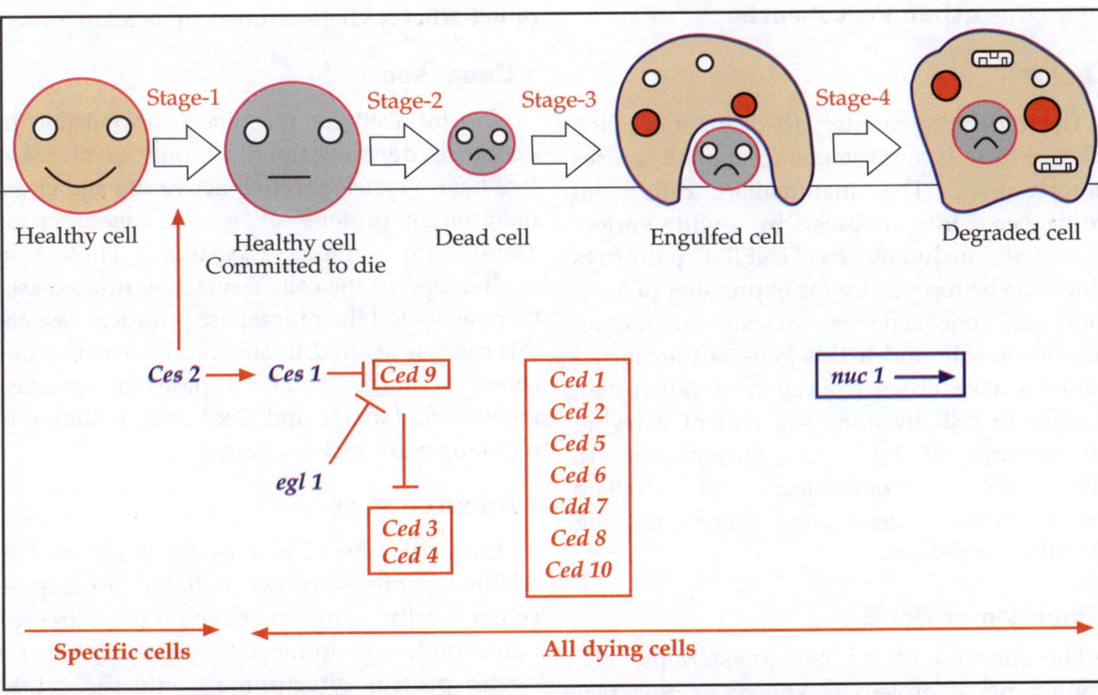


**Fig.21.29 :** *Genetic pathway of apoptosis in* ***C.elegans*** *(After Steller 1995)*

This is fact that *ced 3* and *ced 4* are not only expressed solely in cells that are destined to die, but are expressed also in other cells where normally their action is prevented. The proper control of apoptosis may therefore involves a balance between activation and inhibition of this pathway.

**Stage 3 : Engulfment**

During apoptosis, the neighboring cells engulf the dying cells by the process of phagocytosis. There are some genes viz. *ced 2, ced 5* and *ced* 10 are involved to cause major effects in engulfment, whereas *ced 1, ced 6, ced 7* and *ced 8* are responsible to cause minor effects on engulfment.

**Stage 4 : Degradation**

The engulfed cells are degraded by the action of endonuclease enzyme. The gene *nuc 1* is responsible for the production and regulation of this endonuclease activity.

### 21.13.3 Apoptosis in Mammals and other Vertebrates

#### • *bcl 2*

The vertebrate counterpart of *ced-9* is called *bcl 2*, which is a protooncogene and causes tumorigenesis. The mammalian cells that are triggered into apoptosis by a wide variety of stimuli, including Fas/TNFR-1 pathways which can be rescued by the expression of *bcl 2*. This *bcl-2* oncogene is present on human chromosome 18 and if this gene is transferred to mice leads to absence of cell death rather than increase in cell division. The patient carrying the segment of *bcl 2* of chromosome 18 with the chromosome 14 where immunoglobulin gene locus present causing follicular lymphoma.

#### • Function of Bcl 2

The function of *bcl 2* is mysterious. The product **Bcl 2** protein is known as **Survival factor**. **Bcl 2** family proteins have a single pass transmembrane protein which has a C-terminal membrane anchor and is found in the outer mitochondrial membrane, endoplasmic reticulum and nuclear membrane while the N-terminal end facing the cytosol. Lipid membrane anchor sites where reactive oxygen species are engaged in damage. **Bcl-2** blocks such damage and protects from induced apoptosis (by irradiations, $H_2O_2$ etc.). In **Bcl 2** two critical sites *gly* 145 and *trp*188, are very essential for its action.

#### • Bcl 2 Family

**Bcl 2** belongs to a family whose members can homodimerize and heterodimerize. Two other members are **Bcl-X** characterized in chicken and **Bax** characterized in man. **Bcl-X** is produced in alternatively spliced forms that have different properties. **Bcl-XL** mimics **Bcl 2** and inhibits apoptosis. But **Bcl XS** counteracts the activity of **Bcl-2**.

**Bax** behaves as **Bcl XS**. This suggests that the formation of **Bcl-2** homodimer may be needed to provide the protective form and that **Bcl 2/Bax** or **Bcl-2/Bcl-XS** heterodimers may fail to protect.

#### • Caspases

The intracellular machinery responsible for apoptosis depends upon a family of proteases that have a *cysteine* at their active site and cleave their target proteins at specific *aspertic* acids. These are called **Caspases**. These are synthesized in the cells as inactive **procaspases**. Once activated the procaspase produces caspase, this caspase again activates another caspase by a series of cascades. Finally caspases cause nuclear membrane damage and DNA fragmentation by inducing endonuclease activity.

#### • Adaptor Proteins

The activation of procaspase is initiated by adaptor proteins called initiator procaspase. When cells are damaged or stressed, mitochondria are induced to release the electron carrier protein **cytochrome** c into the cytosol where it binds and activates an adaptor protein called **Apaf-1**.

## Intracellular Pathway

In absence of a trophic factor, **Bad**, a soluble pro-apoptotic protein **Bcl 2** and **Bcl XL**, are inserted into the outer mitochondrial membrane. Binding of **Bad** prevents antiapoptotic proteins from interaction with **Bax**, a membrane bound proapoptotic protein. As a result, ions are influxed through this homodimer **Bax**. It releases cytochrome c from the inner wall of mitochondria to the cytoplasm but the mechanism is not known. Cytochrome c binds with the adaptor protein **Apaf-1**, which promotes **procaspase-9** into active **caspase-9**. This caspase-9 in turn cleaves **procaspase 3** into **Caspase 3**, which causes the cleavage of substrate leading to death (Fig. 21.30).

## Trophic Factor – Mediated Pathways

### Fas receptor

A major pathway that triggers apoptosis in mammalian cells was discovered via the properties of **Fas-receptor**. The two gene loci, one is *gld*, which turns out to lie in the gene that codes the **ligand** for the Fas-receptor and the other is *lpr* which codes **Fas**.

It has been suggested that the apoptotic pathway is triggered by an interaction between the ligand (*gld*-product) and Fas (*lpr* product). The pathway is required for limiting the number of mature lymphocytes. **Fas ligand** binds to the death receptor protein **Fas** on the surface of the target cell. The clustered Fas proteins then recruit intracellular adaptor proteins that bind and aggregate procaspase-8 molecules, which cleave and activate one another and the activated caspase 8 induces apoptosis.

### TNF-receptor

Like Fas, the TNF (tumor necrosis factor) receptor is a cell surface receptor. There is a family of receptors related to TNF and also includes several receptors found on T-lymphocytes and a corresponding family of ligands comprising a series of transmembrane proteins. This suggests that each of these pathways is triggered by a cell-cell interaction, in which the ligand on one cell surface interacts with the receptor on the surface of the other cell.

TNF also exits as cleaved soluble protein, which functions as a soluble growth factor. Through the interactions of TNF (ligand) and one of the TNF-receptors (such as TNF-R1) on the macrophage that trigger the cellular responses like cytotoxicity. The receptor showed the apoptotic response is triggered by an ~ 80 amino acid intracellular domain near the C-terminus. This region is loosely conserved (~28%) between Fas and TNF-R1 and is called **Death Domain** (Fig. 21.31).

Several proteins have been found that interact specifically with the death domain and trigger apoptosis when are transferred into a recipient cells. All of these proteins themselves have death domains and it is possible that a homomeric interaction between two death domains provides the means by which the signal is passed from the receptor to the next component of the pathway.

## ICE Family

**Ced 3** protein of ***C. elegans*** also has homology to the known mammalian protein, the interleukin-1β converting enzyme (ICE), a cysteine protease that cleaves the pro-1L-1β precursor into its active form and the process is inhibited by **Crm A** (an inhibitor of ICE produced by cowpox virus) and also by **Bcl 2**.

There are ~8 mammalian members of the ICE-like family. One is **apopain**. It is possible that more than one protease is involved and are organized into a cascade in which one cleaves another and thereby activates it. The ICE is a caspase. Overexpression of these caspases causes cell death.

## Perforin

Another apoptotic pathway is triggered by cytotoxic T – lymphocytes, which kill target cells by a process that involves the release of granules containing serine proteases and other lytic components. One such component is

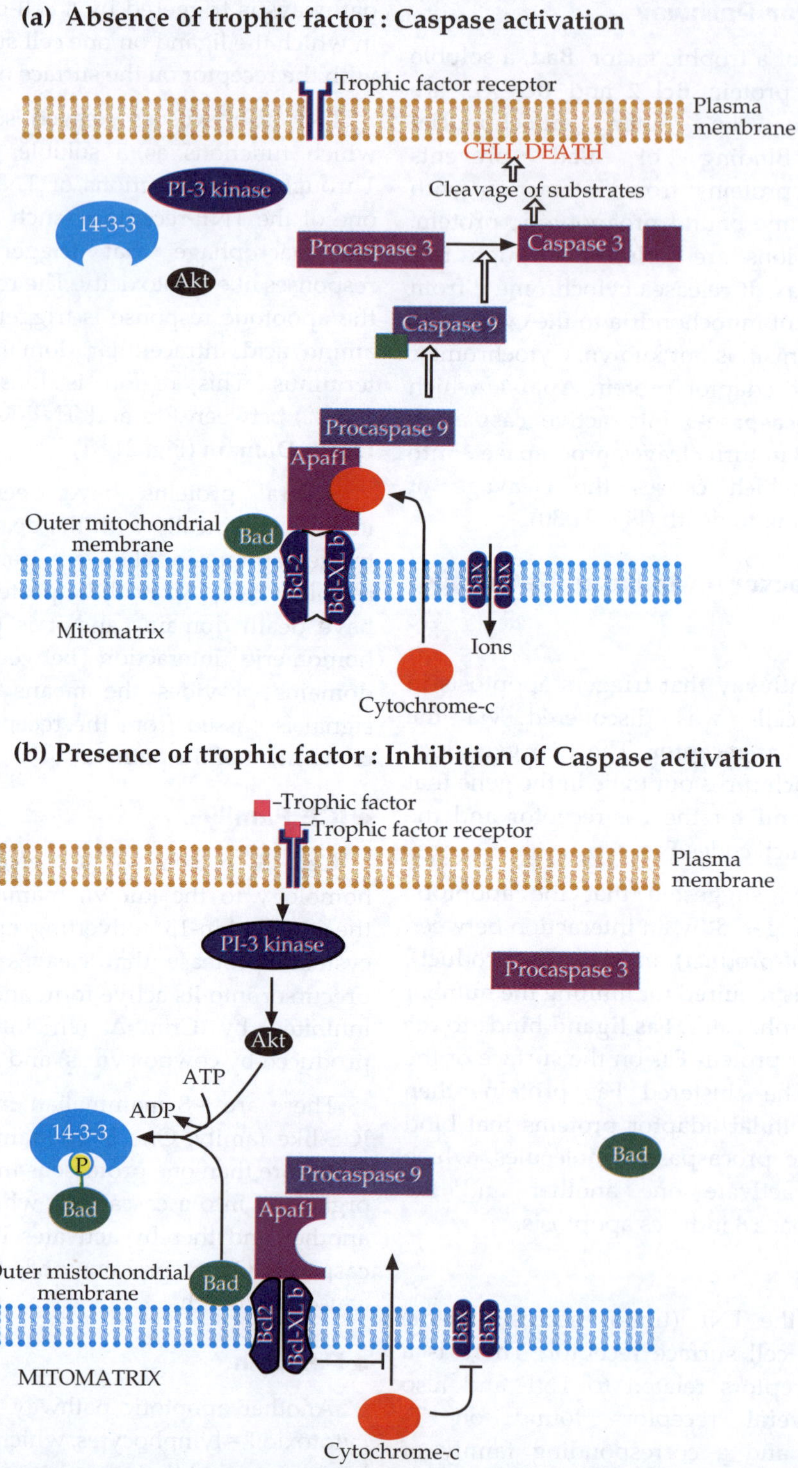


**Fig.21.30 :** *Current models of the intracellular pathways leading to cell death by apoptosis or to trophic factor-mediated cell survival in mammalian cells.*

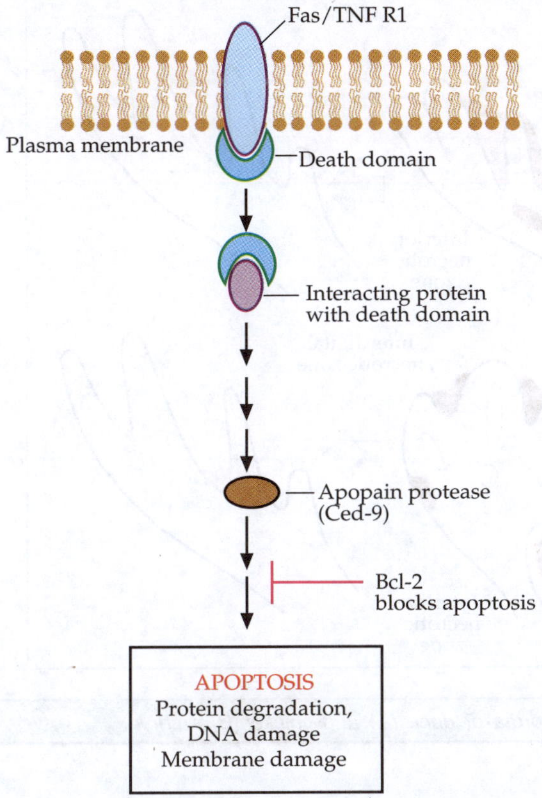


**Fig.21.31 :** *Apoptosis triggered by a receptor with death domain activation.*

**perforin**, which can make holes in the target cell membrane and under some conditions can kill target cells. The serine proteases in the granules are called **granzymes.** In the presence of perforin, granzyme B can induce many of the features of apoptosis, including fragmentation of DNA. It activates ICE-like enzymes called Ich-3, which is necessary for apoptosis in this pathway.

## • Inhibition of Caspase Activation

In some neurons NGF (nerve growth factor) can prevent cell death *in vitro*. Brain-derived neurotrophic factor (BDNF) and neurotrophin-3 (NT3) can also promote the survival of embryonic neurons *in vitro* as well as *in vivo*. Survival factors just like mitogens and growth factors, (NGF) etc. usually bind to the cell surface receptors. Binding of ligand stimulates PI-3, a protein kinase B, which in turn activates a down stream kinase **Akt**. This kinase phosphorylates Bad at sites known to inhibit its pro-apoptotic activity. Bad then forms a complex with **14-3-3 protein.** With Bad sequestered in the cytosol, the anti apoptotic Bcl 2 /Bcl-XL proteins can inhibit the activity of **Bax**, thereby preventing release of cytochrome c and thus the caspase activity is prevented and apoptosis is suppressed (Fig. 21.30).

## 21.13.4 Significance of Apoptosis

Programmed cell death is used to kill unwanted cells during development and homeostasis, for defence and for aging. Usually the cells which have no function, produced in excess, developed improperly, have finished their functions and those are harmful to the body undergo apoptosis. The loss of apoptosis causes the cell improper growth and differentiation that may led to malignant growth, on the contrary excessive or improper apoptosis of the cell may be the cause of different cellular diseases in animals. Therefore, utilizing the mechanism of apoptosis and rational therapeutic measures, certain abnormal cell proliferation can be checked and controlled to prevent mortal diseases in human beings.

## • Apoptosis and the Formation of Digits

Cell death plays an important role in sculpturing the limb. One such case involves the webbing or non- webbing of feet. The difference between chicken's foot and that of a duck is the presence or absence of cell death between the digits. Saunders and Fallon (1966) have shown that after a certain stage, in chick, cells between the digit cartilage are destined to die, and will do so even if transplanted to another region of the embryo or placed into culture, this is called **interdigital necrotic** zone.

The ulna and radius are separated from each other by an interior necrotic zone and the two other regions, the anterior and posterior necrotic

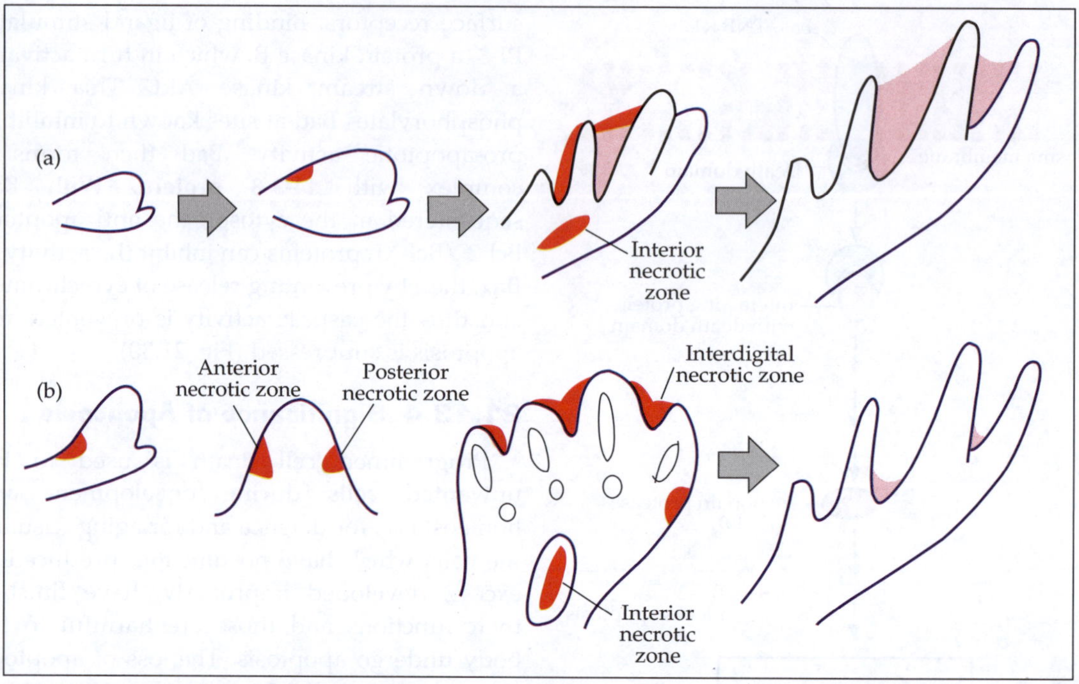


**Fig.21.32 :** *Patterns of Cell death in leg primordia of duck (A) and chicken(B) embryo.*

zones give the further shape to the end of the limbs (Fig. 21.32).

The signal for apoptosis in the autopod is probably provided by the BMP proteins (BMP2, BMP4 and BMP7) are expressed in the interdigital mesenchyme. Blocking of BMP may come from the **Noggin** protein, which is made in the developing digits and in the perichondrial cells surrounding them and its expression inhibits apoptosis.

## Apoptosis and Forming of Joints

In the developing limb, BMP proteins induce the mesenchymal cells either to undergo apoptosis or to become cartilage-producing chondrocytes depending upon the stage of development. Same BMP can induce death and differentiation depending on the age of the target cell. The signal is critical for the formation of joints. Macias *et al* (1997) have shown that during early limb bud stage, BMP2 or BMP7 cause apoptosis. Two days later the same BMPs cause the limb bud cells to form cartilage. In the normal developing limb, BMP 7 promotes cartilage formation, while BMP2 and BMP5 are expressed at the region between the bones, where joints will form. In mice, homozygous for loss of function alleles of **noggin**, no joints form. It appears that the BMP7, in these noggin-defective embryos is able to recruit nearly all the surrounding mesenchymes into the digits (Brunet *et al* 1998). BMP2 and GDF5 proteins either may destroy the mesenchymal cells to form the joint or induce them to rapidly differentiate and join one or other cartilaginous nodule. Thereby a space is made between the nodules and a joint can form.

## Development of Brain and apoptosis

Disruption of normal brain development by blocking apoptosis can be observed. In mice in which *caspase-9* or *Apaf-1* has been knocked out, normal neural apoptosis fails to occur. In caspase-9 deficient mice, the overproliferation of brain neuron is obvious. The enlarged brain protrudes above the face and the limbs are still webbed. It also exhibits thickened ventricle walls and near orbiteration of the ventricles.

There is some evidence that activation of the apoptosis pathway in adult neurons may be responsible for the pathway of Alzheimer's disease and stroke. In these disease fragmentation of DNA is observed in affected areas. This fragmentation into specific sized pieces may be caused due to the digestion of poly ADP ribosepolymerase (PARP) by caspase-3, the PARP is essential for recognition and repair of DNA break.

## Apoptosis and Neuronal Development

It is amazing that during development of central and peripheral nervous system, more than 50% of the neurons die. For instance, in the retina about 80% of the retinal ganglion cells die, while in chick it is 40%. But in the retinas of fishes and amphibians, no retinal ganglion cells appear to die (Patterson 1992).

The survival of any given neuron in the embryo may depend on a combination of agents. Schimidt and Kater (1993) have shown that neurotrophic factor, depolarization and interaction with substrate all combine synergistically to determine neuronal survival. For example, survival of chick ciliary ganglion neurons in culture was promoted by FGF, laminin or depolarization. However FGF did not promote survival when laminin was absent. The neurotrophic factors and environmental agents appear to function by suppressing an apoptotic programme. Deprived growth factors initiate programmed cell death in the vertebrane neurons. Numerous pharmaceutical companies now trying with some therapeutic agents for treatment such as NGF for Parkinson's disease (GDNF), Alzheimer disease (NGF, GDNF), peripheral neuropathies (NGF and NF3) and amyotrophic lateral sclerosis (BDNA, CNTF) etc.

## Amphibian Metamorphosis and Apoptosis

In certain forms of amphibians, metamorphosis is greatly associated with the changes that prepare an aquatic organism for a primary terrestrial existence. The retrogressive changes include the loss of the tadpole's horny teeth and internal gills as well as the destruction of the tail. The anuran nervous system undergoes enormous restructuring during metamorphosis. Some neurons die and other change their specificity. The regression of tail is brought about by apoptosis and it occurs in four stages. Firstly, decrease in protein synthesis in the tail muscle cells. Secondly, by increasing concentration of different lysosomal enzymes. Thirdly, release of these enzymes, which cause cell death and finally, by the activity of macrophases the debris are digested by them. If tail tip is transplanted to tip of the trunk to the region of eye cup or if eye cup is transplanted to tail region, the eye cup is totally protected from apoptosis.

## Alcohol and Apoptosis

Ethanol is the most devastating teratogen in the society. A syndrome, called ***fetal alcohol syndrome***, of birth defects in children has been noticed in alcoholic mothers. Babies are characterized by having small head size, an indistinct philtrum (the ridges that run between the nose and the mouth above the center of the upper lip), a narrow upper lip, smaller brain etc. There is also prominent extra cell death in the front to nasal process and in cranial nerve ganglia. One of the mechanisms of this teratogenic effect of alcohol is that, it induces apoptosis of neurons, possibly by generating superoxide radicals that can oxidize cell membranes and lead to cytolysis (Davis *et al* 1990, Kotch *et al* 1995). Another pathway to apoptosis involves the activation of GABA receptors and simultaneous inhibition of glutamate receptors (Ikonomidou *et al* 2000). Ethanol induced apoptosis can delete millions of neurons from the developing fore brain and cranial nerve ganglia and fronto-nasal process.

## Metamorphosis of Moths and Apoptosis

The process of apoptosis takes place during metamorphosis of *Manducta sexta* (Tobacco hornworm) and in *Antheraea polyphemus* (giant silk moth). During their transition period from caterpillar to pupa, most larval muscles die except intersegmental muscles $A_3$ to $A_6$. The adult then undergoes ecdysis, shedding of unwanted pupal cuticle with the help of these intersegmental muscles, which die only after adult ecdysis is complete. Some neurons that control these muscles also die. The timing of cell deaths is controlled by ecdysone hormone and during apoptosis polyubiquitnation takes place.

## Apoptosis of Thymocytes and Mature T-cells

Immature T-cells are known as thymocytes, which are developed in the thymus and have enormous diversity of T-cell receptors. The 95% of thymocyte population dies before they leave thymus. Because most of the thymocytes that die, are those that express inappropriate T-cell receptors, so that it can react with cells own associated MHC glycoproteins and can avoid autoimmune reaction. Glucocorticoids induce apoptosis, whereas, interleukin-1 and –2 inhibit.

Mature peripheral T-cells, if become autoreactive or autoimmune undergo apoptosis, due to antigens that were not presented to them. Besides, they also die during battle with pathogens. The receptors like Fas, APO-1 and CD95 have recently been demonstrated that activate apoptosis of mature T-cells.

## Apoptosis and Regression of Prostrate Gland

In male rats, the size of the prostrate gland is maintained by the cell death and cell division. Most of the cells of prostrate gland, about 85% of cells, die just after two weeks of birth. This is possibly due to expression of *TRPM-2* gene encoding a protein **clusterin**.

## Apoptosis and Cancer

The $p^{53}$ gene is the most important gene in human cancer. About 50% of the human cancer has been found to be due to the mutation of this gene. It is involved in triple functions, viz. in cell cycle control, in apoptosis and in maintenance of genetic instability. Thus it protects from the production of a tumor.

$p^{53}$ is a tumor suppressor gene and acts to limit the severity of the damage by inducing to commit suicide the mutant cells by apoptosis, which is relatively harmless event for the multicellular organisms. Therefore apoptosis generally reduces or eliminates the occurrence of cancer in the human body.

## Pharmacological Significance

It has been recently shown that **Bcl-2** proteins and **NGFs** are actually survival factors. These survival factors can be used for overcoming unwanted apoptosis. Interleukin–1β converting enzyme (ICE), the poxvirus gene product **(Crm-A)** are also used to inhibit unwanted apoptosis. Following this mechanism treatment in neuro ectodermal cells, fibroblasts etc. can be done to prevent apoptosis.

A mutation in CD95 sometimes cause autoimmune disease, lymphoproliferative syndrome. The mutant activity can be caused by inducing apoptosis of these cells by TNF and CD95 (a cytokine).

Reduced activity of tumor suppressor genes may cause cancer, usually the persons who have a defective $\mathbf{p^{53}}$ gene. In such tumors if $\mathbf{p^{53}}$ gene is introduced can stop the growth of the tumor by inducing their apoptosis. This method is most likely may be the future drug designing against cancer.

## Apoptosis and Evolutionary Significance

During the development of digits in ducks, it has been found that there are fewer interdigital cell deaths and so there is webbing between their toes. In chickens, there is extensive cell death so that the webbing is absent.

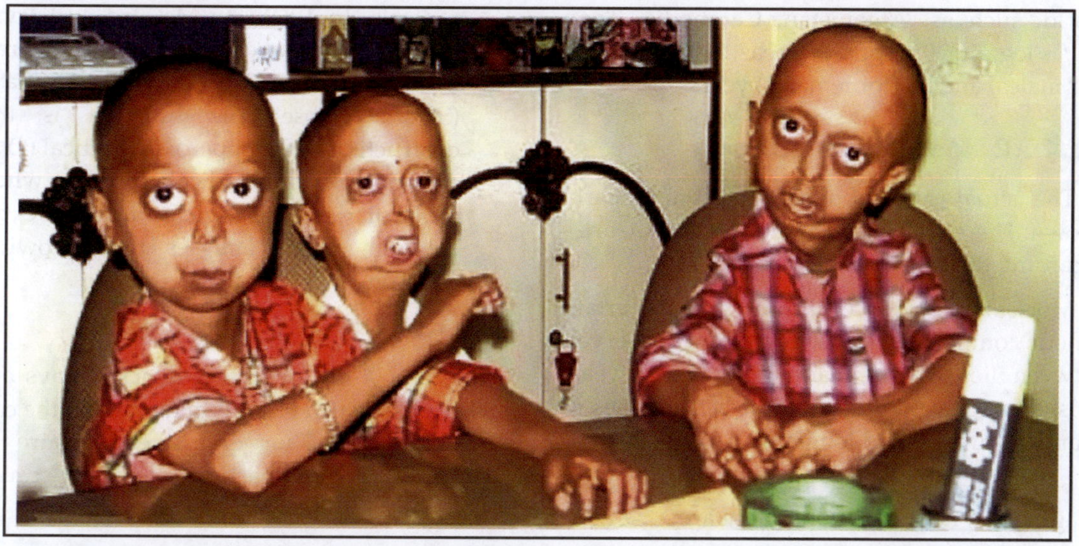

Fig.21.33 : *Three progeria patients (Ali, Ecramul and Rehana)*

In *C. elegans,* sexual dimorphism is evolved due to cell death. HSN neurons control egg laying in hermaphrodites, but die in males in which these neurons are unnecessary. Similar CEM neurons die in hermaphrodites to develop into males. In mammals and also in moth sexual dimorphism arises due to a cell death. Thus it may be stated that, the cells that die before performing any function are evolutionary vestiges of cells that functioned in an ancestral species.

## 21.14 AGING AND SENESCENCE

### 21.14.1 Concept

The general rule of the living beings is that, the organisms will born, attain maturity, become older at a certains age and ultimately die.

Aging is the time-related deterioration of the physiological functions necessary for survival and reproduction. The phenotypic changes of senescence affect all members of the species.

The phenotypic changes of senescence that are characteristic in human being include graying of hairs, sagging and wrinkling of skin, joint stiffness, osteoporosis, muscular lengthening, memory loss, eye sight deterioration and the slowing of sexual irresponsiveness. It has been observed that in humans, **Hutchinson–Gilform Progeria syndrome** causes children to age rapidly and usually die within 12 years in heart attack. The child would have a phenotype similar to that of an old aged person such as hairloss, skin with age spots, transparency of skin, fat distribution, arteriosclerosis and osteoporosis.

There are 48 Progeria patients in the world, three of them are lived in India (Taratala, Kolkata) in a family. They are Rehana (19 yrs.), Ecramul (17 yrs.) and Ali (6 yrs.) (Fig. 21.33)

The maximum life span of the animal is characteristic of a given species. For example, maximum human life-span is estimated to be 121 years (Arking 1998), tortoise to be 150 years, a laboratory mouse is 4.5 years and *Drosophila* survives a maximum of 3 months. Life expectancy is the time of which approximately 50% of the members of a given population is still alive. The life expectancy is not only the characteristic of species but of populations. For example, life expectancy in some areas of the world, such as, Afganistan, Cambodia, Togo etc., is less-tan 40 years, whereas, in USA it is 71 (for males) and 78 (for females) years.

### 21.14.2 Mechanism of Aging

The actual cause of aging is still not clearly known. There are several evidences and theories regarding the cause of aging.

Molecular evidence indicates that certain genetic components of longevity are conserved between flies, worms, mammals and even yeast cells, all appear to use the same set of genes to promote survival and longevity.

Four sets of genes are known to be involved in aging and its prevention. These are

1) DNA repair enzymes
2) Proteins of the insulin signalling pathway.
3) Protein in the mTOR signalling pathway, a cascade that regulates translation.
4) Chromatin remodelling pathway.

#### A . DNA REPAIR ENZYMES

Premature aging syndrome (Progeria) in human and mice appears to be caused by mutations that prevent functioning of DNA repair enzymes. Number of point mutations increases with age and efficiency of the enzymes encoded by our genes decreases. The cells may make greater number of faulty proteins.

a) **Oxidative damage due to cellular metabolism:** Aging may be caused by the accumutation of some by-products of normal cellular metabolism. Reactive oxygen species (ROS) are such substances that are produced by insufficient reduction of substances. These are super-oxide ions, hydroxyl radicals and hydrogen peroxides which are called free radicals. These substances can oxidise the cell membranes, proteins and even nucleic acids.

In 1956 Denham Harman of University of Nebrasca proposed that aging results from tissue damage caused by free radicals. In 1969, Joe McCord and Irvin Fridovich of Duke University discovered the enzyme, **superoxide dismutase** (SOD), whose sole function is the destruction of the superoxide radical ($O_2^-$), a type of free radical formed when molecular oxygen picks up an extra electron. SOD catalyses the following reaction.

$$O_2^-\bullet + O_2^-\bullet + 2H^- \rightarrow H_2O_2 + O_2$$

When X-ray or any radioactive rays are exposed such $H_2O_2$ is generated in the cell cytoplasm. Thus excessive exposure to X-ray or radioactive radiation cause aging.

$H_2O_2$ is highly reactive oxidizing agent. If it is not rapidly destroyed, $H_2O_2$ can break down to hydroxy radicals that attacks cell's macromolecules. $H_2O_2$ is normally destroyed in the cell by the enzyme catalase or glutathione peroxidase.

The superoxides which are formed during oxidative metabolism are destroyed by three different isoforms of SOD, a cytosolic, mitochondrial and extracellular isoform. It is estimated that as much as 1–2% of the oxygen taken into human mitochondria can be converted to $H_2O_2$ rather than to water, the normal end product of respiration. The bacteria and heart that lack the enzyme, these cells are unable to grow in the presence of oxygen. Similarly, mice that are lacking the mitochondrial version of the enzyme (SOD2) are not able to survive more than a weak or so after birth. Conversely, fruit flies genetically engineered to produce large quantities of SOD can live more than 40% longer than untreated control.

Harman proposed that, the better destruction of free radicals would expect the longer life span and they are better able to repair the cellular damage that results from free radical reactions. In an experiment, it has been found that mouse fibroblast cells grown under reduced oxygen condition suffered about one-third as much DNA damage and underwent many more cell divisions before they stopped dividing than the same cells grown at normal oxygen levels. Mouse fibroblasts cultured is 20% $O_2$ suffered three times as much as oxidative DNA damage as human fibroblasts cultured under the same conditions.

Life span of mammals can be increased by severely restricting the calories present in the diet. As first shown in the 1930's, the mice that are maintained on very strict diets typically live 30–40% longer than their life times who are fed diets of normal caloric content. The animals fed calorie-restricted diets exhibit a marked decrease in $O_2^{-}\bullet$ and $H_2O_2$ prouduction, which can explain their longevity. The calorie-restricted diet maintains low blood glucose and triglyceride levels, suggesting that they will be less prone to age related disorders such as diabetes and coronary artery disease.

Lowered blood insulin level may be particularly important in promoting longevity as studied on nematodes and fruit fies suggert that reducing the activity of insulin like hormones can dramatically increases life span in these invertebrates.

In has been found in *Drosophila* that overexpression of the exzyme *catalase* (which degrades peroxides) and *superoxidase-dismutase* cause 30–40% longer life span (Orr and Sohal 1994, Parkes *et. al* 1998).

Lin *et. al* (1998) found that, the fruit flies, mutant *methuselah* gene, which enables them resistant against **Paraquat,** a poison that works by generating ROS within the cell.

Increased synthesis of ROS-degrading enzymes in *C.elegans* makes them more longer life span (Larsen 1993, Vanfleteren and De Vreese, 1996).

Mutations in mice, that cause the loss of certain ROS-degrading enzymes do not cause premature aging (Ho *et. at.1997*, and Melov *et. at.*1998). Normally, mice develop **p66$^{\mathbf{she}}$** protein. Lack of this protein causes cellular resistance to ROS. The p66$^{She}$ proteins through transduction pathway leads to apoptosis upon $O_2$-stress and affects on the life span of mammals.

Vitamin E and C are both ROS-inhibitors. In the invertebrates, particularly in *C. elegans* and flies, vitamin-E with food increases longevity.

b) **Genetic instability:** The rate of DNA damage or mutation enhances aging, because mutation causes synthesis of faulty proteins and enzymes for DNA synthesizing mechanaries. Murray and Holliday (1981) have documented such faulty DNA polymerase in a senescent cell.

DNA repair mechanism is essential for the stability of genome. Tu *et. al* (1996), defected in DNA repair enzymes that can induce premature aging syndromes in humans.

The rate of mitochondrial genome mutation is about 10–20 times faster than the nuclear DNA damage (Johnson *et. at* 1999). Mitochondrial DNA mutation may cause faulty electron transport and production of ROS and also defects in energy production, which led to the process of cell death. Michikawa *et. al* (1999) showed some specific regions for age-related mutations in the mito-genome. This mutated genome replicates in higher rate, thus these mutant genomes become dominated over the normal genome.

c) **Shortening of telomere and p53 :** At the region of the telomeres of the chromosomes, there are a variable number of telemeric repeats. During replication of the DNA, the telomeric ends where 3′ -OH end of a single stranded polynucleotide is overhanged, would not be replicated. As a result, at each time of somatic cell division, it loses 50–100 nucleotides from each of its telomere. This is because, human somatic cells have turned off or fail to produce the enzyme telomerase which is required for the replication of telomeric ends. Therefore, after certain generations, the descerndent cells will inherit defective chromosome and ultimately the shortening of the chromosome becomes maximum and then it will stop division. This process is called **replicative cell senescence.**Normal human fibroblasts typically divide 25-40 tim in the cell culture before they stop. When telomerase in provided to the fibroblasts by inserting an active, telomerase gene, telomere length would then be maintained and the cells would continue to proleferate indefinitely. It has been proposed that this type of control on cell proliferation is important for the maintenance of tissue architechture and aging of animals including the human beings. This has been tested by producing transgenic mice that lack telomerase. Unlike human cells, most rodent cells do not turnoff telomere and therefore their telomerases do not shorten with each cell division.

Cristofalo *et. al* (1998) have got no correlation between telomere length and life span of the animal and also between human telomere length and person's age. Telomerase-deficient mice do not show profound aging defects (Rudolph *et. al* 1999).

p53 is a transcription factor. This is normally inactive in the normal cells. UV radiation or oxidative stress and other factors that cause DNA damage activate p53. The induction of apoptosis or senescence by p53 can be beneficial (for destroying cancer cells) or deleterious (destroying neurons or stem cells). Damaged telomerase activates p53. If repair does not occur, DNA replication halts and apoptosis is initiated. This will reduce the number of stem cells which causes aged phenotype. Shortening of telomere causing degenerative diseases, such as muscular dystrophy ( Sacco et. al.,2010 and Atzmon et. al., 2010). Overexpression of telomerase (which acts as an anti-senescence complex ) in the senescent cells extends longevity without increasing cancer.

## B. INSULIN-SIGNALING PATHWAY

In *Caenorhabditis elegans* , when food is insufficient and overcrowded, it becomes a diapause stage, called **dauer** larva, where aging is suspended. DNA and proteins are resistant to ROS. The insulin signalling pathway controls this pathway. In *C. elegans* the insulin receptor homologue is DAF-2, which is activated during favourable condition.

Down-regulation of insulin-signalling pathway causing longevity by following means:

1) It appears to influence metabolism, decreasing mitochondrial electron transport chain.
2) When DAF-2-receptor is not active, cells increase the production of enzymes that prevent oxidative damages as well as DNA damage enzymes.
3) Lack of insulin signalling decreases fertility. This increase in DNA synthesis enzymes and enzymes that protect against ROS is due to the Foxo/DAF-16 transcription factors
4) This forkhead-type transcription factor is inhibited by insulin receptor (DAF-2) signal.
5) When the signal is absent, Foxo/DAF-16 can function and promote longevity, probably by the expression of genes involved in producing anti-stress proteins

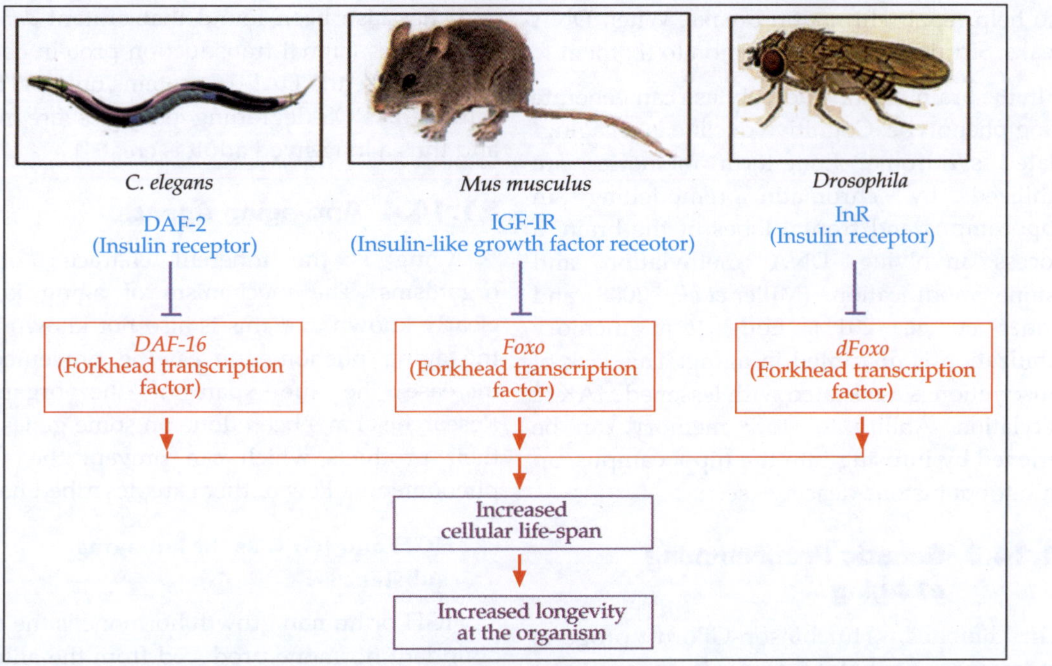


**Fig.21.34 :** Probable pathway for regulating longevity of *C. elegans*, *Mus musculus* and *Drosophila*

as well as lipid signals in the cells that help extended life to those cells nearby (Zhang et. al. 2013) (Fig. 21.34).

In mammals, IGF-pathways are integrated with embryonic development and adult metabolism. Low levels of IGF-1 or loss of function mutation of IGF pathway increases longevity.

In *Drosophila*, mutants of insulin-receptor genes of insulin signalling pathway are sterile. The insulin receptor (InR) is thought to regulate a Forkhead transcription factor, dFoxo (similar to Foxo/ DAF-16 of *C. elegans).* When the *Drosophila dFoxo* gene is activated in fat body, it can increase life span of the fly.

Calorie-restriction is another way of down-regulating the insulin pathway, which may reduce IGF-1 (ligand of IGF-1R) and of circulating insulin. The mechanism is unknown but it does appear to retard age-associated decline of heart beat variability, motor coordination etc.

## C. mTOR PATHWAY

Insulin signalling pathway depresses *Foxo* and at the same time activates mTORC1 , a protein kinase complex) promotes transcription in response to nutrients and hormones. Dietary restriction reduces mTORC1 activity. This reduced level of mTORC1 causes life longer, better protective against age-related cognitive dysfunction and more functional stem cell (Lamming et. al., 2012, Johnson et. al. 2013, Halloran et. al.2012, Majumder et. al. 2012, Yilmaz et. al., 2012).

mTORC1 also increases autophagy, the removal and replacement of damaged organelles and senescent cells (Baker et.al. , 2011).

## D. CHROMATIN MODIFICATION

The *sirtuin* gene encodes histone deacetylation (chromatin-silencing ) enzyme, which prevents many genes from being expressed at the wrong times and places and also help repair chromatin breaks. When DNA breaks, Sirtuin protein is called on to fix them.

In the brain, histone deacetylase can generate aging phenotype. Cognitive decline is an aging-related syndrome. Long-term memories are stabilized by chromatin remodelling in hippocampus and frontal lobes of the brain, a process involving DNA methylation and histone modification (Miller *et.al.*, 2008 and Penner et. al., 2011). Long term memory stabilization is disrupted in aging. This lack of transcription is associated with lessened HAK12 acetylation. Ability to store memory can be retrieved by infusing into the hippocampus, an inhibitor of histone deacetylase.

### 21.14.3 Genetic Programming of Aging

In humans, Hutchinson-Gilord progeria syndrome, a premature aging is caused by a **dominant mutant gene**. A similar syndrome is caused by mutations of the *klotho* gene in mice (Kuro *et. al* 1997) possibly to be involved in suppressing the aging phenotype . The gene product is extremely important in determining the timing of senescence.

Johnson *et. at* (1999) have proposed the presence of DAF-2 signal transduction pathway that affects aging in *C. elegans*.

If **DAF-16** protein becomes functional, inhibits normal metamorphosis of the larva to become adult nematode.

In favourable condition, wild type nematodes make a ligand (insulin-like protein) that activates signal transduction pathway that inhibits the DAF-16 protein function and allows the larva to metamorphase into a short lived wild type adult (Fig. 21.35).

If the wild-type larva is starved, the ligand is being absent, DAF-16 protein becomes functional and creates a long-lived metabolically dormant **dauer** larva by repressing the pathway to adult development by increasing the ROS-degrading enzymes.

It has also been found that mutant *daf-1* or *age-1* genes (signal transduction protein coding genes) cause the DAF-16 proteins only partially inhibited. ROS-degrading enzymes are made and thus a long-lived adult is created.

### 21.14.4 Anti-aging Agents

Aging is the inherent character of all organisms. The mechanism of aging is not clearly known and this is also not known how the aging phenomenon can be prevented to increase the life span of the organism. Researches have been done on some genes and their products which can prevent the aging phenomenon. Few of them are described here.

#### (A) HGH and IGF-1 as the antiaging substances :

HGH or human growth hormone is the most abundant hormone produced from the anterior pituitary gland and released into the blood stream, mostly during deep sleep. The concentration of HGH is maximum upto the age of 20 years but it drastically decreased upto the age of 30 years and then gradually decreased upto 80 years when the concentration becomes near about zero.

Within a few minutes it is converted to a growth factor in the liver. The most important of these growth factors is called insulin-like growth factor-1 (IGF-1) which is also known as somatomedin C. The potency of IGF-1 is ten times more than HGH. Researchers are excited about IGF-1 because of its antiaging properties and a vast potential to heal and improve the body by different ways.

1. The blue print of aging is in the DNA under the hood of the telomere. The end of every chromosome is shortened with each cell division. To reverse aging at the cellular level, the substance is needed which can restore telomere length and the old cells back into young ones. HGH and IGF-1 can restore the telomere and help keep the cells in as healthy a state as possible.

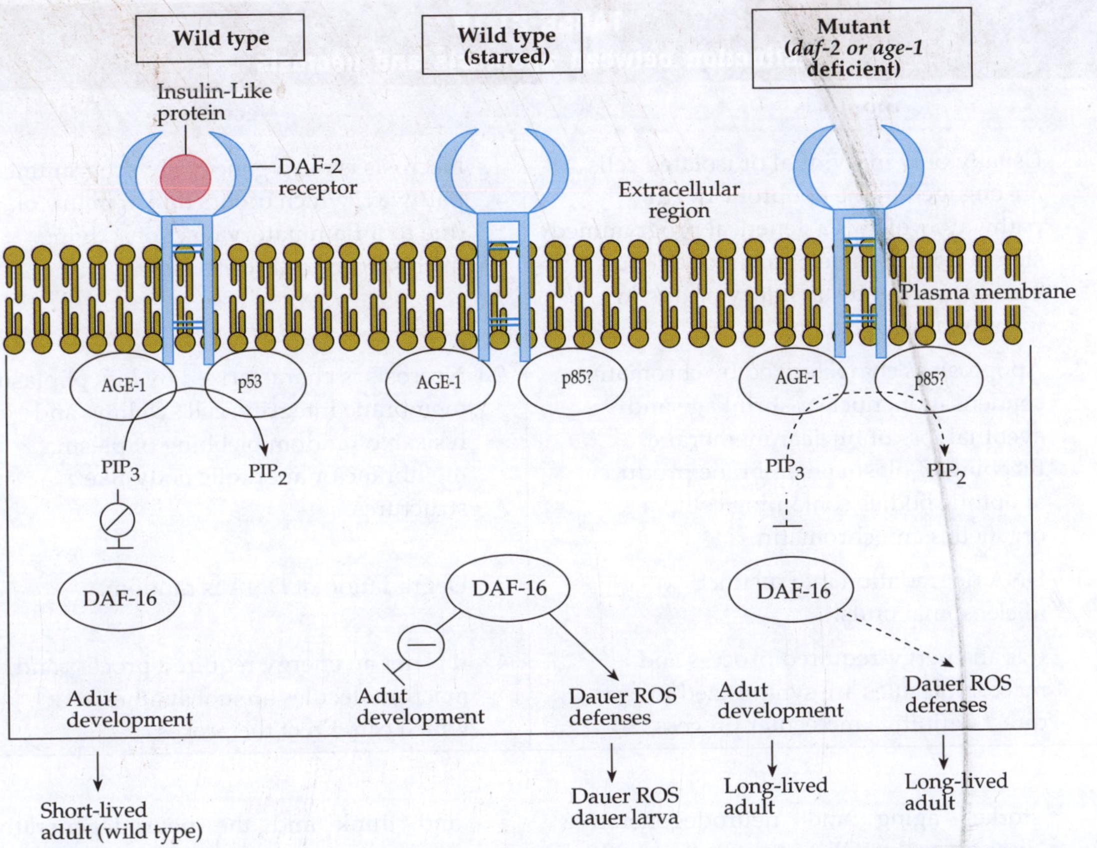


**Fig.21.35 :** *Proposed mechanism for extending the life span of C. elegans through dauer larva pathway.*

2. The genetic material *ie* DNA in the nucleus is under constant attack from oxygen free-radicals, UV-light, heat of the body and other damaging factors. The DNA damage is repaired by the cell's DNA repair system. If the repair system fails affects the cells to age At present supplements of antioxidants such as vitamin C and E can limit the damage of DNA. It has been shown that HGH and IGF-1 can do what antioxidants cannot. HGH and IGF-1 act like carriers to bring the cell the raw materials for renovation and repair. IGF-1 launches the delivery of the nucleic acids right to the nucleus where DNA resides where these are used to repair damage to the DNA. HGH initiates the transport of amino acids into the cell for protein synthesis. Thus these two hormones minimize DNA damage and help heal the cell.

3. By taking IGF-1 directly, one can bypass the pituitary gland which may be "burnt out" with aging and the liver does not have to convert the HGH into IGF-1.

4. HGH reversed the shrinking of the thymus. The experiments were done on cells in culture (Kelth Kelly) where only IGF-1 works not the HGH. But both IGF-1 and HGH work in the living cell. Thus IGF-1 appears to be more potent than HGH in its antiaging action.

5. HGH and IGF-1 may be used to prevent and treat the effects of brain aging. It has momentous implications for brain injury,

**TABLE 21.10**
**Distinction between apoptosis and necrosis**

| Apoptosis | Necrosis |
|---|---|
| 1. Usually only individual or isolated cells are engaged in the apoptotic death pathway, which is a genetical programmed step in normal development of a tissue. This occurs not by an injury or due to inflammatory reactions. | 1. Necrosis is not a genetically programmed pathway, which occurs due to injury or due to inflammatory reactions, dying in clusters of cells or tissues. |
| 2. Apoptosis is characterized by chromatin condensation, nuclear shrinkage and eventual loss of nuclear membrane. Blebbing of plasma membrane produces apoptotic bodies containing cellular organelles and chromatin. | 2. Necrosis is characterized by loss of plasma membrane integrity, cell swelling and lysis. No random blebbing of plasma membrane or apoptotic body-like structures. |
| 3. DNA degradation into distinct nucleosomal units. | 3. Degradation of DNA is random. |
| 4. It is an energy-required process and macromolecules are synthesized to direct definitive molecular process. | 4. It is not an energy required process and macromolecules are not synthesized which can direct the process. |

storke, aging and neurodegenerative diseases as the IGF-1 can stop the death of the brain cells. Barbara Johnston *et al* found that injections of IGF-1 given 2 hrs. after brain injury in fetal lambs rescued the damaged neurons and salvaged cells that would otherwise have died during apoptosis. The treatment was effective in stopping the cell death throughout the brain including the hippocampus, cortex and the areas associated with thinking and memory. The treatment was also effective in the striatum, that plays a role in Parkinson's disease in human.

IGF-1 might be used to inhibit the effects of neonatal hypoxia during birth which can leave a baby with permanent brain damage. IGF-1 can be used in the programed cell death of cardiac cells after a heart attack. Brain tissue is destroyed due to a stroke (CVA) and this cell death may leave the victim unable to walk, talk and think and the neurodegenerative diseases such as Alzheimer's disease, muscular distrophy and multiple sclerosis, IGF-1 may became a weapon against them.

6. IGF-1 has similar properties to insulin and has been shown to improve blood glucose level in type-2 diabetes patients. It also stops protein wasting and lowers total cholesterol and triglycerides after only four days of treatment.
7. IGF-1 has been proved to regenerate damaged peripheral nerves and the nerve ending upto a distance of 6 mm. It increases the sprouting of intranuscular nerves, therefore, this is also known as "long-sought endogenous motor neuron sprouting factor". It regenerates motor neurons of spinal cord, thus, it may be useful in treating amyotropic lateral sclerosis (ALS) and also in peripheral neuropathy.

8. IGF-1 prevents wasting caused during chemotherapy to AIDS and cancers, which cause peripheral neuropathy.

   Thus synthetic IGF-1 has promise effects to prevent apoptosis and aging at cellular level. All the activities of IGF-1 are related to heal the cells, tissues as well as the body which can lead to increase the life span of the organism including human beings.

## (B) *KLOTHO* gene – an antiaging gene

*KLOTHO* gene was discovered by Dr. Kuro-o *et al* in 1997, naming it after one of the mythical Greek fates who controlled the length of human life.

In Aug 26, 2005, they have discovered that this protein prolonging the life in mice, which works by controlling insulin. This discovery possibly sigtnificant in developing anti-aging therapy. It has been observed that mutant mice lacking *klotho* gene appear normal unit about 3-4 weeks old and then begins showing signs of age, such as skin atrophy, osteoporosis, arteriosclerosis and emphysema. The mice died prematurely at about two months. Kuro-o *et al.* created a strain of mice in which *klotho* gene is more active than the normal mice and these mice lived between 19% and 31% longer than normal mice. Studies on the klotho mouse and the *klotho* gene are thus expected to provide new insight into human aging.

High expression of *klotho* gene has been detected in the brain and it would be plausible that *klotho* gene is involved in the regulation of brain aging.

**Klotho** product is a protein, β-glucuronidase, capable of hydrolyzing steroid β-glucuronides. Genetic variants in *klotho* gene has been associated with human aging. This protein has been found to be a circulating factor in the serum that declines with age. This product may be a transmembrane protein and provides some control over the sensitivity of the organism to insulin.

**Principle of action :** The animals resistant to insulin increases their lifespan, this phenomenon is found in all organisms from worms to fruitfly to mice. Higher levels of Klotho in the mice have been found to have a high level of insulin than the normal, suggesting that *klotho* mice are resistant to insulin and Klotho makes them resistant to insulin. The opposite is that *klotho*-mutant mice are more sensitive to insulin. Higher level of Klotho causes the animal diabetic as it is resistant to insulin. This is the Klotho-enhanced side effect.

Klotho delays many of the effects of old age, like, weakening of bones, clogging of the arteries and loss of muscle fitness.

**Mechanism of action of Klotho :**

1. Klotho has an important role to reduce or decrease the oxidative stress which is closely related to aging.
2. Possibly it decreases lipid (malondial dehyde) and DNA (8-hydroxy-2′ deoxyguanosine) peroxide levels in the hippocampus region of the brain because, in *klotho*-mutant these peroxide levels in the hippocampus region is increased at the age of 5 weeks.
3. Pro-death Bax in increased whereas anti-death Bcl-2 and Bcl-XL is decreased and also apoptotic TUNEL-positive cells were detected in the hippocampus region of *klotho*-mutant mice at the age of 7 weeks.
4. In *klotho*-mutant mice, the potent antioxidant, α-tocopherol treatment has been found to prevent lipid accumulation and decreased the number of apoptotic cells. This suggests that **Klotho** protein may be involved in the regulation of antioxidative defence.
5. *klotho* gene product may function as part of a signaling pathway. In 2007, it was discovered that Klotho protein binds to receptors for a metabolic hormone in fat cells, forming a "co-receptor" that enables the hormone to stimulate the processing, of glucose. This in turn can lower blood glucose level in fat cells of mice. This is β-klotho, which may be a possible novel

drug on treating human with obesity and diabetes .

6. *klotho*-deficient mice manifest a syndrome resembling human aging and exhibit impaired endothelium dependent vasodiation and impaired angiogenesis and accelarated arteriosclerosis, suggesting that **Klotho** may protect cardio-vascular system through endothelium derived NO production.
7. *klotho*-deficient mice show increased production of vitamin D, and altered mineral-ion homeostasis is suggested to be a cause of premature aging-like phenotype, because the lowering of vitamin D activity by dietary restriction reverses the premature aging-like phenotypes and prolongs survival in these mutants. These results suggest that the aging-like phenotype were due to Klotho associated vitamin D associated metabolic abnormalities (hyper-vitaminosis).

### (C) Prop-1-an anti-aging substance :

A novel type of pituitary-specific transcription factor, *Prophet of Pit-1* (*Prop-1*) gene expresses in just early embryonic stage in mouse and closely related as a causative gene in combined pituitary hormone deficiency. *Prop-1* gene mutation is a rare cause of hypopituitarism characterized by the development of multiple pituitary hormone deficiencies (MPHD) over time. MPHD (GH, LH, FSH and TSH deficiency) was diagnosed by the possession of short stature (dwarfism), hypogonadism (sterile or near-sterile) and early aging symptoms such as wrinkled skin, obesity, insulin resistance and osteopenia, but have a long life span reaching ages of 80–90 years.

Animal models of GH deficiencies such as Snell mice (*Pit-1* gene mutations), the Ames mice *Prop-1* gene mutation and Laron mice (GH-receptor gene knock out, IGF mutation etc. have a statistically significant higher longevity compared to normal.

On the contrary transgenic mice with excessive GH secretion have premature death of the individual.

**Prop-1** is an essential transcriptional factor for pituitary-specific gene expression in human in normal pituitary but not in the brain tissue.

According to Dolte et al (2001) *Prop* gene mutant is recessive phenotype. In heterozygous state, the individual shows normal phenotype, but homozygous mutants show the abnormal dwarf phenotype. If both the parents are mutant phenotypes do not usually produce offspring.

**Prop-1** protein (transcription factor) acts as an upstream regulator for *Pit-1* gene to induce development of *Pit-1* linage pituitary cell lines GH-, PRL- and TSH- producing cells in the early stage of pituitary organogenesis. Prop-1 is also involved in the function of FSH/LH-producing cells, gonadotrops, since *prop-1* deficiency causing hypogonadism. Therefore, it is thought that Prop-1 might also involved in the development of gonadotropes and hormone production.

## 21.14.5 Epigenetic causes of Aging

Random epigenetic drift may occur and that inappropriate methylation is a factor of aging and cancer.

The monozygotic twins have identical genetic makeup. They start life with very few differences in appearance and behaviour. These twin pairs are nearly indistinguishable in DNA methylation and histone acetylation pattern when young. But both random events and lifestyles may be reflected in phenotypes and accumulate differences with age. Older monozygotic twins exhibit very different patterns of both these epigenetic markers (Bell et. al. 2012). This is called random epigenetic drift.

At each round of DNA replication, the DNA methyl-transferase enzyme must methylate the appropriate cytosine residues and leave the others unmethylated. This is not always done properly and such errors accumulate as with age.

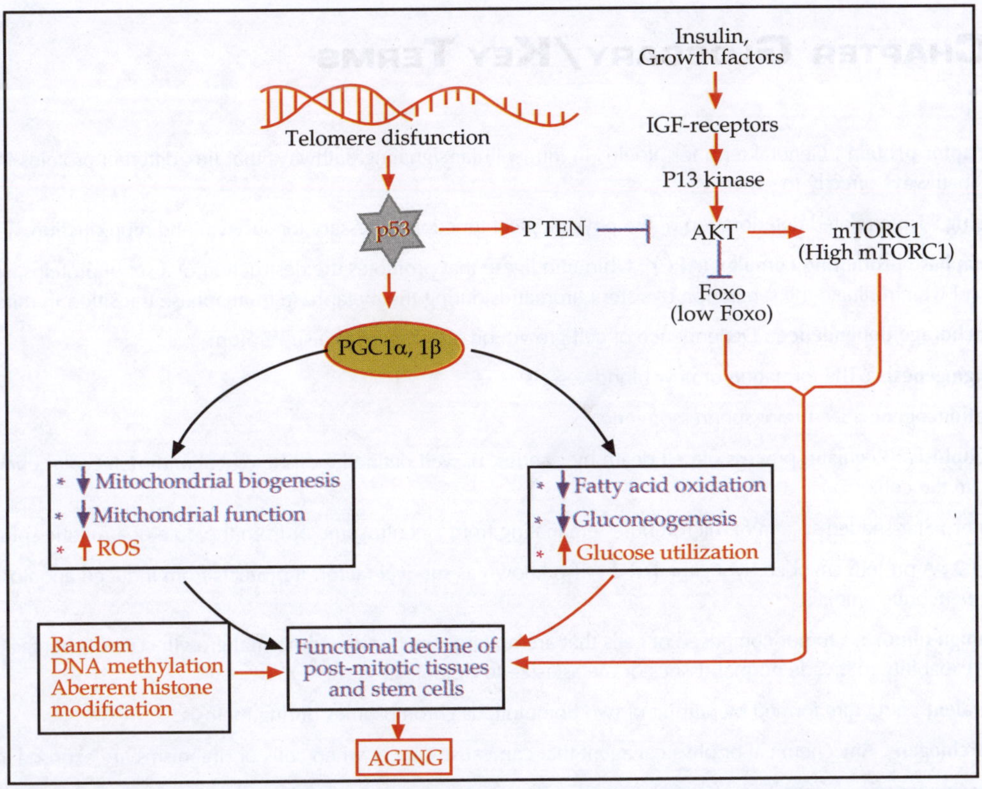


**Fig.21.36 :** Suggestive pathways inducing aging.

The methylation of numerous sites in the genome is directly proportional to the age of the individual (Bocklandt et. al.,2011 and Hannum et. al. 2012). These sites are usually aging-related such as atherosclerosis, cancer and neurodegenerative diseases. DNA methylation-associated inactivation of estrogen-receptor in smooth muscle of vascular system plays an important role in atherosclerosis and also heart disease (Kim et. al.2007).

### 21.14.6 Suggested pathways of Aging

1. p53 is induced by telomere dysfunction and it binds to and repress the expression of PGC1α and PGC1β.
2. Repression of both co-activating transcription factors blocks mitochondrial biogenesis and their functions causing lesser ATP generation but increased production of ROS.
3. PGC lowers fatty acid oxidation and glucogenesis but increases glucose uptake and oxidation.
4. Decline in mitochondrial function and glucose utilization lead to the functional decline in tissue stem cells and post mitotic tissues, causing senescence of long-lived tissues such as neurons and heart.
5. Compromised mitochondrial function can lead to more ROS and iron sulphur clusters which can damage DNA and further activates p53.
6. Active p53 can also block the insulin signalling pathway that causes low level of Foxo transcription factor and high level of mTORC1 complex which actually decline the stem cell.
7. Epigenetic factors also can decrease the activity of particular protein.

# Chapter Glossary/Key Terms

**Adaptor protein :** General term for ptoeins in intracellular signaling pathways that link different proteins in the pathways directly together.

**Aging :** Time related deterioration of the physiological function necessary for survival and reproduction.

**Anaphase promoting complex (APC) :** Ubiquitin ligase that promotes the destruction of a set of proteins, some of which initiate the separation of sister chromatids during the metaphase to anaphase transition in mitosis.

**Anchorage dependence :** Dependence of cell growth on attachment to a substratum.

**Angiogenesis :** The formation of new blood vessels.

**Antioncogene :** See tumor suppressor gene.

**Apoptosis :** Regulatid process of cell death by a series of well defined morphological and molecualar changes in the cell.

**Aster :** Star-shaped system of microtubules emanating from a centrosome or from the pole of a mitotic spindle.

**Bcl 2 :** A protein encoded by a gene bal-2 , also known as survival factor. It protects from induced apoptosis in vertebrate animals.

**Benign tumor :** A tumor composed of cells that are no larger responsive to normal growth controls but lack the capability to invade normal tissues or metastasize to distant sites.

**Bivalent :** Structure formed by pairing of two homologous chromosomes during meiosis.

**Carcinogen :** Any chemical or physical agent that can cause cancer when cells or organisms are exposed to it.

**Carcinogenesis :** Generation of cancer.

**Carcinoma :** A malignant tumor derived from epithelial cell.

**Caspases :** A distinct class of zinc containing cysteine proteases that mediate apoptosis.

**Catastophin :** A protein that destabilizes microlubules during mitotic prophase and capturing events of chromosomes.

**Cdk inhibitor protein (CKI) :** Protein that binds to and inhibits cyclin-Cdk complexes, primarily involved in the control of G1and S-phase.

**Cdk-activating kinase (CAK) :** Protein kinase that phosphorylates Cdks in cyclin-Cdk complex activating the Cdk.

**Cell cycle :** The series of events occurring in a cell between one division and the next.

**Centrosome cycle :** Durplication of the centrosome (during interphase) and separation of two new centrosomes at the beginning of mitosis.

**Check point :** A period before entry into S or M-phase of the cell cycle, a key point at which regulation is exerted.

**Chromatin :** Complex of DNA, histone and monhistone proteins from which eukaryotic chromosomes are formed.

**Cohesin :** The protein that holds sister chromatids together during the period between genome replication and nuclear division.

**Colorectal cancer :** Common carcinoma of the epithelium lining of colon and rectum.

**Condensin :** Complex of proteins involved in chromosome condensation prior to mitosis.

*Contd.*

**Contractitle ring :** Ring containing actin and myosin that forms under the surface of animal cell undergoing cell dividion and contracts to pinch the two daughter cells apart.

**Cyclin :** A regulatory protein whose abundance varies during the cell cycle and which regulates biochemical events in a cell cycle-specific manner.

**Cyclin dependent kinase (Cdk) :** A protein kinase that is catalytically active only when bound to a cyclin of cell into mitosis.

**DNA tumor viruses :** Viruses capable of infecting vertebrate cells transforming them into cancercells. DNA viruses have DNA in the mature virus particle.

**G0-phase :** State of withdrawl from the eukaryyotic cell division cycle by entry into a quiescent G1 phase.

**Granazyme :** The serine protease enzyme, which can induce apoptosis and fragmentation of DNA of the target cell in presence of perforin.

**Kinesin :** Member of a family of motor proteins that use energy released by ATP hydrolysis to move toward the +ve end of a micotubule transporting vesicles or particles in the process.

**Lamin :** A group of intermediate filament proteins that form the fibrous network on the inner surface of the nuclear envelope.

**Mating type :** The euqivalent of male and female for a eukaryotic microorganism.

**M-cdk :** Complex formed in vertebrate cells by an M-cyclin and the corresponding cyclin-dependent kinase.

**M-cyclin :** Type of cyclin found in all eukaryotic cell that promotes the events of mitosis.

**Meiocytes :** The cells where meiosis takes place.

**Metastasis :** Spread of tumor cells from their site of origin and estabilshment of areas of secondary growth.

**Microtubules :** Cytoskeletal fibers (24 nm diameter) that are formed by polymerization of a, b tubulin monomers and exhibit structural and functional polarity. They are important components of cilia, flagella, mitotic spindle etc.

**MPF (mitosis promoting factor) :** A heterogenous protein, composed of a cyclin and cyclin dependent kinase, that triggers entrance of cell into mitosis.

**Multidrug resistance protein (MDR protein) :** Type of ABC transporter protein that can pump hydrophobic drugs (such as anticancer drugs) out of the cytoplasm of eukaryotic cells.

**Oncogenes :** Genes that encode proteins that promote the loss of growth control and the conversion of the cell to a malignant state. These genes have the ability to transform cells.

**p53 :** A tumor suppressor gene, encodes a gene regulatory protein that can repair the DNA damage in a cancer.

**P53 :** Tumor suppressor gene found in mutated in about half of human cancers. It encodes gene regulatory protein that is activated by damage to DNA and is involved in blocking further progression through the cell cycle. This is known as guardian of the genome.

**Perforin :** CTL cell mediate Killing of cells by releasing a lytic component perforin which acts on target cell membrane.

**Phragmoplast :** Structure made of microtubules and actin filaments that forms in the prospective plane of division of a plant cell and guides formation of the cell plate.

**Procaspases :** This is inactive form of caspase.

**Programmed cell death :** See apoptosis.

*Contd.*

**Proto-oncogenes :** A variety of genes that have the potential to subvert the cell's own activities and push the cell toward the malignant state. Protooncogenes encode proteins that have various functions in the cell's normal activities. Protooncogenes can be converted to oncogenes.

**Provirus :** The term for viral DNA when it has been integrated into its host cell's chromosome.

**RNA tumor viruses :** Viruses capable of infecting vertebrate cells, transforming them into cancercells. RNA viruses have RNA in the mature virus particles.

**Sarcoma :** A malignant tumor derived from connective tissue.

**S-Cdk :** Compex formed in vertebrate cells by an S-cyclin and the corresponding cyclin-dependent kinase.

**Securin:** This is an inhibitory protein that inhibits the effect of separase before anaphase.

**Transformed cells :** Normal cells that have been converted to cancer cell by treatment with a carcinogenic chemical, radiation or any infective tumor virus.

**Tumor :** A mass of cells generally derived from a single cell, that is not controlled by normal regulator of cell growth.

**Tumor suppressor genes :** Genes that encode proteins that restrain cell growth and prevent cells from becoming malignant.

# EXERCISE

## A. Long answer type questions :

1. What is benign tumor and malignant tumor? Distinguish between then.
2. Distinguish between the normal cell from cancer cell.
3. Describe the onset and progression of cancer.
4. What is metastasis of the cancer cell? Describe the molecular mechanism of metastasis.
5. Describe the molecular basis of colorectal cancer. Also describe the alternative basis of colorectal cancer.
6. Correlate the genes and cancer.
7. What is oncogene? What is *v-onc* and *c-onc* genes. Describe the genome of RSV.
8. Write a note on DNA *v-onc* genes.
9. What is protooncogene? How protoon-cogenes are activated.
10. What is Tumor suppressor gene? How these are related genetically to induce cancer?
11. How does cell cycle control is related to cancer?
12. How inactivating the $p^{53}$ gene is related to cancer?
13. How telomerase activity is related to cancer?
14. What are carcinogens? How does different careinogens induce carcer?
15. Describe the modern molecular designing of cancer treatment.
16. What are Cdk and Cyclins? Describe different types of Cdk and cyclins. How they are related?

17. How M-Cdk is activated during entry into mitosis?
18. Describe the molecular mechanism of M-Cdk inactivation and creation of $G_1$ phase.
19. Briefly discuss about the escape from $G_1$ to initiate S-phase.
20. Describe the molecular mechanism of initiation of replication in S-phase.
21. Describe the genetic regulation of cell cycle in *S. pombe*.
22. Describe the genetic regulation of cell cycle in *S. cerevisiae*.
23. What do you mean by mitotic check point? What are the probable checkpoints in mitotic cytle? How these checkpoints are regulated by molecular mechanisms?
24. What do you mean by apoptosis? Describe the ultrastructural features of apoptosis?
25. Describe the molecular mechanism of apoptosis in *C. eleganes*.
26. Describe the programmed cell death in mammals and other animals.
27. Discuss the significance apoptosis.
28. Define ageing. Discuss the causes of aging.
29. Describe the genetic programming of aging in animals.
30. How mating types in yeast regulated?
31. Describe the roles of $p^{53}$ as the guardian of the genome.
32. How cancer in regulated epigenetically?
33. What are antiaging agents? Give its examples with their roles.

**B. Short answer type questions :**

1. What are the two heritable properties of cancer cell?
2. What is neoplasm?
3. What are benign and cancerous tumors?
4. What is mestastasis?
5. Distinguish sarcoma and carcinoma?
6. What is adenoma?
7. What is melanoma?
8. What are the cytological changes occur in cancer cells?
9. What is Brittner's milk factor?
10. What is Philadelphia chromosome?
11. What is Burkitts lymphoma?
12. What type of chromosomal abnormality found in cancer cell?
13. What type of metabolic changes occur in cancer cell?
14. What are the changes in aldolase isozymes in cancer cell?
15. What are AFP and CEA? Where does it occur?
16. What is the role of plasminogen activator in cancerous metastasis?
17. What type of surface properties are found in cancer cell?
18. What is immunological survillance?
19. How cancer cell is related to iron transport into cell?
20. What changes occur is cell adhesive substances in cancer cell?
21. What type of cytoskeletal changes are found in cancer cell?
22. What is loss of contact inhibition? Why cancerous cells do form multilayers in culture medium?
23. What is genetic instability?
24. What is the guardian of the genome?
25. What are the key properties of matignant cells?
26. What is monoclonal theory of cancer growth?
27. What is multihit model of cancer induction?
28. What is incubation period of cancer growth?
29. Have there any relationship between the age of the individual and cancer?
30. How angiogenesis is related to cancerous growth? What is HNPCC?

31. What is oncogene and protooncogene?
32. What seven types of proteins are required for controlling cell growth?
33. What are *v-onc* and *c-onc* genes?
34. Give an example of an RNA *v–onc* gene?
35. Give an example of a DNA *v–onc* gene?
36. What are permissive and non-permissive cells?
37. How does papiloma virus induce uterine cancer?
38. How do protoancogenes are activated?
39. What are tumor supporessor genes? How do these genes are related to cancer?
40. How do RB-gene mutation is correlated to cancer?
41. What are heriditary and sporadic retinoblastoma?
42. What is *BRACA-1* tumor suppressor gene?
43. How does it related to breast cancer?
44. How Rb-protein is related to transcriptional activation of many genes that are related to induce cancer?
45. How TGFβ signaling pathway is related to abnormal cell proliferation?
46. How does $G_1$-cell cyle check point control related to cancer induction?
47. How does benzopyrene induce cancer?
48. How does aflatoxin induce cancer?
49. How telomerase activity is related to cancer?
50. What are tumor inditiators and tumor promoters?
51. How does HIV promote Kaposi's sarcoma?
52. What are risk factors of cancer? Give some risk factors that we are subjected?
53. How does radiation is used to resist concer growth?
54. What is multidrug resistance? How such resistance is achieved by cancer cells?
55. How does tamoxifen kill tumor cells?
56. What is Her-2 protein? How it acts on cancer cell?
57. How do chimeric proteins designed to control cancerous growth?
58. What is Gleevec?
59. Define mitosis and meiosis.
60. What are the phases of cell cycle?
61. What is M-phase?
62. What is $G_0$-Phase?
63. What is Cdk? How Cdks are actiated?
64. What is cyclin? What is its function?
65. What types of cyclin are found in the cell cycle of eukaryotes?
66. Tabulate different types of Cdks that bind to cyclins in vertebrates and budding yeast?
67. What is CAK? What is its function?
68. What are the functions of Wee-1 and Cdc 25?
69. What is CKI? What is its function?
70. What is polokinase?
71. What are the function of *nim-1* and *mik-1*?
72. What is condensin? What is its function?
73. What is cohesin? What is its function?
74. What Cdk and cyclins are required for the stimulation of centrosome duplication?
75. What is the role of Cdc-20 APC activity in the cell cycle?
76. What is the role of Hct-1-APC activity in the cell cycle?
77. By what mechanism S-phase is initiated in animal cell?
78. How does pre-replicative complex form in S-phase?
79. How does the origin firing occur for replication?
80. How does replication of DNA occur only once?
81. What are budding yeast and fission yeast?

82. What are checkpoints in the cell cycle?
83. How does unreplicated DNA transmit signal to check $S \rightarrow G_2$ progress?
84. What is spindle attachment checkpoint? How does it occur?
85. What is DNA damage checkpoint? How $G \rightarrow S$ and $G_2 \rightarrow M$ entrance are controlled?
86. What is the role of $p^{53}$ in the checkpoint?
87. What is the role of $p^{21}$ in the entry into mitosis?
88. How ataxia telangiectasia is produced?
89. What is meiocyte?
90. What is the role of progesterone in $G_2$ for entry into meiosis?
91. What is MPF? What is its role for entry into meiosis?
92. What is the role of SPO in budding yeast?
93. What are homotypic and heterotypic division?
94. What is apoptosis? What is its significance?
95. Why apoptosis is extensively studied in *C. elegans*.
96. What do you mean by specificity of cell death?
97. What is the role of ***ced-9*** gene in *C. elegans* ?
98. What is the role of *bcl-2* gene in mammals.
99. What do you mean by *bcl-2* gene family?
100. What is caspase? What is its function?
101. What is Apaf-1 protein? What is its function?
102. What is the role of Bad?
103. What is the role of mitochondria in apoptosis?
103. What is the role of Fas-receptor in apoptosis?
104. What is the role of TNF-receptor in apoptosis?
105. What is ICE? What is it's role in apoptosis?
106. What are granzyme and perforin?
107. Which substances inhibit caspase activation?
108. How do webbing and nonwebbing of feet in ducks and chicken occur during embryogenesis?
109. What is the role of BMP on and noggin in the formation of limb joints.
110. How normal brain development is related to apoptosis.
111. How Alzheimer's disease, heart attack etc. are related to apoptosis?
112. How does neural development is related to apoptosis?
113. How does amphibian metamorphosis is related to apoptosis?
114. What is fetal alcohol syndrome? What are its symptoms? How does its affect brain and other organs?
115. How does apoptosis cause metamorphosis in moth?
116. Why majority of thymocytes undergo apoptosis?
117. How the size of prostate gland in rat is maintained its proper size?
118. How does cancer is related to apoptosis?
119. Have there any relationship between apoptosis and tumor suppressor genes?
120. How the evolution of animals and the apoptosis in related?
121. What you mean by aging and senescence?
122. What are the symptoms of aging?
123. What is progeria disease? What is its symptoms?
124. What is ROS? How these substances are related to aging?
125. What is $p66^{she}$ protein? What is its role in aging?
126. How vitamin C and E are related to aging?
127. What is genetic instability? How it is related to aging?
128. How mitochondrial genome mutation causes aging?
129. What do you mean by telomere shortening? How does it occur? How this event is related to aging in mice? Why most rodents do not undergo aging by telomere shortening?

130. Which gene mutation in mice is related to premature aging?
131. What is the role of DAF-16 proteins in aging of *C. elegans.*
132. How does dauer larva is produced?
133. What do you mean by the mating types in years?
134. What is active mating type locus?
135. How p53 and apoptosis are related?
136. How p53 and cancer are related?
137. How p53 and cell cycle are related?
138. What is comptothecin? How this drug works? Why this is used in cancer treatment?
139. How CpG hypo and hypermethylation causing cancer?
140. How lack of folic acid causes cancer?
141. What is cancer signature? How this is used to detect cancer?
142. What is the role of histone deacetylase in cancer treatment?
143. What are antiaging agents?
144. What are the roles of IGF-1 in antiaging?
145. What are the roles of KLOTHO in antiaging?
146. What are the roles of PROP-I in antiaging?
147. Distinguish apoptosis and necrosis.

22

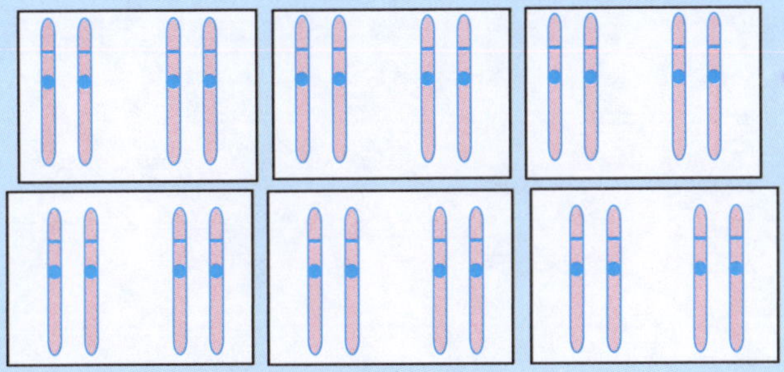

# Human Genome

**CHAPTER AGENDA**

**22.1** Introduction and Nomendature of Human Chromosomes; **22.2** Abnormality in number and structure of Chromosomes; **22.3** Human genetic diseases; **22.4** Genetic and Biochemical disorders; **22.5** Multifactorial disorders in the adult population; **22.6** Hemoglobinopathy; **22.7** Molecular basis of Cystic fibrosis; **22.8** Mechanism of Human Sex determination; **22.9** Human Evolution; **22.10** Origin of Modern Humans; **22.11** Pedigree analysis; Chapter Glossary/Key Terms; Exercise

## 22.1 IDENTIFICATION AND NOMENCLATURE OF HUMAN CHROMOSOMES

J. H. Tjio and A. Leavan in 1956, enabled the determination of correct number, (2n=46) of chromosomes in human beings for first time. The 22 pairs of autosomes were classified according to their length and position of the centromere into seven groups and are identified with letters A—G. The two sex chromosomes X and Y are grouped into group-C and G respectively. Unitil 1970, all chromosomes are placed within such groups but the numbering within the group was more or less tentative (Table 22.1).

The entire chromosome complement of a cell, with each chromosome described in terms of its appearance at metaphase is called it's ***karyotype***.

Kayrotype may be represented by a diagram in which the pairs of homologues are ordered in a series of decreasing size, such an arrrangement is called ***ideogram***. Ideogram is made possible by G-banding technique (Fig. 22.1).

Chromosomes can be identified and classified by different banding techniques. Bands are defined as parts of the chromosomes that appear lighter or darker than adjacent regions when the chromosomes are treated with particular staining methods. When the quinacrine compounds are used as dye to stain chromosomes, then the chromosomes produce fluorescent Q-bands along the chromosomes. Similarly when Giemsa stain is used, chromosomes showed G-bands. Reverse staining method produces R-bands and the heterochromatic regions and centromeric regions are stained by C-banding.

The G-banding pattern of human chromosomes has been identified by the **Paris Conference** (1971). The G-banding pattern arose because of the general use of Giemsa's dye mixture to stain such bands after appropriate treatment of chromosomes. It is to be noted that, according to the decision of Paris Conference (ISCN, 1985), the chromosomes consist of a series of light and dark bands rather than G-bands and interbands. Thus it is appropriate to refer *positive or negative bands*.

A number of cytogeneticists appear to regard the darkly stained bands obtained by G-banding method as G-bands, while, the pale G-bands which stains darkly by R-banding method are described as R-bands. According to Paris Conference, these are referred to as G +ve or R –ve and G-ve or R+ve respectively.

After suitable chemical treatment and staining with Giemsa, the metaphase chromosomes were spread and photographed with a high power microscope and the

**TABLE 22.1**
**Classification of human chromosomes**

| *Group* | *Size and Centromere position* | *Ideogram number* | *Number in diploid cell* |
|---|---|---|---|
| A or I | Large, metacentric or submetacentric | 1–3 | 6 |
| B or II | Large and submetacentric | 4 and 5 | 4 |
| C or III | Medium and submetacentric | 6 – 12, X | 15 (male) or 16 (female) |
| D or IV | Medium and submetacentric | 13 – 15 | 6 |
| E or V | Small and metacentric/submetacentric | 16–18 | 6 |
| F or VI | Small and metacentric | 19 and 20 | 4 |
| G or VII | Smallest and acrocentric | 21, 22, Y | 5 (male), or 4 (female) |

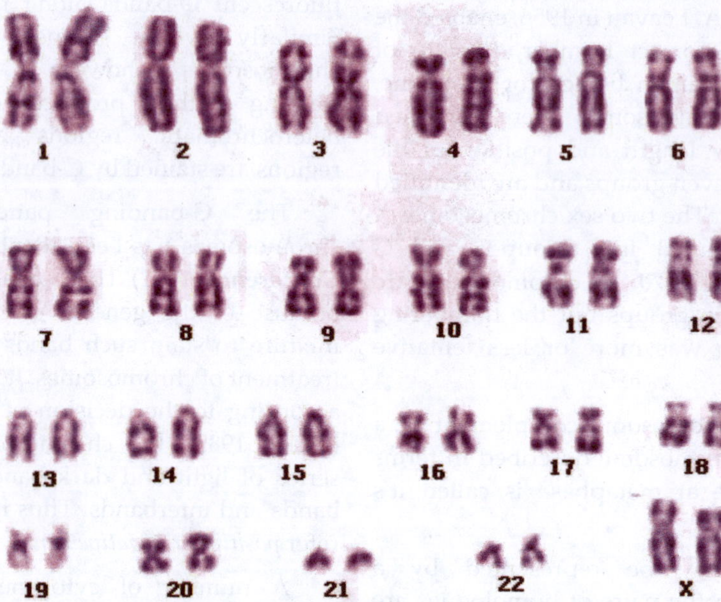

**Fig.22.1 :** *Normal Female Karyo 46(44 + XX)*

individual chromosomes are cut out from the photograph. The chromosomes are then arranged in an orderly fashion in homologous pairs to produce a standard arrangement known as ***karyotype***.

In 1971, a conference on the standarization of human cytogenetics was held in Paris. Confrerees agreed that, to describe extra autosomes, the number of extra chromosomes and microdeletion or microduplication or microtranslocation in the chromosome in an appropriate and simplest way in their karyotype.

This consists first of the total number of chromosomes (in numericals) followed by the sex-chromosome constitution and finally by any abnormalities that are present. Thus the normal male is 46, XY ; a normal female is 46, XX; The Turner Syndrome is 45, XO and a Klinefelter with 47, XXY.

Conference agreed that, to describe extra autosomes, the number of extra chromosome should be placed after the total number of sex-chromosomes with a (+) or (–) sign before the number of the autosome involved. For example, 47, XX+21 is the karyotype of a female with trisomy 21.

The letter "p" symbolizes the short arm and "q" the long arm. The (+) Sign or (–) sign after the p and q indicates the increase or decrease of the arms. For example, 46, XY1q+ means that a male individual with an increase means length of its long arm of chromosome (autosome) no. -1.

Thus if the person is represented by its karyotype as 47, XX, +14p$^+$ symbolizes a female with 47 chromosomes with an additional chromosome no-14 having it's increase in the length of its short arm.

The abbreviations for convenience in presenting chromosome formula. *def* (deficiency), *dup* (duplication), *r* (ring), *inv* (inversion) and *t* (translocation) are used.

In the heterochromatin region, DNA is tightly coiled with histone proteins while in euchromatin region, the DNA is loosely coiled with proteins. Therefore, several protein denaturating agents such as urea, guanidine hydrochloride and various detergents are used for the elimination of these proteins in the heterochromatic regions of the metaphase chromosome. Trypsin pretreatment is widely used for the digestion of proteins in the chromatin which led to sharper band and some extra bands can be identified in the heterochromatin as well as euchromatin regions. Thus microdeletions, duplications and translocations are easily observed in Giemsa-Trypsin-Banding (GTB) technique.

For example, in **cri-du-chat** syndrome (a microdeletion in the short arm of chromosome no-5) is designated as $5p^-$; the karyotype is 46, XX, $5p^-$.

Another human disorder is associated with a chromosome abnormality is **chronic myleocytic leukemia** where deletion of long arm of chromosome-22 was translocated to another chromosome, usually chromosome-9 leaving a microdeficiency in the long arm of chrmosome-22. The karyotype is 46, XX, $9p^+$, $22q^-$.

In **Burkitt's lymphoma**, translacation of chromosome no-14; the karyotype is t ($8q^-$, $14q^+$) ($q^{24}$, $q^{32}$).

A deletion in chromosme 13q (band 14.1) is associated with embryonic tumor **retinoblastoma**.

In this way different types of micro-deletion, duplication and translocation syndromes can be detected by GTB.

## 22.2 ABNORMALITY IN NUMBER AND STRUCTURE OF CHROMOSOMES

Abnormality in chromosome structure and number has been observed in some human beings, which results some metabolic physiological and morphological abnormalities are rarely observed in live born babies and therefore presumably lethal and cause significant number of early abortions. About 30% abortions occur due to chromosome abnormality.

A solitary case of triploid human being 3n=69 was reported in 1960 by Brook and Santesson. This triploid individual had three complete sets of autosome and XXY chromosomes. Consequently, it was a male individual and showed abnormalities in cerebral development, had syndactyly in hands and feet and was small jawed, obese. This triploid individuals survived only upto birth.

### 22.2.1 Aneuploidy in Sex Chromosomes

Aneuploid chromosome numbers involving X-chromosome and resulting phenotypes are given in the Table 22.2

**TABLE 22.2**
**Chromosome constitution and phynotypes in human beings**

| *Sex* | *Chromosome* | *Sex* | *Phenotypes* |
|---|---|---|---|
| XX | disomic | ♀ | normal |
| XO | monosomic | ♀ | Turner's Syndrome |
| XXX | trisomic | ♀ | Super female |
| XXXX | tetrasomic | ♀ | Super female |
| XXXXX | Pentasomic | ♀ | Super female |
| XY | disomic | ♂ | Normal |
| XYY | trisomic | ♂ | Normal (has criminal tendency) |
| XXY | trisomic | ♂ | Klinefelters syndrome |
| XXYY | tetrasomic | ♂ | do |
| XXXY | tetrasomic | ♂ | Mentally retarded extreme KF |
| XXXXY | Pentasomic | ♂ | |

### (a) Klinefelters' Syndrome

Seminiferous tubule dysgenesis is one of the most common forms of primary hypogonadism and infertility in the male with an increased prevalence in mentally retarded males. In 1942, it was first defined as a clinical entity by Klinefelter, Reifenstein and Albright.

**Characteristic features :** Characteristic features of this syndrome which first become

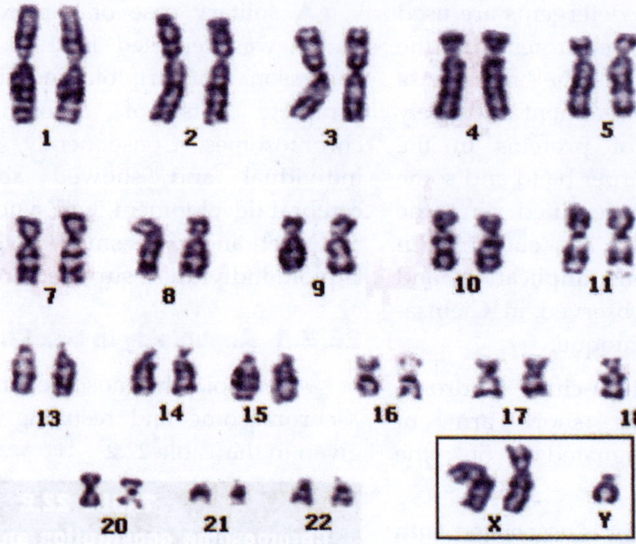


**Fig.22.2 :** *Klinefelters' Syndrome Karyotype 47 (44 + XXY)*

manifest during adolescence were mental retardation, gynecomastia a variable degree of eunuchoidism, small atrophic testes with hyalization of the seminiferous tubules and aggregation of Leydig cells, aspermatogenesis and increased uninary excreation of gonadotropin. Characteristic clinical signs of syndrome are lacking before puberty. The patients tend to be taller than average, mainly because of the disproportionate length of their legs. The patients are uncommonly prone to ill health from a variety of somatic ailments, such as, breast cancer, chronic pulmonary disease, thyroid disease etc.

**Chromosomal constitution :** In 1959, Jacob and Strong and Ford *et al* first reported an XXY-sexchromosome constitution in patients with this disorder. The chromosome constitution of other Klinefelter's syndrome is XXYY (tetrasomic). Besides, XXXY (tetrasomic), XXXXY (pentasomic) extreme KFs may be found (Fig. 22.2).

Normal XX constitution with chromosome number-46 had been identified as KF where $Y_p$ segment of Y chromosome has translocated to the X-chromosome. In $Y_p$ segment *TDF* gene is present which is responsible for the development of testis in $XXY_p$ individuals. Extra copies of genes on the X-chromosome interfere with the male sexual development often preventing testis from functioning normally and reducing the level of testosterone.

**Origin of Chromosomal abnormality :**

1. **Aneuploidy :** XXY males may be developed from nondisjunction of the sexchromosomes during either the first or second meiotic division in either parent or from mitotic non disjunction in the zygote at the time of or following fertilization. The evidence suggests that both meiotic and mitotic errors occur.

   Fertilization of either an XX ovum by a Y-bearing sperm or of an X-ovum by an XY-bearning sperm would yield an XXY zygote.

   Mitotic nondisjuction of the sex-chromosomes in an XY-zygote could yield an XXY and YO daughter cells. Since YO cell line is nonviable, only XXY cell line would survive. This may be caused by anaphase lag in which there is simple loss of a chromosome from one or both of the two daughter cells. Presumably this

 

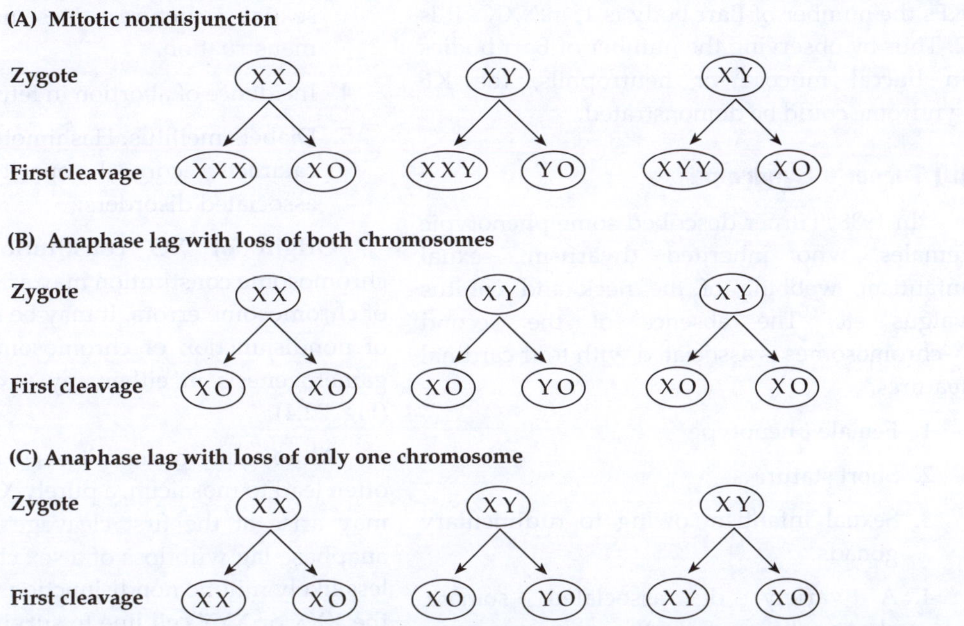


**Fig.24.3 :** *Origin of chromosomal errors in zygotes*

caused by failure of one the equatorial plate during metaphase.

Maternal age-effect in chromosome abnormalities may be a consequence of the long diplotene stage of human ova. They remain suspended in prophase-I from birth to ovulation which may occur for about 40 yrs or longer, this may cause the abnormal spindle formation and non disjunction (Fig. 22.3).

2. **Mosaicism** : Mosaicism is the term applied to individuals with two or more cell lines differing in chromosomal constitution but originating from a single zygote, whcih can arise only from errors in mitosis after fertilization. XXY/XY mosaicism exhibits less severe changes particularly because the normal stem cell line (XY) is present. The sexual function is normal in adult but mental retardation and abnormal skeletal growth is observed.

**Variant forms** : Besides XXY constitution, different variants of KF patients have been observed, such as XXXY and XXXXY etc. The symptoms are like XXY but more pronounced, mental retardation, radioulner synostosis etc.

**Heterochromatin** : It has been demonstrated that in the homogametic XX-female individuals, one X-chromosome gets chracteristically condensed and inactivated. Such chromatin has also been described as facultative heterochromatin, it becomes inactive in certain part of the life cycle and resumes actitity before entering the germ line. The inactivation of X-chromosome was confirmed and observed by Barr and Bertram (1849) as a **Barr body**.

Later Lyon (1872) confirmed the existance of Barry body in normal females, superfemales and in KF males. The number of Barr body is always one less than in the number of X-chromosomes It was established that in the normal females only one X-chromosome is found as **Barr body**.

This is known as **Lyon's hypothesis**. In XXY KFs the number of Barr body is 1, in XXXY it is 2. Thus by observing the number of Barr bodies in buccal mucosa or neutrophils, the KF syndrome could be demonstrated.

## (b) Turner's Syndrome

In 1938, Turner described some phenotypic females, who inherited dwarfism, sexual infantism, webbing of the neck and cubitus valgus etc. The absence of the second X-chromosomes is associated with four cardinal features.

1. Female phenotype
2. Short stature
3. Sexual infantism owing to rudimentary gonads.
4. A variety of associated somatic abnormalities. Sometimes partial sex-chromosome monosomy may be attributed to a structurally abnormal second sex-chromosome, sexchromosome mosaicism involving an XO-cell line or both a structural abnormality and mosaicism. In these patients, sometimes may be associated with the typical clinical picture found in XO patients.

**Phenotypic characteristics :**

1. Micrognathia, epicanthal folds, lowset deformed ears, a fish-like mouth and ptosis are present with varying degree. Neck is short and webbed, besides, cubitus valgus, congenital lymphadema of the feet and hand, renal abnormalities, hypoplastic nails, perceptive hearing loss, unexplained hypertension, mental retardation. Rotation of kidney, horseshoe kidney, duplication of the renal pelvis and ureter are also observed.
2. In most cases, skeleton exhibits localized areas of rarefaction, especially of hands and feet. Short stature.
3. Sexual infantism, genital ducts and external genitalia are female like but immature. Maturation of secondary sexual structures does not occur. No menstruation.
4. Incidence of abortion in fetus is common.
5. Diabets mellitus, Hashimoto's thyroiditis, cataracts, corneal opacity are other associated disorders.

**Origin of XO constitution** : An XO chromosome constitution may arise by a variety of chromosome errors. It may be a consequence of nondisjunction or chromosome loss during gametogenesis in either any sex chromosome (Fig. 22.4).

Although errors of mitosis in normal zygote often lead to mosaicim, a purely XO constitution may arise at the first cleavage division from anaphase lag with loss of a sex chromosome or less likely mitotic nondisjunction with failure of the XXX or XYY cell line to survive. There may be indirect evidence to suggest that loss of one X or a Y chromosome between fertilization and the first cleavage division may be a frequent cause of XO embryo.

Family studies of such X-linked traits such as color blindness suggest that loss of the paternally derived sex chromosome is more common.

Due to presessce of only one X-chromosome in Turner's syndrome, no sex chromatin body is found in the cells.

**Variants of Turner's Syndrome :**

1. Partial sexchromosome monosomy may or may not modify the expression of the classic XO phenotype. This group has usually a structural abnormality of X-chromosome. Loss of $X_p$ part or $Y_p$ part of the sex chromosome of the zygote may be sex-chromatin positive and usual chromosome number 2n = 46.
2. XO/XX mosaicism is the most common finding in patients with sex-chromatin positive gonadal dysgenesis. Patients with mosaicism usually exhibit fewer of the associated somatic anomalies are not

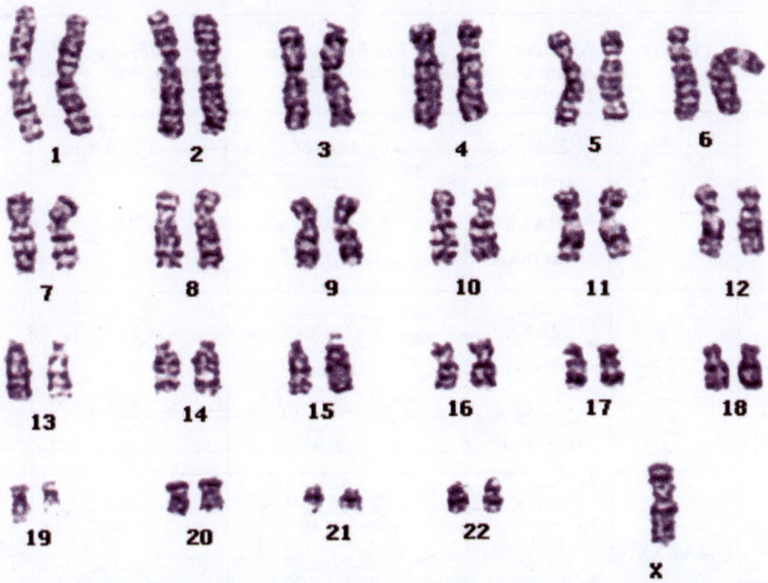


**Fig.22.4 :** *Turner Synbdrome Karyo 45 (44 + XO)*

invariably short and even be fertile. One gonad may be a steak and other may be normal.

Some times, XO/XXX, XO/XX/XXX mosaicism may be produced due to non-disjunction of the X-chromosome during first and second cleavage, thus in the former case two cell lines and in latter case three cell lines are observed.

3. $XO/XX^{I}$ and $XX^{I}$-patients with an $X^{I}$ structural abnormalality (presumably iso-chromosome for the long arm of the X) have an X-chromosome which consists of two long arms but lacks a short arm. Isochromosomes are thought to be due to a transverse division of certromers during second meiotic division of germ cells or during mitosis in the zygote. The sex-chromatin body is larger than the normal. Morishima and Grumbach found two patients one, with $XO/X^{I}O/XX/XXX/XXX^{I}$ and other with five cell lines $XO/X^{I}O/XX/XX^{I}/XXX^{I}$.
4. $XO/XX^{R}$ – A ring chromosome has been described in $XO/XX^{R}$ mosaicism. $X^{R}$ arises by loss of both ends of a chromosome with union of the proximal breaks, as a consequence of variable amount of chromatin material is lost from each arm. The patient is sexchromatin positive as a small body.
5. $XX^{DS}$ and $XO/XX^{DS}$ — Deletion of short arm of an X-chromosome has been described. The heteromorphic X-chromosome in these patients is the late DNA replicating X-chromosome and is the origin of the small sexchromatin body in interphase nuclei.
6. $XX^{DL}$, $XO/XX^{DL}$ — Deletion of long arm of X-chromosome has also been described, but with normal stature.
7. XO/XY, XO/XYY, XO/XY/XYY mosaicism are also observed with ambiguous external genitalia and phenotypic males are found.
8. $XY^{I}$ — Structural abnormalities of Y-chromosome, because of isochromosome of long arm has been reported in Turners' syndrome (Fig. 22.5).

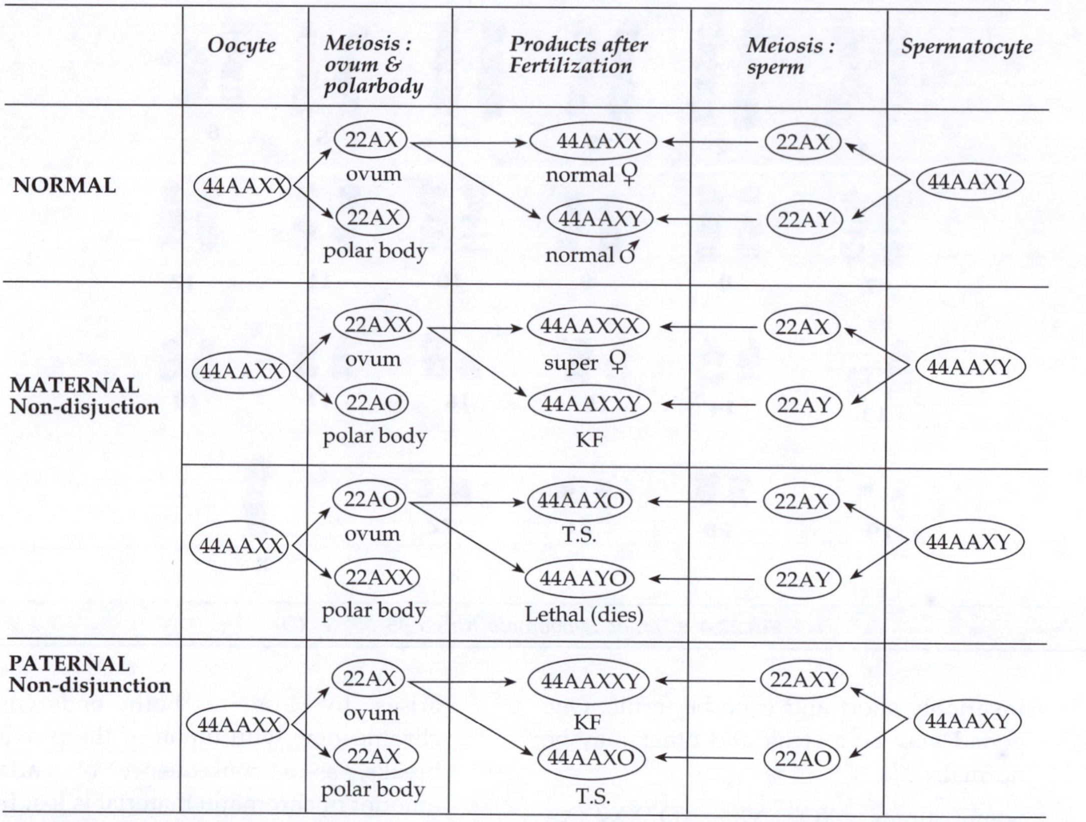


**Fig.22.5 :** *Possible chromosomal patterns might arise in the zygote from non-disjunction of sex chromosome during meiosis in germ cells.*

**Molecular basis of Turner's syndrome** and **Klinefelter syndrome :** Molecular analysis has located the specific genes responsible for the Turner syndrome phenotype. Mutations in the *SHOX* gene which is a part of a large family of Homeobox gene and encodes a transcription factor that is expressed in the embryonic limbs may accounts for the short stature. This gene is located on the distal tip of the chromosomes $X_p$ and $Y_p$ which escape X-inactivation. It is thus normally transcribed in two copies in both males and females. In females with Turner syndrome, only one active copy of the gene would be present, resulting in haploinsufficiency which could be the cause of a short stature.

Similarly, Klinefelters where chromosome constitution is XXY have three active copies (overdose) of the *SHOX* gene resulting into long stature. But long arm of X chromosome ($X_q$) seems primarily contribute to KS phenotypes.

Human androgen receptor (*AR*), previously called *HUMARA*) gene is located in $X_q$ 11.2–q12, is highly polymorphic CAG repeats in exon-1 with normal length 9-37. The CAG expanded repeat is associated with neurological disorder. *AR* contains two methylation sensitive sites close to CAG repeats. There is a positive correlation between CAG length and body height, gynecomastigia and smaller testis and an inverse relationship with bone density, penile length .

In the normal case X-chromosome activation/inactivation ratio is 50% at any chromosomal allele outside the *PAR*s. But in KS the ratio is 80%.

### (c) XXX (Triplo X) females

This was first described by Patricia A, Jacobs in 1959

XXX females are usually normal in appearance occur 1 birth per throusand girls.

Because of Lyonization, in the triple X, two X-chromosomes undergo inactivation forming two Barr bodies, only one X-chromosome is active at any time . Therefore they have a mild effects. The effects include tall stature, microcephaly, epicanthal folds, speach disabilities, weak muscle tone and taller than the average females (because of the over-expression of *SHOX* gene in 3 Xs which escape inactivation).

The cause of XXX is due to maternal nondisjunction during oogenesis or may be due to nondisjunction of cell division during early embryogenesis. Sometimes 46 XX/XXX mosaics may be resulted due to non-disjunction of X chromosome during embryonic development.

### (d) XYY super males

47 XYY is a genetic condition in which human male has an extra Y chromosome which occurs every one in 1000 male births. This was first recorded by Avery Sanford *et al* in 1961.

They have an increased growth velocity from early childhood. The increased gene dosage of three sex chromosome pseudoautosomal regions (*PAR1*) *SHOX* genes has been postulated as a cause of increased stature.

XYY chromosome constitution ususlly occurs as a random event during the formation of sperm due to non-disjunction of Y chromosome during spermatogenesis at anaphase-II or during cell division of post zygotic embryogenesis. Sometimes 46XY/47XYY mosaicism may be found. The XYY is not related to the advancing maternal age. XYY fathers rarely have sons with two Y chromosomes.

It was throught that XYY males indicate that they are more prone to aggressive behaviour, violence and criminal behaviours than XY males and are popularly known as "**Super male**".

Theilgaard (1970) suggested in her study that XYY male is "a difficult child has problems in school, shows excessive day dreaming is a loner, a driflter presents unrealistic future expectations, and manifests impulsiveness with sporadic sudden violence and aggression.

They may have some learning problems such as delayed speach and difficulty with articulation, may have normal to high IQ.

A prenatal or childhood diagnosis of XYY syndrome need not be cause for alarm. Many such children will develop normally no ill effects from their condition. For some, there may be an increased risk of behavioural problems, but environment and upbringing likely will play a greater role in determining how much the individual is affected.

## 22.2.2 Aneuploidy in Autosomes

### 1. Down's Syndrome :

An euploidy for autosomal chromosomes in humans can occur but is probably often lethal. Most frequent autosomal trisomics are those for chrosome - 21, because chromosome 21 is very small and its addition does not cause lethality (Fig. 22.6).

The clinical syndrome associated with this trisomy was first discribed by Seguin 1844 and latter by Langdon Down (1866) and has been known as Down's syndrome (previously Mongolian idiocy).

It is probably the most common congenital abnormality with a frequency of one out of 600 births.

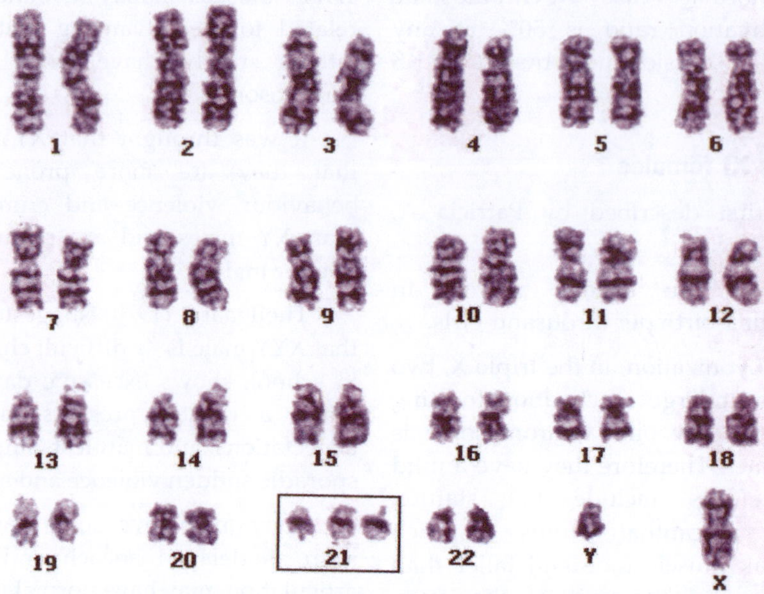


**Fig.22.6 :** *Down's Syndrome Karyotype 47 (44 + XY + Trisomy-21)*

**Characteristics of Down's syndrome :** It is characterized by mental retardation, a short body with stubby fingers, swollen tongue, monkey-like skin ridges on the extemities, slant eyes, sagging mouth, unusual palm and feet, obesity and resembling those of Mongolian races. The life expectancy of those idiotes is about 8–12 years.

**Chromosomal analysis :** In 1957 Leguine, Gautier and Turpin and others showed that trisomy for chromosome, 21 (2n+1 = 47) was an almost constant corollary of Down syndrome. Probably arose through non-disjunction of small chromosome no-21, The gametes would be either with chromosome-21 or with no chromosome no-21. If the former gamete is fertilized with a normal opposite gamete, a male or female trisomic of chromosome no-21 would result.

In about 5% of people with Down syndrome, the normal disomic complement of 46 chromosomes was found but in those instances the additional trisomic chromosome-21 had become attached to one of the larger (D group) chromosome. When a normal homozygote (2n=46) is married with a translocation heterozygote carrying 45 chromosomes, is phenotypically normal but chromosome -21 is translocated to the chromosome no-16. Such translocation heterozygote individuals can produce gametes bearing a normal chromosome no-21 and a $14^{21}$ translocation. When such gametes unite with those produced by normal individual offspring showing Down syndrome that are trisomic for a major part of the chromosome-21. Theoritical proportion of Down's syndrome among viable offspring of this mating is about one third, the actual observed proportion is much less and seems to be dependent upon which parent is the translocation carrier. Down's syndrome appears in about 10% of the offspring of a carrier mother and in about 2% of the offspring of a carrier father (Fig. 22.7).

**Origin :** There is a maternal origin for about 75% of the nondisjunction events that cause

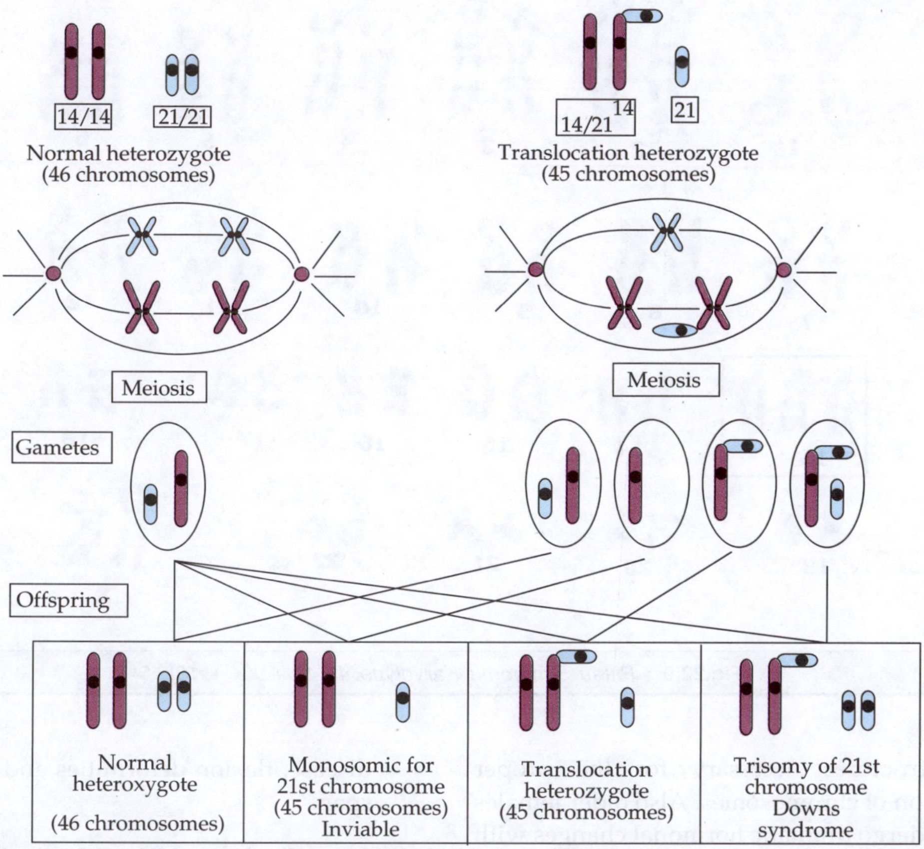


**Fig.22.7 :** *Origin of translocation heterozygote, trisomy and monosomic for chromosome-21*

trisomy-21. In cases ascribed to paternal nondisjunction, age also seems to play a role and father 55 years and older show increased risk of producing offspring with Down's syndrome (Stene *et al* 1977). There is a relationship of incidence of the Down's child with the maternal age (Fig. 22.8).

Among various hypotheses put forth are some based on the fact that each egg of a human female is already partly formed while she is still an unbron fetus. This embryonic egg immediately enters into the prophase of the first meiotic division but does not divide further until it is released during ovulation. The egg remains as much as 40 or more years in older mothers, which is certainly be long enough time to permit weakening of the spindle fibres or

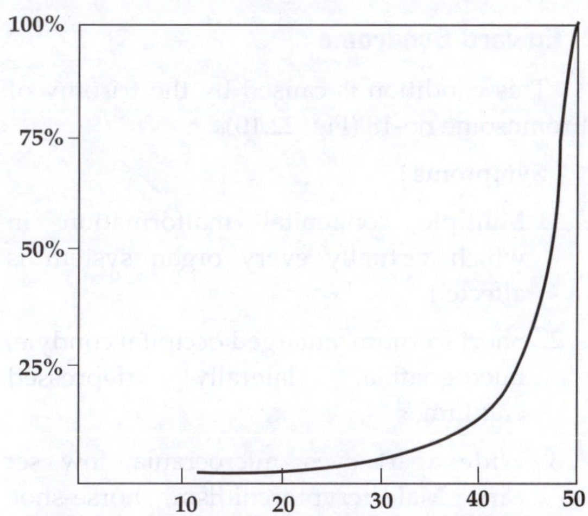


**Fig.22.8 :** *Incidence of Down's syndrome in the children of mothers of different ages.*

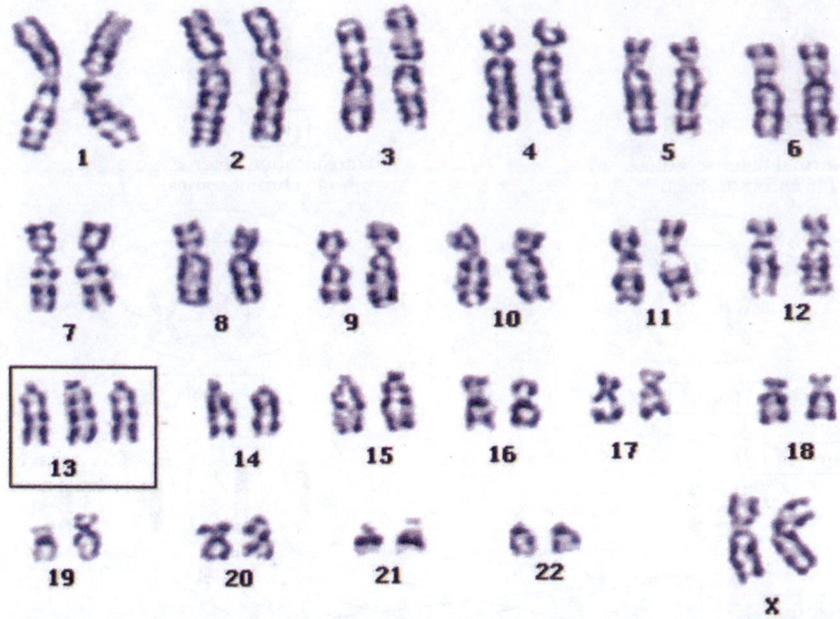


**Fig.22.9** : *Patau Syndrome Karyotype 47(44 + XX + 13)*

other structures necessary for the proper disjunction of chromosomes. Also older females often undergo dramatic hormonal changes with possible side effects on cellular division (Crowly et al, 1979).

### 2. Edward Syndrome

This condition is caused by the trisomy of chromosome no-18 (Fig. 22.10).

**Symptoms :**

1. Multiple congenital malformation in which virtually every organ system is affected.
2. Short sternum, enlarged occipital condyle, micrognathia, laterally depressed cranium.
3. Wide apart eyes, microcrania, low set ears. Male cryptorchidism, horse-shoe kidney.
4. Mental retardation, congenital heart disease, flexion deformities and short life span.

**Genetics and causes of Edwards syndrome**

Most cases of trisomy 18 is called full trisomy 18. The extra genetic material disrupts the normal course of development.

Approximately 5% of people heaving three copies of chromosome 18 in only some of the body's cells called Trisomy18 mosaicism. The severity depends upon the types of cell affected in the body.

Very rarely, a part of long (q) arm of chromosome 18 is translocated to another chromosome. They have normal 46 chromosome elements. If this translocated trisomy 18 with entire q arm present in three copies, the individual may be affected like the full trisomy 18.

**Inheritance pattern:**

1. Most cases of trisomy 18 are not inherited, but occur as random events during the

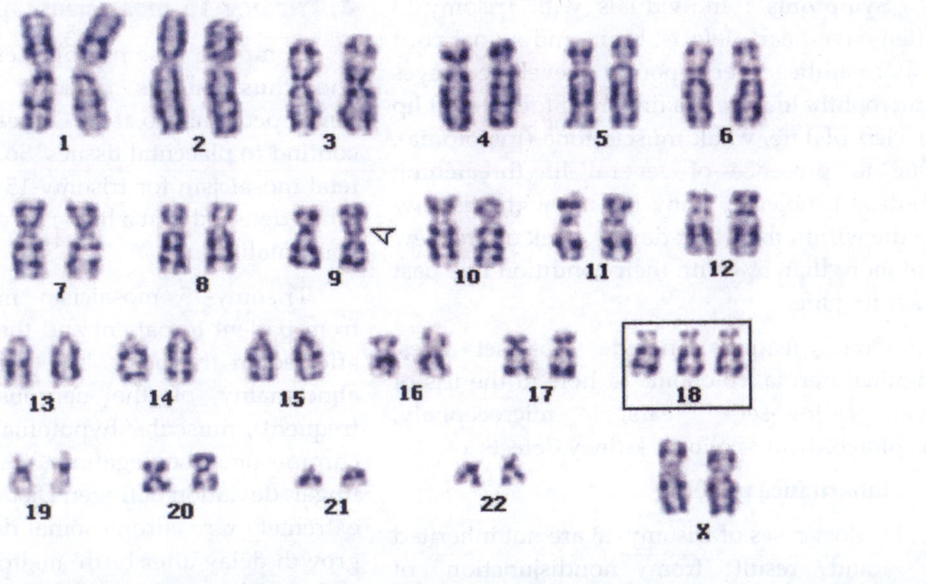


**Fig.22.10 :** *Edward Syndrome Karyotype 47 (44 + XX + 18)*

formation of egg and sperm. An error in the cell division called nondisjunction during oogenesis or spermatogenesis cause abnormal number of chromosomes in eggs and sperms. When these are fertilized with normal gametes, trisomy 18 is resulted.

2. Partial trisomy 18 can be inherited. An unaffected person can carry a chromosome 18 attached to another chromosome, may produce a gamete with one chromosome 18 and another chromosome 18 translocated to another gamete, partial trisomy may be resulted. In live born infants is more likely that the affected females. This is because male fetuses with trisomy are more likely lost due to miscarriage or stillbrith.

Risk rises with rising maternal age. Birth after age 30 yrs the risk increases exponentially upto 45 years. This is because of the weaking of spindle fibres of the ovum during cell division (as found in Downs syndrome).

### 3. Trisomy - 13 or Patau's syndrome

This occurs in 1 in 16000 newborns. Most cases trisomy-13 results from having three copies of chromosome-13 in each cell in the body which disturbs the normal course of development. (Fig. 22.9).

**Chromosome patterns :**

1. Trisomy-13 can also occur when part of chromosome-13 becomes translocated to another chromosome during oogenesis or spermatogenesis when it fertilizes with the normal opposite gametes.
2. In rare cases, only part of chromosome-13 is present in three copies. The physical sign and symptoms in these cases may vary in different individuals.
3. A small number of people with trisomy-13 have an extra copy of chromosome-13 in only some cells of the body. The condition is called *mosaic trisomy-13*. The severity depends upon the type and number of cells that have extra chromsome.

**Symptoms :** Individuals with trisomy-13 often have heart defects, brain and spinal cord abnormailities, very poorly developed eyes (microphthalmia), extra fingers of toes, a cleft lip or cleft platate, weak muscle tone (hypotonia). Due to presence of several life-threatening medical problems, many infants with trisomy-13 die within their first-day or week of life. Few not more than 5% with their condition live past their first life.

Other features include close-set eyes, inguinal hernia, coloboma (a hole in the iris of eye), low-set ears, microcephaly, cryptorchidism, scoliosis, kidney defects etc.

**Inheritance pattern :**

1. Most cases of trisomy-13 are not inherited and result from nondisjunction of Chromosome-13 causing an abnormal egg or sperm with extra one copy of chromosome-13. When these are fertilized with a normal opposite gamate, a trisomy-13 zygote is resulted. The risk of such child for the woman is related to her increased age.
2. Translocation trisomy 13 can be inherited. An unaffected parent can have normal disomy but one of the chromosome-13 is translocated to another chromosome. This person can pass extra chromosome-13 to his/her children.

**Diagnosis and Treatment :** Patients who are at risk to have a translocation due to their family history can have a translocation due to their family history can have a test, called Karyotype, which can determine if translocation is present.

Prenatal testing such as maternal blood screening, fetal ultra sound, Chorionic Villus Sampling or amniocentesis is available to determine if the fetus is affected.

Treatment is generally symptomatic and supportative. Due to multiple abnormalities they usually do not survive past the first month of life.

### 4. Trisomy 15 mosaicism

Complete trisomy-15 is lethal abnormality and thus this is detected in a normally developed embryo at 10-12 week CVS sample is confind to placental tissues. So this is rare. True fetal mosaicism for trisomy-15 is quite rare but when detected is at a high risk of developmental abnormalities.

Trisomy-15 mosaicism may be variable from patient to patient and the tissue and cells affected in the body. The symptoms include, abnormality of the nervous system (very frequent), muscular hypotonia, abnormality in chromosome segregation, Camptodactyly of finger, deviation of finger. Distal trisomy 15q, an extremely rare chromosomal disorder includes. growth delay after birth, malformation of head and facial area, short neck, scoliosis, genital abnormalities, cardiac defects, etc.

**Cause of the disease :**

1. Trisomy-15 may arise due to nondisjunction of chromosome-15 during oogenesis or spermatogenesis which is fertilized by a normal opposite gamate.
2. Trisomy-15 mosaicism may arise due to non-disjunction at the dividing stage of the embryo. This can be detected by CVS or amniocentesis.
3. Uniparental disomy (UPD) may be resulted because of imprinting effects are known for both maternal and paternal UPD-15, DNA studies are always suggested when prenatal diagnosis indicates trisomy mosaicism. Maternal UPD is assocaited with Prader-Willi syndrome while paternal UPD leads to Angelman syndrome. Most trisomy-15 is due to an error in maternal meiosis.
4. Distal trisomy 15q is an extremely rare chromosomal disorder in which the distal portion of the long arm(q) of the 15th chromosome appears three times. This arises due to chromosomal balanced translocation in one of the parents.

5. Trisomy 15q 25q$^{ter}$ exhibits abnormally tall stature, thin finger and toes, scoliosis etc.

**Treatment :** Surgical treatments of the affected organs are recommended. Physicians may regularly monitor the patients with prompt treatment.

### 5. Trisomy 17 mosaicism

Trisomy 17 mosaicism is one of the rarest trisomies in humans. It is often incorrectly called trisomy 17 (which is when three copies of chromosome 17 are present in all cells of the body) which has never been reported in living individuals in the medical literature. Few cases of trisomy 17 mosaicism have been described only a few birth, through a test called CVS or amniocentesis. The signs, symptoms and also severity depend on the location of trisomy in the body parts.

The . **symptoms** reported include, developmental delay, body asymmetry, slow growth and cerebellar hypoplasia etc.

The **cause** of trisomy mosaicism is due to a random event during formation of eggs and ovum and also after fertiliation.

During oogenesis or spermatogenesis, due to nondisjunction of chromosome 17 causes the eggs or sperms with extra one copy of chromocrome 17. When it fertilizes with normal opposite gamete, trisomy 17 is resulted in the zygote.

But when embryos growing, there is a chance of correct the mistake by eliminating this extra chromosome-17 from few cells. This correction process is called *trisomy rescue*. As a result trisomy 17 mosaicism individual is resulted.

In other cases, eggs and sperms are normal, thus zygote is also normal. Nondisjunction occurs when the fertilized egg is growing and dividing. If this error occurs during one of the divisions, it can cause some cells to have abnormal trisomy of chromosome-17 and other cells have normal two copies of chromosome-17. This results trisomy-17 mosaicisms.

## 22.2.3 Partial Deletion Syndromes

### 1. Philadelphia chromosome abnormality

Deletion of the large part of the long arm of chromosome-22 is translocated to one of the larger charmosome usually to no-9. The chromosomal abnormality is found in the bone marrow of 90% of patients suffering from Chronic Myeloid Leukemia. Such leukemic individuals are therefore mosaic with respect to the long arm of chromosome-22 and bear both chromosomally normal and abnormal tissues.

This translocation involves transfer of a 5000 kb region from the end of chromosme 9 carrying *c-abl* to the *bcr* locus 5.8 kb of chromosome-22. Such changes in the conformation of c-Abl protein and activates a latent oncogenic potential. This translocated chromosome is called Philadelphia chromosome (see Fig. 21.21).

**Deletion chromosome - 5 :** A deletion of chromosome 5 results in the *Cri-du-chat* (Cry of cat) syndrome. Children with this syndrome have a small head, low mental ability and they cry in a cat-like manner.

**Partial deletion of chromosome-18 :** It results in a syndrome in which the ears are very large and fingers are very long.

**Delection of the middle part of chromosome - 13 :** This causes a disease called retinoblastoma, a malignant tumor in the eyes and always leads to death in early childhood.

### 2. Cri-du-Chat (Cat's cry) syndrome

This condition was first described by Lejeune and coworkers in 1963 and since reported many times. This disease is associated with a deletion in the short arm of chromosome 5. As can be discerned from its name, this syndrome includes a mewing cat-like cry during infancy.

**Symptoms :**

1. The babies exhibiting to have a peculiar face viewing with a cat cry.
2. Mental retardation, IQ is less than 20.

**TABLE 22.3**
**Chromosomal abnormality diseases in humans**

| *Chromosome-abnormality* | *Syndrome* | *Clinical features* |
|---|---|---|
| Trisomy 21<br>Translocation 13-15/21<br>Translocation 22/21<br>Translocation 21/21 | Downs' | Characteristic facies Mental retardation, hypotonia Congenital heart disease |
| Trisomy 8 | — | Moderate mental retardation. Concomitant strabimas, clinodactyly and other skeletal defects. |
| Trisomy 9 | — | Abnormal facies, skeletal abnormalities, hypoplastic genitalia, congenital heart disease. |
| Trisomy 13 | Pataus | Motor and mental retardation, microcephaly, microophthalmia cleft palate, hare lip, polydactyly and congenital heart disease. |
| Trisomy 18 | Edwards | Motor and mental retardation, flexion deformities, rocker-bottom feet, congenital heart disease. |
| Trisomy 22 | | Mental and motor retardation, microcephaly, abnormal facies and ears. |
| Trisomy 4p | | Abnormal facies, digital abnormalities, foot deformities. |
| Trisomy 9p | | Abnormal facies, large, lowset ears mental retardation, incurved and short 5th digits. |
| $4p^-$ | | Mental retardation, abnormal facies, cleft palate, coloboma, epilepsy, hypospadias, scalp defects |
| $5p^-$ | Cri-du-chat | Mental retardation, micro encephaly, hypertelorism, characteristic cry. |
| $13p^-$<br>13r (ring due to loss of short arm) | | Mental and motor retardation, microcephaly, abnormal facies, abnormal thumbs and ears. |
| $18q^-$ | De Grouchy's | Mental retardation, carp mouth, abnormal ears, tapering fingers. |
| $18q^-$ | De Grouchy's | Mental retardation, ocular abnormalities, abnormal ears, dental decay, CNS abnormalities. |
| 18r | | Combination of $18p^-$ and $18q^-$ features. |
| $21q^-$ | Gdeletion syndrome-I (antimongolism) | Antimongoloid slant eyes, hypertonia, micrognathia, growth retardation, skeletal mal-formations. |
| $22q^-$ | Gdeletion | Epicanthal folds, hypotonia, syndactyly, retarded development. |

3. Broad head , microcephaly
5. Epicanthic fold, braod face, saddle face, widely separated eyes.
6. Low set malformed rotated ears.
7. Abnormal larynx, accessary auricles, oligophrenia and failure to thrive.

**Genetics :** When one of the parent is a translocation heterozygote in whom the short arm of chromosome 5 is translocated to a chromosome of another group ( eg. chromosome no-15 in the D group). Although this parent is normal, he or she will nevertheless produce some unbalanced gametes which carry only the deficient member of the translocation pair.

The affected child receives the deleted chromosome-5 but not the chromosome - 15 to whcih this deleted part is translocated.

Maternal age is also considered to be the cause of this disease.

### 22.2.4 Hermaphrodism and Pseudohermaphrodism

Sex is determined by the composition of the chromosomes in the zygote. When the sex is determined by the sex-chromosomes is called *sex-chromosomal determination* of sex but when the sex is determined by autosomes in called *genetical determination of sex*. In human (and also *Drosophila*) females are XX and males are XY. In human sex chromosomes. X-chromosome has *sxr* gene, while Y-chromosome has *TDF* gene. In presence of Y-chromosome ie *TDF* gene, the *sxr* gene of X-chromosome cannot be expressed.Thus the XY zygote becomes male sex while in presence of only two X chromosmes, the zygote becomes female. Thus the sex is determined by their genotypes of the zygote. This is called *genotypic sex.*

The individuals which possesses female sex determining genotypes will be transformed into a female phenotype such as oviduct, uterus vagina etc. While those having male sex-determining genotypes, the zygote becomes a male phenotype with testis, vasdeferens, prostate gland etc. Every phenotypic sex has their sex-specefic size, vocal cartilage and musculature.

Phenotypic sex depends upon the chromosome number as well as the presence of X and Y chromosomes. They may be super females, supermales, intersex sexes hermaphrodites and pseudohermaphrodites etc.

*Primary sex determination* is the determination of gonads. In mammals, primary sex determination is strictly chromosomal and are not influenced by the environment. Thus a person with XXXXXY having 5 X-chromosomes but only one Y-chromosome whould be a male. In absence of Y, even only presence of one X-chromosome, the individual would be a female.

*The secondary sex charaters*, such as beard, vocal cartilage, musculature, sex-specific size etc. are determined by the hormones secreted from the gonods. In absence of testis, a female phenotype is generated in males, the Mullerian ducts develop while Wolffian duct degenerates. In absence of Y and in presence of only one X (as in the case of Turner's syndrome) originally develops ovaries but these ovaries atrophy before birth and germ cells die before becoming into adult. In absence of gonad (ovary) and due to absence of estrogen hormone, the female secondary sexual characters are not developed.

The testis secretes two hormones, antimullerian hormone (AMH) and testosterone, which is required for the regression of Mullerian duct but the development of male sex organs and secondary sexual characters. Thus *gonadal sex* is of two types, ovary bearing individual of female sex and testis bearing individual of male sex, those having their own primary and secondary sexual characters.

Hermaphrodism is a kind of disorder in gonadal sex where both ovaries and testis are present in either the same or opposite gonads. XO/XY mosaic hermaphrodism occurs where dysgenetic testis may be present with exceedingly rare oocytes with a degree of both secondary sexual characters. Testis on one side and ovary on other side (lateral) or the both testes or ovary in fused (bilateral) or testicular or ovarian tissues on one side and testis or ovary at the other side (unilateral) etc. types of disorders in the gonadal sex are observed.

Y chromosome is translocated to X-chromosome in those tissues where the translocated X-chromosome is inactivated during **dosage compensation**. SRY gene will be turned off, which will result in hermaphrodism.

In a pseudohermephrodism, there is only one type of gonad but the secondary sexual characteristics differ from what would be expected from the gonadal sex. The gonad is testis but the genital duct and genitalia lack full masculinization and display some degree of phenotypic females. This is male pseudoher-maphrodism.

The causes of male pseudohermaphrodism are

1. 3β-hydroxysteroid dehydrogenase enzyme deficiency causes the blockade of early stage of steroidogenesis and testosterone biosynthesis. This is due to mutation of the testosterone hormone synthesizing pathway.
2. Deficiency of C-17 hydroxylase enzyme due to another mutation which is required for the synthesis of C-19 and C-21 steroids from 17α hydroxy-progesterone and 17 α hydroxypregnenolone.
3. Possession of Mullerian duct due to mutation in AMH producing genes in testis.
4. Sometimes the testosterone synthesis is normal but mutation of testosterone receptors causes the hormone ineffective, thus leading to male pseudoher-maphrodism.

In female pseudohermaphrodism, the ovaries and Mullerian derivatives are normally developed and the anatomical ambisexuality is limited to the external genitalia and secondary sexual characters.

The causes of female pseudoher-maphrodism are

1. The congenital virilizing adrenal hyperplasia accounts for most of the female pseudohermaphrodism. This is due to partial C-21 hydroxylase defect, complete C-21 defect, C-11 hyroxylase defect, hydroxysteroid dehydrogenase defect, C-17 hydroxylase defect and due to congenital lipoid adrenal hyperplasia. All are due to mutation in respective genes from which the enzymes are synthesized.
2. Sometimes maternal overproduction of androgens in first trimester causes the fetus to become female hermaphrodism.
3. Overproduction of testosterone from adrenal gland in females causes female pseudohermaphrodism.

### 22.2.5 Chromosomal defects in Azoospermic males

Azoospermia or oligospermia in males is defined as the defects in spermatogenesis and small amount of sperms. It causes sterility.

The cause is usually due to defective development of germinal epithelium in the seminiferous tubules. It may appear due to the failure of hypothalamus to secrete gonadotropin releasing hormone or defects in the production of LH and FSH or testicuar damage due to tuberculosis, syphillis, mumps and malignant infections etc.

Chromosomal abnormalities are the congenital causes of azoospermia in males. It can be documented by a full karyotype analysis or sometimes may be recognised by the presence of Barr-body in the buccal mucosa of the patient. Varieties of chromosomal abnormalilies are found in azoospermic males.

1. Classic Klinefelter's syndrome; where the chromosomal constitution is XXY or XXYY, their buccal smear shows one Barr-body only.

2. XXY/XX, XXY/XY, XXY/XYY etc. mosaic indivuduals where gonad is produced from XXY or XYY cell line, then the normal phenotypic males may become azoospermic; because their testes cannot be able to produce sperm.
3. In poly X and Y disorder in Klinefelters may have a chromosome constitution XXXY, XXXYY, XXXXY etc, their testes become nonfunctional and would result into azoospermia.
4. A mutant XY phenocopy is normal male and the buccal smear showing no Barr-body, may azoospermic if their Y chromosome is defective, the *SRY* gene is deleted or mutated then they show typical Klinefelter but with normal chromosome count.

## 22.3 HUMAN GENETIC DISEASES

Human genetic diseases, ie the diseases caused by the malfunction of certain genes on the chromosomes can be divided into autosome-linked and sex chromosome-linked genetic diseases. Each of them is again divided into dominant and recessive genetic diseases.

### 22.3.1 Autosome-linked Dominant diseases

Some genes are wild in normal persons and remain on the homologous pair of a certain chromosome. But its mutation causes a dominat trait and when is expressed it is present in only one chromosome (heterozygous) or on both chromosomes (homozygous). Therefore, if one of the parent possesses this dominant trait, inherit this disease among 50% of their offspring. If both the parents are heterozygons, 75% of the offspring would get the disease. Such dominant autosomal traits are given in the table 22.4.

**TABLE 22.4**
**Some autosomal dominant traits cause genetic diseases**

| *Name of the disease* | *The genes located on the chromosome numbers* |
|---|---|
| 1. Huntington's chorea | 4 |
| 2. Osteogenesis imperfecta | 7 |
| 3. Marfan's syndrome | 15 |
| 4. Neurofibromatosis | 17 |
| 5. Myotonic dystrophy | 19 and 3 |
| 6. Familial hyperchlesterolemia | 19 |

### 22.3.2 Autosomal Recessive genetic diseases

Some genes are wild in the normal individuals, but after mutation it becomes recessive. When such recessive genes are present in an individual, he or she will suffer from the disease because of it's expression. The heterozygous trait may express the disease to some extent but due to presence of dominant normal gene the severety is very less or not at all.

If the parents both are heterozygous, there is a probability 25% of the offspring to be diseased. On the other hand if the parents are pure normal and diseased homozygous then their offspring would not suffer from the disease severely or not at all. The autosomal recessive traits are given in the table 22.5.

### 22.3.3 Human Sex-linked disease genes

As the males have only one X-chromosomes and females have two X-chromosomes, the

**TABLE 22.5**
**Some autosomal recessive diseased traits in man**

| *Name of the disease* | *genes located on the Chromosome number* |
|---|---|
| 1. Cystic fibrosis | 7 |
| 2. Albinism | 11 |
| 3. Sickle cell anaemia | 11 |
| 4. β-Thalassemia | 11 |
| 5. Phenyl-Ketoneurea | 12 |
| 6. Homocystinuria | 21 |

males are more susceptible to X-linked recessive diseases. If one of the X-chromosomes in females has normal gene then presence of recessive disease gene cannot cause the disease severely or not at all. Similarly Y-linked disease genes are only present in males and so males are the only sufferer of such diseases. X-linked dominant genes are also inherited from both parents. If both the parents are diseased but mother is hererozygous then 50% of their sons and all the daughters would be diseased, but 50% of the daughter is heterozygous diseased. Recessive disease traits show a **criss-cross type of inheritance**.

X-linked dominant diseases are vitamin D resistant rickettes, defects in glucose-6-phosphate dehydrogenase, missing teeth, cleft palate, syndactyly, defective enamel in teeth.

X-linked recessive diseases are haemophilia A and B, night blindness, color blindness, Duchennemuscular dystrophy.

Y-linked genes (holandric genes) are hypertrichosis and several histocompatibility genes.

## 22.4 GENETIC AND BIOCHEMICAL DISORDERS

### 22.4.1 Disorders in Amino acid metabolism

**(a) Phenyl Ketoneuria**

Earliest cases of biochemical mutations were described in man by A.E.Garrod (1909) in his book "Inborn Errors of Metabolism". These are important diseases associated with metabolic break down of *phenylalanine* (Fig. 22.11).

Sequences of biochemical reactions in human beings with the metabolism of *phenylalanine* and various metabolic blocks are shown, which are believed to be caused by the effect of a separately inherited genetic defects on a specific enzyme. For example, in the classic form of phenylketoneuria, a defect in phenylalanine hydroxylase (PAH), prevents the hydroxylation of *phenylalanine*, thereby leading to the accumulation of *phenylalanine* and subsequent neurological damage caused high concentrations of this amino acid. This disease is called as **Follings disease**. Some of the *phenylalanine* also undergoes transamination to phenyl pyruvic acid, which is then excreted with the urine.

Clinically, the child is found to have severe mental retardation due to accumulation of toxic substance in the brain. Elevated level of plasma phenylalanine affects myelination and protein synthesis in the brain cells. Untreated patients have an IQ of less than 20. Due to tyrosine deficiency melanin formation is reduced. Affected children have blonde hair, blue eyes and pigmented region of brain (**Substantia nigra**) may also lack pigment.

The genetic cause of PKU is mutation in the genes encoding component, phenylalanine hydroxylase, located on chromosome 12q24. Several types of mutations such as deletions, insertions and substitutions have been identified. Rare defects include that affects the synthesis of tetrahydroprotein, a cofactor necessary for hydroxylation of phenylalanine or a deficiency of dihydropteridine reductase. This can be diagnosed by **Guthrie test**.

**(b) Alkaptoneuria :**

Block in **alkaptoneuria** leads to the accumulation of homogentistic acid, which is oxidized readily to benzoquinone acetic acid. This then is polymerized into the visible pigment in alkaptonuric urine and also deposited in connective tissues of the body.

This is called **black urine disease**, because patients with alkaptoneuria are asymptomatic as children or young adults, but their urine may turn brown to inky black if left in open air. Pigmentation is due to oxidated form **alkapton**. Pigmentation is noted in the cartilage of ear, sclera and cornea limbus of the eye.

After the age of thirty (due to accumulation of homogentistic acid) the patient begin to develop pain in the weight bearing joints and spines, hips and kness and ribcase can affect breathing. This also casues ochronosis leading to osteoarthritis.

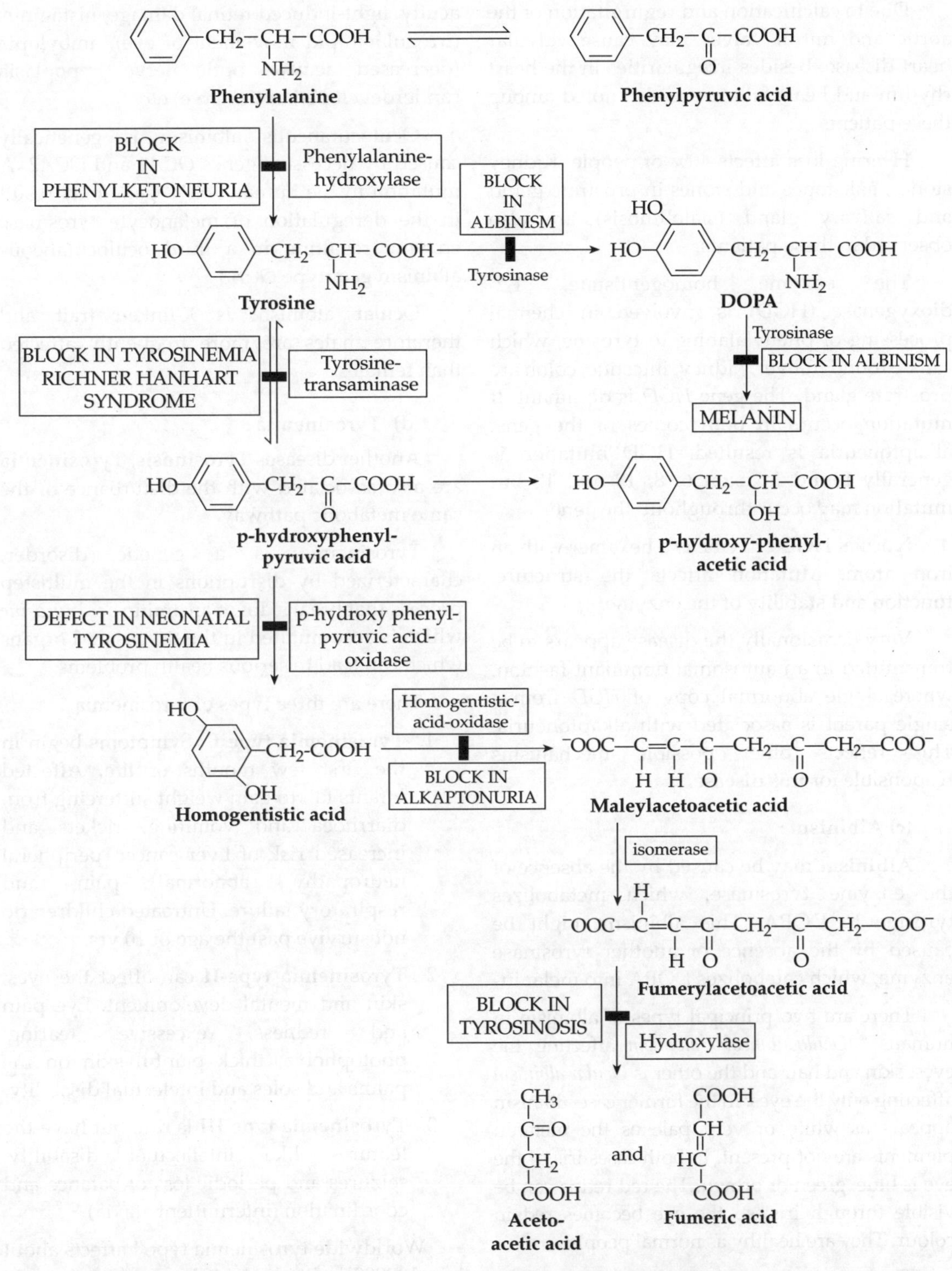


**Fig.22.11 :** *Metabolic pathway in phenylalanine metabolism and some biochemical diseases.*

Due to calcification and regurgitation of the aortic and mitral valves may cause valvular heart disease. Besides irregularities in the heart rhythm and heart failure are also noted among these patients.

Hearing loss affects 40% of people. Kidney stones, gallstones and stones in prostrate gland and salivary gland (sialolithosis) are also observed in these patients.

The enzyme homogentistate, 1,2-dioxygenase (HGD) is involved in chemial processing of phenylalanine to tyrosine, which can be found in liver, kidney, intestine, colon are prostrate gland. The gene *HGD* is dominant. If mutation occurs in both copies of the gene, alkaptoneuria is resulted. HGD mutation is generally found in exon 6, 8, 10 and 13 but mutation may occur throughout the gene.

Normal HGD enzyme is a hexamer with an iron atom. Mutation affects the structure, function and stability of the enzyme.

Very occasionally the disease appears to be transmitted in an autosomal dominant fashion, where single abnormal copy of *HGD* from a single parent is associated with alkaptoneuria. This reflects other possible mechanisms responsible for this disease.

**(c) Albinism :**

**Albinism** may be caused by the absence of the enzyme tyrosinase, which metabolizes tyrosine to DOPA. This albinism might be caused by the absence of another tyrosinase enzyme, which catabolizes DOPA into melanin.

There are two principal types of albinism in humans : *Oculocutaneous albinism* affecting the eyes, skin and hair and the other is *Ocular albinism* affecting only the eyes. in the former case albinism appears as white or very pale as the metanin pigments are not present. In both cases iris of the eye is blue, green or brown. The red retina can be visible through iris, so the eye becomes red in colour. They are healthy as normal people.

The symptoms which are common in albinism are photophobia, reduced visual acuity, light-induced retinal damage, nistagmus (irregular rapid movement of eye), ambylopia (decreased acuity), optic nerve hypoplasia (underdeveloped optic nerve) etc.

Oculocutaneous albinism is genetically caused by necessive genes *OCA1* and *OCA2*. A mutation in the human *TRP-1* gene may result in the deregulation of melanocyte tyrosinase enzyme resulting in a third oculocutaneous albinism genotype *OCA3* .

Ocular albinism is X-linked trait and therefore males are more frequently affected than females.

**(d) Tyrosinemia :**

Another diseases **Tyrosinosis**, **Tyrosinemia** are also associated with the disturbance of the same metabolic pathway.

Tyrosinemia is a genetic disorder, characterized by disruptions in the multistep process that breaks down an amino acid *tyrosine* which is accumutated in the tissues and organs which can lead to serious health problems.

There are three types of tyrosinemia

1. **Tyrosinemia type I :** Symptoms begin in the first few months of life. Affected infants fail to gain weight suffereing from diarrhoea and vomiting, rickets and increased risk of liver cancer, peripheral neuropathy, abnormal pain and respiratory failure. Untreated children do not survive past the age of 10 yrs.
2. **Tyrosinemia type-II** can affect the eyes, skin and mental development. Eye pain and redness, excessive tearing, photophobia, thick painful skin on the palms and soles and intelectual disability.
3. **Tyrosinemia type III** is rare but have the features like intellectual disability, seizures and periodic loss of balance and coordination (intermittent ataxia).

Worldwide tyrosinemia type I affects about 1 in 100000 individuals. it is more common in Quebec, Canada where it occurs 1 in 16000 individuals Tyrosinemia type II is 250000 and type III is rare .

Mutations in *FAH, TAT* and *HPD* genes can cause type I, II and III tyrosinemia respectively.

The *FAH* gene provides instructions for the fumerylaceto acetate hydrolase enzyme which is responsible for final step of tyrosine breakdown. The enzyme produced from the *TAT* gene is tyrosine amino transferase invovled in the first step of tyrosine metabolism. The *HPD* gene provides instructions from making 4-hydroxyphenyl pyruvate dehydrogenase enzyme which is responsible for the second step.

In the liver, these enzymes break down tyrosine and the resulting molecules are excreted by kidney. Mutations of these genes cause a decrease in the activity of one of the enzymes in the breakdown of tyrosine and then the by-products accumulate to a toxic level which can cause damage and death of cells in the liver, kidney, nervous system and other organs.

All are autosomal recessive genes and only in homozygous condition of any one gene can cause tyrosinosis.

Dietary restriction of phenylalanine and tyrosine, use of new drug NTBC (blocks the production of FAH) and gene therapy are recommended.

(e) **Maple Syrap Urine Disease (MSUD) :** MSUD is also called branched-chain ketoacid urea is an autosomal recessive metabolic disorder affecting branched chain amino acids. This is one type of organic acidemia.

Infants with this disease seem healthy at birth but quickly deteriorate. Urine has an odour of sweet-smelling similar to that of maple syrap. The smell is also present in ear wax. It may cause severe brain damage and swelling.

In untreated patients, symptoms include anorexia, vomiting, dehydration, seizure, hypoglycemia, ketoacidosis, pancreatitis and rapid neurological decline, coma and colorectal edema.

The branched chain amino acids are leucine, valine and isoleucine which are present in meat, soy, gluten, whole grain, seeds, beans and pulses. MSUD is a metabolic disorder caused by a deficiency of the branched chain $\alpha$-keto acid dehydrogenase complex (BCK DC) leading to a buildup of the branched chain amino acids and their toxic by products in the blood and urine. The enzyme complex consists of four subunits $E_1\alpha$, $E_1\beta$, $E_2$ and $E_3$. MSUD can result from mutations of any of the four genes. These genes are *BCKDHA, BCKDHB, DBT* and *DLD*. These genes encode 4 proteins that work together as *branched chain $\alpha$-keto-dehydrogenase* complex that is responsble for breakdown of *leucine, valine* and *isoleucine*.

All there genes are autosomal, showing simple Mendelian inheritance.

The MSUD can be classified by the pattern of sign or by its genetic cause.

Classic severe MSUD

Intermediate MSUD

Intermittent MSUD

Thiamine -responsive MSUD

$E_3$-deficient MSUD with lactic acidosis.

As much as 170 human hereditary conditions are known so far to show a loss of enzymatic activity of some of them are listed here in Table 22.6.

### 22.4.2 Disorders in Carbohydrate metabolism

(a) **Galactosemia :** Galactosemia is a disorder that affects the galactose metabolism and an inability to produce energy. Galactosemia is of three types.

• *Classic galactosemia* (type-I) : This is most common and most severe. Affected children often develop feeding difficulties, lethargy, failure to gain weight, yellowing of skin, jaundice, liver damage, sepsis, cataract, spreach difficulties, intellectual disability, loss of functions of ovary (in females)

**TABLE 22.6**
**Some biochemical mutations in human beings**

| Conditions | Phenotypic effect | Enzymes | Normal enzyme activity |
|---|---|---|---|
| **Acatalasia** | Oral gangrene | Catalase | Acts in decomposition of $H_2O_2$. |
| **Alkaptonuria** | Darkening of urine and Arthritis | Homogentistic acid – oxidase | Catalyses transformation of homogentistic acid into Maleylacetoacetic acid |
| **Cretinism** | Thyroid mal-function, mental retardation | Iodotyrosine – deiodinase | Catalyses transformation of tyrosine into thyroxine |
| **Galactosemia** | Liver-enlargement, galactose in urine and blood, Cataracts, mentel deficiency | Galactose – 1 – phophatase, Uridyl– transferase | Catalyses transformation of galactose to glucose |
| **Gaucher's disease** | Presence of Gaucher's cells causing enlargement and destruction of tissues viz. spleen, liver bonemarrow and brain. | Glucocerebrosidase | Catalyses the cleavage of glucose from glucocerebroside. |
| **Glycogen-storage disease** | Liver enlargement caused by accumulation of glycogen | Glucose –6– phosphatase, Branching enzyme, Muscle and liver phosphorylases; Debranching enzymes. | Catalyses transformation of glycogen to glucose. |
| **Huntingtons Chorea** | Progressive mental diterioration | Glutamic acid – decarboxylase | Catalyses synthesis of Gama-amino-butyric acid. |
| **Hypophosphatasis** | Deficient calcification | Alkaline phosphatase | Catalyses hydrolysis of phosphoryl ethanolamine. |
| **Jaundice (congenital non-hemolytic, Crigler Najjar syndrome** | Presence of bile in various tissues | Glucouronyl-transferase | Catalyses transfer of glucouronic acid from uridine diphosphate to bilirubin receptors. |
| **Liesch-Nyhan Syndrome** | Mental retardation, self mutilation spasticity, increased uric acid production. | Hypoxanthineguanine phosphoribosyl transferase | Purine metabolism |
| **Metachromatic Leukodystrophy** | Neurological changes mental regression, Urinary incontinence, death usually by age of 10 yrs. | Arylsulfatase-A | Catabolises sulfatids in normal tissues. |
| **Methmoglobinemia** | Increased proportion of oxidized hemoglobin | NAD-methaemoglobin – reductase | Catalyses the reduction of methaemoglobin into normal hemoglobin. |
| **Nemann-Pick disease** | Accumulation of lipids in reticulo–endothelial cells and destructive changes in nervous system. | Sphingomyelinase | Catalyses hydrolysis of phosphorylcholine from sphingomyelin. |
| **Phenylketonuria** | Mental retardation, excretion of phenylalanine | Phenylalanine-hydroxylase | Converts phenylalanine into tyrosine. |
| **Primaquine — synsitivity (FAVISM)** | Haemolytic anemia | Glucose–6– phorphate – dehydrogenase | Oxidises glucose permitting accumulation of protective levels of glutathione. |
| **Tay-Saches disease** | Mental and motor retardations, death by the age of 2–4 years. | β–D-N-acetyl – hexosaminidase-A | Cleaves the terminal residue from a stored ganglioside (Brain lipid). |

• *Galactokinase deficiency galactosemia* (type II) : It causes fewer medical problems, may develop cataracts.

• *Galactose epimerase deficiency glalactosemia* (type III) : The symptoms may vary from mild to severe and can include cataracts, delayed growth and development, intellectual disability, liver and kidney problems.

Type-I galactosemia occurs 1 in 30000 newborns, Type-II probably affects 1 in 10000 newborns while type III is rare.

Mutations in the *GALT*, *GALK1* and *GALE* genes cause type I, II and III galactosemia respectively. Mutations cause shortage of any of these enzymes allows galactose and related compounds to build up toxic level and accumulate in the tissues and organs, leading to characteristic features of galactosemia (Fig. 22.12).

All these genes are autosomal recessive, the disease is caused only due to presence of recessive gene in homozygous condition.

(b) **Disorders of glucose metabolism :** Hypoglycaemia, *i.e*, the elevated plasma glucose level which causes diabetes mellitus.

This is of three types :

Types-I or early onset diabetes characterised by reduced or absent plasma insulin levels.

Type II or adult onset presents typically as insulin resistance.

MODY or Maturity onset diabetes.

Mutations, in the insulin receptor gene have been associated with type II diabetis. These mutations result in reduction in the number of insulin receptors on the cell's surface or decrease the insulin binding activity level or insulin-stimulated tyrosine kinase activity level. Mutations in mitochondrial DNA and in genes encoding insulin and glucokinase have also been implicated in these disorders. MODY is associated with mutations in the gene encoding glucokinase, located on Chromosome 7p13.

(c) **Disorders of fructose metabolism :** Essential **fructosuria** is caused by a deficiency

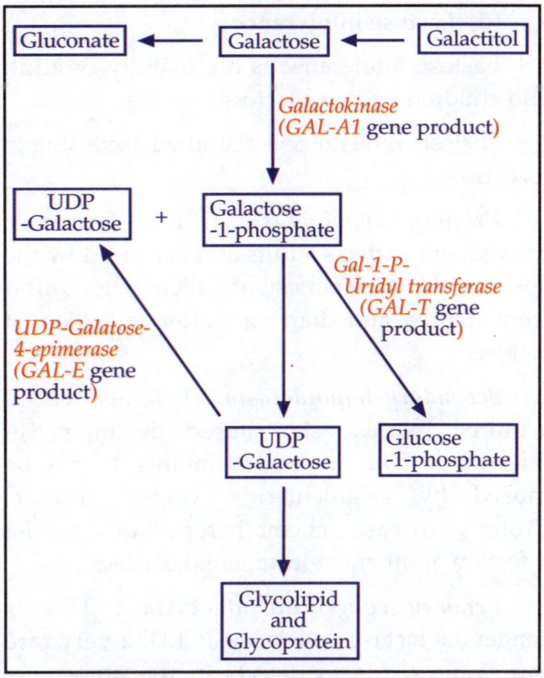


**Fig. 22.12 :** *Galactose metabolism pathway.*

of the enzyme hepatic hexokinase, characterized by incomplete metabolsim of fructose in the liver leading to excretion of fructose in the urine. It does not cause any symptoms.

This is a genetic condition that is inherited in an autosomal recessive manner. Mutations in the *KHK* gene located on the chromosome 2p23.3-23.2 .

Hereditary fructose intolerance or fructosemia is caused by the enzyme aldolase-B. Enzyme deficiency results in an accumulation of fructose-1-phosphate, which inhibits glucose production results in diminished regeneration of ATP. It causes hepatic and renal insufficiency and high degree of mortality. If untreated, causing elevated uric acid, growth abnormalities and can result in coma.

Fructose 1, 6-bisphosphate (FBPase) deficiency is considered as in born error of fructose metabolism. This is a defect of gluconeogenesis. This disorder is manifested by the appearance of hypoglycemia and lactic acidosis neonatally and also life-threatening.

(d) **Lactose intolerance :**

Lactose intolerance is the inabilty of adult and children to digest lactose.

Lactose intolerance is classified according to its causes

***Primary hypolactasia*** : It is a genetic disease, only affects adults and is caused by the absence of lactase persistance allele. They suffer from nausea and diarrhoea after ingestion of lactose.

***Secondary hypolactasia*** : It is also called acquired hypolactasia, caused by injury in intestine in both adults and infants. It may be caused by gastroenteritis, coeliac disease, Crohn's disease chemotherapy or giardia infection or other environmental causes.

***Primary congential alactasia*** : This is congenital lactase deficiency, (CLD) a very rare case, causes due to defects in the autosome-linked recessive allele. They cannot digest lactose from birth even the breast milk due to complete lack to lactase enzyme. The symptoms include abdominal bloating and cramps, flatulence, diarrhoea, nausea, and vomiting.

The *LCT gene provides* the instructions for making lactase. However, analysis of short tandem reapeat polymorphisms (STRPs) surrounding the *LCT* gene have revealed a haplotype that is associated with reduced transcription of *LCT*. The specific DNA sequence in the *MCM6* gene that keeps the *LCT* gene turned on even after breast feeding is stopped. Both *LCT* and *MCM6* genes are lacted on 2q21.

(e) **Glycogen Storage disorders :**

Glycogen storage disorders (GSD is also called glycogenosis and dextrinosis) are a group of inherited diseases that result from a lack of or abnormal functioning of one of the enzymes involved in the glucose to glycogen or the break down of glycogen back to glucose. There are more than 12 types of disorder. Each has a different enzyme lack or malfunction.

Type I GSD is common. Type VIII and X are now classified with type VI.

Most, but not all, GSDs are inherited in a pattern called834 autosomal recessive inheritance. X-linked inheritance pattern is found in type IX.

(1) Type I GSD is known as **Von Glerke** disease. This is due to transport defect of glucose-6-phosphate into microsomal compartment. GSD type 1a is caused by G6Pase deficiency and GSD type 1b is caused by specific translocase T1. The symptoms include low blood sugar, sweating, tremor, convulsions, hepatomegali, weaker muscle, obesity, kidney problems, aching muscles etc.

(b) Type II GSD is known as acid maltase deficiency or **Pompe disease** is a lysosomal disease due to deficiency of the enzyme α-1,4-glucosidase. Glycogen is stored in the tissues causing cardiomyopathy and muscular hypotonia.

(iii) GSD type III is known as **Forbes-Cori disease** or **limit dextrinosis**. Glycogen is stored in liver, muscle and other tissues.

(iv) GSD type IV is known as **amylopectinosis** or **Anderson disease** causing progressive hepatomegaly and accumulations of abnormal polysaccharides. The main clinical features are liver insufficiency and abnormalities of heart and nervous system.

(v) GSD type-V is known as **Mc-Ardle disease** affects skeletal muscle in adults caused by muscle phosphorylase deficiency.

(vi) GSD type VI is also known as **Hers disease** caused by deficiency of hepatic phosphorylase deficiency or deficiency of other enzyems necessary for phosphorylase activation.

(vii) GSD type VII is known as **Tarul disease** arises as a result of phospho-fructokinase (PFK) deficiency, which is located in skeletal muscle and erythrocytes.

Other GSDs are type IX which is caused due to deficiency of the enzyme phosphorylase kinase (PHKA2); type XI or **Falconi-Bickel syndrome** which is caused by deficiency of glucose transporter (GLUT2), type XII or **Red cell aldolase deficiency disease** which is caused by the deficiency of Aldolase A enzyme; type XIII is caused by the deficiency of β-enolase and type O (**Lewis' disease**) is caused by deficiency of glycogen synthase.

Mutations in G6PC gene causes GSD1a and *SLC37A4* gene causes GSD1b. Mutations of these two genes prevent breakdown of glucose-6-phosphate and thus glycogen and fat is stored in the cell and may damage to liver and kidney.

### 22.4.3 Disorders of Lipid metabolism

**(a)** ***Medium chain acyl-Coenzyme-A dehydrogenase deficiency or MCAD.***

MCAD or MCADD is a disorder of fatty acid oxidation due to deficiency of medium chain acyl CoA dehydrogenase enzyme that impairs the body's ability to breakdown medium chain fatty acids (6-12C) into acetyl CoA by the process of β-oxidation in mitochondria. The disease is characterised by hypoglycaemia and sudden death in a fasting condition or vomiting.

MCAD is interited in an autosomal recessive manner. The gene *ACADM* is involved which is located at 1p3, with 12 exons and coding a protein of 421 amino acids. Not only the mutation of this gene, presence of environmental or physiological stressors also responsible for MCDp. Medium chain fatty acid oxidation depends upon cytosolic carnitine and two mitochondrial membrane bound enzymes CPTI and CPTII.

**(b)** ***Long chain and Very long chain acyl-CoA dehydrogenase deficiency (LCAD and VLCAD)***

The LCAD and VLCAD are caused by the deficiency of long chain acyl CoA dehydrogenase activity and very long chain acyl CoA dehydrogenase activity respectively, and thus prevents the body from converting certain fats to energy particularly during fasting.

The symptoms appear during infancy or early childhood include hypoglycaemia, lethergy, muscle weakness and life threatening heart and liver problems.

The condition is inherited in an autosomal recessive pattern. Mutations of the gene *ACADVL* causes VLCAD deficiency in a homozygous condition.

Long-chain 3-hydroxy acyl coA dehydrogenase is 1 of 3 enzymatic activities that make up the trifunctional protein in inner mitochondrial membrane. Other two activities of the protein are 2-enoyl CoA hydratase and Long chain 3-ketoacyl CoA thiokinase. This is specific for C12-C16 chain length. The genes for alpha and beta subunits have been localized in chromosome-2 which are inherited as an autosomal recessive traits. In infants the symptoms appear as acute hypoketoic hypoglycaemia and vomiting after fasting (Fig. 22.13).

**(c)** ***Smith-Lemli-Opitz syndrome (SLOS)***

SLOS is an inborn error of cholesterol synthesis caused by 7-dehydrocholesterol reductase deficiency.

The symptoms include microcephaly, ptosis, short and upturned nose, micrognathia, epicanthal folds. Other symptoms include lowset posteriorly rotated ears, cleft palate or lip, hypoplasia of corpus callosum, polydactyly, syndactyly, congenital heart disease etc. They may have low normal intelligence.

Mutations in *DHCR7* gene casue SLOS. *DHCR7* gene provides instructions for making the enzyme called 7-dehydrocholesterol reductase which is responsible for the final step in the production for cholesterol. Lack of this enzyme prevents formation of cholesterol allowing accumulation of toxic by - products in the blood, nervous systems and other tissues.

*DHCR7* is an autosomal gene, located on chromosome 11q 12-13 Mutations of this gene is recessive allele. SLOS is caused by homozygous condition of this mutant allele.

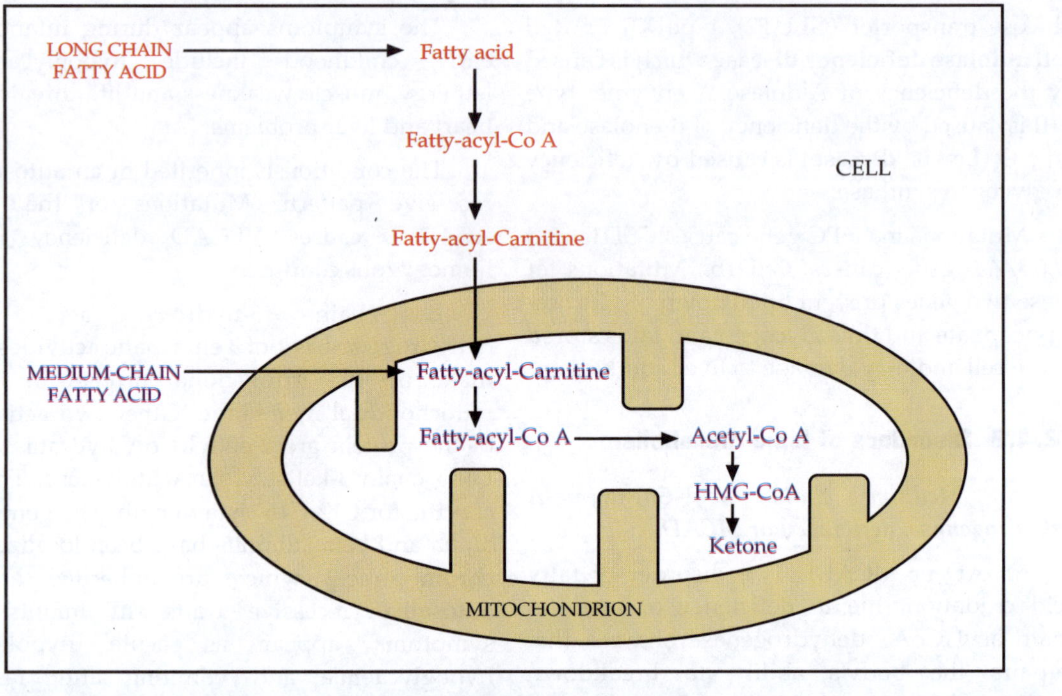


**Fig. 22.13 :** *Fatty acid metabolic pathway*

### 22.4.4 Lysosomal Storage disorders (LSDs)

LSDs (or Larse' soumel) are caused by Lysosomal disfunctions usually due to deficiency of a single enzyme required for metabolism of lipids, glycoproteins.

LSDs are mainly of 4 types by the nature of stored materials involved.

1. (E75) lipid storage disorders, mainly sphingolipidoses (including Gaucher's and Nemann-Pick diseases)

   (E 75.0-E75.1) gangliosidosis (including Tay-Sachs disease

   (E75.2) Leukodystrophies.
2. E(76.0) mucopolysaccharidoses (including Hunter syndrome and Hurler disease)
3. E(77) glycoprotein storage disorder
4. E 77.0 – 77.1 mucolipidoses.

The symptoms include developmental delay, movement disorders, seizures, dementia, deafness and blindness, hepatomegali, spleenomegali, pulmonary and cardiac problems and abnormal growths of bones.

The LSDs are group of autosomal recessive inborn errors of metabolism. Althrough each disorder results from different gene mutations that translate into a dificiency in enzyme activity.

### 22.4.5 Urea Cycle Disorders

***Ornithine Transcarbomylase (OTC) deficiency :***

Ornithine transcarbomylase is an enzyme of urea cycle which normally prevents the accumulation of nitrogenous wastes in the body. OTC deficiency causes toxic ammonia to accumulate in the blood and if its levels become high, causes defects in the nervous system. The symptoms include lethergy, unwilling to eat, breathing problem, unusual body movement and coma, even death.

The *OTC* gene is responsible for the production of the enzyme ornithine transcarbamylase . This is X-linked gene located on Xp21, proximal to dystrophin. Mutations in this gene are of exon deletion and missence type which is recessive. So in females homozygous state causes this disease. Father cannot transmit the disease to his sons.

### 22.4.6 Genetic defects in the Oxidative Phosphorylation (OXPHOS) system

The oxidative phosphorylation system consists of 5 multiprotein complexes and mobile carriers embedded in the inner mitochondrial membrane. The OXPHOS system is under dual genetic control. Defects in OXPHOS system is either maternal (due to mitochondrial gene mutation) or autosomal and X-linked (due to nuclear gene mutation).

The mito-genome encodes 13 peptides and rRNA genes. The nuclear genome encodes the additional genes required for mito-transcription translation, post translational modification and transport. Nuclear-mitochondrial communication is a highly complex process.

Mitochondrial gene mutation involved in mtDNA replication causes progressive opthalmic ophthalmoplegia (PEO), mito DNA depletion system and mitochondrial neurogastrointestinal encephatopathy (MNGIE).

Electron transfer flavoprotein (ETF) is a nuclear encoded protein through which electrons can enter the OXPHOS system. Inherited defects in these proteins can result in glutaric acidemia type II characterised by hypotonia, hypoglycaemia, hepatomegaly and metabolic acidemia. This may cause high degree of mortality among affected neonates.

Pyruvate dehydrogenase (PDH) complex deficiency is caused by mutation of X-linked gene (Xp22) which encodes E1 of PDH complex. The disorder includes lactic acidemia, congenital defects in central nervous system and developmental delay.

### 22.4.7 Defects in transport system

(a) ***Wilson's disease or Hepatolenticular degeneration*** : Wilson's disease is caused by the accumulation of Cu in the liver and brain tissues.

The symptoms of liver disease include tiredness due to hepatic encephalopathy, portal hypertension spelenomegali, ascites, cirrhosis and hepatocellular carcinoma and finally swelling of the brain.

The neuropsychiatic symptoms include parkinsonism, bradykinesia, tremor, seizure, migraine, depression, anxiety and psychosis etc.

Other symptoms are Kayser-Fleischer (KF) ring around the cornea, cataracts, renal tubular acidosis, cardio myopathy and hypoparathyriodism, infertility etc.

The Wilson's disease gene (*ATP7B*) has been mapped to chromosome 13q 14.3 and is expressed primarily in the liver, kidney and placenta. The gene codes for a P-type ATPase that transports copper into bile and incorporates it into ceruloplasm. Mutation of this gene is recessive so, homozygous condition causes this disease.

About 300 mutations of *ATP7B* gene have been described. In Western populations H1069 Q mutation (*his* → *gln* at 1069 position of protein) which in China R778L (*Arg* → *leu* at 778) is very often found.

*PRNP* gene can modify the course of the disease.

(b) ***Menkes Disease (MND)*** : The Menkes disease is known as copper transport disease of *Congenital Hypocupremia* or *Kinky hair syndrome*. This is a disorder that affects copper levels in the body due to defective transport of copper that is absorbed by gastrointestinal tract but cannot be transported from these cells to blood stream. Copper is required as cofactor of many enzymes such as tyrosinase, cytochrome C oxidase and lysyl oxidase. The lysyl oxidase is required for crosslinking collagen and elastin. Reduced enzyme function results in weak cross linkage and weakens the vascular wall and loosening of skin.

The symptoms include sparse kinky hair, mental retardation, hypothermia, seizure, hypopigmented twisted hair, loosening of skin, arterial rupture, hypotonia that may be fatal to early childhood.

Mutations in the *ATP7A* cause MND. The *ATP7A* gene products is important for regulating copper levels in the tissue is toxic. Mutation of *ATP7A* gene causes accumulation of copper in small intestine and kidneys while the brains other tissues have unusually low levels thus reducing the activity of brain, bone, skin, hair, blood vessels and nervous system.

Menkes syndrome is inherited in an X-linked recessive pattern. The gene is located on chromosome Xq13. Therefore only one mutated X-chromosome may cause the disease in males but in females only homozygous state causes the disease. Mutations are noted as missense, nonsense, deletion or splicing defects etc. About one third case, Menkes disease is caused by new mutations without any family background.

(c) ***Acrodermatitis Enteropathica*** : The disease is also known as **Brandt syndrome**, **Danbold-cross syndrome** and **Congenital zinc deficiency**. The disease occurs due to defective absorbtion of Zn.

Symptoms appear in the first few months of birth which include erythomatous patches and plaques of dry scaly skin, eczematous lesions or pustules, alopecia, diarrhoea, inflammation of the nail fold and periorificial (around mouth and anus) dermatitis. The skin lesions may be infected with bacteria, fungi and *Candida albicans.*

A mutation of the gene *SLC39A4* on the chromosome 8q24.3 is responsible for the disorder. The gene encodes a transmembrane protein that serves zinc uptake from intestinal lumen. The disease is fatal if untreated.

(d) ***Hereditary Haemochromatosis (HH-disease)*** : The disease is characterised by excessive intestinal absorption of dietary iron resulting in pathological increase in total body iron stores. The symptoms include, joint and bone pains, cirrhosis of liver, hepatocellular carcinoma, jaundice, type 2 diabetes, erectile disfunction, arthritis and adrenal insufficiency etc.

Iron is stored in liver, heart and spleen thus causing end organ damage *i.e.* cirrhosis of liver, congresive heart failure, diabetes etc fatal life threatening diseases.

The disease is caused by the a HLA class I like gene known as *HFE* located on chromosome *6p21* near the MHC HLA-A3 region which codes for a protein that participates regulation of iron absorption. *HFE* has two common mutations *C282Y* and *H63D*. The *C282Y* is a transition point mutation (guanine $\rightarrow$ adenine at 845 position) resulting missense mutation (*cys* $\rightarrow$ *tyr*).

Homozygosity for *C282Y* mutation is most common. *C282Y/H63D* mutation is so called compound heterozygotes causing iorn overload.

### 22.4.8 Genetic disorders of Haemoglobin structural variants

Besides HbA ($\alpha_2\beta_2$) which is usually 95-98% of total Hb in normal adults, HbA$_2$ ($\alpha_2\partial_2$) 2.0% and HbA$_{IC}$ (glucose at NH$_2$ terminus of β chain) is about 5%.

In newborn HbF ($\alpha_2\gamma_2$) makes up 50-85% HbGower I ($\zeta_2\gamma_2$), Gower II ($\alpha_2\varepsilon_2$) and Port land ($\zeta_2\gamma_2$) are embryonic hemoglobins etc.

Few haemoglobin variants are as follows (Table 22.7)

## 22.5 MULTIFACTORIAL DISORDERS IN THE ADULT POPULATION

Many traits are thought to be influencd not only by multiple genes (Polygenic) but also by environmental factors. These traits are said to be **multifactorial.**

### 22.5.1 Hypertension

Hypertension is defined as having a blood pressue higher than 140 mm Hg systolic pressure and 90 mm Hg diastolic pressure.

**TABLE 22.7**
**Hb variants and their features**

| Name | Globin fold | Amino acid substitution | Features |
|---|---|---|---|
| **UNSTABLE MUTANTS** | | | |
| Brockton | β138 (H16) | *Ala→ Pro* | Hemolytic anaemia, |
| Philly | β35 (C1) | *Tyr→ Phe* | Hemolytic anaemia, increased oxygen affinity |
| Peterborough | β111 (G13) | *Val → Phe* | Hemolytic anaemia, decreased oxygen affinity |
| Stanmore | β111(G13) | *Val → Ala* | Hemolytic anaemia, decreased oxygen affinity |
| Contaldo | α1 or α2 (103) G10 | *His → Arg* | Hemolytic anaemia |
| Hirosaki | α2 43 (CE1) | *Phe → Leu* | Hemolytic anaemia |
| Terre Haute | β106 (G8) | *Leu → Arg* | Hemolytic anaemia |
| **HIGH AFFINITY VARIANTS** | | | |
| Kempsey | β99 (G1) | *Ala → Asn* | Hemolytic anaemia, decreased cooperativity |
| Hiroshima | β146 (HC3) | *His → Asp* | Erythrocytosis, decreases cooperativity, decreased Bohr effect |
| Providence | β82 (EF 6) | *Lys → Thr* | Erythrocyfosis, Low oxygen affinity |
| Helsinki | β82 (EF6) | *Lys → Met* | Erythrocytosis, decreased Bohr effect |
| **LOW AFFINITY VARIANTS** | | | |
| Kansas | β102 (G4) | *Asn → Thr* | Unstable R-state, cynosis,decreased cooperativity |
| Beth Israel | β102 (G4) | *Asn → Ser* | Unstable R-state, Cynosis, decreased cooperativity |
| St. Mande | β102 (G4) | *Asn →Tyr* | Unstable R-state, Cynosis |
| **METHANOGLOBIN VARIANTS** | | | |
| M-Lwate | α1 or α2 (F8) | *His → Tyr* | Methemoglobinemia |
| M-Saskatoon | β63 (E7) | *His → Tyr* | Methemoglobinemia |
| **GLOBIN CHAIN ELONGATION VARIANT** | | | |
| Constant Spring | α2 142 (HC3) | Stop → *Gln* | Microcytosis |
| **VARIANTS WITH MULTIPLE EFFECTS** | | | |
| HbE | β26 (B8) | *Glu → Lys* | Microcytosis, Unstable |
| Warsaw | β42 (CD1) | *Phe → Val* | hemolytic, anaemia, Cyanosis, Heizn body |
| Hammersmith | β42 (CD1) | *Phe → Ser* | Hemolytic anaemia cyanosis |
| Zurich | β63 (E7) | *His → Arg* | Increased oxygen affinity, Heinz, body increased CO affinity |
| Jamaica Plain | β6 (A3) | *Glu → Val* | Hemolytic anaemia, Cynosis |
| | β68 (E12) | *Leu → Phe* | Heinz body, decreased oxygen affinity |
| **OTHER VARIANTS** | | | |
| Hb-Lepore | δ–β fusion gene | | Mild, β-thalassaemia |
| Anti Lepore | β–δ fusion gene | | Mild, β-thalassaemia |
| Gun Hill | deletion of 5 amino acid in β-chain | | β-thalassaemia |
| Hb-Tak | Frame shift mutation | β chain extended 11 residues | |

American Heart Association (AHA) defined the following ranges of blood pressure.

**Causes of hypertension : (Table 22.8 new)**

1. Acute stress and intense exercise
2. Physical inactivity
3. High Na, Low K in the diet
4. Salt-rich diet associoted with processed food and fatty acids
5. Consuming alcohol and use of tobacco
6. Age
7. Obesity and overweight
8. Chronic Kidney disease
9. Adrenal tumor
10. Pheochromocytomia (a cancer)
11. Congenital adrenal hyperplasia
12. Hypothyroidism
13. Pregnancy
14. Sleep apnea

**TABLE 22.8**
**Classification of blood pressure for adults (Defined by American Heart Association)**

| *Category* | *Systolic mm Hg* | *diastolic mm Hg* |
|---|---|---|
| Normal | 90–119 | 60–79 |
| High normal (Prehypertension) | 120–139 | 80–89 |
| Stage 1 hypertension | 140–159 | 90–99 |
| Stage 2 hypertension | 160–179 | 100–109 |
| Stage 3 Hypertension (Hypertensive emergency) | = 180 | = 110 |
| Isolated systolic hypertension | = 140 | < 90 |

**Symptoms :** Hypertension is often referred to as "the silent killer". It may be asymptomatic but long term hypertension can cause arteriosclerosis. The complications include.

1. Heart failure due to enlarged heart.
2. Aneurysm *i.e.* bulge in the wall of arteries which can burst causing severe bleeding in some organs and may cause death.
3. Heart attack or stroke due to narrowing of blood capillaries.
4. Rupture of blood capillaries causing bindness.

**Genetics of hypertension :** Hypertension is related to the family background. Blood pressure is regulated by Renin-Angiotensin system. *AGT* is the most scrutinized gene linked to hypertension. This gene is expressed in several tissues, including liver, adipose tissue, heart, vessel wall, brain and kidney. This gene stretches over only 12 Kb on chromosome 1 (1 q 42-43) and contains 5 exons A promoter found in 1.2 kb region immediatly upstream of 1st exon. An enhancer in found immediately downstream of 2nd polyadenylation site which may cause 40-fold its induction expression of the gene. AGT angiotensinogen protein is 485 amino acid (61 KDa), a glycoprotein. After removal of signal peptides it is 452 amino acids is a substrate of the enzyme renin.

**Gordon syndrome** or **pseudo hypoaldosterism** (PHA) is a condition where aldosterone levels are elevated due to lack of feed back inhibition. It may cause hypertension. The inheritance is due to autosomal dominant pattern exhibiting salt ion mainly from kidneys. The other is multisystem form exhibiting salt loss from kidneys, lung, sweat and salivary glands. *WNK4* and *WNK*1 kinase genes mutations are responsible for this disease.

**Liddle syndrome** is also a PHA caused by disregulation of epithelium sodium channel due to a genetic mutation at the 16p13-p12 locus, an autosomal dominant gene. These channels are found in Kidney renal tubule, lungs and sweat glands. Hypertension is due to increase in extacellular volume of water.

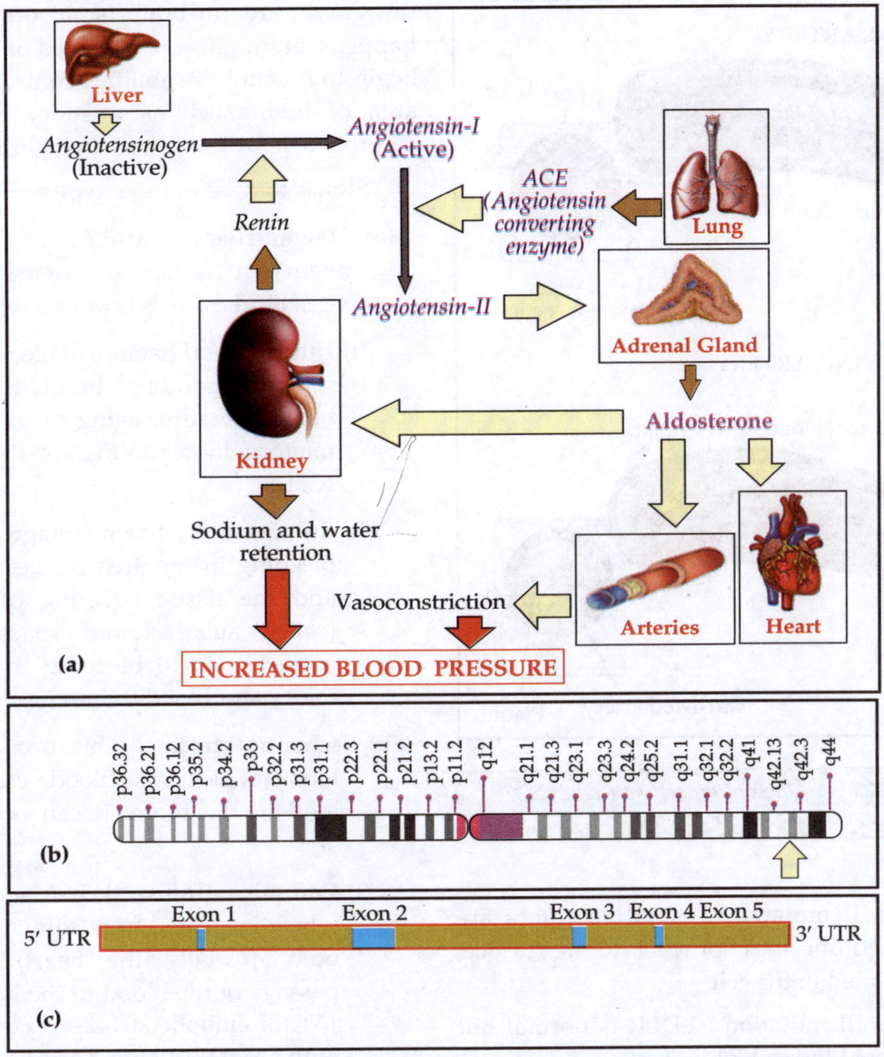


**Fig. 22.14 :** *(a) Renin-Angiotensin pathway in hypertension; (b) Location of AGT gene on chromosome-1; (c) AGT gene stretched on chromosome-1*

## 22.5.2 Coronary Heart Disease (CHD)

CHD is a disease in which plaques build up inside the coronary arteries. These arteries supply oxygen-rich blood to the heart muscle. The plaques in the arteries are called atherosclerosis. Overtime, plaques can harden or rupture or narrow the arteries and reduce the blood or oxygen-rich blood to the heart. It causes cardiac angina, heart attack, pain in shoulder, arms, neck, jaw and back. Heart failure may occur (Fig. 22.15).

For the formation of plaques in arteries, LDL (Low density lipoprotein) is essential. The *LDLR* (LDL-receptor) gene located on 19p is responsible for uptake of LDL-bound cholesterol into the cell. Mutation is dominant, so even in heterozygous condition causes elevated LDL in the plasma. Missense or nonsense submutations of LDLR can be grouped into 5 broad classes.

(i) Class I mutation : Total Lack of LDLR proteins. Heterozygotes have only half of the normal number of receptors.

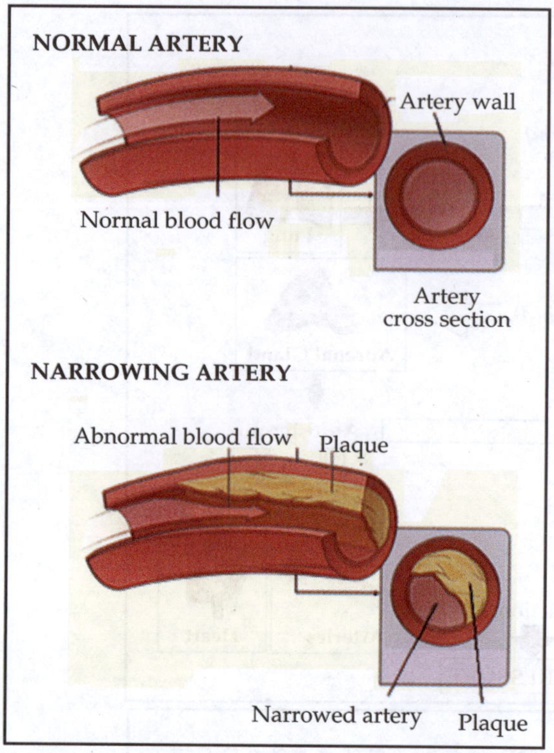


**Fig. 22.15 :** *Atherosclerosis with plaques in the arterial lumen*

(ii) Class II mutation : LDLR receptors are formed but does not reach to the surface, degraded in the cell.

(iii) Class III mutation : LDLR is normal but can not bind to LDL.

(iv) Class IV mutation : LDLR is normal but cannot migrate to their specific coated pits. thus this is defective.

(v) Class V mutation : LDLR can not dissociate from endocytosed LDL and so it can not be recycled.

Mutations in another gene encoding apolipoprotein B are also responsible for LDL in plasma.

### 22.5.3 Stroke

A stroke is a **"brain attack"**. It is a syndrome not a disease . It occurs when blood flow to an area of brain is cut off. When this happens, brain cells are deprived of oxygen and begin to die and the abilities controlled by that area of brain such as memory and muscle control are lost or may lose their ability to speak.

Stokes may be of three types

(a) **Haemorrhage stroke :** The brian aneurysm bursts or weakened blood vessel leakes. This is of two types

(i) **Intracerebral haemorrhage :** Blood leaks into surrounding brain tissue, High blood pressure, aging or arteriovenous malformation (AVM) are the causes of ICH.

(ii) **Subarachnoid haemorrhage :** It involves bleeding in the area between the brain and the tissue covering of the brain (called subarachnoid space). This is caused by AVM, bleeding disorder, head injury and Blood thinner.

(b) **Ischemic stroke :** This occurs when a blood clot blocks the blood vesels carrying blood to the brain. it can occur in two ways :

(i) **Embolic stroke :** When a blood clot which is formed from somewhere in the body (usually the heart) block the passage of the blood to the brain. About 15% of embolic strokes occur in people with atrial fibrilation (Afib)

(ii) **Thrombotic stroke :** This is caused by a blood clot that forms inside one of the arteries supplying blood to the brain, usually due to high cholesterol in the blood and high blood pressure. The clotting may occur in large vessel or small vessels of the brain.

(c) **Transient ischemic attack (TIA) :** When blood flow to a part of the brain stops for a short period of time, is called TIA. It may last for 24 hrs and do not cause permanent brain damage but may be the sign of future stroke attack. TIA is caused by any one of the three ways :

(i) Narrowing of major artery carrying blood to the brain.

(ii) A blood clot in another part of the body

(iii) Narrowing or blocking of smaller blood vessels in the brain.

The risk factors may be grouped into two

(i) The risk factors that we cannot control such as, increasing age, genetic factor, sex (males are more prone) heredity and race.

(ii) The risk factors that can be controlled, such as high blood pressure, tabocco smoking, diabetes, high cholesterol, obesity and physical inactivity, carotid or arterial diseases, transient heart attack, Atrial fibrillation, excesive alcohol intake, use of illegal drugs etc.

A large number of monogenic disorders can cause stroke.

Cerebral small vessel disease is CADSIL (cerebral autosomal dominant arteriopathy with subcortical infracts and leucoencephalopathy) results from mutations of *NOTCH 3* gene. It causes aggregation of granular osmiophilic deposits in the brain vessel causing reduction of blood flow to the brain.

Mutations in the HtrA serine protease encoded by *HTRA-1* gene which is involved in TGF-β signaling is responsible for stroke.

The *COL4A1* gene endoding type IV collagen α-1 chain, is known to cause autosomal dominant porencephaly and infantile hemiparesis causing childhood haemorrhage.

A C-terminal frame-shift mutation of the gene *TREX1* encodes a trunkated DNA-specific 3′ → 5′ exonuclease may cause autosomal dominant retinal vasculopathy with cerebral leucodystrophy resulting visual loss, stroke, dementia in the middle age.

Linkage studies indicated a candidate gene at the 13q 12 locus which is associated with stroke and myocardial infraction. It encodes lipoxygenase activating protein (ALOX5AP) which contributes to risk of stroke by enhancing leucotrience A4 pathway and leukotrience B4 receptors (BLT1 and 2).

Genome-wide association studies and stroke (GWAS) indicated two loci associated with atrial fibrillation. The first is a risk variant on 4q25 is believed to be a gene *PITX 2*, encoding β-catenin regulated transcription factor. The second variant associated with atrial fibrillation in the *ZFHX 3* gene at 16q22. The gene encodes zinc-finger protein.

An association between SNPs in the chromosome 9q21 region and coronary artery disease has been reported by many groups. Genes in this region include the cyclin-dependent kinase inhibitor *CDK 2MA* and CDK2MB and recently discovered non-coding RNA designated *ANRIL* whose function is unknown.

Ischemic heart stroke is associated with an SNP in a member of protein kinase family *PRKCH*. This is a serine threonine kinase.

SNPs in the *CELSRI* (Cadherin EGF LAG seven-pass G-type receptor) gene has been reported.

A multicenter mitochondrial GWAS in ischaemic stroke cases identified 144 SNPs.

A classical syndrome is MELAS (mitochondrial encephalomyopathy lactic acidosis and stoke-like symptoms) is a rare maternally inherited disorder.

Besides genetic causes, some of the known environmental risk factors are hypertension, atherosclerosis, smoking and obesity etc.

### 22.5.4 Schizophrenia

Schizophrenia is a heritable complex mental diaorder. Tremendous effort has been expended in the last two decades to identify genes influencing this disorder.

A schizophrenia gene *ZNF804A* as target for hsa-miR -137 has been found to be associated with schizophrenia etiology. Four loci viz. *CACNA 1C, TCF4, CSMD1, C10, ori 26* are experimentalally validated as hsa-miR-targets.

A schizophrenia gene locus on chromosome 17q21 has been investigated in the families of Latin American ancestry.

A map of 191 SNPs was built across a 5 MB segment from chromosome 13q34 has been genetically linked to schizophrenia. Two overlapping genes *G72* and *G30* transcribed in brain. The enzyme D-amino acid oxidase (DAAO)) is expressed in the brain, which oxidizes D-serine, a protein activator of N-methyl-D-aspartate type glutamate receptor. G72 product is associated with the activation of DAAO and involved in schizophrenia.

In a recent study, family-based association analysis of 36 SSLP and SNP markers implicated two regions separated by ~7 Mb of a gene located in region 6p24-21. The first region is 6p 22.3 with SNPs within 140 Kb gene *DTNBP1* (*disbindin*) are associated with schizophrenia.

SHANK3 a synaptic protein. Two mutations R1117X and R536W were identified in two families with schizophrenia. Mutations of SHANK3 is also associated with autism. So there must be a molecular link between these two neurodevelopmental disorders.

### 22.3.5 Diabetes mellitus

Diabetes mellitus (DM) often simply referred to as diabetes is a metabolic disorder, where in the human body does not produce or properly use insulin, a hormone that is required to convert sugar into energy (Table) 22.9.

**TABLE 22.9**
**The WHO diabetic criteria**

| *Condition* | *2 hrs. after glucose consumption (mg/dl)* | *Fasting glucose (mg/dl)* |
|---|---|---|
| Normal | < 140 | <110 |
| Impaired fasting glycemia | <140 | <110 |
| Impaired glucose tolerance | > 140 | <126 |
| Diabetes mellitus | >200 | >126 |

**Types of diabetes**

1. **Type 1 diabetes :** It results from the condition in which the pancreas fails to produce insulin
2. **Type 2 diabetes :** It results from condition in which the body cells fail to use insulin properly.
3. **Gestational diabetes or Type 3 diabetes :** The condition when the pregnant women, who have never had diabetes before, have a high blood glucose level during pregnancy.
4. **Double diabetes :** Insulin resistant type-1 diabetes (Table 22.10).

**Etiology of type 1 diabetes :** This is characterized by loss of insulin producing β-cells of islets of Langerhans in the pancreas. Onset of disease occurs in the childhood and so that is called **Juvenile diabetes.** Several agents can cause destruction of β cells, viz.,

1. Infection with certain bacterial and viral infections
2. Exposure to food-borne chemicals or toxins such as steroids, dilantin, alloxan, streptozocin thiazide diuretics. Consumption of alcohol can cause destruction of β-cells.
3. Contain syndromes such as Progeria, Turner's, Down's, Prader-Willi etc. syndromes.
4. Exposure to very young infants with Cow's milk where unidentified component triggers the autoimmune reaction against β-cells.

**Etiology of type 2 diabetes :** Pancreas is partially or completely unable to use insulin. This is sometimes referred to as insulin resistance. It is often called **adult-onset diabetes** or **life-style dependent diabetes**. because it depends on the diet, obesity physical inactivity, overeating, genetic factor. The causes are as follows.

**TABLE 22.10**
**Other types of diabetes**

| | |
|---|---|
| 1. Genetic defects of β-cell function | (a) Maturity onset diabetes of the young (MODY)<br>(b) Mitochondrial DNA mutations. |
| 2. Genetic defects in insulin processing and insulin action | (a) Defects in pro-insulin conversion<br>(b) Insulin gene mutation<br>(c) Insulin receptor mutation |
| 3. Exocrine Pancreas defects | (a) Chronic pancreatitis<br>(b) Pancreactomy<br>(c) Cystic fibrosis<br>(d) Haemochromatosis<br>(e) Fibrocalculous pancreatopathy |
| 4. Endocrinopathies | (a) Growth hormone excess<br>(b) Cushing syndrome<br>(c) Hyperthyroidism<br>(d) Glucagonoma |
| 5. Infections | (a) Cytomegalovirus infection<br>(b) Coxsakievirus B |
| 6. Drugs | (a) Glucocorticoids<br>(b) Thyroid hormane<br>(c) β-adrenergic agonists |
| 7. Autoimmunity | (a) Latent autoimmune diabetes of adult (LADA) is also called type 1.5 diabetes. |

1. The receptors on cells in the body failed to be stimulated by insulin (insulin resistance)
2. Simply insufficient availability of insulin.
3. Abnormal, less functionable insulin due to mutation.
4. Mutation in receptor which can not properly transduce glucose metabolism.

**Genetics of type-1 diabetes :** About 18 regions of the genome have been linked with influence the risk of type-1 diabetes, which has been labeled *IDDM-1* to 18 Again each of which may contain several genes. IDDM-1 contains HLA genes (Fig. 22.16).

Development of type-1 is increased by certain variants of the *HLA-DOA1 HLA-DOB1* and *HLA-DRB1* genes which belong to a family of genes called HLA complex.

**Genetics of type 2 diabetes :** To date only two genes, Calpain 10 (*CAPN-10)* and Hepatocyte nuclear factor 4 -alpha (*HNF4A*) have been identified.

1. ***Calpain 10***(*CAPN 10*) **gene :** The calpain 10 is a Calcium-activated enzyme that breaks down protein. Genetic variants of CAPN-10 may alter insulin secretion, insulin action and production of glucose by the liver. The gene is located near the end of long arm of chromosome-2.

It has been found that SNPs in introns of Calpain 10 gene is associated with an increased susceptibility to diabetes. Intron-3 contained SNP-43 also called UCSNP-43 (for University of Chicago) where adenine is switched to guanine. SNPs are also found in intron-6 (SNP-15) and intron-13 (SNP-63) may have the high risk of diabetes SNP-43 C/G individuals have reduced expression of CAPN 10 mRNA and show insulin resistance. In β-cells, blocking RyR2 pathway activates CAPN10 and triggers cells death.

2. ***GCGR*** **(Glucagon receptor) gene :** Glucagon is secreted by alpha cells of Ilets of Langerhans. Its targets are liver, muscle and adipose tissues, induces to release glucose from these tissues.

*GCGR* gene encodes the receptors of glucagon. This is also called *serpentine* (*snake-back*) *receptor*. After binding with glucogon produces cAMP, which stimulates PKA lead to breakdown of glycogen and release glucose. This gene is located on chromosome-17 *Gly* to *Ser* mutation of *GCGR* is linked to diabetes.

3. ***GCK*** **(Enzyme glucokinase)** ***gene*** **:** The enzyme glucokinase encoded by *GCK* gene in chromosome 7 speeds up glucose metabolism and acts as *glucose sensor* in β-cell. Mutant form of this gene causes a rare form of type 2 diabetes.

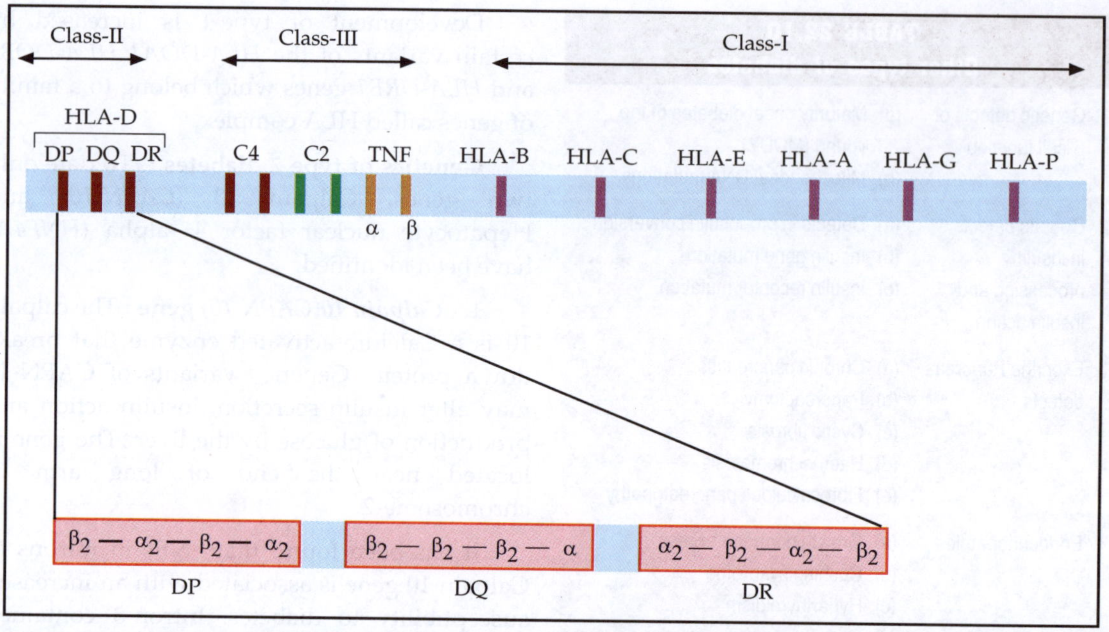


**Fig. 22.16 :** *HLA Locus of Human being*

4. ***GLUT2* (Glucose transporter) *gene*** : The *GLUT 2* gene in chromosome-3 encodes a glucose transporter which regulates entry of glucose into pancreatic β-cells and is thought to be a *glucose sensor*. *GLUT-2* is also found in liver cells.

Mutation in this gene called *SLC 2A2* causes a rare genetic syndrome called **Falconi Bickel-Syndrome** (FBS), where patients exhibit hyperglycaemia afer feeding and hypoglycaemia during fasting. The hyperglycaemia is due to inappropriate glucose uptake in the liver and hypoglycaemia is due to inappropriate insulin secretiion by pancreas.

SNPs in *GLUT-2* gene have been discovered of which T1101 (*Thr* → *Ile*) variants may be associated with Type-2 diabetes.

5. ***HNF 4A* (Hepatocyte nuclear factor 4 alpha) gene** : The *HNF4A* gene is located in chromosome 20 encodes a trancription factor that is found in liver and pancreas. Mutations of this gene causes a rare form of autosomal dominant diabetes.

This gene also regulates the expression of several genes linked with insulin secretion and may cause MODY.

The upstream promoters P1 and P2 have ben found in pancreas. P2 is thought to be the primary transcription site in β cells. Its mutation may cause MODY.

6. ***INS* (Insulin hormone) gene** : Insulin gene *INS* is present in chromosome-11 which encodes insulin hormone. Genetic varient in the 3 untranslated regions of *INS* gene is associated with type 2 diabetes.

A mutant form of insulin called **Chicago insulin** has been found in individuals who have diabetes resembles MODY. This is inherited in an autosomal dominant fashion. In this case *Phe* at position 24 or 25 of insulin B chain (B 25 *Phe* → *Leu* and B24 *Phe* → *Ser*) are associated with diabetes. Actually *Phe* at 24 position is very important in insulin molecule to attach with insulin receptor.

A switch from *Arg*→ *His* at 65 mutation results in proinsulinemia which hinders processing of proinsulin to insulin.

7. ***INSR*** (Insulin receptor) **gene :** *INSR* gene encodes the insulin receptor located in the chromosome 19. Mutations of this gene can cause rare forms of diabetes type-2.

The receptor is known as receptor tyrosine kinase (RTK), a heterodimer of $\alpha$ and $\beta$. subunits, encoded by a single gene with 23 exons. $\alpha$-subunit of liver cell may differ from muscle and adipose tissue. Two isoforms, type-a is without exon-11 and type-b with exon-11.

Mutations in *INSR* gene is rare but severe forms of disease **Leprechaunism** (usually fatal within first two years of life). **Rabson-Mendenhall syndrome** (survive upto 2nd decades) and type A insulin resistance (survive upto middle age).

A heterozygous mutation $985^{Val \rightarrow Met}$ has been found to be more common in the risk of type-2 diabetes.

8. ***ABCC 8* and *KCNJ 11* genes :** *ABCC8* genes are members of ATP-binding cassette transporter. The protein is also known as **SUR** (Sulfonyl urea) receptor. Another protein **Kir 6.2** forms the core of the channel encoded by KCNJ-11 (Potassium inwardly-rectifying channel, subfamily J) gene located in the chromosome 11. Closure of this channel triggers the release of insulin from $\beta$ cells.

Mutations in *KCNJ 11* or *ABCC 8* genes can reduce KATP channel activity leading to increased release of insulin. A rare disorder persistant hyperinsulinemic hypoglycaermia in infancy (PHH-I), while activating mutations of *KCNJ 11* cause permanent neonatal diabetes. The gene has an exon but no introns, encodes a protein of 390 amino acids.

SNPs have been found within *KCNJ 11* gene. At least two of these, *rs 5219* encodes E23K (caused by G$\rightarrow$A mutation resulting *gln* $\rightarrow$ *lys* at codon 23) and *rs 5215* encodes 133V polymorphism, which are associated with impaired insulin response.

Obesity causes elevation of free fatty acids lead to long chain acyl CoA in $\beta$ cells that stimulate KATP channel and inhibit insulin release.

9. **LPL (Lipoprotein lipase enzyme) gene :** *LPL* gene maps to chromosome 8. It has 10 exons and 475 amino acids with signal peptide. This enzyme breaks down triglycerides. Insulin plays a role in regulating LDL synthesis.

Severe mutations in *LDL* gene cause a deficiency that result in type I hyperlipoproteinemia inceasing lipoproteins and triglycerides in blood. SNPs in 3′ end of *LPL* gene were found to be associated with insulin resistance.

The transcription factor *PPARG* (Peroxisome proliferator activated receptor gamma) gene. This gene maps to chromosome 3. It has II exons There are three isoforms. PPAR$\gamma$ is a key regulator of fat cell differentiation. The drug that activate PPAR$\gamma$ increases sensitivity to insulin and lowers blood sugar levels in type 2 diabetes.

### 22.5.6 Osteogenesis Imperfecta

Osteogenesis imperfecta (OI), also known as **brittle bone disease** or **Lobstein syndrome** is a congenital bone disorder, characterised by brittle bones that are prone to fracture (Table 22.11).

People with OI are born with defective connective tissue or without ability to make it, usually because of deficiency of type-I collagen. Eight types of OI can be distinguished *COL1A1* and *COL1A2* genes, both of which code for type I collagen.

**Treatments :** There is no cure of OI. Treatment is aimed at increasing overall bone strength to prevent fracture and maintain mobility. Bisphosphonates can increase bone mass and reduce bone pain and fracture. In severe cases, bones are sugically corrected and rods are placed inside bones, particularly to enable infants to learn to walk. Intravenous bisphosphonates are generally more effective. Intravenous bisphosphonate is **pamidornate**,

**TABLE 22.11**
**Classification of Osteogenesis imperfecta**

| *Type* | *Genes concerned* | *Symptoms and remarks* |
|---|---|---|
| I | Null *COL1A1* allele<br>166240 (1A) and<br>166200 (1B)<br>Autosomal dominant | 1. Blue sclera due to thinner structure<br>2. Insufficient collagen<br>3. Bones fracture easily<br>4. Slight spinal curvture<br>5. Loose joints<br>6. Slight Protrusion of the eyes<br>7. 1A means opalescent teeth absent<br>1B means opalescent teeth present. |
| II | Lethal in perinatal period<br>*COL1A1, COL1A2*<br>259520 Autosomal<br>dominant allele | 1. Insufficient collagen<br>*2. Respiratory problem due to underdeveloped lungs*<br>3. Severe bone deformities and small stature<br>4. **Type IIA** is with broad and short long bones with broad and beaded ribs<br>**Type IIB** is with broad and short long bones with thin ribs, no beading.<br>**Type IIC** is characterised with thin and longer long bones with thin and beaded ribs. |
| III | *COL1A1, COL1A2*<br>166220 Autosomal<br>dominant allele | 1. Collagen is defective<br>2. Bones fracture easily even before birth<br>3. Bone deformity often severe<br>4. Short stature, barrel-shaped rib cage<br>5. Triangular face<br>6. Loose joints<br>7. Blue sclera<br>8. Early loss of hearing<br>This is progressive deforming type with severe physical handicapping |
| IV | COL1A1, COL1A2<br>166220 Autosomal<br>dominant allele | 1. Sufficient collagen<br>2. Bone fracture easily, especially before puberty<br>3. Short stature, spinal curvature barrel shaped rib cage<br>4. Mild bone deformities.<br>5. Early loss of hearing.<br>6. IVA and IVB are characterized by absence or presence of dentinogenesis imperfecta<br>7. Normal coloration of sclera. |
| V | *IFITM5*610967<br>Autosomal dominent<br>allele | 1. More or less similar to type IV<br>2. Histologically mesh-like apperarance of bone<br>3. Calcification of membrane between the two forearm bones, making it difficult to turn the wrist.<br>4. Repair tissue (hyperplastic callus) at the fracture site.<br>5. Long bone bowing. |

*Contd. next page*

| Type | Genes concerned | Symptoms and remarks |
|---|---|---|
| VI | *SERPINE*1 610968 Autosomal recessive allele, a member of serpin family | 1. This is also known as pigment epithelium derived factor (PEDF) the mort powerful endogenous antiangiogenic factor in mammals<br>2. Clinical features similar to type IV but is distinguished histologically by "fish scale" bone appearance when viewed under microscope. |
| VII | *CRTAP* 610682 Autosomal recessive allele | 1. Partial function of CRTAP (cartilarge associated protein) leads to moderate symptoms.<br>2. Similar to type IV & type II<br>3. Short stature<br>4. Small sclera, small head, round face<br>5. Short stature<br>6. Short femur and humerus.<br>7. Acutely angled femur head affects the hip socket. |
| VIII | *LEPRE* 1 610915 Autosomal recessive allele. | 1. Resemble to Lethal TYPE II AND III<br>2. Severe growth deficiency<br>3. Caused by a deficiency of P3H1 (prolyl-3-hydroxylase 1) Leprecan due to *LEPRE 1* gene mutation. |
| Other | Recessive mutation in *TMEM38B* gene on chromosome 9 | This gene encodes TRIC-B, a component of TRIC, a monovalent cation specific channel involved in $Ca^{++}$ release from intracellular store. |

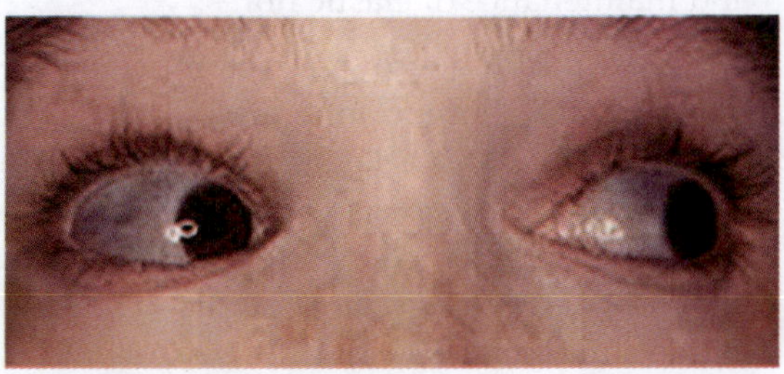

(a)

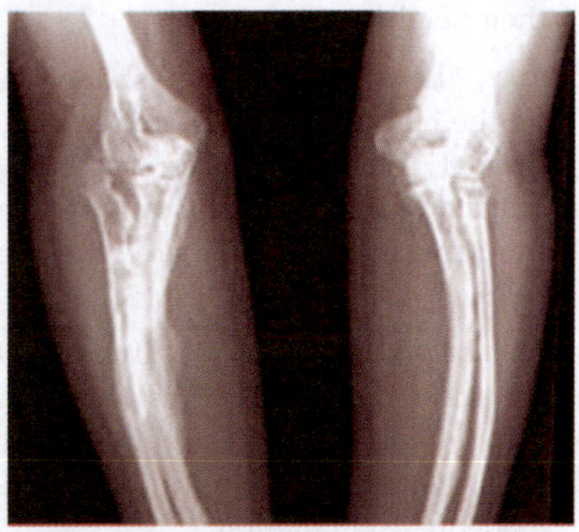

(b)

**Fig. 22.17 :** *Symptoms of osteogenesis imperfecta (a) blue sclera (b) bowing of radio-ulna bones* oral bisphosphonate is **alendornate**. The **residornate** is used for children to increase bone density.

Physiotherapy sometimes improve muscle strength and improve posture.

### 22.5.7 Marfan's syndrome

A French pediatrician Antony Marfan first decribed (1896) a condition in a five year old girl. Marfan's syndrome (MFS) is a genetic disorder of connective tissue. The syndrome is also known as Marfan wrist lift because the positive sign in a person with Marfan's syndrome is the thumb and little finger lverlap, when grasping the wrist of the opposite hand.

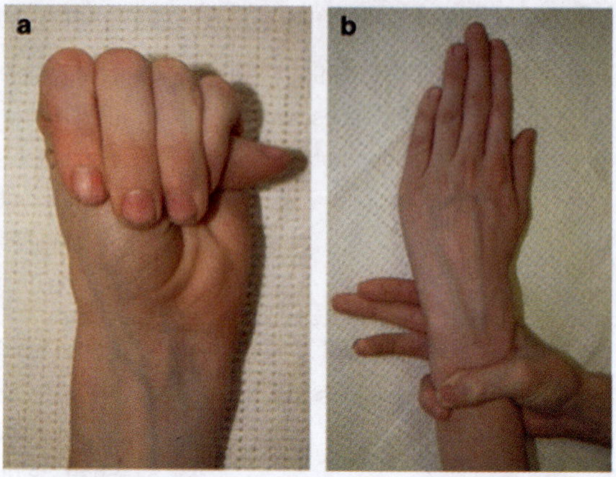


**Fig. 22.18 :** *Marfan syndrome with Marfan wrist lift*

More than 30 different signs and symptoms are variably associated with MFS. The most prominant of these affect the skeletal, cardiovascular and ocular systems but all fibrous connective tissue throughout the body can be affected.

1. *Skeletal system :* Above average height, disproportionately long, slender limbs with thin weak wrists and long toes and fingers. Abnormal lateral curvature of spine (scoliosis), high arched palate, flat feet, hammer toes, stooped shoulder, pain in joints, bones and muscles and small jaws. Early osteoarthritis. Length of two ends of stretched arms is greater than their height.
2. *Eyes* : Lens being kidney-shaped resting on the ciliary body and shifted out of its normal position. Nearsightedness and blurred vision, myopia, corneal flatness exotropia and esotropia are other signs of MFS.
3. *Cardiovascular system :* Undue fatigue, shortness of breath, heart palpitation, racing heart beat, chest pain radiating to back, cold arms and feet due to inadequate circulation.
4. *Lungs :* In spontaneous unilateral pneumothorax, air escapes from a lung and occupies the pleural space between chest wall and lung. Lung is partially compressed or collapsed. This can cause pain, shortedness of of breath, cyanosis, sleep apnea and idiopathic obstructive lung disease.
5. *Nervous system :* Dural ectasia (weakening dura mater on spinal cord) can result in loss of quality of life. Lower backpain, leg pain, abdominal pain, headache etc. Disfunction of autonomic nervous system and spinal cyst may be observed.

**Genetics :** Most individuals with MFS have another affected family member. This is due to autosomal dominant mutation of *FBN1* gene on the chromosome 15, which encodes fibrillin-1, a glycoprotein component of the extracellular matrix. The fibrillin-1 is essential for the proper formation of extracellular matrix, biogenesis and maintenance of elastic fibres.

Transforming growth factor beta (TGF-β) plays an important role in MFS. Fibrillin-1 binds to a latent form of TGF-β and allowed TGF-β levels to rise causing an inflammatory reaction releasing protease enzymes to degrade elastic fibres of extracellular matrix.

**Cytogenetic location :** 15q21.1, which is the long (q) arm of chromosome 15 at position 21.1. (Fig. 22.19)

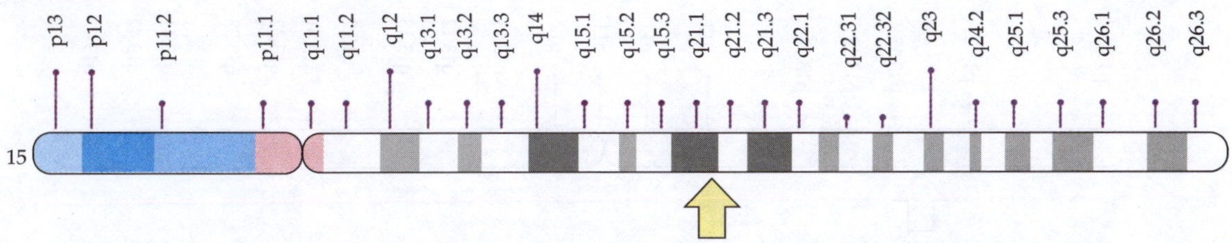


**Fig. 22.19 :** *Cytogenetic location of* ***FBN1*** *gene of Marfan syndrome*

***Molecular location :*** Base pairs 48408306 to 48645788 on chromosome 15 (Annotations Release 108, GRCh38 p7, NCBI).

*Society and Culture* : Studies suggest that Akhenalen, a Pharaoh of Eighteenth Dynasty of Egypt may have suffered from MFS. Abraham Lincoln, 16th President of USA had long hand, long nose, not so wide chest. His descendants are also suffered from this syndrome.

Contribution of public perception of MFS include Flo Hyman, an Olympic silver medalist in women's volleyball (1984) who died suddenly at a match from aortic dissection. jonathan Larson, author and composer of Rent, who also died from aortic dissection with a very short carrier life. Vincent Schiavelly, an actor; Isaish Austin, the basketball player of USA; Arik Einstein, a song writer and singer; Badford Cox; member of rock band Deerhunter; John Tavener; a British composer; Niccolo Paganini, a musical genius; Julias Caesar, greatest ruler and dictator; Sergei Rachmaninev a composer and pianest etc.

The list of MFS is increased when it was learned that Osama Bin Laden who has long fingers and faced difficulty in walking and sitting up straight for long duration and Michel Phelps, 21 olympic gold medalist with 39 world records having a height of 6′4″ and arm span 6′7″ and hypermobile kees (double joints).

### 22.5.8 Familial Hypercholesterolemia (FH)

The Norweigian physian Dr. C. Muller first associated the physical signs, high cholesterol level and autosomal dominant inheritance in 1938. Dr. Joseph L. Goldstein and Dr. Michael S. Brown of Dallas, Texus found increased activity of HMG-CoA reductase activity and then binding of LDL to its receptor as the cause of FH. They later won the 1985 Nobel Prize in Medicine for their discovery of the LDL receptor and its impact on lipoprotein metabolism.

Familial hypercholesterolemia (FH) is a disorder that is passed down through families. It causes LDL (bad cholesterol) level to be very high. The condition begins at birth and can cause heart attacks at an early age.

**Symptoms :**

1. In early years, there may be no symptoms.
2. Yellow fatty skin deposits called Xanthomas over parts of the hands, elbows, knees, ankles and around the cornea of the eye.
3. Cholesterol deposits in the eyelid (Xanthelasma)
4. Chest pain (angina) or other signs of coronary artery disease; may be present at a young age.
5. Cramping of one or both calves when walking.
6. Sores on the toes that do not heal.
7. Sudden stroke-like symptoms, such as trouble speaking, drooping an one side of the face, weakness of a arm or leg and loss of balance.
8. Blood test shows : High level of total cholesterol, high level of LDL, normal triglyceride levels.

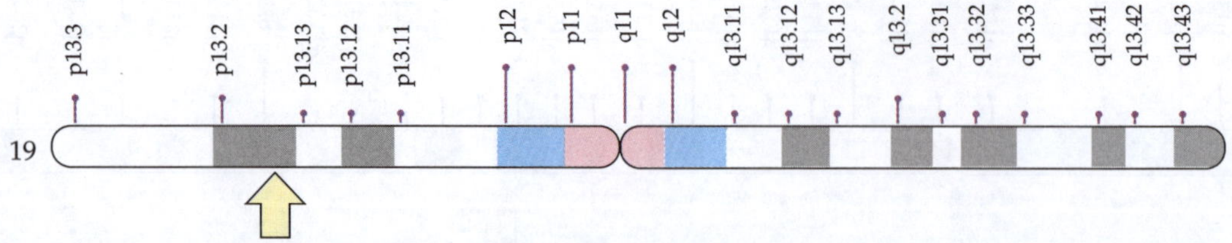


**Fig. 22.20 :** *Cytogenetic location of LDLR gene of Familial hypercholesterolemia disease.*

9. Personal and family medical history include :

   A strong family history of familial hypercholesterolemia or early heart attacks.

   High level of LDL cholesterol in either or both parents.

   People from families with a strong history of early heart attacks should have blood tests done to determine lipid level.

**Diagnosis :** Raised level of total cholesterol, markedly raised level of LDL, normal HDL and triglycerides. Total cholesterol levels of 350-550 mg/dL are typical of heterozygous FH while total cholesterol levels of 650-1000 mg/dL are typical of homozygous FH. 75% of the healthy population would have a lower LDL level. Cholesterol levels can be drastically higher in people with FH who are also obese.

**Geneties of FH :**

The most common genetic defects in FH are LDLR mutations, ApoB mutations, PCSK9 mutations and LDLRAP1 mutations.

The related disease sitosterolemia which has many similarities with FH and also cholesterol accumulation in the tissues, is due to ABCG5 and ABCG8 mutations.

*LDLR* (LDL-receptor) mutation : *LDLR* gene is located on the short arm of chromosome 19 (19p13.1-13.3). It comprises 18 exons and spans 45 kb. The receptor protein contains 839 amino acids in mature form. There is a inversely relation of plasmal LDL levels and LDLR activity (Fig. 22.20).

The mutation is dominant in nature. So single abnormal copy (heterozygote) of FH causes cardiovascular disease by the age of 56 in about 40% of cases. Having two abnoramal copies (homozygote) cause accelerated atherosclerosis in childhood including complications.

There are 5 classes of *LDLR* mutations :

Class I : LDLR is not synthesized at all.

Class II : LDLR is not properly transported from endoplasmic reticulum to Golgi apparatus for expression on the cell surface.

Class III : LDLR does not bind LDL properly on the cell surface due to defects of LDL-R or Apolipoprotein-B.

Class IV : LDLR bound to LDL does not properly cluster in clathrin-coated pits for receptor mediated endocytosis.

Class V : LDLR is not recycled back to the cell surface.

*Apo B* mutation : Apolipoprotein B 100 is the main Apolipoprotein particle. Its gene is located on the small arm of 2nd chromosome (2p24 - p23) and between 21.08 and 21.12 Mb long. FH is associated with the mutation of R3500Q, which causes replacement of arginine by glutamine at position 35000. As a result of mutation ApoB part of LDL binding is reduced to LDLR.

*PCSK 9* mutation : Mutations in the proprotein convertase subtilism/Kexin type 9 (*PCSK 9*) gene were linked to autosomal dominant FH. This gene is located on the first chromosome (1p34.1 – p32 and encodes a 666 amino acid protein that is expressed in the liver. Mutation of *PCSK9* causes FH mainly by reducing the number of LDL-receptor on liver cells.

*LDLRAP1* gene mutation : Abnormalities in *LDLRAP1* also known as *ARH* gene is an autosomal recessive gene causes FH in homozygous recessive condition. Mutations in the protein tend to cause the production of a shortened protein. Its real function is not clear, but it seems to play an important role in the relation between LDL receptor and clathrin coated pits. This is severe than LDLR heterozygote but less severe than LDLR homozygotes.

*Pathophysiology* : LDL cholesterol normally circulates in the body for 2.5 days. ApoB of LDL binds to LDL-receptor on the liver cells, triggering uptake and digestion and thus LDL is removed from the ciruclation. Synthesis of cholesterol by HMG-CoA reductase is suppressed.

Mutations of LDL receptor and/or ApoB causing high LDL level in the blood. It is not known how mutation causes LDLR disfuction in mutations of PCSK9 and ARH.

Due to excess levels of LDL in the circulation, atherosclerosis occurs. In addition to this, smoking, high blood pressure, diabetes, abnormatities in the prothrombin gene *(G20210A)* increase cardiovascular events. A specific genotype of the argiotensis-converting enzyme (ACT) is also found to be a risk of atherosclerosis.

**Prevention and Treatments of FH**

The goal of treatment is to reduce the risk of atherosclerosic heart disease.

- Life style changes
- Change of diet including lowering the amount of fat you eat so that it is less than 30% of your total calories. If you are overweight, losing weight is very helpful.
- To cut saturated fat from the food
- Eliminate trans-fats
- Eat less mutton, beef, pork, chicken.
- Replace full-fat dairy products with low-fat products.
- Eliminate egg yolk and liver of meat.
- Statin drugs are very effective. There include, Lovastatin, Pravastatin, Simvastatin Fluvastatin, Atorvastatin, Pitivastatin, Rasuvastatin, Ezetimibe, Fenofibrate, Gemfibrozil, Nicotinic acid, PCSK9 inhibitors (alirocumab, evolocumab) etc.

People with a family history of this condition, particularly if both parents carry the defective gene, may want to seek genetic couseling.

**Ezetimibe** inhibits cholesterol absorption is the gut is of no overall benefit in FH. Homozygous FH is harder to treat. Only high dose of statin, often in combination may be effective in lowering cholesterol. Lipitamide, an inhibitor of microsomal triglyceride transfer protein was approved by US FDA for the treatment of homozygous FH. The US FDA also approved Mipomersen which inhibits the action of the gene *ApoB* for the treatment of homozygous FH.

For the children suffering from FH the treatment protocol is similar to that of adults but many physicians prefer to use bile acid sequestrants and fenofibrate.

### 22.5.9 Neurofibromatosis

Neurofibromatosis (NF) is neurocutaneous disorder inherited as autosomal dominant genetic syndrome.

Two types of NF, NF1 and NF2 differ with regard of their age of clinical onset, clinical manifestations, gene loci and gene protein products.

**Neurofibromatosis type-1 (NF1)**

NF1 is also known as peripheral neurofibromatosis or Von Recklingausen disease caused by a mutation in or a deletion of the *NF1* gene in a autosomal dominant genetic condition.

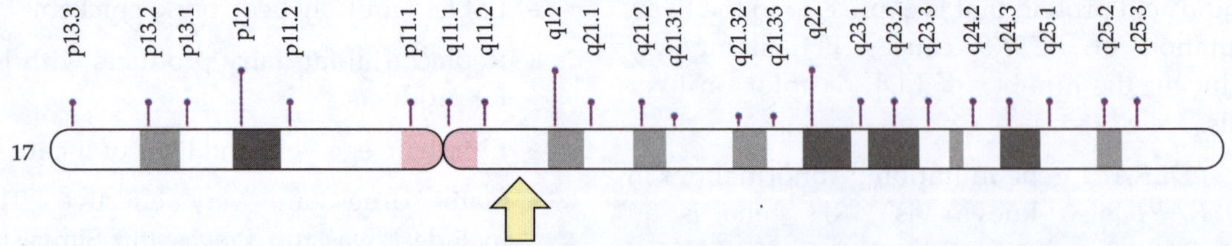


**Fig. 22.21 :** *Cytogenetic location of NF1 gene of Neurofibromatosis*

*NF1* gene (a tumor suppressor gene) product is neurofibromin 1. It activates ras-GTPase involved in cellular signal transduction. When ras-GTPase is switched on" by incoming signals, leading to activation of other proteins, which in turn, activate genes responsible for growth and differentiation. The neurofibromin-1/ras-GTPase suppresses the cell overgrowth.

NF1 phenotype results loss of function mutation of *NF1* gene . The clinical symptoms appear early in life and continue over many years.

**Genetics of NF1**

*NF1* gene is located on the q-arm of chromosome 17, at band 11.2 [17q 11.2], over 100 pathogenic allelic variants, which include mutation, amino acid substitutions, insertions, deletions and chromosomal rearrangements (Fig. 22.21).

The NF1 gene locus is 350 kb. The penetration is nearly 100% .

A mild neurofibromatosis *i.e.* NF1-like syndrome is caused by mutation in the *SPRED1* gene whose location is 15q13.2, called **Legius syndrome**, which is a genetically distinct disorder. *SPRED1* gene codes **Spred -1 - protein,**helps regulate the ras/MAPK signaling pathway which has roles in cellular proliferation and differentiation, cell movement and apoptosis. Legius syndrome does not develop multiple cutaneous neurofibroma or optic gioma and tumorigenic manifestation like NF1.

*Smptoms of NF1 :* NF1 is characterized by changes in skin pigmentation and growth of tumors along nerves in the skin, brain and other parts of the brody and other features such as cafe-au-lait and learning disabilites.

Beginning in early childhood with :

1. Flat patches on the skin that are darker than the surrounding area.
2. The spots increase in size and number with the age of the patients.
3. Freckles in the underarm and groin. Lisch nodules often appear in the iris. Tumors along the optic nerves (optic glioma) may lead to total vision loss.

Adult NF1 symptoms include :

1. Benign tumors just under the skin
2. Tumors also occur in nerves near spinal cord or along nerves elsewhere in the body.
3. Some times tumors may be malignant
4. Have a risk of leukemia and brain cancer.
5. High blood pressure, short stature, macrocephaly, scoliosis and attention defect hyperactivity disorder (ADHD) may occur frequently in affected individuals.

***Neurofibromatosis 2 (NF2)***

Neurofibromatosis 2 (NF2), also called *bilateral acoustic genetic syndrome* caused by mutation in, or a deletion of the *NF2* gene . The *NF2* gene codes for the cytoskeletal protein neurofibromin 2. This gene is located on long arm of chromosome 22 at band 12.2 (22q12.2). Somatic mosaicism is also found in 20-30% cases.

*Symptoms :* NF2 is characterised by vestibular schwannomas (also called acoustic neuroma) which is benign slow-growing tumor of 8th cranial nerve. Meningiomas, ependymomas and schwannomas of the cranial and peripheral nerves also occur. In rare case malignant atrocytoma are reported. It is an adult onset disease as the age at onset, symptoms in between 18 and 24 yrs. The sign includes posterior subscapular lens opacities and cataract. At the age of 30, almost all individuals NF2 develops full fledged symptoms.

Penetrance is 100%. Average life span is 36 yrs. Gradual hearing loss, poor balance, headache etc are the usual symptoms.

*Molecular biology :* Neurofibromin 2 is also called merlin (8 moesin - ezrin-radixin-like protein) is a cytoskeletal protein. The name schwannomin has a role to recognize neurofibromin2 in preventing schwannoma formation.

Merlin is essential to the regulation of contact dependent inhibition of cellular proliferation. It functions at the cell-cell adhesion interface, in transmembrane signaling and in the actin cytoskeleton. Merlin is a tumor suppressor protein, expressed in neurons, schwann cells, oligodendrocytes and leukocytes.

Mutation of *NF2* causes to produce nonfunctional protein product and cannot prevent tumor growth, especially the Schwann cells.

## 22.6 HEMOGLOBINOPATHY

### 22.6.1 Sickle Cell Disease

Sickle cell disease is a group of disorders that affects hemoglobin in RBC. People with this disorder has atypical hemoglobin molecules called **hemoglobin-S**, which can distort RBCs into a sickle or crescent shape (Fig. 22.22).

**Signs and Symptoms :** Signs and symptoms usually begin in early childhood. One of the earliest clinical manifestations is dactylitis at the 6 months of age which may occur with sickle-cell trait and not lasts upto a month. Another feature is acute chest syndrome, fever, chest pain,

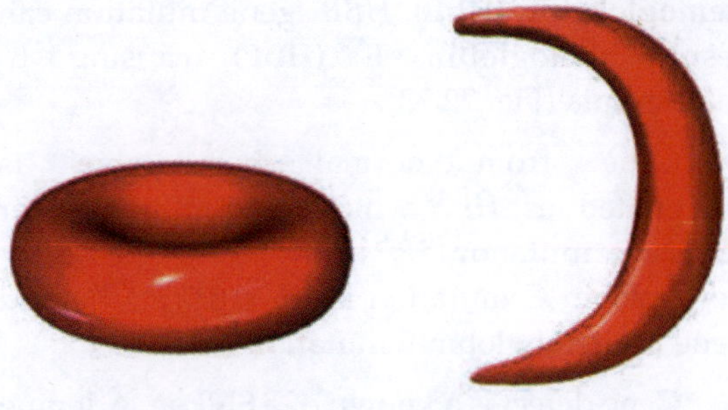


**Fig. 22.22 :** *Normal RBC and Sickled RBC in Sickled cell disease*

difficulties in breathing and pulmonary infiltrate on a chest X-ray.

Severity of symptoms varies from person to person. The symptoms are caused due to breakdown of RBC, which can lead to anaemia, and repeated infections and periodic episode of pain.

Other symptoms include, shortness of breath, fatigue and delayed growth and development of children, yellowing of eyes and skin. Painful episode occurs when stiff and inflexible sickled RBCs get stuck in small blood vessels.

Tissue deprives oxygen that may lead to oxygen damage, especially lung, kidney, spleen and brain. High blood pressure and pulmonary hypertension and heart failure .

Carriers produce 50% normal hemoglobin having symptoms if they are deprived of $O_2$, while climbing a mountain or while severly dehydrated .

**Genetics of sickle - cell disease :** Sickle cell disease is inherited in an autosomal recessive pattern. Point mutation of the gene *HBB* is responsible (which encodes β-subunit of hemoglobin) for this disease due to production of abnormal version of β-globin, known as **hemoglobin-S** (HbS). Other mutations in the *HBB* gene lead to additional abnormal version of β-globin and as **hemoglobin C (HbC)** and

**hemoglobin E (HbE)**. *HBB* gene mutation can result **hemoglobin F (HbF)** causing β-thalassemia (Fig. 22.23).

Gene from normal hemoglobin is designated as $Hb^A$ which is dominant over recessive mutation $Hb^S$ ($\beta^{6\ glu \rightarrow val}$). Gene for hemoglobin C mutation is $Hb^C$ ($\beta^{6glu \rightarrow\ lys}$) and gene for hemoglobin E mutation is $Hb^E$.

Gene defect is a known of a SNP ie, Adenine (A) to Thiamine (T) of β-globin gene. In the normal hemoglobin 6th codon (skipping the start codon *met. i.e.*, actually the 7th codon) is GAA encoding glutamic acid. This is substituted by GTA encoding *valine*, resulting to hemoglobin-S (Fig. 22.24).

| *Genotype* | *Phenotype* | *Nature of hemoglobin* |
|---|---|---|
| $Hb^AHb^A$ | Normal | $\alpha_2{}^A\beta_2{}^A$ |
| $Hb^AHb^S$ | Sickle cell Trait | $\alpha_2{}^A\beta^A\beta^S$ (6 glu →val) |
| $Hb^SHb^S$ | Sickle cell disease | $\alpha_2{}^A\beta_2{}^S$ $(\alpha_2\beta_2{}^{6\ glu \rightarrow\ val})$ |

*HBB* gene is located on short arm of chromosome no - 1L at position 15.5, more specifically $11p^{15.5}$ (Fig. 22.25)

**Cause of sickling :** Molecular mechanism proposed to account for change in shape and viscosity in the stacking of sickle cell molecules in the uniform alignment.

In sickle cell homozygote, in the HbS, *glu* is replaced by *val*, which is hydrophobic, transformed into crystalline type, causing the hemoglobin collapse on itself. When enough Hb collapses, RBC becomes sickling.

In heterozygotes, 50% Hb is normal which prevents formation into crystalline structure preventing from sickling of RBC, except when they are deprived of $O_2$ or in severe dehydration.

**Cause of malaria Protection :** This is an adaptive advantage of heterozygotes. There are several mechanisms.

| | 1 | 2 | 3 | 4 | 5 | 6 | 7 | 8 |
|---|---|---|---|---|---|---|---|---|
| **Hb A** | *Val* | *His* | *Leu* | *Thr* | *Pro* | *Glu* | *Glu* | *Lys* |
| **Hb S** | *Val* | *His* | *Leu* | *Thr* | *Pro* | *Val* | *Glu* | *Lys* |
| **Hb C** | *Val* | *His* | *Leu* | *Thr* | *Pro* | *Lys* | *Glu* | *Lys* |

**Fig. 22.23 :** *Sequence of beta globin chain polypeptide for Hemoglobin.*

1. Defective Hb causes RBC rupture prematurely making *Plasmodium* unable to reproduce and unable to digest hemoglobin.
2. Low level of free heam circulating in the blood carrying sickle cell gene stimulates the production of enzyme *haem-oxygenase-1*. This releases small quantities of carbon monoxide, a gas that in large quantity is highly toxic. Carbon monoxide seems to play a role in preventing accumulation of haem after infection with the parasite, thus protects against disease.
3. The over-active immune response leads to the accumulation of toxic T cells and also phagocytosis by phagocytes to sickle cells.
4. Micro-RNA entering the parasite and tampering with its genome by inhibiting parasitic transformation and contribute to malaria resistance have only been considered more recently which have a very strong supportive evidence.

**Diagnosis :**

1. A mixture of HbS in a reducing solution, such as sodium dithionite gives a turbid appearance, whereas normal Hb gives a clear solution.
2. Abnormal hemoglobin can be detected by gel electrophoresis. Sickle cell hemoglobin HbS and hemoglobin C with sickling (HbSC) – the two most common forms can be identified by the technique.

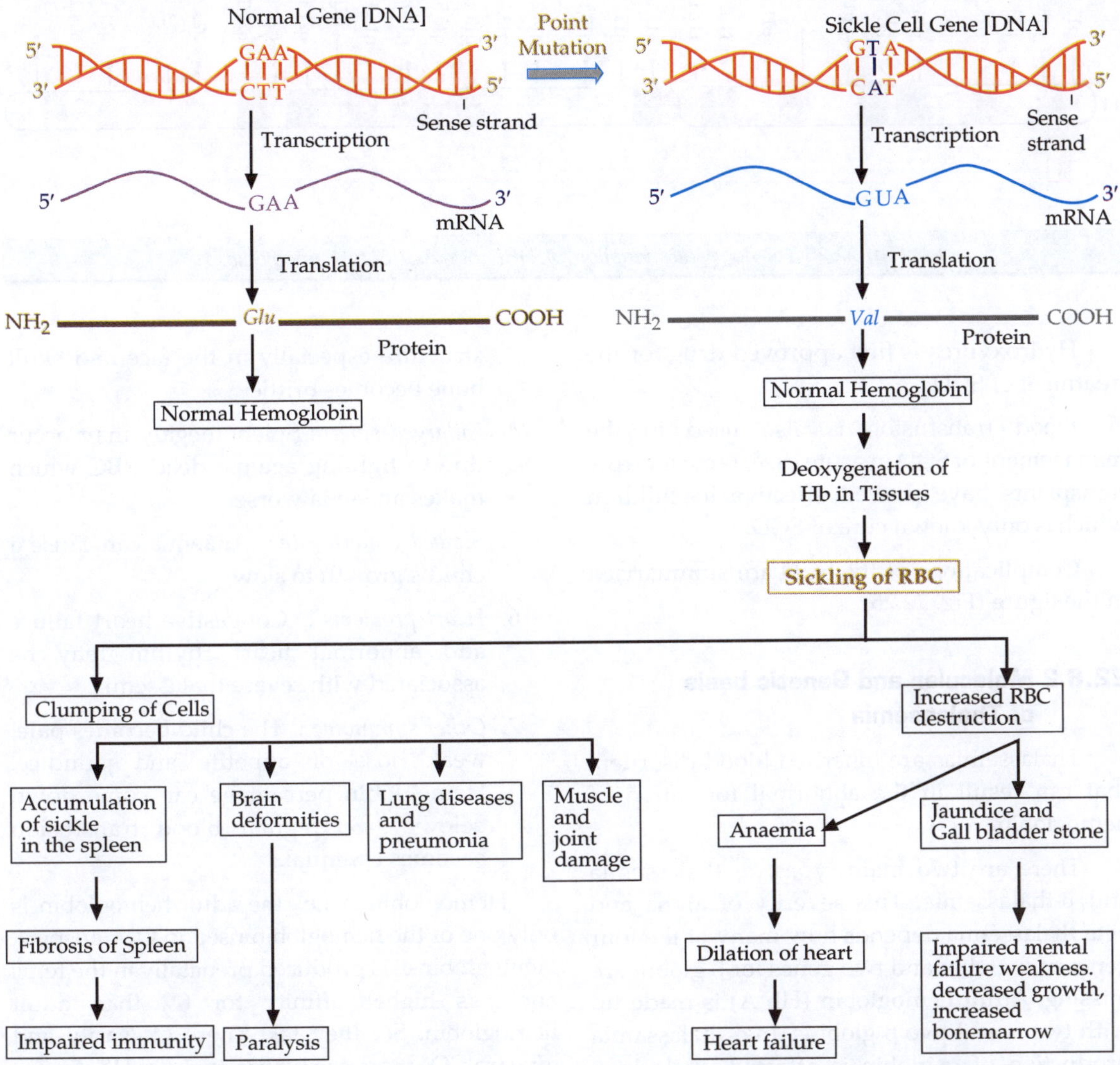


**Fig. 22.24 :** *Molecular mechanism of RBC Sickling and Concequences of Sickle Cell Disease.*

HPLC technique is also used for confirmed diagnosis.

**Management :**

People who are known as carriers of the disease often undergo genetic counseling before they have a child A test to see if an unborn child has a disease takes either a blood sample from the fetus or a sample of amniotic fluid.

Folic acid daily for life is recommended. From birth to five years of age, penicillin daily due to the immature immune system that makes them more prone to early childhood illness is also recommended.

For milder vaso-occlusive crisis, NSAID such as diclofenac or naproxen is used.

Chest crisis can be controlled by antibiotics such as quinolone or macrolide.

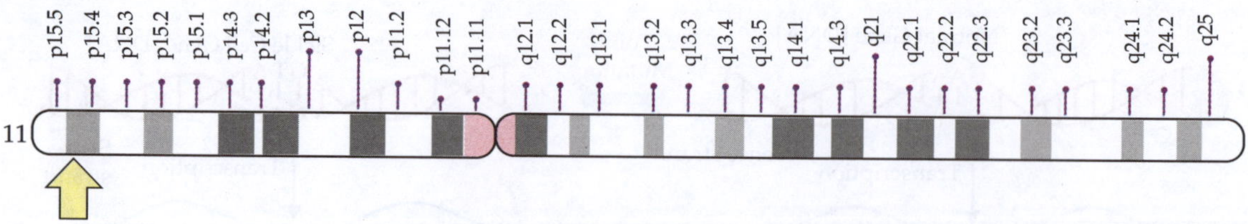


**Fig. 22.25** : *Cytogenetic location of HBB gene of beta hemoglobin*

Hydroxyurea is first approved drug for the treatment of SCD.

Blood transfusion is also used in the management of SCD in acute case. Bone marrow transplants have proved effective in children which is only known cure of SCD.

Complications of the SCD are summarised in the figure (Fig. 22.25)

## 22.6.2 Molecular and Genetic basis of Thalassemia

Thalassemias are inherited blood disorders that can result in the abnormal formation of hemoglobin.

There are two main types, α--thalassemia and β-thalassemia. This severity of alpha and beta thalassemia depends how many of the four genes of α globin and two genes for β globin are missing. Adult hemoglobin (Hb A) is made up with two α and two β globins. In α thalassamia production of α globin is affected while in β thalassemia, β globin is affected.

**Symptoms :**

1. *Iron overload* : Overload of iron in their bodies occurs due to the disease itself or from frequent blood transfusion. Too much iron deposits can damage to heart, liver and endocrine organs.
2. *Infection* : People with thalassemia have an increased risk of infection and severe anaemia.
3. *Bone deformities* : Bone marrow expands which can result in abnormal bone structure especially in the face and skull bone becomes brittle.
4. *Enlarged spleen*: Splenomegaly may occur due to fighting against dead RBC which makes anaemia worse.
5. *Slowed growth rate* : Anaemia can cause a child's growth to slow.
6. *Heart problems :* Congestive heart failure and abnormal heart rhythm may be associated with severe thalassemia.
7. *Other symptoms* : The child becomes pale, weak, loss of appetite and jaundice. Hemoglobin percentage can come down below 7. So regular blood transfusion becomes essential.

Hemoglobin A i.e., the adult hemoglobin is only one of the hemoglobin used in $O_2$ transport. Hemoglobin-F is produced prenatally in the fetus and has higher affinity for $O_2$ than adult hemoglobin. So, they take more $O_2$ easily and give up $CO_2$ more easily than those of Hb-A.

Hb-F is also a tetramer composed of two pairs of peptide chains two α and two unique γ-chains that bear some resemblance with β-chains ($\alpha_2{}^A\gamma_2{}^F$). γ-chain is differing from β-chain by 39 amino acids out of a total 146 amino acids. Usually Hb-F begins to diminish before birth and is practically zero level at 6 months of age. Concurrent with this diminuation of γ-chains in the normal individual is an increase in β-chain production (Fig. 22.26).

Apparently the onset of β-chain production either triggers or is triggered by the decrease in γ. This close relationship is also seen

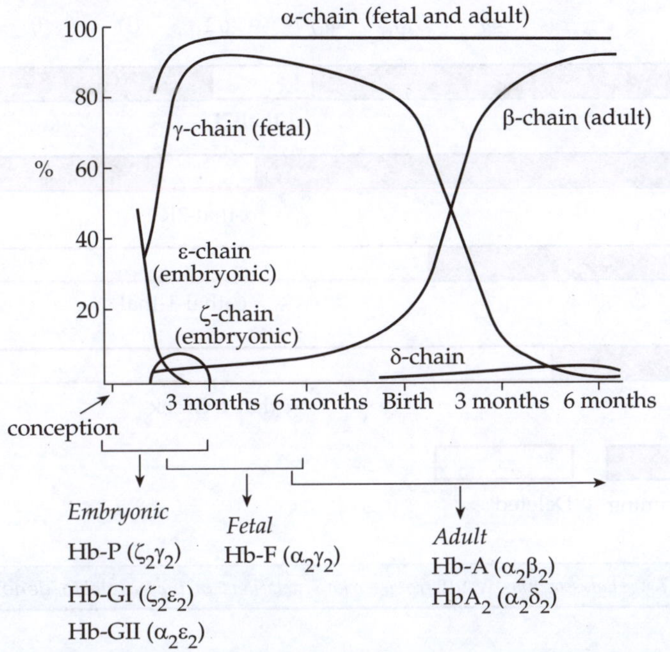


**Fig.22.26 :** *Changes in the amounts of various hemoglobin-chains produced in human subjects from the embryonic period to fetal to adult stages.*

when individuals are suffering from inherited disease.

***Genetics of α–thalassemia :***

The α-thalassemias involve the two closely linked genes and caused by deletion of *HBA1* and *HBA2*. inherited in a Mendelian recessive fashion. Two gene loci and so four alleles exist and located in the chromosome 16p 13.3. The α-thalassemias result in decreased α-globin production . The excess β-globin forms unstable tetramers $\beta_4$ (HbH).

**The deletions that cause the α-thalassemias are**

1. The α-thal-1 deletions are long, varying in location of the left end, with the positions of the right ends located beyond the known genes. They eliminate both the α-genes.
2. The α-thal-2 deletions are short and eliminate only one of the two α genes. The L-form removes 4.2 kb of DNA, encoding $\alpha_2$ gene. It probably results from unequal crossing over, because the ends of the deletion lie in homologous regions just to the right of the $\psi_\alpha$ and $\alpha_2$ genes respectively.

   The R results from the removal of exactly 3.7 kb of DNA, the precise distance between the $\alpha_1$ and $\beta_2$ genes. It appears to have been generated by unequal crossing over between the α1 and $\beta_2$ genes themselves.
3. In wild type, there is (four α genes) at least three or two α genes. With only one α gene, the excess β-chains form the unusual $\beta_4$, which causes Hb-H disease. The complete absence of α gene results in hydrops fetalis (Fig. 22.27).

***Inheritance of α-thalassemia :***

People have two copies of the *HbA1* gene and two copies of *HBA2* gene in each cell. Each

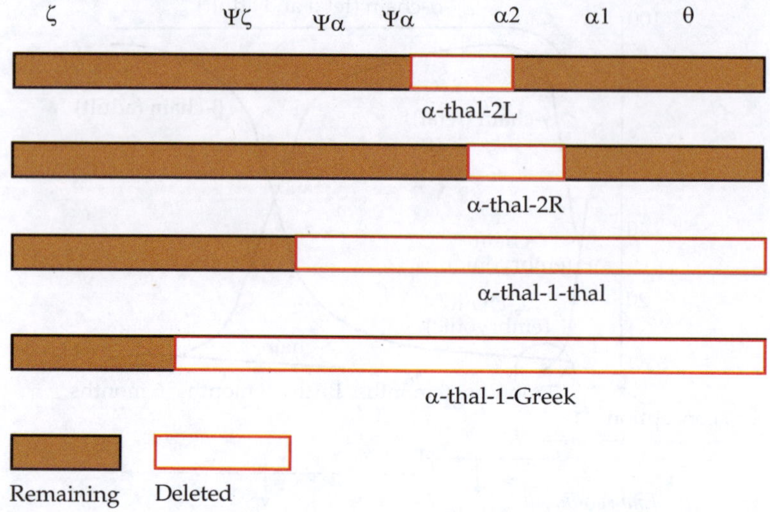


**Fig. 22.27 :** *Thalassaemias result from various deletions in the* α-globin gene cluster.

copy is called allele. For each gene one allele is inherited from a person's father and the other is inherited from mother. As a result, there are four alleles that produce α-globin. Different types of α-thalassemia result from the loss of some or all of these genes (Fig. 22.28)

**Different types of α-thalassemia.**

1. *α-thalassemia major or Hb-Bart syndrome or Hydrops fetalis* : This is resulted from the loss of all four *HbA* alleles. No α-globins are produced. γ-globins or β-globins are produced in excess to form unstable Hb-Bart. They die before birth (still born). If it allowed to birth, excess fluid build up in the fetus called **hydrops fetalis.** They require *in utero* blood transfusion and also life-long blood transfusion and critical medical care.
2. *Silent carrier state* : Loss of one α-globin gene causing no health problems. The amount of α-globin is so small that Hb functions normally.
3. *Hemoglobin constant spring* : Unusual form of silent carrier caused by a mutation of α-globin, discovered in Jamaica. The individual usually experiences no related health problem.
4. *α-thalassemia trait or mild α-thalassemia* : Lack of α-globin is somewhat greater. The patient with mild anaemia but no other symptoms.
5. *Hemoglobin H (HbH) disease* : Lack of α-globin is great enough to cause severe and serious health problems such as, enlarged spleen bone deformities and fatigue. They have abnormal Hb-H that destroys RBC.
6. *Hemoglobin H constant Spring* : More severe than Hb-H disease.
7. *Homozygous constant Spring* : When two constant spring carriers pass their genes on to their child in which one parent is Constant Spring carrier and other is a carrier of α-thalassemia. The condition is less severe than Hb-H Constant Spring.

***Genetics of β-thalassemia :***

β-thalassemias are due to mutations in the *HBB* gene on chromosome 11p 15.5 inherited in an autosomal recessive fashion.

In some, *HBB* mutation is inherited in an autosomal dominant fashion.

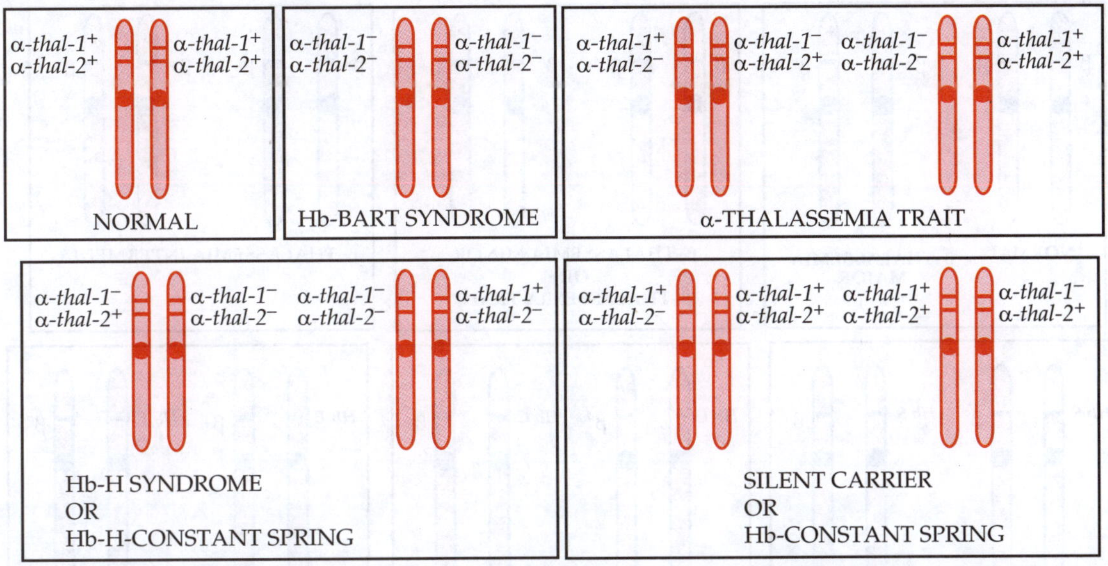


**Fig. 22.28 :** *Genotypes and Phenotypes of α-Thalassemia*

This was reported first in a Irish family with two deletions of 4 and 11 bp in exon-3 interrupted by an insertion of 5 bp in β-globin gene.

The severity depends upon the nature of mutation and presence of mutation in one or both alleles. Normal *HBB* gene is designated as β.

Mutated alleles are called β+ when partial function is observed (either the globin has reduced function or function is normal but is produced in reduced quantity) and $\beta_0$ when no functional globin is produced. (Fig. 22.29)

**The deletions that cause β-thalassemia are :**

1. In rare cases only the β gene is affected. These have a deletion of 600 bp extending from the second intron through the 3′ flanking regions. In the other cases more than one gene of the cluster is affected.
2. β and δ genes differ only ~ 7% in sequence. Unequal crossing over deletes, the material between genes and fusing them together. The fused gene product has β-like chain at N-terminal end while δ-like chain at the C-terminal. This is called **Hb-Lapore** type of hemoglobin.
3. The reciprocal event has been found where fusion lies between normal δ and β genes and thus Hb-antiLapore hemoglobin is formed.
4. Unequal crossing over creates **Hb-Kenya**, where the product contains N-terminal sequence of the $\gamma^A$ gene and the C-terminal sequence of β-gene.
5. There are large number of different hemoglobins that have been arisen through unequal crossing over between them (Fig. 22.30).

**Different types of β-thalassemia :**

1. *β-thalassemia major or Medeterranian anaemia or Cooly's anaemia* : This is caused by $\beta_0/\beta_0$ genetype. No β-globin chain is produced. The symptoms appear within two years of age. They develop yellow skin, jaundice, enlarged liver, heart and spleen. Blood transfusion is required for them.

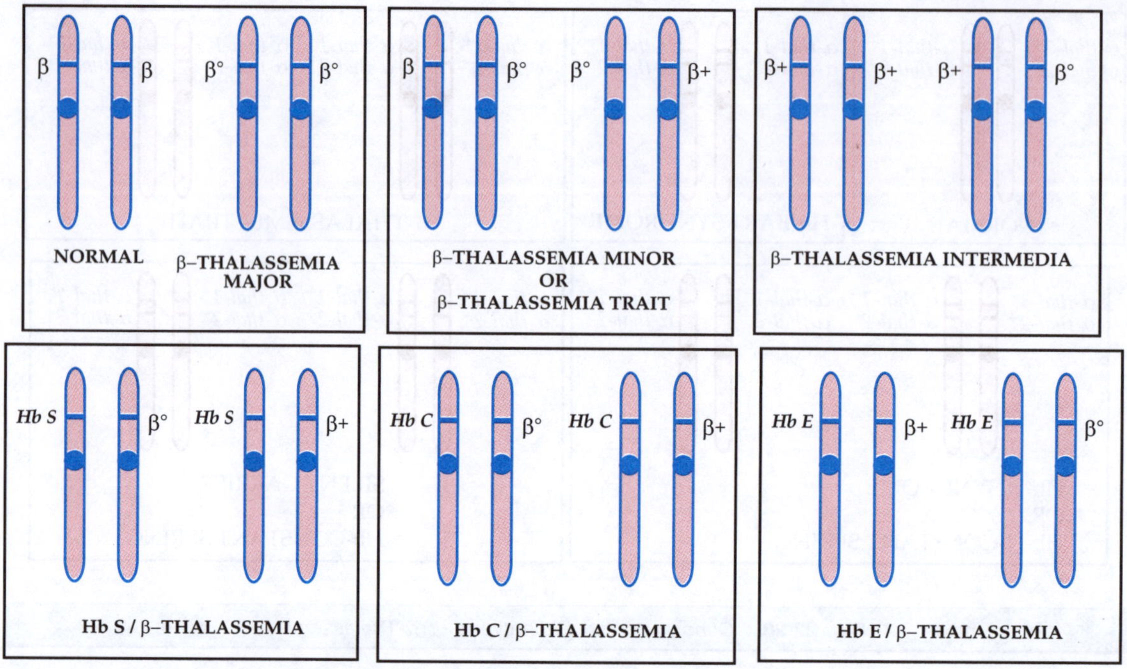


**Fig. 22.29 :** *β-thalassemias associated with hemoglobinopathies*

2. *β-thalassemia intermedia :* This is caused by $\beta^+/\beta^0$ or $\beta^+/\beta^+$ genetype. In this form some HbA is produced. Symptoms appear early in childhood. The affected individuals have mild $\beta^+/\beta^+$ genotype) to moderate ($\beta^+/\beta^0$ genotype) anaemia having slow growth and bone abnormalities.
3. *β-thalassemia minor or β-thalassemia trait :* This is caused by $\beta/\beta^0$ or $\beta/\beta^+$ genotypes. The lack of β-globin is not so great enough to cause health problems other than mild anaemia.
4. *Delta-thalassemia* : About 3% of adult hemoglobin is made up of α and δ chains. β-gene mutation can lead to produce more δ-chain causing $\alpha_2\delta_2$ hemoglobin.

**Thalassemia can coexist with other hemoglobinopathies :**

1. *Hemoglobin E/thalassemia :* (HbE/$\beta_0$ or HbE/$\beta^+$). This is common is Cambodia, Thiland and some parts of India. This is clinically similar to β-thalassemia major or β-thalassemia intermedia.
2. *Hemoglobin S/thalassemia* : (Hb-S/$\beta_0$ or HbS/$\beta^+$). This is common in African and Mediterranian populations. Symptoms like sickle cell anaemia including splenomegaly.
3. *Hemoglobin C/thalassemia* : (Hb-C/$\beta_0$ or HbC/$\beta^+$) This is common in African and mediderranian populations. This is severe hemolytic anaemia (HbC/$\beta_0$) to mild hemolytic anaemia (HbC/$\beta^+$).

**Molecular mechanism of sequential gene expressions of β-globin genes.**

A complex regulatory region is found in the human β-globin gene, which is expressed exclusively in RBC and at a specific time in their development. A complex array of gene regulatory proteins control the expression of the gene, some acting as activators and others as repressors.

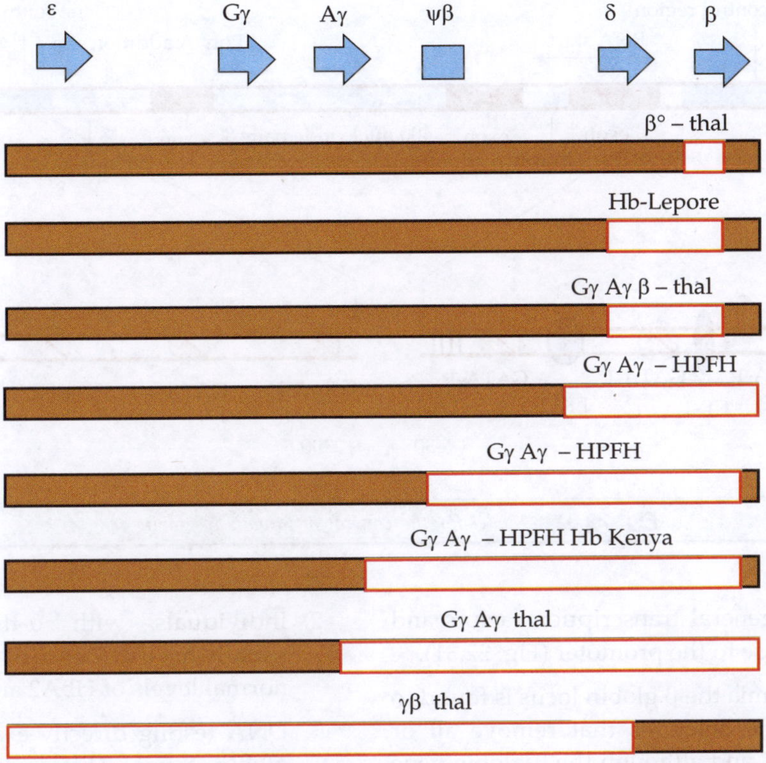


**Fig. 22.30 :** *Deletions in the β–globin gene cluster cause several types of thalassaemias.*

The human β-globin gene is part of a cluster of globin genes. The five genes of the cluster are transcribed exclusively in RBC. Each gene is turned on at different stages of development in different organs. The ε globin gene is expressed in the embryonic yolk sac, γ in yolk sac and the fetal liver, δ and β in the adult bone marrow. The entire cluster appears to be subject to a shared control region called a **locus control region** (LCR), which lies upstream from the gene cluster.

In cells where the globin genes are not expressed (such as brain, skin cells) the whole gene cluster appears tightly packed into chromatin. In the entire gene cluster is still folded into nucleosomes but higher order of packing is decondensed. There are two regulation steps : In the first, the chromatin of the entire globin locus becomes decondensed, which is presumed to allow additional gene regulatory proteins access to the DNA. In the second step, the remaining gene regulation proteins assemble on the DNA and direct the expression of individual genes.

The gene regulatory protein binds to the LCR and interacts through DNA looping. The gene regulatory proteins such as CP1, are found in many types of cells while others, such as GATA-1 are present only in a few types of cells including RBC cells and therefore, are thought to contribute to the cell type specificity of β globin gene expression. Several of the binding sites for GATA-1 overlap those of other gene regulatory proteins, it is thought that occupancy of these sites by GATA excludes binding of other proteins. Once bound to DNA the gene regulatory proteins recruit chromatin remodeling complexes, histone modifying

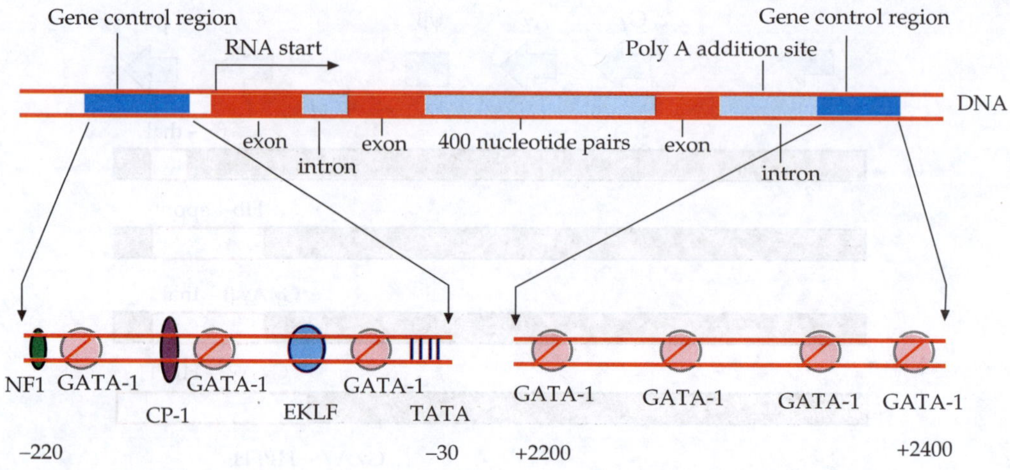


**Fig. 22.31 :** *Model for the control of human β–globin gene.*

enzymes, the general transcription factors and RNA polymerase to the promoter (Fig. 22.31).

In thalassemia the β globin locus is found to have undergone deletions that remove all or part of the LCR and although the β-globin gene and its nearby regulatory regions are intact the gene remains transcriptionally silent even in erythroid cells. Moreover, the α-globin gene in RBC fails to undergo the normal chromatin decondensation step that occurs during erythroid cell development.

**Carrier detection of thalassemia**

Detecting carrier couples can prevent thalassemia and at risk couples can be identified and informed of their genetic risk before having children. A prevention programme includes population screening, counselling and prenatal diagnosis.

The ELISA test for quantitization of HbA2 is used for carrier screening.

Hemoglobin electrophoresis with quantitative HbA2 and HbF.

1. Induviduals with β-thalassemia triat usually having evidence of microcytosis and increased levels of HbA2. HbF is sometimes elevated as well.
2. Individuals with α-thalassemia triat usually have evidence of microcytosis and normal levels of HbA2 and HbF.
3. DNA testing directly examines α and β-globin genes. This is the only way to determine silent α-thalassemia trait and hemoglobin Constant Spring and also for prenatal diagnosis.
4. If a person carries the trait for thalassemia but the partner does not, the child could inherit the trait, the prenatal diagnosis can be done to find wheather the child is carrier or not. But if both the parents are carriers, they must have the option prenatal diagnosis wheather the which is normal, carrier or patient. This can be done by extracting DNA from amniotic fluid after 15 week of gestation and chorionic villus samples (CVS) between 10-12 weeks or later gestation (Fig. 22.32).
5. The sensitive and reliable method based on three multiplex PCR assays is used for rapid detection of seven common α-thalassemia deletions.
6. Molecular characterization of α-thalassemia heterozygocity or homozygocity using Southern blot

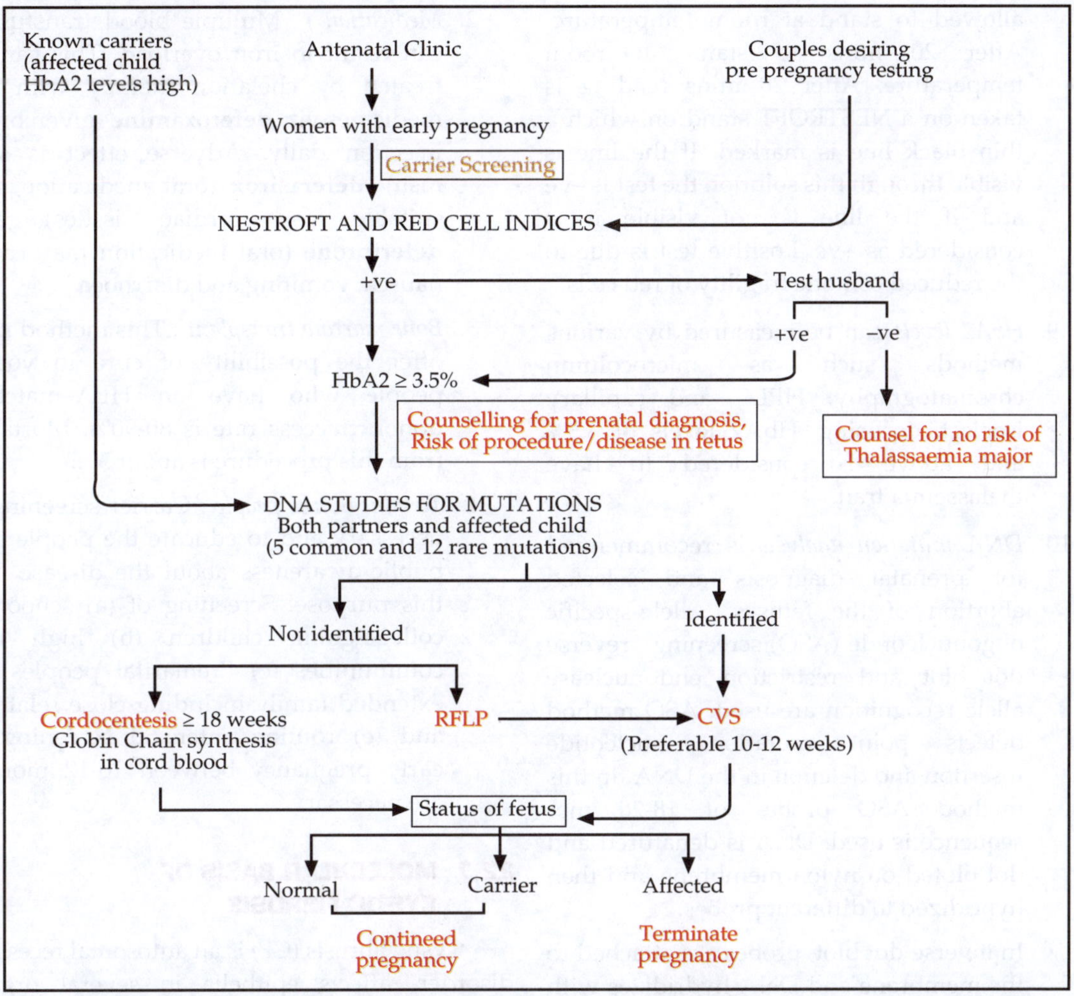


**Fig. 22.32** : *Detection of thalassemia carrier.*

analysis. PCR-based method is more rapid and less expensive. Amplification is done by primers, reagents and the enzyme *AmpliTaq polymerase*. Then 10 μl of product is electrophoresed in a 2% agarose gel, stained with ethidium bromide and visualized on a UV transilluminator.

7. *Red Cell indices* obtained through standard electronic cell counters provide valuable tool for preliminary screening of thalassaemia trait.

Thalassaemia traits in general have reduced mean corpuscular volume (MCV) and reduced mean corpusenlar hemoglobin (MCH) with normal mean corpuscular hemoglobin concentration (MCHC).

8. *Naked eye single tube red cell osmotic fragility test (NESTROFT)* is based on the limit of hypotonicity with the red cell can withstand. In this procedure 2 ml of 0.36% buffered saline is taken is a test tube, 20 ml of whole blood is added to it and it

allowed to stand at room temperature. After 20 mins to stand at room temperature. After 20 mins reading is taken on a NESTROFT stand on which a thin black line is marked. If the line is visible through this solution the test is –ve and if the line is not visible it is considered as +ve. Positive test is due to the reduced osmotic fragility of red cells.

9. *HbA2 levels* can be measured by various methods such as microcolumn chromatography, HPLC and capillary isoelectrofocusing. HbA2 levels of 3.5% and above is considered to have thalassemia trait.

10. *DNA mutation analysis* is recommended for prenatal diagnosis and selected abortion of the fetuses. Allele-specific oligonucleotide (ASO) screening , reverse dot blot and restriction endonuclease allele recognition are used. ASO method detects point mutation, nucleotide insertion and deletion in the DNA. In this method ASO probes of 18-20 mer sequence is used. DNA is denatured and dot bloted on nylon membrane and then hybridized to different probes.

    In inverse dot blot, probes are attached to the membrane and DNA hydridizes with dot, corresponding to the mutation.

**Management of thalassaemia :**

People with thalassemia traits do not require medical or follow-up care after the initial diagnosis. People with β-thalassemia trait should be warned that their condition can be misdiagnosed as the common iron deficiency anaemia.

Following methods are used for the management of thalassaemia :

1. *Blood transfusion :* People with severe thalassaemia requires a blood transfusion regimen which is the first measure in prolonging life.
2. *Medication :* Multiple blood transfusion can result in iron overload. This can be treated by chelation therapy with the medicines viz. **deferoxamine** (given by IV injection daily. Adverse effect is skin rash); **deferasirox** (oral medication, not suitable for cardiac issues) and **deferiprone** (oral medication may cause nausea, vomiting and diarrhoea.)
3. *Bone marrow transplant* : This method may offer the possibility of cure in young people who have an HLA–matched donor. Success rate is 80-90%. Mortality from this procedure is about 3%.
4. *To educate the people :* Carrier screening is necessary and to educate the people and public awareness about the disease. For this purpose. Screening of (a) school or college-going children (b) high risk communities (c) Premarital peoples (d) extended family including close relatives and (e) routine antenatal screening in early pregnancy between 10-12 months are necessary.

## 22.7 MOLECULAR BASIS OF CYSTIC FIBROSIS

Cystic fibrosis (CF) is an autosomal recessive disorder, affects epithelia in several organs resulting in a complex, multisystem disease that includes the exocrine pancreas, intestine, respirtory tract, male genital tract, hepatobiliary system and exocrine sweat glands. CF is sometimes regarded to an **mucoviscidosis.** Dorothy Hansine Andersen (1938) described CF first.

**Symptoms :**

1. **Pancreatic insufficiency :** Pancreatic duct is blocked by viscid mucus secretion causes cystic changes in the pancreas. Trypsin enzyme cannot be released into gut resulting degeneration of pancreatic tissues and also matabsorption of fat and fat soluble vitamins, bulky foamy foul smelling stool.

2. **Sino-pulmonary disease :** Chronic cough, sputum etc viscid secretions injury lung and inflammation block the bronchi, resulting into *bronchiectasis*. Repeated attacks of respiratory infections by *Staphylococcus aureus* and *Pseudomonas aeruginosa* in early life ensure right ventricular failure. End stage lung disease is characterised by extensive damage to airways and pulmonary fibrosis near airways. Maximum death occurs due to respiratory problems.
3. **Gastrointestinal disorder :** Meconium ileus of newborns diagnosed with CF. Pancreatic insufficiency causing haemolytic anaemia, defective coaglutation, skin rashes and deficiency of fat-soluble vitamines.
4. **CF in males :** CF may have congenital absence of vas deferens (CAVD) *i.e.*, hypoplasia or aplasia of vasdeferens and seminal vesicle, obstructive azoospermia, less volume of ejaculated semen, infertility etc are common. Women are not susceptible for any kinds of genital diseases.
5. **Sweat gland :** There is an incease in the concentration of $Na^+$ in sweat secretion, above 8 mM/L.
6. **Trypsinogen :** In CF, trypsinogen is released into the circulation appears to be enhanced by abnormal pancreatic duct secretion. Thus immunoreactive trypsinogen (IRT) levels are elevated.
7. **CF-related diabetis mellitus (CFRDM) :** CFRDM may be present in adults due to reduced insulin secretion (due to reduced number of islet cells) and peripheral insulin resistance.
8. **Hepatobiliary disease :** With elevation of liver enzyme concentration may tend to biliary cirrhosis. This is the second cause of mortality in CF.
9. **Fertility :** More than 95% males are infertile due to azoospermia. A few females have abnormal cervical mucous that may contribute to infertility.

**Genetics of CF :**

CF is a severe autosomal recessive disorder. The gene is known as *CFTR* (Cystic fibrosis transmembrane conductance regulator), located on the long arm of chromosome 7, region 3, bond 1, sub band 2/($7q^{31.2}$). The gene has recently been identified and shown to be approximately 230 kb in size; known as *ABC* gene. A total of 27 exons, each flanked by consensus splice signals. A number of repetitive elements include *Alu* and *Kpn* families and simple repeats, such as, (GT) 17, (GATT) 7, (TA) 14 were detected in close vicinity of some of the exon/intron boundaries (Fig. 22.33).

Although an internal amino acid sequence homology could be detected between the two halves of the polypeptide, especially in the region of the two nucleotide-binding folds NBF1 and NBF2. The lack of alignment of the nucleotide sequence as well as the different positions of exon/intron boundaries do not support the gene duplication events.

*Poly T* tract is located in intron 8 of *CFTR* gene and the CFTR-related disorders depending on its size. The three variants of poly-T tract are 5T, 7T and 9T of which 5T is considered a variably penetrant which is thought to decrease the efficiency of intron-8 splicing.

Short *TG tract* lies just 5′ of the *poly T* tract commonly 11, 12 or 13 in number. Long tract of TG along with short 5T has a strongest effect on intron splicing.

*Deletion of CTT* in the 10th exon 508 th position on the protein causes a loss of *phenylalanine* from the protein. This mutation is maximum in Northern Europe and US population (75%). There are 1500 other mutations that can produce CF.

**Management :**

1. Treatment of pulmonary complications include oral, inhaled or *i.v.* antibiotics, bronchodilators, anti-inflammatory

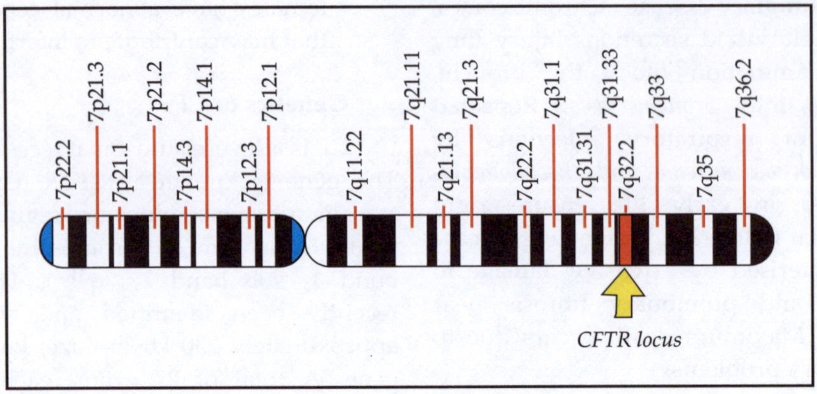


**Fig. 22.33 :** *CFTR gene locus on human chromosome no. 7*

agents, mucolytic agents and chest physiotherapy. Nasal/sinus symptoms require steroids, antibiotics etc.

2. Vitamin supplements are essential
3. Pancreatic insufficiency is treated with oral pancreatic enzyme replacement with meal.
4. Biliary sludging and obstruction and hepatic inflammation are treated with oral *ursodiol.*
5. CAVD-related infertility is managed by ART (Assisted reproductive technology) which includes microscopic sperm aspiration from epididymis. Regular exercise improves clearance of airway secretions. Chest physiotherapy (CPT) is recognised as effective. Routine immunization against pertussis, measles, varicella, *Haemophilus influenza* type B and *Streptococcus pneumonae.* Passive immunization with an anti-RSV monoclonal antibody (Synagis®) is used for younger patients.

Genetic counselling is done to the highly risk individuals.

**Causes :**

The gene product (CFTR protein with 1480 amino acids), is a chloride ion channel important in creating sweat, digestive juices and mucus. This protein possesses two ATP hydrolyzing

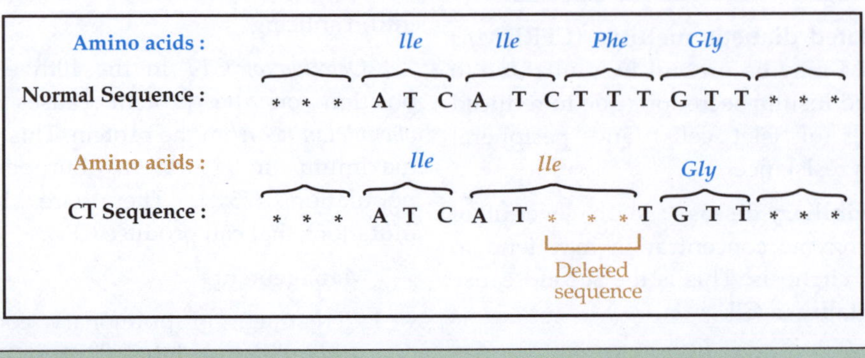


**Fig. 22.34 :** *Showing deletion of CTT bases and eliminating one codon of Phe-amino acid residue in CF-gene*

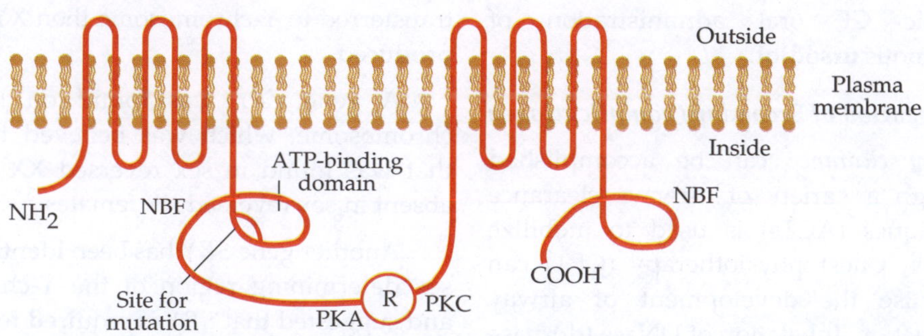


**Fig. 22.35 :** *Typical ABC transporter showing site for mutation in CF.*

domains, which allows the protein to use energy in the form of ATP. It also contains two domains comprising six alpha helices, which allow the protein to cross the cell membrane. A regulatory binding site on the protein allows activation by phosphorylation, mainly by cAMP-dependent protein kinase. The carboxyl terminal of the protein is anchored to the cytoskeleton by a PDZ domain interaction (Fig. 22.35).

This protein is a transmembrane channel controls the flow of $H_2O$ and $Cl^-$ in and out of the cells. When this protein is malfunctioning, these ions cannot flow out of the cell due to a blocked channel and builds up thick mucous in the lung. Due to blocking of ion channels, transmembrane electrical potential is modified and hypothiocyanite, OSCN, cannot be produced by the immune defense system. Thus mucous blocks airway passage, pancreatic duct and intestine. Imunogenic resistance against bacteria ceases, causing bacterial and fungal

| TABLE 22.12 Mutation causing CF are of 4 kinds | |
|---|---|
| *Mutation* | *Mechanisms* |
| 1. Reduced or absent synthesis | nonsense, Frame-shift or splice-junction mutation |
| 2. Block in protein processing | Missense; amino acid deletion |
| 3. Block in regulation of CFTR chloride channel | Missense mutation |
| 4. Altered conductance of CFTR chloride channel | Missense mutation |

infections in the body. About 10% of CF results from a mutation *glycine* in postion 542 being replaced by stop codon causing a truncated protein. Aminoglycoside gentamycin antibiotics interfere with protein synthesis and error correction which is used for the treatment. Another drug *ataluren* is undergoing Phase III clinical trial which can overcome premature stop codon.

**Inheritance :**

Every person inherits two *CFTR gene* — one from each parent, Children who inherit a faulty *CFTR* gene from each parent will have CF.

Children who inherit one faulty gene and one normal *CFTR* gene are CF carriers. They usually have no symptoms of CF and live normal lives. But they can pass the faulty *CFTR* gene to their children.

If both parents are carriers, there is a 25% chance of CF, 25% normal and 50% carrier normal offspring.

**Management of Cystic fibrosis**

(a) ***Prevention of primary manifestations***

1. *Pancreatic insufficiency and malnutrition* are the primary manifestations of CF, which can be managed by pancreatic enzyme replacement and supplement of fat-soluble vitamins and high calorie food.
2. *Biliary cirrhosis* : Endogenous ursodeoxycholic acid level causes lower risk of progression of CF liver diseases. In

chronic CF oral administration of exogenous **ursodiol**.

**(b)** ***Prevention of Secondary complications :***

1. *Airway clearance* can be accomplished through a variety of airways clearance techniques (ACTs) is used to mobilize airway. Chest physiotherapy (CPT) can minimise the development of airway obstruction. Inhalation of DNase (dornase alfa), a mucolytic agent can incrrease cough productivity during CPT. Inhalation of hypertonic saline (3-7%) is also used.
2. *Inhaled and oral antibiotics* are taken against the bacterial infection of the lung.
3. *Immunization* against pertussis, measles, varicella, *Haemophilus influenzae* type B and *Streptococens pneumonac* is done for secondary infection of CF.
4. Risk of osteopenia can be prevented by calcium and vitamin D therapy.
5. Gene therapy is in a research phase only.
6. Genetic counseling of the couples, nearest family member can clarify the genetic status and inheritance of CF. Antenatal screening is also done for the management of CF.

## 22.8 MECHANISM OF HUMAN SEX DETERMINATION

### 22.8.1 Introduction

The primary sex determination is strictly chromosomal and is not influenced by the environment. In human XX-XY mechanism of sex determination is observed. Y-chromosome plays an important role in sex determination.

Y-chromosome has *TDF* (testis determining factor) that organizes the gonad into a testis rather than ovary and X chromosome has *Sxr* (sex-reversal gene). If *TDF* is transferred from Y to X due to abnormal crossing over, XX males would be produced. If *Sxr* of X-chromosome is transferred to Y-chromosome then XY female is produced.

A gene *ZFY* was found on human Y-chromosome, which was believed to be *TDF* that was found in sex reversed XX males but absent in sex reversed XY females.

Another gene *SRY* has been identified in the sex determining region of the Y-chromosome and suggested that *SRY* is required for male sex determination.

Now, it has been found that at the small arm of Y chromosome ($Y_p$), *TDF* gene is localised with about 30–40 milion bases, which has four regions the terminal *IA1* region is 140 kb and next to it IA2 *ZFY* region of 140 kb. The *IA1* region consists of a small region just near to the terminal end called *SRY* which comprises about 250 bp (Fig. 22.36).

In human (mammalian) primary sex determination, there is no"default state". The formation of ovaries and testes is both active gene-directed process. Both have diverged from a common precursor, the bipotential gonad; during which time it has neither female nor male characteristics.

In human, paired gonadal rudiment appear in the intermediate mesoderm, near developing kidney during 4th week of gestation. The ventral portion of the gonadal rudiment is composed of genital ridge epithelium, which proliferates into loose connective mesenchymal tissues. The epithelial layers form sex cords. The germ cells migrate into the gonad during 6th week of gestation and are surrounded by sex cords. In both XX and XY such sex cords are formed and are connected to the surface epithelium.

The conversion of the genital ridge into the bipotential gonad requires *SF1, WT1, LWX 9 and GATA-4* genes.

This bipotential gonad appears to be moved into ovarian developmental pathway in females by *WNT4* FOXL2 and RSPO1 genes while into testicular developmental pathway by *SRY* gene in Y chromosome and some autosomal genes, such as *SOX9*.

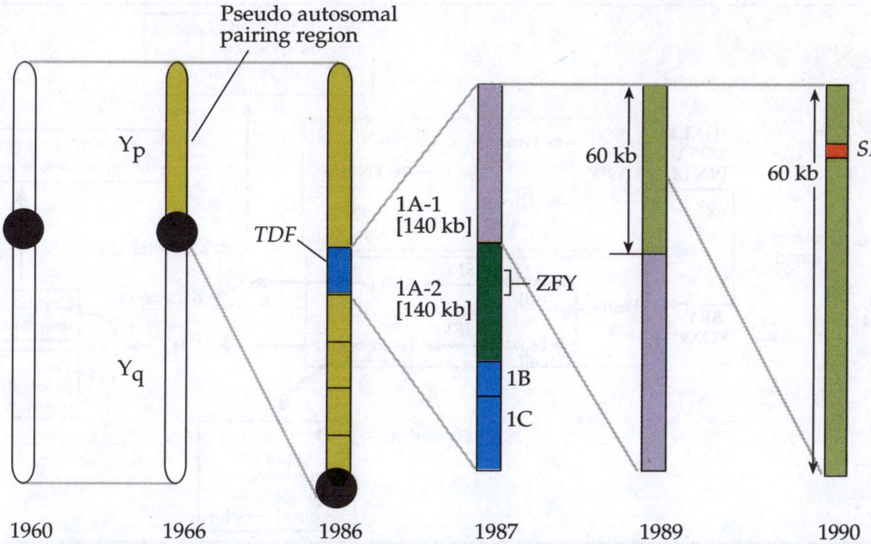


**Fig.22.36 :** *Discovery of the TDF region (30-40 million kb) and SRY region (less than 250 bases only) during the last 44 years.*

Ovary makes these cells and follicular cells, which produce oestrogen and are responsible for the formation of secondary sex organs in females such as uterus, oviduct, cervix, vagina etc. from the Mullerian duct.

Testis first secretes anti Mullerian hormone (AMH) from sertoli cells causing regression of Mullerian duct. Then the Leydig cell of testis produces testosterone causes differentiation of the Wolffian duct into male secondary sexual organs like epididymis, vas deferens, seminal vesicles. Testostorone is then converted into dihydrotestosterone (DHT) which causes morphogenesis of penis and prostrate gland. (Birk *et al* 2000) (Fig. 22.37).

### 22.8.2 *SRY* gene

By analyzing the DNA of XX-male and XY-female, the position of the testis determining gene has been narrowed down to a 35000 b.p.region near the tip of the short arm of Y chromosome. Sinclair *et. al* 1990 discovered a male specific DNA sequence that could encode a peptide of 223 amino acids, which is probably a transcription factor, since it contains a DNA binding domain (helix-turn-helix) called **HMG-box** (high mobility box). This protein is classified as activator influences gene expression by introducing bends and other distortions into DNA (Thomas and Travers 2001) possibly as a prelude to chromatin modification or possibly to bring together proteins attached to non-adjacent sites enabling the bound factors to work together in a structure that has been called *enhanceosome*. It is thought that several testis-specific genes contain *SRY*-binding sites in their promoters and enhancers and thus the developmental pathways to testis formation begin (Cohen *et al* 1994).

### 22.8.3 Evidences of *SRY* gene

The most of the evidences regarding the role of *SRY* gene were based on the *Sry* gene which is present in the mice Y chromosome.

Transgenic insertion of *Sry* DNA into the genome of XX mouse zygote would cause the development of testis.

Koopman and Colleage (1991) took the 14-kb region of DNA that includes the *Sry* gene and

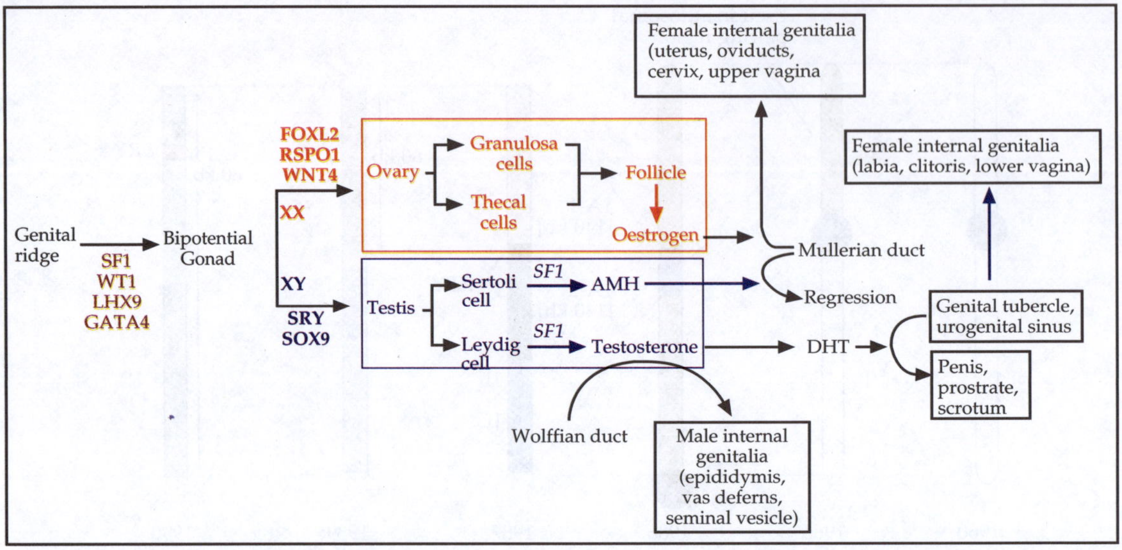


**Fig.22.37 :** *Postulated cascades of sexual phenotypes in mammals*

its regulatory elements and microinjected this sequence into pronuclei of fertilized zygote, several instances of XX embryos develop testis and male accessory organs.

### 22.8.4 Molecular mechanism of sex determination and role of *SRY*

1. When Sry protein binds to its site on DNA, it probably creates conformational changes by unwinding the double helix in its vicinity and bends the DNA as much as 80° (Pontiggia *et al* 1994, Werner *et al* 1995). This bending brings distantly bound proteins to the transcription apparatus into close contact and enables transcription of some important required proteins which are not yet known but needed for testis determination.

2. Recently it has been suggested by Capel (1999) that SRY does not work directly to the genital ridge to convert into sertoli cells. It works through an indirect mechanism.

   SRY in the genital ridge cells induces the cell to secrete a chemostatic factor that permits the migration of mesonephric cells into the XY-gonad. These mesonephric cells induce the gonadal epithelium to become sertoli cells with male-specific gene expression pattern. It is experimentally shown that, cultured XX gonads with either XX or XY mesonephros. The mesonephric cells do not enter the gonads. But cultured XX or XY mesonephros with XY gonads (or transgenic *Sry*, XX gonads) the mesonephric cells did enter the gonad.

   Tilmann and Capel (1999) showed that mesonephric cells are critical for testis cord formation. SRY may function indirectly to create testis by inducing mesonephric cell migration into the gonad.

### 22.8.5 SF1 and its relation with SRY in Sex determination

SF-1 (steroidiogenic factor-1) is a transcription factor may be directly or indirectly activated by SRY.

SF-1 is essential for the transformation of genital ridge into bipotential gonad. But in XX mouse its level declines while in XY mouse it stays at high level and working on both sertoli cells and leydig cells.

In the Sertoli cells SF-1 working in collaboration with Sox-9, which is needed to elevate the level of Anti-Mullerian duct hormone (AMH) transcription (Shen *et al* 1994, Arango *et al* 1999).

In the Leydig cells, SF-1 activates the genes encoding the enzymes necessary for testosterone synthesis.

SRY protein directly or indirectly activates *SF-1* gene and then SF-1 protein is transcribed which is then taking part in male sexual differentiation pathway.

### 22.8.6 Autosomal Sex-reversal gene - *SOX-9*

*SOX-9* is an autosomal gene, encodes a transcription factor that also contains an HMG box. The XX zygote which has an extra copy of *SOX-9* would be developed into a male even in absence of *SRY* (Huang *et. al.*1999).

In mouse homologue to this gene is *Sox-9*, which is expressed only in males (XY) not in female (XX) genital ridges. In males it is expressed just slightly after *Sry* expression.

Sox 9 and SF-1 act synergistically to activate the expresion of *Amh* gene and transcription in Sertoli cell by binding with the promoter of *Amh* gene.

Expression of *Amh* upregulates the binding of SF-1 on its DNA binding site and then WNT-1 is joined to the SF-1 protein.

Another transcription factor, **Gata** upregulates *Amh* expression further (Fig. 22.38).

### 22.8.7 Ovary determining gene (*DAX-1*)

Bernstein *et al* 1980 had reported a peculiar case where two sisters were XY and their Y-chromosome is normal whereas, there is a duplication of a small portion of the short arm of the X-chromosome. Thus-*SRY* signal in Y chromosome is reversed by these two genes. The product of this gene competes with the SRY factors and thus testicular development is suppressed, directing the development of ovary (Bardoni *et. al* 1994).

*Dax-1* is expressed in the genital ridge shortly after *Sry* expression. DAX-1 appears to antagonise the function of SRY and down signals *SF-1* expression (Swain *et al* 1998). Thus it regulates the female sex determination.

### 22.8.8 Autosomal Ovary-determining gene : *WNT 4*

*WNT 4* is an autosomal gene, which is expressed in the genetic ridge while it is still in its bipotential stage. It is maintained in the XX gonads and begins to form ovaries.

In the XX-female mice which lack *WNT 4*, the ovary fails to form properly and some enzymes for AMH and testosterone synthesis are expressed (Vainio *et. al* 1999).

### 22.8 9 *Fgf9* gene

Fibroblast growth factor 9 (*fgf9*) ,whose expression is dependent on Sox9 plays an important role in testis formation.

1. Fgf9 activates the migration of endothelial cells from the adjacent mesonephros into the XY gonad. These endothelial cells form the major artery of the testis and also an important role in inducing Sertoli cell precursors to differentiate into testis cord (Brennan et. al. 2002; Combes et. al. 2009).
2. Fgf9 is required for maintaining *Sox9* gene expression in the presumptive Sertoli cells and directs their formation into seminiferous tubules and their assembly in the testis (Hiramatsu et. al. 2009).
3. Fgf9 acts as both autocrine as well as paracrine factors.
4. Fgf9 represses Wnt4 signalling and also ovarian development by inhibiting β-catenin activity (Maatouk et. al.2008; Jameson et. al. 2012).

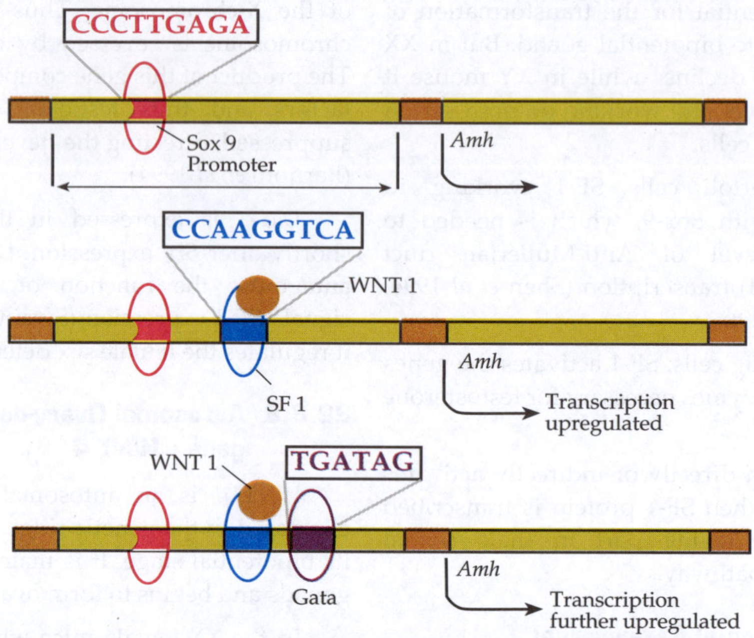


**Fig.22.38 :** *Synergism of Sox 9 and Sf-1 to activate the expression of the Amh gene in sertoli cells*

5. Fgf9 blocks the immediate entry of germ cells into meiosis, thereby directing them to the sperm-forming pathway (Barrios et. al.2010; Bowles et. al.2010)

## 22 .8.10 *R-spondin1* gene

Genital ridge is bipotential where different genes for *Wt1, Wnt4, Lhx9, GATA4* and *Sf1* are expressed. Loss of one function of any one of them prevents the normal development of either male or female gonads. Wnt4 and R-spondin1 are critical in ovary formation. XX gonad with *RSPO1* gene mutation causes to become male (Parma et al. 2006).

1. Rspo1 is a soluble protein. In absence of Y chromosome, it binds to its cell membrane receptor and stimulates the Disheveled protein of the Wnt pathway, making the Wnt pathway more efficient at producing β-catenin.
2. Rspo1 acts in synergy with Wnt4 to produce β-catenin, which activates ovarian development and also blocks the activity of Sox9 (which is necessary for testis determination).

## 22.8.11 TAFII 105 and Foxl 2 Transcription factors

The target for â-catenin is the gene encoding TAFII 105, which is a transcription factor subunit that binds RNA polymerase to promoters. This is seen only in ovarian follicle cells. In absence of TAFII 105, females have small ovaries with few mature follicles.

FoxI 2 is another transcription factor that is strongly upregulated in ovaries. XX female mice homozygous for mutant *Foxl2* alleles develop male-like gonad structure and upregulates Sox9 expression and testosterone production.

## 22.8.12 *Follistatin* gene

Both Foxl2 and Wnt4 pathway are critical activation of*Follistatin* gene (Ottolenghi et. al.2005; Kashimada et.al.2011; Pisarka et.

a.2011). Follistatin is an inhibitor of TGF-β family paracrine factor thought to be responsible for organizing epithelium into granulosa cells of the ovary (Yao et. al.2004). XX female mice lacking Follistatin in the developing gonad undergo partial sex reversal, forming testicle-like structure.

### 22.8.13 Possible molecular mechanism for the initiation of primary sex determination in mammals

#### If SRY is not present :

1. The interactions between paracrine and transcription factors in the developing genital ridge activate *Wnt4* and *Rspo1* (*R-spondin 1*).
2. Wnt4 activates the canonical Wnt-pathway, which is made more efficient by Rspo1.
3. The Wnt pathway causes the accumulation of β-catenin, and large accumulation of β-catenin stimulates further Wnt4 activity. This continual production of β-catenin both induces the transcription of ovary-producing genes and blocks the testis-determining pathway by interfering the SOX9 activity.

#### If SRY is present :

1. It may block β–catenin signalling( thus halting ovary generation)and, along with Sf1, activate the *SOX9* gene.
2. SOX9 activates Fgf9 synthesis, which stimulates testis development and promotes further SOX9 synthesis. SOX9 also prevents β-catenin's activation of ovary-producing genes.
3. SRY may also activate other genes (such as *TCF21* and *NT3*) that help generate Sertoli cells.
4. One of the targets of the Wnt pathway is the *follistatin* gene, whose product organizes the granulosa cells of the ovary. Transcription factor Foxl 2 which is activated in the ovary, is involved in inducing follistatin synthesis.
5. It is fact that the Wnt4 / β-catenin loop specifies the ovaries, whereas a SOX9/ Fgf9 loop specifies the testes. The XY pathway appears to have an earlier initiation; if it does not function, the XX pathway takes over (Sekido and Lovel-Badge 2009; McClelland et al 2012). (Fig 22.39)

### 22.8.14 Brain sex

Recent evidences suggested that sex differences in the brain can be observed even before the maturation of gonads. There may have a direct regulation on brain by the X and Y chromosomes (Arnold and Burgoyne, 2004). Genetic, hormonal and environmental agents all play a role in in sexual behaviours (McCarthy and Arnold 2011;Ngun et al 2011).Several specific regions of brain are to be involved in sex-specific behaviour which is regulated by gonadal steroid hormone and organize the nervous in a sex-specific manner.

**The organization/activationhypothesis**: This hypothesis states the sex-specific brain development and behaviour. The hormone oestradiol is chiefly responsible for determining the male neural pattern.The fetal testosterone can be converted into oestradiol by the enzyme aromatase which occurs in the hypothalamus and limbic system of the brain. Thefetal environment is rich in oestrogen in both males and females, which is produced from gonad and placenta. Oestrogen is bound to á-fetoprotein and inactivates it, but not the testosterone.

1. α-fetoprotein prevents the female brain from receiving circulating oestrogen. Therefore, female mice whose á-fetoprotein genes have knocked out are sterile because GnRH from the brain is down-regulated. On the other hand if these mice are given the aromatase-blocker, normal female pattern of gene expression is established.

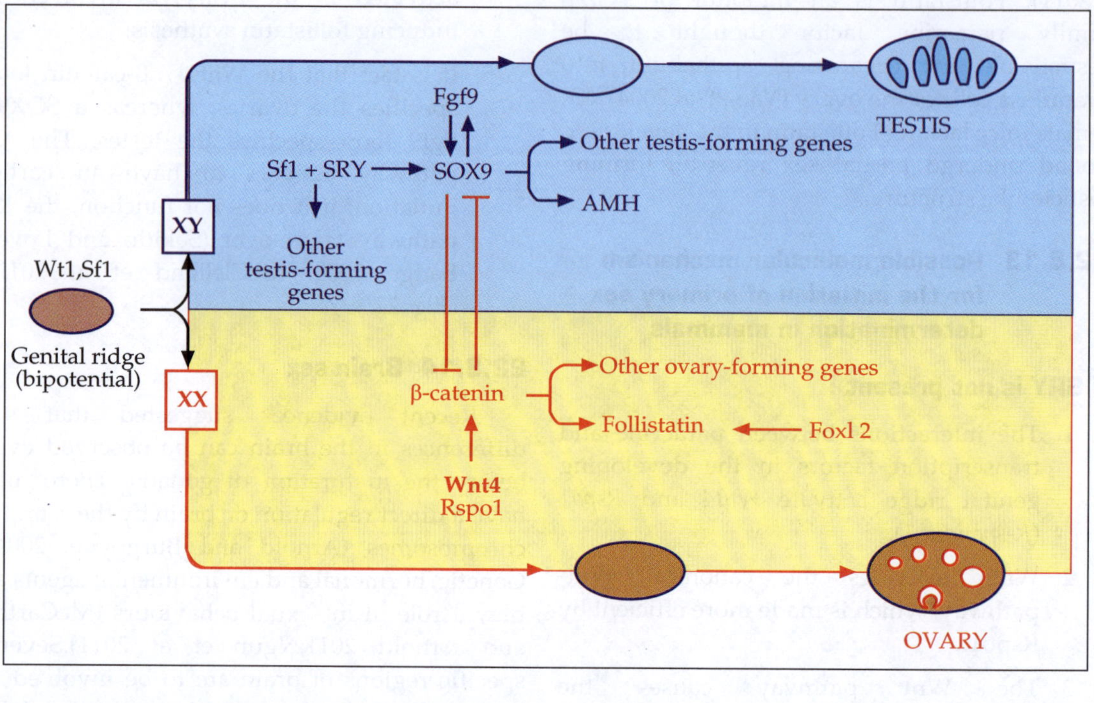


**Fig. 22.39 :** *Possible molecular mechanism for the initiation of primary sex determination in mammals.*

2. Lordosis posture (female rodents that permits the male) is almost abrogated due to the lacking of á-fetoprotein genes.If these mice are given the aromatase-blocker, normallordosis posture in females is established (Bakker and Baum 2008).
3. Prenatal lack of oestrogen andtestosterone may have a critical role for the formation of female brain and after birth, for feminization may require oestrogen. Lordosis behaviour is impaired in female mice whose aromatase gene is knocked out.

**Pheromone sexual behaviour hormone**: Pheromone is a sex-specific chemical secreted in the atmosphere plays an important role in sexual behaviour in rodents. The vomero-nasal organ is responsible for sensing pheromone (such organ is absent in humans).

1. If the genes for pheromone-recognition system or the pheromone-recognition systemitself is removed, males cannot discriminate male to female and attempt to mate both. In such case, female mice lack certain female behaviour, but acquire male-specific courtship behaviour.
2. So. It I thought that both male and female behaviour exist in brain. The pheromone signal distinguishes the male to female brain.
3. In females, feminine pattern is activated and masculine pattern is repressed. On the other hand, in males, masculine pattern is activated and feminine pattern is repressed (Kimchi et. al. 2007).
4. Pheromone signal is thought to take place in the medial pre-optic area/ hypothalamus region of the brain. This region is sexually dimorphic due to prenatal exposure to oestrogen exposure. Pheromone signal activates different sets

of neurons of this region of the brain in the males and females (Baum 2009).

**Brain sex due to intrinsic sex differences**:

1. Studies on the embryonic rat brain with Parkinson disease before gonad maturation indicated that brains from XX embryos have more epinephrine-secreting neurons than XY brains(Beyer et.al. 1991).More than 50 genes were identified (by using microarray and PCR techniques) to express in the sexually dimorphic brain before gonad differentiation.
2. *SRY* gene is expressed in the embryonic, fetal as well as adult brain. SRY is active in substansianigra of male hypothalamus where it regulates the expression of gene for tyrosine hydroxylase enzyme which is essential for dopamine neurotransmitter synthesis.
3. McCarthy and Arnold (2011) stated that there are few hormonally dependent dimorphic structures, but the brain may be monomorphic i.e. the entire brain might be "male" or "female"as a result of sex chromosome differences,
4. Male finches sing; females do not. Testosterone is important in the formation of the song centres in finches. If experimentally testosterone is given to females they sing; but blocking this hormone, males sing without preventing normal development of song centre. Therefore, it seems that development of song centre in the brain is genetically determined without requiring testosterone (Mathews and Arnold 1990).
5. Gynandromorphy of finch where right side of the brain had ZZ (male) sex chromosome and left side had ZY (female) sex chromosome, in an experiment showed(Agate et. al.2002) that they sang and copulate. This is due to the presence of testosterone in the bloodand active song centre in the right side of the brain. This concludes that both intrinsic and hormonal influences are important for song circuit and masculine phenotype in birds.

**Role of experience in brain sex**:

1. One of the most sexually dimorphic regions of rat central nervous system is the spinal nucleus of bulbocavernosus (SNB), which is testosterone-sensitive and larger in males. This controls the pelvic thrusting muscle during mating. But it is interesting that size of SNB neuron becoming smaller when the males mate more frequently. So, it can be seemed that differences in sexual behaviour cause, rather than are caused by, differences in brain structure.
2. Those female pups experience maternal care such as licking and grooming, when they become young also provide such maternal care to their own offspring. This response behaviour is regulated through the oestrogen-responsive neurons of the medial preoptic area (MPOA), a dimorphic region of the brain.When oestrogen binds to its receptor on MPOA neurons, encode genes for oxytocin-receptor. Oxytocin hormone is involved with nursing and grooming.
3. In the MPOA neurons, licking and grooming decreases the amount of DNA methylation of the brain-specific enhancers in the major oestrogen-receptor gene *ERα* in the pups. This enables the Stat5 transcription factor and permits the *ERα* gene to be transcribed at high levels stimulate licking and grooming behaviour. So, differences in parental care gene expression are caused by the experience of the neonatal rats (Cameron et al. 2008 Fig 22.40).
4. Licking and grooming experiences in the rat pups having a highly methylated promoter on *ERα*gene in the anterior

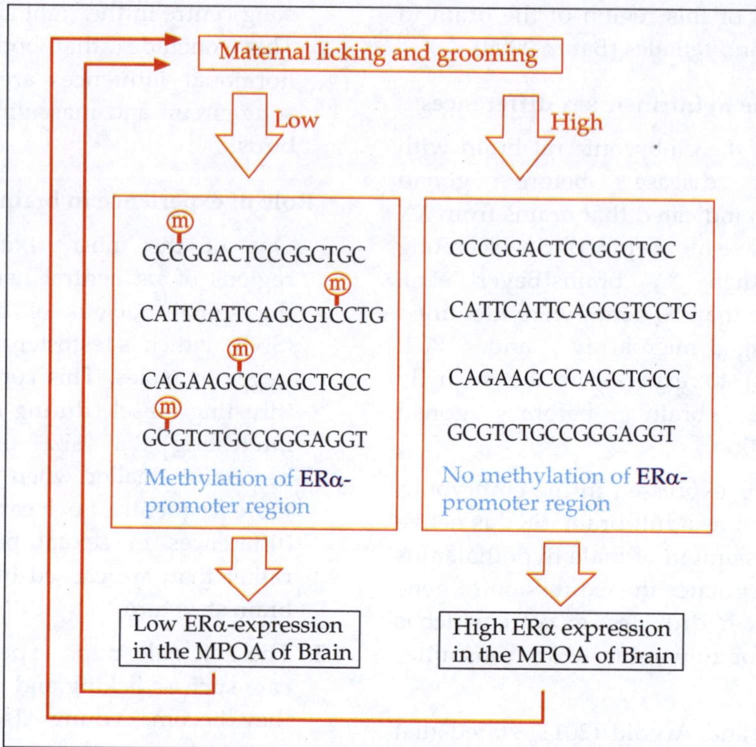


**Fig. 22.40 :** *Differences in parental care gene expression caused by the experience of the neonatal rats.*

paraventricular nucleus (PVN), causing downregulation of oestrogen-receptor in this region.

5. PVN helps regulate Gonadotropins. Rats experiencing low levels of maternal licking and grooming have high levels of oestrogen-receptors in the PVN and correspondingly high levels of gonadotropins. As they mature, these rats get precocious puberty and lack of maternal care to their pups. So, it is clear that experience can create change in gene expressionandneuroanatomy (Cameron et. al. 2008).

**The Brain sex in Humans:**

Though human foetuses have higher levels of oestrogen, α–fetoptrotein does not play any role in the brain development like that of rodents.Moreover, humans do not use pheromones as the primary sex attractants; sight and touch being far more critical. Brain anatomy of homosexual and heterosexuals shows definite differences. Concordance of gender identity between identical twins is only 30%, which is far from 100% expected, if the sexual orientation were genetic (Bailey et. al. 2000). More when they were grownin different environment, their behaviour may be masculine or feminine. Therefore, humans acquire gendered behaviour in a very complex set of interactions between genes, hormones, nerves and environments.

a) An important sex divergence typically occurs in brain development around the eighth week of gestation. In a male embryo, the testes are formed and the XY genotype initiates testosterone production. At birth, the female brain is slightly smaller than a male brain, with fewer brain cells and less brain tissue—which doesn't imply anything about male or female intelligence. It's important to note that presence or lack of a Y chromosome doesn't necessarily determine a person's gender, biologically or socially. A female embryo subjected to high amounts of testosterone might exhibit more "masculinization" than a typical female embryo. The concept of a "female" brain is based on physical characteristics largely present in the brain structures of a majority of individuals with XX genotypes.

b) Dr. Simon Baron-Cohen attempts to account for the sex distinctions in behaviour by referring to three defined brains types:

1. The female brain, which is more empathizing, intuitively figures out how people are feeling and how to treat people with care and sensitivity, systemizer intuitively figures out how things work, or what underlying rules are controlling a system.
2. The male brain, which is more systematizing.
3. The balanced brain, which falls somewhere between the two.

He also states that "Not all men have the male brain, and not all women have the female brain."

c) During pregnancy, women's brains go through many changes. Not only do they physically shrink due to the fetal absorption of Omega-3 fatty acids, but they have to deal with a major influx of hormones like cortisol and progesterone in the brain, and shifts in most hormone levels throughout the body.

d) Male and female brains have other differences in emotional wiring. Women are more vulnerable when it comes to depression. Neuroimage, Hristina Jovanovic 2008, using a PET scan, illustrated greater numbers of serotonin-receptors in female brains. They also believe that women have less of a specific protein that transports serotonin. This may begin to explain differences in depression between men and women, and why women often respond differently to antidepressant medications.

e) Androgens and estrogens determine brain sex during gestation, but some scientists believe testosterone also impacts such cognitive functions as memory, attention and spatial skills. But a typical male brain doesn't guarantee to have a better memory, rather it may make it more likely. The same goes for women and empathy, as well as nurturing because of the presence of oxytocin in the brain during pregnancy and childbirth. This prepares the female brain to be able to care for a new-born.

f) Women's brains seem, to be better at managing stress. Brain regions that are involved in regulating stress also are involved in regulating other functional systems, such as heart regulation (which can affect cardiovascular disease), memory (which can affect aging of the brain and memory decline), and mood and fear (which will affect depression and anxiety disorders.

g) Gene expression changes in the course of normal brain aging are sexually dimorphic. Nicole C. Berchtold (2008) indicates that the male brain gene expression generally remains stable after age 80, whereas in the female brain genes continue to undergo age-related change into the eighth and ninth decades of life.

h) The stress response and its implications for depression and cardiovascular diseases, the aging of the memory circuitry and cognitive decline with implications for the fact that there is higher risk of Alzheimer's among women than men even after adjusting for the fact that women live longer.

i) There are several differences between homosexuals and heterosexuals

1. It is found that in homosexual men and heterosexual women, the blood flowed to the amygdala areas involved in fear and anxiety, whereas in heterosexual men and homosexual women, it tended to flow to pockets linked to aggression.

2. The right hemisphere was found to be slightly larger than the left in heterosexual men and homosexual women, whereas those of homosexual men and heterosexual women were more symmetrical.

3. The corpus callosum is larger in homosexual men than in heterosexual men. The third interstitial nucleus of the hypothalamus has neurons that are packed more together in homosexual men than in heterosexual men.

4. In homosexual men and heterosexual women, there were more connections from the left amygdala. In homosexual women and heterosexual men, there were more connections from the right amygdala.

5. There was a trend for INAH3 to occupy a smaller volume in homosexual men than in heterosexual men; there was no difference in the number of neurons within the nucleus based on sexual orientation.

j) In females, Estradiol influences cognitive function, specifically by enhancing learning and memory in a dose-sensitive manner. Too much oestrogen can have negative effects by weakening performance of learned tasks as well as hindering performance of memory tasks; this can result in females exhibiting poorer performance of such tasks when compared to males.It has been suggested that during development, high levels of oestrogen induce male neural traits to develop while moderate levels induce female traits. In females, defeminizing effects are resisted because of the presence of α-fetoprotein (AFP), a carrier protein proposed to transport oestrogen into brain cells, allowing the female brain to properly develop. The role of AFP is significant at crucial stages of development. Prenatally, AFP blocks oestrogen. Postnatally, AFP decreases to ineffective levels; therefore, it is probable that oestrogen exhibits its effects on female brain development postnatally.

k) Adult male brains have a medial amygdala of greater volume than do adult female brains which is partially due to androgen circulation

l) Oestrogen enhances memory and learning in women, testosterone has been found to enhance memory recall in men. Higher testosterone levels are related to increased brain activation in the amygdala.

m) Oxytocin is positively correlated with maternal behaviours, social recognition, social contact, sexual behaviour and pair bonding. Oxytocin appears at higher levels in women than in men. Vasopressin on the other hand is more present in men and mediates sexual behaviour, aggression and other social functions.

n) 5-HT serotonin levels are higher in women than men while men synthesize serotonin significantly faster than women. Healthy women also have higher 5-HT transport availability in the diencephalon and brainstem areas of the brain.

o) Dopamine function is also increased in women especially dopamine transporter which regulates the availability of receptors.

p) Women are also more dependent on norepinephrine in the formation of long term emotional memories than men are.

## 22.9 HUMAN EVOLUTION

### 22.9.1 Systematic position

"Man" is a primate, belonging to the order **Primates,** because of the presence of prehensile limbs, more or less opposable thumb and hallux. Five digits, flattened nails, rarely claws, with clavicle, the orbit is surrounded by bone, thoracic mammary glands and simple stomach.

Its suborder is **Anthropoidea,** *i.e.* 32-36 teeth, completely closed orbit, two pectoral mammae, richly convoluted cerebral hemispheres covering cerebellum.

It belongs to the group **Catarrhini**, *i.e.* old-world apes, because of the possession of a narrow nasal septum, 32 teeth and non-prehensile tail.

The family is **Hominidae**, having erect posture and development of brain, hind limb to bear the weight of the body.

**History :** T. H. Huxley (1863) made first attempt to the human origin in his book "Man's place in the nature" and visualized apes as the closest relatives.

Darwin directly dealt with the idea in his book "Descent of Man" 1871, where argues a common ancestry of apes and human, Unfortunately, he lacked fossil evidences in support of his view, because in his time, Neanderthal man from Germany and Cro-Morgnon man from France.

Most prehuman fossils were discovered from 1920 onwards. The fossils of human ancestors were unearthed by Eugene Dubois, A Dutch anatomist.

The contribution of Raymond Dart, W.C. Peiliuis and Mary Leaky, their son Richard and Barnard Nigeneo helped in preparing tree of human evolution.

Long discoveries of fossil of human ancestors suggest at least three points.

1. Human evolution is fully consistent with evolation
2. The evolution has been taken place more than 4 million years back.
3. The origin and evolution have taken place is Asia and Africa.

### 22.9.2 Human specialization

(a) *Brain and associated structures :*

1. Larger brain, an average of 1350 cc.
2. Large frontal lobes of Cerebral hemisphere .

This is related to its great capacity of learning, intelligence and their own communicating system.

(b) *Upright Posture*

1. Skull is balanced on the upper end of vertebral column. Foramen of magnum is beneath the skull.
2. Vertebral column is S-shape, called lumber curve which brings the vertebral column upright posture.
3. Ilium bone is expanded to form a basin which supports viscera in the body cavity.

(c) *Bipedalism*

1. Acquired bipedalism with standing on straightend knees.
2. Plantigrade with broad first toe.
3. Hands are specialized for its mobility and can be brought into almost any position in relation to body.

(d) *Teeth and associated structures :*

1. Small incisors, canines are not projected.
2. Simian gap (gap between incisors and canine of upper jaw) is absent.
3. Face is not projected into muzzle called orthognathus face profile due to smaller teeth.

(e) *Other specializations*

1. Loss of hair from the body
2. Prolongation of post-natal development.

**TABLE 22.13**
**Difference between Apes and Man**

| Characters | Apes | Man |
|---|---|---|
| 1. Habit | Mainly arboreal | Terrestrial |
| 2. Head | Occipital condyles directed backwords, Head on the shoulder | Occipital condyle directed downwords, Head on the neck |
| 3. Face | Prognathus | Orthognathus |
| 4. Cranial cavity | 395 cc is Orangutans, 400 cc in Chimpanzee 510 cc in Gorilla | Average 1450 cc (1350 – 1600 cc) |
| 5. Brain | Simple and small | Complex and highly developed |
| 6. Eyebrow ridge | Prominent | Reduced |
| 7. Forehead | Slanting | Broad and straight |
| 8. Jaw | Heavy jaws | Not so heavy |
| 9. Dental arch | U-shaped | Parabola-shaped |
| 10. Teeth | Incisors pointed, canines projecting, 3 premolars, Diastema present | Canines not projected, diastema absent, 2 premolars. |
| 11. Pelvic girdle | Elongated and narrow | Short and broad |
| 12. Posture | Semierect | Erect and Upright |
| 13. Walking | With all four limbs or two hind limbs with body bent forward | Bipedal and erect |
| 14. Sole | Do not lie flat on the ground | Flat on the ground |
| 15. For limbs | Longer than hind limbs for arboreal habit | Shorter than hind limbs for walking |
| 16. Lumber curve | Not prominent | S-shaped lumber curve |
| 17. Hair | Thick hairs on the whole body surface | Small and scanty body hair |
| 18. Great toes | Great toes in hind limb is opposable | Great toe in hind limb is not opposable |

3. Altriceous, *i.e.* babies are helpless, care is taken by the parents after birth and dependent for a long time.

### 22.9.3 Place of Modern Human Evolution

The place of human origin is considered to be Africa, Central Asia, China, Java and India. Fossils of earliest hominids were obtained from Africa, China and Siwalika Hills in India.

There are two theories regarding the origin of modern man.

1. Monophyletic origin or Single Origin hypothesis or Noah's Ark Model : Accrding to this hypothesis, modern man has evolved in a single locality in Africa about 2 million years ago and from where the ancestors were migrated to all other continents of Old world. This was proposed by Willium Howells.

2. Polyphyletic origin or Multiregional hypothesis or Multiple origin of man hypothesis or Candelabra Model : This is presented by Lewin 1987 and Thomas (1992). According to this hypothesis, human evolution has occurred almost simultaneously in different localities in old world after *H. erectus* and spread out the old world. *Homo sapiens* was evolved independently.

### 22.9.4 Characters that developed during Human Evolution :

1. Straight posture, bipedal locomotion, Distinct lumber curve.
2. Increase in size of brain and cranial cavity
3. Flattering of face, loss of supraorbital ridge
4. Formation of chin and narrowing of nose
5. Opposable thumb.
6. Sparse body hair
7. Reduction in the size of canines
8. Increases in intelligence
9. Social and cultural organization

### 22.9.5 Early Human Ancestors

About 25-30 million years ago, ape-humans or hominid stock started descending from the trees and gradually became ground dwellers. They evolved along two lines : apes and man.

1. Those that spent most of their time on trees and occasionally visited to ground : **evolved into apes.**
2. Those that were completely the ground dwellers : **evolved into human.**

Separation of ape and human ancestors occurred at about 5 million years ago.

1. The earliest primates in the Pliocene with their long snouts and claws, somewhat resembled modern tree shrews. They lived in burrows or on trees, they are fruit-eating and tree dwelling.
2. In early Oligocene, anthropoids were diverged into three lines. One to the New World monkeys (Ceboids), second to Cercopithocids or Old World monkeys and the third one is Hominids.
3. The oldest known hominid *Oligopithecus* discovered by Simons *et. al.* (1978) from Egyptian Fayum bed. It had dental formula of apes.
4. In Miocene, *Pliopithecus* probably discended from *Propliopithecus* (probably ancestor of gibbon)
5. Several species of *Dryopithecus* are known who were ancestors to African apes and probably man also.
6. From an unknown group of terrestrial Miocene apes, the ancestral human have evolved.

### 22.9.6 Prior to Ape-Man

1. *Dryopithecus :* The fossils were obtained from rocks of Miocene (about 20-25 million years old) from Africa and Asia. Their fossils from the rocks of Bilaspur (India) have been named *Sivapithecus* and from East Africa *Dryopithecus africanus.*

   They had long arms and legs of almost equal length, semi-erect posture and large canines like those of modern apes. These are supposed to be the common ancestors of apes and man.

2. *Proconsul* : Fossils were obtained from East Africa from Miocene rocks. Their forehead was man–like but canines were very long and pointed like those of apes. These are also called **pre-apes** because from this Chimpanzee and Gorilla had been evolved.
3. *Ramapithecus* : This is regarded to be the forerunner of Hominids, This was obtained from Africa and Asia in the rocks of Miocene and early Pliocene (14-12 million years ago). It has been revealed that the ancestors of Orang-utans possibly giving a branch between 4-6 million years ago. At molecular level of studies and by

DNA-DNA hybridization indicate that human line became separated from Chimpanzee line sometimes between 5.5 and 7.5 million years ago.

They have Man-like feeding habits, small canine, short face, enamelled teeth and walking erect on the ground.

*Australopithecus* is known as ape-man as they had ape-like brain.

The evolution of human from *Australopithecus* onwords is described in the Fig. 22.41 and Table 22.14.

**TABLE 22.14**
**The Ape-man (Australopithecine)**

| | | |
|---|---|---|
| 1. *Australopithecus ramidus* (Ardi) or *Ardipithecus ramidus* | The oldest fossil of *A. ramidus* was discovered in 1992-93 by Gen Suwa, from localities West of the Awash River in Ethiopia. The discovery was revolutionary and lucky, but there is still debate whether ramidus will be regarded as first-species on human line. This is 4.4 million years old. | The fossil is small brained, 50 Kg female, nick name is "Ardi". They had teeth with ape -like and human-like and common ancerter of ape and man, 4 ft tall, bipedal and forest dwellers. |
| 2. *Australopithecus afarensis* | A complete skull of *A. afarensis* female was excavated by D. Johanson in 1975 has become superstar of human evolution lived between 3.9 – 2.9 million years ago. She was named as "lucy", is regarded as **mother of mankind.** | It has eyebrow ridges, low forehead, prognathus face, small brain and long arms, short legs, thin thorax with large belly, 4.5-5 ft height. |
| 3. *Australopithecus anamensis* | Louis Leaky discovered a fossil of 4.1 million years old near Turkana Kenya and Ethiopia. | Mandibles with teeth, more than 4.5 ft height. |
| 4. *Australopithecus africanus* | It was discovered by Dart (1924) in Tuang cave of South Africa. Other fossils were also discovered from South Africa. They live between 3 – 2.3 million years ago. | They had higher and rounded brain case, They can stood upright. Limbs are less adapted for bipedalism. |
| 5. *Australopithecus boisei* (Nutcracker man) | It was discovered by Mary Leakey (1959) at Olduvai Gorge, Tanzania, dated to 1.75 million years ago. | It is 4.5 ft height powerful upper body. Small brain 500-600 cc. Heavy chewing ability, largest molar, 4.5 ft height. |
| 6. *Australopithecus aethiopicus* | This was discovered from West Turkana between 2.6 – 2.2 million years ago. | They have strongly protruding face, megadont teeth, powerful jaw. |
| 7. *Australopithecus robustus* | It was discovered in 1938 by a school boy in South Africa dated between 2–1.2 million years ago. | It has a flatter face, 4 ft 3 inches – 4 ft 7 inches tall, quite well muscled prominent check, and less protruding jaws. It seems that during Pliocene and Pleistocene, a lineage of australo pithecine ran parallel to towards the genus *Homo*. |

**TABLE 22.15**
**Early Homos**

| | | |
|---|---|---|
| 1. *Homo habilis* (Handy man) | Louis Leaky discovered along the Eastern shore of Lake Turkana in Kenya in 1960. The date ranges between 2.5 – 1.6 million years ago. | It is 4.5 ft tall, larger cranial capacity, smaller teeth, rounded brain case. |
| 2. *H. erectus* (The upright man, The Forerunner of Modern man) | Dobois (1891) discovered from Java (Java man) Later it was also discovered from China (Peking man) and also Africa and Europe. It is 1.8 million years old. | It was 5.5 ft in height, heavy brain case, smaller jaw and more projecting nose. Cranial capacity is 950 cc and the arm is more modern. They used stone and fire. |
| 3. *Homo sapiens (The early Human)* | | |
| *(i) Homo sapiens heidelbergensis* (Heidelberg man) | This was found from Heidelberg, Germaany. This is regarded as an ancestor to Neanderthal man dated to be 0.5 million years old. | Jaw is large and heavy and lacks a chin. Teeth are like modern man, heavy eye brow ridge. Cramial capacity is 1100-1300 cc. From these, between 2,00,000 to 50,000 years ago. Neanderthals and Modern man were emerged. |
| (ii) *Homo sapiens neanderthalensis* (Neanderthal man) | Fossils were discovered in 1856 by Fuhirott from cave near Dusseldorf in Neander Valley. They arose some 100000 years ago and flourished in Europe, Asia, North Africa but became extinct about 25000 years ago. | They had heavy bone, wide face, skull with eye brow, low forehead and small chin, Incisors large but teeth are like man. Cramial capacity 1450 cc.<br>They lived in cave, used animal skin for clothing, use stores and fire. Burried dead with flowers. |
| (iii) *Home sapiens rhodesiense* (Rhodesian man) | This was found in Rhodesia in the lime stone cave. | Cranial capacity 1300 cc with receeding forehead and heavy eyebrow ridges. This is more primitive than Java man. |
| (iv) *Homo sapiens fossilis* (Cro-Magnon man, the early modern man) | The fossils were discovered by MacGregar in 1868 from the caves of north-west Italy and caves of France. This was originated about 50000 years ago and existed for about 30000 years or more in Europe and became extinct about 10-20 thousand years ago in the last glacial period. | These are tall, erect posture, body less hairy, prognathus face. Cranial capacity 1650 cc, chin and nose prominent. They were cave dwelars and hunters, use stones and fishing hooks. |
| (v) *Homo sapiens sapiens* (Modern man) | They probably evolved from Cro-Magnon man about 25000 years ago towards the end of last glacial period. They were first appeared in the region of Caspian Sea and migrated eastward, West ward and South ward and Evolved three races<br>(a) Negroid in Africa and Malaysia<br>(b) Caucasian in Europe and North America<br>(c) Mongoloid in China, Siberia and Japan | Modern man is associated with Neolithic Culture. The cultivate and domesticate animals. They live near lakes and ocean, catch fish. Development of technological culture with the use of metals and preparing metalic tools, utensils. Cranical capacity is average 1450 cc. |

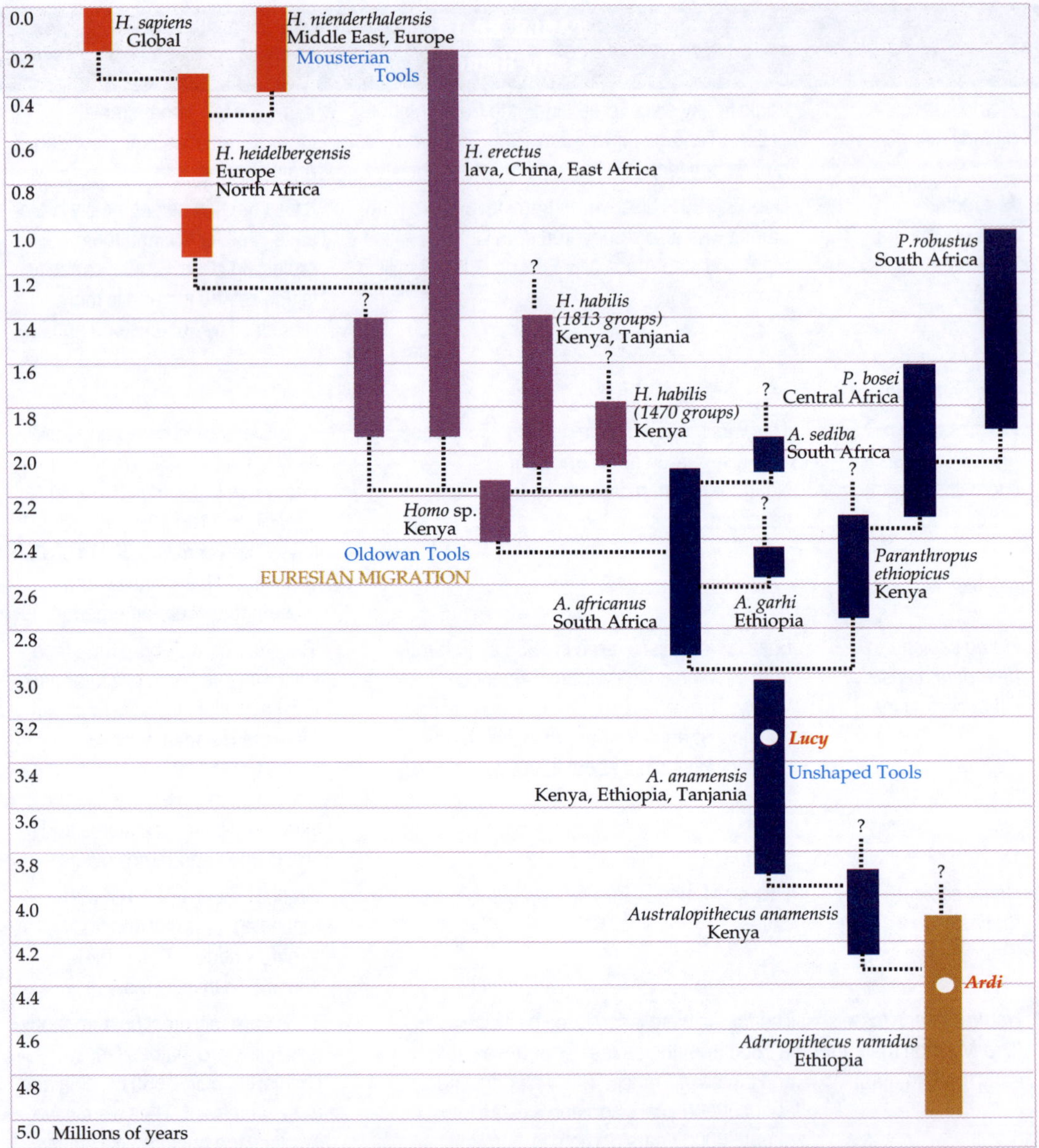


**Fig. 22.41 :** *Human Evolution Tree.*

## 22.10 ORIGIN OF MODERN HUMAN

### 22.10.1 Introduction

*Homo erectus* was the first pre-human species that had been originated in Africa and become geographically dispersed, eventually spreading to all parts of the Old World. The events that followed the dispersal of *H. erectus* are controversial.

There are two hypotheses regarding the origin of modern humans : *viz.* "multiregional" evolution and the "out of Africa" hypotheses.

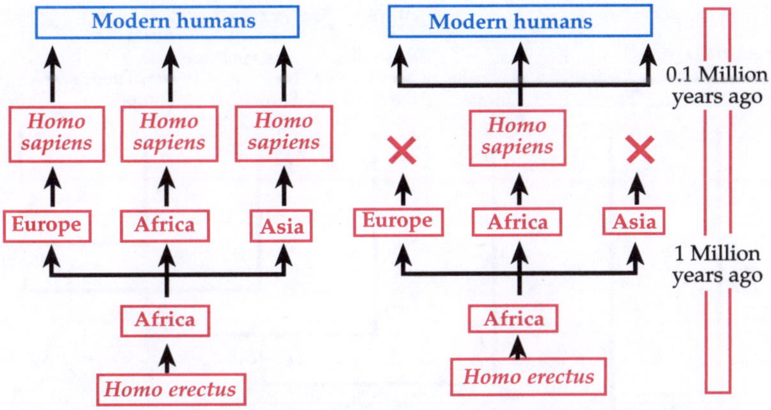


(A) Multi regional evolution (B) The Out of Africa hypothesis

**Fig. 22.42 :** *Two hypotheses for the origins of modern humans*

The multiregional hypothesis, also called "Candelabra" model holds that modern humans in the Old world are descended from H. *erectus* populations that left Africa over one million years ago. Palaeontologists have concluded that from comparisons using fossils, skulls, bones etc. These different populations of different geographic regions remained separate throughout their evolutionary history. There may have been a certain amount of interbreeding between them from different geographic regions (Fig. 22.42).

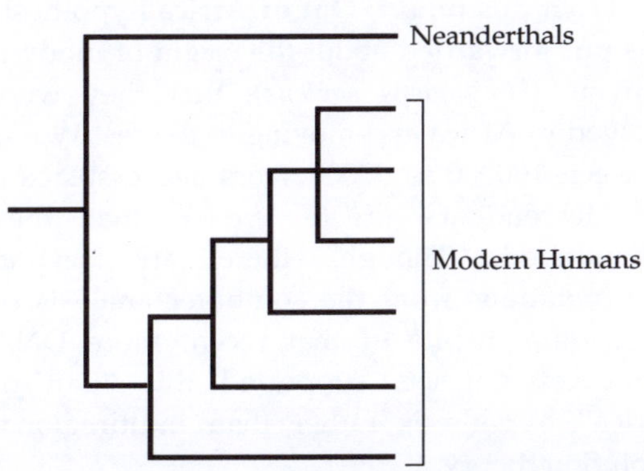


**Fig.22.43 :** *Relationships between Neanderthals and modern humans, as deduced from the ancient DNA sequence obtained from a Neanderthal bone.*

## 22.10.2 About Neanderthals

Neanderthals are extinct hominids who lived in Europe between 30000 and 30000 years ago. They were descended from *Homo erectus* who left Africa about one million years ago.

The last Neanderthals died out 30000 years ago. From its bone, DNA was extracted weighing about 400 mg and subjected to quantitative PCR. The bone fragnment contained about 1300 copies of Neanderthal mito-genome. By carrying out overlapping PCRs, none amplifying more than 170 bp of DNA but together giving a total length of 377 bp.

By comparing sequences obtained from the Neanderthal bone with sequences of six mito-DNA haplogroups from modern humans, a phylogenetic tree was contructed (Fig. 22.43).

In this tree, Neanderthal was positioned on a branch of its own, conneced to the root of the tree but not linked directly to any of the modern human squences.

The Neanderthal's sequence differs from modern human sequences (from all over the world) at an average of 27.2 + 2.2 nucleotide positions. Similar results were obtained when mtDNA from a second Neanderthal's skeleton was examined. The degree of differences

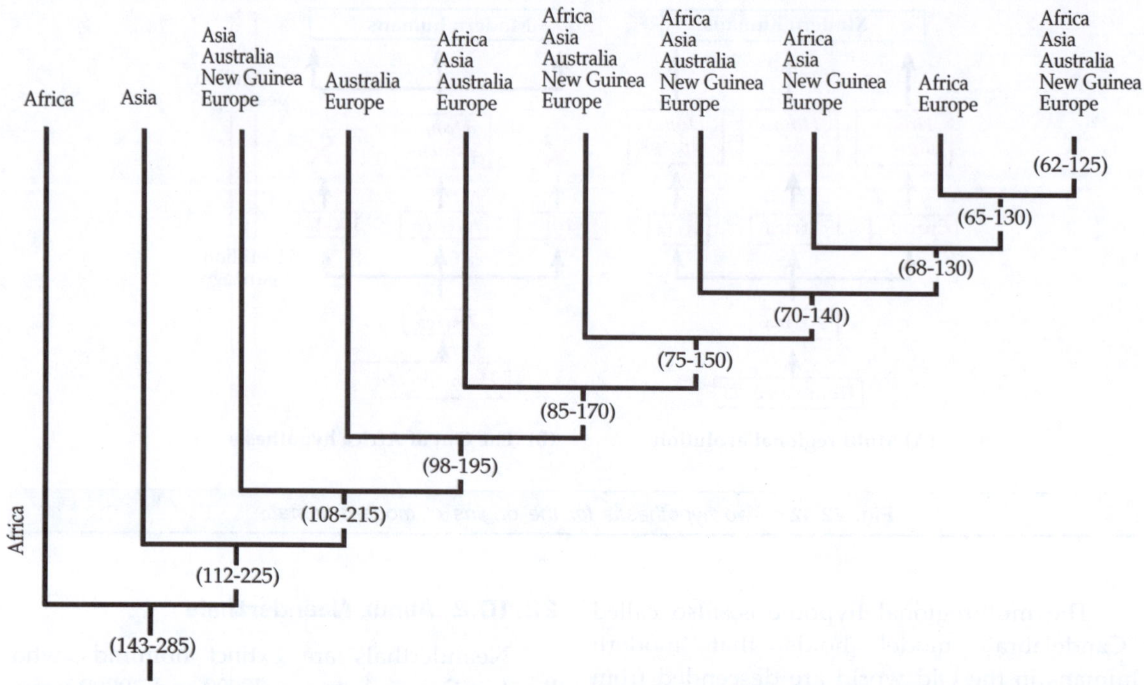


**Fig.22.44 :** *Phylogeny of mitrochondrial DNA from 147 members of indigenous races in five geographic regions. Numerical figures indicate thousands of years ago.*

between Neanderthals and modern European DNA is incompatible with the notion that Neanderthals and modern Europeans were descended from Neanderthals, which strongly supports the "Out of Africa" hypothesis.

### 22.10.3 Studies on mitochondial DNA

In the year 1987, a phylogenetic tree was reconstructed from mitochondrial DNA RFLP data, obtained from 147 humans representing populations from all parts of the world. The tree confirmed that the ancentors of modern humans lived in Africa and they were still there about 200000 years ago. The mitochondrial molecular clock was applied as the interference to make this tree (Fig. 22.44).

The tree shows that "ancestral mitochondrial DNA" from which all modern mitochondrial DNAs are descended, existed between 140000 to 290000 years ago. This mitochondrial genome was located in Africa. The person who possessed it is termed as so called **"Mitochondrial Eve"**, must be a female, because, mitochondrial genome is inherited through female line.

From this report, **Out of Africa** hypothesis was put forwarded about the origin of modern humans (*H. sapiens sapiens*), that they were evolved in Africa and moving to the rest World between 100000 to 50000 years ago displacing the descendents of *H. erectus* that they encountered. Though, there are several interpretations from the computer analysis of these data inspite of that recent more DNA sequences datasets supported this "Out of Africa" hypothesis rather than multiregional evolution theory.

Another interesting postulation is that the modern man has inherited the Y-chromosome from so called **"Y-chromosome Adam"** who was also lived in Africa some 200000 years ago. It is important to note that these ancestral DNAs were still in Africa well after the spread of *H. erectus* into Euresia.

### 22.10.4 Why mito-genome is taken for Evolutionary studies?

1. It is inherited primarily through the maternal lineage and does not orginarily recombine with nuclear DNA.
2. mtDNA remains unchanged from one generation to the next and is homogenous within an individual.
3. Mitochondria lack repair enzymes and mutations can accumulate up to 10 times faster than they can nuclear DNA mutation. The mitochondrial variants present in a single species are called **haplogroups.**
4. Mitochondrial DNA changes have little effects on the viability of the individual.
5. Mito-DNA mutations rate is fairly constant. Thus the differences between their sequences can act as a **molecular clock**, marking the time taken for these DNAs to diverge.
6. A mito-DNA tree can be used as a chronological "tree" and accurate evolutionary clock can be calibrated.

### 22.10.5 Support of Multiregional (single origin) hypothesis

The last common *Homo sapiens* was much more recent, for example only 100000 to 50000 years old, then dispeasal of *H. sapiens* occurred after a one or two million year -old dispersal of *H. erectus.* This would indicate that populations of *H.sapiens* entered localities where *H. erectus* has already been established and eventually replaced these earlier hominids.

1. Researchers find most mtDNA sequence variability among African population, suggesting that these are the oldest mtDNA populations among modern humans and non-African populations are their derivatives.
2. All non-African mtDNA sequences are variants of the African sequence. If the non-African mtDNA has been derived from resident non-African populations, much more non-African variability would be expected.

### 22.10.6 Y-Chromosome genes to trace origin of Human

Mitochondrial DNA acts as only a single genetic limit whose geneology may not necessarily coincide with other genetic untis. Therefore, it is necessary to trace back the non-mitochondrial gene to continents other than Africa. An interesting example is the small Y-chromosome which is inherited exclusively through the male line. Y-chromosome has a non-recombining portion in which mutations can be used to establish both phylogenetic and chronological trees.

For this purpose, Hammer and coworkers (1998) surveyed more than 15000 individuals from all continents of many racial groups and traced all Y-chromosomes to a common ancestor living about 150000 years ago was called "**Y-chromosome Adam**", who was an African. It is important to note that these ancestral DNAs were still in Africa well after the spread of *H. erectus* into Euresia.

### 22.10.7 Other nuclear genes

Nei and Roychoudhury (1993) calculated genetic distances between 26 human populations for 29 different nuclear genes and suggested a single "African origin" for *Homo sapiens* with subsequent widespread geographic divergence.

Mountain and coworkers (1994) presented the polymorphism for *Alu* chromosomal DNA sequences that are specific for humans.

Batzer *et. al* (1994) supported this result and the African ancestry of human origin.

### 22.10.8 Comments

Palaeontologists support the independent multiregional evolution because of the similarities in the anatomy and morphological features in Chinese and Australian hominid fossils, with *Homo erectus* about their eyebrow ridge and cranial size. But the question is that if each population evolved independently, how did they become so similar? The body colour and their minor attributes are due to the expression of genetic traits. Wolpoff (1989), a palaentologist proposed that the exchange of some genes by inter-breeding between then enabled the evolving groups to reach the same modern *Homo sapiens* grade.

## 22.11 PEDIGREE ANALYSIS

### 22.11.1 Concept

A represenation of the ancestry of an individual or family is *pedigree.*

A genetic analysis using information contained within family tree is called *pedigree analysis*. In this approach, the aim is to determine the type of inheritance pattern that a gene follows.

On the basis of the information in a pedigree, geneticists attempt to determine the mode of inheritance of a trait. There are some characteristics in their inheritance of autosomal dominant, autosomal recessive and also sex-chromosomal dominant and recessive genes.

**(a) Dominant inheritance of autosomal genes**

1. Occurs in every generation
2. Every affected child has an affected parent, no generations are skipped.
3. The trait occurs about equally in both sexes.
4. An affected individual with only one affected parent is expected to produce 50% affected offspring . Two affected heterozygous individuals will have 25% unaffected offspring.

*Example* : Polydactyly in human Huntington disease etc.

**(b) Recessive inheritance of autosomal genes :**

1. Affected individuals are not found in each generation.
2. The affected daughters, identical triplets, come from unaffected parents.
3. They represent the first appearance of the tract in the pedigree.
4. Consanguineous mating (mating between close relatives) often produce offspring that have rare recessive and often deleterious traits.

*For example* : Tay Sachs disease

**(c) Sexlinked recessive inheritance**

1. All the affected individuals are sons since, males are hemizygous for the X-chromosome.
2. An affected son would have either a carrier mother and/or affected father. On the other hand an affected daughter might have affected father and carrier or affected mother.
3. Shows criss-cross type of inheritance.
4. 50% of the sons of carrier females should be affected.

*Example* : Colorblind in man

Hemophilia in man.

**(d) Sex-linked dominant inheritance**

1. The trait does not skip generations
2. An affected son must have an affected mother
3. 50% of the children of an affected heterozygous mother are affected.

**TABLE 22.16**
**Examples of some molecules marker genes used in Pedigree analysis of human beings**

| *Disorder* | *Gene Product* | *Pescription* |
|---|---|---|
| (a) **Autosomal recessive** | | |
| 1. Adenine-deaminease deficiency | Adenosine deaminase | Defective immune system, skeletal and neurological abnormalities |
| 2. Albinism (type I) | Tysosine | Inability to synthesize melanin |
| 3. Cystic fibrosis | CF-transmembrane receptor | Water imbalence in tusues of pancreas, intestine, sweat gland and lung |
| 4. Sickle cell anaemia | β-globin | Anaemia |
| 5. Tay-Sachs disease | Hexosaminidase A | Progressive neurodegeneration |
| (b) **Autosomal dominant** | | |
| 1. Osteoporosis | Collagen type-I & II | Brittle and weakened bones |
| 2. Familial hepercholesterolemia | LDL-receptor | Very high LDL in the serum |
| 3. Huntington disease | Huntingtin | Neurodegeneration |
| (c) **Sexlinked Recessive** | | |
| 1. Duchenne muscular dystrophy | Dystrophin | Progressive degeneration of muscle |
| 2. Hemophilia A | Clotting factor VIII | Defect in blood clotting |
| 3. Hemophilia B | Clotting factor IX | Defect in blood clotting |

4. All the daughters, but none of the sons of an affected father are affected.

   *Example* : Ectodermal anidrotic dysplasia, syndactyly, Blood group Xg, Oro-faciodigital syndrome

**(e) Y-linked dominant inheritance (Holandric)**

1. All the males are affected
2. All the females are not affected.

   *Example* : Hypertrichosis

***(f)* Inheritance of sex-limited gene**

1. This is autosomal trait, dominant in males but recesive in females
2. Females are not affected
3. Males are affected in homozygous trait or heterozygous state.
4. Males with homozygous recessive state are not affected.

***(g)* Inheritance of sex-influenced gene**

1. This is autosomal dominant trait and influenced by the sex.
2. In females, heterozygous state, the gene is not expressed, only expressed in homozygous state.

### 22.11.2 Molecular markers in Pedigree analysis

Genetic diseases are frequently used as gene markers in humans for pedigree analysis; the disease state being one allele and the healthy state being a second allele. A geneticist must obtain data from many large pedigrees containing several individuals who exhibit the disorder (Table 22.7).

For example, a neurodegenerative genetic disease called **Tay-Sachs diseases** (TSD), where the victims die in the third or fourth year of life. At the molecular level, the mutation causes **TSD** gene that encodes the enzyme hexosaminidase A (hex A), which is responsible for the breakdown of a category of lipids called $GM_2$ -gangliosides. In TSD, breakdown of lipid does not occur and its accumulation causes neurodegeneration. This is an autosomal recessive gene. Similarly, the autosomal dominant marker gene is used in pedigree analysis is a mutant gene, called Huntington disease gene causing degeneration of neurons in the brain and ultimately death.

This mutant gene encodes a protein called **huntingtin** that is expressed in neurons. The family pedigree of Huntington disease is as follows :

### 22.11.3 Mechanism of Pedigree Analysis

Pedigree analysis is the process of determination of the exact mode of inheritance of a gene when sufficient family information is available.

It gives us

1. the determination of genotypes and phenotypes of past, present as well as future generations.
2. The nature of inheritance, whether sex-linked or autosomal and dominant or recessive.
3. Probable ratio of a gene and segregation are possible.
4. It is essential to have detailed information about the patients (genetic diseases) relatives.

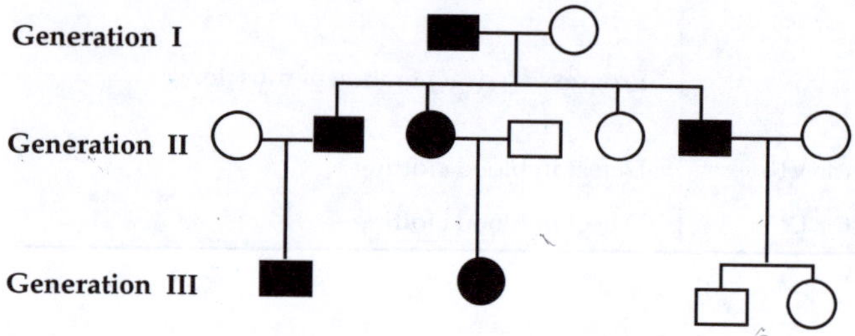


**For pedigree analysis following symbols are commonly used :**

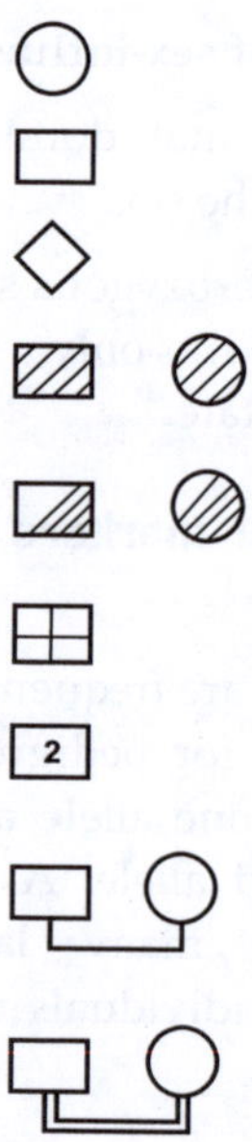

Female

Male

Sibling of unknown sex

Homozygotes male or female, dominant

Heterozygote male or female

Still birth

Two males

Marriage

Marriage between relatives

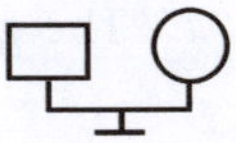
No children

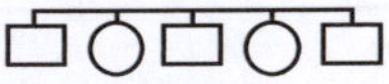
Siblings

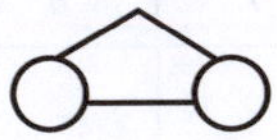
Identical twins

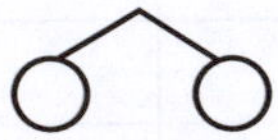
Unidentical twins

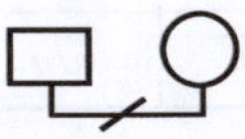
Divorce

Autosomal dominant

Autosomal recessive carriers

Multiple traits

X-linked female carriers

**I, II, III .....** Generations

Abortion

## 22.11.4 Some examples of Pedigree pattern

**Example : 1** Pedegree pattern of an **autosomal dominant** trait. Solid squares and circles indicating the affected males and females while hollow squares and circles are unaffected males and females.

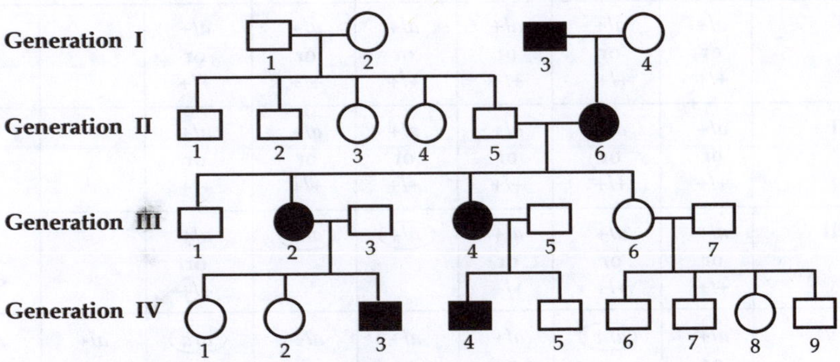

Let the autosomal dominant gene is *"A"* and its recessive allele is *"a"*. The genotypes of the offspring of each generation would be as follows :

| GENERATION | OFFSPRING | | | | | | | | |
|---|---|---|---|---|---|---|---|---|---|
| | 1 | 2 | 3 | 4 | 5 | 6 | 7 | 8 | 9 |
| I | *a*/*a* | *a*/*a* | *Aa* or *AA* | *a*/*a* | | | | | |
| II | *a*/*a* | *a*/*a* | *a*/*a* | *a*/*a* | *a*/*a* | *A*/*a* | | | |
| III | *a*/*a* | *A*/*a* | *a*/*a* | *A*/*a* | *a*/*a* | *a*/*a* | *a*/*a* | | |
| IV | *a*/*a* | *a*/*a* | *A*/*a* | *A*/*a* | *a*/*a* | *a*/*a* | *a*/*a* | *a*/*a* | *a*/*a* |

**Example 2 :** Pedegree pattern of an ***autosomal recessive*** trait. Double line marriage figure indicates consanguineous mating.

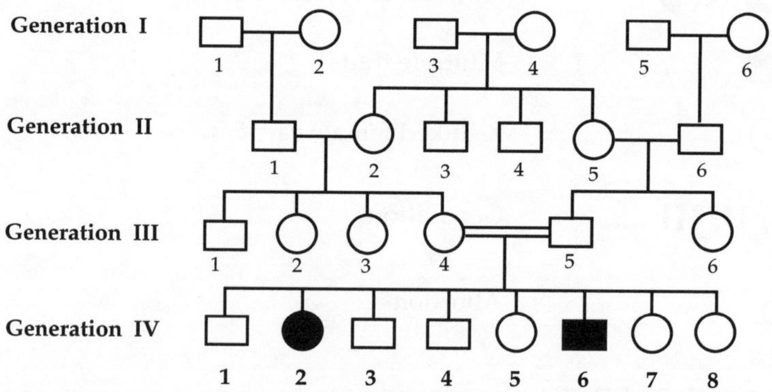


Let the autosomal recessive trait is *"a"* and its normal dominant allele is (+). The genotypes of the offspring is each generation would be as follows :

| GENERATION | OFFSPRING | | | | | | | |
|---|---|---|---|---|---|---|---|---|
| | 1 | 2 | 3 | 4 | 5 | 6 | 7 | 8 |
| I | *a*/+ or +/+ | *a*/+ or +/+ | *a*/+ or +/+ | *a*/+ or +/+ | *a*/+ or +/+ | *a*/+ or +/+ | | |
| II | *a*/+ or +/+ | *a*/+ or +/+ | *a*/+ or +/+ | *a*/+ or +/+ | *a*/+ or +/+ | *a*/+ or +/+ | | |
| III | *a*/+ or +/+ | *a*/+ or +/+ | *a*/+ or +/+ | (*a*/+) | (*a*/+) | *a*/+ or +/+ | | |
| IV | *a*/+ or +/+ | (*a*/*a*) | *a*/+ or +/+ | *a*/+ or +/+ | *a*/+ or +/+ | (*a*/*a*) | *a*/+ or +/+ | *a*/+ or +/+ |

In genration IV, Zygote 2 and 6 are ($a/a$) and others would be ($a/+$) or ($+/+$).

In generation III. zygote no. 4 and 5 would be of genotype $a/+$ and $a/+$ because some of their offspring are ($a/a$) homozygous recessive and other offspring either be $a/+$ or $+/+$ giving dominant phenytypes.

In generation II, zygote no. 1 and 2, any of them certainly have a genotype ($a/+$) while the other is ($a/+$) or ($+/+$).

Again zygote no 5 and 6, any one of them would be $a/+$ and the other be $a/+$ or $+/+$.

In genration I, for parent 1 and 2 or 3 and 4 or 5 and 6, in each case any one of them is $a/+$ and the other be $a/+$ or $+/+$.

**Example 3 :** Pedigree pattern of an X-linked recessive trait. Hollow circle with middle dot indicates carrier females.

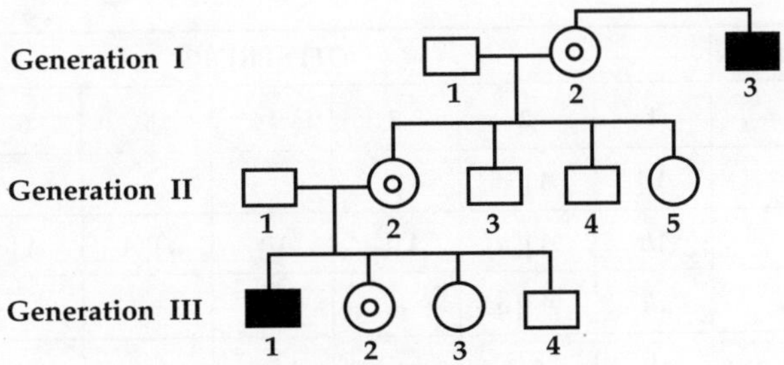


Let the X linked recessive trait is "$a$" and its normal dominant trait is "$A$". Y chromosome does not have their genes.

| GENERATION | OFFSPRING | | | | |
|---|---|---|---|---|---|
| | 1 | 2 | 3 | 4 | 5 |
| I | $A$/↾ | $a$ ‖ $A$ | $a$ \|↾ | | |
| II | $A$/↾ | $a$ ‖ $A$ | $A$ \|↾ | $A$ \|↾ | $A$ ‖ $A$ |
| III | $a$/↾ | $a$ ‖ $A$ | $A$ ‖ $A$ | $A$/↾ | |

In generation I and zygote 1 is male and a dominant gene in its X-chromosome, zygote-2 is carrier heterozygote ($A/a$) female, zygote -3 is male, a recessive gene is present on X-chromosome.

In genration, II, zygote 1, 3 and 4 all are males having a dominant gene on its X-chromosome. Zygote-2 is a carrier female heterozygote ($a/A$), zygote-5 is female dominant homozygote ($AA$)

In generation III, zygote-1 is male, has one recessive gene in X-chromosome and the trait is expressed, zygote-2 is a heterozygote female ($A/a$), zygote-3 is a homozygote female ($A/A$) and zygote-4 is male, having one dominant gene in its X-chromosome.

**Example 4 :** Pedigree pattern of an X-linked recessive trait.

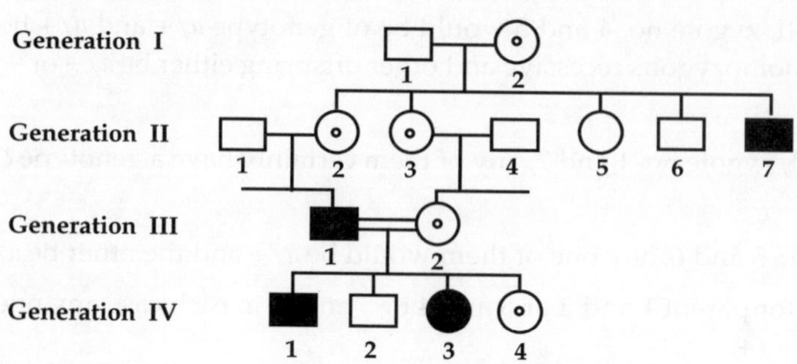

Let, X-linked recessive gene is "a" and its dominant normal gene is "A". Females have two X chromosomes, while males have one X- and one Y-chromosomes. When only one recessive gene is present, affects the offspring. Pedegree analysis would be as follows :

| GENERATION | OFFSPRING | | | | | | |
|---|---|---|---|---|---|---|---|
| | 1 | 2 | 3 | 4 | 5 | 6 | 7 |
| I | *A*/↾ | *A* \|\| *a* | | | | | |
| II | *A*/↾ | *A* \|\| *a* | *A* \|\| *a* | *A*/↾ | *a* \|\| *A* | *A* \|↾ | *a* \|↾ |
| III | *a*/↾ | *A* \|\| *a* | | | | | |
| IV | *a* \|↾ | *A* \|↾ | *a* \|\| *a* | *A* \|\| *a* | | | |

**Example 5 :** Pedigree pattern of **X-linked recessive** trait.

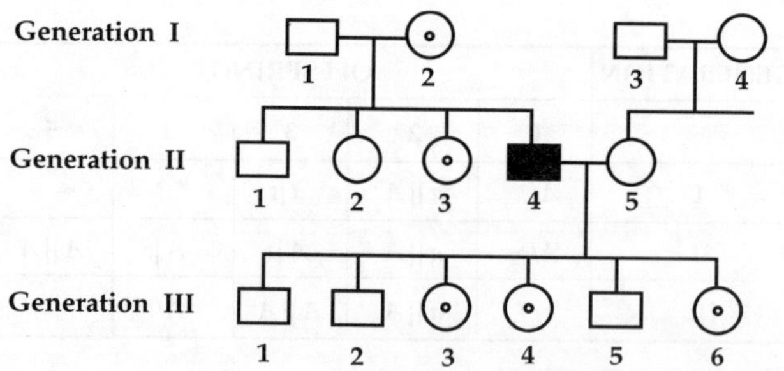

Let, the recessive X-linked trait is "a" and its normal dominant gene is "A". Females carry two X-chromosomes while males carry one X- and one Y-chromosmes. The pedigree analysis is as follows.

| *GENERATION* | *OFFSPRING* | | | | | |
|---|---|---|---|---|---|---|
| | *1* | *2* | *3* | *4* | *5* | *6* |
| I | *A*/↾ | *A* \|\| *a* | *A* \|↾ | *A* \|\| *A* | | |
| II | *A*/↾ | *A* \|\| *A* | *A* \|\| *a* | *a*/↾ | *A* \|\| *A* | |
| III | *A*/↾ | *A* \|↾ | *A* \|\| *a* | *A* \|\| *a* | *A* \|↾ | *A* \|\| *a* |

**Example 6 :** Pedigree pattern of an **X-linked dominant trait**. Solid circles & squares mean affected females and males.

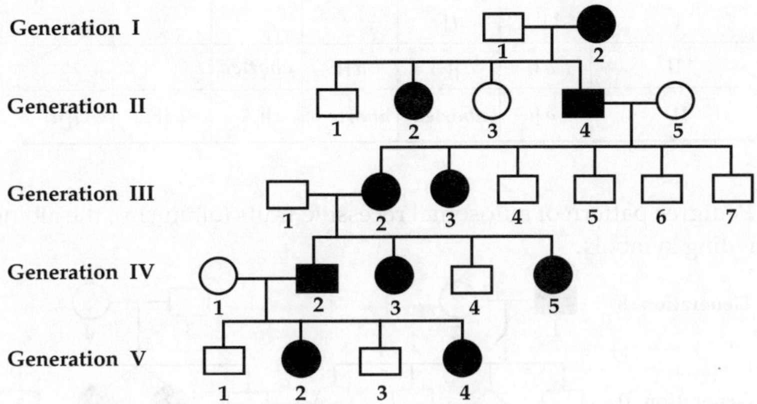


Let, X-linked dominant gene is *"A"* and the recessive gene is *"a"*. In presence of dominant gene, the offspring is affected. The pedigree analysis is as follows :

| GENERATION | OFFSPRING | | | | | | |
|---|---|---|---|---|---|---|---|
| | 1 | 2 | 3 | 4 | 5 | 6 | 7 |
| I | *a* \| ↾ | *A* \|\| a | | | | | |
| II | *a* \| ↾ | *a* \|\| *A* | *a* \|\| *a* | *A*/ ↾ | *a* \|\| *a* | | |
| III | *a* \| ↾ | *a* \|\| *A* | *A* \|\| *a* | *a* \| ↾ | *a* \| ↾ | *a* \| ↾ | *a* \| ↾ |
| IV | *a* \| *a* | *A* \| ↾ | *A* \|\| *a* | *a* \| ↾ | *A* \|\| *a* | | |
| V | *a* \| ↾ | *a* \|\| *A* | *a* \| ↾ | *a* \|\| *A* | | | |

**Example 7 :** Pedigree pattern of an X-linked dominant trait lethal in the hemizygous male. Small circles indicate abortions. Solid circles are the carriers.

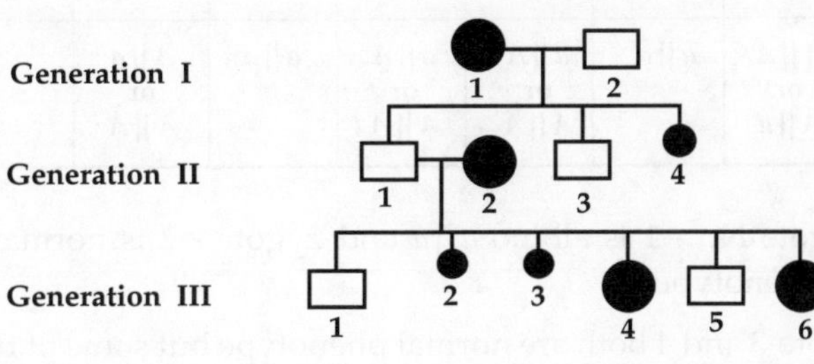


Let, the X-linked recessive gene is *"a"* and the dominant is *"A"*. When it is hemizygous ie in males, it is lethal. The pedigree analysis is as follows.

| GENERATION | OFFSPRING | | | | | |
|---|---|---|---|---|---|---|
| | 1 | 2 | 3 | 4 | 5 | 6 |
| I | *A* \|\| *a* | *a* \| ↾ | | | | |
| II | *a* \|↾ | *a* \|\| *A* | *a* \|↾ | *aborted* | | |
| III | *a* \|↾ | *aborted* | *aborted* | *a* \|\| *A* | *a* \|↾ | *A* \|\| *a* |

**Example 8 :** Pedigree pattern of autosomal recessive traits (albinism), the albino individuals are designated by shading symbols.

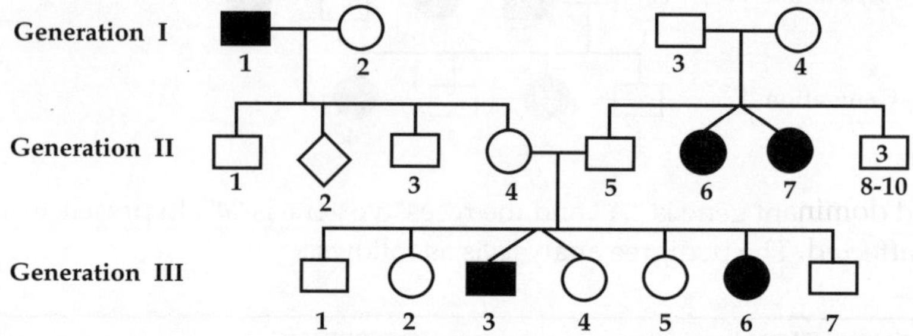


Let the recessive autosomal gene for albinism is *'a'* and its dominant allele is *"A"* which is normal. The normal phenotype would be produced with the genotype (*Aa*) and (*AA*), whereas, albino phenotype is (*aa*). The pedigree analysis would be as follows :

| GENERATION | OFFSPRING | | | | | | | | | |
|---|---|---|---|---|---|---|---|---|---|---|
| | 1 | 2 | 3 | 4 | 5 | 6 | 7 | 8 | 9 | 10 |
| I | *a* \|\| *a* | *A* \|\| *A* or *A* \|\| *a* | *A* \|\| *a* | *A* \|\| *a* | | | | | | |
| II | *a* \|\| A | *A* \|\| *a* | *A* \|\| *a* | *A* \|\| *a* | *A* \|\| *a* | *a* \|\| *a* | *a* \|\| *a* | *a* \|\| *A* or *A* \|\| *A* | *a* \|\| *A* or *A* \|\| *A* | *a* \|\| *A* or *A* \|\| *A* |
| III | *A* \|\| *A* or *A* \|\| *a* | *A* \|\| *A* or *A* \|\| *a* | *a* \|\| *a* | *a* \|\| *A* or *A* \|\| *A* | *a* \|\| *A* or *A* \|\| *A* | *a* \|\| *a* | *A* \|\| *a* or *A* \|\| *A* | | | |

In generation I, zygote No - 1 is albino *a* || *a* and zygote - 2 is normal *A* || *A*, because all the offspring are normal in phenotype.

In generation I, zygote-3 and 4 both are normal phenotype but some of their children are albino, therefore they each must have one *'a'* gene. Therefore, their genotypes are (*Aa*) heterozygote.

In generation II, zygote 4 and 5 are normal in phenotype but some of their children are albino therefore, they certainly have (*Aa*) genes.

In generation III, zygote no 3 and 4 are not identical.

**Example 9 :** Transmission of autosomal dominant trait (eg. chondrodystrophy *ie* a disturbance in the development of the cartilege primordia of the long bones from early life, resulting in arrested growth and peculiar dwarfism with short limbs. The pedigree pattern is as follows.

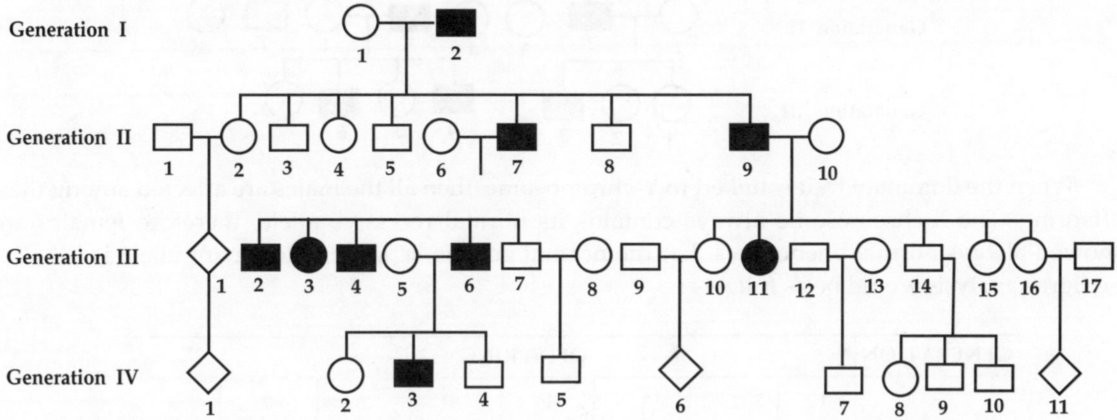

Let, the autosomal dominant trait in "*A*" and its normal recessive allele is "*a*" .

If the zygote is homozygous for dominant its dominant trait, then all the children must be chondrodystrophic, Again the heterogygous one may produce normal as well as chordrodystrophic individuals. The Pedigree analysis is as follows :

| GENERATION | OFFSPRING | | | | | | | | | | | | | | | | |
|---|---|---|---|---|---|---|---|---|---|---|---|---|---|---|---|---|---|
| | 1 | 2 | 3 | 4 | 5 | 6 | 7 | 8 | 9 | 10 | 11 | 12 | 13 | 14 | 15 | 16 | 17 |
| I | $a \Vert a$ | $a \Vert A$ | | | | | | | | | | | | | | | |
| II | $a \Vert a$ | $a \Vert a$ | $a \Vert a$ | $a \Vert a$ | $a \Vert a$ | $a \Vert a$ | $A \Vert a$ | $a \Vert a$ | $A \Vert a$ | $a \Vert a$ | | | | | | | |
| II | $a \Vert a$ | $A \Vert a$ | $A \Vert a$ | $A \Vert a$ | $a \Vert a$ | $A \Vert a$ | $a \Vert a$ | $a \Vert a$ | $a \Vert a$ | $a \Vert a$ | $A \Vert a$ | $a \Vert a$ | $a \Vert a$ | $a \Vert a$ | $a \Vert a$ | $a \Vert a$ | $a \Vert a$ |
| III | $a \Vert a$ | $a \Vert a$ | $A \Vert a$ | $a \Vert a$ | $a \Vert a$ | $a \Vert a$ | $a \Vert a$ | $a \Vert a$ | $a \Vert a$ | $a \Vert a$ | $a \Vert a$ | | | | | | |

In generation II, some of the offspring are chondrodystrophy therefore, generation I-2 zygote is ($A \Vert a$).

In genration II, zygote-1 and 2 all are $a \Vert a$ as they produce all normal offspring. Zygote no 6 produces some dominant traits in their offspring. Therefore, zygote no-7 is $A \Vert a$, like that zygote no. 9 is also ($A \Vert a$).

In generation III, All the chrondrodystrophic zygotes are ($A \Vert a$).

In genration IV, 3rd zygote is also $A \Vert a$ as his mother is ($a \Vert a$).

**Example 10 :** Transmission Y-linked genes the Pedigree pattern is as follows :

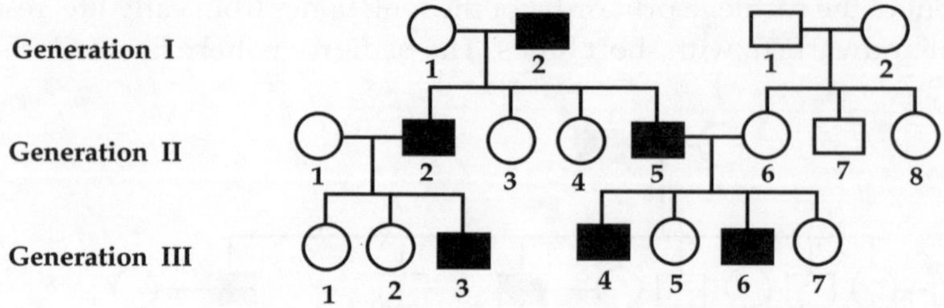


When the dominant trait is linked to Y-chromosome, then all the males are affected among their offspring. The X-chromosome always contains its normal recessive allele, therefore females are showed always normal phenotypes. Let the normal gene is *'a'* and its dominant allele is *'A'*. The pedigree analysis would be as follows :

| GENERATION | OFFSPRING | | | | | | | |
|---|---|---|---|---|---|---|---|---|
| | 1 | 2 | 3 | 4 | 5 | 6 | 7 | 8 |
| I | *a* ‖ *a* | *a* ‖⌈*A* | *a* ‖⌈*a* | *a* ‖ *a* | | | | |
| II | *a* ‖ *a* | *a* ‖⌈*A* | *a* ‖ *a* | *a* ‖ *a* | *a* ‖⌈*A* | *a* ‖ *a* | *a* ‖⌈*a* | *a* ‖ *a* |
| III | *a* ‖ *a* | *a* ‖ *a* | *a* ‖⌈*A* | *a* ‖⌈*A* | *a* ‖ *a* | a ‖⌈*A* | *a* ‖ *a* | |

In generation I, Zygote no - 2 carries dominant mutant allele on the Y chromosome, therefore all their sons showed dominant phenotype, while the zygote no 3 carries normal recessive gene on both X and Y chromosomes.

In generation II, zygote 2 and 5 each has dominant mutant genes on their Y chromosomes, because all of their children in generation II are with dominant phenotypes.

**Example 11 :** X linked dominant gene that causes Muscular dystrophy, a disease, the muscles of limbs are gradually attrophied in any stage of it's life. The pedigree pattern is as sfollows :

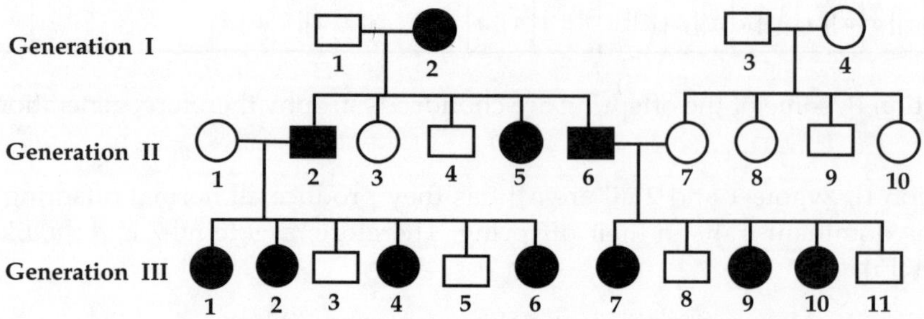


The gene is X-linked because if mother is normal, father is affected then no female children are affected. When mother affected but father is normal then both sons & daughters are affected whereas, when both the parents are normal the children are also normal in phenotype. It is thus assured the trait is X-linked dominant.

Let the recessive gene is *'a'* and its dominant gene is *A* and these genes are present only in X-chromosme. Y-chromosome has no genes of either counterparts. The pedigree analysis is as follows :

| GENERATION | OFFSPRING | | | | | | | | | | |
|---|---|---|---|---|---|---|---|---|---|---|---|
| | 1 | 2 | 3 | 4 | 5 | 6 | 7 | 8 | 9 | 10 | 11 |
| I | $\frac{a}{\rightharpoondown}$ | $\frac{A}{a}$ | $\frac{a}{\rightharpoondown}$ | $\frac{a}{a}$ | | | | | | | |
| II | $\frac{a}{a}$ | $\frac{A}{\rightharpoondown}$ | $\frac{a}{\rightharpoondown}$ | $\frac{a}{a}$ | $\frac{a}{A}$ | $\frac{A}{\rightharpoondown}$ | $\frac{a}{a}$ | $\frac{a}{a}$ | $\frac{a}{\rightharpoondown}$ | $\frac{a}{a}$ | |
| III | $\frac{A}{a}$ | $\frac{A}{a}$ | $\frac{a}{\rightharpoondown}$ | $\frac{A}{a}$ | $\frac{a}{\rightharpoondown}$ | $\frac{a}{A}$ | $\frac{a}{A}$ | $\frac{a}{\rightharpoondown}$ | $\frac{a}{A}$ | $\frac{a}{A}$ | $\frac{a}{\rightharpoondown}$ |

In generation I, from parents I and II, some of the sons and daughters become affected, therefore the mother is heterozygous ($A||a$). In this generation, both the 3rd and 4th zygotes produce all normal sons and daughters, therefore, they carry only recessive genes on X-chromosomes.

In generation II, From parents (1) and (2), all the daughters are affected but males are not, it concludes that the father is affected by carrying A gene on its X-chromosome but mother has two normal genes on their two X-chromosomes. This also true for the parent No (6) and (7).

In generation III the females are all heterozygotes, because their mothers are recessive homozygotes.

**Example 12**

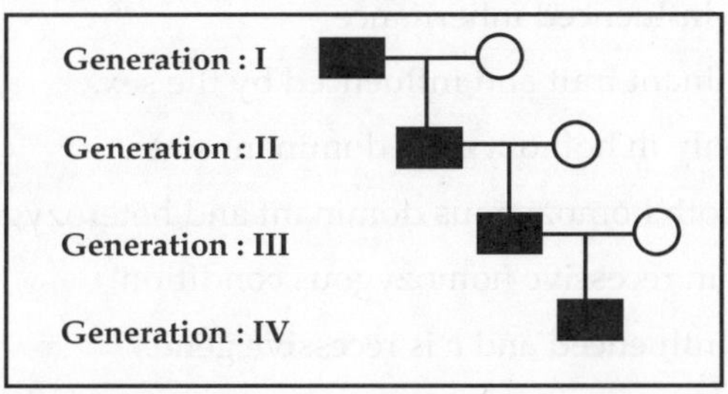


**Solve :**

1. This is sex-limited autosomal trait.
2. Females are not affected
3. This is dominant in males. Therefore, in both homozygous dominant or heterozygous state the trait is expressed, but in homozygous recessive state, males are not affected.

   Let *B* is dominant are *b* is recessive gene. The pedigree is as follows :

| Generation : | Offspring | |
|---|---|---|
| | 1 | 2 |
| I | *BB* or *Bb* | *BB* or *Bb* or *bb* |
| II | *BB* or *Bb* | *BB* or *Bb* or *bb* |
| III | *Bb* | *BB* or *Bb* or *bb* |
| IV | *BB* or *Bb* | |

**Example 13**

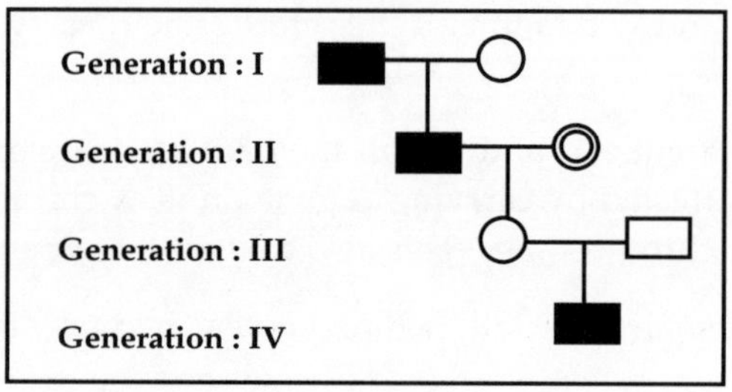


**Solve :**

The pedigree shows sex-influenced inheritance

1. This is autosomal dominant trait and influenced by the sex.
2. Females are affected only in homozygous dominant state.
3. Males are affected in both homozygous dominant and heterozygous state.
4. Males are not affected in recessive homozygous condition.

Let *B* is dominant sex influenced and *b* is recessive gene.

The pedigree is as follows :

| Generation : | Offspring | |
|---|---|---|
| | 1 | 2 |
| I | *BB* or *Bb* | *BB* or *Bb* |
| II | *BB* or *Bb* | *Bb* |
| III | *BB* | *bb* |
| IV | *Bb* | |

## CHAPTER GLOSSARY/KEY TERMS

**Banding pattern in chromosome :** Relatively much larger visible dense regions which are generated by certain staining treatment on chromosomes.

**Barr body :** A condensed mass of chromatin found in the nuclei of placental mammals that contains one or more X-chromosomes. Named for its discoverer Murray Barr.

**Chromosome :** A chromosome with two identical arms and identical genes. The arms are mirror images of each other.

**Dosage compensation :** A phenomenon in which the activity of a gene is increased or decreased according to the number of copies of that gene in the cell.

**Enhanceosome :** A structure formed by DNA bending that comprises a collection of proteins involved in activation of the RNA polymerase II transcription initiation complex.

**Haplogroup :** One of the major sequence classes of mitochondrial DNA present in the human population.

**Heinz bodies :** Abnormal denaturation of hemoglobin and forming precipitation in the cell and are demonstrable by supravital stain.

**Hermaphrodisim :** The animal characterized by both male and female reproductive organs.

**Ideogram :** A diagramatic representation of the G-banding pattern of a chromosome.

**Karyogram :** The entire chromosome complement of a cell, with each chromosome described in terms of its appearance at metaphase.

**Karyotype :** The complete set of chromosomes found in the cells of a particular individual.

**Locus control region :** A DNA sequence that maintains a functional domain in an open active configuration.

**Missense mutation :** An atteration in a nucleotide sequence that converts a codon for one amino acid into a codon for a second amino acid.

**Molecular clock :** A device based on the inferred mutation rate that enables time to be assigned to the branch points in a gene tree.

**Mosaic :** A genetic mosaic is an individual who has two or more genetically different cell lines derived from a single zygote.

**Thalaessemia major :** Homozygous condition of recessive thalassemia gene causing the Hb-A greatly affected.

**Thalassemia :** A disease of RBCs resulting from lack of a and b globin.

**Thalassemia minor :** Abnormalities of Hb-A synthesis is mildly affected due to heterozygous condition of the thalassemia gene.

# Exercise

## A. Long answer type questions :

1. Classify the human chromosomes on the basis of ISCN with examples.
2. Describe the characteristic features, chromosomal constitution and origin of klinefelters, Turners and Down's syndromes.
3. Write a note on partial deletion syndrome with examples.
4. Write a note on cri-du-chat and Edwards syndromes.
5. Write a note on hermaphrodism and pseudohermaphrodism.
6. Describe the causes of azoospermic males.
7. What are the causes of human genetic diseases? give examples.
8. Describe the causes of biochemical mutations in human .
9. Describe the genetic and molecular aspects of sickle cell anaemia.
10. Describe the genetic and molecular aspects of hemophilia.
11. Describe the genetic and molecular aspects of cystic fibrosis.
12. Describe the molecular mechanism of human sex determination and role of SRY.
13. What are the characteristics of inheritance of autosomal dominant, autosomal recessive, sex-linked dominant and sexlinked recessive genes? Write a note on the molecular markers in pedigree analysis.
14. Briefly describe the views of origin of human beings and the roles of mitogenome and Y chromosome as the evidence of evolution studies.

## B. Short answer type questions :

1. How many groups of chromosomes present in human chromosome karyotype?
2. Define karyotype and ideogram.
3. What kinds of techniques are used for chromosome identification.
4. What is G-banding? What is its importance?
5. What are positive and negative bands?
6. What do you mean by G+ve and G–ve and also R+ve and R–ve bands.
7. How a karyotype is made?
8. What were the agreements on the standarization of human cytogenetics held in Paris?
9. What are the symbols of male KF and a female KF?
10. What is the symbol to describe extra autosome, and extra sex-chromosomes.
11. What are the signs of absence or presence of long arm or short arms of chromsomes?
12. What do you mean by the symbol 47, XX, $+14p^{+}$ What are the abbreviations of duplication, deficiency, ring, inversion and translocations?
13. What is GTB? What is its importance in chromosome study? How GTB is done?
14. What is the chromosome karyotype symbol of cri-du-chat syndrome?
15. What is the chromosome karyotype of chronic myleocytic leukemia?
16. What is the chromosome karyotype of Burkitt's lymphoma.
17. What are the symptoms of Klinefelters syndrome?
18. What is the chromosomal constitution of KF?
19. How the chromosomal abnormalities of KF and TS arise during zygotic cleavage and zygote formation from normal parents?
20. How and why maternal age is responsible for KF, TS and Downs syndrome?
21. What is mosaicism? How mosaicism arises in KF and TS patients? What are the symptoms of such mosaicism?
22. What are the variant forms of KF?
23. What are numbers of Barr-bodies in different variants of KF patients?
24. What are the symptoms of Turner's syndrome?

25. What are the causes of XO sex-chromosome constitution?
26. What are the variant form of Turner's syndrome?
27. What is isochromosome of long arm of X-chromosome. How such isochromosome may be found among TS partient?
28. What is ring chromosome? How ring chromosome mosaicism is found in TS patients?
29. What do you mean by $XX^{DS}$ and $XX^{LS}$ chromosome constitution and how mosaicism with such chromosomes in TS may be observed?
30. How and why chromosome of long arms of Y-chromosome causes TS?
31. What is the cause of Down's syndrome?
32. What are the features of Down's syndrome?
33. What is the chromosome constitution of Down's syndrome?
34. What are the causes of origin of Down's syndrome?
35. Why maternal and paternal ages are the causes of Down's syndrome?
36. What is the symptoms of trisomy 17?
37. What is the cause and symptoms of Edward's syndrome?
38. What is the cause and symptoms of Patun's syndrome?
39. What is the symptoms of trisomy-15?
40. What is Philadelphia chromsome? How and when this chromosome is produced?
41. What is the cause and symptoms of cri-du-chat syndrome?
42. What are the symptoms of partial deletion of chromosome-18 and deletion of middle part of chromosome-13?
43. What is the cytology of cri-du-chat syndrome?
44. Write a note on hermaphrodism and pseudohermaphrodisms.
45. What is the cause of hermaphrodism?
46. What are the causes of male pseudohermaphrodism?
47. What are the causes of female pseudohermaphrodism?
48. What is azoospermia? What is its cause? What do you mean by congenital azoospermia?
49. How the autosome-linked genetic diseases are inherited? Give some autosome linked genetic diseases and their locations on the chromosmes.
50. How the autosomal recessive genetic diseases are inherited? Give some examples and their locations on the chromosomes.
51. What do you mean by sex-linked disease? What is the characteristics of such diseases? Give some examples of such traits?
52. Give the examples of X-linked dominant and recessive traits in human being.
53. What is holandric trait?
54. Write notes on Follings disease, alkaptoneuria, albinism, tyrosinosis, tyrosinemia.
55. What is sickle cell anaemia?
56. What do you mean by sickle cell anaemia and sickle cell trait? What are their genetic constitutions?
57. Why the cells become sickle in such homozygous mutants?
58. What are the differences in amino acid sequences in Hb-A, Hb-B and Hb-C hemoglobins?
59. What is the molecular cause of RBC sickling?
60. What are the hemoglobin components of sickle cell trait?
61. What is thalassemia major and thalassemia minor?
62. What is Hb-F? What is its significance?
63. What is physiological jaundice?
64. What is Heinz body? What is its significance?
65. What is $\alpha$–thalassemia? How much it becomes severe?
66. What is hydrops fetalis? What is the cause?
67. What is $\beta$–globin locus?
68. What is the sequence of different types of hemoglobin in the human life from embryonic

to adult stages? How this sequence is controlled?

69. What is cystic fibrosis?
70. What are the symptoms of cystic fibrosis?
71. What are the genetic defects of CF?
72. Describe the molecular defects of CF?
73. What kind of mutation causes sickle cell anaemia trait?
74. How the β globin gene is controlled in human.
75. What are the genes responsible for the human sex determination?
76. Write a note on *TDF, ZFY, SRY, Sxr*.
77. What is bipotential gonad How this bipotential gonad becomes testis or ovary .
78. What is HMG box?
79. What is the function of SF-1 in sertoli cells and in Leydig cells?
80. What kind of chemostatic substance is secreted from XY gonad and how this is involved in testis development.
81. What the role of SOX9?
82. What is the role of AMH?
83. How testicular development is suppressed in XY females with a duplication of short arm of X-chromosome?
84. What is the role of DAX-1?
85. What is the role of WNT-4.
86. What is the probable mechanism of sex determination in mammals?
87. What is pedigree analysis and pedigree?
88. What are the mode of inheritance of dominant autosomal, recessive autosomal, dominant X-linked, recessive X-linked and Y-linked genes.
89. What are the molecular markers in pedigree analysis?
90. What is the first pre-human species and where this had been originated?
91. Define "Out of Africa" and "Multiregional" hypotheses?
92. What are Neandertals? What are the genetic and molecular differences from modern humans?
93. What are mitochondrial Eve and Y-chromosome Adam?
94. Why mitochromsome is considered for human evolutionary studies?

**Excercise I :**

Generation I

Generation II

Generation III

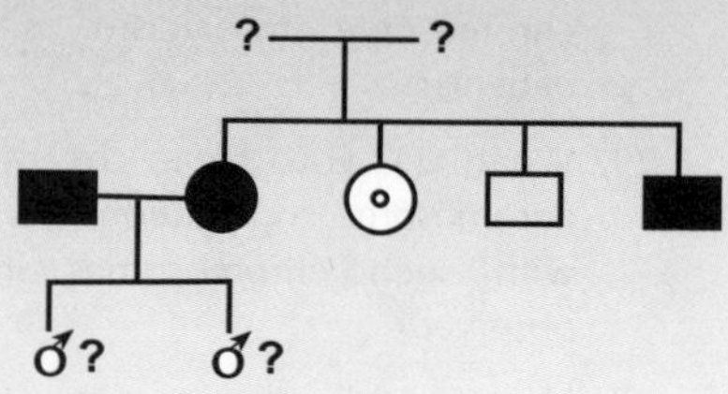

1. Mention the genotypes and phenotypes of the 1st generation.
2. What would be the probability of the sons if the 2nd generation mother is a carrier?
3. Explain the mode of inheritance

**Excercise II**

Generation I

Generation II

Generation III

Generation IV

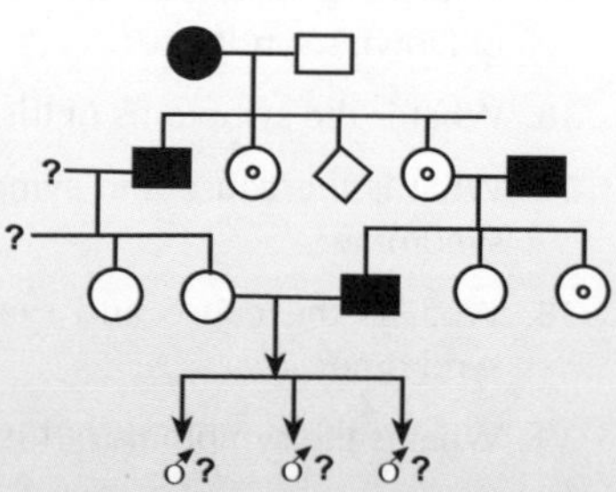

1. State the mode of inheritance.
2. The phenotype of generation II offspring
3. The genotype of the missing (?) second generation parents.
4. The appearance and genotype of IV generation offspring.

# 23

# Human Genome Project

**CHAPTER AGENDA**

## 23.1 CONCEPT

What was the Human Genome Project?

The Human Genome Project (HGP) was the international, collaborative research program whose goal was the complete mapping and understanding of all the genes of human beings. All our genes together are known as our "**genome.**"

Genomes carry the torch of life from one generation to the next for every organism on earth. Each genome is a script, written in a code comprising the four letters A(adenine), T(thymine), G (guanine) and C(cytosine). Genome may be defined as the complete genetic information carried by an individual.

The complete sequence of the genome of several life forms is today available as the new breed of computer savvy molecular biologists is hacking through the thickete of DNA code.

## 23.2 CRITERIA FOR THE SELECTION OF MODEL ORGANISMS IN HUMAN GENOME PROJECT

Human genome is large enough to do research with it. It's genome is 240 times larger than the yeast genome or 1640 times than that of *H. influenzae.* Therefore, few model organisms have been selected to study the comparative genomics with the human genome. The model organisms should have some characteristics.

1. The model organism should be sufficiently closely related, then their genomes might display SYNTENY (i.e. their at least some of their genes are located at similar map positions). It is fact that nearly all human genes have homologs in mice. If the chromosomes are cut into 150 pieces, mixed and matched and then resulted into 21 chromosomes of a mouse.
2. Mapping is significantly easier with a small genome of these model organisms but it likely provides a real boost to equivalent work with the larger genome, eg, the puffer fish, *Fuga rubripes* has a genome of 400 Mb, less than one-seventh the size of human genome but containing approximately same genes.
3. Model organisms have been selected to study or map for some human diseased genes which have homolog in *Drosophila,* yeast and *C. elegans.* Thus it enables hopefully leading to strategies for it's treatment and managements.
4. Comparative genomics gives us the evolution of species, locating the position of genes on the chromoomes and also clinical appraoches.

## 23.3 GOALS AND OBJECTIVES OF HGP

The HGP is not solely aimed at obtaining the complete human genome sequence. The goals are

1. Construction of a comparative genetic map.
2. Identify all the approximate 30000 genes in human DNA.
3. Generation of overlapping clone libraries that span the entire genome.
4. Sequencing entire genome.
5. Improvement in data storage, handling and distribution.
6. Transfer related technologies to the private sector.
7. Address the ethical, legal and social issues that may arise from the project.

## 23.4 IMPORTANCE OF HGP

1. To make a human genome catalog, containing a description of the sequence of every gene in the genome, because, the functions of some of genes remain unknown.
2. To know the sequences of the coding parts as well as regulatory parts of these genes.

3. To know the genes which function incorrectly and give rise to genetic diseases.
4. To understand the mechanism of the action of these diseased genes.

## 23.5 INITIATION OF HUMAN GENOME PROJECT

The Human Genome Project (HGP) was conceived in 1984. But this project was officially initiated in 1st october 1990 in the U.S. under the direction of the National Institutes of Health and the US Department of Energy with a 15 year $ 3 billion plan for completing the human genome sequence. Although the much smaller mitochondrial genome has been sequenced in the early 1980s by Anderson *et. al* (1981).

A second human genome human project was set up by a private company – Celera Genomics of Maryland USA in 1998 (Fig. 23.1).

Both the projects completed a draft of human genome sequence in 2001 and the results were published in the scientific journals "Nature" and "Science" in February of the year (IHGSC, 2001, Venter *et al* 2000). These drafts were not complete sequences, each representing only 83–84% of the entire genome. Most of the remaining 16-17% being made up of sequences at the telomeres and centromeres where only few genes are located.

The HGP is a publicly funded consortium that includes large sequencing centres in US as well as Sanger center in England and laboratories in Japan, France, Germany and China. Additional participants subsequently joined the effort like, Australia, Brazil, Canada, Denmark, Israel, Italy, Korea, Mexico, Netherlands, Russia, Sweedens and Spain. The European Union is also taking part in this project. So it has become a global issue. India is directly and indirectly participating through studies of molecular biology techniques for research and studies of region – specific organisms including human.

**Fig.23.1 :** *Craig Venter*

Although, only incomplete draft, HGP has product were 2.6 billion base pairs of sequences. If in a line of texbook typed with 60 nucleotides of DNA sequence to be written in a line of 10 cm length, the human genome sequence would stretch for 5000 km, ie the distance from Montreal to London or Tokyo to Calcutta or Capetown to Addis Abba or Auckland to Perth. Therefore, sequencing is a harculian task.

The International Human Genome Sequencing Consortium published the first draft of the human genome in the journal Nature in February 2001 with the sequence of the entire genome's three billion base pairs some 90 percent complete. A startling finding of this first draft was that the number of human genes appeared to be significantly fewer than previous estimates, which ranged from 50,000 genes to as many as 140,000.The full sequence was completed and published in April 2003.

## 23.6 PHASES OF HUMAN GENOME PROJECT

Two distinct methods that typically used are:

1. Expressed sequence tags wherein the genes were differentiated into the ones forming a part of the genome and the others which expressed RNAs.
2. Sequence Annotation wherein the entire genome was first sequenced and the functional tags were assigned later.

However, the process that was followed was as follows:

1. The complete gene set was isolated from a cell.
2. It was then cut into fragments.
3. This DNA structure was then amplified with the help of a vector which mostly was BAC (Bacteria artificial chromosomes) and YAC (Yeast artificial chromosomes).
4. The smaller fragments were then sequenced using DNA sequencers.
5. On the basis of overlapping regions, the sequences were then arranged.
6. All this information of the genome sequence was then stored in a computer based program.

In this way the entire genome was sequenced and stored as genome database in computers. Genome mapping was the next goal which was achieved with the help of microsatellites (repetitive DNA sequences).

As the goals of the human genome project achieved, it led to great advancement in research. Today if any disease arises due to some alteration in a certain gene, then it can be traced and compared to the genome database that we already have.

The identification of the sequence or function of a gene in a model organism, for example, the roundworm C. elegans, has the potential to explain a homologous gene in human beings, or in one of the other model organisms. These ambitious goals required and will continue to demand a variety of new technologies that have made it possible to relatively rapidly construct a first draft of the human genome and to continue to refine that draft.

These techniques include:

DNA Sequencing

The Employment of Restriction Fragment-Length Polymorphisms (RFLP)

Yeast Artificial Chromosomes (YAC)

Bacterial Artificial Chromosomes (BAC)

The Polymerase Chain Reaction (PCR)

Electrophoresis

### 23.6.1 RFLP mapping

The initial impetus for human genetic mapping came from the discovery of RFLPs, which were the first highly polymorphic DNA markers to be recognised in animal genomes. In 1987 the first human RFLP map was published comprising 393 RFLPs and 10 additional polymorphic markers (Donis Keller *et al* 1987). This map was developed from the analysis of 21 families, which had an average marker density of one/10 Mb.

In 1994 an international consortium had met and used SSLPs and the large CEPH (Centre d'Etudes du Polymorphisme Humaine in Paris) collection of reference families. The collection contains cultured cell lines from families in which all four grand fathers as well as at least eight second-generation children had been sampled. The map contained 5800 markers , of which over 4000 were SSLPs and had a density of one marker per 0.7 Mb (Murray *et al* 1994).

A subsequent version of the genetic map (Dib *et. al* 1996) took the 1994 map slightly further by inclusion of an additional 1250 SSLPs.

### 23.6.2 STS (Sequence Tagged Site) mapping

The major achievement of the physical mapping of human genome project was of a clone contig map of entire genome using STS screening as well as other clone fingerprinting method. The map consists of 33000 YACs (yeast artificial chromosomes, a high capacity cloning vector constructed from the components of yeast chromosome) containing fragments with an average size of 0.9 Mb (Cohen *et al* 1993). The disadvantage is that YAC Clones may contain two or more pieces of non-contiguous DNA (Anderson 1993). Then in this contig map, the widely separated DNA fragments may, be mistakenly mapped to adjacent positions.

Radiation hybrid mapping of STS markers was adopted by Whitehead Institute/MIT Genome Center, Massachusetts in 1995. A human STS map was published containing 15086 markers, with an average density of 199kb (Hudson *et al*, 1995). Later, additional 20104 STS were published positioning protein coding genes Schuler, *et al* 1996). The resulting map density is one marker per 100 kb.

An integrated map was resulted by comparing genetic and physical maps with clone contig maps that included STS data. This was then used for the sequencing of DNA in Human Genome project.

### 26.6.3 Sequencing of Human Genome

On January 14, NHGRI announced that it will fund a new Genome Sequencing Program (GSP) through multiple FOAs:

RFA-HG-015-001 for Centers for Common Disease Genomics (CCDG)

RFA-HG-015-002 to continue support for the Centers for Mendelian Genomics (CMG)

RFA-HG-015-019 for Genome Sequencing Coordinating Center (GSPCC)

NHGRI also plans to fund several GSP analysis centers in the Spring of 2016.

1. The overall aim of the GSP is to use genome sequencing to identify genes and genomic variants underlying human inherited disease across its full spectrum, including rare diseases likely to be due to rare variants with strong effects (Mendelian), and common, genetically complex diseases that are caused by many variants. As they do this, they will also develop methods, tools, and knowledge intended to enhance the ability of the community to pursue other human inherited diseases.
2. The newly established CCDG will do this for multiple examples of common human inherited diseases and develop technical and project design approaches for using genome sequencing to understand common disease.
3. The CMG will identify genes and variants underlying hundreds of Mende-lianconditions, and in so doing will also develop tools and know-how relevant to applying genome sequencing to Mendelian conditions.
4. In addition, the NHGRI plans to add a separate component to the GSP that will be involved in analyses of the data that take advantage of the range and volume of the data being produced by the program as a whole

The previous iteration of the GSP included two additional components:

1. The Clinical Sequencing and Analysis Centers (CSER). This program is still ongoing.
2. The Genome Sequencing Informatics tools (GS-IT) program, which is ending.

The solicitations for the current program elements are:

RFA-HG-15-001: Centers for Common Disease Genomics (UM1)

RFA-HG-15-019: Genome Sequencing Program Coordinating Center (U24)

Celera used a technique called whole genome shotgun sequencing, employing pairwise end sequencing, which had been used to sequence bacterial genomes of up to six million base pairs in length, but not for anything nearly as large as the three billion base pair human genome.

Celera initially announced that it would seek patent protection on "only 200–300" genes, but later amended this to seeking "intellectual property protection" on "fully-characterized important structures" amounting to 100–300 targets. The firm eventually filed preliminary ("place-holder") patent applications on 6,500 whole or partial genes. Celera also promised to publish their findings in accordance with the terms of the 1996 "Bermuda Statement", by releasing new data annually (the HGP released its new data daily), although, unlike the publicly funded project, they would not permit free redistribution or scientific use of the data.

In March 2000, President Clinton announced that the genome sequence could not be patented, and should be made freely available to all researchers. The statement sent Celera's stock plummeting and dragged down the biotechnology-heavy Nasdaq.

The strategy for sequencing DNA based on YAC libraries had been abandoned because some YAC clones contain non-contiguous DNA. Therefore, a library of 3,00,000 BAC (Bacterial Artificial Chromosome, a high-capacity cloning vector based on the plasmid of *E. coli.*) clones was generated and mapped into the genome forming a "**sequence-ready map**".

The first sequencing of an entire human chromosome-no 22 was published by Dunham *et al* 1999 and sequence of chromosome no-21 by Hattori *et al* (2000).

The genome sequences published are drafts, not complete final sequences. It covers only 96% of the genome. 320 million bp lying predominantly in constitutive heterochromatin region of the chromosomes where DNA is highly packed that contain a few genes. 90% genome that is covered, each part has been sequenced at least four times. 25% has been sequenced the 8-10 times. The draft sequence comprises about 50,000 scaffolds with an average size of 54.2 kb.

## 23.7 IMPLICATIONS OF HUMAN GENOME PROJECT

1. Researchers may be able to identify genes that predispose some individuals to certain diseases or behavioural patterns. For example, 90% addiction to cocaine may be genetic. There is a possibility that there may even be genes that help explain why some people become violent criminals while other living in the same conditions do not.
2. In future, genomics based medicines may be designed which would be person specific. These medicines would selectively target affected cells, thereby having no side effects.
3. This project will help in sequencing the genomics of bacteria useful in energy production, environmental remediation, toxic waste reclamation and industrial processing.
4. It will help to find out the genetic evolution of archaebacteria, eukaryotes and prokaryotes even the evolution of human beings and their races.
5. The project may help in the evironmental protection by detecting bacteria and other organisms that pollute air, water soil and food.
6. It will be possible to develop disease-resistant, insect-resistant and draught-resistant crops.
7. It may help to finding out the function of thousands of unknown genes.
8. Disease free cattles, fowls, farm animals may be developed by this project.
9. It will be possible to access health damage and risks by radiation exposure, exposure to mutagens, teratogens and cancer causing toxins.

There is a programme of genome projects for mouse and rat and plants are being made for a chimpanzee genome project. There will also be additional human genome projects aimed at building up to catalog of sequence variability in different populations.

## 23.8 HOW MANY GENES IN THE HUMAN GENOME?

Oxford researchers claim on Thursday 24 July 2014, more than 90% of human DNA is doing nothing very useful, and large stretches may be no more than biological baggage that has built up over years of evolution

The scientists arrived at the figure after comparing the human genome with the genetic makeup of other mammals, ranging from dogs and mice to rhinos and horses. The researchers looked for sections of DNA that humans shared with the other animals, which split from our lineage at different points in history. When DNA is shared and conserved across species, it suggests that it does something valuable.

Gerton Lunter, a senior scientist on the team, said that based on the comparisons, 8.2% of human DNA was "functional", meaning that it played an important enough role to be conserved by evolution.

"Scientifically speaking, we have no evidence that 92% of our genome is contributing to our biology at all," Lunter told the Guardian.

Researchers have known for some time that only 1% of human DNA is held in genes that are used to make crucial proteins to keep cells – and bodies – alive and healthy. The latest study, reported in the journal Plos Genetics, suggests that a further 7% of human DNA is equally vital, regulating where, when, and how genes are expressed.

But if much of our DNA is so worthless, why do we still carry it around? "It's not true that nature is parsimonious in terms of needing a small genome. Lunter said, "We haven't been designed. We've evolved and that's a messy process. This other DNA really is just filler. It's not garbage. It might come in useful one day. But it's not a burden."

Some of our DNA is left over from ancient viruses that inserted their genetic material into our DNA – or our ancestors DNA – and got mutated to pieces over millennia of evolution. Some still have the ability to jump around in our genomes, adding to the filler as they do so, but are so crippled they cannot break out.

But other scientists take a broader view of what it means for DNA to be functional. Most of the 92%, though 8.2% seems a small portion of DNA to call functional, the meaning of the word is very specific. In the Oxford study, DNA is "functional" if it affects our reproductive fitness.

"Many [DNA] elements that play important roles in human disease are not evolutionarily conserved. Some of these have human-specific functions, some are involved in late-onset diseases like Alzheimer's, and others are simply missed discovered by current comparative

**TABLE 23.1**
**Internet addresses relevent to Human Genome Project**

| Description | Address |
|---|---|
| 1. CEPH (various maps) | http://www.cephb.fr/bio/ceph-genethon-map.html |
| 2. dbEST (EST sequences) | http://www.nebi.nlm.nih.gov/dbEST/ |
| 3. dbSNP (SNP) | http://www.nebi.nlm.nih.gov/SNP/ |
| 4. dbSTS (STS sequences) | http://www.ncbi.nlm.nih.gov/dbSTS/ |
| 5. Genethon (various maps) | http://www.genethon.fr/ |
| 6. Radiation hybrid database | http://www.ebi.ac.uk/RHdb |

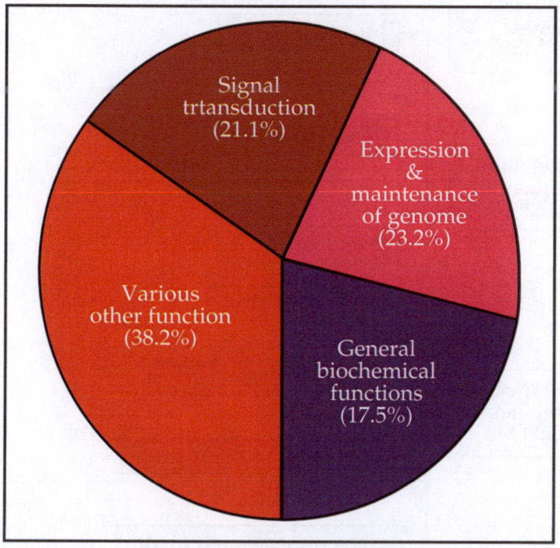


**Fig.23.2 :** *Pie chart showing the categorization of human protein-coding genes*

genomics methods," said Manolis Kellis, a computational biologist at MIT who was not involved in the study. "We cannot simply ignore the remaining 90% of the genome that is not evolutionarily conserved."

Evolution can tell you whether something is important or not important, but it doesn't tell you what that something actually does.

## 23.9 CONTENTS OF HUMAN GENOME

The human genome has only a few hundred genes that are not there in the genome of mice, rats and dogs. It is astonishing that the similarity is observed in the genomes of people of different races. All humans, infact share 99.9% of their DNA. It is the remaining 0.1% of the DNA with subtle differences that makes individuals unique, including their susceptibilities to diseases. A yet another surprise is that hundreds of human genes appear to have resulted from horizantal transfer from bacteria at some point in the vertebrate lineage. It has been found that a set of 223 human proteins has a significant similarity to proteins from bacteria (Fig. 23.2).

### 23.9.1 Functions of Human Genes

The functions of about half of the 30,000 – 40,000 human genes are known. The vast majority code for proteins, less than 2500 specify the various types of non-coding RNA. Almost 23% of the protein-coding genes are involved in expression, replication and maintenance of the genome.20% specify the components of the signal transduction pathways that regulate genome expression and other cellular activities. 17.5% genes are responsible for the production of enzymes to regulate biochemical functions of the cell. Remaining about 38% genes are involved in the activities such as, transport of compounds through the cell membrane, folding of proteins, immune response, synthesis of structural proteins, muscles and cytoskeleton. About 13000 genes are categorised whose functions are not yet known (Fig. 23.3).

### 23.9.2 Exons and Introns

The human genome consists of a series of introns which interrupted the gene into a number of exons. Thus they become split genes. Most human genes are thus become discontinuous with an average of nine exons per gene, although some genes have many more than this. The muscle protein "titin" has as many as 178 exons and in also longest known human gene with 80780 bp. During their expression, the initial RNA that is synthesized is a copy of entire gene including all exons and introns. This is pre-mRNA. It undergoes splicing, the exons are joined to become mRNA, which then directs protein synthesis. Now it is known that this pre-mRNA may undergo alternative or differential splicing to give rise a series of mRNAs containing different combinations of exons and each is specifying a different protein.

The gene also contains sequences from the regions preceeding the first exon and following the last exon which is called 5′ UTR and 3′ UTR (untranslated region) respectively.

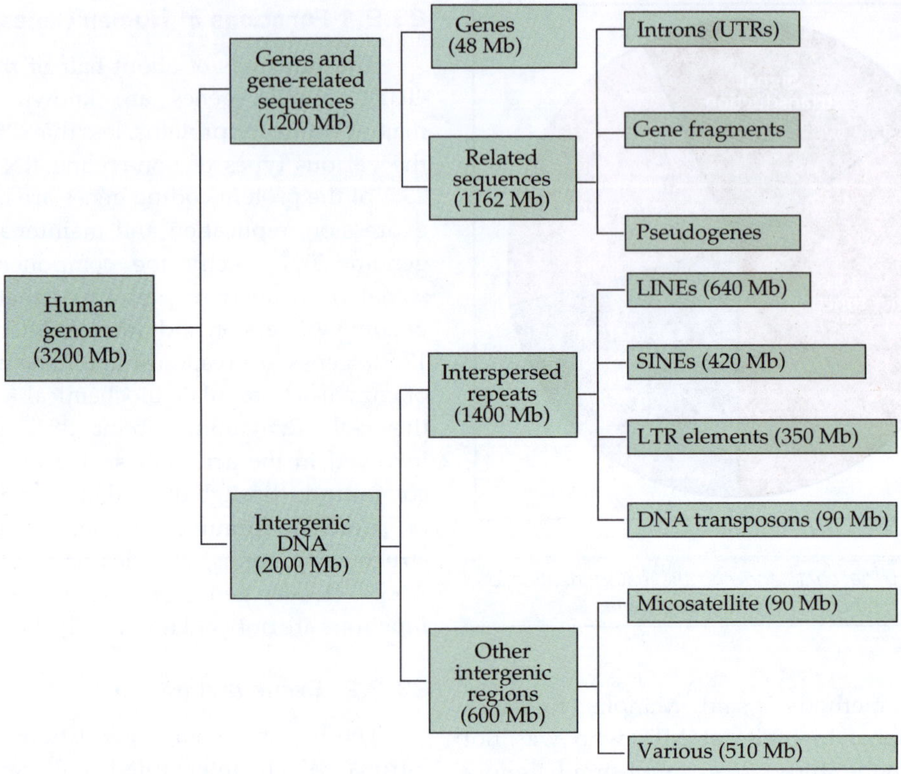


**Fig.23.3 :** *Organization of human genome (Venter, et. al., 2001)*

## 23.9.3 Pseudogenes

Human genome consists of several pseudogenes. Pseudogene is nonfunctional copy of a gene. These are a type of evolutionary relic. They indicate that human genome is continuously undergoing changes.

Pseudogenes are of two types. The conventional pseudogene has been inactivated due to gene mutation. They will no longer be recognisable as a gene relic. *TRY 5* gene in chromosome no 7 is a conventional pseudogene.

A processed pseudogene is thought to arise by integration into genome of a copy of mRNA transcribed from a functional gene by a process called reverse transcription. It possibly does not contain any introns and also lacks upstream of the 5′UTR of the parent gene where actually the signal code sequences are present therefore, this is inactive gene.

## 23.9.4 Repetitive Sequences in Human Genome

There are approximately 62% of the human genome which lack any important function, lies between the genes (*i.e.* intergenic region). These sequences are often called *Junk DNA* sometimes called *selfish DNA*. It mainly constitutes repeats of DNA stretches. But now, molecular biologists assumed that these genes may have some role in the human genome. It has been found that this DNA actually represents an extraordinary trove of information about various biological processes.

Repetitive DNA can be divided into two categories : The interspersed repeats, whose individual repeat units are distributed around the genome in an apparently random fashion. The second is tandemly repeated DNA, whose repeat units are placed next to each other in an

**TABLE 23.2**
**Types and subtypes of interspersed repeats in human genome**

| Types of Repeat | Subtypes | Approximate numer of copies (in thousand) | |
|---|---|---|---|
| **(a) Transposed through RNA intermediate** | | | |
| 1. SINE | Alu | 1090 | 1558 |
| | MIR | 393 | |
| | MIR 3 | 75 | |
| 2. LINE | LINE-1 | 516 | 868 |
| | LINE-2 | 315 | |
| | LINE-3 | 37 | |
| 3. LTR elements | ERV Class I | 112 | 443 |
| | ERV (K) Class II | 8 | |
| | ERV (L) Class III | 83 | |
| | MaLR | 240 | |
| **(b) Transposed not through RNA intermediate** | | | |
| 1. DNA transposons | hAT | 195 | 294 |
| | Tc - 1 | 75 | |
| | PiggyBac | 2 | |
| | Unclassified | 22 | |

array. There are four types of human genome interspersed repeats viz. LINEs, SINEs, LTR elements and DNA transposons. All these are derived from transposable element (a mobile segment of DNA that can move from one place to another place in the genome). Each and every such interspersed repeats consist of few subtypes, which have been described by IGHSC-2001 (Li *et al* 2001) (Table 23.3).

Microsatellites are the tandemly arranged repeated DNA sequences, which are short, upto 13 bp in length. In human genome, the commonest type is dinucleotide repeats with approximately 1,40,000 copies, half of them are the repeats of "CA". Single nucleotide sequence of AAAAA are also common having about 1,20,000 in total.

The dimeric microsatellites can arise by chance mutational events. Replication slippage can then increases the copy number to three, four and more. In Urangutan, gibbon and other

**TABLE 23.3**
**Microsatellites in human genome (IHGSC-2001)**

| Length of repeat unit | Approximate number of copies |
|---|---|
| 1 | 1,20,000 |
| 2 | 1,40,000 |
| 3 | 37,500 |
| 4 | 1,05,000 |
| 5 | 56,000 |
| 6 | 49,000 |
| 7 | 27,000 |
| 8 | 35,500 |
| 9 | 27,500 |
| 10 | 27,500 |
| 11 | 28,000 |

**TABLE 23.4**
**Non coding RNAs in Human genome (IHGSC, 2001)**

| *Types of noncoding RNA* | *Functions* |
|---|---|
| rRNA | Protein synthesis |
| tRNA | Protein synthesis |
| snRNA | mRNA processing |
| snoRNA | rRNA processing |
| 7SLRNA | Type of scRNA, involved in transport of proteins in the cell. |
| 7SKRNA | Types of scRNA, function unknown |
| RNA component of RNase P RNA | Processing of tRNA molecule |
| RNA component of RNase MRP | Proessing of rRNA molecule |
| RNA component of telomerase RNA | Synthesis of telomerase |
| hy RNA | Components of Ro RNA, function unknown |
| valult RNAs | Unknown |
| H 19 | Unknown |
| Xist | X-chromosome inactivation |

species some distance from humans, the sequence 5′ATGTGTGT3′ occurs at the relevant position in the globin pseudogenes. In Gorilla, Baboon, Chimpanzee and human, a single point mutation has changed the sequence to 5′ ATGTATGT3′ with subsequent expansion of the 5′ATGT3′ repeat motif.

TTGTATGTGTGTGTGATG Orangutan

↓ Point mutation

TTGTATGTATGTGATG

↓ Expansion

TTGT ATGT ATGT ATGT ATGT GATG Gorilla Baboon Chimpanzee

↓

TTGT ATGT ATGT ATGT ATGT ATGT GATG Human

### 23.9.5 Non-Coding RNA in the Human Genome

There are some genes which is transcribed into RNAs but are not translated into proteins. These RNAs are called non-coding RNAs. These RNAs perform various functions (Table 23.4).

### 23.9.6 Duplication in Human Genome

No evidence for whole genome duplication has been found, at least not during the recent evolutionary past, but a substantial amount of large segmental duplication has clearly occurred. Duplication events that are inferred to the last 35 million years of evolution of the long arm of human chromosome-22. These duplications have been identified by comparing different parts of the genome, more than 1 kb in length that display 90% or higher sequence similarity. This analysis ignores genome–wide repeat sequences and so locates regions that are probably the products of relativeloy recent duplication events. The pattern of duplications in the long arm of chromosome-22 is fairly typical of the genome as a whole. Individual duplications range from 1-400 kb and there is a distinct bias towards the areas adjacent to the centromeres, and relatively few duplications in the more distal regions of each chromosome arm.

The evolutionary potential of segmental duplications is therefore uncertain. Recombination between a pair of intrachromosomal duplications can result in deletion of the region between the duplications that gives rise to genetic diseases. For example **Charcot-Marie-Tooth syndrome** is developed 5-15 years after birth and is characterised by degeneration of the peripheral nervous system, leading to weakness and difficulty in walking. The syndrome is caused by recombination between a pair of 24 kb segmental duplications on chromosome 17 deleting 1.5 Mb segment of the genome.

## 23.10 EVOLUTION OF HUMAN GENOME

In has been generally accepted that the closest relative of the human being is Chimpanzee which was lived 4.6 to 5.0 million years ago. The human lineage has embraced two genera — *Australopithecus* and *Homo.*

So far, our genome are concerned we have 1.5% extent of the nucleotide sequence dissimilarity from that of Chimpanzee (Hacia, 2001). The difference in coding DNA is less than 1.5% with having many identical sequences. The non-coding DNA dissimilarity is also not more than 3%.

1. Humans lack a 92 bp segment of gene that codes glycolyl-neuraminic acid hydroxylase. This is present on the surfaces of some Chimpanzee cells (Chou *et al* 1998, Muchmore *et al* 1998).
2. There are some gene duplications which are human-specific and Chimpanzee-specific.
3. The alphoid DNA sequences present in human centromere are quite different from the equivalent sequences in Chimpanzee and Gorilla chromosomes (Archidiacono *et al.* 1995).
4. Human genome contains novel versions of *Alu* elements. (Zietkiewicz *et al* 1994).
5. Chimpanzee has 2n=48. The human chromosome no-2 is the product of a fusion between the two Chimpanzee chromosomes.

Four other chromosomes, human chromosome no-5, 6, 9 and 12 also have visible differences to their Chimpanzee counterparts.

How these apes became human is perplexing to molecular biologists? The possible cause lies within the changes in the expression pattern of genes involved in developmental processes and in the specification of interconnections within the nervous system *ie* the Brain. (Normile, 2001). But it is still a mystery what makes us human even though the genome constituents are more or less similar to the apes like Chimpanzee.

## 23.11 MAPPING OF THE GENETIC DISEASES IN HGP

In humans, many diseases result not from infection with pathogens but from a genetic defects. Identification of gene responsible for a genetic disease is important for several reasons.

1. It might provide an indication of the biochemical basis to the disease, enabling therapies to be designed.
2. It might enable a screening programme to be devised, so carrier of the disease can be identified, including at-risk individuals who have not yet developed symptoms and who might get benifit from early treatment.

Several disease causing genes have been isolated viz, the breast cancer and cystic fibrosis genes etc.

Human genome project faces problems on a scale far beyond those that confronted the organizers of the bacterial and yeast genome projects. The problems are as follows

1. Important thing is that, until the HGP got under way, no detailed maps of the human genomes were available. The reason for this is obvious that the conventional genetic analysis is not possible because of controlled breeding experients are unthinkable.

**Table 23.5**
**Some examples of human genetic diseases that have homologs in *S. cerevisiae***

| *Human disease* | *Yeast homolog* | *Function in the yeast genome* |
|---|---|---|
| Amyotrophic lateral sclerosis | *SOD - 1* | Proteins agsinst super oxide |
| Ataxia telengiectasia | *TEL - 1* | Protein kinase |
| Colon cancer | *MSH - 2, MLH - 1* | DNA repair |
| Cystic fibrosis | *YCF - 1* | Metal resistance |
| Myotonic dystrophy | *YPK - 1* | Protein kinase |
| Bloom's disease, Werner's syndrome | *SGS - 1* | DNA helicase |
| Wilson's disease | *CCC - 2* | Copper transport |

2. A biological approach for determining the function of a gene is to create a mutation and then to observe the effect of the mutation to the organism. This is called **gene knockout** mutant in human, which especially causes genetic diseases.

Therefore geneticists cannot built up the genetic map needed for identification and location of diseased genes (mutated genes) on the chromosomes.

Comparative genomics has an important role to play in the study of human disease genes. For this purpose, some model organisms (which are not related al all) have been selected which have homolog of a human disease gene, thus the biochemical functions of human diseased genes can be characterised from these homolog genes.

*Drosophila* holds great promise in this respect. This data already exist for inferring the mode of action of human disease genes that have homolog in *Drosophila* genome.

*S. cerevisiae* genome has some genes which have a known function that provide a clear indication of the biochemical activity of human and yeast (Table 23.5).

It is also observed that all the human genes are present in the mouse genome. Gene knockout study by creating mutations in mouse may lead to the identification of particular genes which cause genetic diseases.

Thus comparative genomics has indicated the possible biochemical basis of the human diseases. Therefore, using model organisms which have homolog genes can be studied for mapping human diseased genes.

## 23.12 ENTIRE HUMAN GENOME IS UNVAILED

Dr. Craig Venter, founder president of Celera Genomics Rockville, Maryland, the private company formed to sequence the human genome in May 1998. The first true complete human genome sequence from a single individual is now available. The paper describing the Venter's genome is published in the **3rd Sept 2007** issue of the journal PLOS BIOLOGY. The genome sequence of the 1st draft which was published in 2001 was rectified, modified and enriched.

1. The degree of genetic variability between maternal and paternal chromosomes is much higher than what has been assumed till date.
2. Another exciting part of the finding is that variation among human to human is substantially higher than what was anticipated from versions of human genome described in 2001. The human to human variation is about 1% not 0.1% as known till date. The result is about ten fold greater. So we are not near identical

clones. The finding gives us a new idea that **human beings are in fact more unique** at the individual genetic level.

3. There are several different kinds of DNA variants within the human genomic SNPs (Single Nucleotide Polymorphism) being the most studied type which is thought to be essential variants implicated in human traits and disease susceptibility. Venter's genome obtained 4.1 million variants covering 12.3 million base pairs of DNA, of which 3.2 millions were SNPs. This is a typical number expected to be found in any other human genome . The personal genomics will give the new possibilities for **personalized medicine** in the near future.

## 23.13 POTENTIAL BENEFITS FROM HUMAN GENOME PROJECT RESEARCH

Rapid progress in genome science and a glimpse into its potential applications have spurred observers to predict that biology will be the foremost science of the 21st century.

Technology and resources generated by the Human Genome Project and other genomic researches are already having a major impact on the research across the life sciences. The HGP research presents the potential for commercial development, industries, wealth opportunities and sales of DNA – based products and technologies in the biotechnology in near future. Some potential applications of HGP researches are described here.

### A. Molecular medicine :

The main objectives of molecular medicines are rapid diagnosis and proper treatments.

1. Improved diagnosis of disease, by analyzing the patient's SNP profile.
2. Earlier detection of genetic predisposition to disease by genetic counseling and amniocentesis.
3. **Rational drug** design, *ie* by acquiring the knowledge about the genetic constitution of the patients. Drugs are designed that will act properly and effectively to cure the individual. It helps to create personalized medicine for proper treatment.
4. Gene therapy for congenital diseases or the disease caused by genetic disorders.
5. Pharmacogenomics which promises to "get the right drug to the right patient" with maximum benefits but fewer side effects.

Detailed genome maps have aided researchers seeking associated with dozens of genetic diseases including myotonic dystrophy, fragile X-syndrome, neurofibromatosis (type-1 & 2), inherited colon cancer, familial breast cancer, Alzheimers disease etc.

### B. Risk-assessment :

Scientists came to know man to man differences for susceptibility and resistance to certain toxic products. This knowledge helps to understand the effects of radiation or other agents especially in terms of cancer. The risk assessment is based on

1. Assessing the health damage and risks caused by radiation exposure, including low dose exposure.
2. Assessing by exposure to mutagenic agents and cancer-inducing agents.
3. Reducing the likelyhood of heritable mutations.

### C. Microbial Genomics :

Microbial Genome program for sequencing bacterial genome has an impact on various aspects

1. New energy sources by discovering microbes which can metabolize readily available renewable resources and development of new energy related biotechnologies.
2. Monitoring the environment to detect pollutants.

3. Protection from biological and chemical warfare
4. The toxic environmental clean up technology which can effeciently and safely destroy pollutants.
5. Biomanufacturing of enzymes, chemicals, and several other industrial products. The enzymes are being used to bleach paper pulp, stone wash denim, remove lipstick from glass ware, breakdown of starch in brewing, and coagulate milk protein for cheese production.
6. Sequencing of microbial genes may help to find new human genes and also may help to find out the disease-producing properties of the pathogen.
7. Microbial genomics help to find out understanding disease vulnerabilities and releaving drug targets.

**D. Bioarchaeology, Anthropology, Evolution and Human migration :**

1. It is possible to study evolution through germline mutations in lineages.
2. Study of different population groups based on mitochondial genome and female genetic inheritance.
3. Study mutations on the Y-chromosome to trace lineage and migration of male.
4. Comparative studies may help to determine the yet-unknown functions of thousands of other genes.
5. Evolution of archea, eukarya and prokarya.

**E. DNA forensic study :**

Scientists use VNTR and other repeat sequences to create DNA profile of induvidual which may help to study DNA forensic science.

1. Identification of criminals and also rectify the wrongly accused crimes.
2. Establish disputed paternity.
3. Help to prosecute the poachers of endangered and protected species.
4. For the detection of pathogens and organisms which pollute the environment; soil and food.
5. Tissue transplantation programmes.
6. Pedigree analysis of livestock breeds and seeds.
7. Authenticate consumables such as caviar and wine.

**F. Agriculture, livestock breeding and bioprocessing**

1. Understanding plant and animal genomes allows us to create stronger and more disease-resistant plants and animals.
2. More nutritious and pesticide-free crops may be produced in agriculture with reduced cost.
3. Insect resistant as well as drought resistant crops are being able to produce.
4. Biotechnology researchers produced genetically engineered food plants which is incorporated with edible vaccines.
5. Genetically engineered tobacco plants can produce a bacterial enzyme which can break down TNT and DNT which can be used to clean such pollutants.

## 23.14 A BRIEF HISTORY FROM MENDEL TO THE HUMAN GENOME PROJECT

### 1856

Gregor Mendel, a 19th century Augustinian monk, is called the father of modern genetics. He used a monastery garden for crossing pea plant varieties having different heights, colours, pod shapes, seed shapes, and flower positions. Mendel's experiments, between 1856 and 1863, revealed how traits are passed down from parents

### 1869

In 1869, Friedrich Miescher isolated a new molecule from the cells' nuclei and called it "nuclein." Nuclein contained hydrogen, oxygen, and a unique ratio of phosphorus to nitrogen. Although, he and other scientists of that time believed proteins were the molecules by which traits passed from parents to children.

### 1952

In 1951, Rosalind Franklin took two sets of high-resolution photos of crystallized DNA fibres and looked at the dimensions of DNA strands, with phosphates on the outside of what appeared to be a helical structure. Franklin's paper on her X-ray diffraction data was published in the same issue of Nature as Watson and Crick's paper introducing their 3-D model of DNA structure.

### 1953

When Francis Crick and James Watson modelled the structure of DNA, they used paper cut-outs of the bases (A, C, G, T) and metal scraps from a machine shop. Their model represented DNA as a double helix, with sugars and phosphates forming the outer strands of the helix and the bases pointing into the center. Hydrogen bonds connect the bases, pairing A–T and C–G; and the two strands of the helix are parallel but oriented in opposite directions. Their 1953 paper notes that the model "immediately suggests a possible copying mechanism for the genetic material."They were awarded Nobel prize in 1955.

### 1961

In the early 1960s, Marshall Nirenberg focused on how DNA directs protein synthesis and the role of RNA in these processes. Their 1961 experiment, using a synthetic messenger RNA (mRNA) strand that contained only uracils (U), yielded a protein that contained only phenylalanine. Identifying UUU (three uracil bases in a row) as the RNA code for phenylalanine was their first breakthrough. Within a few years, Nirenberg's team had cracked the 60 mRNA codons for all 20 amino acids. In 1968, Nirenberg along-with H.G.Khorana shared the Nobel Prize in Physiology and Medicine for their contributions to breaking the genetic code and understanding protein synthesis.

### 1977

In 1977, Frederick Sanger developed the classical "rapid DNA sequencing" technique, now known as the Sanger method, to determine the order of bases in a strand of DNA. Special enzymes are used to synthesize short pieces of DNA, which end when a selected "terminating" base is added to the stretch of DNA being synthesized. Frederick Sanger shared the 1980 Nobel Prize in Chemistry for his contributions to DNA-sequencing methods.

### 1983

The location of the *HD* gene, whose mutation causes Huntington's disease, was mapped to chromosome 4 in 1983, making HD the first disease gene to be mapped using DNA polymorphisms .The mutation consists of increasing repetitions of "CAG" in the DNA that codes for the protein **huntingtin**. The number of CAG repeats may increase when passed from parent to child, leading to earlier HD onset in each generation. The gene was finally isolated in 1993.

### 1983

In 1983 by Kary Mullis, the Polymerase Chain Reaction (PCR) is a relatively simple and inexpensive technology used to amplify or make billions of copies of a segment of DNA. One of the most important scientific advances in molecular biology, PCR amplification is used every day to diagnose diseases, identify bacteria and viruses, and match criminals to crime scenes. PCR revolutionized the study of DNA to such an extent that Dr. Mullis was awarded the Nobel Prize in Chemistry in 1993.

## 1989

In June 1989, researchers identified a small DNA mutation in 70% of **cystic fibrosis** patients, but not in healthy individuals. The discovery of the **CFTR** (cystic fibrosis transmembrane conductance regulator) gene is the single most important discovery to date in CF research.

## 1990

*BRCA1* (***BR**east **CA**ncer* gene **1**) is a "tumour suppressor gene," which normally produces a protein that prevents cells from growing and dividing out of control. However, certain variations of *BRCA1* can disrupt its normal function, leading to increased hereditary risk for cancer. The gene was finally isolated in 1994. Today, researchers have identified more than 1,000 mutations of the *BRCA1* gene, many of them associated with increased risk of cancer, particularly breast and ovarian cancers in women.

## 1990

Beginning in 1984, the U.S. Department of Energy (DOE), National Institutes of Health (NIH), and international groups held meetings about studying the human genome. In 1988, the National Research Council recommended starting a program to **map the human genome**. Finally, in 1990, NIH and DOE published a plan for the first five years of an expected 15-year project.

## 1995

Sequencing the genome of bacterium *Haemophilus influenzae*, reported in May 1995, demonstrated for the first time that random "**shotgun**" sequencing could be applied to whole genomes with speed and accuracy .Shotgun sequencing used powerful computational software to assemble short overlapping DNA fragments, without any preliminary physical map of the genome.

## 1996

At a 1996 summit in Bermuda, leaders of **the Human Genome Project** agreed that all human genomic sequence information generated by centres funded for large-scale human genome sequencing should be made freely available and in the public domain within 24 hours after generation. The "**Bermuda Principles**" were drafted to encourage research and development and to maximize the Human Genome Project's benefits

## 1998

Celera Genomics Corporation founded in 1998 by Craig Venter and the public International Human Genome Sequencing Consortium for sequencing the human genome .

## 1999

Chromosome 22 was chosen to decode because of its relatively small size and its association with several diseases. Seeing the organization of a human chromosome for the first time at the base-pair level paved the way for the rest of the Human Genome Project. Sequencing Chromosome 22 was an international collaboration between scientists in the U.S., England, Japan, France, Germany, and China.

## 2000

In 2000, a consortium of scientists released a substantially complete fruitfly, *Drosophila melanogaster* genome sequence, obtained using several different but complementary sequencing strategies. Groups at the University of California, Berkeley, and Lawrence Berkeley National Laboratory contributed about 25 percent of the sequence, as well as highly detailed genetic maps and a mapped scaffold of partial sequence. Dr. Craig Venter and colleagues at Celera Genomics contributed about 3 million random sequences and computational expertise to assemble the results.

### 6 June 2001

During oxidative phosphorylation the protons flow back from outer chamberinto the mitochondrion only through the**F1 ATPase**. The resulting proton flow spins the rotor of the F1 ATPase. The revolving rotor powers a molecular hammer that bolts together molecules to make a chemical called ATP, which our cells use to store energy. When they go wrong we suffer from heart disease, lung disease, digestive disorders, kidney disease, dementia or cancer.

The new generation of **tailor-made** drugs for everything from cancer to depression is tempting many pharmaceutical companies into the contest. Celera, the firm that sequenced the genome in competition with the publicly funded consortium, has announced its own proteome programme. The computer giant IBM has recently launched a $100m research initiative to build the world's fastest supercomputer with the "grand challenge" of modelling protein folding.

Scientists have already coined a new buzzword - **the metabolome** - that will describe how the pumps, motors, engines and turbines within the **proteome** turn a swirling mass of nutrients into a moving, living cell.

Eventually, putting together the genes, the proteome and the metabolome into nano-scale engineering vessels, scientists may be able to construct the ultimate nanotechnology device: **artificial life**.

### 2001

In 2001, the Human Genome Project international consortium published a first draft and initial analysis of the human genome sequence. At the same time, Craig Venter and colleagues working at Celera Genomics Corporation published another version of the human genome sequence. A wealth of information was obtained from the initial analysis of the human genome draft. For instance, the number of human genes was estimated to be about 30,000 (later revised to about 20,000). Researchers also reported that the DNA sequences of any two human individuals are 99.9 percent identical.

### 2002

In 2002, the international Mouse Genome Sequencing Consortium announced their publication of a high-quality draft sequence of the mouse genome. Scientists were able, for the first time, to compare and contrast the human genome sequences with those of another mammal. More than 90 percent of the mouse genome could be aligned with corresponding regions of the human genome, and each of the two genomes seemed to contain close to 30,000 protein-coding genes.

### 2003

**Human Genome Project completion announced in 2003**, the Human Genome Project's ambitious goals had all been met or surpassed. The sequences produced by the Human Genome Project covered about 99 percent of the human genome's gene-containing regions. Not only was the project finished two-and-a-half years ahead of time, but it was also significantly under budget.

On 7 October 2002 Sir John Sulston, one of the architects of the Human Genome Project, has been awarded the Nobel Prize for medicine.He shares the honour with South African-born Sydney Brenner and American Robert Horvitz for their discoveries concerning genetic regulation of organ development and programmed cell death. Their work in the 1960s and 1970s - which has had such an enormous impact on biological and medical advances - was done with the tiny nematode worm *C.elegans*.

### 22 December 2006

Neanderthals may have clung on in Europe until as recently as 24,000 years ago .Gorham's cave in Gibraltar was home to 15 Neanderthals. Scientists worked out when they inhabited the cave by carbon dating charcoal fragments excavated alongside spear points and basic cutting tools. And in July researchers announced by sequencing the Neanderthal genome using fragments of DNA extracted from fossils. Comparing the sequence with human DNA should tell scientists about what genetic differences make us human.

Bonobos or pygmy chimps (*Pan paniscus*) - which share 98.4% of their genetic makeup with humans - at a sanctuary outside Kinshasa in the Democratic Republic of Congo.

### 9 February 2008

"On the Origin of Species", Darwin made two claims: that there is continuity of species, with each species today being descendants of prior ones, and that natural selection is the mechanism by which species change. In our DNA there is evidence for both, but at the same time our genome is a head-scratching evolutionary enigma.

To see how the continuity of species is written large in our DNA, just take one of your genes. You can typically find a copy of that same gene in many different species. Look closely at the genes and you see just what Darwin would have predicted: our version of the gene is much more similar to the chimp version than, say, to mouse, rat, fish or fly versions. Likewise, the mouse gene is most similar to the rat copy. Contained in the patterns of similarity is the history of the continuity of species - of descent with modification. Darwin was right, species were not just plonked on earth, and each individually created.

### 6 May 2010

Most people living outside Africa can trace up to 4% of their DNA to a Neanderthal origin, a consequence of interbreeding between the two groups after the great migration from the continent.

Anthropologists have long speculated that early humans may have mated with Neanderthals, but the latest study provides the strongest evidence so far, suggesting that such encounters took place around 60,000 years ago in the Fertile Crescent region of the Middle East.

Small, pioneering groups of modern humans began to leave Africa 80,000 years ago and reached land occupied by the Neanderthals as they spread into Eurasia. The two may have lived alongside each other in small groups, they mated , mix their genome, until the Neanderthals died out 30,000 years ago.

The researchers found that modern humans and Neanderthals shared 99.7% of their DNA, which was inherited from a common ancestor 400,000 years ago. Further analysis revealed that Neanderthals were more closely related to modern humans who left Africa than to the descendants of those who stayed. Between 1% and 4% of the DNA in modern Europeans, Asians and those as far afield as Papua New Guinea, was inherited from Neanderthals.

### 30 May 2010

Scientists realised that a mutation produces a specific protein (called "**bcr-abl**") which in turn triggers a cascade of chemical reactions in a patient's body that results in **chronic myeloid leukaemia**,will respond to the use of the drug **Gleevec** that was derived from our new, computer-driven understanding of the genome which will go into remission quite profoundly.

Another example is provided by Crohn's disease, an extremely painful inflammatory disease of the intestine whose origins have, until recently, defied the attention of scientists.

In the last two years, genome-wide studies at several centres have pinpointed around 30 genes that have variants involved in **Crohn's disease**.These genes reveal the pathways that lead to Crohn's and are now allowing drug companies to test their different drugs in order to find one that could block that pathway.

The sequencing of the human genome is already having a medical impact, particularly in the case of **cancer** treatment but that the real improvements still remain out of a reach.

### 19 June 2011

In 1962, the American anthropologist Carleton Coon claimed that "If Africa was the cradle of mankind; it was only an indifferent kindergarten. Europe and Asia were our principal schools."

"Mitochondrial DNA and Human Evolution", was published by Rebecca Cann, Mark Stoneking and Allan Wilson in 1987. For the first time it showed that a tiny and peculiar part of our genome, inherited only through mothers and daughters, derived from an African ancestor about 200,000 years ago. This woman became known as **Mitochondrial Eve**.

After that, the "**out of Africa**" theory really took off. The ancient species *Homo erectus* survived in East Asia and Indonesia but evolved into *Homo heidelbergensis* in Europe and Africa. Then, about 400,000 years ago, *H. heidelbergensis* underwent an evolutionary split: north of the Mediterranean it developed into the Neanderthals, while to the south, in Africa, it became us, modern humans. Finally, about 60,000 years ago *Homo sapiens* began to leave Africa and by 40,000 years ago, with the advantages of more complex tools and behaviours, spread into Asia and Europe, where we replaced the Neanderthals and all the other archaic people outside of Africa. In other words, under our skins, we are all Africans.

One group of scientist continued to support the idea of **multiregional evolution**. It envisaged deep parallel lines of evolution in each inhabited region of Africa, Europe, Asia and Australasia, stretching from local variants of *H. erectus* right through to living people in the same areas today. These lines did not diverge through time, since they were glued together by interbreeding across the ancient world, so modern features could gradually evolve, spread and accumulate, alongside long-term regional differences in things like the shape of the face and the size of the nose.

A different model, known as the **assimilation model**, took the new fossil and genetic data on board and gave Africa a key role in the evolution of modern features. However, this model envisaged a much more gradual spread of those features from Africa than did mine. Neanderthals and archaic people like them were assimilated through widespread interbreeding. Thus the evolutionary establishment of modern features was a blending process rather than a rapid replacement.

When the new Neanderthal genome was compared in detail with modern humans from different continents, the results produced an intriguing twist to our evolutionary story: *the genomes of people from Europe, China and New Guinea lay slightly closer to the Neanderthal sequence than did those of Africans.* Thus if you are European, Asian or New Guinean, you could have 2.5% of Neanderthal DNA in your genetic make-up.

The most likely explanation for this discovery is that the ancestors of today's Europeans, Asians and New Guineans interbred with Neanderthals in North Africa, Arabia or the Middle East, as they existed Africa about 60,000 years ago.

The big picture is that we are still predominantly of recent **African origin** (more than 90% of our genetic ancestry).

### 25 August 2011

The powerful techniques of modern genetics on the fragile and damaged remains of ancient humans, this is concluded that, Hundreds of thousands of years ago, early humans in Africa split into several groups, among them *Homo sapiens*, Neanderthals and their apparent sister species, the Denisovans. The Neanderthals headed for West Asia and Europe, the Denisovans to East Asia. Our ancestors left Africa much later, and arrived in Eurasia where the others had set up home.

### 14 June 2012

Neanderthals have been found to have used tools, to have worn jewellery, and, lastly, to have interbred with our *Homo sapiens* ancestors to such an extent that 4% of every modern European's genome is traceable to Neanderthal origins.

Now comes what could be the final nail in the coffin of the "unintelligent Neanderthals" myth: they might have been the first human species to paint in caves.

World Heritage sites of Altamira, El Castillo and Tito Bustillo. Samples from 50 paintings of different styles were collected and the scientists discovered that a red disc on the wall of the El Castillo cave had to be more than 40,800 years old.

### 5.9.2012

*Breakthrough study overturns theory of 'junk DNA' in genome :*

For years, the vast stretches of DNA between our 20,000 or so protein-coding genes – more than 98% of the genetic sequence inside each of our cells – was written off as "junk" DNA.

The researchers found thatthe DNA outside protein-coding genes within these regions they have identified more than 10,000 new "genes" that code for components that control how the more familiar protein-coding genes work. Up to 18% of our DNA sequence is involved in regulating the less than 2% of the DNA those codes for proteins. In total, Encode scientists say, about 80% of the DNA sequence can be assigned some sort of biochemical function.

Regulatory elements are the things that turn genes on and off. Much of the difference between people is due to the differences in the efficiency of these regulatory elements. There are more variants in the regulatory elements than in the genes themselves.

Genes cannot function without these regulatory elements. If regulation goes wrong, malfunctioning genes can cause diseases including cancer, atherosclerosis, type 2 diabetes, psoriasis and Crohn's disease. Errors in the regulation of a gene known as Sonic Hedgehog, for example, are thought to underlie some cases of human polydactyly in which individuals extra toes or fingers have.

The project has identified about 10,000 stretches of DNA, which the Encode scientists have called non-coding genes, that do not make proteins but, instead, a type of RNA – the single-stranded equivalent of DNA. There are many types of RNA molecule in cells, each with a specific role such as carrying messages or transcribing the DNA code in the first step of making a protein. However, the 10,000 non-coding genes carry instructions to build the large and small RNA molecules required to regulate the actions of the 20,000 protein-coding genes.

These regions are previously thought of as "junk", but are actually vital for controlling the expression of protein-encoding genes. Understanding some of these regulatory elements could help explain some of the environmental triggers for different diseases. Crohn's disease, for example, is a long-term condition that causes inflammation of the lining of the digestive system

### 10.12.2012

*DNA of 100,000 people to be mapped for NHS :*

During an initial three to five-year period, up to 100,000 people with cancer or certain rare diseases will voluntarily have their DNA mapped.We're now getting to the point where the use of genetics in patients can actually help us deliver medicines and understand cancer much better, and to understand a range of diseases in a much more precise way.

An understanding of the genetics of the cancer itself turns out to be crucially important for understanding what's going to happen to you with that cancer and choosing the most appropriate therapies.This will enable us to make ground-breaking discoveries about how cancer works; about who is susceptible to cancer; how we can head it off; what treatments might work and it's something that I hope will mean we can avoid heartache for thousands of people every year who lose a loved one prematurely because they get a cancer that we simply don't know how to deal with.

## 3.1.2013

*Delivering the promise of public health genomics :*

Genomics is often associated with the detection of single gene disorders, such as thalassemia and sickle cell anaemia. It has also the potential to help them tackle the double burden of infectious and non-infectious diseases.

Examples of current research include using genomics to analyse disease outbreaks, examine antibiotic susceptibility and resistance to drugs and identify genetic risk factors for breast cancer. There will be a massive shift in diagnostics towards molecular technology.

The T2D-GENES consortium, funded by the US National Institutes of Health comprises 75 scientists from 27 institutions, including researchers in China and India. The genetic markers that have already been identified as conferring higher risk of diabetes in European populations are also applicable to other ethnic groups; whether there are markers unique to specific populations; and to what extent the same genetic markers confer the same risk when they interact with different environments.

Heritable component accounts for 70-80% of risk for type 2 diabetes but unfortunately even the 60-odd genetic markers for diabetes that have been discovered over the last seven years still only explain less than 10% of heritability."

The Chinese University of Hong Kong team has a 10,000-strong registry of Chinese type 2 diabetes patients and in this cohort they have identified four genetic markers that are associated with increased risk of developing end-stage renal disease. Patients with all four mutations have a six-fold higher risk than those with one or none. Although in the long run genomic knowledge can lead to more cost-effective surveillance and screening, the knowledge is expensive to develop and will inevitably have to compete with essential healthcare services for resources.

## 25.4.2013

Now we are entering the post-DNA era. This century, the descendant of genetic modification has emerged as **synthetic biology**. This takes the principles of gene tinkering, and, just as the pioneers of electronics did, standardises the components so that creating new technologies becomes easier. In the largest synthetic biology meeting in the world at Imperial College London, where the creators of this rapidly maturing field will gather to turn the remixed tools of evolution into ever-more sophisticated circuitry to address global issues including food, fuel and food production. On paper, this circuitry looks like electronics, with transistor-like junctions and gates. But it is in fact DNA, carefully designed and assembled to perform specific logical functions.

We're 10 years on from the completion of the Human Genome Project, we also entered the legal swamp of **DNA patenting**, the idea – currently law – that your genes can be owned by someone else. Two breast cancer genes are the subjects of the key legal test case, which is being addressed by the US Supreme Court , with globally significant ramifications.

Thousands of people in hundreds of labs have worked on generating the various versions of human and other species' genomes over the past few years; the ancient fish the coelacanth became the latest to join the genome club. They have extracted meaningful DNA from all sorts of long-dead organisms, including mammoths and Neanderthals.

In the past few years we have seen startling progress towards reinventing the language of life. That original **four-letter alphabet is now up to at least six**, with the addition of **Z and P** by scientists including Steve Benner at the Foundation for Applied Molecular Evolution in Florida. These new letters don't mean anything yet: it is as if we had added letters to English that could not yet be pronounced. But Benner has incorporated them into a molecule whose alphabet has remained frozen for several billion years. Last year a team in Cambridge led by Vitor Pinheiro re-engineered the struts of the double helix ladder, changing the D in DNA to a host of other molecules, under the catch-all title of "**XNA**". They reproduce, evolve, and have the potential to act as therapeutic drugs, because the body won't recognise them as **rogue DNA.**

DNA technology will continue to grow. But it is our responsibility to allow DNA technology to flourish, while society makes informed decisions about how its fruits are shared. We are in a golden age, an industrial revolution with a single root exactly six decades ago when Watson and Crick discovered DNA structure.

## 1.6.2013

Your DNA is as personal as you can get. It has information about you, your family and your future. Now, imagine it is used – without your consent – to create a mask of your face. Working with the DNA bits left behind by strangers, a Brooklyn artist makes us think about issues of privacy and genetic surveillance.

Heather Dewey-Hagborg, a 30-year-old PhD student studying electronic arts at Rensselaer Polytechnic Institute has the weird habit of gathering the DNA people leave behind, from cigarette butts and fingernails to used coffee cups and chewing gum. She goes to Genspace (New York City's Community Biolab) to extract DNA from the detritus she collects and sequence specific genomic regions from her samples. The data are then fed into a computer program, which churns out a **facial model** of the person who left the hair, fingernail, cigarette or gum behind. Using a 3D printer, she creates life-sized masks – some of which are coming to a gallery wall near you.

Such a process might seem artistically cutting-edge to some. This can help to identify crimes.

One positive example of this influence is the do-it-yourself biology movement. Genspace allows lab members to design workshops, train students and innovate with new technologies.

Dewey-Hagborg has been working on a sculpture from a DNA sample to identify the remains of an unidentified woman. This opens another black box at the connection between law enforcement and what we might call "**DIY forensic science**": here, what is the role of the state versus that of the individual?

## 2.6.2013

*Why do identical twins end up having such different lives?*

The research carried out on the twins left geneticists puzzled. Instead of finding a dozen or so genes for common conditions such as obesity, researchers found that hundreds were involved. In the case of **osteoporosis**, which we once thought was caused by a single mutant gene, we now believe that there may be 500 genes involved – interacting to trigger the disease in people at different ages. These are genes that individually only account for 0.1% of susceptibility for a condition. And even then, these genes, in total, only seem to account for a fraction of the variance we see in the prevalence and severity of these conditions in the population. This phenomenon has a name: it is called **"missing heritability."**

This was shown that the heritability of your age at death is only about 25%. Similarly, there is only a 30% chance that if one identical twin gets heart disease the other one will as well, while the figure for rheumatoid arthritis is only about 15%."

The causes of these differences were due to changes in the human **epigenome**, he realised. Epigenetics is the mechanism by which environmental changes alter the behaviour of our genes. This involves a process known as **methylation**, which occurs when a chemical known as methyl, which floats around the inside of our cells, attaches itself to our DNA.

When it does so, it can inhibit or turn down the activity of a gene and block it from making a particular version of a protein in our bodies. Crucially, all sorts of life events can affect DNA methylation levels in our bodies: diet, illnesses, ageing, chemicals in the environment, smoking, drugs and medicines.

Thus epigenetic changes produce variation in disease patterns. And recent experiments carried out by Spector and his colleagues, in which they have looked at methylation levels in pairs of identical twins, back the theory. "We have studied identical twins who have different tolerances to pain and shown that they have different states of methylation. We have also produced similar results for depression, diabetes and breast cancer. In each case, we have found genes that are switched on in one twin and switched off in the other twin. This often determines whether or not they are likely to get a disease."

Epigenetic changes are not just simple environmental changes, however. They influence a person's genes and can have an effect that can last for two or three generations in extreme cases. For example, studies of the children and grandchildren of pregnant women who endured starvation in the second world war and in China in the 50s have revealed they tended to be smaller and more prone to diabetes and psychosis. These trends are put down to epigenetic changes.

The idea of epigenetic changes explaining the variability in twin (Christine &Barbara) behaviour and illness strikes a chord with Christine. Barbara got married first. When that happens the other twin is left grieving. And later Barbara suffered from leukaemia and has also been divorced. That would leave a mark on anyone. **Luck plays its part.**

## 8.6.2013

*What happened when I had my genome sequenced?*

By the sequencing machines, everyone will be able to hold theirgenome in their hand, and in an iPad on which to download the results, then will be able to surf your genome and find out everything about yourself.

Sequencing the human genome was such a major breakthrough, such huge news when the announcement of the first draft of the human genome was made back in 2001.

**Chemotherapy is just medieval for the treatment of cancer**, It's such a blunt instrument. We're going to look back on it like we do the dark ages. Tumours can now be sequenced and **drugs tailored** to the individual. It's the dawn of **personalised medicine** and it's already happening in the NHS, but with it being the NHS, it's piecemeal and few doctors have ever been trained in genomics, let alone GPs.

People are going to start getting their genomes sequenced and the NHS is going to have to deal with it. Some of the things coming seem as likely as **personalised rocket ships**. In the future, people might not have to have a double mastectomy if she is detected to have the ***BRCA*** gene. She might have a **sensor** in her blood which at the first sign of plasma would send a **cancer ringtone** to her phone, and that is eminently do-able.

Colin Smith, the geneticist, told how he has got mutation on a particular gene. If both copies of that gene are mutated and that gene makes an enzyme that doesn't work at all. It means that if a patient has a particular class of drugs; it would kill the patient. For example, the **immuno suppressant** which is widely used in anti-cancer treatment or transplantation. He found a mutation that means that he – and potentially his children – could die if ever put under anaesthetic. His father had Huntington's, one of the nastiest genetic diseases around, a fatal, neurodegenerative disorder that typically hits in middle age, and which, as the child of an afflicted parent, Smith stands a 50% chance of developing himself. **Most genes aren't fate**. There are so many other things going on – our environment, our epigenetics. But they do have an almost mythical potency in the way that we think about ourselves.

Data of sequencing genome is down loaded and marked"**genetic associations**" within orange button and within purple button, ranging from venous thromboembolism, Crohn's disease and depression to extraversion, eye colour, epilepsy and stroke. Some of them are showing up good, protective genes, and in any case, very few are proved to a high degree. Some literature is suggestive of a link to these traits or conditions, but the study might have been small and not repeated.

Mutation that's associated with an increased risk of stroke; type 2 diabetes; *NRXN3* gene associated with "increased waist circumference"; galactosaemia; genes associated with an increase in smoking behaviour; possible reaction to **flucloxacillin** drugs, a common antibiotic, genes that show a small increase risk of rheumatoid arthritis; variant on *EIF4E2* gene, is associated with **carboplatin** and **paclitaxel** drugs resistant used for **non-small cell lung cancer** treatment.

Early-onset disease in children is a very important area. Take autism, for example. If we can diagnose the day after a child is born, think how powerful that would be, starting treatment then, rather than five or six years later.

A new genetic test, introduced last year, that can test for Down's syndrome, by taking a sample of the mother's blood, rather than by using amniocentesis that carries a risk of miscarriage, has been the most rapidly taken-up test in medical history. What's more, just a few months ago, a team successfully sequenced a **foetus's entire genome** from a simple maternal blood test.

There's more than a whiff of eugenics. Already a company called GenePeeks will match the genes with a potential spouse's and make "**a virtual baby**" to see if you have any recessives lurking that may come together to create a genetic disease.

Already, for a few hundred dollars, one can do a so-called **snip test** that claims to pick up various nasty conditions that might be predisposed to, including **Alzheimer's**, personality traits you may or may not have and information about your ancestors .It is to be noted that the patient takes a daily aspirin to prevent risk of stroke. If they don't include the result for the *APOE* gene, can increase the risk of developing **Alzheimer's**.

## 13.6.2013

*Human genes patent ruling: some clarity but real problem remains:*

The US Supreme Court decision that natural human genes cannot be patented will be greeted with huge cheers by some campaigners and researchers, and anxiety and alarm by others. A patent offers commercial security: a very limited form of assurance that the cost of research might be recovered in sales many years later.

In fact, many genes were identified by scientists funded by medical charities, and the Human Genome Project – a worldwide effort to sequence the entire 3bn-letter alphabet of human DNA – grew out of such research. British, US, Japanese and European scientists in one consortium took the decision to publish every finding immediately, so that the information was freely available and could not be patented. But another initiative, led by the scientist Craig Venter in the US, also raced to sequence the human genome with the intention of patenting as much commercially valuable information as possible. For more than a decade, researchers and pharmaceutical companies alike have had to address two competing philosophies.

One side has argued that to patent a gene necessarily limits other, separate research on the same length of DNA that might be of profound medical importance; the other that without the commercial protection of a patent, no drug, treatment or diagnostic test might be developed at all.

The US Supreme Court decision now leaves both sides with some clarity. However, the real problem so far with genetic research is that the human genome has turned out to be far more complex and difficult to understand than everybody had once hoped, and inherited diseases linked to a single gene, such as cystic fibrosis, remain without a cure, long after the DNA blueprint was first identified.

It was clear that at the end of these projects we would not have cracked the code of our brains, and cured autism, Alzheimer's and stroke. Perhaps we will be able to understand our brains a little better, but certainly not completely resolve their complexity nor deconstruct how our personalities are written in our brains.

### 1.9.2013

*'Should parents be told about a disease their child might get?'*

Yuk Ming Dennis Lo in 1997, he and colleagues published the unusual news that **fragments of an unborn baby's DNA circulate freely in its mother bloodstream in significant quantities**. Then he was astonished that no one saw the full implications of the discovery, based upon detecting pieces of **Y-chromosome** in the blood of women carrying male foetuses. They didn't realise how far this technology could go. They thought you could use it only to tell the sex of the baby.

Chronic villi sampling (CVS) and amniocentesis are used for diagnosing a child's every genetic disease and trait well before its birth. Lo found cell-free foetal DNA floating freely in the watery portion of women's blood, the plasma, he spent nearly a decade looking in the wrong place. It took a decade more work before he arrived at the application of his ideas in a test for Down's syndrome, the most common chromosomal abnormality.

In late 1996, Lo was reading recent medical papers and came across two reports describing how tumour DNA could sometimes be found floating freely in the blood plasma of cancer patients. The idea of a blood test revealing information about a foetus suddenly seemed attainable again. "**I thought a baby living in a mother is a little bit like cancer growing in a patient. So, if cell-free tumour DNA can exist in a patient's blood, surely there can be some cell-free foetal DNA in a pregnant mother's blood.**" Within a few days, by the easily replicable method of briefly boiling the plasma of women carrying male foetuses and using PCR to look for evidence of the Y chromosome, Lo had his result. "**I couldn't believe it. We had wasted eight years of our lives by looking at the wrong part of the blood,**" he says now. "**The plasma was the thing we had been putting down the drain.**"

Shortly after the discovery, he began work on a maternal blood test for Down's syndrome in a foetus, reporting a number of possible methods before achieving one with the necessary level of accuracy. The condition is caused by a person having three rather than two copies of chromosome 21. Lo's method, published in 2008, is based on a technique (so called **"next-generation sequencing"**) that involves sequencing and counting millions of randomly chosen DNA pieces in a mother's plasma to see if there are more than normal from chromosome 21. The US Company Sequenom, which Lo works with to license his inventions, first made the test available in the US in 2011. That test was recently expanded to look also for Edwards and Patau syndromes, caused by extra copies of chromosomes 18 and 13 respectively.

By sequencing the entire genome of a foetus non-invasively, parents will try to know their baby's genetic future and a disease their child might get in 40 years' time when we don't know what medicine will be like then.

### 15.9.2013

*How the diminutive zebra-fish is having a big impact on medical research*

This is a fish that has acquired a startling scientific importance in recent years and which is now playing a key role in unravelling the roles of all the 20,000 genes inside the human body. A creature best known as an aquarium pet has become a scientific star and seeking to become model human diseases.

In fact, the zebra-fish, ***Danio rerio***, is not so much useful for modern biological research as indispensable. In combination with its transparency and its remarkable growth rate, the zebra-fish's genetic structure is surprisingly close to that of *Homo sapiens*.

As a result, scientists have already used the fish to pinpoint the functions of hundreds of human genes. "Thanks to the completion of the Human Genome Project 10 years ago, we discovered the structures of all the 20,000 or so genes that make up the human constitution," says Derek Stemple, head of mouse and zebra-fish genetics at the Sanger. We have learned what some genes do but the roles of the vast majority remain a mystery – and that is where the zebra-fish comes in.

"About 70% of our genes turn out to have a zebra-fish counterpart. More to the point, if you look at genes that cause disease in human, 84% of these have zebra-fish analogues. That is why the Welcome Trust has paid so much money to study the zebra-fish at the Sanger Institute."

Successes achieved by comparing human and zebra-fish genomes include discoveries of several previously unknown genes that are involved in rare forms of muscular dystrophy; of genetic pathways involved in human embryo development and heart physiology; and drugs that are now being tested as future treatments for skin cancer. The work of Dr Tim Chico, consultant cardiologist at the University of Sheffield, provides another example. "The same pathways and genes that made my heart and your heart are responsible for switching on heart development in zebra-fish,"

We have a library of many thousands of compounds that might be the next best drug for heart disease. With zebra-fish we can very quickly screen them to see if the compounds have an effect. We can switch off genes and see how the zebra-fish re-grows vessels to repair damage. If we could switch the right genes on in humans then we could live longer and survive better after a heart attack.

Our aim is to find out the function of a gene when it has not been mutated, when it is in its normal state,because zebra fish have so many close counterparts to the genes *of Homo sapiens* that will also tell us the function of the human gene.

To do this, researchers – once they have created their mutated zebra-fish males – breed them with untreated, normal female zebra-fish. The males' mutations are then passed on to a new generation of zebra-fish. This first generation of fish is then crossbred to create a second generation in which some fish possess two copies of the same mutated gene – one from their mothers, one from their fathers – and which will clearly manifest itself in the physiology of the young fish.

Recently found one family of zebra-fish, created through mutation research, that completely lacked pigmentation and there is a clear link indicating the ***slc22a7b*** gene is involved in pigmentation. More to the point, there is a human equivalent to that gene which we now believe is responsible for coding for genes that are involved in pigmentation in humans.

Another example of the value of the zebra-fish to medicine is provided by research carried out by Carss at the Sanger. She works on a form of **muscular dystrophy** known as **dystroglycanopathy**, which is generally found in babies and young children and causes weakness and loss of movement. Using zebra-fish, Carss has discovered that mutations in the genes ***B3galnt2*** and ***GmppB*** produced embryos that were small and bent compared to healthy embryos.

"The zebra-fish embryos with the disrupted genes have structural and functional defects that mimic the symptoms of children with dystroglycanopathy," adds Carss. "It is very strong evidence that the mutations we found in

*B3galnt2* and *GmppB* cause **dystroglycanopathy** in children. Knowing these genes are involved gives us clues as to what treatments we might be able to give these children. For good measure, zebrafish embryos could be used to test these treatments."

In one set of experiments carried out by Zon, added various drugs to zebra-fish embryos and discovered one, called **prostaglandin E2**, that increased their levels of blood stem cells – and by inference blood stem cell levels in humans. These cells, which are made in our bone marrow, are the precursors of all the types of cells that make up our blood including white cells that form our immune system. The discovery could be significant, because it could be used to enhance stem cell transplants for patients, in particular those suffering from cancers. "Bone marrow is destroyed during chemotherapy and has to be replaced in patients once their treatment is finished. If a patient doesn't have a relative whose bone marrow matches theirs, a doctor will use blood stem cells taken from umbilical cords. These are routinely stored in cord banks today. Transfusions of cord blood can restore patients' immune systems. However, these cords hold only a few cells and we need to find ways to boost blood stem cell numbers quickly while patients are immune compromised. Prostaglandin E2 – which we pinpointed from our work on zebra-fish – suggests a way for us to do that."

In leukaemia patients who had undergone chemotherapy, it was found that cord blood transfusions that were treated with prostaglandin restored white blood cells and platelets several days earlier compared with patients who had no prostaglandin added to their cord blood transfusions. It is a very promising development.

The Sanger Institute has funding to study 8,000 sets of crossbred mutant zebra-fish from which its scientists expect to pinpoint the function of 80-90% of all human genes.

"So far, we have sequenced the genomes of around 3,000 mutant zebra-fish and identified mutations in about half of all protein-coding genes," says Stemple. We make all this information publicly available via centres such as the Zebra-fish International Resource Centre in Oregon, and the European Zebra-fish Resource Centre in Karlsruhe, Germany. We also send samples of frozen sperm from each of the mutant strains of zebra-fish we have created to these centres so they can be archived there. Scientists anywhere in the world can then ask to use this frozen sperm to create a strain of zebra-fish with a particular mutation. Drugs that might treat diseases linked to the human equivalent of this gene can then be tested to find the most effective.

"We are developing an enormously powerful tool this way, one that will pinpoint the functions of our all genes and help us create new medicines that can tackle diseases linked to those genes. And it is all happening thanks to the zebra-fish."

### 20.9.2013

The biochemist Frederick Sanger and his group was the first to work out the precise composition of the entire genome of any organism when they figured out the structure of the DNA of the virus **Phi X 174**. Although the virus was a relatively modest life form, it nevertheless contained 5,400 of the chemical bases that link together in chains in the creation of DNA. The Sanger Sequencing Method for decoding the structure of DNA was the main technique used in 1990 for the Human Genome Project, the massive research effort aimed at discovering the composition of every one of the thousands of human genes.

While proteins were known to consist of large numbers of amino acids, the basic chemical building blocks of life, the details remained a mystery of how many amino acids there were of each kind and how they were arranged in a particular molecule. He perfected a way of unravelling the complete amino acid sequence of even the most complex of proteins. He came up with a technique using a special marking agent, now known as **Sanger's reagent**, for breaking the long chains of amino acids in protein molecules into short fragments. He then worked out their constitution and gradually pieced together the structure of the whole molecule. Sanger spent 10 years carefully identifying small fragments of the insulin molecule and working out their composition to arrive at its structure. By 1953 he not only had the exact sequence of amino acids for insulin, but had also shown the precise but quite small differences that existed between the insulin of different mammalian species. For this work he won the 1958 Nobel prize in chemistry.

### 15.10.2013

*Human Brain Project: building a perfect model of the human brain using 'big data' to trace the electronic signals that zing between neurons :*

A fundamental postulate of neuroscience is **Hebb's rule** – that neurons that fire together wire together. Markram, a brain researcher, his son, Kai was diagnosed with **Asperger's,** an autism spectrum disorder. At the time, psychiatrists were saying that autistic children had no empathy, that they were unable to form a theory of mind. But actually Markram found that Kai could be intensely emotional about certain things and that he seemed to know things about what you are thinking that most people don't know.

Instead, Markram and his wife Kamila, a neuroscientist, performed a series of experiments on rats to test a new theory. Using an anti-epilepsy medicine, **valproic acid**, that causes birth defects that mimic autism, Markram found that certain networks of brain cells in the acid-treated rats were much more sensitive than normal. They also found that the brain cells in autistic rats had notably more connections: their brains were "**hyperconnected**", enhancing the flow of information. Finally, they discovered that the **amygdala**, a part of the brain responsible for fear processing, had a tendency to form new connections, possibly explaining the intense fear the autistic rats developed.

The Markrams' hypothesis is that **the brains of autistic individuals are similarly hyperconnected and "hyperexcitable"**. Rather than suffering from a deficit in perceptual abilities, autisms experience the world too intensely and so take refuge by turning inward, hence his phrase "**intense world theory**" to explain the disorder. '"People like Kai have jacked-up brains," he says. "They have to withdraw to protect themselves."

Once these changes have been identified, Markram argues neuroscientists will be in a better position to draw up hypotheses about the underlying biological causes and test the hypotheses in his brain simulation. For instance, one patient diagnosed with **schizophrenia** and another diagnosed with **depression** might share the same mutated gene. Conversely, two patients diagnosed with schizophrenia might be found to have different gene mutations. In either case, the goal is to do away with the current classification system based on the subjective ordering of symptoms and syndromes and replace it with one that adheres more closely to **biological signatures**.

Markram put all the diseases on the table and start working out mathematically how they are related to each other. By accumulating data on different cell types and the genes that encode for the expression of particular proteins and ion channels, Markram was able to model the electrical prosperities of the synapses and a form a picture of how they communicated and formed links with synapses in other parts of the column. Using his **Blue Gene** computer, he then ran statistical simulations to predict structures in parts of the column for which there was no experimental data. The final stage was to compare his model to the brains of real rats in his wet lab.

To date, Markram's team have simulated 100 interconnected columns and every week, Blue Gene "runs" a new model of the cortical column, incorporating the latest data from experiments, as well as the data on ion channels. This ion channel data is automatically uploaded to *channelpedia.net* – a user-editable website that collates similar data from papers published across PubMed.

Whatever thinking about Markram's vision, one thing is certain: simulating a human brain will require epic computing power, which is why one of the key sub-goals of the project is to stimulate research into an alternative approach known as **neuromorphic computing**.

The principle behind neuromorphic computing, the computer's processors are designed to spit out lots of tiny bundles of information as and when it suits them, much as a neuron spikes in response to a certain threshold of electrical activity.

One such project is **SpiNNaker**, short for spiking neural architecture. It combines the best of analogue and digital computing and replaces neurons with custom-designed microchips powered by low wattage ARM processors designed to mimic the spiking patterns seen in the human brain. One of the limitations of using microchips is that you cannot possibly wire them with the same complexity as neurons and dendron. But what you can do is exploit the fact that an electronic wire is much faster than a biological wire and can carry several signals sequentially, one after another. As Professor Steve Furber, who heads SpiNNaker, explains: "The solution we came up with was basically when a neuron goes 'ping' this is represented as a very small packet in an electronic communication network. We then move that packet very quickly around the system to many different places and keep the size of the packets very small compared with a **supercomputer**."

Just as in a real brain, communications are initiated whenever a sender wants to send, and signals arrive at the receiver unheralded and must be handled, ready or not. Using this method, Furber, a division co-leader on the Human Brain Project, eventually hopes to be able to move 10 billion packets a second around his network. The problem is this will still only be equivalent to modelling about one billion neurons, or 1% of a human brain, in real time.

If these approaches are successful the result could be a computer capable of running a thousand times faster than a biological brain but with energy costs many times lower than a conventional supercomputer. The possibilities do not end there, however. Markram also envisages connecting his brain simulation to a robot equipped with sensors and simultaneously recording what the robot is seeing and hearing as it explores a physical environment.

By correlating the auditory and visual signals with the simulated brain activity as the robot learns about the world, researchers could then introduce distortions to the simulation – so as, say, to mimic the wiring of an autistic brain – and then hit the replay button. In theory, it should then be possible step inside a 3D hologram of the simulation and experience the world as an autist experiences it and, at the same, watch what is going on in the autist's mind.

## 20.2.2014

*Neanderthal Man: In Search of Lost Genomes* :

SvantePääbo realised that if intact DNA could be recovered from Neanderthals (who became extinct about 30,000 years ago) and other early human ancestors, comparing the DNA of the genome with modern humans and great apes would dramatically increase the number of deductions that could be made concerning human evolution. Chimpanzee can't speak, make fire or make weapons; Neanderthals had certainly mastered two of these (and probably the third) genes but it's likely that they lacked the genes and traits that account for our dominant role on the planet.

Mummies are 2,000-5,000 years old and comparing their DNA with that of people from modern Egypt could perhaps answer the question: what became of the ancient Egyptians?

Was the population replaced by incomers or do some of their characteristic genes live on?

The mummies' DNA was badly degraded and Pääbo also came to realise that ancient human remains were often multiply overlaid with DNA from later human contact and bacterial contamination. To overcome this he began to develop techniques of ultra-cleanliness and adopted the new method of amplifying small pieces of DNA to make them readable.

Then in 1991 a well-preserved body was disgorged by a glacier in the Tyrol. Ötzi, as he was named, was 5,300 years old and Pääbo honed his technique on this serendipitous find. Ötzi's DNA was similar to that of any modern southern European, except that he lacked the mutation that allows adults to digest milk, a gene known to have spread rapidly in the past 5,000 years. The first Neanderthal DNA sequences were published in 1997, but it took another 13 years of painstaking work before the landmark, full Neanderthal genome, based on three individuals, was published in a 174-page section of Science in May 2010.

The science of human evolution has been dogged by two opposing dogmas – the "**Out of Africa**" hypothesis and the "**multiregional**" hypothesis. Out of Africa, the dominant theory, claims that modern humans originated in Africa about 200,000 years ago, entered Europe, Asia and Polynesia 50-60,000 years ago (they seem to have reached Australia before Europe), by which time all other forms of **proto-humans (hominins)** were extinct or about to become so. It is known that the first hominin to leave Africa, Homo erectus, reached China by 1.8m years ago, so the multiregionalists believe that various groups of hominins coexisted from this time on and evolved in situ rather than only in Africa. Modern humans and Neanderthals diverged about 300,000 years ago and certainly met up again at some point, probably in the Middle East about 90-100,000 years ago, because modern Europeans and Asians, but not Africans, have 1.5-2.1% of Neanderthal DNA. Pääbo has shown that there was interbreeding between, at the present count, four distinct lines of hominin. So a **hybrid of the two theories** is now plausible: essentially Out of Africa but with some complicated interactions thereafter.

A recent major break-through is that modern humans have only **96 changes in protein-coding genes** compared with Neanderthals. That is, almost every modern human across the world surely has these altered genes.. Several of them are related to **brain development**. We are now edging closer and closer to an answer to that elusive question – **what was it that made us human**?

### 11.5.2014

*The genes that we share with trees, and the link between polonium and cancer from cigarettes :*

## PLANT AND ANIMAL /HUMAN GENOME

The last common parent of animals and plants lived between 1.1 and 1.8bn years ago. But the clues to the past remain. There are still many genes in plants (including trees) and animals (including humans) that are related to each other.

Related genes do not have identical DNA sequences, however, they show enough similarity that we can tell the two genes shared a common parent millions or billions of years ago." But just how many of our genes are "related" to those of the greenery? "Different estimates suggest that between 40-55% of the genes in the human genome are related to genes found in plants," says Schnable.

The percentage of the total DNA shared between a human and a tree is quite small and will vary a lot depending on the tree species. The genome of a pine tree is seven times as large as our own human genome, while the genome of a papaya tree is only 1/10th as large as the human genome.

## CANCER-TOBACCO-POLONIUM 210 LINK

A Tobacco leaves – and hence cigarettes – do indeed contain polonium-210, a radioactive isotope that hit the headlines in 2006 when ex-spy Alexander Litvinenko was poisoned with a dose that was apparently slipped into his tea. That cigarette smoke contains polonium-210 was reported in the 1960s. In soil, naturally occurring radium-226 (a decay product of uranium) undergoes a decay pathway that leads to lead-210 and hence polonium-210. Calcium phosphate fertilisers, often used on tobacco plants, that are contaminated with such radionuclides are also a source of polonium-210. As well as taking up radioactive elements from the soil through their roots, tobacco plants may also trap them from their air by means of tiny, sticky hairs and pores on their leaves.

Polonium-210 emits alpha particles (helium nuclei) as it decays, which have a high energy and can damage DNA, for example by deletion of segments, and cause cell death. When cigarette smoke is inhaled, these substances accumulate in localised areas within the lungs. Studies over the years have looked at the effects of this radiation on the lungs. A report from 1982 suggested that smoking one and a half packets of cigarettes a day for a year exposes the lungs to a radiation dose that is equal to **having 300 chest x-rays over 12 months**, however a more recent study revised this to 28 chest x-rays in a year for a smoker who consumed 20 cigarettes a day for 12 months. A study from the 1970s found exposing the lungs of hamsters to polonium-210 can give rise to cancers, suggesting it could do the same in humans.

Most interestingly, the levels of polonium-210 found to induce tumours in these rodents was less than a fifth of that a smoker would inhale over 25 years if they consumed two packets a day.

While polonium-210 is one of many carcinogens that enter the lungs through smoking, it has been linked to a shift in the type of lung cancers seen in smokers over recent decades – a trend that appears to correlate with an increase in the use of calcium phosphate fertilisers.

The authors of one 2011 paper estimate that polonium-210 could be responsible for "120 to 138 deaths per 1,000 regular smokers over a 25-year period" while another estimates the direct risk to be four cases of lung cancer per 10,000 smokers per year.

## 2.7.2014

*Less than 10% of human DNA has functional role, claim scientists :*

More than 90% of human DNA is doing nothing very useful, and large stretches may be no more than biological baggage that has built up over years of evolution, Oxford researchers claim.

The scientists arrived at the figure after comparing the human genome with the genetic makeup of other mammals, ranging from dogs and mice to rhinos and horses.

The researchers looked for sections of DNA that humans shared with the other animals, which split from our lineage at different points in history. When DNA is shared and conserved across species, it suggests that it does something valuable.

GertonLunter, a senior scientist on the team, said that based on the comparisons, **8.2% of human** DNA was "functional", meaning that it played an important enough role to be conserved by evolution."Scientifically speaking, we have no evidence that **92%** of our genome is contributing to our biology at all,"

Researchers have known for some time that only **1% of human DNA** is held in genes that are used to make crucial proteins to keep cells – and bodies – alive and healthy. The latest study, reported in the journal Plos Genetics, suggests that a further **7% of human DNA** is equally vital, regulating where, when, and how genes are expressed.

The other DNA really is just filler. It's not garbage. It might come in useful one day. But it's not a burden."

Some of our DNA is left over from ancient viruses that inserted their genetic material into our DNA – or our ancestors DNA – and got mutated to pieces over millennia of evolution. Some still have the ability to jump around in our genomes, adding to the filler as they do so.

Though 8.2% seems a small portion of DNA to call functional, the meaning of the word is very specific; it affects our **reproductive fitness**.

"Many [DNA] elements that play important roles in human disease are not evolutionarily conserved. Some of these have human-specific functions, some are involved in late-onset diseases like Alzheimer's, and others are simply missed by current comparative genomics methods," said ManolisKellis, a computational biologist at MIT who was not involved in the study. "We cannot simply ignore the remaining 90% of the genome that is not evolutionarily conserved."

### 3.8.2014

*DNA research: this is the age of the genome*:

This is the age of the genome, a time when doctors are turning to techniques that will allow them to sequence a patient's whole complement of genes swiftly and cheaply, making it possible to diagnose susceptibilities to diseases such as diabetes and proneness to conditions such as cancer long before they have established themselves in a person's body. We already have the ability to generate the basic genetic data for such tasks

In cases involving cancers, two genomes from a patient's tissue are likely to be sequenced: one from their normal tissue and another from their tumour. Scientists will then compare them to pinpoint how normal tissue turned cancerous. At the same time, people with rare diseases, usually children, will have their DNA compared with that of close relatives, again to pinpoint the roots of their condition.

It is highly welcomed for several reasons. For a start, it offers medicine a new way to think about tackling disease: by tracking changes in a person's DNA before they cause ailments and by finding ways to block such disease pathways and so **prevent illnesses** from developing.

The new project will inevitably lead to a vast increase in amounts of patient data kept on computers. Protecting that while still allowing companies some access so they can develop **new drugs** will not be easy. Yet it will be crucial to the success of the new project that this protection is ensured. Leaks will lead to a loss of faith among patients whose support for the project is crucial and will have to be prevented at all costs.

### 5.1.2015

*All cancers are caused by a combination of bad luck, the environment and heredity :*

5 January 2015 Last modified on 1 June 2017

In fact the genomics revolution is already upon us. For example, 10 years ago it took over 12 months and cost over £1,000 to analyse ***BRCA1*** and ***BRCA2*** (the two most important genes for hereditary breast and ovarian cancer), but today we can do this as an NHS service for less than half the cost in a matter of weeks. This type of genetic testing is very important in cancer prevention as it identifies individuals at high risk because they have inherited a gene mutation. Moreover, a targeted drug for *BRCA1*/*BRCA2*-related cancers has just been authorised by the European Medicines Agency, 20 years after the discovery of these genes. We are rapidly moving beyond single-gene analysis for complex genetic conditions and we now have the ability to simultaneously analyse 4,300 disease-causing genes for less than £1,000. The 100,000 genomes project will accelerate this process and provide much-needed data that will allow better clinical interpretation of the genetic code.

Professor Bert Vogelstein of Johns Hopkins University asserts: "**All cancers are caused by a combination of bad luck, the environment and heredity**" (Report, 2 January). His thesis appears to hold that cancers that he cannot attribute to a cause must therefore be down to no cause –*i.e.*"**bad luck**".

## 19.3.2015

*Do your genes determine your entire life? Environment is almost always more influential than genes :*

19 March 2015 Last modified on 11 May 2017

Professor Tim Spector has been studying identical twins at King's College London for more than 20 year and told that identical twins were always more similar than brothers or sisters or non-identical twins. At the time "social scientists hated the idea" those genes were an important determinant of who we were, "particularly in those rather controversial areas like **IQ, personality and beliefs".** As "one of the many scientists who took the gene-centric view of the universe for granted", Spector wanted "to prove them wrong, and to prove that there's nothing that's not genetic to some extent".

The launch in 1990 of the Human Genome Project, which aimed to map the complete sequence of human DNA, came at the beginning of a decade that would mark the high point of optimism about how much our genes could tell us. Daniel Koshland, then editor of the prestigious journal Science, captured the mood when he wrote: "The benefits to science of the genome project are clear. Illnesses such as manic depression, Alzheimer's, schizophrenia, and heart disease are probably all **multigenic** and even more difficult to unravel than cystic fibrosis. Yet these diseases are at the root of many current societal problems." Genes would help us uncover the secrets of all kinds of ills, from the psychological to the physical.

Genes were no longer simply the key to understanding health: they have become the skeleton key for unlocking almost all the mysteries of human existence. For virtually every aspect of life – criminality, fidelity, political persuasion and religious belief – someone would claim to find a gene for it. In 2005 in Hall County, Georgia, Stephen Mobley tried to avoid execution by claiming that his murder of a Domino's pizza store manager was the result of a mutation in the monoamine oxidase A (*MAOA*) gene. The judge turned down the appeal, saying that the law was not ready to accept such evidence. The basic idea, however, that the low-*MAOA* gene is a major contributing cause of violence has become widely accepted, and it is now commonly called the "**warrior gene**".

Almost all inherited features or traits are the products of **complex interactions of numerous genes**. However, the fact that there is no one genetic trigger has not by itself undermined the claim that many of our deepest character traits, dispositions and even opinions are genetically determined. The concept of epigenetics shows how many inherited traits only get "**switched on**" in certain environments. Most of **this switching on and off** occurs very early in life – either *in utero* or in early childhood.

The key concept is the heritability. We are often told that **many traits are highly heritable**: happiness, for instance, is around 50% heritable. Such figures sound very high. But they do not mean what they appear to mean to the statistically untrained eye.

The common mistake people make is to assume that if, for example, **autism is 90% heritable,** then 90% of autistic people got the condition from their parents. But heritability is not about "chance or risk of passing it on", says Spector. "It simply means how much of the variation within a given population is down to genes. Crucially, this will be different according to the environment of that population.

Spector told that **IQ** which has a heritability of 70% on average. In the US, around Harvard, it's above 90%,because people selected to go there tend to come from middle-class families who have offered their children excellent educational opportunities. Having all been given very similar upbringings, almost all the remaining variation is down to genes. In contrast, if you go to the Detroit suburbs, where deprivation and drug addiction are common, the IQ heritability is "close to 0%", because the environment is having such a strong effect. In general, Spector believes, **"Any change in environment has a much greater effect on IQ than genes,"** as it does on almost every human characteristic. That's why if you want to predict whether someone believes in God, it's more useful to know that they live in Texas than what their genes are.

Tim Spector's view that **environment** is almost always more influential than genes.

### 1.4.2016

*Who needs sex to make babies? Pretty soon, humans won't ?*

1 April 2016 Last modified on 1 June 2017

I confidently predict that people will still be having sex in 20 to 40 years' time, but they will be using sex to conceive their babies much less often. Two biomedical advances are going to change how humans reproduce: whole genome sequencing and stem cell technology.

For over 25 years now, some babies have been born after something **called pre-implantation genetic diagnosis (PGD).** Three- to five-day-old embryos have some of their cells removed and subjected to genetic testing. Parents and doctors then decide, based on the test results, which embryos to transfer into the womb in the hope of making a baby. Last year 3,000 to 4,000 babies were born in the US after PGD without any obvious safety problems.

PGD will soon get much better, becoming what I call "**easy PGD**." Cheap whole genome sequencing is one reason. The first whole human genome was sequenced in 2003 at a cost of about £350m. Today, a whole human genome sequence costs around £1,000; in 20 to 40 years, it will be far less. It can now look at an embryo's whole genome. That will make PGD much more useful to parents.

The big problem with PGD is that it requires *in vitro* fertilisation (IVF).It is not easy. Harvesting eggs from a woman's ovaries is expensive, uncomfortable, and somewhat risky.

Stem cell technologies will bypass egg harvesting. Instead we will take a woman's skin cells; turn them into so-called "induced pluripotent stem cells"; turn those cells into eggs, and mature the eggs in the lab. This would not only greatly reduce the cost, discomfort and risk of IVF, but would allow each woman reliably to produce hundreds of eggs (or more). It already has worked in mice and the first steps have been taken with humans.

The result will be easy PGD. A couple who wants children will visit a clinic – he will leave a sperm sample; she will leave a skin sample. A week or two later, the prospective parents will receive information on 100 embryos created from their cells, telling them what the embryos' genomes predict about their future. Prospective parents will then be asked what they want to be told about each embryo .Then they will select which embryos to move into the womb for possible pregnancy and birth.

**Easy PGD** will not produce **super-babies**. Genes aren't that important. But it will produce children who have little or no chance of some serious diseases; better than normal chances of avoiding other diseases; preferred hair or eye colours; slightly better chances of high maths, sports, or musical ability; and who are of the parents' preferred sex. The health and behaviour differences are likely to be about the same as the average differences between being born to rich parents and poor parents – not enormous, but not trivial. New gene-editing technologies such as CRISPR may eventually make it possible to edit embryos, but easy PGD, and its selected embryos, will be safe, effective, and available years sooner. I suspect selection also will be more attractive to those many parents who want children "like themselves" – but like the best of themselves, not the worst.

These would not be **designer babies**

To many people this sounds like fiction. And of course, it does raise difficult and important questions – from safety, fairness, and coercion, to family structures and whether it's "just plain wrong".

Could it really happen? I think so. Many parents will want it, if only to avoid the 1-2% risk of having a child with a severe early genetic disease. Health systems will find it cost-effective to no longer have to provide care for children who are born sick. Clinics will want the business, and governments will be reluctant to interfere in parental choice – at least in some places.

Its reception will vary from country to country. We expect the US, much of east Asia, Australia, and some other countries to allow or even encourage easy PGD. Germany and Italy, probably not. The UK will be interesting. As opposed to America's Wild West, the UK has the Human Fertilisation and Embryology Authority, which has allowed, with limits, new reproductive technologies based on both safety and perceived moral concerns. What will it do with easy PGD?

Before long many countries – as well as individual couples – will have to make these choices. Cheap sequencing and stem cell technologies are inevitable, driven mainly by non-reproductive uses. To choose wisely, for ourselves and for our countries, we all need to learn more about this burgeoning of genetic choice, its likely paths and consequences. The time to begin is now.

## 29.5.2016

*'As long as we study life, it will be read': the Selfish Gene* :

29 May 2016 Last modifiedon 2 May 2017

It's 40 years since Richard Dawkins suggested, in the opening words of **The Selfish Gene** .According to Dawkins' theory, the base unit of evolution is the individual gene.Since evolutionary fitness is measured in terms of passing on your genes to the next generation, Dawkins theorized that each gene acted in a way that would allow it the best opportunity to be replicated and passed on to the next generation.

Dawkins explains how the **selfish gene** can also be a **subtle gene**. The world of the selfish gene revolves around savage competition, ruthless exploitation, and deceit, and yet, Dawkins argues, acts of apparent altruism do exist in nature.

But in fact, Dawkins said, it was the gene itself that was trying to survive, and it just so happened that the best way for it to survive was in concert with other genes in the impermanent husk of an individual.

This gene-centric view of evolution also began to explain one of the oddities of life on Earth – the behaviour of social insects. What is the point of a drone bee, doomed to remain childless and in the service of a totalitarian queen? Suddenly it made sense that, with the gene itself steering evolution, the fact that the drone shared its DNA with the queen meant that its servitude guarantees not the individual's survival, but the endurance of the genes they share. The Anglo-Indian biologist JBS Haldane put it: "**Would I lay down my life to save my brother? No, but I would to save two brothers or eight cousins.**"

Imagine the mutation of the normal lens allele, creating a third allele ($T_{super}$) that produces a super transparent lens protein. The population now contains three alleles, $T_{low}$, $T_{normal}$, and $T_{super}$. Individuals possessing the $T_{super}$ allele detect prey, on average, at slightly higher frequencies, and thus have more food, and they more frequently detect predators and therefore are eaten slightly less frequently. As a consequence, on average, they have more offspring than individuals possessing $T_{normal}$. Over many, many generations, the frequency of the $T_{super}$ allele will increase in the population, whereas the frequencies of the $T_{normal}$ and Tlow alleles will decrease, and perhaps disappear altogether. This is called evolution by natural selection: the frequencies of the three alleles have changed as a consequence of their reproductive effects. Over time, a population will acquire alleles that produce proteins that better solve critical reproductive problems, and lose alleles that produce proteins that less effectively solve these problems. There is widespread agreement that evolution by natural selection is responsible for the origins of the sophisticated organs and tissues like hearts, lung, livers, etc., that enable organisms to reproduce.

Because, in a population of a given size, the increase in the frequency of $T_{super}$ must decrease the frequencies of the other alleles, biologists began saying that different alleles were 'competing'. (Usually, but not always, alleles increase their frequency by causing individuals possessing them to produce, on average, more offspring.) Dawkins, highlighting the iron-clad logic that alleles increase their frequency in the population if they cause more copies of themselves to be made relative to other alleles, and that by increasing their own frequency, they decrease the frequency of the alternative (competing) alleles, termed genes '**selfish**'. Alleles increase their frequency at the expense of other allele

Once the gene became the dominant idea in biology in the 1990s there followed a technological goldrush – the Human Genome Project – to find them all. Many of these areas were genetic control switches, the on and off buttons to tell genes where and when to function. Some are just the decaying remains of genes whose function have been lost in time.

The establishment of the first selfish gene, might have occurred deep in the geological crannies in the ocean floors some 4bn years ago. Life has been continuous on this planet ever since – on a sort of single evolutionary tree. We share dozens of genes with our most distant relatives, single-celled bacteria and archaea. These are probably the most successful – the most selfish – of any genes, since their existence spans the entire duration of life on Earth. The Selfish Gene has attained its own literary and scientific immortality: as long as we study life, it will be read.

### 5.6.2016

*We've learned to read our genes. Now we need to start writing them :*

5 June 2016 Last modified on 22 February 2017

In 2003, biologists from the Human Genome Project announced that they had learned how to read an entire human genome. A few days ago, they revealed that researchers have reached the stage where they want to build the genetic instructions that form the blueprint for living cells. The idea, outlined in Science last week, is exciting, audacious and also controversial. In fact, the idea goes back to the results of the original Human Genome Project that are now providing greater understanding of the causes of cancer, heart disease and schizophrenia while also shedding light on human evolution.

This information has certainly catalysed genetics, but we can only learn so much from simply reading our genetic code. For a start, there is the puzzling fact that only about 2% of the sequences that make up our genes actually direct the production of proteins. This leaves nearly 98% of the human genome apparently unaccounted for andtrying to elucidate the role of this 98% "**junk DNA**". In the process, we will learn the importance of how genes and genomes are ordered and regulated and how this changes in disease states.

The proposed project, provisionally called Human Genome Project is led by Professor LefBoeke, of New York University, and Professor George Church, of Harvard. Both are distinguished scientists; their proposal faces a number of problems. For a start, there is the cost of making the DNA base pairs that are strung together to form a gene and which they need to create their **artificial genomes**.

Genomes have already been synthesised. In 2010, Craig Venter and colleagues at the J Craig Venter Institute synthesised a simple bacterial genome, while in Britain, Tom Ellis's lab at Imperial College London and Patrick Cai's lab at the University of Edinburgh are collaborating with an international consortium known as Synthetic Yeast 2.0. It is working towards the synthesis of the 12 million base pairs that make up all 16 chromosomes of baker's yeast and expects to complete the work by 2018.

But human chromosomes are huge in comparison. The largest human chromosome is made up of 249 million base pairs and would need an enormous amount of highly expensive DNA for its creation. At present, estimates suggest it would cost around $100m (£69m) to create a human genome. And that is just the cost of making the DNA. The technology to handle these long and fragile lengths of DNA and place them into mammalian cells where they can be grown and studied does not exist at present. However, these are just the sorts of technologies the project's researchers believe they could develop.

But is the project ethical? Is this another route to the creation of **designer babies**? This project has certainly been billed as controversial – but is that fair? Medical researchers already replace sections of human DNA in cell lines, which are grown in laboratories, to investigate how specific human genes work and to establish what happens when they go wrong. There are very tight regulations concerning such research. We should also note that the HGP-write project is explicit about only developing cell lines and not altering ova or embryos.

In short, this is not a sinister route to the creation or cloning of babies by stealth. In fact, its proponents are adamant that they want this project to be carried out with public involvement. Common goals for both the public and for the scientist would be identified from the start as part of an open debate. If we can do that, we can then determine how best to move the science of genetics into the latter half of the 21st century.

## 11.9.2016

*Why our DNA isn't the whole story of ourselves:*

11 September 2016 Last modified on 22 February 2017

Each individual of the human being bears the part of human gene pool temporarily. "There is no one alive who is youer than you." So said Dr Seuss, who could have added "and there never has nor ever will be, too." Your genome, the total collection of DNA that resides in your cells, is yours alone for all of human history. That precise remix of your parents' DNA will never be repeated, even if you are an identical twin.

We are in the era of the genome, where reading this unique coded script,you cangive a drop of blood on a slide for an analysis of your ancestry or your risk factor for various diseases or traits, or even your likelihood of sporting success. These are at best trivial – and at worst a form of astrology.Reading our genome indulges our solipsism and craving for simple answers – but human variation is infinite.

The patterns of inheritance are actually not nearly as clear as we once thought. Eye colour is the classic example: there is a gene which determines blues or browns, and browns are dominant over blues. But there's another gene for green, and so far, 13 other genes have been shown to have a significant effect on eye colour. It is effectively impossible to predict the colour of a child's eyes, based on their parents', and every combination of parent and child is possible, including blue-eyed parents making brown-eyed kids.

We now came to know that genomes are uniquely complex, and with everyone's experience being unique, too, human variation is infinite. We know that most diseases and traits are governed by many – dozens, sometimes hundreds – of genes, in concert with every unique life lived.

So **DNA is not a blueprint**, or an instruction manual, as it is sometimes described. Your genome alone won't reveal your personality, or explain your behaviour. It won't tell you how intelligent, how tall, how violent, how beautiful, you will be, nor what gender or sexuality or sport you will prefer. We are more brilliantly, frustratingly, complicated than that. We learned recently that people bearing the name Rutherford have a motto: by neither fate nor chance – which is oddly fitting.

The human genome is an epic sprawling saga that culminates in you. In it there are tales of your ancestors, of the history of our species, of disease, famine, culture, and a lot of sex.

**12.9.2016**

*Human DNA string:*

12 September 2016 .Last modifiedon 2 May 2017

Sixteen years ago, British researcher Ewan Birney launched an unusual sweepstake. At the time, scientists were completing the Human Genome Project, the international effort to unravel the genetic makeup of human beings. But how many individual human genes would be revealed when the project was completed, Birney wondered? So he asked the world's top geneticists to each bet a dollar on the outcome.

A total of 460 geneticists – including several Nobel winners – stepped up to make their predictions. Some believed the project would show humans have up to 250,000 genes. After all, we are extraordinarily complex creatures, it was argued. Surely we must have a huge number of genes to control the manufacture of the proteins from which our densely connected neural circuits are made. Other researchers stuck at around 150,000 while most plumped for a figure above 70,000. Birney chose 48,000. The lowest guess, by US geneticist Lee Rowen, was 25,947.

Then, in 2003, the Human Genome Project revealed the true figure. We have about 20,000 genes. "The best experts in the world were all mistaken," writes Rutherford. "And they were not just a little bit out." Our much-vaunted understanding of how DNA rules our bodies, minds and lives, gleaned in the latter half of the 20th century, was shown to rest on rather shaky intellectual ground.

Humans turn out to have fewer genes than a roundworm or a banana or a grain of rice. Yet scientists had no inkling our complement of genes was so meagre. As Rutherford notes: **"The greatest achievement of the Human Genome Project was working out exactly how little we knew."**

Biology researcher Ewan Birney challenged the world's top geneticists to predict the outcome of the Human Genome Project.

We have discovered that modern humans once interbred with our Neanderthal predecessors; and demonstrated that **the idea of race is an illusion**. Indeed, on this last point, Rutherford is unequivocal. "Genetics has shown that people are different and these differences cluster according **to geography and culture** but never in a way that aligns with the traditional concepts of **human races**."

**17.9.2016**

*Adam Rutherford review – genes, race and rewriting the human story :*

17 September 2016 Last modified on 2 May 2017

The neat family trees and branch lines charting the steady progress of evolution, and illustrations of the ascent of humans, in which we evolve step by step from bent-over apes to straight-backed *Homo sapiens,* are not just simplistic.

If you take the notion that you have two parents, that they each also had two parents, and work backwards to an ever expanding family tree, then by the time you reach the eighth century and Charlemagne you will have accounted for 137,438,953,472 individuals, more people than have ever existed in total on the planet. Family trees, it seems, collapse and fold in; they zigzag across generations to produce a bewilderingly entangled mesh.

In untangling this mesh, Rutherford aims at no less than a retelling of human history.

In the first half of his book, Rutherford charts how we came to be. The "**Out of Africa**" argument is alive and well, but it's complicated. "The dates and overall flow has profoundly changed with evidence provided by ancient DNA." In their great migrations *Homo sapiens* were both "mobile and horny". A toe bone of a female Neanderthal who died 50,000 years ago in the Siberian Altai mountains exposes ancient humans' inclination to mate with other species. Denisovans from the nearby Denisova caves also contributed to the modern human gene pool.

The second half explores the trickier question of who we are now, and the profound consequences of the extraordinary Human Genome Project (HGP) – the sequencing of the 20,000 genes, spread across 23 pairs of chromosomes comprised of 3bn letters of genetic code that contain the instructions that make us human.

Rutherford is especially illuminating on the nebulous concept of race, how it both does and doesn't exist. In 1972 an academic paper asserted that there was more genetic difference within so-called races than there was between them. A black Jamaican can be more closely linked genetically to a white Englishman than to a black Nigerian. It all depends what you select for. In trying to group people, if for instance you select for adaptation to altitude, then genetically you'll find a connection between Nepalese and Ethiopians.

In "**genome-wide association studies**" researchers take a sample of people with a particular condition and look for variants in changes to DNA that are not found in people who don't have the condition. **Tay-Sachs disease**, long regarded as a "Jewish condition", isn't any more. As Rutherford points out, with "careful genetic counselling" it has all but vanished among Ashkenazi Jewish populations. DNA analysis shows how sickle cell trait, once identified with sub-Saharan Africans and their more immediate new world descendants, is actually also found in the Middle East, the Philippines and southern Europe.

That example allows Rutherford to demonstrate how evolution can give with one hand and take away with the other. Sickle cell trait evolved to give protection against malaria (specifically from the parasites *Plasmodium falciparum* and *Plasmodium vivax*), whereas the full-blown sickle cell disease (with two copies of the gene) is a serious, sometimes life-threatening condition.

## 1.8.2017

*A fertilised human egg. '**Crispr** makes it possible to manipulate a genome in the way that we can alter the words in a word processor.' :*

3 August 2017 Last modified on 3 August 2017

The news that a team of scientists from America and Korea have corrected a genetic defect in single-cell embryos is tremendous. In the short term it affirms the revolutionary principles of the gene editing technique known as **Crispr** – or, formally, **Crispr-Cas9** . In the medium term it holds out the prospect – if the law changes – of eliminating some single-gene defects from entire families, since embryos treated in this way will no longer transmit the defective form of the gene.

**Crispr** makes it possible to manipulate a genome in the way that we can alter the words in a word processor. Very small identifying stretches of **DNA around a defective gene can be targeted and then deliberately broken.** The hope is that when the cell repairs the break, it does so without the original error. When the DNA is copied at the next cell division, only a functioning version of the gene is reproduced. When this is done early enough, at the embryo stage, the change does not last only for the patient's lifetime, but is transmitted to all their descendants, too.

Most scientists extremely cautious about applying the technique to humans. The process by which genes are used to build the bodies around them is extremely complex and we understand what happens when it goes wrong much better than when it goes right. Crispr, although it appears to be very precisely targeted, **can make errors analogous to a badly framed** search-and-replace request, changing gene sequences that are far from the intended targets.

Attempts to extend this technique to human embryos, in China, are reported to have run into problems with mosaicism, where some, but not all, the copies of the relevant gene are changed, so that the embryo develops with different regions expressing different variants of the same gene.

Embryo selection with parental consent to eliminate such diseases would be a good thing. Pre-implantation genetic diagnosis allows the screening of embryos that are at risk of devastating single-gene disorders in the context of IVF and that eliminates vast amounts of human misery. For some conditions, couples tragically will not get "healthy" embryos – all will carry one or two copies of a mutated gene and these will cause disease in the child. The pressure to attempt gene editing in such early-stage embryos will be very great.

**Crispr** itself has great promise as a way to investigate some forms of infertility, and as a weapon against cancer and other scourges. Chinese researchers are already investigating its uses against seven different cancers. Research using Crispr on embryos has been licensed by the Human Fertilisation and Embryology Authority in this country already. Caution as well as optimism is in order.

## Chapter Glossary/Key Terms

**Alternative splicing :** The production of two or more mRNAs from a single pre-mRNA by joining together different combinations of exon.

***Alu* element :** An example of LINE, a particular short DNA sequence found in many cpoies on the chromosomes of humans and other primates.

**Exon :** A coding region within a discontinuous gene.

**Gene knockout :** A mouse that has been engineered so that it carries an inactivated gene.

**Horizantal gene transfer :** Movement of genes sideways between unrelated organisms.

**Intron :** A noncoding region within a discontinuous gene.

**Junk DNA :** Defective selfish DNA that is of no use to the host cell it inhabits and which can no longer move or express its genes.

**Long interspersed element (LINE) :** Long sequence found in multiple copies that makes up much of the moderately repetitive DNA of mammals.

**Minisatellite (VNTR) :** A type of simple sequence length polymorphism comprising tandem copies of repeates that are a few tens of nucleotides in length.

*Contd.*

**Pseudogene :** An inactivated and nonfunctional copy of a gene.

**Repetitive DNA :** A DNA sequence that is repeated two or more times in a DNA molecule or genome.

**Restriction fragment length polymorphism (RFLP) :** A restriction fragment whose length is variable because of the presence of polymorphic restriction site at one or both ends.

**Sequence tagged sites (STS) :** A DNA sequence that is unique in the genome.

**Short interspersed element (SINE) :** Short repeated sequence that makes up a significant fraction of the moderately or highly repetitive DNA of mammals.

**Simple sequence length polymorphism (SSLP) :** Any array of repeat sequences that display length variation.

**Single code :** A short sequence at the N-terminus of some proteins that directs the protein across a membrane.

**Splicing :** The removal of introns from the primary transcript of a discontinous gene.

**Synteny :** Refers to a pair of genomes in which at least some of the genes are located at similar map positions.

**Titin :** A protein component of muscle fibre.

**Yeast artificial chromosome (YAC) :** A high-capacity cloning vector constructed from the components of a yeast chromosome.

# EXERCISE

## A. Long answer type questions :

1. Write a brief note on the criteria of the selection of model organisms.
2. Write the goals and objectives of HGP.
3. What is the importance of HGP.
4. Write a brief history of HGP.
5. What are the phases of HGP and what tools are taken for this purpose?
6. What are the implications of HGP?
7. How many genes are present in the human genome?
8. Write a note on the contents of human genome.
9. Briefly describe the evolution of human genome.
10. In HGP, how the mapping of the genetic diseases were done?
11. What was unvailed in the human genome when HGP is completed.
12. Describe the potential benefits that we get from HGP.

## B. Short answer type questions :

1. What is genome?
2. Why model organisms are taken in HGP in place of human genome?

3. What are the criteria for a suitable model organism that can be used in HGP?
4. What is synteny?
5. What are the goals and objectives of HGP?
6. What is genome catalog? How it helps to study human genome.
7. When HGP was conceived but when the project was officially initiated.
8. When Celera Genomics sets up HGP?
9. When and by which organizations, the draft of the HGP was published? What was the results?
10. How HGP becomes a global issue and which countries were then participated in this issue?
11. What tools and techniques are taken in HGP for genome sequencing.
12. When and by whom first RFLP maps were published?
13. When and how SSLPs are used to map genomes from the samples of first and second generations?
14. How STS becomes useful to establish clone conting map of entire genome?
15. What kind of vector is used in STS mapping and why? What are the advantages of such mapping?
16. What are the results of STS mapping in HGP?
17. What is "sequence ready map"? How this is generated?
18. Why YAC library is abundoned and BAC clones were taken into account?
19. When entire sequencing was done with chromosome-22 and chromosome-21?
20. What are the implications of HGP?
21. How many genes are present in human genome? Why this figure is fewer than the anticipated.
22. What are the contents of human genome?
23. All humans do not share only 0.1% of the DNA. What are these unshared part of DNA?
24. Why some human proteins have some similarity with the proteins from bacteria?
25. What are the functions of human genes?
26. What is the average number of exons in humans genes?
27. What is the longest known genes in human beings and how many base pairs and exons it contains?
28. What are 5′ UTR and 3′ UTR? Where do they occur? What are their characteristics?
29. What is conventional pseudogene? Give example?
30. What is processed pseudogene? What are their characteristics? Why this becomes inactive?
31. What are junk DNA or selfish DNA? What are their compositions?
32. How many junkDNAs are present in human genome?
33. What are interspersed repetitive DNA and tandemly repetitive DNA? What are the examples?
34. How do they derived?
35. How the dimeric microsatellites are increased in their copy number?
36. What are the functions of noncoding RNAs?
37. Have there any duplications of genes in human genome?
38. What is the cause of Charcot-Marie-Tooth syndrome? What are the characteritics?
39. What are the genome differences among humans and chimpanzee?
40. What are the mysteries that only few genome difference can make chimpanzee to become human?
41. Why identification of genes of the genetic diseases is essential?
42. Why genetic maps of human genes are not possible?
43. How the comparative genomics becomes an important tool for studying human diseases genes?
44. How *Drosophila*, mouse and *S. cerevisiae* become model organisms for comparative genomics?

45. When the complete human genome was unvailed and by whom?
46. How the first draft (published in 2001) was rectified, modified and enriched in the final version?
47. In the final form what percent of genes were found to be varying from human to human?
48. How many SNPs are found in human genome?
49. What are the objectives of molecular medicine?
50. What is rational drug design?
51. What are the basis on which risk assessment can be done?
52. What is the impact of microbial genomics?
53. What are the importance in the study of bioarcheology, anthropology, evolution and migration of human, forensic DNA and live stock breeding?

Crb2 and Cmpt8 cause **dystroglycanopathy** in children. Knowing these genes are involved gives us clues as to what treatments we might be able to give those children. For good measure, zebrafish embryos could be used to test these treatments.

In one set of experiments carried out by Zon, added various drugs to zebra-fish embryos and discovered one called **prostaglandin E2** that increased their levels of blood stem cells – and by inference blood stem cell levels in humans. These cells, which are made in our bone marrow, are the precursors of all the types of cells that make up our blood including white cells that form our immune system. The discovery could be significant, because it could be used to enhance stem cell transplants for patients, in particular those suffering from cancers. Bone marrow is destroyed during chemotherapy and has to be replaced in patients once their treatment is finished. If a patient doesn't have a relative whose bone marrow matches theirs, a doctor will use blood stem cells taken from umbilical cords. These are routinely stored in cord banks today. Transfusions of cord blood can restore patients' immune systems. However, these cords hold only a few cells and we need to find ways to boost blood stem cell numbers quickly while patients are immune compromised. Prostaglandin E2 – which we pinpointed from our work on zebra-fish – suggests a way for us to do that."

In leukaemia patients who had undergone chemotherapy, it was found that cord blood transfusions that were treated with prostaglandin restored white blood cells and platelets several days earlier compared with patients who had no prostaglandin added to their cord blood transfusions. It is a very promising development.

The Sanger Institute has funding to study 8,000 sets of crossbred mutant zebrafish from which the scientists expect to pinpoint the function of 50-60% of all human genes.

"So far we have sequenced the genomes of around 3,000 mutant zebra-fish and identified mutations in about half of all protein-coding genes," says Stemple. "We make all this information publicly available via centres such as the Zebra-fish International Resource Centre in Oregon and the European Zebra-fish Resource Centre in Karlsruhe, Germany. We also send samples of frozen sperm from each of the mutant strains of zebra-fish we have created to these centres so they can be archived there. Scientists anywhere in the world can then ask to use this frozen sperm to create a strain of zebra-fish with a particular mutation. Drugs that might treat diseases linked to the human equivalent of this gene can then be tested to find the most effective.

"We are developing an enormously powerful tool this way, one that will pinpoint the functions of our all genes and help us create new medicines that can tackle diseases linked to those genes. And it is all happening thanks to the zebra-fish."

The biochemist Frederick Sanger and his group was the first to work out the precise composition of the entire genome of any organism when they figured out the structure of the DNA of the virus Phi X 174. Although the virus was a relatively modest life form, it nevertheless contained 5400 of the chemical bases that link together in chains in the creation of DNA. The Sanger Sequencing Method for decoding the structure of DNA was the main technique used in 1990 for the Human Genome Project, the massive research effort aimed at discovering the composition of every one of the thousands of human genes.

While proteins were known to consist of large numbers of amino acid, the basic chemical building blocks of life, the details remained a mystery of how many amino acids there were of each kind and how they were arranged in a particular molecule. He perfected a way of unravelling the simple amino acid

24

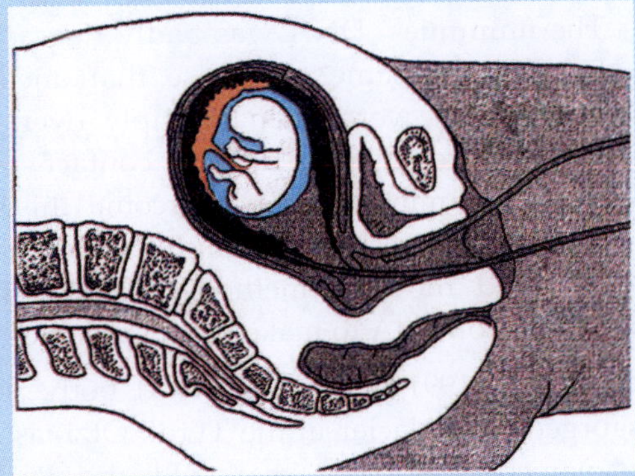

# Eugenics

**CHAPTER AGENDA**

## 24.1 CONCEPT

Eugenics was defined by Sir Francis Galton in 1883, an eminent British scientist and a cousin of Charles Darwin in his book *Hereditary Genius*. According to him, eugenics is *"the science of improving human stock by giving the more suitable races or strains of blood a better chance of prevailing speedily over the less suitable"*.

Eugenic improvement could be gained in two ways. *Positive eugenics* emphasized reproduction by good people — that is, those who exhibit desirable traits. Such people should reproduce with each other and do so often so that "good blood" will become more prevalent. *Negative eugenics* emphasized the necessity of limiting reproduction of those with "bad blood" so that undesirable traits would be lost from the population. Thus positive eugenics does not try to force such a reproductive policy on society but rather hoped that all "enlighted people would voluntarily perform this duty to the human race. But in negative eugenics, the "bad blood" — would not be voluntarity chose to limit their reproduction for the good of the human race. Therefore, it is thought to be essential for the state to 'legislate a negative eugenics policy to limit reproduction among those deemed unfit meaning people who are alcoholics, insane, epileptic, criminals or just plain poor.

During the formative years of eugenics, many scientists were eager to take part, such as Charles Davenport, who in 1910 became the head of the Eugenic Record office, a laboratory supported by Mrs. E. H. Harriman and Luther Burbank. Many other famous people were also allied with the eugenics movement including George Bernard Shaw and H.G. Wells (the President of Stanford University), David Starr Jordan and Theodore Roosevelt. The American Eugenics Society was formed in 1923. This organization published *A Eugenics Catechism,* a book designed to explain laypersons the benefits and methods of eugenics. In 1935 the American Society published a book entitled *"Tomorrow's Children : The Goal of Eugenics"*. In its preface the author, Ellsworth Huntington noted that every one who contributed to the publication effort agreed that "everything possible should be done to encourage large families in the right kinds of homes and to discourage them in undesirable homes".

Garland Allen, in 1975, argues that eugenics movement is primarily a social program of the upper class. On the other hand Elof. Axel Carlson suggests in his review "Human Imperfection : Unresolved Responses" that the eugenics movement had extensive grass-roots support and becomes a popular cause of all but the most dispute. The eugenics movement grew out of a unique combination of social, economic, political and scientific influences.

## 24.2 ASSISTED REPRODUCTIVE TECHNOLOGY

The manipulations of reproduction in animals and humans are collectively considered under Assisted Reproductive Technology (ART). The objective of ART is to increase the number of progeny of the desired species. ART includes *in vitro* fertilization (IVF) and intracytoplasmic sperm injection (ICSI), as well as some more experimental procedures such as Gamete Intrafallopian Transfer (GIFT), Zygote Intrafallopian Transfer (ZIFT), Cytoplasmic Transfer, and Assisted Hatching.

### 24.2.1 *In vitro* Fertilization

IVF is the abbreviation for *in vitro* fertilization, a procedure that involves retrieving eggs and sperms from female and male partners repectively and placing these gametes together in a petridish to enhance fertilization. After the eggs have begun dividing, they are then transferred into the female partner's uterus where implantation and embryo development will occur as in a normal pregnancy.

IVF was originally developed in the early 1970s to treat infertility caused by blocked or damaged fallopian tubes. By 1978, 25th July, the first IVF baby, Louise Brown, was born in England. Since then, the number of IVF procedures performed each year has increased and the success has improved significantly. Because IVF was the first ART procedure developed and widely publicized in the US, many people mistakenly think that IVF is the only treatment option for infertile couples. Less than 3% of all patients who seek medical treatment actually receive *in vitro* fertilization as a treatment option. Most infertile couples who seek evaluation and treatment respond positively to the less involved treatment options such as hormonal therapies and artificial insemination.

Some types of infertility in both females and males require *in vitro* fertlization. Following are some examples of such infertility.

- **Female infertility :**

1. **Tubal infertility :** This is caused by the damaged or nonfunctional fallopian tubes where the fertilization takes place.
2. **Nonfunctional or absence of ovaries :** If the female has nonfucntional ovaries or ovaries are absent, then a donor female is selected who donates her ovum but this is then fertilized by hasband's spermatozoa *in vitro*. The embyo is then transferred to the infertile recipient mother.
3. **Non functional or absence of uterus :** In this case a host mother is selected whose uterus is hired for the development of embryo. But the ovum of the infertile female is fertilized *in vitro* with her hasband's spermatozoa.
4. **Idiopathic infertility :** There is no explanation medically or physiologically in such case of female infertility.

- **Male infertility :**

1. **Oligospermia :** For normal fertility the sperm concentration in human semen should be 15-20 million/ml. A reduced level of sperms is called oligospermia.
2. **Azoospermia :** Absence or very low concentration of motile sperms in the semen is called azoospermia. This may be due to congenital defects or due to other physiological causes.

- **Assessment of female patients :**

1. She should be physically fit to carry resultant pregnancy and can withstand surgical procedures.
2. Her ovaries should be accessible for oocyte.
3. Her uterus should have the capability to accept the embryo and continue full term of 9 month pregnancy.

- **Different Steps of IVF technique**

**Step 1 : Ovarian stimulation and Monitoring**

Ovarian stimulation causes several mature eggs to be produced for retrieval, fertilization and transfer to increase the possibility that at least one will result pregnancy.

1. Various hormonal medications are used to stimulate the ovaries to develop as many ovarian follicles as possible. In addition to stimulating multiple follicle development, these medications are also used to control the timing of ovulation for egg retrieval, which is called **ovarian hyperstimulation** or **superovulation.**
2. Ovarian stimulation involves the use of follicle stimulating hormone (FSH). This hormone is necessary to stimulate multiple oocyte development. FSH is a gonadotropin, which stimulates to develop eggs from ovaries. In some circumstances, another gonadotropin, luteinizing hormone (LH) may be added to the FSH.
3. FSH is available in the forms of **Metrodin** and **Fertinex**. Metrodin, a purified form of FSH that is administered by injection into the muscle. Recently in 1995, Fertinex is released as a purified form of FSH that is

self administered by injection just under the skin. Daily injections are given until the optimal follicle development is observed, generally 5-7 days.

4. Careful physician monitoring is necessary. Following the final dosage of FSH, the use of Human Chorionic Gonadotropin (hCG), by injection, is needed to stimulate the timed and synchronized release of eggs from the follicle. **Profasi**, **Pregnyl**, or other generic versions of hCG are available by prescription. In instances, GnRH (gonadotropin releasing hormone) may be administered to trigger ovulation.

5. For monitoring the patient, ultrasound scans provide an actual image of the ovaries and aid in monitoring follicle growth, beginning approximately day eight of the cycle. The physician monitors the growth, number, size of each follicle and the signs of difficulty that require alterations in treatment.

5. Blood tests are typically performed every day in order to monitor levels of estrogen (estradiol). These tests determine the optimal timing of adminstering hCG to stimulate the follicles to release the eggs.

**Step 2 : Egg Retrieval**

Once the follicle has ruptured, the physician attempts to remove as many eggs as possible. Not all the eggs retrieved will be used in the current IVF cycle. Unhealthy eggs and any egg that fails to fertilize are not used. Any successfully fertilized eggs that are not needed for trnasfer in the first IVF cycle may be cryopreserved for use in the later cycle. Two methods used to retrieve eggs : ultrasound guided aspiration and laparoscopy.

1. Ultrasound guided aspiration is performed under sedation or general anesthesia.The ultrasound image allows accurate aspiration attepts because the physician can guide the needle into each follicle in order to withdraw the egg. After recovering the eggs, these are transferred to a sterile container for fertilization in the laboratory.

2. In laparoscopy, after general anesthesia, the laparoscope is inserted into the abdominal cavity, which contains the aspiration system that uses light suction to restrieve the egg from the follicle. This can be instantly examined under a powerful microscope.

But now ultrasound guided aspiration method is used due to its lesser risk.

**Step 3 : Fertilization**

1. A semen sample is collected from the male partner approximately two hours before the retrieval of eggs from the female partner.

2. The sperms are then processed, a procedure called sperm washing using various laboratory techniques. Thus the only healthy and active sperms remain in the semen sample.

3. The sperm is then incubated in protein-supplemented media for 3-4 hours. The incubation results in sperm capacitation.

4. The retrieved eggs are also cultured in protein supplemented media for about 6–8 hours.

5. The mature healthy eggs are then placed together in the laboratory culture medium with selected and capacitated sperms. They are incubated at a temperature identical to that of the woman's body. After approximately 48 hours, the eggs that have successfully fertilized and are growing normally, are called embryos.

6. Sometimes, they are called **pre-embryos** since they can still split and give rise to identical twins. These embryos are then ready for the next step to transfer them into the uterus of the female partner.

**Step 4 : Embryo transfer**

1. The embryos are placed in a catheter, which is a tubular instrument used to transport the embryos from the laboratory container to the womb.
2. The physician inserts the catheter through the famale partner's vagina and cervix in order to insert the embryos (maximum three) directly into the uterus. This is performed without anesthesia. Normal implantation and maturation of the embryo are required to achieve pregnancy.
3. Luteal phase support is given by administration of progesterone for about 14 days. By this time, the diagnosis of pregnancy can be assessed by estimating hCG in the blood.
4. In instances where fertilization has been achieved, but after a number of cycles, implantation into the uterus fails, the physician may suggest "**assisted hatching**".
5. **Assisted hatching** is a novel approach for proper implantation of the embryo in the endometrium. In certain women, particularly above 40 years age, natural hatching (removal of zona pellucida by the embryo itself) does not occur and then outside assistance is required. For this purpose, a Laser is used to make a small hole in the zona pellucida of the embryo prior to inserting it into the uterus.When the embryo is transferred into the uterus, it hatches and gets implanted. During this course of assisted hatching for 3–4 days the women are kept on steroids to suppess mother's immunity and antibiotics are given to prevent infection from bacteria.

8. Optimum number of embryos are transferred to achieve successful pregnancy. If there are any remaining embryos that are not needed for transfer in this cycle, cryopreservation may be an option to save the embryos for other IVF procedures in future cycles. Frozen embryos have been thawed and used in later cycles that resulted in pregnancy. This will reduce the cost, risk of hyper-stimulation, egg retrieval, fertilization procedures etc.

- **Success Rates of IVF**

The rate of delivery of live babies per retrieval depends upon age. The recent (1997) statistics are 30.7 live births/100 cycles for women under the age of 35. The success rate drops to 25.5% for women 35–37 years of age and to 17.1% for women 38–40. After 40 years of age, the success rate is less than 5%. This decline is most likely due to the declining quality of eggs in women as women advance in age past 40.

The success rate of IVF is rather low due to some reasons.

1. Increased risk of abortions
2. Multiple pregnancy
3. Low birth weigh baby

and 4. Premature delivery.

- **Multiple birth problem in IVF**

Although IVF procedure is quite successful in achieving pregnancy in many women, it does carry the risk of multiple-births. It is well known that the transfer of more embryos increases the chance of pregnancy, but it also increases the risk for multiple births.

The multiple-birth infants are predisposed to many health problems including malformations, infant death, pre-term delivery and low birth weight. Babies born prematurely and at low birth weight are at risk for life long health problems, including cerebral palsy and chronic respiratory problems. In addition, the mothers who carry multiple infants are also at risk for many health conditions and complications such as, high blood pressure, diabetes etc.

A recent study (Schieve *et al* 1999) investigated how the following three factors affected birth rates and the chance for having multiple births in women undergoing IVF.

1. The woman's age
2. The number of embryos transferred into uterus during IVF.
3. The quality of the embryo.

It has been found that, women in their 20's and lower 30's (30–34) have the highest birth rate when two embryos were transferred and extra-embryos cryopreserved. Women at age 35 and over, achieved higher birth rates if more than three embryos were transferred, however the birth rates were still lower compared to women under age 35. Cryopreservation of extra embryos did not affect birth rates in women over age 35.

The rate of multiple-birth's was dependent on the age of the women and the number of embryos cryopreserved. Women at age 35 and over, achieved higher birth rates if more than three embryos transferred. When 3 embryos were transferred, the multiple birth rate was 46% for women of age 20–29. The rate decreased to 39% for women age 40–44 when 7 or more embryos were transferred. Therefore, younger women were at a greater risk for multiple births compared to older women, even though the number of embryos transferred may have been lower.

Women having multiple births are given the option of aborting some of the embryos in order that the remaining one or two will be at less risk for the serious medical complications. Many women and couples have moral qualms about doing this, and it may be especially difficult for a women who has spent years attempting to become pregnant to abort some of the embryos she is carrying.

- **Donor eggs and donor sperms**

For women who experience failure of their ovarian function and older women with poor quality oocyte or eggs, the use of donated eggs from another female may be the best option to achieve conception. Women with congenital abnormalities, women who have previously been treated with radiation or chemotherapy for cancer, women who have repeatedly failed with prior IVF attempts and women with recurrent miscarriages, may also consider this option.

Use of donor eggs in an IVF procedure involving retrieval of the donor's egg, fertilization with male partner's sperm and transfer to the female partners uterus.

Donor sperm can also be used with IVF when there is no female infertility factors.

### 24.2.2 Intra-Cytoplasmic Sperm Injection (ICSI)

Intracytoplasmic sperm injection or ICSI was developed to treat couples who previously had a very poor probability of achieving fertilization due to male partner's extremely low numbers of normal viable sperms. Here, a single sperm is injected into the cytoplasm of the egg. This treatment, when combined with IVF, allows these couples a more favourable probability of achieving conception. ICSI has replaced micromanipulation techniques of partial zona dissection (PZD) and subzonal insertion (SUZI).

- **Causes of male infertility**

1. **Azoospermia :** Sperm can be completely absent in the ejaculate.
2. **Oligospermia :** Men with low concentrations of sperm in the ejaculate.
3. **Asthenospermia :** Poor motility of the sperm, do not have the forward swimming motion sufficient to make the journey from the ejaculation site in the female's vagina, through the reproductive tract to unite with the egg in the fallopian tube .
4. **Teratospermia :** Men whose sperms have an increased percentage of abnormal shapes and forms.

5. Other causes that prevent fertilization due to inability to bind and penetrate the cytoplasm of the egg.

Male factor infertility may be caused by

1. Blockages, varicoceles or abnormalities of the ejaculatory ducts causing low quantities of sperm in the ejaculate.
2. Men who have had injury to their male reproductive organs, some neurological disorders, or surgery may have an absence of sperms in the ejaculate.
3. Men who have had radiation and chemotherpy treatments for cancer, may have low or no sperm present in the ejaculate.
4. Men who have provided semen samples prior to undergoing cancer treatments and major surgeries of their reproductive organs are condidates of ICSI due to the limited number of sperm available to achieve conception with ART procedure.

**Step 1 : Ovulation, Stimulation and Monitoring**

The same process used in the other ART procedures to induce ovulation is used with ICSI.

**Step 2 : Sperm Extraction**

1. Semen samples can be obtained through masturbation. The sperm sample will be evaluated and processed to select only the healthy, viable sperm for the fertilization procedure.
2. When there is an absence of sperm in the ejaculate, surgical extraction procedures are performed.
3. Microsurgical epididymal sperm aspiration (MESA) is used when sperms are unable to move through the genital duct due to uncorrectable blockage, congenital absence of vasdeferens or seminal vesicles. The sperms directly extracted from epididymis are not motile but contain the normal chromosome number to produce normal babies.
4. Sperms can also be aspirated from the testicles in a surgical procedure called testicular sperm aspiration (TESA). These sperms are also typically not motile and mature, but they do contain the normal genetic material to produce normal babies.

**Step 3 : Egg Retrieval**

This step is same as in the other ART procedures.

**Step 4 : Micromanipulation and Fertilization**

1. The cumulus cells that support the surrounding oocyte or egg are removed. This allows to visualize the oocyte's maturity and suitability to undergo the ICSI procedure.
2. ICSI has been proven successful with only one viable sperm and one viable egg that are able to fertilize. It involves the insertion of a single sperm directly into the cytoplasm of a mature egg using a microinjection pipette or thin glass needle. Thus ICSI bypasses both the needs to have the sperm swim through the reproductive tract to reach the egg and to have the sperm penetrate the egg.
3. The failure is typically due to egg damage in the insertion process, eggs whose plasma membranes are too difficult to pierce or fertilized eggs that fail to divide or stop developing for some unknown reasons.

**Step 4 : Embryo Transfer**

Transfer of the fertilized embryo can be accomplished by insertion into the uterus or fallopian tube as with IVF.

### 24.2.3 Partial Zona Dissection (PZD)

The zona pellucida is opened by a sharp instrument or by chemical dissolution. A single sperm is then directly injected into cytoplasm of the oocyte through this micropuncture of zona pellucida by a micropipette or a fine glass needle. The sperm head then moves through cytoplasm as a normal course of fertilization.

### 24.2.4 Sub-Zonal Insertion (SUZI)

Zona pellucida is opened by the same technique used in PZD. The sperms, 1-30 in number, are injected into the area between the zona and the egg membrane. Only one sperm would fertilize the egg.

### 24.2.5 Gamete Intra-Fallopian Transfer (GIFT)

GIFT is a variation of IVF. It is often used when IVF facilities are unavailable and procedure is most often recommended for couples with unexplained infertility with the female partner having at least one open fallopian tube. GIFT is also recommended for patients whose infertility is due to the cervical or immunological factors, mild endometriosis or selected case of male infertility.

In GIFT, fertilization occurs naturally within the fallopian tube of the female partner, instead of in the laboratory as with IVF. The female must have at least one normal fallopian tube.

GIFT is a procedure that involves ovarian stimulation, egg retrieval same as IVF. Mixture of sperm and ovum is directly placed into the fallopian tube by a laparoscopic surgery to foster fertilization inside the female's body.

In terms of deliveries per retrieval, GIFT has a higher success rate than IVF, regardless of the woman's age and regardless of whether male factor infertility problem is present. GIFT is sometimes selected, based on a couple's religious beliefs that prohibit conception outside the body. With GIFT, the actual fertilization cannot be observed.

### 24.2.6 Zygote Intra-Fallopian Transfer (ZIFT)

ZIFT is another variation of IVF. It is often called *tubal embryo transfer*. Like IVF the ovarian stimulation, egg retrieval and sperm manipulation etc. steps are taken and fertilization in the laboratory is maintained but the difference is that in ZIFT, the zygote within 24 hours is transferred into the fallopian tube not in the uterus. The actual fertilization of the eggs is observed and confirmed in the laboratory by ZIFT.

### 24.2.7 Oocyte Cytoplasm Transfer (OCT)

Egg cytoplasm contains many substances and organellies like mitochrondria, mRNA etc. which are essential for the cell growth and cell division during developmental procedure. In oocyte cytoplasm transfer technique, cytoplasm from a donor oocyte is transferred into the host oocyte. Usually the oocytes of older women do not contain sufficient amount of important cytoplasmic substances and therefore they are capable of being fertilized but do not seem to be either activated, dividing or implanting. Cytoplasm from a donor oocyte, provided by a younger woman or by oocytes frozen at an earlier time in the host's life can be injected into the host's oocyte and *in vitro* fertilization could then take place.

Transfer of a small amount of cytoplasm is done by a tiny needle. Sometimes a large amount of cytoplasm is required, then donor's cytoplasm is fused with the recipient cytoplasm by applying electricity.

### 24.2.8 Intra-Vaginal Culture (IVC)

In this technique, the retrieved oocyte and sperms are taken into a sealed container with appropriate culture medium. This is then held in the vagina where sperm fertilizes the ovum in body's own termperature and environment. After two or three days the dividing zygotes are transferred to the uterus for further developmemt. The rate of success is very low.

### 24.2.9 Ethical issues

Assisted reproductive technology becomes popular and by this technology infertile couples have got their babies. However, this technology has opened some ethical and legal concerns, some of which are mentioned here.

1. The ART is only for the wealthy and costs few lakhs of rupees for a cycle of ICSI. This technique is beyond of reach to the unweathly persons. If curing infertility is the goal, then should the focus be on a high-tech medicine or on public health efforts centering on eliminting sexually transmitted diseases, which are the main causes of infertility.
2. Is there a 'right' to have a genetically related child? Are procedure designed allow 50 year old women to have babies?
3. It becomes an unregulated business by the fertility clinics.
4. What would be the status of a frozen embryo? Who has rights to keep the embryos if the couple should divorce?
5. High doses of fertility drugs are not safe. There is a link between hormones and reproductive cancers. The ovarian hyperstimulation is frequently associated with complications, sometimes even life threatening. The ovarian **hyper-stimulation syndrome** is more severe in women undergoing extensive cycles of ART.
6. Multiple pregnancy causes an increased risk for anaemia, diabetes and premature labor, low birth weight and also linked with mortality and morbidity of both patient and baby.
7. Ovarian hyperstimulation causes maturation of multiple follicles, thus there is a risk of early menopause.

## 24.3 GENETIC TESTING

### 24.3.1 Concept

The term genetic testing refers to the use of testing methods to discover if an individual carries a genetic abnormality. Therefore, genetic testing is the analysis of individuals with regard to their genes or gene products. In many cases, the goal is to determine if an individual carries a mutant gene.

The genetic screening refers to population - wide genetic testing. This testing method is used to determine if an individual is a heterozygous carrier for or has a genetic disease.

### 24.3.2 Application of Genetic testing

**(a) Protein level analysis :** In many cases, single gene mutations that affect the function of cellular proteins can be examined at the protein level

1. If a gene encodes an enzyme, biochemical assays to measure that enzyme activity may be available. For example, the Tay-Sachs disease involves a defect in the enzyme **HexA**. This enzyme can be assayed by using an artificial substrate in which 4-methylumbelliferone (MU) is covalently linked to N-acetylglucosamine (GLcNAc). Hex-A enzyme cleaves this bond and releases MU which is fluorescent.

   $$\text{MU} - \text{GlcNAc} \xrightarrow{\text{HexA}} \underset{\text{fluorescent}}{\text{MU}} + \text{GlcNAc}$$

   The fluorescence is measured by fluorometer. In normal human, high fluorescence is observed. But in homozygous diseased person no fluorescence is observed if a small sample of cell is incubated with MU-GlcNAc. Heterozygous individual will show moderate or 50% level of fluorescence which is expected to be intermediate between normal and homozygous mutants.
2. If the disease is caused by the defective mutant proteins but not an enzyme then Western blotting technique is used. The proteins can be detected using primary antibodies which first bind to the protein. A secondary antibody is used which tagged with certain enzymes or

radiolabeled that can bind to the primary antibodies. Thus the protein can be identified. ELISA&RIA are based on this technique. β-thalassemia can be detected by this technique.

**(b) DNA or Chromosome level analysis :**

1. Some diseases are to be detected at DNA level where single gene mutation is the cause. The cloning of several human genes such as those involved in Duchenne muscular dystrophy, cystic fibrosis and Huntington disease have made it possible to test for affected invididuals or those with carriers of this disease.
2. About 5% of infant deaths are related to genetic abnormality caused by changes in chromosome number and structure. With regard to testing, changes in chromosome number and structure, chromosome karyotyping is done with GTB under light microscope. The probability of the occurrence of this disease is related to the age of the parent, particularly, the mother, of above 35 yrs. of age.

**(c) Genetic screening** can be performed prior to birth. For this purpose, amniocentesis and chorionic villus sampling are the usual practices. The couples with a history of previous chromosome defect child, Downs syndrome, Klinefelter's syndrome, Turners syndrome Cri-du-chat syndrome etc. or having such abnormalities in their family, are advised genetic testing.

**(d)** *In situ* hybridization, a modern technique in which a radioactive or fluorescent DNA probe is used to hybridize directly with the mutant gene. If the gene is present, then the probe hybridizes with the gene. Computer imaging method is used to assign each fluorescently labeled probe with a differently coloured.

**(e)** DNA sequencing is now used to discover diseased genes directly with comparing the normal genes by computer analysis.

**(f)** Altered restriction sites are very important for genetic testing. A gene-mutation may alter the presence of a particular rstriction enzyme site. This can be detected by gel electrophoresis to identify the restriction site of a particular enzyme.

**(g)** RFLP linkage is used for gentic testing of certain disease causing alleles. For example: β-globin gene is cloned which is radiolabeled to make a probe. Blood sample from the suspected sickle cell anaemia person is taken, DNA is isolated and digested with *Hpa I* restriction enzyme and subjected to electrophoresis, β-globin gene can be detected by Southern hybridization technique with radiolabeled probe.

### 24.3.3 Limitations of Genetic testing

Genetic testing and screening are medical practices but with many social and ethical dimensions.

1. The person who learns that he or she is a carrier of a genetic disease, such as Huntingtons disease or familial breast cancer would become mentally shocked from these fatal diseases. This is unethical. Though some argue that people have a right to know about their genetic make up.
2. Another issue is privacy : the Medical insurance company or the Employer would discriminate them if they came to know about the genetic makeup of the person.
3. It is unethical when gentic testing tells to their parent that the disease of their children is not treatable or the onset of the disease would occur at their adult stage.

Therefore, the persons usually avoid the genetic testing of the disease to themselves as well as to their future children.

## 24.4 GENETIC COUNSELING

Genetic counseling is a medical speciality with responsibility for educating people about genetic diseases, treatments and potential reproductive choices.

Particularly in the developed countries, genetic counseling for couples who believed that there may be a risk of producing a defective child has now routine aspect of medical practice. These parents may either voluntarily abstain from having any child or may undergo selective abortions after ascertaining it through **antenatal diagnosis**.

1. The genetic counsellor should first be able to identify the disease. Therefore he or she would be a clinician as well as a geneticist also.
2. The person seeking genetic counseling will be those having a family history of disease and the parents may like to know the chances of having child free of that disease.
3. The couple may have one abnormal child and would like to know the chances of having a normal child on the next pregnancy. If the defect is known to be a single recessive gene but both the parents are normal, then there is a chance of 75% normal among their children. The parents may like to give birth to such a child who may be a carrier although in future he or she will face the same problem like the parents.
4. Without a precise diagnosis, it is not possible to give reliable gentic counseling since certain disorders, though superficially similar may be inherited differently. For example, **Hunter's syndrome** and **Hurler's syndrome**, both present similar clinical features but clouding of the cornea does not occur in the former condition. Further, Hunter's syndrome is an X-linked recessive trait and therefore the unaffected sister of an affected boy may be at risk of having affected children. Hurler's syndrome is an autosomal recessive disorder and in this condition there is, therefore, no chance of an unaffected sister having affected children provided she does not marry a near relative who might also carry the mutant gene.
4. It is always advisable to check that the disease in question is infact genetic and not due to some environmental factors. For example, congenital deafness is often due to a rare recessive gene but it may also result from intrauterine infection with rubella during the first three months of pregnancy, which may also cause other abnormalities in fetus, such as congenital heart disease and eye defects. If it can be shown in a particular case that congenital deafness was due to maternal rubella, then there would be no chance of recurrence in subsequent children.
5. In some cases detection of heterozygote may also be useful and possible.
   (a) When a heterozygote, though phenotypically normal, produces a particular enzyme activity intermediate to those found in two homozygotes. Its presence can be detected using electrophoresis. In such cases, if a biochemistry laboratory is available, deficiency like HGPRT (hypoxanthene - guanine-phosphoribosyl transferase) in *Lesch-Nyhann* syndrome in heterozygote condition can be detected from the blood sample.
   (b) When a heterozygote, produces two forms of their products, one is normal and other is mutant, then these two proteins can be separated by electrophoresis. Thus the nature of heterozygotes can be easily identified.
   (c) If the defect is due to the abnormality in the chromosome structure or number, then with the availability of a cytogenetics laboratory such an abnormality in the heterozygote condition can be identified.

7. When a pregnant woman is known to have a chance of having a child with a genetic defect, it may be desirable to diagnose the condition in the fetus by the technique called amniocentesis.
8. After counseling of genes, it is probable to rectify the disease by adding genetic material to the diseased person only to their somatic cells, which is known as gene therapy.

## 24.5 PRENATAL DIAGNOSIS

When a pregnant woman is known to have a chance of bearing a child with a genetic defect, it may be desirable to diagnose the condition in the fetus. If the father is affected with a dominant or if both parents are heterozygous for a rare recessive gene, the antenatal diagnosis with selective abortion of affected fetus is required. For that purpose, antenatal diagnosis is achieved by the techniques, amniocentesis and chorionic villus sampling (CVS).

### 24.5.1 Amniocentesis

Amniocentesis is a common prenatal test for diagnosing genetic disorders in the growing fetus.

**Procedure :** About 5–10 ml, of fluid is removed by transabdominal amniocentesis around the 15 to 18 weeks of gestation. For that purpose, a thin hollow needle is inserted into the womb/uterus and removed with some amount of amniotic fluid that surrounds the fetus. Ultrasound is used to guide the insertion of this needle into the amniotic sac (Fig. 24.1).

The specimen is centrifuged. The cellular part is grown in a culture medium in the laboratory for one to two weeks. These cells are then karyotyped and used to test for chromosomal abnormalities. A combination of PCR and hybridization methods used for this purpose. The supernatant after centrifugation is used to test various inborn errors of metabolism. Test results usually are available within three weeks. The presence of fluorescent body (F-body) and sex chromatin body confirm the sex of the fetus.

**Safety :** If it is performed by a skilled practitioner, amniocentesis is quite safe for both mother and the fetus. This technique, however, possesses a slight risk of miscarriage. The procedure also carries an extremely low risk of uterine infection (less than one in thousand), which also can cause miscarriage.

**Outcome :** Although diagnosis of a serious genetic abnormality in a fetus can help parents take the timely decision to terminate that pregnancy, advances in prenatal therapy are making it possible to treat some birth defects before birth in the womb, resulting in the birth of healthy babies.

**Application :**

1. This is valuable in X-linked disorders which can yet be diagnosed *in utero* (eg Duchenne muscular dystrophy). In this way a known carrier mother can be guaranted a daughter who will not be affected (though she might be a carrier) for if fetus is a male, the parents may decide on termination since there is a 50% chance of an affected fetus.
2. Amniotic fluid cells can also be cultured and from the study of this material, it is possible not only to determine the sex of the fetus but also to diagnose cytogenetic abnormalities and certain inborn errors of metabolism in the fetus.
3. At present the main application of such studies is in the antenatal diagnosis of Down's syndrome and many centers now offer amniocentesis to all pregnant woman over the age of 40 years, because of their increased risk of having a child with this disorder.
4. **Anencephaly** and **Open spina bifida** are associated with raised levels of $\alpha$–fetoproteins in amniotic fluid.
5. The cultured cells can be tested in various ways eg. karyotype, enzyme production

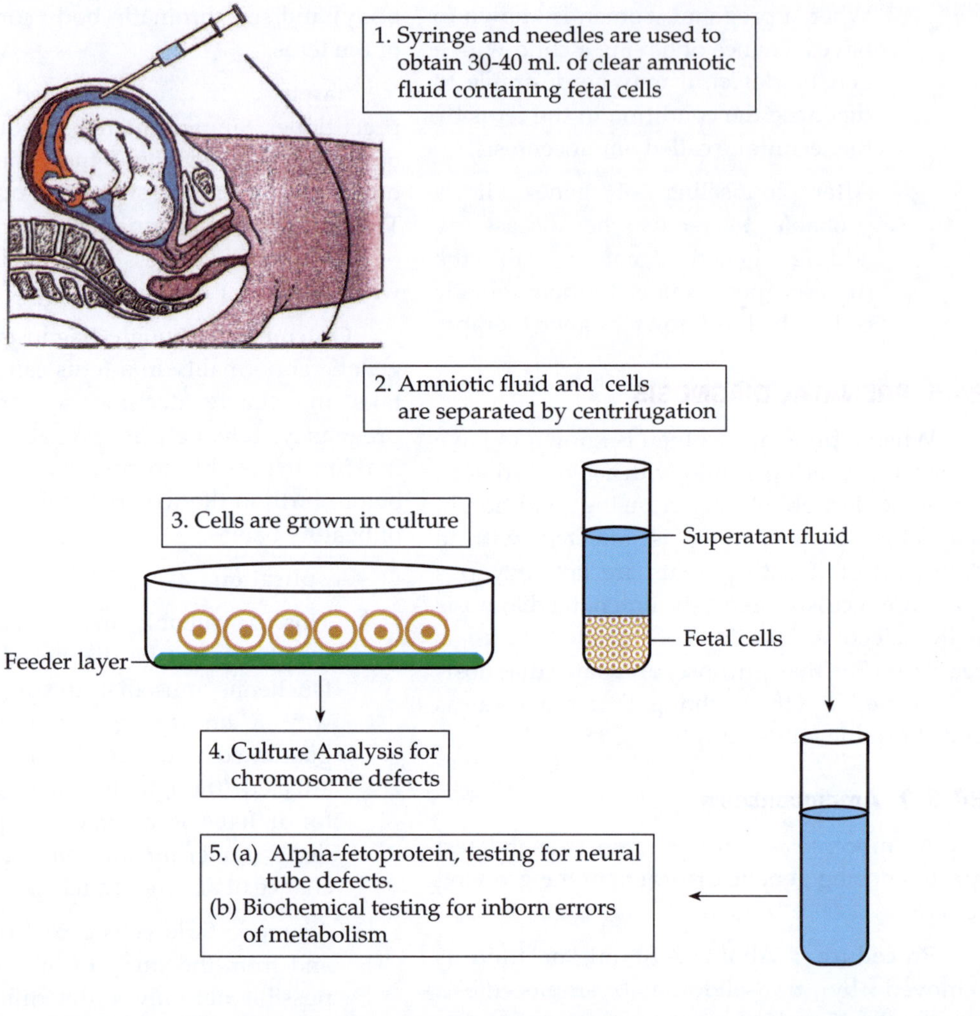


**Fig.24.1** : *Technique for amniocentesis*

and restriction site pattern analysis of its DNA and now at least 35 diseases can be identified by this technique. At present, it is possible to identify the disease within two months of pregnancy.

6. Number of disease-specific DNA probes is also increasing at a fast rate, so that antenatal disgnosis by DNA analysis or linkage should be possible for all single gene defects. In recent years the disease thalassemia can be detected by the use of antenatal diagnosis and now in **Cypriot community in Britain**, the percentage of thalassemia has been fallen from 30% to 2%.

7. Lastly, it is recommended for abortion of fetus only if the defect is detected by this method. In USA, there is a campaign against abortion and therefore, also against antenatal diagnosis. In such cases there will be birth of defective children and these may become the patients for gene therapy.

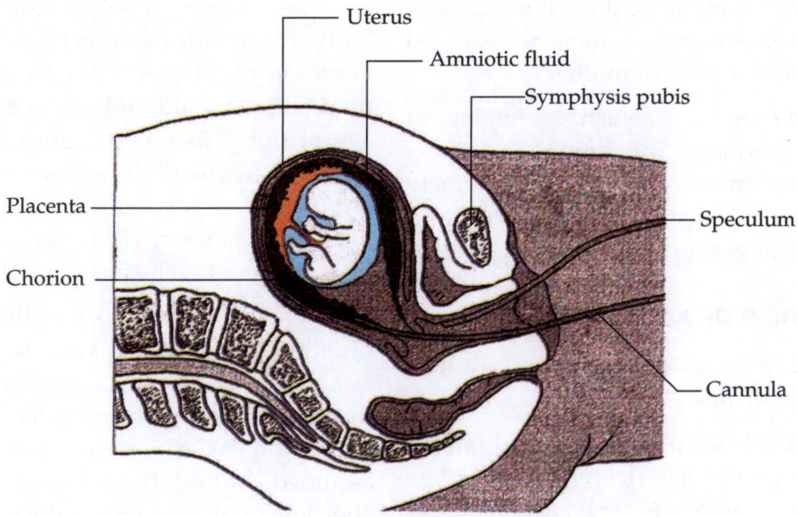


**Fig.24.2 :** *Chorionic villus sampling*

### 24.5.2 Chorionic Villus Sampling

Chorionic villus sampling (CVS) involves removing pieces of the chorionic villi, embryonic tissue that anchors the fetus to the uterine wall and serves a nutritional function until the placenta develops. These pieces can be obtained either by puncturing the mother's abdominal wall with a needle as in amniocentesis or by inserting a catheter through the cervix (Fig. 24.2).

A tube is inserted through the cervix to contact the chorionic villi. Portions of the villi are then removed by suction. Fetal cells are separated from fluid and from any maternal tissue. There are usually enough cells in this sample to directly perform karyotypic as well as biochemical and hybridization tests.

CVS has the distinct advantage of allowing earlier diagnosis — tissue can be obtained from the eighth week through the 12th week of pregnancy, allowing therapeutic abortion during the first trimester. CVS has a slightly increased risk of miscarriage compared to amniocentesis but it is fact that by this method early diagnosis is possible.

## 24.6 EMBRYONIC DIAGNOSIS

In recent years it is possible to perform genetic diagnosis using material obtained from a single cell. The DNA of the cell is isolated and PCR is used to amplify the desired target sequences. Following amplification, the target DNA can easily be tested by using hybridization procedure.

Embryonic diagnosis is successfully used during *in vitro* fertilization. The prospective parents (both are assumed to be heterozygous for a recessive fatal disease, say, cystic fibrosis), donate eggs and sperms for *in vitro* fertilization. Many eggs are fertilized, but only some survive to begin dividing. The survivors are cultured until they reach the eight-cell stage. At this time, one cell is removed from each embryo. This seven-celled embryos are further cultured and continue normal development into a full embryo, while the removed single cell is subjected to genetic testing for **cystic fibrosis**. Some of the embryos (about 25%) may be found to have two copies of CF genes. These embyos are destroyed without ever being implanted — as are many embryos during the normal course of *in vitro* fertilization. Other homozygous normal or heterozygous embryos can be implanted into the uterus of mother.

The implications of such technological advances are enormous. It is easy to imagine a future time when many genes can be routinely diagnosed, ensuring that children do not suffer from a number of genetic disorders.

## 24.7 DIAGNOSIS OF ADULT

Diagnosis of genetic diseases in adult is more plausible because

1. It is relatively simple since a blood sample can provide the material for some enzyme diagnostic tests as well as the cells necessary for hybridization based tests.
2. Screening can be applied to individuals with clear informed consent.
3. The results are not usually used to make decisions about abortion.

An adult is usually diagnosed to determine whether the parents are heterozygous for a particular trait or not. Therefore they are allowed to make reproductive choices. For example, if both the parents are heterozygous for a recessive lethal gene which may affect 25% of their children with defect gene. Then they are pursued to take prenatal diagnosis of their fetus whether it suffers from the disease.

The Huntington's disease is caused for a dominant mutant gene which can be diagnosed by the test based on hybridization. This fatal disease symptoms are much delayed as late as the age of 40 yrs. The adult patient may be homozygous or heterozygous. As it is a dominant autosomal gene, the male or female offsping will have the same chance to suffer from this disease.

## 24.8 GENETIC SCREENING

Genetic screening is highly organized attempts to use accurate and reliable gentic diagnostic tests on a specific target group for genetic disorder.

The target groups are usually the individuals with increased risk for the disease. For example, Down's syndrome occurs more frequently in children born to mothers over the age of thirty five, cystic fibrosis which occurs mostly frequently within the caucasian population, sickle cell anaemia occurs mostly within African-American population, Tay-Sachs disease occurs exclusively in Ashkenazi Jews.

Genetic screening is not different from that of individual genetic diagnosis. It is possible to establish a screening program that would diagnose almost all features having the gene for Huntington's disease. If the positive diagnosis is assumed, would be followed by therapeutic abortion, which would reduce the number of individuals in the next generation who will suffer from such a disease.

In USA, almost every baby is screening within the first few days of birth for genetic disease phenylketonuria taking a very little amount of blood. If the disease is diagnosed early, the infant's diet can be modified to prevent mental retardation caused by this disease.

A successful screening programme must offer immediate, real and tangible benifits to the diagnosed individuals.

## 24.9 GENE THERAPY

### 24.9.1 Concept

Gene therapy is the insertion of genes into an individual's cells and tissues to treat a disease and hereditary diseases in particular.

Gene therapy involves the treatment of diseases by introduction of corrective or therapeutic DNA into cells and maintenance of the corrective genetic material within the modified cells and its offspring.

### 24.9.2 Objectives of Gene therapy

1. To replace missing or defective genes.
2. To deliver genes that catalyze the destruction of cancer cells or cause cancer

cells to revert back into normal.

3. To deliver viral or bacterial genes as a form of vaccination
4. To deliver genes that promote the growth of new tissue or stimulate regeneration of damaged tissue.

Gene therapy differs from conventional medical treatments in that treating the symptoms; gene therapy addresses the underlying genetic causes of disease at their origin *i.e.*, the DNA.

### 24.9.3 Strategies of somatic cell Gene therapy

1. Augmentation of gene
2. Gene replacement
3. Targeted inhibition of gene expression.
4. Targeted killing of specific cells

### 24.9.4 The factors that kept Gene therapy away from becoming an effective treatment for genetic diseases

1. *Immune response* : Any foreign object which is nonself to human, is introduced into the body, the immune system attacks the invaders and mount immune responses against the object. It is very possible that the foreign genes may create a potential risk when the gene therapy is repeated in patients.
2. *Short-lived nature of gene therapy* : The therapeutic DNA which is introduced into the body must remain functional as long as it remains there. After death or destruction of these cells and their descendants, the gene therapy would become non-effective. Therefore, the main objective of gene therapy would be such that the therapeutic DNA must be long-lived and stable.
3. *Problems with integrating therapeutic DNA* : The therapeutic DNA which is integrated into the genome prevents long term benifits if the cells are dividing rapidly. Then they will have to undergo multiple rounds of gene therapy.
4. *Problems with viral vectors* : Viruses are the main choice of vectors for gene therapy. But they may create certain potential problems to the patients, such as its toxicity, immune and inflammatory responses. In addition, there is always a fear that viral vector may recover its ability to cause disease.
5. *Multigene disorders* : The most commonly occurring disorders, such as heart disease, high blood pressure, Alzheimer's disease, arthritis and diabetes are caused by the combined effects of variations of many genes. Such a multigene disorder would be difficult to treat effectively by using gene therapy, because gene therapy is usually successful in single gene disorder diseases.
6. *Ethical problem* : There are some ethical questions which make the gene therapy to keep away from effective treatment.
   - What is normal and what is disorder and who will decide?
   - Are disabilities the diseases? Do they need to be cured or prevented?
   - Does searching for a cure demean the lives of individuals presently affected by disabilities?
   - Is somatic gene therapy more or less ethical than germline gene therapy? In cases of somatic gene therapy, the procedure may have to be repeated in future generation?
   - Priliminary attempts at gene therapy are exorbitantly expensive. Who will pay for their use?

### 24.9.5 Current status of Gene therapy research

1. University of California, Los Angeles, research team gets genes into the brain using liposomes coated with polymer

called polythene glycol (PEG). The transfer of genes into the brain is a significant achievement, because viral vectors are too big to get across the "blood brain barrier". The method has potential for treating Parkinson's disease.

2. The most modern approach is the use of RNA interference or gene silencing to treat *Huntington's disease*. A very small piece of dsRNA (called interferring RNA) is used to degrade the mRNA produced by defective genes which cause the disease. The protein which causes the disease is not produced.
3. New gene therapy approach repairs errors in mRNA derived from defective genes. Technique has potential to treat the blood disorder thalassemia, cystic fibrosis and some cancers.
4. Gene therapy for treating children with X-SCID (Severe combined immuno-deficiency) or the "**Bubble boy**" disease is now stopped as the treatment caused leukemia in one of the patients (in Oct 2002).
5. Gene therapy in mice is successfully done to treat sickle cell anaemia.

### 24.9.6 Weismann Barrier

U.S. Food and Drug Administration defined a "transgenic animal" as an aminal which is altered by the introduction of recombinant DNA through human intervention. This includes two classes of animals; those with **heritable germline** DNA alterations and those with **somatic non-heritable** alterations. Examples of the first class include animals with germline DNA altered through methods requiring *ex vivo* manipulation of gametes or early embryonic stages or embryonic stem cell lines. Examples of the second class include animals with somatic cell DNA alterations achieved through gene therapy approaches, such as, direct plasmid DNA injection or virally mediated gene transfer.

Somatic cell gene therapy involved replacing a defective gene with a healthy gene in order to alleviate a disease. With this type of gene therapy the replaced gene would only affect the host not inherited by the next generation because it would die when the host died.

Germline gene therapy concerned with genetic changes which would be transmitted from the patient to their children because it affected the germ cells (sperms or ovum).

The work of 19th century biologist August Weismann was an early step in the founding of the science of genetics, and like any part of any science is subject to review in light of new data. Athough the principle was seriously questioned at times in the 20th century, the research of Paul Krammerer and Trofim Lysenko failed to weaken the principle among the greater scientific community.

The Weismann barrier is the principle that "**hereditary information moves only from germline genes to body cells but never in reverse.**" In more precise terminology hereditary information moves only from germline to somatic cell. But soma to germline feedback is impossible.

This theory is very important as it has implications for human gene therapy. If the Weismann barrier is not permeable, then genetic treatments of somatic cells may actually result in an inheritable change to the genome, resulting in a change in an individual.

**Criticism :** In the late 20th century there have been criticisms of an impermeable Weismann barrier.

1. *Horizantal gene transfer* : This also called **lateral gene transfer**, is the natural transfer of DNA from one species to an unrelated species, especially interkingdom gene transfer. If a certain gene is present in the genome of all individuals of all species and if it is confirmed that it is a case of horizantal gene transfer, then the gene must has

passed the Weismann barrier. Direct uptake of foreign genetic material by the germ line is suggested by the evidence. Bushman (2002) used the term "**germ-line tropism**". It is seemed that some retroviruses are able to insert themselves in the germline and that integrated gene (DNA) can become part of the gene pool of that species. Such endogenous retroviruses have been demonstrated in mice pigs and humans. They originate from retroviral infection of germ-line cell, followed by a stable integration in the genome of the species.

2. *Immune system* : A controversial theory of Edward J Steeles suggests that endogenous retroviruses carry new versions of V-genes from soma cells in the immune system to the germ-line cells.
3. *Other experiments* : Mohan Raizada *et al.* at the University of Florida have delivered a therapeutic gene, inserted in a modified virus into the hearts of rat that are predisposed to high blood pressure and these rats as well as two subsequent generations were protected from hypertension. The notion is that the AT1R-AS is integrated into the parental genome and is transmitted to the offspring. The possibilities that lack of a blood-gonadal barrier and the presence of significant numbers of undifferentiated germ cells in the neonatal rat cannot be ruled out.

   A report on Human Inheritable Genetic Modifications published on Sept 2000 by the American Association for the Announcement of Science stated that it is very likely that some of the adult gene therapy trials in the US have had unintentional impacts on germ lines. According to Normal Nevin, Chairman of governments' Gene Therapy Advisory Committee "a proposal for *in utereo* gene therapy is unlikely to be approved, because of the risk of accidentally introducing germline changes.

## 24.10 VECTORS FOR GENE DELIVERY SYSTEM IN GENE THERAPY

### 24.10.1 Concept

A carrier molecule called a **vector** must be used to carry the therapeutic gene and to deliver it to the target cells of the patient. An ideal vector system would have some following characteristics.

1. The vector must have an adequate carrying capacity.
2. This is to be undetectable by the immune system
3. It would be non-inflammable.
4. It would be safe with preexisting lung inflammation.
5. It must have long duration of expression and/or have the ability to be safely readministered.

The vectors of gene transfer may be of viral or non viral type. The pros and cons of these vectors are as follows.

**Pros of viral vectors :**

1. High transduction efficiency.
2. Having an ability to infect different cells.
3. Evolved mechanisms for endosomal escape.
4. Natural transportation mechanism of DNA into nucleus.

**Cons of viral vectors :**

1. May cause strong immune reactions against viral proteins prohibit multiple adminsitration.
2. Possibility of chromosomal insertion and proto-oncogene activation.
3. Complicated synthesis process.
4. Limitation of delivered gene size.

5. Toxicity and contamination of live viruses.

**Pros of non-viral vectors :**

1. Having low immunogenicity
2. Can be made to be non-toxic
3. Easy to synthesize and having a chance of quality control for mass production
4. Potentially targetable.
5. No limit on plasmid size.
6. No integration
7. Can be administered as drug

**Cons of nonviral vectors :**

1. Low transfection efficiency.
2. Currently most vehicles are toxic at high doses.
3. No natural tropism, endosomal escape or nuclear transport mechanisms.

## 24.10.2 Viral vectors

- **RNA Viruses :**

RNA retroviruses are used for the transfer of gene during gene therapy. Examples of such viruses are

1. Murine leukemia virus (MuLV)
2. Human immunodeficiency virus (HIV)
3. Human T-cell lymphotropic virus (HTLV)

Retroviruses efficiently integrate the genetic material and only a single copy of the provirus at a given chromosomal site and rearrangement of the host genome are not introduced.

The main problem is that this gene can be inserted into an arbitrary position, say, within the important gene of the genome and may cause **insertional mutagenesis**. This may cause uncontrolled cell division and cancer.

For the integration of genes into the cell or embryo by retroviruses, following criteria may be used.

1. The oncogenic part and the deleterious part of the retroviral genome should be eliminated.
2. The foreign gene is expressed under the control of the strong viral promoter located at the sequence called long terminal repeat (LTR)
3. The recombinant molecule would be transported to a special packaging cell line that harbours an integrated provirus with all its genes intact but lacking the sequence recognised by the packaging apparatus. Otherwise the virus particles produced by provirus may assemble to produce infectious virus particles and be removed from the cell.

**Advantages of using retroviruses**

1. Acts as replication-defective gene transfer vector.
2. Long term expression of transgene (stable)
3. Randomly integrated into genome
4. Wide host range
5. Viral gene promoter also controls the expression of transgene.
6. High efficiency of infection (transduction)
7. Insert size upto 8 kb.
8. Viral genes absent.
9. Well studied system.

**Disadvantages of retroviruses as vector**

1. Integration is random and even cause insertional mutagenesis
2. It has a capacity to carry therapeutic gene is small.
3. Infectivity is limited to dividing cells.
4. Inactivation by complement cascades of our immune system.
5. Safety
6. Low titers ($10^5 - 10^7$/ml)

- **DNA virus vectors :**

Except retroviruses, several DNA viruses have been found suitable as vectors for gene therapy. These are

1. Adenoviruses
2. Adeno-associated viruses (AAV)
3. Herpes simplex virus (HSV)
4. Pox viruses.

**(a) Adenoviruses as delivery system :** Adeno-viruses are dsDNA viruses, cause rspiratory, intestinal and eye infections in humans.

When these viruses infect a host cell, they introduce their DNA molecules into the host, but its genetic material is not integrated into the gènome, only left free in the cell cytoplasm. This DNA molecule transcribes like a gene of the host cell, but not replicated. Therefore, the descendant cells do not have this adenoviral gene. Therefore, readministration is required. For its use in gene therapy certain changes may have to be done.

1. Replication - deficient adenovirus vectors can be generated by replacing $E_1$ or $E_3$ gene which is essential for replication.
2. The recombinant vectors are then replicated in cells that express the products of the $E_1$ and $E_3$ genes and can be generated in very high concentrations.
3. Cells infected with recombinant adenovirus can express the therapeutic gene, but because essential genes for replication are deleted, the vectors can not replicate

**Advantages of the use of adenoviruses**

1. They have high transduction efficiency
2. Produce high expression of therapeutic genes.
3. Do not integrate into host chromosome
4. Infect replicating and nonreplicating both types of cells.
5. High viral titer ($10^{10}$ – $10^{12}$/ml)
6. Insert gene size more than 30 kb.

**Disadvantages of the use of adenoviruses**

1. Viral genes must be in vector
2. Induce immune respone in the host body.
3. Viral proteins can be expressed in host following vector administration.
4. Viral DNA does not integrate into the host genome.
5. Do not produce long term gene expression.

**(b) Adenoasociated viruses :** These are the classes of ssDNA viruses that can insert their genetic material at a specific site on chromosome-19.

**Advantages of the use of AAV**

1. These are not associated with diseases
2. Can obtain high titered virus stocks ($10^9$–$10^{10}$/ ml)
3. Having small genome that is easy to manipulate.
4. They integrate into a specific region of the human genome at chromosome 19
5. The integration is stable.
6. They infect both dividing and nondividing cells.
7. Contain no viral genes and have no immunity problems.

**Disadvantages of the use of AAV**

1. Difficult to obtain large viral stocks
2. Small capacity of gene sequence, only 4.5 kb of DNA.

### 24.10.3 Non-viral vectors

Non-viral vectors can be divided into two broad classes which can use two methods of delivery — physical method and chemical methods.

**Physical methods** involve taking plasmids and forcing them into the cell by electroporation, microinjection, ultrasound sonication or particle bombardment.

**Chemical methods** use lipids polymers or proteins that will complexed with DNA, condensing it into particles and directing it into the cells.

1. **Microinjection :** This is carried out by intramuscular injection of a naked DNA plasmid But the expression has been very low.
2. **Electroporation :** Short electrical pulses of high field strength are used to increase the permeability of the plasma membrane and facilitate entry of DNA into the cell if DNA is in contact with the membrane.
3. **Particle bombardment :** Some microprojectiles are made by tungsten or gold particles coated with DNA are accelerated to a very high velocity by using a gene gun directly into the cell. This is promising but limited to dermal tissues and has low rate of stable integration.
4. **Liposomes :** Artificial phospholipid vesicles in which DNA is encapsulated. The lipids can fuse with the lipid bilayer of the cell membrane, releasing the DNA inside the cell and the lipid is incorporated. This is highly reproducible and more efficient, non pathogenic, no immunity problem, but low transfection efficiency, low rate of stable integration.

   A number of protocols have been considered for preparing the liposomes for delivery of DNA.

   (a) Sonication may be used to disperse the phospholipids, though it may destroy DNA.

   (b) Anionic lipids such as phosphatidyl serine with $Ca^{++}$ may allow the entrapment of large DNA molecule.

   (c) The fusion proteins of sendai virus may be incorporated which enables fusion of liposome into plasma membrane.

   (d) Liposomes may be incorporated with a protein ligand with DNA may be targeted to the cell surface receptors.

   (e) Antibodies may be attached to liposomes to target cells and also hormone receptors are used for this purpose.
5. **Cationic lipids :** Polycations are hydrophobic long chain cations such as polyethylene glycol (PEG), poly-L-lysine, Poly-L-ornithine or DEAE dextran with or without metal ions such as $Zn^{++}$, Li, $Cs^+$, $K^+$, $Na^+$ or $Mg^{++}$ etc. These are organised into a bilayer micelles. If this structure meets DNA, they recoganize to colloid DNA/lipid complexes. The structure of these complexes depends on the nature of the cationic lipid.
6. **Cationic liposomes :** These are positively charged lipids bind to –vely charged DNA and cause perterbations in the plasma membrane and fuse with it. The DNA then enters into cytoplasm.

   **Advantages :**
   - Form stable complex
   - Can carry large sized DNA
   - Can target to specific cells
   - Does not induce immunological reactions

   **Disadvantages :**
   - Low transfection efficiency
   - Transient expression
   - Inhibited by serum
   - Some cell toxicity.
7. **Calcium phosphate – mediated DNA uptake.** Plasmid DNA is mixed with $CaCl_2$ solution at isotonic phosphate

buffer to precipitate DNA-Ca-phosphate on the surface of the cell. This is then osmotically shocked to facilitate DNA uptake by treatment with polyvinyl alcohol at pH-7 Calcium or dimethyl sulfoxide to encourage endocytotic uptake of precipitate.

This method is suitable for cells growing in monolayers or in suspension, but not those growing as clumps.

Some cell lines are adversely affected by the Ca-precipitate due to its toxicity

## 24.11 GENE THERAPY ON SOME DISEASES

In USA, there is a campaign against abortion and therefore, also against antenatal diagnosis. In such cases, there will be births of defective children and these may become patients for gene therapy.

If a child is diagnosed to carry a defective gene leading to disability, one may like to get this gene replaced by a normal functional gene. This is gene therapy theory. Gene therapy can be used at three different levels, viz. *patient therapy, embryo therapy and germline therapy*. The gene therapy is performed agsinst inherited diseases, tumors and cancer.

### 24.11.1 Patient therapy

Cells with healthy gene may be introduced into the affected tissue so that healthy gene overcomes the defect without affecting the inheritance of the patient. For this purpose several steps are followed.

1. The defective genes should be identified and their dominance or recessiveness should be clearly known.
2. The normal healthy genes of the identified defective genes should be isolated.
3. The normal healthy gene should be placed in the cell into the correct site where it can function.

The main problems of the gene therapy are that, the inherited gene may not function. The corrected cells which were introduced may be out numbered by the defective resident cells.

### 24.11.2 Cancer Gene therapy

First clinical gene transfer was achieved in 1989 in USA. The marker gene *Neo R*(neomycin resistance) introduced into tumor infiltrating lymphocytes and then these cells are transferred into the advanced cancer patients.

Numerous cancer gene therapy trials *ex vivo* as well as *in vivo* are currently being conducted, their objective is to kill the disease cell artifically or by enhancing the immune response.

**For example :**

1. Retroviruses are used to delivery HSV-tk gene for brain tumor, non small cell lung cancer, ovarian cancer therapy.
2. Retroviruses are used to deliver *MDR1* gene for breast cancer, colorectal cancer, renal-cell carcinoma etc.
3. Retroviral *IL-4* gene therapy is used for breast cancer, malignant melanoma, myelogenous leukemia and some tumors.
4. Similarly, *IL2* gene therapy by retroviruses is used in some melanomas and carcinomas.
5. In a few cases, the gene therapy approach has focused on targeting single gene, such as *TP53* gene for the therapy of ovarian cancer and delivery of antisense *KRAS* gene in the case of some forms of non small cell lung cancer.

The strategies of gene therapy for tumors and cancers are targeted to reduce the tumor cells is still 100% success, because if a cell is still remained, the tumor may recur.

1. Usually the lymphocytes infiltrate into the tumor cells called TILs (Tumor-infiltrating lymphocytes). The gene therapy is considered to be a form of adaptive immunotherapy, where a gene encoding a cytokine, tumor necrosis factor -$\alpha$ (TNF-$\alpha$) is transferred to TILs collected from solid tumors by a retrovirus recombinant

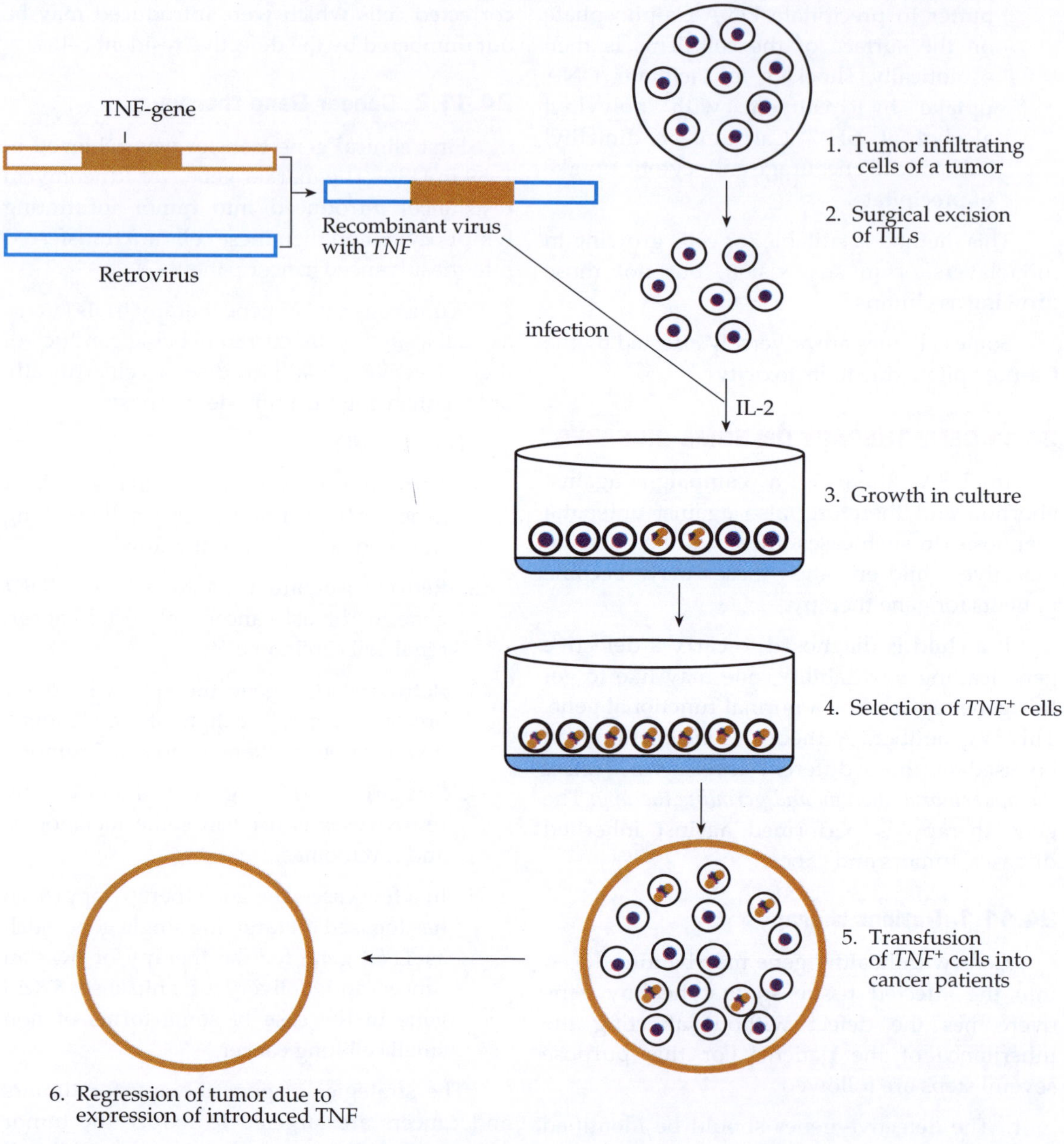


**Fig.24.3 :** *Genetic modification of TILs and gene therapy to such cancer patient.*

vector. Such as infected T-cells acquire increased anti-tumor efficacy and when it is infused in sufficient amount, the tumor cells are destroyed (Fig. 24.3).

2. In another gene therapy protocol, the tumor cells are genetically modified by insertion of interleukins, TNFα, TNF-γ, granulocyte macrophage colony stimulating factor (GM-CSF) and these cells are reimplanted into the tumor. It has been found to regress the tumor.

3. In addition to cytokine genes, other genes such as *foreign HLA antigen* genes have been transferred to tumor genes. *HLA-B7* or *β2 microglobulin* genes have been inserted to the tumors of patient lacking *HLA-B7* by liposomes which will provoke the immune system to destroy the tumor.
4. The fibroblast cells are used for long term tissue culture. *IL-2* and *IL-4* genes are transferred to skin fibroblasts, grown in culture and are used for the treatment of breast cancer, colorectal cancer, melanoma and renal carcinoma.
5. A strategy has been taken for *in vitro* gene therapy for a brain tumor **glioblastoma multiforme**. The retroviral producing cells (VPCs) were implanted into the growing tumor cells using stereotatic MRI. This retrovirus transfers a gene encoding a "prodrug" Herpes Simplex Thymidine kinase (HSV -tk) into tumor cells. This reagent confers sensitivity to the drug "gancyclovir" and converts into its mono-phosphorylated form *gcv-P*. Then cellular kinases convert it into *gcv-PPP* (triphosphate), which is a potent inhibitor to DNA polymerase. The replication is inhibited and ultimately lead to death of the cell. The adjacent cells that have not taken up that *HSV-tk* gene may also be distroyed. This effect is called *by-stander effect*. Possibly, this effect is due to diffusion of *gcv-PPP* through gap junctions to the neighbouring cells.

### 24.11.3 Gene therapy for inherited diseases

1. The first apparently successful gene therapy was initiated in 1990, the patient was a 4 years old girl, a named Ashanthi De Silva, was suffering from a recessively inherited disease ADA (adenosine deaminase deficiency). The ADA patients suffer from severe combined immuno-deficiency (SCID). The gene is very small and easy to culture. Thus it enables *ex vivo* gene therapy. By this method the $ADA^-$ lymphocytes are infected with retroviral recombinant ADA normal genes. Thus $ADA^-$ lymphocytes are changed into $ADA^+$ cells. These $ADA^+$ cells are selected by an appropriate selectable markers (such as neomycin-resistance) in retrovirus. Suitable $ADA^+$ cells are cultured and reintroduced into the patient. This is actually a treatment, not a cure. At present a dozen of such trials have been done in USA, Itali and other places.
2. For the treatment of human *galactosemia disease* by genetic engineering, C.R.Merril M.R. Geiger and J. C Petricciani (1971) have treated human fibroblast cells from a galactosemia heterozygote in tissue culture with phage bearing the *gal* operon from bacterial cells and found what appeared to be enzyme activity in the fibroblasts which persisted throughout cell divisions. This indicates that bacterial bacteriophage DNA can enter human cells and at least some of the DNA can undego replication and transcription in human cells.
3. *Familial hypercholesterolemia* is a disorder caused by a dominantly inherited deficiency of LDL (low density lipoprotein) receptors which are normally synthesized in the liver and is characterised by premature coronary artery disease. The death occurs by severe myocardial infraction in late childhood. The pathogenecity is due to missense mutation in the *LDLR* gene. The gene therapy involved surgical removal of a portion of the left lobe of the patient's liver. These cells are infected with retrovirus containing a normal *LDLR* gene. These genetically modified cells were then infused back into the patient with a catheter through the portal vein and implanted into liver. Such gene therapy improved the patient for a long period (Grossman *et. al.*, 1994).

**Fig.24.4 :** *R. Michael Blaese, MD with AshanthiDeSilva (left) and Cindy Kisik at the IDF 2013 National Conference, June 29*

4. *Cystic fibrosis (CF)* is an autosomal recessive disease. The defect of this gene causes the defective transport of chloride ions through epithelial cells of lung . The gene is *CFTR* which encodes a cAMP regulated chloride channel. The lung tissue culture method is not known, therefore adenovirus vectors or liposomes are used to carry this gene. The gene with adenoviruses have been transferred to the lung epithelium *in vivo.* Though liposome-based gene therapy trial is used.
5. Duchenne muscular dystrophy (DMD) is a severe disease caused by X-linked recessive gene, the patient suffers from progressive muscle deterioration. Suitable gene therapy approches have been difficult to conceive because muscle cells are at post-mitotic stage and therefore retroviral transfer is impossible. Adenovirus vectors are used to transfer normal gene *in vitro* for their expression to continue over the course of life time of the patient. *DMD* locus is Xp21.

### 24.11.4 Germline Gene therapy

To insert a new gene into a fertilized ovum (zygote) and modify the body of the offspring and their discendants and also by this technique some genetic diseases are corrected by elimination of the deleterious genes, is called germline gene therapy. Therefore, germline gene therapy would seek to eliminate "bad" genes from the population. Germline gene therapy is inheritable.

At the present time, technical difficulties prevent even the consideration of germ cell gene therapy in humans.

1. *In vitro* fertilization of the ovum is essential. For that purpose numerous eggs are required for *in vitro* manupulation and only a small percentage of these would survive in each required step : genetic alteration, fertilization, selection and implantation.
2. The insertion of normal gene into embryo takes place at post zygotic level, either directly by microinjection or by the aid of

a virus. But the most difficult aspect is that insertion of DNA (gene) into the specific location of chromosome is obviously impossible.

3. The third problem is that the inserted DNA into host chromosome may have been found to become inactive.
4. As the insertion of gene is random process, it might activate or inactivate certain genes and will cause serious difficulties for the developing embryos.

Therefore, germline gene therapy still now is restricted to mouse, rabbits, fishes and other animals except humans.

Wivel and Walters (1993) stated two possible cases where germline gene therapy might be justified.

1. When both the parents are afflicted with a recessive autosomal disorder, so that 100% of their offspring would be expected to have it. Though this is an exceptionally rare situation.
2. When both the parents are heterozygous for a recesive genetic disorder, they would have a 75% chance of having a phenotypically normal child. Screening can be carried out during pregnancy, followed by selective abortion of fetus if it is found homozygous recessive allele. In these cases germline therapy may be considered as an alternative to abortion.

Wivel and Walter's view is that such monogenetic deficiency deseases as Lesch Nyhan syndrome, Tay-Sachs desease and metachromatic leukodystrophy are the candidates for the types of genetic therapy.

The implications of germ cell gene therapy are tremendous, far greater than those of somatic cell gene therapy. By this, it become possible to correct for a whole host of genetic diseases including cystic fibrosis phenylketoneuria and Tay-Sachs diseases. Daniel Koshland (past editor in chief of the journal "*Science*") expressed that if a child destined to have permanently low IQ could be replaced by a gene, to become a normal child, why do we argue against it? The improvement would produce "Super indivuduals". In a recent symposium on Engineering the Human Genome (UCLA, 1998), J. D. Watson was explicit about using gene therapy technique for enhancement "I mean, if we could make better human beings by knowning how to add genes, why shouldn't we do it?"

The arguments against germline gene therapy come from several sources. Dranks (1994) has been found a very little medical good coming from germ-line gene therapy. He thought that

1. There are very few candidates for such a procedure
2. The homozygous recessive parents are rare.
3. In case of two heterozygous parents may include *in vitro* fertilizations which may discard several viable embyos and also able to identify those embryos which are not at risk.
4. During germline gene therapy. There might even lead to mutations, because the insertion of gene is random and not to a particular location in the egg.
5. To achieve heritable correction, it will be necessary to achieve replacement of the defective gene by the inserted gene and this has not yet been possible.

## 24.12 EUPHENICS

The symptomatic treatment of genetic diseases of human is called *euphenics*, which deals with the control of several inherited diseases in human, espectially inborn errors of metabolism in which the missing of defective enzyme has been identified.

1. Phenylketoneuria is determined by an autosomal recessive gene. Babies are unable to metabolise properly an amino acid phenylalanine and once the child is

detected, a diet free of phenylalanine is imposed and the child can develop normally.

2. One possible measure for the future would be to supply the known missing enzyme to individuals that would allow their cells to complete the required biochemical reaction. Some attempts have been made but immunological difficulties made it unsuccessful.
3. Scientists studying the two anaemias of human, one is thalassemia and other is Lapore anaemia in homozygous mutations at β-chain locus of globin gene. Hope that they will discover the factors regulating the β-chain activity and thereby increasing the amount of β-chain synthesis.
4. If the mechanism regulating Hb synthesis in the fetus and the adult can be discerned, they might be able to cure lethal conditions such as thalassemia and sickle cell anaemia by suppressing the abonormal β-chains and allowing fetal γ-chain to be produced instead.
5. Cancer and heart diseases are thought to have some heritable components. A.K. Altman (1972) has shown that heart disease may be inherited as an autosomal dominant trait and those have such incidence in the family they may take care to their life habits such as refrain from smoking and avoid high fat diet.

## 24.13 STEM CELL AND GENE THERAPY

### 24.13.1 Introduction

Stem cells have the ability to give rise to specialized cells, which can differentiate and make specific organs of the body. These cells are also known as **master cells**, as they get differentiated into different cell types and are the fundamental building blocks for all tissues in the body. They get differentiated into blood, brain, muscle, skin and all other tissues.

Stem cells are of three types : totipotent, pluripotent and multipotent, each representing a different stage in cell development.

A fertilized cell is considered to be a **totipotent**, meaning that it's potential is total, it can give rise to all the different types of cells in the body. If this zygote divides into two cells and separate them, each would develop a full grown embryo and ultimately into adult. So 2-called stage is also totipotent.

The inner cell mass of the blastocyst contains **pluripotent** cells, which can capable of developing into any tissue in the body except those needed to develop a fetus.

Stem cells that can give rise to multiple different cell types are generally called **multipotent cells**. These cells are found in mature tissues and are formed by body to replace worn out cells in tissues and organs.

Stem cells isolated from human embryos are called *human embryonic stem cells.* The technique of isolating and growing such cells in the laboratory was discovered in 1988. The embryos from which human embryonic stem cells are derived are typically four or five days old and are a hollow microsopic ball of cells called the blastocyst. The blastocyst includes three structures the **trophoblast**, which is the layer of cells that surronds the blastocyst, the **blastocoel** which is a hollow cavity inside the blastocyst and the **inner cell mass**, which is a group of approximately 30 cells at one end of the blastocoel. The inner cell mass gives rise to the hundreds of highly specialised cells to make up an adult organisms (Fig. 24.5).

At present human pluripotent cell lines have been developed from many sources.

1. **Special pupose embryos :** Embryos are created through *in vitro* fertilization for the sole purpose of extracting their stem cells.
2. **Cloned embryos :** Embryos are cloned in labs using somatic cell nucelar transfer (SCNT) method for harvesting their stem

cells. This has been tried only on animals till now. It this, enucleated animal egg is fused with a normal somatic cell. The fused cell is totipotent in nature and by cell division, it soon forms blastocysts from which stem cells can be removed.

3. **Aborted fetuses :** Stem cells are taken from fetuses in early development that have been aborted.
4. **Umbilical cord :** Umbilical cord blood contains **neonatal stem cells** which are pluripotent. These cells can be harvested during parturition. The procedure for collecting cord blood is painless and poses no threat to the baby or the mother. Immediately after a baby is born, the umbilical cord is clamped which serves the link between the baby and the placenta. Soon after the neonate is separated from placenta the latter is placed in a sterile supporting structures in such a manner that the umbilical cord hangs through the support. A four to eight inch long umbilical cord is cleaned with alcohol. Blood is then drawn by inserting a needle into the umbilical vein. The blood flows into the sterile blood bag cavity and that completes the blood collection. Approximately 100 ml of blood can be collected from the placenta. It is then tested for the diseases and usability. The stem cells may be spun out of the collected blood and saved cryogenically for later use. Cryopreservation is done in frozen state storage combined with cryoprotectant substance formulated to protect the cells from damage during freezing and subsequent thawing cycles. These cells remain frozen at –196°C and can be stored for several years.
5. **Adult tissues or organs :** Stem cells are obtained from adult tissues, particularly from bone marrow or peripheral blood stem cell. Gearhart and Thompson identified and isolated stem cells from human fetuses had the same surface proteins as teratocarcinoma cells and confirmed their common origin. Teratocarcinoma is the wrong type of tissue in the wrong place. Muscle cells in the brain or gut cells in the heart are the examples. Researchers found that these stem cells under various conditions, coax the cells into growing mature tissues resembling gut, neurons and cartilages. Thus it has been proved that these are pluripotent stem cells.
6. **Cadavers :** Isolation and survival of neuron progenitor cells from human post-mortem tissues (up to 20 hrs after death) have been reported and provide the additional source of human stem cell.

### 24.13.2 Culturing Stem cells

Stem cells are artificially grown in a laboratory by employing cell culture techniques. Human embryonic stem cells are isolated by transferring the inner cells mass from the blastocyst, into a culture dish. It contains the usual culture medium that is used in the tissue culture. The inner surface of the dish is typically coated with mouse embryonic skin cells that have been treated so that they will not divide. This coating layer of cells is called a feeder layer. This cell layer on the botton of the culture dish gives the inner cell mass cells a sticky surface to which they anchor. Furthermore, these feeder cells release nutrients into the culture medium. But the demerits are that there is a risk of viruses or other macromolecules in the mouse cells that may be transmitted to the stem cells in culture.

However, now the scientists have devised the ways of growing embryonic stem cells without this mouse feeder cells. Polystyrene, PVC, polycarbonate, teflon, thermanox etc. layers are used for this purpose. The substrate surface may be treated to improve cell attachment by purified fibronectin or collagen.

Over a course of several days the cells of the inner cell mass proliferate and begin to crowd the culture dish.

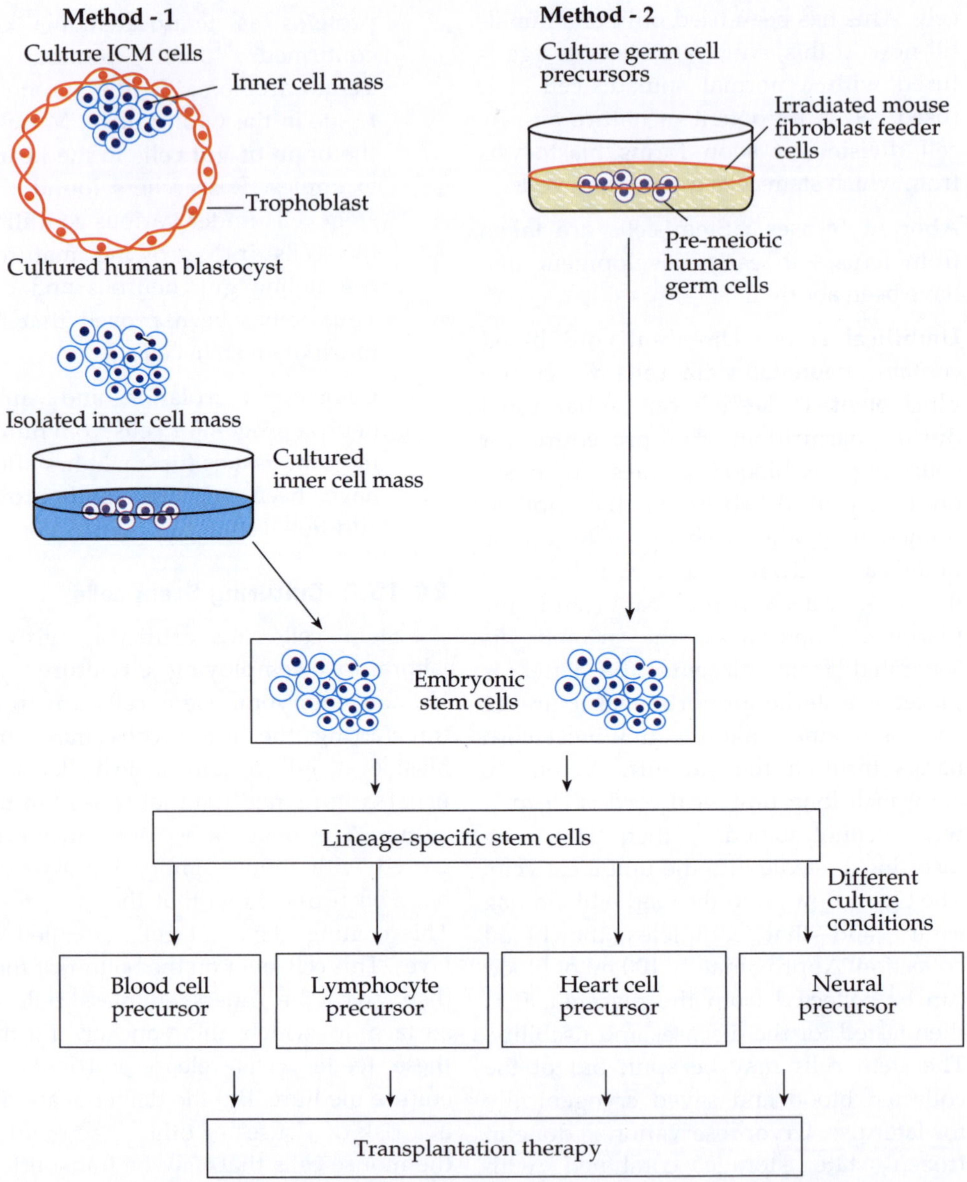


**Fig.24.5 :** *Schematic diagram of stem cell transplantation therapy*

These are then removed gently into several fresh sub-cultuers and the process is repeated many times. After six months or more, the original few cells of inner cell mass yield millions of embryonic stem cells. These cells would be pluripotent in nature and genetically alike. Therefore these are referred to as an embryonic stem cell-line. These may be cryopreserved for future use.

### 24.13.3 Testing Stem cells

Before any use of the preserved stem cell, it is evident to test these cells whether it is absolutely fit for the purpose; These tests include :

1. It ensures that the cells are capable of long term self-renewal and they look healthy and remain undifferentiated.
2. Another important test is that the presence of a protein called Oct-4, which the undifferentiated cells typically make. Oct-4 is a transcription factor, helps the genes turn on or off at the right time.
3. Any chromosomal damage present in these stem cells certainly be examined under microscope. This damage cause genetic changes in the cells.
4. The cells are again cultured even after freezing, thawing and replating.
5. The cells must be examined whether the cells are still pluripotent or not. This is done by allowing the cells to differentiate spontaneously in the cell culture or manipulating the cells so they will differentiate to form specific cell-types, or injecting the cells into a immuno-suppressed mouse to test for the formation of a benign tumor called teratoma.

### 24.13.4 Problems with Embryonic Stem cells

Embryonic stem cells are pluripotent, it does not mean that they will perform on command. In cells, a battery of options and factors control their differentiation. Growth factors, compressive and/or twisting movements, electrical charges coupled with the unique chemical cocktail of the embryonic tissue provide cues and impetus to the stem cell. Under these influences, an entire cascade of genes is switched on or off, shaping the embryo.

Actually in cultures, the ESC materializes as *"embryoid bodies"* teratocarcinoma which happens to occur when ESCs linger latent in the body, undetected and non-interfering till one day; some cellular trigger-kick starts their dormant mechanism. Their pluripotent nature comes to force and soon they are out of control and the tissues are developed in the wrong places.

Basically, ESC research depends on the knowledge about growth factors. For example, retinoic acid for neuron transformation, BMP4 for muscle and tendon cells etc. But the rate of transformation is low. So during ESC therapy, correct combination and correct order of application coupled with proper interplay of physical forces are to be maintained. Joel Greenberger and RY Houck at University of Pittsburgh Medical Center, USA, have devised a robitised system by means of which growth factors can be evaluated. Image analysis software plus automated cell sampling and monitoring (shape, growth, surface protein, genes turn off or on) have been already identified for growth factors needed to make the hematopoietic stem cells pass through several cell divisions without becoming specialized.

The human pluripotent stem cells derived from embryo would be genetically different from the recipient. Hence, tissue incompatibility and immune rejection would definitely be a major problem. Besides storing of ESC becomes aged. Modern genetic engineering creates an "Universal" cell that would applicable to all. SCNT may be a way to overcome this problem. In this process the nucleus of the donor egg is removed, so all the genetic material in the blastocyst subsequently formed would come from the patient and the question of immune rejection would not rise.

### 24.13.5 Working with Adult Stem cell

A lot of ethical and moral questions are being raised against the use of embryonic/fetal stem cell research because the removing the inner cell mass, to some one seems to a murder. Adult stem cell thus becomes alternative to fetal stem cells.

Adult stem cells have to be de-differentiated to get a clean state. Stem cells from adults have not been isolated for all tissues of the body. Cardiac stem cells or pancreatic islets stem cells in humans have not been isolated yet.

Adult stem cells are often present in only very miniscule quantities. Moreover, these are very difficult to isolate and purify. With age, this miniscule number also starts decreasing. This is particularly true in the case of neuronal stem cell.

In some adult tissues such as bone marrow, muscle and brain, discrete populations of adult stem cells generate replacements for cells that are lost through normal wear and tear, injury or disease. A number of experiments over the last several years have raised the possibility that stem cells from one tissue may be able to give rise to cell types of a completely different tissue, a phenomenon known as *plasticity*. For example, blood cells becoming neurons, liver cells that can be made to insulin producing Langarhan's cells, hematopoietic stem cells can develop into heart muscle etc.

The adult stem cells contain more DNA abnormality, caused by sunlight, toxins and defects in replication which may be acquired during the course of lifetime. This weakness might limit the usefulness of adult stem cells.

The potential advantage of using stem cells from an adult is that patient's own cells could be expanded in culture and then reintroduced into the patient. The use of patient's own adult stem cell would mean that the cells would not be rejected by the immune system. This represents a significant advantage, as immune rejection is a difficult problem that can only be circumvented with immunosuppressive drugs.

### 24.13.6 Transfer of Gene into Stem cells

Gene therapy aims to deliver genetic materials to the appropriate cells of the patient in a specific, efficient and safe manner. Genes need to be targeted at the nuclei of the cells. This is done best through the delivery vehicles called vectors.

Currently attenuated or modified versions of viruses are used as vectors. Viruses have a natural ability to target and deliver their genetic cargo into the host cells. Most commonly, retroviruses, adenoviruses and adnoassociated viruses are used for the delivery of genetic material into human cells.

Before these viruses are employed for gene therapy, their disease-causing components must be removed. The correct copy of the gene is then inserted into the virus which is now act as vectors. The modified viruses cannot reproduce in the patient but retain the ability to deliver the genetic material.

Liposomes, proteins and complexes of DNA are also used efficiently for transferring genes.

Before using retroviruses as a cloning vector, several modifications are required. First, the retrovirus must be able to accept a nonviral gene and incorporate it into the viral RNA. Second, any deleterious genes in the retrovirus must be removed or inactivated. Third, to maintain the transferred gene inside a host cell, the ability of the retrovirus to replicate should be destroyed so that no new viral particles are created and the host cell remains intact.

But the problem is that retroviral vectors are able to carry only relatively small pieces of RNA and the host cell must be actively dividing in order for viral DNA to be incorporated into its chromosome.

### 24.13.7 *Ex vivo*, *In situ* and *In vivo* Gene therapy

There are several ways of using somatic gene therapy, one of which is *ex vivo* or outside human body" strategy. In this approach, a few cells are taken from the patients body and are artificially grown in the laboratory. They are incubated with vectors to introduce in them with healthy genes, after which they are reintroduced into the patient. As the vector inserts the genetic material with the therapeutic gene into the diseased cells the latter begin producing the missing proteins and thus start behaving normal. This strategy is mainly used for blood cells, because many genetic defects after the functioning of one or more types of these cells. But blood cells have a limited life span. Hence, corrected cells slowly disappear necessitating periodic treatment.

Another way to use somatic cell gene therapy is *in situ* treatment. In this method, genes are introduced directly into the tissue where they are needed. *In situ* treatment is used for several diseases. Persons suffering from cystic fibrosis have impaired lungs, caused by a defective gene. In such a case, the healthy genes could be directly introduced into the bronclial linings of the impaired lungs of the patients. Similarly, inserting specific genes directly into the muscle tissue could treat muscular distrophy. The *in situ* treatment is not yet fully safe for public use, as genes are inserted randomly into various body tissues.

The more practical approach for gene therapy is called *in vivo* or "in the body" gene therapy, involves the direct applications of retroviral vectors to human tissue. However this therapy has not been very successful. In the treatment of cystic fibrosis, attenuated versions of adenoviruses are being used.

### 24.13.8 Applications of stem cell Gene therapy

An application of stem cell research is to improve our understanding of the basic processes that take place in normal cell development in order to better remedy the errors, in these processes, that occur in diseases like cancer, and birth defects and also screening new drugs and toxins.

The potential therapeutic applications of stem cells can be expanded through genetic modifications to produce enzymes or factors such as insulin, before being transplanted into the body. Stem cells can also be modified to resist certain infections. For example, studies underway to create stem cells resistant to HIV. Once implanted, these stem cells would repopulate the diseased immune system of AIDS patients with cells resistant to the disease. Genetic modification can reduce the risk of transplant rejection between individuals and between species.

Stem cells offer the opportunity of transplanting a live source for self-recognition. Bone marrow transplants (BMTs) are the well known clinical applications of stem cell transplantation. BMT can repopulate the marrow and restore all the different cell types of the blood after high doses of chemotherapy and/or radiotherapy, our main defense used to eliminate endogenous cancer cells.

Stem cells are progenitor cells which are now being developed for many clinical applications. Some are described below :

1. **Skin replacement :** Keratinocyte stem cells reside in the hair follicle and can be removed when a hair is plucked. These cells are cultured to form an epidermal cells and provide tissue for an autologous graft. There is no problem of rejection. Such surgical grafts may be used for various ulcers and burn victims.

2. **Brain cell transplantations :** Neural stem cells are now being locatized in both embryonic and adult tissues. Potential targets of neural stem cell transplants include storke, spinal cord injugy, some neurodegenerative diseases such as Parkinson's disease, Alzhaimer's disease etc.

   Parkinsons' disease involves the loss of cells that produce the neurotransmitter dopamine. Fetal cell transplantation of stem cells for Parkinson's diseases has been reported to produce dopamine. Though some side effects have been recorded but further studies are needed and onging.

3. **Treatment for diabetes :** Normally, insulin is produced and secreted by cellular structures called β–cells of the islets of Langerhans in the pancreas. Insulin expressing cells from mouse stem cells have been generated and are self assembled to produce a structure resembling pancreatic islets to produce insulin. These synthetic islets may utilize for the treatment of diabetic patients.

4. **Treatment for heart and kidney diseases :** In February 2002, scientists had

successfully transplanted kidney–like organs in cows. They had created a cloned cow embryo and allowed to develop into fetus. Then they harvested fetal tissue from the clones and transplanted it into the donor cows, In the three months of observation following transplantation, no signs of rejection were observed in the transplant recipient.

Professor Loren Field of Indiana University School of Medicine (USA) and her colleagues and another team of scientists at Standford University School of Medicine in California (USA) have injected stem cells in hearts of mice that have suffered from a heart attack. They announced an improvement in how their hearts pumped blood and speculated that instead to changing into heart muscle cells as had been hoped, the stem cells may have helped the damaged heart by recruiting new blood vessels to help heart muscle cells that would have otherwise died. It is fact that stem cells failed to turn into heart muscle cells.

The promise of stem cell therapy and gene therapy is an exciting one, but significant technical hurdles remain that will only be overcome through years of intensive research.

## Chapter Glossary/Key Terms

**Amniocentesis :** The technique of sampling amniotic fluid to determine genetic abnormalities by the presence of certain chemicals or defective fetal cells.

**Antenatal diagnosis :** Genetic testing of the fetus to know the condition of the future child for selective abortion of the affected fetus.

**Blastocoel :** The fluid-filled cavity in the blastula.

**Chorion :** An outermost extra embryonic membrane of amniotes. It contains ectoderm and somatic layer of mesodern and surrounds the whole embryonic symtems of embryo. In placental mammals it contributes to the structure of placenta.

**Chorionic villus sampling (CVS) :** Sampling a tiny portion of the fetal part of the placenta to determine genetic or congenital defects.

**Enzyme-linked immunosorbent assay (ELISA) :** The technique of detecting very small amounts of specific proteins utilizing antibodies linked to enzymes that catalyze the formation of coloured products.

**Eugenics :** Controlling the gene pool of human species by selective breeding, "the science of improving human stock by giving more suitable races prevailing speedily over the less suitable".

*Contd.*

***Ex vivo* gene therapy :** Gene therapy involving the removal of affected cells from a patient, correction of the genetic defect, then reintroduction of the corrected cells into the patient.

**Gene therapy :** Adding genetic materal to a person so that a defect or disease can be corrected to date, applied only to somatic cells in humans.

**Genetic counseling :** A medical speciality with responsibility for educating people about genetic diseases treatments and potential reproductive choices.

**Genetic diagnosis :** Method used to determine whether a particular genetic defect is present in an individual.

**Genetic screening :** Highly organized attempts to use accurate and reliable genetic diagnostic tests on a specific target groups of genetic disorders.

**Karyotyping :** A method of photographing the complete set of chromosomes for a particular cell type and organizing them into homologous pairs based on size and shape.

**Lateral gene transfer :** Movement of genes sideways between unrelated species.

**Masturbation :** Hand manipulation of semen by mechanical way from the male reproductive organs.

**Probe :** Defined DNA or RNA fragment radioactively or chemically labeled that is used to detect specific nucleic acid sequence by hybridization.

**Restriction enzyme :** An endonuclease that cleaves DNA at the specific sequence.

**Restriction fragment length polymorphism (RFLP) :** A difference in restriction fragment length between very similar DNA molecules; RFLP analysis is used to detect relatively small differences between DNA molecules used in DNA typing and genetic disease detection.

**Semen :** Product of male reproductive system, includes sperm and sperm-carrying fluid.

**Severe combined immunodeficiency disease (SCID) :** A genetic disease characterized by a deficient immune system and caused by defective gene for the enzyme adenosine deaminase (ADA).

**Stem cells :** Cells from which differentiated cells derive.

**Trophoblast :** The outer wall of the mammalian blastocyst, concerned with nutrition of embryo within.

**Tumor infiltrating lymphocytes (TILS) :** T cells that can invade and distroy turmors.

# EXERCISE

## A. Long answer type questions :

1. Write a note on eugenics.
2. What is ART? Give the names of different types of ART.
3. What is IVF? What are the causes of male and female infertility that can be treated with IVF? How the assessment of the female patient can be done?
4. Describe different steps of IVF technique.
5. What are the problems and success rates of IVF?
6. What is ICSI.
7. What are the male factor infertility causes?
8. Describe different steps of ICSI.
9. What is PZD and SUZI.

10. Describe the GIFT technique.
11. Describe ZIFT, OCT and IVC.
12. What are the ethical problems of ART?
13. What do you mean by genetic testing? What are its applications and limitations?
14. What is genetic counseling? What are the criteria for a genetic counseling?
15. What do you mean by prenatal diagnosis?
16. Describe the procedure, safety, outcome and applications of amniotcentesis?
17. Write a note on CVS.
18. Write a note on embryonic diagnosis and adult diagnosis.
19. Write a note on genetic scrcening.
20. What is gene therapy? What is its objective? What are the strategies of somatic cell gene therapy?
21. What factors kept gene therapy away from an effective treatment for genetic diseases?
22. What is the current status of gene therapy research?
23. Write a note on Weismann barrier.
24. What are the vectors for gene delivery system in gene therapy.
25. What are the pros and cons of viral and nonviral vectors for gene delivery?
26. What kinds of viral vectors are used for gene delivery.
27. What are the advantages and disadvantages of retroviruses as vectors for gene delivery in gene therapy?
28. What kinds of DNA virus vectors are used for gene delivery?
29. What are the advantages and disadvantages of adenoviruses and AAV as vectos for gene delivery in gene therapy?
30. What are the nonviral vectors used in gene delivery in gene therapy?
31. Write a notes on liposome-mediated gene delivery in gene therapy?
32. What do you mean by patient therapy? Write a note on cancer gene therapy.
33. Give some benefits of gene therapy for inherited diseases.
34. What is germline gene therapy? What are the technical difficulties faced in germline gene therapy?
35. Why germline gene therapy restricted to animals?
36. What are the cases where germline gene therapy may be justified?
37. What are the arguments against germline gene therapy?
38. Write a note an euphanics.
39. What do you mean by stem cell? What are their sources? How the stem cells are cultured?
40. Why and how stem cells are tested for stem cell therapy?
41. What are the problems of gene therapy with embryomic stem cells?
42. What do you mean by adult stemcell? What is the potential advantages of such stem cells in gene therapy.
43. Describe different techniques for the transfer of genes into stem cells.
44. Write a note on *ex vivo* and *in vivo* gene therapy.
45. Briefly describe the applications of stem cell gene therapy.

**B. Short answer type questions :**

1. Define eugenics.
2. What are positive engenics and negative eugenics?
3. What are the objectives of eugenics?
4. What is ART? What are the objectives?
5. Who was the first IVF baby?
6. What kinds of male and female infertility can be heated with IVF?
7. What are tubal infertility and idiopathic infertility?

8. Distinguish oligospermia and azoospermia.
9. What is the concentration of sperm in the semen of normal male?
10. What is superovulation? How superovulation is done? What are the available forms of FSH in the market? How these are administered for ovarian hyperstimulation.
11. What is the role of HCG? What are the generic version of HCG available in the market?
12. How the ovulation is monitored?
13. What is egg retrieval? How this is done in IVF?
14. What are the objectives of egg retrieval?
15. Why ultrasound guided method of egg retrieval is usually done than the laparoscopy method?
16. How the sperm capacitation is done in IVF?
17. What are the steps of embryo transfer into uterus of female partner?
18. What is the role of progesterone in embryo transfer?
19. What is assisted hatching? When such assisted hatching is recommended? How this assisted hatching is performed?
20. Why cryopreservation of excess embryos is done?
21. How the success rate of IVF depends upon the age of the mother?
22. What are the reasons for low success rate of IVF?
23. What do you mean by multiple birth problem in IVF? What are the problems associated with such multiple birth in both baby and mother?
24. What are the factors that cause multiple births in IVF?
25. What qualities of eggs and sperms should be maintained?
26. What is ICSI? What types of patients are used for ICSI?
27. What are the causes of male and female infertility.
28. What are the steps of ICSI?
29. How micromanupulation and fertilization are done in ICSI?
30. What is PZD? How it is done?
31. What is SUZI? How it is done?
32. What is GIFT? To whom this technique is recommended?
33. What is the difference between GIFT and IVF?
34. What are the similarities of GIFT and IVF?
35. Describe the GIFT procedure.
36. What is ZIFT?
37. What is tubal embryo transfer?
38. What is the difference between ZIFT and IVF?
39. What is OCT? What is the objective of OCT?
40. What is IVC? Describe the method.
41. Why the ART becomes popular?
42. What are the ethical and legal problems regarding IVF?
43. What kinds of complications arise due to drug induced superovulation?
44. What is hyperstimulation syndrome?
45. What is genetic testing?
46. What is genetic screening?
47. What is the objective of protein level analysis for genetic testing? Give examples.
48. How enzyme HexA is monitored in Homozygous or heterozygons Tay-Sachs patients?
49. How DNA or chromosome level analysis is done for genetic testing?
50. What is genetic screening?
51. When the genetic screening is performed?
52. What practices are used for genetic screening?
53. How a gene mutation can be tested for genetic testing?
54. How *in situ hybridization* technique is used for genetic testing?
55. How RFLP is used for genetic testing?

56. What are the limitations of genetic testing?
57. What do you mean by genetic counseling?
58. What is antenatal diagnosis?
59. What are the criteria of the genetic counseling?
60. What type of couples seeking genetic counseling?
61. What is the purpose of prenatal diagnosis?
62. What is amniocentesis?
63. How the amniotic fluid is taken out in amniocentesis?
64. How the male of female is taken out in amniocentesis?
65. How chromosomal or metabolic abnormalities are determined in amniocentesis?
66. What are the risk and safety of amniocentesis?
67. What are the applications of amniocentesis?
68. What is chorionic villus? What is CVS?
69. How CVS is performed? What is its advantages?
70. What is embryonic diagrnosis? When this is done?
71. Why adult diagnosis of genetic disease is more plausible? How this is done?
72. What is the significance of genetic screening?
73. What is gene therapy?
74. What are the objectives of gene therpy?
75. What is the difference of gene therapy from conventional therapy?
76. What are the stategies taken for somatic cell gene therapy.
77. What are the causes that kept the gene therapy unpopular?
78. What are the ethical problems that the gene therapy keep away from the effective treatments?
79. Give some current strategies of gene therapy.
80. How modern gene-therapy used PEG and RNA-interferance for Parkinson's and Huntington's diseases?
81. What is Bubble boy disease? How this can be cured by gene therapy?
82. What do you mean by Weismann barrier?
83. What is lateral gene transfer?
84. What is germline tropism? How this occurs?
85. What are the characteristics of an ideal vector?
86. What are the pros and cons of viral vectors?
87. What are the pros and cons of non-viral vectors?
88. What kinds of RNA viruses are used for gene therapy?
89. What are the criteria for the retroviral insertion of genes in gene therapy?
90. What are the advantages and disadvantages of retroviral mediated gene therapy?
91. What DNA viruses are used for gene delivery?
92. What modifications should be done before adenovirus mediated gene therapy?
93. What are the advantages and disadvantages of adenoviral delivery system?
94. What are the advantages and disadvantages of the use of AAV?
95. What physical methods are used for gene therapy?
96. What chemical methods are used for gene therpy?
97. What are liposomes? How these are used for gene therapy? What are their advantages and disadvantages?
98. What are the different protocols for liposome-mediated gene therapy?
99. What are the advantages and disadvantages of cataionic liposome mediated gene therapy?
100. What is the protocol for calcium phosphate mediated DNA uptake? What are the advantage and disadvantage.
101. Define gene therapy, what are the three levels of gene therapy?
102. What are the steps for patient gene-therapy.

103. What are the problems of patient gene-therapy.

104. When and where first cancer gene therapy was done?

105. Which marker gene was used?

106. What is the objectives of cancer gene therapy?

107. Give some examples of cancer gene therapy which are currently being successful.

108. What is TIL? What is the source of TIL? How TIL is used for cancer gene therapy.

109. How the genetically modified cells are used for cancer gene therapy?

110. What do you man by *by-stander effect*?

111. Describe the strategy of *in vitro* gene therapy for a brain tumor by a prodrug (HSV-tk) gene?

112. What was the case of first successful gene therapy? What is ADA deficiency? How gene therapy was done on the ADA patient?

113. How the galactosemia disease is treated by gene therapy?

114. What are the cause and symptoms of familial hypercholesteromia disorder? How this diseased patient can be treated by gene therapy?

115. What are the causes and symptoms of cystic fibrosis? How this CF patients can be treated by gene therapy?

116. Why liposomes or adenovirus vectors are used for such gene therapy?

117. What are the cause and symptoms of DMD? How these patients are treated by gene therapy? Why retroviral transfer is not possible?

118. What do you mean by germline gene therapy?

119. What are the characteristics of germline gene therapy?

120. What are the problems to achieve germline gene therapy in human?

121. What are the possible cases where germ-line gene therapy might be justified?

122. Give examples of these cases. Why germline gene therapy has a greater implications than somatic cell gene therapy.

123. What are the arguments against germline gene therapy?

124. What do you mean by euphanics?

125. What are stem cells? Why these are called master cells?

126. What ae the three types of stem cells?

127. What is totipotent cells? Give example.

128. What is pluripotent cell? Give example.

129. What is multipotent cell? Give example?

130. What is humanembryonic stem cell?

131. How embryonic stem cells are isolated from blastocyst.

132. What is inner cell mass of blastoiyst? Where does it occur?

133. What are the sources of human exbyronic stem cell?

134. What is special purpose embryo? How this can be created?

135. What is cloned embryo? What method is used for harvesting such cells? Describe the protocol of this method?

136. What is neonatal stem cell? Where does it occur? What is the protocol for harvesting the cell? What is the advantage of this method? How these cells can be preserved for future use?

137. What adult tissues harbour stem cells?

138. How the stem cells from inner cell mass of blastocyst may be cultured.

139. What is feeder layer? What is its problem to use?

140. What kinds of tests are done before use of stem cells?

141. Why Oct-4 protein is tested before the use of stem cells? How the preserved cells are examined whether these are still pluripotent or not?

142. What are the battery of option and factos that contol the differentiation and proliferation of embryonic stem cells?

143. What are embryoid bodies? What are their fates.

144. Why during ESC therapy, correct combination and correct order of application are to be maintained?

145. What are the disadvantages of ESC therapy?

146. What are adult stem cells? Why this is very difficult to isolate?

147. What is plasticity? Give examples? What are the problems of adult stem cell therapy? What are their advantages?

148. How the genes are transferred to stem cells for gene therapy?

149. What are *in vivo* and *ex vivo* gene therapy? Give examples.

150. Give some applications of stem cell therapy?

25

# Hardy-Weinberg Equilibrium and it's Implications

**CHAPTER AGENDA**

## 25.1. DEFINITION

In 1908 G. H. Hardy, an English mathematician and W. Weinberg, a German physician, independently discovered that *"An equilibrium is established between frequencies of alleles in a random mating population. It was also shown that the relative gene frequencies remain unaltered from one generation to the next, regardless of their dominance and recessive relationship."* A mathematical relationship called Hardy-Weinberg theorem was developed to explain the equilibrium. This is known as **Hardy-Weinberg Law** (Fig. 25.1).

## 25.2. FREQUENCIES OF TWO ALLELES AT A SINGLE LOCUS

When two individuals, heterozygous for the same gene e.g. *Aa* are crossed (*Aa* × *Aa*), they segregate in a ratio *1AA : 2Aa : 1aa*. This ratio can be obtained by simple binomial expansion.

$$(A+a)^2 = 1AA + 2Aa + 1aa$$

In this case, frequencies of *A* and *a* are the same, i.e., 0.5.

**In a population, the frequencies of two alleles belonging to a particular gene are not always the same** and therefore, in a random mating population, the above ratio of 1 : 2 : 1 is not always available.

Suppose, "*p*" represents the frequency of *A* and "*q*" represents the frequency of *a* (where *p*+*q*=1), then these frequencies "*p*" and "*q*" can also be realized in the form of gametes carrying *A* and *a*. In other words, the proportion of gametes carrying *A* will be "*p*" and the proportion of gametes carrying *a* will be "*q*". The probabilities of individuals obtained from such a population can be achieved like this:

| ♂ \ ♀ | A(p) | a(q) |
|---|---|---|
| A(p) | $AA(p^2)$ | Aa(pq) |
| a(q) | Aa(pq) | $aa(q^2)$ |

This leads to the formulation of Hardy-Weinberg equation: $p^2 (AA) + 2pq(Aa) + q^2 (aa)$.

Here gene frequency of $A = p^2 + \frac{1}{2}2pq = p^2 + pq = p(p+q) = p$

Gene frequency of $a = q^2 + \frac{1}{2}2pq = q$

This equation would essentially be obtained in every case after one generation of random mating, if factors like mutation, selection and migration do not operate (Fig. 25.2).

It is possible to prove algebraically that population having genotype frequencies expressed, as $p^2 + 2pq + q^2$ will be in equilibrium.

**Mating :**

| ♂ \ ♀ | $AA(p^2)$ | $Aa(2pq)$ | $aa(q^2)$ |
|---|---|---|---|
| $AA(p^2)$ | $p^4$ | $2p^3q$ | $p^2q^2$ |
| $Aa(2pq)$ | $2p^3q$ | $4p^2q^2$ | $2pq^3$ |
| $aa(q^2)$ | $p^2q^2$ | $2pq^3$ | $q^4$ |

**Result :** See table 25.1

Therefore, in this generation, the frequency of *A* and *a* alleles are as follows:

$$AA\,(p^2) + Aa\,(2pq) + aa\,(q^2)$$

Here gene frequency of

$$A = p^2 + \frac{1}{2}2pq = p\,(p+q) = p$$

Gene frequency of

$$a = q^2 + \frac{1}{2}2pq = q\,(p+q) = q$$

The frequency of the genes is in equilibrium.

## 25.3 APPLICATION OF HARDY-WEINBERG PRINCIPLE

### Problem 1

Among humans, the difference between those who can taste and those who cannot taste the chemical phenyl thio-carbamide (PTC), resides in a single gene difference with two

**Fig. 25.1 :** *(a) G. H. Hardy and (b) Wilhelm Weinberg*

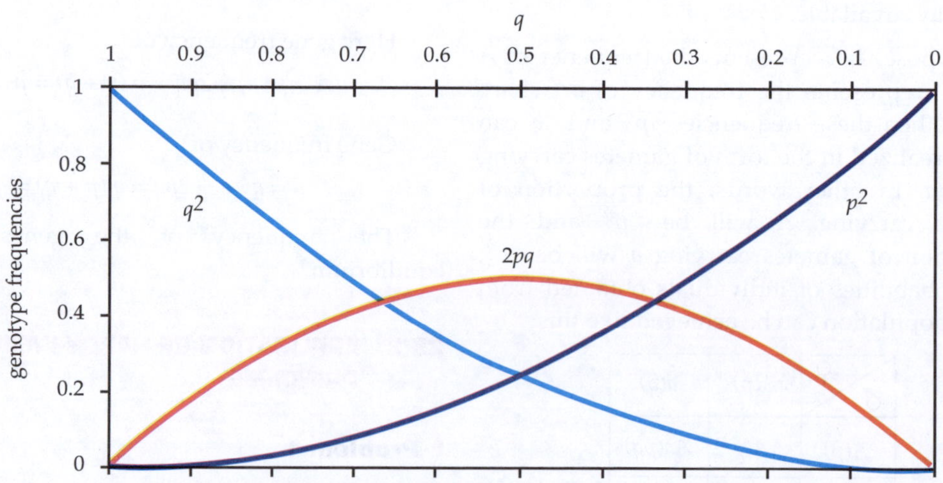


**Fig. 25.2 :** *Common way of visualizing the expectations of Hardy-Weinberg Principle in the plot p2, 2pq and q2 as a function of allele frequencies.*

**TABLE 25.1**
**Result of genotypic frequencies after second generation**

| *Types of mating* | *frequency* | *Frequency ratios of offspring* | | |
|---|---|---|---|---|
| | | *AA* | *Aa* | *aa* |
| $AA \times AA$ | $P^4$ | $P^4$ | | |
| $AA \times Aa$ | $2p^3q$ | $P^3q$ | $p^3q$ | |
| $AA \times aa$ | $P^2q^2$ | | $p^2q^2$ | |
| $AA \times Aa$ | $2p^3q$ | $P^3q$ | $p^3q$ | |
| $Aa \times Aa$ | $4P^2q^2$ | $P^2q^2$ | $2p^2q^2$ | $p^2q^2$ |
| $Aa \times aa$ | $2pq^3$ | | $pq^3$ | $pq^3$ |
| $AA \times aa$ | $p^2q^2$ | | $p^2q^2$ | |
| $Aa \times aa$ | $2pq^3$ | | $pq^3$ | $pq^3$ |
| $aa \times aa$ | $q^4$ | | | $q^4$ |
| | | $p^4 + p^3q + p^3q + p^2q^2$ <br> $= p^2 (p+q)^2$ <br> $= p^2 \times 1$ <br> $= p^2$ | $2pq (p^2 + 2pq + q^2)$ <br> $= 2pq (p+q)^2$ <br> $= 2pq \times 1$ <br> $= 2pq$ | $q^2 (p^2 + 2pq + q^2)$ <br> $= q^2 (p+q)^2$ <br> $= q^2 \times 1$ <br> $= q^2$ |

alleles $T$ and $t$. The allele for testing $T$ is dominant over the $t$, so that heterozygous $Tt$ and homozygous $TT$ would be tasters whereas homozygous $tt$ will be only non-tasters. If we were to chose an initial population compared with an arbitrary number of each genotype, then we can calculate the frequencies of those genes after many generations.

Let us, for example upon an island, a group of children in the ratio 0.4 $TT$ : 0.4 $Tt$ : 0.2 $tt$. The gene frequencies in this newly formed population are therefore

$$T = 0.4 + 0.4 \times \frac{1}{2} = 0.6$$

$$t = 0.2 + 0.4 \times \frac{1}{2} = 0.4$$

The types of random mating combinations and their relative frequencies in this population would be as follows :

**Mating :**

| ♂ \ ♀ | $TT$ (0.4) | $Tt$ (0.4) | $tt$ (0.2) |
|---|---|---|---|
| $TT$ (0.4) | 0.16 | 0.16 | 0.08 |
| $Tt$ (0.4) | 0.16 | 0.16 | 0.08 |
| $tt$ (0.2) | 0.08 | 0.08 | 0.04 |

**Result :** Table 25.2

It is to be noted that the gene frequencies have not changed. For $T$, gene frequencies = $0.36 + \frac{1}{2} \times 0.48 = 0.6$

For $t$ the gene frequencies =

$$0.16 + \frac{1}{2} \times 0.48 = 0.4$$

The result is exactly same as before.

Therefore, in the population the gene frequency is in equilibrium.

**TABLE 25.2**
**Result of genotypic frequencies in the next generation**

| *Types of mating* | *frequency* | *Frequency ratios of offspring* | | |
|---|---|---|---|---|
| | | *TT* | *Tt* | *tt* |
| *TT* × *TT* | 0.16 | 0.16 | | |
| *TT* × *Tt* | 0.16 | 0.08 | 0.08 | |
| *TT* × *tt* | 0.08 | | .08 | |
| *TT* × *Tt* | 0.16 | 0.08 | 0.08 | |
| *Tt* × *Tt* | 0.16 | 0.04 | 0.08 | 0.04 |
| *Tt* × *tt* | 0.08 | | 0.04 | 0.04 |
| *TT* × *tt* | 0.08 | | 0.08 | |
| *Tt* × *tt* | 0.08 | | 0.04 | 0.04 |
| *tt* × *tt* | 0.04 | | | 0.04 |
| | | 0.36 | 0.48 | 0.16 |

### Problem 2

In a population of an island containing 0.25 MM blood group: 0.70 MN: 0.05 NN. Check the population whether it is in equilibrium or not.

Gene frequency of M = $0.25 + \frac{1}{2} \times 70 = 0.6$

$N = 0.5 + \frac{1}{2} \times 70 = 0.4$

In the second generation, the genotypic ratio would be $p^2$ (MM) : $2pq$ (MN) : $q^2$ (NN)

That is, 0.36 (MM) : 0.48 (MN) : 0.16 (NN)

The gene frequency in the second generation for M = $0.36 + \frac{1}{2} \times 0.48 = 0.6$

$N = 0.16 + \frac{1}{2} \times 0.48 = 0.4$

It is exactly same as before.

Therefore, the gene frequency of the given population is in equilibrium.

## 25.4 RESULT OF RANDOM MATING IN A POPULATION WITH THREE ALLELES

If there are three alleles at a locus, the Hardy Weinberg principle is simply expanded. If these are $A_1$, $A_2$ and $A_3$ and their respective frequencies are $p$, $q$ and $r$, then $p+q+r = 1$.

If there is random mating between all possible gametes, the genotypes and their values will be as follows:

**Mating :**

| ♂ \ ♀ | $A_1(p)$ | $A_2(q)$ | $A_3(r)$ |
|---|---|---|---|
| $A_1(p)$ | $A_1A_1(p^2)$ | $A_1A_2$(pq) | $A_1A_3(pr)$ |
| $A_2(q)$ | $A_1A_2(pq)$ | $A_2A_2(q^2)$ | $A_2A_3(rq)$ |
| $A_3(r)$ | $A_1A_3$(pr) | $A_2A_3(qr)$ | $A_3A_3(r^2)$ |

**Result :**

| Genotypes | Frequency |
|---|---|
| $A_1A_1$ | $p^2$ |
| $A_1A_2$ | $2pq$ |
| $A_1A_3$ | $2pr$ |
| $A_2A_3$ | $2qr$ |
| $A_2A_2$ | $q^2$ |
| $A_3A_3$ | $r^2$ |
| Total | $p^2 + q^2 + r^2 + 2pq + 2pr + 2qr$ |
| | $= (p + q + r)^2$ |
| | $= 1$ |

## 25.5 SIGNIFICANCE OF HARDY-WEINBERG PRINCIPLE

1. It helps to estimate, whether a population is in equilibrium or not.
2. It helps to determine whether random mating has taken place in a population.
3. It helps to realize why frequencies of dominant alleles do not increase in a population.
4. When frequency of one allele is known, genotypic frequencies of a population in the equilibrium state can be determined.
5. It helps to determine the allelic frequencies and the genotypic frequencies with the help of recessive genotype.

   For example,

   **Albinism** is caused due to recessive autosomal gene. In a population 9 albinism persons have been counted in 250000 individuals.

   Let use, gene for albinism is *a*

   Normal gene is *A*

   In the equilibrium condition, the three genotypes of the population *AA* ($p^2$) , *Aa* ($pq$) and *aa* ($q^2$) where *aa* will represent the albino.

   The frequency of *aa* genotype $= \frac{9}{250000}$

   or $q^2 = \frac{9}{250000}$ or $q = \frac{3}{500} = 0.006$

   Hence, the frequency of gene *A* is $1 - 0.006 = 0.994$

   Therefore, number of heterozygous carrier *Aa* is

   $2 \times .006 \times 0.994 \times 250000 = 2982$

6. Evolution cannot occur unless the equilibrium is upset. The elemental forces of evolution, such as mutation, selection, migration and genetic drift, disturb the equilibrium.

   (i) *Role of mutation :* Let us, consider, a population with two alleles of a gene *A* and *a*, the respective frequencies of which are $p$ and $q$. if $\mu$ is the rate of mutation from *A* to *a*, then rate of change in gene frequencies $\Delta p = -\mu p$.

   So, after one generation, frequency of *A* gene becomes $p - \mu p = p(1-\mu)$

   If rate and direction of mutation remain unaltered after second generation, frequency of *A* gene becomes $p(1-\mu) - p\mu(1-\mu)$

   $$= p(1-\mu)(1-\mu)$$
   $$= p(1-\mu)^2$$

   In this manner, after n generations, frequency of *A* gene will be $p(1-\mu)^n$.

   Though rate of mutation is very small and is counteracted by reverse mutation, a little change in gene frequencies due to mutation is sufficient to disturb the genetic equilibrium of the population.

   (ii) *Role of selection* : Selection is a mechanism that affects reproductive success of a genotype. If the individual carries one allele which is more fertile and produce viable offsprings than the other allele, the frequency of the former will increase relative to the latter. This change also disturbs the genetic equilibrium of the population.

   (iii) *Role of migration* : Migration refers to the influx of individuals from one population to another, both of which maintain an entirely distinct gene frequency with respect to other. In simple meaning migration is the introduction of new individuals with new genotypes into Mendelian population. The population from which the individuals are migrating is the migrant and which receives the migrating is the recipient populations.

   Suppose, the black allele (*B*) is higher in the insect population Y than X. Let, a random sample from the X population is migrated to the population Y. If $q_x$ and $q_y$ representing the white alleles in the original population and a fraction ($m$) of the total number of individuals now present in Y population, then a new frequency is established ($q'_y$) in the Y-population.

So, $q'_y = (I - m)\, q_y + mq_x$

Then, the change in frequency of white allele in the population after one generation will be

$\Delta q = q'_y - q_y$

$=(1 - m)q_y + mq_x - q_y$

$= - m\,(q_y - q_x)$

When numerical values are added into this equation and value of $q_y$ changes significantly upsetting the equilibrium of the Hardy-Weinberg equation.

(iv) *Role of genetic drift* : Genetic drift is the random fluctuation of gene frequency due to chance occurrence in a finite population. It is easily visualized in a small sample. In the large population, the change in allele frequencies in some individuals may be corrected by some others in the population.

For example,

According to Mendelian principle, a pair of heterozygote parents ($Cc \times Cc$) can produce offspring with genotype $CC : Cc : cc$ in a ratio $\frac{1}{4} : \frac{1}{2} : \frac{1}{4}$. If in a population of two such parents' produce only two offspring, the possible genotypes of the offspring and their probabilities and allelic ratio would be as follows.

Parent : $Cc \times Cc$

Offspring : (See table no. 25.3)

Allelic frequencies in the parents are both 0.5 for C and c, that are most expected among the offspring s. But the result is :

(i) Frequencies of alleles in the offspring remain same as in possibilities 3 and 4.

The probability is $\frac{1}{4} + \frac{2}{16} = \frac{6}{16}$

(ii) Probability of increase in the frequency of C and hence decrease in c in possibilities (1) and (5) is $\frac{1}{16} + \frac{1}{4} = \frac{5}{16}$

**TABLE 25.3**
**Result after mating between *Cc* × *Cc***

| *Possibility* | *Genotype of offspring* | *Probability* | *Ratio of alleles* | |
|---|---|---|---|---|
| | | | C | c |
| 1. | CC and CC | $\frac{1}{4} \times \frac{1}{4} = \frac{1}{16}$ | 1.0 | 0 |
| 2. | cc and cc | $\frac{1}{4} \times \frac{1}{4} = \frac{1}{16}$ | 0 | 1.0 |
| 3. | Cc and Cc | $\frac{1}{2} \times \frac{1}{2} = \frac{1}{4}$ | 0.5 | 0.5 |
| 4. | CC and cc | $2\left(\frac{1}{4} \times \frac{1}{4}\right) = \frac{2}{16}$ | 0.5 | 0.5 |
| 5. | CC and Cc | $2\left(\frac{1}{4} \times \frac{1}{2}\right) = \frac{1}{4}$ | 0.75 | 0.25 |
| 6. | Cc and cc | $2\left(\frac{1}{2} \times \frac{1}{4}\right) = \frac{1}{4}$ | 0.25 | 0.75 |

(iii) Probability of decrease in the frequency of C and hence increase in "c" in possibilities

(2) and (6) is $\frac{1}{16} + \frac{1}{4} = \frac{5}{16}$

Thus chance of deviation from expected is $\frac{5}{16} + \frac{5}{16} = \frac{10}{16}$, which is actually greater than the chance that it will remain same as parents. Even, either *C* or *c* allele completely disappears from the off-springs [possibility (2) or (1)] with a probability $\frac{1}{16} + \frac{1}{16} = \frac{2}{16}$.

## 25.6 EXCEPTIONS OF HARDY- WEINBERG PRINCIPLE

1. **Non-random mating :** Random mating is one of the key assumptions of Hardy-Weinberg principle. If the mating is not random i.e., have the preference of opposite sex, the population fails to show equilibrium. Such random mating is called assortive mating.

2. **Unequal survival :** When zygotes resulted from random mating suffers from different survival rates, genotypic frequencies of the individuals of these zygotes will fail to show equilibrium state.

3. **Subdivided population :** A large single inbreeding population is called **panmictic population**. But in nature, populations are subdivided into groups. Such subdivisions of population will result in violation of equilibrium.

## 25.7 ATTAINMENT OF EQUILIBRIUM AT TWO OR MORE LOCI

We now consider the products of two independently assorting gene-pair differences simultaneously. For example, *Aa* and *Bb*, the number of genotype increases to $3^2$ *i.e., AABB, AABb, AaBB.* etc.

If *p*, *q*, *r* and *s* be the gene frequencies of *A*, *a*, *B* and *b* respectively, then the equilibrium ratios of their genotypes are expressed as

$$(pr + ps + qr + qs)^2$$
$$= p^2r^2AABB + 2p^2rsAABb + 2p^2s^2AAbb \text{ ...... ........}q^2s^2aabb.$$

Here, we see that *pr*, *ps*, *qr* and *qs*, which are the equilibrium frequencies of the gamete *AB*, *Ab*, *aB* and *ab* respectively and when the gametic frequencies have reached those equilibrium values, the equilibrium genotypic frequencies will also have been reached.

If we begin with a cross of heterozygotes $AaBb \times AaBb$, the gene frequencies are equal, i.e., $p = q = r = s = 0.5$. Then the gametic frequencies of *AA*, *Ab*, *aB* and *ab* would be equal i.e., 0.25. Thus, within one generation the genotypic equilibrium would be reached.

If we begin with a population with genotypes $AABB \times aabb$, only two types of gametes *AB* and *ab* are produced and then equilibrium for all genotypes cannot be reached in the next generation, because *AAbb* and *aaBB* etc genotypes are missing.

The gametes those in "repulsion" (*Ab* and *aB*) and those in coupling (*AB* and *ab*). The frequencies of genes in repulsion and coupling be the same therefore, we would expect that the products of frequencies of coupling gametes and repulsion gametes are same at equilibrium.

If there is a difference in the coupling and repulsion products in the initial population then, changes in the gametic frequencies will must occur. Suppose this difference disequilibrium value is *d*. When product of frequencies of repulsion gametes has a greater value than the product of frequencies of coupling gametes, the value of *d* is positive. Then, at equilibrium, this fraction will have been added to each coupling gametes and subtracted from each of the repulsion gametes.

Similarly, if *d* is negative, the reverse operation will occur.

Thus, after generation value of *d* will be diminished and finally into zero.

### Example

Calculate the difference disequilibrium and the equilibrium frequencies of gametes for a population in which the frequencies of two unlinked gene pairs *A-a* and *B-b* are $A = B = 0.6$ and $a = b = 0.4$ and the initial genotypic frequencies are $AABB = AAbb = aaBB = 0.3$ and $aabb = 0.1$.

**Solution :**

**Equilibrium frequencies of gametes**

| *Initial population* | *Gametes* type | *initial frequency* | *equilibrium frequency* |
|---|---|---|---|
| *AABB* | *AB* | 0.3 | 0.3 + *d* |
| *AAbb* | *Ab* | 0.3 | 0.3 – *d* |
| *aaBB* | *aB* | 0.3 | 0.3 – *d* |
| *aabb* | *ab* | 0.1 | 0.1 + *d* |

Difference disequilibrium

= (Repulsion products) – (coupling products)

= (*Ab*) (*aB*) – (*AB*) (*ab*)

= 0.3 × 0.3 – 0.3 × 0.1 = 0.6

**Attainment of equilibrium**

| *Genera-tion* | *Amount added (AA, bb) Substracted Ab, aB* | *Proportion of disequilibrium remaining* | *Gametes* *AB* | *Ab* | *aB* | *aa* |
|---|---|---|---|---|---|---|
| 1 | | 1.0d | 0.3 | 0.3 | 0.3 | 0.1 |
| 2 | 0.5*d* | 0.5d | 0.33 | 0.27 | 0.27 | 0.13 |
| 3 | 0.75*d* | 0.25d | 0.345 | 0.255 | 0.255 | 0.145 |
| 4 | 0.875*d* | 0.125d | 0.3525 | 0.2475 | 0.2475 | 0.1525 |
| . . . . | . . . . | . . . . | . . . . | . . . . | . . . . | . . . . |
| Equili-brium | *d* | 0 | 0.36 | 0.24 | 0.24 | 0.16 |

Within 4 to 5 generations, more than 90% of this difference from equilibrium frequency has been attained by all gametes or less than 10% of disequilibrium value remains.

If the two loci are linked i.e., on the same chromosome, the chances of different types of gametes will depend upon the crossing over frequencies between them. Therefore, equilibrium would be delayed accordingly as the linkage between the two loci are closer.

## 25.8 SEX LINKAGE AND ATTAINMENT OF EQUILIBRIUM

The females are chromosomally XX and males XY, five genotypes can occur for a sex linked pair of alleles *A* and *a*. These are in females *AA*, *Aa* and *aa* while in males *A* and *a*.

If we assign the frequencies of *A* and *a* are *p* and *q* respectively then, in females the equilibrium genotypic values would be $p^2$ (*AA*), 2*pq*(*Aa*) and $q^2$(*aa*). While in males, the equilibrium genotypic values would be *p*(*A*) and *q*(*a*). These frequencies can be proved algebraically.

**Mother's genotypes and frequencies**

| Father's genotypes and frequencies: ♂ \ ♀ | *AA*($p^2$) | *Aa*(2*pq*) | *aa*($q^2$) |
|---|---|---|---|
| *A*(*p*) | $p^3$ | $2p^2q$ | $pq^2$ |
| *a*(*q*) | $p^2q$ | $2pq^2$ | $q^3$ |

**Result :** See table 25.4

### Example

If we begin a population with the proportions 0.2*A* : 0.8*a* in males and 0.2*AA* : 0.6*Aa* : 0.2*aa* in females. Then in females, frequency of *A* is $0.2 + \frac{1}{2} \times 0.6 = 0.5$ and in males 0.2. What are the equilibrium frequencies of all 5 genotypes and how long will it take for these frequencies to be attained?

Since one X in males and two Xs in females then $p = \frac{1}{3}$ of males and $\frac{2}{3}$ of females =

$0.2 \times \frac{1}{3} + \frac{2}{3} \times 0.5 = 0.4$ and the frequencies of *a* i.e., $q = 1 - 0.4 = 0.6$.

Thus, according to our methods the equilibrium frequencies of *A* and *a* in areas are *p* : *q*, i.e., 0.4 : 0.6.

The equilibrium frequencies of *AA*, *Aa* and *aa* in females would be $(0.4)^2$, 2 × 0.4 × 0.6 and $(0.6)^2$ *i.e.*, 0.16, 0.48 and 0.36 respectively.

**TABLE 25.4**
**Result of the Cross of sex-linked alleles**

| Mating | | Offspring | | | | |
|---|---|---|---|---|---|---|
| | | Females | | | Males | |
| Type | Frequency | AA | Aa | aa | A | a |
| $AA \times A$ | $p^3$ | $p^3$ | | | $p^3$ | |
| $Aa \times A$ | $2p^2q$ | $p^2q$ | $p^3q$ | | $p^2q$ | $p^2q$ |
| $aa \times A$ | $pq^2$ | | $pq^2$ | | | $pq^2$ |
| $AA \times a$ | $p^2q$ | | $p^2q$ | | $p^2q$ | |
| $Aa \times a$ | $2pq^2$ | | $pq^2$ | $pq^2$ | $pq^2$ | $pq^2$ |
| $aa \times a$ | $q^3$ | | | $q^3$ | | $q^3$ |
| Total : | | $p^2(p+q)$ $= p^2$ | $2pq\,(p^2+2pq+q^2)$ $= 2pq\,(p+q)^2$ $= 2pq$ | $q^2\,(p+q)$ $= q^2$ | $p\,(p^2+2pq+q^2)$ $= p\,(p+q)^2$ $= p$ | $q\,(p^2+2pq+q^2)$ $= q\,(p+q)^2$ $= q$ |

Equilibrium will not be reached in a single generation, because males inherit their X-chromosomes only from their mothers, the frequency of a sex linked gene among them is the same as its maternal frequency.

Therefore, a founding population with a maternal frequency of *A* equal to 0.5 will produce male offspring with the same frequency of *A*. (*i.e.*, 0.5).

The female offspring inherit one paternal and one maternal X-chromosome. So, the frequency of a sex-linked gene among them will be the average of paternal and maternal frequencies *i.e.*, $\frac{0.2+0.5}{2} = 0.35$.

Thus, in the first generation of random mating the equilibrium value of 0.4 will not be reached by the daughters and will be exceeded by the sons.

Again in the second generation, the frequency among female offspring would be $\frac{0.35+0.5}{2} = 0.425$. whereas, the equilibrium values of the male offspring would be 0.35.

In this way, after each generation the equilibrium frequency of male and female offspring will come close together and finally into equilibrium after certain generations.

## 25.9 ESTIMATION OF EQUILIBRIUM FREQUENCIES OF CODOMINANCE IN NATURAL POPULATION

The equilibrium gene frequencies can be reliably estimated from the observed genotypic frequencies and then it can be easily compared to their expected values. By this way co-dominance at MN blood group locus can be taken into account.

**Example-1**

104 people were classified into their genotypic frequencies 0.59 *MM*; 0.34 *MN* and 0.07 *NN*.

The gene frequency of *M*

$$= 0.59 + \frac{1}{2} \times 0.34 = 0.76.$$

Gene frequency of *N*

$$= 0.07 + \frac{1}{2} \times 0.34 = 0.24.$$

At equilibrium, expected genotype frequencies should be $(0.76)^2$ *MM*, $(2 \times 0.76 \times 0.24)$ *MN*, $(0.24)^2$ *NN* or 0.58 *MM*, 0.36 *MN* and 0.06 *NN*.

The difference between observed and expected genotypic frequencies can be tested for goodness of fit by chi-square method.

| | *MM* | *MN* | *NN* | *Total* |
|---|---|---|---|---|
| Observed | 61 | 36 | 7 | 104 |
| Expected | 60 | 38 | 6 | 104 |
| Obs – exp | 1 | –2 | 1 | |
| $(\text{Obs}-\text{exp})^2$ | 1 | 4 | 1 | |
| $\frac{(\text{obs - exp})^1}{\text{expected}}$ | 0.0167 | 0.11 | 0.167 | $\chi^2_{1df} = 0.294$ |

Here, for chi-square test, degree of freedom = number of phenotypes – number of alleles = 3 – 2 = 1. If the chi-square value is less than the tabulated value, then the hypothesis is accepted, i.e., the observed data is in equilibrium.

### Example-2

Under random mating by 741 couples, data was collected by Matsunaga and Itoh for *MN* locus in a Japanese town. The observed genotypic frequencies were 0.274 *MM*, 0.502 *MN* and 0.224 *NN*.

The genotypes of the populations are to be tested and expected frequencies of mating combinations are to be calculated.

Here, gene frequency of

$$M = 0.274 + \frac{1}{2} \times 0.502$$

$$= 0.274 + 0.251 \quad = 0.525$$

and gene frequency of

$$N = \frac{1}{2} \times 0.502 + 0.224$$

$$= 0.251 + 0.224 \quad = 0.475$$

The expected frequencies would be

$MM = (0.525)^2 = 0.276$

$MN = 2 \times 0525 \times 0.475 = 0.499$

$NN = (0.475)^2 = 0.225.$

Expected frequency of

$$M = 0.276 + \frac{1}{2} \times 0.499$$

$$i.e., p = 0.5255$$

and expected frequency of

$$N = 1 - 0.5255$$

$$i.e., q = 0.4745$$

It is obvious that the genotypes of the population are in equilibrium for this locus.

| ♂ \ ♀ | $MM(p^2)$ | $MN(2pq)$ | $NN(q^2)$ |
|---|---|---|---|
| $MM(p^2)$ | $p^4$ | $2p^3q$ | $p^2q^2$ |
| $MN(2pq)$ | $2p^3q$ | $2p^2q^2$ | $2pq^3$ |
| $NN(q^2)$ | $p^2q^2$ | $2pq^3$ | $q^4$ |

| *Mating* | *Expected frequencies* | *Expected number* |
|---|---|---|
| *MM* × *MM* | $P^4 = 0.0760$ | 56.3 |
| *MM* × *MN* | $4p^3q = 0.2749$ | 203.7 |
| *MM* × *NN* | $2p^2q^2 = 0.1244$ | 92.2 |
| *MN* × *MN* | $4p^2q^2 = 0.2487$ | 184.3 |
| *MN* × *NN* | $4pq^3 = 0.2251$ | 166.8 |
| *NN* × *NN* | $q^4 = 0.0509$ | 37.7 |
| | **1.0000** | **741** |

It the observed number is given then we can compare it with the expected frequencies by chi-square method which can test for goodness of fit between MN-system of blood groups.

## 25.10 ESTIMATION OF EQUILIBRIUM FREQUENCIES OF DOMINANCE IN NATURAL POPULATION

When the effect of one allele is completely dominant, the heterozygous genotype (*Aa*) cannot be distinguished phenotypically from the homozygous (*AA*) dominant one. Then the allelic frequencies and genotypic frequencies can be determined with the help of recessive genotypes.

**TABLE 25.5**

| | | Female Parent phenotypes | | |
|---|---|---|---|---|
| | | Dominant | | Recessive |
| Male parent phenotypes | | $p^2(AA)$ | $2pq\ (Aa)$ | $q^2(aa)$ |
| Dominant | $p^2\ (AA)$ | $p^4$ | $2p^3q$ | $p^2q^2$ |
| | $2pq\ (Aa)$ | $2p^2q$ | $4p^2q^2$ | $2pq^3$ |
| Recessive | $q^2\ (aa)$ | $p^2q^2$ | $2pq^3$ | $q^4$ |

| Parent (genotypes) | frequency | frequency of recessive phenotypes |
|---|---|---|
| $Aa \times Aa$ | $4p^2q^2$ | $\frac{1}{4} \times 4p^2q^2 = p^2q^2$ |
| $Aa \times aa$ | $4pq^3$ | $\frac{1}{2} \times 4pq^3 = 2pq^3$ |
| $aa \times aa$ | $q^4$ | $= q^4$ |

For example : Cystic fibrosis (CF) is caused due to recessive autosomal gene. In a population 9 Cystic fibrosis, persons have been counted in 250000 individuals.

Let use gene for CF is = $a$

Normal gene is $A$

In the equilibrium condition, the three genotypes of the populations $AA(p^2)$, $Aa\ (2pq)$ and $aa(q^2)$, where $aa$ will represent the CF.

The frequency of $aa$ genotype = $\frac{9}{250000}$

or $q^2 = \frac{9}{250000}$

or $q = 0.006$

Hence, the frequency of gene $A$ is 1 – 0.006 = 0.994.

Therefore, number of heterozygous carriers $Aa$ is $2 \times 0.006 \times 0.994 \times 250000 = 2982$.

High frequencies for carriers of recessive traits such as Albinism, Tay-Sachs disease and alkaptonuria, etc are found unexpected heterozygous condition.

From the above example, we are able to detect the value of recessive allele as the square root of the frequency of homozygous recessives assuming that Hardy Weinberg equilibrium has been reached. But do not provide any supporting evidence that $AA$ and $Aa$ are in equilibrium.

Snyder has devised a test for the presence of genetic equilibrium when family data are available. This is based on the expected frequencies of recessives produced by the parental mating combinations. Such as, a mating between two dominant phenotypes may produce recessive phenotypes when they are heterozygous. Only if one parent is homozygous dominant, then the offspring would express dominant phenotypes. Therefore, expected recessive phenotypes would be available only when the crosses are $Aa \times Aa$, $Aa \times aa$ and $aa \times aa$. Their frequencies can be calculated from the table 25.5.

When the parents are dominant phenotypes i.e., $AA \times AA$, $Aa \times AA$ and $Aa \times Aa$

Their frequencies would be

$$= p^4 + 4p^3q + 4p^2q^2$$

So, the fraction of recessive offspring when parents are dominant phenotypes would be

| TABLE 25.6 | | | | | | |
|---|---|---|---|---|---|---|
| Parents | | Offspring | | | Frequency of Nontasters among offspring | |
| Mating | No. of couples | Taster | nontaster | Total | Observed | Expected |
| taster × tastes | 425 | 929 | 130 | 1059 | 0.123 | 0.122 |
| taster × nontaster | 289 | 483 | 278 | 761 | 0.365 | 0.349 |
| nontaster × nontaster | 86 | (5) | 218 | 223 | | |

$$\frac{p^2q^2}{p^4 + 4p^3q + 4p^2q^2}$$

$$= \frac{p^2q^2}{p^2(p+2q)^2} = \frac{q^2}{(p+q+q)^2} = \frac{q^2}{(1+q)^2}$$

Similarly, when one of the parent is recessive phenotype and other is dominant phenotype (i.e., $Aa \times aa$),

Then their frequencies would be

$$= 2p^2q^2 + 4pq^3$$

So, the fraction of recessive offspring when parents are dominant phenotype would be

$$\frac{2pq^3}{2p^2q^2 + 4pq^3}$$

$$= \frac{2pq^3}{2pq^2\ (p+2q)} = \frac{q}{(p+q+q)} = \frac{q}{1+q}$$

From the family data, at equilibrium, the expected frequencies can be obtained from the following data.

1. When parents are dominant phenotypes, the expected frequency of recessive phenotypes = $q^2/(1+q)^2$
2. When one parent is dominant phenotype, while the other parent is recessive phenotype, the expected frequency of recessive phenotype = $q/(1+q)$
3. When both of the parents are recessive phenotypes, the expected frequency of recessive phenotype = $q^2$.

### Example

Snyder performed a test for equilibrium of the alleles for the ability to taste phenylthiocarbamide from 800 couples and the result was as follows. See table 25.6.

Here, total no. of parents = 800 × 2 = 1600.

Frequency of nontasting alleles derived from both heterozygous and homozygous parents = 289 + 86 × 2 = 461

Then, the value of

$$q = \sqrt{\frac{461}{1600}} = \sqrt{0.288} = 0.537$$

Therefore, the expected frequency of recessive offspring from taster × taster parents should be

$$\frac{q^2}{(1+q)^2} = \frac{(0.537)^2}{(1.537)^2} = 0.122$$

The expected frequency of recessive from taster × nontaster combinations

$$\frac{q}{1+q} = \frac{0.537}{1.537} = 0.349$$

Both the expected values fit with the observed proportions closely.

## 25.11. CHANGES IN ALLELE FREQUENCIES

### 25.11.1 Concept

Populations change over time. The number of individuals in a population may increase or decrease, depending upon food resources,

**TABLE 25.7**

| | *AA* | *Aa* | *aa* |
|---|---|---|---|
| 1. $P_1$ | 100 | 100 | 100 |
| 2. $F_1$ | 100 | 90 | 80 |
| 3. Average progeny per individual in $F_1$ (or, reproductive success or survival success) | 1.0 | 0.9 | 0.8 |
| 4. Relative fitness ($w = \frac{\text{(reproductive success of individual genotype)}}{\text{reproductive success of best genotype}}$ | 1.0 | 0.9 | 0.8 |
| 5. Reproduction in fitness or selection coefficient (s) where ($s = 1-w$) | 0 | 0.1 | 0.2 |

climate, weather and availability of breeding areas; predators, parasites and disease-causing organisms can also play a role. At the genetic level, a population may change because of selection, mutation migration and random genetic drift. The first three are directional whereas, the last one is random process. These natural processes can change the allele frequencies thereby altering the fundamental makeup of the population.

Evolution cannot occur unless the equilibrium is upset. The elemental forces of evolution are selection, migration, mutation and genetic drift.

### 25.11.2. Natural Selection

The most critical process that changes gene frequency is natural selection. Natural selection is the process that promotes adaptation and keeps the disorganizing effects of the other processes, such as mutation, migration and genetic drift in check. Thus it accounts for the adaptive and highly organized nature of living creature. The parameter commonly used to measure natural selection is "**Darwinian fitness**" or **relative fitness (*w*)** also called **selection value** or **adaptive value**.

### 25.11.3 Darwinian fitness

Fitness is a measure of the "reproductive efficiency" of a genotype. Natural selection operates by differential reproduction. Accordingly fitness is often expressed as a "relative and not absolute" measure of reproductive efficiency. For mathematical convenience, geneticists usually assign "fitness value" = 1 to the genotype with the highest reproductive efficiency.

Let, at a certain locus, there are three genotypes (*AA*), (*Aa*) and (*aa*). For every one progeny produced by *AA*-homozygote, the heterozygote *Aa* also produces one progeny but the *aa* homozygote produces only 0.8 progeny. Then the fitness of (*AA*), (*Aa*) and (*aa*) are 1,1 and 0.8 respectively ( See table 25.7).

Looking in terms of fitness, '*A*' therefore may be considered to possess a "superior fitness" or "adaptive value" relative to '*a*', which is now considered to be deleterious. In extreme cases, this deleteriousness may be such that no *aa* individuals are produced as in the case of lethal genes. In such cases '*w*' will be zero (0). Therefore both relative fitness $w$ and selection coefficient $s$ may vary from 0 to 1.

### 35.11.4. Selection Coefficient

Usually it is considered that a "force" or a factor acts on each genotype to reduce its relative fitness. This force has been called "Selection coefficient" or 's'. In the previous example, *s* has no effect on (*AA*) but on *aa* the effect is 0.2 i.e. 20%.

We can therefore, define 's' as the amount of reduction on the fitness of a genotype. The relative fitness of the best genotype cannot usually exceed the value 1.

The selection coefficient $s = 1 - w$ (fitness of the genotype concerned).

### 25.11.5 Effect of Natural Selection

The ultimate outcome of natural selection may be either the elimination of one or another allele or a stable polymorphism with two or more alleles.

- **Gametic Selection**

**Meiotic drive** or **segregation distortion** may be considered as one form of gametic selection in which gametes carrying a particular gene show preferential survival, there is of no number difference between dominant and recessive genes, since both genotypes are phenotypically expressed.

The population can then be considered to consist of "A" genotypes with a frequency 'p' and 'a' genotypes with frequency *q*. The fitness of "A" is considered to be 1. The fitness of its relatively deleterious allele 'a' is reduced to a coefficient of "s". Then, after one generation of selection will cause the following changes (See table 25.8):

The selection is proceeding very slowly, therefore, 's' is very small and *qs* in the denominator can be safely ignored.

Therefore $\Delta q = -sq\,(1-q)$

This relation can be summarized for n generations by the following formula.

$$sn = \log_e \frac{q_0\,(1-q_n)}{q_n\,(1-q_0)} \qquad = 2.303 \log_{10} \frac{q_0\,(1-q_n)}{q_n\,(1-q_0)}$$

- **Zygotic selection**

In most higher animals and plants selection occurs in the zygotic stage. The effectiveness of selection depends upon the degree of dominance. If the dominance is complete, the selection occurs only against the recessive homozygotes (e.g., *aa*) whereas, heterozygote is shielded from selection and persists for many generations.

**TABLE 25.8**

| | Genotypes | | Total |
|---|---|---|---|
| | *A* | *a* | |
| 1. Initial frequency | $p_0$ | $q_0$ | 1 |
| 2. Fitness | 1 | $1-s$ | |
| 3. Frequency after selection | *p* | $q(1-s)$ | $p+q-qs = 1-qs$ |
| 4. Fraction of selection frequency | $\frac{P}{1-qs}$ | $\frac{q(1-s)}{1-qs}$ | |

5. Change in the frequency of "a" $= \Delta q = q_i - q$

$$= \frac{q(1-s)}{1-qs} - q = \frac{q - qs - q + q^2 s}{1-qs} = \frac{-qs(1-q)}{1-qs}$$

**TABLE 25.9**

| | Genotypes | | | Total | frequency of a |
|---|---|---|---|---|---|
| | *AA* | *Aa* | *aa* | | |
| 1. Initial frequency | $p^2$ | $2pq$ | $q^2$ | 1 | $q$ |
| 2. Fitness | 1 | 1 | 0 | | |
| 3. Frequency after selection | $p^2$ | $2pq$ | 0 | $p(p+2q)$ $= p(1+q)$ | |
| 4. Relative frequency | $\frac{p^2}{p(1+q)}$ | $\frac{2pq}{p(1+q)}$ | 0 | | $\frac{1}{2}\left[\frac{2pq}{p(1+q)}\right]$ |
| | $=\frac{p}{1+q}$ | $=\frac{2q}{1+q}$ | | | $=\left[\frac{q}{1+q}\right]$ |
| 5. Change in frequency $= \Delta q = \frac{q}{1+q} - q = \frac{-q^2}{1+q}$ | | | | | |

**1. Change in gene frequency of a gene that is lethal in homozygous condition (i.e., *s* =*1*)**

Let, we begin with a population in which *aa* is lethal but *AA* and *Aa* are normal. The gene frequency then changes for *a* after one generation would be as follows (See Table 25.9) :

If the value of $q$ initially is large then the decreasing change in relative frequency will occur. But if the value of $q$ is small, then the denominator *1+q* becomes 1. Then the change in relative frequency would be approximately $q^2$, i.e., no change in its value. Thus selection against recessive lethal genes is quite inefficient when the genes are present in low frequency because only a very few recessive homozygotes are formed.

**2. Change in frequency of a gene that is deleterious but not lethal in recessive homozygous condition (i.e., 0<*s*<1)**

When the recessive homozygotes are deleterious but are not lethal, the selection coefficient (s) lies between 0 and 1. The change in relative gene frequency would be occurred after one generation is described as follows (See table 25.10)

From the above deduction, it is evident that when *a* is rare, the product $sq^2$ is very small, and then the denominator becomes nearly 1. Under these conditions $\Delta q$ would be essentially $-sq^2$. Therefore, for a small value of $q$, the change in gene frequency per generation is quite small. On the other hand, for the larger value of $q$, the change in $q$ is also larger and reaches a maximum value when $q = \frac{2}{3}$.

The phenomenon of industrial melanism has been best studied in the moth *Biston bitularia* in England. Until the middle of nineteenth century these moths were a uniformly peepered light gray colour. Then darkly pigmented variants started to appear in the industrial regions, where the vegetation has gradually blackened owing to polution from shoot and other wastes. In some localities the dark varieties have almost completely replaced the light ones.

- **Change in frequency for one generation of selection against a dominant deleterious gene**

The selective sequence is reversed in the case of dominant allele. The dominant allele is

**TABLE 25.10**

| | Genotypes | | | Total | Frequency of a |
|---|---|---|---|---|---|
| | AA | Aa | aa | | |
| 1. Initial frequency | $p^2$ | $2pq$ | $q^2$ | 1 | $q$ |
| 2. Fitness ($w$) | 1 | 1 | $1-s$ | | |
| 3. Frequency after selection | $p^2$ | $2pq$ | $q^2(1-s)$ | $p^2+2pq+q^2(1-s)$ $=1-sq^2$ | |
| 4. Relative frequency | $\frac{p^2}{1-sq^2}$ | $\frac{2pq}{1-sq^2}$ | $\frac{q^2(1-s)}{1-sq^2}$ | | $\frac{1}{2}\times\frac{2pq}{1-sq^2}+\frac{q^2(1-s)}{1-sq^2}$ $=\frac{q(1-sq)}{1-sq^2}$ |

5. Change in relative frequency

$$\Delta q = \frac{q(1-sq)}{1-sq^2} - q = \frac{q(1-sq)-q(1-sq^2)}{1-sq^2} = \left[\frac{-sq^2(1-q)}{1-sq^2}\right] = \left[\frac{-sq^2p}{1-sq^2}\right]$$

then selected against the recessive, which is now favoured. If the dominant allele is deleterious then the fitness is les than 1, and if it is lethal fitness would be zero.

The change in frequency of dominant alleles under selection after one generation would be as follows (See table 25.11) :

**TABLE 25.11**

| | Genotypes | | | Total | Frequency of A |
|---|---|---|---|---|---|
| | AA | Aa | aa | | |
| 1. Initial frequency | $p^2$ | $2pq$ | $q^2$ | 1 | p |
| 2. Fitness ($w$) | $1-s$ | $1-s$ | 1 | | |
| 3. Frequency after selection | $p^2(1-s)$ | $2pq(1-s)$ | $q^2$ | $1-sp(2-p)$ | |
| 4. Relative frequency | $\frac{p^2(1-s)}{1-sp(2-p)}$ | $\frac{2pq(1-s)}{1-sp(2-p)}$ | $\frac{q^2}{1-sp(2-p)}$ | | $\frac{p^2(1-s)}{1-sp(2-p)}+\frac{1}{2}\frac{2pq(1-s)}{1-sp(2-p)}$ $=\frac{p-sp}{1-sp(2-p)}$ |

5. Change in relative frequency of A

$$\Delta p = \frac{p-sp}{1-sp(2-p)} - p = \frac{p-sq-p+2sp^2-sp^3}{1-sp(2-p)} = \frac{-sq(1-p)^2}{1-sp(2-p)}$$

**TABLE 25.12**

| *Genotype* | *Dark* | *Light* | *Total* |
|---|---|---|---|
| (a) Number released | 154 | 64 | 218 |
| (b) Number captured | 82 | 16 | 98 |
| (c) Survival rate $\frac{\text{No. captured}}{\text{No. released}}$ | $\frac{82}{154} = 0.53$ | $\frac{16}{64} = 0.25$ | |
| (d) Relative fitness ($w$) | $\frac{0.53}{0.53} = 1$ | $\frac{0.25}{0.53} = 0.47$ | |
| (e) Selection coefficient ($s$) | 0 | $1 - 0.47 = 0.53$ | |

From the above discussion, it is evident that if $s$ is small $\Delta p$ is effectively equal to $[-sp\,(1-p)^2]$,

Since, $1-p$ is $q$ and $1-q = p$, then $\Delta p$ would be $-sq^2(1-q)$ or $\Delta p$ is identical to $\Delta q$ at low selection coefficient.

- **Predation by birds**

The replacement of light forms by dark forms of *Biston bitularia* in industrial regions is due to differential predation by birds. On the tree trunk darkened by pollution, the light gray forms become conspicuous while the dark forms are well camouflaged. H.B.D Kettlewell (1962) released marked dark and light moths near Birmingham which is a heavily industrialized area. The proportion of recaptured moths were 53% for the dark form and 25% for the light form. Since the fertility of the two forms is about the same, we may assume that relative fitness determined exclusively by the survival rate mostly due to predation (See table 25.12).

We do not know the frequency to heterozygotes, then we have to calculate $q$ from the total population.

$$q^2 = \frac{64}{218} = 0.2937$$

$$q = \sqrt{0.2937} = 0.541$$

So, $p = 1 - q = 1 - 0.541 = 0.459$

$2pq = 2 \times 0.549 \times 0.459 = 0.496$

$p^2 = (0.459)^2 = 0.210$

$q^2 = 0.293$

So, $p^2 + q^2 + 2pq = 0.210 + 0.293 + 0.496$

$= 0.999$ or 1

Selection coefficient $s = 0.53$

$$\Delta q = \frac{-spq^2}{1-sq^2} = \frac{-0.53 \times 0.459 \times 0.541^2}{0.845} = \boxed{-0.084}$$

- **Changes in frequency in one generation of selection against a deleterious gene that shows no dominance (i.e., the effect is additive)**

When the dominance of the advantageous allele is incomplete, heterozygotes will show the effect of a deleterious gene since the heterozygous phenotype is at least partially deleterious. If the dominance is incomplete, the heterozygote has a phenotype exactly intermediate to that of the two homozygotes, its selection coefficient will be exactly half that of the deleterious homozygotes. The change of allelic frequency would be calculated as follows (See table 25.13):

- **Heterozygous advantage and changes in frequencies of a gene in one generation of selection**

Various conditions permit the establishment of an equilibrium through which

**TABLE 25.13**

| | Genotypes | | | Total | Frequency of a |
|---|---|---|---|---|---|
| | AA | Aa | aa | | |
| 1. Initial frequency | $p^2$ | $2pq$ | $q^2$ | 1 | $q$ |
| 2. Fitness ($w$) | 1 | $1-s$ | $1-2s$ | | |
| 3. Frequency after selection | $p^2$ | $2pq(1-s)$ | $q^2(1-2s)$ | $(1-2sq)$ | |
| 4. Relative fitness | $\frac{p^2}{1-2sq}$ | $\frac{2pq(1-s)}{1-2sq}$ | $\frac{q^2(1-2s)}{1-2sp}$ | | $\frac{1}{2} \times \frac{2pq(1-s)}{1-2sq} + \frac{q^2(1-2s)}{1-2sq}$ $= \frac{q-sq(1+q)}{1-2sq}$ |
| 5. Change in reative frequency of $a$ | | | | | |

$$\Delta q = \frac{q-sq(1+q)}{1-2sq} - q = \frac{q-sq-sq^2-q+2sq^2}{1-2sq} = \frac{-sq(1-q)}{1-2sq}$$

both alleles may remain indefinitely within the population. One such condition is based on the constant selective coefficients, is known as **overdominance**. It is observed when the heterozygote has superior reproductive fitness to both the homozygotes. Then the heterozygotes (*Aa*) have a fitness of 1 while the fitness of homozygotes *AA* and *aa* are (1–s) and (1–t) respectively. The changes in frequency of *'a'* in a single generation would be as follows (See table 25.14) :

When $\Delta q = 0$, i.e., equilibrium has been reached, $pq(ps-qt)$ would be equal to zero or p or q would be zero.

If $p$ or $q = 0$, both the genes will not be present in the population at the same time and balance or equilibrium will absent.

**TABLE 25.14**

| | Genotypes | | | Total | Frequency of a |
|---|---|---|---|---|---|
| | AA | Aa | aa | | |
| 1. Initial frequency | $p^2$ | $2pq$ | $q^2$ | 1 | q |
| 2. Fitness ($w$) | $(1-s)$ | 1 | $(1-t)$ | | |
| 3. Frequency after selection | $p^2(1-s)$ | $2pq$ | $q^2(1-t)$ | $1-p^2s-q^2t$ | |
| 4. Relative fitness | $\frac{p^2(1-s)}{1-p^2s-q^2t}$ | $\frac{2pq}{1-p^2s-q^2t}$ | $\frac{q^2(1-t)}{1-p^2s-q^2t}$ | | $\frac{1}{2} \times \frac{2pq}{1-p^2s-q^2t} + \frac{q^2(1-t)}{1-p^2s-q^2t}$ $= \frac{q(1-qt)}{1-p^2s-q^2t}$ |
| 5. Change in relative frequency of a | | | | | |

$$\Delta q = \frac{q(1-qt)}{1-p^2s-q^2t} - q = \frac{q(1-qt)-q(1-p^2s-q^2t)}{1-p^2s-q^2t} = \frac{pq(ps-qt)}{1-p^2s-q^2t}$$

The equilibrium will be established if $ps - qt = 0$ or $ps = qt$

$$\text{or, } \frac{p}{q} = \frac{t}{s} \quad \text{or, } \frac{p}{p+q} = \frac{t}{t+s} \quad \text{or, } p = \frac{t}{s+t}$$

$$\text{similarly } q = \frac{s}{s+t}$$

From the above deduction, it is evident that, if $s$ and $t$ are constant values, both $p$ and $q$ will reach a stable equilibrium, i.e., if $q$ departs from the equilibrium value, selection pressure will force it back.

If $\Delta q$ is positive, the gene frequency $q$ increases again if $\Delta q$ is negative, $q$ decreases. The negative or positive value of $\Delta q$ depends on whether $q$ is above or below its equilibrium value.

When $q$ is below the equilibrium value, $\Delta q$ is positive and acts to increase the value of $q$ so that the equilibrium is reached. On the other hand, when $q$ is above the equilibrium value, $\Delta q$ is negative and acts to decrease the value of $q$ toward the same equilibrium. Thus both the alleles remain in the population at frequencies $p$ and $q$ so long as the selection pressure coefficients confer superior fitness on the heterozygotes.

The persistence of different genotypes through heterozygote superiority is an example of *balanced polymorphism*, a term invented by Ford (1940) to describe the preservation of genetic variability through selection. The polymorphism has been examined at the chromosome level as well as genetic level. One prominent example of polymorphism that overdominance causes the sickle cell gene in human, where heterozygotes ($Hb^A/Hb^S$) survive the malarial parasite more successfully than other normal $Hb^A/Hb^A$ or sickle cell homozygotes ($Hb^S/Hb^S$). This gene persists in notable frequencies in geographical areas where malaria is endemic and heterozygotes offer protection against malaria.

## 25.12 UNSTABLE EQUILIBRIUM

If any disturbance of equilibrium frequencies causes one of the genes to go to "fixation" then, they are considered to be unstable.

One type of such unstable equilibrium may be observed in the case of heterozygotes at a gene locus with two alleles. If both homozygotes have equal adaptive values and the heterozygote is inferior, then the equilibrium is produced only when the frequency of each of the two alleles is exactly equal to 0.5. Any slight departure from these frequencies will cause the less frequent alleles to have proportionately more of its genes in heterozygous than the more frequent allele. In this case one allele will gradually diminished and eliminated and other allele would go to fixation.

Suppose, gene frequency of '*A*' is 0.6 and '*a*' is 0.4. Heterozygotes are lethal, then we can calculate the elimination of gene '*a*' in the population through unstable equilibrium.

1. Initial gene frequency
   $AA = 0.6\ (p)\ aa = 0.4(q)$
2. After first generation
   $AA = p^2 = (0.6)^2 = 0.36$ will survive
   $aa = q^2 = (.4)^2 = 0.16$ will also survive

and, $Aa = 2.pq = 2 \times .6 \times .4 = .48$ will not survive

$$\text{Thus, frequency of } A = \frac{0.36}{0.52} = 0.69$$

$$\text{frequency of } a = \frac{0.16}{0.52} = 0.31$$

3. Initial gene frequency at second generation
   $AA = 0.69 \qquad aa = 0.31$
4. After second generation:
   $AA = (0.69)^2 = 0.476$ will survive
   $aa = (0.31)^2 = 0.096$ will survive.

and, $Aa = 2 \times 0.69 \times 0.31 = 0.4278$ will not survive,

$$\text{Frequency of } A = \frac{.476}{572} = 0.83$$

$$\text{and } a = \frac{0.096}{0.572} = 0.17$$

Thus within a few generations, the *A* gene would go to fixation and *a* gene would be eliminated.

Example of such unstable equilibrium may be observed in human Rh blood group system where Rh negative mother (*rr*) bears an Rh positive child (*Rr*) dies as a result of hemolytic disease. It is observed that Rh-negative gene is infrequent, few Rh-negative mothers are found and the heterozygote has a lower selection coefficient.

## 25.13 MUTATION RATES

In a population, gene frequency is affected by the frequency of mutations. If gene *'A'* is continuously mutated to *'a'* but the reverse mutation does not occur, then the frequency of mutant *'a'* will increase from generation to generation. After a long time the mutant gene can fully replace the normal *"A"* gene.

Let, $p_0$ is the initial frequency of gene *'A'* and the rate of mutation is $u$ per generation.

So, after one generation the gene frequency of *"A"* is reduced to $p_0(1-u)$.

In the next generation the frequency of *'A'* gene would be $u \times p_0\ (1-u)$. Therefore, the frequency of gene 'A' would be

$$p_0(1-u) - up_0(1-u)$$
$$= p_0(1-u-u+u^2)$$
$$= p_0(1-u)^2$$

After, n generation,. the frequency of gene *'A'* would be $= p_0(1-u)^n$

The value of $u$ is very small. Therefore, the value of $(1-u)^n$ after a large enough generations will approach zero and then *"A"* will disappear.

It may be assumed that mutant *'a'* may again be mutated back to *"A"* with a rate $v$ because mutation does not occur in only one direction.

If the initial frequency of allele *'A'* is $p_0$ and *'a'* is $q_0$, after a single generation of mutation, will produce a frequency of *'A'* is $(p_0 + vq_0)$ and the frequency of *'a'* is $(q_0 + up_0)$.

Change of frequency of allele *'a'* is

$$\Delta q = up_0 - vq_0.$$

From this equation, it can be assumed that as the value of $p$ is large and $q$ is small, $\Delta q$ would be large and $q$ would increase rapidly. Again as *'q'* increases, $p$ decreases and then $\Delta q$ would diminish in size. At a certain point $p$ and $q$ will be balanced in relation to their mutation frequencies, then $\Delta q = 0$. This is called **mutational equilibrium** ($\hat{q}$).

So, at equilibrium condition

$$\Delta q = 0 = up - vq$$

or, $up = vq$

or, $u(1-q) = vq$ because $(p = 1-q)$

$$u = q(u+v)$$

$$\hat{q} = \frac{u}{u+v}$$

Similarly $\hat{p} = \dfrac{v}{u+v}$

Then $\dfrac{\hat{p}}{\hat{q}} = \dfrac{v}{u+v} \Big/ \dfrac{u}{u+v} = \dfrac{v}{u}$

When there is equality between the mutation rates i.e. $u = v$, the equilibrium gene frequencies $\hat{p}$ and $\hat{q}$ will be identical.

If the initial frequency of *'a'* is $q_0$ and after 'n' generations, the frequency reaches to $q_n$. The formula $(u+v)n = \log_e \dfrac{(q_0 - \hat{q})}{(q_n - \hat{q})}$ may be obtained through calculus. [the value of $\log_e = 2.718$.]

This formula can be converted to use the common logarithms to the base 10, then the formula would be $(u+v)n = 2.303 \log_{10} \dfrac{(q_0 - \hat{q})}{(q_n - \hat{q})}$.

For example, if the mutation rates $u = 0.00005$ and $v = 0.00003$, the equilibrium frequency

$$\hat{q} = \frac{u}{u+v} = \frac{0.00005}{0.00005 + 0.00003} = \frac{5}{8} = 0.625$$

$$\hat{p} = \frac{v}{u+v} = \frac{3}{8} = 0.375$$

Then, from the above formula, the value of n (generations), can be calculated when the mutational equilibrium would be established.

$$(0.00008)n = \log_e \frac{0.125 - 0.625}{0.375 - 0.625}$$

$$= \log_e 2$$

$$= 0.69315$$

$$\text{Then, } n = \frac{0.69315}{0.00008} = 8664 \text{ generations}$$

If the rate of mutation is $5 \times 10^5$ or less, the equilibrium would probably rarely occur. Therefore, to reach equilibrium, mutation rates would subject to a variety of modifying genes.

Kimura *et al* have pointed out that the chances for a reverse mutation to occur at a specific amino acid site on a protein is probably very small and mutational equilibrium should not be expected. For example, a gene coding 200 amino acids has 600 nucleotides. If at any position one nucleotide substitution occurred during mutation. Then 1800 possible mutations would provide an exact reversion of previously existing codon. So reverse mutation chance is more than thousand times smaller and can safely be ignored as a factor enabling mutation rate equilibria to be reached for single nucleotide or single amino acid.

## 25.14 EQUILIBRIUM BETWEEN MUTATION AND SELECTION

Mutation produces both dominant and recessive deleterious alleles; on the other hand, selection tries to eliminate both of them. Thus selection and mutation have opposite effects with respect to deleterious alleles. The net effect of these two processes will be nil.

### 35.9.1 Deleterious Recessive Allele

We have seen that the changes in gene frequency per generation for a deleterious recessive "a" with frequency $q$ are at a loss $\Delta q = \frac{sp^2(1-q)}{1 - sq^2}$ per generation.

If 's' is small, the denominator can be considered one and loss in frequency is then $sq^2(1-q)$ *i.e.*, $spq^2$.

But the frequency of recessive allele 'q' will however increase by the mutation rate ($u$) of $A \rightarrow a$ is "$u.p$". There will be an equilibrium between mutation and selection when

$$up = spq^2$$

$$\text{or, } u = sq^2 \quad \text{or, } q^2 = \frac{u}{s} \quad \text{or, } q = \sqrt{\frac{u}{s}}$$

From the above equation, we can say that the frequency of 'a' is directly proportional to the square root of 'u' and inversely proportional to the square root of 's'.

When $s = 1$ i.e., selection coefficient is 1 or say fitness is zero due to lethality or sterility in homozygous condition, the value of $q$ becomes $\sqrt{u}$, i.e., the square root of mutation rate.

**Example :** If the rate of mutation $u = 10^{-5}$ then, the frequency of lethal allele

$$q = \sqrt{u} = \sqrt{10^{-5}} = 0.003$$

Again if the mutant allele "a" is not lethal but recessive and the value of $s = 0.1$,

Then, the frequency of the allele

$$q = \sqrt{\frac{u}{s}} = \sqrt{\frac{10^{-5}}{0.1}} = 0.01$$

Therefore, the frequency of mutant recessive deleterious allele is three times higher than that of the recessive lethal allele.

### 25.14.2 Deleterious Dominant Alleles

In the case of deleterious dominant allele, the frequency of $p$ will decrease owing to the selection but will increase due to mutation. We know that selection against a dominant allele of gene frequency $p$ results in a change of

$$\Delta p = \frac{-sp(1-p)^2}{1 - sp(2-p)}$$

Now if $s$ is very small, then $\Delta p$ approaches to $-sp(1-p)^2$.

Again, the mutation rate from recessive to dominant "$u$" produces new dominant alleles at a frequency of $uq$ or $u(1-p)$.

Equilibrium between selection and mutation then occur when

$$sp \times (1-p)^2 = u(1-p)$$

$$\text{or, } p(1-p) = \frac{u}{s}$$

Again, $p$ is small because the dominant allele is selected against. Then $(1-p)$ can be considered as 1. Then the equation becomes :

$$p = \frac{u}{s}$$

When $s = 1$

*i.e.* the dominant mutation is lethal, then $p = u$ i.e., mutation rate.

**Example :**

If mutation rate = $10^{-5}$ then $p$ would be $10^{-5}$ *i.e.*, 300 times smaller than that of the recessive lethal (0.003), since $q = \sqrt{u}$.

The heterozygous for the alleles *Aa* will also express the trait. Its frequency is $2pq$. As $p$ is very small, $q$ will nearly one, then the frequency $2pq$ is equivalent to $2p$.

Example:

1. A disease Achondroplesia, the mutation frequency is $5 \times 10^{-5}$ and 20% can reproduce.

   $w = 0.2$ or $s = 0.8$.

   Then equilibrium frequency $p = \frac{u}{s}$
   $= 5 \times 10^{-5}/0.8 = 6.25 \times 10^{-5}$

   This will also express in $2pq$

   Again since, $q \simeq 1$

   Then $2pq = 2p = 2 \times 6.25 \times 10^{-5}$
   $= 1.25 \times 10^{-4}$

   So, the result is that 1.25 individuals/10000 which is indeed the frequency of Achondroplesia may develop in population.

2. The mutation rate of Down's syndrome is $\frac{1}{700}$

   Their selection coefficient $s = 1$
   *i.e.*, fitness = 0

   *i.e.*, none of them can reproduce.

   Then $p = \frac{u}{s} = \frac{u}{1} = u = \frac{1}{700} = 0.0014$

   This will also express in $2pq$

   Since $q \simeq 1$

   Then $2pq = 2p = 2 \times 0.0014 = 0.0028$.

   So, 28 births per 10000 individuals in the population will develop Down's syndrome.

## 25.15 CHANGES IN ALLELE FREQUENCIES DUE TO MIGRATION

Migration or "gene flow" refers to the influx of individuals from one population to another, both of which maintain an entirely distinct gene frequency with respect to other. In simple meaning, *migration is the introduction of new individuals with new genotypes into Mendelian population*. The population from which the individuals are migrating is the migrant and which receives the migratings is the *recepient population*.

Assume that individuals from surrounding populations migrate at a certain rate into a local population and there interbreed with the residents.

Suppose, the black allele (*B*) is higher in the insect population "Y" than "X". Let a random sample from X-population is migrated to the Y-population and vice versa. If Q and $Q_0$ representing the white recessive alleles in the original population and a fraction 'm' of the total number of individuals now present in Y population, then a new frequency is established $Q_1$ in the Y population.

So, $Q_1 = (1-m)\,Q_0 + mQ$

Then change in frequency of white allele in the Y- population after one generation will be

$$\Delta Q = Q_1 - Q_0$$
$$= (1-m)\,Q_0 + mQ - Q_0$$
$$= -m\,(Q_0 - Q)$$

When numerical values are added into this equation and value of $Q_0$ changes significantly, upsetting the equilibrium of the Hardy-Weinberg equation.

From the above equation it is evident that greater the proportion of migrant individuals and the greater is the difference between allelic frequencies, the greater, $\Delta Q$ becomes. Notice that $\Delta Q$ will be zero only when either m=0 or $Q_0 - Q = 0$. Therefore, unless migration stops, the allelic frequency will continue to change until it becomes the same in the local population, as in the surrounding population (i.e., $Q_1 - Q = 0$).

After first generation, the difference in allele frequency between the local and surrounding population will be :

$$Q_1 - Q = (1-m)\,Q_0 + mQ - Q$$
$$= (1-m)\,Q_0 - (1-m)Q$$
$$= (1-m)\,(Q_0 - Q)$$

After second generation, the difference in allele frequency will be

$$Q_2 - P = (1-m)Q_1 + mQ - Q$$
$$= (1-m)\{(1-m)Q_0 + mQ\} + mQ - Q$$
$$= (1-m)^2Q_0 + mQ - m^2Q + mQ - Q$$
$$= (1-m)^2Q_0 - (1-m)^2Q$$
$$= (1-m)^2\,(Q_0 - Q)$$

After 't' generations of migration, the difference in allele frequency will be :

$$Q_t - Q = (1-m)^t \times (Q_0 - Q)$$

or $$Q_t = (1-m)^t\,(Q_0 - Q) + Q$$

Rearranging the equation we also get

$$(1-m)^t = \frac{Q_t - Q}{Q_0 - Q}$$

Rate of *Gene flow* (m) can be calculated from the above equation after a certain time as well as after the number of generations.

**Example :**

In USA, people of mixed Caucasian and Black descent are considered members of black population. Racial admixture can be seen as a process of gene flow from the Caucasian to the Black populations. The frequency of $R^o$ allele at the locus determining the Rhesus blood group is Q = 0.028 in U.S. Caucasian populations. Among the African populations from which the Black came, the frequency of $R^0$ is 0.630 and which can be considered as the initial allele frequency of U.S. Black population $Q_0 = 0.630$. The African ancestors of US Blacks came to USA about 300 years or 10 generations ago; hence t = 10 and the frequency of $R^o$ among US Blacks is at present is $Q_t = 0.446$.

From the deduction we get

$$(1-m)^t = \frac{Q_t - Q}{Q_0 - Q}$$

Substituting the values of various parameters we have :

$$(1-m)^{10} = \frac{0.446 - 0.028}{0.630 - 0.028} = 0.694$$

$$\therefore (1-m) = \sqrt[10]{0.694} = 0.964$$

$$m = 0.036$$

So, the gene flow from US Caucasians to US Black population has occurred at the rate equivalent to as an average of 3.6% per generation and after 10 generations of these gene flow left $(1-m)^{10} = 0.694$ of all genes in US Blacks derived from their African ancestors and 1 – 0.964 = 0.036 or somewhat 3.6% of their genes derived from their Caucasian ancestors.

## 25.16 CHANGES IN ALLELE FREQUENCIES DUE TO GENETIC DRIFT

**Genetic drift** is the random fluctuation of gene frequency due to chance occurrence in a finite population. The random genetic drift is also known as **Sewell-Wright effect**.

Genetic drift is caused by the fact that real populations are limited in size rather than infinite, so that gene frequency changes because of sampling errors.

A random drift can be easily visualized by an example. If a coin is tossed 1000 times, expected number of heads will be roughly 500 and tail of 500. But the experimental result may be of 510 heads and 490 tails or the ratio may be near about it. It is sure that there would not be a result of 700 heads and 300 tails in the tossing experiment. But if we may have 7 heads and 3 tails, this fluctuation in result may be due to small sampling.

Similarly, if only a few parents are chosen to begin a new generation, such a small sample of genes may deviate widely from the gene frequency of the previous generation.

The extent of deviation of samples for any size of population can be estimated mathematically by standard deviation $\sigma = \sqrt{\dfrac{pq}{N}}$

Where $p$ is the frequency of one allele, $q$ is the other and N is the number of genes sampled.

For diploid parents, each carrying two genes, then $\sigma = \sqrt{\dfrac{pq}{2N}}$

When we begin with a large population where N = 5000, $p$ and $q$ are both equal to 0.5 then

$$\sigma = \sqrt{\frac{0.5 \times 0.5}{2 \times 5000}} = 0.005$$

This means that values of small population will usually vary around 0.5 ± 0.005 i.e., between 0.495 and 0.505.

But if there are two parents in the population and the allelic frequencies remain same then $\sigma = \sqrt{\dfrac{0.5 \times 0.5}{2 \times 2}} = 0.025$. The mean values of such population will vary around 0.5 ± 0.25 ie between 0.25 and 0.75. Again if the next population remains small and next generation begins with either of the extremes i.e. 0.25 and 0.75, the standard deviation is $\sqrt{\dfrac{0.25 \times 0.75}{2 \times 2}} = 0.22$.

The following generation may have the frequency of the allele reduced to 0.25± 0.22 i.e., a range of 0.03 to 0.47 (almost to zero) or may be increased to 0.75 ± 0.22 i.e., 0.53 to 0.97 (almost to one).

If such small population continues each generation that allelic frequency may be eliminated or predominantly fixed in the population. When N is large, the rate of fixation is slow.

The number of parents is therefore an important value for the determination of drift and is called **effective population size** ($N_e$). It differs from the observed population size because not all members of a population are necessarily parents. If there are 300 pairs of mating parents then the effective population size is 600.

Population size is also reduced if one of the sexes is present in reduced number, so that the percentage of the next generation is limited by this sex.

For example, if out of a total population of 1000, 30 males mated to 300 females to produce next generation, the effective population size is more than 60 but less than 250.

Wright has expressed the relationship as $N_e = 4N_fNm/N_f{+}N_m$

Where $N_f$ = number of parental females and

$N_m$ = number of parental males.

Therefore, in the above case,

$$N_e = \frac{4 \times 300 \times 30}{360} = 100$$

Wright has therefore proposed that genetic drift may be quite important in changing gene frequencies among populations when their effective population size is small.

### Founder principle :

Occasional $N_e$- size reductions can cause a drastic effect on gene frequencies even in one or two generations. **Founder principle** (Mayr 1942) is that a population may occasionally send forth only a few founders to begin a new population. Whatever genes and chromosome arrangements, these founders take with them, either beneficial or detrimental, have a good chance of becoming established in the new population.

For example, if we take 5 founder birds, one male and one female bird among them by chance become heterozygous for a rare gene *'c'*. Therefore, in the population 2 of every 10 gametes will carry *'c'* gene *i.e.* frequency of *'c'* gene is 0.2. In the next generation the frequency of *aa* homozygotes would be $0.2 \times 0.2 = 0.04$ i.e., 4% in the population. Such an usual allele frequency and phenotype in isolated new colony is possibly due to Founder's principle.

The human population, in Amish of Lancaster, Pennsylvania, three couples in the year 1770 founded a population one of them were carrier of the recessive gene, a combination of dwarfism and polydactylism. The colony virtually isolated from the rest of the world. Now about 13% of the individuals in the colony are estimated to carry this mutant gene and 60 cases (out of 17000) of such abnormality has now been occurred in this population, which is more than the rest of the world population.

### Bottleneck effect :

Theoretically, the number of individuals of a species tends to remain approximately constant in a locality. Stebbins proposed the bottleneck effect which states that a species may be very abundant in one year and may be rare in another year. When it is rare, the small population is of a special significance because they are the sources for another built up of species. Such small populations are called **bottleneck**.

For example, Roberts has shown that, on the Atlantic Ocean Island of Tristan de Cunha, one couple, the founder of the population was settleled there in 1816. In 1855 they contributed more than 25% of the genes. But in 1961 approximately 45% of genes present, which can ascribe only 5 ancestors. The lack of uniformity is due to the reduction in the size of population that occurred by chance in 1856 and 1885. After each of these bottlenecks, there were marked effects on the composition of gene pool caused by relative changes in the contribution of certain ancestors.

## 25.17 PROBLEMS ON H.W. EQUILIBRIUM

### Problem 1

At a particular locus, there are two alleles *B* and *b*. The mutation rate of *B* to *b* is $3.5 \times 10^{-4}$, whereas the mutation rate of *b* to *B* is $6 \times 10^{-8}$. What is the equilibrium frequency of the *b* allele, assuming no other factors are operating in this population to disturb the Hardy-Weinberg equilibrium.

**Solution :**

We, let $q = f(b)$

$$\mu = 3.5 \times 10^{-4}\ (B \xrightarrow{\mu} b)$$

$$\nu = 6 \times 10^{-8}\ (b \xrightarrow{\nu} B)$$

We then simply substitute μ and ν into the equation

$$\hat{q} = \frac{\mu}{\mu + \nu} = \frac{3.5 \times 10^{-4}}{3.5 \times 10^{-4} + 6 \times 10^{-8}} = 0.9998$$

### Problem 2

In a laboratory, colony of fruit flies, the fitness of the genotypes of an electrophoretic locus (malate dehydrogenase) are determined, *FF*, *FS* and *SS* have fitness of 0.85, 1.0 and 0.6 respectively. What is the equilibrium frequency of the slow allele (*S*)? [Where *F* = fast]

**Solution :**

As fitness of three genotypes *FF*, *FS* and *SS* are given, and then the locus is exhibiting heterozygote advantage with selection coefficients of the two homozygotes of

$s_1 = 1 - 0.85 = 0.15$

$s_2 = 1 - 0.6 = 0.4$

If q is the frequency of the slow allele(s) then using equation for

$$\hat{q} = \frac{s_1}{s_1 + s_2} = \frac{0.15}{0.15 + 0.4} = 0.27$$

**Problem 3**

In a particular population with two alleles at a locus, the frequency of *AA* individuals = 0.25, *Aa* = 0.5 and *aa* = 0.25. If the *Aa* genotype fitness is 1, *Aa* = 0.8 and *aa* = 0.6, what will the frequencies of *A* and *a* be in the next generation? Assume mutations do not occur.

**Solution :**

The allele frequencies of *A* and *a* in the next generation may be calculated as per following table :

| | Genotypes | | | |
|---|---|---|---|---|
| | AA | Aa | aa | Total |
| 1. Genotypic frequencies | 0.25 | 0.5 | 0.25 | 1 |
| 2. Fitness ($w$) | 1 | 0.8 | 0.6 | |
| 3. Contribution to the gene pool (genotypic frequencies after selection) | 1 ×0.25 = 0.25 | 0.8 ×0.5 = 0.4 | 0.6 ×0.25 = 0.15 | 0.25 + 0.4 + 0.15 = 0.8 |
| 4. Relative genotypic frequencies after selection | 0.25/0.8 = 0.3125 | 0.4/0.8 = 0.5 | 0.15/0.8 = 0.1875 | |

Allelic frequencies after selection

$$f(A) = 0.3125 + \frac{1}{2}(0.5) = 0.3125 + 0.25 = 0.5625$$

$$f(a) = 0.1875 + \frac{1}{2}(0.5) = 0.1875 + 0.25 = 0.4375$$

**Problem 4**

In three different populations, the relative fitness of genotypes differing in respect to one pair of genes *A* and *a*, was found to be as follows :

| Population | Relative fitnesses | | |
|---|---|---|---|
| | AA | Aa | aa |
| 1 | 0.5 | 1.00 | 0.00 |
| 2 | 0.75 | 1.00 | 0.50 |
| 3 | 0.90 | 1.00 | 0.80 |

(a) Assuming that only selection is operating on these genotypes, what are the equilibrium frequencies of the genes *A* and *a* in each of these population?

(b) If all three of these populations began with exactly the same gene frequencies, A =0.40, a = 0.60 explain which of these populations would approach their equilibrium gene frequencies fastest?

**Solution :**

(a) In all populations, fitness value of heterozygote (*Aa*) is 1.00, exhibits heterozygote advantage.

**In population 1**

| | ***AA*** | ***Aa*** | ***aa*** |
|---|---|---|---|
| Relative fitness (*w*) | 0.5 | 1.00 | 0.00 |
| Selection coefficient ($s = 1-w$) | 0.5 ($s_1$) | 0 | 1 ($s_2$) |

The equilibrium frequencies of gene *A* ($\hat{p}$) will be

$$\hat{p} = \frac{s_2}{s_1 + s_2} = \frac{1}{0.5 + 1.0} = \frac{1}{1.5} = 0.66$$

$$\text{and } \hat{q} = \frac{s_1}{s_1 + s_2} = \frac{0.5}{1.5} = 0.33$$

**In population 2**

| | ***AA*** | ***Aa*** | ***aa*** |
|---|---|---|---|
| Relative fitness (*w*) | 0.75 | 1.00 | 0.50 |
| Selection coefficient ($s = 1-w$) | 0.25 ($s_1$) | 0 | 0.50 ($s_2$) |

Equilibrium frequencies of gene *A* ($\hat{p}$) will be

$$\hat{p} = \frac{s_2}{s_1 + s_2} = \frac{0.5}{0.25 + 0.5} = \frac{0.5}{0.75} = 0.66$$

Equilibrium frequencies of gene *A* ($\hat{q}$) will be

$$\hat{q} = \frac{s_1}{s_1 + s_2} = \frac{0.25}{0.75} = 0.33$$

**In population 3**

| | ***AA*** | ***Aa*** | ***aa*** |
|---|---|---|---|
| Relative fitness (*w*) | 0.9 | 1.00 | 0.80 |
| Selection coefficient (*s*) ($s = 1-w$) | 0.1 ($s_1$) | 0.00 | 0.20 ($s_2$) |

Equilibrium frequencies of *A* ($\hat{p}$)

$$= \frac{s_2}{s_1 + s_2} = \frac{0.20}{0.10 + 0.20} = \frac{0.20}{0.30} = 0.66$$

Equilibrium frequencies of gene *a* ($\hat{q}$)

$$\frac{s_1}{s_1 + s_2} = \frac{0.1}{0.3} = 0.33$$

**(b)** The equilibrium frequencies for *A* and *a* allele are same in all the three populations.

So, if all three of these populations began with exactly the same gene frequencies (*A* = 0.40 and *a* = 0.60) then all three populations would reach the equilibrium frequencies at the same period of time.

### Problem 5

Consider a population in which the frequency allele "*A*" = *p* = 0.7 and the frequency of allele "*a*" = *q* = 0.3, and where the alleles are codominant. What will be the allele frequencies after one generation if

(a) W*AA* = 1.0, W*Aa* = 0.9 and W*aa* = 0.8

(b) W*AA* = 1.0, W*Aa* = 0.95 and W*aa* = 0.9

(c) W*AA* = 1.0, W*Aa* = 0.99 and W*aa* = 0.98

(d) W*AA* = 0.8, W*Aa* =1.0 and W*aa* = 0.8

**Solution :**

From the allelic frequencies of *A* (*p* = 0.7) and a (q = 0.3) the equilibrium genotype frequencies for the different combinations will be as follows:

| *AA* | *Aa* | *aa* |
|---|---|---|
| $p^2 = (0.7)^2 = 0.49$ | $2pq = 2 \times 0.7 \times 0.3 = 0.42$ | $q^2 = 0.3 \times 0.3 = 0.09$ |

**(a)**

| | AA | Aa | aa | Total |
|---|---|---|---|---|
| 1. Initial genotypic frequencies | 0.49 | 0.42 | 0.09 | 1 |
| 2. Fitness (*w*) | 1 | 0.9 | 0.8 | |
| 3. Genotypic frequency after selection | 1 × 0.49 = 0.49 | 0.9 × 0.42 = 0.378 | 0.8 × 0.09 = 0.0792 | 0.9472 |
| 4. Relative genotypic frequency after selection | $\frac{0.49}{0.942} = 0.52$ | $\frac{0.378}{0.942} = 0.40$ | $\frac{0.0792}{0.942} = 0.0836$ | 1 |

Allelic frequency after selection for "*A*"

$$p_1 = 0.52 + \frac{1}{2}(0.41) = 0.52 + 0.2 = 0.72$$

Allelic frequency after selection for "*a*"

$$q_1 = 1 - 0.72 = 0.28$$

(b)

| | AA | Aa | aa | Total |
|---|---|---|---|---|
| 1. Initial genotypic frequencies | 0.49 | 0.42 | 0.09 | 1 |
| 2. Fitness ($w$) | 1 | 0.95 | 0.9 | |
| 3. Genotypic frequency after selection | $1 \times 0.49 = 0.49$ | $0.95 \times 0.42 = 0.399$ | $0.9 \times 0.09 = 0.081$ | 0.97 |
| 4. Relative genotypic frequency after selection | $\frac{0.49}{0.97} = 0.50$ | $\frac{0.399}{0.97} = 0.41$ | $\frac{0.081}{0.97} = 0.08$ | |

Allelic frequency after selection for "$A$"

$$p_1 = 0.50 + \tfrac{1}{2}(0.41) \quad = .50 + 0.205 \quad = 0.705$$

Allelic frequency after selection for "$a$"

$$q_1 = 1 - 0.705 \quad = 0.295$$

(c)

| | AA | Aa | aa | Total |
|---|---|---|---|---|
| 1. Initial genotypic frequencies | 0.49 | 0.42 | 0.09 | 1 |
| 2. Fitness ($w$) | 1 | 0.99 | 0.98 | |
| 3. Genotypic frequency after selection | $1 \times 0.49 = 0.49$ | $0.99 \times 0.42 = 0.4158$ | $0.98 \times 0.09 = 0.0882$ | 0.994 |
| 4. Relative genotypic frequency after selection | $\frac{0.49}{0.994} = 0.49$ | $\frac{0.4158}{0.994} = 0.41$ | $\frac{0.0882}{0.994} = 0.088$ | |

Allelic frequency after selection for "$A$"

$$p_1 = 0.49 + \tfrac{1}{2}(0.41) \quad = 0.49 + 0.205 \quad = 0.695$$

Allelic frequency after selection for "$a$"

$$q_1 = 1 - p_1 \quad = 1 - 0.695 \quad = 0.305$$

(d) In this case, selection operates on both the homozygotes, where there is no selection on heterozygote, so exhibiting heterozygote advantage.

The allelic frequencies after selection can be calculated directly from the following formula.

$$q_1 = \frac{q(1 - s_2 q)}{1 - s_1 p^2 - s_2 q^2}$$

Where, $q = 0.3$, $p = 0.7$,

$s_1 = 1 - WAA = 1 - 0.8 = 0.2$ $\quad$ $s_2 = 1 - Waa = 1 - 0.8 = 0.2$

Therefore, $q_1 = \frac{0.3(1 - 0.2 \times 0.3)}{1 - 0.2(0.7)^2 - 0.2(0.3)^2} = \frac{0.3 \times 0.94}{1 - 0.098 - 0.018} = \frac{0.282}{1 - 0.116} = 0.287$

and $p_1 = 1 - q_1 = 1 - 0.287 = 0.713$

### Problem 6

Two small separated human populations, A and B have respective frequencies of phenylthiocarbamide (PTC) tasters caused by of a dominant gene of 0.85 and 0.25. If 50% of population B comes from population A each generation, what will be the frequency of the tasting gene in population B after (a) 1, (b) 5, (c) 10 generations?

**Solution :**

**In population-A**

Tasters = 0.85

So, nontaster = 1– 0.85 = 0.15

If allelic frequency for nontaster (t) = f (t) = $q_A$

Then $q_A^2 = 0.15$

or, $q_A = \sqrt{0.15} = 0.39$ and $p_A = 1 - 0.387 = 0.61$

**In population B**

Tasters = 0.25

So, nontaster = 1– 0.25 = 0.75

If allelic frequency for nontaster (t) = f (t) = $q_B$

Then $q_B^2 = 0.75$

Or, $q_B = \sqrt{0.75} = 0.87$

And $p_A = 1 - 0.87 = 0.13$

When 5% of population-B comes from population A, each generation, the frequency of the tasting gene ($p_1$) in population-B after

**(a)** After -1 generation, it will be as follows :

According to the formula

$p_1 = p_B(1 - m^2) + p_A \times m$

Where, m is the frequency of immigrant = 0.05, $p_B = 0.13$ and $p_A = 0.61$

Then, $p_1 = 0.13\ (1 - 0.05) + 0.61 \times 0.05$

$= 0.13 \times 0.95 + 0.0305 \quad = 0.1235 + 0.0305 \quad = 0.1585$

**(b)** After 5 generations, it can be calculated by an alternative formula.

$$p_t = (1 - m)^t (p_o - p_m) + p_m$$

Where, $p_t$ = gene frequency after t generation

$m$ = proportion of migrates (= 0.05)

$p_o$ = gene frequency of resident population ($p_B$) (= 0.13)

$p_m$ = gene frequency of migrant population ($p_A$) (= 0.61)

$t$ = no. of generations (= 5)

Then $p_t = (1 - 0.05)^5 (0.13 - 0.61) + 0.61$

$= (0.95)^5 (-0.48) + 0.61 \quad = 0.773 (-0.48) + 0.61 \quad = -0.371 + 0.61 \quad = 0.239$

Therefore, after 5 generations gene frequency for taster in population B will be increased further to 0.239 from original 0.13.

**(c)** After 10 generation it can be calculated by the same formula

$P_{10} = (1\text{-}0.05)^{10} (-0.48) + 0.61$

$= (0.95)^{10} (-0.48) + 0.61 \quad = 0.598 (-0.48) + 0.61$

$= -0.287 + 0.61 \quad = 0.323.$

**Problem 7**

If the frequency of the "N" allele is 0.25 in a native population 0.32 in a Conglomerate population and o.4 in a migrant population, what percentage of the "n" allele in the Conglomerate population was derived from the migrant population.

**Solution :**

If f(N) = $p$ then,

$p_o = 0.25$, $p_m = 0.4$ and $p_1 = 0.32$

So, the value of immigrants (m) can be calculated by the formula

$p_1 = p_o (1-m) + p_m \times m$

or, $0.32 = 0.25 (1-m) + 0.4\, m$

or, $0.32 = 0.25 - 0.25m + 0.4m$

or, $0.15m = 0.32 - 0.25$

or, $0.15m = 0.07$

or, $m = 0.07/0.15 = 0.46$ ( ≡ 46%)

**Problem 8**

The ability of certain people who taste a chemical called PTC is governed by a dominant allele "T" , and the inability to taste PTC by its recessive allele "$t$". If a 24% of a population is homozygous taster and 40% is hoterozygous taster. What is the gene frequency of "$t$"?

**Solution :**

Let, the gene frequency of taster is p and non-taster is q.

Therefore, homozygous taster $p^2$ = 24% = 0.24

heterozygous taster 2pq = 40% = 0.40

and non-tasters are $q^2$ = 100 – (24 + 40)% = 36% = 0.36

Therefore $q = \sqrt{0.36} = 0.6$

The gene frequency of $t = 0.6$

**Problem 9**

One hundred persons from a small town in Pennsylvania were tested for their MN blood types. The genotypic data are : MM 41; MN 38 and NN 21: Calculate gene frequency of M and N. Is the population in Hardy-Weinberg equilibrium?

**Solution :**

| Genotype | MM | MN | NN | Total |
|---|---|---|---|---|
| **Number of individuals** | 41 | 38 | 21 | 100 |
| **Genotypic frequency** | 0.41 | 0.38 | 0.21 | |
| **Gene frequency of M** | $= 0.41 + \frac{1}{2} \times 0.38 = 0.6$ | | | |
| **Gene frequency of N** | $= 0.21 + \frac{1}{2} \times 0.38 = 0.4$ | | | |

Expected number of genotypes will be

$$MM = p^2 = (0.6)^2 = 0.36$$

$$MN = 2pq = 2 \times 0.6 \times 0.4 = 0.48$$

$$NN = q^2 = (0.4)^2 = 0.16$$

Gene frequency of M $= 0.36 + \frac{1}{2} \times 0.48 = 0.6$

Gene frequency of N $= 0.16 + \frac{1}{2} \times 0.48 = 0.4$

The gene frequency of observed and expected numbers are same

So the population is in Hardy-Weinberg equilibrium

**Problem 10**

Among a Jewish Community of Central European ancestry, about 1 in 3600 children is borne with Tay-Sachs disease. Derive what fraction of the individuals in this population are carrierrs?

**Solution :**

Let the gene frequency of the Tay-Sachs diseases is q

Therefore $q^2 = \frac{1}{3600}$

$$q = \frac{1}{60} = 0.017$$

Then $p = 1 - q = 0.983$

The carriers are heterozygous

i.e. $2pq = 2 \times 0.98 \times 0.017$

$= 0.0334$

i.e., 3.34%

### Problem 11

In a human population of 100 people. The blood group is as follows

Group A = 17

Group B = 17

Group AB = 2

Group O = 64

If this population is in equilibrium what are the allelic frequencies.

**Solution :**

Blood group of human is due to $I^A$, $I^B$ and $i$ alleles. If their frequencies are p, q and r respectively then the genotypic frequency would be as follows.

| Genotype | Genotypic frequency | Phenotype |
|---|---|---|
| $I^AI^B$ | $p^2$ | A |
| $I^Ai$ | 2pr | A |
| $I^BI^B$ | $q^2$ | B |
| $I^Bi$ | 2qr | B |
| $I^AI^B$ | 2pq | AB |
| $ii$ | $r^2$ | O |

Here genotypic frequency of group O is $r^2 = 0.64$ ; $r = 0.8$

The genotypic frequency of group A

is $p^2 + 2pr = 0.17$

$p^2 + 0.16p - 0.17 = 0$

$(p + 0.17)(p - 0.1) = 0$

So, $p = 0.1$

The genotypic frequency of group B

$q = 1 - (p + r) \quad = 1 - 0.9 = 0.1$

Therefore gene frequency of

$I^A = p = 0.1$

$I^B = q = 0.1$

$i = r = 0.8$

### Problem 12

The sex-linked recessive disease hemophilia in a population constitutes 1% in man.

What are the expected frequency of hemophilia among men and women?

What are the expected genotypes among women.

**Solution :**

Suppose the frequency of hemophilic gene is q for males (XY) and $q^2$ for females (XX)

It is 1% in man *ie* q = 0.01

The expected frequency of hemophilia is 1% in man and $q^2$ i.e. $(0.01)^2 = 0.0001$ or 0.01% in females

The expected genotypes among females

are homozygous normal = $p^2 = (0.99)^2 = 0.98$

heterozygous carrier = $2pq = 2 \times .99 \times 0.01 = 0.0198$

homozygous hemophilic = $q^2 = (0.01)^2 = 0.0001$

**Problem 13**

In human, about one man in 20 is colour blind (a sex linked recessive trait) What proportion of women would be expected to the colour blind and carriers?

**Solution :**

Suppose, the gene frequency of colour blind is

$$\text{males is } q = \frac{1}{20} = 0.05$$

frequency of normal gene p = 1 – 0.05 – 0.95

The gene frequency of colour blind gene in

$$\text{females} = q^2 = (0.05)^2 = 0.0025$$

Expected genotypes among females

homozygous normal = $p^2 = (0.95)^2 = 0.9025$

heterozygous carrier = $2pq = 2 \times .95 \times 0.05 = 0.0095$

homozygous color blind = $q^2 = (0.05)^2 = 0.0025$

**Problem 14**

Genotypes of leopard frogs from a population were determined for a locus that encodes the enzyme malate dehydrogenase. The following numbers of genotypes were observed.

| Genotype | Number |
|---|---|
| $M^1M^1$ | 20 |
| $M^1M^2$ | 45 |
| $M^2M^2$ | 42 |
| $M^1M^3$ | 4 |
| $M^2M^3$ | 8 |
| $M^3M^3$ | 6 |
| Total | 125 |

(i) Calculate the genotypic and allelic frequencies of the population.

(ii) What would be the expected number of genotypes if the population were in HWE?

**Solution :**

Hints : This is a codominant multiple allele locus, Let gene frequency of $M^1$, $M^2$ and $M^3$ as p, q and r repectively .

Then genotypic frequencies of $M^1M^1 = p^2$, $M^1M^2 = 2pq$, $M^2M^2 = q^2$, $M^1M^3 = 2pr$, $M^2M^3 = 2qr$ and $M^3M^3 = r^2$.

Then calculate the values of p, q and r.

## Chapter Glossary/Key Terms

**Allele :** One of a pair or series, of alternative forms of a gene that occur at a given locus in a chromosome.

**Allele frequency :** The proportion of one allele relative to all alleles at a locus in a population.

**Binomial expansion :** Exponential multiplication of an expression consisting of two terms connected by a plus (+) or minus (–) sign such as (a+b).

**Bottle neck effect :** Occassional reduction of population may happen in some year when a small population is the source of next build up of abundance, they are called bottlenecks. Their genetic makeup will determine the gene pool of the next large population and the phenomenon is called bottle neck effect.

**Codominant alleles :** Alleles that produce independent effects when heterozygous.

**Darwinian fitness :** The relative efficiency of a gene to be transmitted to subsequent generations is expressed as Darwinian fitness.

**Dominance :** A condition in which one member of an allele pair is manifested to the exclusion of the other.

**Founder's effect :** A few individuals isolated from the parental population may start a new population. The genotypes of the founders eventually get established in the new population and the phenomenon is called founder's effect.

**Frequency :** The number of repeated occurrences of a score or case in the sample.

**Gene flow :** The spread of genes from one breeding population to another by migration, possibly leading to allele frequency changes.

**Gene frequency :** See allele frequency.

**Genetic drift :** Changes in allele frequency in small breeding populations due to chance fluctuations.

**Genetic equilibrium :** condition in a group of interbreeding organisms in which the allele frequencies remain constant over time.

**Genotype frequency :** The frequency of different genotypes found within a population.

**heterozygous :** An organism with unlike members of any given pair or series of alleles that consequently produces unlike gametes.

*Contd.*

**Homozygous :** An organism with like members of any given pair of series of alleles that consequently produces like gametes.

**Locus :** A fixed position on a chromosome that is occupied by a given gene or one of its alleles.

**Mendelian population :** A natural interbreeding unit of sexually reproducing plants or animals sharing a common gene pool.

**Mutation :** A change in the DNA at a particular locus in an organism.

**Natural selection :** Differential survival and reproduction in nature that favours individuals those are better adapted to their environment, elimination of less fit organisms.

**Overdominance :** A condition in which heterozygtes are superior to either of the associated homozygotes.

**Population :** The totality of the statistical data forming a subject of investigation.

**Selection coefficient :** A number that measures the fitness of a genotype relative to a standard.

**Sewell Wright effect :** The random fluctuation of gene frequency due to chance occurrence in a finite population also called genetic drift.

## Exercise

**A. Long answer type questions :**

1. Define Hardy-Weinberg law.
2. Deduce the Hardy-Weinberg law with two alleles at a single locus.
3. Briefly describe the applications of Hardy-Weinberg principle.
4. Briefly deduce the results of random mating in a population with three alleles.
5. Briefly describe the significance of Hardy-Weinberg principle.
6. What are the exceptions of Hardy-Weinberg principle?
7. Describe the principle of attainment of equilibrium at two or more loci with appropriate example.
8. Describe the principle of attainment of equilibrium of sex-linked gene in the population with example.
9. Brifly describe with example of codominant gene and its attainment of equilibrium in the natural population.
10. Briefly describe with example of dominant gene and its attainment of equilibrium in the natural population.
11. Write a note of Darwinian fitness and selection coefficient.
12. Write a note on gametic selection and zygotic selection.
13. Briefly deduce the change in freqauency for one generation of selection against a dominant deleterions gene.
14. Write a note on predation of birds on the selection coefficient of moth.
15. What is heterozygous advantage? Deduce the change in frequencies of a gene in one generation selection.

16. Write a note on unstable equilibrium.
17. Describe how H.W. equilibrium is affeted by migration, mutation and genetic drift.
18. What is mutation rate and mutational equilibrium? What is their relationship.
19. Write a note on Founder principle and Bottleneck effect.

**B. Short answer type questions :**

1. What is Hardy-Weinberg law?
2. What is gene (or allelic) frequency?
3. What is genotypic frequency?
4. Define the Hardy-Weinberg equation with example.
5. What is the result of random mating in the population with three alleles?
6. What is the significance of Hardy-Weinberg principle?
7. What are the elemental forces of evolution that upset the equilibrium?
8. How mutation of gene upsets equilibrium?
9. What is the role of selection to upset equilibrium?
10. What is the role of migration to upset equilibrium?
11. What is the role of genetic drift that upset equilibrium?
12. What are the exceptions of Hardy-Weinberg principle?
13. What is panmictic population?
14. What are the genotypic equilibrium values in males or females of two alleles?
15. When the parents are dominant phenotypes what would be the fraction of recessive offspring in equilibrium?
16. When one of the parent is recessive phenotype and other parent is dominant phenotype, what would be the fraction of recessive offspring in equilibrium?
17. When both parents are recessive phenotype, what would be the fraction of recessive offspring in equilibrium state?
18. What is Drarwinian fitness?
19. What is the measure of reproductive efficiency of a genotype?
20. What is the highest and lowest fitness value?
21. What is selection coefficient?
22. What is the mathematical relationship between fitness and selection coefficient?
23. What do you mean by gametic selection?
24. When selection is proceeding very slowly what is the change of frequency of recessive allele?
25. What is zygotic selection? Why heteroxygotes are shieled from selection and persists for many generations?
26. Calculate the change in gene frequency of a gene that is
    (i) lethal in homozygous state.
    (ii) deleterious but not lethal in homozygous state
    (iii) dominant deleterious
    (iv) deleterious but shows no dominance (the effect is additive)
27. What do you mean by deleterious gene?
28. What is overdominance?
29. What is balanced polymorphism?
30. What is unstable equilibrium?
31. What is mutational equilibrium?
32. When $\hat{p}$ and $\hat{q}$ become identical?
33. What is the relative effects of mutation and selection with respect to deleterious alleles?
34. What are migrants, and recepient population?
35. What do you mean by genetic drift?
36. What is Sewell-Wright effect?
37. What is effective population size?
38. What is Founder principle? Give example.
39. What is bottleneck effect? Give a suitable example.

# 26

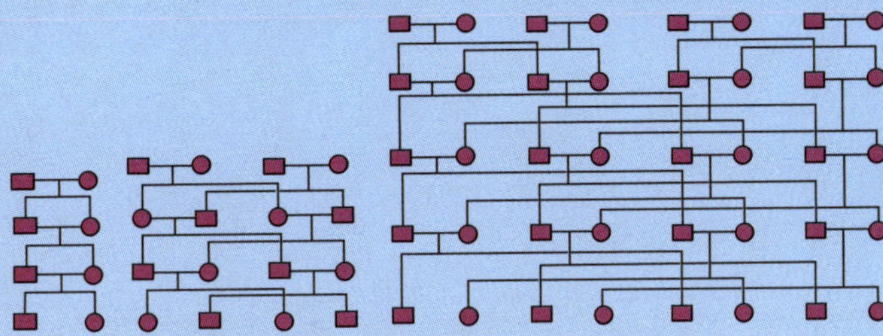

# Inbreeding and Heterosis

**CHAPTER AGENDA**

**26.1** Inbreeding; **26.2** Heterosis and Hybrid vigour; Chapter Glossary/Key Terms; Exercise

## 26.1 INBREEDING

### 26.1.1 Concept

Mating between relatives is called **inbreeding**. The major effect of inbreeding is the increased frequency of homozygotes in the population; though it has very little influence on overall gene frequencies. The rare recessive gene may appear in the homozygotic condition at a higher frequency in the inbreeding population. Inbreeding has been associated with some unfavourable biological effects. This is the cause why marriages between close relatives have been forbidden.

### 26.1.2 Measurement of Inbreeding

In diploid, when two alleles at a locus are descended from the same gene, they are called **identical** (*AA*). Homozygotes may occur when each of the two alleles are not descended from the same gene, but homozygous for genes of separate origin called **similar**. For example, a mating between first cousins may produce a homozygote containing genes of identical origin and at the same time also produce an individual homozygous for genes of separate origin (Fig. 26.1). The measurement of probability that two genes in a zygote are identical is called **inbreeding coefficient (F)**.

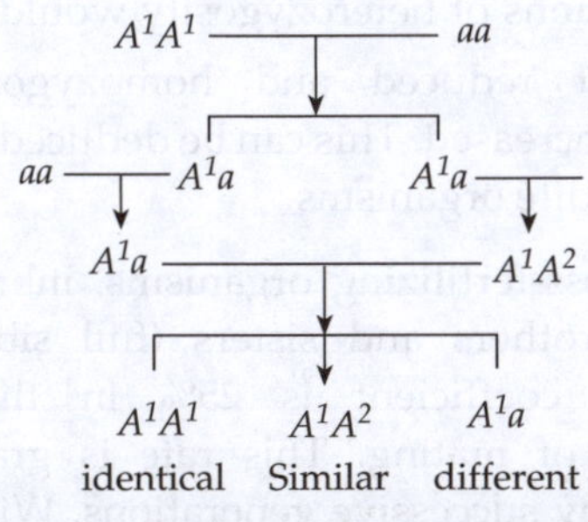


**Fig.26.1 :** *Three possible combinations of alleles as a result of a first cousin mating.*

Let us, assume a population of a marine hermaphrodite is begun with 50 (≡N) diploid individuals, none of which carry the same allele at the particular locus. So, there are 100 alleles in the population, designated as $A^1$, $A^2$, .....$A^{100}$.

There are 100(= 2N) kinds of gametes, or may be said $\frac{1}{100}(=\frac{1}{2N})$ of the gametes are identical.

In the next generation, there will again be 2N different kinds of gametes produced by new parents and the probability of inbreeding is again $\frac{1}{2N}$. Some of these gametes are produced by heterozygotes and also some by homozygous parents. This extra population of identical gametes will increase the chance of forming new identical homozygotes.

Now, if the probability of newly arisen identical homozygote is $\frac{1}{2N}$, then the probability of the remaining zygotes $(1-\frac{1}{2N})$ will have identical genes, is the **inbreeding coefficient** of the previous generation.

Thus, initial inbreeding coefficient $F_0 = 0$

Inbreeding coefficient of generation – 1

$$= F_1 = \frac{1}{2N}$$

Inbreeding coefficient of generation – 2

$$= F_2 = \frac{1}{2N} + (1-\frac{1}{2N})F_1$$

Inbreeding coefficient of generation – 3

$$= F_3 = \frac{1}{2N} + (1-\frac{1}{2N})F_2$$

Thus,

Inbreeding coefficient of generation – n

$$= F_n = \frac{1}{2N} + (1-\frac{1}{2N})F_{n-1}$$

### 26.1.3 Panmictic Index

Panmictic index (P) is the measure of the relative amount of random – mating heterozygosity that is diminished by inbreeding. Therefore P = 1 – F or F = 1 – P

We know, $F_n = \frac{1}{2N} + [1-\frac{1}{2N}]F_{n-1}$

then, $1 - P_n = \frac{1}{2N} + (1 - \frac{1}{2N})(1 - P_{n-1})$

or, $- P_n = -1 + \frac{1}{2N} + (1 - \frac{1}{2N})(1 - P_{n-1})$

or, $- P_n = - P_{n-1} + \frac{1}{2N} P_{n-1}$

$= - P_{n-1}(1 - \frac{1}{2N})$

Thus, $P_n = P_{n-1}(1 - \frac{1}{2N})$

The loss of heterozygosity by random mating for any generation is therefore equal to the factor $\frac{1}{2N}$.

In dioecious animals, self-fertilization is not possible, then this rate is reduced to $\frac{1}{2N+1}$.

Again we right,

$$P_n = P_{n-1}(1 - \frac{1}{2N})$$

$$= P_{n-2}(1 - \frac{1}{2N})^2$$

Since, $P_{n-1} = P_{n-2}(1 - \frac{1}{2N})$

$$= P_{n-3}(1 - \frac{1}{2N})^3$$

$$= P_0(1 - \frac{1}{2N})^n$$

as n = decreases to 0

$P_0$ = initial panmictic index of the base population

Suppose, in an inbreeding population, two alleles "*A*" and "*a*" will be a proportion of F identical homozygotes according to the inbreeding coefficient.

Therefore, *AA* and *aa* homozygotes will be in a genotypic frequencies of *p*F and *q*F.

The remaining individuals (1–F) will bear genotypes whose frequencies are determined by Hardy – Weinberg equilibrium $p^2(AA) : 2pq(Aa) : q^2(aa)$.

Thus, the three genotypes will have the following frequencies.

$$AA = p^2(1-F) + pF$$
$$= p^2 + pF(1-p) = p^2 + pqF$$
$$Aa = 2pq(1-F) = 2pq - 2pqF$$
$$aa = q^2(1-F) + qF = q^2 + pqF$$

From above frequencies, it is evident that increase in the frequency of each type of homozygote by a factor of pqF, comes through the reduction in the frequency of heterozygotes.

When, inbreeding is absent, then F=0 and then the genotypic frequency is same as that of Hardy Weinberg equilibrium.

When inbreeding is complete, i.e., F=1, the frequency of *Aa* heterozygote is equals to zero. It means that only *AA* and *aa* genotypes would be present in a $p : q$ ratio.

### 26.1.4 Systematic Inbreeding

In inbreeding system, each generation produces individuals all of whom have the same coefficient of inbreeding. In such a system homozygosity is expected to rise in each generation. If it begins with a completely heterozygous population, after "n" generations the proportions of heterozygosity would be $\frac{1}{2^n}$ i.e., almost reduced and homozygosity is gradually increased. This can be deduced for the hermaphrodite organisms.

For cross-fertilizing organisms, inbreeding between brothers and sisters (full sibs), the inbreeding coefficient is 25% in the first generation of mating. This rate is gradually decreased by successive generations. Within 10 generations, the inbreeding coefficient is about 90% (Table 26.1).

The first cousin mating system involves two pairs of parents in each generation. The rate of inbreeding becomes slower than the full sib mating.

The second cousin mating, involves four pairs of parents in each generation (Fig. 26.2).

**TABLE 26.1**
**Results of selfing after n generations**

| Generation | Proportion of genotypes *AA* | *Aa* | *aa* | Showing the cross |
|---|---|---|---|---|
| 0 | | 1 | | *Aa* |
| 1 | $\frac{1}{4}$ | $\frac{1}{2}$ | $\frac{1}{4}$ | *AA* $\frac{1}{4}$, *Aa* $\frac{1}{2}$, *aa* $\frac{1}{4}$ |
| 2 | $\frac{3}{8}$ | $\frac{1}{4}$ | $\frac{3}{8}$ | $\frac{1}{8}$, $\frac{1}{4}$, $\frac{1}{8}$ |
| 3 | $\frac{7}{16}$ | $\frac{1}{8}$ | $\frac{7}{16}$ | $\frac{1}{16}$, $\frac{1}{8}$, $\frac{1}{16}$ |
| 4 | $\frac{15}{32}$ | $\frac{1}{16}$ | $\frac{15}{32}$ | $\frac{1}{32}$, $\frac{1}{16}$, $\frac{1}{32}$ |
| 5 | $\frac{31}{64}$ | $\frac{1}{32}$ | $\frac{31}{64}$ | $\frac{1}{64}$, $\frac{1}{32}$, $\frac{1}{64}$ |
| 10 | $\frac{1023}{2048}$ | $\frac{1}{2048}$ | $\frac{1023}{2048}$ | $\frac{1}{2048}$, $\frac{2}{2048}$, $\frac{1}{2048}$ |
| n | $\frac{2^n - 1}{2^{n+1}}$ | $\frac{1}{2n}$ | $\frac{2^n - 1}{2^{n+1}}$ | $\frac{1}{2^{n+1}}$, $\frac{1}{2^n}$, $\frac{1}{2^{n+1}}$ |

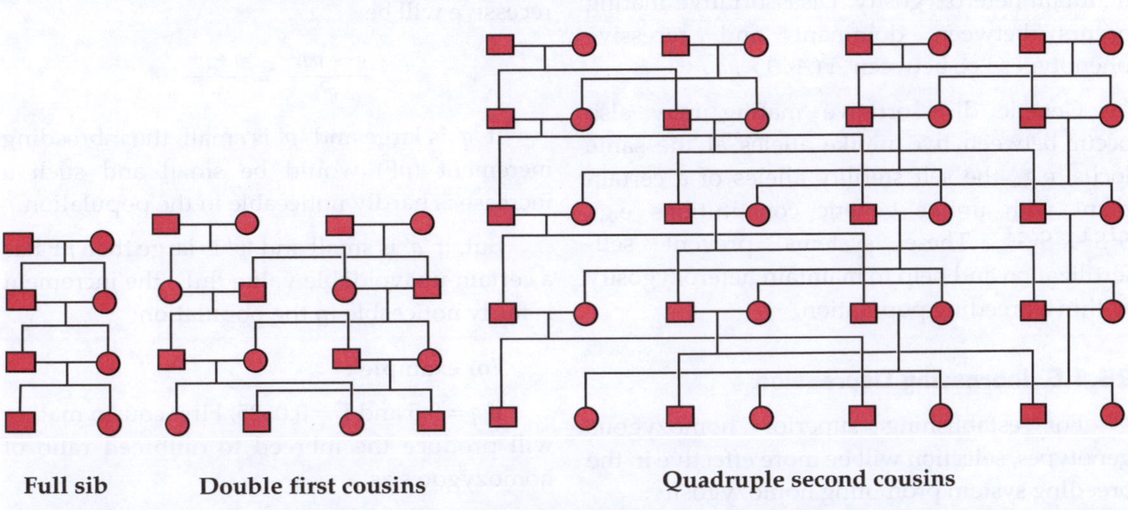


**Fig.26.2 :** *Different mating schemes showing different numbers of individuals used to perpetuate the population each generation.*

### 26.1.5 Assortative and Disassortative mating

In genetic assortative mating, the parents are sorted and mated together on the basis of their genetic relationship. The systematic mating such as selfing, sib-mating, first cousin mating, second cousin mating are to be considered here.

In phenotypic assortative mating, the parents are mated with their similar phenotypes, may be dominant phenotypes or may be recessive phenotypes e.g., between $AA \times AA$ or $Aa \times Aa$ or $AA \times Aa$ and also between $aa \times aa$. If such crosses are continued for a long time, heterozygotes would be eliminated and the population becomes polarized into two groups, homozygous dominants (*AA*) or recessives (*aa*). The genes on other locus (*Bb* or *Cc*) would not be homozygous.

In phenotypic assortative mating, if more than one locus is considered e.g., $A(A/a)\ B(B/b) \times A(A/a)\ B(B/b)$ and $aabb \times aabb$ or etc., the progress to homozygosity for these loci will evidently be slower, because *AaBB, AABb or AaBb*, etc., heterozygotes would be produced.

Phenotypic disassortative mating, involves the mating of unlike phenotypes. It tends to maintain heterozygosity. Disassortative mating occurs between dominant and recessive phenotypes i.e., between $A\ (A/a) \times aa$ .

Genetic disassortative mating may also occur between two unlike alleles at the same locus, e.g., the self sterility alleles of a certain plant with unlike genetic constitutions e.g., $S^1S^2 \times S^2S^3$. These systems prevent self-fertilization and help to maintain heterozygosity within a breeding population.

### 26.1.6 Inbreeding Depression

For establishing superior homozygous genotypes, selection will be more effective in the breeding system promoting homozygosity.

There are numerous devices ensuring cross-fertilization and the maintenance of various levels of heterozygosity. When such normal crossbreeding patterns are obstructed by enforced breeding, one of its prime results would be inbreeding depression.

**Deduction :** In a population at equilibrium, frequencies of genotypes $AA=p^2$, $Aa=2pq$ and $aa=q^2$, and the inbreeding coefficient is "F".

Then, in an inbreeding population, '*A*' and '*a*' alleles will be in a proportion of F identical homozygotes. Therefore, *AA* and *aa* homozygotes will be in a frequency of $p$F and $q$F respectively.

The remaining individuals (1–F) will bear genotypes whose frequencies are determined by Hardy Weinbing equilibrium $p^2(AA) : 2pq(Aa) : q^2(aa)$.

Thus, the three genotypes will have the following frequencies.

$$AA = p^2(1\text{–F}) + p\text{F} = p^2 + pq\text{F}$$

$$Aa = 2pq(1\text{–F}) = 2pq - 2pq\text{F}$$

$$aa = q^2(1\text{–F}) + q\text{F} = q^2 + pq\text{F}$$

If a recessive disease with genotype *aa* occurs with a frequency $q^2$ in random outbreed population, its frequency will be increased by $pq$F in an inbred population. The ratio of inbreed and outbreed frequency of homozygous recessive will be

$$\frac{q^2 + pq\text{F}}{q^2} = \frac{q + p\text{F}}{q}$$

If '$q$' is large and '$p$' is small, the inbreeding increment ($p$F) would be small and such a increase is hardly noticeable in the population.

But, if '$q$' is small and '$p$' is large then $p$F has a certain unavoidable value thus, the increment is fairly noticeable in the population.

**For example :**

If $q = 0.5$ and $\text{F} = 0.0625$, First cousin mating will produce the inbreed to outbreed ratio of homozygotes as

$$\frac{0.5 + 0.5 \times 0.0625}{0.5} = 1.06$$

**TABLE 26.2**
**Average value of genotypes when recessives have lower quantative values**

| Genotype | Quantitative | Before inbreeding | | After inbreeding | |
|---|---|---|---|---|---|
| | | Frequency | frequency × value | frequency | frequency × value |
| AA | $v$ | $p^2$ | $p^2v$ | $p^2 + pqF$ | $p^2v + pqvF$ |
| Aa | $v$ | $2pq$ | $2pqv$ | $2pq - 2pqF$ | $2pqv - 2pqvF$ |
| aa | $-v$ | $q^2$ | $-q^2v$ | $q^2 + pqF$ | $-q^2v - 2pqvF$ |
| Total | | | $v(p^2-q^2) + 2pqv$ $= v(p-q) - 2pqv = Q$ | | $v(p^2-q^2) + 2pqv - 2pqvF$ $= v(p-q) + 2pqv - 2pqvF$ $= Q - 2pqvF$ |

But $q = 0.005$ then the ratio would be

$$\frac{0.005 + 0.995 \times 0.0625}{0.005} = 13.43$$

Again, if $q = 0.0005$ then the ratio would be

$$\frac{0.0005 + 0.9995 \times 0.0625}{0.0005} = 126$$

As the value of '$q$' decreases, the inbreed homozygosity is increased with respect to outbreed homozygosity.

One may assume that as the frequency of recessive (lethal) gene is small, the frequency of such families would be small where homozygosity of such lethal gene would be occurred.

But it is fact that, there are different kinds of deleterious genes which are present as recessive alleles, and due to inbreeding, different inbred families will often produce such homozygotes of different deleterious genes (Table 26.2).

If a gene has a quantitative effect equal to $v$, the dominant genotype may be considered +v and homozygous recessive $-v$, then from the Table 26.2 we have a reduction in quantitative value upon in breeding is $-2pqv$F, which arises from the exact reduction in quantitative value of the heterozygotes.

In incomplete dominance, the change is somewhat diminished, In absence of dominance, the quantitative value is midway between both homozygotes.

Therefore, the four primary features of inbreeding are as follows:

1. Increase in frequency of homozygotes.
2. Increase in variability between different inbred families.
3. Reduction in value of quantitative character in the direction of recessive values.
4. The dependence of this reduction in value upon dominance.

If these inbreeding effects are multiplied for many gene loci, there may be a large reduction in value of many traits, including those that affect fitness and survival.

G. H. Shull (1909) and E. M. East (1908) studied the effects of inbreeding in corn for 30 generations independently and observed that their yielding ability was reduced. This effect is due to

1. A number of lethal and sub-vital traits appear in the early generations of selfing.
2. The material rapidly separates into distinct lines, which become increasingly uniform for differences in various morphological and functional characteristics.

3. Many of the lines decrease in vigour and fecundity even in most favourable culture medium.
4. The lines that survive show a general decline in size and vigour.

In a study on rats, it was found that by continuous brother sister mating for 25 generation, the progenies compared favourably with crossbred stock as control. In *Drosophila,* inbreeding results in a rapid loss of vigour.

## 26.2 HETEROSIS AND HYBRID VIGOUR

Heterosis may be defined as the superiority of the hybrid over its parents. This term was first used by Shull (1914) for the first time. The superiority is due to crossbreeding between unrelated or distant related stock. It results in hybrid vigour.

Whaley (1944) described the hybrid vigour that denotes the manifest effects of heterosis.

The increased vigour of the $F_1$ hybrid may be taken as **luxuriance**. But in heterosis, increased fertility is accompanied in the process while in luxuriance, the hybrid may show fertile or poorly fertile form.

### 26.2.1 Importance and Use

1. A phenomenon observed by the early hybridizers was that when cross-fertilization was made, there was a general increase in size, yield etc. in the $F_1$ generation plants.
2. The plants in the $F_1$ generation were more vigorous than either of their parents and if crossed no further, this vigorousness decreased in the future generations. From those days it has been a point of interest for both the biologists and the horticulturists.
3. It serves a very useful practical purpose to the farmers by an increase in the yield of grains and other economic products.
4. Heterosis is much more pronounced in naturally cross-fertilized plants and more so when inbred lines are crossed.
5. Heterosis is observable in many characters such as height, size, reproductiveness, earliness in flowering, health, viability, resistance of pests, drought and disease etc.
6. The superiority of the hybrid is soon lost, if the $F_1$ hybrids and progenies are allowed to be self fertilized.
7. In cases where propagation is by seeds, an increased number of hybrids can be effected by producing a large number of hybrid seeds every year. For this purpose, the parents are selfed every year and maintained pure. In plants like sugarcane, potato etc., which are vegetatively propagated, the problem of loss of hybrid vigour does not arise.
8. An increase in vigour due to hybridization has been noted in cases of barley, maize, wheat, onion, brinjal, tomato, cucumber, sugarbeet. sugarcane, coconut, cotton, tobacco, sunflower and even in the fungus like *Penicillium*.
9. Hybrids of beans, the numbers of nodes, leaves and pods are greater than the parents, but gross size of the plant remains unaffected.
10. Though heterosis has a great practical utility, still it has not been possible to utilize this method in all the hermaphrodites, and normal crop plants for their improvement.

### 26.2.2 Theories of Inbreeding Depression and Heterosis

A number of theories have been put forwarded to explain inbreeding depression and related phenomena of heterosis and hybrid vigour. These are briefly described below.

**(a) Physiologic Stimulus or heterozygosity hypothesis or overdominance hypothesis :** Shull (1910) proposed that heterosis is due to some kind of physiologic stimulus produced by the union of dissimilar gametes. The superiority of the heterozygotes has been proposed to be due to the production of different kinds of products by two kinds of alleles present. Thus, they acquire metabolic advantage. The hybrid may produce a unique "hybrid substance" completely different from either of the homozygous products, e.g., In corn, the hybrid possesses an alcoholdehydrogenase enzyme, which is active and stable. But in their homozygous parents the enzymes were inactive or unstable. Another example is found in AB-antigen in human blood group is chemically different from A or B group antigens of their homozygous parents.

Another type of hybrid metabolism occurs when heterozygote produces intermediate amount of same substance that is produced in different quantities by parent homozygotes. For example, heterozygote sickle cell anemic patient produces both normal hemoglobin and sickle hemoglobin. These heterozygotes are believed to be resistant from falciperum – malaria as well as hemolytic anaemia and thrive well than the normal dominant or recessive homozygotes in malaria prone areas.

Various workers have given different names to this hypothesis, such as single gene heterosis, cumulative action of divergent alleles and stimulation of divergent alleles. Fisher (1930) called it as **superdominance**.

The hypothesis assumes that the heterozygous combination $a_1a_2$ at a single locus is superior to either of the homozygous combinations $a_1a_1$ or $a_2a_2$. In the heterozygotes the superiority is due to the sum up of both the products of the alleles.

East in 1936 elaborated the hypothesis and proposed that there is a series of alleles, say $a_1a_2a_3$...... of gradually increasing functions (i.e., formation of more effective growth factors) and different combinations in heterozygotes have different grades of superiority. Such series of heterozygous superiority is observed in multiple allelic series of blood group antigens in man.

**(b) Greater initial capital hypothesis :** According to Ashby (1930), heterosis is nothing else, but the continued maintenance of an initial advantage gained in the size of the embryo, which he termed as the greater initial capital. Other workers have challenged the validity of his hypothesis.

**(c) Dominant factor hypothesis :** Proposed by Devenport (1908) and supported by Bruce, Keeble and Pellew in the year 1910 independently. According to this hypothesis it has been assumed that, a cross fertilizing species consists of a large number of genetically different individuals which may carry deleterious recessive mutant genes that are concealed in the heterozygotes due to presence of a dominant allele. In the inbreeding individuals, such deleterious mutant recessive genes might come close together in the homozygotes.

In this hypothesis, the harmful effects of recessive alleles are suppressed by dominant alleles. According to the dominance hypothesis, a mating between two inbred lines leads to a heterotic hybrid because each inbred line is homozygous for a unique set of deleterious genes, but carries the advantageous dominant alleles for the deleterious recessives in the other inbred line. As a result a chromosome pair in the hybrid possesses dominant alleles for many or all the deleterious recessives.

$$AA\ bb\ CC\ dd \quad \times \quad AA\ bb\ CC\ dd$$

$$\downarrow$$

$$AA\ bb\ CC\ dd \text{ ..................} F_1$$

Here the harmful effects of $b$ and $d$ are not suppressed and so in inbreeding, the hybrid will show no heterosis.

$$AA\ bb\ CC\ dd \times aa\ BB\ cc\ DD$$
$$\downarrow$$
$$Aa\ Bb\ Cc\ Dd \ldots\ldots\ldots\ldots\ldots(F)$$

In this cross the harmful effects of *a*, *b*, *c* and *d* recessive genes are masked by their corresponding dominant alleles.

In support of this theory, Quinby and Karper (1946), observed that heterosis in Sorghum (*MaMa*) which is attained significantly late in maturity and produces greater weight of grain than their both homozygous *"MAMA"* and *"mama"* parents. Crow (1940) calculated the 5% increase of heterosis of an equilibrium population, which is measured in terms of selection advantage.

The objections against the dominant hypothesis are that

1. The above hypothesis shows no clearcut explanation on the isolation of homozygous for all dominant genes.
2. There is no symmetrical distribution of $F_2$ generation, i.e., the distribution curve should be skewed, because dominant and recessive phenotypes would be distributed according to the binomial expansion of $\left[\frac{3}{4}+\frac{1}{4}\right]^n$.

**(d) Linked-favourable dominant gene hypothesis :** To overcome the objections of dominant hypothesis, Jones (1917) proposed that linked, dominant and growth favouring genes are brought from the both parents into the $F_1$ generation, which also counteract any ill effect of the recessive genes. Heterosis is due to the complementary actions of these genes.

At present there is no evidence which of these mechanisms is responsible for heterosis. It seems likely that dominance is sufficient to explain the superiority of the hybrids, though, there is no conclusive evidence about the mechanism of heterosis.

## Chapter Glossary/Key Terms

**Assortative mating :** Mating in which the partners are chosen because they are phenotypically similar.

**Disassortative mating :** Inbreeding in which individuals with unlike phenotypes preferentially mate with each other.

**Heterosis :** Superiority of heterozygous genotypes in respect to one or more traits in comparison with corresponding homozygotes.

**Hybrid vigor :** See "heterosis".

**Inbreeding :** Mating of genetically related individuals.

**Inbreeding coefficient :** The probability of autozygosity.

**Inbreeding depression :** A depression of vigor or yield due to inbreeding.

**Outbreeding :** Mating of unrelated individuals.

**Panmictic population :** A population in which mating occurs at random.

**Population :** A group of actually or potentially interbreeding individuals of a species, more correctly known as Mendelian population.

**Probability :** The relative frequency of the events, cases or scores of a given type among a very large or almost infinite number of total events, cases or scores.

# EXERCISE

**A. Long answer type questions :**

1. What is inbreeding? How could you measure the inbreeding coefficient of n generations?
2. Define panmictic index? Deduce the change in frequencies of homozygous and heterozygous genotypes after random mating when inbreeding is absent and complete.
3. Describe the results of systematic inbreeding after n generation.
4. What is assortative and disassortative mating? Deduce the results of phenotypic assortative mating where parents are with similar phenotypes and where more than one locus is considered.
5. What is inbreeding depression? Deduce the inbreeding depression and the ratio of inbreed and outbreed frequency of homozygous recessive. What are the primary effects of inbreeding depression and also the causes of such effects.
6. What are heterosis and luxuriance? Distinguish between them. Briefly describe its importance and uses in biology.
7. Describe different theories regarding the inbreeding depression and heterosis.
8. How the homozygosity is increased in selfing (hermaphrodite organisms)?
9. What would be the inbreeding coeficients when cross-fertilization occurs beetween two full sibs? How this coefficient is gradually decreased within 10 generations.
10. What is first cousin mating?
11. What is abortative mating?
12. What happens when phenotypic assortative mating is continued for a long time where the paraents are of similar phenotypes? What would be happend for the genes of other loci?
13. Phenotypic anortative mating considering more than one locus, what would be happened about the production of homozygosity?
14. What is phenotypic disassortative mating what would be its result?
15. What do you mean by inbreeding depression?
16. How inbreeing increases the frequency of double recessive genotypes in the population? What would be happened if such occurs in population?
17. What happens if the frequency of recessive allele "q" is large or small in the inbreeding population?
18. What are the primary effects of inbreeding?
19. Why and how inbreeding affects on the fitness and survival of the organisms?
20. What is heterosis?
21. What do you mean by hybrid vigour?
22. What do you mean by luxuriance?
23. Distinguish between luxuriance and hybrid vigour?
24. What is the effect of cross breeding between distantly related strains in $F_1$?
25. How such distantly related cross breeding exerts beneficial effects on agricultural and horticultural plants?

**B. Short answer type questions :**

1. What is inbreeding?
2. What is the major effect of inbreeding.
3. What is the genetic cause of marriage between close relatives forbidden?
4. What is inbreeding coefficient?
5. What is panmictic index?
6. How the frequency of homozytgote is increased and heterozygotes decreased in an inbreeing population?
7. How the gene frequency becomes same as Hardy-Weinberg equilibrium if the inbreeding is absent? and when inbreeding is complete what would be the genotypic ratio in the population?

26. What kinds of heterosis is observed in distant crosses?
27. If $F_1$ superior hybrids are allowed to self fertilized, what would be the result?
28. What are the theories regarding inbreeding depression and heterosis?
29. What is superdominance?
30. What you mean by physiologic stimulus hypothesis?
31. What is greater initial capital?
32. What is dominant factor hypothesis? Discuss the hypothesis with examples? What are the objections against this hypothesis.
33. What is linked-favourable dominant gene hypothesis?

27

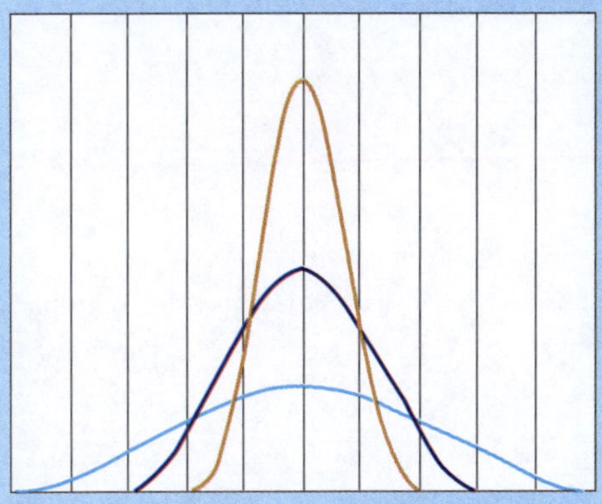

# Quantitative Genetics

## CHAPTER AGENDA

## 27.1 CONCEPT

Genetic analysis of complex characteristics or characteristics influenced by multiple genetic factors is called **quantitative genetics.**

Continuous characteristics displays a number of possible phenotypes which must be described by quantitative measurement.

## 27.2 CHARACTERISTICS OF QUANTITATIVE TRAITS

A gene or chromosomal region that contributes to the expression of quantitative characteristics is called **quantitative trait locus** (QTL).

Quantitative or discontinuous traits possess only a few phenotypes. These characteristics are the types studied by Mendel. These traits fall into discrete categories. In analyzing crossing involving these types of traits, each offspring can be put into a particular phenotypic category. Such attributes are called *discontinuous traits.*

Quantitative traits show a continuum of phenotypic variation within a group of individuals. Many characteristics vary continuously along a scale of measurement with many overlapping phenotypes.

Quantitative characteristics include height, weight and blood pressure in humans; growth rate in mice, seed; weight in plants and milk production in cattle.

Quantitative characteristics arise from two phenomena. Many are **polygenic** i.e. they are influenced by genes at many loci. If many loci take part, many genotypes are possible, each producting a slightly different phenotype. The second quantitative characteristics often arise when environmental factors affect the phenotype, because environmental differences result in a single genotype producing a range of phenotypes.

Most continuously varying characteristics are both polygenic and influenced by environemtnal factors and these characteristics are said to be multifunctional.

## 27.3 TYPES OF QUANTITATIVE CHARACTERISTICS

A continuous characteristics can theoritically assume any value between two extremes, the number of phenotypes is limited only by our ability to precisely measure the phenotype. For example, height of humans is a continuous characteristics because, within certain limits, people can theroritically have any height.

Some characteristics are not continuous but are nervertheless considered quantitative, because they are determined by multiple genetic and environmental factors. This **meristic characteristics**, which is measured by whole numbers. For example, the litter size of a female mouse may have 4, 5 or 6, but not 4.32.

Another type of quantitative characteristics is a **threshold chracteristics,** which is simply present or absent. Although, threshold characterisitcs exhibit only two phenotypes, they are considered as quantitative because they are determined by multiple genetic and environmental factors. For example diseases are often such threshold characteristics becuase, many factors, both genetic and environmental, contribute to disease susceptibility.

## 27.4 TYPES OF QUANTITATIVE TRAITS

1. **Anatomical traits :** Height and weight of human, number of bristles in *Drosophila,* ear length is corn, degree of pigmentation in flower and human skin.
2. **Physiological traits :** Metabolic traits, speed of running and flight, ability to withstand harsh temperatures, milk production in mammals.
3. **Behavioural traits :** Mating calls, courtship rituals, ability to learn a maze, ability to grow or move toward light.
4. **Complex diseases :** Diabetes, hypertension, arthritis, obesity etc.

## 27.5 POLYGENIC INHERITANCE

George Udny Yule, a mathematician, proposed in 1906 that several genes acting together could produce continuous chracteristics. This hypothesis was later confirmed by Herman Nilsson-Ehle, working on wheat and tobacco. Ronald Fisher demonstrated that the inheritance of quantitative characteristics could indeed be explained by the cumulative effects of many genes, each following Mendel's laws of inheritance.

If two individuals homozygous for different alleles at a single locus ($A_1A_1 \times A_2A_2$) and resulting $F_1$ is interbred ($A_1A_2 \times A_1A_2$), then one-fourth of the $F_2$ should be homozygous like each of the original parents. If the original parents are homozygous for different alleles at two loci, then $\frac{1}{4} \times \frac{1}{4} = \frac{1}{16}$ of the $F_2$ should resemble one of the original homozygous parents. Generally $\left(\frac{1}{4}\right)^n$ will be the number of individuals in the $F_2$ progeny that should resemble each of the original homozygous parents, where n equals the number of loci with a segregating pair of alleles that affect the chracteristics. This equation provides us with a possible means of determining the number of loci influencing a quantitative characteristics.

## 27.6 QUANTITATIVE TRAIT LOCUS (QTL)

The trait, usually polygenic in nature that can be described with numbers called *quantitative trait.*

A gene or chromosomal region that contributes to the expression of quantitative characteristics, called **quantitative trait locus** (QTL).

### 27.6.1 QTL mapping

In recent years, numerous genetic markers have been identified and mapped with the use of recombinant DNA techniques, making it possible to identify QTLs by linkage analysis. These molecular markers are RFLPs and microsatellites, that serve as reference points along the chromosomes and these markers have been used to contruct detailed genetic maps of several genomes of species including, some model organisms such as *Drosophila, Arabidopsis, Caenorhabdites,* mice etc; some agricultural important plants, such a corn, rice and tomatoes as well as some livestocks such as cattle, pigs, sheep, chicken etc.

Eric Lander and David Botstein, in 1989 extended a technique to identify QTLs. The basis of QTL mapping is the association between genetically determined phenotypes (quantitative traits) and the molecular markers such as RFLPs and microsatellites.

Two strains of crops were taken, which differ in two ways.

1. They must differ with regard to a quantitative traits of interests. For example, the strain of large fruits and the other stain of small fruits. There are more than one unknown gene, which designate the sites, promoting large fruit and at the same site that promotes small fruit.
2. The two strains differ with their molecular markers.

Suppose, a diploid plant, showing their four pairs of chromosomes. The left one is the strain produces large fruit and right one is the strain produces small fruit. The left stain having "X" regions at the different sites of their chromosomes for promoting large fruit. The right strain also has "X" regions at the same site that promote small fruit. The chromosomes have different marker regions for RFLPs or microsatellites designated as 1A and 1B, 2A and 2B, and so on. A and B denote the two markers on the chromosomes of two strains at the same site (Fig. 27.1).

For the purpose of QTL mapping, analysis of a large number of markers and offspring are to be involved and the data are to be analyzed by computer programs that can be associated statistically the phenotypes with particular

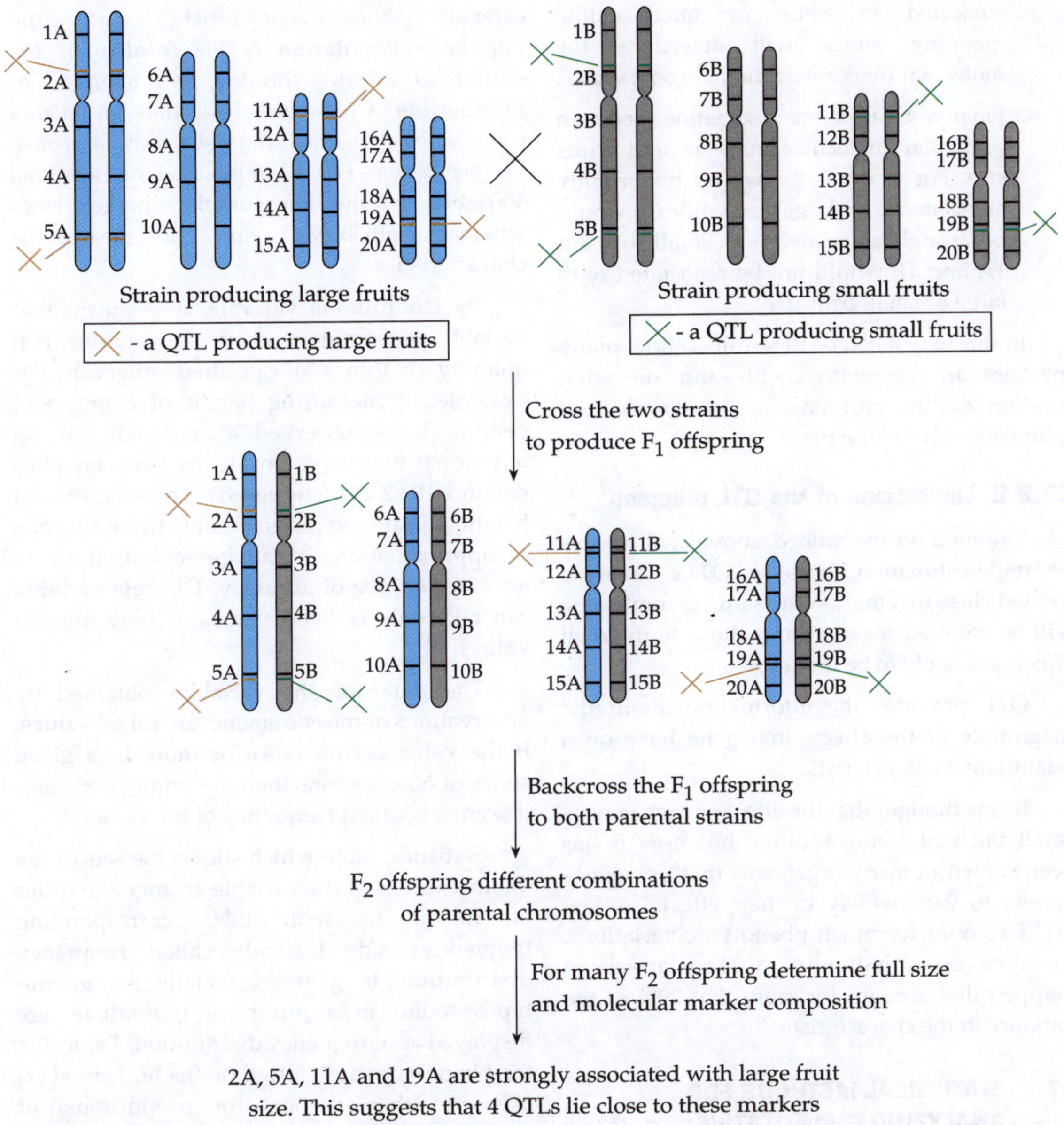


**Fig.27.1 :** *General strategy for QTL mapping via molecular markers.*

markers, because markers are present throughout the genome.

The protocol of QTL mapping is based on

1. Mating the two inbred strains to produce $F_1$ offspring.
2. Backcrossing the $F_1$ offspring to the parental stocks. As a result, the $F_2$ offspring, would have different combinations of parental chromosomes.
3. The $F_2$ offspring are first examined by the fruit size and then their sample cells are

subjected to RFLP or microsatellite mapping which will determine the molecular markers on their chromosomes.

4. Finally, to find an association between particular molecular markers and fruits size. For example 2A would be strongly associated with large size while 2B would be strongly associated with small size. But 1A and 1B would not be associated with large or small fruit size.

In this way it can be determined how many markers are associated with and on what location on the chromosomes are assocaited with fruit's size of the plant.

### 27.6.2 Limitations of the QTL mapping

The method mentioned above will always be underestimation, because QTLs that are located close together on the same chromosome will be counted together and those with small effects are likely to be missed.

QTL provides the information about the magnitude of the effects that gene have on a quantitative characteristic.

It was thought that the effect of each gene is small but equal and additive but now it has been shown in many organisms that polygenes appear to vary widely in their effects. A few QTLs account for much phenotypic variations. In some cases individual QTLs have been mapped that account for more that 20% of the variance in the characteristic.

## 27.7 STATISTICAL METHODS FOR ANALYZING QUANTITATIVE CHARACTERISTICS

### 27.7.1 Concept

*Statistics* is a collection of informations in numerical terms. Informations in numerical terms are collected by census or survey or any other methods are called *raw data. Data* is a collection of observations expressed in numerical figures. *Sample* is a portion of a population which is examined with a view to estimate the characteristics of the population.**Population** ***is the totality of the statistical data forming a subject of information.*** **Characteristics** *means the quality possessed by an indivudual, person, object or item of the population.* For example, height, age etc. **Variable** is the measurable characteristics whereas attributes are non-measurable characteristics.

By **Continuous variable,** it is meant that variable, which can assume for its value any real quantity within a specified interval. For example, in measuring height of a group of people, it is observed that height of an individual may have any value between 146.8 cm and 183.2 cm (supposed). Thus increase of height measureing gives the statistician to scope of approximation, it can be measured to an arbitrary degree of accuracy. **Discrete variable** can take only isolated values, *ie* only integral values.

The data for the variables obtained by observations or measurements are called **values.** If the value occurs twice or more in a given series of observations then the number of times it occurs, is called **frequency** of the value.

Statistical table which shows the sets of the distinct values of the variable arranged in order of magnitude with their corresponding frequencies side by side called **frequency distribution**. In genetics, usually the **phenotypes** found in a group of individuals are displayed as a frequency distribution. Typically, the phenotypes are plotted on the horizantal (x) axis and the numbers (or proportions) of individuals with each phenotype are plotted on the vertical (y) axis.

Many quantitative characteristics exhibit a symmetrical (bell shaped) curve called a *normal distribution*. Normal distributions arise when a large number of independent factors contribute to a measurement. Quantitative characteristics are frequently affected by numerous genes and environemtnal factors, so their phenotypes often exhibit normal distributions. The distributions may be skewed and bimodal.

### 27.7.2 Measurement of Central tendency

A typical value *i.e.* the average of the whole set of observation usually occupies a central position, so that some observations are larger and some others are smaller than it, averages are also known as measures of **central tendency**. There are three measures of central tendency – mean, median and mode.

#### Mean

The arithmatic mean of the score of the sample is called simply a **mean** ($\bar{x}$).

This is obtained by dividing the sum of the given values by their numbers.

1. For attributes, if the variables are denoted by x and if n values of x are given, viz., $x_1$, $x_2$, $x_3$ ............$x_n$, then the mean of x is

$$\bar{x} = \frac{x_1 + x_2 + x_3 + \ldots\ldots\ldots\ldots + x_n}{n}$$

$$= \frac{1}{n}\sum_{i=1}^{n} x_i$$

2. For discrete variables, where $x_1$, $x_2$, $x_3$ ............... $x_n$ are the different observed values of x with the frequency $f_1$, $f_2$, $f_3$ .......$f_n$, then

$$\text{mean } \bar{x} = \frac{1}{n}\sum_{i=1}^{n} x_i f_i$$

3. For continuous variable.

$$\bar{x} = A + \frac{\sum u_i f_i}{n} \times c$$

Where A = assumed mean

$$u_i = \frac{x_i - A}{c}$$

c = difference of class boundary.

#### Median

Median is that value of the variable which divides the series into two equal parts such that half of the total number of values are less than or equal to it and half are greater than or equal to it. The score below which lies exactly 50% of all the scores of the sample.

1. **For simple series :** If the given values of x are arranged in an increasing or decreasing order of magnitude, then the middlemost value in the arangement is **median.**

   When the number of values, n = odd, then the middlemost value $\frac{n+1}{2}$th, is the median of x.

   When n is even, there may be no unique median. The value between $\frac{n}{2}$th and $(\frac{n}{2}+1)$th of x would be taken as median.

2. For grouped or continuous variable.

$$\text{Median} = x_i = \frac{\frac{n}{2} - n_i}{f_0} \times c$$

Where, $x_i$ = Lower boundary of class where median lies

$n_i$ = Cumulative frequency upto lower boundary

$f_0$ = Frequency of the class where median lies

c = Width of the class.

#### Mode :

The score occurring most frequently in the sample is called **mode.**

It can be easily obtained from the simple series and from ungrouped variables by observing the value of x which occurs most frequently.

For grouped or continuous variables

$$\text{Mode} = x_i + \frac{f_0 - f_{-1}}{2f_0 - f_{-1} - f_{+1}} \times c$$

Where, $x_i$ = Lower boundary of the modal class

$f_0$ = Frequency of the modal class

$f_{-1}$ = Frequency of the previous class interval of the modal class

$f_{+1}$ = Frequency of the next class bondary of the modal class

c = Width of the class.

### 27.7.3 Standard deviation and Variance

Standard deviation is defined as "the square root of the mean (average) of the squares of deviations from the mean. It is designated as σ.

If $x_1, x_2, x_3$ ...................... $x_n$ be the series of values of the variable and $\bar{x}$ is their mean, then standard deviation is defined by the equation :

- **For large sample where n>30**

$$\sigma = \sqrt{\frac{(x_1-\bar{x})^2 + (x_2-\bar{x})^2 + (x_3-\bar{x})^2 + ....... + (x_n-\bar{x})^2}{n}}$$

$$= \sqrt{\frac{\sum (x_i-\bar{x})^2}{n}} \quad \text{or} \quad \sqrt{\frac{\sum x_i^2}{n} - \left(\frac{\sum x_i}{n}\right)^2}$$

In a discrete frequency distribution table

$$\sigma = \sqrt{\frac{\sum (x_i-\bar{x})^2 f}{n}} \quad \text{or} \quad \sqrt{\frac{\sum x_i^2 f_i}{n} - \left(\frac{\sum x_i^2 f_i}{n}\right)^2}$$

In grouped or continuous frequency table

$$\sigma = \sqrt{\frac{\sum u_i^2 f_i}{n} - \left(\frac{u_i f_i}{n}\right)^2} \times c$$

Where, $u_i = \frac{x_i - A}{c}$

A = assumed mean

c = width of the class

- **For small samples,** standard deviation is the square root of average squared deviation from the mean, divided by the degree of freedom

$$\text{Standard deviation (s)} = \sqrt{\frac{\sum (x-\bar{x})^2}{n-1}}$$

$$\text{or,} \quad s = \sqrt{\frac{\sum x^2 - n\bar{x}^2}{n-1}}$$

Variance ($s^2$) is defined as the average squared deviation from the mean, divided by the degree of freedom.

*i.e.*, variance = (standard deviation)$^2$

For large size sample :

$$\text{Variance} = \frac{\sum (x-\bar{x})^2}{n}$$

For small size sample :

$$\text{Variance} = \frac{\sum (x-\bar{x})^2}{n-1}$$

Variance indicates the variability of a group of measurements or how spread out the distribution is. Distribution may have the same mean but different variances. The larger the variance, the greater the spread of measurements in a distribution about it's mean (Fig. 27.2).

The standard deviation is in the same units as the original measurements, whereas the variance is expressed in units squared. Therefore, standard deviation is often preferred for describing the variability of a measurement.

### 27.7.4 Sampling

Biologists frequently need to describe the distribution of phenotypes exhibited by some group of individuals and constantly confronted with the problem that the population is too large for a complete census. One solution is to measure a smaller fraction of individuals, called a **sample**, and use measurements made on the sample to describe the population.

**Sampling** denotes the selection of a part of the aggregated statistical material with a view to obtain information about the whole.

The selected part, which is used to ascertain the characteristics of population is called **sample.**

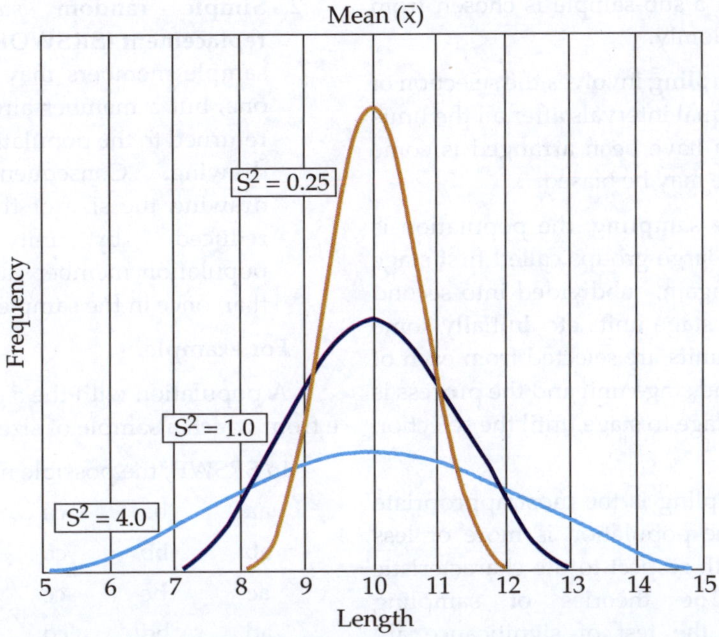


**Fig.27.2 :** *The variance provides information about the variability of a group of phenotypes*

The total number of members of the population and the number included in the sample are called **population size** and **sample size** respectively.

A true mean is the mean of infinitely large number of readings of a parameter. In experiments, it is not possible for us to try to collect a reasonably small number of readings which are representatives of the large population and in this way we are sampling the universe of possible readings.

A sample should never be selected but collected randomly. The true mean and standard deviation will coincide with the mean and standard deviation of the sample, which are affected by the following factors.

1. Size of the sample.
2. Variability of the readings – shorter range of data, the variability is lesser.
3. Frequency distribution of means.
4. Standar d error of the mean.
5. Degree of freedom – the number of values of a sample which are freely variable without affecting the mean.
6. Significance – the difference between the experimental results and the control results.

**Random and non-random samplings**

Sampling from the population may be of different types, but is classified mainly into random sampling and nonrandom sampling.

**Random sampling** is the process of selection of a group of units in such a manner that every unit of the population has got no equal chance and are not being included in the sample. It may be purposive sampling, systemic sampling and multistage sampling.

In **Purposive sampling** , a sample is selected on the basis of individual judgement of the sampler. So, there is much scope for bias and the degree of accuracy is not known.

In **stratified sampling**, the population is subdivided into several **strata** by purposive method and then a sub-sample is chosen from each of them randomly.

**Systemic sampling** involves the selection of sample units at equal intervals after all the units in the population have been arranged is some order. The sample may be biased.

In **multistage sampling,** the population is first divided into large groups called first stage units. These are again, subdivided into second stage units, third stage units etc. Initially some of the first stage units are selected from each of which some second stage unit and the process is carried on from stage to stage until the selection of ultimate units.

Random sampling is the most appropriate in cases when the population is more or less homogeneous with respect to the characteristic under study. The theories of sampling distribution and the test of significance are based on random sampling only.

**Sampling error** : In sampling, the composition of the sample is a matter of chance and if a proper process of selection is employed, the results obtained from sample cannot be expected to represent the characteristics of population in toto. Some error or discripancy is inevitable. This is called **sampling error**. The magnitude of such errors depends on the size of the sample and the variability of the population.

**Simple random sampling :**

The drawing of a sample from a given population may be done in a variety of ways; sampling may be with or without replacement.

1. **Simple random sampling with replacement (SRSWR)** : In this case the members of a sample are drawn from the population one by one and after each drawing, the member drawn is put back to the population once its nature is noted. The size and composition of the population remain unchanged throughout the sample operation and the same population member may appear more than once in the sample.

2. **Simple random sampling without replacement (SRSWOR)** : In this case, the sample members may be drawn one by one, but a member already drawn is not returned to the population before any new drawing. Consequently, after each drawing the size of the population gets reduced by unity and the same population member cannot appear more than once in the sample.

**For example,**

A population with the 5 elements, a, b, c, d, e from which a sample of size 2 is to be taken.

In SRSWR, the possible number is 5×5 = 25.

| | | | | |
|---|---|---|---|---|
| aa | ba | ca | da | ea |
| ab | bb | cb | db | eb |
| ac | bc | cc | dc | ec |
| ad | bd | cd | dd | ed |
| ae | be | ce | de | ee |

In SRSWOR, the possible number is 4×5 = 25.

| | | | | |
|---|---|---|---|---|
| ab | ba | ca | da | ea |
| ac | bc | cb | db | eb |
| ad | bd | cd | dc | ec |
| ae | be | ce | de | ed |

Suppose a sample of size "n" is to be taken from a population size N,

In SRSWR, if the n units of the sample are drawn from the population one by one, after each drawing the individual selected being returned to the population in such a way that at each drawing each of the N members of the population gets the same probability $\frac{1}{N}$ of being selected.

In SRSWOR, if the 'n' units of the sample are drawn from the population one by one, the members obtained at any drawing not being returned to the population in such a way that at each drawing, each of the remaining members of the population gets the same probability, *eg*, at the i-th drawing, the probability $\frac{1}{N-i+1}$ of being selected.

In SRSWR, $N^n$ possible samples with distinct permutations each with probability $\frac{1}{N^n}$.

In SRSWOR, $^NC_n = \frac{N!}{n!\,(N-n)!}$ possible samples with distinct "combinations" each with a probability $\frac{1}{^NC_n}$.

### 27.7.5 Standard error

Standard error of the statistic is the standard deviation calculated from the sampling distribution of the statistic.

Let, $x_1, x_2, x_3 ..........x_n$ be a random sample of size n drawn from a specialized population. On the basis of this sample, let us calculate the value of a certain statistic, say sample mean

$$\bar{x} = \frac{(x_1 + x_2 + x_3 + ....... + x_n)}{n}$$

We repeat the process of drawing a random sample of the fixed size n, a large number of times, and calculate the value of the statistic (mean) for each sample. This relative frequency distribution of these sample means when the number of samples considered is infinitely large, is called **sampling distribution of sample mean.**

The standard deviation calculated from the sampling distribution of a statistic is called **standard error.**

Stardard error (SE) gives the measure of dispersion of the statistic.

SE depends upon the sample size. As sample size increases, SE decreases.

SE is used to set up confidence limits for population parameters and in tests of significance.

SE of sample mean $\bar{x}$ or sample proportion (p) are used to find confidence limits for the population mean (μ) and the population proportion (P) respectively.

1. If $\bar{x}$ is the mean calculated from the random sample of size "n" and SD of the population is σ, then

$$SE = \frac{\sigma}{\sqrt{n}}$$

When the population size is infinitely large or the sample is drawn with replacement.

2. $SE = \frac{\sigma}{\sqrt{n}}\sqrt{\frac{N-n}{N-1}}$, when the population size N is finite, but the sample is drawn without replacement.

3. If $\bar{x_1}$ and $\bar{x_2}$ denote the means, calculated from independent random samples of sizes $n_1$ and $n_2$, drawn from two populations with standard deviation $\sigma_1$ and $\sigma_2$, then SE of $(\bar{x}_1 - \bar{x}_2) = \sqrt{\frac{\sigma_1^2}{n_1} + \frac{\sigma_2^2}{n_2}}$.

### 27.7.6 Scatter diagram, Correlation and Regression

**Scatter diagram** : When statistical data relating to a bivariate frequency distribution, each pair of observation having a geometrical measurement of two points on a graph paper, the values of one variable being shown along the X-axis and the other corresponding variable along the Y-axis. If there are n pairs of observations, finally a graph paper will contain 'n' points. This diagrametie representation of bivariate data is known as **scatter diagram**.

A scatter diagram indicates the nature of association between the two variables.

**Correlation** : The degree of association between two or more variables is called **correlation.** If, with the increase in the values of one variable, the values of the other variable is also found to increase in general or on the average, then the two variables are said to be **positively correlated**. Here the pattern of dots on the scatter diagram shows a linear path diagonally across the graph paper from the bottom left-hand corner to the top right (Fig. 27.3).

If, on the otherhand, with the increase in the value of one variable that of the other variable decreases on the average, then the two are said to be **negatively correlated**. Here the patterns of dots be such as to indicate a straight line path from the upper left-hand corner to the bottom right, i.e., the association is indirect, high values of one variable being associated with low values of the other.

The values of one variable increases, the value of the other variable remains constant on the average, this is said to be a case of **zero correlation**. Here the dots do not indicate any straight line tendency but a swarm concentrated around a curved line.

When the dots lie exactly on the straight line, the correlation is perfect, when both variables increase with a increase of other, then its degree of correlation is +1 and when one vairable increases with the decrease of the other variables, is said to be degree of correlation is –1.

**Correlation coefficient :** Correlation between characteristics are measured by a **correlation coefficient** (designated as "r"). It measures the degree of association between two or more variables. The value of corelation coefficient ranges from –1 to +1. The absolute value of correlation coefficient provides information about the strength of association between the variables.

To determine how the characteristics are correlated , we first obtain the covariance (cov) of x and y.

$$Cov_{xy} = \frac{\sum(x-\bar{x})(y-\bar{y})}{n-1}$$

Where n = the number of xy pairs

**The Pearsons correlation coefficient** (r or $r_{xy}$) is obtained by dividing the cov of xy by the product of the standard deviations of x and y.

$$r = \frac{Cov(x, y)}{Sx\ Sy}$$

**Test of correlation coefficient :** In sampling from a bivariate normal population, the sampling distribution of sample correlation coefficient (r) is far from normal even for large sample size (n). Therefore, tests for correlation coefficient is $\rho = 0$ or $\rho \neq 0$, i.e. whether the variables are uncorrelated or correlated in the population.

It may be assumed that when n>500 *ie* very large sample, the sample correlation coefficient r may be assumed to follow roughly a normal distribution with mean ρ (i.e., population correlation coefficient) and standard error (SE of r) = $(1-\rho^2)/\sqrt{n}$.

Hence, $z = \frac{r-\rho}{SE\ of\ r}$ has approximately a standard normal distribution.

This test statistic is used to test the hypothesis $H_0(\rho=\rho_0)$, i.e., the sample may be assumed to have arisen from the population.

95% confidence limits = r ± 1.96 × SE of r

99% confidence limits = r ± 2.58 × SE of r

Where SE of $r = \frac{1-r^2}{\sqrt{n}}$.

**Regression :** The word "regression" is used to denote estimation or prediction of the average value of one variable for a specialized value of the other variable.

The estimation is done by means of suitable equation derived on the basis of available bivariate data, this is called *regression equation* and its geometrical representation is called the *regression curve.*

In simple linear regression, the relationship between the variables is assumed to be linear. The estimate of y (say y′) is obtained from the equation of the form.

$y-\bar{y} = b_{yx}(x-\bar{x})^2$. This is known as regression equation of y on x, $b_{yx}$ is regression coefficient of y on x.

The estimate of x (say x′) from another equation of the form.

$x-\bar{x} = b_{xy}(y-\bar{y})$, have $b_{xy}$ regression coefficient of x on y.

The statistic that measures how much one variable changes on average, with a unit change in another variable is called **regression coefficient.**

The regression coefficient of "x" on "y" is

$$b_{xy} = \frac{Cov(xy)}{Var(y)} = r\frac{\sigma_x}{\sigma_y}$$

Thus the regression equation of "x" on "y" becomes

$$x = \bar{x} + \frac{r\sigma_x}{\sigma_y}(y - \bar{y})$$

The error variance var(e) = $\sigma_y{}^2(1 - r^2)$

## 27.8 QUANTIFYING GENETIC VARIABILITY

The variability observed for quantitative characters in a segregating population. It is often quantified using statistical calculations.

**Variance :**

$$S^2 = \frac{(x_1-\bar{x})^2 + (x_2-\bar{x})^2 + (x_3-\bar{x})^2 + ...... + (x_N-\bar{x})^2}{N}$$

$$= \frac{1}{N}\sum(x_i - \bar{x})^2$$

$$= \frac{\sum x_i^2 - \frac{\sum x_i 2}{N}}{N}$$

Where,

x = the variable

$x_i$ = the i–th measurement

N = number of observations

$$\bar{x} = \text{mean} = \frac{x_1 + x_2 + x_3 .................. x_n}{N}$$

$$= \frac{1}{N}\sum x_i$$

The variations observed between individuals when they are measured for most quantitative traits may be caused by genetic differences and occasionally by interaction between genotypes and environment. Accurate quantitative prediction cannot be made because genotypes act differently on different environment.

We may consider the observed phenotypic variance ($V_p$) has three components, viz., genotype variance ($V_G$), environmental variance ($V_E$) and interaction of genotypes and environments ($V_{GE}$) i.e., $V_P = V_G + V_E + V_{GE}$

(i) The environmental variance ($V_E$) includes all variations of the environment, not caused by genetic differences such as growth factors, birth sequences etc.

(ii) The genotype-environmental interactions $V_{GE}$ are those in which the differential environment interferes with the expression of the genes differentially.

(iii) The genotypic variance ($V_G$) is the phenotypic differences arise from a variety of sources represented by their genetic constitution. It may be again divided into three components:

Additive measurement ($V_A$) of different alleles present in the genotype when there is a quantitative value of each allele of genes (e.g., multiple factors)

The alleles interact with each other in the same gene pair producing dominant effects ($V_D$).

The epistatic – hypostatic interaction ($V_I$) between the alleles of the gene.

Therefore, genetic variance,

$V_G = V_A + V_D + V_I$

and then, $V_P = V_A + V_D + V_I + V_E + V_{GE}$

These values may be estimated in appropriate experimental design. Clayton, Morris and Robertson measured the number of abdominal bristle in *Drosophila* population. They found that phenotypic variance was reduced by 61% in the uniform population, i.e., 61% of the variance is the component of $V_G$, and remaining 39% may be considered to be the $V_E$ and $V_{EG}$.

When two inbred lines are crossed, the $F_1$ can be used as estimates of environmental variance. The $F_1$ mean value would be expected to be exactly intermediate to both parents if the genetic effects are additive. Departure from this genetic effects are additive. Departure from this mid parental value would indicate the effect of dominance.

The dominance effect may be toward either a phenotypic increase ($A_2A_2$) or decrease ($A_1A_1$). Beginning from the mid parental value and going towards each of the homozygotes is an additive increment, "a" then the difference between parental values is 2a.

If the dominance is complete then d = a, the phenotypic value of the $F_1$ heterozygote is like either to $A_1A_1$ or to $A_2A_2$. The ratio $\frac{d}{a}$, i.e., the degree of dominance would be 1. If dominance is lacking then d = 0, i.e., the relationship between these alleles is wholly additive. Then degree of dominance is also zero.

When a single gene pair $A_1$ and $A_2$ is segregating, there are three distinct genotypes in the $F_2$ in a proportion $\frac{1}{4}A_1A_1 : \frac{1}{2}A_1A_2 : \frac{1}{4}A_2A_2$.

If the departure from the mid-parental value is d, then $A_1A_1 = -$ a,

$A_1A_2$ = d and $A_2A_2$ = + a.

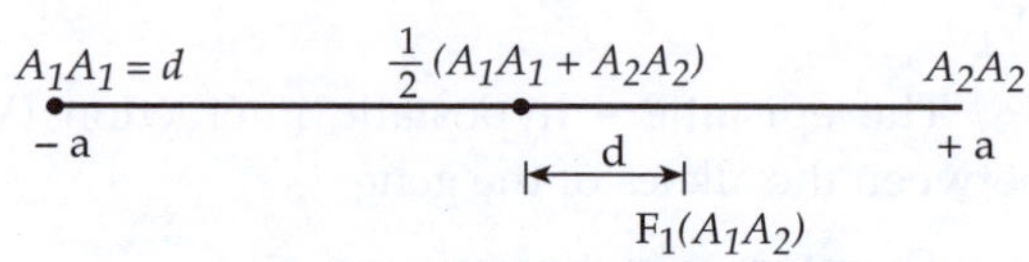


The $F_2$ mean would be :

$$\frac{1}{4}(-a) + \frac{1}{2}(d) + \frac{1}{4}(+a) = \frac{1}{2}(d)$$

The variance [*i.e.* if $f(x - \bar{x})^2$]

$$= \frac{1}{4}\left(-a - \frac{d}{2}\right)^2 + \frac{1}{2}\left(d - \frac{d}{2}\right)^2 + \frac{1}{4}\left(a - \frac{d}{2}\right)^2$$

$$= \frac{1}{4}\left(a^2 + ad + \frac{d^2}{4}\right) + \frac{d^2}{8} + \frac{1}{4}\left(a^2 - ad + \frac{d^2}{4}\right)$$

$$= \left(\frac{a^2}{2} + \frac{d^2}{4}\right)$$

If we designate $a^2$ as A, $d^2$ as D and environmental component as E, then the total variance in $F_2$ is $\frac{A}{2} + \frac{D}{4} + E$

When the $F_2$ segregating population is grown along with parents $P_1$ and $P_2$ and also with $F_1$ hybrids, the mean variance exhibited by parents and hybrid which give the estimate of the environmental variance.

Therefore,

$$V_p = V_G + \frac{V_{P_1} + V_{P_2} + V_{F_1}}{3}$$

$$\text{or } V_G = V_P - \frac{V_{P_1} + V_{P_2} + V_{F_1}}{3}$$

## 27.9 ESTIMATION OF HERITABILITY

Heritability in **broad sense**, is measured by the following formula

$$H^2 = \frac{V_G}{V_P} = \frac{\text{Genotypic variance}}{\text{Phenotypic variance}}$$

It is to be noted that $H^2$ (or $h^2$) is the common statistical symbol of heridity. It does not signify the square of heritability.

However this ($H^2$) does not tell us what proportion of an individual's phenotype is due to genotype and also the dependence of its environment where the individual grows. Therefore, the geneticists prefer to estimate the heritability in **narrow sense** ($h^2$), which is based on the knowledge about gene action.

It is obvious that environmental variance should be low and the genetic variance is high. It means that phenotype of the individual is greatly affected by genetic differences and slightly by environmental variance i.e., $V_P = V_G + V_E$. In extreme cases, there is no environmental variance at all on the phenotypic variance i.e., $V_E = 0$, e.g., ABO blood group system in humans.

If, the environmental variance is low, complete dominance is lacking, interaction is absent. Two alleles at a locus controlling a quantitative trait i.e., genetic variability is determined by additive variance or $V_G = V_A$ [because, we know $V_G = V_A + V_D$ and $V_D = 0$]. Then the phenotype of the parent would be the accurate indication of its offspring's genotype.

The ratio between additive variance and the total phenotypic variance is the measure of the inheritance or the estimate of heritability in narrow sense.

$$h^2 = \frac{V_A}{V_P}$$

Greater value of $h^2$ indicates the better are the chances that selected individuals will maintain their superiority of the population as a whole.

Heritability is a measure of the resemblance between relatives. It can be estimated by evaluating the degree of resemblance. The correlation between the relatives can be used to obtain the correlation coefficient or regression slope, (b) which indicates the additive variance ($V_A$).

When the regression curve is large, the heritability is considered to be high. At zero the heritability is absent.

For the regression of offspring on one parent, heritability is twice to the regression coefficient i.e., $h^2 = 2b$.

When mid point value is used, heritability is equal to the regression coefficient ie. $h^2 = a$.

In regression equation $Y = \overline{Y} + b(X - \overline{X})$, Y is considered as the measurement of individual offspring and X as the measurement of the male or female parent or as the mid parental value. If more than one offspring is measure for each parent or set of parents, the average measurement of this group of offspring can be used.

If N number of trials, X representing the number of bristles on the mother of each set of daughters. Y is the average number of bristles in the female offspring then the regression coefficient can be calculated by the following formula.

$$b = \frac{\sum XY - \frac{\sum X \sum Y}{N}}{\sum X^2 - \frac{(\sum X)^2}{N}}$$

## 27.10 CALCULATING HERITABILITY

There are several ways to measure the heritability of a characteristic.

**(a) Heritability by elimination of variance components :** We have seen that $V_p = V_G + V_E + V_{GE}$

If we eleminate environmental variance *ie* $V_E = O$, then $V_{GE}$ would also be zero, because no genetic environmental interaction can be taken place. Thus $V_P$ becomes equal to $V_G$.

Theoritically $V_E = 0$ means that all the individuals are raised in exactly the same environment, but this is virtually impossible.

Again, in genetically identical individuals, the $V_G$ is equal to zero, then $V_P$ would be equal to $V_E$. In such case, if we cloned identical homozygous individuals in a defined environment, then we can measure their phenotypic variance to estimate $V_E$.

Using the value of $V_E$ on these genetically identical individuals, we can obtain the $V_G$ of the variable individual by using formula.

$V_G$ of genetically varying individual = $V_P$ (of genetically varying individual) – $V_E$ (of genetically identical individual)

The broad sense heritability of a genetically variable individual would be calculated as

$$H^2 = \frac{V_G}{V_P}$$

Heritability of white spotting in guinea pigs was estimated by Sewal Wright by following method.

1. He first measured the phenotypic variance of a genetically variable population $V_P = 573$.
2. He then generated genetically identical homozygous guinea pigs by inbreeding technique. He measured their phenotypic variance in white spotting and obtained the value of $V_P = 340$. Here $V_G = 0$, therefore $V_P = V_E$.

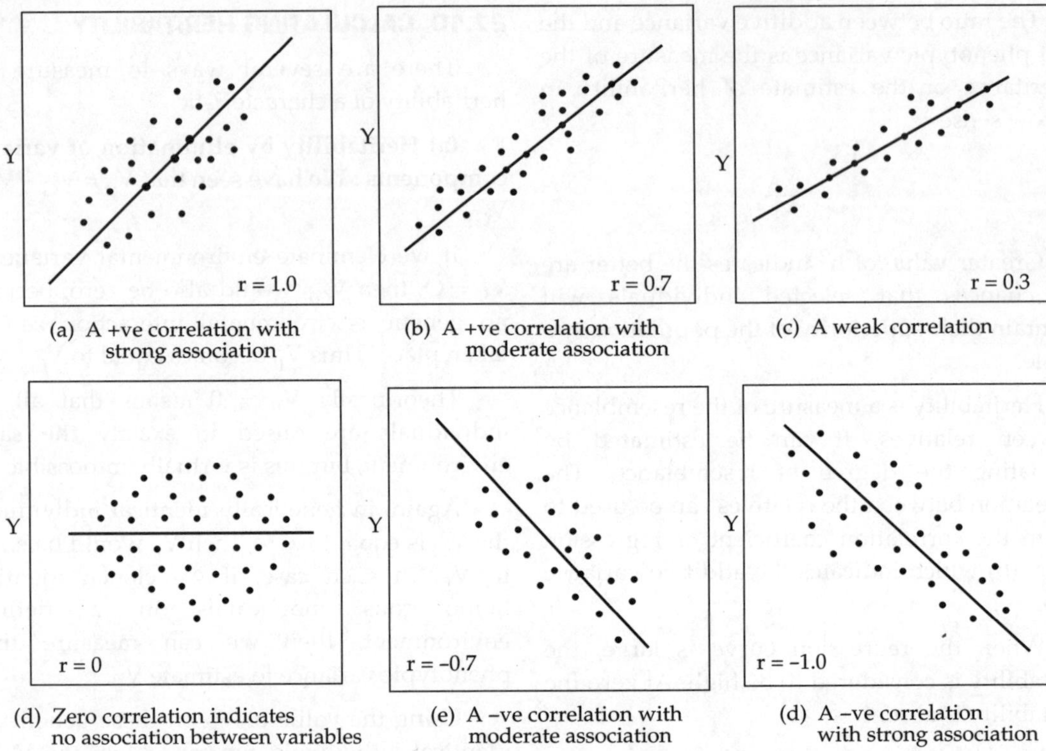


**Fig.27.3 :** *The correlation coefficient describes the relation between two or more variables.*

3. From this, he assumed the value as environmental variance for the original population.

   Thus the genetic variance

   $$V_G = V_P - V_E = 573 - 340 = 233$$

4. From this, the broad sense heritability can be calculated

   $$H^2 = \frac{V_G}{V_P} = \frac{233}{573} = 0.41$$

This implies that 41% of the variation in the spotting of guinea pigs in the experiment was due to differences in genotype.

(b) **Heritability by parent – offspring regression :** Here heritability is estimated by comparing the phenotype of parent with offspring. When offspring resemble more with their parents than their unrelated ones, their phenotypic variance is due to their genetic differences, because they have common genes with their parents.

We have to then calculate the narrow-sense heritability to measure the characteristic on a series of parents and offspring. If we plot the mean parental phenotype on x-axis with mean offspring phenotype on y-axis of a series of parents and offspring, there would be three types of regression coefficients which are equals to $h^2$.

1. When $h^2 = 0$, *i.e* there is no narrow – sense heritability, the genetic differences do not contribute to the phenotypic differences among individuals. The offspring would have no phenotypic similarity like that of unrelated relationships. The points will be scattered randomly, generating a regression coefficient of zero (Fig. 27.3d).

2. When $h^2 = 1.0$, the phenotypic differences are additive genetic differences of their parents. Then the regression coefficient is 1.0 (Fig. 27.3a).
3. When $h^2 < 1.0$, genes and environment both contribute to the difference in phenotype. The regression coefficient provides information about the magnitude of the heritability and the regression coefficient lies between 0 and 1.0 (Fig. 27.3b and c).

The regression of mean phenotype of the offspring against the mean phenotype of parents, *ie* the narrow-sense heritability would be equal to the regression coefficient.

$h^2$ = b (regression of mean offspring against mean of both parents)

When we calculate the regression of the mean offspring phenotype against the phenotype of one parent, the narrow-sense heritability equals twice the regression coefficient.

$h^2 = 2 \times$ b (regression of mean offspring against mean of one parent.)

This is because half of the genes of the offspring come from one parent.

Thus to obtain heritability, we must double the value of regression coefficient.

(c) **Heritability and degrees of relatedness** : Heritability is calculated by comparing the phenotypes of individuals having different degrees of relatedness. This method is based on the concept that more closely related individuals have more genes that they have common.

For example, the monozygotic twins have 100% of their genes in common, whereas, the dizygotic twins have only 50% common genes. We can calculate the broad sense heritability by the following formula.

$$H^2 = 2(r_{MZ} - r_{DZ})$$

Where $r_{MZ}$ and $r_{DZ}$ are the correlation coefficients of monozygotic and dizygotic twins respectively. Here, it assumes that the two individuals of a MZ twin pair experience environments that are no more similar to each other than those experienced by the two individuals of DZ pairs.

## 27.11 SOLVED PROBLEMS

### Problem 1

Find mean, median, mode, variance and standard deviation from the following tables.

**Table 1 :** Annual milk production (hundred pounds) by two-year old Jersey cows.

60, 74, 58, 61, 56, 55, 57, 54, 42, 65

**Table 2 :** Number of members of hundred families

| Family member | frequency |
|---|---|
| 1 | 1 |
| 2 | 8 |
| 3 | 20 |
| 4 | 31 |
| 5 | 34 |
| 6 | 4 |
| 7 | 2 |
| | n = 100 |

**Table 3 :** A gouped frequency distribution data collected from a population

| Class boundary | Frequency |
|---|---|
| 0–10 | 5 |
| 10–20 | 10 |
| 20–30 | 30 |
| 30–40 | 35 |
| 40–50 | 10 |
| 50–60 | 9 |
| 60–70 | 1 |
| | n = 100 |

**Solution :**

**Table 1 :**

**(i) mean**$(\bar{x}) = \frac{1}{N}\Sigma x = \frac{60+74+58+61+56+55+57+54+42+65}{10}$

$= \frac{582}{10} = 58.2$ hundred pounds per year

**(ii) Median :** Arranging the figures in increasing order 42, 54, 55, 56, 57, 58, 60, 61, 65, 74
n = 10, therefore, the average of 5th and 6th figure would be medium
5th term = 57
6th term = 58
The median is $= \frac{57+58}{2} = 57.5$ hundred pounds/year

**(iii) Mode :** Here the value of x is maximum in the case where yield is maximum 74 pounds/year.

Hence, the mode is 74 hundred pounds/year.

**(iv) Variance and Standard deviation :**

| x | $x_i - \bar{x}$ | $(x_i - \bar{x})^2$ |
|---|---|---|
| 60 | 1.80 | 3.24 |
| 74 | 15.80 | 249.64 |
| 58 | –0.20 | 0.04 |
| 61 | 2.80 | 7.84 |
| 56 | –2.20 | 4.84 |
| 55 | –3.20 | 10.24 |
| 54 | –4.20 | 17.64 |
| 57 | –1.20 | 1.44 |
| 65 | 6.80 | 46.24 |
| 42 | –16.20 | 262.44 |
| | | $\Sigma(x_i - \bar{x})^2 = 603.60$ |

**Variance** $= \frac{\Sigma(x_i - \bar{x})^2}{n-1}$, because n is not very large $= \frac{603.60}{9} = 67.07$

**Standard deviation =** $\sqrt{S_x^2} = \sqrt{67.07} = 8.19$

**Table 2 :**

| x | f | *xf* | Cumulative frequency | $x_i - \bar{x}$ | $(x_i - \bar{x})^2$ |
|---|---|---|---|---|---|
| 1 | 1 | 1 | 1 | – 3.09 | 9.55 |
| 2 | 8 | 16 | 9 | – 2.09 | 4.37 |
| 3 | 20 | 60 | 29 | –1.09 | 1.19 |
| 4 | 31 | 124 | 60 | –0.09 | 0.008 |
| 5 | 34 | 170 | 94 | 0.91 | 0.83 |
| 6 | 4 | 24 | 98 | 1.91 | 3.65 |
| 7 | 2 | 14 | 100 | 2.91 | 8.47 |
| | n = 100 | 409 | | | 28.068 |

(i) **Mean** $= \frac{409}{100} = 4.09$

(ii) **Median =** There are two middle values $\frac{n}{2}$th and $(\frac{n}{2}+1)$th ie 50th and 51st values.

Therefore, the median is the average of 50th and 51st values.

Here 50th and 51st values are 4 each.

Therefore, the **Median** is 4.

(iii) **Mode** is the highest frequency.

Here the highest frequency is 34 of the class 5.

Hence, the mode is 5.

(iv) **Variance** $= \frac{1}{N}\Sigma(x_i - \bar{x})^2 = \frac{28.068}{100} = 0.28068$

(v) **Standard deviation :** $\sqrt{\text{Variance}} = \sqrt{0.28068} = 0.529$

**Table 2 :**

| Class boundary | mid value $x_i$ | $f_i$ | $u_i$ | $u_i f_i$ | Cumulative frequences | $u_i^2 f_i$ |
|---|---|---|---|---|---|---|
| 0–10 | 5 | 5 | –3 | –15 | 5 | 45 |
| 10–20 | 15 | 10 | –2 | –20 | 15 | 40 |
| 20–30 | 25 | 30 | –1 | –30 | 45 | 30 |
| 30–40 | 35 | 35 | 0 | 0 | 80 | 0 |
| 40–50 | 45 | 10 | 1 | 10 | 90 | 10 |
| 50–60 | 55 | 9 | 2 | 18 | 99 | 36 |
| 60–70 | 65 | 1 | 3 | 3 | 1 | 9 |
| | | | | $\Sigma u_i f_i = -34$ | | $\Sigma u_i^2 f_i = 170$ |

1. **Mean :** Let, assumed mean is A = 35, c = Class boundary, $u_i = \frac{x_i - A}{c}$

$$\text{mean } (\bar{x}) = A + \frac{\sum x_i f_i}{n} \times c$$

$$= 35 + \frac{-34}{100} \times 10 \quad = \quad 35 - 3.4 \quad = \quad 31.6$$

2. **Median :** Here the median class is 30–40. Lower boundary of median class = 30

$$\textbf{Median} = x_i + \frac{\frac{n}{2} - n_i}{f_0} \times c$$

$$= 30 + \frac{\frac{100}{2} - 45}{35} \times 10 \quad = 35 + \frac{5}{35} \times 10 \quad = 30 + 1.428 \quad = 31.428$$

3. **Mode :** Lower boundary of modal class (highest frequency) = 30

$$\textbf{Mode} = x_i + \frac{f_0 - f_{-i}}{2f_0 - f_{+1} - f_{-1}} \times c$$

$$= 30 + \frac{35 - 30}{2 \times 35 - 30 - 10} \times 10 \quad = 30 + \frac{50}{30} \quad = 30 + 1.66 \quad = 31.66$$

4. **Standard deviation** $= \sqrt{\frac{\sum u_i^2 f_i}{n} - \left(\frac{\sum u_i f_i}{n}\right)^2} \times c$

$$= \sqrt{\frac{170}{100} - \left(\frac{-34}{100}\right)^2} \times 10 \quad = \sqrt{1.70 - 0.1156} \times 10 \quad = 0.9404 \times 10 \quad = 9.404$$

**Variance** = $(SD)^2 = (9.404)^2 = 88.4352$

### Problem 1

Mean weight and standard deviation of a large number of fishes are 0.3 Kg and 0.2 Kg respectively. If 100 fishes are taken at a time, find its standard errors.

**Solution :**

Mean $\mu = 0.03$, $\sigma = 0.2$, $n = 100$

Then S.E of mean $= \frac{\sigma}{\sqrt{n}} = \frac{0.2}{\sqrt{100}} = 0.02$

### Problem 3

A simple random sample of size 10 is drawn without replacement from a finite population consisting of 50 units. If the population S.D. is 6.25, what would be the S.E. of sample mean?

**Solution :**

Here n = 10, N = 50, σ = 6.25

$$\text{Then S.E. of mean} = \frac{\sigma}{\sqrt{n}} = \sqrt{\frac{N-n}{N-1}} = \frac{6.25}{\sqrt{10}} \times \sqrt{\frac{50-10}{50-1}} = 1.79$$

**Problem 4**

Calculate the SE of mean from the data

| x | 11 | 12 | 13 | 14 | 15 | 16 | 17 | 18 | 19 | 20 | 21 | 22 |
|---|---|---|---|---|---|---|---|---|---|---|---|---|
| f | 1 | 1 | 2 | 5 | 12 | 18 | 23 | 16 | 13 | 4 | 3 | 2 |

**Solution :**

| $x_i$ | $f_i$ | $x_i f_i$ | $x_i^2 f_i$ |
|---|---|---|---|
| 11 | 1 | 11 | 121 |
| 12 | 1 | 12 | 144 |
| 13 | 2 | 26 | 338 |
| 14 | 5 | 70 | 1050 |
| 15 | 12 | 180 | 2880 |
| 16 | 18 | 288 | 4896 |
| 17 | 23 | 391 | 7038 |
| 18 | 16 | 288 | 5472 |
| 19 | 13 | 247 | 4940 |
| 20 | 4 | 80 | 1680 |
| 21 | 3 | 63 | 1323 |
| 22 | 2 | 44 | 698 |
| | n = 100 | 1700 | 30580 |

$$\text{Sample mean } \bar{x} = \frac{\Sigma x_i f_i}{n} = \frac{1700}{100} = 17$$

$$\textbf{Sample S.D.} = \sqrt{\frac{n\Sigma fx^2 - \Sigma(fx)^2}{n(n-1)}} = \sqrt{\frac{30580 \times 100 - 2890000}{100 \times 99}} = 4.12$$

Statistically, variance of the mean is calculated as $\frac{1}{N}$ of the variance of the sample

$$\text{so, SE} = \frac{\sigma}{\sqrt{n}} = \frac{4.12}{\sqrt{100}} = 0.412$$

**Problem 5**

From the table calculate sample mean, variance of the sampling distribution of means, sampling standard deviation of mean, population standard deviation and standard error of the sample mean.

Table : Possible samples (with replacement)

| Sl. no. | Sample values | | Total | Sample mean |
|---|---|---|---|---|
| 1 | 3 | 3 | 6 | 3 |
| 2 | 3 | 7 | 10 | 5 |
| 3 | 3 | 11 | 14 | 7 |
| 4 | 3 | 15 | 18 | 9 |
| 5 | 7 | 3 | 10 | 5 |
| 6 | 7 | 7 | 14 | 7 |
| 7 | 7 | 11 | 18 | 9 |
| 8 | 7 | 15 | 22 | 11 |
| 9 | 11 | 3 | 14 | 7 |
| 10 | 11 | 7 | 18 | 9 |
| 11 | 11 | 11 | 22 | 11 |
| 12 | 11 | 15 | 26 | 13 |
| 13 | 15 | 3 | 18 | 9 |
| 14 | 15 | 7 | 22 | 11 |
| 15 | 15 | 11 | 26 | 13 |
| 16 | 15 | 15 | 30 | 15 |

**Solution :**

Here $N^n = 4^2 = 16$, N=4, n=2 without replacement

| Sample mean ($\bar{x}$) | frequency | $\bar{x}f_i$ | $(\bar{x}-9)^2 f_i$ |
|---|---|---|---|
| 3 | 1 | 3 | 36 |
| 5 | 2 | 10 | 32 |
| 7 | 3 | 21 | 12 |
| 9 | 4 | 36 | 0 |
| 11 | 3 | 33 | 12 |
| 13 | 2 | 26 | 32 |
| 15 | 1 | 15 | 36 |
| | N = 16 | 144 | 160 |

$$\bar{X} = \frac{\Sigma x_i f_i}{N} = \frac{144}{16} = 9$$

$$\text{Variance of } \bar{X} = \frac{\Sigma(\bar{x}-\bar{X})^2 f_i}{N} = \frac{160}{16} = 10$$

Standard deviation of sample mean s = $\sqrt{10}$ = 3.162

Standard deviation of population mean $\sigma = \sqrt{10 + 10} = 4.47$

[Because variance is additive, ie, two distributions with variances of 10 each is combined]

Variance = 20

SE of $\bar{x} = \frac{\sigma}{\sqrt{n}} = \frac{\sqrt{20}}{\sqrt{2}} = \sqrt{10} = 3.162$

### Problem 6

Calculate sampling mean, sampling variance, sampling SD, population variance, population SD and SE of the mean.

**Table : Samples (without replacement)**

| Sl. no. | Sample values | | Total | Sample mean |
|---|---|---|---|---|
| 1 | 3 | 7 | 10 | 5 |
| 2 | 3 | 11 | 14 | 7 |
| 3 | 3 | 15 | 18 | 9 |
| 4 | 7 | 11 | 18 | 9 |
| 5 | 7 | 15 | 22 | 11 |
| 6 | 11 | 15 | 30 | 13 |

### Solution :

Here n = 2 and N = 6 without replacement

| Sample mean ($\bar{x}$) | frequency | $\bar{x}f$ | $\Sigma(\bar{x} - \bar{X})^2 f$ |
|---|---|---|---|
| 5 | 1 | 5 | 16 |
| 7 | 1 | 7 | 4 |
| 9 | 2 | 18 | 0 |
| 11 | 1 | 11 | 4 |
| 13 | 1 | 13 | 16 |
| | N = 6 | $\Sigma\bar{x}f = 54$ | $\Sigma(\bar{x} - \bar{X})^2 f = 40$ |

Sampling mean $\bar{X} = \frac{\Sigma\bar{x}f}{N} = \frac{54}{6} = 9$

Sampling var of mean $= \frac{40}{6} = \frac{20}{3}$

Sampling SD of mean $= \sqrt{\frac{20}{3}} = 2.58$

Population var $= \frac{20}{3} + \frac{20}{3} = \frac{40}{3} = 13.33$

$$\text{Population SD} = \sqrt{\frac{40}{3}} = 5.16$$

$$SE = \frac{\sigma}{\sqrt{n}} = \sqrt{\frac{N-n}{N-1}} = \frac{\sqrt{40}}{\sqrt{3}\sqrt{2}} \times \sqrt{\frac{4-2}{4-1}} = \frac{\sqrt{20} \times \sqrt{2}}{3} = 2.108$$

**Problem 7**

Find the coefficient of correlation from the following pairs of observations and also find the two regression equations

(1, 3), (2, 2), (3, 5), (4, 4), (5, 6)

**Solution :**

| $x_i$ | $y_i$ | $x_i - \bar{x}$ | $y_i - \bar{y}$ | $(x_i - \bar{x})^2$ | $(y_i - \bar{y})^2$ | $(x_i - \bar{x})(y_i - \bar{y})$ |
|---|---|---|---|---|---|---|
| 1 | 3 | –2 | –1 | 4 | 1 | 2 |
| 2 | 2 | –1 | –2 | 1 | 4 | 2 |
| 3 | 5 | 0 | 1 | 0 | 1 | 0 |
| 4 | 4 | 1 | 0 | 1 | 0 | 0 |
| 5 | 6 | 2 | 2 | 4 | 4 | 4 |
| $\Sigma x_i = 15$ | $\Sigma y_i = 20$ | | | $\Sigma(x_i - \bar{x}) = 10$ | $\Sigma(y_i - \bar{y}) = 10$ | $\Sigma(x_i - \bar{x})(y_i - \bar{y}) = 8$ |

$$\bar{x} = \frac{\Sigma x_i}{n} = \frac{15}{5} = 3$$

$$\bar{y} = \frac{\Sigma y_i}{n} = \frac{20}{5} = 3$$

$$Cov_{xy} = \frac{\Sigma(x_i - \bar{x})(y_i - \bar{y})}{n-1} = \frac{8}{5-1} = \frac{8}{4} = 2$$

$$S_x^2 = \frac{\Sigma(x_i - \bar{x})^2}{n-1} = \frac{10}{5-1} = \frac{10}{4} = 2.5$$

$$S_y^2 = \frac{\Sigma(y_i - \bar{y})^2}{n-1} = \frac{10}{5-1} = \frac{10}{4} = 2.5$$

$$S_x = \sqrt{2.5} = 1.581$$

$$S_y = \sqrt{2.5} = 1.581$$

$$\text{Correlation coefficient (r)} = \frac{Cov\ xy}{S_x\ S_y} = \frac{2}{\sqrt{2.5} \times \sqrt{2.5}} = \frac{2}{2.5} = 0.8$$

$$\text{Regression coefficient } (b_{yx}) = \frac{\text{Cov } xy}{S^2_x} = \frac{2}{2.5} = 0.8$$

$$b_{xy} = \frac{\text{Cov } xy}{S^2_y} = 0.8$$

Thus the linear prediction equations become

$$y - \bar{y} = b_{yx}(x - \bar{x})$$

$$\text{or, } y - 4 = 0.8\,(x - 3) \quad \text{or, } y = 4 + 0.8\,(x - 3)$$

$$\text{or, } \quad y = 0.8x + 1.6$$

and

$$y - \bar{y} = b_{xy}(x - \bar{x})$$

$$\text{or, } y - 4 = 0.8\,(x - 3) \quad \text{or, } y = 4 + 0.8\,(x - 3)$$

$$\text{or, } \quad y = 0.8x + 1.6$$

**Problem 8**

A random sample of 1600 pairs of observations from a bivariate normal population shows a correlation coefficient of 0.74. Is it likely that the population correlation coefficient is 0.8? Also find 99% confidance limits for correlation coefficient in the population.

**Solution :**

The Null hypothesis is that $H_0(\rho = 0.8)$

$n = 1600$

Observed value of $r = 0.74$

Expected value of $r = 0.8$

$$\text{SE of } r = \frac{1 - \rho}{\sqrt{n}} = \frac{1 - (0.8)^2}{\sqrt{1600}} = 0.009$$

$$\text{The test statistic } z = \frac{r - \rho}{\text{SE of } r} = \frac{0.74 - 0.8}{0.009} = -6.67$$

Since (z) = 6.67 is larger than 2.58, z is highly significant and Null hypothesis is rejected. Concluded that the population correlation coefficient is not = 0.8.

$$\text{SE of } r = \frac{1 - r^2}{\sqrt{n}} = 0.0113$$

99% confidence limit for $\rho$ are

$$r \pm 2.58 \times \text{SE of } r$$

$$= 0.74 \pm 2.58 \times (0.0113)$$

$$= 0.74 \pm 0.0291$$

$$= 0.7691 \text{ and } 0.7309$$

## Chapter Glossary/Key Terms

**QTL mapping :** The determination of the location of QTLs using mapping methods such as genetic crosses coupled with the analysis of molecular marker.

**Quantitative trait :** A trait, usually polygenic in nature, that can be described with numbers.

**Quantitative genetics :** The area of genetics concerned with the traits that can be described in a quantitative way.

**Quantitative trait loci (QTLs) :** The locations on chromosomes where the genes that influence quantitative trait reside.

**Polygenic inheritance :** It refers to the transmission of traits that are governed by two or more different genes.

**Continuous variation :** Variation not represented by distinct classes. Individuals grade into each other and measurement data are required for analysis. Multiple genes are usually responsible for this type of variation.

**Heritability :** Degree to which a given trait is controlled by inheritance.

**Broad-sense heritability :** In quantitative genetics, the proportion of the total phenotypic variance is the genotypic variance.

**Narrow-sense heritability :** In quantitative geneties the proportion of the phenotypic variance that is due to the additive effects of alleles.

**Correlation :** A statistical association between variables.

**Restriction fragment length Polymorphism (RFLP) :** Genetic variation within a population in the lengths of DNA fragments that are produced when chromosomes are digested with particular restriction enzymes.

**Discontinuous trait :** A trait in which each offspring can be put into a particular phenotypic category.

## Exercise

**A. Long answer type questions :**

1. What are quantitative traits? What are the characteristics of quantitative traits?
2. Describe different types of quantitative traits?
3. What do you mean by polygenic inheritance?
4. What is QTL? What is the principle of QTL mapping? Describe the protocol for QTL mapping.
5. Define mean, median, mode, standard deviation and variance.

6. What is a sample and sampling? Describe different basis of random samples?
7. Distinguish between SRSWR and SRSWOR with examples.
8. Define sampling distribution of sample mean and standard error.
9. What do you mean by scatter diagram and correlation? Describe positive, negative and zero correlation.
10. Define and deduce correlation coefficient.
11. What are regression and regression curve? Deduce the regression equation.
12. What is variance? What is phenotypic variance? Define three components of phenotypic variance.
13. How the phenotypic variance is measured?
14. What do you mean by broad sense and narrow sense heritability? Describe their significance in the estimation of heritability.
15. Describe and deduce different methods of the measurement of heritability of a characeristic.

**B. Short answer type questions :**

1. What is quantitative genetics? What kind of characters are described by quantitative measurement?
2. What is QTL?
3. What is discontinuous trait?
4. How the quantitative characteristics arise in the organism?
5. What is multifunctional trait?
6. What is meristic characteristics? Give example?
7. What is threshold characteristics? Give example? Why this is quantitative characteristics?
8. Give some examples of quantitative traits?
9. What is anatomical trait? Give example?
10. What is phyiological trait? Give example?
11. What is behavioral trait? Give example?
12. What is polygenic inheritance? Give example?
13. What are quantitative trait and quantitative trait locus?
14. What is the basis of QTL mapping?
15. Give the protocol of QTL mappping?
16. What are the limitations of QTL mapping?
17. Define statistics, data, sample, population, characteristics, variables, continuous variable, discrete variable, values, frequency and frequency distribution.
18. What do you mean by central tendency?
19. Define mean, median and mode and their measurements.
20. Define standard deviation and also their measuremetns for small smaple and large sample?
21. What is variance? What is its measurement?
22. Distinguish between variance and standard deviation.
23. What are sample size and population size?
24. When sample mean and standard deviation are deviated from the popultion mean and standard deviation?
26. What is degree of freedom?
27. What is random sampling?
28. Define purposive, stratified systemic and multistage sampling?
29. What do you mean by sampling error?
30. What are SRSWR and SRSWOR? Give examples.
31. Define standard error?
32. Define sampling distribution of sample mean?
33. Calculate SE from random sample size n is infinite large drawn with replacement or without replacement.
34. What do you mean by scatter diagram? What is correlation? What do you mean by positively, negatively or zero correlation?
35. What are +1 and –1 correlation?
36. What is correlation coefficient?
37. What is covariance of x and y?
38. What is Pearson's correlation coefficient?

39. What test statistic is used for assuming the significance of the correlation coefficient?
40. What is regression?
41. What are regression equation and regression curve?
42. What is regression coefficient? Deduce error variance?
43. What are the components of phenotypic variance? Define environmental, genotypic and genetic environmental variations?
44. What are the components of $V_G$?
45. What do you mean by heritability in broad sense and narrow sense? What is its measure?
46. Why geneticists prefer narrow sense heritability? When the phenotype of parent would be the accurate indication of the genotype of the offspring?
47. What the greater value of $h^2$ indicates?
48. When heritability is high or zero, what would be the situation of regression curve?
49. When $h^2$ = 2b or b what would be the situation of regression coefficient?

28

# Behavioural Genetics

**CHAPTER AGENDA**

**28.1** Concept; **28.2** Different types of twins; **28.3** Conjoint twins; **28.4** Twin studies; **28.5** Twin studies by correlation method; **28.6** Adoption studies; **28.7** Phenocopy; **28.8** Nurturing behavior in mice; **28.9** Nest-cleaning behaviour in honey bees; **28.10** Biological rhythm in *Drosophila*; **28.11** Sexual preference in *Drosophila*; **28.12** Human Genetic diseases caused by expanding trinucleotide repeats; **28.13** Neurodevelopmental disorders and Genomic imprinting; **28.14** Neurodegenerative Alzheimer's disease; **28.15** A neurodegenerative disease Duchenne muscular dystrophy; **28.16** Lesch-Nyhan Syndrome : A behavioural disorder; **28.17** A neurodegenerative Tay-Sachs disease in human; **28.18** A neurodegenerative disease in human : Phenyl-ketoneuria; **28.19** Aggressive, impulsive and violent behavior in human; **28.20** Schizophrenia : a severe psychiatic disorder in human; Chapter Glossary/Key Terms; Exercise

## 28.1 CONCEPT

Behavior refers to a coordinated neuromuscular response to changes or signals in the external and internal environments. The behavior of animals includes a wide range of activities which are associated with feeding, courtship, reproduction, communication, remembering the previous events, intelligence, learning and many other usual activities for living. The genetic determinants of these behaviors are only now beginning to be identified through experimental works. Some particular behaviors in honeybees, *Drosophila*, mice as well as human beings are discussed with their genetic analyses in this chapter.

## 28.2 DIFFERENT TYPES OF TWINS

1. **Identical or monozygotic twins** come from a single zygote that splits into two. This separation can occur upto 12th day of conception, around the time the egg is implanting in the uterus. They share 100% of their DNA and are of same sex.
2. **Fraternal or dizygotic twins** are formed when the mother releases two eggs and both get fertilized. Such twins share 50% of their DNA. They may or may not be of same sex.
3. **Monoamniotic or monochorionic** twins are identical twins that are not separated by any membranes in the womb. They are at a higher risk for tangling of the umbilical cord. (Fig. 28.1).
4. **Half identical twins or polar body twins** are formed when an egg splits prior to fertilization and each half receives a separate sperm. The twins share 75% of their DNA.
5. **Half fraternal twins** are such that when two eggs are released by the ovaries and each egg is fertilized by a different father. The twins share 25% of their DNA.
6. **Conjoint twins** are also called **Siamese twins** (because, the most famous pair of conjoint twins was Eng and Chang Bunker born in Siam, Thailand on May 10, 1811 and died on Jan 12, 1874) are a type of monozygotic twins who fail to separate completely, perhaps because they split very late in development. (Fig. 28.2)

**Fig.28.1 :** *Two MZ twin sisters (in the middle) and their two MZ twin maternal uncles (on the two sides)*

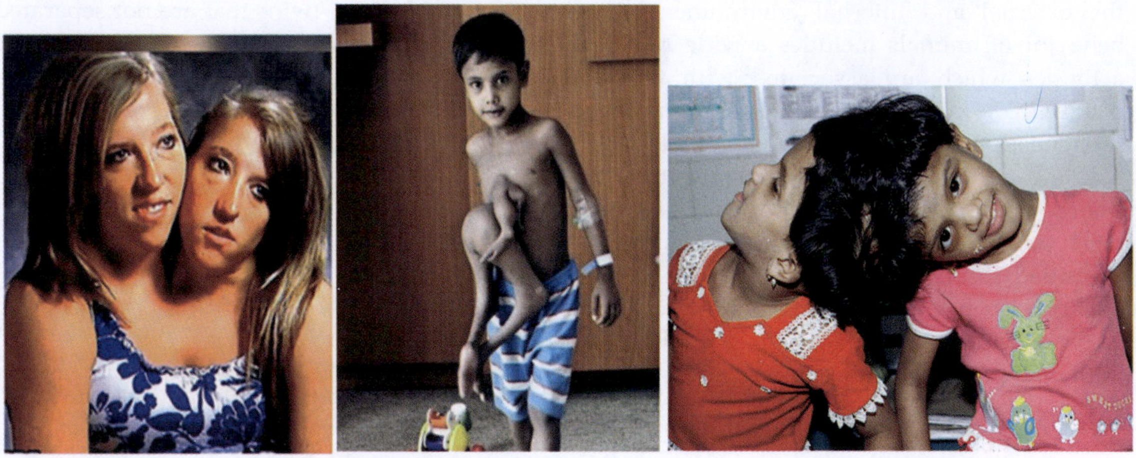

(a) Dicephalus twin (Abby and Brittany) (b) Parasitic twin (c) Cephalopagus twin

**Fig.28.2 :** *Three different conjoint twins*
*(a) Dicephalus twin (Abby and Brittany), (b) Parasitic twin, (c) Cephalopagus twin.*

## 28.3 CONJOINT TWINS

Over the past 500 years, about 600 surviving sets of conjoint twins have been documented. The incidence of such conjoint twins is very low, occurring only once in every 10000 births or so, with at least half being stillborn. Of the live births only two-thirds make it beyond day one. The overall survival rate is between 5-25%. Interestingly more than 90% of the survivors are female twins. The phenomenon is more common in Africa, China as well as Vietnam where US war defoliant **Agent orange** has been implicated. But what triggers the formation of conjoint twins is still not known.

The conjoint twin formation is due to rarely errors, which take place in the initial stage around the end of the second week of conception and the division stops before the separation is completed. The fetus continues to develop, growing into two babies that are fused together. Thus conjoint twins originate from a single fertilized egg and are therefore always identical and of the same sex. They can be detected as early as the 10th to 14th week of pregnancy by ultrasonography.

**Types of conjoint twins :**

(a) Complete and symmetrical twins : Two nearly normal babies sharing some parts of their body, union never involves heart and umbilicus. This may be of different types.

1. *Craniopagus (2%) :* Cranial union only,
2. *Pygopagus (19%)* : Posterior union of the rump.
3. *Thoracopagus (35%) :* Anterior union of the upper half of the trunk. It always involves sharing of the heart.
4. *Cephalopagus :* The anterior union of the upper half of the body with two faces on opposite sides of a conjoint head is extremely rare. The heart is sometimes involved.
5. *Parapagus (5%) :* also called *diprosopus*, which involves lateral union of the lower

half, extending variable distances upward. The heart is sometimes involved.

6. *Omphalopagus (30%) :* Involves anterior union of the mid trunk *ie* lower breast bone to waist.
7. *Ischiopagus (6%) :* Anterior union of the lower half of the body. Heart is not involved.
8. *Dicephalus :* Separate head and neck with one body.

(b) Incomple or heteropagus : Two dissimilar twins with rare organizations.

1. *Parasitic twins :* Asymmetrical conjoint twins, one twin being small, less formed, and dependent upon the other.
2. *Fetus in fetu :* Situation in which the imperfect fetus is contained completely within the body of its sibling.

Separation of the conjoint twins is a problem. Those are joined together by skin or ligament, the sepaation is not a problem. But if the twins sharing the vital organs such as the heart and the liver, the separation can lead to death of one or both. This poses many ethical and moral questions.

Conjoint twins have no personal space, privacy whether they think alike or not, have to perforce go everywhere together.

The behaviour and IQ have been studied on these conjoint twins. Although their genetic components are like that of identical twins, their immotional reactions to specific events and experiences may be quite dissimilar. The Iranian conjoint twins have quite different personalities. If one wanted to bend and pick something from the floor, the other would have to go along with it though she may have wanted to look at the sky at the same point of time.

Giacomo and Giovanni Battista Tocci, the blended twins (see fig 28.1c), each boy controled only one leg and they never coordinate their movements and therefore never learned to walk without assistance. But they were able to write, one was left -handed and other right-handed and each had artistic talents.

The famous pair of conjoint twins was Eng and Chang Bunker, the Siamese twins died within hours of each other at the age of 62 years. They married sisters Sarah and Adelaide Yates, respectively and fathered 21 children between them.

## 28.4 TWIN STUDIES

### 28.4.1 Concept

Twins are of two kinds : those that are no more alike than ordinary brothers and sisters (expect that they are of the same age) and those that are so much alike that it is often difficult to distinguish them apart. The first are known as **fraternal twins**, the second as **identical twins**. Identical twin births form about one-fourth of the total twin births.

Fraternal twins develop from two separate eggs and each fertilized by a separate sperm cell. They are originated from two separate zygotes, therefore, they are known as *dizygotic twins* (DZ). These fraternal twins are no more alike than nontwin children in the same family.

Identical twins develop from a single egg and zygote which in the course of development becomes two by the division of the developing zygote into two separate embryos.The division of the zygote is fully down in the middle of the body, so that the left half of the embryo becomes one twin, the right half the other one. In exceptional instances, the divided zygote by further division, gives rise to identical triplets, quaduplets and rarely quintuplets. The identical twins are referred to as *monozygotic twins* (MZ) as they are developed from a single zygote and also referred to as *monoval twins* as they are developed from a single ovum.

### 28.4.2 Concordance and discordance among Identical Twins

In genetics, the degree to which pairs of individuals exhibit the same trait and phenotypically similar is called *concordance*. On the other hand, the degree of phenotypically dissimilar trait, exhibited by the pair of individuals is called *discordance.*

Identical twins, who are reared together have very much the same environement as well as the same heredity and they show a remarkable extent of resemblances. They appear to have similarities only to their facial features but also to their general physical build, their deportment, their facial expression and often such slight details as the manner in which they hold their heads upon being photographed.

### 28.4.3 Finger-prints

No two fingerprints are ever exactly alike, not even those of corresponding fingers of left and right hands of the same person. But the finger prints of left and right hands are often very similar in their general pattern, though they may also be very different in details.

The fingerprints of identical twins are often similar in their general pattern. In general it may be stated that the **fingerprints of identical twins are about as much alike on the average as are those of the left and right hands of the same person.** This is because, the left hand of one identical twin and right hand of the other would be left and right hands of the same person if the zygote is not divided into two.

Actually, the left and right sides of a person's body are mirror images of each other though not always, the symmetry reversal is applied in the case of identical twins, *i.e.* the fingerprints of the left hand of one twin are sometimes mirror images of those of the right hand of the other. Sometimes, fingerprints of corresponding hands are mirror images.

### 28.4.4 Pattern of Whorl on the Crown of the Head

Pattern resemblances and mirror images are often strikingly shown by the whorl of the hair on the crown of the head in the case of identical twins, one is right-handed and the other is left-handed whorl.

### 28.4.5 Left and Right-Handedness

There is somewhat of a tendency for identical twins to be opposite handed *ie* one is right-handed and the other is left-handed. This tendency is not universal but such tendency is more often than the fraternal twins.

The greater percentage of left handedness is observed in the identical twin populations. One theory of left-handedness is that left-handed people are always or at least usually, members of an identical twin pair, the other members often having died before going further development. However, this theory, though possibly true, has little evidence in its support.

### 28.4.6 Handwriting

Identical twins show a resemblance, in their handwriting particularly when they are reared together and have had same teacher and same environment. However when identical twins are reared apart from early infacy their environments differ more widely , they do not show the same degree of resemblance as that of twins who were reared together.

### 34.4.7 Mental Ability

Identical twins are alike not only physically but also mentally. Intelligence test shows that they are, on the average, much more alike in aptitude than are fraternal twins.

Intelligence tests were made by Muller on a pair of identical twins reared apart from early child-hood. Similar test was also made by Newman, Freeman and Holzinger on 19 pairs of twins reared separtely, 50 pairs each of identical twins and fraternal twins reared together and 52 nontwin siblings reared together. The intelligence measured by the Stanford-Binet IQ test. The highest IQ rating among the twins reared apart was 127. The next highest was 122. The result was as follows :

| Case | IQ | Score of twins | difference |
|---|---|---|---|
| I | 85 | 97 | 12 |
| II | 66 | 78 | 12 |
| III | 99 | 101 | 2 |
| IV | 89 | 106 | 17 |
| V | 89 | 93 | 4 |
| VI | 102 | 94 | 8 |
| VII | 105 | 106 | 1 |
| VIII | 92 | 77 | 15 |
| IX | 102 | 96 | 6 |
| X | 122 | 127 | 5 |
| XI | 92 | 116 | 24 |
| XII | 116 | 109 | 7 |
| XIII | 94 | 95 | 1 |
| XIV | 85 | 84 | 1 |
| XV | 91 | 90 | 1 |
| XVI | 90 | 88 | 2 |
| XVII | 115 | 105 | 10 |
| XVIII | 96 | 77 | 19 |
| XIX | 88 | 79 | 9 |

The result showed that there tends to be a correlation in the rating of the members of a pair – *low in one twin tends to go with medium and high with high.* The *correlation* in the ratings can be explained only on the basis of heredity. The difference in the intelligence of the two pairs must be due in part at least to a difference in their heredity.

The nonidentical twins also show some correlation in their IQ ratings, but the correlation is not as great as that shown by identical twins even though the nonidenticals were reared together and the identicals were reared apart.

The degree of correlation of the twins in that investigation was also calculated mathematically. The *correlation coefficient* of 1 would mean complete agreement (same score always) between the membes of a twin pair. A coefficient of 0 would mean no more agreement than between any two persons chosen at random.

It is seen that the coefficient for (i) identical twins reared together is 0.881 (ii) non-identical twins reared together is 0.631 (iii) identical twins reared apart is 0.767, which is intermediate between the values for identicals and nonidenticals reared together.

This shows that, despite their separate environments, the identicals still are more alike, on the average, than nonidenticals.

The conclusion from the twin studies is that, first, the differences in intelligence of people are due partly to heredity, partly to environment. However, even though to environments are somewhat different (as those of twins reared apart), both might still be "normal" in the sense that both allow for normal mental development and the twin studies show that **when the environment is normal, exceptional intelligence depends largely on exceptional heredity.**

### 28.4.8 Susceptibility to Tuberculosis

Studies were made by Von Verschuer on a number of persons who were members of twin couples. It was found that when one twin has tuberculosis, the other also had it in 65% of the couples studied, but for non-identical twins the figure was 25%. This indicates that susceptibility to tuberculosis has an hereditary basis though, of course, the environment plays an important part in the spreading of the infection.

The agreement of two members of a twin couple with regard to a given tract as when both are tubercular is sometimes referrred to as *concordance* (++) and their disagreement as discordance(+–). In the above case, the concordance with respect to tuberculosis is 65% for identical twin pairs and 25% for fraternal twin pairs. The concordance is significantly greater for identical twins than fraternal twins because of the heredity.

### 28.4.9 Occurrence of Cancer

M.T. Maclin in his investigation observed that percentage of having same kind of cancer in identical twin (94.7%) is greater than that of nonidentical twins (58.3%).

Dizygotic twins share, on average, 50% of their genetic material. When a disorder has a genetic component, both identical twins are more likely to exhibit the disorder than are both nonidentical twins.

Geneticists evaluate the concordance for a disorder, which is the degree to which it is inherited, by calculating the percentage of twin pairs in which both twins exhibit the disorder relative to pairs where only one twin shows the disorder. Theoritically for diseases that are caused by a single gene, concordance among identical twins, should be 100%. For dizygotic twins, concordance for dominant disorders is expected to be 50% assuming that only one parent is a heterozygous individual. For recessive diseases concordance among dizygotic twin would be 25% if we assume that both parents are heterozygous carriers. The actual value may not be so becasue some disorders are not completely panetrant or one twin may have a disorder due to new mutation that occurred after fertilization.

## 28.5 TWIN STUDIES BY CORRELATION METHOD

The monozygotic twins are rare (0.3% of live births) and they usually are reared together (MZT) during their childhood and adolescence. In some cases, the MZ twins are separated early in life and are subsequently reared apart (MZA). The MZA twins provide a unique opportunity to study the genetic component of complex behavioral phenotypes.

Similarly the dizygotic twins may be reared together (DGT) in their early life or adolencence, or may be reared apart (DGA) from their early life.

British scientist Francis Galton in the late nineteenth century has developed a statistical procedure to quantify the phenotypic similarity between twins.

The degree of similarity is measured by the correlation coefficient whch is symbolized by "r" and it lies between 0 and 1. The value $r=0$ means that the samples are phenotypically unrelated, having no relationship. The value $r=1$ means that they are phenotypically identical to each other. Thus the value of r nearer to 1 means their similarity is closer.

The complex phenotype results from the combined effects of genetic and environmental factors. If, T represents the quantitative measure of the trait under study, we have the simple expression

$$T = \mu + g + e$$

Where, $\mu$ = mean value of trait in the population

g = deviation from the mean due to genetic factors

e = deviation from the mean due to environmental factors.

If we assume, "g" influences the phenotype in an additive fashion and that the genetic and environmental factors affecting the phenotype are independent of each other that the hypothesis is that, correlation coefficient "r" for each relationship represents the proportion of the total variation of the trait, that is due to the genetic and environmental factors shared by the individuals.

For MZT twins, the correlation coefficient r estimates the proportion of the total variance in the trait that is due to genetic factors ($H^2$) and also the proportion that is due to the shared environmental factors ($C^2$).

Thus, $r = H^2 + C^2$

For MZA twins, which are genetically identical but they do not share the common environment. Then the r estimates the effects of the identical genotypes, which is $H^2$.

Thus, $r = H^2$

For DZ twins, the individuals have 50% identical genetic variability ($\frac{1}{2}H^2$), So, when they reared apart (DZA), the r estimates the only genetic variability.

Thus, $r = \frac{1}{2}H^2$

For DZT, the r estimates the genetic variability plus the same environmental variability ($C^2$).

Thus, $r = \frac{1}{2}H^2 + C^2$

For unrealated induviduals reared together (URT), having only the common environment. Then r simply estimates its common environmental variability ($C^2$).

Thus $r = C^2$

In the case of human the broad-sense heritability can be estimated by correlation method for two complex human traits viz, intelligence and personality of the twin.

**Intelligence** : Intelligence is an inherent characteristics of human beings and this complex trait is influenced by both genetic and the environmental factors. It is a constellation of mental abilities including the skills needed to

(i) define and understand words

(ii) think of words rapidly

(iii) analyze mathematical relationships

(iv) analyze spatial relationship

(v) memorize and recall informations

(vi) perceive similarities and differences among objects.

(vii) Formulate rules, principles and concepts for solving problems and understanding situations.

Psychologists and geneticists characterize and quantify these abilities as a statistic called **intelligence quotient** or **IQ** which indicates the person's intelligence.

The IQ is determined by dividing the person's mental age as determined by the test score by his or her chronological age and then multiplying by 100. Thus, a 10-year old boy whose test score is equivalent to the test score of 11 years, then his IQ would be $\frac{11}{10} \times 100 = 110$. IQ scores are scaled so that mean of the population is 100 with standard deviation 15.

1. For IQ scores, the correlation coefficients of both MZT and MZA are very high in the range of about 0.7–0.8.
2. On the otherhand, the DZ twins tend to be lower because they share 50% of their genes.
3. The IQ of unrelated individuals, even reared together, will show a correlation coefficient zero or nearer to zero.

The analyses strongly suggest that the IQ score has a large genetic component rather than the environmental one. The IQs of adopted children are more strongly correlated with the IQ's of their biological parents than with those of their adoptive parents.

MZA twins have shown a correlation coefficient of 0.7 *ie* 70% of the variation in IQ scores is attributed by the genetic variability of the population.

**Personality** : Personality is another inherent characteristics of human beings. But there is no such reliable tests like IQ test to determine the personality of a person, but essentially, the personality is influenced by genetic factors. Psychologists make use of many different tests to measure personality characteristics and others to measure vocational and social interests.

The genetic analysis of personality in general population has come from the Minnesota, Study of Twins Reared Apart, a long term project directed by Thomas Bouchard. They have taken 50 pairs of MZA twins from all over the world and each of them were subjected to more than 50 hours of medical and psychological evaluations including testing for intelligence and personality traits.

They observed that the overall variation in personality is as much as 50%. The correlation coefficient for the personality test score of MZA twins ranges from 0.39 to 0.50. Thus the broadsense heritability for these traits is reasonably high.

Many studies have been performed on the conditions such as manic depression, schizophrenia and alcoholism etc genetic traits occurring among MZ and DZ twins. It has been found that the trait alcoholism among MZ twin pairs is 55% of the time. On the otherhand the DZ cotwin is alcoholic only 28% of the cases. This greater concordance for alcoholism between MZ twins suggests that this trait is influenced by genetic factors.

## 28.6 ADOPTION STUDIES

### 28.6.1 Concept

The children separated from their biological parents soon after birth and are adopted by another person with whom they have no genetic relationship. These children have no more genes in common with their two adoptive parents, only they do share the common environment. On the otherhand the adopted child has 50% of their genes in common with each of their biological parents but do not share the same environment with them.

The similar characteristics shown by both adopted child and adoptive parents are due to the environmental factors, not by gentic factors. On the otherhand the similar characteritics shown by adopted child and the biological parents are due to genetic factors, not due to the environmental factors. Thus, comparison of adopted child with the adoptive parent and biological parent helps to determine the role of genetic as well as environmental factors on the variation of human beings.

### 28.6.2 Adoption studies and Obesity

In 1986, geneticists published the results of a study of 540 people who had been adopted in Denmark between 1924 and 1947. They used a measurement called the **"body-mass index"** i.e., the body weight divided by height. On the basis of body-mass index, sex and age, the adopted persons were divided into four classes : thin, median weight, overweight and obese. They obtained a strong relationship between the body-mass index of adopted person with their biological parents not with their adoptive parents. This investigations concluded that the genetic factors influence the adult body weight.

### 28.6.3 Adoption studies and Alcoholism

Study on alcoholic addiction was carried out on 1775 Sweedish adoptees who had been separated from their mothers at an early age and raised by biologically unrelated adoptive parents. They distinguished two groups of alcoholics. Type-1 alcoholics (men and women) who typically develop problems with alcohol after age of 25. They lose control of the ability to drink in moderation. They drink in binges and usually nonaggressive during drinking bout.

Type-II alcoholics largely of males, who begin drinking before the age of 25 or before, they actively seek out alcohol but do not binge and tend to be impulsive, thrill-sicking and aggressive while drinking.

They study disclosed that type-I alcoholism is usually required for both a genetic predisposition and exposure to rearing environment in which alcohol is consumed and typed-II alcoholism is appeared to be highly hereditary. It is developed among males whose biologicial father was also type-II alcoholies. A male adoptee where biological father is type-II alcoholic was nine times as likely to become alcoholic as was an adoptee whose biological father was not an alcoholic. However, alcoholism is a complex behavioural characteristics that is influenced by many factors, not strictly depend upon the genetic characteristic.

## 28.7 PHENOCOPY

The phenotype that is produced by environmental effects, is same as the phenotype produced by a genotype is called *phenocopy*. This is a nonhereditary change.

In fruit flies, for example, the autosomal recessive mutation *eyeless* produces greatly reduced eyes. The eyeless phenotype can also be produced by exposing the larvae of normal flies to sodium metaborate.

The epilepsy, for example in human may result from either genetic or environmental causes. As a result, the definitive diagnosis of an inherited abnormality requires family pedigree data or other informations indicating that the condition is inherited, in addition to the appropriate phenotypic manifestations in an individual.

In 1960 and 1961, it was noted that a considerable number of German and British Commonwealth babies were being born with shortened limbs giving a flipper-like appearance called **phocomelia.** The cause was due to the dietary changes to the atom bomb testing explosion. This trait arose from the use of a drug thalidomide in early stage of gestation by the mothers. The trait has also been recorded in some families which is inherited among their offspring.

## 28.8 NURTURING BEHAVIOUR IN MICE

Jennifer Brown and coworkers discovered the gene *fos B* in mice, which is expressed in the brain and plays an important role in the behavioural expression. They cloned the gene, transferred it to the diploid ES cells and developed chimeric mice. These chimeric mice are allowed to reproduce. From these offspring, they were succeeded in establishing a strain of mice heterozygous for *fos* mutants. When these were intercrossed, homozygous mutant offsprings appear. These mice, though having normal appearance but they consistently failed to nurture their youngs. Usually the normal wild mice create a nest, clean their pups, crouch over them to warm and nurse them, and bring them back to the nest if they go away from the nest. But the homozygous mutant *fosB* mice do not exhibit these behaviours.

They described that *fosB* gene is expressed in the pre-optic area of the hypothalamus within 6 hours of pup presentation. The induction of FosB transcription factor presumably results from a signaling cascade within the cells of hypothalamus. It is then targeted to the specific genes for their expression which are essential for the nurturing behaviour in mice.

## 28.9 NEST CLEANING BEHAVIOUR IN HONEYBEES

Some strains of honeybee have been found to have "nest cleaning behaviour" and they maintain their hives hygienic. The behaviour includes the removal of dead larvae after uncapping the cell. On the otherhand, some other strains do not exhibit this behaviour of nest cleaning.

Walter Rothenbuhler (1964) reported that nest cleaning behaviour in honeybee is controlled by two independently assorted genes. It has been found that when nonhygienic, haploid drones are crossed with hygienic diploid queens. All the diploid worker offspring were nonhygienic. Thus it has been assumed that nonhygienic behaviour gene is dominant over hygienic gene. Again, when haploid drones ($ur$, $u^+r$, $ur^+$, $u^+r^+$) derived from the unfertilized eggs of $F_1$ queen ($u^+u\ r^+r$) were back crossed with the $P_1$ queen ($uu\ rr$), four classes of offspring were obtained in $F_2$.

1. With hygienic behaviour.
2. Workers uncapped the cells with dead larvae but unable to remove larvae.
3. Workers did not uncapped the cells with dead larvae but able to remove the dead larvae from the uncapped cells.
4. Workers neither uncapped the cells with dead larva nor able to remove these larvae.

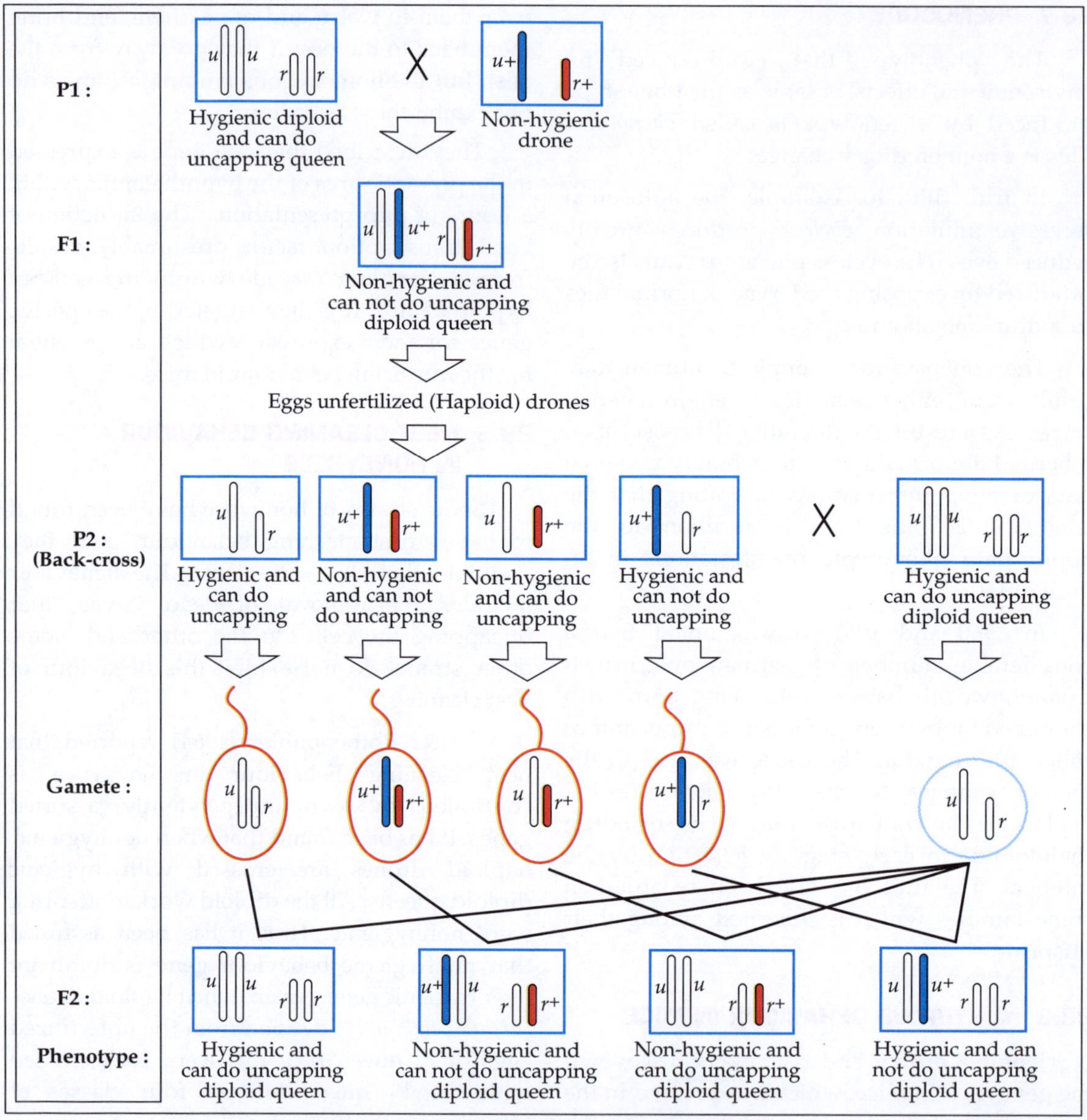


**Fig.28.3 :** *Inheritance pattern of hygienic behavior in honeybees where two alleles (u and $u^+$, r and $r^+$) control uncapping and removal of dead larvae.*

Rothenbuhler suggested that genes each with two alleles control the nest cleaning behaviour which may be designated as

$u$ = uncapping behaviour (recessive)

$u^+$ = with nouncapping behaviour (dominant)

$r$ = dead larvae-removing behaviour (recessive)

$r^+$ = with no dead larvae-removing behaviour (dominant) (Fig. 28.3)

**Molecular mechanism :** A chemical signal is given off by the cells with dead larvae which possibly attracts the hygienic workers not the nonhygienic ones. Once a cap is removed, the chemical signal might become strong enough to trigger the expression of the other gene which determines the removal behaviour. The genotype (uu$r^+$r) workers, initial signal may be sufficient to trigger the uncapping behaviour but after the cell is uncapped, it may become so strong that it inhibits the removal behaviour.

## 28.10 BIOLOGICAL RHYTHM IN *DROSOPHILA*

*Drosophila* exhibits both 24-hr (circadian) and short-term (ultradian) rhythmic behaviour.

1. The 24-hrs locomotor activity can be measured by placing the fly in a darkened glass tube and shining a narrow beam of red light across the tube. The fly cannot perceive red light, therefore, the light does not affect their locomotory movements. At the exit of beam of light an electronic photoreceptor cell is placed to record the interruption of light beam due to movement through the tube.
2. The result shows a 24-hr cycle of locomotory movement which is synchronized with the emergence from their pupal case. Thus the flies which eclose at night or morning, their movement is also observed at the night or morning respectively.
3. The rhythm persists if the cultures are reared in a standard day/night cycles.

   If the culture is transferred to complete darkness, the fly's circadian clock triggers eclosion at what would be morning in a 24-hr cycle without looking light or dark.

   *Drosophila* shows ultradian rhythms which are associated with courtship rituals between males and females. Each *Drosophila* has their own distinctive courtship behaviour including approaching to each other, wings of the male extends 90° angle and vibrate, generating a song for the attraction of females, and then copulate. The males repeat the ritual again but the females do not.
4. Ronald Konopka and Seymour Benzer discovered that this rhythmic behaviour is controlled by an X-linked recessive gene. Mutagenized males by EMS (ethylmethane sulfonate) when mated with a female with attached X-chromosomes, it has been found that this mutation is transferred from the father to his sons (Fig. 28.4).

These stocks of *Drosophila* in which X-chromosomes were mutagenized in males were then tested for abnormalities in their circadian eclosion rhythm under such free running conditions. Among 2000 stocks, they found three abnormal eclosion rhythms :

(a) Arrhythmic, *ie*, the males emerged at all times

(b) The males emerged on a 19-hr cycle

(c) The males emerged on a 28-hr cycle

They mapped the chromosomes and identified that the mutations are located at some intervals at the left end of X-chromosome. The complementation analysis disclosed that all three mutations were alleles of the same gene. The gene was named as *per* gene or *period* gene.

**Molecular biology of the rhythm :** Konopka and Benzer (1984) discovered that

1. The arrhythmic mutation is *per°*, which is due to a premature **stop codon** in the codon sequence of the gene
2. The short period mutaiton is $per^s$ gene and the long-period mutaiton is $per^L$, both are missense mutations that cause single amino acid substitutions in the **Per** protein (wild type).
3. In wild type files, the *per* RNA and **Per** protein oscillate on a 24-hr cycle. The protein is produced as the dusk approaches and persists through the night

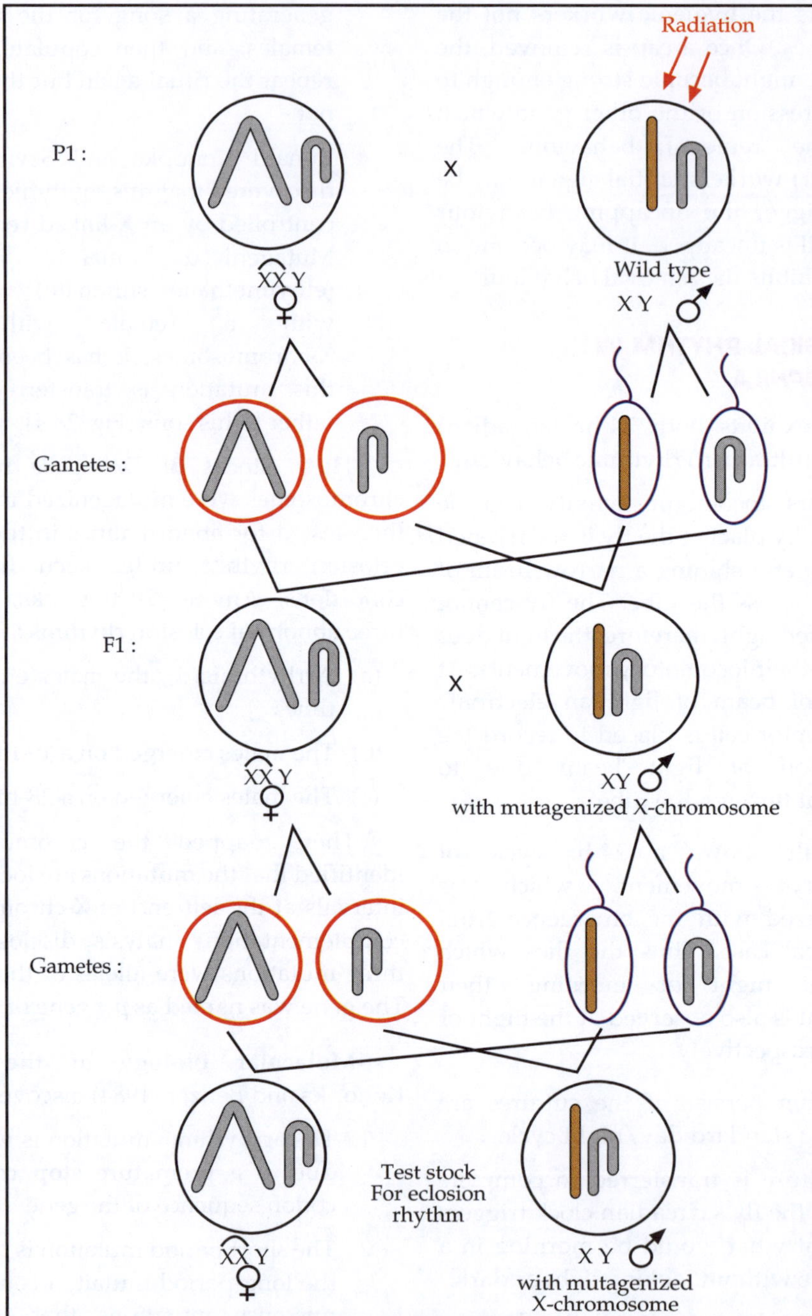


**Fig.28.4 :** *Scheme to induce X-linked rhythm mutants in Drosophila*

and by the dawn, it is nearly abolished. Thus it has been supposed that **Per** protein is a molecular oscillator in the biological rhythm.

4. There are five other autosomal genes such as *timeless* (*tim*), *clock* (*clk*), *cycle* (*cyc*), *cryptochrome* (*cry*) and *double time* (*dbt*)

**Tim** protein interacts with **Per** to form **Tim/Per** complex.

**Clk** and **Cyc** products of *clk* and *cyc* genes are the basic helix-loop-helix (bHLH) transcription factors that positively regulate the expression of *per* and *tim* genes. However, the expressioin of *per* and *tim* genes are negatively regulated by their own products.

**Cry** protein is a photoreceptor protein and **Dbt** protein has a kinase activity.

**Regulatory mechanism**

1. **Per, Clk** and **Cyc** contain a stretch of amino acids, called **PAS-domain** (The name is obtained from **Per, Arnt**, **Ahr** and **Sim**)
2. **PAS** domains fascilitate dimerization between polypeptides. Thus **Clk** and **Cyc** dimerize to form **Clk-Cyc** complex, similarly **Per** dimerizes with **Tim.**
3. During the day time, the **Clk** and **Cyc** transcription factors bind as a heterodimer to the enhancer upstream of promoter in both *per* and *tim* genes. Thus these genes are stimulated to transcribe *per* RNA and *tim* RNA.
4. These RNAs move from nucleus to cytoplasm and translate separately into **Per** and **Tim** proteins. These proteins remain monomers in the cytoplasm throughout the days.
5. During the night, these two proteins **Per** and **Tim** form heterodimers and migrate from cytoplasm again back to the nucleus.
6. In the nucleus, **Per-Tim** heterodimer may form complex with **Clk** and **Cyc.**
7. Then **Clk** and **Cyc** cannot dimerize to become an active transcription factor and thus synthesis of **Per** and **Tim** is down regulated.
8. At the dawn, **Tim** and **Per** which were present in the nucleus are degraded because **Tim** is light sensitive. The **Cyc** and **Clk** again tend to form dimers and become acitve and activate *per* and *tim* genes. Thus the 24-hr cycle is continued.
9. Another gene in *Drosophila* has been discovered which is known as *clock* gene. The product **Clock** protein is a bHLH transcription factor and is expressed in many tissues. The human and mouse homologous *clock* genes have been isolated and studied to understand the clock mechanism and rhythmic behaviour.

Joseph Takahashi and colleagues (1994) discovered *clock* gene in mouse, which is a dominant autosomal gene. They observed the mutation of this gene that causes abnormality in their rhythm activity. The trait is inherited. In complete dark condition the rhythm is lengthened to 27-28 hours or may be lost. In mouse there are two special small areas in the hypothalamus of the brain, which lie just above the crossing of optic nerves, called suprachiasmatic nuclei. Each center consists of about a million of neurons. This region plays an important role in the circadian rhythm of mice (Fig. 28.5).

## 28.11 SEXUAL PREFERENCE IN *DROSOPHILA*

Kulbir Gill (1963) reported his discovery at the Annual Meeting of the American Society of Zoologists, a new male-sterile *Drosophila* which in homozygous condition did not attempt to mate with females even though they courted them. Jeffrey Hall and coworkers carried out experiments to map the mutations and given the name to the mutation as *fruitless* (*fru*), the male sterility.

In 1996, Lisa Ryner and coworkers established that *fru* gene encodes a zinc-finger type transcription factor that regulates the genes for male sexual behaviour and male sexual preference in *Drosophila.*

Genetic experiments by Barbara Taylor had suggested that *fru* gene might control a branch in the *Drosophila* sex determination pathway.

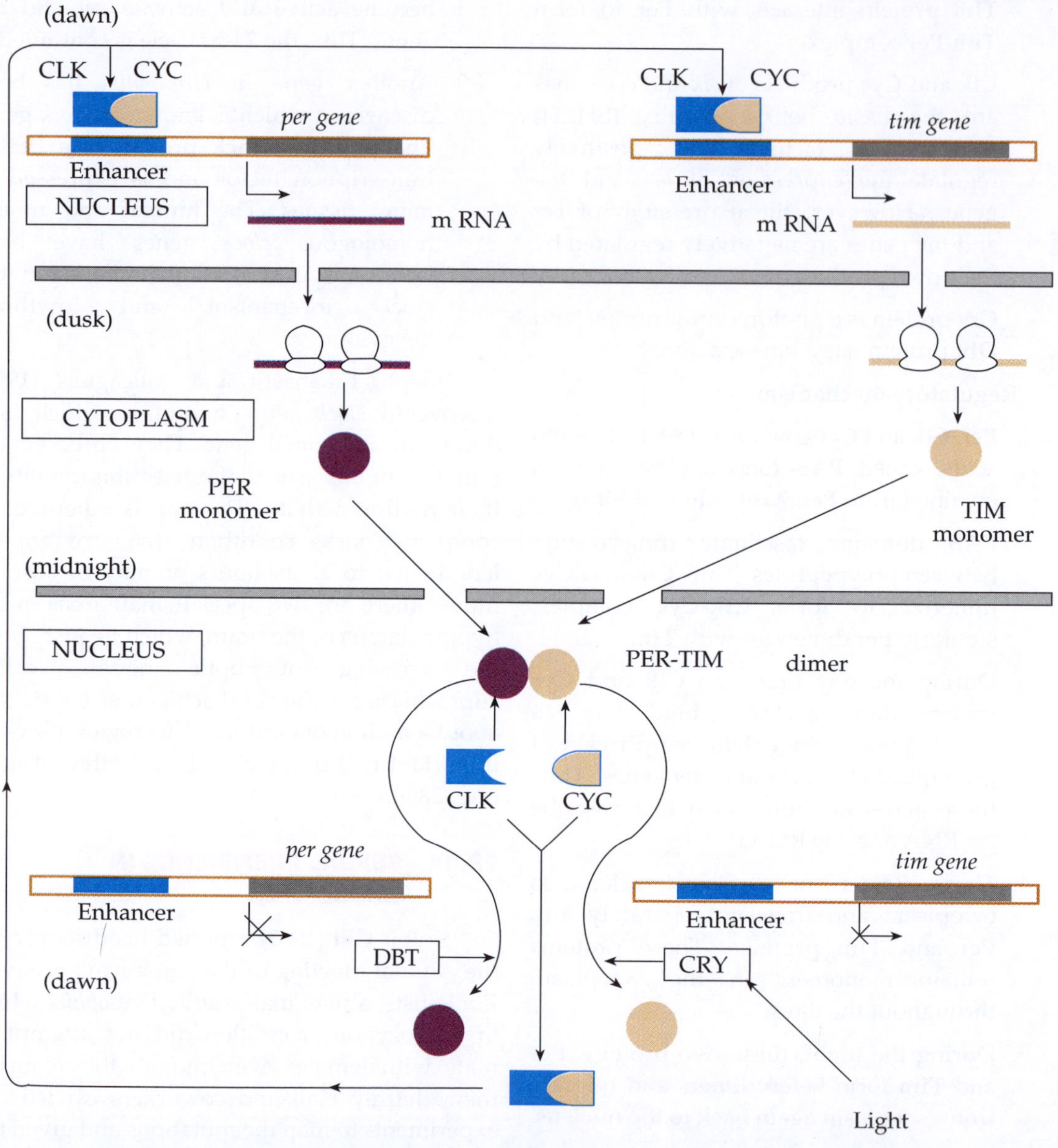


**Fig.28.5 :** *Possible molecular mechanism governing biological clock in Drosophila during one 24-hour cycle.*

The *sxl*-gene product SXL, regulates the splicing of the transcripts from *sxl* and *tra* genes. The *tra* gene product, denoted as TRA along with TRA-2 are also the regulators of splicing of the *dsx* transcript.

In males and females, *dsx* transcript splicing produces male DSX and female DSX proteins which regulate the sex-specific gene-expression and sexual differentiation in *Drosophila.*

Taylor observed that the formation of a particular **abdominal muscle in males** was not controlled by the *dsx* gene. This finding implied that the sex determination must be regulated by another unidentified genetic pathway. This

**TABLE 28.1**
**Some diseases caused by expanding trinucleotide repeats**

| Disease | Repeated sequence | No of copies of repeat | |
|---|---|---|---|
| | | Normal range | Disease range |
| 1. Spinal and bulbar muscular atrophy (SMBA) (X-linked) | CAG | 11 – 33 | 40 – 62 |
| 2. Fragile X-syndrome (FRAX) | CGG | 5 – 54 | 50 – 1500 |
| 3. Jacobsen syndrome | CGG | 11 | 100 – 1000 |
| 4. Spinocerebellar ataxia (SCA1) | CAG | 4 – 44 | 21 – 130 |
| 5. Autosomal dominant cerebellar ataxia | CAG | 7–19 | 37 – 220 |
| 6. Myotonic dystrophy (MD) | CTG | 5 – 37 | 44 – 3000 |
| 7. Huntington desease (autosomal dominant) | CAG | 9 – 37 | 37 – 121 |
| 8. Friedreich ataxia | GAA | 6 – 29 | 200 – 900 |
| 9. Dentatorubral pallidoluysian alrophy | CAG | 7 – 25 | 49 – 75 |
| 10. Myoclonus epilepsy | CCCCGCCCGCG | 2 – 3 | 12 – 13 |

unknown gene might encode the *sex-specific transcription factors.* This gene might be regulated by itself post-transcriptionally or by TRA and TRA-2 etc splicing-factor proteins.

Ryner and her colleagues cloned the *fru* gene which is located in chromosome-3 having the 13-nucleotide TRA/TRA-2 RNA binding sites. Its expression is regulated at the splicing level by TRA and TRA-2 proteins.

The *fru* gene has multiple promoters and its expression is limited to a relatively small number of neurons in the central nervous system of *Drosophila.*

In males, TRA protein is not produced and therefore *dsx* mRNA and *fru* RNA are spliced in a male-specific way, leading to mRNA that encodes male-specific transcription factors, DSX-male and FRU-male.

These transcription factors regulate the sex-specific target genes for male-sexual anatomy and male-sexual behaviour.

But in females, TRA and TRA-2 proteins regulate the splicing of *dsx*-mRNA ad *fru*-mRNA. As a result female-specific DSX and FRU proteins are produced. These are transcription factors. Female-specific DSX protein stimulates target genes for female sexual anatomy. But the role of female-specific FRU protein is not known, possibly this also performs an essential function (Fig. 28.6).

## 28.12 HUMAN GENETIC DISEASES CAUSED BY EXPANDING TRINUCLEOTIDE REPEATS

### 28.12.1 Concept

Expanding trinucleotide repeats have been found in several human diseases. The number of copies of trinucleotide repeat often correlates with the severity or age of onset of the disease. The number of copies of the onset of the repeat also correlates with the instability of trinucleotide repeats : when more repeats are present, the probability of expansion to even more repeats increases. This instability leads to a phenomenon known as **anticipation,** in which diseases caused by trinucleotide repeat expansions become more severe in each generation (Table 28.1).

At the present time, more than a dozen distinct diseases have been attributed to

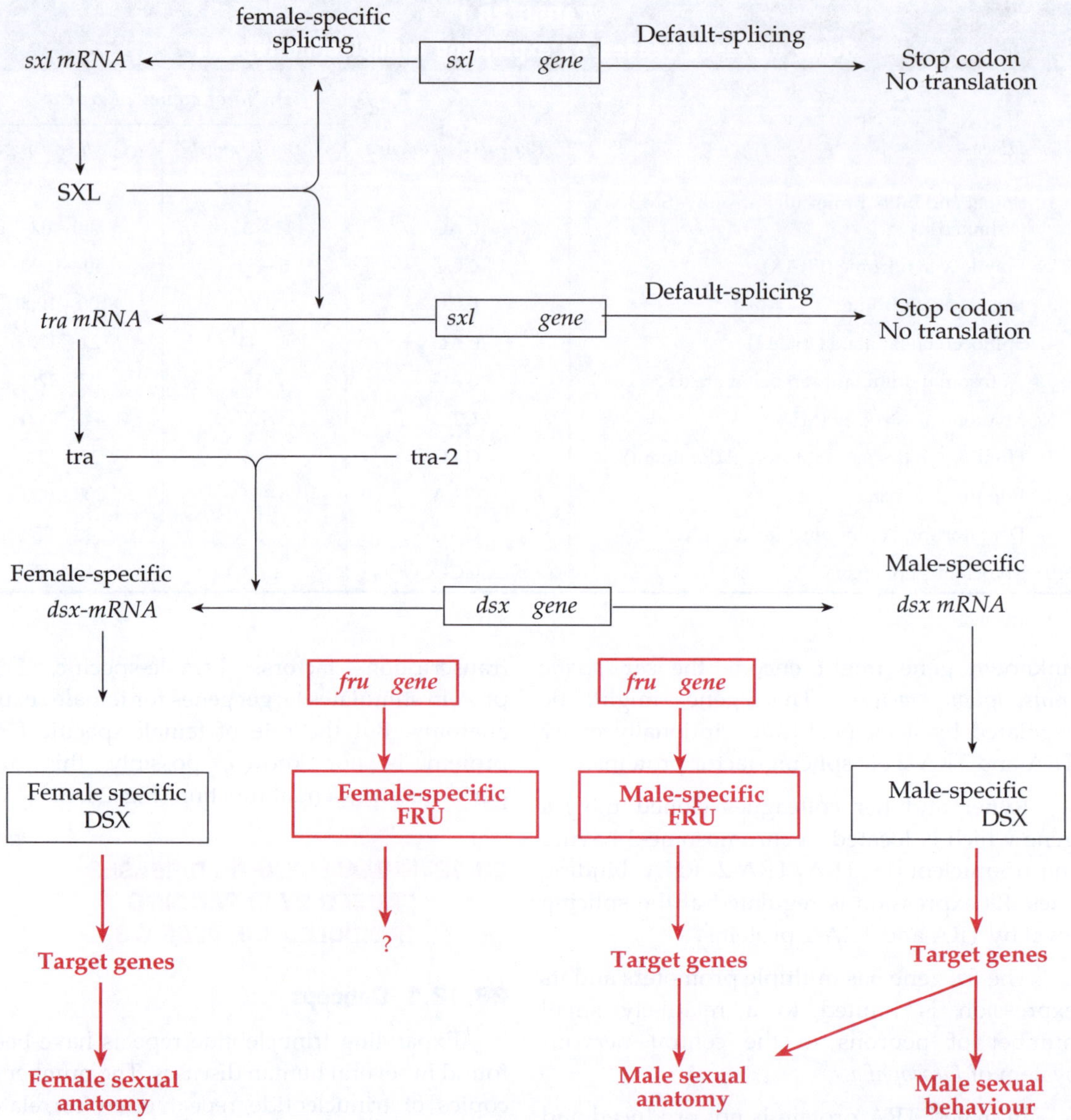


**Fig.28.6 :** *Role of sxl, tra, tra-2, dsx and fru genes of Drosophila in sex determination and sexual behaviour determination.*

expansion of trinucleotide repeats. These diseases fall into two basic categories. Type-I diseases are all neurodegenerative disorders that result from the expansion of the number of the reapeats of a CAG trinucleotide within the coding portion of the mutant gene. For example, Huntington's disease, SMBA, SCAI etc. Type II diseases arise from the expansion of a variety of trinucleotides, not only CAG, which may be present in a part of the gene but does not encode amino acids. For example, Fragile X-syndrome, MD etc.

### 28.12.2 Huntington's disease

The Huntington's disease (HD) or Huntington's chorea is a fatal neuro-degenerative disorder that follows an autosomal dominant (chromosome No. 4p) pattern of inheritance. People who inherit the HD mutation suffer a gradual loss of neurous mainly in the caudate nucleus and putamen located in the cerebral region of the brain. Both of these areas are imporatnt for the coordination of body movement. Other nerves are also affected.

In fact, persons who are homozygous for the HD allele are no more seriously affected than heterozygotes. This observation indicates that the mutant huntingtin polypeptide causes the disease, not because it fails to carry out a particular function, but because it acquires some type of toxic property, which is referred to as a *gain-of-function* mutation.

The major symptoms of this disease which usually occurs during middle age, leading to changes in personality, unable to control their movements, their speech is disturbed, they sometimes become depressed and they become psychotic. As the disease progresses, most patients undergo significant intellectual decline such as difficulty in acquiring and recalling informations and they are unable to organize informations. Death in early age is occurred.

*HD* gene was isolated in 1993 and the protein that it codes **huntingtin** was identified shortly thereafter.

The normal *HD* gene, which is stably transmitted contains between 6–35 copies of the CAG nucleotide in its coding region. Thus the normal **huntingtin** polypeptide contains a stretch of 6–35 *glutamine* residues in its primary structure. This protein functions normally, though their normal conformation is polymorphic as it has 6–35 glutamine residues, as long as the length of the polyglutamine tract remains below approximately 35 *gln* residues.

The presence of one abnormal allele in heterozygous condition is sufficient to cause disease. This is a very puzzling feature that the number of CAG repeats in a mutant allele often increases dramatically from one generation to the next.

The molecular basis of HD remains unclear. One hypothesis is that the excessively large polyglutamine tract within mutant HD is toxic to certain types of neurons in the brain which causes aggregation of proteins in neurons.

Another hypothesis is that when the length of polyglutamine tract exceeds 35, the protein or its fragment undergoes abnormal folding and binds to other mutant HD molecules to form insoluble aggregates like those of Alzheimer's disease or binds to a number of other proteins *viz* transcription factors such as TBP and CBP which are involved in regulation of gene expression, because in patients, these transcription factors are mostly found with these mutant HD proteins in brain neurons. This hypothesis was experimentally proved in genetically engineered mice where their brain cells lack the ability to produce CREB. These mice exhibited same type of neurodegeneration as in the case of animals carrying mutant *HD* gene. Thus it is seemed that part of the brain affected by HD is particularly dependent for survival upon CREB dependent transcription.

### 28.12.3 Friedreich's ataxia

Friedreich's ataxia is a rare neurological disease characterized by the progessive loss of voluntary muscular coordination (ataxia) and heart enlargement. In 1863, a German physician Nikolaus Friedreich described first about this disease.

The disease affects both males and females and diagnosed in the childhood. The disease is caused by a 5′ -GAA-3′ trinucleotide repeat in the first intron of Friedreich's ataxia gene, which is located on chromosome no-9. The normal individual has 8–30 copies of this repeat, but when the repeat is as many as 1000 may cause the disease. This GAA tract may form a tripple helix which inhibits the transcription of Friedrich's gene and causes a reduced amount

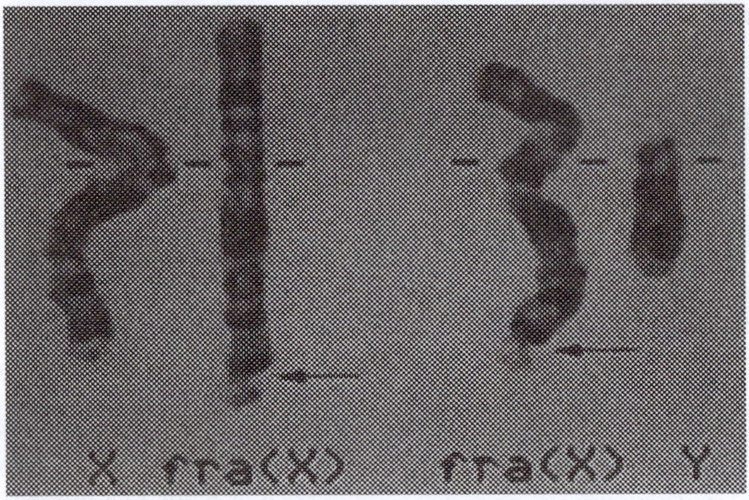


**Fig.28.7 :** *Showing the location of the FMR1 gene, that causes FXS. The gene is located in the fragile area of the X-chromosome.*

of the protein, **frataxin**, normally found in human mitochondria, possibly it is involved in the regulation of export and import of iron into mitochondria.

## 28.12.4 Fragile X Syndrome (FXS)

In 1943, Martin and Bell have shown that a particular form of mental retardation (later known as fragile X-syndrome) was X-linked. In 1969, Herbert Lubs developed chromosomal test for fragile-X. The test was not used extensively until late 1970's . In 1991, the *FMRI* gene was identified.

Fragile X syndrome is a form of mental retardation caused by a mutated gene (recessive trait) on the X-chromosome with a variable expression and incomplete penetrance, 30% of all carrier women are also affected.

Fragile X syndrome is the most common form of inherited mental retardation. The symtoms of this disease is more severe in boys than in girls.

The syndrome is called "fragile-X" because there exists a fragile site or gap at the end of a long arm of the X-chromosome in lymphocytes of affected patients when grown in a folate deficient medium (Fig. 28.7).

**Symptoms :** Children and adults with FXS have varying degrees of mental retardation or learning disabilities and behavioural and emotional problems including autistic-like features. Males tend to be more severely affected than females. The symptoms of FXS differ among boys and girls.

**Physical problems :** Boys with fragile-X appear normal at birth. However, developmental delays become apparent as they grown older. Most of the boys show mild to severe mental retardation. Common physical traits include large protruding ears; a long narrow face with a prominent chin and forehead; Double-jointed fingers, flat feet, puffy eyelids and enlarged testis after puberty. Some other physical signs are with high arched palate, flattened nasal bridge, vertical creases of soles, long philtrum, and antimongoloid stant (Fig. 28.8).

**Behavioural problems :** Girls with fragile X syndrome have fewer signs of the disorder, though some of them have large ears.

**Fig.28.8 :** *A little boy with fragile X-syndrome, having slightly elongated face and prominent ears.*

FXS children may have delays in developmental milestones, such as learning how to sit, walk and talk. Males with FXS may get stuck an one topic, and talk about that one thing constantly. Affected children may have frequent tantrums and difficulties paying attention. They often are highly anxious and easily overwhelmed by what's going on around them. They may have some unusual behaviours such as hand flapping, hand biting and poor self stimulating behaviour.

Poor sensory skills and mathematical ability are sometimes found in conjunction with good reading skills. Affected girls tend to be shy and socially withdrawn, and to have particular difficulty with mathematics (Fig. 28.8).

**Medical problems :** Most children with FXS do not have serious medical problems and generally have a normal life span. However, about 20% develop seizures, which generally can be controlled with medications. Children with FXS also may be at increased risk of inner ear infections (otitis media), vision problems (including near-sightedness and lazy eye) and digestive disorders (including gastro-oesophageal reflux). About 50% of them will develop a heart condition called mitral valve prolapsus during adulthood.

**Genetics of FXS :** Fragile X syndrome is caused by a mutation in the *FMR-1* (Fragile X Mental Retardation) gene located on the X-chromosome. The *FMR-1* gene appears to play a role in early development, so it causes developmental delays in its mutated form. However, this gene appears to be able to exist in what researchers call a **pre-mutated** form for several generations of a family. With each generation, the gene becomes closer to **full mutation** until it results in FXS.

Boys are more likely to develop more severe symptoms, because they have only one copy of X. Because girls have two X-chromosomes, the abnormal gene on one X-chromosome might be balanced by a normal gene on the other X-chromosome. They are designated as carriers and would have 50% chance of inheriting her fragile X-gene.

The gene that causes the disease is designated as *FMR-1*, which appears in three forms, that are defined by the number of repeats of a pattern of DNA called **CGG** Repeats.

Individuals with less than 54 CGG repeats have a normal gene.

Individuals with 55–200 CGG repeats have a **premutation** which means they carry an unstable mutation which can expand in future generations.

Individuals with over 200 repeats have a full mutaion which causes fragile -X syndrome.

Normally, the *FMR-1* gene produces an important protein called **FMRP.** When the gene is turned off, the individual does not make fragile X mental retardation protein (FMRP). The lack of this specific protein causes fragile X-syndrome.

**Premutaion :** Some of the maternal grand fathers of the boys with FXS carry the "premutation" on their X-chromosome and may develop a progressive shaking and unsteadiness as they get older, which may be designated as Fragile-X-Tremor/Ataxia syndrome (FXTAS). "Ataxia" refers to a problem with co-ordination and balance. The "tremor" (shaking) and ataxia in FXTAS are due to damage to a part of the brain called the cerebellum and its connections.

In more rare cases, mothers of boys with FXS carry the premutation can also develop FXTAS.

FXTAS generally comes on slowly in men over 50 years. Problems may include

1. Tremor ie shaking that can occur with activity or at rest.
2. Poor balance
3. Poor hand coordination and unclear speech
4. Slow movements, stiff muscles, lack of facial expression and poor balance that may look like Parkinson disease (PD).
5. Fainting, that occurs with standing due to a drop in blood pressure and problems with excretion that suggest problems with the autonomic nervous system that has an effect on heart rate, blood pressure and sweating.

Many doctors are not familiar with this disease because of it's lesser occurrence and the symptoms and signs are typical with Parkinson's disease. However, special studies such as an MRI of the brain is helpful because it shows some typical changes in an area close to the cerebellum called the middle cerebeller peduncle. It is very important for families with FXTAS to get genetic counseling because all the daughters of men with FXTAS will carry the gene defect. this means that these daughters can have sons with mental retardations and the daughters herself may go through early menopause and rarely even developed FXTAS.

**Diagnosis :** The disease is diagnosed by PCR on the X-chromosomes of affected individuals for a fragile area and the *FMR1* gene. This fragile area generally results from a lack of folate, which causes triplet repeats in the fragile area of the X-chromosome. The more triplet repeats there are on the X-chromosome, the more severely affected the individual will be.

A health care provider may recommend that a child be tested for FXS if he or she has mental retardation, developmental delay or autism, especially if the child has physical or behavioural characteristies of FXS or if there is a family history of FXS or mental retardation of unknown cause. A health care provider also may recommend testing if a woman who is planning a pregnancy has a family history of FXS or any mental retardation.

FXS can be diagnosed before birth by amniocentesis and chorionic villus sampling to determine whether a baby of a carrier mother has inherited the full mutation.

**Inheritance of FXS :** Fragile X-syndrome can be passed from a carrier mother to her children. A woman is considered a carrier of FXS if she has either a premutation (55 – 200 trinucleotide repeates within her *FMR-1* gene) or a full mutation (greater than 200 trinucleotide repeats). A carrier of a pre-mutation generally has no symptoms (though it has now been thought to have an increased risk of early menopause prior to age 40. Approximately one-third to one-half of female carriers of a full mutation will exhibit signs of a fragile X-syndrome but are usually less severely affected than males with full mutations.

A premutation carrier mother has a 50% chance of passing along the abnormal gene to her baby during each pregnancy. Some children who inherit the abnormal gene will have a premutaion and no symptoms of FXS.

However, **the number of repeats may expand when the gene is passed from mother to child.** As a result, some children of carrier mothers inherit the full mutation (more than 200 repeats) and show symptoms of FXS.

A woman who carries full mutation has a 50% chance of passing along the full mutation in each pregnancy. Most boys who inherit the full mutation display symptoms of FXS, while only up to half of girls do.

A man can also be an unaffected carrier of a premutation in the fragile X-gene. An unaffected carrier male will pass on the premutation to all his daughter but not to his sons. The daughters generally have no symptoms of FXS, but they are carriers of premutation that may be passed

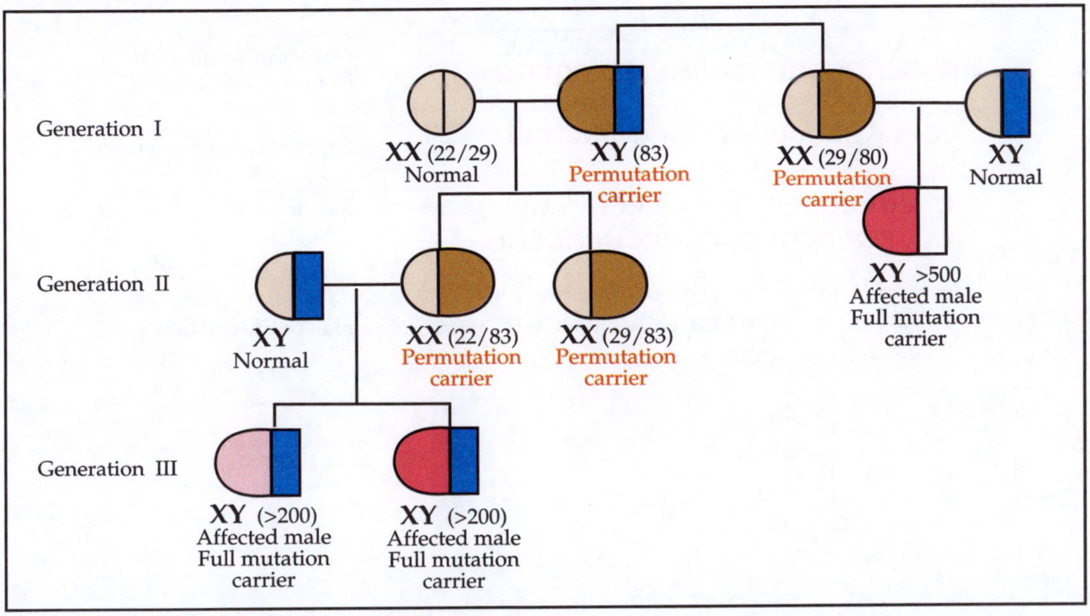


**Fig.28.9 :** *Pedigree analysis of Fragile X-syndrome*

on to the their children. This is to be noted that **in males, the premutation does not usually expand in size when passed on to his daughters.**

**Treatment :** There is currently no cure for FXS. However, an individualized treatment plan, beginning during the preschool years can help affected children reach their full potential. Most children with FXS can get benefit from treatment by a team of health professionals and special educators. The members of the team may include speech/language therapists, physical and occupational trainers, special educators, psychologists and pediatricians.

The children with FXS can be benefited from medications which include antidepressants, stimulants (such as, *Ritalin*, used for hyperactivity) and antiseizure drugs. Folic acid has been found to improve hyperactivity and attention deficits in some preadolescent males with FXS. In addition, medications to control gastrooesophageal reflux and ear infections are also used. Surgical correction of heart defects is sometimes necessary. Other treatment is symptomatic and supportive.

**Anticipation and the Sherman Paradox :** This genetic disease can not be comparable with the mode of inheritance of other genetic diseases. Anticipation causes subsequent generations in a family to be more severely affected by a disease. This is because due to **increase in the number of triplet repeats** in the fragile area of X-chromosome through the generations. It also causes the disease to strike with a greater frequency. This pattern of inheritance caused by anticipation is known as Sherman Paradox (because, this was first identified by Sherman *et al.)*

Because of the Sherman Paradox, 20% of the males with fragile X chromosome remain unaffected and have unaffected daughers, but sons and grandsons of these daughers have a high probability of being affected and being severely affected (Fig. 28.9).

**Prognosis of FXS :** Prognosis of the disease is more positive than that of other

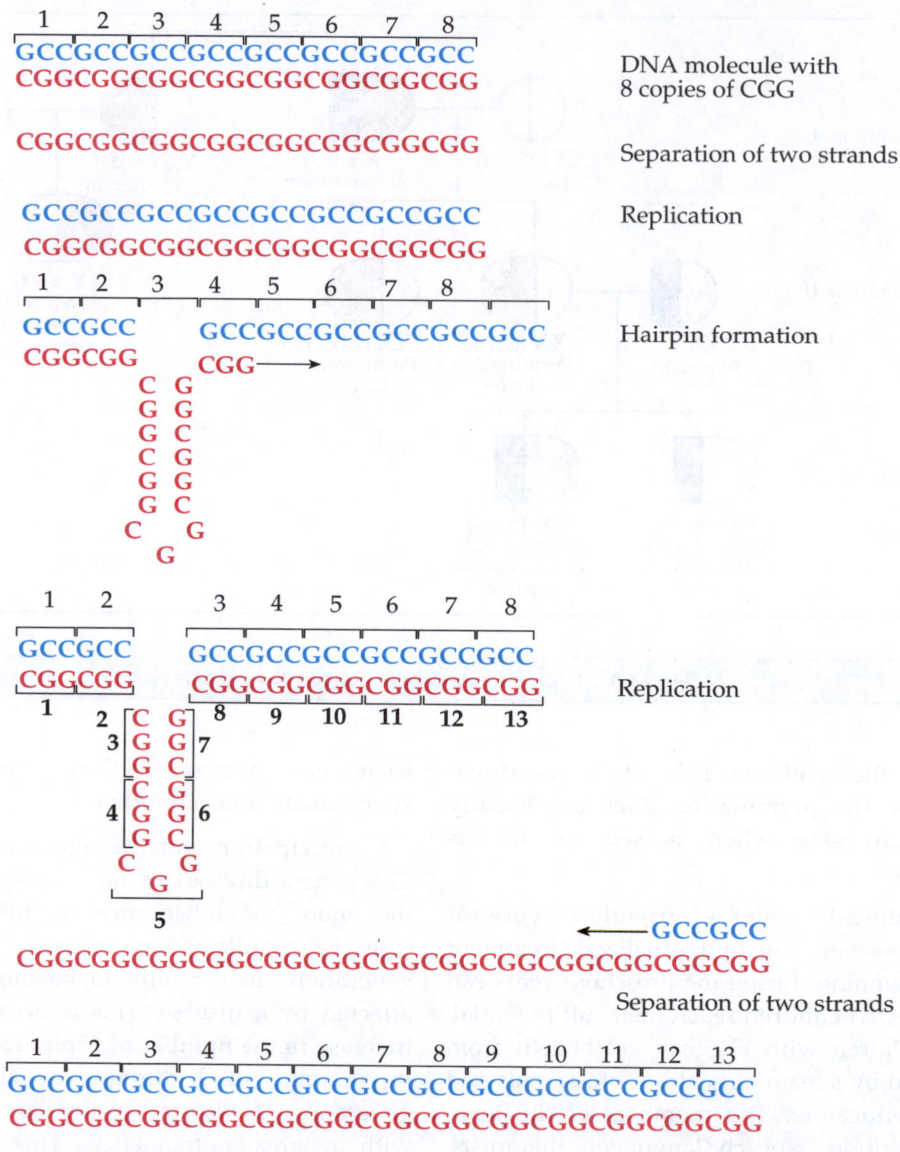


**Fig.28.10 :** *Increase to trinucleotide sequence by STRAND SLIPPAGE*

X-linked diseases, but it depends upon the degree of a affected region of X-chromosome and repetitions of CGG triplets. Less affected individuals may be able to have a job and live on their own but to make them potential, approapriate training and supervision are essential. These individuals can survive upto 60 years. They are also successful in the special schools.

## 28.12.5 Mechanism of expansion of trinucleotides

The mechanism that leads to the expansion of trinucleotide repeats is not completely

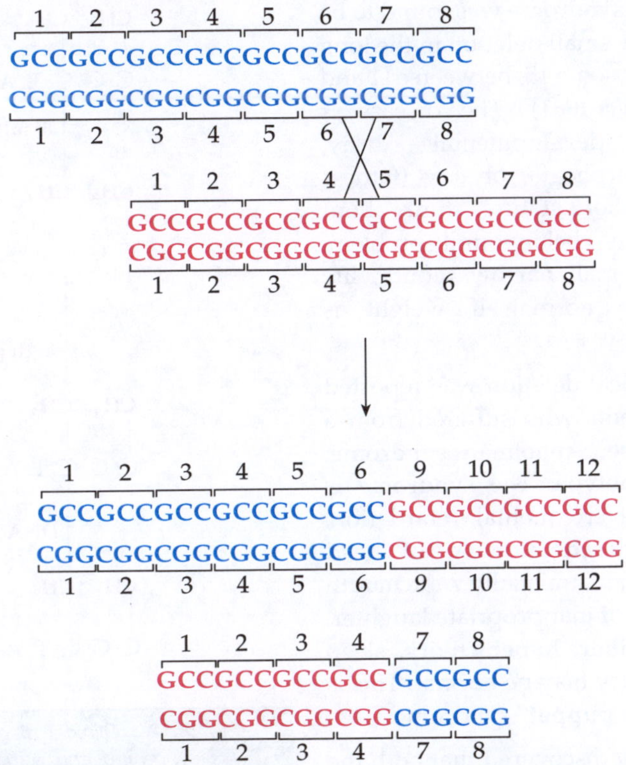


**Fig.28.11** : *Increase of trinucleotide sequence by UNEQUAL CROSSING-OVER*

understood. **Strand slippage** in DNA replication and crossing over between misaligned repeats are two possible sources of expansion.

Strand slippage may occur when one nucleotide strand forms a small loop. If the looped-out nucleotides are on the newly synthesized strand, an insertion results. At the next round of replication, the insertion will be incorporated into both strands of the DNA molecule. On the otherhand if the looped-out nucleotides are on the template strand, then deletion is resulted and is perpetuated in subsequent replication.

Misaligned pairing may cause unequal crossing over, which also results in insertion and deletion.

The trinucleotide repeats or homopolymeric repeats of the same base in a row are prone to strand slippage and unequal crossing over. Stretches of more repeats are more likely to undergo strand slippage.

Thus both strand slippage and unequal crossing over produce duplicated copies of sequences which in turn promote further strand slippage and unequal crossing over. This chain of events may explain the **phenomenon of anticipation** often observed for expanding trinucleotide repeats (Fig 28.10 & 28.11).

## 28.13 NEURODEVELOPMENTAL DISORDERS AND GENOMIC IMPRINTING

Three neurodevelopmental disorders, Prader-Willi syndrome, Angelman syndrome and Rett syndrome are the results of deregulation of imprinted genes.

The Prader-Willi syndrome was found to be associated with a very small deletion in the long arm of human chromosome 15, between q11 and q13 (Ledbetter *et al*, 1981). The disease is characterized by developmental delay, cryptorchidism, hyperphagia, obesity (fatness due to overeating) short stature, think about food 24 hours a day, behavioural problem, mental retardation, small narrow mouth, life expectancy may be normal if weight is controlled.

In 1987, an identical deletion was reported in a number of patients who suffered from a very different disease, Angelman syndrome, with a distinct phenotype. The syndrome is characterized by severe mental retardation, seizures, lack of speech, slowing of head growth, puppet-like gait, unusually wide mouth prominent chin bouts of inappropriate laughter, autistic – like behaviour, hyperactivity, sleep disorder, life expectancy may be normal. This is also known as "**happy puppet**" syndrome.

In 1989, Knoll *et al* discovered that both the syndromes are caused by the same chromosomal deletion; the Prader-Willi syndrome was always caused by the defects involving paternally derived chromosome, while Angelman syndrome was always caused by deletions in the maternally derived chromosomes. There are several mechanisms leading to "missing" allele including *de novo* deletion of a large region of chromosome 15 encompassing the Prader Willi syndrome/ Angelman syndrome locus, uniparental disomy and ICR mutations. In about 24% of cases, Angelman syndrome results from clasic gene mutation, though, such classic gene mutation has not beeen seen in any patients with Prader - Willi syndrome so far.

**Clinical diagnosis :** Clinical diagnosis of both these syndromes can be carried out by detection of differential pattern of DNA methylation, *ie*, 5-methyl cytosine in DNA samples; by bisulfite-PCR method. The genomic DNA sample is denatured and treated with sodium bisulfite ($NaHSO_3$), a sulfite ($-SO_3$) group is added to the 6-position of cytosine only if the cytosine is unmethylated. Then it is subjected to high pH, the sulfonated cytosines are converted to uracil. This is amplified by PCR using two specific primers for the region of interest, followed by sequencing of the PCR product. The methylated-C will read as Cytosine, while every unmethylated C will read as T (Fig 28.12).

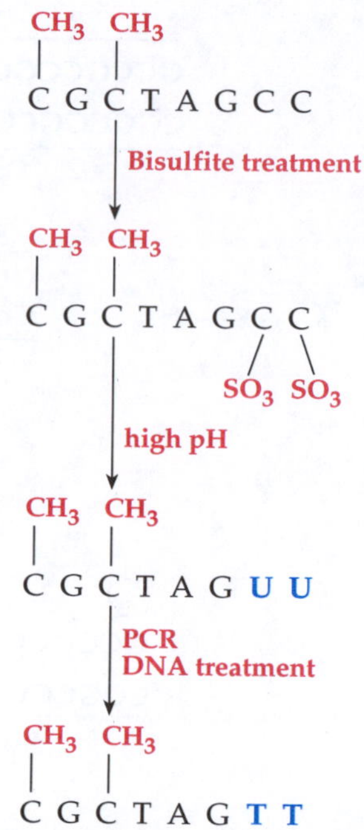


**Fig.28.12 :** *Clinical diagnosis of Prader-Willi syndrome and Angelman syndrome.*

**Neurodevelopmental disorders :** The genes involved in Prader-Willi syndrome encode proteins that are produced from the paternally derived chromosome. These include *SNRPN*, a gene which encodes the small ribonucleoprotein is polypeptide **SmN**, that is found in the fetal and adult brain, an ZEN127, a zinc-finger protein of unknown function. The hypopigmentation is found in both syndromes is probably due to loss of the *P* gene which is involved with pigment production. It is possible that the hypothalamic problems, such as overeating, associated with Prader Willi syndrome might result from the loss of SNRPN. The production of this protein is found mainly in the hypothalamic regions of the brain and in the olfactory cortex. No candidate gene is known for the symptoms of the Angelman syndrome.

**Molecular biology :**

*Deletion of imprinted Gene locus* : The genes responsible for PWS and AS are paternally or maternally imprinted. AS results from the lack of expression of a single gene *UBE3A* which codes for a protein called E6-AP, ubiquitin-protein ligase **UBE3A,** an enzyme involved in the binding of substrate prior to ubiquitinylation. The paternal allele of *UBE3A* is silenced in AS. Therefore, if the maternal allele is deleted, the individual will develop AS, because, he or she will not have an active copy of the *UBE3A* gene.

The contribution of the paternally expressed protein-coding genes and the snoRNAs to Prader-Willi syndrome remains unclear, though numerous paternally expressed genes present in the imprinted region. These genes are :

1. *MKRN 3* (makorin ring finger protein 3) mediates ubiquitin conjugating enzyme E2-dependent ubiquitinylation and is expressed in all tissues.
2. *MAGEL2* (melanoma antigen-like gene-2) is expressed in the brain.
3. *NDN* (necdin), a nuclear protein is expressed in neurons and at high levels in the hypothalamus, is involved in post mitotic neuron-specific growth suppression.
4. *SNURF* (SNRPN upstream reading frame proteins) and *SNRPN* (small nuclear ribonucleoprotein accociated polypeptide N) form an extremely complex locus which encodes many novel human brain (HB II) sno RNAs. These RNAs are expressed with introns of the SNURF-SNRPN large transcript (>148 exons) and undergo alternative splicing.
5. Several other transcripts serve as an antisense RNA for *UBE3A* gene controlling the expression of paternal gene *UBE3A* allele. This UBE3A is expressed in both paternal and maternal alleles in most human tissues (hippocampus and cerebellum) but it is silenced by antisense RNA in paternal chromosomes.

In Prader-Willi syndrome, maternally imprinted alleles are inactive. If these genes of paternal chromosome are deleted, the Prader-Willi syndrome is resulted (Fig. 28.13).

*Uniparental Disomy* **:** The effect of imprinting can also be seen in those rare cases of Prader-Willi and Angelman syndromes due to uniparental disomy of chromosome 15. In these cases, both copies of chromosome 15 come from either male or the female parent. Uniparental disomy can occur during early development. Those people with both sets of chromosome-15 from their mothers have the absence of paternal genes in this region and develop Prader-Willi syndrome. Those people who have paternal uniparental disomy have Angelman syndrome (Nicholls, 1994). The methylation patterns in this region of chromosme 15 are consistent with the hypothesis that methylation may be the mechanism to distinguish the maternal and paternal genes (Driscoll *et al* 1992; Mowery-Rushton *et al* 1996, Glenn *et al* 1996).

*Mutation of Imprinting Region :* The imprinting center is about 100 kb long and includes exon1 of the *SNRNP* gene. Dittrich *et al* (1996) have found novel transcripts originating from this region, representing alternatively splicing RNAs of the *SNRPN* transcript. Interestingly, these novel exons are only seen to be expressed from the paternal chromosome. In patients with Angelman or Prader-Willi syndromes have either deletions or mutation in this area. These mutations and deletions prevent the maternal to paternal imprinting switch in Angelman syndrome families and prevent the maternal to paternal switch in Prader Willi families. Therefore it is possible that the imprint center is needed to

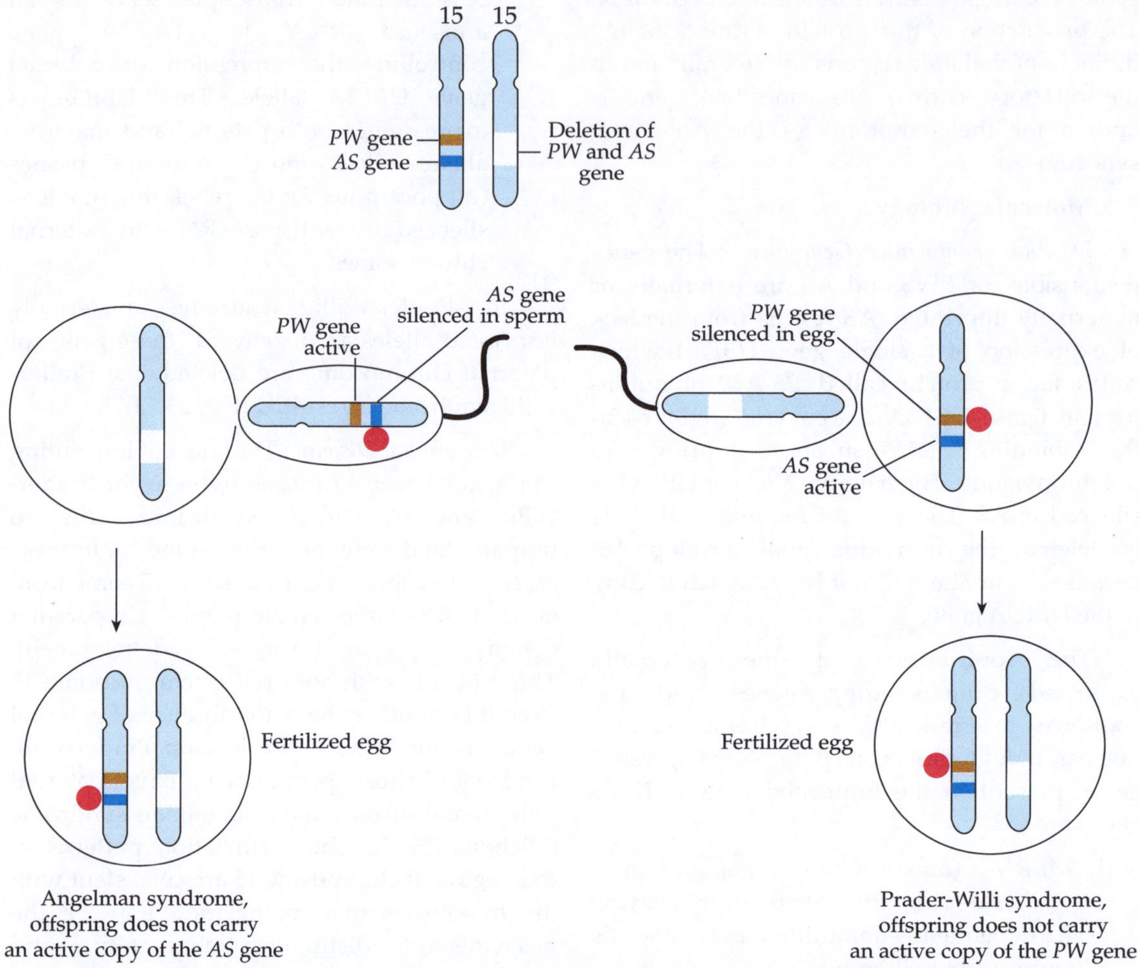


**Fig.28.13 :** *Role of imprinting (red circle) in the development of Angelman and Prader-Willi syndromes.*

regulate alternate RNA splicing in the SNRPN gene transcript (Fig. 28.14).

1. The imprinting region (ICR) is unmethylated on the paternal chromosome and directs expression bidirectionally to all imprinted genes in this region including the *UBE 3A* antisense gene.

   Methylation at the ICR on the maternal chromosome requires a region located >30 kb further upstream called the Angelman syndrome (AS) element. AS element has an open chromatin structure that directs the ICR element to become methylated and thus this silences all the paternally expressed genes on the maternal chromosome. But due to absence of *UBE 3A* antisence RNA, the maternal UBE 3A is expressed.

2. When the ICR, controlling the *Igf 2r* imprinted region, is unmethylated on the paternal chromosome, the antisense noncoding RNA (*Air* RNA) is expressed and then the paternal *Igf2r* allele is silenced.

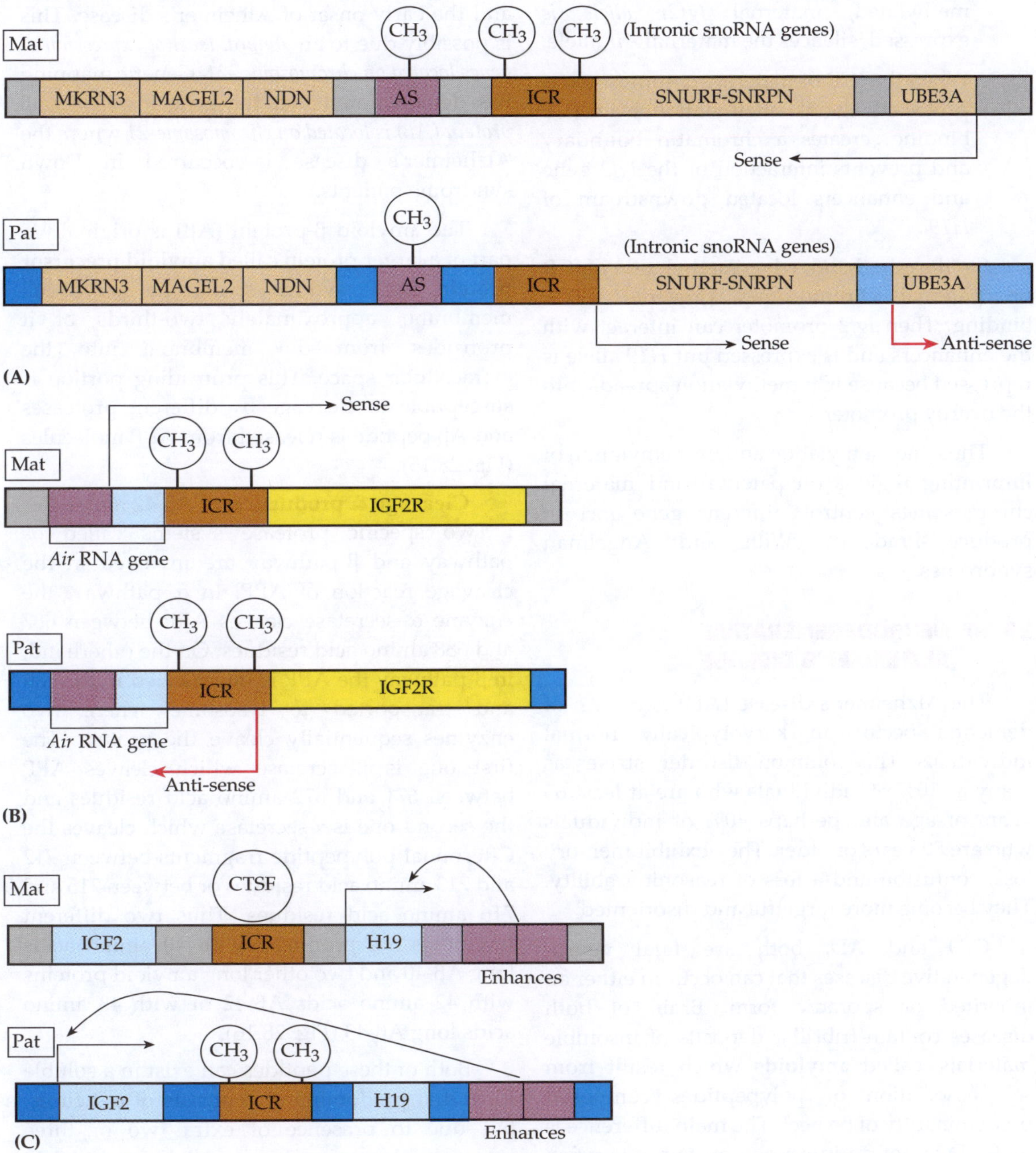


**Fig.28.14 :** *Schematic representation of regulatory mechanisms for three imprinted domains (A) Imprinting region at the SNURF-SNRPN gene (B) IGF-2R locus and (C) IGF-2-H19 locus.*

When the ICR on maternal chromosome is methylated, maternal *Igf2r allele is* expressed, silences the maternal *Air* allele.

3. When the ICR of maternal chromosome is protected against methylation by CTCF binding, creates a chromatin boundary and prevents interaction of the *Igf2* gene and enhancers located downstream of *H19*.

On the otherhand, when methylation of ICR on paternal chromosomes prevents CTCF binding. Then *Igf2* promoter can interact with the enhancers and is expressed but *H19* allele is repressed because ICR methylation spreads into the nearby promoter.

Thus, the methylation and unmethylation of imprinting regions on paternal and maternal chromosomes control different gene loci to produce Prader - Willi and Angelman syndromes.

## 28.14 NEURODEGENERATIVE ALZHEIMER'S DISEASE

The Alzheimer's disease (AD) is a form of dementia occurs in karyotypically normal individuals. This common disorder, strikes as many as 10% of individuals who are at least 65 years of age and perhaps 40% of individuals who are 80 years or older. They exhibit memory loss, confusion and a loss of reasoning ability. They become more forgetful and disoriented.

CJD and AD, both are fatal neuro-degenerative diseases that can occur in either an inherited or sporadic form. Brain of both diseases contain fribrillar deposits of insoluble materials, called **amyloids** which result from self association of polypeptides composed predeminantly of β-sheet. The main difference is that AD is not an infectious protein like prion protein which is the cause of CJD.

The Down syndrome is caused by the trisomy of chromosome -21, which is a major cause of mental retardation, the symptoms usually appeared shortly after birth. They exhibit varying degrees of mental impairment, increased susceptibility to infectious diseases and the early onset of Alheimer's disease. This is possibly due to an *abnoral level of expression of genes located on chromosome -21*. Genetic mapping has demonstrated that the gene for *amyloia β protein (Aβ) is located on chromosome-21* where the Alzheimer's disease is occurred in Down syndrome patients.

The amyloid β-protein (Aβ) is originally a part of a larger protein called **amyloid precursor protein (APP)**, which spans the nerve cell membrane, approximately two-thirds of it protrudes from the membrane into the extracellular space. This protruding portion is susceptible to cleavage by different proteases and Aβ peptide is released from APP molecules (Fig. 28.15).

**Cleavage & production of Aβ-42 molecules** : Two specific protease systems called α-pathway and β-pathway are involved in the cleavage reaction of APP. In α–pathway, the enzyme α–secretase cleaves APP between 687 and 688 amino acid residues. On the otherhand, in β-pathway the APP is internalized in the cell and transported to lysosome where two enzymes sequentially cleave the protein. The first one is β-secretase which cleaves APP between 671 and 672 amino acid residues and the second one is γ-secretase which cleaves the C-terminal polypeptide fragments between 712 and 713 amino acid residues or between 715 and 716 amino acid residues. Thus two different fragments are produced with 40 amino acids long Aβ-40 and two other long amyloid proteins with 42 amino acids Aβ-42 or with 43 amino acids long Aβ-43 (Fig. 28.16).

Both of these peptides can exist in a soluble form that predominantly consists of α–helices, but due to presence of extra two or three hydrophobic amino acids Aβ-42 and Aβ-43 have the tendency to refold spontaneously into β-pleated sheet. These long proteins have the potential to cause Alzheimer's disease, because these proteins tend to form small oligomer complexes and tend to aggregate to form fibrils, which are visible under electron microspe.

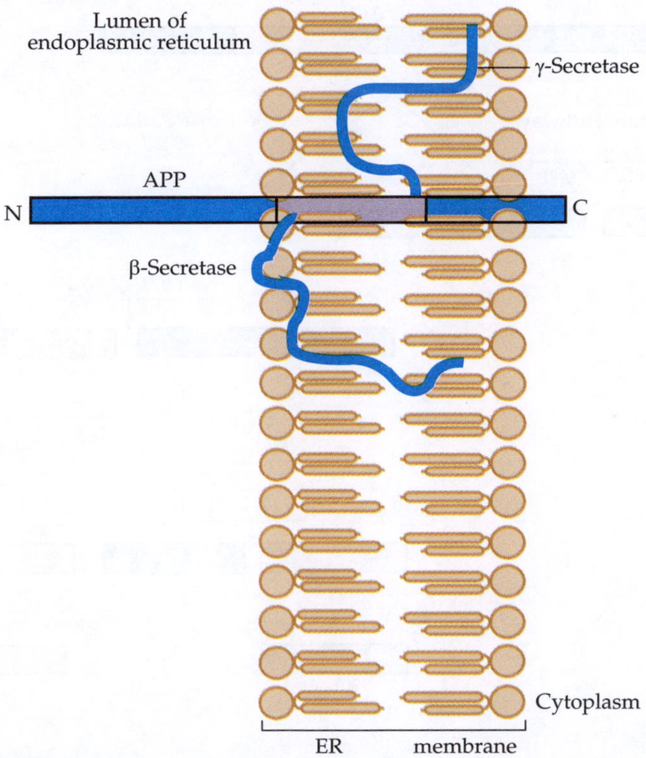


**Fig.28.15 :** *Location of Amyloid precursor protein (APP) and the two enzymes $\beta$ and $\gamma$ secretase in the ER membrane*

These aggregates are probably insoluble and toxic to nerve cells.

The patients, with or without trisomy of chsomosome no-21, *ie* in Down syndrome patients, excessive amounts of these amyloid proteins have been found to be deposited in the extracellular spaces where they form senile plaques.

Overproduction of these long proteins can be caused by mutation in the *APP* gene or in genes *PS 1* and *PS 2* that encode γ-secretase.

Both PS 1 and PS2 proteins, are known as **Presenilins** encoded by two genes *PS1* and *PS2* located on chromosome-14 and chromosome-1 respectively. Early onset of Alzheimers is due to the dominant mutations in these genes. The mechanism of the excessive production of long Aβ protein is not clearly known by these mutant genes. These proteins are located in neural membranes and they may mediate signaling processes that influence APP transport into lysosome and proteolytic cleavage of this protein.

When studied in artificial bilayers, cholesterol and sphingolipids tend to pack tightly to form a microdomain, which are referred to as "lipid rafts". The lipid rafts are thought to provide local environment for cell surface receptors to interact with other membrane proteins that transmit signals from the extracellular space to the cell interior. It has been speculated that two of the proteins involved in Alzheimer's disease, amyloid precursor protein and gamma secretase might be concetrated in lipid rafts. It might explain why cholesterol-lowering drugs dicrease the risk of developing AD. Lowered cholesterol level would decrease raft formation, which in

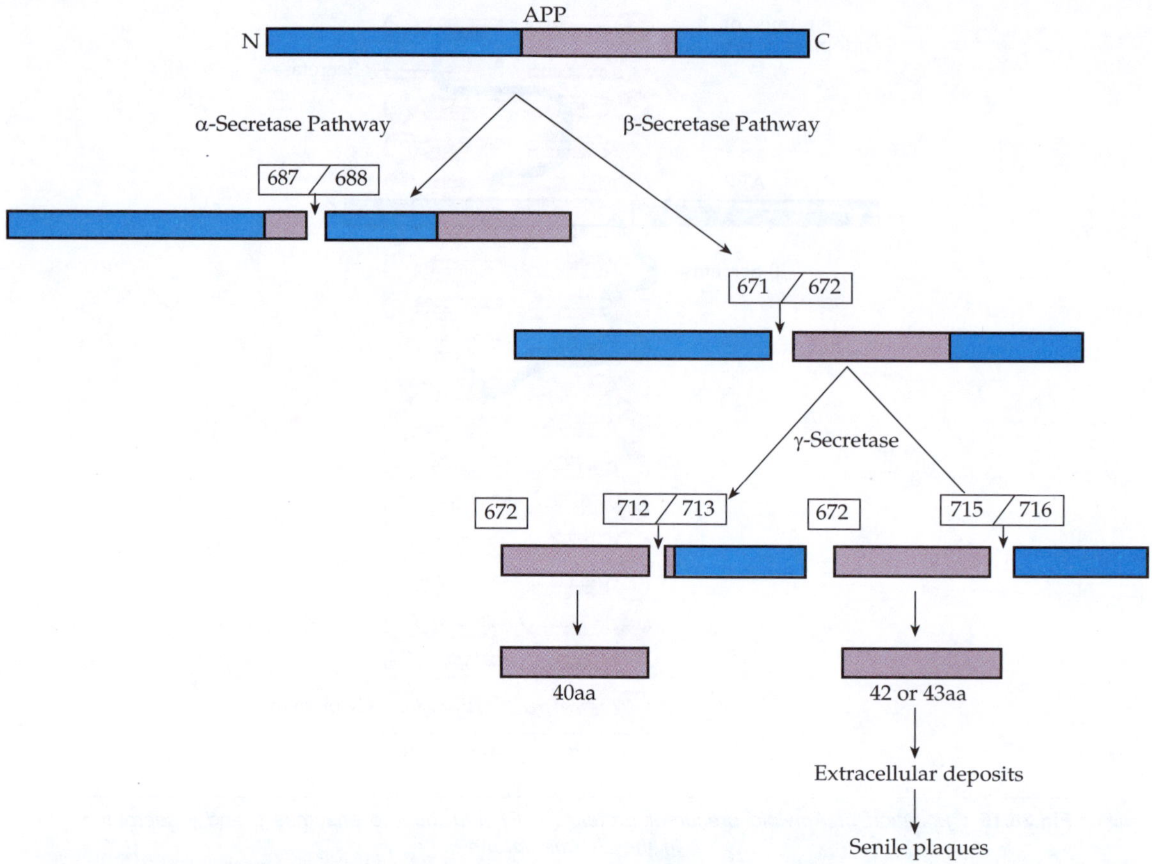


**Fig.28.16 :** *Alternate pathways for cleavage of APP to form Aβ polypeptides*

turn would likely decrease the production of the disease producing amyloid β-peptide.

## 28.15 A NEURODEGENERATIVE DISEASE : DUCHENNE MUSCULAR DYSTROPHY (DMD)

DMD is most common and devastating fatal disease that strikes nearly 1 in 3500 males but rare in females. This is a degenerative sex-linked disease of muscles. At birth, affected boys appear normal. The first symptom is mild muscle weakness appearing between 3 and 5 years of age. The child stumbles frequently, has difficultly climbing stairs and is unable to rise from sitting position. In time, the arm and leg muscles become progressively weaker. By the age of 11, those affected patients are usually confind to a wheel chair and by age 20, most persons with DMD have died.

DMD was first recognized in 1852 and the disease was fully described by Benjamin. A Duchenne, in 1861. This disease is an X-linked recessive trait, the males inherited through unaffected mothers.

Louis Kunkel and his colleagues at Harvard Medical School, in 1985, first observed a DMD boy with a deletion on the short arm of X-chromosome. They located and cloned the piece of gene responsible for this disease and shortly after the gene of DMD was determined and the protein encoded by this gene was isolated. This large protein is called "**dystrophin**".

The dystrophin gene is the largest known human gene. The transcribed sequence is 2.5 million nucleotides in length including 79 introns. It takes over 16 hours to produce a single transcript, of which more than 99% is removed during splicing to generate a mature mRNA only with 12000 nucleotides. The protein consists of 4000 amino acid residues.

The patients with DMD have a defect in the gene that encodes dystrophin.

Dystrophin is a very large protein that constitutes 5% of the membrane-associated cytoskeleton in muscle cells. It crosslinks actin filaments into a supportive cortical network and attaches this network to a glycoprotein complex in the muscle membrane. The membrane complex also binds to proteins in the extracellular matrix. Thus the internal cytoskeleton is connected to the extennal matrix via dystrophin membrane glycoprotein linkage. The DMD patients lack functional dystorphin. Therefore, the membrane of the muscle is not supported by cortical cytoskeleton and presumably is easily damaged by the stress of repeated muscle contraction.

## 28.16 LESCH-NYHAN SYNDROME : A BEHAVIOURAL DISORDER

The Lesch-Nyhan syndrome (LNS) is an inborn error of metabolism. This X-linked trait is caused by mutations in the gene encoding the enyme hypoxanthine-guanine phosphoribosyltransferase (HPRT). Children with this genetic disorder, which becomes manifest by the age of 2 years, are mentally retarded and badly coordinated. They exhibit a ceaseless and involuntary writhing movement. They are extremely hostile and show compulsive self-destructive tendencies : they mutilate themselves by biting off their fingers, toes and lips.

Purine and pyrimidine bases are recycled by Salvage pathway. Hypoxanthine and guanine arise continually as breakdown products of nucleic acids. These free hypoxanthine and guanine are salvaged by the enzyme HPRT. A lack of this crucial enzyme results in a rise in PRPP levels, which leads to a general increase in *de novo* purine synthesis . The brain is especially dependent on the salvage pathway. Normally this enzyme is expressed at higher levels in the brain than in other tissues of the body. Thus the precursors are accumulated in the nervous tissues and joints of the organs. Thus the behavioural disorders associated with LNS may result from abnormally low purine levels in the brain tissue.

## 28.17 A NEURODEGENERATIVE TAY-SACHS DISEASE IN HUMAN

Tay-Sachs disease is a metabolic error, inherited as autosomal recessive trait. Children with Tay-Sachs disease appear healthy at birth but become listless and weak at about 6 months of age. Gradually and rapidly their physical and neurological conditions worsen, leading to blind and deafness and eventually death at the age of 2–3 years.

Tay-Sachs disease is rare in most populations. But in the Ashkenazi Jewish people of Central Europe, the disease occurs in about 1 in 36000 and about 1 in 30 adult carries the mutant gene as heterozygous state in these populations.

The mutation that causes Tay-Sachs disease is located in the *HEXA*-gene which encodes the enzyme hexasaminidase. This enzyme acts on a complex lipid ganglioside $G_{M2}$ cleaving it into a smaller ganglioside $G_{M3}$ and N-acetyl-D galactosamine.

The function of ganglioside $G_{M3}$ is to coat nerve cells, insulating them from events occuring in neighbouring cells and thus speeding up the transmission of nerve impulses.

In absence of this enzyme, ganglioside $G_{M3}$ accumulates and smoothens nerve cells in the brain causing swelling and builds up a complex lipid on neurons block their action potential leading to deterioration of the nervous system and eventually to paralysis. In heterozygous condition, one copy of the gene in one chromosome produces half the normal amount of the enzyme which is enough to ensure the $G_{M2}$ ganglioside to be broken down normally and therefore, heterozygotes are usually healthy.

Although the molecular defects responsible for this disease is known, there is no effective treatment for this disorder. Treatment with missing enzyme is not feasible as the enzyme does not penatrate the blood-brain barrier. Somatic cell gene therapy is not also possible. It can be detected prenatally by amniocentesis. Recently a sensitive DNA test has been developed to test for one cell of 8-cell stage of embryo during *in vitro* fertilization. If found normal, then the 7-cell embryo is implanted for complete development.

## 28.18 A NEURODEGENERATIVE DISEASE IN HUMAN : *PHENYLKETONURIA*

Phynylketonuria (PKU) was first described by Asjborn Folling, a Norwegian physician and biochemist in 1934, and observed some retarded children gave off an odour musty odor. This odour is due to the presence of phenylpyrivicacid present in their urine.

PKU is a genetic disorder that when untreated, is characterized by mental retardation, eczema, and light hair, eyes and skin. The disorder arises because of a defect in the gene that codes for phenylalanine hydroxylase (PAH), a live enzyme that normally metabolizes amino acid phenylalanine. The level of this phenylalanine during early infancy and childhood is critical for growth and brain development. Too little phenylalanine limits growth, again too much of this amino acid produces mental retardation. In PKU, the enzyme PAH is defective, cannot convert phenylalanine into tyrosine, the amino acid which is essential for the growth of brain.

**PKU allele :** The symptoms of PKU are caused by the mutant recessive allele, located on the long arm of chromosome 12. In homozygous mutant state, the individual cannot produce the functional enzyme PAH. However, in regard to the activity of the enzyme, PKU exhibits incomplete dominance, *i.e.* in heterozygons condition, the person would have 50% of the enzyme activity, but still can maintain plasma conentration of phenylalanine in the normal range and are free of symptoms of PKU.

PKU has more than 400 alleles at the *PAH* locus, exhibiting multiple allele series. Thus, people with PKU exhibit much variability in their ability to metabolize phenylalanine. This individual variation is explained by a particular alleles possessed by a person with PKU. Some persons are with PKU are *compound heterozygote ie*, they possess two different mutant alleles at the *PAH* locus. The severity of the disease in determined by which less severe PAH mutation present in these persons.

**PKU is a multifunctional trait :** It has been observed that some untreated persons with PKU genotype with elevated blood concentration of phenylalanine may be with normal intelligence than some patients with lower concentration of phenylalanine in the blood. This is possibly because of individual differences in the entry of phenylalanine to the brain.

**PKU as the maternal genetic cause :** The question arises why do the children of normal genotype, born to woman with PKU, has the features of PKU? The answer is that, if a pregnant woman has abandoned her low - phenylalanine diet, her blood level of phenylalanine are likely to be high, would likely pass through placenta and act on the brain to cause mental and developmental retardation to the fetus. Thus the mother's genotype affects the PKU phenotype of the child.

***PAH locus :*** The *PAH* gene is located on the long arm of chromosome-12 in the region 12q23.2. This is about 90000 bp long with 13 exons. It encodes an mRNA with 2400 nucleotides long. Thus the PAH enzyme consists of 452 aminoacids.

The *PAH* locus has several sites at which transcription can be initiated. The most 5′ of

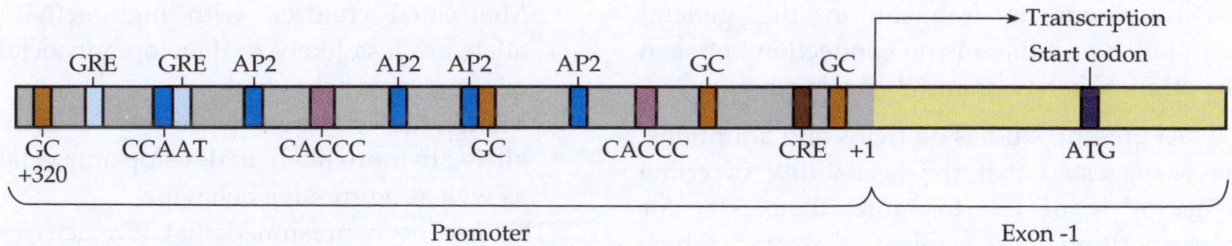


**Fig.28.17 :** *PAH locus for phenylketonuria showing its promoter which contains a number of regulatory sequences, that serve as binding sites for transcriptional activator proteins.*

these sites is 154 bp upstream of the initiation codon.

Immediately upsteam of these transcription start sites is the core promoter for the gene. It lacks TATA box. Farther upstream, there is a number of binding sites for transcription activator proteins including GC box and CAAT box and several other regulatory sequences (Fig. 28.17).

**Mutations at the *PAH* locus :** More than 450 mutations have been observed throughout the world. 30 of these mutations are naturally occurring variants, do not cause diseases, called polymorphisms, Remainders are disease-causing mutants. The mutations are of different types viz. Missense (67%), deletions (14%), splice (12%), nonsense (6%) and insertion (1%). Splicing usually causes removal of exon-11.

**Complicating factors :**

1. It has been observed that, some siblings who have the exact same *PAH genotype* have very different mental abilities. Therefore, it might be assumed that the effect is both genetic as well as environmental that causes the blood phenylalanine level to damage brain.
2. The phenotype of compound heterozygotes is determined by the possession of the mildest mutant allele, because, the PAH locus is multiple allele series.
3. Complications arise when foetus is normal but mother is PKU with elevated phenylalanine in her blood which could damage the brain of the fetus.
4. The cofactor tetrahydrobioprotein ($BH_4$) which is essential for the functioning of PAH. Therefore, symptoms of PKU may arise due to mutation at the loci that code $BH_4$. Such PKU patients are responsive to treatment with $BH_4$.

**Treatment of PKU :** PKU can be effectively treated by the dietary restriction of phenylalanine. Phenylalanine is an essential amino acid and therefore it cannot be completely eliminated from the diet. Therefore, the diet should be so restricted that the blood concentration of phenylalanine remains low within the range of 120-360 µmol. Low phenylalanine diet must be initiated just after birth. Therefore, the concentration of phenylalanine must be monitored in the blood weekly or biweekly. Low phenylalamine diet is also restricted throughout the life because in adult stage, high phenylalamine may cause reduced attention span, slow information-processing abilities, slow reaction time, increased muscle tone and tremor.

## 28.19 AGGRESSIVE, IMPULSIVE AND VIOLENT BEHAVIOR IN HUMAN

In 1960s, researchers reported that Y-chromosome is associated with the violent crime behaviour in human. These studies were based on the sample-inmates in the prison. The extra Y chromosome may cause such antisocial behavior. But recent studies disclosed that extra

Y-chromosome is frequent in the general population and there is no connection between the criminal behavior and Y-chromosome.

At present, studies on twins and adoptions, have suggested that the heritability of crime behavior is of 0% to more than 50% for predisposition to violent factor, which represents the degree of a trait stems from genetic factors. The remaining possible effect of crime behaviour is acquired from the environmental factors in early life.

Molecular biologists have found a link between the aggressive behaviour and a gene on X-chromosome that codes for the enzyme monoamine oxidase A (MAOA). This enzyme metabolizes several neurotransmitters in the brain such as dopamine and serotonine, thus preventing excess neurotransmitters from interfering with communication among neurons.

$$R\text{-}CH_2\text{-}\overset{(+)}{N}H_3 + O_2 \xrightarrow[\text{monoamine oxidaze}]{H_2O} RCHO + \overset{(+)}{N}H_4 + H_2O_2$$

Abnormal criminal behavior has been observed in a Dutch family where there is a chain termination mutation in exon 8 of the *MAOA* gene. But there was no informations on environmental effects influencing the behavior.

A number of functional length polymorphism in the transcriptional control region of *MAOA* gene has been chracterized.

A tandem repeat of 30 bp is present in 3, 3.5, 4 and 4.5 copies at the promoter region of *MAOA* gene. The 3.5 and 4 copies of such repeats are transcribed more MAOA enzyme rapidly and efficiently. These are *high-activity alleles.*

The repeats of 3 or 5 copies produces less MAOA enzyme called *low-activity alleles.*

There is a convincing evidence which has been established in Newzealand in 2002, where these repeat polymorphisms that influence aggressive behavior are dependent on the early environment of the child from their birth to adulthood. In this experiment 1037 males were taken. The results were that

1. Maltreated children with high activity allele are less likely to develop antisocial or aggressive behaviour.
2. Maltreated children with low activity allele are more likely to develop antisocial as well as aggressive behavior.

This has been presumed that low activity allele carrying males produce less amount of MAOA which cannot mobilize sufficient amount of dopamine and serotonine. They become four times more likely to be aggressive, impulsive, antisocial and commit violent crimes.

Females also inherit two alleles in their two X-chromosomes but the effects are easier to study in males because of the presence of only one X-chromosome.

Researchers tried to establish the aggressive behaviour on both great apes and old world monkeys with the *MAOA* gene. The same 30 bp repeats or a shorter 18 bp repeats in the *MAOA* gene was found in apes and Old World (Asian and African) monkeys carried these alleles. But in New World (South American) monkeys do not have such alleles. It has also been observed that the repeat polymorphism in the rhesus macaque *MAOA* gene promoter region influences aggressive behavior. This is to be noted that the expression of this gene is also dependent on the early environment of the animal concerned (Fig. 28.18).

## 28.20 SCHIZOPHRENIA : A SEVERE PSYCHIATIC DISORDER IN HUMANS

Schizopherenia is the illness with symtoms corresponding most closely to the popular conception of the madman. During the acute phase of their illness to eperience.

1. Hallucinations, most commonly in the form of threatning or unfriendly voices.
2. To express bizarre delusions with little or no appreciation of why it is that their ideas are unacceptable to those around them.
3. Severe depression, mental illness, mania and delirium.

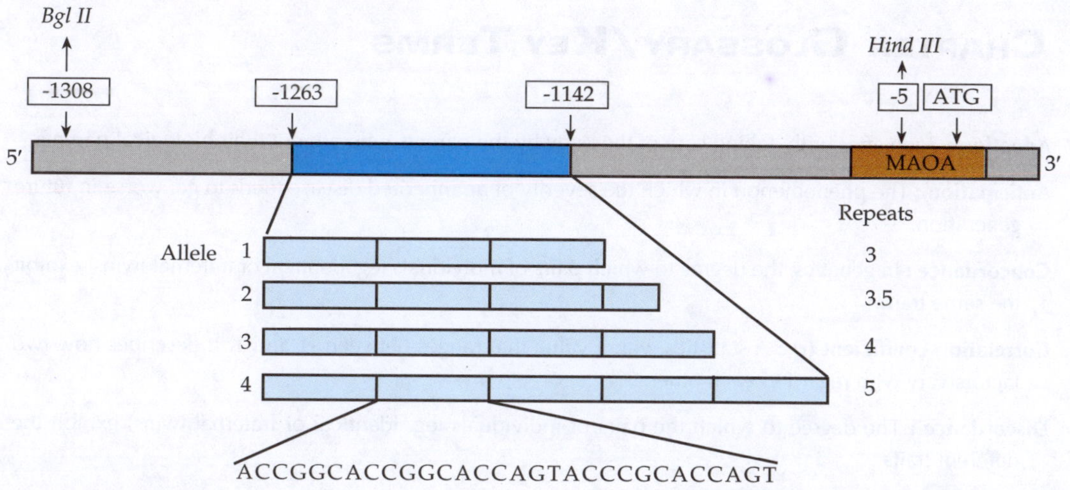


**Fig.28.18 :** *Functional polymorphism in the MAOA gene is linked to aggressive, impulsive and violent behavior.*

4. Paranoid delutions in which the patient believes that he or she is surrounded by hostile forces which watch him and secretly intervene to do him harm.
5. These patients tend to have little insight into the fact that they are ill and in need to treatment.

Twin and adoption studies showed conclusively that the risk of developing schizophrenia is increased among relatives of affected individuals. The complex mode of its transmission seemed that the trait is governed by more than one gene (polygenic).

A number of loci have been described to be present on chromosomes 1, 5, 6, 8, 10, 12, 13, 17 and 22. The pupative susceptibility genes for which the most promising follow-up data are available are those encoding :

1. **Dysbindin** (DTNBP1, also known as **dystrobrevin** binding protein-1) located on chromosome 6.
2. **Neuregulin-1** (NRG1) in chomosome 8
3. **Disrupted in schizophrenia 1**(DISC 1) in chromosome 1.
4. **D-amino acid oxidase** (DAO) in chromosome 12.
5. **D-amino acid oxidase activator** (DAOA) in chromosome 13.
6. **Regulator of G-protein signaling 4 (RGS 4)** in chromosome 1.

Several other genes may encode several other proteins and enzymes which are not still known. Of these, DTNBP1 and NRG1 have been so far known to be very strong, but their functions are still not known. Variation in mRNA expression of **dysbindin** may confer risk by presynaptic effects on glutamate trafficking or release, particularly in the hippocampus region of the brain. The Neuregulin is thought to encode more than 15 proteins with a diverse functions in the brain including cell-cell signaling, axon guidance, synaptogenesis, glial differentiation, myelination and neuro-transmission etc. Therefore, altered expression or splicing of neuregulin may confer risk. This is also fact that defective regulation leading to excessively high concentrations of noradrenaline may be a factor in the development schizophrenia.

## CHAPTER GLOSSARY/KEY TERMS

**Adoption :** Soon after birth, taking care of the baby by the parents who are not their biological parents.

**Anticipation :** The phenomenon in which the severity of an inherited disease tends to get worse in future generation.

**Concordance :** In genetics, the degree to which pairs of individuals (eg identical or fraternal twins) exhibit the same trait.

**Correlation coefficient (r) :** A statistics with a value that ranges between -1 and 1. It describes how two factors vary with regard to each other.

**Discordance :** The degree to which the pairs of individuals (eg. identical or fraternal twins) exhibit the different traits.

**Dizygotic twins :** Twins formed from separate pairs of sperm and egg cells.

**DNA fingerprinting :** A technology to identify a particular individual based on the properties of their DNA.

**Dystrophin :** A protein that attaches to the inside of the muscle cell plasma membrane and stabilizes the membrane during muscle contraction. Mutations of the gene encoding this protein.

**Fraternal twins:** Same as dizygotic twins.

**Huntingtin :** The protein contains 6-35 *gln* residues in its primary structure produced by *HD* gene. Mutant protein produces Huntington disease in human.

**Identical twins :** Same as monozygotic twins.

**Imprinted gene :** By a process of genomic imprinting the gene whose expression depends on whether it has been inherited from a male or a female parent.

**Intelligence Quotient (IQ) :** This indicates the person's intelligence. This is determined by dividing the mental age and the test score by the individuals chronological age and then multiplying by 100.

**Monozygotic twins :** Twins that are genetical identical of each other and are formed from a zygote of same sperm and egg.

**Phocomelia :** Congenital defects in the limbs.

**Sherman Paradox :** The pattern of inheritance of Fragile-X-syndrome caused by anticipation.

**Strand slippage :** The one strand of DNA forms a loop and this looped-out nucleotides are on the newly synthesized strand, an insertion results and at the next round of replication the insertion is incorporated into both the strands of the replicated DNA molecules. Thus leads to the expansion of trinucleotide sequence.

# Exercise

## A. Long answer type questions :

1. Describe the different types of twins and their causes of origin.
2. What is conjoint twin? Classifly different types of conjoint twins.
3. Define concordance and discordance. Describe different methods of twin studies and results.
4. Describe the twin studies by correlation method about their intelligence and personality.
5. Describe the adoption studies on some hereditary characters.
6. Write a note on phenocopy.
7. Write a note on nurturing behaviour in mice and its inheritance.
8. Describe the genetics of nest cleaning behaviour in honeybees.
9. Describe the molecular mechanism of biological rhythm in *Drosophila*.
10. Describe the molecular mechanism of sexual preference in *Drosophile*.
11. Describe the molecular mechanism and genetics of Huntington's disease.
12. What do you mean by ataxia, Write a brief note on Friedreich's ataxia.
13. What are symptoms, physical problems, behavioural problems and medical problems of FXS? Describe the genetices and inheritance of FXS.
14. Write a note on premutation.
15. Write a brief note on diagnosis and treatment of FXS?
16. Briefly describe the mechanism of expanding trinucleotide sequence.
17. Describe the causes and symtoms of Prader-Willi syndrome and Angelman syndrome. Briefly describe their molecular biology of diseases.
18. Describe the cause, symptoms and molecular biology of DMD.
20. Write a note on Lesh-Nyhan syndrome.
21. Write a brief note on Tay-Sachs disease.
22. Briefly describe the cause, symptoms and genetics of PKU.
23. Describe the molecular biology of aggressive behaviour in human.
24. Describe the cause and symptoms of schiezophrenia in human.

## B. Short answer type questions.

1. What is behaviour?
2. Which activities of the animal are included in the behaviour?
3. What is monozygotic twin? How does it occur? How much of genes these twins share?
4. What is dizygotic twin? How does it form? How much of genes they share?
5. What are the causes of monoamniotic twin, polar body twin, half fraternal twin and conjoint twin? What are their causes to be formed?
6. What is Siamese twin?
7. Waht do you mean by complete (symmetrical) and incomplete (asymmetrical) conjoint twins?
8. Define craniopagus, pygopagus, thoracopagus, cephalopagus, parapagus, omphalopagus, ischiopagus and dicephalus conjoint twins.
9. What do you mean by parasitic twins and fetus in fetu twins.
10. What is concordance and discordance among the identical twin?
11. What would be the pattern of fingerprints in identical twins?
12. What would be the left or right handedness among identical twins?
13. What would the conclusion from the results of IQ test of various twins.

14. What are the causes of susceptibility of diseases or occurrence of cancer among twins.
15. What are MZT, MZA, DGT and DGA?
16. What would the results when r=0 and r = 1?
17. What would be the relations between r, $H^2$ and $c^2$ in MZA, DZA, DZT and URT individuals?
18. What kinds of IQ scores can be obtained in MZT and DZT and also among URT?
19. What may be the results of personality expression among DZT and MZT about some genetic factors such as alcoholism?
20. What is adoption? What do you mean by adoptive parent and biological parents? What kinds of interactions occur between adoptive child with adoptive parent as well as biological parents?
21. What is the result of adoption studies on the obesity or alcoholism properties?
22. What kind of results are obtained in adoption studies with alcoholism? What are the comments of such results?
23. What do you mean by phenocopy? How do these individuals can be produced? Give examples.
24. Give the names and functions of nurturing behaviour genes in mice? How do they function?
25. What genes are involved in the nest cleaning behaviour in honeybees? What is the molecular mechanism of such behaviour?
26. What is circadian and ultradian rhythms?
27. What kinds of abnormal eclosion rhythms are produces by X-chromosome mutation in males by EMS?
28. Which gene is responsible for eclosion behaviour?
29. What are $per^O$, $per^S$ and $per^L$ mutations.
30. What are the autosomal genes responsible for the biological rhythm of *Drosophila*.
31. What is the role of Clk and Per proteins in the biological rhythm of *Drosophila*?
32. What is *fru* gene? What is its function? How *fru* gene controls *Drosophila* sex determination?
33. What is the role of *dsx* gene in *Drosophila* sex determination?
34. What do you mean by trinucleotide repeats?
35. Define anticipation?
36. What are the two types of diseases attributed to the expansion of trinucleotide repeats?
37. What is the symptoms of HD?
38. What type of mutation occurs in HD gene?
39. What is the gene product of *HD* gene? What is its composition in wild and mutant alleles?
40. How heterozygous state causes the disease?
41. What is the molecular basis of the function of the mutant protein?
42. What is the cause of Friedreich's ataxia?
43. What is the function of frataxin?
44. How frataxin causes the disease?
45. What is the symptoms of FXS?
46. What is fragile X? What is the cause of such fragility?
47. What is the physical problems of such FXS boys?
48. Why the girls have fewer signs of the disorder of FXS.
49. What are behavioural problems of FXS?
50. Why the girls have fewer signs of the disorder of FXS.
51. What are behavioural problem of FXS?
52. What are the medical problems of FXS?
53. What is pre mutation and full mutation in FXS?
54. What is the characteristic repeats of bases found in FMR-1 gene.
55. What is FMRP?
56. What is FXTAS?
57. What are the problems of FXTAS in men of 50 years?
58. How the diagnosis can be done for FXS?
59. What would be recommended to a child to test FXS by a health care personal?

60. How the child can be diagnosed an FXS before birth?
61. When a woman is considered to be a carrier of FXS?
62. What is the chance of a premutaiton carrier mother to pass the abnormal gene to her babies?
63. What is the chance of a full mutaiton carrier mother to inherit the abnormal gene to her babies?
64. A premutation man how inherit the FXS to three daughters and sons?
65. Why in males the premutaiton does not expand in size to his daughters?
66. What kind of treatment or improvement of the patients with FXS can be done?
67. What is the difference of FXS from the other genetic diseases?
68. What is anticipation and its causes?
69. What do you mean by Sherman Paradox?
70. What is prognosis of the FXS patients?
71. What are the causes of expansion of trinucleotide repeats?
72. What do you mean by strand slippage?
73. How such mechanism increases the trinucleotide sequence?
74. How unequal crossing over causes increase in trinucleotide sequence?
75. What is the cause of Prader-Willi-syndrome? What is it's symptoms?
76. What is the cause Angelman syndrome? What is its symptoms? Why this is called happy puppet syndrome?
77. What is the principle of diagnosis of Prader-Willi and Angelman syndromes?
78. What is bisulfite–PCR? Describe the protocol of bisulfite –PCR?
79. Which genes ae responsible for Prader-Willi syndrome?
80. What is the bisulfite product product? Where does it found?
81. What is the function?
82. Why Prader-Willi patients suffer from overeating problem?
83. Why PWS is paternally derived and AS is maternally derived syndromes?
84. What paternally expressed genes are expressed in PWS?
85. Which gene is not expressed in AS but expressed in PWS?
86. How maternal uniparental disomy results PWS and paternal uniparental disomy results AS? What are the causes of maternal to paternal imprinting switches in PWS and AS?
87. What are the symptoms of AD?
88. What are the similarities and dissimilarities of AD and CJD?
89. What are amyloids?
90. What is the similarity between AD and Down syndrome at molecular and genetic levels?
91. What is APP? Where does it located?
92. What amyloid protein is responsible for AD? How this protein is formed and causes AD?
93. Why the AD protein causes symptoms in Down syndrome?
94. What is presenilins? Which genes encode them?
95. What is the cause of early onset of AD?
96. What is the effect of APP and $\gamma$-secretase on lipid raft.
97. Why and how cholesterol lowering drug decreases the risk of developing AD?
98. Give a name of sex-linked muscle degenerative disease?
99. How DMD is inherited by the males?
100. What is dystrophin? What is its function?
101. What is the characteristics of dystrophin gene?
102. What is the cause of DMD?
103. What are the cause and symptoms Lesch-Nyhan syndrome?

104. Why and how precursors of nucleotide bases are accumulated in the brain and nervous tissues?

105. What are the cause and symptoms of Tay-Sachs disease?

106. Among which populations the Tay-Sachs disease is mostly found?

107. What is the molecular mechanism of Tay-Sachs disease?

108. Why heterozygons Tay-sachs are healthy?

109. Why treatment with missing enzyme is not feasible for the treatment of Tay-sachs disease.

110. What is the cause of musty odor in the urine in PKU?

111. What are the sympotoms of PKU?

112. What is the cause of PKU?

113. Why heterozygous state of PKU is free from the disease?

114. What is the cause of variant severity of the PKU?

115. Why the children of normal genotype may have features of PKU of a woman with PKU?

116. How mother's genotype affects the PKU phenotype of the normal child?

117. What is the characteristics of *PAH* locus? What do you mean by the polymorphism of the *PAH* lucus?

118. What is the role of tetrahydrobioprotein in PKU?

119. What is the role of MAOA in aggressive behavior?

120. What are high-activity and low-activity alleles in MAOA gene?

121. What is the genetic and molecular cause of aggressive behavior?

122. What is the symptoms of schizophrenia?

123. What is the mode of transmission of schizophrenia?

124. Which genes are responsible for schizophrenia?

# 29

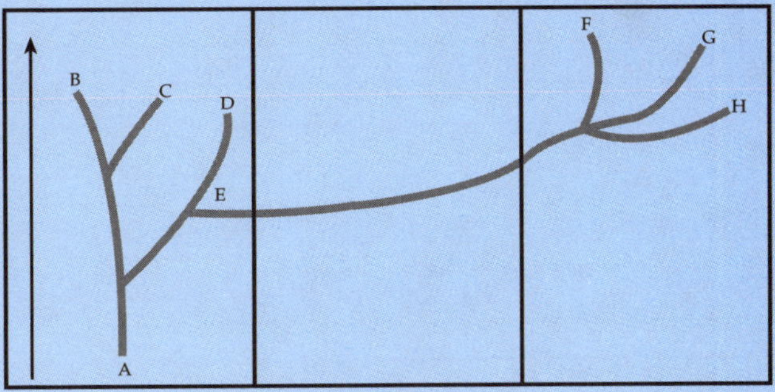


# Theories of Evolution

**CHAPTER AGENDA**

## 29.1 LAMARCKISM

Jean Baptiste Lamarck (1744-1829), a French biologist, was the first person to propose a definite theory of Organic evolution in the year 1809 in "Philosophic Zoologique". He proposed that changes in organisms in course of time, not only the outcome of direct action of the environment, but also it acts on the internal structure in an indirect way. So, his theory is best known as the theory of "The inheritance of acquired characters". Lamarck's idea makes the light upon the compromize of Buffon's and Darwin's views of evolution.

### 29.1.1 Theory

1. *Principles of Use and Disuse* : In every animal which has not passed the limit of its development, a more frequent and continuous use of any organ gradually strengthens, develops and enlarges that organ, and gives it a power proportional to the length of time it has been so used, while the permanent disuse of any organ imperceptibly weakens and deteriorates it, and progressively diminishes its functional capacity until it finally disappears.
2. *The Inheritance of Acquired Characters* : The changes, which have taken place during its lifetime due to environment or use or disuse are known as "acquired characters". These modifications *i.e.*, the acquired characters are inherited by its offspring over a period of time. He also thought that an animal in some way may exert its will to live and determine the course of evolution.

### 29.1.2 Support of Lamarckism

To explain his theory, which was based on the ideas direct environmental effect over living organisms use and disuse and inheritance of acquired traits, Lamarck used examples like long neck of Giraffe, limblessness in snakes, webbed feet of ducks, blindness of moles and also dimorphism of submerged and aerial leaves in aquatic plants.

1. Giraffe, found in Africa has to fed on foliage of trees and required an effort to reach the leaves. Thus by continuous effort of stretching the neck and forelimbs increased in each generation and so the present giraffe possesses a long neck and forelimbs.
2. A snake crawling through thick bushes and grass has to stretch its body to pass through and has consequently become elongated, in passing through space, the limbs were not used and so they finally disappear by continuous disuse. The long tongue was put out to feel and become continuous protrucible sensory organs to detect objects.
3. The eyes of cave dwelling animals were not used in the dark and were eventually lost through disuse.
4. Kammerer performed experiments on salamanders. The *S. arta* found in the cold part of the Alps are black in colour, while *S. maculosa* living in Alps. He placed *S. arta* in yellow boxes and *S. maculosa* in black boxes. He found that in course of time the former acquired yellow patches and were inherited by its progeny, while the later becomes black in colour.
5. Besides, other biologists have put support on Lamarckism with some experiments such as Guyer's experiment on induced inheritance of immunity, Mc Dougall experiments on hereditary transmission of the training effect in rat. Harrison's demonstration on the production of melanic mutation etc.

### 29.1.3 Critical Analysis of Lamarck's proposition

Lamarck's theory is simple but is largely rejected because of the effects of environment or of use and disuse, of called acquired character produces variations, which were never inherited. So, he faced much social and scientific criticisms.

1. The first proposition of Lamarck suggests the tendency to increase of size. While the evolutionary trend in a certain groups of organisms has been found to be associated with increase of size but there are many cases where evolution proceeds through a reduction in size, e.g., many ferns and conifers which become extinct were gigantic trees and the more highly evolved flowering plants are actually smaller in size.
2. The second Lamarckian principle is that new organs result from new needs, is quite manifestly not true. He also believed that the environment acted through the nervous systems, in other words the desire of the animal leads to the formation of new structures. This would mean that the man who mused that "Birds can fly so why cannot I" should have sprouted wings and taken to the air.
3. The third proposition of Lamarck was that organs would develop due to its use and degenerate due to its disuse, which may be correct as far as growth of an organ within the lifetime of an individual. But the powerful arm muscles of blacksmith, acquired by continuous work are not inherited to their offspring.
4. The fourth and final proposition of Lamarck was that the inheritance of acquired characters during the lifetime of the individual.

Darwin's concept of pangenesis also tides over the Lamarckian crisis. He assumed that the inheritance of acquired characters does not happen on the concept of Lamarck. He imagined the hereditary particles are known as PANGENES OR GEMMULES produced in the lifetime of an individual by each and every part of the body, these pangenes are discharged into the circulation of blood and collected together to form the germ cells and the germ cells produce zygote and inherited by their offspring.

August Weismann (1892) advocated that the living organism composed of two types of materials, "somatoplasm and germplasm", which are quite different. The zygote divides into cells having the same hereditary qualities as the parent cells. Some daughter cells become differentiated into body or somatic cells but the undifferentiated cells become germ cells. The germ cells produce the next generation and there is an unbroken linkage from generation to generation. Any variations must be present in the germ cells, if they are to be inherited. He proved that acquired characters affect the body and are somatic, they cannot be inherited, and they do not affect the germ cells.

For strengthening his concept he performed extensive experiments on white mice. He artificially cut the tail of parent mice even for about 22 generations till the mice produced all with tail, *i.e.*, these are not inherited even for a long generation.

Besides, these negative experimental evidences for discrediting Lamarckian theory, there are certain experimental evidences, which have tried to support it.

1. Mc Dougall conducted learning experiments in rats and from the result obtained he tried to suggest that learning as an acquired character can be inherited. In his experiments, rats were dropped into a tank of water from which, there were two exits, one is lighted and other dark. A rat leaving by the lighted exit received on electric shock, while leaving by the dark exit received no shock. Thus after the number of trials a particular rat to learn always to select the dark exit without any shock. These rats were then bred and their descendants were similarly studied. It appeared that the learning behavior is increased from generation to generation and so Mc Dougall concluded that learning, an acquired trait is inherited from generation to generation.

2. F.B. Summer reared the white mice at 20-30°C, because of which they developed longer bodies, tail and feet, when these mice were bred at lower temperatures their offspring showed their normal proportions of size.

## 29.2. NEO-LAMARCKISM

Lamarckism cannot explain origin of new species and the origin and adaptations remain unsolved. Kammerer's experiment on salamander, Guyer's experiments on induced inheritance of immunity, Mc Dougall's experiments on training effect on rat, Harrison's experiment of melanic mutation in moth etc. gave strong support to this theory. But Weishman's experiment and many other scientists strongly objected the theory and told inheritance of acquired character is not occurred in this way. Poyne (1911) has shown an excellent example to demonstrate the failure of production of Lamarckian effects by disuse in *Drosophila*.

Modern biologist after the discovery of genes and their role in hereditary throw much light on the origin and inheritance of hereditary variations.

Lamarckian acquired characters are phenotypic variations and they cannot affect the genotypes. But it is fact that phenotypic variations are the results of interactions of genotypes and the environment. So, there is a relationship between the changes of genotypes and changes of phenotypes.

Waddington has developed a new evolutionary point of view, which tries to make a compromise between Lamarckian theory and the selection theory, which is called **genetic assimilation**.

According to C.H. Waddington, genetic assimilation is a process by which acquired character is converted into inherited character, depends upon selection, acting on genotypes of several generations. This genetic assimilation is referred to as Neo-Lamarckism and thus Lamarckism is newly modified and re-established.

According to Goodrich (1934), the characters of all organisms are to some extent inherited and some extent acquired. The genetic assimilation may arise from the joint action of genotypes and environment. Suppose, an organism is reared in an environment "E", which shows the phenotype "P" while if it is reared in "F", it will show phenotype "P1", then those features in which "P1" differs from "P" may be considered as acquired character and those features in which 'P1' resembles with 'P' can be designated as inherited character with reference to this peculiar change of environment.

### 29.2.1 Phenomenon

From the previous example, let, a sub-population is transferred into another environment "E", and shows phenotype "P1", so P1 – P is the acquired character in that subpopulation. Again it is transferred to the former environment 'E' it will show characters separate from P and P1 but as P2. Then the degree in which P2 resembles P1 is the original acquired character has converted into inherited one.

### 29.2.2 Mechanism

The mechanism of selection may be natural or artificial acting on the genotype for many or several generations and genetic assimilation is brought about by selection (natural or artificial) acting on genotypes in the subpopulations, which transferred from E to E1.

### 29.2.3 Experimental Evidences

1. **Waddington's experiment (1952-53) :** 21 to 23 hours old pupae of *Drosophila melanogaster* was subjected to 40°C temperature shock for 4 hrs, several abnormalities were produced. One of which is a breaking or even complete absence of posterior cross vein in wings. These selected stocks were maintained by breeding in every generation and

continued with abnormal temperature. After 14 generations the broken or post crossveinless is produced in absence of temperature shock. So, the acquired characters have become genetically assimilated and then inherited in the next generations.

2. **Bateson's experiment :** Like Waddington, Bateson selected other abnormalities as the breakage of anterior crossvein, extra crossvein and distorted or dumpy phenotype by abnormal 40°C treatment for $4\frac{1}{2}$ hours of 16-28 hours aged pupae. After 25 generations, this dumpy character is generally assimilated.

Waddington (1959), in another experiment produced *Drosophila* with enlarged anal papillae by adding NaCl in normal culture medium. This character is genetically assimilated after 21 generations.

### 29.2.4 Analysis

Genotypes of assimilated stocks have been analyzed by crossing method and the results of the experiments were analyzed.

1. Waddington (1953) showed that in assimilated crossvein stock, the 2nd and 3rd autosomes and X-chromosome had a tendency to produce the character but 3rd one had strongest effect and many genes determined the character.
2. Bateson also has drawn in her experiment and showed that
   (a) Without post crossvein has strongest effect of the 3rd chromosome with a great number of gene loci.
   (b) Without anterior crossvein has 2nd and 3rd chromosomes equal effect.
   (c) Extra crossvein has 2nd chromosome strong effect.
   (d) Dumpy phenotype was due to assimilation of an allele *"dp"*.

### 29.2.5 Conclusion

Thus modern genetics makes the fact crystal clear that whatever changes are induced in the genotype, the change is not necessarily in the genotype but the change of phenotype is due to the introduction of genetic assimilation in normal and artificial environment by producing genetic variation in a normal random mating population after some generations. Therefore, the acquired character is inherited. In this way Lamarckism is resynthesized by modern geneticists and coined the name Neo-Lamarckism.

## 29.3 THE VOYAGE OF THE BEAGLE

After completion of his degree at Cambridge, Charles Darwin, in 1831, has received an invitation from expeditionary ship, H.M.S. Beagle to join them as biologist. He took the offer and the ship sailed on December 27, 1831 from Davenport under the leadership of Captain Robert Fitzroy. The ship sailed through Praia in the Cape Verde islands, through coasts of South America into the Pacific to the Galapagos Islands.

The 5-year voyage on the Beagle enabled Darwin to observe and think about a relatively wide range of organisms and geological formation. He collected many animals and plants from the Brazilian tropical forests. At Punta Alta, on the coast of Argentina, he unearthed fossil bone of 20ft high giant sloth, *Megatherium*, the hippopotamus-like *Toxodon*, the giant armadillo, *Glyptodon* etc. He gathered evidence showing the distribution of marine shells at various places above sea level. At the Bay of Concepcion at the coast of Chile, he experienced a severe earthquake.

Darwin's visit to Galapagos, the lava-ridden islands of the coast of Equador 500 miles away from the mainland, was the single event that led him to the central conceptions of his evolutionary theory. He collected many animals from here, which he had already noted on the mainland but due to different localities, these were not always occupied by similar species.

In Galapagos island, there insect-eating warbles and woodpeckers were absent but various species of finches, usually seed-eating are found.

He collected nearly 20 varieties of small sized birds, which differ mainly in shape, and size of beak and colour of plumage. These birds are called **Darwin finches**. The general bird fauna of these islands show affinity with American species but Darwin's finches were reported from South America mainland. Therefore, Darwin concluded that American mainland species were the original ones from which different forms migrated to the different islands of Galapagos and adapted to the environmental conditions of these islands. These adapted forms are considered to be the new species (Table 29.1).

**TABLE 29.1**
**Classification of different finches**

**A. Ground Finches:**

1. Large ground finch (*Geospiza magnirostris*)
2. Medium ground finch (*G. fortis*)
3. Small ground finch (*G. fuliginosa*)
4. Sharp- beaked ground finch (*G. difficilis*)
5. Cactus ground finch (*G. scandens*)
6. Large cactus ground finch (*G. conirostris*)

**B. Tree finches :**

7. Vegetarian tree finch (*Camarhynchus crassiortris*)
8. Large insectivorous tree finch (*C. psittacula*)
9. Large insectivorous tree finch on Charles island (*C. pauper*)
10. Small insectivorous tree finch (*C. parvulus*)
11. Wood pecker finch (*C. pallidus*)
12. Mangrove finch (*C. heliobates*)

**C. Warbler like finches:**

13. Warbler finch (*Certhidea olivacea*)
14. Cocos finch (*Pinaroloxias inornata*)

At present 14 species of finches specialized to feed on cacti, seeds and insects. Some insectivorous finches have evolved behavioural features common to woodpeckers, like long pointed beak and clinging feet. None of them resemble to the parental seed-eating finches of South American mainland.

Most probably, a few seed-eating finches or perhaps a single previously mated female had reached Galapagos islands from mainland in distant past. In the absence of competition the population of finches diversified and become adapted to different habitats or ecological niches and evolved into new species. Thus geographical isolation has led to the development of reproductive isolation and thereby to the origin of new species. This type of speciation is called **allopatric speciation** (Fig. 29.1 & 29.2).

On 2nd October 1836, Beagle reached the shore of England. Darwin completed his first writing "The Voyage of Beagle" in 1837. He took more 20 years to reach his revolutionary conclusion. By June of 1858 he completed the draft of his book on species, which was greatly encouraged by his botanist friend Sir Joseph Dalton Hooker and geologist Charles Lyell.

## 29.4. DARWINISM

In 1st July 1858, two Englishmen published jointly, in the "Proceedings of the Linnean Society", papers on a new concept, of evolution. This concept, the theory of the natural selection was destined to influence greatly the thinking of modern man in many different fields and to become the basis of most modern biological concept of evolution. These two naturalists were Charles Robert Darwin (1802-82) and Alfred Russel Wallace (1823-1913).

Darwin-Wallace explanation of the way in which evolution occurs may be generalized as follows :

*"The change in species by the survival of an organismal type exhibiting a natural variation that gives it an adaptive advantage in an environment,*

TREE FINCHES
Large Insectivorous finch
C. psitacula
Wood-peaker Finch
C. pallidus
Mangrove finch
C. heliobetes
Small Insectivorous finch
C. parvulus
Veg tree finch
C. crassirostris
Medium Insectivorous finch
C. pauper
CACTUS-EATING FINCHES
Large cactus-eating ground finch
G. conirostris
Small cactus-eating ground finch
G. scandens
WRABLER FINCHES
Gray Wrabler finch
C. fusca
Green Wrabler finch
C. olivacea
Small-sized ground finch
G. fuliginosa
Sharp-beaked ground finch
G. difficilis
Medium-sized ground finch
G. fortis
Large-sized ground finch
G. magnirostris

**Fig.29.1 :** *Species of finches observed by Darwin in the Galapagos Island.*

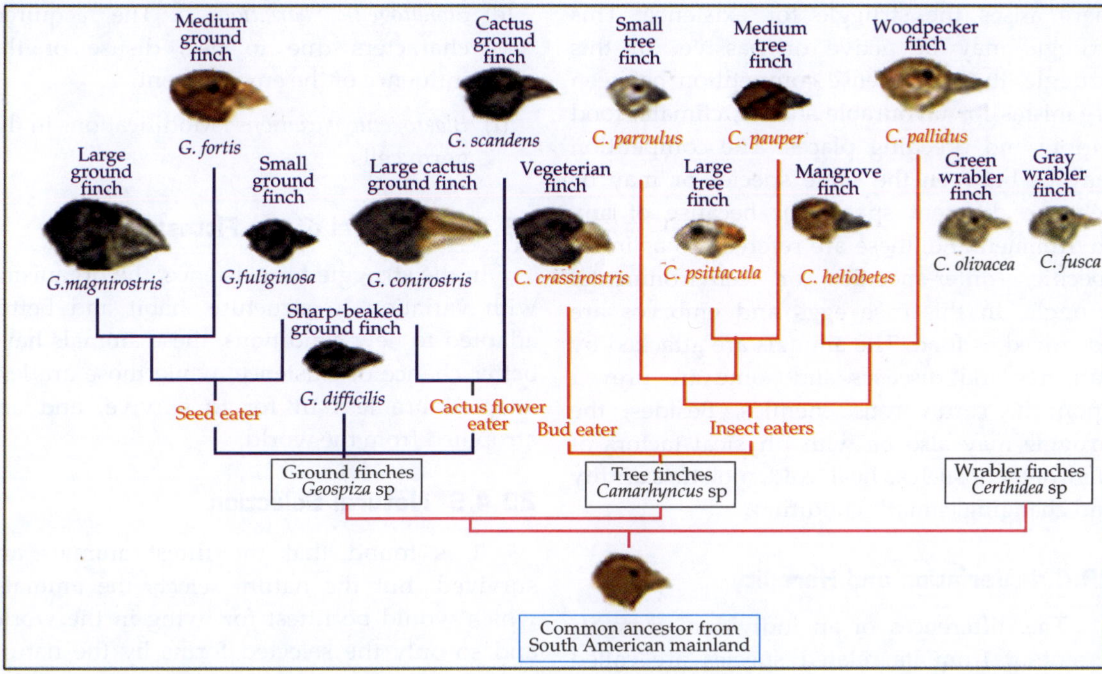


**Fig.29.2 :** *Evolution tree of Darwin's finches showing beak adaptations of the individuals species.*

*thus leading to a new environmental equilibrium in evolution by natural selection."*

Thus natural selection is a continuous process of trial and errors on the gigantic scale, for all living matter is involved. The theory is based on six fundamental principles around a concept of natural selection, which has summarized by Wallace.

### 29.4.1 Prodigality in Production

Reproduction is the basic characteristics of the living organism. If organisms are very fertile they have capacity for rapid increase in number due to enormous reproduction rate. If reproduction is remained unchecked the world could not hold all the animals. Even a slow breeder elephant produces 6 youngs once between the age of 30 and 90 years. If this continues for 500 years then a single pair of these would be 15 million of descendents provided they lived for 90 years. But after a time organism reaches a condition of reproductive equilibrium in which the numbers are maintained at a relatively constant level, as long as the environment remained unchanged. The great fertility of animals is accomplished by great destruction because there are checks upon increase, so that the total number of animals remains almost stationary.

### 29.4.2 Constancy of Food and Space

The food and space on the earth are usually remained constant and the extraordinary power of fertility, the huge number of animals result crowdness and this condition results in the competition of life for shelter and food.

### 29.4.3 Struggle for Existence

As a result of prodigal rate of reproduction, Darwin reasoned that there must be a competition among individuals of both the same and different species for food and space. So, there arises the struggle for existence. This struggle may be active or passive. In this struggle, there is intense competition between organisms for favourable shelter, climate, food supply and breeding places. The competition may be between the same species or may be between different species or because of any environment. So, these are refereed to as intra-specific, inter-specific or environmental struggle. In this case eggs and embryos are destroyed as food. The animals are attacked by parasites and diseases and some are preyed upon the carnivorous enemies. Besides, the struggle may also be with physical factors of environment such as heat, cold, moisture aridity and changing climatic condition.

### 29.4.4 Variation and Heredity

The differences of an individual from its parent or from its related species are called variations, without which evolution is not possible.

The resemblance of an individual to its relatives and parents is called heredity. The variation and heredity is intimately correlated. Variation helps to fit an animal into its environment and their offspring are likely to inherit the favourable variations because of heredity. Variations give rise to new characters and heredity passes them into new generations. Any variations of an individual are useless for evolution unless they are inheritable. Variations are of different kinds:

(a) *Meristic Variation* : Changes in the number of repeated parts of an animal.

(b) *Substantive variation* : Changes in the size shape, colour, structure of an animal or in its parts.

(c) *Continuous variation* : Changes are with small gradations, which fluctuate on either sides of an average condition.

(d) *Discontinuous variation* : New or more or less conspicuous characters, which appear suddenly and spontaneously.

(e) *Somatogenic variations* : The acquired characters due to use, disuse or the influence of the environment.

(f) *Blastogenic variations* : Modifications in the germ cells.

### 29.4.5 Survival of the Fittest

In the struggle for existence, the organisms with variation in structure, habit and better adapted to new conditions, these animals have better chance of existence, while those are less adapted are less fit for to survive, and are atrophied from the world.

### 29.4.6 Natural Selection

It is found that the fittest animals are survived. But the nature selects the animals, which would be fittest for living in the world and so only the selected forms by the nature would survive in the world while other will degenerate and ultimately perish.

In animals there is a struggle for mating. Males often have to fight for females with their horns, canine teeth, body size and strength. Thus there is sexual selection in the nature. Certain characters such as plumage of male birds, wooing dance, pleasant scents in butterfly and lovely songs of birds have usually developed by males.

Some of the characters are introduced by man during domestication. These changes would involve by hybridization. These are *artificial selection.*

Darwin said that the artificial selection, which is brought about by man could produce such a result in a short period than natural selection whereas natural selection would be more effective over the long period of geological time.

### 29.4.7 Inductions & Deduction of Darwinism

| Inductions | Deduction |
|---|---|
| Prodigality of Reproduction<br>Constancy of food & Space | Struggle for existence |
| Struggle for existence<br>Omnipotence of variation amongst the individuals | Survival of the fittest |
| Survival of the fittest<br>Operation of Natural Selection amongst the survivors | Speciation |

The concept of Darwin i.e., the Natural selection was supported much by Weismann and regarded the Darwinism as the principal cause of evolution.

### 29.4.8 Critical analysis of Darwinism

In the 19$^{th}$ century, gradually the people began to loose confidence on Darwinism and evolutionary studies become more and wide-spread. Bateson, first opposed the Darwinism concept of continuous variation of Nature, Many other workers convinced that Natural selection was unable to accept evolution as the slow and continuous accumulation of minute advantageous mutations.

1. de Vries, discovery on *Oenothera*, believed that the origin of hereditary variations is through mutation and disproved the role of Natural Selection.
2. The rediscovery of Mendelism by Correns, de Vries and Tschermark (1900) wanted to put forward the mutation is sharp and discontinuous while the continuous variations are widespread in nature are not inheritable.
3. Genetists (Goldschmidt, Muller, Morgan and Fisher) did not believe Natural selection.
4. Biometry did not recognize the idea of Natural Selection (Person, Weldon).
5. Experimental embryologists under the leadership of Roux and Spemann contradicted the classical concept of recapitulation.

**Criticism of Darwinism :**

1. Darwin accepted the occurrence of variations, but did not explain the actual mechanism of variation.
2. Natural Selection cannot account for the beginning of organs.
3. Natural Selection does not explain degeneration of organs.
4. Natural Selection may select favourable individuals but does not explain the origin of species.
5. Darwin believed in blending inheritance but modern genetics has proved beyond doubt that blended inheritance does not occur. Modern genetics establishes that the inheritance is particulate and the particles are borne on the chromosomes.
6. Darwin indirectly accepted the Lamarckian idea of Inheritance of acquired characters in the form of Pangenesis hypothesis, which cannot be acceptable in the light of knowledge of modern genetics.
7. Lastly, some persons have objected Natural Selection because it is essentially a materialistic doctrine, depending as it does purely of the law of character.

**Conclusion :**

T. H. Morgan was the great critic of Darwinism but later on with his genetical researches became an upholder of Darwinism and a new compromise school was sprang up and Darwinism took a rebirth.

## 29.5. NEO-DARWINISM

A new compromise school sprang up to be called the neo-Darwinism. The school placed the theory of Natural Selection on a solid basis and

Darwinism took a rebirth. T. H. Morgan was the great critic but later on with his genetical researches became an upholder of Darwinism.

**Efficacy of neo-Darwinism**

Neo-Darwinism has enabled us to analyze how the Natural Selection is working in the environment and given an idea of the *status quo* of the species. The Natural Selection has two aspects-

1. *The stabilizing aspects* by which the Natural Selection keeps down the deleterious mutant genes and thus it protects and stabilizes the developmental pattern of the species.
2. *Dynamic aspects* of the Natural Selection allow the species to maintain its hold on the changing environmental condition and thus it establishes new genotypes that are suited to the new condition.

The concept of selection gets greatest support from Mendelian laws of heredity. The genes of the organism, which is called the **corporate genotype**. It determinates the cause of development in the environment. The efficacy of neo Darwinism is represented here.

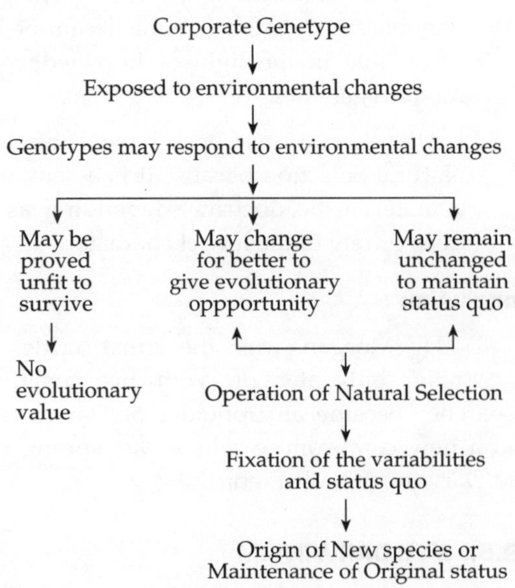


**Multiple forces of neoDarwinism**

1. **Role of environment** : which is a directive force in evolution and the source of genetic variabilities.
2. **Role of reproduction :** for the production of endless variety of the genotype. The relationship between reproduction, mutation and Natural Selection is represented here :

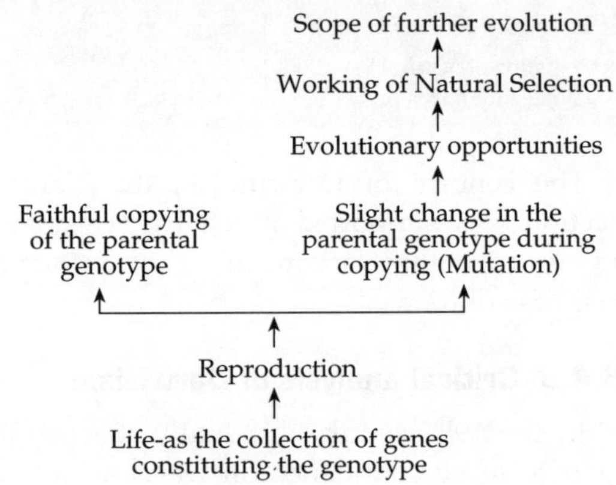


3. **Role of mutation :** For the introduction of new genes into the genotype in an organized pattern. These novel genes are produced by the process of mutation and provide new material for Natural Selection.
4. **Stabilizing the species by Natural Selection :** Mutations provided new evolutionary opportunities and selection mechanism. The mutations are stabilized continuously to produce new species.

For example, a moth, *Biston* sp. found in Manchester, has two species, *B. butalaria,* a lighter variety and *B. carbonaria,* a darker variety. In 1848 before industrialization, *B. butalaria* was prevalent. But with the advent of industrialization the light variety is being vanished while the dark variety becomes dominant. The darken form is the mutant form. Full industrialization makes the surroundings darker and the darker varieties are stabilized by the Natural selection because of their greater survival value.

5. **Adaptation is the outcome of Selection :** The adaptive value of the species is improved by mutation. Thus the interaction between the genetic variabilities and Natural Selection produces greater adaptive plasticity. The dynamic aspect of Natural Selection establishes new genotypes adapted to new conditions.

**Comments :** According to neo-Darwinism, the adaptations result from multiple force and Natural Selection is only one of these multiple forces.

Neo-Darwinism also believed that characters are not inherited as such. But there are character determiners, which control only the development.

The ultimate characters would be resulted out due to the interaction of determiners, activity of the organisms and the environment during development.

Due to lack of present understanding of genetics neo-Darwinism seems to be incomplete and partly wrong.

## 29.6. SYNTHETIC THEORY OF EVOLUTION

During later half of the 19th century and at the beginning of 20th century, many ideas had been put forward for explaining the inheritance of variations from one generation to successive generations and also for explaining the evolution.

Rediscovery of Mendel's laws of Heredity by Correns, de Vries and Tschermak (1900) made it clear that the characters are not mixed in the offspring and more than one pair of contrasting characters are inherited independently.

Discovery of **mutation theory** by Hugo de Vries (1886, 87) stated the sudden changes in the characters *i.e.*, mutation is the cause of origin of new species.

Wagner (1868) suggested the role of geographic isolation in the role of speciation.

All the modern concepts in cytology, genetics, cytogenetics, population genetics and evolution gave a way for the formulation of a theory, which is called **modern synthesis** around 1930's by S. Wright, H. J. Muller, Th. Dobzansky, R. B. Goldschmidt, J. S. Huxley, R. A. Fisher, J. B. S. Haldane, Earnest Mayr and G.L. Stebbins.

According to G.L. Stebbins 1971, the modern synthetic theory of evolution recognizes 5 basic types of processes.

1. Gene mutation
2. Changes in chromosome number and structure.
3. Genetic recombination.
4. Natural Selection
5. Reproductive isolation.

The first three processes are called the genetic variability. Genetic variability in populations and natural selection are two main elemental forces of evolution. Adaptations are the outcome of interaction of these forces along with isolation (the physical force), which assists in the accumulation of variations in a group of individuals of a population and in the populations of a species.

### Genetic variability in the population:

Group of individuals of a species living in the given geographical area and freely interbreeding in nature is called **population**.

The total gene content of all organisms of a population is called **gene pool**. These organisms share a part of the same gene pool and thus have a free gene flow.

Change in the gene pool of a population may bring about genetic variability.

Gene mutation's and genetic recombination's are the causes of genetic variation at individual level whereas chromosome aberrations and hybridization are the causes of genetic variations at population level.

1. **Gene mutations :** Gene mutations are sudden changes in the number or sequence of nucleotides or nitrogenous bases in DNA molecule. These are
   (i) Frame shift mutations: which are caused by one or more nucleotides added or deleted from the DNA?
   (ii) Substitution mutations : which are caused by the substitution of one or more nitrogenous bases by other ones. It may be a transition or transversion.

   Mutations help the animal to survive in the changing environment and take an important role in evolution.

2. **Genetic Recombinations :** At the time of gamete formation (during meiosis), crossing over (i.e., exchange of chromosome segments) resulted in a new combination of dominant and recessive genes. This genetic recombination enables the accumulation of advantageous characters in their gene pool and thus accelerates evolution process.

3. **Chromosomal changes :** At population level, genetic variations are introduced by
   (a) Chromosomal aberrations :
      (i) Changes in number of genes:

      Deletion or deficiency - loss of one or more genes.

      Duplication – addition of one or more genes.

      (ii) Changes in arrangement of genes

      Inversion – rotation of a block of genes in a chromosome at 180°

      Translocation – exchange of parts between nonhomologous chromosomes.

   (b) Changes in number of chromosomes :
      (i) Changes involving entire sets:

      Haploidy- having only one set of chromosomes (n).

      Polypliody – having more than two sets of chromosomes.

      (ii) Changes in individual chromosomes from a set.

      Monosomic – loss of one chromosome from one set (2n-1)

      Polysomic–addition of one or more chromosomes to one set (2n +1) or (2n + 2).

      Nullisomic – loss of both chromosomes of a pair (2n –2).

   (c) Hybridization : Hybridization is the intermingling of genes of two populations of a species which are otherwise separated. This can occur either by migration or artificial crossbreeding by man.

   In struggle for existence, only those organisms manage to survive that are well adapted to the environment. The natural selection selects and favours the multiplication of those genetic variations, which are of adaptive value to the organism or to the population.

4. **Natural Selection :** By the interaction of organism and environment, the appropriate genotype should be inherited. But there is no role of determinants in Natural Selection. Different types of selections are observed.
   (a) *Directed selections* : Sometimes, Natural Selection directs a new phenotype gradually in a new changing environment. E.g., *Biston* sp. A moth has two species. *B. butalaria* (light variety) and *B. carbonaria* (darker variety). Before industrialization in 1848, *B. butalaria* was dominant; gradually the dark variety takes it's position due to dark environment. Today, *B. butalaria* is fully vanished and darker variety becomes dominant.

(b) *Stabilizing Selection* : Sometimes Natural Selection stabilizes the characters of a population. E.g., in Africa, the human population has sickle cell anaemia gene (*s*) as a recessive character. When it is homozygous (*ss*), the person will die before becoming adolescence. Only *Ss* hybrid or *SS* normal person will survive. But it is fact that *Ss* hybrid is more resistant than *SS* to falciperum malaria. This shows that Natural Selection favoured the sickle celled character because it has survival value in malaria-infected regions.

(c) *Disruptive selection* : In a homogenous population, more than one phenotypes are observed. E.g., In Africa, the male butterfly (*Papilio dardanus*) does not show mimicry. But the female butterfly mimics with distasteful Donaid butterfly. Thus they save themselves from their enemies.

5. **Reproductive isolation :** Mechanisms that prevent successful reproduction between members of two or more populations (viz. closely related species) have descended from the same original population are called reproductive isolation. E.g., Seal (*Mirounga leonina*) in North pole is segregated by a vast land of 3000 miles from South polar seal (*M. angustirostris*) and isolated reproductively.

### Conclusion :

It has already been mentioned that, the first three types of processes provide the genetic variability, without which, change cannot be taken place. The natural selection and reproductive isolation guide populations or organisms into adaptive channels.

In his book, Stebbins gave analogy and compared the motor car with the evolution;

1. Mutation - with the fuel (petrol) of the motor car.
2. Genetic recombination– with the engine of the car
3. Natural Selection – with the driver of the car.
4. Changes in the number and structure of the chromosomes with the axillator.
5. Reproductive isolation – with the road traffic signal.

In addition to these, three accessory processes may affect the working of these five basic points.

1. Migration of individuals from population to another.
2. Hybridization between races or closely related species both increase the amount of genetic variability available to a population.
3. The effects of chance acting on small populations may alter the way in which Natural Selection guides the cause of evolution.

However, according to Ernst Mayer (1970), recent synthesis theory includes adaptive response, mutational limitations, epigenetic limitations, mutation, recombination and Natural Selection.

## 29.7. MUTATION THEORY

Hugo de Vries (1848- 1935) a Dutch Botanist published the mutation theory in 1901 to explain the process of mutation.

Before him, in 1869 Waggen designated mutation as a smallest perceptible in the temporal series of forms in a species *Ammonites*. These changes have a definite direction and their gradual accumulation with the passage of time leads to appearance of types progressively in more distinct form from the ancestors.

de Vries (1901) defines mutation as the form of "the mutation theory".

*"I designate the statement that the properties of organisms are built from certain distinct units or intergrades which are so numerous between the*

*external forms of plants and animals exist; these units are not more than the molecules of chemistry".*

Mutation is then, a drastic change in one of the unit which present in the genes. de Vries proceeds to define the disconnections between his theory and Darwin's theory of Natural Selection, the later assumes that usual or the so called individual variability in the starting point of the origin of new species.

But according to mutation theory "the two types of this variability are completely independent. I hope to show that the usual variability, *i.e.* the independent variability cannot lead to the real over-stepping of the species units even in the most instance stepping selection".

On the other hand, "each mutation sharply completely separates the new forms and an independent species from which it arose".

de Vries studied on the variations of plants in his garden and revealed two important facts:

1. **The occurrence of elementary species** : Among many wild and domesticated species there are varieties with small differences, which breed upon themselves.
2. **The mutations in *Oenothera lamarckiana*** (Evening primrose, a garden plant with yellow flower, which opens at evening) :

   In Holland this plant often grows in wild condition in an abundant potato field. de Vries found certain varieties of this plant which looked very different from the normal. He brought this and cultivated in the garden, found 7 types, which breed and these varieties are the mutants.

After breeding of 8th generations de Vries classified these mutants as follows;

(a) *Progressive species* : Due to the addition of certain characters.

(i) *Oenothera gigas* – A stouter with large leaves and flowers.

(ii) *O. rubrinervis* – Red veined leaves and stems.

(b) *Retrogressive species* : Due to loss of some normal characters.

(iii) *O. nariella* – the dwarf form

(iv) *O. laevifolia* – smooth narrow leaves.

(v) *O. brevistylis* – shorter style.

(c) *Degressive species* : Very weak form not likes to survive in nature.

(vi) *O. albida* – Pale whitish plant.

(vii) *O. oblongo*- With oblong leaves on weak dwarf plant.

Besides these 7 mutants, he also obtained two other types, which did not breed true but was given rise to mutants like the parent *O. lamarckiana*. These two are grouped together.

(d) Inconstant species :

(viii) *O. lata* – board leaves.

(ix) *O. scintellans* – No broad leaves.

Starting these 9 types of plants from the field, breeding for 8 years found that 7 same mutants arrived from stock parental forms year after year. So, he concluded as follows:

1. New elementary species appears certainly and attains a full constancy at one.
2. The same new species are produced in large numbers of individuals. The same mutants obtained again and again, so there is a greater chance of selection by nature.
3. The mutability is something fundamentally different from fluctuating variability.
4. Mutation takes place in random and in all directions.

This is because the mutation may mean either gain or loss or may involve any types of characters.

From all these, de Vries formulated extremely important theory, which stands co-establishment of the material on which the theory is based, was found later. Even de Vries noticed that *O. lamarckiana* is inconstant species unlike the more usual true breeding species. The reason of this inconstancy has now being found cytologically.

The chromosome number of *O. lamarckiana* is 2n = 14, but it not has been derived from the same kind of parent. From two sets of chromosomes "GAUDENS COMPLEX and VELANS COMPLEX".

Among the zygotes, formed from Gaudens complex X Gaudens complex or Velans complex X Velans complex, are homozygous true breeding forms, fail to survive. When the cross is Gaudens complex X Velans complex i.e., heterozygous, only survive to form the common *O. lamarckiana*.

The *O. lamarckiana* is a hybrid known as complex heterozygote, which is stable and powerful and likely to chromosomal mutations. Many of the mutants obtained by de Vries were not actually mutants.

On de Vries sense, chromosomal mutations are more unstable. Of these, mutations obtained by this the first one are known as tetraploid (*O. gigas*). *O. rubrinervis* and *O. narella* are due to recombination of chromosomes. *O. laevifolia* is a true gene mutant.

So, de Vries put mutation theory with a very abnormal species. Now by the modern genetists and molecular biologists agreed with this theory that mutation is one of the main cause of evolution.

## 29.8. ISOLATING MECHANISM AND IT'S ROLE IN EVOLUTION

The pre-requisite for speciation is reproductive isolation.

Mechanisms that prevent successful reproduction between members of two or more populations (viz. closely related species) that have descended from the same original population, are called **isolating mechanisms**.

The significance of isolating mechanisms in speciation first of all recognized by the post Darwinian evolutionist, Dobzansky (1937).

### 29.8.1 Types of Isolating Mechanism

Most modern evolutionist such as Mecham (1961), Myar (1948, 1970), Stebbins (1966, 1971) etc. have classified the reproductive isolating mechanisms into two classes, again these are divided into sub types :

**A. Pre-mating or Pre-zygotic isolating mechanisms :**

(i) Habitat isolation

(ii) Seasonal or temporal isolation

(iii) Ethological isolation.

(iv) Mechanical isolation.

(v) Gametic isolation.

**B. Post-mating or Post-zygotic isolating mechanisms :**

(i) Gametic mortality.

(ii) Zygotic mortality.

(iii) Developmental hybrid sterility.

(iv) Segregational hybrid sterility.

(v) Hybrid inviability or weakness.

(vi) $F_2$ breakdown.

It is further recognized that, for these, reproductive isolation to evolve, the separated populations of an original single group must be separated spatially or geographically or by time. So, a discussion of these three types of isolations should be made.

1. **Isolation by time :** During the course of evolution, some species simply transformed into a new species through accumulating genetic differences. With the study of sequential fossil records, G.C. Simpson told that horse evolved some 16 million years ago in Eocene by successive changes produced by thousands of favourable mutations of many genes in course of evolution.

2. **Isolation by distance or spatial isolation :** A large distance apart from its native

place may act as an isolating factor for a species. For example, Wrens (bird) of South America are found all over the continent but the wrens of one region differ from those of the other in colour pattern, size and habitat and tend to produce subspecies.

3. **Geographical isolations :** Geographical barriers are river, desert, glacier, mountain or ocean; all of which prevent interbreeding between the separated populations and in course of time different mutations are incorporated in their gene pool and ultimately speciation occurs. Again when these two groups come in contact do not interbreed.

The classic example is illustrated by Darwin for finches. He found there 26 groups of finches in the Galapagos island. Only 5 of these groups were same as the finches of mainland. The other 21 types were peculiar to the groups of islands forming species and subspecies.

Another example is the elephant seal, *Mirounga leonina* occurs in cool water of Southern Australia, New Zealand. A close relative Northern elephant seal *M. angustirostris* is found in the western coast of North America. These two forms are very similar but due to separation of 3000 miles apart they become another species (allopatric species).

**A. Pre-zygotic isolating mechanism :** This mechanism prevents contact between the species when they are reproductively active. It may be caused by following reasons:

(i) *Habitual isolation* : When two closely related species will thrive in different ecological conditions within the same territory, no hybrid between them will occur. But when these are taken to the laboratory, hybrids between them can be made. Thus their respective gene pools are isolated physically but not physiologically.

Such type of isolation is mostly observed in plants, because of their sedentary habit, but it is not very effective isolating mechanism in the mobile animals.

Two subspecies of the American mouse *Peromyscus maniculatis* inhabit regions that share a common boundary. But the hybrids between them in the laboratory have not been found in the nature. The explanation of such isolation is that one subspecies lives in the forest and other on sandy beaches.

(ii) *Seasonal isolation* : Two groups of organisms exist in exactly the same ecological area but do not interbreed because they become sexually mature at different times of the year. For example, in the North-Eastern United States, three species of frog, *Rana pipens, Rana sylvatica, Rana clamitans,* all mate in the same ponds at different times, which is effective barrier for gene exchange.

(iii) *Ethological or Behavioural isolation* : Behavioural isolation mechanisms are barriers for mating due to incompatibilities in behaviour. It is based on the production and reception of stimuli by the sex partners. The specific stimuli (visual, auditory, tactile, olfactory or chemical) help two sexes for the stimulation and recognition of each other during courtship.

E.g., Females are attracted by the calls of conspecific males in frogs and toads; melodious songs of male insects and birds; light signals by male fire flies, pheromones in moths, butterflies and some mammals etc. have a significant role in ethological isolation.

(iv) *Mechanical isolation* : Mechanical isolation is provided due to differences in the structure of the genital organs of different species. (Lock and Key theory of Dufour 1844) and therefore, cross pollination (in plants) and copulation (in animals) may not be easily brought about).

According to Mayr (1970) the genitalic apparatus in animals are complicated structures due to pleotropic by-product of many genes of the species. Any change in genetic constitution may result in a change in the structure of genitalia.

(v) *Gametic isolation* : It has been postulated that sperm can tolerate only narrow range of physiological conditions such as pH, temperature. Besides, the sperm may encounter an antigenic reaction in the genital tract of the female. Sperm may die if the environment in the genital duct of female is not suitable. This is gametic isolation.

B. **Post Zygotic Isolating Mechanism :** This is the mechanism by which the growth of the zygotes and the individuals is prevented after fertilization.

(i) *Zygotic mortality* : Zygote may die due to several cytological, genetical, embryological, molecular biological, biochemical and physiological reasons. It may also be regarded as **physiological isolation**.

(ii) *Hybrid inviability* : If the fertilization takes place among the different species, hybrid inviability occurs. According to Haldane's rule, interspecific crosses result in progeny that are all of same sex.

(iii) *Development of Hybrid sterility* : Sometimes, intraspecific crosses may result in the abnormal development of gonads and abnormality in the gamete formation, thus the hybrid becomes sterile e.g., Horse X Zebra, Cattle X Buffalo. This is termed as **haplontic sterility** when the sterility is set in haploid and **dioplontic sterility** where the sterility is brought about before meiosis in diploid tissues (Muntzing, 1930).

(iv) *Segregational Hybrid sterility* : This may result from the abnormality in segregation at meiosis. This is caused by spindle abnormality asynapsis, desynapsis etc. Therefore, this is also known as **genetic** or **cytogenetic isolation** e.g., **Raphanobrassica** (Radish X Cabbage) got 9 chromosomes from Radish and 9 from cabbage and thus unable to take up equatorial position at metaphase. Mule is also sterile due to same causes.

(v) *$F_2$ breakdown* : It is found that, in both plants and animals, hybrids may be fertile, but their progenies are sterile. Thus their second generation ($F_2$) is failed to reproduce. This is called $F_2$- breakdown e.g., $F_2$- hybrids of *Gossypium arboreum* × *G. herbaceum* and *G. barbadense* × G. hirsutum are either missing or very weak.

### 29.8.2 Genetics of Isolating Systems

Detailed analysis of the genetics of isolating mechanisms in *Drosophila* has revealed that many of their mutations, such as yellow, white, bar eye etc. influence the mating success of the mutant individuals. Further studies have established that the behavioural and mechanical isolations have a highly complex genetic basis. Thus it can be concluded that the isolating mechanisms that protect every species might have a considerable number of genes that are involved.

### 29.8.3 Role of Isolating Mechanisms

1. It increases the efficiency of mating.
2. In allopatric population, selection pressure, random mutation and genetic drift bring about the genetic divergence and heritability, which enables the different populations in subspeciation.
3. Subspeciation is the first step of speciation. If the genetic divergence is more, then the speciation occurs.
4. When isolation breaks down, again inbreeding may occur. If the isolation brings about speciation, hybrids become sterile, weak and inviable. Sometimes mostly in plants, such inbreeding may result in speciation by polyploidy in the nature.

Therefore, isolating mechanism is very important in the origin and evolution of the species.

## 29.9. ORIGIN OF SPECIES

According to Mayr, "species are groups of potentially interbreeding natural populations that are reproductively isolated from other groups".

Dobzansky said" species are formed at once when actually or potentially inbreeding arrays of Mendelian population become segregated into two or more reproductively isolated arrays", *i.e.*, a species is the most inclusive Mendelian population. Therefore they cannot interbreed or can produce viable fertile offspring and little or no gene flow occurs between them. Their evolutionary path remains separate and distinct. Such biological definition is in fact not applicable to non-living records or fossils. So, palaeontologists take the morphological basis of species definitions. Though there are some organisms which are morphologically alike are isolated reproductively into separate species *e.g., Drosophila pseudoobscura and D. persimilis.*

Pre-Darwinian scientists including Darwin himself considered "Origin of species" as evolution. It can be considered into two broad headings: (A) Transformation of species in time and (B) Multiplication of species in space.

### 29.9.1 Transformation of species in time

A species has originated from a previous one without multiplication of the parental one.

Simpson recognizes two ways of such transformation :

(a) **Phyletic evolution :** A species transforms into new species rather than an increase in the total number of existing species in course of time. That is, from species "a" through "b" and "c" into species "d" without splitting.

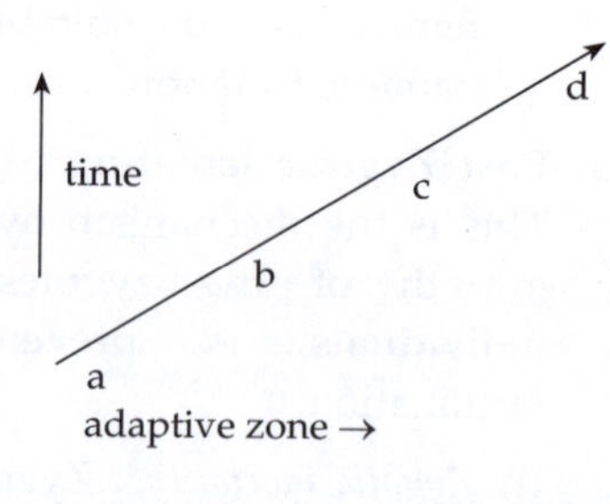


Geologists prefer the term **anagenesis** for phyletic evolution when one species becomes extinct by gradually evolving into another.

The genetic change that leads to phyletic origin can be distinguished into two types.

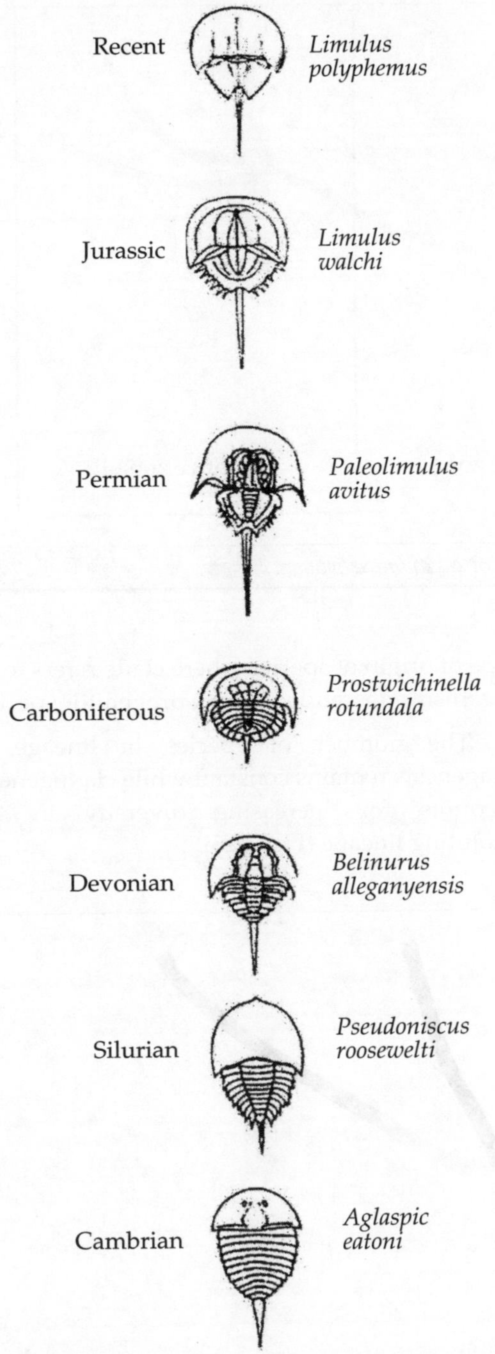


**Fig.29.3 :** *Phyletic origin of horse-shoe crab.*

(i) **Autogenous transformations :** The change may be produced by mutation, recombination and selection but not by the incorporation of genes from different species.

(ii) **Allogenous transformation :** The change is produced by the incorporation of genes from different species.

The phenotypic changes were relatively small over long period of time, which can be seen in the phyletic evolution in horseshoe crabs (Fig. 29.3).

(b) **Quantum evolution :** The rapid shift of a population to a new equilibrium distinctly unlike the ancestral condition, thus leading to originate higher taxonomic categories such as new orders, classes etc. This is rare. E.g., two-winged insects derived from the four – winged insects.

It is extremely unlikely that a single change mutation would cause all of the many changes in the physiology and morphology of the organism that would be necessary to produce a type sufficiently well adapted to a new mode of existence to be considered a new order.

Origin of higher taxonomic groups occurs in a single rather small pre-adapted populations of a species to which a new ecological niche becomes available and during this short transitional period some transitional forms are also being existed.

The fossil record of horse (Equuidae) showed that they have evolved and diversified within the browsing adaptive zone. The pre-adaptive change appears to the development of larger and higher crowned teeth required to grind up the vegetation. These teeth were preadaptive for grazing. The transitional forms of the browsing and grazing animals strongly support in favour of this (Fig. 29.4).

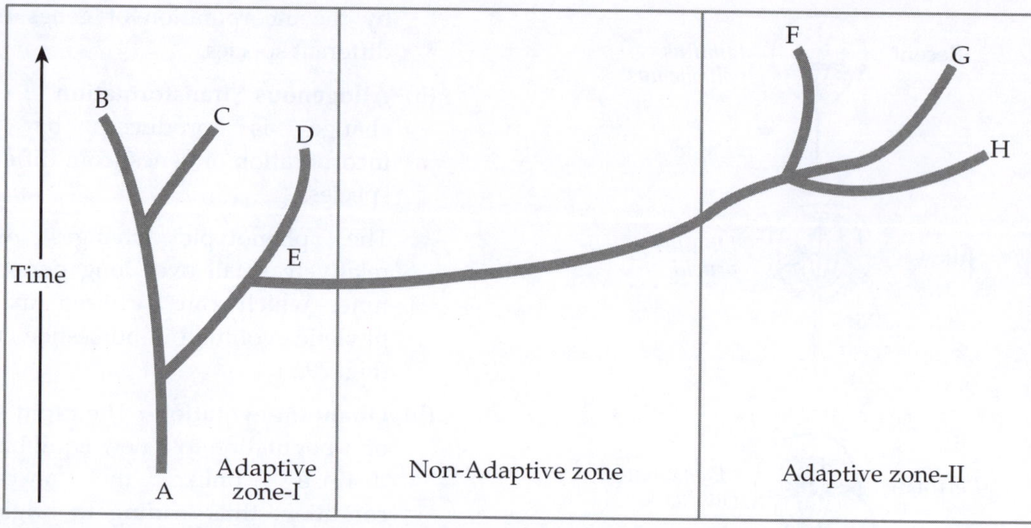


**Fig.29.4 :** *Hypothetical views of quantum evolution.*

### 29.9.2 Multiplication of species in space or Speciation

Speciation means formation of species, in this process one species divides into two or more reproductively isolated lineages. Geologists prefer the term **cladogenesis** for this type of origin of species where **clade** refers to all organisms descended from a progenitor species.

The number of species in lineage of anagenesis remains constant while cladogenesis accounts for increasing diversity in the evoluting lineage (Fig. 29.5).

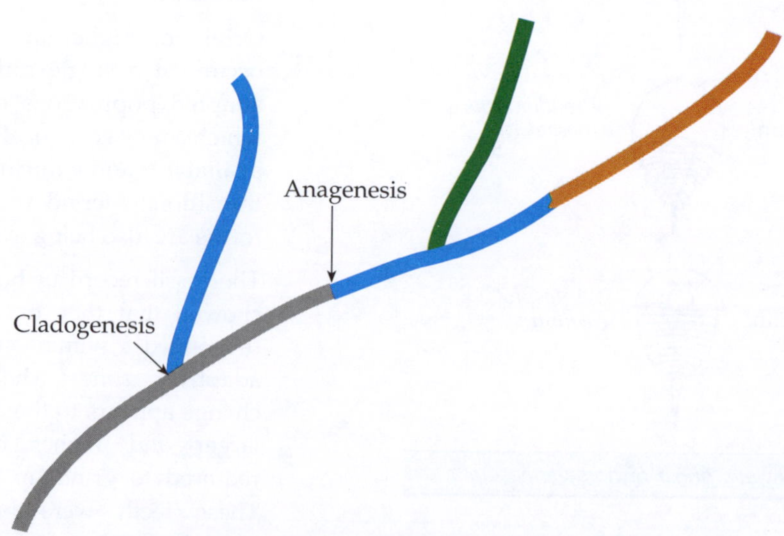


**Fig.29.5 :** *Diagramatic representation of origin of species by phyletic evolution (anagenesis) and speciation (cladogenesis)*

Mayr (1973) grouped them into two broad classes :

(a) Instantaneous speciation

(b) Gradual speciation.

(a) **Instantaneous speciation through individuals :** The sudden origin of new species, new higher taxa or quite generally of new-types by some sort of SALTATION *i.e.,* a change by leap across a discontinuity (by de Vries) also called **macrogenesis**. (or by complete genetic reconstruction). Such an event will produce a "**hopeful monster**" as Goldschmidt (1940) called it, which will become the ancestor of evolutionary linkage.

Modern genetic studies have shown that the mutation is not enough to establish a "hopeful-monster". There are many causes that are essential.

(i) *Speciation through chromosomal aberrations* : Cytological studies have revealed that the closely related species often differ more conspicuously in their karyotype than in their morphology. These include differ in chromosome number, number of metacentric and acentric chromosomes, presence of para-centric and pericentric inversions or of supernumerary chromosomes.

Chromosomal polymorphism is well known in *Drosophila* in its different species.

Chromosomal mutations would lead to evolutionary advantage, which includes inversions, translocations and duplications.

Most structural rearrangement of chromosomes inhibits or prevents crossing over in heterozygotes. A new gene-arrangement may "lock up" a coadapted gene sequence and by protecting it from crossing over creates a new gene called "super gene" that leads to increase in genic heterozygous inferiority and strengthen cyto-mechanic isolating mechanisms.

(ii) *Speciation through polyploidy* : Though polyploidy is rarer but about one third of all species of plants (except conifers) have arisen by polyploidy. In animals only parthenogenetically reproducible groups do the same. Lumbricoid earthworms, turbellarians and certain weevils have shown that polyploidy is the principal method of their speciation.

(b) **Gradual Speciation through population :** Gradual divergence of populations until they have reached the level of species distinctness is called gradual speciation. Two modes of gradual speciation have been postulated.

1. ***Geographical or Allopatric speciation*** : A new species develops from a population that is geographically isolated from its parental species and during this period they promote or ensure reproductive isolation with its parent species. This is **allopatric speciation**.

Allopatric speciation requires

(i) Spatial isolation of sub-population from the remainder ancestral species.

(ii) Divergent selection pressure that established new barriers of reproductive isolation based upon a large genetic difference (Fig. 29.6).

The intermediate stages in this process of speciation are called **incipient species** or **geographical isolates**. E.g., in genus *Drosophila,* different degree of divergence is demonstrated by Patterson and Stone (1952), which ranges from partial

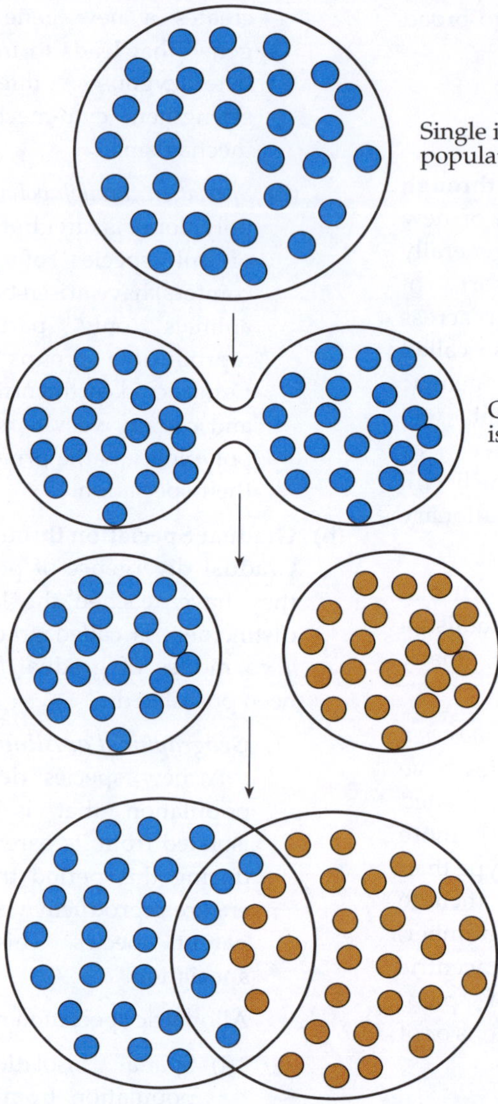


**Fig.29.6a :** *Simplified diagram of allopatric speciation.*

strain isolation to subspecies divergence, to closely related species to distantly related species.

Spatially segregated populations of a species differ in morphology, anatomy, cytology, physiology etc. Occurrence of such variation is called **geographic variation**. This is mostly found in birds and mammals and insects and are differing from each other to some extent in their ecology. Therefore, ecological isolation may become well established between geographic isolates as a step to speciation. In genus *Drosophila*, sterility barrier is found to have geographic variation, such as *D. virilis*, *D penissularis* etc.

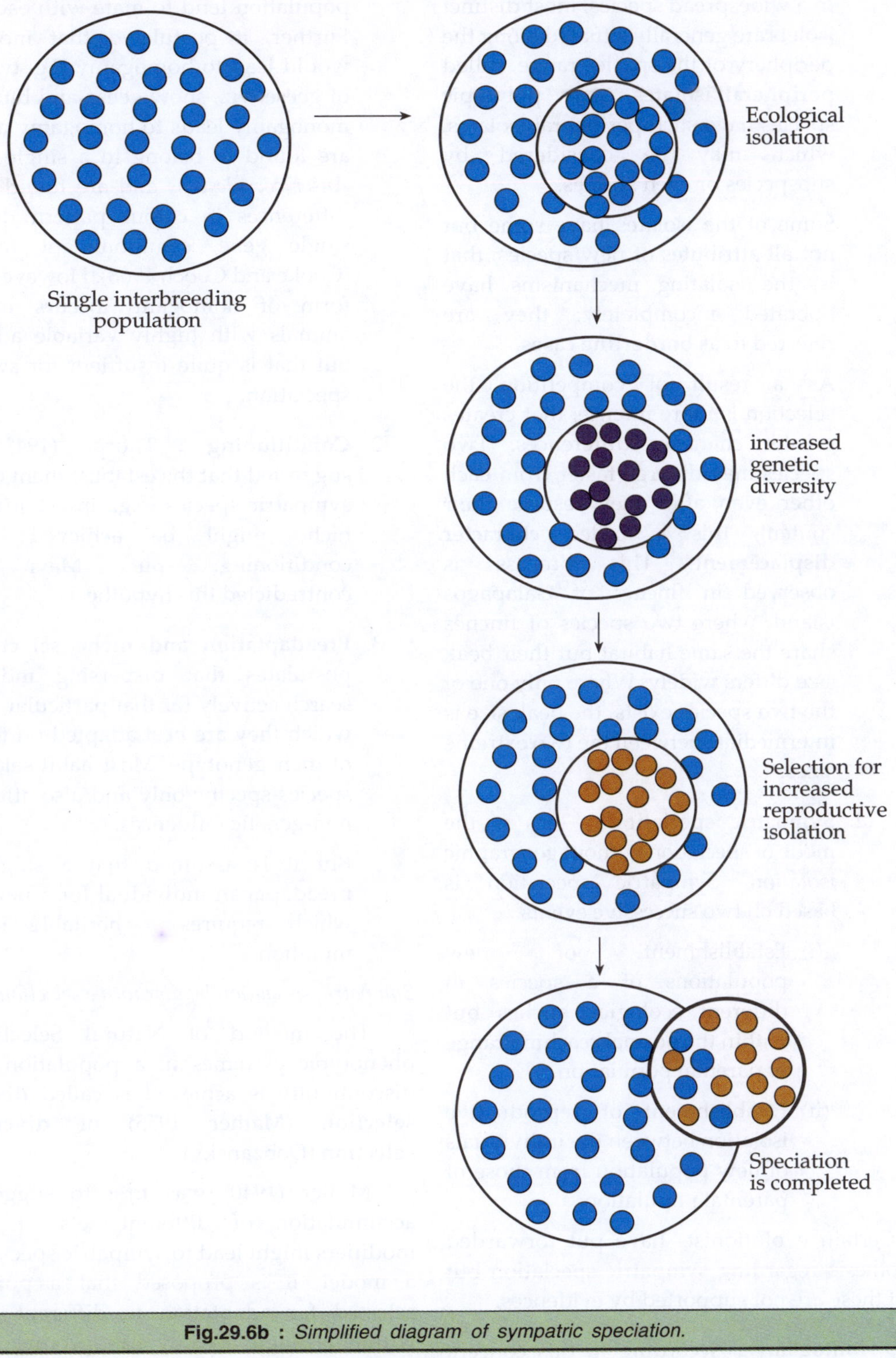


**Fig.29.6b :** *Simplified diagram of sympatric speciation.*

In a widespread species, most distinct isolets are generally situated along the periphery of the species range, called **peripheral isolates**. Many polytypic species have such peripheral isolates, which may be considered by subspecies or even species.

Some of the isolates have some but not all attributes of new species, that is, the isolating mechanisms have operated incompletely; they are referred to as **borderline cases**.

As a result of competition the selection is more intense, that creates greater character differences. Two species may diverge faster from each other even after they resume their content, this is called **character displacement**. This process is observed in finches of Galapagos island, where two species of finches share the same habitat but their beak size differs widely. Where only one of the two species exists, the beak size is intermediate between the two extreme sizes.

2. **Sympatric speciation** : This is the mode of speciation without geographic isolation. Sympatric speciation is based on two successive events
   (i) Establishment of new populations of a species in different ecological niches but within the normal reaching range of parental population.
   (ii) Establishment of reproductive isolation between the individuals of new population from those of parental population.

Certain evolutionists have put forwarded hypothesis regarding sympatric speciation but all of these are not supported by evidences.

1. **Homogamy :** According to this concept the most similar individuals of a population tend to mate with each other. Further, it postulated that monogamy would lead to homogamy E.g. two kinds of geese, viz, snow geese and blue geese, monogamy leads to homogamy and both are found to belong to a single species, *Anser coerulescens* and are found to have differences in colour pattern due to a single gene, semidominant for blue. (Cooke and Cooch 1968). However, a mild form of homogamy occurs in many animals with highly variable adult size but that is quite insuffient for sympatric speciation.

2. **Conditioning** : Thorpe (1945) *et al* suggested that the establishment of a new sympatric species (e.g., insects) in a new niche might be achieved through conditioning. But Mayr (1947) contradicted this hypothesis.

3. **Preadaptation and niche selection :** It postulates that dispersing individuals search actively for that particular niche to which they are best adapted on the basis of their genotype. Most habit selection is species-specific only and also affected by non-genetic influences.

   But it is assumed that a single gene preadapts an individual for a new niche, which requires a heritable systemic mutation.

*Sympatric speciation by disruptive selection :*

The method of Natural Selection for phenotypic extremes in a population until a discontinuity is achieved is called **disruptive selection** (Mather 1955) or **diversifying selection** (Dobzansky).

Muller (1940) was first to suggest that accumulation of different sets of specific modifiers might lead to sympatric speciation. In a model, it is proposed that a population selected for adaptation to different habitats within a single locality can produce genetic variability leading to polymorphism. This

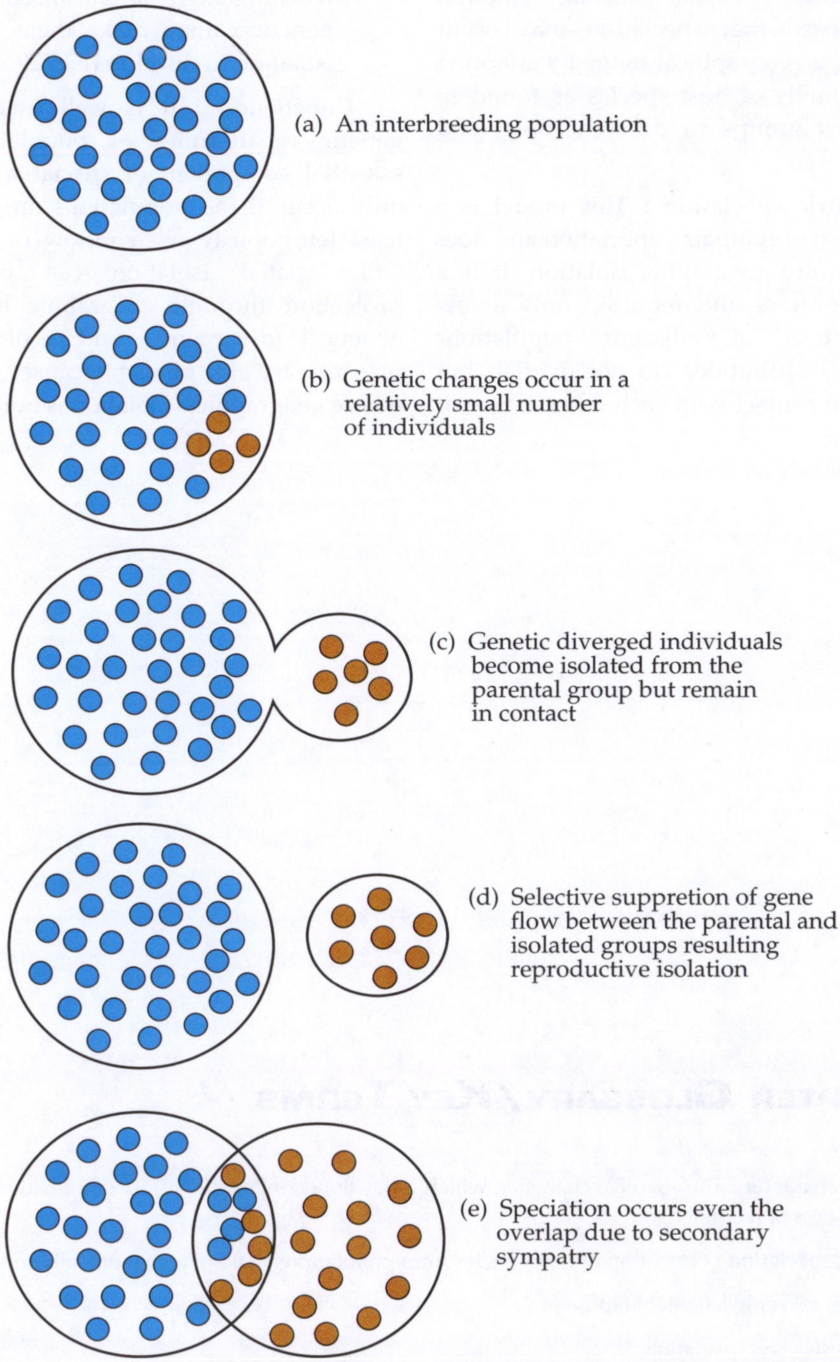


**Fig.29.7 :** *(a) to (e) Model of Parapatric speciation*

phenomenon is known as **disruptive selection** found in butterfly *Papilio dardanus*. Another model proposed that speciation may occur within a single geographical range by adapting to different kinds of host species as found in various insect groups to different host food plants.

(c) **Parapatric speciation :** This model is a variation of sympatric speciation and does not require geographic isolation. It is a rapid process and required only a few individuals of adjacent populations whose distributions do not overlap but come in contact with each other at one or more points. The structural rearrangement of chromosomes or other genetic causes make them reproductive isolation to develop (Fig. 29.7).

**Conclusion :** It is well established that genetic repatterning of populations is the essential component of speciation, which can only occur if the populations are protected at least temporarily from inflow of alien genes. Only spatial isolation can provide this protection through geographic barriers. The genetical divergence and ecological niche pressure are also plausible causes of speciation where geographical isolation is not required.

## Chapter Glossary/Key Terms

**Acquired character :** The adaptive character, which is developed in the life history of individuals through the process of learning.

**Allopatric speciation :** Formation of new species from populations that are geographically separated.

**Anagenesis :** See phyletic evolution.

**Cladogenesis :** See speciation.

**Gene pool :** All the genes present in the breeding individuals of a population at a given time.

**Heredity :** Resemblance among individuals related by descent, transmission of traits from parent to offspring.

**Incipient species :** Because speciation is a slow and gradual process, immediate stages in the process of speciation are observed in nature, called incipient species.

**Mutation :** A change in the DNA at a particular locus in an organism.

**Natural selection :** Differential survival and reproduction in nature that favours individuals those are better adapted to their environment, elimination of less fit organisms.

**Parapatric speciation :** A model of speciation, in which adjacent populations without sufficient geographic isolation may develop reproductive isolation and become new species.

**Phyletic evolution :** The process of origin of species from a parental one without multiplication of the latter.

**Quantum evolution :** The kind of evolution or speciation in one or a few generations by rapid change through genetic drift and selection.

**Speciation :** The process in which one parental species splits into two or more reproductively isolated lineages (new species).

**Sympatric speciation :** Formation of new species from the populations that inhabit the same or overlapping geographical areas.

**Variation :** The occurrence of differences among individuals.

# EXERCISE

**A. Long answer type questions :**

1. Describe Lamarckism. Comment on it's support and criticism.
2. How Lamarkism is modified and newly reestablished? Describe the phenomenon of genetic assimilation. Give some experimental evidences genetic assimilation and how the neoLamarkism is reestablished through genetic assimilation.
3. Describe the voyage of the Beagle and Darwins expedition on Galapagos island.
4. What are Darwin funches? How did he classify funches found on Galapagos island? What was his conclusion?
5. Describe the Darwin-Wallace explanation on origin of species by natural selection. What are the drawbacks of Darwinism?
6. Though Darwin's theory of origin of species was criticized by several naturalists several others were tried to uphold the hypothesis? Describe the multiple forces that support the Darwinism and conclude the concept.
7. What is the synthetic theory of evolution? Why it is called so? What are the 5 basic points of this theory proposed by G.L.Stebbins? Briefly comment on these five basic points with examples? How Stebbins concluded this theory by an analogy of a motor car with the 5 basic points of evolution?
8. Briefly describe de Vries mutation theory of evolution with his novel experiments of *Oenothera* sp.
9. What do you mean by isolating mechanism? Describe different types of isolating mechanisms and their roles in evolution and origin of species?

10. Define species? Describe the transformation of species in time with examples.
11. What is speciation? What do you mean by instantaneous and gradual speciation?
12. Describe allopatric, sympatric and parapatric mode of speciation.

**B. Short answer type questions.**

1. What is principles of use and disuse?
2. What do you mean by acquired characters.
3. What do you mean by the inheritance of acquired characters?
4. What are the two ideas of Lamarckism?
5. How the neck and forelimb of giraffe are elongated in their evolution?
6. Give an example where the organ of the body is reduced through disuse.
7. What do you mean by pangenes of gemmules?
8. What is Weismann germplasm-somatoplasm concept of evolution?
9. What was the Mc Dougall's experiment on rats? and what was its conclusion?
10. What is genetic assimilation.
11. Describe Goodrich concept to genetic assimilation and the quantity of inherited character and acquird character.
12. What was the experiment of Waddington on genetic assimilation?
13. What is the voyage of the Beagle?
14. Why the galapagos island is famous?
15. What are Darwin finches?
16. Who were the two Englishmen published jointly the new concept of natural selection?
17. What is prodigality in production? What is its effect?
18. What is the result of constancy of food and space on prodigality in reproduction?
19. What is struggle for existance? What types of struggle may be observed? What kinds of inter and intraspecific struggle are observed.
20. What is variation and what is heredity.
21. What are their relationships in evolution?
22. Define different kinds of variations?
23. What do you mean by survival of the fittest?
24. What is natural selection?
25. What is artificial selection?
26. What are the stabilizing aspects of natural selection?
27. What are the stabilizing aspects of natural selection?
28. What is corporated genotype? What is its role?
29. What are the multiple forces of neoDarwinism?
30. Why neoDarwinism seems to be incomplete and partly wrong?
31. What is modern synthesis?
32. What are the five basic types of process in synthetic theory of evolution? and what are the elemental forces of evolution.
33. What are population and gene poof?
34. What is genetic variability? What are the causes of genetic variability at individual level and population level?
35. What is the role of mutation in evolution?
36. How genetic recombination accelerates evolution?
37. Which events introduce genetic variation at population level?
38. What is the role of hybridization in evolution?
39. Define different types of selection?
40. How the genetic variability and natural selection are interrelated during evolution?
41. What is mutation?
42. What are the results of mutation studies by de Vries?
43. What are progressive species, retrogressive species degressives species and inconstant species? What are their types of mutation described by genetics?

44. What are gaudens complex and velans complex and what was the assumptions of de Vries about mutation with these complexes?
45. What is prerequisite for speciation?
46. What is isolating mechanism?
47. What are the two types of isolating mechanism?
48. What do you mean by isolation by time and distance?
49. Define geographical isolating mechanism.
50. What do you mean by pre-zygotic and post-zygotic isolating mechanisms.
51. Define with examples of habitual seasonal, ethological, mechanical, gametic isolations.
52. Define with examples of zygotic mortality, hybrid inviability, hybrid sterility and $F_2$ breaknown.
53. What are haplontic sterility and diplontic sterility?
54. What is physiological isolation?
55. What is genetic or cytogenetic isolation?
56. What is *Rephanobrassica*.
57. What do you mean by genetic isolating systems?
58. What are the roles of isolating mechanisms in evolution?
59. What is a species?
60. What do you mean by transformation of species in time?
61. What is phyletic evolution?
62. What is anagenesis? What are the genetic changes during phyletic evolution.
63. What is autogenous and allogenus transformation?
64. What is quantum evolution? Give an example?
65. What do you mean by multiplication of species in space?
66. What do you mean by speciation?
67. What is cladogenesis?
68. What is clade?
69. Distinguish between anagenesis and cladogenesis?
70. Define instantaneous speciation through individuals?
71. What is macrogenesis?
72. What is hopeful monster?
73. What is super gene?
74. Define gradual speciation through population?
75. What is allopatric speciation? What are their requirements?
76. What do you mean by incipient species.
77. What is geographic variation?
78. What are peripheral isolates?
79. What are borderline species?
80. What is character displacement?
81. What is sympatric speciation? What are the two events of sympatric speciation?
82. How homogamy, conditioning and preadaptation contradict sympatric speciation?
83. What do you mean by disruptive selection? Give example.
84. What do you mean by parapatric speciation?
85. What are the causes of speciation where geographical isolation is not required?

# 30

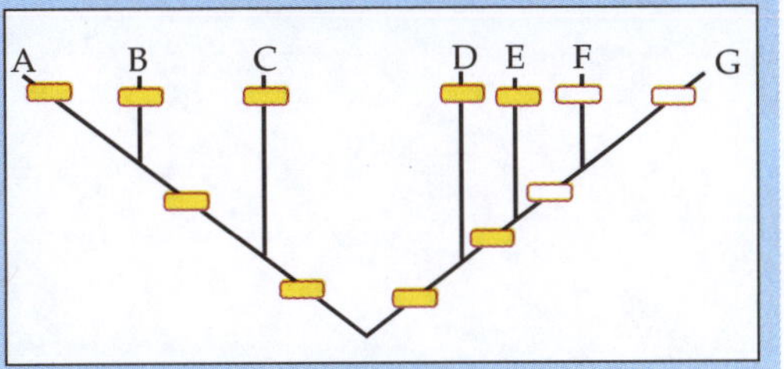


# Molecular Phylogenetics

**CHAPTER AGENDA**

**30.1** Concept; **30.2** Phenetics; **30.3** Clades and Cladistics; **30.4** Methods of Cladistic analysis; **30.5** Problems encountered in the Construction of a Cladogram; **30.6** DNA-based phylogenetic trees; **30.7** Difference between DNA-based Phylogenetic tree and Species tree; **30.8** Tree reconstruction; **30.9** Synonymous codon; Chapter Glossary/ Key Terms; Exercise

## 30.1. CONCEPT

Genome is evolved by gradual accumulation of mutations. The amount of differences in nucleotide sequence between a pair of genomes should indicate how recently these two shared a common ancestor. The objectives of molecular phylogenetics are to work out the evolutionary relationships between two or more genomes by comparing the amount of changes in nucleotides in course of evolution.

Phylogeny means a classification scheme that indicates the evolutionary relationships between organisms. To construct a classification or to infer a phylogeny, a relevant data are obtained by examining variable characters, mainly morphological characters and are being compared.

Nuttall in 1950s showed the molecular data, which can be, used in phylogenetics but this approach was not widely adopted because of its technical limitations.

Recently, a large number of techniques have been discovered which can easily provide the sequences of DNA molecules as amino acid sequences in the protein molecules. These techniques are base upon immunological data, protein electrophoresis, DNA-DNA hybridization data, PCR, RFLPs, SSLPs and SNPs etc. Thus molecular phylogenetics came into the light.

## 30.2 PHENETICS

The degree of similarity was traditionally one of the criteria on which the recognition of taxa had been based. Such similarity can be determined by recording similarities and differences in a large number of variables. The book "Principles of Numerical Taxonomy (1963)" by Sokal and Sneath became the classical text of the new school of numerical phenetics. A second greatly revised edition by them was appeared in 1973.

Numerical Phenetics is the methodology of assembling individuals into taxa on the basis of an estimate of unweighted overall similarity.

**Definition:**

*In biology, phenetics also known as taximetrics, is an attempt to classify organisms based on overall similarity, usually in morphology or other observable traits, regardless of their phylogeny or evolutionary relation.*

It is closely related to numerical taxonomy which is concerned with the use of numerical methods for taxonomic classification.

### 30.2.1 Operational taxonomic unit (OTU)

**Definition:**

*OTU is an operational definition used to classifying groups of closely related individuals.* The term was introduced by Robert. R. Sokal and Peter. H.A. Sneath in the context of Numerical Taxonomy.

Operational taxonomic unit is a name for individuals, populations, species or higher taxa classified by numerical methods.

Pheneticists rejected the taxa with OTU and phenetically different individuals are to be treated as different OTUs. They employ four criteria to determine whether or not a given classification satisfactorily represents the probable relationship of the included taxa.

1. Closeness to the original similarity matrix
2. Maximal similarity within the taxa
3. Maximum predictive value
4. Stability of classification.

### 30.2.2. Taxonomic character

A taxonomic character is any attribute by which a member of a taxon differs or may differ from a member of another taxon. For example, feather colour of swans. White vs Black.

### 30.2.3 Signifier

It means the "sign bearer", i.e., the features varies from one organism to another. The feather would be the signifier; feather black and feather white would be the characters.

### 30.2.4 Character state or Signifier state

The characters are divided into character states i.e., one or two specific variations of characters that constitute a signifier, such as blue or brown eyes. When character present in two states, called binary mode and when character is more than two states, called as multiple mode.

### 30.2.5 Preparation of Data-matrix and Similarity-matrix

For the preparation of data-matrix and similarity-matrix, data set is constructed in the forms of a table, which defines specific character states, each of which is coded with assigned numbers (generally 0-3).

### 30.2.6 Data-matrix

Data-matrix is a tabulation of differences between species (or other taxa) in rows as characters / signifiers and column as taxa.

From the dataset data matrix is prepared with the mnemonics and character states code of all imaginary OTUs.

### 30.2.7 Data matrix table

The data matrix table usually has a row of cells representing each character and acolumn of cells representing each taxon; ideally. Every cell most be filled.( Table 30.1).

The simplest codes are those with two character states,e.g. Present vsAbsent; Red vs White. These characters are coded 0 and 1.

Characters may have more than two component character states. Thecodes may be designated as 0, 1, 2, 3.......

**TABLE 30.1**
**Character mnemonics, character states and codes of an immaginary insect species**

| *Character mnemonics* | *State definition* | *Code* |
|---|---|---|
| CrVn (Crossvein) | Absent<br>present | 0<br>1 |
| CsMg (Costal wing margin) | curved in at the base<br>curved out at the base | 0<br>1 |
| NkSw (Neck curved) | in behind eyes<br>out behind eyes for about length of an eye<br>out behind eyes for more than length of eye<br>quadrately swollen behind eye | 0<br>1<br>2<br>3 |
| ClyL (Clypeus) | projecting beyond rest of head<br>end of clypeus is even with rest of head | 0<br>1 |
| CoLC (Collar) | Incomplete<br>Complete | 0<br>1 |
| PrEx (Pronotal expansion) | absent from posterior angle<br>rounded apically<br>acute apically | 0<br>1<br>2 |
| PrLb (Pronotum position) | medially without a transverse groove<br>medially with an incompete transverse groove<br>medially with complete grooves producing 2 grooves<br>longer than basal pert of the wing | 0<br>1<br>2 |

**TABLE 30.2**
**Data-matrix table of immaginary 8 different insect species (A to B) indicating their mnemonics and code number**

| *Mnemonics* | *A* | *B* | *C* | *D* | *E* | *F* | *G* | *H* |
|---|---|---|---|---|---|---|---|---|
| CrVn | 0 | 1 | 0 | 0 | 1 | 0 | 0 | 1 |
| CsMg | 0 | 1 | 1 | 1 | 0 | 0 | 1 | 1 |
| NkSw | 0 | 1 | 2 | 3 | 0 | 1 | 2 | 3 |
| ClyL | 0 | 1 | 0 | 2 | 0 | 1 | 0 | 1 |
| CoLC | 1 | 0 | 1 | 0 | 1 | 0 | 1 | 0 |
| PrEx | 0 | 1 | 2 | 0 | 1 | 2 | 0 | 1 |
| PrLb | 1 | 0 | 2 | 3 | 1 | 0 | 2 | 3 |
| MmbL | 1 | 0 | 2 | 1 | 0 | 2 | 1 | 0 |

When the final form of each character has been decided upon, the data matrix may be drawn and the cells must be filled with appropriate character state code for each character and each taxon. (Table 30.2)

### 30.2.8 Distance matrix/Similarity matrix

1. Measures of distance between taxa can arise from observational technique used (e.g. melting temperature in DNA-DNA hybridization) or can be obtained by transforming character data into distance data.
2. Distance measures can be calculated by comparing character states of several taxa to determine the overall similarity or difference between each possible pair of taxa. The differences are coded and assembled into a data matrix.
3. Then a coefficient of similarity between each possible pair of taxa is calculated by comparing all character state of each taxon with those of avery other taxon or OUT. The coefficients are assembled into a similarity matrix.
4. Both the columns and the rows in a similarity matrix are for taxa. The cells contain a measure of similarity or distance between each possible pair of taxa.

5.A matrix for n number of taxa requires calculation of (n2-n)/2 similarity measures. Thus, a matrix of 8 taxa, the data set requires 28 calculations.

6.Manhattan distance: Manhattan distance is the simplest similarity coefficient to calculate. The formula for this distance between each pair of taxa is expressed as follows:

$$\sum_{i=1}^{n} |j-k|$$

7.It is calculated by finding the sum of the absolute differences between the character states of each character for each possible pair of taxa. (Table 30.3 )

### 30.2.9 Cluster analysis

Grouping of the phenetically most similar taxa on the basis of a similarity matrix is called cluster analysis. Therefore, taxa in the similarity matrix must be listed in one's best approximation of the final order of similarity. Thus it requires to place taxa with the lowest similarity coefficients close together.(Table 30.4)

**TABLE 30.3**
**Similarity matrix Manhattan distance**

| | A | B | C | D | E | F | G | H |
|---|---|---|---|---|---|---|---|---|
| A | X | 8 | 7 | 8 | 3 | 7 | 4 | 11 |
| B | 8 | X | 9 | 8 | 7 | 5 | 8 | 5 |
| C | 7 | 9 | X | 7 | 9 | 6 | 3 | 8 |
| D | 8 | 8 | 7 | X | 11 | 9 | 4 | 3 |
| E | 5 | 7 | 9 | 11 | X | 9 | 4 | 3 |
| F | 7 | 5 | 6 | 9 | 8 | X | 9 | 10 |
| G | 4 | 8 | 3 | 4 | 7 | 9 | X | 7 |
| H | 11 | 5 | 8 | 3 | 8 | 10 | 7 | X |

**TABLE 30.4**
**Similarity matrix Manhattan distance rearranged by similarity**

| | A | E | G | C | F | D | B | H |
|---|---|---|---|---|---|---|---|---|
| A | X | 3 | 4 | 7 | 7 | 8 | 8 | 11 |
| E | 3 | X | 7 | 9 | 8 | 11 | 7 | 8 |
| G | 4 | 7 | X | 3 | 9 | 4 | 8 | 7 |
| C | 7 | 9 | 3 | X | 9 | 7 | 9 | 8 |
| F | 7 | 8 | 9 | 7 | X | 11 | 5 | 10 |
| D | 8 | 11 | 4 | 7 | 11 | X | 8 | 3 |
| B | 8 | 7 | 8 | 9 | 5 | 8 | X | 5 |
| H | 11 | 8 | 7 | 8 | 10 | 3 | 5 | X |

Cluster analysis method explained here is called the unweighted pair group method using arithmetic average (UPGMA) and is a commonly used distance method. This cross averaging method is also known as average linkage.( Fig 30.1)

A primary cluster always consists of two taxa that are closer to one another either is to any other taxon.

Secondary clusters contain more than two but only one primary cluster. But no secondary cluster may exist.

| | A | E |
|---|---|---|
| G | 4 | 7 |
| C | 7 | 9 |

$\frac{4+7+7+9}{4} = 5.75$

| | B | F |
|---|---|---|
| D | 8 | 5 |
| H | 11 | 10 |

$\frac{8+5+11+10}{4} = 8.5$

| | D | H |
|---|---|---|
| A | 8 | 11 |
| E | 11 | 8 |

$\frac{8+11+11+8}{4} = 9.5$

| | G | C |
|---|---|---|
| D | 4 | 7 |
| H | 4 | 8 |

$\frac{4+7+4+8}{4} = 5.75$

| | G | C |
|---|---|---|
| B | 8 | 9 |
| F | 9 | 6 |

$\frac{8+9+4+8}{4} = 8.0$

| | A | E |
|---|---|---|
| B | 8 | 7 |
| F | 7 | 8 |

$\frac{8+7+7+8}{4} = 7.5$

| | A | E | G | C |
|---|---|---|---|---|
| D | 8 | 11 | 4 | 7 |
| H | 11 | 8 | 7 | 8 |

$\frac{8+11+4+7+11+8+7+8}{8} = 8.0$

| | A | E | G | C | D | H |
|---|---|---|---|---|---|---|
| B | 8 | 7 | 8 | 9 | 8 | 5 |
| F | 7 | 8 | 9 | 6 | 9 | 10 |

$\frac{8+7+8+9+8+5+7+8+9+6+9+10}{12} = 7.833$

| | A | E | G | C |
|---|---|---|---|---|
| D | 8 | 11 | 4 | 7 |
| H | 11 | 8 | 7 | 8 |
| B | 11 | 8 | 7 | 8 |
| F | 7 | 8 | 9 | 7 |

$\frac{8+11+4+7+11+8+7+8+8+7+8+9+7+8+9+7}{16} = 7.937$

***Fig.30.1** : Cluster analysis and calculation of Manhattan distances between different taxa*

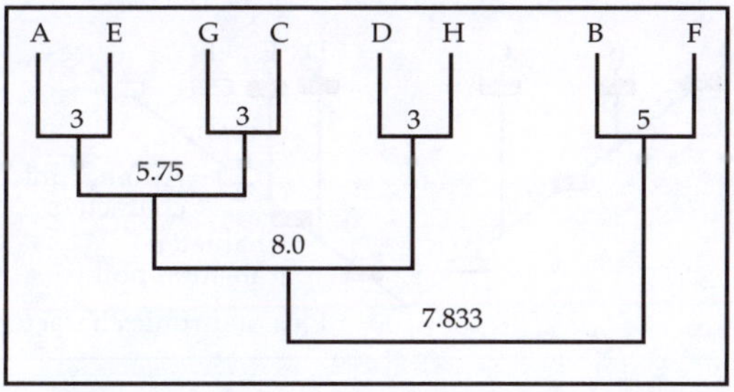


**Fig.30.2 :** *Phenogram and cluster analysis.*

Tertiary clusters are the clusters of clusters.

Here the cluster are prepared would have smallest average value. (Fig30.2)

## 30.3 CLADES ANS CLADISTICS

### 30.3.1 Clades

*Clade means a group of organisms that consists of a common ancestor and all its lineal descendants, and represents a single branch of a tree of life.* So clades are monophyletic

### 30.3.2 Cladistics

*Cladistics is an approach to biological classification in which organisms are categorized based on shared derived characteristics that can be traced to a group's most recent common ancestor and are not present in more distant ancestors.* Therefore, members of a group are assumed to share a common history and are considered to be closely related.

### 30.3.3 Distinction between Phenetics and Cladistics

Phenetics attempts to classify organisms based on overall similarity, typically in morphology, without regard for their evolutionary relationships. Basically, it's classification based on how similar to the organisms look. A single category in a phenetic classification system may contain organisms that have different evolutionary histories but have developed similar morphological features through convergent evolution.

Cladistics attempts to classify organisms based on their evolutionary lineage. In a cladistic classification system, a single category, known as a clade, contains the most recent common ancestor of all organisms in the clade as well as all organisms descended from that ancestor. The organisms in a single clade may be morphological different, but they share an evolutionary relationship. Organism's that have developed similar morphological characteristics through convergent evolution will generally be in different clades.

So in summary, the basic different between phenetics and cladistics is that cladistics is based on evolutionary relationships whereas phenetics is based on morphology.

### 30.3.4 Cladogram

1. The outcome of a cladistic analysis is a cladogram, a tree-shaped diagram (dendrogram) that is interpreted to represent the best hypothesis of phylogenetic relationships. This is based on the pattern of synapomorphies (a homologous character shared by two or more taxa and inferred to have been present in the nearest common ancestor neither in earlier ancestor nor in taxa outside this group.
2. Each branching point in a cladogram represents a speciational event, which potentially gives rise to a holophyletic taxon (a group that consists of all the descendants of its most recent common ancestor). No branch of a cladogram can be based on plesiomorphiccharactors (ancestral characters).

Cladists adopt two conventions for the construction of a cladogram. (fig. 30.7)

1. Sister groups which are placed at a same distance from the ancestral species.
2. The sister taxon that have retained more primitive characters is placed on the left branch of dichotomy

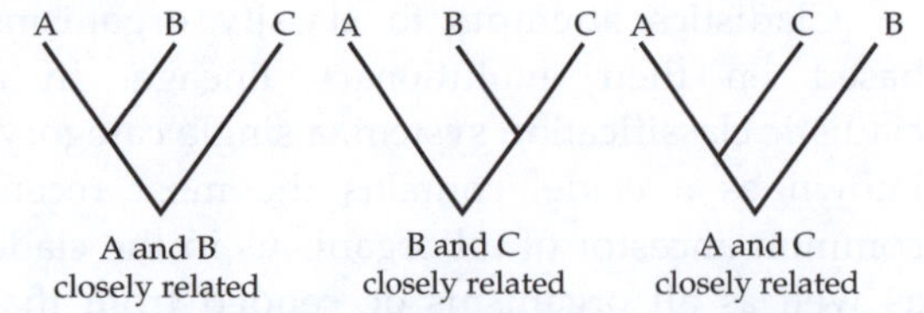


**Fig. 30.3 :** *Three taxa (A, B and C) on a dicotomous cladogram*

### 30.3.5 Principle of Parsimony

When cladistic analysis allows for the construction of several possible cladograms, that one is considered to be best which is "shortest" i.e., has the smallest number of changes in character states (branching points). This is called **Principle of Parsimony**.

### 30.3.6 Data matrix

The character states that are to be used in a cladistics analysis are assembled into a data matrix in which characters are coded to indicate the sequence from plesiomorphic (ancestral) to apomorphic ( derived) . The most primitive character state is given the number "zero" and the increasingly derived character states are given sequentially higher numbers. PPimental and Riggins (1987) provide a helpful discussion of coding methods. ( Fig. 30.4)

More recently, pattern cladists have recognized that cladogram is actually a diagram of the distribution of synapomorphic characters. The cladagram is constructed by considering inherited characters, derived characters and branching point where character transition has occurred (Fig. 30.5).

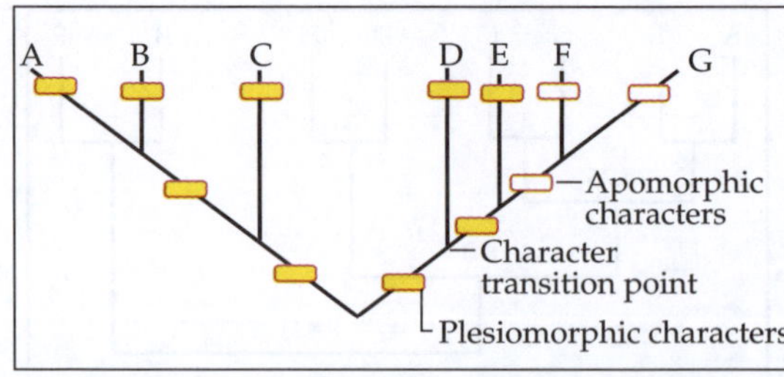


**Fig.30.5 :** *Diagramatic representation of a cladogram*

## 30.4 METHODS OF CLADISTIC ANALYSIS

Cladistic analysis is defined as the analysis of character of organisms to infer the evolutionary branching sequence of a group's phylogeny.

1. **Parsimony method :** Parsimony is the principle stating that, that tree is best which is "shortest", *i.e.*, has the smallest number of character state changes.
2. **Compatibility method :** Compatibility is a method in which "that tree is selected, which is compatible with the largest number of characters and is thus believed to have the fewest **homoplasies** (*i.e.*, possession by two or more taxa of a character derived not from the nearest common ancestor but through convergence, parallelism or reversal).
3. **Maximum likelihood method :** which generally have been applied only to molecular data. The tree for which the probability of observing the data is highest is chosen as maximum likelihood estimate of the phylogeny.

Characters

| Taxa | | a | b | c | d | e |
|---|---|---|---|---|---|---|
| | X | 0 | 0 | 0 | 0 | 0 |
| | Y | 0 | 0 | 0 | 0 | 1 |
| | Z | 1 | 1 | 1 | 1 | 1 |

Data matrix

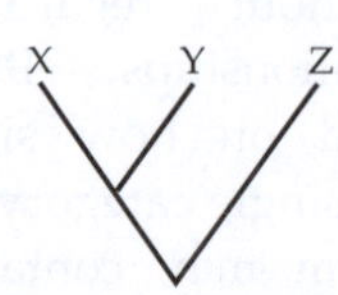


Cladogram

**Fig.30.4 :** *Data matrix and cladogram.*

In molecular phylogeny the term **operational taxonomic unit** (or OTU) is used to describe the organisms being compared when a tree is constructed from morphological data. OTU is sometimes also used by molecular phylogeneticists as a synonym for "gene or other nucleotide sequence" but it is perhaps best avoided because a gene is not strictly speaking a taxonomic unit.

Taxonomic unit is a component of a classification scheme, such as "species". To describe a gene as a taxonomic unit runs the risk of confusing a gene tree with a species tree.

## 30.5 PROBLEMS ENCOUNTERED IN THE CONSTRUCTION OF A CLADOGRAM

1. Blunders: Numerical analysis consists of a long series of steps, errors such as wrong copying of number creep in easily. The best test is to translate the cladogram back into a data matrix and compare it with the original data matrix. If they do not match, a blunder has been committed.
2. Unsupported empty internodes: Dichotomies are found in some trees that are not supported by any apomorphies. The result is an "empty"internode. The maintenance of such empty internodes is unjustified. If such internode is eliminated, a trichotomy or polytomy will result.
3. The unwitting use of Plesiomorphic character state: One internode is given a character state and its sister internode is labelled as being without it. This is not admissible in a cladogram. Such contrasting character state of this sort on sister internodes are diagnostic keys rather thancladogram.
4. Taxa without apomorphies: Sometimes, it happens that no apomorphic character states can be found to give a character state to a terminal taxon. This may be due to terminal sibling species or the taxon is paraphyletic.
5. Unwise choice of Character state: The use of different sets of character states may lead to entirely different classifications. The major problem is to establish exactly which character states are unreliable.
6. Incompletely studied taxa: It is impossible to study every feature of every species in the study group. In small taxa, character states may not be known because of a lack of certain immature forms, sex and available species. In large taxa these problems are compounded.

Henning(1966) said that no one expect the author "to present the phylogenetic sister-group relations more accurately than they are known" and he warned workers about the need to point out weakness in their studies.

## 30.6. DNA-BASED PHYLOGENETIC TREES:

**FEATURES** : The objective of most phylogenetic studies is to reconstruct the tree-like pattern that describes the evolutionary relationships between the organisms being studied.

The topology of this tree comprises external nodes. If we like to show the relationship between four genes A, B, C, D then the tree comprises four external nodes, each representing one of the four genes that we have compared.

There are two internal nodes representing ancestral genes.

The lengths of the branches indicate the degree of difference between the genes represented by the nodes. The degree of differences is calculated when the sequences are compared.

The unrooted tree means that it is the tree is only an illustration of these genes, but it does not tell us their evolutionary pathways.

Rooted tree provides information on the past evolutionary events that have led to the organisms or DNA sequences being studied. An organism or DNA sequence that is used to root

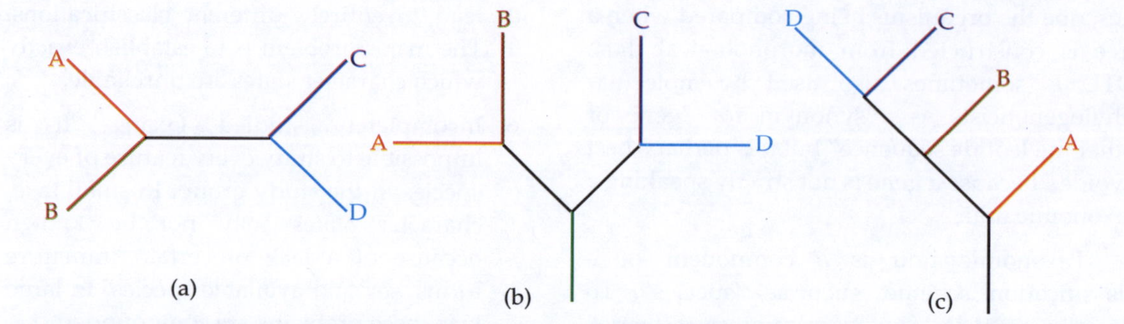


**Fig.30.6 :** *Types of phylogenetic tree (a) unrooted tree (b) rooted tree*

a phylogenetic tree called "out-group". Therefore a homologous gene, which we know, is less closely related to such A, B, C, and D, etc. genes to each other, is to be located first to obtain the root of the tree (Fig. 30.6).

For example, four homologous genes in a tree come from human, chimpanzee, gorilla and orangutan. Then an out-group- homologous gene from primate, such as baboon can be chosen because we know from fossil records that baboons split away from the primate lineage before the time of common ancestor of the other four species (Fig. 30.7).

A tree obtained by phylogenetic analysis is known as **inferred tree** because most phylogenetic data analyses are prone to

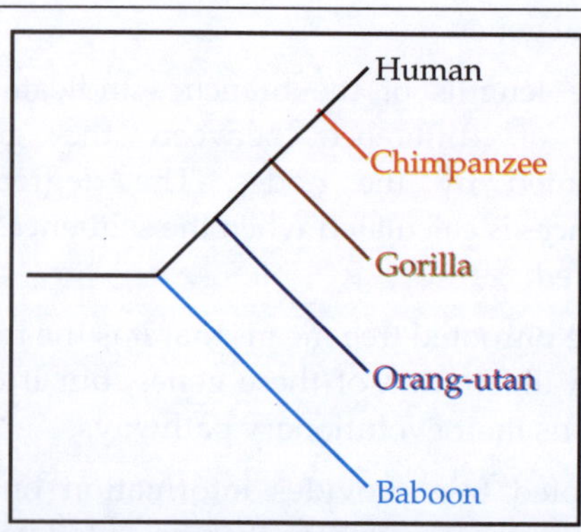


**Fig.30.7 :** *Showing the use of out-group in a rooted tree*

uncertainties, which may differ in some respects from the true tree.

## 30.7 DIFFERENCE BETWEEN DNA-BASED PHYLOGENETIC TREE AND SPECIES TREE

**Species tree** is based mainly on morphological comparisons whereas, **gene tree** is constructed from comparisons between the sequences of **orthologous genes** (i.e. the genes derived from the same ancestral sequence) and is based on the molecular data with all advantages. Therefore, gene tree is more accurate and less ambiguous.

The difference from the species tree is that:

1. An internal node in a gene tree represents the divergence of an ancestral gene into two genes with different DNA sequences, which occurs by mutation.
2. An internal node in a species tree represents the speciation event (Fig. 30.8).

## 30.8 TREE RECONSTRUCTION

There are four steps for the construction of gene tree carried out with DNA sequences.

(a) **Aligning the DNA sequences and obtaining the comparative data that would be used to reconstruct the tree :** This is the critical part for the construction of true tree. The sequence of DNA is to be

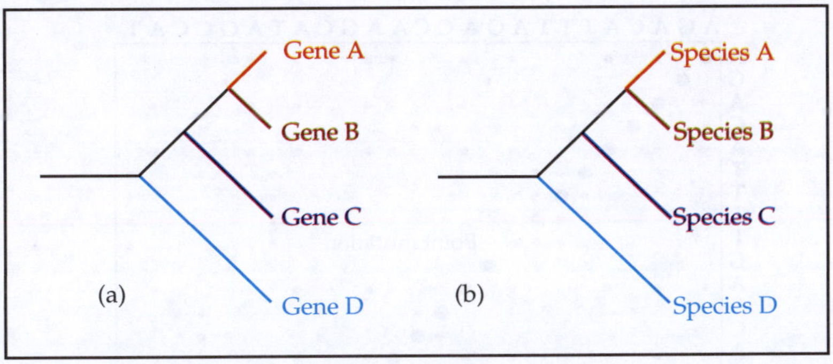


**Fig.30.8 :** *A gene tree (a) and a species tree (b)*

examined whether they are homologous or not. If they are not homologous then they do not share a common ancestor and the resulting tree will have no biological relevance. But if they are homologous by definition it may be assumed that they may be derived from a common ancestral sequence and there is sound basis of phylogenetic tree.

Once the two DNA sequences have been found to be homologous, then their nucleotides are compared. It is very difficult to compare the **indels** (the position in an alignment between two DNA sequences where the insertion and deletion have occurred).

The alignment of some pairs of sequences can be made by eye observation.

**Dot matrix** method is used for the alignment of more complex gene pairs. In this method two sequences are written out on the X- and Y- axes of a graph. The dots are placed in the squares of the graph paper at position corresponding to identical nucleotides in two sequences. The alignment is indicated by diagonal series of dots, broken by empty squares where the sequences have nucleotide differences and shifting from one column to another at places where "indels" occur (Fig. 30.9).

Mathematical approaches to sequence alignment have also been devised. Distance measures can be calculated by comparing character-states of several taxa or genes to determine the overall similarity or difference between each possible pair of taxa or genes. The differences are coded and assembled into a data matrix called **distance matrix**.

Then a coefficient of similarity between each possible pair of taxa is calculated by comparing all character state of each taxon or gene, with those of every other taxon or OTU. The coefficients are assembled into a **similarity matrix**.

Both the columns and the rows in a similarity matrix are for both taxa. The cells contain a measure of similarity or distance between each possible pair of taxa (genes).

To build stepwise all possible trees in **Branch and Bound method** some computer programs are employed. The most widely used of these packages are PAUP (Phylogenetic Analysis Using Parsimony) which is the most comprehensive package of parsimony inference of phylogenies. It runs on MS-DOS, Apple-Macintosh and other machines.

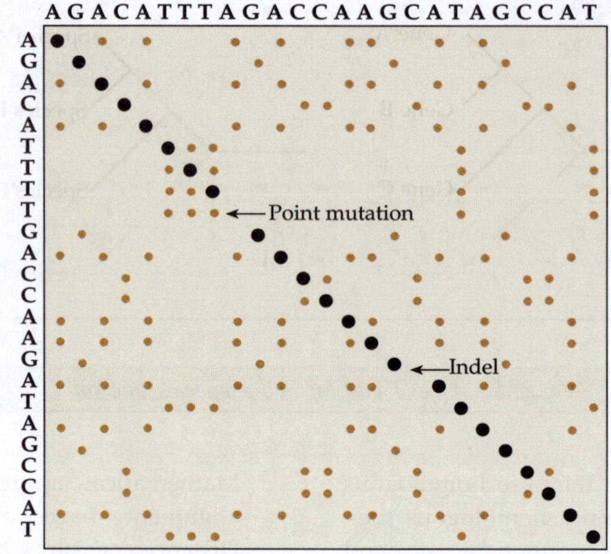


**Fig.30.9 :** *The dot matrix technique for sequence alignment (Adapted from Genome-2, TA Brown, 2002)*

The tree building programs in PAUP are more accurate one and are able to handle relatively large data sets (Eernisse, 1998). PHYLIP (Phylogeny Inference Package) especially suitable for particular data set. The programs are slow but work on many different computers. Other popular packages include PAML (Yang 1997) Mac Clade and HENNING 86 etc.

(b) **Manhattan distance and Eucledean distance :** This is the simplest similarity coefficient to calculate. The formula for this distance between each pair of taxa is expressed as follows.

$$\sum_{i=1}^{n} |j-k|$$

It is calculated by finding the sum of the absolute differences between the character states of each character for each possible pair of taxa.

**Eucledean distance :** This is also known as taxonomic distance, this coefficient measures the distance between two taxa in multidimensional space and is widely used in phenetic studies Eucledian distance is derived by conncecting points j and k with line creates a right angle, to which pythagorean theorem $c^2 = a^2 + b^2$ may be applied to find the distance c between j and k, the values for sides a on X- and b on Y-axes.

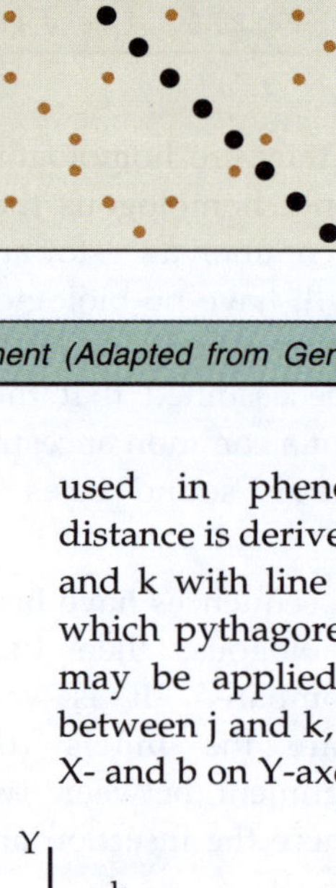


$$\text{Eucledean distance } c = \sqrt{(X_j - X_k)^2 + (Y_j - Y_k)^2}$$

For example :

| Character | Taxa j | Taxa k |
|---|---|---|
| X | 9 | 4 |
| Y | 3 | 10 |

$$\text{Distance } \sqrt{(9-4)^2 + (10-3)^2} = 8.6$$

Adding a third character z requires a three dimensional space and the addition of a z axis to taxnomic space

Formula then becomes

$$c^2 = (X_j - X_k)^2 + (Y_j - Y_k)^2 + (Z_j - Z_k)^2$$

For n number of characters

$$c = \sqrt{\sum_{i=1}^{n} (X_{ij} - X_{ik})^2}$$

The Eucldean distance can be simplified so that for all the characters of each pair of taxa j and k the expression becomes

$$\sqrt{\sum_{i=1}^{n} (j-k)^2}$$

(c) **Converting alignment data into a phylogenetic tree :** The multiple sequence alignment is converted into numerical data that can be analyzed mathematically in order to reconstruct the tree. The simplest approach is to convert the sequence information into a distance matrix which is simply a table showing the evolutionary distances between all pairs of nucleotide sequences in a data set.

The evolutionary distance is expressed as the number of nucleotide differences per nucleotide site for each sequence pair. For example, A and B are 20 nucleotides in length and have four differences, corresponding to an evolutionary difference of $\frac{4}{20} = 0.2$. There is no multiple substitutions (called multiple hits). Multiple substitutions occur when a single site undergoes two or more changes, e.g., ancestral sequences. ....AGTC.... gives rise to ....ACTC.... and ....ATTC..... There is only one nucleotide difference between the two modern sequences but there have been two nucleotide substitutions, then, the evolutionary difference is $\frac{2}{20} = 0.1$.

To avoid this problem, **distance matrices** for phylogenetic analysis are usually constructed using mathematical methods that include statistical devices for estimating the amount of multiple substitutions that have occurred. The distance matrix is used to establish the lengths of the branches connecting these two sequences in the reconstructed tree.

**Example :**

**Multiple alignments :**

A – AGGCCAAGCCATAGCTGTCC

B – AGGCAAAGACATACCTGACC

C – AGGCCAAGACATAGCTGTCC

D – AGGCAAAGACATACCTGTCC

**Distance matrix :**

| | A | B | C | D |
|---|---|---|---|---|
| **A** | — | 0.20 | 0.05 | 0.15 |
| **B** | 0.20 | — | 0.15 | 0.05 |
| **C** | 0.05 | 0.15 | — | 0.10 |
| **D** | 0.15 | 0.05 | 0.10 | — |

**Cluster analysis :** Grouping of the most similar nucleotide sequence of genes on the basis of a similarity matrix. Thus it requires placing the genes with the lowest similarity coefficients close together.

| | A | B | C | D |
|---|---|---|---|---|
| **A** | × | 0.05 | 0.15 | 0.20 |
| **B** | 0.05 | × | 0.1 | 0.15 |
| **C** | 0.15 | 0.1 | × | 0.05 |
| **D** | 0.20 | 0.15 | 0.05 | × |

The cluster analysis method explained here is called **unweighted pair group method using arithmatic average** (UPGMA) and is a commonly used distance method. This cross-averaging method is also known as average linkage. A primary cluster always consists of two genes that are closer to one another either to any other genes.

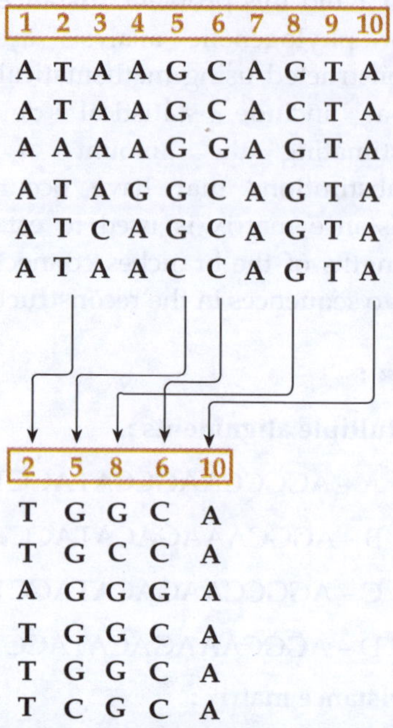


**Fig.30.10 :** *Construction of a new multiple alignment for boot-strap analysis*

Secondary clusters contain more than two but only one primary cluster. But no secondary cluster may exist.

Tertiary clusters are clusters of clusters. Here the clusters are prepared would have the smallest average value (Fig. 30.10).

The average value is calculated by following method

|   | B | D |
|---|---|---|
| A | 0.2 | 0.05 |
| C | 0.05 | 0.1 |

$$\text{Average value is } \frac{0.2 + 0.05 + 0.15 + 0.1}{4}$$

$$= \frac{0.4}{4} = 0.1$$

The **neighbour joining method** (Saitou and Nei; 1987) is a tree building procedure that uses the distance matrix approach. Initially it is assumed to have

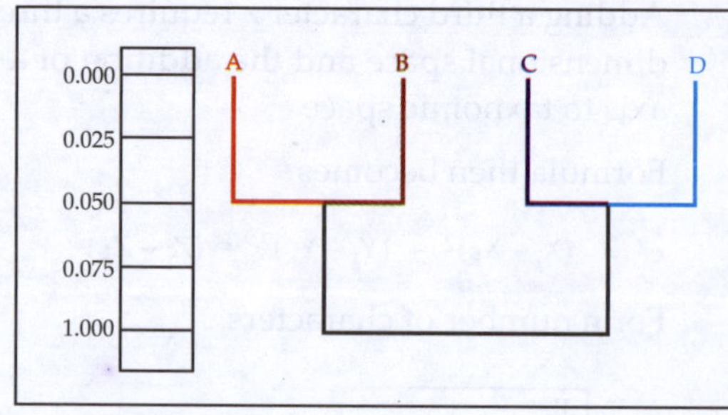


**Fig.30.8 :** *Phenogram using Manhattan distance*

one internal node from which branches are leading to radiate all the DNA sequences. In the next step a pair of sequences is chosen at random, removed from the start and are attached to a second internal node, connected by a branch to the center of the start. Distance method is used to calculate the total length of the branch. The sequences are returned to their original position. Another pair is taken for calculating branch length. This process is repeated. The shortest total branch length is to be identified which will be neighbours in the final tree (Fig. 30.11).

This process is repeated for 2nd pair of neighbouring sequence and then 3rd pair of neighbouring sequence and so on.

**The maximum parsimony method** (Fitch, 1977) is an approach that decides between different phylogenetic tree topologies identifying the one that involves the shortest evolutionary pathway. This method is more rigorous. Even a high-speed computer is not able to check every one of these trees in a reasonable time.

(d) **Assessing the accuracy of a reconstructed tree :** The accuracy test of the reconstructed tree has been devised by Hillis (1997), Whelan *et al* (2001). The method to carry out is a boot-strap analysis. In this method a new alignment is built up by taking columns at random from the real

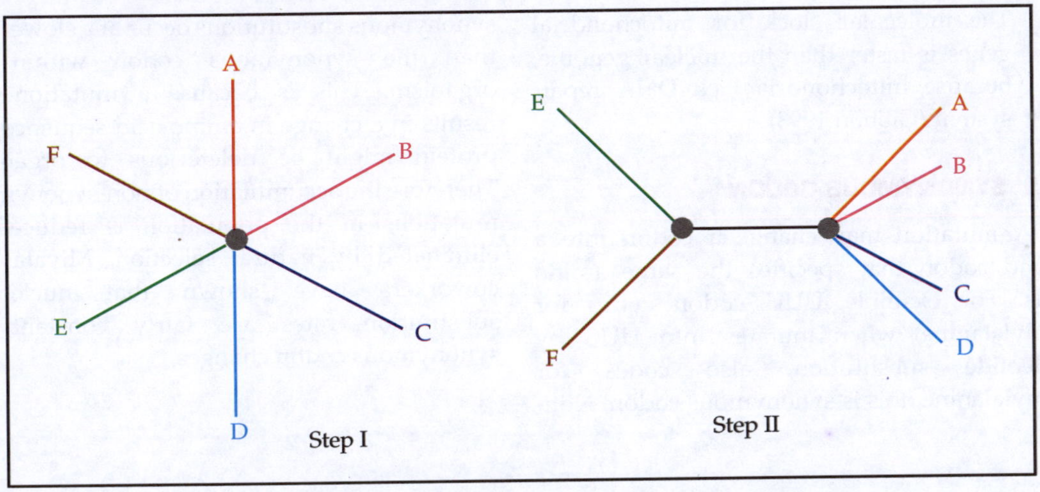


Fig.30.12 : *Neighbour joining methods for tree construction*

alignment. The new alignment comprises sequences that are different from the original but have similar pattern of variability. We may think that it would obtain the same tree (Fig. 30.12).

(e) **Molecular clock for estimation of time of divergence** : The molecular clock hypothesis was first proposed in the early 1960s, states that nucleotide substitutions (or amino acid substitutions, if protein sequences are being compared) occur at a constant rate. This means that the degree of differences between two sequences can be used to assign a date to the time at which their ancestral sequence diverged. Therefore, molecular clock must be calibrated so that we know how many nucleotide substitutions to expect per million years. The calibration is usually achieved by reference to the fossil records.

For example, fossil record suggested that the recent common ancestor of Human and Orangutans lived 13 million years ago.

Therefore, to calibrate the Human molecular clock, we compare the DNA sequences of Human and Orangutans to determine the amount of nucleotide substitution that has occurred and also to obtain the rate of substitutions per million years.

The number of substitutions is determined for a pair of homologous genes from human and orangutans.

If number of substitutions = $x$

Number per lineage = $\frac{x}{2}$

Number per lineage per million years

$$= \frac{x}{2 \times 13}$$

At one time it was thought that there might be a universal molecular clock that applied to all genes in all organisms. But now it is realized that the molecular clocks are different in different organisms and are variable even within a single organism (Strauss, 1999). The species with a short generation time is likely to accumulate DNA replication error at a faster rate than a species with a longer generation time. This explains that rodents have a faster molecular clock than primates (Gu and Li 1992).

The molecular clock for mitochondrial genes is faster than the nuclear genome, because mitochondria lack DNA repair system (Gibbon 1998).

## 30.9 SYNONYMOUS CODON

A mutation may change a codon into a second codon that specifies the same amino acids. For example UUU codon codes for phenylalanine, when mutates into UUC by nucleotide substitution, also codes for phenylalanine, this is synonymous codon. Non-synonymous substitutions occur at a slower rate than the synonymous codon within the organism. This is because a mutation that results in a change in amino acid sequence of a protein might be deleterious to organism. Therefore the accumulation of non-synonymous mutations in the population is reduced or eliminated by natural selection. Miyata and coworkers have shown that nucleotide substitution rates are fairly constant for synonymous codon changes.

## CHAPTER GLOSSARY/KEY TERMS

**Cladistics :** A phylogenetic approach that stresses the importance of understanding the evolutionary relevance of the characters that are studied.

**Data matrix :** A tabulation of differences between species for (or other taxa) in rows (characters) and columns (taxa).

**Distance matrix :** A table showing the evolutionary distance between all pairs of nucleotide sequence in a dataset.

**Distance method :** A mathematical approach to alignment of nucleotide sequences.

**Euclidean distance :** A coefficient measuring the distance between two taxa in multidimensional space.

**Gene tree :** A phylogenetic tree that describes the evolutionary relationships between a group of genes.

**Holophyletic :** Pertaining to a group that consists of all the descendents of its most recent common ancestor.

**Hybridization :** The attachment to one another by base pairing of two complementary polynucleotides.

**Indel :** A position in an alignment between two DNA sequences where an insertion or deletion has occurred.

**Inferred tree :** A tree obtained by phylogenetic analysis.

*Contd.*

**Manhattan distance :** A similarity coefficient consisting of the absolute differences between the characters of each signifier for every possible pair of taxa.

**Maximum parsimony method :** The method for reconstruction of a phylogenetic tree based on maximum parsimony (shortest evolutionary pathway).

**Molecular clock :** A device based on the inferred mutation rate that enables times to be assigned to the branch points in a gene tree.

**Neighbour-joining method :** A method for reconstruction of phylogenetic tree.

**Numerical phenetics :** A classificatory approach which is based on the numerical typing of as many characters as possible.

**Operational taxonomic unit (OTU) :** One of the organisms composed in a phylogenetic analysis.

**Orthologous gene :** Homologous genes located in the genomes of different organisms.

**Paralogous gene :** Two or more homologous genes located in the same genome.

**Paraphyletic taxa :** The group of sequences that excludes some members of a clade in a phyletic tree construct.

**Parsimony :** An approach that decides between different phylogenetic tree topologies by identifying the one that involves the shortest evolutionary pathway.

**Phylogenetic tree :** A diagramatic resentation of inferred lines of descent, based on palaeontological, morphological, molecular or other evidences.

**Plesiomorphic character state :** The character state possessed by a remote common ancestor of a group of organisms.

**Polymerase chain reaction (PCR) :** A technique that results in eponential amplification of a selected region of a DNA molecule.

**Restriction fragment length polymorphism (RFLP) :** A restriction fragment whose length is variable because of the presence of a polymorphic restriction site at one or both ends.

**Signifier :** A feature that varies from one organism to another.

**Signifier state :** The particular expression of a signifier in a given organism. In taxonomic analysis, a signifier state is most often the same as a character as traditionally defined.

**Simlarity approach :** A rigorous mathematical approach to alignment of nucleotide sequence.

**Simple sequence length polymorphism (SSLP) :** An array of repeat sequences that display length variation.

**Single nucleotide polymorphism (SNP) :** A point mutation that is carried by some individuals of a population.

**Sister group :** In a dicotomous cladogram, the two holophyletic groups that descended from their commoin ancestor.

**Species tree :** A phylogenetic tree that describes the evolutionary relationships between a group of species.

**Synonymous codon :** The codon which is changed into a second codon by mutation that specifies the same amino acid.

**Taxonomic character :** Any attribute of a member of a taxon by which it differs or may differ from a member of different taxon.

# Exercise

**A. Long answer type questions :**

1. What is OTU? How OTU is used for the classification of the animals. Define taxonomic character and its important in taxonomy.
2. What is the importance of data matrix and data matrix table in the taxonomy?
3. Write a note on cladistics.
4. Describe different methods of cladistic analysis.
5. What is cladogram? What are their components? What is the principle of cladogram.
6. What are the features of DNA based phylogenetic trees? What are the differences between species tree and gene tree?
7. Describe different methods of tree construction.
8. Write a note on dot matrix method of tree construction.
9. Write a note on Branch and Bound method of tree construction.
10. Write a note on Manhattan and Eucledean method of tree construction.
11. What methods are used to convert alignment data into a phylogenetic tree?
12. Write notes on distance matrix, cluster analysis, UPGMA, maximum parsimony method.
13. What principles are used in molecular clock for estimation of time of divergence?
14. Write a note on synonymous codon and mutation rate.

**B. Short answer type questions.**

1. What do you mean by molecular phylogeny? What is it's objective?
2. What is phylogeny? How a phylogeny can be constructed?
3. How the modern phylogeny could be done?
4. What do you mean by numerical phenetics?
5. What do you mean by operational taxonomic units?
6. What is taxonomic characters?
7. What do you mean by the term "signifier".
8. What is character states? What is signifier state?
9. What do you mean by binary mode and multiple mode of character states?
10. What is data matrix?
11. What is data matrix table? How the characters are coded in the data-matrix table?
12. What is cladistics?
13. Why in cladistics equal weightage is not given to all characters?
14. What are apomorphic and plesiomorphic characters?
15. What do you mean by cladistic analysis.
16. What is the principle of parsimony method used for cladistic analysis.
17. What do you mean by homoplasies?
18. What is the principle of compatibility method used for cladistic analysis.
19. What is the principle of maximum likelihood method used for claadistic analysis?
20. Why gene or other nucleotide sequence is avoided to take them as a taxonomic unit?
21. What would be the risk of confusion if we take gene as a taxonomic unit?
22. What is a cladogram? On which the cladogram is based?
23. What is synapomorphic, plesiomorphic and apomorphic characters?
24. What are holophyletic taxon and paraphyletic taxon?
25. What are the two converntions for the construction of a cladogram?

26. What is the principle of Parsimony?
27. How the character states are coded in the cladistic analysis.
28. What are the three characters recognized to draw the cladogram?
29. What is the objective of DNA-based phylogenetic trees?
30. What do you mean by the nodes and internodes and branches of a DNA based phylogenetic tree?
31. What is meant by unrooted phylogenetic tree?
32. What is meant by rooted phylogenetic tree?
33. What is "out group"?
34. What do you mean by inferred tree? Why it is called so?
35. What do you mean by orthologous gene?
36. Why gene tree is more accurate?
37. What is the main difference of gene tree from a species tree?
38. What are the four steps for the construction of gene tree?
39. What is the sound basis of construction of phylogenetic tree?
40. What are indels?
41. What is dot matrix? How dot matrix is done?
42. What is distance matrix?
43. What is similarity matrix? How the matrix is prepared?
44. Give some computer methods for construction of trees.
45. Define Manhattan distance and Eucledean distance.
46. What is cluster analysis?
47. What do you mean by UPGMA?
48. What is primary cluster? What is secondary cluster?
49. What is teritiary cluster?
50. What is neighbour joining method of tree building?
51. What do you mean by maximum parsimony method?
52. What is the principle of assessing the accurary of a reconstructed tree?
53. What is molecular clock hypothesis in evolution?
54. How the calibration of time is done?
55. What is the principles of calibration of molecular clock?
56. Why the calibration of molecular clock is not similar within species?
57. Why molecular clock is faster in mitochondrial DNA?
58. What is synonymous codon?
59. Why mutation of synonymous codon is faster than nonsynonymous codon?

# 31

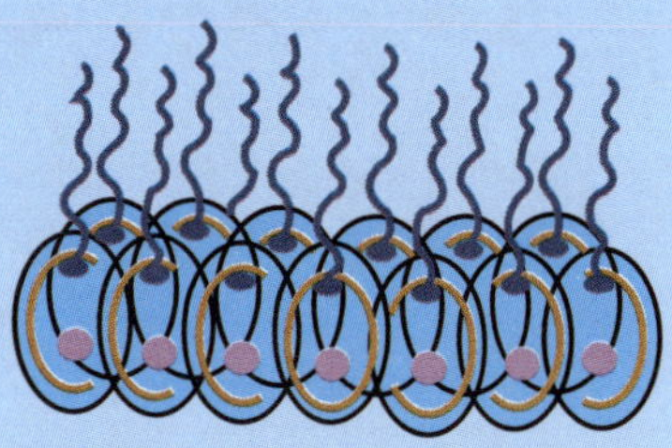

# Evolution at Molecular Level

**CHAPTER AGENDA**

**31.1** Molecular evolution; **31.2** Molecular evolution by nucleotide substitution; **31.3** Pseudogenes and it's evolutionary significance; **31.4** Molecular evolution by amino acid substitution; **31.5** Karyotypic evolution and Speciation; **31.6** Genetic distance; **31.7** Evolutionary rates; **31.8** Origin of life; **31.9** Recent concept of Origin of Prokaryotes; **31.10** Origin and Evolution of Metazoa; Chapter Glossary/Key Terms; Exercise

## 31.1. MOLECULAR EVOLUTION

At molecular level, the process of evolution involves the insertion, deletion or substitution of nucleotides in the DNA (gene), which may cause a change in the amino acid sequence of the product.

Until the late 1960's the techniques for protein sequencing did not become a routine and rapid DNA sequencing was not developed until 10 years after that. Early studies were therefore dependent largely on indirect assessment of DNA or protein variations using one of three methods.

1. **Immunological data**, which involves measurements of amount of cross-reactivity seen when an antibody specific for a protein from one organism is mixed with the same protein from a different organism. For example, if human β-globin is injected into a rabbit that the rabbit makes an antibody that binds specifically to the protein. The antibody also will cross-react with β-globins from other vertebrates, because these β-globins have similar structures to the human serum. The degree of cross reactivity depends on how similar the β-globin being tested is to the human protein, providing the similarity data used in the phylogenetic analysis.
2. **Protein electrophoresis**, which is used to compare the electrophoretic properties and hence degree of similarity of proteins from different organisms. This has been used useful for comparing the proteins of the members of same species and also for closely related species.
3. **DNA-DNA hybridization data** are obtained by hybridizing DNA samples from the two organisms being compared. The stability of the DNA-DNA hybrids between two individuals depends upon the degree of similarity between the nucleotide sequences of the two DNAs, which is measured by determining the melting temperature. Stable hybrids having a higher melting temperature. According to Mc Carthy and others, for each 1% difference in nucleotide composition between two samples of DNA, the thermal stability of the hybrid molecule is lowered by 1.6°C. For example, the single copy portion of cattle DNA is hybridized to single copy DNA from sheep and pig, the approximate reduction in thermal stability for these two hybrid DNAs turns out to be 6°C (3.7% mismatching) and 12°C (7.5% mismatching), indicating a significantly further evolutionary distance between cow and pig than between cow and sheep.

During 1980s DNA-based phylogenies began to be carried out on a large scale. Now a large number of techniques have been evolved for the analysis of DNA *viz.* PCR, RFLPs, SSLPs and SNPs, particularly for intraspecific studies as those aimed at understanding migrations prehistoric human populations.

## 31.2 MOLECULAR EVOLUTION BY NUCLEOTIDE SUBSTITUTION

DNA-DNA hybridization has been used in attempts to analyze phylogenetic relationship between birds and between hominoid primates but this technique does not provide exact sequence informations.

Recently, complete DNA sequence data have been obtained for only some small viruses and small number of genes in other organisms.

One example of molecular characterization of a gene cluster isolated by recombinant DNA technique is that of the β globin genes. In human, this gene is present on chromosome no. 11 with a span of 60kb. and are present as seven linked loci cluster. All of these genes apparently arose by a process of gene duplication although two are pseudogenes. In Gorillas and Chimpanzees and old world monkeys, a similar organization of the five functional genes are found. In New world monkeys, there is an apparent absence of one of the functional genes, which indicates their early divergence from an ancestral group which is the lemur-like primates. The genes responsible for embryonic and fetal development and adult β-globin each possesses three exons and two introns. The non-functional pseudogenes are related to functional genes but are inactivated by mutations such as deletion, duplication or nucleic acid substitution.

## 31.3 PSEUDOGENES AND IT'S EVOLUTIONARY SIGNIFICANCE

In multicellular organisms, a wide variety of DNA sequences are found, which are of no apparent use. Some of these sequences are defective copies of functional genes and are therefore called **pseudogenes**.

Pseudogenes have been reported in human beings, mouse and *Drosophila*.

### 31.3.1 α and β Globin Pseudogenes

**In Primates :** The division of globin chains into α-like and β-like is supported by the structure of the protein and by the organization of the genes. The entire β-like family is defined by its ability to combine directly with the α–chain. The zeta chain is defined by its ability to combine with the embryonic β-like chains. Each type of globin turns out to be coded by genes organised into a single cluster. In man the α-cluster lies on chromosome no-11 and β-cluster lies on chromosome no-16 (Fig. 31.1).

Each cluster was discovered by the ability of genomic fragments to hybridize with probes representing adult globin mRNA. This analysis led to the discovery of further genes, some representing known or unknown embryonic globins, other comprising non-functional pseudogenes.

The organization of these genes in other higher primates is very similar. For example, the β-clusters of gorilla and baboon are virtually indistinguishable from that of man. All of the genes are transcribed from left to right and they lie in the order of developmental expressions : 5′-embryonic-fetal-adult-3′.

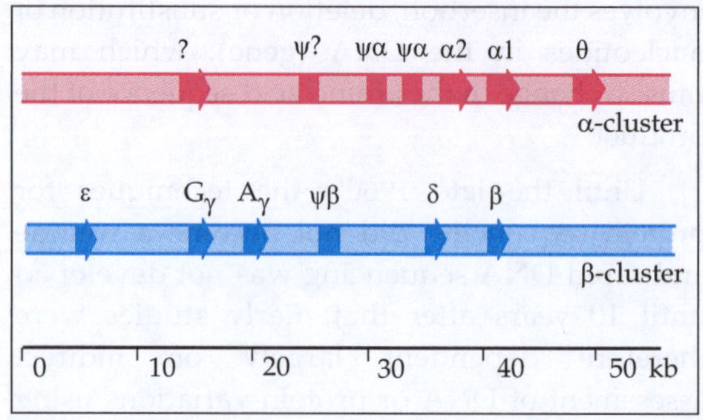


**Fig.31.1 :** *α and β cluster genes in primates (human)*

Stretching over 50kb, the β-cluster contains five fundamental genes: ε, Gγ, Aγ, δ and β and one pseudogene ψβ lies between Aγ and δ. The two γ genes differ in their coding sequence in only one amino acid. The G-varient has glycine at position 136, whereas, A-varient has alanine at that position.

The more compact α-cluster extends over 28kb and includes one active ζ (zeta), one nonfunctional ζ -gene, one ψα pseudo-α-gene, two α-genes and one θ-gene of unknown function. The existence of two α-genes, coding for the identical protein was suspected previously on the basis of genetic evidence.

**In other vertebrates :** A similar general organizations have been found in other vertebrate globin gene clusters, but details of the type of members of genes may vary (Fig. 31.2).

In rabbit, 4 β-like genes have been identified, two embryonic, one pseudogene and one adult gene. Again the functional genes lie in their order of expression 5′ → 3′.

In goat, there are seven β-like globin genes. Two are embryonic, one fetal, two adult and two pseudogenes.

In the mouse, there must be at least nine β-like globin genes. Seven genes so far have been identified. These include the two adult β-genes, the major being expressed at greater level than minor. $\beta h_3$ and $\beta h_2$, whose sequences

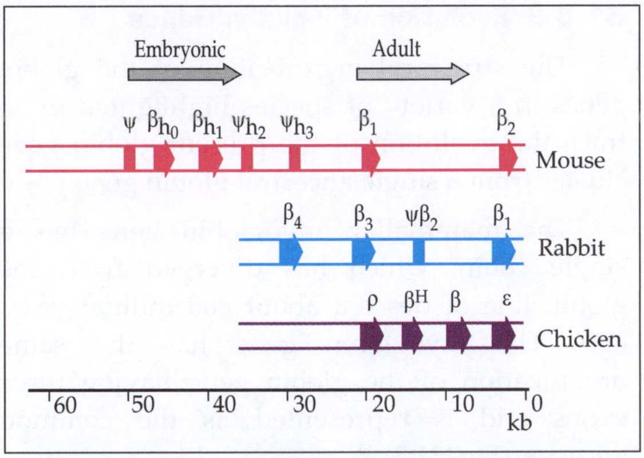


**Fig.31.2 :** *Cluster of β-globin pseudogenes in other vertebrates.*

do not seem to fit with known mouse globin types and these may be pseudogenes.

There may be more members of a gene family, both functional and nonfunctional then we would suspect on the basis of protein analysis. The extra functional genes may represent duplicates that code for identical peptides or they may be related to proteins.

The pseudogenes show varying relationship with the functional genes and can be analyzed only at the level of DNA sequence.

In the mouse genome, some additional pseudogenes have been found that are not the part of the clusters. The α-cluster consists of one embryonic and two adult genes. Two identified pseudogenes each lie on different chromosomes from the cluster. There may be others. These pseudogenes must have originated by translocation events that moved a gene away from the cluster.

Pseudogenes possess the sequences that are related to those of the functional genes, but that cannot be translated into a functional protein.

Some pseudogenes have the same general structure as functional genes with sequences corresponding to exons and introns in the usual locations. They are rendered inactive by **MUTATIONS** that prevent any or all of the stages of gene expression. The changes can take the form of abolishing the signals for initiating transcription, preventing splicing at the exon-intron junctions or terminating translation prematurely.

Usually, a pseudogene has several deleterious mutations, presumably because once it ceased to be active, there was no impediment to the accumulation of further mutations. Pseudogenes of this type have been found in many systems including globin, immunoglobulins, histocompatibility antigens etc.

A typical example is the rabbit pseudogene $\psi\beta_2$ which has the usual organization of exons and introns and is related most closely to the functional gene $\beta_1$. But there is a deletion of one base pair at codon 20 of $\psi\beta_2$, causing a frame shift that would lead to termination shortly after initiation of translation. Several point mutations have changed later codons representing amino acids that is highly conserved in the β-globins.

Neither of the two introns any longer possess boundary sequences that can form adequately to the GT-AG rule, so probably the introns could not be spliced out even if the gene is transcribed.

The mouse $\psi h_3$ gene has an interesting property. It precisely lacks both introns. Its sequence can be aligned with the α globin mRNA. The apparent tune of inactivation coincides with the original duplication, which suggests that the original inactivating events may have been associated with the loss of introns. Without introns, the gene may have been unable to function and thus will have begun immediately to collect mutations. But how does it occur? This could take the form of insertion of a reverse transcript into the genome, perhaps carried by a retrovirus or of pairing between the mRNA and one strand of DNA at some stage of a recombination process.

In the α globin genes of the goat, there are two adult species $\beta^A$ and $\beta^C$. Each of these has a pseudogene a few kb upstream from it, called $\psi\beta^Z$ and $\psi\beta^X$. The two pseudogenes are better related to each other than to the adult β-globin genes, in particular, they share several inactivating mutations. Also, the two adult β-globin genes are better related to each other than to the pseudogenes. This implies that an origin of ψβ→β structure was itself duplicated giving two functional β genes, which have diverged further into $\beta^A$ and $\beta^C$ genes and two nonfunctional genes, which have developed into the current pseudogenes.

### 31.3.2 Origin of Pseudogenes

Gene duplication, rearrangement and variation are the important factors for the evolution as the slow accumulation of point mutations in the individual genes.

A gene cluster can expand or contract by unequal crossing over when recombination occurs between nonallelic genes. When two copies of a gene on each chromosome, an occasional misalignment allows pairing between them. Thus generates nonreciprocal recombinant chromosomes one of which has a duplication of gene and other has deletion. The first recombinant can increase the copies of the gene from two to three to more, while the second has a decrease from two to one. The corresponding exons of adjacent gene copies are likely to be well enough related to support pairing. Thalassemias result from the mutations that reduce or prevent synthesis of either α or β globin. The occurrence of unique crossing over in the human globin gene cluster is revealed by the nature of certain thalassemias.

One of the possible origin of pseudogenes was based on the assumption that most pseudogenes are flanked by a short repeat of 6-21 bases. It suggests that mRNA or snRNA itself becomes incorporated into DNA or into retrovirus RNA followed by the incorporation of retroviruses.

The reverse transcript of mRNA or snRNA was synthesized as cDNA, which subsequently becomes integrated. The insertion of this cDNA due to staggered cleavage of genomic DNA at a specific site.

### 31.3.3 Evolution of β-globin Genes

The structural organization of the globin genes in a variety of species highlighted us to trace the evolution of the present globin gene cluster from a single ancestral globin gene.

The mammalian myoglobin gene has a single chain, which has diverged from the globin line of descent about 800 million years ago. The myoglobin gene has the same organization of the globin gene having three exons and is represented as the common ancestor (Fig. 31.3).

The leghemoglobin in plants, which is related to the globin gene, may represent the ancestral form, which has four exons and in between them has three introns.

In some primitive fishes like lamprey and hagfishes, have only one globin chain. That must have arose from the exon fusion of the leghemoglobin. As a result, three exons and in between, two introns resulted. Other view is that by introducing intron into the middle exon, leghemoglobin might have arisen.

The next stage of evolution among vertebrates were found in *Xenopus* where two globin genes α and β of both larval and adult types. The cluster must therefore have evolved by duplication of linked α and β genes, followed by divergence between the individual copies.

About 350 million years ago separation of α and β globin genes must has been resulted from a transposition in the mammalian/avian ancestors. The separate clusters of α and β globin genes in both mammals and birds have been physically separated before they have been diverged from their common ancestors probably 270 millions of years ago.

Now, these two clusters are expanded by further duplication and inactivation by unequal crossing over or by incorporation with retroviruses and established into the separate chromosome.

Most mutations that change the amino acid sequence are deleterious and will be eliminated

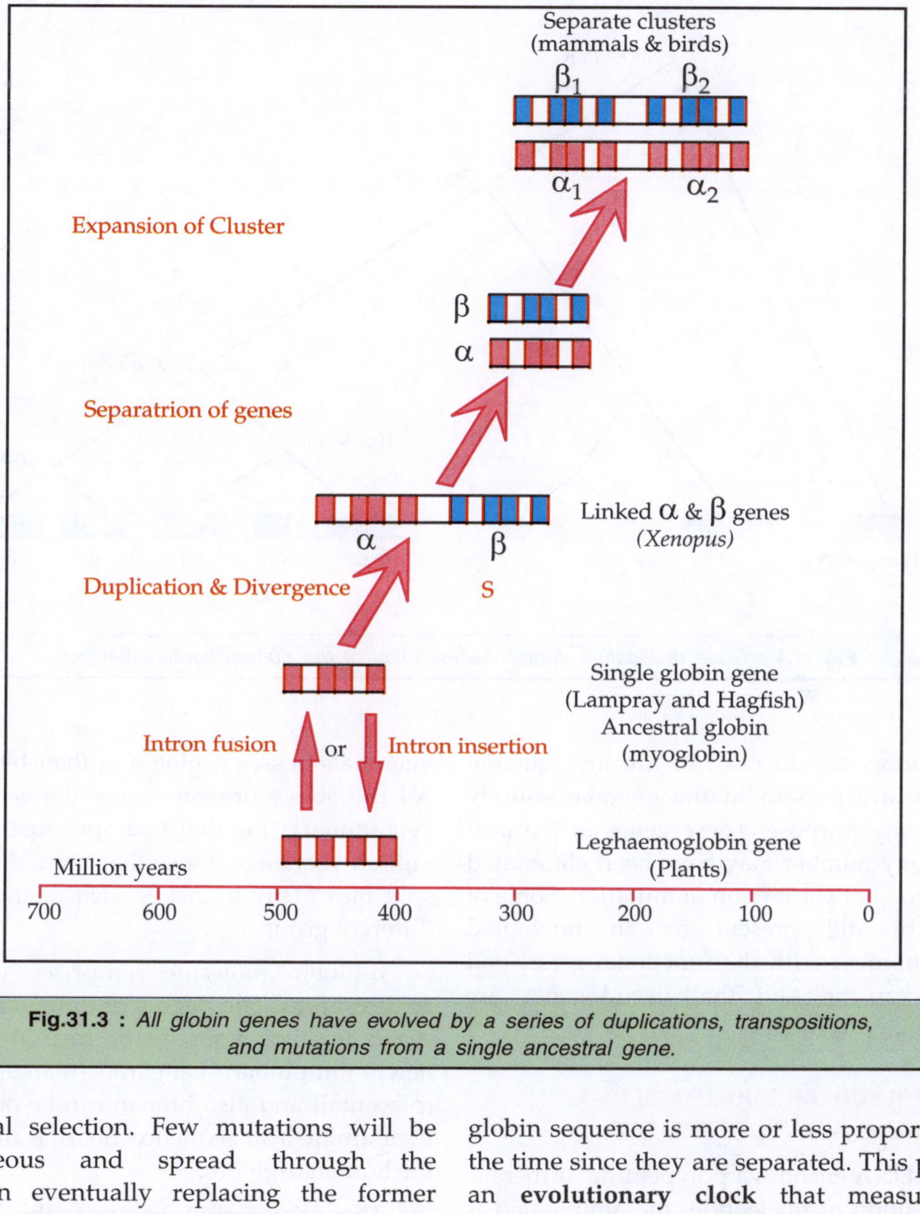


**Fig.31.3 :** *All globin genes have evolved by a series of duplications, transpositions, and mutations from a single ancestral gene.*

by natural selection. Few mutations will be advantageous and spread through the population eventually replacing the former sequence. The coding region can be distinguished into potential replacement sites and silent sites. The mutation of the replacement sites alters the amino acid, which may cause deleterious, neutral or advantageous to the organism. The mutations on the silent sites do not change in the proteins.

It is evident that the silent site divergence is much greater than the replacement site divergence. The divergence between any pair of globin sequence is more or less proportional to the time since they are separated. This provides an **evolutionary clock** that measures the accumulation of mutations at an apparently even rate during evolution.

Replacement site divergences between pairs of β-globin genes allow the history of the human cluster to be reconstructed. This tree accounts for the separation of classes of globin genes. Duplications of individual genes are of unknown origin. The time of the α and ζ divergence is not known (Fig. 31.4).

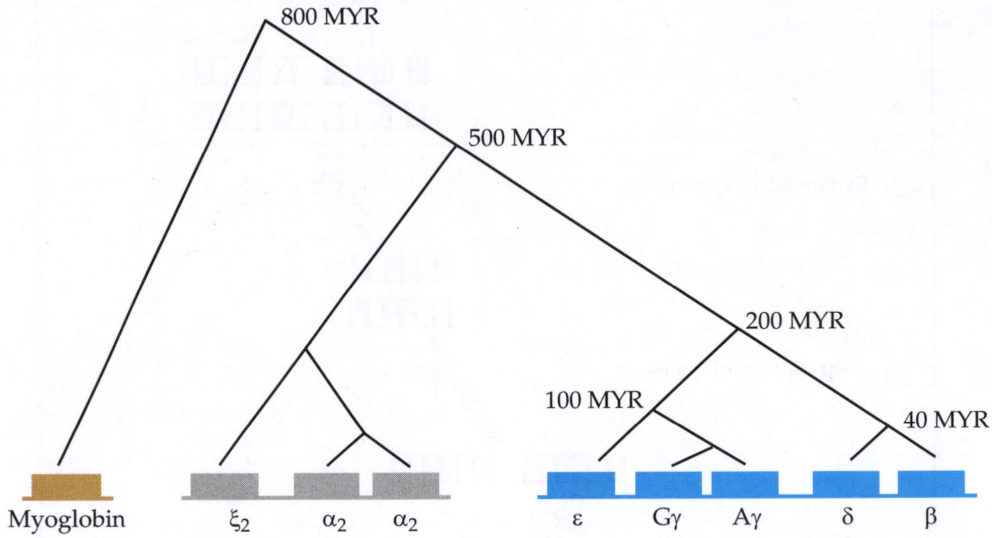


**Fig.31.4 :** *Gene duplication during the evolution of the human hemoglobin gene.*

Pseudogenes do not full fill any function and they are present in the genome entirely without any purpose. These genes in the past time in any number may have been eliminated by deletion or by accretion of mutation. Some of them are still present as an unwanted accompaniment with the functional genes and thus it can be said that pseudogenes are **evolutionary dead ends.**

## 31.4 MOLECULAR EVOLUTION BY AMINO ACID SUBSTITUTION

The DNA encodes a polypeptide. If there is a substitution of nucleotide, the amino acid is also substituted at that region, as a result a changed polypeptide is produced. By comparing related sequences of amino acids, the molecular details of evolution can be analyzed.

Evolution of the α-globin polypeptide of hemoglobin in several vertebrate groups can be analyzed. Five major classes of vertebrates – the cartilagenous fishes, the bony fishes, the amphibians, the marsupials and placental mammals posses α-globin in their hemoglobin. All the above organisms are derived from an evolutionary line that had appeared about 500 million years ago. Since that time, this line has split into many branches each giving rise to a different groups.

α-globin molecule comprises 141 amino acid residues. The degree of differences among shark (cartilagenous fish), carp (bony fish), newts (amphibia), kangaroo (marsupials) cow (placental) and also human can be observed in their amino acid sequence. Shark is most unlike the human α-globin.

The relationship between the degree of difference (D) and the evolutionary time can be used to estimate the rate at which α-globin has evolved.

For instance, the human and carp evolutionary lines. The common ancestor of these organisms existed about 400 million years ago, so the total evolutionary time that has elapsed since the two lines diverged is 800 million years. During this time human and carp

**TABLE 31.1**
**The data given bellow described the rate of amino acid substitution per year site per in α-globin in different vertebrates : (source M. Kimura)**

| *Animal* | *Common ancestor existed (million years ago)* | *Total evolution time (million years)* | *Degree of difference of aminoacids in α-globin* | *$\frac{D}{7}$(amino acid substitution per site per year)* |
|---|---|---|---|---|
| Shark | 440 | 880 | $\frac{79}{141} = 0.5602$ | $\frac{0.5602}{880} = 0.6 \times 10^{-5}$ M.Y. |
| Carp | 400 | 800 | $\frac{68}{141} = 0.482$ | $\frac{0.482}{800} = 0.6 \times 10^{-5}$ Million years |
| Newt | 350 | 700 | $\frac{62}{141} = 0.4397$ | $\frac{0.4397}{700} = 6.28 \times 10^{-4}$ M.Y. |
| Kangaroo | 135 | 270 | $\frac{27}{141} = 0.1914$ | $\frac{0.1914}{270} = 7.09 \times 10^{-4}$ M.Y. |
| Cow | 70 | 140 | $\frac{17}{141} = 0.12056$ | $\frac{0.1205}{140} = 8.6 \times 10^{-4}$ M.Y. |

α-globins have accumulated differences in 68 amino acid sites. The degree of difference is $\frac{68}{141} = 0.482$ difference per amino acid site, suggesting that α-globin has evolved at a rate of $\frac{D}{T} = 0.482$ amino acid substitutions per site over 800 million years or $0.6 \times 10^{-9}$ substitutions at each site per year (Table no. 31.1).

An evolution tree indicating the differences in number of amino acids of α-globin in different vertebrates, when compared with human can be drawn (Fig. 31.5).

The substitution of amino acids in a particular site may be changed more than once and such a change can not be identified, which may be about one substitution per one amino acid site is about one billion years in the case of α-globin.

M. Kimura proposed the **neutral theory** of **molecular evolution** which postulates that the majority of the molecular changes are caused by the random fixation of selectively neutral mutations. The probability of random fixation of selectively neutral mutation is equal to the mutation rate. Therefore according to his theory the rate of evolution (molecular evolution) is completely determined by the force of mutation.

Some mutations may cause no change in the function of polypeptides such a case the rate of evolution is low.

The neutral theory of evolution is called **non-Darwinian theory of evolution**, because in the neutral theory, species do not get better by fixing beneficial mutations and this theory has little or no place for selection in the positive Darwinian sense.

## 31.5. KARYOTYPIC EVOLUTION AND SPECIATION

Comparisons of chromosome banding patterns within animal groups such as mammals, birds, reptiles, amphibians and fishes and also between representatives of particular taxonomic groups have been accomplished. Today taxomists employed structure of chromosomes and has proved to be a stable and broadly representative of phylogenetic change. Thus, data from comparisons of chromosome-banding patterns in members of different species have a broad phylogenetic significance.

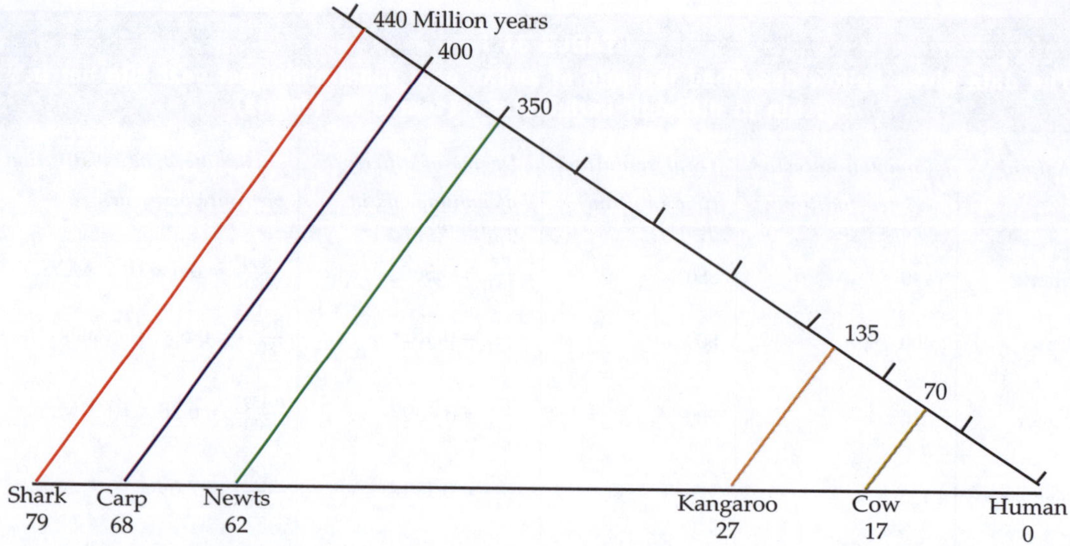


**Fig.31.5 :** *Evolution of the α -globin polypeptide of hemoglobin in some vertebrate groups.*

Karyological studies on banding arrangements of the chromosomes of human (*Homo sapiens*), Chimpanzee (*Pan trogodytes*), Gorillas and Orangutans have been noted that the 24 pairs of chromosomes in the great apes are reduced to 23 pairs in human because of the fusion of two different chromosomes into a single (No-2) human chromosome. This fusion event along with some other changes (e.g., inversions in chromosome –1 and 18) must have taken place somewhat after human line is separated from a human-chimpanzee common ancestor. These banding arrangements indicate that human has a closer evolutionary relationship to chimpanzees than to Gorilla and a more distant one to Orangutans.

Karyological changes bring about the speciation in natural populations.

For example, *Homo sapiens* a line has been diversed from the *Pan trogodytes* line. A. D. Stock (1973) compared the banded chromosomes of these two species and noted some structural differences between them (Fig. 31.6).

1. Human chromosome-2 has been evolved by centric fusion of two chromosomes of *Pan trogodytes*.
2. Chromosome 4, 5, 9, 12, 17 and 18 of the two species, each differ by a single pericentric inversion.
3. A pericentric inversion distinguishes chromosome 8 of the two species.
4. Chromosome 1 and 9 have a difference in heterochromatin content.

These karyological changes established in the species level are used as a measure phylogenetic change.

Evolutionary changes in karyotype brought about by translocations have emerged from comparative cytogenetic studies on species of *Drosophila*.

The ancestral or simplest chromosomal complement is found as five pairs of rod-shaped and one pair of dot-like chromosomes is *D subobscura*, *D. virilis* and other.

One of the rod-shaped chromosomes is the X-chromosome. Translocation of X-chromosome and one of the autosomes give rise to *D. pseudoobscura* and *D. persimilis* where one pair of V-shaped X-chromosomes, three pairs of rod-like and a pair of dot-like autosomes.

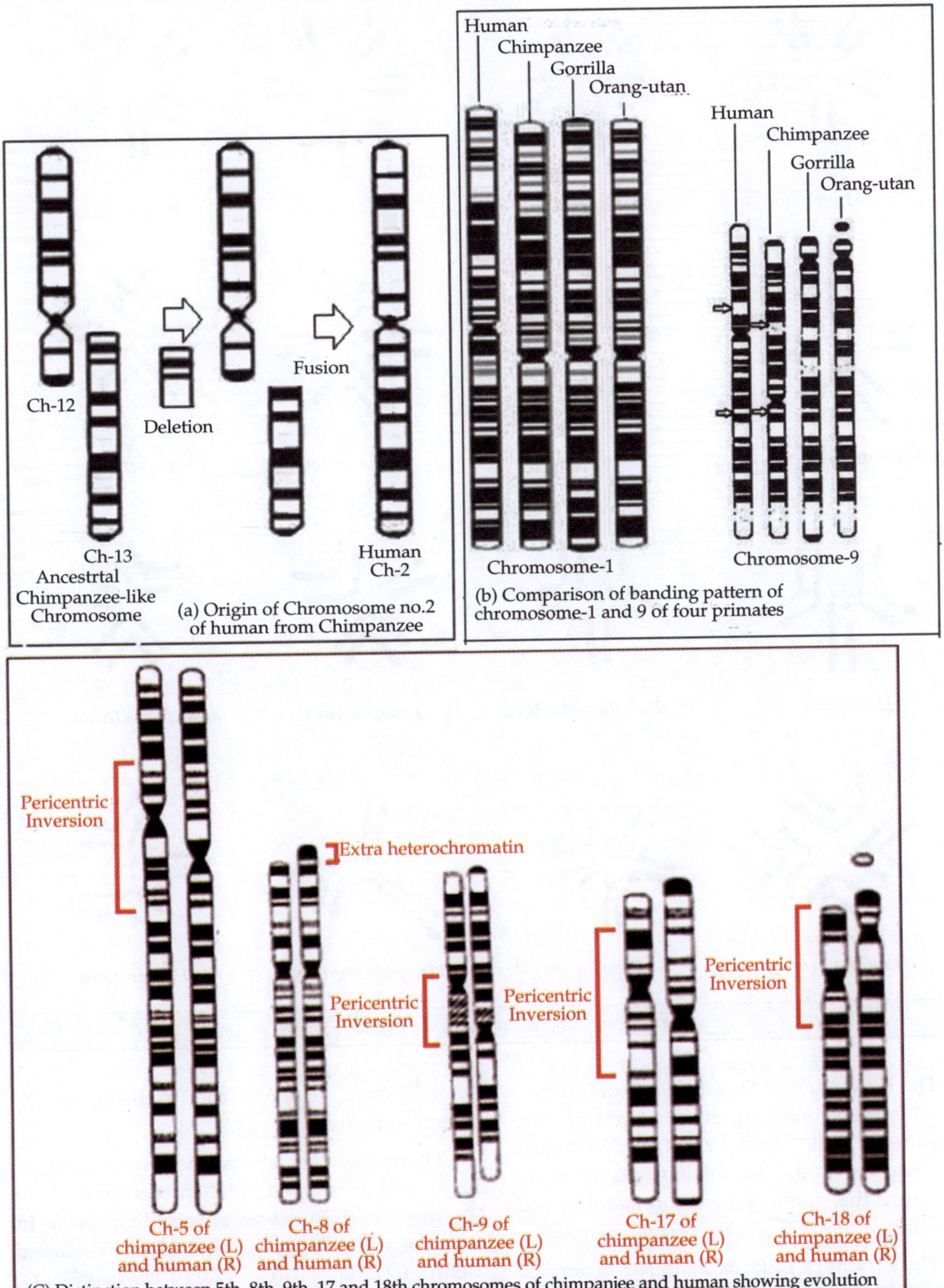


(a) Origin of Chromosome no.2 of human from Chimpanzee

(b) Comparison of banding pattern of chromosome-1 and 9 of four primates

(C) Distinction between 5th, 8th, 9th, 17 and 18th chromosomes of chimpanjee and human showing evolution

**Fig.31.6 :** *Banding pattern of the chromosomes of human, chimpanjee, gorilla and Orangutan in respective order from left to right.*

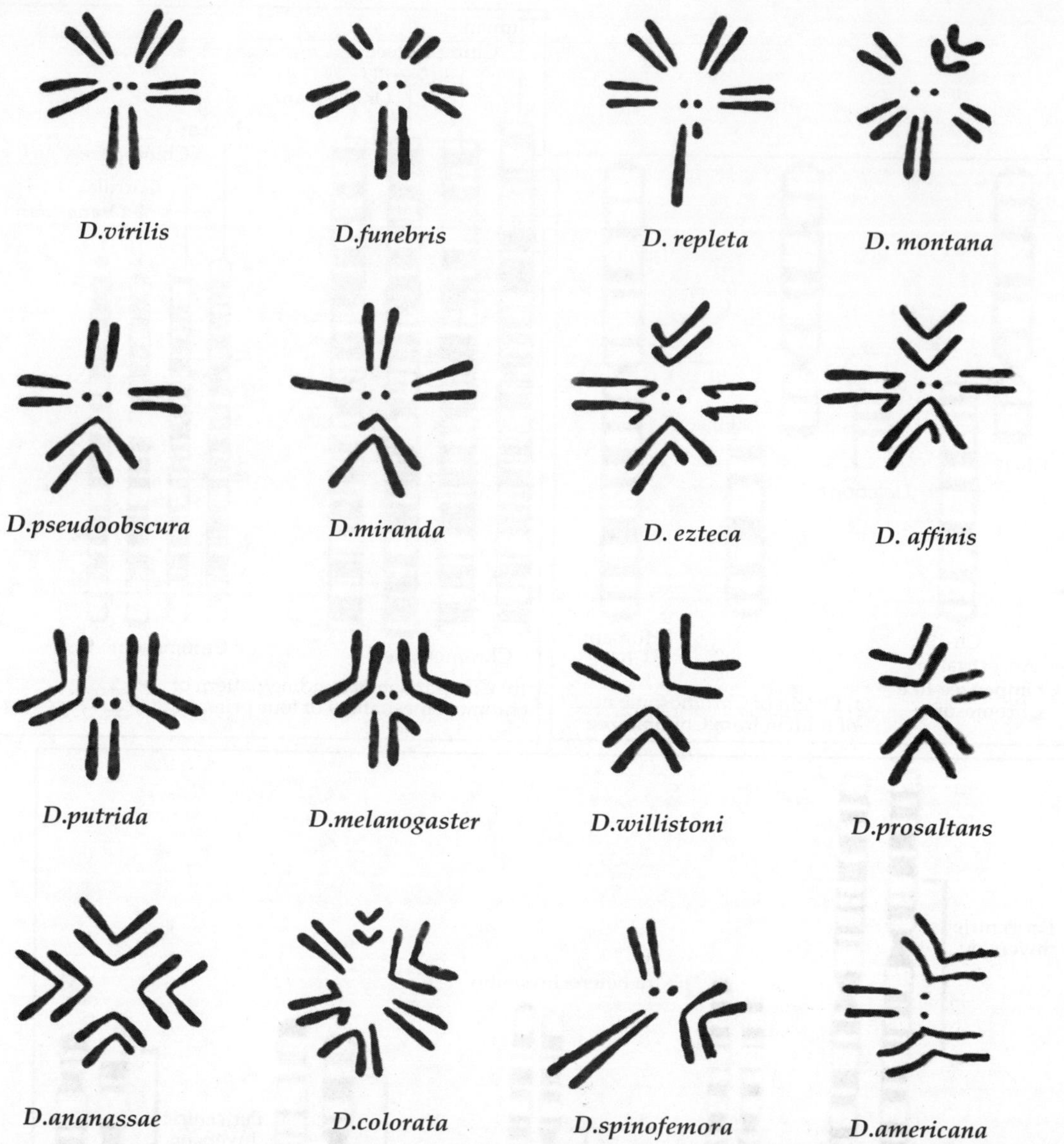


**Fig.31.7 :** *Chromosome complements in males of certain species of Drosophila.*

The Karyotype of *D. willistoni* exhibits two more translocations combine two of the autosomal rods into another V-shaped autosome within a median centromere and cause the dot to join the remaining rod (Fig. 31.7).

The karyotype of *D. melanogaster* is derived from the two translocations that tie together four rod-shaped autosomes to become two V-shaped one, leaving the rod-shaped X-chromosome free.

Therefore, the genes that are borne in the rod shaped X-chromosome in *D. melanogaster; D. subobscura* and *D. virilis* lie in one of the two arms of V-shaped X-chromosome in *D. pseudoobscura, D. persimilis* and *D. willistoni.*

## 31.6 GENETIC DISTANCE

In the taxonomy, subspecies or race is an aggregate of local populations of a species inhabiting a geographic subdivision of the range of the species and differing taxonomically from other populations of the species.

Geneticists have characterized races as the populations of the same species that markedly differ from each other. Therefore, races share the gene pool of the entire species although they are sufficiently separated to exhibit individually unique gene frequencies. Races differ in the relative frequency of a particular gene but these differences do not prohibit gene exchange between the races of the same species.

Usually differences among human populations have not reached the point where one population is fixed for one allele at a particular locus and another population is fixed for a different allele. But when a population shows fixation for one allele, other populations are always polymorphic for it. To calculate genetic divergences under such circumstances, Nei proposed one procedure in calculating indices of genetic identity (I) and genetic distance (D) between races of human beings such as Caucasians, Africans, Greater Asians, Amerindians and Australoid groups.

**TABLE 31.2**
**Calculation of genetic distance (D) and genetic identity by Nei's procedure (source from Stickberger) for two loci in Caucasians and Africans races.**

| *Locus* | *Allele* | *Caucasians* | *Africans* |
|---|---|---|---|
| **Acid protein** | $P_a^1$ | $P_1=0.21$ | $P_2 = 0.14$ |
| | $P_a^2$ | $q_1 = 0.79$ | $q_2 = 0.86$ |
| **ABO-blood group** | A | $p_1 = 0.24$ | $p_2 = 0.19$ |
| | B | $q_1 = 0.06$ | $q_2 = 0.16$ |
| | O | $r_1 = 0.70$ | $r_2 = 0.65$ |

$$\text{Genetic identity (I)} = \frac{\text{Arithmatic mean of the products of allele frequencies}}{\text{Geometric mean of the homozygote frequencies}}$$

$$I = \frac{[(p_1 \times p_2) + (q_1 \times q_2) + (r_1 \times r_2)]/\text{number of loci}}{\sqrt{[(p_1^2 + q_1^2 + r_1^2) \times (p_2^2 + q_2^2 + r_2^2)]/(\text{number of loci})^2}}$$

$$\text{or, } I = \frac{[(0.21 \times 0.14) + (0.79 \times 0.86) + (0.24 \times 0.19) + (0.06 \times 0.16) + (0.70 \times 0.65)]/2}{\sqrt{[0.21^2 + 0.79^2 + 0.24^2 + 0.06^2 + 0.70^2] \times [0.14^2 + 0.86^2 + 0.19^2 + 0.16^2 + 0.65^2]2^2}}$$

$$\text{or, } I = \frac{1.2190/2}{\sqrt{(1.2194)\,(1.2434/4}} = 0.9899$$

Therefore, genetic distance $= -\ln I$

$= -\ln 0.9899$

$= 0.0101$

The value of genetic identity (I) ranges from zero (no similar alleles between the two populations) to one (complete similarity of alleles and frequencies).

When I = 1, then genetic distance is zero,

When I, approaches zero, D can increase to very large values, indicating that the alleles at some or many loci have been replaced one or more times.

Using this procedure, Nei and Roychoudhury estimated that when averaged over many loci, genetic distance in humans (D) accumulates at some constant rate that may roughly be 3.75 million years per unit of D. Thus for the 85 loci that allow comparisons among the three major races, the estimated times when these races initially diverged from each other.

e.g., Caucasian from Asian, where D = 0.019

The estimated time of divergence

$= 0.019 \times 3.75$ million years.

$= 41000 \pm 15000$ years ago

Similarly, Caucasian from African, where D = 0.032

The estimated time of divergence of races

$= 0.032 \times 3.75$ million years

$= 113000 \pm 34000$ years ago.

Coyne and Orr (1997) pointed out that when the species in a pair are closely related i.e. genetic distance between them is small, (for example 0.5) they are clearly more isolated from each other when they are sympatric than when they are allopatric. For allopatric populations to achieve reproductive isolation requires a much greater genetic distance (D = 0.54) than reproductively isolated sympatric populations (0.04).

As a rough estimate, they proposed that speciation requires approximately 200000 years among taxa that became sympatric and approximately 2.7 million years among taxa that remain allopatric.

## 31.7. EVOLUTIONARY RATES

To estimate the rate of evolution is one of the unanswered problems. Palaeontologists have estimated the rate of evolution. Some of them prefer to measure the rates in term of chronological time (*i.e.*, geological duration and period) whereas, other group prefers to measure biological time (*i.e.*, number of generations.) But the unsolved questions are that what morphological or molecular features should we use to measure rates and how do we determine the number and kinds of genes involved?

In completeness of fossil records, absence of intermediate evolutionary groups etc. are the problems for determination of evolutionary rate. On the other hand taxonomic difficulties also arise due to presence of "lumper" and 'Splitter' groups that combine or split the groups of organisms respectively into different taxonomic categories.

Palaeontological method has classified the rate of evolution in two categories. One is the slower rate i.e., "bradytely" and the other is faster rate i.e., "tachytely".

All living fossils show bradytellic rate of evolution. Most of them are able to survive early in history, they have colonized a difficult but persistent environment. Rare animals have been able to cross such adaptive threshold but most of them are able to continue without any evolution. The examples are *Lingula, Neopilina, Latimeria* etc.(Fig. 31.8).

Among mammals, evolution of artiodactyls is considered to have occurred at tachytelic rate. Simpson has coined the term *"quantum evolution"* to such rapid rate of evolution. These are marked by expansion of parental stock into new adaptive zones and origin of new taxa.

Haldane proposed the rate of evolution in the term of the amount of changes in character divided by elapsed time and is generally in *darwin* units. The rate depends upon the completeness of fossil record, valid phylogenetic information and accurate chronology. According to this, the rate of evolution is measured by the equation :

$$\text{rate} = \frac{\ln \bar{X}_{t_2} - \ln \bar{X}_{t_1}}{(t_2 - t_1)}$$

Where, $\bar{X}$ is the degree of difference in the character's average dimension from time $t_1$ to time $t_2$. *ln* is the natural logarithms base e = 2.718.

For example, a small femur in a rodent lineage that is increased by 0.1 *darwin* evolved twice as fast as a much larger elephant femur that was changed by only 0.05 *darwin*.

The evolutionary rate differences probably rely upon various factors.

1. The structure of populations-their size, genetic variability and distribution.
2. Adaptive and developmental constraints that dictate the structures and functions that organisms are able to achieve.
3. Changes in the direction and intensity of selection at different times in different groups.

Evolution by continuous progressive changes has been called **phyletic gradualism**, which seems to be a very slow process. The rate is calculated geologically or biologically.

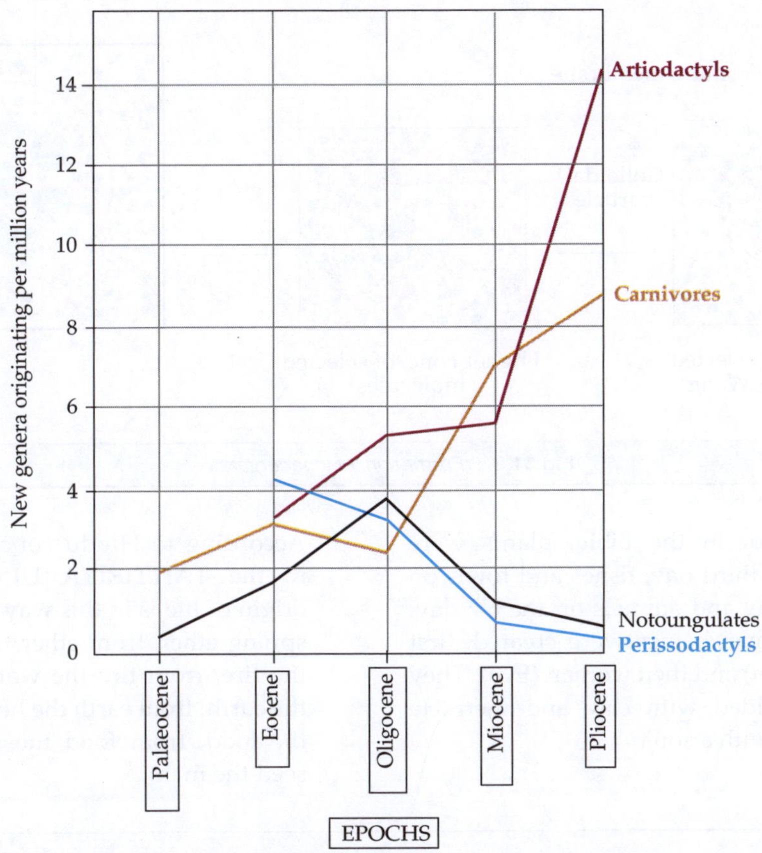


**Fig.31.8 :** *Evolutionary rates measured in terms of new genera originating per million years in four orders of mammals during the Tertiary period.*

Evidences from fossil records indicate that the rate in this process is 0.5 to several million years per species. The drawbacks or criticisms are that it requires about 800 million years for the diversification of life since the origin of metazoa.

Gould and Stanley postulated that the **punctuated equilibrium** process which indicates that most changes occur extremely rapid (cladogenesis) at the time of initiation of new groups, but most of their history passes with little change (stasis), and punctuated by rapid macroevolutionary period, during which new taxa arise through entirely new causes and mechanism.

## 31.8 ORIGIN OF LIFE

Origin of life on the earth has been called the "mystery of mysteries". Surely an even mystery is the origin of the very first living thing.

### 31.8.1 Ancient concepts

There are many non-scientific and scientific ideas on the problem. Most of them are quite bizarre and merely having a historical significance.

1. According to the **special creation** theory, the life is mysterious force or vital force, was originally created by a super natural

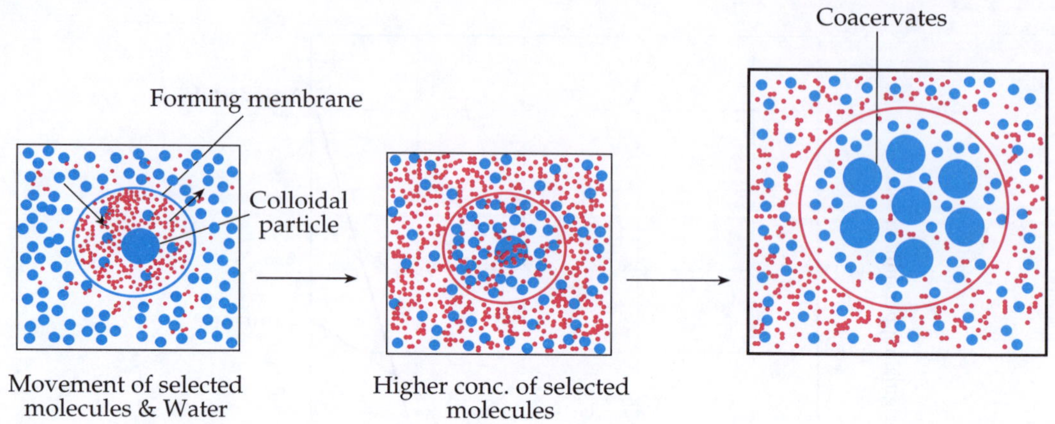


Fig.31.9 : *Formation of coacervates*

power God. In the Bible, plants were created on third day, fishes and fowls on the fifth day and animals on the 6th day. Lastly, human beings were created, first man (Adam) and then woman (Eve). They were moulded with clay and then He furnished with a soul.

According to Hindu concept, elaborated in the TAITTIRIYA UPANISHAD the origin of life is in this way "From Brahma sprang ether, from ether the air, from air the fire, from fire the water, from water the earth, from earth the herbs, from herbs the food, from food the seed and from seed the man".

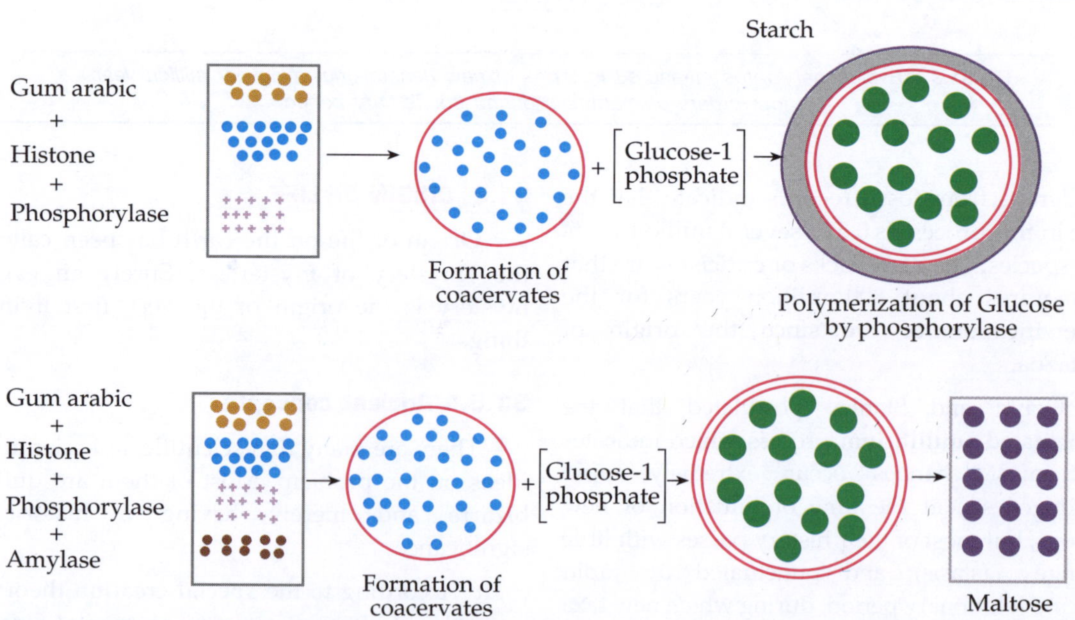


Fig.31.10 : *Synthesis and hydrolysis of starch in coacervates with enzymes*

2. According to Aristotle the birth of living creatures from like-species, **spontaneous generation** from non-living matters occurred, such as maggots from rotting meat, insect from damp soil. A. Spallanzani (1765) tested the theory of spontaneous generation of microbes in a flask. But Louis Pasteur (1828 –1895) devised several experimental means by which the spontaneous generation of microbes was disapproved.
3. A theory, the **cosmozoic theory**, was based on the assumption that life matter, has always existed somewhere in the cosmos and these were carried to the earth by means of spores by meteorites.

All the above theories were non-scientific, only based on the philosophical thinking. None of these theories can satisfy the modern concept of life-form and function.

### 31.8.2 Modern Biochemical Theory

Russian biochemist A.I. Oparin (1894- ) was, the first to suggest that a long evolution of chemical substances occurred before life actually originated. In his "The origin of life On Earth" in 1924, he provided a biochemical explanation of origin of life. *According to him, origin of life occurred along the origin and evolution of earth and it's atmosphere.* The primordial atmosphere of earth had water, methane and ammonia from which, a colloidal mixture of biologically important macro-molecules (lipids, proteins, carbohydrates, nucleic acids etc) are formed called the **coacervates**. These nonliving coacervates behave as a biological system from which the life has been originated through selection, reproduction etc. (Fig. 31.9 & 31.10).

Similar observations were made by an English biologist J. B. S. Haldane (1929) about the origin of life. Both of these scientists got the ideas from the studies of biochemistry made by Sir F. G. Hopkins and both were of the opinion that the gradual transmutation of inorganic compounds into organic ones.

S. Miller and H.Urey in 1953 attempted first the prebiotic synthesis in the laboratory condition. Cairns and Smith (1971) described the model of evolution of living systems into protocell and represented it on a phylogenetic tree (Fig. 31.11).

The trunk of the figure consists of simple gene and gene – protein associations which can be regarded as heterotrophic and which evolved into heterotropic protocell. Photosynthesis developed among some of these lineages, which thus become autotrophic. Within the autotrophic protocell the genetic code was refined and translation developed, until it attained its modern form. One of the more modernistic autotrophic protocell species became the common ancestor of all living organisms, diversifying into heterotrophic as well as autotrophic prokaryotes and leading to eukaryotic descendents.

### 31.8.3 Structure of primitive Earth

1. **Lithosphere :** The earth's lithosphere contains Crust, Mantle and Core.

   Crust contains Al, Fe, Ca, Mg, Na and K. It is generally solid but flows under tectonic stress.

   Mantle contains silicates of Mg and Fe. It is solid but flows under stress.

   Core contains only Fe-Ni only. Outer part is liquid, central part is probably solid.

2. **Atmosphere :** Primitive earth was without an atmosphere. Volcanic gases might be considered mainly of **juvenile water vapour**, which is released from water of crystallization and variable amounts of $CO_2$, $N_2$, $SO_2$, HCl, $B_2O_3$ and lesser amount of $H_2$, $CH_2$=CO, $NH_3$ and HF but no $O_2$. Therefore it is assumed that primitive atmosphere was a *reducing atmosphere* consisting mainly $H_2$, $CH_4$, $NH_3$, water vapour and noble gases.

   According to Urey (1962), Abelson (1966), Fox and Dose (1972), this reducing

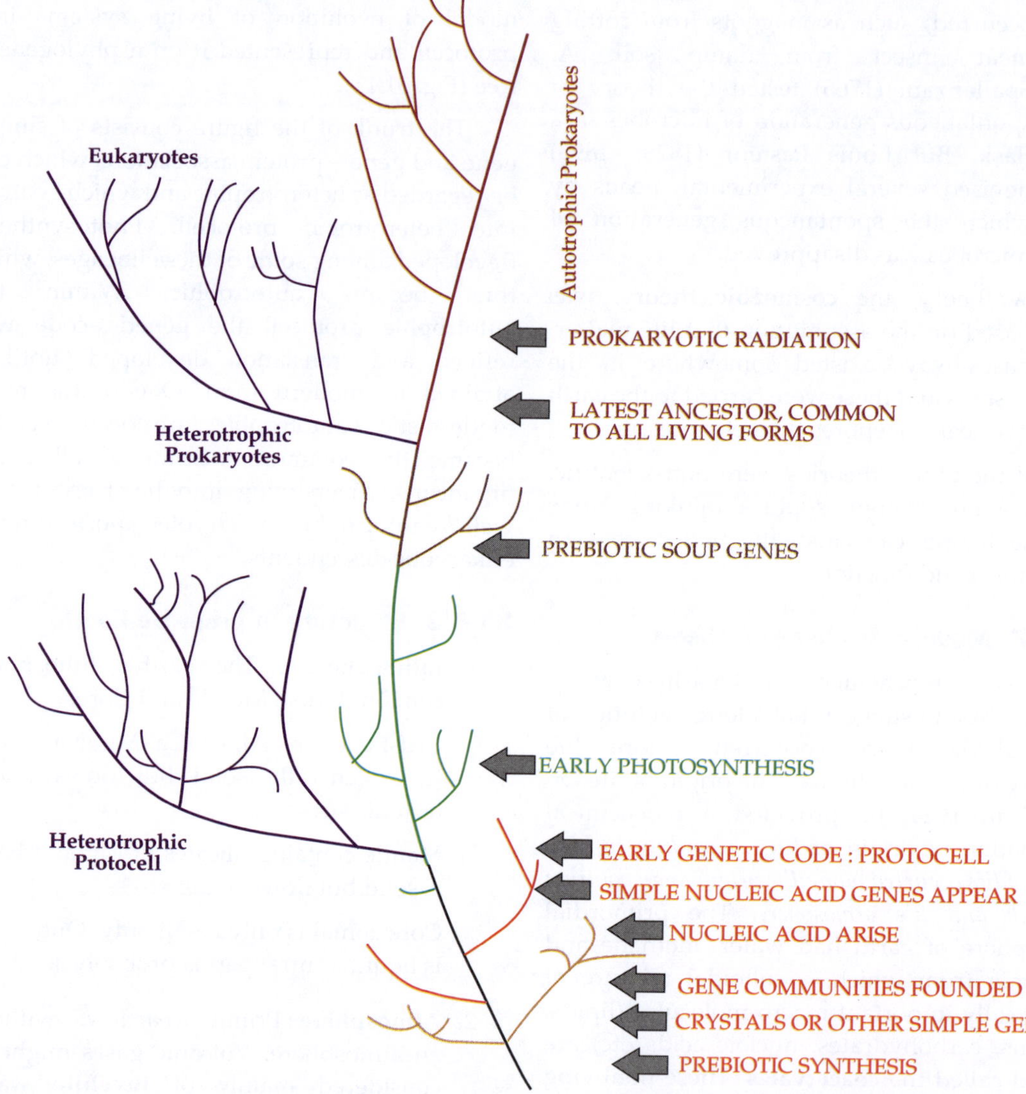


**Fig.31.11 :** *Some of the important events during the rise of living system and their evolution into protocell, represented a phylogenetic tree. (Modified from Cairns-Smith, 1971)*

atmosphere has already disappeared before a significant accumulation of organic compounds from the constituents of the secondary structure.

3. **Hydrosphere :** The vast quantities of $H_2$ and $O_2$ under great pressure and heat below the surface formed water. This water escaped through fissures of the rocks and is known as JUVENILE WATER

as atmospheric vapour. Gradually, the temperature of the earth's surface lowers significantly, the rains continued unceasingly for thousand of years with lightening discharge. Thus the rocks dissolves and the minerals are dissolved thus the water become 3%salt content. Oxides, sulphates are formed. Thus creating an organic media.

**Availability of Energies :**

The possible sources of energy available on the primitive earth are follows :

(i) Solar radiation, particularly UV radiation.

(ii) High energy radiation- $\alpha$, $\beta$ and $\gamma$-radiations from $U^{238}$, $U^{235}$, $Th^{232}$ and $K^{38}$, volcanic heat.

(iii) Electric discharge, hydrothermal veins, microwaves, supersonic shock waves etc.

These sources of energy contributed to the molecular evolution.

### 31.8.4 Experimental support of Oparin's hypothesis

In 1942, a Mexican scientist A.L. Herrera synthesized SULPHOBES (organized microstructures with the appearance of cells) from Ammonium –thio-cyanate and formalin and he also reported the formation of two amino acids and pigments, but he failed to correlate his findings with the problem of origin of life.

### 31.8.5 Miller and Urey's Experiment

Stanley Miler and his teacher, Harold Urey in 1953 devised an apparatus that simulated the conditions of the surface of the pre-biological earth and analyzed the molecular forms that arose. The apparatus consists of exposing water vapour to electric shock of 75000 volts (to represent the lightening of thunder storms) in an ammonia and methane atmosphere (the atmosphere of the early earth). After two weeks of treatment, Miller chromatographed the final solution and found many organic compounds including both carbohydrates and amino acids etc. such as *Ala, Gly, Glu, Asp*. Many of the compounds were important metabolic intermediates of present day organisms.

Later many other scientists tried to produce many other organic substances in this method. These are polypeptide chains, nucleotides etc. (Fig. 31.12)

### 31.8.6 Experiment by Siddney Fox

Recently simple organic compounds have been detected in interstellar dust, clouds by radio-astronomical techniques. The first three important isomers in pre-biotic syntheses; formaldehyde, (which can give rise to sugars), HCN (from which amino acids and adenine can be derived) and the cyanoethylene (from which pyridines are formed) (Orgel, 1973).

But Oparin has postulated that larger molecular aggregates called coacervates are produced, which initiates the reassembly of different organic compounds into a natural crystalline lattices, those play an important role in the biogenesis process.

Siddney Fox and his collaborators mixed all twenty amino acids and heated them on volcanic rock in an oven at 170°C for two hours. The surface of the rock was sprinkled with water and allowed to cool. The residues, which they obtained were examined under microscope as millions of small spheres similar to size and shape to yeast cells. Fox designated them as PROTEINOIDS OR MICROSPHERES. They possess polypeptides, a double-layered surface with semipermeable properties and a capacity to carryout enzymatic reactions, notably oxidation and having a power of reproduction by budding (Fig. 31.13).

From this experiment Fox (1968) Lehninger (1970), Fox and Dose (1972) suggested the models for *self assembly theory*, which holds that protobiogenesis occurred due to inherent property of self organization of the chemical molecules and thus micromolecules to macro-

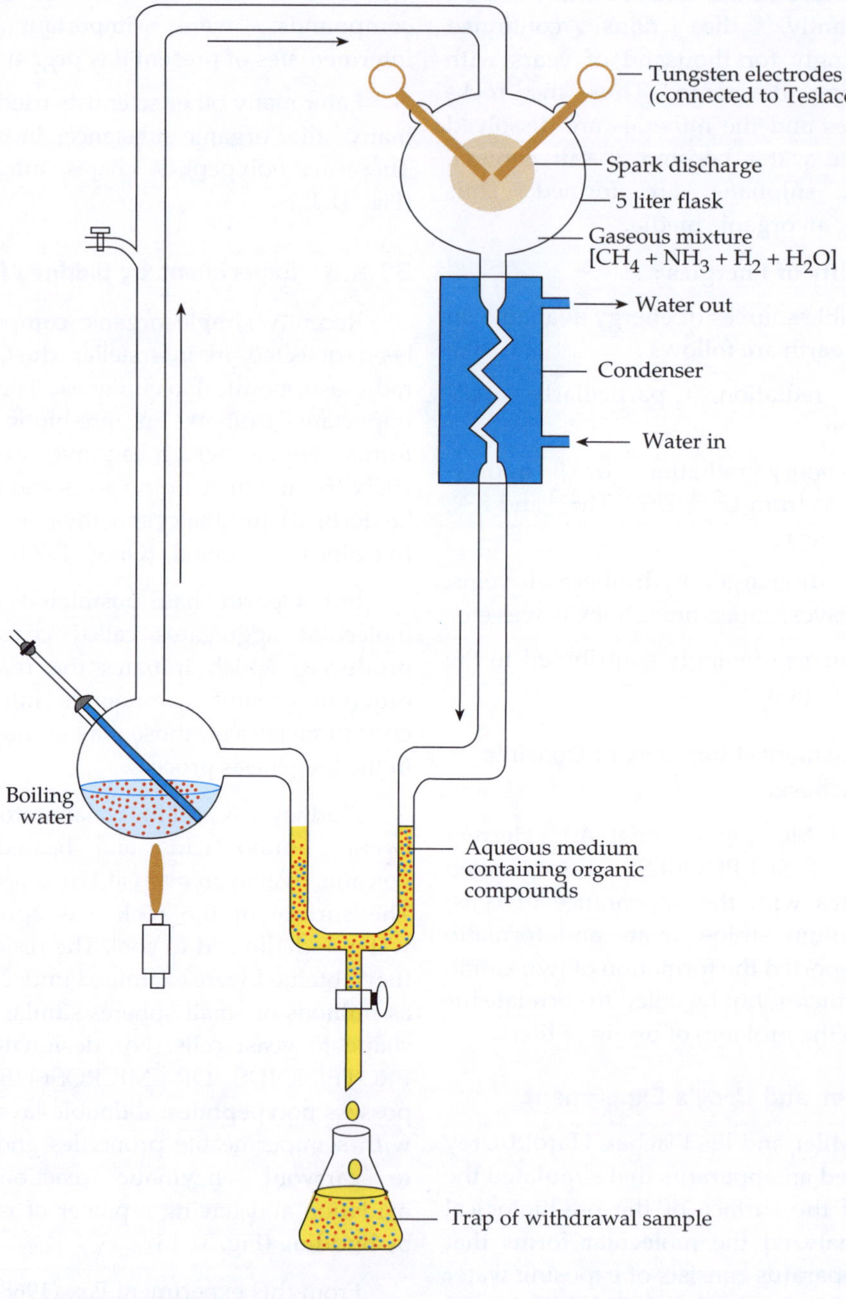


**Fig.31.12 :** *Diagramatic representaiton of apparatus Miller (1953) used to demonstrate the synthesis of organic compounds by electrical discharge in a reducing atmosphere.*

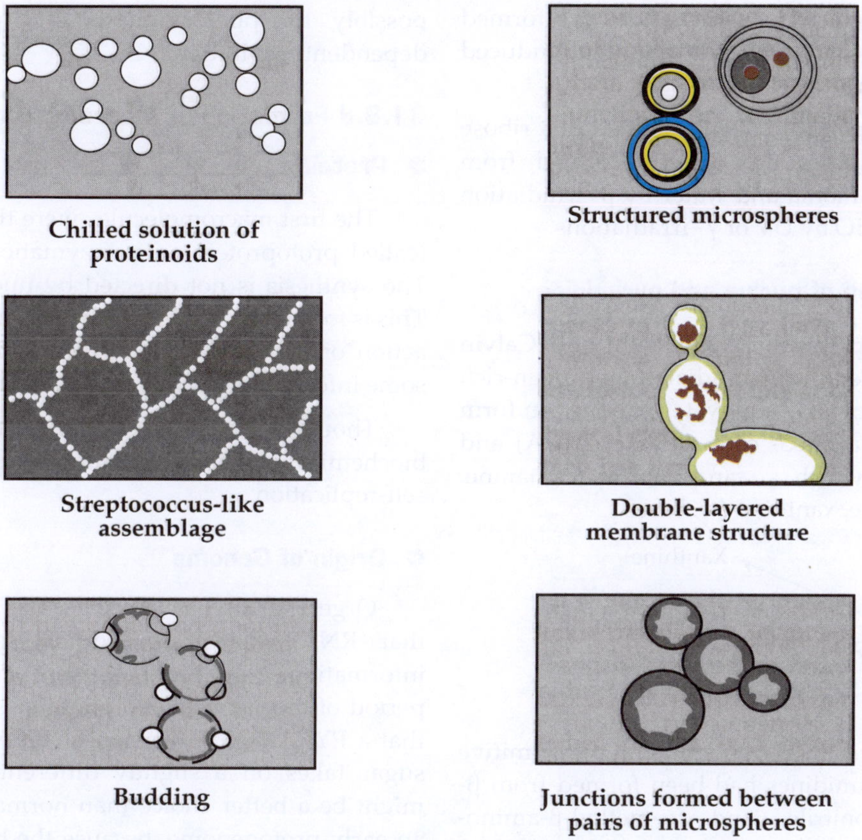


**Fig.31.13 :** *Various forms of proteinoid microspheres*

molecules to an organized cell- like micro-system had been evolved.

### 31.8.7 Formation of Micromolecules

The molecules, which have mol. wt. below 100D, are called micromolecules. The possible modes of formation of some biologically important micromolecules are as follows:

#### ● Formation of Amino acids: (According to Miller, 1958)

$$RCHO + NH_3 + HCN \longrightarrow \underset{\displaystyle NH_2}{R{-}\overset{}{\underset{|}{C}}H{-}CN} + H_2O$$

$$\underset{\displaystyle NH_2}{R{-}\underset{|}{C}H{-}CN} + H_2O \longrightarrow \underset{\displaystyle NH_2}{R{-}\underset{|}{C}H{-}COOH} + NH_3$$

#### ● Formation of Hydrocarbons and Fatty acids

Miller (1955) demonstrated that formic acid; acetic acid, propionic acids and their derivatives, glycolic acid and lactic acids are formed when $CH_4$, $NH_3$, $H_2$ and water vapour are exposed to spark discharge.

Formaldehyde and glyceraldehyde have been reported to condense into sugars such as fructose, cellobiose, sorbose, xylulose under prebiotic conditions.

Some higher monosaccharides are formed by aldol condensation or alkali-induced condensation.

Ponnampermura (1965) claimed that ribose and deoxyriboses are directly formed from methane, ammonia and water by β- irradiation or from HCHO by UV or γ –irradiations.

### • Formation of purine and pyrimidine

Ponnampermura (1965), Palm and Calvin (1962) reported that β-irradiated Hydrogen-rich atmosphere of $CH_4$ and water vapour can form 4-aminoimidazole-5- carboxamide (AICA) and adenine, which can form guanine, hypoxanthine, xanthine etc. bases.

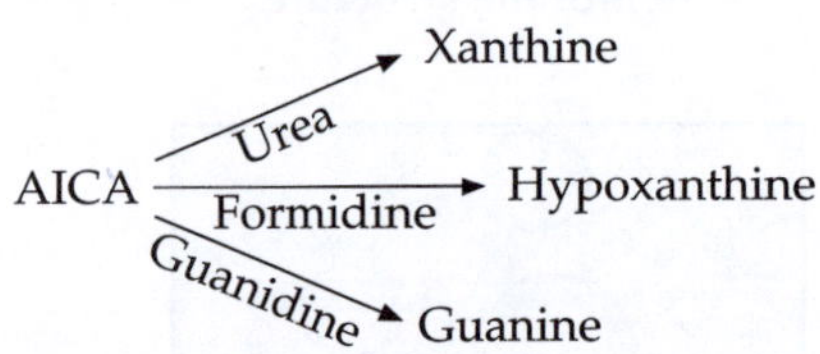


Ferrin *et al* (1963) reported that the primitive earth of pyrimidines had been formed from β-amino-acrylonitrile and α-methyl-β-amino-acrylonitrile.

### • Formation of nucleosides and related compounds

Wachenldt and Fox (1967) demonstrated that nucleosides are phosphorylated with polyphosphoric acid at 0–22°C. The nucleosides are evolved during the later phase of molecular evolution before their function of co-enzymes and constituents of genetic material taken by other compound. Lipmann (1965) and Kulaev (1970) considered the inorganic pyrophosphate to be the primitive group carrier in biological systems.

### • Origin of porphyrin

Pyrroles, the probable precursor of porphyrin were likely formed from acetylene and HCN or acetylene and $NH_3$ in the primitive earth. Later on, this porphyrin is used as chlorophylls, hemoglobin and chromatophores possibly for photosynthesis and porphyrin-dependent respiration.

## 31.8.8 Formation of Macromolecules

### • Proteins

The first macromolecules were the proteins (called protoprotein), are enzymatic in nature. The synthesis is not directed by nucleic acids. This is formed by random polymerization by the action of thermal energy. These proteins have some informations called proto-information.

Though proteins are required to catalyze biochemical reactions but cannot carry out their self-replication.

### • Origin of Genome

Orgel (2000) has received the possibility that RNA was preceeded by some other informational molecule at the very earliest period of biochemical evolution and concluded that a PYRANOSYL version of RNA, in which sugar takes on a slightly different structure, might be a better choice than normal RNA for an early protogenome, because the base-paired molecules that it forms are more stable (Beier *et al* 1999, Eschenmoser 1999). The same is true for Peptide Nucleic Acid (PNA), a polynucleotide analog in which the sugar-phosphate backbone is replaced by amino acids (Fig. 31.14).

PNA has been synthesized in the test tube and has been shown to form base pairs with normal polynucleotides.

But there is no indication of either pyranosyl RNA or PNA that have evolved in the prebiotic soup.

**(a) The RNA world :**

The major breakthrough came in the mid 1980's when it was discovered RNA could have catalytic activity. These are called the RIBOZYMES that can carryout three types of biochemical reactions such as self-cleavage, cleavage of other RNAs and synthesis of peptide bonds by rRNA of ribosomes.

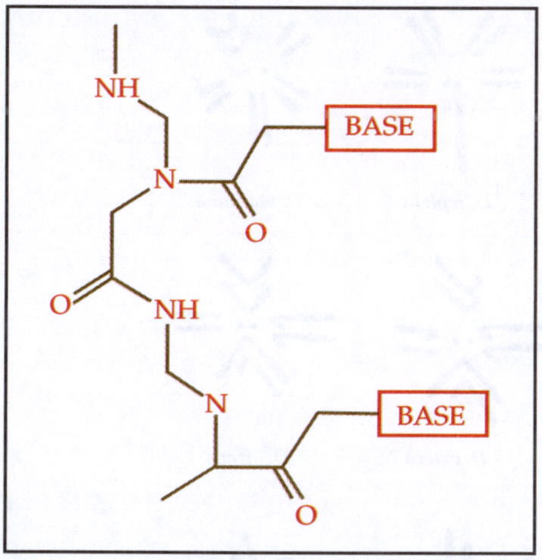


**Fig.31.14 :** *A short chain of peptide-nucleic acid*

In a test tube, synthetic RNA molecules have been shown to carryout other biologically relevant reactions such as synthesis of ribonucleotides (Unrau and Bartel 1998), synthesis of copying of RNA molecules (Ekland and Bartel 1996, Johnston *et al* 2000) and transfer of an RNA-bound amino acid to a second amino acid forming a dipeptide. Thus the first biochemical system could have been centered entirely on RNA (Fig. 31.15).

It has been postulated that RNA molecules initially replicated in a slow haphazard fashion simply by acting as template for binding of complementary nucleotides, which is polymerized spontaneously. This is certainly not accurate and therefore, a large variety of RNA sequences have been generated. Some of them acquired ribozyme properties; they then direct their own more accurate self-replication.

Natural Selection is operated so that a most efficient replicating system become predominant. This efficient system enabled RNAs to increase in length without loosing their sequence specificity. Thus the RNA becomes as complex as group-I intron and rRNAs.

This first genetic material of RNA is called "**naked gene**" or "**protogenome**". These genes are self replicating and able to direct simple biochemical reactions such as energy metabolism.

The reactions might have become compartmentalized within lipid membranes, forming the first cell like structure and encapsulating one or more protogenomes and providing the RNAs with an enclosed environment in which more controlled biochemical reactions could be carried out.

Presumably the first membrane-bound cells were formed by the spontaneous assembly of a set of amphipathic phospholipid molecules.

**(b) The DNA world :**

One of the several unanswered questions regarding biochemical evolution is that how catalytic activity of the cell is transferred to the protein-enzymes. The more recent suggestion is that protein catalysis is more efficient because of the inherent flexibility of folded polypeptides compared with the greater rigidity of base-paired RNAs (Csermely, 1997).

Besides, enclosure of RNA protogenes within membrane vesicles could have prompted the evolution of the first proteins (Walter *et al*, 2000).

The main function of the protogenomes was to specify the construction of the catalytic proteins. But it is not clear **"whether the ribozymes became the coding molecules or coding molecules are synthesized by the ribozymes"** (Fig. 31.16 & 31.17).

Due to relative instability of the RNA phosphodiester bond, it becomes less suitable for coding function. Therefore DNA, the more stable compound seems to be inevitable, which is probably synthesized by reverse-transcriptase enzyme. Uracil is replaced by its methylated derivative thymine. The adoption of double stranded DNA certainly enables it from repairing the damage.

Thus the first DNA genome comprised many separate molecules and each specifying a single protein. The improved efficiency of gene

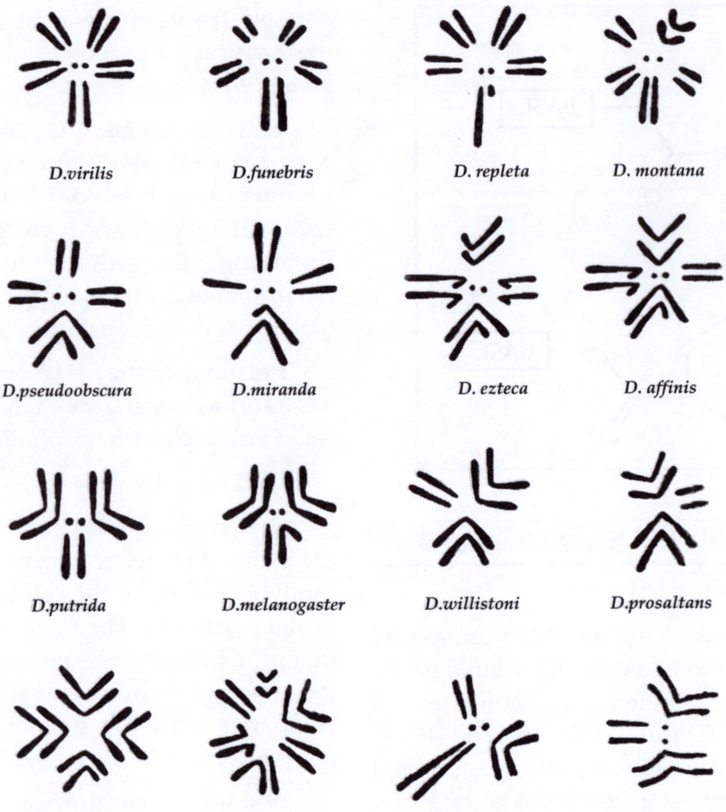


**Fig.31.15 :** *Copying of RNA molecule in the early RNA world*

during reproduction and propagation, these are linked together into a chromosome.

### 31.8.9 Protocell

The protoproteinaceous cell-like entities are called **protocell or protobionts**. It lacked lipid and nucleic acid but had a definite spherical shape and reproduced by budding and derives nutrients from prebiotic soup. It is suggested that protocells were formed as an outcome of a stepwise accumulation of traits directed by selection pressure and took one billion years to progress from molecular aggregates to biological level.

These protocells become fully heterotrophic to draw amino acids, nitrogen bases, cofactors, enzymes, inorganic salts and energy-rich molecules.

Later it synthesizes porphyrins and become able to trap solar energy by photosynthesis. It acquires the genetic material DNA and protein synthesizing materials. Thus DNA-RNA protein system is established.

The integration of organismal activities into a genetically medicated pattern took the form of the contemporary cell.

## 31.9 RECENT CONCEPTS OF THE ORIGIN OF PROKARYOTES

The living organisms can be classified on the basis of their cell structure into two groups: the eukaryotes and prokaryotes.

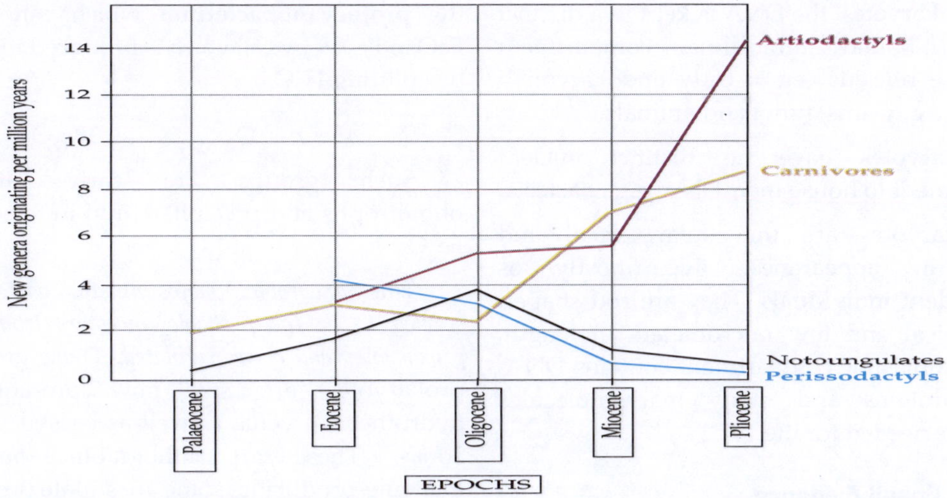


**Fig.31.16 :** *Conversion of a coding molecule into the progenitor of the first DNA genome*

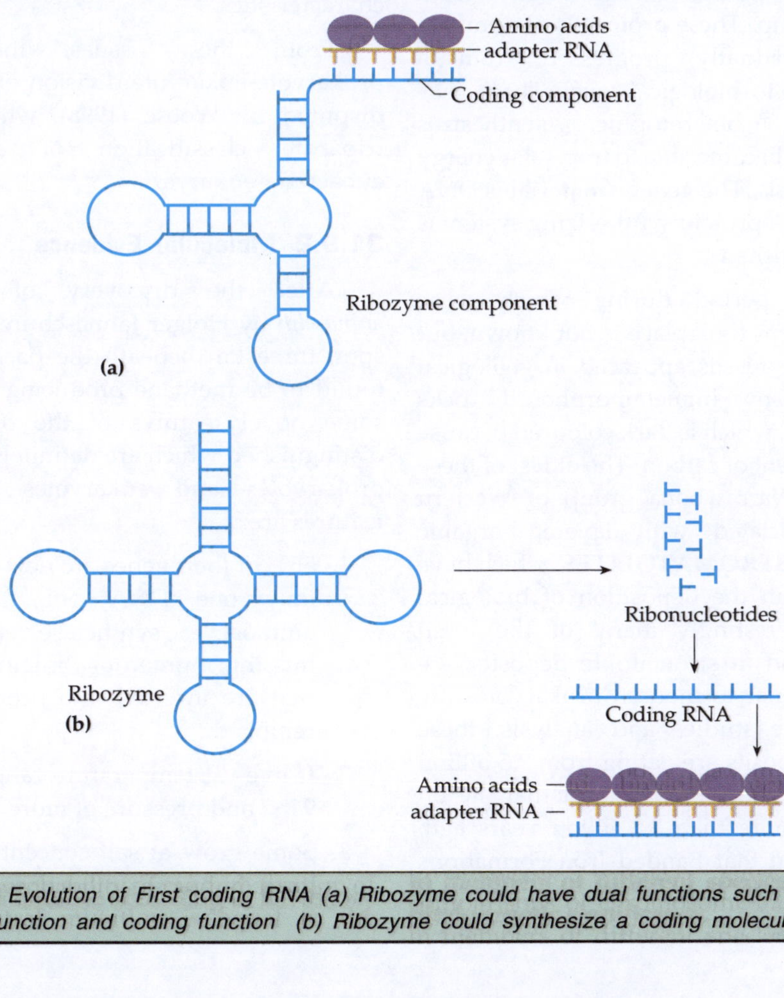


**Fig.31.17 :** *Evolution of First coding RNA (a) Ribozyme could have dual functions such as catalytic function and coding function (b) Ribozyme could synthesize a coding molecule*

In eukaryotes, the DNA is kept in a distinct membrane-bound intracellular compartment called the nucleus (eu = truly and karyon = nucleus) e.g. plants, fungi and animals.

Prokaryotes have no distinct nuclear compartment to house their DNA. e.g., bacteria.

Prokaryotes are unicellular, small and simple in appearance, live mostly as independent individuals. They are rod shaped or spherical and few micrometers in length. Their cytoplasmic compartment contains DNA, RNA, proteins and many macromolecules which are needed for life.

### 31.9.1 Fossil Evidence

The protocells which lack lipid and nucleic acid but had a definite spherical shape and reproduce by budding, derived nutrient from the prebiotic soup. These protocells accumulate traits and gradually progressed from a molecular level to biological level. These cells become fully heterotophic, synthesizes porphyrins and became able to trap solar energy by photosynthesis. The genetic material is DNA and a DNA-RNA protein synthesizing system is gradually established.

The exact period during which these evolutionary steps took place is not known, but various cell-like fossils appeared in geological strata are mostly unmetamorphosed rocks called **CHERTS**, which is dark coloured because of the high content of carbon. The oldest of these cherts are in Warrawoona group of Western Australia, associated with layered organic deposits called **STROMATOLITES**, which have been arisen from the deposition of biological organisms. Interestingly many of the fossil organisms found in stromatolite deposits, are remarkably similar to modern prokaryotes. By $C^{13}/C^{12}$ isotope studies and analysis, these stromatolite deposits are dating from 3.5 billion years ago, supporting the concept that life on Earth existed more than 3.8 billon years ago. Cloud suggested that Banded Iron Formations (B1F), the oldest of which dates 3.76 billion years ago may also had been formed biologically by the **protocyanobacterium** which can change FeO to $Fe_2O_3$ by $O_2$ which is produced in the cell by splitting $H_2O$.

$$4FeO + O_2 \longrightarrow 2Fe_2O_3$$

Such groups are early anaerobic phototrophs and precipitate iron in the form of $Fe_2O_3$.

*This anaerobic photosynthetic bacteria are seemed to be the probable ancestors from which prokaryotes had been originated.* These groups of prokaryotes are still now present in hydrothermal vents as well as coastal volcanic zones. These are lithographic anaerobic methane-producing, some are sulfate producing or organographic hot stream vents. Peculiar is that these groups show some similarities with eukaryotes and also have some novel characteristics.

From these issues, the traditional prokaryote-eukaryote division of life (Mayr) is disputed by Woese (1998), who proposed a tripartite classification of archaebacteria-eubacteria-eukarya.

### 31.9.2 Molecular Evidence

After the discovery of *Methanococus jannaschii* by Holger Jannasch in 1982 from hot spot, three km beneath the pacific ocean was found to be methane producing organism and some novel features of the organism were distinguished which are definitely distinct from prokaryotes and eukaryotes. These novel features are :

1. 56% of their genes are new to science e.g., only one DNA pol., several tRNA aminoacyl synthetase enzymes are missing; numerous "inteins" are known that are inserted into proteins and then removed.
2. It lives at temperature ranging from 68°-94°C and pressure of more than 200 atm.
3. Some grow at salt concentration upto 10 times higher than that of sea water.

4. Oxygen kills it.
5. It is autotroph, utilizing, $CO_2$, $N_2$, and $H_2$ and can produce $CH_4$.
6. Besides these novel genes, they have some prokaryotic genes (eg, transport of $K^+$ and $Na^+$) and eukaryotic genes (e.g., replication, transcription, translation and histone genes).

Prokaryotes lack nuclear envelope, divide by binary fission, lack mitotic spindle, centrioles, endoplasmic reticulum, Golgi bodies etc. They also lack split genes, *i.e.*, genes are interrupted by producing alternative segments of exons (expressing sequences) and introns (intervening sequences). The origin of split genes was described by two hypotheses.

Doolittle (1978) and others favoured "**intron early**" hypothesis : cellular organisms ancestral to both prokaryotes and eukaryotes probably had such intron-exon structures. But these were mostly abandoned in prokaryotic lines because increased intensity of selection streamlined DNA replication and improved transcription efficiency.

An "intron late" hypothesis suggests that introns first inserted into full length eukaryotic genes after *eukaryotes had separated from prokaryotes*, *i.e.*, gene assembly did not depend on the initial use of introns to connect and shuffle the molecular exons. The introns are recent origin in eukaryotes (Logsdon *et al* 1998).

A decision between two hypotheses is yet to come. But the question, how did introns enter into eukaryotes genes? Why did they became so prevalent and why are they maintained? One answer was thought by modern molecular biologists that introns are mobile DNA sequences that can splice themselves out as well as targeted to its specific target site, acting like a mobile transposon-like element.

Woese *et al* (1998) have catalogued the presence and frequencies of various sequences in the 16 S RNA component of ribosomes and showed that archaebacteria occupy an intermediate evolutionary position between eubacteria and eukarya. Theorists have therefore suggested that no one group derived from any other, rather they all derived from a common cellular ancestor or from a community of early cells in which mutation rates were high and genes were being freely exchanged – a population of PROGENOTES (Woese, 1998) (Fig. 31.18).

In favour of this concept it is evidenced that

1. Similar mode of DNA replication *i.e.*, new nucleotides are added to the 3′ end of the molecule.
2. A common genetic code.
3. A similar protein synthesizing system.
4. Similar membrane structure
5. Similar mechanism of active transport through the membrane.

It has been assumed that in the ancestral organism, probably had enzymes involved in glycolysis; Kreb cycle and urea cycle and gained lower rate of mutation due to attainment of DNA by replacing RNA as the genetic material.

### 31.9.3 Conclusion

The subsequent events are still not clear. Many scientists proposed that eubacteria and eukaryotes arose from Aarchaea. (Darnell, Poole *et al* 1998). Eukaryotes directly from prokaryotes (Cavalier – Smith, 1991).

Roser *et al* (1998), Pennisi (1998), Rowlands *et al* (1994) aggreed with the suggestion which is based on the sequence. similarities among 16S RNA that the possible phylogenetic tree is "unrooted" *i.e.*, there is no root for the origin of common ancestor. The tree shows that

1. There is a close tie between animal & fungi and widely separated from flagellates, *Entamoeba*, diplomonads, ciliates, microsporida which are called Protista.
2. *Giardia*, has a position as an earliest Eukaryotic offshoot which lacks mitrochondria. It can be assumed that its

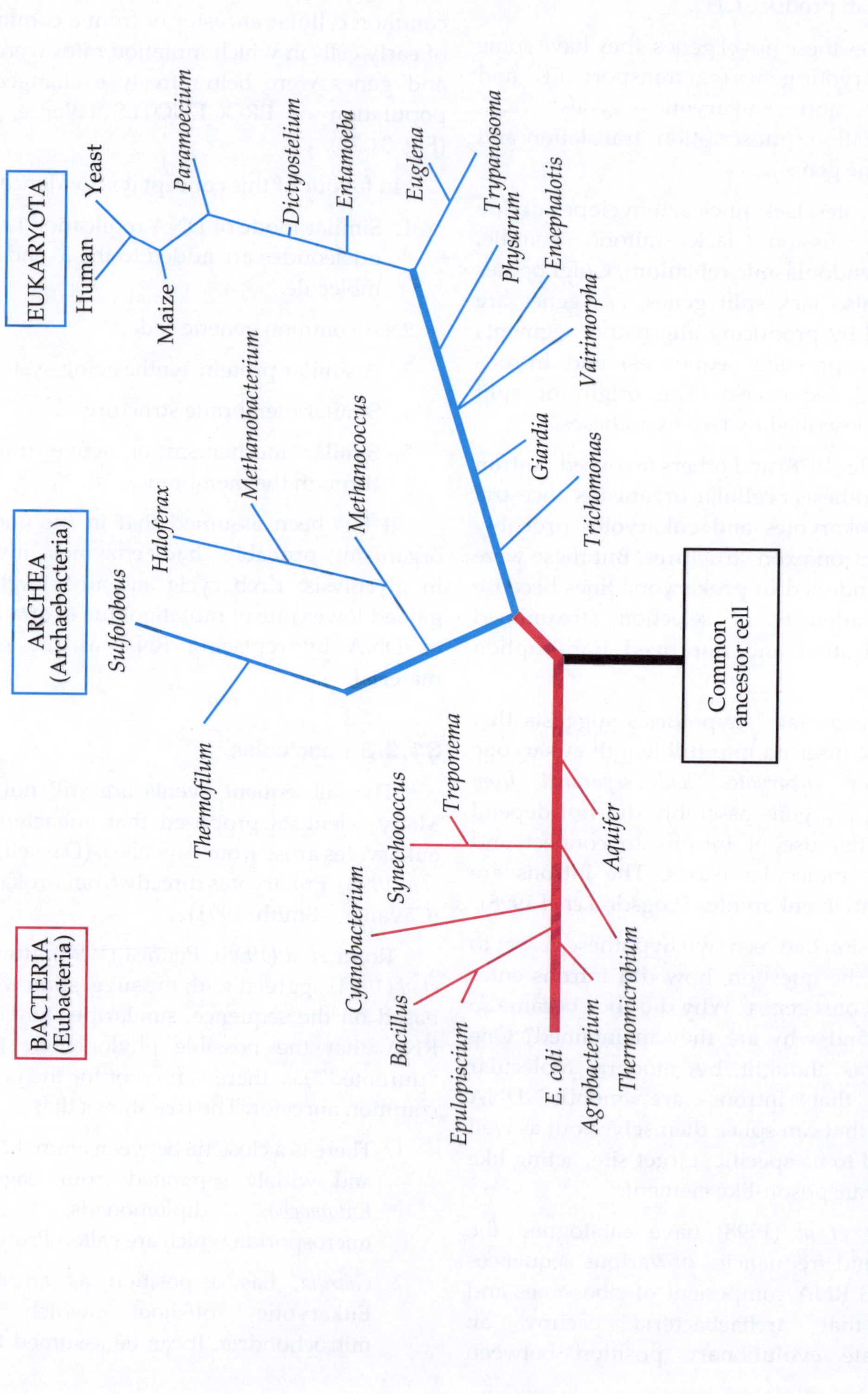


Fig.31.18 : Phylogenetic diversity of organisms

ancestors have maintained bacterial symbionts .

3. There is a closer connection between eukaryota and archaea that between eukaryotes and bacteria (Fig. 31.19).

## 31.10 ORIGIN AND EVOLUTION OF METAZOA

### 31.10.1 Characteristics of Metazoans

1. Metazoans are multicellular, motile heterotrophic organisms that develop from embryos.
2. The surface epithelial layer is specialized for protective function, then sensory and nervous structures, while the internal layer becomes digestive system. Cells and layers in an intermediate situation have a supporting function.
3. Collagen fibres are distinctive products of metazoans.
4. The metazoan sperms are monoflagellated and occurred in all eukaryotic organisms.
5. The body tissue of metazoa is differentiated into a somatic part which carries on the regular life activities. This part dies but the germinal part is immortal by means of reproduction.

We still do not know how the changes led to the appearance of metazoans (multicellular animal eukaryotes). But by the beginning of the Cambrian period (545 million years ago) many differently skeletonized groups materialized. Yet the origin and earliest evolution of the metazoan phyla can not be documented from fossil evidences.

From the fossils that we do have, from comparative studies among living organisms and from interpretations of the functional significance of primitive characters, it is possible to produce models of metazoan origin and diversifications. Now the biologists accepted the views that most, if not all, existing metazoan phyla had a common ancestry, but how did unicellular, ancentry transform into metazoan descendants? is a pertinent question among them. But all the theories are based on two possibilities.

The first possibility is that the metazoan status was achieved by the coming of two or more cells forming a colony and remain as a symbiotic association.

The second possibility is that the animals arose from a single cell which becomes multinucleated syncytial mass by nuclear division without cytoplasmic division to give rise to multicellular animals.

### 31.10.2 Colonial theories

**A. Colonial flagellate theory**

It is widely accepted that metazoans have evolved from protozoans.

(a) *Butschli theory :* According to Butschli, the plate- like form, such as *Gonium* was the ancestral metazoan type. It becomes first into two layers and later curved into a sphere (Fig. 31.20).

(b) *Lankester theory :* According to Lankester 1874, the ancestral metazoan was a morula-like solid colony, such as *Synura* or *Pandorina*. The outer external flagellated cells are used for food taking, the inner layer, which gets separated and served the digestion function.

The main criticism is that inner cell layer i.e., endoderm formation by such primary delamination is rare in Metazoa. Besides without mouth the inner layer would be useless.

(c) *Colonial blastaea/gastrea theory :* This theory was proposed by Hackel (1874-75) which was heavily dependent on recapitulation theory, suggesting that the metazoans arose through a hollow spherical colony of flagellated protozoans not unlike the colony of *Volvox* but lacking chloroplast.

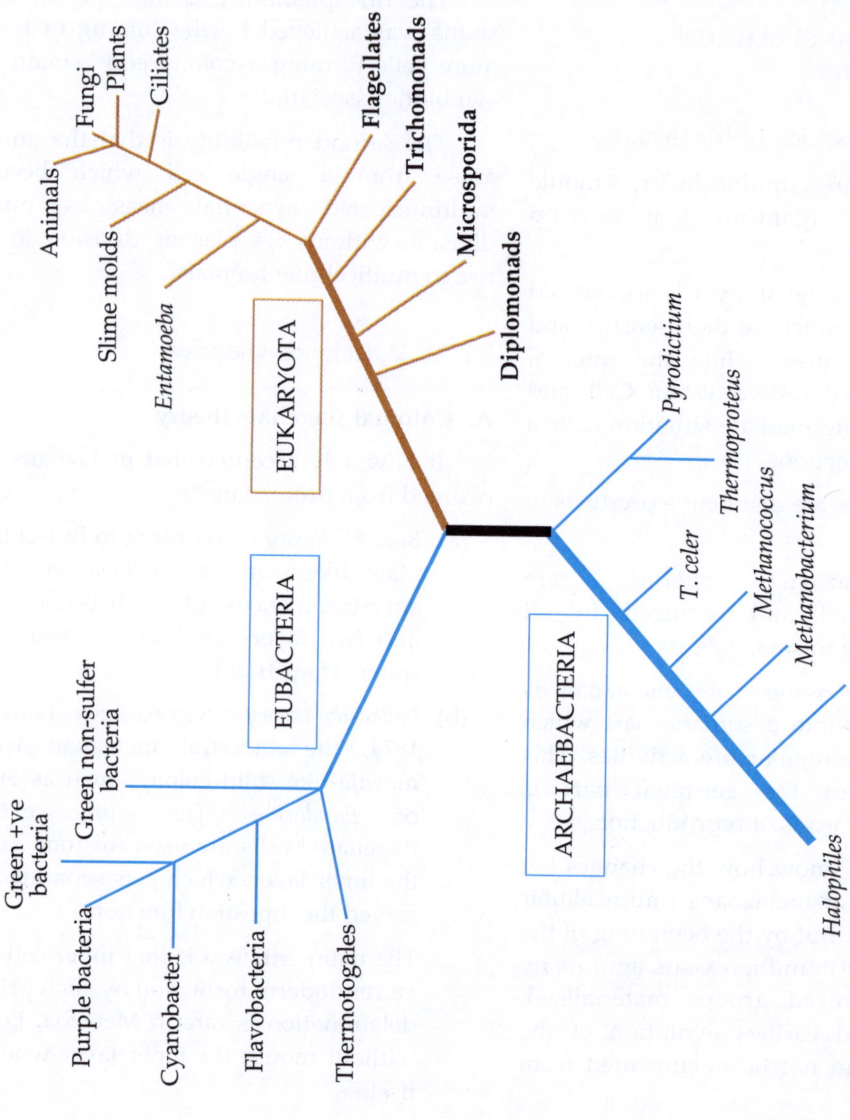


**Fig. 31.19 :** *Phylogeny of Achaea, Eubacteria and Eukarya (Sagin, 1991; Wheelis, et al 1992 and Roger et, at, 1998)*

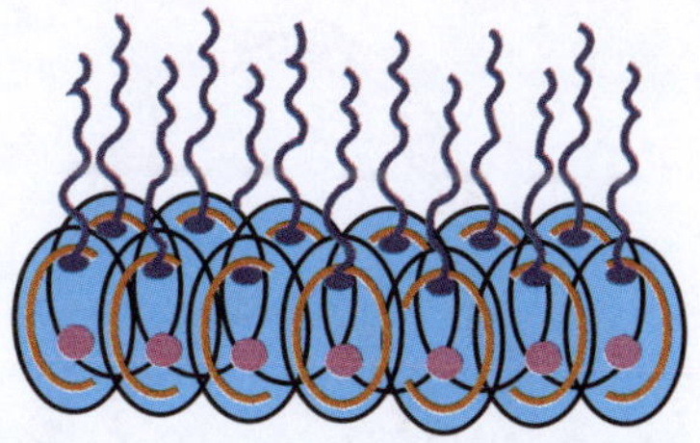

Fig.31.20 : *Gonium sp.*

This is called BLASTAEA (or blastula) by Hackel.

He claimed that the, blastaea has been specialized into two poles, to become gastrula or GASTREA, the anterior pole for locomotion and posterior pole for digestion. The later cells undergo invagination to form blastopore and a cup like cavity, the archenteron.

**Support :**

1. Blaslula and gastrula stages in the embryonic development of higher organisms support the Hackel's recapitulation theory.
2. In sponges and cnidarians the gastrea hypothesis may be supported due to its diploblastic gastrula structures.

**Criticism :**

1. The major objection is that gastrulation by invagination is not common in the embryological development of many metazoans. Even in cnidarians, (the hypothetical gastrea), endoderm is formed by ingression of ectodermal cells, not by invagination (Fig. 31.21).

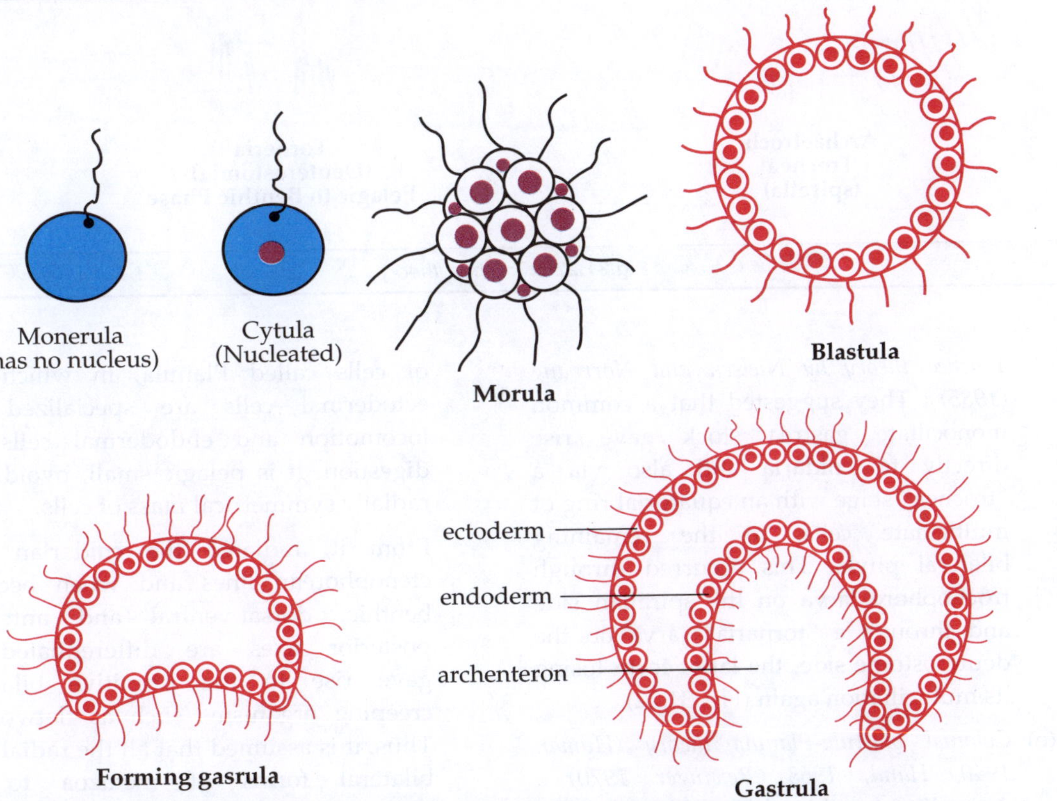


Fig.31.21 : *Stages in the evolution of multicellular organisms (Blastula-Gastrula hypothesis)*

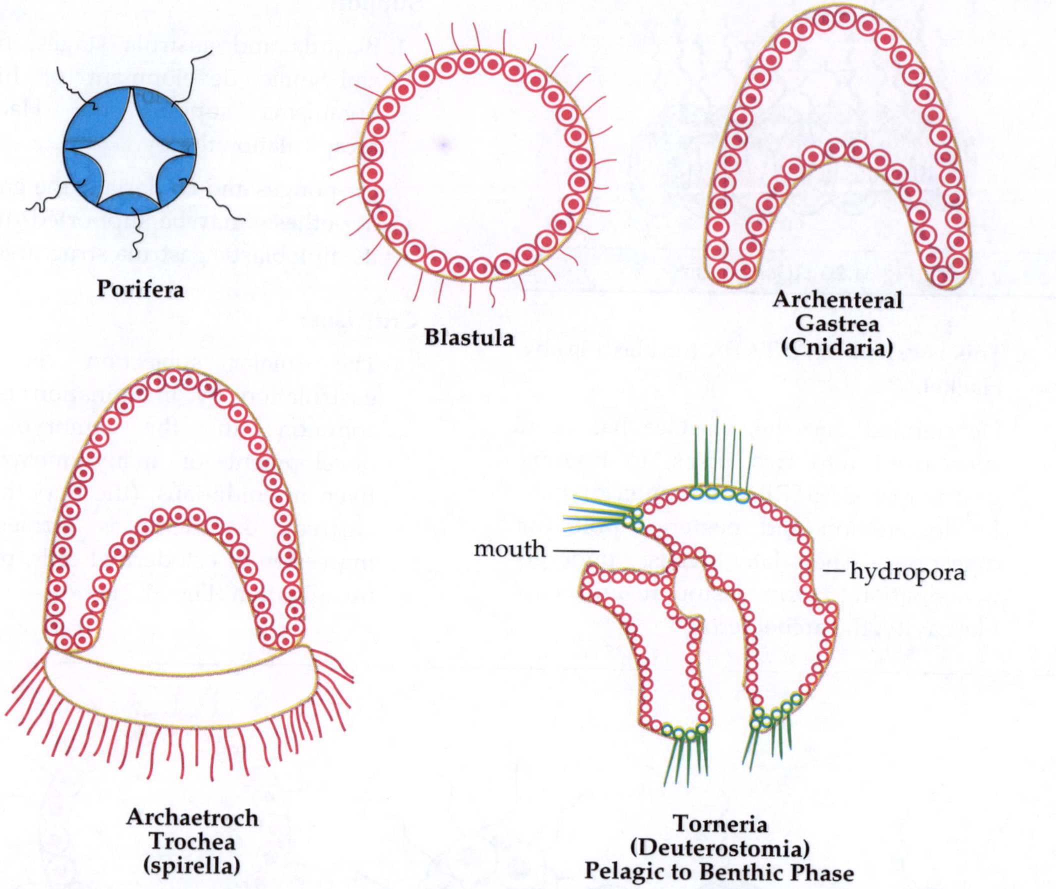


**Fig.31.22 :** *Trochea theory*

(d) *Trochea theory by Nielsen and Norrvang (1985)* : They suggested that a common monociliate gastrea stock gave rise directly to cnidaria and also via a "trochea" stage with an equatorial ring of multiciliate cells, to the remaining bilateral phyla. This occurred through trochophore larva on the spiralian side and through a "tornaria" larva on the deuterostome side, the latter form losing its multiciliation again (Fig. 31.22).

(e) *Colonial blastula-Planula theory (Hyman 1940, Hand, 1963, Reisinger 1970)* : According to this theory blastula was followed by the formation of a solid ball of cells called Planula, in which the ectodermal cells are specialized for locomotion and endodermal cells for digestion. It is pelagic small, ovoid and radially symmetrical mass of cells.

From it, radiated the cnidarian and ctenophorean lines and when become benthic, dorsal-ventral and anterior-posterior axes are differentiated to gave rise to the primitive bilateria creeping organisms such as flatworms. Thus, it is assumed that all the radial and bilateral forms of metazoa to be monophyletic in origin from flagellate ancestors (Fig. 31.23).

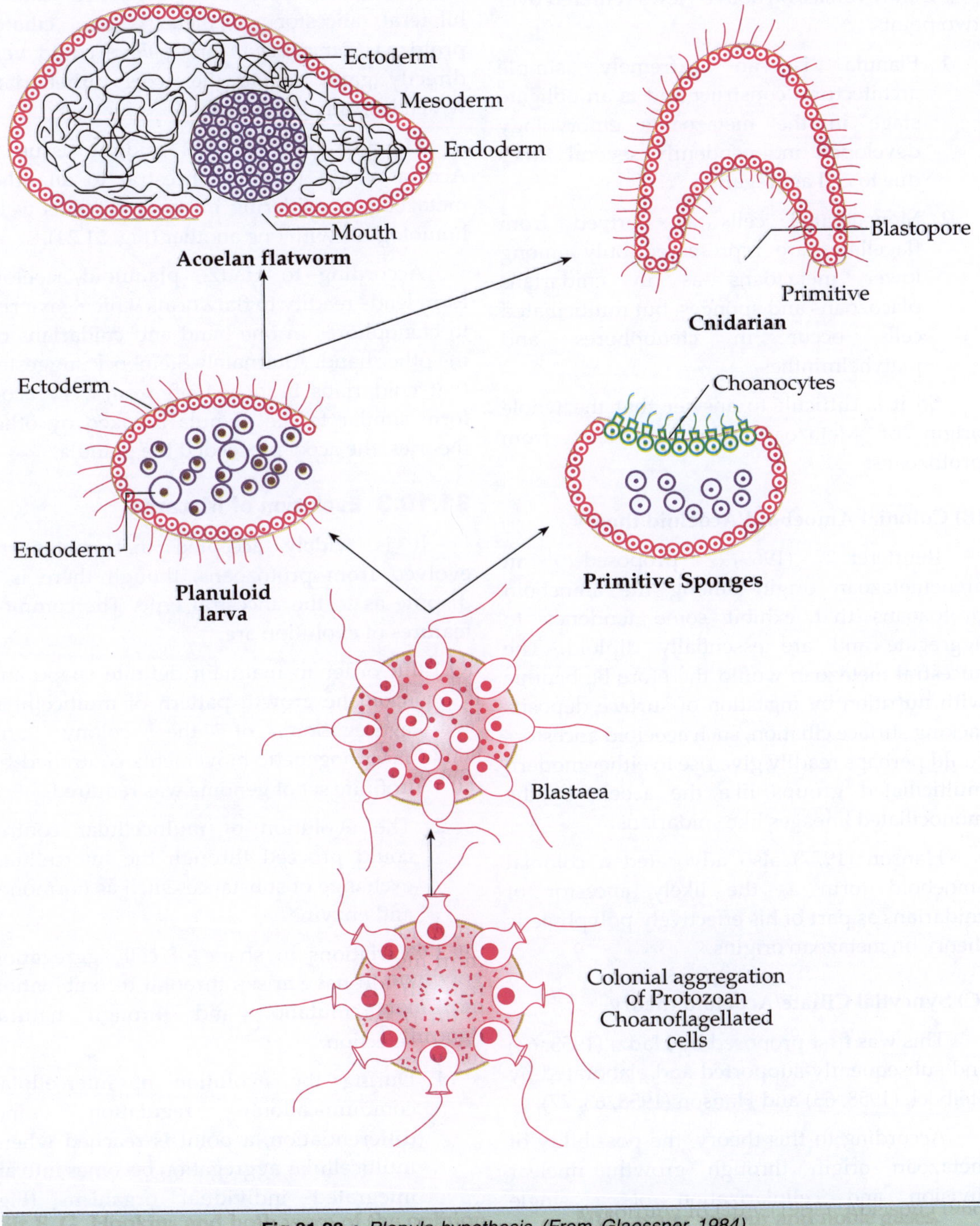


**Fig.31.23 :** *Planula-hypothesis (From Glaessner 1984)*

**Remark :**

Controversies on above views centered over two points:

1. Planula is an extremely simple architectural construct and is an obligate stage in the metazoan's embryology developed independently several times due to cell aggregation.
2. Monociliated cells as derived from flagellates are represented only among lower metazoans as in cnidarians placozoans and sponges, but multiciliated cells occur in ctenophores and platyhelminthes.

So it is difficult to answer that the whole origin of Metazoa is monophyletic from protozoans.

**(B) Colonial Amoeboid/Acoeloid theory**

Reutterer (1969) proposed an archemetazoan origin among the amoeboid protozoans that exhibit some tendency to aggregate and are essentially diploid. The ancestral metazoan would therefore be benthic with nutrition by ingestion of surface deposits lacking surface ciliation, such acoeloid ancestors could perhaps readily give rise to either modern multiciliated groups like the acoela or the monociliated lineages like cnidarians.

Hanson (1977) also advocated a colonial amoeboid form as the likely ancestor of cnidarians as part of his effectively polyphyletic theory on metazoan origins.

**(C) Syncytial Ciliate/Acoeloid theory**

This was first proposed by Hadzi (1953, 63) and subsequently supported and elaborated by Steibock (1958, 63) and Hanson (1958, 63, 77).

According to this theory, the possibility of metazoan origin through growth, nuclear division and cellularization of a single protozoan, rather than by aggregation of several. His theory also explained that a bilateral ancestor of metazoa i.e., ciliated protozoa (*Paramoecium* or *Opalina*) could very directly gave rise to the acoel turbellarians which lack any gut lumen.

He also believed that midgut tissue in Acoela would then be ancestral to all other metazoans considering many features as to be homologous with one another (Fig. 31.24).

According to Hadzi, planuloid/acoeloid form leads readily to flatworms which gave rise to ctenophores in one hand and cnidarians on the other hand. Alternately Steinbock suggested that cnidarians branched off from very acoel form similar to the planula invoked by other theories, the acoel preceeded the planula.

### 31.10.3 Evolution of Metazoa

It is widely accepted that metazoans evolved from protozoans, though there is a dispute as to the ancestral type. The common features of evolution are.

1. In order to maintain definite shape and size, the growth pattern of multicellular aggregation of the colony and morphogenetic movements controlled by definite set of genome was required.
2. The evolution of multicellular control could proceed through the intercellular exchange of substances such as hormones and enzymes.
3. Variations in shape of cell aggregation could have arisen through recombination and mutation and through natural selection.
4. During the evolution of intercellular communication, regulation and differentiation, a point is reached where multicellular aggregation becomes into an integrated individual organism (Fig. 31.24).

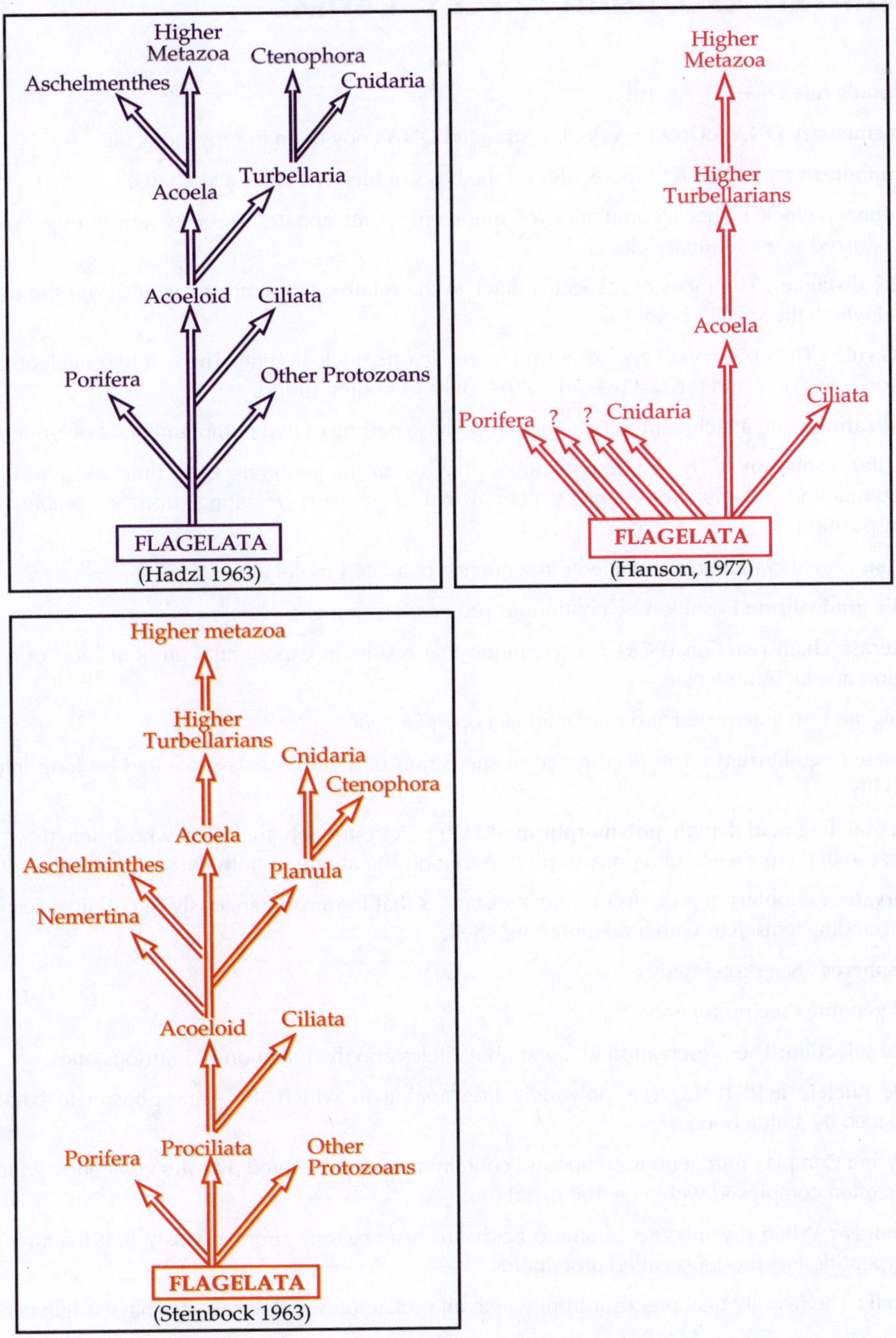


**Fig.31.24 :** *Evolutionary pathways of Metazoa*

## Chapter Glossary/Key Terms

**Chembon's rule :** See GT-AG rule.

**Complementary DNA (cDNA) :** A double-stranded DNA copy of an mRNA molecule.

**Electrophoresis :** Separation of molecules on the basis of their net electrical charge.

**Evolutionary clock :** The accumulation of mutations at an apparently even rate during evolution is recognized as evolutionary clock.

**Genetic distance :** The races of a species differ in the relative frequency of genes from the same gene pool which the species belongs.

**GT-AG rule :** The commonest type of intron in eukaryotic nuclear gene. The first two nucleotides of the intron is 5′ GT 3′ and the last two are 5′ AG 3′ of its coding strand.

**Hybridization :** The attachment to one another by base pairing of two complementary polynucleotides.

**Molecular evolution :** The gradual changes that occur in genomes over time as a result of the accumulation of mutations and structural rearrangements resulting from recombination and transposition.

**Mutation :** An alteration in the nucleotide sequence of a DNA molecule.

**Phyletic gradualism :** Evolution by continuous progressive changes.

**Polymerase chain reaction (PCR) :** A technique that results in exponential amplification of a selected region of a DNA molecule.

**Pseudogene :** An inactivated and nonfuctional copy of a gene.

**Punctuated equilibrium :** The occurrence of speciation events in bursts separated by long intervals of stability.

**Restriction fragment length polymorphism (RFLP) :** A restriction fragment whose length is variable because of the presence of a polymorphic restriction site at one or both ends.

**Coacervates :** Droplets of proteins or other substances that form spontaneously in colloidal suspensions, surrounding temselves with a membranous shell.

**Microspheres :** See proteinoids.

**Naked genome :** see protogenome.

**Natural selection:** The preservation of favourable alleles and the rejection of injurious ones.

**Peptide nucleic acid (PNA) :** A polynucleotide analog in which the sugar-phosphate backbone is replaced by amide bond.

**Porphyrin :** Complex nitrogenous compound containing four substituted pyrroles covalently joined into a ring, often complexed with a central metal ion.

**Proteinoids :** When dry mixture of amino acids are heated, they spontaneously link together to yield polypeptide-like products called proteinoids.

**Protocell :** The hypothetical precusor from which all prokaryotes and eukaryotes have originated.

**Protogenome :** An RNA genome that existed during the RNA world.

**Ribozyme :** An RNA molecule that has catalytic activity.

**RNA world :** The early period of evolution when all biological reactions were centered on RNA.

*Contd.*

**Blastula :** An animal embryo after cleavage and before gastrulation, usually consists of a hollow sphere, the walls of which are composed of a single layer of cells.

**Chert :** Ancient sediments mostly of unmetamorphored rocks, present in various locations of the world.

**Fossil :** Any remains of an organism which lived in the distant past. It may be whole or part of the body of the organism, intact or altered, an impression or even an artefact made by it.

**Gastrula :** An embryo in the process of gastrulation the stage of development during which the blastula with its single layer of cells turns into a three-layered embryo, made up of ectoderm, endoderm and mesoderm, often enclosing an archenteron.

**Metazoa :** Multicellular organism, usually develops from an embryo.

**Prokayote :** An organism whose cells lack a distinct nucleus.

**Stromatolite :** The organo-sediments precipitated on the ocean floor as a result of growth and metabolic activities of prokaryotic micro-organisms.

**Syncytium :** A cell-like structure comprizing a mass of cytoplasm and many nuclei.

# EXERCISE

## A. Long answer type questions :

1. Describe briefly different methods of indirect assessment of molecular evolution.
2. What do you mean by molecular evolution by nucleotide substitution? Briefly describe the method.
3. What is pseudogene? Why it is called so? Describe the $\alpha$ and $\beta$ globin pseudogenes in primates and other vertebrates.
4. How pseudogenes were evolved? Why pseudogenes are evolutionary dead end?
5. Write a note on the evolution of globin genes from its ancentral gene.
6. Describe the molecular evolution by amino acid substitution.
7. Briefly describe neutral theory of molecular evolution? Why this is called non-Darwinian theory of evolution?
8. What do you mean by Karyological evolution? How human beings were evolved from great apes?
9. How different species of *Drosophila* have been originated by karyological changes?
10. What is genetic distance? Write a note on genetic distance?
11. Write a note on evolutionary rates.
12. Describe the different theories of origin of life.
13. Who proposed the modern biochemical theory? What was the modern biochemical theory?
14. Describe the phylogenetic tree of evolution of living system given by Cairns and Smith.
15. Briefly describe the structure of primitive earth.
16. Desceribe the experiment of Miller and Urey on the prebiotic synthesis on primitive earth.

17. Describe the experiments of Siddney Fox *et. al.* From the experiment what was suggested by them?
18. Briefly narrate the formation of different micromolecules on the primitive earth surface.
19. Describe the origin of genome?
20. Briefly narrate the RNA world?
21. How RNA becomes the protogenome?
22. Describe the process of transformation of the RNA world into the DNA world.
23. Write a note on protocell.
24. Discuss in brief about the recent concept of origin of prokaryotes.
25. Give the fossil evidences on the origin of prokaryotes.
26. Write a note on the molecular evidence on the origin of prokaryotes.
27. Describe in brief about the origin and evolution of metazoa.
28. What are the characteristics of metazoa?
29. Write briefly the colonial theory of origin of metazoa.
30. Write a note on colonial amoeboid theory and acoeloid theory of metazoan origin.

**B. Short answer type questions.**

1. What do you mean by molecular evolution?
2. What are the methods used for the indirect assessment of DNA or protein in an organism to evaluate molecular evolution?
3. How immunological data can be used to assess molecular evolution?
4. How DNA-DNA hybridization methods can be used to assess molecular evolution?
5. What is pseudogene? Why it is named so?
6. Give the sequence of $\alpha$ and $\beta$ globin genes in human.
7. Give the sequence of globin genes in goat, rabbit and mouse?
8. Give the characteristics of $\psi\beta_2$ in rabbit.
9. What is the interesting property of $\psi h_3$ gene in mouse.
10. How $\beta^A$ and $\beta^B$ genes in goat indicate its origin?
11. What is leghemoglobin? How does globin gene originated?
12. Why pseudogenes are the evolutionary dead ends.
13. Why myoglobin gene is regarded as the common ancestor of all the three types of globin genes.
14. How fish globin gene has been evolued from leghetmoglobin gene?
15. How the $\alpha$ and $\beta$ globin genes of *Xenopus* had been evolved?
16. How $\alpha$ and $\beta$ globin genes have been separated in mammals and birds?
17. What are the causes of expansion the $\alpha$ and $\beta$ clusters of globin genes?
18. What is evolutionary clock? How the mutations favours establishment of the globin genes in the organisms in course of evolution?
19. What is the principle of molecular analysis of evolution?
20. What is the relationship between the degree of differerce and evolutionary time?
21. How the rate of $\alpha$–globin gene can be estimated by knowing the evolutionary lines of the gene?
22. What is neutral theory of molecular evolution?
23. Why neutral theory of molecular evolution is regarded as non-Darwinian theory of evolution?
24. What are the differences in banding pattern between great apes and humans?
25. What karyological changes bring about the speciation from chimpazee to human?
26. What were the chromosome complements found in *D. subobscura* and *D. virilis*?
27. How *D. pseudoobscura* and *D. persimilis* were evolved by cytological changes?
28. How cytological changes give rise to *D. willistoni*.
29. How *D. melanogaster* was evolved by cytological changes?

30. What is a race? Why the races or subspecies are not regarded to be a species?
31. How human beings have polymorphic traits?
32. How genetic divergence can be calculated by Nei's method?
33. How the index of genetic identity can be calculated?
34. What do you mean by a value of zero genetic identity and a value of one genetic identity?
35. What is the relationship between genetic identity and geneitc distance.
36. What is the meaning of genetic identity approaches to zero?
37. How the time divergences can be calculated from the genetic distances during the evolution of Asian to Caucasian and from African to caucasian races.
38. How sympatric and allopatric speciation are influenced by genetic distance between a pair of closely related species?
39. What are biological time and chronological times for the measurement of rate of evolution?
40. What are the problems to estimate evolution rate?
41. What are the lumper and spliter groups in taxonomy?
42. What are bradytely and tachytely?
43. How the bradytellic animals are persisted in the world? Give examples.
44. What is quantum evolution? What are their importance in evolution? Give example.
45. What do you mean by Darwin unit of evolution rate? How this can be measured?
46. What are the factors that rely the evolutionary rate?
47. What is phyletic gradualism?
48. What is punctuated equilibrium process of evolution?

1. What is special creation theory of origin of life? What are written in Bible and Upanishad about it?
2. Comment on spontaneous generation concept of origin of life.
3. What is cosmozoic theory of origin of life?
4. What was the concept of Oparin on origin of life?
5. What was the components of primordial atmosphere?
6. What are coacervates?
7. What are steps of Cairns and Smith model for the origin of life, heterotrophs, autotrophs, protocell prokaryotes eukaryotes?
8. What was the structure of primitive earth?
9. What are the constituents of earth's atmosphere?
10. What is juvenile water?
11. What are the sources of energy available on primitive earth surface?
12. Describe the Miller and Urey's experiment on origin of life? What are the amino acids they obtained?
13. What chemicals Siddney Fox detected in the interstellar dust? What was his comments.
14. What was the experiment devised by Siddney Fox and his colleagues? What was his comment on the experiment?
15. What are proteinoids? What are their characteristics? What is "self assembly theory"? Who proposed this theory?
16. What are micromolecules?
17. How do amino acid hydrocarbons, fatty acids, purine and Pyrimidine, nucleotides and porphyrin were formed in the primitive earth surface?
18. What are macromolecules on primitive earth surface?
19. What is protoprotein? What was its properties?
20. What do you mean by proto-information?
21. What is the drawback of protein to be considered as genetic material?
22. What is pyranosyl version of RNA? Why this is of better choice for an early protogenome?
23. What is RNA?
24. What do you mean by the RNA world?
25. What are ribozymes? What are their properties?

26. Why this is considered as the first biochemical system in the lfe?
27. How ribozymes were formed in the early earth surface? What was their advantage over the simple RNA as genome?
28. What is naked genome or protogenome? What was its characteristics? How this protogenome become a cell-like structure?
29. Why protein enzyme is more efficient than ribozymes?
30. What is RNA world?
31. Why RNA is unsuitable for coding function than that of DNA?
32. How RNA world was transformed into DNA world?
33. What was the property of first DNA genome? How the chromosomes were evolved?
34. What is protocell? What was its characteristics?
35. How the cell reproduced and derived nutrients?
36. How protocells become heterotroph and also become autotrophs?

1. Define eukarya and prokarya?
2. What are cherts?
3. What are stromatolites? What is the importance of such deposits?
4. What is BIF? What is its characteristics.
5. What is the probable ancestor of prokaryotes from which they arose?
6. What is protocyanobacterium? Where did it present?
7. What is its characteristics?
8. What is the characteristics of *Methanococcus Jannaschii*?
9. What are the intron early and intron late hypotheses? What is the conclusion of these two theories.
10. What is the progenotes hypothesis of Woese? Give reasons in favours of this hypothesis.
11. What is the significance of 16SRNA in evolution?
12. What is the conclusion about the origin of prokaryotes.
13. What are the characterisitics of metazoa?
14. Comment on Butschli theory of origin of metazoa?
15. What is Lankester theory of origin of metazoa? What is its demerit?
16. What is the major thinking of colonial blastaea/gastrea theory of metazoan origin? What are their merits and demerits?
17. Write a note on Trochea theory of metazoan origin?
18. Briefly discuss the colonial blastula-planula theory of metazoan origin.
19. What would be the conclusion of colonial flagellate theory of metazoan origin.
20. What is archimetazoa? What is its characteristics? What is its importance?
21. Write a note on acoeloid theory of origin of metazoa?

# Bibliography


Abbas, A.K., A.H. Lichtman and S. Pillai (2007), *Cellular and Molecular Immunology*, 6th edn., Saunders Elsevier.

Abbas, A.K., and A.H. Lichtman (2003), *Cellular and Molecular Immunology*, 5th edn, Saunders

Acheson, N.H. (2007), *Fundamentals of Molecular Virology*, John Wiley and Sons.

Adam M and Dick M (2014), *Food Microbiology*, Medi Tech, Delhi, India.

Adhikari, S. and A. K. Sinha (1973), *Fundamentals of Biology of Animals*, New Central Book Agency, vol-3, Kolkata, India.

Agarwal, R.A. et al *Animal Physiology and Biochemistry*. S. Chand and Company Ltd. India.

Agarwal, R.A., Anil K. Srivastava and Kaushal Kumar (2013), 5th edn., S. Chand and Company Ltd., NewDelhi 110055.

Agarwal, V.K. and Usha Gupta (2001), *Chordata Embryology and Histology*. S. Chand and Company Ltd. India.

Alberts, B., et al, (2002) *Molecular Biology of The Cell*. 4th edn., Garland Science.

Alberts, Bruce et *al*. (2008), *Molecular Biology of The Cell*, 5th edn., Garland Science.

Alberts, Bruce, et *al* (2004), *Essential Cell Biology* 2nd edn. Garland Science.

Alcamo, I. Edward. (2001), *DNA technology : The Awesome Skill*, 2nd edn., Harcourt Academic Press.

Allison, Lizabeth A (2007) *Fundamental Molecular Biology*. Blackwell Publishing.

Aneja, K.R. (2003), *Experiments in Microbiology Plant Pathology and Biotechnology*, 4th edn., New Age International Publishers India.

Annadurai, B (2008), *A Textbook of Immunology and Immunotechnology*. S. Chand and Company Ltd. India.

Arther, GH. (1975), *Veterinary Reproduction and Obstetrics*. 4th edn. ELBS.

Atlas, Ronald M (2015), *Principles of Microbiology*, McGraw Hill Education (India) Private Litd., New Delhi, India.

Attenburg, Edgar (1970) *Genetics*, Revised edn. Oxford and IBH Publishing Co.

Austen, K. Frank, S.J. Burakoff, F.S. Rosen and T.B. storm (2001), 2nd edn., Blackwell Science.

Bains, W, (2004), *Biotechnology from A to Z*, 3rd edn, Oxford University Press.

Balasubramanian D, CFA Bryee, K. Dharmalingam J. *Green and Kunthala Jayaraman* (2009), University Press India, Limited India.

Balasubramanian, D, et *al* (2007), *Concepts in Biotechnology*, Universities Press, India.

Banerjee A.K. and N. Banerjee (2006), *Fundamentals of Microbiology and Immunology*, New Central Book Agency (P) Ltd. India.

Banerjee, A.K. and N. Banerjee (2006), *Fundamentals of Microbiology and Immunology*, New Central Book Agency (P) Ltd., India.

Banerjee, P.K. (2006), *Problems on Genetics, Molecular Genetics and evolutionary Genetics*, 1st edn., New Central Book Agency. Kolkata.

Banerjee, Pranab Kumar (2014), *Introduction Biophysis*, S. Chand and Company Ltd., New Delhi 110055.

Bazzett, Terence. J. (2008), *An Introduction to Behaviour Genetics*. Sinauer Associates Inc. Publishers.

Bell, G.H. et *al* (1976), *Textbook and Physiology and Biochemistry, 9th edn*, ELBS and Churchill Livingstone.

Benjamin. S. Weeks (2012), *Alcamo's Microbes and Society*, 3rd edn., Jones and Bartlett Learning, USA.

Bergey, DH, (2014), *Wastewater Microbiology*, 1st edn., Meditech, NewDelhi, India.

Bhattacharya, S. and J. Sinha (2006), *A Textbook of Immunology*, Academic Publishers, Kolkata, India.

Black, J.G. (2008), *Microbiology*, 7th edn., John Willey Sons Inc.

Black, Jacquelyn G and Laura J, Black (2015), 9th edn., *Microbiology : Principles and Exploration*, Wiley.

Bourgaize, David (2003), *Biotechnology Demystifying the Concepts.* Pearson Education.

Brooker, Robert J (2005), *Genetics Analysis and Priciples*, 2nd edn., McGraw Hill.

Brooker, Robert. J. (2009), *Genetics Analysis and Principles*, 3rd edn., McGraw-Hill International edition.

Brooker, Robert. J. (2015), *Genetics : Analysis and Principles*, 5th edn., McGraw Hill Education.

Brooks, G.F., J.S. Butel and S.A. Morse (2004), *Jawetz, Melnick and Adelberg's Medical Microbiology*, 23rd edn. McGraw Hill.

Brown, T.A. (2002), *Genome 2*, 2nd edn, Wiley-Liss.

Brown, T.A. (2004), *Genetics A Molecular Approach*, 3rd edn., BIOs Scientific Publishers.

Brown, T.A. (2006), *Gene Cloning and DNA Analysis : An Introduction.* 5th edn. Blackwell Publishing.

Brown, T.A. (2007), *Genomes 3*, Garland Science NewYork and London.

Brown, T.A. (2016), *Gene Cloning and DNA Analysis : An Introduction* (7th edn.), Wiley Blackwell.

Brown, T.A. T(2018), *Genome 4*, Garland Science.

Brown, Terry (2012), *Introduction to Genetics : A molecular approach*, 1st edn., Garland Science, NewYork.

Cappuccino. J.G. and N. Sherman (2002), *Microbiology A Laboratory Mannual*, 6th edn., Pearson education.

Carey Nessa (2015), *Junk DNA Icon*, Book Ltd. London.

Cassimeris, Lynne, Vishwanath R Lingappa and George Plopper (2011), *Lewin's Cells*, 2nd edn., Jones and Bartlett Publishers.

Chakraborty, A (1996), *Immunology*, Tata McGraw Hill Publishing Company Ltd. New Delhi, India.

Chakraborty, A.K. (2003), *Immunology II*, N.L. Publishers, Siliguri, India.

Chakraborty, P (2013), *A Textbook of Microbiology,* 3rd edn., New Central Book Agency, Kolkata.

Chakraborty, P. (2001), *ATextbook of Microbiology,* 2nd edn., New Central Book Agency (P) Ltd., India.

Chakraborty, P. (2003), *A Textbook of Microbiology, 2nd edn.,* New Central Book Agency (P) Ltd. India.

Chandra, Suresh (1997), *Essentials of Community Medicine,* New Central Book Agency (P) Ltd., India.

Channarayappa (2006), *Molecular Biotechnology Principles and Practices,* University Press (India) Private Limited.

Channarayappa (2010), *Cell Biology,* University Press (India) Priate Ltd., Hyderabad 500029, India.

Chatterjee, C.C. (1973), *Human Physiology* Vol-I 8th edn. New Central Book Agency. India.

Chatterjee, G.C. 1977, *Human Physiology,* Vol-1 Medical Allied Agency, Kolkata, India.

Chattopadhyay, S. (2002), *Life, Origin, Evolution and Adaptation,* Books and Allied (P) Ltd. Kolkata, India.

Chaudhury, Sujit. K. (2001), *Concise Medical Physiology,* 3rd edn., New Central Book Agency. Kolkata, India.

Clark, P. David (2005) *Molecular Biology Understanding the Genetic Revolution,* Elsevier.

Coico, R., G. Sunshine and E. Benjamini (2003), *Immunology,* 5th edn., A. John Willey and Sons Inc. Publication.

Cooper, Geoffrey M. and Robert E. Hausman (2007), *The Cell A Molecular Approach,* 4th edn. ASM Press and Sinauer Associates Inc.

Cornelissen Cynthia Nau, Bruce D Fisher and Richard A. Harvey (1913), *Lipipincott's illustrated reviews,* 3rd edn., Wolters Kluwer, India Pvt. Ltd., NewDelhi.

Cowan, M.K. and K.P. Talaro (2006), *Microbiology : A System Approach,* McGraw Hill Higher education.

Cox, Michael. M. and David. L. Nelson (2008), *Lehninger Principles of Biochemistry,* 5th edn. W.H.Freeman and Company NewYork.

Craig, Nancy L, Orna Cohen-Fix, Rachel Green, Carol W Greider; Gisela Storz and Cynthia Wolberger (2010). *Molecular Biology – Principles of Genome Function.,* Oxford University Press.

Craig, Nancy L., Oma Cohen — Fix; Rachel Green, Corol Gre, der, Grisela Storz and Cynthia Wolberger (2014), 2nd edn., *Molecular Biology : Principles of Genomes Function.* Orford University Press.

Crueger Wulf, Anneliese Crueger and K.R. Aneja (2017), 3rd edn., *Biotechnology, A Textbook of Industrial Microbiology,* Meditech, NewDelhi, India.

Dale Jeremy W, Malcoln Von Schantz and Nick Plant, (2012), *From Genes to Genomes : Concepts and Application of DNA Technology,* 3rd edn., Wiley-Blackwell.

Dale, J.W. and S.F. Park (2004), *Molecular Genetics of Bacteria.* 4th edn., John wiley and Sons Ltd.

Dale, Jeremy W. and Malcom von Schantz (2007), *From Genes to genomes* 2nd edn., John Wiley and Sons, Ltd.

Daniel, L. Hartl and Maryellen Ruvolo (2012), *Genetics, Analysis of Genes and Genomes,* 8th edn., Jones and Bartlett Learning.

Das, A (2006), *Physiology and Biochemistry,* Books and Allied (P) Ltd. Kolkata, India.

Das, Debajyoli, Arati Das (2003), *Statistics in Biology and Psychology.,* Academic Publishes, Kolkata, India.

Das, H.K. (2004) *Textbook of Biotechnology,* Wiley Dreamtech India Pvt. Ltd.

Das, H.K. (2007), *Textbook of Biotechnology,* 3rd edn. Wiley India (P) Ltd.

Das, N.G. (1997), *Statistical Methods,* M. Das and Co. Calcutta, India.

Dassanayak e, Ranil. S. and Y.I.N. Silva, Gunawardene (2011), *Genomic and Proteomic Techniques : In Post Genomic Era,* Narosa Publishing House, India.

David A. Micklos, Bruce Nash and Uwe Hilgert (1913), Cold Spring Harbor Laboratory Press, N. York.

De, Robertis, E.D.P. and E.M.F. De Robertis Jr (2001), *Cell and Molecular Biology,* 8th edn. Lippincott Williams and Wilkins.

Delves, Peter. J., Seamus. J. Martin, Dennis. R. Burton and Ivan M. Roitt (2011), *Roitt's, Essential Immunology,* 12th edn., Wiley-Blackwell.

Doan Thao, Roger Melvold, Susan Viselli, and Carl Waltenbough (2013), *Lippincott's illustrated Reviews,* 2nd edn, Wolters Kluwer (India) Pvt. Ltd. NewDelhi.

Dubey, R.C. and D.K. Maheshwari (2004), *A textbook of Microbiology,* S. Chand and Company Ltd., India.

Falconer, D.S. and Trudy F.C. Mackey (1998), *Introduction to Quantitative Genetics* 4th edn. Longman group Ltd.

Flint, S.J., L.W. Enquist, V.R. Racaniell and A.M. Skalka (2004), *Principles Virology* , 2nd edn., ASM Press, Washington, D.C.

Freifelder, D. (2003) *Molecular Biology,* 2nd edn., Narosa Publishing House.

Gangal Sudha (2007), *Principles and Practice of Animal Tissue Culture,* Universities Press (India) Ptv. Ltd.

Gangani, S.D. (2017), *Human Genetics* (5th edn.), ELSEVIER.

Gardner, Eldon John, et *al* (2002), *Principles of Genetics*, 8th edn., John Wiley and Sons, Inc.

Geha Raif and Luigi Notarangelo (2012), 6th edn. *Case Studies in Immunology,* Garland Science, Newyork, London.

Ghosh, Sankar Kumar (2012), *A Textbook on DNA Barcoding,* Books Space, 22A College Row, Kolkata 70009, India.

Gilbert, S.F. (2000), *Developmental Biology* 6th edn Sinauer Associates, Inc, Publishers, Sunderland, Massachusetts.

Gilbert, Scott F. (2014), 10th edn., *Developmental Biology*, Sinauer Asociates Inc. Sunderland USA.

Gilbert, Scott. F (2000), *Developmental Biology*, 6th edn. Sinauer Associates Inc-Publishers.

Glazer, A.N. and Hiroshi Nikaido (2008), *Microbial Biotechnology : Fundamentals of Applied Microbiology,* 2nd edn., Cambridge University Press.

Goldsby, R.A., T.J. Kindt, B.A. Osborne and J. Kuby (2003), *Immunology,* 5th edn., W.H. Freeman and Company, New York.

Goon, A.M., M.K. Gupta and B. Dasgupta (1981), *Basic Statistics,* 2nd edn., The World Press Private Limited. Kolkata, India.

Griffiths Anthony J.F., Susan R Wessler, Sean B. Carroll and John Doebley (2015), *Introduction of Genetic Analysis* (11th edn.), W.H. Freeman and company New York.

Griffiths, Antony, J.F. et *al* (2008), *Introduction to Genetic Analysis*, 9th edn., W.H. Freeman and Company, NewYork.

Gulbert Scott-F 2014, 10th edn., *Developmental Biology*, Sinauer Associates Inc. USA.

Gupta, P.K. (1995), *Genetics,* Rastogi Publications India.

Gupta, P.K. (2002), *Cell and Molecular Biology,* 2nd edn., Rastogi Publications. India.

Hancock, J.T. (2008), *Molecular Genetics*, Viva Books Private Limited, India.

Haridas N., (2015), 1st edn., *Biochemistry for Medical Students*, New Central Book Agency, Kolkata.

Hartl, Daniel. L and Elizabeth. W. Jones (2009), *Genetics Analysis of genes and genomics.* 7th edn. Jones and Bartlett Publishers.

Hartl, Daniel.L. 2011, *Essential Genetics A Genomics Perspective*, 5th edn., Jones and Bartlett International Student edn.

Hartwell, Leland H (2008), *Genetics from Genes to Genomes,* 3rd edn. McGraw Hill International edition.

Hartwell, Leland H., Michael. L. Goldberg, Janice A. Fischer and Leroy Hood (2018), *Genitics : From Genes to Genomes,* 6th edn., McGraw Hill Education.

Helmreich, E.J.M. (2007), *The Biochemistry of Cell signaling,* Oxford University Press.

Helmreich, E.J.M. (2007). *The Biochemistry of Cell Signaling.* Oxford University Press.

Holde Van, Kensal. E (2006), *Principles of Physical Biochemistry,* 2nd edn. Pearson Prentice Hall.

Howe Christopher (2016), *Gene Cloning and Manipulation* (2nd edn.), Cambridge University Press.

Ingraham. J.L. and C.A. Ingraham (2004), *Introduction to Microbiology : A case History Approach.* 3rd edn., Thomson Books/Cole.

Ingram, J.L. and C.A. Indram (2002), *Introduction to Microbiology,* 2nd edn., Thomson Books/Cole.

Jeffrey C. Pommerville (2011), Alcamo's *Fundamentals of Microbiology,* 9th edn., Jones and Bartlett Publishers, Sudbury, Massachusetts.

Joshi, P. (2007), *Genetic Engineering,* 2nd edn. Agrobios (India).

Kapil Arti and C.S. Bhaskaran (1913), Anantanaryan and Panikar's , *Testbook of Microbiology,* 9th edn., Universities Press (India) Pvt. Ltd.

Kar, Ashutosh (2007), *Pharmaceutical Microbiology,* New Age International Publishers, India.

Karp, Gerald (2005), *Cell and Molecular Biology Concepts and experiments,* 4th edn., John Wiley and Sons, Inc.

Karp, Gerald (2010), *Cell Biology,* 6th edn., John Wiley and Sons Inc. Singapore.

Karp, Gerald, 7th edn., *Cell Biology,* Wiley.

Kaushik, P. (2004), *Microbiology,* S. Chand and Company Ltd. India.

Khopkar, SM (1985), *Basic Concepts of Analytical Chemistry.* Wiley Eastern Limited.

Kindt, T.J., R.A. Goldsby and B.A. Osborne (2007), *Kuby Immunology,* 6th edn., W.H. Freeman and Company, New York.

Klaus Kalthoff 2001, 2nd edn., *Analysis of Biological Development,* McGraw Hill, International Edition.

Klug Willium S, Michael R. Cummings, Charlotte A. Spencer and Michael A Palladino (2016), 10th edn., Pearson India Education Services Pvt. Ltd.

Klug, William S. *et al* (2009), *Concepts of Genetics* 9th edn. Pearson.

Klug, William S., Michael R. Cummings, Charlotte A. Spencer and Michael A Palladino (2016), *Concept of Genetics,* 11th edn., Pearson.

Kothari, Manu L., Lopa. A. Mehta, Sadhana. S. Roychoudhury (2012), 5th edn., *Essentials of Human Genetis.,* University Press (India) Private Limited, AP, India.

Krebs, J.E., E. Goldstein and S.T. Kilpatrick (2011), *Lewin's Genes X,* Jones and Bartlett Publishers Sudbury, Massachusetts.

Krebs, Jocelyn. E, Elliott S. Goldstein and Stephen, T. Kolpatrick (2018), Lewin's *GENE XII,* Jones & Bartlett Learning, 5 Wall Street, MA.

Kreuzer, H. and A. Massey (2001), *Recombinant DNA and Biotechnology,* 2nd edn, ASM Press, Washington, D.C.

Kurup Soumya (2015), *Biochemistry Wave,* Letter Wave Books India.

Latchman David S., (2nd edn.), *Gene Control Garland Science,* Taylor & Francis Group, New York and London.

Latha, P. Madhavee (2012), *Textbook off Immunology,* S. Chand and Company Ltd. RamNagar, New Delhi 110055.

Lesk Arther M (2017), *Introduction to genomics,* Oxford University Press, 3rd edn.

Lesk, Arthur M. (2007), *Introduction to Genomics*, Orford University Press.

Lesk, Arthur. M., (2016) , *Introduction to Protein Science :Architechture, Function and Genomics,* 3rd edn., Oxford University Press.

Lewin, Benjamin (2000), *Genes VIII,* Oxford University Press.

Lewin, Benjamin (2008), *Genes IX,* Jones and Bartlett Publishers.

Lewin, Benjamin *et al* (2007), *Cells,* Jones and Bartlett Publishers.

Lodish, H. e*t al* (2008), *Molecular Cell Biology*, 6th edn., W.H. Freeman and Company. NewYork.

Lodish, Harvey. e*t al,* (2001) *Molecular Cell Biology,* 4th edn. WH. Freeman and Company.

Macleod, John. (1978), *Davidson's Principles and Practice of Medicine,* 12th Edn., eLBL and Churchill Livingstone.

Madigan, M.T., J.M. Martinko, P.V. Dunlap and D.P. Clark (2009), *Brook Biology of Microorganisms,* 12th edn., Pearson International.

Mahesh, S and A.B. Vedamurthy (2003), *Biotechnology 4,* New Age International (P) Limited.

Maier, R.M., I.L. Pepper and C.P. Gerba (2006), *Environmental Microbiology*, Academic Press, Elsevier.

Mair, R.M., I.L. Pepper and C.P. Gerba (2006), *environmental Microbiology*, Academic Press.

Male, D., J. Brostoff, D.B. Roth and I. Roitt (2006), *Immunology*, 7th edn., Mosby Elsevier

Maloy, S.R., J.E. Cronan Jr. and D. Freifelder (1994), 3rd edn., Jones and Bartlett Psublishers Inc.

Mandal, S. (1996) *Fundamentals of Human Genetics.* New Central Book Agency (P) Ltd. Kolkata.

Martens, Thomas R. and Robert L. Hammer Smitth (2015), *Genetics Laboratory Invertigation*, 14th edn. Pearson.

Micklos, David, A., Greg A. Freyer and David A. Crotty, (2003), *DNA Science : A First Course*, 2nd edn., Cold Spring Harbor Laboratory Press, New York.

Miglani Gurbachan S. (2013) *Gene Regualtion*, Narosa Publishing House India.

Miglani Gurbachan. S. (2014), 1st edn., *Gene expression*, Narosa Publishing House.

Miglani, Gurbachan. S. (2014), *Gene Expression*, Narosa Publishing House, India.

Miglani, Gurbachan. S. (2015), 1st edn., *Essentials of Molecular Genetics.*

Miglani, Gurbanchan, S. (2015), *Essentials of Molecular Genetics*, Narosa Publishing House, India.

Mitra, D., *et al* (2006), *Studies in Botany*, 7th edn., Moulik Library, Kolkata, India.

Moat A.G., J.W. Foster ad M.P. Spector (2002), *Microbial Physiology*, 4th edn., John Wiley and Sons. Inc. Publication.

Mudili, J. (2007), *Introductory Practical Microbiology*, Narosa Publishing House, India.

Murphy, K, P. Travers and M. Walport (2008), *Janway's Immunobiology*, 7th edn., Garland Science.

Narayanan, P. (2003), *Essentials of Biophysics* New Age International (P) Limited, Publishers, India.

Nester, E.W, D.G. Anderson, C.E. Roberts jr and M.T. Nester (2009), *Microbiology, A Human Perspective*, 6th edn., McGraw Hill International edn.

Nester, E.W., D.G. Anderson, C.Evans Roberts, Jr, and M.T. Nester (2007), *Microbiology : A Human Perspective*, 5th edn., McGraw Hill Higher education.

Nicholl, Desmond S. (2010), *An Introduction to genetics Engineering* (3rd edn.), Cambridge University Press.

Nicholl, Desmond. S.T. (2007), *An Introduction to genetic engineering,* 2nd edn., Cambridge University Press.

Nunnally, B.K. (2005), *Analytical Techniques in DNA sequencing,* 1st edn., Taylor and Francies group.

Nussbaum, R.L., Roderick R. Mclnnes, Huntington, F., Willard (2012), Thomson & Thomson, *Genetics in Medicine,* 8th edn., Elsevier.

Padmini E. (2015), *Biochemical Calculations and Biostatistics,* Books and Allied (P) Ltd., Kolkata, India.

Pandian, M.R. and B.S. Kumar (2007), *Immunology and Immunotechnology,* Panima Publishing Comporation, India.

Parija, Subhas Chandra (2012), *Textbook of Microbiology and Immunology,* 2nd edn., Reed Elsevier India Private Limited, India.

Parija, Subhash Chandra (2009) : *Textbook of Microbiology and Immunology,* Elsevier.

Pathak, S and U. Palan (2005), *Immunology : Essential and Fundamental,* 2nd edn., Capital Publishing Company, India.

Pathok, Sulabha and Urmi Palan (2011), *Immunology Essential and Fundamental,* 3rd edn., Capital Publishing Company, New Delhi.

Pelczar, Jr. M.J., E.C.S. Chan and N.R. Krieg (2004), *Microbiology,* Tata McGraw Hill Publishing Company Limited.

Pennington, S.R and M.J. Dunn (2002), *Proteomics from protein sequence to function,* Viva Books Private Limited.

Peppler, H.J. and D. Perlman (2004), *Microbial Technology : Microbial Processes,* 2nd edn., Vol. II, Academic press, elsevier, India Pvt. Ltd.

Peppler, H.J. and D.Perlman (2004), *Microbial Technology : Microbial processes,* 2nd edn., Vol. I Academic Press, elsevier India Pvt. Ltd.

Pierce, Benjamin A (2005), *Genetics : A Conceptural Approach,* 2nd edn. WH Freeman and Company.

Pierce, Benjamin A. (2008), *Genetics : A conceptual approach,* 3rd edn., W.H. Freeman and Company, New York.

Pierce, Benjamin, A. (2010), *Genetics : A conceptual Approach,* 5th edn., W.H. Freeman and Company.

Pierce, Benjamin. A. (2012), *Genetics — A conceptual Approach,* 4th edn., W.H.Freeman and Company, New York.

Pommerville, J.C. (2004), *Alcamo's Fundamentals of Microbiology.* 7th edn., Jones and Bartlett Publishers, Sudbury, Massachusetts.

Prescott, L.M., J.P. Harley and D.A. Klein (2005), 6th edn., McGraw Hill Higher eduction.

Prescott, L.M., J.P. Harley and D.A. Klein (2005), 6th edn., McGraw Hill Higher education.

Primrose S.B. and R.M. Twyman (2014), *Principles of Gene Manipulation and Genomics,* 7th edn., Wiley Blackwell.

Primrose, S.B. (2001), *Molecular Biotechnology,* 2nd edn., Panima Publishing Corporation, New Delhi

Purohit, S.S. (2004). *Biotechnology Fundamentals and Applications,* 3rd edn., Student edition, India.

Purohit. S.S. (2004), *Microbiology : Fundamentals and Applications,* 6th edn., Student edition, Jodhpur, India.

Rajagopal, K. (2012), *Recombinant DNA Technology and Genecits Engineering,* Tata McGraw Hill Education Private Limited, India.

Rajendran, P. and P. Gunasekaran (2006), *Microbial Bioremediation.* MJP Publishers, Chennai, India.

Rao, C.V. (2005), *Immunology : A textbook,* Narosa Publishing House, India.

Rastogi Smita and Neelam Pathod (2012), *Genetic Engineering,* Oxford University Press, Dehis , India.

Rastogi Veer Bala (2015), 3rd edn., *Biostatistics.* Meditech, NewDelhi, India.

Rastogi veer Bala (2016), *Principles of Molecular Biology,* Meditech, NewDelhi, India.

Rastogi Veer Bala (2016), *Principles of Molecular Biology.,* Meditech, NewDelhi, India.

Rastogi, S.C. (2007), *Biotechnology Principles and Applications.* Naraso Publishing House.

Rastogi, Smita and Neelam Pathak (2009), *Genetic Engineering,* Oxford University Press.

Ray, Samit. and Arun K. Roy (2006) *Biodiversity Biotechnology,* New Central Book Agency, Kolkata.

Rej., Swapan Kumar (2015), 1st edn., *General Concepts of Histology and Endocrinology,* New Central Book Agency, Kolkata.

Rob, Phillips, Jane Kondev, Julie Therrot and Nigel Orme (2009), *Physical Biology of the Cell,* Garland Science, Taylor and Francis Group, LLC, NewYork, USA.

Roy, R N (1999), *A Text Book of Biophysics* New Central Book Agency (P) Ltd. Kolkata, India

Roy, R N (2001), *Medical Biophysics* Books and Allied (P) Ltd. India.

Roy, R.N. (2011), *Heredity, Genetics and Genetical Diseases,* New Central Book Agency, Kolkata.

Russel, Peter J. (2006), *iGenetics,* 2nd edn. Pearson.

Russel, Peter J. (2017), *Genetics : A Molecular Approach,* 3rd edn., Pearson.

Rustagi, Monika (2016), 1st edn. *Bacterial metabolism,* Meditech, NewDelhi, India.

Saha Indranil and Bobby Paul (2016), *Essentials of Biostatistics* (2nd edn.), Academic Publishers, Kolkata.

Sambamurty A.V.S.S. *Molecular Biology* Narosa Publishing House.

Sambamurty, A.V.S.S. (2007), *Molecular Genetics* Narosa Publishing House, India.

Sateesh, M.K. (2003), *Biotechnology-5,* New Age International (P) Limited.

Satyanarayana, U (2002) *Biochemistry,* Books and Allied (P) Ltd., Kolkata

Satyanarayana, U. (2005) *Biotechnology,* Book and Allied (P) Ltd. Kolkata.

Schaff, Christian P., Johannes Zschocke and Lorraine Potocki (2012), *Human Genetics : From Molecules to Medicine,* Wolters Kluwer/ Lippincott Williams and Wilkins Health.

Schulz, G.E. and R.H. Schirmer (2009), *Principles of Protein Structure,* 1st edn., Springer International edition.

Scott F. Gilbert (2014), *Developmental Biology,* 10th edn., Sinaur Associations Inc. Publisher, Sunderland, MA, USA.

Sharma, VK. (1991), *Techniques in Microscopy and Cell Biology,* Tata McGraw Hill Publishing Company Limited. New Delhi.

Shetty, N. (2005), *Immunology : Introductory textbook,* New Age International (P) Limited Publishers. India.

Shukla Rajiv and Bindu Sarkar 2017, *Cell Structure and Function*, MediTech, NewDelhi, India.

Sinden, Richard R. (1994), *DNA Structure and Function.* Academic Press

Singh K.P. 2016, 1st edn. *Concepts of Molecular Genetics,* MediTech, New Delhi, India.

Singh, B.D. (2001), *Plant Breeding* Kalyani Publishers India.

Sinnott, Edmund W. (1973), *Principles of Genetics,* 5th edn. Tata McGraw-Hill Edition.

Snustad, D. Peter and Michael J Simmons (2010), *Principles of Genetics,* 5th edn., John Wiley and Sons, Inc.

Snustad, D. Peter and Michael, J. Simmons (2012), *Genetics,* 6th edn., John Wiley and Sons Inc.

Snustad, D. Peter and Michael. J. Simmons (2006) *Principles of Genetics.*, 4th edn., John Wiley and Sons Inc.

Stanier, R.Y., John L. Ingraham, M.L. Wheelis and P.R. Painter (2005), *General microbiology*, 5th edn., Macmillan Press Ltd. U.K.

Stent, G.S. and R. Calendar (2002), *Molecular Genetics An Introductory and Narrative*, 2nd edn., CBS Publishers and Distributors, India.

Strickberger M.W. (3rd edn.), *Evolution*, Jones and Bartlett Publishers.

Strickberger, Monroe W. (1985) *Genetics.* 3rd edn., Prentice-Hall of India Private Limited.

Strickberger, Monroe W. (2017), *Genetics* (3rd edn.), Pearson India Education Service Pvt. Ltd.

Sudha Gangal, 2007, *Principles and Practice of Animal Tissue Culture.* University Press (India) Pvt. Ltd. 3-5-819, Hyderguda, Hyderabad, India.

Synder, L and W. Champness (2007), *Molecular Genetics of Bacteria,* 3rd edn., ASM Press Washington DC.

Talaro, K.R. (2005), *Foundations in Microbiology,* 5th edn., McGraw Hill.

Tamarin, Robert H (2006), *Principles of Gentics,* 7th edn. Tata McGraw-Hill Editions.

Tom Strachan and Andrew Read (2011), *Human Molecular Genetics* (4th edn.), Garland Science, Canada.

Tortora, G.D., B.R. Funke and C.L. Case (2004), *Microbiology : An Introduction,* 8th edn., Pearson education.

Tortora, G.J., B.R. Funke and C.L. Case (2008), *Microbiology* , 9th edn., Pearson.

Tortora, Gerald J, Berdell R. Funke and Christine L. Case (2016), 11th edn., Pearson.

Trivedi, Dipali. J and Paras, S. Shrimankar (2016), *Kapur and Suri's Basic Human Genetics,* (3rd edn.) The Heath Science Publisher, Madras, India.

Tropp Burton E. (2012), *Molecular Biology : Genes to Proteins* (4th edn.), Jones and Bartlett, Student Edition.

Tropp, Burton E. (2008), *Molecular Biology — Genes to Proteins,* 3rd edn., Jones and Bartlett Publishers.

Twyman R.M. (2001), *Developmental Biology,* Viva Books Private Limited. India

Twyman, R.M. (2002), *Advanced Molecular Biology,* Viva Books Private Limited.

Twyman, R.M. (2008), *Principles of Proteomics,* Taylor and Francies Publication.

Upadhay, Avinash e*t al* (2003), *Biophysical Chemistry : Principles and techniques,* Himalaya Publishing House.

Vasanthakumari, R. (2007), *Textbook of Microbiology,* BI Publications Pvt Limited. New Delhi.

Waiters, M.J., N.L. Morgan, J.S. Rockey and G. Higton (2002), *Industrial Microbiology : An Introduction,* Blackwell Science.

Watson, J.D., Tania, A. Baker, Stephen P. Bell, Alexander Gann, Michael Levine and Richard Losik (2008), *Molecular Biology of the Gene*, 6th edn., Cold Spring Harbour Laboratory Press, New York.

Watson, James D. (2017), *Molecular Biology of the Gene* (7th edn.), Pearson.

Watson, James D. et *al* (2007), *Recombinant DNA Genes and Genomes—A short Course* 3rd edn. W.H. Freeman and Company. N.Y.

Watson, James D., et. *Al.* (2007) *Molecular Biology of the Gene*, 5th edn., Pearson education.

Weaver, Robert F. (2005), *Molecular Biology,* 3rd edn., McGraw Hill.

Weaver, Robert F. (2008), *Molecular Biology,* 4th edn. McGraw-Hill International edition.

Weaver, Robert. F. (2008), *Molecular Biology,* 4th edn., McGraw-Hill International edition.

Weinberg Robert A. 2nd edn. *The Biology of Cancer,* Garland Science NewYork and London.

Weir, D.M. and J. Stewart (1997), *immunology,* 8th edn., Churchill Livingstone.

Wheelis, M.L. (2008), *Principles of Modern Microbiology,* Jones and Bartlett Publishers.

Willey, J.M. , L.M. Sherwood and C.J. Woolverton (2008), Precott, Harley and Klein's Mirobiology, 7th edn. McGraw Hill Higher education.

Willey, Joanne. M., Linda M. Sherwood and Christopher. J. Woolverton (2011), *Prescott's Microbiology*, 8th edn., McGraw Hill International edition.

Williums, Robert. H. (1974), *Textbook of Endocrinology,* Kothari Books Depot. India.

Wilson, G.B. and John H Morrison (1966), *Cytology* 2nd edition. Van Nostrand Reinhold Company.

Wilson, John and Tim Hunt (2008), *Molecular Biology of the Cell The Problem Book.* 5th edn. Garland Science.

Wilson, Keith and John Walker (2010), *Principles and Techniques of Biochemistry and Molecular Biology,* 7th edn., Cambridge University Press.

Winter, P.C. et *al* (2002), *Instant notes in Genetics,* Viva Books Privates Limited, India.

Wolpert Lewis and Cheryll Tickle 2011, Oxford University Press, 4th edn.

# Index

## Numeric & Symbol

## A

## B

# C

## D

## E

# F

## G

## H

## I

## J



## K

# L

## M

## N

# O



# P

## Q



## R

## S

# T

## U

# V



# W



# X

## Y



## Z